THIRD EDITION

# The
# Complete
# Antiques
# Price
# List

Books by Ralph M. and Terry H. Kovel

The Complete Antiques Price List
Know Your Antiques
American Country Furniture 1780–1875
A Directory of American Silver, Pewter and Silver Plate
Dictionary of Marks—Pottery and Porcelain

THIRD EDITION

# The Complete Antiques Price List

A guide to the 1971 market
for professionals, dealers, and collectors

**ILLUSTRATED**

**by Ralph M. and Terry H. Kovel**

CROWN PUBLISHERS, INC., NEW YORK

Third Printing, February, 1971
© 1970 by Crown Publishers, Inc.
Library of Congress Catalog Card Number: 68-9064
Printed in the United States of America
Published simultaneously in Canada by
General Publishing Company Limited

This book is devoted to "how much" but dedicated
to an organization and a driving force
that have done the impossible with "too little":
To Betty Cope, and her station WVIZ,
educational TV of Cleveland, Ohio

# INTRODUCTION

Investors in antiques have once again seen their collections rise in value. The housewife who bought a few pieces for the living room can get more enjoyment from her purchases knowing they are now worth more, not less, than when she first found them.

Buying antiques takes skill and information, even though the prices are rising each year.

The value of an antique can be judged in many ways: by its intrinsic value if it is made of silver or another precious metal or stone, by its historic or nostalgic value to the owner, or by its sale value in a recognized sale or auction. This book records the "asked for" prices of antiques in auctions, ads, antique shops, and shows. Each price indicates an actual piece that was offered for sale, and the piece is described by the seller. If identical antiques were offered at different prices, a range has been given which includes the highest and lowest prices. Each price listed in the book has been taken from an antique offered for sale between July 1969 and June 1970. No price shown is just an estimate or even a suggested figure. All antiques listed are perfect and working, except for a few very rare pieces.

Please note, however, that the prices are those paid by collectors. If you want to offer an antique for sale, unless you are selling to another collector you must expect a dealer to pay less than the listed price. Dealers do have overhead and the cost of doing business to absorb. As a general rule you can expect to receive from 50 percent to 70 percent of the listed price. At least you can use this as a guide.

All the antiques listed in this edition of THE COMPLETE ANTIQUES PRICE LIST are items sold within the last year at auctions, shows, or through mail-order ads. It is possible that some pieces priced in last year's book do not appear in this new edition. This is because we have been unable to find a sale price for a particular antique in this year's market. Prices are changing so quickly that it is impossible to give an accurate price by quoting a sale that is over one year old.

Antiques sell at different prices in different parts of the country. The West Coast market is higher for bottles and for pioneer relics. The East Coast seems more interested in regional items. Buffalo pottery, for example, is sold at its highest prices in the New York State region. The antique trading newspapers and the advertisements in magazines have equalized the market in many respects, and mail-order antiques have become big business. If a price in the book appears low or high, perhaps the regional difference has influenced the seller.

A computer was used to produce this list as accurately, completely, and quickly as possible. The subject headings and certain punctuation marks were used as guides for the computer program. All pressed-glass patterns, for example, are listed under "pressed glass" and not under the pattern name. The item name, such as bowl, tray, pitcher, etc., is listed next. The pattern name is then listed, and any other important information, including color, size, and unusual features, is added. To look up a Lord's Supper bread tray of pressed glass, look under "pressed glass, tray, bread, Lord's Supper." If you do not find an item where you first expect to find it, please try a different category. Organs, pianos, music boxes, records, and many other items are listed under the title "music." All fabrics are listed under "linen" "Store" has the odds and ends used in a country store that would not fit under the headings of "wooden," "iron," etc. This year we have included many more cross-reference entries, which should help to make the book easier to use.

In this edition all bottles are listed under "bottle." To locate Beam bottles and their prices, look under bottle, Beam. All silver is listed under silver with a subheading, for instance, silver, sterling; silver, coin; silver plate, etc. Some depression glass is included under the proper glass factory name. Several new categories such as Phoenix glass, Niloak pottery and Newcomb pottery have been included. Because this book is a report of actual sales, many new items have appeared under general headings such as store, wooden, iron, etc.

Pictures have been included. Each picture is fully captioned and priced in the book. The abbreviation "illus." at the end of an entry indicates that a picture is nearby. The problem of space has made it impossible to put every picture on the exact page where it belongs, but because the pictures are in alphabetical order, the items can easily be found. Unfortunately, no range of price could be given for an illustrated piece. Only the exact price for which the pictured piece was sold is included. The pictures were loaned to us with all the information, and each item pictured was sold during the past year. In a few cases, a pair of antiques is priced although only one of the pair is pictured.

# ACKNOWLEDGMENTS

We are sorry but it is impossible for us to answer any requests for appraisals by mail, although we welcome any suggestions about either the content or category indexing for our next edition. We have tried to be accurate but cannot be responsible if any mistakes in pricing do appear.

---

To all the dealers who knowingly or unknowingly added to this book by offering antiques for sale, our thanks. To the following dealers, our special thanks for the use of their pictures: Aladdin Antiques of Sanbornville, New Hampshire; Alley Antiques of Birmingham, Alabama; Antiques & Uniques of Oxford Pennsylvania; Barton Kinkead Battaile of Lexington, Kentucky; G. Bittner's Sons of Louisville, Kentucky; Mark Boultinghouse of Lexington, Kentucky; Helen E. Brook Antiques of Esmond, Rhode Island; Paula Clark of Monessen, Pennsylvania; Corner Flower Shop of New Bedford, Massachusetts; Country Squire Antiques of Lexington, Kentucky; Darcia Antiques of South Pasadena, California; Dorothy M. Fadour of Bethel, Maine; Theresa & Arthur Greenblatt of Freeport, New York; Hathaway and Bowers, Inc., of Santa Fe Springs, California; Frank Hyatt of Kenman, New York; Edwin Jackson of New York, New York; Rosemary B. Jury of Knoxville, Tennessee; Elaine Kent of Newton, Massachusetts; Manitowoc Submarine Memorial Association of Manitowoc, Wisconsin; Norma Jeanne's Dolls of Pittsburgh, Pennsylvania; Garth Oberlander of Garth's Auction Barn of Delaware, Ohio; Pennypacker Auction Centre of Kenhorst, Reading, Pennsylvania; Yetta Rosen of Mattapan, Massachusetts; Guy and Gladys Saulsbury of Spicer, Minnesota; Stone's Antiques of Tulsa, Oklahoma; Temptation Gallery of Nashville, Tennessee; Noel E. Tomas of West Hartford, Connecticut; The Trojan Horse of Paris, Illinois; and Clara H. Welches of Huntington, Indiana.

An extra thank you must go to Garth's Auction Barn, Delaware, Ohio, for the rush service offered when some special pictures were needed. We also want to admit that without our staff, especially Debbie Herman and Pauline Jaffee, this book could never have been completed on time.

ABC PLATES OR CHILDREN'S ALPHABET PLATES WERE POPULAR
FROM 1780 TO 1860. THE LETTERS ON THE PLATE WERE
MEANT AS TEACHING AIDS FOR THE CHILDREN WHO WERE
LEARNING TO READ. THE PLATES WERE MADE OF POTTERY,
PORCELAIN, METAL, OR GLASS.

| | |
|---|---|
| ABC PLATE, AESOP'S FABLES, 8 1/4 IN. DIAM., 3...........ILLUS.. | 30.00 |
| ABC MUG, BLUE, BOY AT DESK, GIRL AT CHRISTMAS TREE.............. | 22.50 |
| ABC MUG, PINK & WHITE, TEN ANIMALS & ALPHABET ON TOP EDGE...... | 7.50 |
| ABC PLATE, ANIMALS FOR EACH LETTER, GERMANY, CUP.............. | 15.00 |
| ABC PLATE, B IS FOR BOBBY'S BREAKFAST, CHILDREN, ANIMALS, STAFFORDSHIRE........................................... | 25.00 |
| ABC PLATE, BLUE TRANSFER OF BULLDOG, SAYS MY FACE IS MY FORTUNE, 6 IN.................................................. | 22.00 |
| ABC PLATE, BOUQUET OF FLOWERS IN CENTER, FROSTED, 6 IN......... | 18.00 |
| ABC PLATE, BOY FALLS OFF HORSE, 6 3/4 IN...................... | 12.50 |
| ABC PLATE, CARNIVAL GLASS, MARIGOLD.......................... | 32.50 |
| ABC PLATE, CHILD & DOG....................................... | 5.00 |
| ABC PLATE, CHILD IN CENTER, RAISED LETTERS, PORCELAIN.......... | 20.00 |
| ABC PLATE, CHILDREN, ANIMALS, VERSES, CLEAR.................... | 15.00 |
| ABC PLATE, CLEAR, FROSTED GIRL IN CENTER, MARKED CLAY'S CRYSTAL WORKS, 8 IN........................................... | 25.00 |
| ABC PLATE, CLOCK CENTER, CLEAR, 6 IN........................... | 12.00 |
| ABC PLATE, CLOCK CENTER, VASELINE GLASS, 7 IN.................. | 20.00 |
| ABC PLATE, CLOCK FACE CENTER, NUMERALS, ALPHABET ON MARGINS, NOTCHED BORDER............................................ | 23.50 |
| ABC PLATE, CLOCK FACE, CLEAR, 6 IN............................. | 22.50 |
| ABC PLATE, CLOCK, CLEAR...................................... | 14.00 |
| ABC PLATE, CLOCK, SCALLOPED EDGE, GLASS, 7 IN.................. | 28.50 |
| ABC PLATE, EAGLE CENTER, TIN................................. | 32.00 |
| ABC PLATE, ENGLISH PAPER BOY SCENE, 8 1/2 IN.................. | 15.00 |
| ABC PLATE, FOOTBALL, BASEBALL, PAIR...................ILLUS.. | 35.00 |
| ABC PLATE, FRANKLIN'S PROVERBS, 6 IN. DIAM., 4.........ILLUS.. | 60.00 |
| ABC PLATE, FROSTED CHILD'S HEAD, VASELINE GLASS............... | 15.00 |
| ABC PLATE, GIRL PICTURE IN CENTER, GLASS, 6 IN................ | 15.00 |
| ABC PLATE, GREEN, RAISED LETTERS, FROSTED CHILD'S HEAD, CLAY'S CRYSTAL WORKS............................................ | 45.00 |
| ABC PLATE, HARRY BAITING LINE, 5 3/4 IN....................... | 17.00 |
| ABC PLATE, HEN & CHICKENS, 6 IN............................... | 12.50 |
| ABC PLATE, HI DIDDLE DIDDLE, TIN.............................. | 8.50 |
| ABC PLATE, HI DIDDLE DIDDLE, TIN, 8 1/2 IN.................... | 14.00 |
| ABC PLATE, HI DIDDLE DIDDLE, TIN, 8 3/8 IN.................... | 22.00 |
| ABC PLATE, HI DIDDLE DIDDLE, TIN, 9 IN........................ | 18.00 |
| ABC PLATE, HORSE DECOR, PORCELAIN, ADAMS, 7 1/4 IN............ | 15.00 |
| ABC PLATE, JUMBO CENTER, TIN................................. | 17.50 |
| ABC PLATE, LITTLE RED RIDING HOOD, WOLF, PORCELAIN............ | 17.50 |
| ABC PLATE, MARY HAD A LAMB, TIN.............................. | 14.50 |
| ABC PLATE, MARY HAD A LAMB, TIN, 8 IN. DIAMETER............... | 24.00 |
| ABC PLATE, MINIATURE, TIN, 2 1/4 IN........................... | 15.00 |
| ABC PLATE, MOTHER HEN WITH CHICKS IN CENTER, CLEAR, 6 IN....... | 12.00 |
| ABC PLATE, NATIONS OF THE WORLD, ENGLAND, IRONSTONE........... | 15.00 |
| ABC PLATE, NURSERY VERSE, EMBOSSED ALPHABET AROUND EDGE, STAFFORDSHIRE............................................ | 8.00 |
| ABC PLATE, PAPER BOY SCENE, ENGLAND, 8 1/2 IN................. | 15.00 |
| ABC PLATE, PRESSED GLASS, SIGNED............................. | 9.50 |
| ABC PLATE, RABBIT CENTER, FROSTED, 6 IN....................... | 18.00 |
| ABC PLATE, RABBITS, CHILDREN, 7 1/4 IN........................ | 12.50 |
| ABC PLATE, RAISED ALPHABET, DISH OF ICE CREAM IN CENTER, 2 3/4 IN. DIAMETER........................................ | 8.00 |
| ABC PLATE, RAISED LETTERS, MILITARY SCENE, CRIMEAN WAR, STAFFORDSHIRE............................................ | 20.00 |
| ABC PLATE, ROBINSON CRUSOE, 8 1/4 IN. DIAM., 2.........ILLUS.. | 20.00 |
| ABC PLATE, SANCHO PANZA & DAPPLE, FROSTED, 6 IN............... | 18.00 |
| ABC PLATE, SCULPTURED CHILD'S FACE IN CENTER, SIGNED CLAY CRYSTAL WORKS............................................ | 25.00 |
| ABC PLATE, SEASIDE SCENE, BATHING AT BRIGHTON, STAFFORDSHIRE, 7 IN....................................... | 16.00 |
| ABC PLATE, STORK CENTER, FROSTED............................. | 18.00 |
| ABC PLATE, TIN............................................... | 15.00 |
| ABC PLATE, TIN, 6 IN.............................. 8.50 TO | 15.00 |
| ABC PLATE, TIN, 7 1/2 IN..................................... | 12.00 |
| ABC PLATE, TOM THUMB, TIN.................................... | 12.00 |
| ABC PLATE, WHITE, GOLD LETTERS & RIM, PORCELAIN, GERMANY, 6 IN... | 6.50 |
| ABC PLATE, WHO KILLED COCK ROBIN, PICTURE, TIN................ | 8.50 |
| ABC PLATE, WHO KILLED COCK ROBIN, TIN, 8 IN. DIAMETER......... | 24.00 |
| ABC PLATE, WILD ANIMALS, THE LION, STAFFORDSHIRE.............. | 16.50 |
| ABC PLATE, YELLOW ALPHABET, RED BORDER, CENTER CATS PLAYING WITH YARN, TIN........................................... | 13.00 |
| ABC RATTLE, HANDLE, WHISTLE, FOR A GOOD GIRL, TIN............. | 17.00 |
| ABC, PLATE, BEADED EDGE, MILK GLASS, 7 IN. DIAMETER........... | 16.50 |
| ABC, PLATE, CLOCK CENTER..................................... | 17.00 |

ABC FOOTBALL PLATE

ABC AESOP'S FABLES PLATE

ABC ROBINSON CRUSOE PLATE

ABC FRANKLIN'S PROVERBS PLATE

```
    ADAMS CHINA WAS MADE BY WILLIAM ADAMS AND SONS OF
    STAFFORDSHIRE,ENGLAND.THE FIRM WAS FOUNDED IN 1769 AND
    IS STILL WORKING.
ADAMS,BOWL,CHINESE DECOR,10 IN. WIDE........................    12.00
ADAMS,BOWL,TUNSTALL,CRIES OF LONDON,TURNIPS & CARROTS,
   4 IN.DEEP.................................................    87.50
ADAMS,CRACKER BARREL,BLUE JASPERWARE,BAIL,MARKED ADAMS,
   TUNSTALL,ENGLAND.........................................    75.00
ADAMS,CUP & SAUCER,DEEP PINK...............................    19.00
ADAMS,CUP & SAUCER,PINK,GARDEN SPORTS,HANDLELESS...........    24.00
ADAMS,CUP PLATE,SEASHELL DESIGN,MARKED.....................    35.00
ADAMS,DISH,CANDY,PINK,SQUAT,BULBOUS,FLARING RIM,LID,
```

```
3 IN.HIGH.........................................................  7.50
ADAMS,DISH,VEGETABLE,SCHNECTADY ON MOHAWK RIVER,PINK,
   10 IN.LONG.....................................................  85.00
ADAMS,JAR,CRACKER,BLUE,WHITE,HUNTING SCENE,ENGLAND..........  47.50
ADAMS,MUG,BLACK,BERMUDA COAT OF ARMS,CREAM COLOR LINING,
   MARKED........................................................  35.00
ADAMS,PLATE,ATHEN PATTERN,8 1/2 IN.........................  12.50
ADAMS,PLATE,BIRD,BY JOHN JAMES AUDUBON,BLACK ON WHITE,
   10 1/2 IN.....................................................  20.00
ADAMS,PLATE,CALEDONIA,PURPLE,10 1/2 IN.DIAMETER............  25.00
ADAMS,PLATE,COLUMBUS,MULBERRY,6 IN.........................  18.50
ADAMS,PLATE,COLUMBUS,MULBERRY,8 1/2 IN.....................  37.50
ADAMS,PLATE,COLUMBUS,PINK,9 1/2 IN.........................  32.50
ADAMS,PLATE,MACBETH,ORANGE BORDER,FISH,URN,FLORAL,10 IN.....  22.00
ADAMS,PLATE,PALESTINE,PINK & GREEN,8 1/2 IN.................  17.50
ADAMS,PLATE,PINK LUSTER,7 IN...............................  8.00
ADAMS,PLATE,PINK,VIEW NEAR CONWAY,NEW HAMPSHIRE,9 IN........  39.00
ADAMS,PLATE,SIR JOHN FALSTAFF,ORANGE BORDER,FISH,URN,FLORAL,
   9 IN..........................................................  22.00
ADAMS,PLATTER,LAKE GEORGE,PINK,13 1/4 IN....................  67.50
ADAMS,SOUP,COLUMBUS,BLACK & WHITE,CIRCA 1835,10 5/8 IN......  24.00
ADAMS,TEAPOT,CREAMER,SUGAR,TRAY,PANELS,RIBS,IRONSTONE,
   WM.ADAMS & SONS...............................................  40.00
ADAMS,TUREEN,SOUP,CATTLE SCENERY,BLUE,WHITE,IRONSTONE....... 150.00
ADAMS,TUREEN,SOUP,GREEN GROUND,PURPLE FLORAL,GOLD,TRAY,
   LADLE,CALYX WARE..............................................  60.00
ADAMS,TUREEN,VEGETABLE,BOTHWELL CASTLE,CLYDESDALE,BLUE,
   FLOWER FINIAL.................................................  90.00
ADAMS,TUREEN,VEGETABLE,FLOWER FINIAL,BOTHWELL CASTLE,
   STAFFORDSHIRE.................................................  95.00
ADVENTURINE,BOWL,RUFFLED,MATCHING UNDERPLATE HAS TURNOVER
   PIECRUST RIM..................................................  75.00
         AGATA GLASS WAS MADE BY JOSEPH LOCKE OF THE NEW
      ENGLAND GLASS COMPANY OF CAMBRIDGE,MASSACHUSETTS,AFTER
      1885. A METALLIC STAIN WAS APPLIED TO NEW ENGLAND
      PEACHBLOW AND THE MOTTLED DESIGN CHARACTERISTIC OF
      AGATA APPEARED.
AGATA,SPOONER,BLUE-GREEN,MOTTLING,3 1/2 IN. X 4 1/4 IN.HIGH. 695.00
AGATA,TUMBLER.........................................ILLUS.. 445.00
AGATA,TUMBLER,GREEN........................................ 450.00
AGATA,TUMBLER,PINK........................................ 495.00
AGATA,VASE,LILY,11 1/2 IN...............................1,160.00
AGATE,BOTTLE,SNUFF,BROWN,1780-1880,JADE STOPPER............ 100.00
AGATE,BOTTLE,SNUFF,CARNELIAN,1780-1880,JADE STOPPER.........  90.00
AGATE,BOTTLE,SNUFF,FRUIT FORM,BLUE,VINES,LEAFAGE........... 160.00
AGATE,BOTTLE,SNUFF,GRAY,1780-1880......................... 275.00
AGATE,BOTTLE,SNUFF,GRAY,1780-1880,QUARTZ STOPPER........... 160.00
AGATE,BOTTLE,SNUFF,SOOCHOW,1780-1880...................... 400.00
AGATE,BOX,BRASS TRIM,HINGED COVER,2 IN. X 3 IN. X
   1 1/2 IN.TALL.................................................  15.00
AGATE,BOX,STRIATE,RED,CRYSTAL DEPOSITS,CHASED SCROLL SILVER
   BORDER........................................................ 150.00
AGATE,COFFEEPOT,CIRCA 1780,11 IN. HIGH..................... 300.00
AGATE,URN,PAIR,NUMBERED 4 & 6,MATCHING CLAM SHAPE DISH,EAGLE
   ON BOTTOM.....................................................  25.00
```

AGATA TUMBLER

```
AGATE,VASE,CARNELIAN,CHIH LUNG,POLYPORUS FUNGUS,
  5 1/4 IN.HIGH.....................................................  150.00
```

AKRO AGATE GLASS WAS MADE IN CLARKSBURG,WEST VIRGINIA,
FROM 1932 TO 1951. BEFORE THAT TIME THE FIRM MADE
CHILDREN'S GLASS MARBLES. MOST OF THE GLASS IS MARKED
WITH A CROW FLYING THROUGH THE LETTER A.

```
AKRO AGATE,ASHTRAY,GREEN,3 IN...........................................  4.75
AKRO AGATE,BOWL,CHILD'S,GREEN,COVER.....................................  1.50
AKRO AGATE,BOWL,GREEN,HALF MOON-SHAPED,RAISED FLORAL,2 X 3 X
  5 IN.LONG...........................................................  7.00
AKRO AGATE,BOWL,PANELED,SCALLOPED,GREEN MARBLE,5 1/2 IN.....  5.00
AKRO AGATE,BOWL,5 1/4 IN. X 2 IN.HIGH...................................  4.50
AKRO AGATE,BOX,POWDER,BLUE,LID,SIGNED A-KROS RAREST.....  49.00
AKRO AGATE,BOX,POWDER,BLUE,WOMEN,SIGNED,6 1/2 IN.TALL.......  49.00
AKRO AGATE,BUTTER PAT,2 1/4 IN..........................................  2.50
AKRO AGATE,CACHEPOT,YELLOW-ORANGE MOTTLE,MARKED,4 IN....  6.50
AKRO AGATE,DISH,BOAT SHAPE,GREEN,8 IN.LONG,3 IN.WIDE,
  3 IN.DEEP...........................................................  12.00
AKRO AGATE,DISH,YELLOW,OVAL,MARK,6 IN.LONG,3 IN.WIDE,
  2 1/2 IN.HIGH.......................................................  6.50
AKRO AGATE,DISHES,CHILD'S,EIGHT PIECES..................................  18.50
AKRO AGATE,FLOWERPOT,GREEN,3 1/2 IN. HIGH...............................  5.00
AKRO AGATE,FLOWERPOT,ORANGE,3 1/2 IN. HIGH..............................  5.00
AKRO AGATE,HOLDER,MATCH,BUTTERSCOTCH MARBLE GLASS...........  3.00
AKRO AGATE,HOLDER,MATCH,HORN OF PLENTY,ORANGE,WHITE........  10.00
AKRO AGATE,JAR,MEXICALI,SOMBRERO LID,PUMPKIN COLOR & WHITE,
  COVER...............................................................  32.50
AKRO AGATE,MARBLE,100...................................................  6.00
AKRO AGATE,MARBLE,3 IN.DIAMETER.........................................  1.50
AKRO AGATE,PITCHER,CHILD'S,BLUE,SIX PINK GLASSES.......  14.00
AKRO AGATE,PITCHER,CHILD'S,BLUE-GREEN,CRISSCROSS BAND,FOUR
  TUMBLERS............................................................  12.00
AKRO AGATE,PITCHER,SUGAR,CREAMER,CHILD'S,ORANGE............  4.75
AKRO AGATE,PLANTER,CARAMEL & WHITE......................................  8.50
AKRO AGATE,PLANTER,DAFFODILS,5 1/2 IN...................................  7.50
AKRO AGATE,PLANTER,GREEN,MARK,5 IN......................................  6.00
AKRO AGATE,PLANTER,GREEN,WHITE,5 1/2 X 3 IN.............................  6.00
AKRO AGATE,PLANTER,ORANGE,WHITE,LEAVES,BLOSSOMS,5 1/2 IN. X
  3 IN................................................................  6.00
AKRO AGATE,PLANTER,ORANGE,WHITE,5 1/2 X 3 IN............................  6.00
AKRO AGATE,PLATE,CHILD'S,BLUE,SET OF 4..................................  4.00
AKRO AGATE,POT,FLOWER,SHADES OF ROSE,IVORY & ORANGE,3 IN....  4.00
AKRO AGATE,SHOT GLASS,PAIR..............................................  4.00
AKRO AGATE,SUGAR,CREAMER,FOUR CUPS & SAUCERS,CHILD'S,GREEN..  5.50
AKRO AGATE,TEA SET,CHILD'S,MULTICOLORED,SIGNED,16 PIECES....  9.00
AKRO AGATE,TEA SET,CHILDS,6 PIECES......................................  6.50
AKRO AGATE,TOOTHPICK,CORNUCOPIA,GREEN TO WHITE,SIGNED.......  10.00
AKRO AGATE,TOOTHPICK,VASE IN HAND,ORANGE COLOR TO WHITE,
  SIGNED..............................................................  15.00
AKRO AGATE,TUMBLER,MEXICALI,CREAMY,PUMPKIN SLAG.............  10.00
AKRO AGATE,URN,CORNUCOPIA,GREEN.........................................  4.50
AKRO AGATE,VASE,BROWN SWIRL RIBBED BODY,FLARED RIM,3 IN.HIGH  6.50
AKRO AGATE,VASE,GREEN...................................................  10.00
AKRO AGATE,VASE,HAND,ORANGE,MARKED......................................  10.00
AKRO AGATE,VASE,HORN OF PLENTY,3 IN.,PAIR...............................  10.00
AKRO AGATE,VASE,ORANGE & CREAM,FLAT.....................................  6.00
AKRO AGATE,VASE,URN SHAPE,BLUE SLAG,MARKED..............................  6.00
AKRO AGATE,VASE,URN SHAPE,ORANGE MOTTLE,PEDESTAL,SCALLOPED
  RIM,3 1/4 IN........................................................  6.50
ALBERTINE,JAR,CRACKER,APRICOT GROUND,APPLE BLOSSOM LIMBS &
  FLORAL..............................................................  275.00
```

ALBUMS WERE POPULAR IN VICTORIAN TIMES TO HOLD THE
MYRIAD PICTURES AND CUTOUTS FAVORED BY THE COLLECTORS.
ALL SORTS OF SCRAPBOOKS AND ALBUMS CAN STILL BE FOUND.

```
ALBUM,BROWN & TAN VELVET,RED PAGES,BRASS CORNERS,BRASS HEART
  FRAME...............................................................  16.00
ALBUM,CARDS,ADVERTISING & ALBUM,1880S,350...............................  30.00
ALBUM,GREEN-FIGURED VELVET,BRASS CORNERS,MIRROR,HANDLED
  HOLDER,DRAWER.......................................................  41.50
ALBUM,PHOTO,GOLD EDGE,ORNATE CLASP,5 IN. X 6 IN. X 1 3/4 IN.  5.98
ALBUM,PHOTO,GREEN VELOUR,HEART SHAPE MIRROR INSERT,GOLD
  FLORAL BOUQUET......................................................  18.00
ALBUM,PHOTO,PICTURE OF U.S.S.MAINE ON COVER.............................  35.00
ALBUM,PHOTO,WORLD WAR I SNAPSHOTS WITH DESCRIPTIVE CAPTIONS.  7.50
ALBUM,PHOTOGRAPH,LEATHER,DATED 1865.....................................  15.00
ALBUM,PICTURE,TOOLED LEATHER COVER,BRASS CLASP,PATENT 1881..  15.00
```

ALBUM,RED VELVET,NICKEL LETTERS,ALBUM,ON COVER,GOLD-EDGED
  PAGES,CLASP...................................................    16.00
ALBUM,VELVET,BROWN,GOLD-EDGED PAGES,8 1/2 X 11 IN............     7.50
ALEXANDRITE,PLATE,HONEYCOMB PATTERN,CRIMPED EDGE,5 3/4 IN...   350.00
  ALPHABET PLATE,SEE ABC PLATE


             AMBER GLASS IS THE NAME OF ANY GLASSWARE WITH THE
             PROPER YELLOW-BROWN SHADE. IT WAS A POPULAR COLOR
             AFTER THE CIVIL WAR.
AMBER,BASKET,EIGHT PANELS,9 1/2 IN.HIGH.......................    10.25
AMBER,BASKET,EYEWINKER PATTERN ON EDGE,LEAF PATTERN IN
  CENTER,FOOTED...............................................    20.00
AMBER,BASKET,PANELED,9 IN.HIGH...............................    30.00
AMBER,BELL,ROSE IN SNOW,BRASS HANDLE.........................    18.50
  AMBER,BOTTLE,SEE BOTTLE,AMBER
AMBER,BOWL,BERRY,DAISY & BUTTON,PANELED,SCALLOPED,EIGHT
  SAUCE DISHES................................................    85.00
AMBER,BOWL,BIRCH LEAF,PORTLAND GLASS CO.,10 1/2 X 7 1/4 IN..    22.50
AMBER,BOWL,DAISY & BUTTON,GRAPE LEAVES,BOAT SHAPE,FOOTED....    39.50
AMBER,BOWL,FINGER,TREE OF LIFE...............................    15.00
AMBER,BOWL,OVAL,SHELL & TASSLE...............................    22.50
AMBER,BOWL,PUNCH,PANELED,BLOWN,ORNATE BRASS COVER & UNDER
  PLATE......................................................    85.00
AMBER,BOWL,ROSE,APPLIED SIX CRYSTAL FEET,BLOWN..............    38.00
AMBER,BOWL,ROSE,LION LEGS,4 1/2 X 3 1/4 IN...................    25.00
AMBER,BOWL,SHELL & TASSEL,BOAT SHAPE,SILVER FRAME,10 IN.LONG    65.00
AMBER,BOWL,TEN PANELS,CAMBRIDGE,12 IN.DIAMETER...............     7.00
AMBER,BOX,DIAMOND PATTERN,COVER..............................     7.50
AMBER,BOX,JEWEL,ENAMELED,CHECKERBOARD,FORGET-ME-NOTS,BRASS
  HINGE,HANDLES..............................................   150.00
AMBER,BOX,WHITE ENAMELED FLORAL,HINGED LID,4 1/2 X 3 IN.....    25.00
AMBER,BUTTER,DEWEY...........................................    26.50
AMBER,BUTTER,LID IS FACE OF WATCH............................    47.00
AMBER,CAKE STAND,DAISY & BUTTON,THUMBPRINT,9 1/4 IN..........    37.50
AMBER,CAKE STAND,WILLOW OAK..................................    27.50
AMBER,CAKE STAND,1000-EYE,THREE KNOB STEM,10 IN.DIAMETER....    37.50
AMBER,CAKESTAND,DAISY & BUTTON,THUMBPRINT,9 1/4 IN..........    37.50
AMBER,CANDLEHOLDER,ETCHED TOP,SIGNED SINCLAIRE,4 1/2 X
  3 IN.HIGH,PAIR.............................................    57.50
AMBER,CANDLESTICK,DOLPHIN,6 IN.,PAIR.........................    15.00
AMBER,CANDLESTICK,PANELED,WARRIOR BAND IN GILT,
  12 3/4 IN.TALL,PAIR........................................   110.00
AMBER,CANOE,SALT.............................................    12.00
AMBER,CASTOR,PICKLE,CANE PATTERN INSERT......................    65.00
AMBER,CASTOR,PICKLE,DAISY & BUTTON,QUADRUPLE PLATE SILVER
  HOLDER.....................................................    59.00
AMBER,CASTOR,PICKLE,DAISY & BUTTON,SILVER FRAME & COVER.....    75.00
AMBER,CASTOR,PICKLE,HONEY,DAISY & BUTTON,ORNATE HOLDER,
  RESILVERED,FOOTED..........................................    77.50
AMBER,CELERY,DAISY & BUTTON,PANELS...........................    37.50
AMBER,CELERY,DIAMOND PATTERN,TWO HANDLES.....................    45.00
AMBER,CHAMPAGNE,CUT DESIGN,5 1/2 IN.HIGH,SET OF 8...........    35.00
AMBER,COMPOTE,BLOCK & STAR,COVER,6 IN. X 10 IN..............    24.00
AMBER,COMPOTE,CATHEDRAL PATTERN,OPEN,8 1/4 IN. X 8 1/4 IN...    35.00
AMBER,COMPOTE,CATHEDRAL PATTERN,RUFFLED,9 IN.DIAMETER,
  6 1/2 IN.HIGH..............................................    28.00
AMBER,COMPOTE,DAISY & BUTTON WITH CROSSBAR,LOW STANDARD.....    22.50
AMBER,COMPOTE,DAISY,BUTTON IN BLOCK,SQUATTY FOOTED,9 IN.....    22.50
AMBER,COMPOTE,GRAPES,VINE,FOOTED,OPEN........................    35.00
AMBER,COMPOTE,INVERTED THUMBPRINT,OPEN,7 IN.................    22.50
AMBER,COMPOTE,JELLY,OPEN,WHEAT & BARLEY,4 IN.DIAMETER,
  4 1/2 IN.HIGH..............................................    18.50
AMBER,COMPOTE,OPEN-LATTICED EDGE,BASKETWEAVE STEM,7 IN.HIGH.    37.50
AMBER,COMPOTE,OPEN,1000 EYE,SQUARE TOP,RIBBED STEM,
  8 1/4 IN.DIAMETER..........................................    32.50
AMBER,COMPOTE,PRESSED DIAMOND PATTERN,OPEN,PEDESTAL FOOT,
  6 IN.TALL..................................................    25.00
AMBER,COMPOTE,PRESSED DIAMOND,OPEN,7 1/2 IN. X 5 IN.........    15.00
AMBER,COMPOTE,THOUSAND EYE,THREE KNOB BASE,OPEN,9 IN.ROUND..    42.50
AMBER,COMPOTE,THREE PANEL,FOOTED,7 IN........................    18.00
AMBER,COMPOTE,THREE PANELS,8 1/2 IN. X 3 1/2 IN.HIGH........    19.50
AMBER,COMPOTE,WHEAT & BARLEY,COVER,FINIAL,12 1/4 IN.HIGH....    57.50
AMBER,COMPOTE,WILD FLOWER,TWISTED SILVER HANDLE,8 X 11 IN...    32.50
AMBER,CONSOLE SET,GOLD BORDER,13 IN.BOWL,PAIR
  3 IN.CANDLESTICKS..........................................    15.00
AMBER,CREAMER & SUGAR,OPEN,C IN TRIANGLE.....................     7.50
AMBER,CREAMER,HOBNAIL,THUMBPRINT BASE........................    15.00
AMBER,CREAMER,ROSE IN SNOW PATTERN...........................    35.00
AMBER,CREAMER,SPIREA BAND PATTERN,5 1/2 IN.TALL.............    12.50

```
AMBER,CREAMER,WILD FLOWER.....................................  18.00
AMBER,CRUET,BULBOUS,ENAMELED LILY DESIGN,BLUE HANDLE &
   STOPPER....................................................  25.00
AMBER,CRUET,DIMPLED SIDES,BLOWN,APPLIED HANDLE,STOPPER,
   7 IN.TALL..................................................  27.00
AMBER,CRUET,EMERALD GREEN HANDLE & STOPPER,ETCHED INITIAL,
   7 IN.HIGH..................................................  32.00
AMBER,CRUET,ENAMELED FLORAL,BEE,PANELED,STOPPER..............  35.00
AMBER,CRUET,PINCHED-IN SIDES,APPLIED AMBER HANDLE,STOPPER,
   7 IN.TALL..................................................  27.00
AMBER,CRUET,PINCHED,BLUE APPLIED HANDLE & STOPPER...........   48.00
AMBER,CRUET,PINK & BLUE ENAMELING,PEDESTAL BASE,RIBBED,
   8 IN.TALL..................................................  42.00
AMBER,CRUET,S REPEAT PATTERN,CLEAR,STOPPER...................  15.00
AMBER,CRUET,SIX BOTTLE,DAISY & BUTTON,SILVER HOLDER..........  85.00
AMBER,CRUET,WINE,ENAMEL LAVENDER FIRS,GREEN VINE,8 SMALL
   CUPS,HANDLED...............................................  46.50
AMBER,CUP,PUNCH,INVERTED THUMBPRINT,APPLIED BLUE HANDLE.....   28.00
AMBER,DECANTER,RINGED BOTTOM,MUSHROOM STOPPER,SIGNED STUART,
   ENGLAND....................................................  23.00
AMBER,DECANTER,WHISKEY,TRAY,FIVE PEDESTAL SHOT GLASSES,
   PANELED....................................................  35.50
AMBER,DECANTER,WINE,ENAMEL,HAND-PAINTED WHITE FLORAL,BLUE
   GRAPES,6 WINES.............................................  85.00
AMBER,DECANTER,WINE,ENAMELED WHITE FLORAL,BLUE GRAPES,BLOWN,
   6 WINES....................................................   5.00
AMBER,DISH,CANDY,LACY BRASS COVER SET WITH COLORED JEWELS...   16.50
AMBER,DISH,FLAT RAYS PATTERN,RUFFLED,9 IN....................  12.50
AMBER,DISH,FROSTED LION COVER,DATED 1889,LACY BASE..........   75.00
AMBER,DISH,SAUCE,HOLLY,BEADED,4 1/2 IN...................... 135.00
AMBER,DISH,SAUCE,WILD FLOWER,THREE FOOTED....................   4.00
AMBER,DISH,SAUCE,1000-EYE,FLAT...............................   5.50
AMBER,EYECUP,JUST-RITE,MARKED W.E.M.CO.......................   4.00
AMBER,FIGURINE,HEN,WHITE HEAD,5 1/2 IN.......................  75.00
AMBER,FLASK,14 RIBS ON EACH SIDE,1/2 PINT....................  25.00
AMBER,GOBLET,BASKET WEAVE....................................  27.50
AMBER,GOBLET,CANE............................................  22.50
AMBER,GOBLET,DAISY & BUTTON,THUMBPRINT.......................  27.50
AMBER,GOBLET,DAISY & BUTTON,THUMBPRINT,FLASHED...............  27.50
AMBER,GOBLET,HOBNAIL.........................................  20.50
AMBER,GOBLET,MAPLE LEAF......................................  15.00
AMBER,GOBLET,ROSE IN SNOW....................................  22.50
AMBER,GOBLET,SPIREA BAND.....................................  14.50
AMBER,GOBLET,STAR OF DAVID...................................  12.50
AMBER,GOBLET,THOUSAND EYE....................................  21.00
AMBER,GOBLET,WILD FLOWER.....................................  22.50
AMBER,HEN ON NEST,5 IN.......................................  35.00
AMBER,ICE BUCKET,PANELS,SILVER COLLAR & HANDLES..............  20.00
AMBER,INKWELL,DIAMOND SHAPE,FACETED HINGED LID,4 IN.........   20.00
AMBER,JAR,COFFEE,SCREW ON TIN COVER..........................  15.00
AMBER,JAR,POWDER,HONEY,DIAMOND POINT COVER,FINIAL,SIGNED
   CAMBRIDGE..................................................  12.00
AMBER,JAR,SNUFF,LORILLARD,1872...............................  12.50
AMBER,JAR,WAN-ETA-COCA.......................................   5.00
AMBER,JUG,HOBNAIL,BLOWN,8 IN.HIGH............................  45.00
AMBER,KNIFE REST,FACETED ENDS,3 1/4 IN.......................   8.50
AMBER,LAMP,DAISY & BUTTON FONT,RIBBED BRASS SHANK,SQUARE
   IRON BASE..................................................  35.00
AMBER,LAMP,LIGHTHOUSE,TWO PARTS,HEXAGONAL,6 IN.HIGH.........   22.50
AMBER,MUG,ALE,TWO LION HEADS,EMBOSSED,6 IN...................   8.00
AMBER,MUG,BUTTERFLY..........................................  17.00
AMBER,MUG,CHILD'S FACE IN WREATH MEDALLION...................  15.00
AMBER,MUG,DEER & DOG.........................................  18.00
AMBER,MUG,HOBNAIL............................................   7.00
AMBER,MUG,LIGHTHOUSE ON ONE SIDE,SHIP ON OTHER,SKIRTED
   BOTTOM,3 IN.HIGH...........................................  12.75
AMBER,MUG,RELIEF MOSQUITOES,RABBITS..........................  39.50
AMBER,NAPKIN RING,TRIANGLE SHAPE,LARGE STAR WITH BUTTON,
   2 IN.WIDE..................................................  10.00
AMBER,PITCHER,DAISY & BUTTON,PANELS,9 IN.TALL................  25.50
AMBER,PITCHER,DAISY & BUTTON,SCALLOPED TOP,APPLIED HANDLE,
   TANKARD,9 IN...............................................  75.00
AMBER,PITCHER,ENAMELED BLUE LILIES,WHITE FLORAL,BLUE HANDLE,
   9 3/4 IN...................................................  35.00
AMBER,PITCHER,MILK,BASKET WEAVE..............................  17.00
AMBER,PITCHER,MILK,DAISY,BUTTON,X BAR........................  29.50
AMBER,PITCHER,WATER,APPLIED BLUE HANDLE,BLOWN................  37.00
AMBER,PITCHER,WATER,HOBNAIL,BULBOUS,APPLIED REEDED HANDLE,
   7 1/2 IN.TALL..............................................  40.00
AMBER,PITCHER,WATER,HUMMINGBIRD..............................  38.75
```

AMBER,PITCHER,WATER,INVERTED RIB,BLUE APPLIED HANDLE,BULBOUS    65.00
AMBER,PITCHER,WATER,SWIRLS,BLUE APPLIED RIBBED HANDLE,
  9 1/2 IN................................................    47.50
AMBER,PITCHER,WATER,WILD FLOWER..............................    37.50
AMBER,PITCHER,WATER,WILLOW OAK...............................    44.50
AMBER,PITCHER,WATER,1000 EYE,11 1/2 IN.,ONE TUMBLER..........    85.00
AMBER,PLATE,BREAD,CUPID & VENUS,11 1/2 IN....................    35.00
AMBER,PLATE,BREAD,WHEAT & BARLEY,HANDLES,ROUND...............    16.50
AMBER,PLATE,CAKE,DEEP-EMBOSSED GOLD BORDER,OCTAGONAL,
  10 IN.DIAMETER..........................................    15.00
AMBER,PLATE,CAKE,PANELED,APPLIED HANDLES,CAMBRIDGE,
  11 1/2 IN...............................................     6.00
AMBER,PLATE,DAHLIA,7 IN....................................    25.00
AMBER,PLATE,DOG HEAD CENTER,5 1/2 IN.......................    16.00
AMBER,PLATE,QUEEN'S JUBILEE,QUEEN VICTORIA 50TH YEAR,
  1837-1857..............................................    45.00
AMBER,POKAL,HAND-PAINTED ROBED FLEMISH WOMAN,PRUNTS,PEDESTAL
  BASE,16 IN.............................................    65.00
AMBER,RELISH BOAT,OVAL,TWO HANDLES,OLD IMPERIAL MARK.......    10.50
AMBER,ROLLING PIN.........................................    19.00
AMBER,SALT & PEPPER,FROSTED...............................    95.00
AMBER,SALT,DAISY & CUBE...................................    12.00
AMBER,SALT,FACET CUT,SIX SIDED,1 3/4 X 1/2 IN.............     3.00
AMBER,SALT,MASTER.........................................     5.00
AMBER,SALT,MASTER,DUCK,FROSTED............................    12.50
AMBER,SALT,MASTER,HOBNAIL,SQUARE,2 3/4 IN.................    10.00
AMBER,SALT,MASTER,STAR BOTTOM.............................     5.00
AMBER,SALT,PANELED ROSE...................................     9.00
AMBER,SALT,1000 EYE.......................................    15.00
AMBER,SAUCE,DAISY & BUTTON,SCALLOPED,DEEP.................     9.50
AMBER,SAUCE,DAISY,BUTTON,CROSSBAR,FOOTED..................     6.50
AMBER,SAUCE,DIAMOND QUILTED,FOOTED........................     8.00
AMBER,SAUCE,HOBNAIL,FAN TOP...............................    13.00
AMBER,SAUCE,ROSE SPRIG,PORRINGER HANDLE,FLAT,4 IN.........     8.75
AMBER,SAUCE,WILD FLOWER,FLAT,4 IN.........................     6.00
AMBER,SHAKER,SALT & PEPPER,KLONDYKE CURVE,FROSTED,PAIR.....    95.00
AMBER,SHAKER,SALT,BLOCK...................................     8.50
AMBER,SHAKER,SALT,THUMBPRINT,ENAMELED FLOWERS,BULBOUS.....    22.00
AMBER,SHOE,DAISY BUTTON,MOCCASIN SHAPE,4 7/8 IN...........    18.50
AMBER,SITZ BATH,DAISY & BUTTON............................    80.00
AMBER,SLIPPER,DAISY & BUTTON,MOCCASIN SHAPE,4 1/2 IN.LONG...    20.00
AMBER,SPOONER,BEADED OVAL WINDOWS.........................    19.50
AMBER,SPOONER,CHILD'S,SHAPE OF FISH.......................    18.00
AMBER,SPOONER,WILD FLOWER.................................    17.50
AMBER,STEIN,ENAMELED FIGURE...............................    42.00
AMBER,SUGAR,HOBNAIL,RUFFLED TOP,PLAIN BASE,COVER..........    15.00
AMBER,SYRUP,PANELED HORIZONTAL THUMBPRINT,PEWTER TOP.......    30.00
AMBER,SYRUP,RIBBED SWIRL,APPLIED AMBER HANDLE,ACID FINISH,
  WHEELING...............................................    65.00
AMBER,SYRUP,THUMBPRINT,SWIRL BASE,PEWTER LID,DATED JAN.29,
  84.....................................................    35.00
AMBER,TIEBACK,2 1/2 IN.,PAIR..............................     6.00
AMBER,TOOTHPICK,ANVIL.....................................    30.00
AMBER,TOOTHPICK,BARREL,PICKET.............................     9.50
AMBER,TOOTHPICK,COAL SCUTTLE..............................    27.50
AMBER,TOOTHPICK,COAL SCUTTLE,DAISY & BUTTON...............    27.50
AMBER,TOOTHPICK,DAISY & BUTTON,HAT........................    12.50
AMBER,TOOTHPICK,FISH......................................    20.00
AMBER,TOOTHPICK,FOOTED....................................    12.50
AMBER,TOOTHPICK,HOBNAIL...................................    12.00
AMBER,TOOTHPICK,HOLLY BAND PATTERN........................    40.00
AMBER,TOOTHPICK,S REPEAT..................................     8.50
AMBER,TOOTHPICK,VERMONT...................................    23.50
AMBER,TOOTHPICK,WITCH KETTLE,CANE.........................     9.50
AMBER,TOOTHPICK,WITCH KETTLE,DAISY & BUTTON...............     9.50
AMBER,TRAY,CELERY,RAISED LEAF.............................     6.00
AMBER,TRAY,MOSES IN THE BULRUSHES,THREE SMALL FEET,8 3/4 X
  6 3/4 IN...............................................    45.00
AMBER,TRAY,WATER,BASKET WEAVE.............................    22.50
AMBER,TRIVET,3 FISH MAKE THE LEGS,SIGNED VERLYS,FRANCE......    18.00
AMBER,TUMBLER,DAISY & BUTTON..............................    18.00
AMBER,TUMBLER,DAISY & BUTTON,THUMBPRINT...................    13.50
AMBER,TUMBLER,HOBNAIL.....................................     7.50
AMBER,TUMBLER,HONEYCOMB,DAISY & BUTTON....................    18.00
AMBER,TUMBLER,INVERTED THUMBPRINT,BENNINGTON TYPE.........     8.50
AMBER,TUMBLER,PANELS,SOME CLEAR,ETCHED VINTAGE............    25.00
AMBER,TUMBLER,STIPPLED,FLEUR-DE-LIS.......................    18.50
AMBER,TUMBLER,WINE,INVERTED THUMBPRINT,4 IN.TALL.........     7.50
AMBER,VASE,APPLIED AQUA STRIPES,6 IN.TALL.................    15.00
AMBER,VASE,CELERY,TWO PANEL...............................    14.00

AMBER,VASE,LEAF & FLOWER SPRAYS,ETCHED,RIBBON BANDS,FAN
  SHAPE,7 3/4 IN............................................ 35.00
AMBER,VASE,SCROLL,ROUGH PONTIL,13 IN.TALL,7 IN.DIAMETER..... 37.50
AMBER,WINE SET,SILVER-FOOTED TRESTLE,HOOPS,BARREL,SIX
  GLASSES.................................................... 21.00
AMBER,WINE,CLEAR STEM & FOOT,PAIR........................... 12.00
AMBER,WINE,HOLLOW STEM,5 3/4 IN.TALL,SET OF 8............... 20.00
AMBER,WINE,1000-EYE,THREE KNOBS............................. 10.00


     AMBERINA IS A TWO-TONED GLASSWARE MADE FROM 1883 TO
  ABOUT 1900. IT WAS PATENTED BY JOSEPH LOCKE OF THE NEW
  ENGLAND GLASS COMPANY. THE GLASS SHADES FROM RED TO
  AMBER.
AMBERINA,SEE ALSO,MT.WASHINGTON,BACCARAT,PLATED AMBERINA
AMBERINA,BOTTLE,BULBOUS,10 IN.HIGH.......................... 87.50
AMBERINA,BOTTLE,COLOGNE,BACCARAT,SWIRL DESIGN,STOPPER,
  8 IN.TALL................................................. 30.00
AMBERINA,BOWL,FINGER,FUCHSIA,DIAMOND-QUILTED................ 80.00
AMBERINA,BOWL,FINGER,FUCHSIA,INVERTED THUMBPRINT,
  4 1/2 IN.DIAMETER......................................... 65.00
AMBERINA,BOWL,FINGER,PLATE,FUCHSIA TO YELLOW,VENETIAN
  DIAMOND PATTERN...........................................250.00
AMBERINA,BOWL,FUCHSIA,FLUTED,LIBBEY,5 1/2 IN.DIAMETER,
  UNDERPLATE................................................200.00
AMBERINA,BOWL,FUCHSIA,ROLLED-OVER TOP,SCALLOPED,SIGNED
  LIBBEY,10 IN..............................................295.00
AMBERINA,BOWL,FUCHSIA,TRIANGULAR,MT.WASHINGTON..............175.00
AMBERINA,BOWL,ROSE,INVERTED THUMBPRINT,EGG SHAPE,NARROW
  NECK,AMBER FEET...........................................110.00
AMBERINA,BOWL,SIGNED C IN TRIANGLE,10 1/2 IN................ 60.00
AMBERINA,BUTTER PAT,DAISY & BUTTON,SQUARE,CLOVERLEAF CORNERS 15.00
AMBERINA,CASTOR,PICKLE,RIBBED,INVERTED THUMBPRINT,SILVER
  PLATE HOLDER..............................................225.00
AMBERINA,CELERY,DAISY & BUTTON............................. 35.00
AMBERINA,CELERY,DIAMOND-QUILTED,SQUARE SCALLOPED TOP,
  6 1/2 IN.HIGH.............................................160.00
AMBERINA,CELERY,RIBBED,DARK RED TO SMOKY AMBER,GROUND
  PONTIL,NEW ENGLAND........................................115.00
AMBERINA,CELERY,THUMBPRINT,SCALLOPED RIM,NEW ENGLAND,
  6 3/4 IN.HIGH.............................................225.00
AMBERINA,COMPOTE,FUCHSIA,AMBER WAFER BASE,BALUSTER STEM,
  SIGNED LIBBEY.............................................250.00
AMBERINA,CREAMER & SUGAR,DAISY & BUTTON.................... 89.50
AMBERINA,CREAMER,WREATH CHERRIES,RED AT BASE,GOLD IN CENTER,
  RED AT TOP................................................ 18.00
AMBERINA,CRUET,FUCHSIA.....................................145.00
AMBERINA,CRUET,FUCHSIA,INVERTED THUMBPRINT,SQUAT BODY,AMBER
  STOPPER...................................................250.00
AMBERINA,CRUET,INVERTED THUMBPRINT,AMBER HANDLE,CUT STOPPER,
  6 IN.HIGH.................................................145.00
AMBERINA,CRUET,THUMBPRINT..................................135.00
AMBERINA,CRUET,WINE,INVERTED THUMBPRINT,RUFFLED EDGE,WHITE
  CUT STOPPER...............................................150.00
AMBERINA,CRUET,WINE,RUFFLED EDGE,CLEAR REED HANDLE,CUT
  STOPPER,9 IN..............................................135.00
AMBERINA,CUP,PUNCH,BERRY PATTERN,N MARK,SET OF 6........... 50.00
AMBERINA,CUP,PUNCH,FUCHSIA TOP,3 1/4 IN. X 2 1/2 IN.HIGH.... 65.00
AMBERINA,CUP,PUNCH,FUCHSIA,DIAMOND-QUILTED,AMBER REED
  HANDLES,SET OF 4..........................................300.00
AMBERINA,CUP,PUNCH,FUCHSIA,DIAMOND-QUILTED,AMBER RIBBED
  HANDLE....................................................122.00
AMBERINA,CUP,PUNCH,FUCHSIA,DIAMOND-QUILTED,AMBER HANDLE..... 79.50
AMBERINA,CUP,PUNCH,FUCHSIA,DIAMOND-QUILTED................. 80.00
AMBERINA,CUP,PUNCH,FUSCHIA,REEDED,SET OF 6.................400.00
AMBERINA,CUP,PUNCH,INVERTED THUMBPRINT,BLUE & RED SPOT IN
  PONTIL.................................................... 67.00
AMBERINA,CUP,PUNCH,INVERTED THUMBPRINT,CLEAR APPLIED HANDLE. 45.00
AMBERINA,CUP,PUNCH,THUMBPRINT,REEDED HANDLE,2 5/8 IN.TALL... 95.00
AMBERINA,CUP,TODDY,INVERTED THUMBPRINT..................... 45.00
AMBERINA,DECANTER,RUFFLED TOP,INVERTED THUMBPRINT,REEDED
  CLEAR HANDLE..............................................185.00
AMBERINA,DISH,BUTTER,FUCHSIA,INVERTED THUMBPRINT,DAISY &
  BUTTON BASE...............................................110.00
AMBERINA,DISH,BUTTER,INVERTED THUMBPRINT,DAISY & BUTTON
  AMBER BASE................................................140.00
AMBERINA,DISH,CHEESE,COVER,7 IN.HIGH,7 1/2 IN.ACROSS BASE...350.00
AMBERINA,DISH,FLARED,RUFFLED,SHALLOW,7 IN.,SIGNED LIBBEY....165.00
AMBERINA,DISH,ICE CREAM,DAISY & BUTTON,SQUARE,CUT CORNERS,
  5 3/4 IN.................................................. 60.00

| | |
|---|---:|
| AMBERINA,GLASS,JUICE,BABY INVERTED THUMBPRINT,OVERALL GOLD DECOR | 85.00 |
| AMBERINA,GOBLET,SAWTOOTH SWIRL,LOW STEM,SIGNED,BACCARAT | 26.00 |
| AMBERINA,ICE BUCKET,THUMBPRINT,CUT RAYED BASE,6 3/4 X 4 1/4 IN.HIGH | 190.00 |
| AMBERINA,ICE CREAM SET,DAISY & BUTTON,SCALLOPED CORNERS, PLATTER,4 PLATES | 635.00 |
| AMBERINA,LAMP,HALL,DIAMOND-QUILTED | 139.50 |
| AMBERINA,LAMP,HALL,DIAMOND-QUILTED,CYLINDER SHAPE | 147.50 |
| AMBERINA,MUG,BABY THUMBPRINT | 45.00 |
| AMBERINA,MUG,CORSET SHAPE | 59.00 |
| AMBERINA,MUG,CRANBERRY SHADING TO AMBER,SWIRL PATTERN,AMBER HANDLE | 65.00 |
| AMBERINA,PITCHER,HOBNAIL,SQUARE TOP | 277.00 |
| AMBERINA,PITCHER,INVERTED THUMBPRINT,7 IN | 75.00 |
| AMBERINA,PITCHER,MILK,AMBER REEDED HANDLE,WHEELING,6 1/2 IN. | 72.50 |
| AMBERINA,PITCHER,MILK,DAISY & BUTTON,TANKARD,SANDWICH GLASS, 5 1/4 IN | 250.00 |
| AMBERINA,PITCHER,MILK,HERRINGBONE PATTERN | 125.00 |
| AMBERINA,PITCHER,MILK,WHEELING,AMBER REED HANDLE | 72.50 |
| AMBERINA,PITCHER,PANELED,APPLIED ROPE AROUND NECK,FORMS HANDLE,8 7/8 IN | 195.00 |
| AMBERINA,PITCHER,QUILTED,CLEAR THREADED HANDLE,5 3/4 IN | 165.00 |
| AMBERINA,PITCHER,THUMBPRINT,10 IN.HIGH | 175.00 |
| AMBERINA,PITCHER,WATER,FUSCHIA,INVERTED THUMBPRINT, 7 1/2 IN.HIGH | 160.00 |
| AMBERINA,PITCHER,WATER,INVERTED THUMBPRINT,TREFOIL TOP, BULBOUS | 175.00 |
| AMBERINA,SHADE,ALLOVER EMBOSSED,IRIS,FLARED,RUFFLED,4 1/2 X 5 1/4 IN | 55.00 |
| AMBERINA,SHAKER,PEPPER,BABY INVERTED THUMBPRINT,PEWTER TOP, 4 IN.TALL | 35.00 |
| AMBERINA,SHAKER,SALT,THUMBPRINT,ENAMEL | 49.00 |
| AMBERINA,SHERBET,COLONIAL PATTERN | 35.00 |
| AMBERINA,SHOE,HIGH-BUTTON,FUCHSIA,RIBBED INTERIOR,FLINT, 7 1/2 IN.TALL | 110.00 |
| AMBERINA,SPOONER,FUCHSIA,DIAMOND-QUILTED,SCALLOPED SQUARE TOP,4 1/2 IN | 135.00 |
| AMBERINA,TOOTHPICK,BABY DIAMOND-QUILTED,BARREL SHAPE,2 X 2 1/2 IN.HIGH | 95.00 |
| AMBERINA,TOOTHPICK,BARREL SHAPE,ROUND TOP,BABY DIAMOND QUILTED | 95.00 |
| AMBERINA,TOOTHPICK,DATED,PAT.SEPT.1930 | 50.00 |
| AMBERINA,TOOTHPICK,DIAMOND-QUILTED,FUCHSIA AT TOP, TRICORNERED | 125.00 |
| AMBERINA,TOOTHPICK,DIAMOND-QUILTED | 65.00 |
| AMBERINA,TOOTHPICK,DIAMOND-QUILTED,BARREL SHAPE | 115.00 |
| AMBERINA,TOOTHPICK,DIAMOND-QUILTED,BARREL SHAPE,2 IN. X 2 1/2 IN.HIGH | 95.00 |
| AMBERINA,TOOTHPICK,DIAMOND-QUILTED,GROUND PONTIL,DEEP RUBY TOP | 75.00 |
| AMBERINA,TOOTHPICK,FUCHSIA HALFWAY DOWN,BARREL,2 1/2 IN.HIGH | 95.00 |
| AMBERINA,TOOTHPICK,FUCHSIA,DAISY & BUTTON | 145.00 |
| AMBERINA,TOOTHPICK,FUCHSIA,DIAMOND-QUILTED,SQUARE TOP,NEW ENGLAND | 125.00 |
| AMBERINA,TOOTHPICK,SQUARE TOP,NEW ENGLAND | 95.00 |
| AMBERINA,TOOTHPICK,THREE-CORNERED | 110.00 |
| AMBERINA,TUMBLER,BABY THUMBPRINT,ENAMELED LEAVES & FLORAL, REVERSE | 95.00 |
| AMBERINA,TUMBLER,DIAMOND-QUILTED,3 3/4 IN.TALL | 50.00 |
| AMBERINA,TUMBLER,FUCHSIA | 78.00 |
| AMBERINA,TUMBLER,FUCHSIA HALFWAY TO AMBER,DIAMOND-QUILTED | 62.00 |
| AMBERINA,TUMBLER,FUSCHIA TO YELLOW,BABY THUMBPRINT,4 IN.TALL | 42.50 |
| AMBERINA,TUMBLER,FUSCHIA,DIAMOND-QUILTED | 65.00 |
| AMBERINA,TUMBLER,INVERTED THUMBPRINT | 38.00 |
| AMBERINA,TUMBLER,INVERTED THUMBPRINT,BLOWN,3 3/4 IN.TALL,SET OF 4 | 182.50 |
| AMBERINA,TUMBLER,INVERTED THUMBPRINT,SIGNED LIBBEY,4 IN.TALL | 65.00 |
| AMBERINA,TUMBLER,JUICE,BABY THUMBPRINT | 35.00 |
| AMBERINA,TUMBLER,RAINDROP,ONE LARGE BURST BUBBLE INSIDE | 26.00 |
| AMBERINA,TUMBLER,SWIRL PATTERN,POLISHED PONTIL,4 IN. TALL | 60.00 |
| AMBERINA,TUMBLER,WATER,DEEP GOLD COLR TO DEEP RED, DIAMOND-QUILTED | 85.00 |
| AMBERINA,VASE,2 HANDLES,SIGNED LIBBEY,9 IN. X 6 IN | 295.00 |
| AMBERINA,VASE,APPLIED SWIRLED PETALS,8 IN.HIGH | 110.00 |
| AMBERINA,VASE,BUD,APPLIED SWIRL DECOR,8 1/4 IN.HIGH | 95.00 |
| AMBERINA,VASE,BUD,SIGNED LIBBEY,12 IN.HIGH | 250.00 |
| AMBERINA,VASE,BULBOUS BOTTOM,TULIP TOP,INVERTED THUMBPRINT, AMBER TO ROSE | 125.00 |
| AMBERINA,VASE,CELERY,DEEP FUCHSIA,STRIPED,9 1/2 IN.TALL | 110.00 |

AMBERINA,VASE,CELERY,FUCHSIA,INVERTED THUMBPRINT,FLUTED TOP,
  NEW ENGLAND........................................................ 225.00
AMBERINA,VASE,CELERY,SQUARE SCALLOPED TOP,FUCHSIA,
  6 1/2 IN.TALL...................................................... 135.00
AMBERINA,VASE,DIAMOND-QUILTED,ACID CUT,10 IN.HIGH........... 275.00
AMBERINA,VASE,FLORIFORM,TURNIP SHAPE BODY,FUCHSIA,
  3 1/2 IN.TALL...................................................... 187.50
AMBERINA,VASE,FUCHSIA,LILY,PANELS,ROUND FLAT BASE,
  7 1/4 IN.HIGH...................................................... 175.00
AMBERINA,VASE,FUCHSIA,SIGNED LIBBEY,10 1/2 IN............... 330.00
AMBERINA,VASE,FUSCHIA,INVERTED THUMBPRINT,TWO HANDLES,
  4 1/4 IN.HIGH...................................................... 135.00
AMBERINA,VASE,INVERTED THUMBPRINT,GOLD FINISH,10 IN......... 195.00
AMBERINA,VASE,INVERTED THUMBPRINT,SCALLOPED TOP,7 IN.HIGH,
  PAIR.............................................................. 110.00
AMBERINA,VASE,LILY,PANELED BODY,THREE-LIPPED TOP,FUCHSIA,
  12 IN.HIGH........................................................ 175.00
AMBERINA,VASE,PALE GOLD COLOR TO PINK,THUMBPRINT,RUFFLED,
  8 IN.............................................................. 95.00
AMBERINA,VASE,QUILTED PATTERN,BULBOUS BOTTOM,FIVE-SIDED TOP,
  5 IN.............................................................. 75.00
AMBERINA,VASE,RED TO RUST TO BROWN TO TAN,9 IN.TALL........ 50.00
AMBERINA,VASE,RIDGED,SIGNED LIBBEY AMBERINA,5 IN.HIGH...... 255.00
AMBERINA,VASE,TULIP,AMBERINA,SIGNED LIBBEY,11 IN.HIGH...... 350.00
AMBERINA,WHISKEY,FUCHSIA,VENETIAN DIAMOND BODY,2 1/2 IN.HIGH 110.00


    AMETHYST GLASS IS ANY OF THE MANY GLASSWARES MADE IN
    THE PROPER DARK PURPLE SHADE. IT WAS A COLOR POPULAR
    AFTER THE CIVIL WAR.
AMETHYST,BONBON,SILVER DEPOSIT,LID,6 1/2 IN.DIAMETER........ 28.00
AMETHYST,BOTTLE,BARBER,BUST OF LADY WITH LONG HAIR,
  VEGEDERMA,BLOWN................................................... 75.00
AMETHYST,BOTTLE,PERFUME,ATOMIZER,MULTICOLORED ENAMELED
  SCROLLS,5 1/2 IN.................................................. 32.00
AMETHYST,BOTTLE,SCENT,PEWTER SCREW TOP...................... 35.00
AMETHYST,BOTTLE,TWO SIDES INDENTED TO TOUCH INSIDE,BLOWN
  STOPPER........................................................... 25.00
AMETHYST,BOWL,BERRY,BLUE ENAMELED FORGET-ME-NOTS,ORANGE
  BERRIES,6 SAUCES................................................. 59.00
AMETHYST,BOWL,COIN DOT,6 1/2 IN............................. 16.00
AMETHYST,BOWL,FINGER,CUT TO CLEAR,MATCHING SAUCER,SET OF 12. 200.00
AMETHYST,BOWL,FINGER,POLISHED PONTIL........................ 14.00
AMETHYST,BOWL,FLAT BASE,CLEAR,4 1/2 IN.HIGH,8 1/2 IN.RIM.... 32.50
AMETHYST,BOWL,PEAR SHAPE,GRAPE PATTERN,BRASS STEM,MARBLE
  BASE............................................................. 40.00
AMETHYST,BOWL,POLISHED PONTIL,FOOTED,12 IN.,CANDLESTICK,
  FOOTED,11 IN..................................................... 30.00
AMETHYST,BOWL,POND LILIES,CATTAILS,8 IN.DIAMETER........... 18.00
AMETHYST,BOWL,PUNCH,TWO-PIECE,12 CUPS....................... 85.00
AMETHYST,BOWL,ROSE,RIBBED,ENAMELED GIRL HOLDING EWER,GOLD,
  BLOWN............................................................ 26.00
AMETHYST,BOWL,STRETCH GLASS,TURNED-IN EDGES,BLACK GLASS
  STAND,FENTON..................................................... 32.00
AMETHYST,BOWL,THREE FRUIT,NORTHWOOD,9 IN.................... 50.00
AMETHYST,BOWL,TROUT & FLY,MILLERSBURG....................... 125.00
AMETHYST,BOX,ORMOLU,FOOTED,ENAMELED,5 IN.................... 42.50
AMETHYST,BUTTER,S REPEAT,FLASHED,GOLD,COVER................. 65.00
AMETHYST,CANDLEHOLDER,3-FOOTED,PAIR......................... 10.00
AMETHYST,CANDLEHOLDER,THUMBCUT STEM,PAIR.................... 25.00
AMETHYST,CANDLESTICK,BLACK,PAIR............................. 8.00
AMETHYST,CANDLESTICK,8 1/2 IN.HIGH,PAIR............ 22.00 TO 25.00
AMETHYST,CHRISTMAS TREE LIGHT,JAR HOLDS CANDLE,FASTENED BY
  FINE WIRE........................................................ 4.75
AMETHYST,COMPOTE,CRYSTAL FIGURINE STEM...................... 22.50
AMETHYST,COMPOTE,ETCHED,CLEAR TOP........................... 18.00
AMETHYST,CREAMER & SUGAR,SILVER OVERLAY,OPEN................ 8.00
AMETHYST,CREAMER & SUGAR,STRUTTING PEACOCK.................. 92.50
AMETHYST,CRUET,GOLD TRIM,STOPPER............................ 87.50
AMETHYST,CRUET,YELLOW,ENAMELED FLORAL IN PINK,BLUE,WHITE,
  STOPPER,9 IN..................................................... 83.00
AMETHYST,CUP,LOVING,DANCING GIRLS,STIPPLED HEART,7 IN.HIGH.. 11.50
AMETHYST,DARNER,BLOWN....................................... 8.00
AMETHYST,DECANTER,FOUR WINES,PAIRPOINT...................... 65.00
AMETHYST,DECANTER,QUILTED PATTERN,BLOWN STOPPER,PAIR........ 40.00
AMETHYST,DECANTER,RAISED ENAMEL,STOPPER,FRANCE,10 IN.TALL... 65.00
AMETHYST,DECANTER,SILVER OVERLAY,FLOWER DESIGN.............. 22.50
AMETHYST,DISH,BLACK,ROOSTER COVER,RED COMB,8 1/2 IN......... 25.00
AMETHYST,DISH,SWAN,BLACK,9 IN............................... 18.00
AMETHYST,FLASK,NAILSEA TYPE,7 IN. X 4 IN.................... 125.00

| | |
|---|---|
| AMETHYST,JAR,POWDER,COVER IS ONE HUGE ROSE.................. | 18.50 |
| AMETHYST,JAR,SWEET MEAT,BARREL SHAPE,CRYSTAL OVERLAY,SILVER TOP.......................................................... | 55.00 |
| AMETHYST,LAMP,CHIMNEY,RING,SHADE,10 IN...................... | 60.00 |
| AMETHYST,LAMP,FINGER,LITTLE BUTTERCUP....................... | 28.00 |
| AMETHYST,LAMP,LITTLE BUTTERCUP,APPLIED HANDLE............... | 37.50 |
| AMETHYST,LAMP,OIL,NO.2,CLEAR,PATENTED 1911 AROUND COLLAR, 10 IN....................................................... | 12.00 |
| AMETHYST,MUG,CHILD'S........................................ | 8.00 |
| AMETHYST,PITCHER,ENAMELED FLORAL............................ | 45.00 |
| AMETHYST,PITCHER,IMPERIAL GRAPE,SIX TUMBLERS................ | 225.00 |
| AMETHYST,PITCHER,WATER,ENAMELED FLOWERS AND LEAVES.......... | 9.50 |
| AMETHYST,PITCHER,WATER,SWIRL,DEEP PONTIL,BLOWN,10 IN.HIGH... | 55.00 |
| AMETHYST,SALT,MASTER,PAIRPOINT,BOAT SHAPE,PEDESTAL.......... | 17.00 |
| AMETHYST,SAUCE,DIAMOND QUILTED,FOOTED....................... | 14.00 |
| AMETHYST,SAUCE,MILLERSBURG,DEEP............................. | 30.00 |
| AMETHYST,SHOE,LADY'S,STIPPLED DETAILS....................... | 16.50 |
| AMETHYST,TOOTHPICK,SILVER DECOR............................. | 15.00 |
| AMETHYST,TUMBLER,ICED TEA,SET OF 4.......................... | 10.00 |
| AMETHYST,TUMBLER,SILVER DECOR,SET OF 6...................... | 55.00 |
| AMETHYST,VASE,BLACK,ENAMELING,SANDWICH GLASS,12 IN.HIGH,PAIR | 95.00 |
| AMETHYST,VASE,BLACK,TWO FIGURES ON FRONT,HANDLES,7 IN...... | 8.50 |
| AMETHYST,VASE,BLACK,WHITE ENAMEL SCROLLS,DOTS,PORCELAIN MEDALLION,CASED............................................. | 95.00 |
| AMETHYST,VASE,DIAMOND POINT,10 3/8 IN....................... | 17.50 |
| AMETHYST,VASE,ENAMEL,LILY-OF-THE-VALLEY,DAISIES,WHITE BEADING,PAIR............................................... | 195.00 |
| AMETHYST,VASE,ETCHED GRAPE & LEAF DESIGN,PAIRPOINT, 6 1/2 IN.TALL........................................... | 35.00 |
| AMETHYST,VASE,FLOWERS,GOLD,1867............................. | 20.00 |
| AMETHYST,VASE,FLUTED TOP,5 1/2 IN.TALL,3 IN.DIAMETER,PAIR... | 10.00 |
| AMETHYST,VASE,HANDKERCHIEF,WITH CRYSTAL,9 IN.TALL........... | 100.00 |
| AMETHYST,VASE,HYACINTH,BLOWN................................ | 16.00 |
| AMETHYST,VASE,OVERSHOT,ROUND BASE,STICK TOP,TWIST IN CENTER, 6 IN.HIGH.................................................. | 35.00 |
| AMETHYST,VASE,PEACOCK AND FLORAL PATTERN,12 X 7 IN.......... | 18.00 |
| AMETHYST,VASE,PINK & GREEN IRIS,ALLOVER GOLD FLORAL,BLOWN, PANELED,10 IN............................................. | 38.00 |
| AMETHYST,VASE,SINCLAIRE,S IN WREATH,4 1/4 X 5 IN.HIGH....... | 12.50 |
| AMETHYST,VASE,STIPPLED IN GOLD,MEDALLION,LOBES,WEITZ, HANNOVER LABEL............................................. | 125.00 |
| AMETHYST,WINE,BELL SHAPE,CLEAR KNOB STEM,5 IN. X 3 IN.,SET OF 6..................................................... | 50.00 |
| AMPHORA,VASE,APPLIED FLOWERS,4 GOLD HANDLES,SIGNED AMPHORA-TEPLITZ............................................ | 45.00 |
| AMPHORA,VASE,VINTAGE DECOR,GOLDEN LIZARD HANDLE,SIGNED AMPHORA-TEPLITZ............................................ | 45.00 |
| ANDIRON,BRASS,PAIR,GEORGIAN,4 PIECES,15 IN. HIGH............ | 100.00 |
| ANDIRON,PAIR,BRASS,BALL-TOP,19TH CENTURY,4 PIECES.......... | 125.00 |
| ANDIRON,PAIR,BRASS,4 PIECES,30 IN. HIGH.................... | 160.00 |
| ANDIRON,PAIR,BRONZE,OWL-FORM,8 PIECES,22 IN. HIGH.......... | 375.00 |
| ANDIRON,PAIR,GEORGE III,BRASS URN-TOP,19 IN. HIGH.......... | 120.00 |
| ANDIRON,PAIR,GILDED,WROUGHT IRON,7 PIECES.................. | 90.00 |
| ANDIRONS,HAND-WROUGHT,RING TOP,18TH CENTURY,IRON........... | 65.00 |

ART GLASS MEANS ANY OF THE MANY FORMS OF GLASSWARE
MADE DURING THE LATE NINETEENTH CENTURY OR EARLY
TWENTIETH CENTURY. THESE WARES WERE EXPENSIVE AND MADE
IN LIMITED PRODUCTION. ART GLASS IS NOT THE TYPICAL
COMMERCIAL GLASSWARE THAT WAS MADE IN LARGE QUANTITIES,
AND MOST OF THE ART GLASS WAS PRODUCED BY HAND METHODS.
ART GLASS, SEE ALSO, SEPARATE HEADINGS SUCH AS BURMESE,
MOTHER-OF-PEARL, SATIN GLASS, TIFFANY, ETC.

| | |
|---|---|
| ART GLASS,BASKET,EMERALD GREEN,RUFFLED & CRIMPED RIM,CLEAR HANDLE,BLOWN............................................. | 35.00 |
| ART GLASS,BASKET,WHITE,APPLIED AMBER EDGE,HANDLE,LEAF ON EACH SIDE,6 IN............................................ | 19.50 |
| ART GLASS,BOWL,BLUE OPALINE BIRDS,NEST IS BOWL,SIGNED E.ZEN.,FRANCE............................................. | 28.00 |
| ART GLASS,BOWL,FRUIT,OPAQUE GLASS,STACKED COBRA HEADS ON HOMO GLASS,GILT........................................... | 55.00 |
| ART GLASS,BOWL,RED,IRIDESCENT,CRIMPED EDGE,IMPERIAL........ | 42.50 |
| ART GLASS,BOWL,ROSE,BLUE,RIBBED,TURNED-IN TOP,3 1/2 IN..... | 75.00 |
| ART GLASS,BOWL,ROSE,GREEN,MILK GLASS SPIRAL STRIPE OVERLAY, IRIDESCENT............................................... | 55.00 |
| ART GLASS,BOWL,ROSE,WHITE GROUND,CRYSTAL & CRANBERRY CRIMPED LEAF..................................................... | 45.00 |
| ART GLASS,BOX,POWDER,SATIN,COBALT,LADY PORTRAIT ON LID, SIGNED MUGS............................................... | 25.00 |

ART GLASS,CENTERPIECE,GREEN IRIDESCENT,RIBBED,OPALESCENT PEDESTAL,LIBBEY........................................ 350.00
ART GLASS,DISH,GREEN,WHITE MOTTLING,LARGE-BRIM HAT SHAPE, 8 IN................................................... 22.50
ART GLASS,INKWELL,BUTTERFLY SHAPE,IRIDESCENT,BRASS HINGED LID.................................................... 65.00
ART GLASS,LAMP,FAIRY,BLUE,SATIN GLASS,DIAMOND-QUILTED,CLARKE BASE...................................................
ART GLASS,MUG,PINK OVERLAY,GOLD BUTTERFLY,HANDLED............ 67.00
ART GLASS,MUG,PINK OVERLAY,GOLD BUTTERFLY,HANDLED............ 18.00
ART GLASS,POWDER,HAND-PAINTED FLORAL,COVER.................. 38.00
ART GLASS,SHADE,GOLD THREADS,BLUE IRIDESCENT LILY PADS,GOLD COLOR LINING................................................ 29.00
ART GLASS,SHADE,GREEN FEATHER DESIGN,SIGNED BY HENRY WINTER. 32.00
ART GLASS,SHADE,PASTEL GREEN TO OPALESCENT,DIAMOND LATTICE.. 43.00
ART GLASS,SHADE,SQUARE,FLUTED,BLUE INTERIOR,GOLD OUTSIDE, PAIR..................................................... 50.00
ART GLASS,TUMBLER,BROWN,GOLD AVENTURINE,DIMPLED SIDES, 3 1/2 IN................................................. 20.00
ART GLASS,VASE,BLUE GROUND,APPLIED AMBER BRANCH,CHERRIES, CRIMPED TOP.............................................. 175.00
ART GLASS,VASE,BLUE GROUND,GOLD MOTTLING,AVENTURINE,UNION CITY GLASS CO............................................ 50.00
ART GLASS,VASE,BLUE,CLEAR RUFFLED TRIM,LILIES,LEAVES,HAND PAINTED,PAIR............................................. 45.00
ART GLASS,VASE,CONE,PINK OVERLAY,RUFFLED EDGE,METAL SERPENTINE HOLDER........................................ 32.00
ART GLASS,VASE,CREAM COLOR,FEATHER AROUND CENTER,PINK LINING,10 IN.............................................. 75.00
ART GLASS,VASE,GREEN THREADED............................. 8.50
ART GLASS,VASE,OPAQUE,SMOKY TO MEDIUM BLUE,ENAMEL FLORAL, 16 IN.HIGH.............................................. 35.00
ART GLASS,VASE,WHITE SATIN,APPLIED LILY DECOR,GREEN LEAVES.. 45.00
ART NOUVEAU,SEE ALSO GLASS,FURNITURE,ETC.
ART NOUVEAU,ARMCHAIR,FRENCH,BROCADE,WALNUT..........ILLUS.. 475.00
ART NOUVEAU,BOOKEND,GIRL FIGURE WITH FLOWING HAIR,GOLD COLOR,PAIR.............................................. 20.00
ART NOUVEAU,BOX,JEWEL,GOLD COLOR,ROSE DECOR ON LID,BLUE SATIN LINING........................................... 15.00
ART NOUVEAU,BROOCH,GOLD.................................. 50.00
ART NOUVEAU,BROOCH,SILVER & ENAMEL,DATED 1903............. 50.00
ART NOUVEAU,BROOCH,SILVER & ENAMEL,PEARL................. 70.00
ART NOUVEAU,BROOCH,14-KARAT GOLD,TIFFANY FAVRILE GLASS SCARAB................................................. 150.00
ART NOUVEAU,BUCKLE,AMERICAN SILVER,WILLIAM B.KERR & CO...... 50.00
ART NOUVEAU,EWER,ROSENBERG,THE HAGUE,PORCELAIN,8 IN. HIGH... 250.00
ART NOUVEAU,INKSTAND,BRASS,2 PIECES....................... 40.00

ART NOUVEAU ARMCHAIR

```
ART NOUVEAU,JUG,ROSENBERG,THE HAGUE,9 1/2 IN. HIGH.........   110.00
ART NOUVEAU,LAMP,SILVER-PLATED & STAINED GLASS,SCHOOL OF
    PETER BEHRENS...........................................   900.00
ART NOUVEAU,MIRROR,CHILD'S,GOLD LEAF,2 IN...................     3.50
ART NOUVEAU,PENDANT,PEARLS,ENGLISH,GOLD & ENAMEL...........    50.00
ART NOUVEAU,RING,GOLD,TIFFANY FAVRILE GLASS SCARAB,1 1/8 IN.
    LONG...................................................   350.00
ART NOUVEAU,TABLE,CENTER,FRENCH,INLAID,WALNUT........ILLUS..   350.00
ART NOUVEAU,VASE,AUSTRIAN CERAMIC,PAIR,19 3/4 IN. HIGH......   100.00
ART NOUVEAU,VASE,ENGLISH CERAMIC,TOOTH & CO.,1867,17 1/2 IN.
    HIGH...................................................   250.00
ART NOUVEAU,VASE,ROSENBERG,THE HAGUE,16 1/4 IN HIGH.........   250.00
ART NOUVEAU,VASE,ROSENBERG,THE HAGUE,19.IN. HIGH...........    60.00
ART NOUVEAU,VASE,ROYAL DUX PORCELAIN,PAIR,BOHEMIAN,FIGURAL..   300.00
ASTER TAPESTRY,DISH,POWDER,COVER,JAPANESE...................    52.00
```

ART NOUVEAU FRENCH TABLE

```
ASTER TAPESTRY,TEAPOT,JAPANESE.............................    78.00
```

AURENE GLASS WAS MADE BY FREDERICK CARDER OF NEW YORK
ABOUT 1904. IT IS AN IRIDESCENT GOLD GLASS,USUALLY
MARKED AURENE OR STEUBEN.

```
AURENE,SEE ALSO STEUBEN
AURENE,BASKET,GOLD IRIDESCENT,SIGNED,NUMBERED,8 IN. X
    12 IN.HIGH.............................................   450.00
AURENE,BASKET,MINIATURE,GOLD IRIDESCENT,SIGNED,4 X 6 IN.HIGH  295.00
AURENE,BOWL,BLUE,HIGHLIGHTS,SIGNED & NUMBERED 2852,9 IN.....   295.00
AURENE,BOWL,BLUE,SINGLE FOOT,SIGNED,3 1/2 IN.HIGH,
    8 IN.DIAMETER.........................................   235.00
AURENE,BOWL,BLUE,TURNED-IN SCALLOPED TOP,SIGNED & NUMBERED..   235.00
AURENE,BOWL,CLOVERLEAF SHAPE,SILVER IRIDESCENCE,4 X
    2 IN.HIGH.............................................   200.00
AURENE,BOWL,GOLD,CALCITE,8 IN. X 2 IN......................    80.00
AURENE,BOWL,MINIATURE,MOTTLED SILVER STRETCHED BORDER,
    SIGNED,3 1/2 IN.......................................   128.00
AURENE,CANDLESTICK,TWISTED STEM,IRIDESCENT,GOLD,10 IN.,PAIR.   265.00
AURENE,COMPOTE,GOLD IRIDESCENT,SIGNED,5 IN.DIAMETER X
    6 IN.HIGH.............................................   225.00
AURENE,COMPOTE,GOLD,DRAPED TOP,DISC & RIBBED BUBBLE STEM,
    PAPER LABEL...........................................   250.00
AURENE,COMPOTE,GOLD,ENTWINED STEM,SIGNED,7 IN.WIDE X
    7 IN.HIGH.............................................   295.00
AURENE,COMPOTE,TWISTED STEM,GOLD IRIDESCENT,SIGNED,7 IN.HIGH
    X 7 IN.WIDE...........................................   295.00
AURENE,CUP & SAUCER,DEMITASSE,STERLING SILVER,GOLD LINER,
    SIGNED................................................    90.00
AURENE,CUSPIDOR,LADY'S,GOLD,FLUTED EDGE,SIGNED.............   175.00
AURENE,DARNER,BLUE,SIGNED AURENE,F.CARDER.................   250.00
AURENE,DECANTER,GOLD,SIX MATCHING CORDIAL GLASSES.........   500.00
AURENE,DECANTER,TRAY,FOUR CONE-SHAPED LIQUOR GLASSES,GOLD,
    SIGNED................................................   650.00
AURENE,DISH,CANDY,GOLD,SIGNED AURENE 532,FRED CARDER,4 1/2 X
    1 3/4 IN..............................................   165.00
AURENE,FLOWER FORM,GOLD WITH BLUE IRIDESCENT,10 IN.HIGH.....   110.00
AURENE,FROG,FLOWER,BLUE IRIDESCENT,4 IN...................    75.00
AURENE,GOBLET,GOLD COLOR,RED-GOLD INTERIOR,VENETIAN,SIGNED..   175.00
```

AURENE,GOBLET,GOLD,BLUE TWISTED STEM,SIGNED................... 125.00
AURENE,GOBLET,SWIRLED STEM SHADED TO BLUE BASE,SIGNED &
    NUMBERED................................................. 195.00
AURENE,JAR,STRAIGHT SIDES,COVER,BAIL,SIGNED.................. 385.00
AURENE,LIQUOR SET,TRAY,BOTTLE HOLDER,FOUR FOOTED GLASSES,
    STEUBEN................................................... 600.00
AURENE,LIQUOR,GOLD,TWISTED STEM,SIGNED HAVILAND,4 IN.HIGH,
    SET OF 4................................................. 240.00
AURENE,LIQUOR GLASS,DIMPLED SIDES,IRIDESCENT,SIGNED,STEUBEN,
    2 1/4 IN................................................. 115.00
AURENE,NAPPIE,RED & BLUE IRIDESCENCE,GOLD HANDLE,5 X
    2 IN.HIGH............................................... 250.00
AURENE,PERFUME,BLUE,SIGNED & NUMBERED........................ 295.00
AURENE,PERFUME,GOLD,BELL SHAPE,SIGNED & NUMBERED............ 195.00
AURENE,PERFUME,GOLD,BLUE HIGHLIGHTS,STOPPER,SIGNED,
    7 1/2 IN.HIGH........................................... 295.00
AURENE,PERFUME,GOLD,FOOTED,SIGNED........................... 150.00
AURENE,SALT,FLUTED,SIGNED,269 SILVER,GOLD................... 70.00
AURENE,SALT,GOLD,PEDESTAL,NO.3067.......................... 110.00
AURENE,SALT,PEDESTAL,GOLD & BLUE IRIDESCENT,SIGNED......... 98.00
AURENE,SHADE,GREEN,SILVER BAND,SIGNED,10 IN.DIAMETER....... 200.00
AURENE,TAZZA,FLOWER-LIKE TOP,TWISTED STEM,SIGNED,
    10 1/2 IN.HIGH.......................................... 370.00
AURENE,VASE,BLUE TO GOLD COLOR,PEARL SHAPE BODY,FLUTED TOP,
    4 1/4 IN................................................ 135.00
AURENE,VASE,BLUE-GOLD,IRIDESCENT,THREE PRONG,SIGNED,STEUBEN. 185.00
AURENE,VASE,BLUE,PEDESTAL FOOT,SIGNED,8 1/4 IN. X 3 IN...... 225.00
AURENE,VASE,BLUE,RIBBED,5 1/2 IN.HIGH...................... 210.00
AURENE,VASE,BUD,GREEN-GOLD,FOOTED,RIBBED,SIGNED,MARKED
    NO.562,5 IN.HIGH........................................ 150.00
AURENE,VASE,GOLD IRIDESCENT,BLUE RIM & BASE,SIGNED,7 IN..... 55.00
AURENE,VASE,GOLD IRIDESCENT,BULBOUS BODY NARROWING AT NECK,
    FLARED RIM.............................................. 95.00
AURENE,VASE,GOLD IRIDESCENT,SWIRL,SIGNED,12 1/2 IN.HIGH..... 250.00
AURENE,VASE,GOLD,IRIDESCENT,PINCHED RIM,SIGNED,4 1/2 IN..... 125.00
AURENE,VASE,GOLD,RUFFLED TOP,SQUAT,TRIFOOTED,3 1/2 IN.TALL.. 100.00
AURENE,VASE,GOLD,SIGNED.................................... 135.00
AURENE,VASE,JACK-IN-THE-PULPIT,GOLD,SIGNED................. 195.00
AURENE,VASE,STEUBEN,BLUE,ACID CUT,6 IN. X 12 IN.HIGH....... 695.00
AURENE,VASE,STICK,BLUE,SIGNED & NUMBERED,13 IN.HIGH........ 275.00
AURENE,VASE,STICK,PIERCED SILVER HOLDER,PAIRPOINT,
    6 1/2 IN.HIGH........................................... 85.00
AURENE,VASE,TRUMPET,FOLD-DOWN TOP RIM,BLUE,11 3/4 IN.HIGH... 250.00
AURENE,VASE,URN SHAPE,GOLD,SIGNED,7 IN.HIGH................ 125.00


    AUTO PARTS AND ACCESSORIES ARE COLLECTORS ITEMS TODAY.
AUTO,BREATHER PIPE,MODEL T,UNUSED........................... 12.50
AUTO,CARBURETOR FOR MODEL T FORD,HOLLY-DETROIT PAT.1914,
    BRASS................................................... 7.00
AUTO,DUSTER,LINEN,TWO...................................... 10.00
AUTO,GAS TANK,CAP,BRASS SEDIMENT BULB,HUPMOBILE,1909....... 30.00
AUTO,GASOLINE PUMP GLOBE,PEERLESS.......................... 35.00
AUTO,GOGGLES,LADY'S,MESH,SMOKE GLASS,CASE................. 5.00
AUTO,HEAD LAMP,HANDLE,BRASS,11 IN.HIGH.................... 35.00
AUTO,HEADLIGHT GLASS,WARNER-LENZ,PAT.JUNE 1912,NO.35,
    8 1/4 IN.DIAMETER....................................... 22.00
AUTO,HEADLIGHT,LEFT,KEROSENE,BRASS,BUICK,1902............. 35.00
AUTO,HOLDER,FLOWER,TURQUOISE GLASS,TRUMPET FLARE,8 IN...... 9.00
AUTO,HOLDER,LICENSE PLATE,FOR MODEL A FORD................. 3.50
AUTO,HOOD ORNAMENT,EAGLE,FLYING........................... 5.00
AUTO,HOOD ORNAMENT,FLYING MAN,CHROME...................... 12.00
AUTO,HOOD ORNAMENT,LADY,FLYING............................ 7.50
AUTO,HORN,BRASS,RUBBER BULB,23 IN.LONG.................... 18.00
AUTO,HORN,BULB TYPE,BRASS................................. 45.00
AUTO,HORN,KING OF THE ROAD,BRASS,12 IN.LONG............... 50.00
AUTO,HORN,MODEL T,HAND-OPERATED BY PUSH ROD............... 20.00
AUTO,HORN,TAXI,BRASS,BULB TYPE............................ 42.50
AUTO,HUB CAP,MODEL T,BRASS................................ 5.00
AUTO,HUB CUP,BRASS,EARLY FORD............................. 4.50
AUTO,HUB CUP,IRON,EARLY FORD.............................. 3.50
AUTO,LAMP,BRASS,DIETZ REGAL MOTOR,PAT.DATES ON PARTS 1887 TO
    1903.................................................... 45.00
AUTO,LAMP,FORD,BLACK,EDMUNDS & JONES,1914................. 13.50
AUTO,LAMP,FORD,BRASS,PAINTED BLACK,BEVEL GLASS,JNO.W.BROWN
    CO.,MODEL 110........................................... 45.00
AUTO,LAMP,KEROSENE,IRON,9 1/4 IN.HIGH..................... 15.00
AUTO,LAMP,SIDE,BRASS...................................... 15.00
AUTO,LICENSE PLATE,NEW YORK STATE WORLD'S FAIR,1940........ 4.25
AUTO,LIGHT,SIDE,KEROSENE,RED,GREEN,CLEAR GLASS,FOR FORD
    MODEL 115............................................... 20.00

```
AUTO,LIGHT,TAIL & STOP,1921 STUDEBAKER,BRACKET..............   10.00
AUTO,MIRROR,BRACKET,MODEL T................................    5.00
AUTO,MOTORMETER,CADILLAC...................................   20.00
AUTO,RADIATOR CAP,MODEL T,BRASS............................    3.00
AUTO,RADIATOR ORNAMENT,SMALL ANGEL,METAL...................    6.50
AUTO,SPEEDOMETER,GOES UP TO 60,STEWART,4 IN.FACE...........   15.00
AUTO,TAILLIGHT,RED,DODGE,1928..............................    7.00
AUTO,TAILLIGHT,FORD,MODEL 5 40,PAIR........................   25.00
AUTO,TIRE PUMP,POLISHED BRASS & IRON.......................   20.00
AUTO,TURNSIGNAL KIT FOR MODEL A FORD,CIRCA 1930............   50.00
AUTO,VASE,BENZER,MARIGOLD,ALUMINUM BRACKET.................   12.00
AUTO,VASE,BLUE CAMPHOR-LIKE GLASS..........................   18.00
AUTO,VASE,CUT & ETCHED FLOWER,HOLDER.......................   11.00
AUTO,VASE,GREEN GLASS,HOLDER...............................    8.50
AUTO,WHEEL LOCK,TWO KEYS,PATENTED AUG. 25,1914,IRON........   18.50
  AVON,SEE BOTTLE,AVON
```

```
        BACCARAT GLASS WAS MADE IN FRANCE BY LA COMPAGNIE DES
      CRISTALLERIES DE BACCARAT,LOCATED ABOUT 150 MILES FROM
      PARIS. THE FACTORY WAS STARTED IN 1765. THE FIRM WENT
      BANKRUPT AND BEGAN OPERATING AGAIN ABOUT 1822. FAMOUS
      CANE AND MILLEFIORI PAPERWEIGHTS WERE MADE THERE DURING
      THE 1860-1880 PERIOD. THE FIRM IS STILL WORKING NEAR
      PARIS MAKING PAPERWEIGHTS AND GLASSWARES.
BACCARAT,ATOMIZER,COBALT BUTTON PATTERN,GOLD COLOR METAL
  TOP,CUT GLASS...........................................   20.00
BACCARAT,BOBECHE,LACY,PAIR................................    9.00
BACCARAT,BOTTLE,BUDDHA SHAPE,SIGNED.......................   22.00
BACCARAT,BOTTLE,COLOGNE,METAL DISPENSER,PAPER SIGNATURE,
  5 1/2 IN...............................................    32.00
BACCARAT,BOTTLE,CUT DIAMOND PATTERN,SIGNED,7 1/2 IN.......   35.00
BACCARAT,BOTTLE,INK,BOULLE LAP DESK.......................  675.00
BACCARAT,BOTTLE,PERFUME,COLUMN LEAF DESIGN,BLUE TRIM,PAPER
  LABEL,PAIR.............................................    60.00
BACCARAT,BOTTLE,PERFUME,HEAVY GROUND STOPPER,PANELED,4 IN...  12.00
BACCARAT,BOTTLE,PERFUME,RED TO CLEAR,SWIRL,STOPPER,7 IN.HIGH  30.00
BACCARAT,BOTTLE,WATER,AMBERINA SWIRL,7 IN.HIGH,5 IN.DIAMETER  27.00
BACCARAT,BOWL,CENTERPIECE,BRASS PEDESTAL BASE,SWIRLED
  CRYSTAL TOP............................................   125.00
BACCARAT,BOWL,CENTERPIECE,SILVER BASE,ENAMEL CHERUBS,
  TRUMPETS,CUT DISH......................................   250.00
BACCARAT,BOWL,DEPOSE SWIRL,RUBINA COLOR,TURNED-DOWN
  SCALLOPED EDGE.........................................    49.50
BACCARAT,BOX,CRYSTAL,SAWTOOTH CUT,DORE TRIM,HINGED........   145.00
BACCARAT,BOX,PERFUME,TUMBLER,COLUMN LEAF DESIGN,RED TRIM...   50.00
BACCARAT,CANDLEHOLDER,DIAMOND POINT,SIGNED,7 IN.HIGH......    25.00
BACCARAT,CANDLESTICK,GOLD DECOR,SIGNED,FLINT,8 1/2 IN.HIGH,
  PAIR...................................................    90.00
BACCARAT,CANDLESTICK,SWIRLED,CLEAR,SIGNED,8 IN.,PAIR......    45.00
BACCARAT,CHANDELIER,TWELVE-LIGHT,DRIP PANS,AMETHYST BEAD
  CHAIN,46 IN............................................   800.00
BACCARAT,COLOGNE,SWIRLS,CLEAR TO CRANBERRY,STOPPER,
  5 1/2 IN.HIGH..........................................    35.00
BACCARAT,COMPOTE,AMBER OVERLAY,DIAMOND-QUILTED,SCALLOPED
  TOP,SIGNED.............................................    85.00
BACCARAT,COMPOTE,DIAMOND-QUILTED,SCALLOPED,LOW PEDESTAL,
  GREEN,SIGNED...........................................    20.00
BACCARAT,COMPOTE,GREEN SWIRL,PEDESTAL,SIGNED,6 IN.DIAMETER..  25.00
BACCARAT,DECANTER & TRAY,11 1/2 IN. HIGH,SIGNED...........   210.00
BACCARAT,DECANTER,LIQUOR,BRONZE OVERLAY,WOMAN WITH CHILD,
  SCROLL DESIGN..........................................    85.00
BACCARAT,DISH,CANDY,PINK,SWIRL PATTERN,SIGNED,5 IN. X
  2 IN.HIGH..............................................    32.00
BACCARAT,DISH,DENTIFRICE,SIGNED,FRANCE....................   45.00
BACCARAT,DISH,DEPOSE,SWIRL PATTERN,OBLONG,COVER,SIGNED....   25.00
BACCARAT,DISH,PIN,RUBINA SWIRL,SIGNED,5 X 2 IN............   18.50
BACCARAT,DISH,RELISH,RUBY-FLASHED BUTTONS,GOLD TRIM,CLEAR,
  OBLONG,SIGNED..........................................    25.00
BACCARAT,EPERGNE,SINGLE,ORMOLU BASE,CLEAR CRYSTAL VASE....   135.00
BACCARAT,FIGURINE,GAME COCK,FROSTED,2 3/4 IN.TALL,PAIR....    35.00
BACCARAT,GOBLET,LACY,CIRCA 1840...........................    35.00
BACCARAT,HOLDER,IVY,WIDE SWIRL RIB SIDES & BASE,7 1/2 X
  2 IN.TALL..............................................    15.00
BACCARAT,HOLDER,RING,AMBERINA,SWIRL,SIGNED................    25.00
BACCARAT,HOLDER,TOOTHBRUSH,VASELINE,PEWTER STEM,HOLDS THREE
  BRUSHES................................................    18.00
BACCARAT,INKSTAND,BOLD DESIGN,SIGNED......................    70.00
BACCARAT,JAR,COOKIE,BRASS LID & BAIL,SIGNED...............    50.00
BACCARAT,JAR,SWIRL,CLEAR,COVER............................    28.00
BACCARAT,LAMP,CANDLESTICK,KEROSENE,CHIMNEY,SWIRLED PATTERN,
```

```
  BASE.......................................................... 175.00
BACCARAT,PAPERWEIGHT,PANSY,MAUVE PETALS,STAR CUT BASE,
  2 1/8 IN.DIAMETER............................................. 225.00
BACCARAT,PAPERWEIGHT,PANSY,RAYED BASE,2 1/2 IN.DIAMETER..... 225.00
BACCARAT,PAPERWEIGHT,RED DOUBLE CLEMATIS,FACETED,
  3 3/16 IN.DIAMETER........................................... 750.00
BACCARAT,PAPERWEIGHT,RED DOUBLE CLEMATIS,LEAVES,
  2 7/16 IN.DIAMETER........................................... 650.00
BACCARAT,PAPERWEIGHT,RED PERIWINKLE,STAR CUT BASE,
  2 1/2 IN.DIAMETER..........................................1,800.00
BACCARAT,PAPERWEIGHT,ROSE,THOUSAND PETAL TYPE,STAR CUT BASE,
  2 5/8 IN...................................................2,300.00
BACCARAT,PAPERWEIGHT,SALMON PINK DOUBLE CLEMATIS,
  3 1/8 IN.DIAMETER..........................................2,750.00
BACCARAT,PAPERWEIGHT,SULFIDE,ABRAHAM LINCOLN,BLUE DOUBLE
  OVERLAY,G.P.,1953 60000&'M &'NA&)GO1&H&2HGO1MA&+ZN)&-G&OB&  600.00
BACCARAT,PAPERWEIGHT,SULFIDE,ABRAHAM LINCOLN,BLUE GROUND,
  WINDOWS...................................................... 300.00
BACCARAT,PAPERWEIGHT,SULFIDE,ABRAHAM LINCOLN,BLUE GROUND,
  1953......................................................... 250.00
BACCARAT,PAPERWEIGHT,SULFIDE,ABRAHAM LINCOLN,WHITE JASPER
  GROUND,1953.................................................. 475.00
BACCARAT,PAPERWEIGHT,SULFIDE,ADLAI STEVENSON,RED BASE....... 115.00
BACCARAT,PAPERWEIGHT,SULFIDE,BENJAMIN FRANKLIN,BLUE GROUND,
  SIGNED G.P................................................... 500.00
BACCARAT,PAPERWEIGHT,SULFIDE,DWIGHT EISENHOWER,BLUE GROUND,
  CENTRAL STAR................................................. 370.00
BACCARAT,PAPERWEIGHT,SULFIDE,GEORGE WASHINGTON,RED GROUND,
  G.P.,1953.................................................... 275.00
BACCARAT,PAPERWEIGHT,SULFIDE,GEORGE WASHINGTON,RED GROUND,
  SIGNED G.P................................................... 190.00
BACCARAT,PAPERWEIGHT,SULFIDE,JOHN F.KENNEDY,BLUE GROUND,
  OVERLAY...................................................... 325.00
BACCARAT,PAPERWEIGHT,SULFIDE,JOHN F. KENNEDY,GREEN FLASH
  GROUND....................................................... 150.00
BACCARAT,PAPERWEIGHT,SULFIDE,JOHN F.KENNEDY,PURPLE GROUND,
  CUT STAR..................................................... 400.00
BACCARAT,PAPERWEIGHT,SULFIDE,JOHN KENNEDY,RED,GREEN,FACETS,
  SIGNED A.DAVID............................................... 255.00
BACCARAT,PAPERWEIGHT,SULFIDE,LAFAYETTE,BLUE GROUND,SIGNED
  B.G.P.,1955.................................................. 225.00
BACCARAT,PAPERWEIGHT,SULFIDE,LAFAYETTE,DOUBLE OVERLAY,
  B.G.P.,1953.................................................. 350.00
BACCARAT,PAPERWEIGHT,SULFIDE,LAFAYETTE,FACETED,SIGNED
  B.G.P.,1955.................................................. 275.00
BACCARAT,PAPERWEIGHT,SULFIDE,POPE JOHN,STAR CUT BASE........ 125.00
BACCARAT,PAPERWEIGHT,SULFIDE,POPE JOHN XXIII,RED BASE,
  FACETED,SIGNED............................................... 125.00
BACCARAT,PAPERWEIGHT,SULFIDE,POPE JOHN XXIII,SIGNED A.DAVID
  1964......................................................... 250.00
BACCARAT.PAPERWEIGHT,SULFIDE,POPE JOHN XXIII,SIGNED A.DAVID
  PARIS,1963................................................... 80.00
BACCARAT,PAPERWEIGHT,SULFIDE,POPE PIUS XII,SIGNED A.DAVID
  1955......................................................... 100.00
BACCARAT,PAPERWEIGHT,SULFIDE,POPE PIUS,RED GROUND,FACETED
  SURFACE...................................................... 100.00
BACCARAT,PAPERWEIGHT,SULFIDE,ROBERT E. LEE,BLUE WAFFLE-CUT
  GROUND,1954.................................................. 175.00
BACCARAT,PAPERWEIGHT,SULFIDE,ROBERT E.LEE,FACETED,SIGNED B.,
  MAR.1954..................................................... 200.00
BACCARAT,PAPERWEIGHT,SULFIDE,THEODORE ROOSEVELT............. 100.00
BACCARAT,PAPERWEIGHT,SULFIDE,THEODORE ROOSEVELT,AMETHYST
  BASE......................................................... 125.00
BACCARAT,PAPERWEIGHT,SULFIDE,THOMAS JEFFERSON,DOUBLE
  OVERLAY,G.P.,1953............................................ 375.00
BACCARAT,PAPERWEIGHT,SULFIDE,THOMAS JEFFERSON,SIGNED G.P.,
  1953......................................................... 200.00
BACCARAT,PAPERWEIGHT,SULFIDE,WASHINGTON,PINK OVERLAY,
  WINDOWS,FLUTES............................................... 475.00
BACCARAT,PAPERWEIGHT,SULFIDE,WILL ROGERS,DEEP CUT BASE...... 85.00
BACCARAT,PAPERWEIGHT,SULFIDE,WILL ROGERS,GOLD BASE.......... 125.00
BACCARAT,PAPERWEIGHT,SULFIDE,WINSTON CHURCHILL,BLUE GROUND,
  1953......................................................... 725.00
BACCARAT,PAPERWEIGHT,TWELVE SIGNS OF THE ZODIAC............. 110.00
BACCARAT,PAPERWEIGHT,TWO STRAWBERRIES,LEAVES,
  2 3/8 IN.DIAMETER..........................................2,800.00
BACCARAT,PAPERWEIGHT,WHEAT FLOWER,LEAVES,STAR CUT BASE,
  2 7/16 IN..................................................1,800.00
BACCARAT,PAPERWEIGHT,WHITE POMPON,LEAVES,2 5/8 IN.DIAMETER.. 550.00
BACCARAT,PAPERWEIGHT,YELLOW DOUBLE CLEMATIS,STAR CUT BASE,
```

```
18 IN.TALL.........................................................    80.00
BACCARAT,LAMP,TABLE,ROPE DESIGN,LACE SHADE.....................        60.00
BACCARAT,MUG,LACY,CIRCA 1845,2 3/4 IN.HIGH,PAIR..............          77.00
BACCARAT,MUSTARD,AMBER & CLEAR PANELS,CLEAR TOP,CUT STAR,
  PEWTER DIPPER.................................................       35.00
BACCARAT,PAPERWEIGHT,1846,GEOMETRIC CANES,2 7/8 IN.DIAMETER.          800.00
BACCARAT,PAPERWEIGHT,1848,MILLEFIORI,ANIMAL SILHOUETTES,
  2 5/16 IN....................................................       475.00
BACCARAT,PAPERWEIGHT,1848,MILLEFIORI,ANIMAL SILHOUETTES,
  4 IN.DIAMETER.............................................2,400.00
BACCARAT,PAPERWEIGHT,ANEMONE,CENTRAL FLOWER,STAMENS,STALK,
  LEAVES.....................................................       350.00
BACCARAT,PAPERWEIGHT,APRICOT COLOR POMPON,CANES,
  2 9/16 IN.DIAMETER.......................................1,500.00
BACCARAT,PAPERWEIGHT,BELLFLOWER,STAR CUT BASE,
  2 3/4 IN.DIAMETER.........................................1,200.00
BACCARAT,PAPERWEIGHT,BLUE PERIWINKLE,STAR CUT BASE,
  2 1/2 IN.DIAMETER.........................................1,200.00
BACCARAT,PAPERWEIGHT,BLUE PRIMROSE,MAUVE MARKINGS,
  3 1/8 IN.DIAMETER...........................................   950.00
BACCARAT,PAPERWEIGHT,BLUE CARPET GROUND,ANIMAL SILHOUETTES,
  CANES.....................................................2,300.00
BACCARAT,PAPERWEIGHT,BLUE DOG ROSE,WHITE STAR DUST STAMENS,
  2 3/8 IN....................................................   400.00
BACCARAT,PAPERWEIGHT,BUTTERFLY,AMETHYST BODY,CANES,
  3 1/8 IN.DIAMETER.........................................1,200.00
BACCARAT,PAPERWEIGHT,BUTTERFLY,PRIMROSE,2 15/16 IN.DIAMETER.2,700.00
BACCARAT,PAPERWEIGHT,CANES FESTOONED WITH A FLORAL CHAIN,
  3 1/8 IN.ACROSS.............................................   290.00
BACCARAT,PAPERWEIGHT,CLEAR,LAFAYETTE MEDALLION,SIGNED WITH B
  & DATED....................................................   185.00
BACCARAT,PAPERWEIGHT,CLEMATIS BUDS,WHITE,PINK,
  2 11/16 IN.DIAMETER......................................1,800.00
BACCARAT,PAPERWEIGHT,COG WHEEL DESIGN,GREEN CENTER,BLUE
  BACKGROUND,3 IN.............................................   395.00
BACCARAT,PAPERWEIGHT,DOG ROSE,STALK,LEAVES,MINIATURE,
  2 IN.DIAMETER...............................................   525.00
BACCARAT,PAPERWEIGHT,DOG ROSE,STAR CUT BASE,
  3 1/16 IN.DIAMETER..........................................   900.00
BACCARAT,PAPERWEIGHT,DOUBLE CLEMATIS,2 3/4 IN.DIAMETER......   550.00
BACCARAT,PAPERWEIGHT,DOUBLE CLEMATIS,FACETED,
  2 5/8 IN.DIAMETER...........................................   650.00
BACCARAT,PAPERWEIGHT,DOUBLE CLEMATIS,2 13/16 IN.DIAMETER....4,250.00
BACCARAT,PAPERWEIGHT,DOUBLE CLEMATIS,TWO ROWS OF WINDOWS ON
  SIDES.....................................................1,150.00
BACCARAT,PAPERWEIGHT,FESTOONS INTERTWINE CANES,
  3 1/4 IN.ACROSS.............................................   289.00
BACCARAT,PAPERWEIGHT,FLAT BOUQUET,CLEMATIS,PANSIES,FACETED,
  3 1/8 IN..................................................1,600.00
BACCARAT,PAPERWEIGHT,FLAT BOUQUET,PRIMROSE,CLEMATIS,
  THUMBPRINTS,3 IN..........................................2,500.00
BACCARAT,PAPERWEIGHT,MILLEFIORI,1968.........................   125.00
BACCARAT,PAPERWEIGHT,MILLEFIORI,ALTERNATE CLEAR CRYSTAL,
  FLOWER CANES...............................................   125.00
BACCARAT,PAPERWEIGHT,MILLEFIORI,CIRCLES OF FLOWER CANES,
  CENTER MOTIF...............................................   125.00
BACCARAT,PAPERWEIGHT,OUR LADY OF LOURDES.....................    50.00
BACCARAT,PAPERWEIGHT,PANSY,MAUVE,YELLOW,HONEYCOMB CANE,
  2 7/8 IN.DIAMETER...........................................   850.00
BACCARAT,PAPERWEIGHT,PANSY,MAUVE,YELLOW,THUMBPRINT,STAR CUT
  2 11/16 IN................................................1,000.00
BACCARAT,PAPERWEIGHT,YELLOW POMPON,FACETED,2 5/8 IN.DIAMETER1,600.00
BACCARAT,PAPERWEIGHT,YELLOW PRIMROSE,STAR CUT BASE,
  2 7/16 IN.DIAMETER........................................1,800.00
BACCARAT,PAPERWEIGHT,ZODIAC,AQUARIUS,TRANSLUCENT BLUE,SIGNED     55.00
BACCARAT,PAPERWEIGHT,ZODIAC,CANCER,TRANSLUCENT BLUE,SIGNED..     55.00
BACCARAT,PAPERWEIGHT,ZODIAC,VIRGO,TRANSLUCENT BLUE,SIGNED...     55.00
BACCARAT,PERFUME ATOMIZER,LABEL,BALL,AMBERINA................    19.50
BACCARAT,PERFUME,FRENCH......................................    22.00
BACCARAT,PERFUME,SWIRL RIB,VASELINE GLASS....................    22.00
BACCARAT,PITCHER,TAUPE,WHITE-MOTTLED,APPLE BLOSSOMS,FAN,
  BIRDS,10 1/4 IN.............................................    55.00
BACCARAT,RELISH,SWIRL,SIGNED,9 1/2 IN........................    19.00
BACCARAT,RING TREE,AMBERINA SWIRL,MARKED.....................    16.50
BACCARAT,SALT,MASTER,DEEP PURPLE,LACY,FOOTED,BOAT SHAPE.....     20.00
BACCARAT,TOOTHPICK TRAY,LIGHT AMBER SWIRL,SIGNED............     17.00
BACCARAT,TRAY,PIN,AMBER,SIGNED,1 1/4 IN.HIGH X 5 IN.LONG....     14.00
BACCARAT,TRAY,SWIRLED,SCALLOPED,CRANBERRY,13 X 9 IN.........     65.00
BACCARAT,TUMBLER,SULFIDE,PORTRAIT,ST.MADELAINE,INSCRIPTION,
  3 1/2 IN...................................................   110.00
```

BACCARAT,VASE,BLUE,CUT TO CLEAR GEOMETRIC DESIGN,
   11 1/2 IN.TALL.................................................  75.00
BACCARAT,VASE,CUT DIAMOND BAND,SIGNED,8 IN.TALL X
   6 IN.SQUARE.................................................... 60.00
BACCARAT,VASE,GREEN CRYSTAL,ENAMEL FLORAL,HORSES,MOUNTAINS,
   8 IN.,PAIR.................................................... 85.00
   BAG,BEADED,SEE BEADED BAG


   MECHANICAL BANKS WERE FIRST MADE ABOUT 1870. ANY BANK
   WITH MOVING PARTS IS CONSIDERED MECHANICAL,ALTHOUGH
   THOSE MOST COLLECTED ARE THE METAL BANKS MADE BEFORE
   WORLD WAR I. REPRODUCTIONS ARE BEING MADE.
BANK,ACROBATS,MECHANICAL,GYMNASTICS,PAINT.................... 325.00
BANK,ADVERTISING,RED GOOSE SHOES,SHAPE OF GOOSE,IRON........  20.00
BANK,ALWAYS DID 'SPISE A MULE,NEGRO ON BENCH,WIRE WHIP,
   PAINT,MECHANICAL............................................ 125.00
BANK,AUNT JEMIMA WITH SPOON,IRON,STILL......................  18.00
BANK,BANK BUILDING,CUPOLA,STEPS,IRON,STILL..................  14.00
BANK,BANK BUILDING,GOLD PAINT,IRON,4 IN.....................   8.00
BANK,BANK BUILDING,IRON,2 1/2 IN.SQUARE,4 1/2 IN.TALL.......  12.00
BANK,BANK BUILDING,STILL,IRON,3 1/2 IN.HIGH.................  15.00
BANK,BANK BUILDING,TWO DOOR,IRON,5 1/2 IN...................  12.50
BANK,BARREL,HAPPY DAYS,CHEIN,TIN............................  12.00
BANK,BASEBALL PLAYER,IRON,STILL.............................  20.00
BANK,BEAR,STANDING,BRASS....................................  35.00
BANK,BEAR,STANDING,STILL,IRON...............................  25.00
BANK,BEAR,STANDING,STILL,IRON,6 1/2 IN.HIGH.................  20.00
BANK,BEARS ROBBING BEEHIVE,IRON.............................  45.00
BANK,BEEHIVE WITH BEES,STILL,IRON...........................   9.50
BANK,BELL SHAPE,GOLD IRIDESCENT.............................   2.00
BANK,BEN FRANKLIN THRIFT,REGISTERING,TIN....................  15.00
BANK,BILL IKEN,STILL,IRON........................... 9.50 TO  15.00
BANK,BLACK BEAUTY...........................................  20.00
BANK,BLACKPOOL TOWER........................................  45.00
BANK,BOTTLE,FIGURAL,BEAR, SNOW CROP SYRUP,  7 IN............   5.00
BANK,BOTTLE,LINCOLN.........................................   5.50
BANK,BOY SCOUT,STILL,IRON...................................  22.50
BANK,BRUNSWICK PHONOGRAPH,COPPER............................  18.00
BANK,BUFFALO,PENNY,IRON.....................................  14.50
BANK,BUILDING,CITY,FOUR TURRETS ON TOP,IRON,4 1/2 IN.HIGH...  15.00
BANK,BUILDING,CUPOLA,IRON,3 1/4 IN..........................  15.00
BANK,BUILDING,CUPOLA,IRON,4 3/4 IN.HIGH.....................  15.00
BANK,BUILDING,EMPIRE STATE,STILL,IRON.......................  15.00
BANK,BUILDING,NO.305,IRON,5 1/2 IN..........................  22.50
BANK,BUILDING,TIN...........................................   6.00
BANK,BULLDOG,SITTING,STILL,IRON.............................  19.00
BANK,BULLDOG,STILL,IRON.....................................  25.00
BANK,BUST OF GENERAL PERSHING,1918,STILL....................  22.50
BANK,BUSTER & TIGE,STILL,IRON...................... 20.00 TO  35.00
BANK,CATHEDRAL,RED,BLUE,SLOT,TIN,4 IN.HIGH..................  10.00
BANK,CHARLIE MCCARTHY,SAYS FEED ME I WILL SAVE YOU MONEY,
   9 1/2 IN....................................................   9.00
BANK,CHEST,PIRATE,LOCK,STILL,IRON...........................  18.00
BANK,CHEST,WOOD.............................................  12.00
BANK,CHURCH,CHEIN,TIN.......................................  15.00
BANK,CIRCUS HORSE,FRONT FEET ON BARREL,TWO SLOTS,PAINT,IRON.  24.00
BANK,CLOCK DIAL ON FRONT, IT'S SAVINGS TIME,ALBANY,N.Y.,
   WOODEN......................................................   2.00
BANK,CLOCK,NEW HAVEN,TAMBOUR SHAPE,7 1/2 IN.WIDE............  22.50
BANK,DEER WITH ANTLERS,GOLD PAINT,IRON......................  18.00
BANK,DIME REGISTER,CHEIN,TIN................................  12.00
BANK,DIME REGISTER,FIRST DIME LOCKS,LAST DIME UNLOCKS AT
   $10,CHEIN,TIN...............................................   5.00
BANK,DOG ON TURNTABLE,MECHANICAL,IRON.......................  95.00
BANK,DOG,IRON,5 IN.LONG.....................................   2.00
BANK,DONKEY WITH SADDLE,STILL,IRON..........................  19.50
BANK,DRESSER SHAPE,WOODEN,8 IN.TALL,5 1/4 IN.WIDE...........   5.00
BANK,DRUM,GOD BLESS AMERICA,TIN.............................  10.00
BANK,EAGLE IN RELIEF,CARNIVAL GLASS,4 1/2 IN.TALL...........   7.00
BANK,ELEPHANT WITH HOWDAH,STILL,IRON,3 IN...................  22.00
BANK,ELEPHANT,IRON..........................................   9.50
BANK,ELEPHANT,IRON,3 IN.HIGH,4 IN.LONG......................  15.50
BANK,ELEPHANT,IRON,6 1/2 X 5 IN.............................   2.00
BANK,ELEPHANT,MOVES TRUNK,NICKEL-PLATED.....................  45.00
BANK,FERRYBOAT,ON WHEELS,STILL,IRON.........................  22.50
BANK,FIDO DOG ON PILLOW,STILL...............................  25.00
BANK,FIGURAL,BEAR,GLASS.....................................   3.00
BANK,FIREPROOF,MOSLER SAFE CO.,TIN,2 IN.HIGH................   5.00
BANK,GAS HEATER,SAYS GEM,ABENDROTH BROS.,N.Y.,IRON..........  25.00

```
BANK,GENERAL PERSHING,SILVER PAINT,STILL....................    15.00
BANK,GLASS WORLD GLOBE,3 1/2 IN. DIAMETER...................     8.00
BANK,GOOD LUCK,BILLIKEN,SEATED ON A TWO-STEPPED PLATFORM,
   6 1/2 IN...............................................    19.75
BANK,GRAF ZEPPELIN,DIRIGIBLE SHAPE,GRAY PAINT,IRON,5 IN.LONG    15.00
BANK,HALLS EXCELSIOR.......................................    35.00
BANK,HAT,STILL,IRON........................................    25.00
BANK,HORSE ON TUB,STILL,IRON...............................    18.00
BANK,HORSE PRANCING,STILL,IRON.............................    12.50
BANK,HORSE,BLACK BEAUTY,IRON...............................    22.50
BANK,HORSE,OVAL BASE,STILL,IRON............................    27.00
BANK,HORSESHOE,IRON,STILL..................................    25.00
BANK,HOUSE,CAPE COD,STILL,IRON,4 IN. X 4 IN................    18.50
BANK,HOUSE,CENTER CHIMNEY,FRONT STEPS,IRON,3 IN.HIGH.......     9.95
BANK,HOUSE,CENTER CHIMNEY,FRONT STEPS,IRON,2 1/4 X 3 IN.HIGH     9.95
BANK,HOUSE,RED,IRON,3 IN...................................    12.00
BANK,HOUSE,STILL,IRON......................................     4.00
BANK,HOUSE,WHITE,STENCIL,TIN,3 1/4 IN.LONG.................    18.00
BANK,IDEAL SECURITY COMBINATION SAFE,IRON,5 1/2 IN.........    20.00
BANK,INDEPENDENCE HALL,BACK COVER,STILL,IRON,10 1/4 IN.TALL.    90.00
BANK,INDIAN,BUFF ENAMEL,IRON,6 1/2 IN.TALL.................    12.50
BANK,JUG,STILL,POTTERY,4 IN.HIGH...........................    15.00
BANK,LIBERTY BELL,CARNIVAL GLASS,MARIGOLD..................     3.00
BANK,LIBERTY BELL,GLASS,INCISED WORDING,4 1/2 IN.HIGH......     5.00
BANK,LIBERTY BELL,PHILADELPHIA SESQUICENTENNIAL............     9.00
BANK,LIBERTY BELL,SESQUICENTENNIAL,1926,IRON...............    20.00
BANK,LIBERTY BELL,SQUARE BASE,CENTENNIAL 1776-1876.........    25.00
BANK,LIBERTY BELL,STILL,HOUCK,POTTSTOWN,PENNSYLVANIA,METAL,
   5 IN.HIGH..............................................    15.00
BANK,LIBERTY BELL,STILL,IRON...............................    22.00
BANK,LION,GOLD-COLORED,IRON................................    10.50
BANK,LION ON WHEELS,STILL..................................    25.00
BANK,LION,STANDING,IRON....................................    11.75
BANK,LION,STILL,IRON,5 IN..................................    12.50
BANK,MAILBOX SHAPE,STILL,MARKED U.S.MAIL & EAGLE,2 1/2 X
   5 IN.LONG..............................................    17.50
BANK,MAILBOX,GREEN,STILL,IRON..............................     9.50
BANK,MAMMY,IRON,WITH SPOON.................................    25.00
BANK,MANTLE CLOCK SHAPE,FIVE COIN REGISTER,TIN.............    25.00
BANK,MECHANICAL,BUILDING,COLUMBIAN EXPOSITION
   ADMINISTRATION,IRON....................................    75.00
BANK,MECHANICAL,BULLDOG,SEATED.............................   105.00
BANK,MECHANICAL,CABIN,DARKY IN DOORWAY,JUNE 1885...........    70.00
BANK,MECHANICAL,CABIN,TRAP DOOR ON BOTTOM,PAT.1875,IRON.....    65.00
BANK,MECHANICAL,CHIEF BIG MOON,IRON........................   185.00
BANK,MECHANICAL,CLOWN,CHIEN,TIN...................  12.50 TO    15.00
BANK,MECHANICAL,COLUMBIAN EXPOSITION,ADMINISTRATION
   BUILDING,IRON..........................................    75.00
BANK,MECHANICAL,COW KICKING................................   400.00
BANK,MECHANICAL,DENTIST....................................   150.00
BANK,MECHANICAL,DINAH............................  85.00 TO   250.00
BANK,MECHANICAL,DOG ON TURNTABLE.................  75.00 TO   134.00
BANK,MECHANICAL,ELEPHANT,CHEIN,TIN.........................    25.00
BANK,MECHANICAL,ELEPHANT,MAN IN HOWDAH,IRON........110.00 TO   160.00
BANK,MECHANICAL,HALL'S EXCELSIOR,IRON......................    60.00
BANK,MECHANICAL,INDIAN SHOOTING BEAR.......................   130.00
BANK,MECHANICAL,JOLLY N,HIGH WHITE HAT, PATENT MARCH 14,
   '82...................................................    80.00
BANK,MECHANICAL,JOLLY N,HIGH HAT,TAKES PENNY, BLINKS
   EYES,ENGLAND..........................................   250.00
BANK,MECHANICAL,JOLLY N,WITH HAT,STARKIES
   PATENT...........................................  35.00 TO    45.00
BANK,MECHANICAL,JOLLY N,HIGH HAT...........................   375.00
BANK,MECHANICAL,LILLIPUT...................................   188.50
BANK,MECHANICAL,LITTLE JOE.......................  50.00 TO   180.00
BANK,MECHANICAL,MONKEY TIPS HAT,J.CHEIN,TIN,5 1/2
   IN.HIGH........................................  10.00 TO    95.00
BANK,MECHANICAL,MULE ENTERING BARN,REPLACED KEY PLATE......   125.00
BANK,MECHANICAL,ORGAN MONKEY,CAT & DOG,IRON................   145.00
BANK,MECHANICAL,PADDY & HIS PIGS,PAINT.....................   250.00
BANK,MECHANICAL,PIG IN HIGH CHAIR..........................   175.00
BANK,MECHANICAL,PONY,TRICK,PAINT...........................   100.00
BANK,MECHANICAL,SANTA BY CHIMNEY...........................   115.00
BANK,MECHANICAL,SANTA CLAUS................................   145.00
BANK,MECHANICAL,SPEAKING DOG...............................   125.00
BANK,MECHANICAL,SPEAKING DOG,CHILD SEATED IN CHAIR,DOG,DATED
   1885,IRON.............................................    95.00
BANK,MECHANICAL,TAMMANY HALL.........................ILLUS..    60.00
BANK,MECHANICAL,TANK & CANNON..............................   195.00
BANK,MECHANICAL,THE DARKTOWN BATTERY.......................   175.00
```

```
BANK,MECHANICAL,TRICK DOG,IRON.....................................  75.00
BANK,MECHANICAL,TRICK DOG,SIX-PIECE BASE........................  135.00
BANK,MECHANICAL,UNCLE SAM.............................ILLUS..  120.00
BANK,MECHANICAL,WILLIAM TELL..........................95.00 TO  135.00
BANK,MULE,SADDLE,STILL,4 1/2 IN................................  18.00
BANK,NATIONAL SAFE,COMBINATION LOCK,IRON,3 3/4 X 5 IN.HIGH..  11.75
```

TAMMANY HALL MECHANICAL BANK          UNCLE SAM MECHANICAL BANK

```
BANK,OWL,TURNS HEAD.................................75.00 TO  125.00
BANK,PADDY & HIS PIGS,MECHANICAL,PAINT.......................  250.00
BANK,PIANO BABY TYPE GIRL,SOFT COLORS,CHALK..................   25.00
BANK,PIG IN A SUITCASE,PORCELAIN,GREEN.......................    9.00
BANK,PIG,CARNIVAL GLASS......................................    6.00
BANK,PIG,GREEN & BROWN MARBLE GLAZE POTTERY..................   15.00
BANK,PIG,SAYS  THE WISE PIG,THRIFTY,ONE PENNY,TWO KEEPS WOLF
    AWAY,  IRON..............................................   20.00
BANK,PIG,SITTING,STILL,IRON........................15.00 TO   20.00
BANK,PIG,STANDING,IRON,7 1/4 IN.WIDE.........................   19.00
BANK,PIGGY,COBALT BLUE.......................................    6.00
BANK,PIRATE CHEST,SKULL,CROSSBONES,METAL,STILL...............   12.40
BANK,PIRATE SITTING ON CHEST,GILT METAL......................   12.00
BANK,PIRATES CHEST,PENNY,PIRATE & SKELETON & CROSSBONES ON
    SIDE,TIN.................................................    5.00
BANK,PONY,TRICK,MECHANICAL,PAINT.............................  100.00
BANK,POODLE,BROWN,GLAZED,POTTERY,9 IN.TALL...................   45.00
BANK,POPEYE,BLUE ON SILVER,TIN,2 1/2 IN.SQUARE,1/2 IN.HIGH..    6.00
BANK,POPEYE,DIME REGISTER,COPYRIGHT 1919,AUTOMATIC..........   10.00
BANK,POPEYE,DIME,TAN,1929....................................   10.00
BANK,POTTERY,BROWN,SIGNED METZ BREW CO.,OMAHA,6 IN.HIGH.....    9.50
BANK,PRANCING HORSE,PAINT,IRON.....................12.00 TO   17.00
BANK,PRESTO,STILL,IRON.......................................   25.00
BANK,PUPPY,PAINTED,IRON,STILL................................   12.50
BANK,PUPPY WITH A FLY ON HIS HIP,IRON,5 IN.HIGH..............   18.00
BANK,PUPPY,BEE,BOW,STILL,IRON................................   20.00
BANK,RABBIT,STILL,IRON.......................................   22.50
BANK,RADIO,MAJESTIC,STILL....................................   25.00
BANK,REARING HORSE ON PLATFORM...............................   18.00
BANK,REGISTER,UNCLE SAM.............................3.00 TO   15.00
BANK,REPLICA OF PLYMOUTH ROCK,RAISED 1620 ON SIDE,GRAY
    FINISH,REDWARE...........................................   15.00
BANK,ROLLER SAFE,IRON,1889...................................   18.50
BANK,ROOSTER,STILL,IRON......................................   25.00
BANK,ROYAL SAFE DEPOSIT,COMBINATION ON DOOR,IRON,6. 18.00 TO   25.00
BANK,SADDLE & COWBOY BOOTS,BRONZED METAL.....................   12.00
BANK,SAFE DEPOSIT,COMBINATION,IRON,5 1/4 IN..................   20.00
BANK,SAFE SHAPE,SAYS KEY LOCK SAFE,J.& E.STEVENS CO.,
    PAT.1897,IRON............................................   11.75
BANK,SAFE,ARABIAN,STILL,IRON.................................   30.00
BANK,SAFE,COMBINATION ON DOOR,ROYAL SAFE DEPOSIT,IRON,
```

```
   6 IN.HIGH.................................................    25.00
BANK,SAFE,COMBINATION,HANDLES,STENCIL,HART MFG.,DETROIT,
   MICH.,5 IN.HIGH.........................................    20.00
BANK,SAFE,JAPANESE,STILL,IRON...............................    35.00
BANK,SAFE,KENTON BRAND,KENTON HARDWARE,OHIO,4 IN............    15.00
BANK,SAFE,PAT.1896,IRON,3 1/4 IN.HIGH.......................    15.00
BANK,SAFE,PATENTED 1896,3 1/4 IN.HIGH.......................    15.00
BANK,SAFE,SAVINGS DEPOSIT,KENTON BRAND,KENTON HARDWARE,OHIO,
   4 IN.HIGH...............................................    15.00
BANK,SAFE,STILL,RED PANELS,BLACK GROUND,IRON,3 3/4 IN.......    15.00
BANK,SANTA BY CHIMNEY,MECHANICAL............................   115.00
BANK,SANTA CLAUS BY STUMP,STILL.............................    35.00
BANK,SATCHEL,IRON,6 IN.LONG,3 IN.HIGH.......................    15.00
BANK,SCOUTMASTER,PENNY,IRON.................................    24.50
BANK,SIX-SIDED BUILDING,OPENWORK WITH BIRDS,6 IN.TALL,STILL.    25.00
BANK,SQUIRREL,GRAY,POTTERY,6 IN.TALL........................     7.50
BANK,ST.BERNARD DOG WITH PACK ON BACK,PATENT 1900,STILL,IRON    28.50
BANK,STAGECOACH,BRONZED METAL...............................    12.00
BANK,STANDING ELEPHANT,RED PAINT,IRON,STILL.................    22.00
BANK,STATE BANK,CUPOLA ON TOP OF BUILDING,3 IN..............    20.00
BANK,STATUE OF LIBERTY,IRON.................................    14.50
BANK,TAJ MAHAL,IRON,4 IN....................................    14.00
BANK,TAMMANY,MECHANICAL,IRON................................    60.00
BANK,TAN,WORLD WAR I,STILL,IRON.............................    30.00
BANK,TANK,IRON,1918.........................................    15.00
BANK,TEXAS BOOK.............................................     3.50
BANK,THEODORE ROOSEVELT,STILL,IRON..........................    20.00
BANK,THREE MONKEYS,SEE,HEAR,SPEAK NO EVIL,STILL,PORCELAIN...    18.00
BANK,THRIFTY PIG BANK,IRON..................................    18.00
BANK,TIME SAFE,DOOR OPENS WHEN CLOCK SHOWS CORRECT TIME,
   3 1/2 X 7 IN............................................    32.00
BANK,TRICK DOG,MECHANICAL...................................    75.00
BANK,TURKEY,STILL...........................................    15.00
BANK,U.S.MAIL,IRON,3 1/2 IN.HIGH............................    15.00
BANK,UNCLE SAM WITH MONEY BAG,MECHANICAL....................    85.00
BANK,UNCLE SAM,CASH REGISTER,TIN............................    10.00
BANK,UNIVERSAL,PAT.1905,SHONK & CO.,5 IN....................    25.00
BANK,WALKING ELEPHANT,GOLD PAINT,IRON,4 X 3 IN.,STILL.......    15.00
BANK,WHITE KITTEN WITH A BLUE NECK BOW,IRON,5 IN.HIGH.......    18.00
BANK,WILLIAM TELL,MECHANICAL................................   135.00
BAROMETER,ANEROID,BANJO TYPE CASE,OAK,36 IN.................    87.50
BAROMETER,BANJO SHAPE CASE,SHELL & FLORAL MEDALLIONS,
   G.MASPERO,MAHOGANY......................................    70.00
BAROMETER,BANJO,HYGROMETER,THERMOMETER,A.MANTEGANI,WISBEACH,
   38 1/2 IN...............................................   150.00
BAROMETER,BANJO,SILVERED REGISTER DIAL,ROSEWOOD,THESOLILI,
   LONDON,41 IN............................................   250.00
BAROMETER,COTTAGE,STORM GLASS,THERMOMETER,LABEL.............     9.50
BAROMETER,DESK STYLE,BRASS CASE,GERMANY,3 1/2 IN............     8.00
BAROMETER,MAHOGANY,JAMES TONEY......................ILLUS..    45.00
```

JAMES TONEY MAHOGANY BAROMETER

BAROMETER,STICK,ENGRAVED IVORY REGISTER PLATES,ROSEWOOD,
  LOFTUS,LONDON............................................. 125.00
BAROMETER,STICK,GEORGE III,F.HENDERSON,EDINBURGH,39 IN.HIGH.  200.00
BAROMETER,STICK,IVORY REGISTER DIAL,MAHOGANY,W.GILBERT,
  BELFAST,36 IN............................................. 200.00
BAROMETER,STICK,IVORY REGISTER DIAL,ROSEWOOD,E.C.WOOD,
  LONDON,36 IN.HIGH........................................ 175.00
BAROMETER,STICK,SILVERED REGISTER DIAL,MAHOGANY,34 IN.HIGH..  150.00
BAROMETER,THERMOMETER,HYGROMETER,SPIRIT LEVEL,JOSEPH
  ALEXANDER,NORWICH........................................ 160.00
BAROMETER,WALL,CIRCULAR REGISTER PLATE,CARVED GILT WOOD
  BEZEL,40 IN.............................................. 250.00
  BARSOTTINI,SEE BOTTLE,BARSOTTINI


       BASALT IS A BLACK STONEWARE MADE BY MIXING IRON AND
       OXIDES INTO A BASIC CLAY. IT IS VERY HARD AND CAN
       BE FINISHED ON A LATHE. WEDGWOOD DEVELOPED HIS FAMOUS
       BLACK BASALT IN 1769,WHICH WAS AN IMPROVEMENT ON A
       SIMILAR WARE MADE IN STAFFORDSHIRE,ENGLAND,AS EARLY
       AS 1740. BASALT IS STILL BEING MADE IN ENGLAND AND ON
       THE CONTINENT.
BASALT,CREAMER,BLACK ON BLACK,CLASSIC FIGURES,MARKED
  WEDGWOOD.................................................   50.00
BASALT,INKWELL,ROUND,THREE QUILL HOLES,RAISED PANELS,INCISED
  A.......................................................   22.00
BASALT,SUGAR,INDIVIDUAL,OPEN,SIGNED WEDGWOOD,ENGLAND........    3.00


       BATTERSEA ENAMELS ARE ENAMELS PAINTED ON COPPER AND
       MADE IN THE BATTERSEA DISTRICT OF LONDON FROM ABOUT
       1750 TO 1756. MANY SIMILAR ENAMELS ARE MISTAKENLY
       CALLED BATTERSEA.
BATTERSEA,BOX,BLUE BASE,ENAMEL, MAY YOU BE HAPPY ........... 125.00
BATTERSEA,BOX,BLUE ENAMEL,PINK,YELLOW & ORCHID FLORAL,HINGED
  LID,4 IN................................................. 135.00
BATTERSEA,BOX,GREEN BASE,TOP FLORAL DESIGN,1 IN.DIAMETER.... 100.00
BATTERSEA,BOX,GREEN ENAMEL,WHITE INSIDE,ACORN SHAPE,
  3 IN.LONG............................................... 350.00
BATTERSEA,BOX,PATCH,ENAMELED,2 IN.DIAMETER.................   89.00
BATTERSEA,BOX,PATCH,ROSE BASE,WHITE LID,BLACK CROWN,
  FRIENDSHIP SINCERE......................................   67.50
BATTERSEA,BOX,PILL, ESTEEM THE GIVER,  ENAMEL,BLUE.........   45.00
BATTERSEA,BOX,SAYS UNITY,PEACE & CONCORD ON COVER,ONE INCH
  DIAMETER............................................... 125.00
BATTERSEA,BOX,WRESTLING SCENE,2 1/2 IN.WIDE,1 IN.HIGH....... 165.00


       BAVARIA WAS A DISTRICT WHERE MANY TYPES OF POTTERY AND
       PORCELAIN WERE MADE FOR CENTURIES. THE WORD BAVARIA
       APPEARS ON MANY PIECES OF NINETEENTH-CENTURY CHINA,
       BAVARIA,GERMANY,APPEARED AFTER 1871.
BAVARIAN,BERRY SET,PINK & RED FLOWERS,PINK RIM,1 LARGE &
  6 SMALL BOWLS...........................................   25.00
BAVARIAN,BERRY SET,PINK,GREEN,GILT,BLUE FLOWERS,HAND-PAINTED  21.00
BAVARIAN,BOWL,BERRY,BERRY BLOSSOMS,GOLD BORDER,
  ARTIST-SIGNED,4 SAUCERS.................................   40.00
BAVARIAN,BOWL,BERRY,GRAPE DECOR,GREEN,GOLD BORDER,SCALLOPED,
  6 SAUCES...............................................   60.00
BAVARIAN,BOWL,BERRY,WHITE,GREEN SNOWBALLS,PINK FLOWERS,GOLD,
  11 IN..................................................   10.00
BAVARIAN,BOWL,BIRD & FLORAL CENTER,YELLOW TO BLUE BORDER,
  ROYAL CROWN............................................   20.00
BAVARIAN,BOWL,FLORAL CENTER,OPENWORK AROUND SIDES,SCHUMANN,
  8 1/2 IN...............................................   25.00
BAVARIAN,BOWL,PINK ROSES,GOLD TRIM,2 5/8 IN. DEEP,
  10 1/2 IN.DIAMETER.....................................   10.50
BAVARIAN,BOWL,STRAWBERRIES,SIGNED DEKALB..................   28.50
BAVARIAN,BOX,POWDER,BLUE,LAVENDER VIOLETS,GREEN LEAVES,
  HAND-PAINTED,GILT......................................   32.00
BAVARIAN,BUTTER CHIP,WHITE,GOLD BAND,MARKED BAVARIA & CROWN,
  SET OF 6...............................................   12.00
BAVARIAN,CHOCOLATE POT,FLORALS,Z.C.& CO..................   30.00
BAVARIAN,CHOCOLATE POT,MIGNON,LARGE ROSES,GILT TRIM & HANDLE  25.00
BAVARIAN,CHOCOLATE POT,PINK ROSES,GOLD,CINDER MARK,6 CUPS &
  SAUCERS................................................   45.00
BAVARIAN,CHOCOLATE POT,WHITE GROUND,PINK ROSES,BLUE
  FORGET-ME-NOTS,GOLD....................................   28.00
BAVARIAN,COCOA POT,FLORAL,GOLD TRIM,4 CUPS & SAUCERS........  24.00
BAVARIAN,CREAMER,CHILDS,HAND-PAINTED DECOR,MARKED

```
    SELB-MITTERLACH................................................  4.00
BAVARIAN,CUP & SAUCER,CHOCOLATE,YELLOW & PINK FLORAL,GOLD,
    GREEN......................................................  6.50
BAVARIAN,CUP & SAUCER,DEMITASSE,PINK,RED ROSES,GOLD EDGE,
    GOLD HANDLE................................................ 11.00
BAVARIAN,CUP & SAUCER,FRUITS...................................  6.50
BAVARIAN,CUP & SAUCER,HOLLY,BERRIES,GOLD HANDLE & EDGE...... 13.50
BAVARIAN,CUP & SAUCER,PINK ROSES,FORGET-ME-NOTS,
    ARTIST-SIGNED,MARK........................................ 10.50
BAVARIAN,CUP & SAUCER,PORCELAIN,COPPER LUSTER,SELB
    HUTSCHENREUTHER........................................... 20.00
BAVARIAN,CUP & SAUCER,TWO-HANDLED CUP,STRAWBERRIES,GOLD,
    ARTIST-SIGNED............................................. 10.00
BAVARIAN,CUP & SAUCER,WILD ROSE SPRAYS,CROSSED SWORD MARK... 10.00
BAVARIAN,DISH,CANDY,FLUTED,RUFFLED,PINK TO ROSE SHADING,
    ROSES,MONBIJOU............................................ 12.00
BAVARIAN,DISH,CANDY,OPENWORK EDGE,DRESDEN TYPE FLOWERS,
    HANDLE,MARK............................................... 12.00
BAVARIAN,DISH,RELISH,PINK POPPIES,HAND-PAINTED,GOLD HANDLES. 12.50
BAVARIAN,FIGURINE,ELEPHANT,TRUMPETING,YELLOW PORCELAIN,
    MARKED,5 IN.HIGH.......................................... 15.00
BAVARIAN,GRAVY BOAT,ATTACHED PLATE,FIORELLA................. 10.00
BAVARIAN,HAIR RECEIVER,HATPIN HOLDER,TRAY,POWDER BOX,YELLOW,
    WHITE ROSES............................................... 35.00
BAVARIAN,HAIR RECEIVER,PINK & BLUE FLORAL,GILT,HAND-PAINTED,
    Z S & CO..................................................  8.00
BAVARIAN,HAIR RECEIVER,POWDER JAR,YELLOW FLOWERS,GOLD TRIM.. 20.00
BAVARIAN,HAIR RECEIVER,WHITE GROUND,VIOLETS,GOLD TRIM....... 10.00
BAVARIAN,HOLDER,HATPIN,BLUE FORGET-ME-NOTS,GOLD TRIM TOP &
    BOTTOM,5 IN............................................... 15.00
BAVARIAN,HOLDER,HATPIN,GOLD-PAINTED,Z S & COMPANY........... 10.00
BAVARIAN,HOLDER,HATPIN,PINK & YELLOW ROSES,GOLD TRIM....... 12.50
BAVARIAN,HOLDER,HATPIN,PINK ROSES,BLUE GROUND,OPEN TOP,
    MARKED.................................................... 12.50
BAVARIAN,HOT PLATE,BLUE DECOR..............................  3.50
BAVARIAN,JAR,CRACKER,BLUE GROUND,PINK ROSES,GREEN LEAVES ON
    WHITE BAND................................................ 29.50
BAVARIAN,JAR,CRACKER,ROSES,LILIES OF THE VALLEY,
    HAND-PAINTED,HANDLES...................................... 16.50
BAVARIAN,JAR,CRACKER,YELLOW,GREEN,CERISE TULIPS,GOLD SPRAYS,
    HANDLE.................................................... 18.50
BAVARIAN,JUG,CASTOR,HANDLE,ORANGE,GOLD,OIL.................  5.00
BAVARIAN,JUG,CASTOR,HANDLE,ORANGE,GOLD,VINEGAR.............  5.00
BAVARIAN,MUG,HAND PAINTED,GRAPES,GOLD TRIM,LIZARD HANDLE.... 12.00
BAVARIAN,MUG,SHAVING,GOLD BANDS,INITIALED C.H.MC L.,CROSSED
    SWORD MARK................................................  9.50
BAVARIAN,MUG,SHAVING,LADY'S,WHITE,PINK FLORAL,TURQUOISE,
    SHELF,SCHOENBERG.......................................... 18.50
BAVARIAN,PITCHER,DUTCH GIRL,ORANGE,WHITE,WILLIAM GOEBEL,
    DOLLMAKER................................................. 12.00
BAVARIAN,PITCHER,ROSE DECOR................................  8.50
BAVARIAN,PITCHER,SOUVENIR,SCENE,ONSET,MASSACHUSETTS,WHITE,
    3 IN......................................................  3.50
BAVARIAN,PITCHER,SQUATTY,PURPLE GRAPE CLUSTERS,GILT HANDLE,
    3 TUMBLERS................................................ 50.00
BAVARIAN,PLATE,ALLOVER ORCHID,PINK,WHITE IRIS,9 1/2 IN..... 25.00
BAVARIAN,PLATE,APPLE LYING IN GRASS,HAND-PAINTED UNDER
    GLAZE,7 3/4 IN............................................  7.50
BAVARIAN,PLATE,BLUE GROUND,THREE LARGE WHITE CLEMATIS,
    9 5/8 IN..................................................  7.50
BAVARIAN,PLATE,BLUE,YELLOW ROSE,WHITE BORDER,HUTSCHENREUTHER
    SELB.,6 IN................................................ 10.00
BAVARIAN,PLATE,BREAD,GOLD MEDALLION CENTER,GIVE US THIS DAY,
    FLORAL.................................................... 10.50
BAVARIAN,PLATE,BREAD,PASTEL FLOWER SPRAY IN CENTER,10 IN.... 10.50
BAVARIAN,PLATE,BROWN TO TAN,ROSES,Z S & CO.,6 IN.,SET OF 4.. 30.00
BAVARIAN,PLATE,CAKE,BERRIES,RAISED DECORATION,BLOSSOMS,9 IN.  9.00
BAVARIAN,PLATE,CAKE,RED & PINK ROSE CENTER,IRIDESCENT GOLD
    RIM,HANDLES...............................................  5.00
BAVARIAN,PLATE,CAKE,RED & PINK ROSES,PIERCED HANDLES........  6.50
BAVARIAN,PLATE,CAKE,SIGNED 1938 PAINTED BY MARY
    LINDENBERGER,AGE 76....................................... 12.50
BAVARIAN,PLATE,CAKE,YELLOW & PURPLE GRAPES,OPEN HANDLES,
    HAND-PAINTED..............................................  5.50
BAVARIAN,PLATE,CAKE,YELLOW ROSES,HEAVY GOLD,10 IN.......... 11.00
BAVARIAN,PLATE,CHERRY DESIGN,GOLD BORDER,MARK MALMAISON,
    6 IN...................................................... 13.00
BAVARIAN,PLATE,CHOP,FLOCK OF BLUE BIRDS IN CENTER,BIRD
    BORDER.................................................... 19.50
BAVARIAN,PLATE,CHOP,VIOLETS,GOLD TRIM,CZECHOSLOVAKIA,
```

```
      MATCHING BOWL.........................................   25.00
BAVARIAN,PLATE,CHOP,WHITE AND YELLOW ROSES,RAISED ENAMEL....   35.00
BAVARIAN,PLATE,COIN GOLD RIM,YELLOW ROSES,HAND-PAINTED,6 IN.    3.75
BAVARIAN,PLATE,DEEP,HANDLE EFFECT ON 2 SIDES,RED & PINK
      ROSES,11 IN.......................................       16.50
BAVARIAN,PLATE,DESSERT,GREEN,IVORY COLOR,FLORAL,MARKED
      TIRSCHENREUTH,6...................................       38.50
BAVARIAN,PLATE,DINNER,DELMONTE,PAIR........................     7.50
BAVARIAN,PLATE,GAME,DUCK,REEDS,ROSE GARLAND BORDER,7 1/2 IN.   12.50
BAVARIAN,PLATE,GAME,PARTRIDGE IN GREEN SHRUBBERY,PINK
      CLOUDS,13 IN.......................................       35.00
BAVARIAN,PLATE,GAME,QUAIL IN CENTER,PINK ROSES ON BORDER,
      7 1/4 IN...........................................       15.00
BAVARIAN,PLATE,GAME,QUAILS,MEDALLION,GOLD LACE BORDER,
      BEEHIVE MARK.......................................       67.50
BAVARIAN,PLATE,GAME,SCENE,DEER,FAWN,PINE TREES,HAND-PAINTED,
      8 1/2 IN...........................................       25.00
BAVARIAN,PLATE,GRAIN,MARKED R.C.KRONACH,CROSSED SWORDS,
      CROWN,8 1/2 IN.....................................        6.00
BAVARIAN,PLATE,GREEN & CREAM,FRUIT BLOSSOMS,HAND-PAINTED,
      8 1/4 IN...........................................        4.50
BAVARIAN,PLATE,GREEN BAND,STRAWBERRIES,HAND-PAINTED,
      FAVORITE,SIGNED....................................        3.50
BAVARIAN,PLATE,GREEN,SILVER,ROSES ON BORDER,PANSIES IN
      CENTER,2 HANDLES...................................       12.00
BAVARIAN,PLATE,HAND PAINTED,APPLES,ORANGE,GREEN,BEIGE,GOLD,
      SIGNED KOCH........................................       15.00
BAVARIAN,PLATE,HANGING,HAND PAINTED,PINK DOGWOOD,GOLD,
      MARKED,PAIR........................................       15.00
BAVARIAN,PLATE,HUNT SCENE,ORANGE & GOLD BAND,GERMANY,
      6 1/2 IN...........................................       20.00
BAVARIAN,PLATE,IVORY FRUIT PATTERN,BLACK KNIGHT,MARKED,SET
      OF 4..............................................        18.00
BAVARIAN,PLATE,IVORY GROUND,HAND-PAINTED BORDER,
      9 IN.DIAMETER......................................        4.50
BAVARIAN,PLATE,IVORY,GREEN BAND,VIOLETS,HAND-PAINTED,LOUISE,
      7 IN..............................................         4.00
BAVARIAN,PLATE,LAVENDER,MORNING GLORIES,ARTIST-SIGNED,
      8 1/2 IN...........................................        7.50
BAVARIAN,PLATE,MIGNON PATTERN,SCALLOPED EDGE,PINK FLORAL
      BAND,SET OF 4......................................        6.50
BAVARIAN,PLATE,PEARLIZED CENTER,TWO BUTTERFLIES,BLUE BORDER,
      SIGNED............................................        10.00
BAVARIAN,PLATE,PICTURE OF UNION STATION,KANSAS CITY,MO.,
      J.C.LOUISE.........................................       10.00
BAVARIAN,PLATE,PINK,YELLOW ROSES,GIVE US THIS DAY,HANDLES,
      9 IN..............................................         8.00
BAVARIAN,PLATE,POPPIES,GOLD TRIM,HAND-PAINTED,8 1/4 IN......     6.00
BAVARIAN,PLATE,PORTRAIT,QUEEN LOUISE,GOLD GRAPES,CIRCLE
      BORDER,7 1/2 IN....................................       22.00
BAVARIAN,PLATE,SCENE,TWO HORSES & RIDERS,OPEN EDGE,7 IN.....   11.00
BAVARIAN,PLATE,SENTA,CLUSTERS OF PEACHES WITH BLOSSOMS,
      TRANSFER DESIGN....................................        8.00
BAVARIAN,PLATE,SOUVENIR,FLORIDA,WHITE,SCENE,MAN PICKING
      GRAPEFRUIT........................................         8.50
BAVARIAN,PLATE,TIGER LILY,SAXE............................      8.00
BAVARIAN,PLATE,VIOLET MOTIF,ARTIST-SIGNED,6 IN.............    8.00
BAVARIAN,PLATE,VIOLET MOTIF,HAND-PAINTED,SIGNED B.E.HOOKER,
      6 IN..............................................         8.00
BAVARIAN,PLATE,WATER LILIES,ARTIST-SIGNED,9 IN.............    7.00
BAVARIAN,PLATE,WHITE & PINK POND LILIES IN WATER,
      HAND-PAINTED,6 IN..................................        3.00
BAVARIAN,PLATE,WHITE,GOLD DECOR & BORDER,10 1/2 IN.........    9.00
BAVARIAN,PLATE,WHITE,GREEN,PURPLE GROUND,PINK & GREEN
      GOOSEBERRIES......................................        16.50
BAVARIAN,PLATE,WHITE,PINK ROSE,LEAVES,HUTSCHENREUTHER SELB.,
      6 IN..............................................        10.00
BAVARIAN,PLATE,WILD CANARY & VIOLETS,ROBIN & BLUEBERRIES,
      7 1/2 IN.,PAIR.....................................       25.00
BAVARIAN,PLATE,YELLOW AND PINK ROSES,10 IN.................    6.75
BAVARIAN,PLATE,YELLOW ROSES,GRAY LEAVES,GOLD TRIM,MARKED,SET
      OF 6..............................................        75.00
BAVARIAN,PLATTER,SMALL PINK ROSES AROUND BORDER,4 PLATES....   25.00
BAVARIAN,POT,CHOCOLATE,HAND-PAINTED ROSES,MARK.............   11.00
BAVARIAN,SHAKER,SALT & PEPPER,LILY OF THE VALLEY DECOR,
      MARKED GALLUP......................................       12.50
BAVARIAN,SHAKER,SUGAR,PASTEL COLOR GROUND,VIOLETS,FOLIAGE,
      GILT..............................................        15.00
BAVARIAN,SUGAR BOWL,YELLOW,PURPLE,GREEN,PANSIES,KNOBBED
      COVER.............................................        35.00
BAVARIAN,TEAPOT,CREAMER,SUGAR,PINK ROSES,GOLD TRIM..........   30.00
```

BAVARIAN,TEAPOT,INDIVIDUAL,PINK & WHITE FLORAL,GOLD TRIM,
  ARTIST-SIGNED............................................. 15.00
BAVARIAN,TRAY,BACHELOR BUTTONS,GOLD,GREEN,HAND PAINTED,
  SIGNED WATTEAU............................................ 15.50
BAVARIAN,TRAY,DARK GREEN GROUND,DARK RED ROSES,WIDE GOLD
  BORDER,MARKED............................................. 15.00
BAVARIAN,TUREEN,LOUISE,GOLD & WHITE........................... 12.50
BAVARIAN,VASE,GOLD,DOUBLE HANDLES,MARK,SIGNED SARAH COYLE,
  8 1/2 IN.TALL............................................. 12.00
BAVARIAN,VASE,LAVENDER GROUND,VIOLETS,HAND-PAINTED,GOLD,BALL
  SHAPE..................................................... 12.00
BAYONET,SEE WEAPON,BAYONET
BEADED BAG,GOLD COLOR WITH WHITE PEARL COLOR,7 IN. X 5 IN...  2.25
BEADED BAG,GREEN CARNIVAL GLASS,DRAWSTRING TOP.............. 20.00
BEADED BAG,GREEN,MEDALLION IN RELIEF,SMALL.................   3.50
BEADED BAG,IRIDESCENT TIERS OF FRINGE,DRAWSTRING,
  CZECHOSLOVAKIA............................................ 10.00
BEADED BAG,MADE IN BELGIUM....................................  9.00
BEADED BAG,MULTICOLOR BEADED FLOWER,TRIM,HANDLE,SATEEN
  GROUND,DATE 1925.......................................... 15.00
BEADED BAG,WHITE LEATHER LINING,CHINA........................ 39.50
BEADED,PURSE,DRAWSTRING,IRIDESCENT,CZECHOSLOVAKIA........... 10.00
BEADED,PURSE,7 IN.HIGH.......................................  8.00
BEAM,SEE BOTTLE,BEAM


BEEHIVE,AUSTRIA,OR BEEHIVE,VIENNA,CHINA INCLUDES ALL
THE MANY TYPES OF DECORATED PORCELAIN MARKED WITH THE
FAMOUS BEEHIVE MARK. THE MARK HAS BEEN USED SINCE THE
EIGHTEENTH CENTURY.
BEEHIVE,BUTTER PAT,MOSAIC DECOR,QUATREFOIL SHAPE,CUTOUT
  CORNERS................................................... 20.00
BEEHIVE,CUP & SAUCER,DEMITASSE,COLORFUL COUPLE,GOLD SCROLL
  HANDLE.................................................... 15.00
BEEHIVE,JAR,POWDER,COVER,CIRCULAR PANEL,COURTING LOVERS,
  BLUE,GOLD,FOOTED..........................................  9.00
BEEHIVE,PLAQUE,FIGURES IN CENTER,GREEN & GOLD FLANGE,RED
  CORNERS,15 IN............................................ 135.00
BEEHIVE,PLATE,BLUE,CLASSIC SCENE,SIGNED ANGELICA KAUFFMANN,
  6 1/4 IN.................................................. 12.50
BEEHIVE,PLATE,BLUE,COBALT RIM,GOLD,MYTHOLOGICAL SCENE IN
  CENTER,SIGNED............................................. 47.50
BEEHIVE,PLATE,CAKE,MAIDENS & CUPID,RED & GOLD BORDER,MARK,
  10 IN..................................................... 27.00
BEEHIVE,PLATE,CAKE,TWO MAIDENS,CUPID,RED & GOLD BORDERS,MARK
  & AUSTRIA................................................. 27.00
BEEHIVE,PLATE,CLASSICAL FIGURES,RED,GOLD TRACERY,AUSTRIA,
  9 1/4 IN.................................................. 40.00
BEEHIVE,PLATE,COLORFULLY-DRESSED LADIES,MAGENTA BORDER,
  PIERCED,MARK.............................................. 32.50
BEEHIVE,PLATE,FRUIT,GERMANY,9 IN............................. 50.00
BEEHIVE,PLATE,GARRICK BETWEEN COMEDY & TRAGEDY,SIGNED
  REYNOLD,7 IN.............................................. 18.00
BEEHIVE,PLATE,LIGHT BLUE,PINK FLORAL,GREEN LEAVES,8 1/2 IN.. 25.00
BEEHIVE,PLATE,MAIDENS,DOVE,ANGELS,ARTIST KARL LARKEN,AUSTRIA 30.00
BEEHIVE,PLATE,PORTRAIT OF LADY WITH LOW-CUT GOWN,RED,GREEN,
  WHITE BORDER.............................................. 75.00
BEEHIVE,PLATE,PORTRAIT,BLUE,IRIDESCENT GROUND,RAISED GOLD,
  SIGNED WAGNER............................................ 150.00
BEEHIVE,PLATE,PORTRAIT,COBALT,GOLD,SIGNED WEH,9 1/2 IN...... 55.00
BEEHIVE,PLATE,PORTRAIT,GOLD,9 IN............................. 60.00
BEEHIVE,PLATE,ROYALLY DRESSED LADIES IN WOODLAND SCENE,
  PIERCED,MARK.............................................. 32.00
BEEHIVE,PLATE,THREE MAIDENS,DOVE,ANGEL,MARK & AUSTRIA,SIGNED
  KARL LARKEN............................................... 30.00
BEEHIVE,PLATE,WHITE,ALLOVER FLORAL,PINK,GREEN,8 1/2 IN...... 25.00
BEEHIVE,PLATE,WOMAN,CHERUB,MAGENTA & GREEN GROUND,7 IN...... 16.00
BEEHIVE,TRAY,BREAD,DEER,DOE RIM PANELS,BE INDUSTRIOUS,IOWA
  CITY...................................................... 75.00
BEEHIVE,URN,PINK,BLUE GROUND,GOLD,FOUR SCENES,LADIES,
  CHERUBS,14 IN.,PAIR...................................... 425.00
BEEHIVE,VASE,BLUE,GOLD,BROWN,10 IN........................... 45.00
BEEHIVE,VASE,LADY,CHILD ON COW,MAIDEN,RED,GOLD,SIGNED
  E.BOUCHERS................................................ 75.00
BEEHIVE,VASE,MINIATURE,MEDALLION WITH LOVERS,MAROON TRIM,
  GOLD BEADING.............................................. 60.00


BELLS HAVE BEEN MADE OF CHINA,GLASS,OR METAL. ALL TYPES
ARE COLLECTED.
BELL,BOLSHEVIK SCENE,ANIMAL CARVINGS,HANDLE IS VULTURE,

BRONZE,5 3/4 IN.................................................1,200.00
BELL,BRASS,BURNISHED,3 IN.DIAMETER,FOUR ON LEATHER STRAP....  20.00
BELL,BRASS,28,LEATHER STRAP,FIRE DEPARTMENT,FULTON,MISSOURI. 175.00
BELL,BUCKLE-SHAPE GRIP,INCISED BANDS,IRON CLAPPER,BRONZE,
  4 IN.TALL..................................................   8.50
BELL,CALF,BRASS,ON LEATHER STRAP,2 1/2 IN....................   8.00
BELL,CALL,DOLL,STOCKING FACE,CIRCA 1895......................   6.00
BELL,CAMEL,ENGRAVED,BRASS,THREE,WOVEN CORD...................  10.00
BELL,CHIANTEL FONDEUR,BRONZE,IRON HANDLE,4 IN.HIGH...........  15.00
BELL,CHIMES,DINNER,BOX TYPE FOR WALL,LIBERTY CO.,9 1/2 IN. X
  11 IN.....................................................   15.00
BELL,CHIMES,DINNER,RAILROAD,MALLET................... 19.75 TO  25.00
BELL,CHIMES,SHAFT,BRASS......................................  20.00
BELL,CHURCH,IRON,24 IN.DIAMETER..............................  47.50
BELL,CLOWN,BRASS,ENGLAND.....................................  15.00
BELL,COMBINE,HORSE TEAM......................................   7.00
BELL,COTTER-PINNED,BRASS,47 ON DOUBLE LEATHER STRAP..........  75.00
BELL,COW,10 GRADUATED SIZES,LEATHER STRAP,GILDED COPPER
  COLOR.....................................................   19.50
BELL,COW,BRASS-PLATED STEEL,RIVETED AT SIDE,5 1/2 IN.LONG...   5.00
BELL,COW,BRASS,5 IN.HIGH.....................................  10.00
BELL,COW,COPPER,STRAP HOLDER,4 IN.TALL,4 1/2 IN.DIAMETER....  10.00
BELL,COW,HAND-FORGED CLAPPER,BRONZE,2 1/2 IN. X 4 IN. X
  4 IN.TALL.................................................    8.50
BELL,COW,HAND-FORGED,SQUARE CLAPPER,CHAIN,IRON..............   15.00
BELL,COW,IRON,3 1/2 IN.......................................   5.00
BELL,COW,RECTANGULAR FRAME ON TOP FOR STRAP,BRONZE,4 X
  3 3/4 IN.HIGH.............................................    8.00
BELL,CROSS ON TOP,SAYS SANTA BARBARA,1786,3 IN..............    8.50
BELL,CRUISER MESS CALL,FOUR CHIMES,IVORY STRIKER,
  PAT.1889-1925,8 IN........................................   22.00
BELL,CUTTER,GRADUATED ON BRASS STRAP,BRASS,4................   18.50
BELL,DESK,BRASS,ROUND WALNUT BASE............................  14.00
BELL,DESK,ORNATE FOOTED STAND,MARKED PAT.APPLIED 1863,
  5 1/2 IN.HIGH.............................................   16.00
BELL,DESK,TAP TYPE,ORNATE BASE,DATED 1856...................   12.00
BELL,DINNER CHIMES,RAILROAD,MALLET,FOUR CHIMES..............   19.95
BELL,DINNER GONG,5 BRASS BELLS WITH BRASS BARS,WOOD STAND,
  XYLOPHONE TYPE............................................   45.00
BELL,DINNER,CLEAR,ENAMELED FLORAL,4 1/2 IN..................   22.50
BELL,DINNER,ORNATE HANDLE,STERLING SILVER,3 1/2 IN..........    7.50
BELL,DINNER,STERLING SILVER..................................  12.00
BELL,DINNER,STORK HANDLE,BRASS...............................   5.00
BELL,DOOR,FRONT READS TURN,BRASS & IRON......................   7.50
BELL,DOOR,PULL TYPE,BRASS....................................   5.50
BELL,DOOR,PULLS THROUGH DOOR,BRASS...........................  15.00
BELL,DUTCH LADY CARRIES FLOWERS IN APRON,BRASS,2 1/4 IN.HIGH   9.50
BELL,DUTCH LADY,BRASS........................................   9.50
BELL,EAGLE HANDLE,BRASS,2 7/8 IN.DIAMETER,5 IN.TALL.........   15.00
BELL,EL CAMINO,SAN DIEGO,PAT.1914...........................   12.00
BELL,ETCHED BASE,CLEAR,FROSTED HANDLE,COLUMBIAN EXPOSITION,
  1893......................................................   45.00
BELL,FARM,ARM PULL,36 IN.YOKE,HILLSBORO,OHIO,1888,IRON,
  18 IN..................................................... 100.00
BELL,FIGURAL,FORM OF SERPENT,6 IN.,HAMMER FOR STRIKING,
  BRONZE...................................................   12.00
BELL,FIGURAL,TORTOISE,PRESS HEAD OR TAIL,TORTOISESHELL BACK,
  IRON......................................................  89.50
BELL,GONG,BACKPLATE SCREWS TO WALL,BRASS,4 5/8 IN.DIAMETER..   8.75
BELL,GONG,STREETCAR.........................................   25.00
BELL,HAND,BRASS,3 IN.DIAMETER................................  10.00
BELL,HAND,BRASS,3 1/2 IN.DIAMETER............................  15.00
BELL,HAND,BRASS,4 IN.DIAMETER................................  18.00
BELL,HAND,BRASS,5 IN.DIAMETER,8 1/2 IN.HIGH.................   22.50
BELL,HAND,BRASS,5 3/4 IN.DIAMETER,9 IN.HIGH.................   27.50
BELL,HAND,BRASS,6 IN.DIAMETER,10 IN.HIGH....................   32.50
BELL,HAND,BRASS,7 1/4 IN.DIAMETER,12 IN.HIGH................   45.00
BELL,HAND,BRONZE,6 IN.DIAMETER,10 IN.HIGH...................   35.00
BELL,HAND,BULL'S-EYE DECOR,BRASS,BRASS HANDLE,11 IN. X
  6 1/4 IN.DIAMETER.........................................   60.00
BELL,HAND,SCHOOL,BRASS,2 3/8 IN..............................   2.00
BELL,HAND,SCHOOL,BRASS,2 5/8 IN..............................   2.50
BELL,HAND,SCHOOL,BRASS,3 3/8 IN..............................   3.50
BELL,HAND,SCHOOL,BRASS,4 IN..................................   5.00
BELL,HAND,SCHOOL,BRASS,5 IN..................................   6.50
BELL,HAND,SCHOOL,BRASS,6 IN..................................   9.00
BELL,HAND,SCHOOLMASTER,WOODEN HANDLE,BRASS,7 1/2 IN.HIGH X
  4 IN.DIAMETER.............................................   11.75
BELL,HAND,SCHOOLMASTER,WOODEN HANDLE,6 IN.HIGH,
  3 1/4 IN.DIAMETER.........................................    6.95
BELL,HAND,SMOOTH,BRASS,4 POUNDS,6 IN........................   20.00

```
BELL,HAND,TEACHER,ENGRAVED,BRASS,4 IN......................        9.00
BELL,HAND,TEACHER,ENGRAVED,BRASS,5 IN......................       12.00
BELL,HAND,TEACHER,ENGRAVED,1878,BRASS,3 1/4 IN.............        7.00
BELL,HAND,TEACHER'S,ENGRAVED,BRASS,3 IN....................        6.00
BELL,HAND,TOWN CRIER,WOODEN HANDLE,BRASS,11 1/4 IN. HIGH....       39.75
BELL,HARNESS SADDLE,TWO BRASS BELLS ON EMBOSSED BRASS STRAP,
   6 IN.LONG...............................................        9.00
BELL,HORSE,LACQUERED,BRASS,2 3/4 IN........................        4.00
BELL,INDIA,BRASS,GRADUATED FROM 1 3/4 IN. TO 2 1/2 IN.,6...       20.00
BELL,INSCRIBED 42ND ST.TROLLEY,BRONZE......................       25.00
BELL,KINGS CROWN SHAPE,WHITE CROSSED BANDS,JEWELED,GOLD,
   TURQUOISE,RUBIES........................................       32.00
BELL,LADY WITH HOOPSKIRT,BRASS,4 IN.HIGH...................       14.00
BELL,LADY,VICTORIAN ERA,PORCELAIN,3 3/4 IN.HIGH............       25.00
BELL,LOCOMOTIVE,MOUNTED,BRASS..............................       75.00
BELL,LOCOMOTIVE,STEAM,STACK,BRASS,15 IN.DIAMETER,BRASS
   FRAME,21 IN.HIGH........................................      600.00
BELL,MAN FINIAL,ENAMELED,CHINA.............................       13.50
BELL,MARKED 1878 SAIGNELEGIER,CHIANTEL,FONDEUR,BRONZE,STRAP
   HANDLE,4 IN.............................................        9.50
BELL,NAPOLEON,BRASS,4 3/4 IN.HIGH..........................       14.00
BELL,OPEN SHAFT,THREE ON A SIDE............................       17.00
BELL,PLANTATION,BRASS,8 IN.................................       20.00
BELL,PLANTATION,ENGRAVED,BRASS,WEIGHS 6 POUNDS,7 1/2 IN.....      25.00
BELL,PLANTATION,ENGRAVED,BRASS,1874,8 IN...................       25.00
BELL,PLANTATION,ENGRAVED,BRASS,7 1/2 IN.DIAMETER...........       25.00
BELL,PLANTATION,ENGRAVED,1874,8 IN.........................       25.00
BELL,PULL,MARKED BEVIN,8 IN.DIAMETER.......................       18.00
BELL,QUEEN ANNE,BRASS,3 1/2 IN.HIGH........................       14.00
BELL,RINGER,SHAPE OF TORTOISE,PRESS HEAD FOR RING,IRON,
   TORTOISE SHELL..........................................       89.50
BELL,SCHOOL,BLACK HANDLE,BRASS.............................        7.50
BELL,SCHOOL,BRASS,4 IN.DIAMETER............................       10.00
BELL,SCHOOL,BRASS,9 IN.TO TOP OF HANDLE....................       25.00
BELL,SCHOOL,BRASS,BLACK WOODEN HANDLE,8 IN.................       18.00
BELL,SCHOOL,BRASS,WOODEN HANDLE,5 1/2 IN.HIGH..............        6.50
BELL,SCHOOL,BRASS,WOODEN HANDLE,7 IN.HIGH...........  4.50 TO     12.50
BELL,SCHOOL,BRASS,WOODEN HANDLE,8 IN.HIGH..................       12.00
BELL,SCHOOL,IRON,250 LBS...................................      150.00
BELL,SCHOOLHOUSE,WEIGHS 200 POUNDS.........................      150.00
BELL,SCHOOLMASTER,HAND,BRASS,WOODEN HANDLE,2 5/8 IN. X
   5 1/4 IN.HIGH...........................................        4.75
BELL,SHAFT,4 BRASS BELLS ON BRASS STRAP....................       20.00
BELL,SHEEP,LEATHER HOLDER,2 IN.HIGH,3 IN.WIDE..............        6.50
BELL,SHIP,BRASS,10 IN.DIAMETER.............................       45.00
BELL,SHIP,BRASS,6 1/2 IN.TALL..............................       45.00
BELL,SHIP,BRASS,8 IN.DIAMETER..............................       25.00
BELL,SHIP,U.S.N.,IRON,10 IN.TALL,9 1/2 IN.DIAMETER.........       25.00
BELL,SLEIGH,7-FOOT STRAP,2-IN.DIAMETER,30..................        6.50
BELL,SLEIGH,7-FOOT STRAP,3-IN.DIAMETER,30..................        9.00
BELL,SLEIGH,18,STRAP 55 IN.LONG............................       19.75
BELL,SLEIGH,25 ON NEW STRAP,BUCKLE.........................       42.50
BELL,SLEIGH,30 BRASS BELLS ON LEATHER STRAP................       45.00
BELL,SLEIGH,32 IRON BELLS ON STRAP.........................       30.00
BELL,SLEIGH,41 BELLS ON STRAP,84 IN.LONG...................       40.00
BELL,SLEIGH,54-IN.STRAP,18.................................       19.75
BELL,SLEIGH,BRASS,LEATHER STRAP,30.........................       25.00
BELL,SLEIGH,BRASS,ON LEATHER STRAP,36 BELLS,43 IN.LONG.....
BELL,SLEIGH,BRASS,ONE-INCH DIAMETER,LEATHER STRAP,28.......       22.50
BELL,SLEIGH,BRASS,ONE-INCH DIAMETER,30,RED VELVET-LINED
   STRAP..................................................        40.00
BELL,SLEIGH,BRASS,STRAP,18.................................       48.00
BELL,SLEIGH,BRASS,STRAP,9..................................       18.50
BELL,SLEIGH,BRASS,36 ON STRAP..............................       45.00
BELL,SLEIGH,BRASS,9 ON ORIGINAL CANVAS STRAP...............       14.50
BELL,SLEIGH,CONICAL SHAPE,ORNATE STRAP & BUCKLE,22.........       25.00
BELL,SLEIGH,DOUBLE STRAP,BRASS BELLS,3 1/2-IN.DIAMETER,44...      45.00
BELL,SLEIGH,ENGRAVED,BRASS,FASTENED BY COTTER PINS,31 ON
   7-FOOT STRAP............................................       50.00
BELL,SLEIGH,ENGRAVED,POLISHED,GRADUATED,BRASS,30,8-FEET-LONG
   STRAP..................................................        85.00
BELL,SLEIGH,FASTENED TO 7-IN.STRAP BY COTTER PINS,ETCHED,
   BRASS,31...............................................        55.00
BELL,SLEIGH,GRADUATED FROM 1 IN. TO 2 1/2 IN.,BRASS,19 ON
   STRAP..................................................        75.00
BELL,SLEIGH,GRADUATED SIZES ON LEATHER STRAP,17............       25.00
BELL,SLEIGH,GRADUATED,LEATHER STRAP,BRASS,18...............       40.00
BELL,SLEIGH,LEATHER STRAP,39...............................       35.00
BELL,SLEIGH,MARKED PAT.1876,BRASS,THREE ON 7 1/4-IN.LONG
   LEATHER STRAP..........................................         2.75
BELL,SLEIGH,NICKEL-PLATED,1 1/2-IN.DIAMETER,30 BELLS ON A
```

```
7-FOOT STRAP.......................................................    15.00
BELL,SLEIGH,NICKLE-PLATED,30 ON STRAP,PAIR....................   100.00
BELL,SLEIGH,ONE SIZE,NICKLE ON BRASS,36,LEATHER STRAP.......    65.00
BELL,SLEIGH,PAT.1872,42 BELLS,ONE-IN.DIAMETER,92-IN.LEATHER
  STRAP............................................................    40.00
BELL,SLEIGH,POLISHED,THREE ON A SIDE,3-IN.TO
  1 1/2-IN.GRADUATION,STRAP.........................................    40.00
BELL,SLEIGH,SHAFT,THREE CLAPPERS IN EACH BELL,METAL BRACKET,
  BRASS,4..........................................................     9.75
BELL,SLEIGH,STRAP,EIGHTEEN,54 IN.LONG.........................    19.75
BELL,SLEIGH,SWEDEN,SET OF 4...................................    18.50
BELL,SLEIGH,THREE IRON BELLS ON IRON STRAP,PAINTED BLACK....    10.00
BELL,SLEIGH,UPPER SECTION OCTAGON SHAPE,NICKEL PLATE,STRAP,
  23...............................................................    22.00
BELL,STORE,ON HEAVY SPIRAL METAL SPRING,SPIKE,BRASS..........    12.50
BELL,STORE,SPRING,RINGS WHEN DOOR OPENS,BRASS................     8.75
BELL,STRING OF FIVE GRADUATED HIMALAYAN GONGS,3- TO
  6-IN.DIAMETER....................................................    25.00
BELL,TABLE,BIRD HANDLE,BRASS,3 1/2 IN.HIGH....................     2.00
BELL,TABLE,BRASS,BURNISHED,EBONY HANDLE,5 IN.TALL............     8.50
BELL,TABLE,BRASS,EBONY HANDLE,3 1/2 IN.TALL..................     6.50
BELL,TABLE,HOLLOW REPOUSSE DESIGN,STERLING SILVER HANDLE,
  1900.............................................................     8.00
BELL,TABLE,PUSH-BUTTON,SILVER METAL,3 1/4 IN. X 2 1/4 IN....     3.50
BELL,TAP,EMBOSSED FLORAL DECOR ALLOVER,MAKER MERIDEN COMPANY    10.00
BELL,TAP,SILVER PLATE OVER BRASS & IRON,PAW FEET,ORNATE
  BASE,DATED 1858..................................................     9.75
BELL,TEACHER,HAND,BRASS,4 1/2 IN. X 8 1/2 IN.HIGH............    16.50
BELL,TEACHER'S,BRASS,3 1/2 IN.................................    11.00
BELL,TEMPLE,SHINTO,1867,BRONZE...............................    65.00
BELL,THREE GRADUATED BELLS IN FRAME,HEART-SHAPED HANDLE,
  BRASS,6 1/2 IN...................................................    18.00
BELL,TOPPED BY FIST,CIRCA 1820,BRASS,2 3/4 IN.HIGH..........    18.00
BELL,TORTOISE,SHELL BACK,IRON,PRESS HEAD OR TAIL & BELL
  RINGS...........................................................    89.50
BELL,TOWN CRIER,HAND,WOODEN HANDLE,11 1/4 IN.HIGH,
  6 5/8-IN.DIAMETER................................................    39.75
BELL,TURKEY,BRASS............................................     3.50
BELL,WEDDING,ENAMEL,FIGURAL TOP,BRONZE,10 IN.HIGH...........   155.00
BELL,WHISTLE,NAVY,BOSUN,JAPANESE,ENGRAVED MARKINGS,ANCHOR,
  BRASS,5 IN.......................................................    12.00
BELL,WITH HANGER,C.S.BELL CO.,HILLSBORO,OHIO,IRON,16 IN.....    65.00
BELL,WOMAN FINIAL,ENAMELED,CHINA.............................    13.50


     BELLEEK CHINA WAS MADE IN IRELAND,OTHER EUROPEAN
     COUNTRIES,AND THE UNITED STATES. THE GLAZE IS CREAMY
     YELLOW AND APPEARS WET. THE FIRST BELLEEK WAS MADE IN
     1857.
  BELLEEK,SEE ALSO,LENOX
BELLEEK,BASKET,HEART SHAPE,IMPRESSED IRELAND,4 1/2 IN.LONG..    50.00
BELLEEK,BOWL,BASKET WEAVE,APPLIED ROSES,THISTLES,CLOVER ON
  RIM,HANDLES......................................................    95.00
BELLEEK,BOWL,HEART SHAPE,BLACK MARK,IRELAND,6 IN. X
  6 IN.LONG........................................................    28.50
BELLEEK,BOWL,KETTLE SHAPE,THREE LEGS,SECOND MARK,IRELAND,
  4 1/2 IN.........................................................    38.00
BELLEEK,BOWL,ROSE,GREEN RIBBON,2 3/4 IN.DIAMETER............    30.00
BELLEEK,BOWL,ROSE,RUFFLED,GREEN MARK,3 IN...................    10.00
BELLEEK,BOWL,ROSE,SWIRLED,APPLIED FLORAL,BERRIES,LEAVES,
  PEARL LUSTER.....................................................    25.00
BELLEEK,BOWL,SHELL,TWO SHELL FEET,4 1/4 X 1 3/4 IN.HIGH.....    32.00
BELLEEK,BOWL,SPIRAL SHELL PATTERN,IRELAND,3 1/2 IN.DIAMETER.    30.00
BELLEEK,BOWL,WITCHES CAULDRON,TWO HANDLES,IRELAND,4 IN. X
  4 1/4 IN.........................................................    38.00
BELLEEK,BOWL,YELLOW LINING,8 1/4 IN.DIAMETER................    75.00
BELLEEK,CANDLESTICK,WREATHS,SILVER OVERLAY,SILVER TOP,
  BOTTOM,LENNOX,PAIR...............................................    37.50
BELLEEK,CAULDRON,GREEN SHAMROCK DECOR,THREE LEGS,BLACK MARK,
  4 IN. HIGH.......................................................    30.00
BELLEEK,CREAMER & SUGAR,BASKETWEAVE,SHAMROCKS,TWIG HANDLES,
  GREEN MARK.......................................................    22.50
BELLEEK,CREAMER & SUGAR,INDIVIDUAL,BASKET WEAVE,DAISY,GREEN
  MARK.............................................................    25.00
BELLEEK,CREAMER & SUGAR,SHAMROCK DECOR,TWIG HANDLE,FOOTED,
  MARK.............................................................    40.00
BELLEEK,CREAMER & SUGAR,SHELL & GREEN SHAMROCK PATTERN,
  IRELAND..........................................................    56.00
BELLEEK,CREAMER & SUGAR,SHELL PATTERN,GREEN SHAMROCKS,BLACK
  MARK,IRELAND.....................................................    30.00
BELLEEK,CREAMER & SUGAR,SHELL PATTERN,PINK ROPE HANDLE,
  FERMENAGH,IRELAND................................................    35.00
```

BELLEEK,CREAMER & SUGAR,SHELL,GREEN BORDER,BLACK MARK,HOUND
  & HARP......................................................... 45.00
BELLEEK,CREAMER & SUGAR,SHELL,YELLOW BORDER,BLACK MARK,HOUND
  & HARP......................................................... 44.00
BELLEEK,CREAMER & SUGAR,WHITE,SHELL DESIGN,PINK TRIM,SHELL
  FEET,MARK..................................................... 47.50
BELLEEK,CREAMER & SUGAR,WHITE,SHELL DESIGN,YELLOW HANDLES,
  BLACK MARK.................................................... 30.00
BELLEEK,CREAMER,BASKET WEAVE,SHAMROCK,BLACK FERMANAGH MARK,
  3 3/4 IN...................................................... 20.00
BELLEEK,CREAMER,BASKET WEAVE,ROPE HANDLE,IRELAND,GREEN MARK,
  4 IN.......................................................... 12.50
BELLEEK,CREAMER,GREEN LEAVES,IRELAND,GREEN MARK,4 1/2 IN.... 11.50
BELLEEK,CREAMER,GREEN SHAMROCKS,BASKETWEAVE................. 40.00
BELLEEK,CREAMER,OPEN SUGAR,BASKET WEAVE,GREEN SHAMROCK
  DECOR,IRELAND................................................. 12.50
BELLEEK,CREAMER,OPEN SUGAR,OVAL BOWL,PINK EDGE............. 100.00
BELLEEK,CREAMER,RAISED LEAVES,FLOWERS,ROPE HANDLE,BLACK
  MARK,HARP,TOWER............................................... 35.00
BELLEEK,CREAMER,ROSE,SILVER INLAY,FOOTED,WILLETT............ 25.00
BELLEEK,CREAMER,SHELL,CORAL HANDLE,IRELAND,BLACK MARK,
  4 IN.HIGH..................................................... 19.00
BELLEEK,CREAMER,SHELL,PINK HANDLE & BORDER,BLACK MARK,HOUND
  & HARP....................................................... 25.00
BELLEEK,CREAMER,SUGAR,GREEN,GOLD RIM,FINIAL,HANDLES,GREEN
  DECOR,WILLET.................................................. 15.00
BELLEEK,CUP & SAUCER,APRICOT COLOR,PINE CONES,PALETTE MARK,
  AMERICAN...................................................... 12.50
BELLEEK,CUP & SAUCER,DEMITASSE,CREAM,RIBBED DESIGN,BLACK
  MARK,IRELAND.................................................. 20.00
BELLEEK,CUP & SAUCER,DEMITASSE,SHELL SHAPE,SHELL FEET,PINK
  TRIM,IRELAND.................................................. 38.00
BELLEEK,CUP & SAUCER,GRASSES PATTERN,FIRST MARK,IRELAND..... 38.00
BELLEEK,CUP & SAUCER,GREEN & CREAM PANELS,FLUTED,GREEN
  HANDLE........................................................ 32.00
BELLEEK,CUP & SAUCER,IRIDESCENT SHELL,SWIRLED,GREEN EDGES,
  FOOTED CUP.................................................... 22.00
BELLEEK,CUP & SAUCER,SHELL PATTERN,BLACK MARK,HOUND & HARP.. 16.50
BELLEEK,CUP & SAUCER,SHELL PATTERN,GREEN SHAMROCKS,YELLOW
  LINED,IRELAND................................................. 15.00
BELLEEK,CUP & SAUCER,SHELL PATTERN,IVORY COLOR,GREEN TINTS,
  BLACK MARK.................................................... 28.50
BELLEEK,CUP & SAUCER,SHELL,GREEN RIM & HANDLE,BLACK MARK,
  HOUND & HARP.................................................. 17.50
BELLEEK,CUP & SAUCER,SHELL,GREEN,SHELL FEET................. 35.00
BELLEEK,CUP & SAUCER,WHITE & BLUE SCENIC,WINDMILL,HOUSE,
  WATER,WILLET.................................................. 35.00
BELLEEK,CUP & SAUCER,WHITE,ECHINUS PATTERN,BLACK MARK,
  IRELAND....................................................... 40.00
BELLEEK,CUP & SAUCER,WHITE,GREEN EDGE & HANDLE,RIPPLE
  PATTERN,BLACK MARK............................................ 18.50
BELLEEK,CUP & SAUCER,WHITE,NOSEGAYS,PALETTE MARK,AMERICAN,
  HAND-PAINTED.................................................. 12.50
BELLEEK,DISH,HEART SHAPE,GREEN FERMANAGH MARK,6 IN.......... 18.00
BELLEEK,DISH,LEAF SHAPE,GREEN,WHITE FLORAL,ARTIST'S PALETTE
  MARK.......................................................... 28.50
BELLEEK,FIGURINE,SEA HORSE,IRIDESCENT,PEARL LUSTER,BASE,
  BLACK MARK.................................................... 58.00
BELLEEK,HARP,6 IN.HIGH..................................... 90.00
BELLEEK,HOLDER,HATPIN,SILVER DEPOSIT ON WHITE,LEAF PATTERN,
  WILLET,5 IN................................................... 20.00
BELLEEK,HOLDER,HATPIN,WHITE,WILLET......................... 15.00
BELLEEK,JARDINIERE,EGGSHELL COLOR,SHAMROCKS,LEAVES,BRANCH
  LEGS,MARK.................................................... 100.00
BELLEEK,JUG,BANDS OF PATTERNS,LEAVES,ZIGZAG,RIBBING,HARP
  HANDLE,IRELAND................................................ 58.00
BELLEEK,JUG,LOOPS,LEAVES,CHEVRONS,RIBBING,HARP-SHAPE HANDLE,
  IRELAND....................................................... 52.00
BELLEEK,MUG,BASKET WEAVE,SHAMROCKS,GREEN,BROWN,IRELAND,
  2 3/4 IN.HIGH................................................. 36.00
BELLEEK,MUG,BROWN GROUND,ACORNS,OAK LEAVES,LENOX,5 IN.HIGH.. 28.00
BELLEEK,MUSTARD POT,BEEHIVE SHAPE,SHAMROCK DESIGN,IRELAND,
  CASTLE MARK................................................... 26.50
BELLEEK,MUSTARD POT,GOLD TRIM,HANDLES,SPOON,PALETTE MARK,
  LENOX......................................................... 36.00
BELLEEK,PITCHER,APPLIED FLORAL,7 IN.HIGH.................. 110.00
BELLEEK,PITCHER,CLUSTERS OF PURPLE & PINK GRAPES,GOLD BASE,
  WILLET,14 IN.................................................. 72.00
BELLEEK,PITCHER,EARS OF CORN,CHICKEN,HEAD IS HANDLE,BACK IS
  SPOUT,MARK.................................................... 75.00
BELLEEK,PITCHER,WHITE SHELL WARE,BLACK MARK,4 1/2 IN.HIGH... 20.00

BELLEEK,PLATE,BASKET WEAVE,GREEN SHAMROCKS,BLACK MARK,
   IRELAND,7 IN................................................ 12.00
BELLEEK,PLATE,BASKET WEAVE,SHAMROCKS,BLACK MARK,
   6 3/8 IN.DIAMETER.......................................... 8.50
BELLEEK,PLATE,CAKE,BASKET WEAVE PATTERN,SHAMROCK SPRAYS,TWO
   HANDLES.................................................... 37.50
BELLEEK,PLATE,CAKE,BASKET WEAVE,GREEN SHAMROCKS,TWIG
   HANDLES,IRELAND............................................ 25.00
BELLEEK,PLATE,SHAMROCK SPRAYS,BASKET WEAVE BORDER,BLACK
   MARK,6 3/4 IN.............................................. 15.00
BELLEEK,PLATE,SHELL PATTERN,YELLOW BORDER,BLACK MARK,
   8 1/2 IN.................................................. 17.50
BELLEEK,PLATE,SHELL,YELLOW BORDER,BLACK MARK,HOUND & HARP,
   7 1/2 IN.................................................. 16.50
BELLEEK,SALT,INDIVIDUAL,ROSE DECOR,CIRCA 1881,BY WILLETS.... 8.00
BELLEEK,SALT,INDIVIDUAL,TAN & GOLD GROUND,BLUE FLORAL,
   WILLETS................................................... 5.00
BELLEEK,SALT,PINK ROSES ON MEANDERING VINES,OPEN,SIGNED
   WILLETS................................................... 12.00
BELLEEK,SALT,PINK TRIM,TEAR SHAPE,SECOND MARK,IRELAND....... 18.00
BELLEEK,SALT,SHELL,PINK TRIM,OPEN,BLACK MARK,HOUND & HARP... 14.50
BELLEEK,SALT,SHELL,YELLOW TRIM,OPEN,BLACK MARK,HOUND & HARP. 14.50
BELLEEK,SALT,SWAN SHAPE,WILLET,3 IN.LONG................... 16.00
BELLEEK,SALT,WHITE,GOLD & GREEN ENAMEL DOTS,OPEN,MARK,SET OF
   6......................................................... 30.00
BELLEEK,STEIN,GREEN,WHITE ROSES,SIGNED LOUIE BENEDICT
   BALDWIN,1907.............................................. 18.50
BELLEEK,SUGAR,BASKET WEAVE,SHAMROCK,OPEN,BLACK FERMANAGH
   MARK,2 IN................................................. 20.00
BELLEEK,TEA STRAINER & HOLDER,SIGNED L IN CIRCLE & ARTIST
   PALETTE................................................... 17.00
BELLEEK,TEAPOT,CREAMER,OPEN SUGAR,WHITE,SEASHELL & CORD
   PATTERN,FOOTED............................................ 135.00
BELLEEK,TEAPOT,IRELAND,HARP,TOWER,CREAMER,SUGAR,6 CUPS &
   SAUCERS,MARK.............................................. 275.00
BELLEEK,TEAPOT,LIMPET DESIGN,PINK TRIM,IRELAND............. 85.00
BELLEEK,TEAPOT,SHELL PATTERN,GREEN SHAMROCKS,BLACK MARK,
   IRELAND................................................... 30.00
BELLEEK,TEAPOT,SWAN BODY,SWAN HEAD,NECK,BILL FOR SPOUT,
   IRELAND,MARK.............................................. 55.00
BELLEEK,TRAY,GRAY TRANSFER OF BELLEEK FACTORY,LANDSCAPE,
   IRELAND,9 IN.............................................. 65.00
BELLEEK,TRAY,RIBBED SHELL PATTERN,GREEN SEAWEED ON SIDES,
   MARK...................................................... 110.00
BELLEEK,TRAY,SHELL MOTIF,PINK EDGE,SHELL HANDLES,HARP & DOG
   MARK...................................................... 110.00
BELLEEK,TUMBLER,DEEP FLUTING,YELLOW LUSTER LINING,IRELAND,
   4 1/2 IN.HIGH............................................. 32.00
BELLEEK,TUMBLER,GOLD RIM,IRELAND,3 1/2 IN.HIGH............. 24.00
BELLEEK,TUMBLER,MUSTACHE,PLAIN,FLUTED..................... 65.00
BELLEEK,VASE,APPLIED DECOR,GREEN MARK,PAIR................ 78.00
BELLEEK,VASE,BLUE,GRAY,CRANES,BLACK MARK,11 IN.HIGH........ 38.00
BELLEEK,VASE,BULBOUS,CREAM GROUND,SHAMROCKS,FLORAL,IRELAND,
   5 7/8 IN.................................................. 27.50
BELLEEK,VASE,PEARLY LUSTER ON PEARL WHITE,THISTLE,SCALLOPED,
   MARK...................................................... 22.00
BELLEEK,VASE,ROSE,WHITE,PURPLE MORNING GLORIES,WILLET,
   13 1/4 IN................................................. 44.00
BELLEEK,VASE,THISTLE ON EACH SIDE,SCALLOPED,PEARLY LUSTER,
   5 1/2 IN.HIGH............................................. 25.00
BELLEEK,VASE,THREE-PRONG,TREE TRUNK,SHAMROCK PATTERN,BLACK
   MARK,6 IN................................................. 37.50
BELLEEK,VASE,VIOLETS,HAND-PAINTED,SINGLE HANDLE,AMERICAN.... 50.00
BELLEEK,VASE,WHITE GROUND,PURPLE & WHITE IRIS,WILLET,
   9 1/2 IN.................................................. 42.50
BELLEEK,VASE,WHITE,APPLIED FLOWERS,FOUR TWIG FEET,5 IN.HIGH. 75.00
BELLEEK,VASE,WHITE,SWIRL.................................. 35.00
BENNINGTON TYPE,CUSPIDOR,GREEN & BROWN.................... 22.00
BENNINGTON TYPE,CUSPIDOR,MOTTLED BROWN.................... 15.50
BENNINGTON TYPE,CUSPIDOR,MOTTLED,RAISED SCALLOP DECOR,
   ROCKINGHAM................................................ 12.50
BENNINGTON TYPE,DISH,VEGETABLE,BROWN & TAN SHADING,OVAL,7 X
   10 IN.LONG................................................ 35.00
BENNINGTON TYPE,DISH,7-IN.DIAMETER,2 IN.DEEP.............. 5.00
BENNINGTON TYPE,JUG,STONE,GALLON,DRUM SHAPE,UTAH LIQUOR CO.,
   COBALT.................................................... 125.00
BENNINGTON TYPE,MILK PAN,10-IN.DIAMETER,2 3/4 IN.DEEP...... 6.00
BENNINGTON TYPE,PITCHER,MILK,MOTTLED,WREATH DESIGN ON SIDES,
   6 IN.HIGH................................................. 15.00
BENNINGTON TYPE,PITCHER,MOTTLED BROWN & WHITE,CORN PATTERN,
   7 IN...................................................... 16.50

BENNINGTON TYPE,PITCHER,MOTTLED BROWN,7 1/2 IN.TALL......... 25.00
BENNINGTON TYPE,PLATE,PIE,BROWN.......................... 18.00
BENNINGTON TYPE,PLATE,PIE,DARK BROWN,10 1/4 IN............ 20.00
BENNINGTON TYPE,PLATE,PIE,PUMPKIN,YELLOW,9 1/4-IN.DIAMETER.. 5.00
BENNINGTON TYPE,PLATE,PIE,PUMPKIN,YELLOW,11 1/4-IN.DIAMETER. 6.00
BENNINGTON TYPE,PLATE,PIE,10 1/2-IN.DIAMETER.............. 25.00
BENNINGTON TYPE,TEAPOT,REBECCA AT THE WELL............... 60.00
BENNINGTON TYPE,TEAPOT,REBECCA AT THE WELL,ROCKINGHAM GLAZE. 38.50

BENNINGTON WARE WAS THE PRODUCT OF TWO FACTORIES
WORKING IN BENNINGTON,VERMONT. BOTH FIRMS WERE OUT OF
BUSINESS BY 1896. THE WARES INCLUDE THE BROWN AND
YELLOW MOTTLED POTTERY,PARIAN,SCRODDLE,STONEWARE,
GRANITEWARE,YELLOW WARE,AND STAFFORDSHIRE-LIKE VASES.
BENNINGTON,SEE ALSO,ROCKINGHAM
BENNINGTON,BOTTLE,COACHMAN,1849 MARK...................... 225.00
BENNINGTON,BOWL,BARBER,BROWN ENAMEL,SIGNED NORTON 1849...... 187.00
BENNINGTON,CREAMER,COW,SADDLE COVER,ROCKINGHAM GLAZE........ 82.00
BENNINGTON,CROCK,WIDE MOUTH,BALUSTER,BLUE FLORAL,NORTON,
     STONEWARE.............................................. 48.00
BENNINGTON,CUSPIDOR,ENAMEL,FLINT,SIGNED,CIRCA 1849,6 1/4 X
     4 IN.HIGH.............................................. 95.00
BENNINGTON,CUSPIDOR,PANELED,POURING HOLE................... 20.00
BENNINGTON,DISH,VEGETABLE,RAISED TULIPS IN BOTTOM,10 IN..... 25.00
BENNINGTON,JAR,TOBACCO,BROWN MOTTLING,LYMAN FENTON & CO.,
     MARK,7 1/4 IN.......................................... 76.00
BENNINGTON,JUG,GRAY STONEGLAZE,FLOWERS,SIGNED E.& L.P.NORTON 25.00
BENNINGTON,JUG,NARROW NECK,BULGING SHAPE,MARKED NORTON &
     FENTON................................................. 48.00
BENNINGTON,MUG,FROG IN THE BOTTOM,TOUCH OF GREEN,4 X 4 IN... 125.00
BENNINGTON,PIPE,WOODEN STEM............................... 8.00
BENNINGTON,PITCHER,EMBOSSED DEER,DOGS,GRAPES,HOUND HANDLE,
     2 1/2 GALLON........................................... 165.00
BENNINGTON,PITCHER,FRUIT DESIGN,8 1/2 IN................... 17.50
BENNINGTON,PITCHER,HUNTER,DOG,6 IN.HIGH................... 62.50
BENNINGTON,PITCHER,HUNTER,DOGS,BIRDS...................... 75.00
BENNINGTON,PITCHER,POND LILY PATTERN,PARIAN,RIBBON MARK,
     8 1/2 IN............................................... 150.00
BENNINGTON,PLATE,PIE,PUMPKIN,YELLOW,9 1/4-IN.DIAMETER...... 5.00
BENNINGTON,TOBY,PITCHER,FLINT ENAMEL,SIGNED,6 1/4 IN.HIGH... 295.00
BENNINGTON,WASHBOARD..................................... 60.00
BENNINGTON,WASHBOARD,YELLOW POTTERY,IMPRESSED MARK,1849..... 95.00
BICYCLE,CHILD'S,THREE-WHEEL,UPHOLSTERED BACK & SEAT,CIRCA
     1869,IRON.............................................. 100.00

BILSTON ENAMELS WERE PAINTED ON COPPER AS EARLY AS
1760 IN BILSTON,ENGLAND. SEVERAL FACTORIES WORKED IN
THE AREA.
BILSTON,BOX,SNUFF,ENAMEL,ALAS LOVES DART GONE IN MY HEART,
     BLUE,OCHER............................................. 185.00

BING AND GRONDAHL IS A FAMOUS DANISH FACTORY MAKING
FINE PORCELAINS FROM 1853 TO THE PRESENT. THEIR
CHRISTMAS PLATES ARE ESPECIALLY WELL KNOWN. THESE ARE
LISTED UNDER CHRISTMAS PLATES.
BING AND GRONDAHL,SEE ALSO,CHRISTMAS PLATE
BING & GRONDAHL,BOTTLE,CHERRY HEERING,BLUE & WHITE,LABELS,
     STAMP.................................................. 30.00
BING & GRONDAHL,PERFUME,RELIEF FLORAL,BLUE,WHITE,PEAR SHAPE,
     3 1/2 IN............................................... 30.00
BING & GRONDAHL,PLATE,MOTHER'S DAY........................ 75.00
BIRDCAGE,ARCHITECTURAL FORM,CANTED ROOF,ON STAND,PAINTED.... 30.00
BIRDCAGE,RECTANGULAR,REMOVABLE TRAYS,STAND,PAINTED BLUE..... 100.00

BISQUE IS AN UNGLAZED BAKED PORCELAIN. FINISHED BISQUE
HAS A SLIGHTLY SANDY TEXTURE WITH A DULL FINISH. SOME
OF IT MAY BE DECORATED WITH VARIOUS COLORS. BISQUE
GAINED FAVOR DURING THE LATE VICTORIAN ERA WHEN
THOUSANDS OF BISQUE FIGURINES WERE MADE.
BISQUE,BASKET,WHITE,2 PUPPIES INSIDE,3 IN.................. 8.00
BISQUE,BOTTLE,RAISED BABY'S HEAD,SCROLLS,PASTELS,GOLD DECOR,
     2 3/4 IN............................................... 4.50
BISQUE,BUST,BOY,GIRL,PASTEL,PEDESTAL,10 1/2 IN.TALL,PAIR.... 28.50
BISQUE,CANDLEHOLDER,BOY SITS ON LEAF,HOLDS FLOWER,
     2 1/4 IN.HIGH.......................................... 10.00
BISQUE,DWARF,RED CAP,4 IN................................ 4.00
BISQUE,EPERGNE,THE FRUIT PICKERS......................... 25.00
BISQUE,FIGURINE,ADVERTISING,BABY IN CHAIR,MELLINS FOOD,OUR
     BABY................................................... 15.00

| | |
|---|---:|
| BISQUE,FIGURINE,BABY IN DIAPER SWING | 15.00 |
| BISQUE,FIGURINE,BABY ON CUSHION,APRICOT COLOR,4 1/2 IN | 12.00 |
| BISQUE,FIGURINE,BATHING BEAUTY,DIVING POSITION,OLD-FASHIONED SUIT | 20.00 |
| BISQUE,FIGURINE,BOY & DOG,LABEL,12 IN | 39.00 |
| BISQUE,FIGURINE,BOY IN SAILOR SUIT,BOAT IN HAND,LEANING ON STUMP,SIGNED | 20.00 |
| BISQUE,FIGURINE,BOY ON POTTY | 12.00 |
| BISQUE,FIGURINE,BOY WITH BASKETBALL AT FEET,MARKED GERMANY, 5 IN.HIGH | 6.00 |
| BISQUE,FIGURINE,BOY,COLONIAL COSTUME,PALE PINK.LAVENDER,GOLD DOTS | 15.00 |
| BISQUE,FIGURINE,BOY,COLONIAL,PASTEL,FRANCE,6 IN | 12.00 |
| BISQUE,FIGURINE,BOY,GIRL,PILLOWS,MATTRESS,FOUR-POSTER BRONZE DORE BED | 290.00 |
| BISQUE,FIGURINE,BOY,HOLDS BLUE WICKER BASKET,SEATED,GIRL, 10 1/2 IN.,PAIR | 75.00 |
| BISQUE,FIGURINE,BOY,TOP HAT,MONOCLE,UMBRELLA UNDER ARM,1890, 8 3/4 IN | 30.00 |
| BISQUE,FIGURINE,BUST OF ELDERLY MAN,GRAY BEARD,SIGNED, GERMANY,5 1/2 IN | 25.00 |
| BISQUE,FIGURINE,CAT,GRAY STRIPES,GOLD COLOR BOW,SEATED, 5 1/4 IN.TALL | 18.00 |
| BISQUE,FIGURINE,CHINESE WOMAN SEATED,HEADS NODS, 5 1/2 IN.TALL | 25.00 |
| BISQUE,FIGURINE,DOG,BONZO,MARKED COPYRIGHT BY GEORGE E.STEDDY,GERMANY | 10.00 |
| BISQUE,FIGURINE,ELF,RED DEVIL ATTIRE,MUSICIANS,CONDUCTOR, EIGHT | 37.00 |
| BISQUE,FIGURINE,GERMAN BOY & GIRL,HOLD PUPPIES,7 IN.,PAIR | 30.00 |
| BISQUE,FIGURINE,GIRL HOLDING KITTEN,TREE,GREEN,WHITE,GOLD, 14 IN.TALL | 55.00 |
| BISQUE,FIGURINE,GIRL HOLDS TRAY,BOY HOLDS CANE,WEARING TAMS, 11 IN.,PAIR | 125.00 |
| BISQUE,FIGURINE,GIRL WITH HOE,GOLD DECOR,MARK,FRANCE, 9 IN.HIGH | 18.00 |
| BISQUE,FIGURINE,MAID IN VICTORIAN DRESS,7 3/4 IN.TALL | 15.00 |
| BISQUE,FIGURINE,MOTHER DOG & TWO PUPPIES,SAYS GERMANY 1839 | 15.00 |
| BISQUE,FIGURINE,NEGRO BOY EATING WATERMELON,STRAW HAT,3 IN | 15.00 |
| BISQUE,FIGURINE,ONE LADY,ONE MAN,23 IN.,PAIR | 200.00 |
| BISQUE,FIGURINE,PEASANT BOY,PIPE IN MOUTH,TREE,FLORAL, FRANCE,11 IN.TALL | 42.00 |
| BISQUE,FIGURINE,PUG-DOG,BLUE COLLAR,BELLS,2 1/4 IN.TALL | 14.00 |
| BISQUE,FIGURINE,SHEPHERD,SHEPHERDESS,MUTED COLORS,FRANCE, 10 1/2 IN.,PAIR | 65.00 |
| BISQUE,FIGURINE,WHITE,BOY WITH GUN,BIRD & DOG,9 1/2 IN | 24.00 |
| BISQUE,FIGURINE,WOMAN FEEDING WHITE ROOSTER,10 IN | 6.00 |
| BISQUE,FIGURINE,WOMAN SITTING SIDESADDLE ON DONKEY,DOG, CHANTILLY,FRANCE | 95.00 |
| BISQUE,FIGURINE,WOMAN,SIGNED GARDINER,RUSSIA,8 1/4 IN.HIGH | 250.00 |
| BISQUE,HEN,2 1/2 IN | 2.00 |
| BISQUE,HOLDER,MATCH,DOUBLE,BOY,GIRL WITH BASKETS | 12.00 |
| BISQUE,INKWELL,CHICK,HEAD LID,TIN FEET | 10.00 |
| BISQUE,JAR,TOBACCO,DARK GIRL,OPEN MOUTH,KERCHIEF FORMS THE COVER | 24.00 |
| BISQUE,MATCH HOLDER ..........................ILLUS.. | 20.00 |
| BISQUE,MATCH HOLDER,BOY ON SIDE,5 IN.TALL | 12.00 |
| BISQUE,MATCH HOLDER,GIRL WITH DOG,4 1/2 IN.HIGH | 8.50 |
| BISQUE,MATCH HOLDER,MAN SITTING ON PIPE,RED COAT,BULLDOG PEEPING | 10.00 |
| BISQUE,NODDER,LADY,MOVES HEAD & HANDS | 55.00 |
| BISQUE,NODDER,PIG,WEARS TAN & GOLD SUIT,HOLDS BOUQUET OF FLOWERS,BASE | 22.00 |
| BISQUE,PIANO BABY WITH CAT | 38.00 |
| BISQUE,PIANO BABY WITH DOG | 38.00 |
| BISQUE,PIANO BABY,BLOND GIRL,TOES IN HAND,RECLINES,DUTCH CAP,7 IN | 15.00 |

BISQUE MATCH HOLDER

```
BISQUE,PIANO BABY,BOY,SITTING,PLAYING PATTY-CAKE,PASTEL
  COLORING.............................................  49.50
BISQUE,PIANO BABY,CAT LEAPING FROM BOWL,9 IN.............  65.00
BISQUE,PIANO BABY,HAND-PAINTED,5 IN.,PAIR................   7.50
BISQUE,PIANO BABY,HOLDING YELLOW SHOE,BLUE DRESS,PINK &
  WHITE BONNET........................................... 40.00
BISQUE,PIANO BABY,LITTLE GIRL DRESSED IN PINK NIGHTDRESS,
  5 IN.,PAIR............................................  12.00
BISQUE,PIANO BABY,NEGRO EATING WATERMELON,4 IN.HIGH......  38.00
BISQUE,PIANO BABY,ON TUMMY,RAISED FEET,HOLDS RATTLE,GREEN
  DRESS,HEUBACH.........................................  92.00
BISQUE,PIANO BABY,PLAYING WITH HER TOES,SITTING,YELLOW
  RUFFLED FROCK.........................................  85.00
BISQUE,PIANO BABY,SEATED,HOLDS CUP,WEARS NIGHTIE,RUFFLES,
  BOWS,12 IN............................................  75.00
BISQUE,PIANO BABY,SITTING ON PILLOW WITH DOG,4 IN.......    3.50
BISQUE,PIANO BABY,SITTING,PLAYING WITH HANDS,7 IN.......   10.75
BISQUE,PIANO BABY,8 IN..................................   22.00
BISQUE,PIANO BABY,8 1/2 IN.LONG,PAIR....................   60.00
BISQUE,PIANO DOLL,BOY,LYING ON BACK HOLDING BALL........  115.00
BISQUE,PIANO DOLL,KICKER,7 1/2 IN.TALL..................   65.00
BISQUE,PIANO DOLL,PLAYING WITH TOES,HUBECK..............   75.00
BISQUE,PIANO DOLLS,PAIR................................. 195.00
BISQUE,POTTY BABE,BLACK.................................   10.00
BISQUE,STATUETTE,FRENCH,18TH-CENTURY,GIRL,6 1/4 IN.TALL.   50.00
BISQUE,TOOTHPICK,GIRL SITTING ON OPEN PURSE HOLDING STRINGS. 6.50
BISQUE,TOOTHPICK,SHOE,GERMANY...........................    3.00
BISQUE,VASE,CHERUB ON WINGED SLEIGH,GREEN & PINK,GOLD
  BEADING,5 3/4 IN......................................  12.50
BISQUE,VASE,ORPHAN ANNIE,SANDY..........................   15.00
BISQUE,VASE,TREE TRUNK SHAPE,LIMB HANDLES,FLORAL,GIRL WITH
  BASKET,26 IN.......................................... 138.00
BISQUE,VASE,2 RABBITS DANCING UNDER BLEEDING HEART SPRAYS,
  FOOTED...............................................  85.00
```

```
     BLACK AMETHYST GLASS APPEARS BLACK UNTIL IT IS HELD TO
     THE LIGHT,AND A DARK PURPLE CAN BE SEEN. IT WAS MADE IN
     MANY FACTORIES FROM 1860 TO THE PRESENT TIME.
BLACK AMETHYST,BASKET,BASKET WEAVE DECOR,HANDLE,SMALL SIZE..  8.50
BLACK AMETHYST,BOWL,GREEK KEY,GOLD FLOWERS,MARK,FOOTED,
  4 1/2 IN..............................................  10.00
BLACK AMETHYST,BOX,GOLD COLOR DRAGON,HINGED LID,
  5 IN.DIAMETER.........................................  30.00
BLACK AMETHYST,FLASK,INDIAN & BIRD DESIGN,CLEAR STOPPER.....  20.00
BLACK AMETHYST,LAMP,FROSTED CLEAR FONT.......................  40.00
BLACK AMETHYST,SWAN,OPEN,9 IN.LONG..........................  42.50
BLACK AMETHYST,VASE,BUD,HAND PAINTED........................   7.00
BLACK AMETHYST,VASE,BULBOUS,FLUTED TOP,6 1/2 IN.............   4.00
BLACK AMETHYST,VASE,HEART-SHAPED MEDALLION,TWO LADIES,
  SCALLOPED,HANDLES.....................................  22.50
BLACK AMETHYST,VASE,IRIS DECOR,6 1/2 IN.....................   6.50
BLACK AMETHYST,VASE,RAISED DESIGN IN HEART,TWO HANDLES......  30.00
BLACK AMETHYST,VASE,RUFFLED TOP,FOOTED,7 1/2 IN.HIGH,PAIR...  25.00
BLACK AMETHYST,VASE,11 IN...............................   15.00
BLANC DE CHINE,BUDDHA,SEATED,7 1/2 IN.HIGH..............   75.00
```

```
     BLOWN GLASS WAS FORMED BY FORCING AIR THROUGH A ROD
     INTO MOLTEN GLASS. EARLY GLASS AND SOME FORMS OF
     ART GLASS WERE HAND BLOWN. OTHER TYPES OF GLASS WERE
     MOLDED OR PRESSED.
BLOWN GLASS,BAR GLASS,BOLD CUT FACETING,ENGRAVED VINTAGE
  TOP,1840,FOOTED.......................................  20.00
BLOWN GLASS,BOTTLE,WATER,ENGRAVED FLOWER & FERN DECOR.......  10.00
BLOWN GLASS,BOWL,FINGER,TRAY,EMERALD GREEN,SIX SETS.........  60.00
BLOWN GLASS,BOWL,FLUTED,ENAMELED,FLORAL,BUTTERFLY,PURPLE.... 110.00
BLOWN GLASS,BOWL,ROSE,RIGAREE,CLEAR.....................   12.00
BLOWN GLASS,CRUET,MAN,MEGAPHONE-SHAPED,DAISIES ENCIRCLE
  BODY,STOPPER..........................................  20.00
BLOWN GLASS,CRUET,WINE,CLEAR,HAND-PAINTED DECOR,BALL
  STOPPER,GERMANY.......................................  39.50
BLOWN GLASS,DECANTER,DARK GREEN,METALLIC TRIM & STOPPER,
  ENGLAND...............................................  75.00
BLOWN GLASS,DECANTER,THREE DOUBLE RIGAREE NECK RINGS,
  STOPPER,PINT SIZE.....................................  62.00
BLOWN GLASS,DEMIJOHN,GREEN,CROOKED NECK..................   55.00
BLOWN GLASS,EGG,WHITE...................................    4.00
BLOWN GLASS,JAR,BISCUIT,CLEAR,LID,14 IN.HIGH,6-IN.DIAMETER..  32.00
BLOWN GLASS,LAMP BASE,TURQUOISE,ROMAN KEY,BLOWN IN THE MOLD,
  11 IN.,PAIR...........................................  60.00
```

```
BLOWN GLASS,LAMP,COURTING,CAMPHENE,OCTAGON SHAPE...........    25.00
BLOWN GLASS,PERFUME,BLUE,ENAMEL LILY-OF-THE-VALLEY DECOR,
   STOPPER,4 IN.................................................    15.00
BLOWN GLASS,PITCHER & BOWL,CLEAR................................   135.00
BLOWN GLASS,SYRUP,PEWTER TOP...................................    14.50
BLOWN GLASS,VASE,SAPPHIRE BLUE SWIRL,CLEAR APPLIED RUFFLE,
   11 IN.TALL.................................................    48.00
BLOWN GLASS,VASE,TRUMPET SHAPE,GREEN,APPLIED DECOR,
   10 IN.HIGH,PAIR...........................................    75.00
BLOWN GLASS,WHISKEY TASTER,RIM ON NECK,FREE-BLOWN,AQUA,
   2 1/2 IN.................................................    22.00
BLUE AMBERINA,BOWL,ON REEDED CURLICUE LEGS,9 IN.ACROSS......   560.00
   BLUE GLASS,SEE COBALT BLUE
   BLUE ONION,SEE ONION


        BLUE WILLOW PATTERN HAS BEEN MADE IN ENGLAND SINCE
        1780. THE PATTERN HAS BEEN COPIED BY FACTORIES IN MANY
        COUNTRIES INCLUDING GERMANY,JAPAN,AND THE UNITED
        STATES. IT IS STILL BEING MADE. WILLOW WAS NAMED FOR A
        PATTERN THAT PICTURES A BRIDGE,BIRDS,WILLOW TREES,AND A
        CHINESE LANDSCAPE.
BLUE WILLOW,BOWL,RICE..........................................     6.00
BLUE WILLOW,BUTTER PAT.........................................     3.25
BLUE WILLOW,BUTTER PAT,ENGLAND,3 IN.,SET OF 4.................    10.00
BLUE WILLOW,BUTTER PAT,MARKED,NUMBERED,ENGLAND,
   3 1/4 IN.DIAMETER,6........................................    12.00
BLUE WILLOW,CUP & SAUCER,LARGE CUP,DEEP SAUCER...............     9.50
BLUE WILLOW,CUP,MARKED WITH SHIELD,TWO LIONS,ENGLAND........     3.00
BLUE WILLOW,DISH,CHEESE,ROUND,COVER..........................    37.50
BLUE WILLOW,DISH,SOAP.........................................     3.50
BLUE WILLOW,DISH,VEGETABLE,OPEN,ENGLAND,8 1/2 X 7 IN........     6.00
BLUE WILLOW,DISH,VEGETABLE,OPEN,GERMANY,7 1/2 X 9 1/2 IN....     7.00
BLUE WILLOW,DISH,VEGETABLE,OPEN,INCISED NUMERALS,
   8 1/2 IN.SQUARE...........................................     7.50
BLUE WILLOW,PEN HOLDER........................................    10.50
BLUE WILLOW,PEPPER POT,FOOTED.................................    45.00
BLUE WILLOW,PLATE,ALLERTON,9 IN..............................     6.00
BLUE WILLOW,PLATE,ENGLAND,9 IN...............................     5.00
BLUE WILLOW,PLATE,HOSTESS,BLUE,WHITE,FIVE SECTIONS,
   J.STEVENSON,ENGLAND.......................................     6.00
BLUE WILLOW,PLATE,RIDGWAY,9 1/2 IN...........................     5.50
BLUE WILLOW,PLATE,SCALLOPED,ALLERTON,8 3/4 IN................     4.00
BLUE WILLOW,PLATE,WEDGWOOD,9 3/4 IN..........................     5.50
BLUE WILLOW,PLATTER,ALLERTON,11 1/4 IN. X 9 1/8 IN..........     9.50
BLUE WILLOW,PLATTER,LONGTON,ENGLAND,18 IN....................    24.00
BLUE WILLOW,PLATTER,MARKED E,18 IN...........................    24.50
BLUE WILLOW,PLATTER,MARKED GERMANY,11 X 8 IN.................     6.00
BLUE WILLOW,PLATTER,PORCELAIN,OVAL,19 IN. X 15 1/2 IN.......    18.00
BLUE WILLOW,PLATTER,13 IN. X 16 IN...........................    10.00
BLUE WILLOW,PLATTER,16 IN.....................................     8.00
BLUE WILLOW,PLATTER,8 1/2 IN. X 11 1/2 IN....................     5.00
BLUE WILLOW,POT,PEPPER,FOOTED.................................    45.00
BLUE WILLOW,SAUCER,WEDGWOOD...................................     3.00
BLUE WILLOW,SAUCER,18TH CENTURY.......................ILLUS..     9.00
BLUE WILLOW,SUGAR,COVER,ALLERTON.............................     8.75
BLUE WILLOW,TEA SET,CHILD'S,16 PIECES........................    10.00
BLUE WILLOW,TUREEN,COVER,ALLERTON............................    23.00
BLUE WILLOW,TUREEN,GRAVY,COVER,7 3/4 IN.LONG,5 IN.HIGH......    18.50
BLUERINA,BOWL,PIECRUST RIM,CURLIQUE LEGS,9 1/2 IN.ACROSS....   630.00
```

18TH CENTURY BLUE WILLOW SAUCER

BOEHM,EDWARD MARSHALL,MADE POTTERY IN TRENTON,NEW
  JERSEY,STARTING IN 1949. HIS BIRD FIGURINES HAVE
  ACHIEVED WORLDWIDE RECOGNITION.
BOEHM,BLACKBIRD,REDWING,MALE,FEMALE,IN CATTAILS,13 &
  14 1/2 IN.,PAIR.........................................1,500.00
BOEHM,BOBOLINK,MALE,BLACK,BROWN,ORANGE PLUMAGE,ON SUGAR
  CANE,14 3/4 IN..........................................  750.00
BOEHM,BOBWHITE QUAIL,6 1/2 & 7 1/2 IN.,PAIR.........ILLUS..8,500.00
BOEHM,BULL,BRAHMAN,WHITE,GRAY,BISQUE,14 IN.HIGH.............2,000.00
BOEHM,BUNTING,INDIGO BLUE PLUMAGE,ON CHEROKEE ROSE BRANCH,
  PEDESTAL BASE..........................................  150.00
BOEHM,CARDINAL,MALE,FEMALE,GRAPE LEAVES,BERRIES,10 IN. &
  15 IN.,PAIR............................................1,750.00
BOEHM,CARDINAL,MALE,FEMALE,GRAPEVINE,BERRIES,10 & 15 IN.....1,600.00
BOEHM,CEDAR WAXWING,BLACKBERRIES,11 IN.HIGH,PAIR...........6,500.00
BOEHM,CEDAR WAXWING,MALE,FEMALE,BLACKBERRIES,11 IN.HIGH,PAIR6,000.00
BOEHM,CEDAR WAXWING,MALE,FEMALE,FLEDGLINGS,BERRIES,11 1/2 &
  12 IN.,PAIR............................................4,250.00
BOEHM,CHICKADEE,BLACK-CAPPED,HOLLY BRANCHES,8 3/4 IN.HIGH...  175.00

BOEHM BOBWHITE QUAIL

BOEHM,CHIPMUNK,WHITE,SITS ON HIND LEGS,FOREPAWS DRAWN TO
  CHEST,3 1/2 IN..........................................  200.00
BOEHM,DISH,SHELL,FLUTED,PEG FEET,WHITE,HANDLE,BISQUE,
  8 1/2 IN...............................................   50.00
BOEHM,DISH,SWEETMEAT,SCROLL HANDLE,OVAL,7 1/2 IN.,PAIR......  120.00
BOEHM,DUCK,MALLARD,CATTAILS,5 1/2 IN.,PAIR.................1,300.00
BOEHM,FIGURINE,CUPID WITH HORN,BISQUE,5 1/2 IN.HIGH.........  225.00
BOEHM,FIGURINE,CUPID,HARP,BISQUE,5 1/2 IN.HIGH.............  225.00
BOEHM,FIGURINE,DOG,COLLIE,TAN,WHITE,CHIP ON EAR,
  8 1/2 IN.HIGH..........................................  200.00
BOEHM,FIGURINE,DOG,POODLE,RECLINING,GREEN COLLAR,WHITE,
  BISQUE,5 IN.LONG.......................................  100.00
BOEHM,FIGURINE,DOG,SPANIEL,WHITE COAT,BROWN-BLACK SPOTS,
  6 3/4 IN.HIGH..........................................  100.00
BOEHM,FIGURINE,DOG,SPANIEL,WHITE,BISQUE,5 IN.HIGH..........  200.00
BOEHM,FIGURINE,GUARDIAN ANGEL,KNEELS ON CUSHION,SPREAD
  WINGS,7 IN.HIGH........................................1,750.00
BOEHM,FIGURINE,MADONNA & CHILD,8 IN.HIGH...................  325.00
BOEHM,FIGURINE,MADONNA,MATCHING BASE,WHITE PORCELAIN,SIGNED,
  10 3/4 IN..............................................   95.00
BOEHM,FIGURINE,MADONNA,UPPER HALF FIGURE,BLUE & WHITE
  GARMENT,HALO,8 IN......................................  375.00
BOEHM,FIGURINE,POPE PIUS XII,BUST,CEREMONIAL ROBES,
  7 1/2 IN.HIGH..........................................  225.00
BOEHM,FIGURINE,ST.FRANCIS OF ASSISI,BISQUE,12 1/2 IN.HIGH...  400.00
BOEHM,FIGURINE,ST.FRANCIS OF ASSISI,DOVE,FAWN,12 1/2 IN.HIGH1,000.00
BOEHM,FIGURINE,ST.JOSEPH,CHRIST CHILD,INSCRIBED SAMPLE,
  14 IN.HIGH.............................................  375.00
BOEHM,FIGURINE,STALLION,ARABIAN,REARING,OVAL BASE,REPAIRED,
  10 1/2 IN..............................................  300.00
BOEHM,GEESE,CANADIAN,MALE,FEMALE,GOSLINGS,OVAL BASE,5 &
  7 IN.,PAIR.............................................  325.00

```
BOEHM,GOLDFINCH,BROWN,YELLOW PLUMAGE,OPEN BEAK,4 1/2 IN.,
  PAIR.................................................... 175.00
BOEHM,GOLDFINCH,MALE,FEMALE,SCOTTISH THISTLE,11 1/4 IN.,PAIR  800.00
BOEHM,GOOSE,CANADIAN,MALE,FEMALE & GOSLINGS,BASE,5 &
  7 1/2 IN.,PAIR......................................... 400.00
BOEHM,GROUSE,RUFFED,COCK,HEN,OVAL BASE,11 1/2 IN.,PAIR......3,500.00
BOEHM,HORSE,GRAY,WHITE,BRIDLE,SADDLE,GRASSY BASE,14 IN.HIGH.4,500.00
BOEHM,JAY,GREEN,MALE,FEMALE,PERSIMMON TREE,BASE,REPAIRED,
  PAIR...................................................1,000.00
BOEHM,KINGLET,GOLDEN CROWN,MALE,FEMALE,ORIENTAL POPPIES,
  BISQUE,13 IN.............................................. 650.00
BOEHM,KINGLET,GOLDEN CROWN,ORIENTAL POPPIES,11 IN.HIGH......1,100.00
BOEHM,MOCKINGBIRD,MALE,FEMALE,IN MORNING GLORY,11 1/2 &
  12 1/2 IN.,PAIR........................................1,600.00
BOEHM,PITCHER,CLUSTER OF GRAPE LEAVES,GRAPES,SCROLL HANDLE,
  8 1/2 IN................................................. 200.00
BOEHM,PTARMIGAN,MALE,FEMALE,THIRD PIECE OF SMALL ROCK,PAIR,
  3 PIECES...............................................1,750.00
BOEHM,QUAIL,BOBWHITE,MALE,FEMALE,SPECKLED BROWN PLUMAGE,
  PLINTH,PAIR............................................1,600.00
BOEHM,QUAIL,MEARNS,GLASS EYES,7 1/2 & 15 IN.,PAIR....ILLUS.1,200.00
BOEHM,REDSTART,AMERICAN,FEMALE,MALE,FLOWERING DOGWOOD,
  11 1/4 IN.HIGH........................................... 700.00
```

BOEHM QUAIL, GLASS EYES

```
BOEHM,REDSTART,AMERICAN,GROUP,FLOWERING DOGWOOD,
  11 1/4 IN.HIGH........................................... 750.00
BOEHM,ROBIN,ON ROCKY MOUND,DAFFODILS,12 1/2 IN.HIGH........1,800.00
BOEHM,ROOSTER,BANTAM,BLACK TAIL,BASE,REPAIRS,IMPERFECTIONS,
  11 1/2 IN................................................. 50.00
BOEHM,SPARROW,WHITE THROAT,PERCHED ON STALK ENTWINED WITH
  WILD ROSES............................................... 225.00
BOEHM,STALLION,BELGIAN,GRAY,WHITE,BRAIDED MANE,TAIL,
  ROSEBUDS,RIBBON........................................3,000.00
BOEHM,TUFTED TITMICE ON STALKS OF SNOW-LADEN SUMAC PANICLES,
  13 1/4 IN..............................................1,000.00
BOEHM,TUMBLER PIGEON,WHITE,GRAY PLUMAGE,FAN-SHAPED CREST ON
  HEAD,PAIR............................................... 125.00
BOEHM,WARBLER,BLUE,BLACK-THROATED,MOUNTAIN LAUREL,
  10 1/2 IN.HIGH.........................................2,500.00
BOEHM,WARBLER,CERULEAN,GROUP OF TWO BIRDS,WILD ROSE,WOODEN
  PLINTH.................................................4,000.00
BOEHM,WARBLER,PARULA,TWO BIRDS,TREE TRUNK,BISQUE,16 IN.HIGH. 900.00
BOEHM,WARBLER,YELLOWTHROAT,ON CRIMSON EYE MALLOW,PEDESTAL
  BASE.................................................... 225.00
BOEHM,WHIPPET,MALE,FEMALE,ON BASE,REPAIRED,5 1/2 IN.,PAIR...1,600.00
BOEHM,WOOD THRUSH,BABY,CIRCULAR BASE,4 1/2 IN.HIGH.......... 125.00
BOEHM,WOODCOCK,ON MUDDY BANK,LEAFAGE,11 IN.HIGH...........1,600.00
BOEHM,WREN,CAROLINA,SUGAR MAPLE LEAVES,GROUP OF MALE &
  FEMALE,14 IN.LONG......................................4,500.00
```

BOHEMIAN GLASS IS AN ORNATE,OVERLAY,OR FLASHED GLASS
MADE DURING THE VICTORIAN ERA. IT HAS BEEN REPRODUCED
IN BOHEMIA,WHICH IS NOW A PART OF CZECHOSLOVAKIA. GLASS
MADE FROM 1875 TO 1900 IS PREFERRED BY COLLECTORS.

| | |
|---|---:|
| BOHEMIAN GLASS,BEAKER,CENTRAL PANEL,VIEW,RAISED LOZENGES ON BASE.......................................................... | 15.00 |
| BOHEMIAN GLASS,BEAKER,ENGRAVED SCENES,AMBER TO CLEAR, 4 1/2 IN.TALL................................................ | 27.50 |
| BOHEMIAN GLASS,BEAKER,RUBY FLASH,PANEL,ENGRAVED,LANDSCAPE, 4 1/8 IN................................................... | 35.00 |
| BOHEMIAN GLASS,BELL,BLUE,DEER & PINE TREE.................. | 16.00 |
| BOHEMIAN GLASS,BELL,DINNER,RUBY............................ | 17.50 |
| BOHEMIAN GLASS,BOTTLE,BARBER,GRAPE & VINE,NO STOPPER....... | 50.00 |
| BOHEMIAN GLASS,BOTTLE,BARBER,RED........................... | 15.00 |
| BOHEMIAN GLASS,BOTTLE,COLOGNE,ETCHED DESIGN,7 IN.TALL,PAIR.. | 100.00 |
| BOHEMIAN GLASS,BOTTLE,SCENT,ORIENTAL DESIGN,MATCHING STOPPER,4 1/2 IN............................................. | 36.00 |
| BOHEMIAN GLASS,BOWL,AMBER CUT TO CLEAR,BOAT SHAPE, BUTTERFLIES,FLOWERS......................................... | 35.00 |
| BOHEMIAN GLASS,BOWL,FOOTED.............................ILLUS.. | 135.00 |

BOHEMIAN GLASS BOWL, FOOTED

| | |
|---|---:|
| BOHEMIAN GLASS,BOWL,ROSE,ETCHED LILY PAD PATTERN............ | 35.00 |
| BOHEMIAN GLASS,BOWL,ROSE,RED & CLEAR PINWHEEL & FAN,FOOTED, 6 X 6 IN................................................... | 34.50 |
| BOHEMIAN GLASS,CANDLEHOLDER,SATIN CUT INSET IN CENTER, ETCHED,9 IN.,PAIR........................................... | 65.00 |
| BOHEMIAN GLASS,CASTOR SET,FOUR BOTTLE,FROSTED LANDSCAPES, SILVER HOLDER.............................................. | 55.00 |
| BOHEMIAN GLASS,CHAMPAGNE,VINTAGE PATTERN,RUBY.............. | 24.00 |
| BOHEMIAN GLASS,COLOGNE,CUT WHITE OVERLAY,ORNATE GILT DECOR.. | 165.00 |
| BOHEMIAN GLASS,COLOGNE,DEER,TREES,PINE BRANCHES,WILD ORCHIDS,CUT,STOPPER....................................... | 75.00 |
| BOHEMIAN GLASS,COMPOTE,DEER PARK,COVER,DEEP RUBY........... | 28.00 |
| BOHEMIAN GLASS,COMPOTE,RED,GOLD GRAPE PATTERN,5 1/2 IN...... | 25.00 |
| BOHEMIAN GLASS,CRUET,DEER,CASTLE,SIGNED VOLMER,1898......... | 35.00 |
| BOHEMIAN GLASS,CRUET,GRAPE & LEAF DESIGN,STOPPER........... | 15.00 |
| BOHEMIAN GLASS,DECANTER,CASED PANELS,BURNISHED GOLD DESIGN, RED,7 1/2 IN.............................................. | 38.50 |
| BOHEMIAN GLASS,DECANTER,CUT GLASS,WHITE OVERLAY VINTAGE PATTERN,STOPPER........................................... | 75.00 |
| BOHEMIAN GLASS,DECANTER,RED,OVERLAY,ETCHED VINTAGE PATTERN, 15 3/4 IN................................................. | 57.00 |
| BOHEMIAN GLASS,DECANTER,STOPPER,DEEP RED,FIVE PEDESTAL CORDIALS.................................................. | 50.00 |
| BOHEMIAN GLASS,DECANTER,VINTAGE GRAPE,ETCHED LEAVES,GRAPES, RED,STOPPER.............................................. | 40.00 |
| BOHEMIAN GLASS,DECANTER,VINTAGE PATTERN,RUBY,DATED 1896,SIX WINES.................................................... | 125.00 |
| BOHEMIAN GLASS,DECANTER,WINE,CUT RUBY GLASS............... | 27.50 |
| BOHEMIAN GLASS,DECANTER,WINE,RED & CLEAR PINWHEEL & FAN, 17 IN.HIGH................................................ | 39.50 |
| BOHEMIAN GLASS,DISH,BUTTER,ETCHED DEER,CASTLE,ROUND,COVER, RUBY GLASS................................................ | 47.50 |
| BOHEMIAN GLASS,DISH,NUT,ETCHED,OCTAGONAL,FLORAL,DEER,RUBY, 4 X 3 X 1 IN.............................................. | 26.00 |
| BOHEMIAN GLASS,GOBLET,CENTRAL PANEL,ENGRAVED,DIANA,GRASSY KNOLL,DEER,DOG............................................ | 20.00 |
| BOHEMIAN GLASS,GOBLET,ENAMEL,SILVER,MULTICOLOR,PUNCH,JUDY, SCROLLS.................................................. | 75.00 |
| BOHEMIAN GLASS,GOBLET,PRISM DECOR,AMBER RIBBON,ENGRAVED, SHORT STEM,FOOT........................................... | 40.00 |
| BOHEMIAN GLASS,GOBLET,TOPOGRAPHICAL,BLUE & PINK FLASH, PANELS,5 IN............................................... | 15.00 |
| BOHEMIAN GLASS,JAR,POWDER,DEER & BIRD PATTERN,RUBY......... | 18.00 |

BOHEMIAN GLASS,JUG,SYRUP,DEER & CASTLE DESIGN,SILVER-PLATED

```
    SPRING TOP....................................................   18.00
BOHEMIAN GLASS,LAMP,RUBY & FROSTED,BAND ON FONT,BURNER,MILK
  GLASS BASE...................................................   30.00
BOHEMIAN GLASS,LUSTRE,ONE ROW CRYSTAL PRISMS,CIRCA 1890,
  14 IN.TALL,PAIR.............................................  135.00
BOHEMIAN GLASS,MUG,PANELS,ETCHED,TWO SCENES,BUILDING,GAZEBO,
  RED.........................................................   30.00
BOHEMIAN GLASS,MUG,TWO FROSTED BARS FOR WRITING NAME OF
  USER,4 1/8 IN...............................................   20.00
BOHEMIAN GLASS,PERFUME,PALE YELLOW,ENGRAVED,STOPPER,SIGNED..   15.00
BOHEMIAN GLASS,PITCHER,DEER & CASTLE,RUBY,SIX TUMBLERS......   55.00
BOHEMIAN GLASS,PLATE,DEER,CASTLE,BIRDS,9 IN.................   22.50
BOHEMIAN GLASS,PLATE,PORTRAIT,LADY,9 3/4 IN.................   20.00
BOHEMIAN GLASS,SHAKER,SUGAR,FROSTED DEER PATTERN,RED........   50.00
BOHEMIAN GLASS,SPILL HOLDER,BLUE ON CLEAR,GOLD BAND,
  MONOGRAM,THUMBPRINT.........................................   60.00
BOHEMIAN GLASS,STEIN,CUT FLOWERS,THUMBPRINT,CRANBERRY,
  OVERLAY,COVER...............................................   60.00
BOHEMIAN GLASS,TOOTHPICK,BIRD & CASTLE.....................   18.00
BOHEMIAN GLASS,TRAY,RED VINTAGE PATTERN,8-IN.DIAMETER......   20.00
BOHEMIAN GLASS,TUMBLE UP,RUBY,TWO PIECE....................   37.50
BOHEMIAN GLASS,TUMBLER,AMBER FLASH,FACETED,ENGRAVED GRECIAN
  LADIES......................................................  130.00
BOHEMIAN GLASS,TUMBLER,ENGRAVED,MEDALLIONS,FLORAL MOTIF,
  STAG,BUSHES.................................................   20.00
BOHEMIAN GLASS,TUMBLER,GOLD AND COLORED OVERLAY,SET OF 4....   22.00
BOHEMIAN GLASS,TUMBLER,RUBY & YELLOW,CUT TO CLEAR,GRAPES,
  THUMBPRINT BASE.............................................   55.00
BOHEMIAN GLASS,TUMBLER,WINDOWS,SCROLLING,ROSEBUDS,OPAQUE,
  WHITE.......................................................   20.00
BOHEMIAN GLASS,VASE,BLUE,DEER,CASTLE,9 1/2 IN...............   95.00
BOHEMIAN GLASS,VASE,FROSTED INSET HAS BIRD ON LIMB,FLARED
  TOP,9 IN.,PAIR..............................................   65.00
BOHEMIAN GLASS,VASE,GOLD COLOR FLORAL,GREEN OPENWORK AT
  BOTTOM,8 IN.................................................   15.00
BOHEMIAN GLASS,VASE,GREEN,GOLD FLORAL DECOR,MEDALLIONS,
  15 IN.,PAIR.................................................  300.00
BOHEMIAN GLASS,VASE,RED GROUND,DEER,CASTLE,FLOWERS,
  10 IN.TALL..................................................   45.00
BOHEMIAN GLASS,VASE,RED OVERLAY,FOUR CUT PANELS,FOUR FLORAL
  PANELS......................................................   62.00
BOHEMIAN GLASS,VASE,RUBY OVERLAY ON CRYSTAL,PANELS,DAISIES,
  FLARED,8 IN.................................................   62.00
BOHEMIAN GLASS,WATER SET,GRAPE & LEAF PATTERN,RUBY,SEVEN
  PIECE.......................................................   55.00
BOHEMIAN GLASS,WATER SET,VINTAGE PATTERN,SEVEN PIECE.......   75.00
BOHEMIAN GLASS,WINE,CHALICE SHAPE,FLORAL,RUBY-JEWELED KNOB
  STEM,SET OF 6...............................................  330.00
BOHEMIAN GLASS,WINE,ETCHED GRAPE DESIGN,HAND-BLOWN,RUBY.....   12.50
BOHEMIAN GLASS,WINE,RED....................................   18.00
BONE DISH,FLORAL DECOR,ALFRED MEAKIN,SET OF 6.............   18.00
BONE DISH,GOLD EDGE DESIGN,HANLEY,ENGLAND,MEAKIN...........    2.00


     BOTTLE COLLECTING HAS BECOME A MAJOR AMERICAN HOBBY.
   THERE ARE SEVERAL GENERAL CATEGORIES OF BOTTLES SUCH AS
   HISTORIC FLASKS,BITTERS,HOUSEHOLD,FIGURAL,AND OTHERS.
BOTTLE,7-UP,LABEL,BROWN,QUART.............................    4.50
BOTTLE,12-PANEL MOLD,BLOWN,ROUGH PONTIL...................    5.00
BOTTLE,A CENTURY OF PROGRESS,1833-1933,BUILDING,CLEAR,SCREW
  CAP.........................................................    9.50
BOTTLE,A.H.BULL EXTRACT OF SARSAPARILLA,OPEN PONTIL.......   34.00
BOTTLE,ADIRONDACK SPRING,WESTPORT,N.Y.,EMERALD............   65.00
BOTTLE,ALE,THREE MOLD,BLACK GLASS,IMPROVED PONTIL........    8.00
BOTTLE,AMBER,CIGAR SHAPE,MARSHALL,4 3/8 IN. LONG.........    7.50
BOTTLE,AMBER,GUITAR.......................................    9.00
BOTTLE,AMBER,JEN-SAL,MARKED 0-750,9 IN...................    2.50
BOTTLE,AMBER,SNUFF,JADE STOPPER,18TH-19TH CENTURY.........  700.00
BOTTLE,AMBER,SNUFF,MOLDED,CORKED,ORIGINAL LABEL & SNUFF,
  SQUARE......................................................   18.50
BOTTLE,AMBER,SNUFF,THREE DOTS.............................    3.00
BOTTLE,ANDERSON BROS.,E.ST.LOUIS,ILL.,CLEAR..............    2.50
BOTTLE,ANDERSONS DERMADOR.................................    8.00
BOTTLE,APOTHACARY JAR,PAUL MASSON........................   14.90
BOTTLE,APOTHECARY,BROWN,WHITE & GOLD PORCELAIN LABEL,
  STOPPER,PAIR................................................    7.50
BOTTLE,APOTHECARY,GLASS INSERT,STOPPER,R.BENZ CO.,
  6 1/2 IN.HIGH..............................................    5.00
BOTTLE,APOTHECARY,GOLD & WHITE PORCELAIN LABELS,GLASS
  STOPPER,7 IN.TALL..........................................    9.50
BOTTLE,APOTHECARY,SQUARE,AMBER,QUART,LABEL...............   10.00
```

BOTTLE,ARMANETTI,HARRY HOFFMAN.......................................  11.95
BOTTLE,AROMATIC SCHNAPPS,SCHIEDAM,UDOLPHOWOLLE,AMBER.........  22.00
BOTTLE,ATLAS STRONG SHOULDER,LID,QUART..............................  5.00
BOTTLE,ATOMIZER,BLUE TO CLEAR CUTTING,OVERLAY,4 1/2 IN......  14.00
BOTTLE,ATWOODS GENUINE PHYSICAL,DUG,FIVE STAR..............  35.00
BOTTLE,ATWOODS JAUNDICE BITTERS,AQUA..............................  6.00
BOTTLE,AVON,ANGELS,GILT................................................  7.45
BOTTLE,AVON,BARBER................................... 17.00 TO  25.00
BOTTLE,AVON,BARBER,WITH CONTENTS..................................  26.00
BOTTLE,AVON,BAROMETER,FULL CONTENTS.............................  5.00
BOTTLE,AVON,BATH URN...................................................  13.00
BOTTLE,AVON,BAY RUM JUG................................................  7.50
BOTTLE,AVON,BELL........................................................  15.00
BOTTLE,AVON,BOAT,BRASS TOP,WITH CONTENTS.....................  6.00
BOTTLE,AVON,BOAT,SILVER COLOR.......................................  8.00
BOTTLE,AVON,BOOK,WITH CONTENTS....................................  3.00
BOTTLE,AVON,BOOT,AMBER................................................  3.95
BOTTLE,AVON,BOOT,AMBER,GILT TOP,8 OZ............................  8.00
BOTTLE,AVON,BOOT,GREEN,SILVER TOP.................................  6.00
BOTTLE,AVON,BOOT,MAJORETTE..........................................  3.95
BOTTLE,AVON,BUD VASE...................................................  5.95
BOTTLE,AVON,CANDLEHOLDER,PERFUMED,OLIVE COLOR GLASS.........  16.50
BOTTLE,AVON,CANDLEHOLDER,PERFUMED,MILK GLASS.................  15.00
BOTTLE,AVON,CANDLEHOLDER,REGENCE,TALL...........................  11.90
BOTTLE,AVON,CANDLESTICK,SILVER COLOR............ 9.90 TO  15.00
BOTTLE,AVON,CANDLESTICK,WITH CONTENTS,PAIR.....................  30.00
BOTTLE,AVON,CANNON.................................. 11.90 TO  22.50
BOTTLE,AVON,CANNON,CONTENTS.........................................  14.50
BOTTLE,AVON,CASEY'S LANTERN,AMBER................................  15.00
BOTTLE,AVON,CASEY'S LANTERN,GREEN................................  22.50
BOTTLE,AVON,CASEY'S LANTERN,RED....................................  22.50
BOTTLE,AVON,CHRISTMAS CANDLE........................................  8.95
BOTTLE,AVON,CHRISTMAS TREE..........................................  3.50
BOTTLE,AVON,CHRISTMAS TREE ORNAMENTS,RED.......................  4.00
BOTTLE,AVON,CHRISTMAS TREE,GOLD COLOR............................  4.00
BOTTLE,AVON,CLOCK.................................... 4.00 TO  6.00
BOTTLE,AVON,COLOGNE,WILD ROSE,1 OZ..............................  4.50
BOTTLE,AVON,CRUET,MILK GLASS....................... 10.00 TO  13.95
BOTTLE,AVON,CRYSTAL GLORY............................................  10.00
BOTTLE,AVON,CUP,DEMITASSE,BLUE & WHITE............ 4.00 TO  5.95
BOTTLE,AVON,CUP,DEMITASSE,ROSE......................................  4.95
BOTTLE,AVON,CUP,DEMITASSE,WILD ROSE,FULL CONTENTS............  3.50
BOTTLE,AVON,DECANTER,MALLARD,GREEN................................  6.00
BOTTLE,AVON,DECISION...................................................  18.00
BOTTLE,AVON,DINNER BELL................................................  4.95
BOTTLE,AVON,DOLLARS & SCENTS...................... 13.00 TO  22.50
BOTTLE,AVON,DOLLARS & SCENTS,WITH CONTENTS.....................  25.00
BOTTLE,AVON,DOLPHIN................................. 4.50 TO  7.00
BOTTLE,AVON,DUCK.......................................................  7.00
BOTTLE,AVON,EIGHT CAR..................................................  3.50
BOTTLE,AVON,EXCALIBUR,FULL CONTENTS.............................  5.00
BOTTLE,AVON,FLASK,ALPINE..............................................  37.50
BOTTLE,AVON,FLING......................................................  .75
BOTTLE,AVON,FOOTBALL HELMET,BLUE.................. 4.50 TO  6.45
BOTTLE,AVON,FOOTBALL HELMET,GOLD...................................  5.45
BOTTLE,AVON,GAVEL................................... 7.50 TO  15.00
BOTTLE,AVON,GOLDEN ANGEL..............................................  5.50
BOTTLE,AVON,GOLDEN APPLE............................ 6.00 TO  7.50
BOTTLE,AVON,GOLDEN HEIRLOOM,WITH CONTENTS......................  19.00
BOTTLE,AVON,GUN,WITH CASE.............................................  17.50
BOTTLE,AVON,HEART.......................................................  37.50
BOTTLE,AVON,HEART,FAN TOP..............................................  7.95
BOTTLE,AVON,ICICLES................................. 2.50 TO  3.45
BOTTLE,AVON,JUG,BAY RUM............................. 10.00 TO  12.50
BOTTLE,AVON,KEG,BAY RUM............................. 12.50 TO  14.00
BOTTLE,AVON,KEY NOTE................................ 9.90 TO  16.95
BOTTLE,AVON,LANTERN,RED............................. 15.00 TO  20.00
BOTTLE,AVON,MALLARD DUCK............................ 5.00 TO  7.50
BOTTLE,AVON,MALLARD,WITH CONTENTS.................................  7.00
BOTTLE,AVON,MAN'S BOOT,GOLD TOP.....................................  5.95
BOTTLE,AVON,MAN'S BOOT,SILVER TOP...................................  7.95
BOTTLE,AVON,MISS LOLLYPOP.............................................  3.00
BOTTLE,AVON,OWL PIN....................................................  10.00
BOTTLE,AVON,PEACH SODA................................................  12.50
BOTTLE,AVON,PIPE DREAM.............................. 10.00 TO  17.50
BOTTLE,AVON,PISTOLS,DUELING,WITH CASE............. 11.90 TO  17.50
BOTTLE,AVON,PONY POST............................... 6.00 TO  8.50
BOTTLE,AVON,PUMP.................................... 4.00 TO  6.00
BOTTLE,AVON,RIVIERA................................. 6.00 TO  7.95
BOTTLE,AVON,ROYAL ORB............................... 12.50 TO  21.00
BOTTLE,AVON,SABER......................................................  4.00

```
BOTTLE,AVON,SCHOOL BELL..................................        18.00
BOTTLE,AVON,SCIMITAR........................... 8.50 TO         17.50
BOTTLE,AVON,SCIMITAR,FOAM CASE................. 9.00 TO         10.00
BOTTLE,AVON,SEASHELL.....................................         5.00
BOTTLE,AVON,SIX CAR......................................         3.50
BOTTLE,AVON,SNAIL............................. 3.50 TO          6.00
BOTTLE,AVON,SNAIL,WITH CONTENTS..........................         6.50
BOTTLE,AVON,STEER HORNS....................... 13.90 TO        22.95
BOTTLE,AVON,STEIN,6 OZ...................................         5.95
BOTTLE,AVON,STEIN,8 OZ........................ 8.00 TO         14.95
BOTTLE,AVON,STERLING SIX CAR,WITH CONTENTS...............         4.50
BOTTLE,AVON,STRAIGHT EIGHT CAR...........................         3.25
BOTTLE,AVON,STRAIGHT EIGHT CAR,WITH CONTENTS.............         4.50
BOTTLE,AVON,TALL PONY POST...............................        12.50
BOTTLE,AVON,THREE HEARTS ON TRAY.........................        15.00
BOTTLE,AVON,TOWN PUMP....................................         4.95
BOTTLE,AVON,TOWN PUMPS,CONTENTS,BOX......................         5.00
BOTTLE,AVON,URN,MILK GLASS...............................        14.00
BOTTLE,AVON,URN,OPAL GLASS,WITH CONTENTS.................        13.50
BOTTLE,AVON,VIKING HORN....................... 8.90 TO         20.00
BOTTLE,AVON,WARRIOR,FROSTED..............................         5.45
BOTTLE,AVON,WARRIOR,SILVER & BLUE........................        14.95
BOTTLE,AVON,WARRIOR,COBALT.................... 3.95 TO          9.00
BOTTLE,AVON,WARRIOR,CONTENTS,4 OZ........................         2.50
BOTTLE,AVON,WARRIOR,FROSTED,WITH CONTENTS................         5.00
BOTTLE,AVON,WARRIOR,FULL CONTENTS,6 OZ...................         4.00
BOTTLE,AVON,WEATHER OR NOT.................... 3.99 TO          5.00
BOTTLE,AVON,WINDJAMMER,PAPER LABEL.......................         7.50
BOTTLE,AYER'S CHERRY PECTORAL,OPEN PONTIL................        11.00
BOTTLE,AYER'S HAIR VIGOR,COBALT BLUE,STOPPER,7 IN........        18.00
BOTTLE,AYER'S SARSAPARILLA...............................         4.00
BOTTLE,AZTEC GOD,GREEN,CERAMIC...........................        17.00
BOTTLE,B-BAR BITTERS,PORCELAIN SPOUT,BITTERS ENGRAVED....        11.75
BOTTLE,BABY NURSER,THERMOLAC MFG. CO.,BOSTON,MASS.,PAT.JUNE
   20,1911.............................................        35.00
BOTTLE,BABY,SEATED,KISS SNOOKUMS,5 IN....................        18.50
BOTTLE,BABY'S,EMBOSSED DOGS,8 OZ.........................         4.50
BOTTLE,BABY'S,KITTENS....................................         6.00
BOTTLE,BALLANTINE,DUCK........................ 14.95 TO        21.95
BOTTLE,BALLANTINE,GOLF BAG.................... 15.90 TO        19.95
BOTTLE,BALLANTINE,GOLF CLUBS.............................        14.95
BOTTLE,BALLANTINE,KNIGHT.................................        19.95
BOTTLE,BALLANTINE,OLD CROW CHESSMAN......................        11.95
BOTTLE,BALLANTINE,SILVER KNIGHT..........................        14.95
BOTTLE,BALLAST,ROUND BOTTOM,BLOB TOP,AQUA................         4.50
BOTTLE,BAR,ENAMELED NELSON'S ROCK CORN WHISKEY...........        15.00
BOTTLE,BAR,HERDON,EMBOSSED,CLEAR.........................        15.00
BOTTLE,BAR,RYE,LIGHT AMETHYST............................        18.00
BOTTLE,BAR,WHISKEY,STRAIGHT-SIDED,MASSACHUSETTS..........        17.50
BOTTLE,BARBER,AMBER,PRESSED GLASS,STOPPER................        22.50
BOTTLE,BARBER,AMETHYST,ENAMEL FLORAL.....................        40.00
BOTTLE,BARBER,APPLE GREEN,PAINTED FLOWERS,HAND-BLOWN,PEWTER
   STOPPER.............................................        25.00
BOTTLE,BARBER,BAY RUM,AMBER..............................         3.50
BOTTLE,BARBER,BAY RUM,LADY IN BLUE,COLOGNE,LADY IN PINK,
   PEWTER TOP,PAIR.....................................        75.00
BOTTLE,BARBER,BAY RUM,WATER,WHITE FROSTED GLASS,PAIR,
   MATCHING JAR........................................        23.50
BOTTLE,BARBER,BAY RUM,WITCH HAZEL,NO STOPPERS,CLAMBROTH,PAIR    24.00
BOTTLE,BARBER,BROWN,SATIN GLASS,CRYSTAL STOPPER..........        22.00
BOTTLE,BARBER,CLEAR,MILK GLASS STOPPER...................         4.50
BOTTLE,BARBER,CLEAR,PANELED DESIGN,ROUGH PONTIL,CIRCA 1864,
   PAIR................................................        35.00
BOTTLE,BARBER,COBALT,ENAMEL TRIM.........................        30.00
BOTTLE,BARBER,COBALT,SILVER SWAG DECOR IN FLEUR-DE-LIS
   SHAPE,6 1/2 IN......................................        30.00
BOTTLE,BARBER,CRANBERRY FLASH,STOPPER....................        23.50
BOTTLE,BARBER,CRANBERRY,WHITE LOOPINGS,SATIN,PEWTER STOPPER,
   10 3/4 IN...........................................        85.00
BOTTLE,BARBER,CRUDE LIP,ROUGH PONTIL,ENAMELED FLOWERS,
   AMETHYST............................................        50.00
BOTTLE,BARBER,ENAMEL DECOR,AMETHYST,PAIR.................        55.00
BOTTLE,BARBER,FLASHED IRIDESCENT,ENAMELED FLORAL,
   MAROON-CRANBERRY....................................        22.50
BOTTLE,BARBER,FOUR SIDES,TWO OVAL,AMBER SATIN............        22.50
BOTTLE,BARBER,GREEN,ENAMEL DECOR.........................        40.00
BOTTLE,BARBER,GREEN,PASTEL FLORAL,RAISED WHITE ENAMEL....        25.00
BOTTLE,BARBER,GREEN,WHITE ENAMEL LATTICE & DAISIES,
   HAND-BLOWN..........................................        35.00
BOTTLE,BARBER,HOBNAIL....................................         5.00
BOTTLE,BARBER,MARKED WATER,STERLING SILVER DECOR,MILK GLASS.    14.00
```

BOTTLE,BARBER,MILK GLASS,PORCELAIN STOPPER.................... 12.50
BOTTLE,BARBER,OPAQUE,PEWTER STOPPER.......................... 10.00
BOTTLE,BARBER,RIBBED,OPEN PONTIL,BLOWN,COBALT............... 32.00
BOTTLE,BARBER,ROUGH PONTIL,ENAMELED FLOWER,CRANBERRY GLASS.. 15.00
BOTTLE,BARBER,SWIRLED RIB PATTERN,INVERTED THUMBPRINT BASE,
  AMBER.................................................... 62.50
BOTTLE,BARBER,WITCH HAZEL,STERLING SILVER DECOR,MILK GLASS.. 14.00
BOTTLE,BARCLAY PATENT SPIRAL GROOVE......................... 5.00
BOTTLE,BARDENHEIERS WINE,VINES & GRAPE CLUSTERS,BROWN,1930.. 4.00
BOTTLE,BARREL,DESIGNED BY ISAAC NEWTON PIERCE,DATED 1865,
  PRESSED GLASS........................................... 15.00
BOTTLE,BARREL,FOOD CONTAINER,JOSHUA WRIGHT,PHILA.,AQUA,
  10 1/2 IN.TALL.......................................... 37.50
BOTTLE,BARREL,GREEN,6 HOOPS ON TOPS & BOTTOM,MARKED LAM A &
  F,1/2 GAL............................................... 15.00
BOTTLE,BARREL,PICKLE,EMERALD GREEN,8 IN..................... 15.00
BOTTLE,BARREL,PICKLE,EMERALD GREEN,9 3/4 IN................. 25.00
BOTTLE,BARSOTTINI,ANTIQUE AUTO.............................. 5.99
BOTTLE,BARSOTTINI,ANTIQUE BOURBON CERAMIC................... 14.95
BOTTLE,BARSOTTINI,ANTIQUE CARRIAGE.......................... 5.99
BOTTLE,BARSOTTINI,BARREL ON WAGON........................... 16.95
BOTTLE,BARSOTTINI,CANNON.................................... 17.95
BOTTLE,BARSOTTINI CLOCK..................................... 22.00
BOTTLE,BARSOTTINI,CLOWN..................................... 3.95
BOTTLE,BARSOTTINI,ELK HEAD.................................. 15.95
BOTTLE,BARSOTTINI,GALLIANO CARABINIERE...................... 14.95
BOTTLE,BARSOTTINI,HORSE..................................... 10.95
BOTTLE,BARSOTTINI,LOVE BIRDS................................ 11.95
BOTTLE,BARSOTTINI,OWL....................................... 11.95
BOTTLE,BARSOTTINI,ROMAN COLISEUM.................... 8.95 TO  9.35
BOTTLE,BARSOTTINI,TRIBUNE................................... 10.95
BOTTLE,BAVARIAN BREWING CO.,COVINGTON,KY.,BROWN............. 3.50


        BEAM BOTTLES ARE MADE TO HOLD KENTUCKY STRAIGHT BOURBON
        MADE BY THE JAMES B.BEAM DISTILLING COMPANY. THE BEAM
        SERIES OF CERAMIC BOTTLES BEGAN IN 1953.
BOTTLE,BEAM,ANNIVERSARY WHITE FOX........................... 50.00
BOTTLE,BEAM,ANTIOCH................................ 11.00 TO 14.00
BOTTLE,BEAM,ANTIQUE TRADER......................... 9.90 TO  24.50
BOTTLE,BEAM,ARIZONA................................ 9.95 TO  25.00
BOTTLE,BEAM,ARMANETTI.............................. 12.50 TO 14.00
BOTTLE,BEAM,ASHTRAY,IVORY COLOR............................. 35.00
BOTTLE,BEAM,BASEBALL........................................ 10.00
BOTTLE,BEAM,BING CROSBY..................................... 15.95
BOTTLE,BEAM,BIRTHDAY FOX.................................... 75.00
BOTTLE,BEAM,BLACK HORSE..................................... 17.50
BOTTLE,BEAM,BLUE BOY........................................ 9.90
BOTTLE,BEAM,BLUE DAISY............................. 7.50 TO  8.00
BOTTLE,BEAM,BLUE DELFT............................. 8.50 TO  16.00
BOTTLE,BEAM,BLUE FOX,ANNIVERSARY,LABEL...................... 75.00
BOTTLE,BEAM,BLUE SAILBOAT................................... 7.50
BOTTLE,BEAM,BOAT,IVORY,LABELS,BLACK CORK.................... 35.00
BOTTLE,BEAM,BROADMOOR.............................. 9.50 TO  11.95
BOTTLE,BEAM,BROWN HEAD KENTUCKY............................. 18.00
BOTTLE,BEAM,BUFFALO HUNT.................................... 2.50
BOTTLE,BEAM,CABLE CAR.............................. 6.50 TO  11.00
BOTTLE,BEAM,CAMEO BLUE...................................... 6.00
BOTTLE,BEAM,CANASTA,BLACK................................... 25.00
BOTTLE,BEAM,CAT............................................. 12.00
BOTTLE,BEAM,CAT,TAN......................................... 12.00
BOTTLE,BEAM,CHEYENNE CENTENNIAL.................... 10.95 TO 13.00
BOTTLE,BEAM,CHURCHILL DOWNS,KENTUCKY DERBY.................. 32.50
BOTTLE,BEAM,CIVIL WAR,NORTH........................ 42.00 TO 43.90
BOTTLE,BEAM,CIVIL WAR,SOUTH........................ 43.90 TO 44.00
BOTTLE,BEAM,CLEOPATRA,RUST......................... 4.90 TO  7.50
BOTTLE,BEAM,CLEOPATRA,YELLOW....................... 15.90 TO 18.50
BOTTLE,BEAM,COLORADO........................................ 49.90
BOTTLE,BEAM,DANCING SCOT.................................... 14.00
BOTTLE,BEAM,DOE.................................... 32.95 TO 38.50
BOTTLE,BEAM,DOG.................................... 75.00 TO 85.00
BOTTLE,BEAM,DUCK................................... 49.00 TO 52.50
BOTTLE,BEAM,EAGLE.................................. 14.50 TO 16.50
BOTTLE,BEAM,ELK............................................. 14.95
BOTTLE,BEAM,ELK CENTENNIAL.................................. 35.00
BOTTLE,BEAM,EXECUTIVE,1955.................................. 225.00
BOTTLE,BEAM,EXECUTIVE,1957.................................. 80.00
BOTTLE,BEAM,EXECUTIVE,1959.................................. 95.00
BOTTLE,BEAM,EXECUTIVE,1961.................................. 90.00
BOTTLE,BEAM,EXECUTIVE,1962.................................. 60.00
BOTTLE,BEAM,EXECUTIVE,1963.................................. 52.50

```
BOTTLE,BEAM,EXECUTIVE,1964.................................    52.50
BOTTLE,BEAM,EXECUTIVE,1965.................................    75.00
BOTTLE,BEAM,EXECUTIVE,1966,CASE............................    33.50
BOTTLE,BEAM,FISH.................................. 49.90 TO    60.00
BOTTLE,BEAM,FISH,GOLD SPECKLED HIGHLIGHTS..................   350.00
BOTTLE,BEAM,FLORIDA........................................    11.50
BOTTLE,BEAM,FLORIDA SHELLS......................... 5.95 TO    13.50
BOTTLE,BEAM,FLORIDA SHELLS,PAIR............................    25.00
BOTTLE,BEAM,FOREMOST,1956,GREEN,GOLD,ONE-OF-A-KIND,
    AUTHENTICITY LETTER....................................5,000.00
BOTTLE,BEAM,FOREMOST,BLACK,GOLD............................   135.00
BOTTLE,BEAM,FOX............................................    31.00
BOTTLE,BEAM,GENIE..........................................     6.00
BOTTLE,BEAM,GENIE,SMOKED CRYSTAL...........................     5.90
BOTTLE,BEAM,GRAND CANYON...................................    32.90
BOTTLE,BEAM,GRAY SLOT.............................. 7.50 TO    10.00
BOTTLE,BEAM,GRECIAN............................... 6.50 TO     7.50
BOTTLE,BEAM,HAROLD CLUB,BLUE SLOT................. 18.00 TO    25.00
BOTTLE,BEAM,HAROLD CLUB,GRAY SLOT..........................    15.00
BOTTLE,BEAM,HAROLD CLUB,SILVER OPAL........................    21.90
BOTTLE,BEAM,HARRY HOFFMAN..................................    10.00
BOTTLE,BEAM,HAWAII,LABELS..................................    80.00
BOTTLE,BEAM,HEMISFAIR......................................    17.50
BOTTLE,BEAM,ILLINOIS.............................. 11.00 TO    12.50
BOTTLE,BEAM,JUG,TURQUOISE..................................     6.00
BOTTLE,BEAM,KANSAS.........................................    74.90
BOTTLE,BEAM,KATZ KAT,BLACK.................................    32.00
BOTTLE,BEAM,KATZ KAT,YELLOW................................    34.50
BOTTLE,BEAM,KENTUCKY.............................. 12.95 TO    15.00
BOTTLE,BEAM,KENTUCKY BLACK HEAD............................    15.00
BOTTLE,BEAM,KENTUCKY BROWN HEAD............................    18.00
BOTTLE,BEAM,KENTUCKY CARDINAL..................... 46.90 TO    57.50
BOTTLE,BEAM,KENTUCKY DERBY,PINK................... 10.95 TO    14.00
BOTTLE,BEAM,KENTUCKY DERBY,RED.............................    12.95
BOTTLE,BEAM,KENTUCKY DERBY,RED ROSE........................    25.50
BOTTLE,BEAM,KENTUCKY WHITE HEAD............................    17.50
BOTTLE,BEAM,LARAMIE.................................ILLUS..    15.00
BOTTLE,BEAM,LAS VEGAS............................. 12.95 TO    20.00
BOTTLE,BEAM,LAST CHANCE JOE................................    15.00
BOTTLE,BEAM,LOMBARD LILAC......................... 11.90 TO    18.00
BOTTLE,BEAM,MAN IN BARREL,NO.1.............................   475.00
BOTTLE,BEAM,MANITOWOC,WISCONSIN,SUBMARINE...........ILLUS..    12.50
BOTTLE,BEAM,MARINA CITY........................... 55.00 TO    79.90
BOTTLE,BEAM,MARK ANTHONY...................................    22.00
BOTTLE,BEAM,MONTANA........................................    99.00
BOTTLE,BEAM,MUSICIANS ON A WINE CASK.............. 13.50 TO    15.00
BOTTLE,BEAM,NEBRASKA.............................. 12.50 TO    15.00
BOTTLE,BEAM,NEVADA.........................................    88.50
BOTTLE,BEAM,NEW HAMPSHIRE.......................... 8.95 TO    19.00
BOTTLE,BEAM,NEW JERSEY,BLUE................................   135.00
BOTTLE,BEAM,NEW JERSEY,GOLD COLOR................. 67.50 TO    75.00
BOTTLE,BEAM,NEW MEXICO............................ 8.95 TO     13.00
```

BEAM BOTTLE, LARAMIE

BEAM BOTTLE, SUBMARINE

```
BOTTLE,BEAM,NEW YORK WORLD'S FAIR.................. 27.50 TO    30.00
BOTTLE,BEAM,NORTH DAKOTA,1964..................... 65.00 TO    85.00
BOTTLE,BEAM,NURSE & CHILD........................            5.95
BOTTLE,BEAM,NURSE & CHILD,SOLDIER & GIRL,PAIR...............   10.90
BOTTLE,BEAM,OHIO.......................................       16.00
BOTTLE,BEAM,OLD CABIN STILL,HILLBILLY,QUART...............    25.00
BOTTLE,BEAM,OLYMPIAN............................... 7.50 TO    10.00
BOTTLE,BEAM,ON THE TERRACE......................... 8.50 TO     9.90
BOTTLE,BEAM,OREGON................................ 47.50 TO    49.90
BOTTLE,BEAM,PENNSYLVANIA.............................ILLUS..   11.00
BOTTLE,BEAM,PHEASANT.............................. 17.00 TO    18.95
BOTTLE,BEAM,PINCH......................................       15.00
BOTTLE,BEAM,PISTOL,DUELING,PAIR........................       15.00
BOTTLE,BEAM,POLITICAL,1960,ELEPHANT....................       15.00
BOTTLE,BEAM,POLITICAL,1956,PAIR........................       35.00
BOTTLE,BEAM,POLITICAL,1960,PAIR........................       35.00
BOTTLE,BEAM,POLITICAL,1964,DONKEY......................       12.00
BOTTLE,BEAM,POLITICAL,PAIR.............................       30.00
BOTTLE,BEAM,PONDEROSA..................................       10.95
```

BEAM BOTTLE, PENNSYLVANIA

```
BOTTLE,BEAM,PONY EXPRESS.......................... 8.95 TO    14.00
BOTTLE,BEAM,PUSSY WILLOW...............................        7.00
BOTTLE,BEAM,QUEEN MARY GOLD FOX........................       65.00
BOTTLE,BEAM,RAM..................................129.00 TO   140.00
BOTTLE,BEAM,RAM,THERMOMETER............................       24.95
BOTTLE,BEAM,REDWOODS,CALIFORNIA................... 11.95 TO    13.00
BOTTLE,BEAM,RENO CENTENNIAL....................... 10.90 TO    16.50
BOTTLE,BEAM,RICHARDS,NEW MEXICO................... 8.90 TO    12.00
BOTTLE,BEAM,ROBIN......................................       10.95
BOTTLE,BEAM,ROSE DELFT.................................       11.00
BOTTLE,BEAM,ROYAL EMPEROR..............................       10.00
BOTTLE,BEAM,RUIDOSO............................... 8.95 TO    14.00
BOTTLE,BEAM,RUIDOSO,POINTED EAR................... 34.95 TO    45.00
BOTTLE,BEAM,SAILBOAT,MILK GLASS,LABELS.................        7.50
BOTTLE,BEAM,SAN DIEGO............................. 7.50 TO    13.00
BOTTLE,BEAM,SANTA FE,CENTENNIAL........................      195.00
BOTTLE,BEAM,SPACE NEEDLE...............................       33.00
BOTTLE,BEAM,ST.LOUIS...................................       25.00
BOTTLE,BEAM,ST.LOUIS ARCH..............................       17.50
BOTTLE,BEAM,TABBY CAT..................................       11.00
BOTTLE,BEAM,THAILAND.............................. 10.95 TO    75.00
BOTTLE,BEAM,VIP,1967...................................      400.00
BOTTLE,BEAM,VIP,1968...................................      375.00
BOTTLE,BEAM,BEEFEATER............................. 60.00 TO    90.00
BOTTLE,BEAM,WEST VIRGINIA CENTENNIAL.............135.00 TO   165.00
BOTTLE,BEAM,WHITE HEAD KENTUCKY........................       17.50
BOTTLE,BEAM,WOODPECKER.................................       10.95
BOTTLE,BEAM,WORLD WAR CHARLIE..........................       40.00
```

```
BOTTLE,BEAM,WYOMING..........................................  68.00 TO    80.00
BOTTLE,BEAM,YOSEMITE.........................................   9.00 TO    14.00
BOTTLE,BEAM,YUMA RIFLE.......................................  40.00 TO    44.90
BOTTLE,BEAM,ZIMMERMAN,CHERUB,PAIR............................              16.00
BOTTLE,BEAM,ZIMMERMAN,LAVENDER CHERUB........................               7.50
BOTTLE,BEAR,BLACK,SCREW TOP,11 1/2 IN........................              18.00
BOTTLE,BEAVER,AMETHYST,QUART.................................              12.50
BOTTLE,BEEF TONIC,RECTANGULAR PANELED CORNERS,7 IN...........               6.00
BOTTLE,BEEFEATER,FIBER STATUE................................              20.00
BOTTLE,BEER,BOURNE 30 DENBY EMBOSSED ON BOTTOM...............              12.50
BOTTLE,BEER,EMBOSSED SEMINUDE,AQUA...........................               2.50
BOTTLE,BEER,GREEN,PEWTER BANDS & HANDLE,PORCELAIN CLAMP ON
   TOP.......................................................              50.00
BOTTLE,BEER,MILK GLASS,9 IN..................................              14.00
BOTTLE,BEER,RED,QUART........................................               7.00
BOTTLE,BEER,ROYAL RUBY,8 OZ..................................              14.00
BOTTLE,BEER,RUBY,QUART.......................................              20.00
BOTTLE,BEER,S.R.ERVEN,PHILADELPHIA,SQUAT,GREEN...............              20.00
BOTTLE,BEER,THREE-PIECE MOLD,DARK OLIVE AMBER................               3.00
BOTTLE,BINOCULAR,FULL SIZE,BLACK.............................               5.00
BOTTLE,BISCHOFF,DACHSHUND....................................              31.90
BOTTLE,BISCHOFF,PLATE........................................              39.90
BOTTLE,BISSO,SOPHIA..........................................              22.00
BOTTLE,BITTERQUELLE,APPLIED COLLAR,OLIVE GREEN,9 IN..........               6.00
BOTTLE,BITTERQUELLE,WHITTLED,ROUND,GREEN.....................               6.00
BOTTLE,BITTERS,A.S.HOPKINS UNION,CONTENTS,LABELS,AMBER.......              20.00
BOTTLE,BITTERS,ABBOTT,MINIATURE,PEWTER STOPPER,LABEL.........              10.00
BOTTLE,BITTERS,AMBER,TIPPECANOE..............................              60.00
BOTTLE,BITTERS,ATWOOD'S JAUNDICE,SCREW TOP...................               3.00
BOTTLE,BITTERS,ATWOOD'S JAUNDICE,CORK TOP,AQUA...............               4.00
BOTTLE,BITTERS,ATWOOD'S JAUNDICE,FORMERLY MOSES ATWOOD,
   GEORGETOWN,CORK...........................................               4.00
BOTTLE,BITTERS,BROWN'S IRON,HONEY AMBER......................              35.00
BOTTLE,BITTERS,BROWN'S IRON..................................              19.00
BOTTLE,BITTERS,BURDOCK BLOOD,AQUA............................              12.00
BOTTLE,BITTERS,BURDOCK BLOOD,EMBOSSED........................              18.00
BOTTLE,BITTERS,CLARK'S COMPOUND MANDRAKE.....................              40.00
BOTTLE,BITTERS,CLARK'S SHERRY WINE,AQUA............  35.00 TO               50.00
BOTTLE,BITTERS,CLEAR,ROUND,EMBOSSED..........................              20.00
BOTTLE,BITTERS,COLE BROTHERS.................................              23.00
BOTTLE,BITTERS,COLUMBO PEPTIC................................              23.00
BOTTLE,BITTERS,D.LANGLEY'S ROOT & HERB BITTERS,REVERSED 99..              28.00
BOTTLE,BITTERS,DR.BOYCES TONIC,AQUA,PINT.....................              32.00
BOTTLE,BITTERS,DR.HARTERS,SAMPLE SIZE........................              35.00
BOTTLE,BITTERS,DOYLES HOP,AMBER,1872,9 1/2 IN.TALL. 20.00 TO               30.00
BOTTLE,BITTERS,DR.BAXTER MANDRAKE,EMBOSSED...................              12.00
BOTTLE,BITTERS,DR.BAXTER'S MANDRAKE,CLEAR....................               8.00
BOTTLE,BITTERS,DR.BULL'S.....................................              12.00
BOTTLE,BITTERS,DR.FLINTS QUAKER,AQUA.........................              25.00
BOTTLE,BITTERS,DR.FLINTS QUAKER,EMBOSSED.....................              25.00
BOTTLE,BITTERS,DR.HARTERS,WILD CHERRY,PINT...................              40.00
BOTTLE,BITTERS,DR.HENDLEYS WILD GRAPE ROOT,AQUA..............              60.00
BOTTLE,BITTERS,DR.HOOFLANDS GERMAN...........................              32.00
BOTTLE,BITTERS,DR.HOSTETTERS STOMACH,BLACK...................              95.00
BOTTLE,BITTERS,DR.HUNTINGTONS GOLDEN TONIC,SIX STAR,NO.182,
   HONEY AMBER...............................................              69.95
BOTTLE,BITTERS,DR.J.HOSTETTER'S STOMACH BITTERS..............              10.00
BOTTLE,BITTERS,DR.J.SWEETS,EMBOSSED..........................              35.00
BOTTLE,BITTERS,DR.LANGLEYS ROOT & HERB.......................              23.00
BOTTLE,BITTERS,DR.LANGLEYS ROOT & HERB,BOSTON,AQUA,PINT.....              20.00
BOTTLE,BITTERS,DR.LANGLEYS,99 UNION ST.,SHORT NECK...........              10.00
BOTTLE,BITTERS,DR.SOLOMONS GREAT INDIAN,AQUA.................              65.00
BOTTLE,BITTERS,DR.STEPHEN JEWITTS BITTERS,RINDGE,N.H.,OLIVE
   AMBER.....................................................             200.00
BOTTLE,BITTERS,DRAKES PLANTATION,AMBER,LABEL.................              40.00
BOTTLE,BITTERS,DRAKES PLANTATION,SIX LOG,AMBER...............              30.00
BOTTLE,BITTERS,ELECTRIC BRAND,H.E.BUCKLEN & CO.,CHICAGO,
   ILL.,AMBER................................................              20.00
BOTTLE,BITTERS,ELECTRIC,EMBOSSED.............................              16.00
BOTTLE,BITTERS,EMERSON EXCELSIOR BOTANIC,BY E.H.BURNS,
   AUGUSTA,MAINE.............................................              12.00
BOTTLE,BITTERS,FORESTINE BLOOD BITTERS,WAX-SEALED,PAPER
   LABEL.....................................................             125.00
BOTTLE,BITTERS,GERMAN HOPS,EMBOSSED..........................              55.00
BOTTLE,BITTERS,GOFF'S HERB,EMBOSSED,AQUA.....................               7.50
BOTTLE,BITTERS,INDIAN RESTORATIVE,EMBOSSED...................              25.00
BOTTLE,BITTERS,IRON BITTERS,EMBOSSED.........................              27.00
BOTTLE,BITTERS,I.W.HARPER,APPLIED MOUTH,AMBER................              12.00
BOTTLE,BITTERS,J.PINKERSTONS WAHOO & CALISAYA BITTERS,AMBER.              35.00
BOTTLE,BITTERS,JEWETTS,WHITTLED,OPEN PONTIL,AQUA.............              70.00
BOTTLE,BITTERS,LASHS,CONTENTS,SEAL & LABELS INTACT,AMBER....              20.00
```

```
BOTTLE,BITTERS,LASHS,NATURAL TONIC LAXATIVE,AMBER..........      12.00
BOTTLE,BITTERS,LASHS,SAN FRANCISCO,ROUND,AMBER.............      18.00
BOTTLE,BITTERS,LOG CABIN,DRAKES PLANTATION BITTERS.........      22.00
BOTTLE,BITTERS,MALT BITTERS CO.,AMBER......................      35.00
BOTTLE,BITTERS,MOSES ATWOOD'S JAUNDICE,EMBOSSED,AQUA.......       6.00
BOTTLE,BITTERS,MOUNTAIN ROOT...............................      15.00
BOTTLE,BITTERS,NIGHTCAP,TRIANGULAR,LIGHT AMETHYST..........      75.00
BOTTLE,BITTERS,OLD SACHEM,EMBOSSED.........................     135.00
BOTTLE,BITTERS,PEPSIN CALISAYA,EMERALD GREEN...............      48.00
BOTTLE,BITTERS,POOR MAN'S FAMILY,AQUA......................      45.00
BOTTLE,BITTERS,PRICKLY ASH BITTERS CO......................      29.00
BOTTLE,BITTERS,REX BITTERS COMPANY,ROUND,AMBER,EMBOSSED....      25.00
BOTTLE,BITTERS,REX KIDNEY & LIVER,AMBER,EMBOSSED...........      25.00
BOTTLE,BITTERS,SANBORN'S KIDNEY & LIVER VEGETABLE LAXATIVE..     70.00
BOTTLE,BITTERS,TIPPECANOE,SHAPED LIKE LOG,CANOE ON SIDE.....     75.00
BOTTLE,BITTERS,TONICA,LABLE,CONTENTS,EMBOSSED...............     25.00
BOTTLE,BITTERS,UNICUM,LABELS,BUDAPEST,GREEN.................      6.50
BOTTLE,BITTERS,W.F.SEVERA,TWO LABELS,EMBOSSED...............     40.00
BOTTLE,BITTERS,WALKER V,ROUND,AQUA.........................       9.00
BOTTLE,BITTERS,WILLARDS GOLDEN SEAL,AQUA...................      60.00
BOTTLE,BITTERS,WILLIAM ALLEN'S CONGRESS,IMPRESSED PANELS,
   AQUA,10 1/4 IN..........................................     120.00
BOTTLE,BITTERS,YERBA BUENA,AMBER...........................      70.00
BOTTLE,BLACK BAR WHISKEY,INVERTED HOBNAILS,PONTIL,BLUE.....      45.00
BOTTLE,BLACK GLASS,APPLIED SEAL,EMBOSSED A.S.C.R.,CIRCA
   1790,QUART.............................................       59.00
BOTTLE,BLOUNT SPRINGS,NATURAL SULFUR,S OVER B TRADEMARK,BLUE     24.00
BOTTLE,BLUE BOTTLE EXTRACTS,RECTANGULAR,COBALT.............       6.00
BOTTLE,BOLS,BALLERINA......................................      12.50
BOTTLE,BOLS,CREME DE MENTHE,DELFT,SQUAT....................      10.75
BOTTLE,BRANDY,FROSTED CHERUBS HOLDING CLEAR GLOBE,PONTIL,
   DESPOSE,SIGNED..........................................      35.00
BOTTLE,BRANTS INDIAN PULMONARY BALSAM,PONTIL...............       3.00
BOTTLE,BRISTOL'S EXTRACT OF SARSAPARILLA,OPEN PONTIL.......      34.00
BOTTLE,BRISTOL'S SARSAPARILLA..............................      14.00
BOTTLE,BROWN IRON BITTERS,SQUARE,CRUDE MOLD,AMBER..........      20.00
BOTTLE,BROWNS INDIAN QUEEN.................................     200.00
BOTTLE,BROWNS SARSAPARILLA,AQUA............................       8.00
BOTTLE,BROWNS SARSAPARILLA,AQUA,PINT.......................      12.00
BOTTLE,BUFFALO HUNT........................................       5.00
BOTTLE,BUFFALO LITHIA WATER................................       5.00
BOTTLE,BUFFALO MINERAL SPRINGS WATER,APPLIED LIP,EMBOSSED
   LADY..................................................        11.00
BOTTLE,BUNKER HILL PICKLES,HONEY AMBER,7 3/4 IN............      18.00
BOTTLE,BURDOCKS BLOOD BITTERS..............................      10.00
BOTTLE,BURNHAMS BEEF WINE & IRON,SLOPED SHOULDERS,OLIVE
   GREEN.................................................         2.75
BOTTLE,C.H.MAYER & CO.,HAMMOND,IND.,WHITE PORCELAIN TOP,
   AMBER,8 IN.............................................       10.00
BOTTLE,C.HEIMSTREET & CO.,COBALT..........................       12.00
BOTTLE,C.W.ABBOTTS,ROUND,AMBER............................        7.00
BOTTLE,CABIN SHAPE,AMBER..................................        3.50
BOTTLE,CALABASH,HUNTER & FISHERMAN........................       45.00
BOTTLE,CALFIG SYRUP OF FIGS...............................        3.00
BOTTLE,CAMEL SADDLE,HAND-BLOWN............................       30.00
BOTTLE,CANADA DRY,CARNIVAL GLASS,MARIGOLD.................       12.00
BOTTLE,CAPTAIN,ONION,SQUAT,OPEN PONTIL,BLACK GLASS,CIRCA
   1700..................................................        65.00
BOTTLE,CAPTAIN,SQUATTY,ONION,FREE BLOWN,PONTIL,CIRCA 1700...    135.00
BOTTLE,CARAFE,MARKED LIBBEY,HOBSTARS,DIAMOND,CUT GLASS.....      43.00
BOTTLE,CARRIE NATION......................................        9.00
BOTTLE,CASE GIN,A.B.M.,TAPERED,OLIVE GREEN,8 IN...........        4.00
BOTTLE,CASE GIN,DARK OLIVE................................        7.50
BOTTLE,CASE GIN,EMBOSSED,OLIVE GREEN......................       14.00
BOTTLE,CASE GIN,FLARED MOUTH,FREE BLOWN,BLACK GLASS,CIRCA
   1790..................................................        16.00
BOTTLE,CASE GIN,FREE BLOWN,COLLAR TOP,BLACK GLASS,CIRCA
   1810..................................................        10.00
BOTTLE,CASE,PANELED CORNERS,BLOB MOUTH,AQUA...............       14.00
BOTTLE,CASTOR,HONEYCOMB CUT,ETCHED FLOWERS,ROUND..........        7.00
BOTTLE,CASTOR,INVERTED THUMBPRINT,NEW SILVER TOPS,SET OF 5..     35.00
BOTTLE,CATHEDRAL PICKLE,GREEN,14 IN.......................       65.00
BOTTLE,CATHEDRAL,BLUE.....................................        7.00
BOTTLE,CATHEDRAL,PICTURES BEEHIVE & BEES,MARKED 1 POUND PURE
   HONEY,AQUA............................................         8.50
BOTTLE,CATSUP,10-SIDED....................................        5.00
BOTTLE,CATSUP,8-SIDED.....................................        5.00
BOTTLE,CELLO,SCALES ON BACK,PALE AMBER,8 1/2 IN...........       22.00
BOTTLE,CHAMPAGNE,G.H.MURNUM,CORK,LABELS,GREEN,21 IN.HIGH...      16.50
BOTTLE,CHAMPAGNE,LABEL,CORK,1928,BLACK GLASS..............        5.00
BOTTLE,CHARLES H.FLETCHER,EMBOSSED,AQUA...................        2.00
```

BOTTLE,CHEMUNG SPRING WATER,THIS BOTTLE IS LOANED AND NEVER
TO BE SOLD................................................... 35.00
BOTTLE,CHERRY HEERING,BLUE & WHITE,LABELS,STAMP,TAX,BING &
GRONDAHL..................................................... 30.00
BOTTLE,CHESTNUT,CLEAR OLIVER AMBER,5 IN....................... 80.00
BOTTLE,CHESTNUT,W.JERSEY,SWIRL,TAPERED LIP,BULBOUS,11 IN...... 150.00
BOTTLE,CHICAGO WATER TOWER.................................... 17.50
BOTTLE,CHICKEN ON NEST,10 X 4 1/2 IN.......................... 25.00
BOTTLE,CIAO LIQUORE,ITALIAN,MINIATURE......................... 2.50
BOTTLE,CLARK & WHITE NEW YORK,SEEDS,WHITTLE MARKED,GREEN,
PINT......................................................... 25.00
BOTTLE,CLARK & WHITE,LARGE C,WHITTLED,PINT.................... 22.00
BOTTLE,CLARKE & SON,NEW YORK,SARATOGA TYPE,BLACK GLASS........ 95.00
BOTTLE,COACHMAN,GENEVER VAN DUNCK,AMBER....................... 70.00
BOTTLE,COCA-COLA,SEE COCA-COLA
BOTTLE,COCA MARIANI........................................... 7.00
BOTTLE,COCA MARIANI,WHITTLED,IRIDESCENT,GREEN................. 7.50
BOTTLE,COLOGNE,1000 EYE,FACETED KNOB STOPPER,2 5/8 X
7 1/2 IN.HIGH................................................ 9.00
BOTTLE,COLOGNE,BLUE,BLOWN,AMBER STOPPER,MARKED 54 IN GOLD..... 20.00
BOTTLE,COLOGNE,COSMOS DESIGN,SIGNED C.G.CO.,CUT GLASS......... 28.00
BOTTLE,COLOGNE,CUTOUT DECOR,BIRDS,FLOWERS,PANELS,SILVER BASE
& COLLAR..................................................... 35.00
BOTTLE,COLOGNE,EIFFEL TOWER,FROM HEMISFAIR.................... 3.00
BOTTLE,COLOGNE,ENAMELED SCENE,GROUND PONTIL,STOPPER,
3 3/4 IN.HIGH................................................ 25.00
BOTTLE,COLOGNE,LACY SCROLL,HOUR GLASS SHAPE,AQUA,
5 5/8 IN.TALL................................................ 32.50
BOTTLE,COLOGNE,MULTICOLORED FLOWERS,ST.CLAIR................. 15.00
BOTTLE,COLOGNE,PAPERWEIGHT,CLEAR FACETED STOPPER,BUBBLE
INSIDE....................................................... 18.50
BOTTLE,COLOGNE,PINECONES,HAND-PAINTED,GROUND STOPPER,
6 1/2 IN.,PAIR............................................... 13.00
BOTTLE,COLOGNE,SCENE,GIRL IN WOODS,WINTER,POLISHED PONTIL,
CUT STOPPER.................................................. 25.00
BOTTLE,COLOGNE,SHAPE OF LADY'S SHOE,3 IN..................... 4.00
BOTTLE,COLOGNE,SILVER OVERLAY,FLOWERS,LEAVES,CIRCA 1850,PAIR 65.00
BOTTLE,COLOGNE,TWO CRYING DOGS,HAND-COLORED FACES,PINT....... 15.00
BOTTLE,COLOGNE,VASELINE GLASS................................ 18.50
BOTTLE,COLOGNE,WHITE OPALESCENT GLASS,SKIRT SHAPE,BALL
STOPPER,BRISTOL.............................................. 22.50
BOTTLE,CONGRESS & EMPIRE,PINT................................ 16.50
BOTTLE,CONGRESS & EMPIRE,QUART............................... 16.50
BOTTLE,CONGRESS WATER..............................20.00 TO 25.00
BOTTLE,CONGRESS WATER,LARGE C & SARATOGA,N.Y.,APPLIED LIP,
7 3/4 IN..................................................... 28.00
BOTTLE,CORDIAL,CLEAR,GREEN,STOPPER,GILT,SIX PEDESTAL-TYPE
GLASSES...................................................... 8.00
BOTTLE,CORDIAL,PINE TREE TAR,DARK GREEN...................... 35.00
BOTTLE,CORDIAL,TREE TAR,L.Q.C.,WISHARTS,GREEN,PINT........... 20.00
BOTTLE,CRABFELDERS WHISKEY,AMBER,5 3/4 IN.................... 4.75
BOTTLE,CREME DE MINT,HORSESHOE,CLOVER,GOOD LUCK,GREEN.
11 1/2 IN.................................................... 5.75
BOTTLE,CROCK,MARKED COWDEN & WILCOX,GALLON................... 7.00
BOTTLE,CROSSBONES,SKULL...................................... 5.50
BOTTLE,CROWN SHAPE,PURPLE.................................... 3.50
BOTTLE,CRYSTAL BACK,PEACH BRANDY IN LARGE ENAMEL SCRIPT...... 16.00
BOTTLE,CURTIS & PERKINS CRAMP & PAIN KILLER,BANGOR,ME.,
CYLINDER..................................................... 10.00
BOTTLE,D.EVANS CAMOMILE PILLS,OPEN PONTIL,AQUA............... 10.00
BOTTLE,D.JAYNES TONIC VERMIFUGE,OPEN PONTIL.................. 12.00
BOTTLE,DAISY,F.E.WARD & CO.,AQUA.PINT........................ 6.50
BOTTLE,DALTON SARSAPARILLA,LABEL............................. 18.00
BOTTLE,DANAS SARSAPARILLA.................................... 10.00
BOTTLE,DANDY,CLEAR,QUART..................................... 27.00
BOTTLE,DANT,AMERICAN LEGION.................................. 9.95
BOTTLE,DANT,BOSTON TEA PARTY.......................ILLUS.. 7.75
BOTTLE,DANT,EAGLE........................................... 2.50
BOTTLE,DANT,PATRICK HENRY.................................... 9.95
BOTTLE,DANT,REVERSE EAGLE..........................ILLUS.. 25.00
BOTTLE,DANT,WASHINGTON CROSSING DELAWARE..................... 9.95
BOTTLE,DANT,WRONG WAY CHARLIE............................... 24.95
BOTTLE,DECANTER,B-BAR,OHIO RIVER,PONTIL..................... 17.50
BOTTLE,DECANTER,CRYSTAL,EGG SHAPE,STOPPER,SIGNED ORREFORS,
6 IN.,PAIR................................................... 85.00
BOTTLE,DECANTER,CUT GLASS,STAR-CUT FLAT-TOPPED STOPPER,CIRCA
1810,PAIR.................................................... 85.00
BOTTLE,DECANTER,EISENHOWER,AMETHYST,WHEATON-NULINE.......... 10.00
BOTTLE,DECANTER,ENAMELED FLORAL,ROSES,OVERLAY,STOPPER,
CZECHOSLOVAKIA............................................... 45.00
BOTTLE,DECANTER,FEATHERED RINGS AROUND NECK,MARK CORK GLASS

BOSTON TEA PARTY DANT BOTTLE

REVERSE EAGLE DANT BOTTLE

| | |
|---|---|
| CO.,PAIR............................................ | 125.00 |
| BOTTLE,DECANTER,FIGURAL,ROOSTER,CRYSTAL BODY,SILVER HEAD, STOPPER,BASE | 135.00 |
| BOTTLE,DECANTER,FOUR-PART,SPIRITS,PRESSED GLASS............ | 50.00 |
| BOTTLE,DECANTER,GREEN,QUILTED PATTERN,CLEAR HANDLE,BLOWN STOPPER,10 IN.. | 35.00 |
| BOTTLE,DECANTER,GREEN,SILVER OVERLAY,FLORAL,LEAVES,STOPPER, 9 1/4 IN.. | 18.50 |
| BOTTLE,DECANTER,INTAGLIO DAISY,MITER CUT LEAVES & FERN,CUT GLASS,11 IN.. | 60.00 |
| BOTTLE,DECANTER,INVERTED THUMBPRINT,PEDESTAL FOOT,STOPPER, AMBER.. | 25.00 |
| BOTTLE,DECANTER,LIGHT GREEN,ENAMEL FLORAL,CLEAR STOPPER, 9 1/4 IN.HIGH.. | 19.00 |
| BOTTLE,DECANTER,LILIES OF THE VALLEY,OLIVE GREEN,HAND-BLOWN, STOPPER.. | 35.00 |
| BOTTLE,DECANTER,OHIO RIVERBOAT,BLOWN IN MOLD,BLOWN STOPPER.. | 25.00 |
| BOTTLE,DECANTER,PITTSBURGH,APPLIED NECK RINGS,RED FLORAL, RIBS,FLINT.. | 95.00 |
| BOTTLE,DECANTER,RIB,DRAPE,SNAPPED PONTIL,MOLD-BLOWN,14 IN., PAIR.. | 40.00 |
| BOTTLE,DECANTER,RIVER BOAT TYPE,STOPPER MARKED NO.10,SIGNED LIBBEY.. | 87.50 |
| BOTTLE,DECANTER,STERLING SILVER OVERLAY,12 IN.HIGH,TUMBLER.. | 72.50 |
| BOTTLE,DECANTER,SWIRL RIBS,VINTAGE COPPER WHEEL ENGRAVING, BLOWN,STOPPER.. | 12.00 |

BOTTLE,DECANTER,THREE-MOLD,THREE DOUBLE RIGAREE NECK RINGS,
BLOWN...................................................... 70.00
BOTTLE,DECANTER,VIENNESE SCENE,AMETHYST,SILVER OVERLAY,
8 1/2 IN................................................... 27.75
BOTTLE,DECANTER,WINE,BLUE ENAMEL FLORAL,WHEAT,CRYSTAL,TWO
WINES...................................................... 20.00
BOTTLE,DECANTER,WINE,HAND-PAINTED FLORAL,VERSE IN GERMAN
SCRIPT,12 IN............................................... 18.50
BOTTLE,DECANTER,WINE,PETTICOAT FORM,BLOWN,9 1/2 IN.HIGH..... 25.00
BOTTLE,DEMIJOHN,OLIVE AMBER,15 IN.HIGH...................... 40.00
BOTTLE,DEMIJOHN,SAYS HOE LARGER LIENER,ORANGE BLOESEEM,
STOPPER,PAIR............................................... 75.00
BOTTLE,DIAMOND PATTERN,FLIP GLASS,SANDWICH,QUART........... 150.00
BOTTLE,DICKEL,HORN......................................... 4.90
BOTTLE,DILL'S BALM OF LIFE,THE DILL CO.,NORRISTOWN,PA.,AQUA. 4.00
BOTTLE,DOSE,JOHN WYETH..................................... 5.00
BOTTLE,DOUBLE EAGLE,AQUA,1/2 PINT.......................... 37.50
BOTTLE,DOUBLE EAGLE,PITTSBURGH,PENNA.,AQUA,1/2 PINT........ 43.00
BOTTLE,DOUBLE EAGLE,RINGED TOP,PINT,AQUA................... 40.00
BOTTLE,DR.BAKERS PAIN PANACEA,SMALL.................ILLUS.. 16.00
BOTTLE,DR.BAKERS PAIN RELIEF,AQUA.......................... 5.00
BOTTLE,DR.BAXTERS,PALE SMOKY GREEN......................... 11.00
BOTTLE,DR.BOYCES TONIC BITTERS,AQUA,PINT................... 32.00
BOTTLE,DR.CALDWELLS SYRUP PEPSIN........................... 2.00
BOTTLE,DR.COX BARB WIRE LINIMENT........................... 3.00
BOTTLE,DR.D.JAYNES ALTERNATIVE,AQUA........................ 13.50
BOTTLE,DR.D.JAYNES EXPECTORANT,PHILA.,TUBULAR PONTIL,AQUA,
1/2 PINT................................................... 20.00
BOTTLE,DR.FENNERS KIDNEY & BACKACHE CURE,LABEL IN ENGLISH,
GERMAN,AMBER............................................... 25.00
BOTTLE,DR.FENNERS KIDNEY & BACKACHE CURE,AMBER............. 35.00
BOTTLE,DR.HARTERS BITTERS,SAMPLE SIZE...................... 35.00
BOTTLE,DR.J.F.CHURCHILL,HYPOPHOSPHITE,PECTORAL............. 3.00
BOTTLE,DR.J.G.B.SIEGERT & HIJOS,WHITTLED,GREEN............. 10.00
BOTTLE,DR.J.G.B.SIEGERT & SONS,GREEN....................... 7.00
BOTTLE,DR.KENNEDYS PRAIRIE WEED............................ 14.00
BOTTLE,DR.KILMERS SWAMP ROOT KIDNEY CURE,BINGHAMTON,N.Y.,
AQUA,3 1/4 IN.............................................. 4.00
BOTTLE,DR.KILMERS SWAMP ROOT KIDNEY,LIVER & BLADDER CURE,
EMBOSSED,AQUA.............................................. 3.00
BOTTLE,DR.KILMERS SWAMP ROOT KIDNEY REMEDY,CYLINDER,AQUA.... 7.50
BOTTLE,DR.KILMERS SWAMP ROOT,RECTANGULAR,AQUA.............. 3.00
BOTTLE,DR.MC LANES,AMERICAN WORM SPECIFIC,PONTIL,AQUA,
3 1/2 IN.LONG.............................................. 14.00
BOTTLE,DR.MC MUNNS ELIXIR OF OPIUM,CYLINDER,PONTIL,AQUA,
4 1/4 IN................................................... 7.50
BOTTLE,DR.MILES MEDICAL CO................................. 2.50
BOTTLE,DR.NORTONS TASTELESS WORM DESTROYER,HONEY AMBER,4 IN. 5.00
BOTTLE,DR.PEPPER,INDENTED LETTERS.......................... 2.50
BOTTLE,DR.W.B.CALDWELL'S SYRUP PEPSIN,PEPSIN SYRUP CO.,AQUA. 4.00
BOTTLE,DR.WISTARS BALSAM................................... 5.00
BOTTLE,DR.WISTARS BALSAM,OPEN PONTIL....................... 20.00
BOTTLE,DR.WOODS SARSAPARILLA & WILD CHERRY BITTERS,AQUA,OPEN
PONTIL..................................................... 75.00
BOTTLE,DRAKES PLANTATION,SIX LOGS.......................... 35.00
BOTTLE,DRESSER,BULBOUS,BLUE,IVORY,FLORAL,STOPPER,PORCELAIN,
FRANCE..................................................... 15.00
BOTTLE,DRESSER,PAINTED PINK ROSE,SATIN FINISH,STOPPER,9 IN.. 15.00
BOTTLE,DRESSER,RAISED LADY CAMEO,STOPPER,MILK GLASS,PAIR.... 19.00
BOTTLE,DU QUOIN BOTTLING,DU QUOIN,ILL.,GREEN............... 2.50
BOTTLE,DUFFY MALT WHISKEY,BROWN,25 OZ...................... 6.00
BOTTLE,DURKEE CHALLENGE SAUCE,AQUA......................... 22.00
BOTTLE,DYOTTVILLE GLASS WORKS,AQUA,6 1/2 IN.HIGH........... 15.00
BOTTLE,E.HALLS BARREL...................................... 95.00
BOTTLE,E.KIDERLEN,7 1/2 IN................................. 30.00
BOTTLE,EL DORADO BREWING,STOCKTON,CALIFORNIA,11 1/2 IN...... 5.00
BOTTLE,EMANUEL COLLEGE SEAL,PONTIL,CIRCA 1810.............. 70.00
BOTTLE,EMBOSSED BARRELS,SAYS G.O.BLAKES RYE & BOUR.WHISKEY.. 4.50
BOTTLE,EMBOSSED GORDON,DRY GIN,LONDON,ENGLAND,AQUA......... 12.50
BOTTLE,EMBOSSED PURE LEMON ACID,PONTIL,LABEL,CONTENTS...... 13.00
BOTTLE,ENAMELED FLORAL ON TOP & STOPPER,BLOWN,BROWN,SQUARE,
9 1/2 IN.TALL............................................. 12.50
BOTTLE,ESSENCE,LEMON,LEAF SPRAYS,DOUBLE POINT TOP,PORCELAIN,
FRANCE..................................................... 9.50
BOTTLE,ESSENCE,PURPLE GRAPE,GREEN LEAF TRIM,PORCELAIN,
FRANCE,4 1/4 IN............................................ 8.50
BOTTLE,EXCELSIOR SPRING,OLIVE GREEN,PINT................... 25.00
BOTTLE,EYEWASH,EYECUP ON GROUND STOPPER,WYETH,COBALT....... 12.00
BOTTLE,EZRA BROOKS,ANNAPOLIS TECUMSEH,BUST,BRONZE COLOR.... 14.00
BOTTLE,EZRA BROOKS,ANTIQUE CANNON......................... 14.75
BOTTLE,EZRA BROOKS,ANTIQUE PISTOL......................... 8.25
BOTTLE,EZRA BROOKS,ARCH................................... 11.50

```
BOTTLE,EZRA BROOKS,BEAR.............................. 7.50 TO   12.50
BOTTLE,EZRA BROOKS,CABLE CAR.........................ILLUS..    12.50
BOTTLE,EZRA BROOKS,CIGAR-STORE INDIAN................ILLUS..     8.25
```

DR. BAKER'S PAIN
PANACEA BOTTLE

CIGAR STORE INDIAN
BOTTLE, EZRA BROOKS

CABLE CAR BOTTLE, EZRA BROOKS

```
BOTTLE,EZRA BROOKS,DICE..................................         8.50
BOTTLE,EZRA BROOKS,DUELING PISTOL........................        14.00
BOTTLE,EZRA BROOKS,FOREMOST MAN..........................        14.00
BOTTLE,EZRA BROOKS,GRIZZLY BEAR................. 8.25 TO         14.00
BOTTLE,EZRA BROOKS,HAROLD'S CLUB LUCKY 7 RED DICE.. 14.00 TO     16.50
BOTTLE,EZRA BROOKS,HAT...................................        12.00
BOTTLE,EZRA BROOKS,INDIAN................................        12.00
BOTTLE,EZRA BROOKS,IRON HORSE............................        14.00
BOTTLE,EZRA BROOKS,KATZ CAT..............................        14.00
BOTTLE,EZRA BROOKS,MR.FOREMOST...........................        14.00
BOTTLE,EZRA BROOKS,OIL DERRICK.................. 7.50 TO         14.00
BOTTLE,EZRA BROOKS,PISTOL................................         8.00
BOTTLE,EZRA BROOKS,PISTOL,STAND..........................        10.90
BOTTLE,EZRA BROOKS,POTBELLY STOVE.............. 8.25 TO          14.00
BOTTLE,EZRA BROOKS,QUEEN OF HEARTS.......................        14.00
BOTTLE,EZRA BROOKS,RENO ARCH................... 14.00 TO         16.50
BOTTLE,EZRA BROOKS,TECUMSEH,WITH CONTENTS................        14.95
BOTTLE,EZRA BROOKS,WINSTON CHURCHILL........... 10.25 TO         16.50
```

```
BOTTLE,FATHER JOHN'S MEDICINE.................................     3.00
BOTTLE,FIGURAL,ALARM CLOCK SHAPE..............................     4.00
BOTTLE,FIGURAL,BABY BLACKAMOOR,CLEAR & FROSTED................    26.00
BOTTLE,FIGURAL,BABY,CRYING,CLEAR,6 1/2 IN.HIGH................    35.00
BOTTLE,FIGURAL,BASE VIOLA,AMBER...............................     8.00
BOTTLE,FIGURAL,BEAR,BLACK,ENAMELED OVER CLEAR,SMIRNOFF........    10.00
BOTTLE,FIGURAL,BELL TOWER,WATCHTOWER..........................    21.50
BOTTLE,FIGURAL,BINOCULAR,FULL SIZE,BLACK......................     5.00
BOTTLE,FIGURAL,BIRD,HEAD FORMS STOPPER,MILK GLASS,8 IN.TALL...    10.00
BOTTLE,FIGURAL,BIRD,HEAD FORMS STOPPER,MILK GLASS,10 IN.TALL..    12.00
BOTTLE,FIGURAL,BUST OF GEORGE WASHINGTON,MINIATURE............     6.50
BOTTLE,FIGURAL,BUST OF REGINA ELENA,CLEAR,BLOWN...............    30.00
BOTTLE,FIGURAL,CABIN,STILL,HILLBILLY,PINT.........  25.00 TO      45.00
BOTTLE,FIGURAL,CABIN,STILL,HILLBILLY,QUART....................    22.50
BOTTLE,FIGURAL,CHERUB HOLDING CLOCK,PAINTED CLOCK FACE,
   FRANCE,14 IN.HIGH.........................................    25.00
BOTTLE,FIGURAL,CHERUB HOLDING MEDALLION,CLEAR,13 3/4 IN.
   HIGH......................................................    16.00
BOTTLE,FIGURAL,CHRISTMAS TREE.................................    35.00
BOTTLE,FIGURAL,CLOWN,BANK.....................................     3.00
BOTTLE,FIGURAL,CLOWN,HEAD IS STOPPER,HAND BLOWN IN
   MULTICOLORS,PAYASO........................................     6.50
BOTTLE,FIGURAL,EGYPTIAN PITCHER...............................    17.50
BOTTLE,FIGURAL,ELEPHANT,BANK..................................     4.00
BOTTLE,FIGURAL,ELEPHANT,SITTING,UPRAISED TRUNK HAS CORK,
   8 1/2 IN.TALL.............................................    12.50
BOTTLE,FIGURAL,FISH,ASHTRAY...................................    17.50
BOTTLE,FIGURAL,GEORGE WASHINGTON,BY OLEAN CO.,PAT.1936........    30.00
BOTTLE,FIGURAL,GIRL WITH PARASOL..............................    10.00
BOTTLE,FIGURAL,GROVER CLEVELAND,FROSTED,9 IN..................    70.00
BOTTLE,FIGURAL,GUITAR,BROWN,16 IN.............................     5.00
BOTTLE,FIGURAL,HUNTER,LADY,PAIR...............................    25.00
BOTTLE,FIGURAL,IMPERIAL CROWN,VICTYLITE,OSHKOSH,WIS.,MADE IN
   ITALY,AMBER...............................................     8.00
BOTTLE,FIGURAL,IRISHMAN ON BARREL,ENAMEL......................    25.00
BOTTLE,FIGURAL,KAHLUA GODDESS,FERTILITY GODDESS,PAIR..........    35.00
BOTTLE,FIGURAL,KITTY,BANK,ORIGINALLY HELD SOFT DRINK,4 X
   7 IN.HIGH.................................................     3.50
BOTTLE,FIGURAL,LADY,RED,YELLOW COLONIAL STYLE DRESS,HOLDS
   FAN,PORCELAIN.............................................    12.50
BOTTLE,FIGURAL,LINCOLN,BANK,CLEAR,8 3/4 IN....................     5.50
BOTTLE,FIGURAL,MAN,GALLIANO...................................     2.90
BOTTLE,FIGURAL,MAN,STILL,CABIN,FIFTH..........................     8.90
BOTTLE,FIGURAL,MAN,STILL,CABIN,QUART..........................    15.90
BOTTLE,FIGURAL,MONK,BENNINGTON TYPE,10 1/2 IN.HIGH............   150.00
BOTTLE,FIGURAL,MR.CARTER,MRS.CARTER,PAIR......................    25.00
BOTTLE,FIGURAL,NEGRO BABY,PARTLY FROSTED,FRANCE...............    26.00
BOTTLE,FIGURAL,OWL,BROWN......................................    10.50
BOTTLE,FIGURAL,OWL,ENAMEL,GLASS EYES,6 3/4 IN.TALL............    22.50
BOTTLE,FIGURAL,OWL,RED...............................  8.50 TO    10.50
BOTTLE,FIGURAL,PISTOL,LABEL SAYS BARSOTTINI VINO ROSSO,
   ITALY,LINED BOX...........................................    15.00
BOTTLE,FIGURAL,QUEEN ELIZABETH................................    10.00
BOTTLE,FIGURAL,RAISED GOLD CAT OVER GREEN CRYSTAL,12 1/2 IN...    11.00
BOTTLE,FIGURAL,REVOLVER,SCREW TOP,AMBER,9 3/4 IN..............    12.00
BOTTLE,FIGURAL,RIVER QUEEN BOAT.....................  10.50 TO    11.75
BOTTLE,FIGURAL,ROOSTER,ASHTRAY................................    17.50
BOTTLE,FIGURAL,SAILOR.........................................     1.00
BOTTLE,FIGURAL,SENORITA,HEAD FORMS STOPPER,MILK GLASS,
   10 IN.TALL................................................    12.00
BOTTLE,FIGURAL,SMILING INDIAN,BUBBLY GREEN,LIMA,PERU,FEDERAL
   LAW......................................................    22.00
BOTTLE,FIGURAL,TAYLOR CASTLE..................................     9.00
BOTTLE,FIGURAL,VIOLIN,BLUE,HANGER,PAIR........................    45.00
BOTTLE,FIGURAL,VIOLIN,EARS,CLEAR..............................     5.00
BOTTLE,FIGURAL,WEEPING HOUND,PURPLE...........................    11.50
BOTTLE,FIGURINE,MADONNA,COBALT BLUE,10 IN.TALL................     3.00
BOTTLE,FIGURINE,MADONNA,HAND-BLOWN,PONTIL,1932,COBALT,
   13 IN.TALL................................................     3.00
BOTTLE,FIGURINE,MADONNA,HAND-BLOWN,PONTIL,1932,AMBER,
   13 IN.TALL................................................     3.00
BOTTLE,FIGURINE,MADONNA,HAND-BLOWN,PONTIL,COBALT,10 IN.TALL...     3.00
BOTTLE,FIGURINE,MADONNA,PONTIL,AMBER,1932,13 IN.TALL..........     4.00
BOTTLE,FIGURINE,MADONNA,PONTIL,COBALT BLUE,1932,13 IN.TALL...     4.00
BOTTLE,FIRE EXTINGUISHER,CORSET SHAPE,ICE BLUE,PAIR..........    32.50
BOTTLE,FISH SHAPE,COD LIVER OIL,AMBER,1 PINT..................     6.50
BOTTLE,FISH SHAPE,COD LIVER OIL,AMBER,1/4 PT..................     7.50
BOTTLE,FISH,AMBER,10 IN.......................................     8.50
BOTTLE,FISH,BROWN...............................ILLUS..             5.00
BOTTLE,FISH,CORK TOP,AMBER,8 1/4 IN...........................    18.00
BOTTLE,FISH,CORK TOP,AMBER,9 3/4 IN...........................    18.00
```

BROWN FISH
BOTTLE

| | |
|---|---:|
| BOTTLE,FITZGERALD,COAT OF ARMS | 2.00 |
| BOTTLE,FITZGERALD,DECANTER,FLAGSHIP | 6.49 |
| BOTTLE,FITZGERALD,DECANTER,MONTICELLO | 6.49 |
| BOTTLE,FITZGERALD,LEPRECHAUN | 5.00 |
| BOTTLE,FLASK,ALBANY GLASS WORKS,CLEVENGER,AMETHYST | 25.00 |
| BOTTLE,FLASK,AMERICAN EAGLE,AQUA | 67.50 |
| BOTTLE,FLASK,AMERICAN EAGLE,PONTIL,G-11 73 | 100.00 |
| BOTTLE,FLASK,BOTTOM HALF ENCASED IN PEWTER,TOP HALF IN LEATHER,1865 | 3.95 |
| BOTTLE,FLASK,CAPT.BRAGG,TAYLOR-WASHINGTON,AQUA,QUART | 90.00 |
| BOTTLE,FLASK,CLAMSHELL,LAY-DOWN | 18.75 |
| BOTTLE,FLASK,CLASPED HANDS,SHIELD,STARS,UNION,MEDALLION, REVERSE,AQUA,QT | 47.50 |
| BOTTLE,FLASK,CLYDE GLASS WORKS,N.Y.,EMBOSSED ON FACE,AQUA, PINT | 35.00 |
| BOTTLE,FLASK,COFFIN,EMBOSSED,EMERALD,8 OZ | 12.00 |
| BOTTLE,FLASK,CORNUCOPIA & BASKET OF FLOWERS,OLIVE GREEN, 1/2 PT | 55.00 |
| BOTTLE,FLASK,CORNUCOPIA,BASKET,OLIVE GREEN,PINT | 50.00 |
| BOTTLE,FLASK,CORNUCOPIA,EAGLE,OLIVE GREEN,PINT | 75.00 |
| BOTTLE,FLASK,CORNUCOPIA,EAGLE,X TO LEFT,PINT,AQUA | 90.00 |
| BOTTLE,FLASK,CRYSTAL,STERLING HINGED LID & JACKET, STEEPLECHASE SCENE | 15.00 |
| BOTTLE,FLASK,DOUBLE EAGLE,BLUE,PINT | 34.00 |
| BOTTLE,FLASK,DOUBLE EAGLE,CUNNINGHAM & CO.,PITTSBURGH,AQUA, QUART | 47.50 |
| BOTTLE,FLASK,EAGLE,AQUA,QUART | 45.00 |
| BOTTLE,FLASK,EAGLE,BASKET OF FRUIT,OLIVE COLOR,MARKED KEENE, PINT | 95.00 |
| BOTTLE,FLASK,EAGLE,12 STARS,CLEAR,GEORGE WASHINGTON, 1732-1932,8 IN.TALL | 10.00 |
| BOTTLE,FLASK,EMBOSSED ANCHOR AND CHAIN,1/2 PT. | 9.00 |
| BOTTLE,FLASK,EMBOSSED E.R.BETTERTON & CO.,DISTILLERS, CHATTANOOGA,TENN | 7.00 |
| BOTTLE,FLASK,ENCASED PEWTER & LEATHER COVER,PEWTER TOP, 1/2 PINT | 8.50 |
| BOTTLE,FLASK,FIGURAL, A CHAMPAGNE GIRL,  PURPLE GRAPES, FRUIT,STOPPER | 14.50 |
| BOTTLE,FLASK,FIGURAL,APACHE DANCERS,PORCELAIN | 32.50 |
| BOTTLE,FLASK,FIGURAL,COMIC SAILOR,PORCELAIN | 30.00 |
| BOTTLE,FLASK,FIGURAL,FLAPPER HOLDS WHISKEY BOTTLE,PORCELAIN. | 30.00 |
| BOTTLE,FLASK,FIGURAL,HAPPY MOON FACE,PORCELAIN | 25.00 |
| BOTTLE,FLASK,GREEN,LEATHER COVERED,ORANTE KEY OPENS STOPPER. | 125.00 |
| BOTTLE,FLASK,HISTORICAL,LIBERTY WITH EAGLE,WILLINGTON GLASS CO.,GREEN | 135.00 |
| BOTTLE,FLASK,HISTORICAL,SAPPHIRE BLUE,QUART | 475.00 |
| BOTTLE,FLASK,HISTORICAL,SUMMER-WINTER,BIRD,BUBBLY,GX19,AQUA, QUART | 49.50 |
| BOTTLE,FLASK,HISTORICAL,WASHINGTON-TAYLOR,BUBBLY,GI-49,AQUA, PINT | 45.00 |
| BOTTLE,FLASK,KNIGHTS OF PYTHIAS BIENNIAL,BOSTON,1908,EMBLEM, AMBER | 8.50 |
| BOTTLE,FLASK,LOTION BOTTLE,STAMPED SEARS,AMBER,1/2 PINT | 10.00 |
| BOTTLE,FLASK,OAK LEAVES & ACORNS DECOR,COPPER,SIGNED JAMES DIXON | 25.00 |
| BOTTLE,FLASK,OLD SETTLER WHISKEY,PEORIA,ILL.,LABEL,AMBER | 12.00 |
| BOTTLE,FLASK,OLIVE GREEN,PONTIL,GII-72 | 85.00 |
| BOTTLE,FLASK,OVAL-SHAPED SADDLE,BLOWN,OLIVE GREEN,IN WICKER & TIN HOLDER | 35.00 |

```
BOTTLE,FLASK,PAUL JONES,EMBOSSED,AMBER......................      10.00
BOTTLE,FLASK,PERSIAN SADDLE................................      14.95
BOTTLE,FLASK,PEWTER........................................       5.00
BOTTLE,FLASK,PIG,C.F.KNAPP,PHILA.,CLEAR,2 OUNCES...........      35.00
BOTTLE,FLASK,PIKES PEAK,MAN,KNAPSACK,CANE,FOR PIKES PEAK,
  1/2 PINT................................................      42.00
BOTTLE,FLASK,PIKES PEAK,APPLIED RING TOP,AQUA,PINT.........      70.00
BOTTLE,FLASK,PINK,STAFFORDSHIRE,CIRCA 1830.................      55.00
BOTTLE,FLASK,PINT,BIGELOW-KENNARD STERLING,CRYSTAL.........      35.00
BOTTLE,FLASK,RESURGAM,BALTIMORE GLASS WORKS,ANCHOR IN
  REVERSE,AQUA,PINT.......................................      68.50
BOTTLE,FLASK,RICHMOND,AMERICAN GLASS PLATE NO.259.........     500.00
BOTTLE,FLASK,SADDLE,FREE-BLOWN,EMERALD GREEN,CIRCA 1700,
  9 IN...................................................      23.50
BOTTLE,FLASK,SCENT,AMETHYST QUARTZ,GOLD,DIAMOND,CABOCHON
  SAPPHIRE,RUSSIA.....................................1,000.00
BOTTLE,FLASK,SCROLL & STARS,ROUGH PONTIL,AQUA,QUART.......      35.00
BOTTLE,FLASK,SCROLL,RINGED LIP,IRON PONTIL,AQUA,QUART.....     115.00
BOTTLE,FLASK,SHEAF OF WHEAT,MARKED WESTFORD,CONNECTICUT,
  AMBER,HALF PINT........................................      70.00
BOTTLE,FLASK,SMALL BOY FIREMAN HOSING DOWN FIREWATER BOTTLE,
  PORCELAIN..............................................      32.50
BOTTLE,FLASK,SPIRIT,W.H.JONES & CO.,BOSTON,TRADEMARK 1851,
  SILVER CAP.............................................       7.50
BOTTLE,FLASK,STODDARD TYPE,WHITTLED,SNAP CASE,AMBER.......      21.50
BOTTLE,FLASK,STONEWARE,PINT...............................      25.00
BOTTLE,FLASK,SUMMER,WINTER,PONTIL,AQUA,PINT,GX-15.........      70.00
BOTTLE,FLASK,TAYLOR & WASHINGTON,AQUA,PINT................      45.00
BOTTLE,FLASK,TAYLOR & WASHINGTON,AQUA,QUART...............      55.00
BOTTLE,FLASK,THE NAME ST.JOSEPH ASSURES PURITY............       9.00
BOTTLE,FLASK,THE WALDORF CAFES,SAN FRANCISCO,1915,NEW YEARS,
  PINT,CLEAR.............................................       9.75
BOTTLE,FLASK,TURTLE,CLEAR,GROUND MOUTH,PEWTER TOP.........      20.00
BOTTLE,FLASK,UNGLAZED POTTERY,PINT........................      25.00
BOTTLE,FLASK,UNION A F MADE,CLEAR.........................       5.00
BOTTLE,FLASK,UNION,CLASPED HANDS,13 STARS,REVERSE EAGLE,
  BLUE,1/2 PT............................................     110.00
BOTTLE,FLASK,UNION,STAR IN CIRCLE ON SHOULDER,AMBER.......       6.00
BOTTLE,FLASK,UNION,WHITTLED,AMBER.........................      10.00
BOTTLE,FLASK,WASHINGTON & TAYLOR,AQUA,PINT................      65.00
BOTTLE,FLASK,WHITNEY GLASS WORKS EMBOSSED ON BOTTOM,AQUA,
  AMBER,PAIR.............................................      30.00
BOTTLE,FLAT SIDES,RAISED STAR,PINT,AMBER..................       6.50
BOTTLE,FLORA BOTTLING WORKS D TRACO PROP,AQUA.............       2.50
BOTTLE,FLORIDA WATER,AQUA,6 IN............................       3.50
BOTTLE,FOLEY KIDNEY PILLS,FOLEY & CO.,CHICAGO,CLEAR,
  EMBOSSED,CORK..........................................       2.50
BOTTLE,FRANZIA,CALIFORNIA PORT,MINIATURE..................       2.00
BOTTLE,FREE BLOWN CYLINDER,BLACK GLASS,CIRCA 1790.........      15.00
BOTTLE,FREE BLOWN,DIP MOLD,BLACK GLASS,QUART..............       8.00
BOTTLE,FRENCH DRESSING,FLORAL,OIL,VINEGAR,CUT GLASS,HAWKES,
  JUNE 1916..............................................      17.00
BOTTLE,FRIEDRICHSHALL COPPEL & CO.,MINERAL WATER FROM
  ENGLAND,QUART..........................................      20.00
BOTTLE,FROSTILE HOLMES FRAGRANT,ELMIRA,N.Y.,U.S.A.,CLEAR..       6.00
BOTTLE,FRUIT JAR,ALL RIGHT,PRESERVE,AQUA,QUART............      22.00
BOTTLE,FRUIT JAR,ANCHOR MASON,QUART.......................       2.00
BOTTLE,FRUIT JAR,AQUA,GLOBE,1 PINT,DATED 1886.............      15.00
BOTTLE,FRUIT JAR,ATLAS E-Z SEAL,AQUA LID..................      10.00
BOTTLE,FRUIT JAR,ATLAS E-Z SEAL,SQUATTY PINT,AQUA.........       3.00
BOTTLE,FRUIT JAR,ATLAS,GOOD LUCK,FOUR-LEAF CLOVER,QUART....       3.50
BOTTLE,FRUIT JAR,BALL DELUXE JAR..........................       2.00
BOTTLE,FRUIT JAR,BALL MASON,PERFECT NO.6,BLUE,QUART.......       3.50
BOTTLE,FRUIT JAR,BALL SURE SEAL...........................       2.00
BOTTLE,FRUIT JAR,BALL,STANDARD,AQUA,QUART.................       2.50
BOTTLE,FRUIT JAR,BEAVER,AQUA,QUART........................      12.50
BOTTLE,FRUIT JAR,BEAVER,CLEAR,QUART.......................      12.00
BOTTLE,FRUIT JAR,BEAVER,CLEAR,1/2 GALLON..........12.00 TO      13.50
BOTTLE,FRUIT JAR,BLUE,ZINC COVER,PAT.NOVEMBER 30,1858.....       4.50
BOTTLE,FRUIT JAR,BUFFALO BALL BROS..MONOGRAM B.B.G.M.CO.,
  AQUA,QUART.............................................      15.00
BOTTLE,FRUIT JAR,C.U.THOMSEN & SONS,PITTS.,PA.,WAX SEALER,
  TIN LID,QUART..........................................      12.00
BOTTLE,FRUIT JAR,CLAMPS,BALL IDEAL,1908,AQUA,QUART........       2.50
BOTTLE,FRUIT JAR,CLARK'S PEERLESS,AQUA,PINT...............      12.00
BOTTLE,FRUIT JAR,CLARK'S PEERLESS,QUART...................       6.00
BOTTLE,FRUIT JAR,CLARK'S PEERLESS,1/2 GALLON..............       7.00
BOTTLE,FRUIT JAR,CLEAR,GLASS LID WITH CLAMP,CHINESE
  INSCRIPTION,PINT.......................................       4.75
BOTTLE,FRUIT JAR,CLYDE MASON'S IMPROVED EMBOSSED ON FRONT,
  CLEAR.................................................      11.00
```

| | |
|---|---|
| BOTTLE,FRUIT JAR,COHANSEY,AQUA............................... | 9.00 |
| BOTTLE,FRUIT JAR,COHANSEY,AQUA,QUART......................... | 10.00 |
| BOTTLE,FRUIT JAR,CROWN,GREEN-AMBER,1/2 GAL................... | 8.00 |
| BOTTLE,FRUIT JAR,CROWN IMPERIAL,TWO-PIECE LID,PINT........... | 6.00 |
| BOTTLE,FRUIT JAR,DICTATOR,PRESERVE,AQUA,QUART................ | 20.00 |
| BOTTLE,FRUIT JAR,DREY IMPROVED,WIRE CLAMP,PINT............... | 3.00 |
| BOTTLE,FRUIT JAR,ECONOMY,SUN-COLORED......................... | 6.00 |
| BOTTLE,FRUIT JAR,EMBOSSED MELLINS FOOD,AQUA,TIN LID,3 IN. X | |
| 6 IN.TALL................................................... | 3.50 |
| BOTTLE,FRUIT JAR,ESKEY FOOD,BROWN,1/2 GALLON................. | 5.00 |
| BOTTLE,FRUIT JAR,EUREKA,CLEAR LID & CLAMP,18 OUNCE,PINT..... | 10.00 |
| BOTTLE,FRUIT JAR,FLACCUS,STEER HEAD,EMBOSSED,SIMPLEX LID.... | 35.00 |
| BOTTLE,FRUIT JAR,FRANKLIN DEXTER,QUART....................... | 10.50 |
| BOTTLE,FRUIT JAR,FRUIT KEEPER,GREEN,QUART.................... | 16.95 |
| BOTTLE,FRUIT JAR,GEM,MIDGET,TWO-PIECE TOP.................... | 10.00 |
| BOTTLE,FRUIT JAR,GILCHIST,QUART.............................. | 16.00 |
| BOTTLE,FRUIT JAR,GILKA,EIGHT-SIDED,AMBER,QUART............... | 10.00 |
| BOTTLE,FRUIT JAR,GLASS LID,WIRE HANDLE,AMBER,GLOBE,DATED | |
| 1886........................................................ | 25.00 |
| BOTTLE,FRUIT JAR,GLASS SCREW LID,CLEAR,CROWN,CANADA,PINT.... | 3.00 |
| BOTTLE,FRUIT JAR,GLOBE,AMBER,QUART........................... | 17.50 |
| BOTTLE,FRUIT JAR,GLOBE,AMBER,1/2 GALLON...................... | 18.50 |
| BOTTLE,FRUIT JAR,GLOBE,AQUA,PINT............................. | 14.00 |
| BOTTLE,FRUIT JAR,GLOBE,RED-AMBER............................. | 22.50 |
| BOTTLE,FRUIT JAR,GLOBE,2 QUART............................... | 6.00 |
| BOTTLE,FRUIT JAR,GOLDEN STAR,CLEAR SHOO-FLY,STAR,PINT........ | 7.00 |
| BOTTLE,FRUIT JAR,GOOD LUCK,1/2 GALLON........................ | 3.00 |
| BOTTLE,FRUIT JAR,GRAY POTTERY,GLASS LID,T SNAP,SHERWOOD..... | 7.50 |
| BOTTLE,FRUIT JAR,GREEK KEY,SAFETY VALVE,AQUA,1/2 GALLON..... | 27.50 |
| BOTTLE,FRUIT JAR,GREEN MOUNTAIN,PINT......................... | 8.00 |
| BOTTLE,FRUIT JAR,H & R ON BASE,WAX SEALER,AQUA,1/2 GALLON... | 4.00 |
| BOTTLE,FRUIT JAR,H.PETTIT,AQUA,PINT.......................... | 10.00 |
| BOTTLE,FRUIT JAR,HERON PICKLE JAR,METAL COVER................ | 23.00 |
| BOTTLE,FRUIT JAR,HORMEL GOOD FOODS,OVAL,PINT................. | 2.50 |
| BOTTLE,FRUIT JAR,HORMEL,OVAL,PINT............................ | 6.00 |
| BOTTLE,FRUIT JAR,J.ELWOOD LEE,AMBER,QUART.................... | 30.00 |
| BOTTLE,FRUIT JAR,JEANETTE,MATCHED LID........................ | 3.00 |
| BOTTLE,FRUIT JAR,KEYSTONE MASON,TWO QUART.................... | 8.00 |
| BOTTLE,FRUIT JAR,KEYSTONE-EMBOSSED IN CIRCLE,ONE-PIECE LID.. | 6.50 |
| BOTTLE,FRUIT JAR,KING,PINT.................................... | 8.50 |
| BOTTLE,FRUIT JAR,KING,QUART.................................. | 8.00 |
| BOTTLE,FRUIT JAR,KINSELLA,QUART.............................. | 8.00 |
| BOTTLE,FRUIT JAR,KNOULTON,AQUA,QUART......................... | 20.00 |
| BOTTLE,FRUIT JAR,LECTRIC,PINT................................ | 4.00 |
| BOTTLE,FRUIT JAR,LECTRIC GM,PINT............................. | 5.00 |
| BOTTLE,FRUIT JAR,LIGHTENING,AMBER,QUART............. 16.00 TO | 20.00 |
| BOTTLE,FRUIT JAR,LIGHTENING,AQUA,QT.......................... | 4.00 |
| BOTTLE,FRUIT JAR,LIGHTNING,AMBER,1/2 GALLON.................. | 16.00 |
| BOTTLE,FRUIT JAR,LIGHTNING,DARK AMBER,TWO QUART.............. | 20.00 |
| BOTTLE,FRUIT JAR,LIGHTNING,PUTNAM TRADEMARK,PINT............. | 4.00 |
| BOTTLE,FRUIT JAR,LIGHTNING,TRADEMARK,LID DATED APRIL 25, | |
| 1882,AMBER.................................................. | 22.00 |
| BOTTLE,FRUIT JAR,LIGHTNING,WHITTLED,AMBER,QUART.............. | 16.50 |
| BOTTLE,FRUIT JAR,LIGHTNING,1882,AMBER,QUART.................. | 15.00 |
| BOTTLE,FRUIT JAR,LITTLE RIVER PICKLE JAR,GLASS COVER........ | 18.50 |
| BOTTLE,FRUIT JAR,LOCKPORT MASON IMPROVED,CLEAR,SCREW TOP | |
| WITH GLASS.................................................. | 3.00 |
| BOTTLE,FRUIT JAR,MARION,1/2 GALLON........................... | 5.00 |
| BOTTLE,FRUIT JAR,MASON,AQUA,ONE QUART........................ | 2.00 |
| BOTTLE,FRUIT JAR,MASON,AQUA,TWO QUART........................ | 2.00 |
| BOTTLE,FRUIT JAR,MASON,BALL PERFECT,MEASURE ON SIDE,AMBER, | |
| 1/2 GALLON.................................................. | 15.00 |
| BOTTLE,FRUIT JAR,MASON,BALL,AMBER,1/2 GALLON................. | 19.00 |
| BOTTLE,FRUIT JAR,MASON,BLUE,QUART.....................ILLUS.. | 6.00 |
| BOTTLE,FRUIT JAR,MASON,CG-GG EMBLEM,1858,QUART............... | 8.00 |
| BOTTLE,FRUIT JAR,MASON,DATED 1858,QT......................... | 2.00 |
| BOTTLE,FRUIT JAR,MASON,DATED 1858,1/2 GAL.................... | 2.00 |
| BOTTLE,FRUIT JAR,MASON,DATED 1858,5 IN....................... | 5.50 |
| BOTTLE,FRUIT JAR,MASON,PAT.NOV.30,1853,AQUA,QT............... | 5.00 |
| BOTTLE,FRUIT JAR,MASON,PAT.1858,CFJC ON FRONT,CLYDE,N.Y. ON | |
| BACK........................................................ | 3.00 |
| BOTTLE,FRUIT JAR,MASON,PATENT NOVEMBER 30,1858,QUART........ | 2.50 |
| BOTTLE,FRUIT JAR,MASON,RED KEY,1/2 GALLON.................... | 9.00 |
| BOTTLE,FRUIT JAR,MASON,SMALL MOUTH,PINT...................... | 7.50 |
| BOTTLE,FRUIT JAR,MASON,WHITNEY,PAT.1858,AQUA,QUART........... | 4.50 |
| BOTTLE,FRUIT JAR,MASON,ZINC TOP,MILK GLASS LINER,PATENT | |
| NOV.1858,QUART.............................................. | 6.00 |
| BOTTLE,FRUIT JAR,MASON,1858,LIGHT OLIVE GREEN............... | 9.25 |
| BOTTLE,FRUIT JAR,MASON,1858,MIDGET,ONE-PIECE LID............ | 7.00 |
| BOTTLE,FRUIT JAR,MASON C.F.J.CO.IMPROVED MIDGET,TWO-PIECE | |
| LID......................................................... | 7.00 |

BLUE MASON BOTTLE

```
BOTTLE,FRUIT JAR,MASON IMPROVED,QUART........................    4.50
BOTTLE,FRUIT JAR,MASON MIDGET,C.F.J.CO.,ONE-PIECE LID.......    5.00
BOTTLE,FRUIT JAR,MASON MIDGET,PAT.DATE,ONE-PIECE LID........    5.00
BOTTLE,FRUIT JAR,MASON MIDGET,KEYSTONE-EMBOSSED,ONE-PIECE
   LID.......................................................    6.50
BOTTLE,FRUIT JAR,MASON TRADEMARK CFJ,QUART..................    3.00
BOTTLE,FRUIT JAR,MASON'S IMPROVED,TWO-PIECE LID,PINT........    5.00
BOTTLE,FRUIT JAR,MASON'S PAT.1858,KEYSTONE IN CIRCLE,QUART..    3.00
BOTTLE,FRUIT JAR,MASON'S PATENT NOV.30,1858,MIDGET..........    8.50
BOTTLE,FRUIT JAR,MASON'S STAR,PINT.........................    3.00
BOTTLE,FRUIT JAR,MASONS UNION,WHITTLED,AQUA,EMBOSSED
   U.S.TREASURY SHIELD......................................   37.50
BOTTLE,FRUIT JAR,MILLVILLE ATMOSPHERIC,QUART...............   16.00
BOTTLE,FRUIT JAR,MILLVILLE ATMOSPHERIC,TWO QUART...........   10.00
BOTTLE,FRUIT JAR,MILLVILLE ATMOSPHERIC,WHITALLS PATENT,JUNE
   18,1861................................................   27.50
BOTTLE,FRUIT JAR,MILLVILLE,QUART..........................   14.50
BOTTLE,FRUIT JAR,MILLVILLE,WHITTLED,2 QUART...............   15.50
BOTTLE,FRUIT JAR,P.LORILLARD,GLASS TOP,1872,QUART..........    9.75
BOTTLE,FRUIT JAR,QUICK SEAL,1908,CLEAR...................    2.00
BOTTLE,FRUIT JAR,RAU,GROOVE RING,QUART....................   25.00
BOTTLE,FRUIT JAR,RIBBED,EMBOSSED,MILK GLASS,2 1/2 IN.TALL,3.    8.50
BOTTLE,FRUIT JAR,ROOT MASON,AQUA,QUART....................    3.00
BOTTLE,FRUIT JAR,ROOT MASON,1/2 GALLON....................    5.00
BOTTLE,FRUIT JAR,SAFETY VALVE,PINT.......................    5.00
BOTTLE,FRUIT JAR,SAFETY VALVE,1895.......................    9.00
BOTTLE,FRUIT JAR,SAFETY,AMBER,GALLON.....................   35.50
BOTTLE,FRUIT JAR,SAFETY,AMBER,QUART......................   35.00
BOTTLE,FRUIT JAR,SALZMAN,AMBER,1/3 GAL...................    6.00
BOTTLE,FRUIT JAR,SALZMAN,EIGHT-SIDED,AMBER,QUART.........    8.00
BOTTLE,FRUIT JAR,SAYS MAGIC FRUIT JAR,AQUA,QUART.........   28.00
BOTTLE,FRUIT JAR,SCHRAM ECONOMY.........................    3.00
BOTTLE,FRUIT JAR,SECURITY SEAL,CLEAR,QUART...............    6.50
BOTTLE,FRUIT JAR,SELCO..................................    2.00
BOTTLE,FRUIT JAR,SIMPLEX,1/2 PINT........................    9.00
BOTTLE,FRUIT JAR,SMALLEY NU SEAL........................    4.00
BOTTLE,FRUIT JAR,STERLING MASON,QUART...................    1.50
BOTTLE,FRUIT JAR,SURE SEAL,BLUISH AQUA,1910..............   12.50
BOTTLE,FRUIT JAR,SWAYZE'S IMPROVED MASON................    1.50
BOTTLE,FRUIT JAR,SWAYZE'S IMPROVED MASON,QUART...........    4.00
BOTTLE,FRUIT JAR,TELEPHONE,GLASS CLOSURE,AQUA,PINT.......    4.00
BOTTLE,FRUIT JAR,THE GEM,C.F.J.CO.,1/2 GALLON............    7.00
BOTTLE,FRUIT JAR,THE GEM,QUART..........................    4.00
BOTTLE,FRUIT JAR,THE GEM,SHIELD ON REVERSE,DATED BASE,QUART.    8.50
BOTTLE,FRUIT JAR,THE GEM,2 QUART........................    4.00
BOTTLE,FRUIT JAR,THE HERO,QUART.........................   12.00
BOTTLE,FRUIT JAR,THE HERO,1 1/2 QUART...................   12.00
BOTTLE,FRUIT JAR,THE HEROINE,2 QUART....................   15.00
BOTTLE,FRUIT JAR,THE MARION JAR.........................    5.50
BOTTLE,FRUIT JAR,THE PEARL,QUART........................   35.00
BOTTLE,FRUIT JAR,THE QUEEN,WREATH OF DATES,CLEAR LID,AQUA,
   QUART...................................................   12.00
```

BOTTLE,FRUIT JAR,TRADEMARK MASON'S IMPROVED,AQUA,PINT....... 5.00
BOTTLE,FRUIT JAR,UNION FRUIT JAR,A & D.H.CHAMBERS,PITTS.,
  GREEN,GALLON............................................... 16.50
BOTTLE,FRUIT JAR,VICTORY,SHIELD............................. 5.00
BOTTLE,FRUIT JAR,W.W.LYMAN,FULL CIRCLE,PATENT DATES......... 12.00
BOTTLE,FRUIT JAR,WEIDEMAN,PINT............................. 5.00
BOTTLE,FRUIT JAR,WHITTLED,PATENT,CLYDE,AQUA,MASON,QUART..... 7.00
BOTTLE,FRUIT JAR,WIRE CLOSURE,CLEAR,LID,QUART.............. 1.50
BOTTLE,FRUIT JAR,WIRE CLOSURE,LID,BLUE,QUART.............. 2.00
BOTTLE,FRUIT JAR,WOODBURY IMPROVED,WCW EMBLEM,TWO QUART..... 28.00
BOTTLE,FRUIT JAR,WOODBURY,AQUA,QUART....................... 13.50
BOTTLE,FRUIT JAR,WOODBURY,WCW EMBLEM,TWO QUART............. 25.00
BOTTLE,FRUIT JAR,WOODBURY,WHITTLED,QUART................... 25.00
BOTTLE,FRUIT JAR,ZINC LID,TEARDROPS....................... 2.50
BOTTLE,G.W.WESTON,SARATOGA,PINT........................... 25.00
BOTTLE,GALLIANO SOLDIER....................... 13.00 TO 15.00
BOTTLE,GALLIANO,FIGURAL,SOLDIER,ONE GALLON,39 IN.HIGH....... 48.00
BOTTLE,GARGLING OIL,GREEN................................. 7.00
BOTTLE,GARNIER,DUCK........................... 13.00 TO 24.90
BOTTLE,GARNIER,EIFFEL TOWER............................... 15.00
BOTTLE,GARNIER,FIGURAL,ROOSTER,MAROON..................... 18.00
BOTTLE,GARNIER,FOO DOG...................................
BOTTLE,GARNIER,NATIVE GIRL UNDER TREE..................... 19.75
BOTTLE,GARNIER,PARROT..................................... 24.90
BOTTLE,GARNIER,RED ROOSTER,LABELS......................... 30.00
BOTTLE,GARNIER,TEAPOT....................................
BOTTLE,GEISHA GIRL,PURPLE................................. 15.00
BOTTLE,GEORGE WASHINGTON,BUST............................. 4.00
BOTTLE,GEORGE WASHINGTON,CLEAR,9 1/2 IN................... 12.50
BOTTLE,GIN,CASE,OLIVE GREEN............................... 7.50
BOTTLE,GIN,CASE,SIX DOTS,6-POINT STAR,AMBER............... 9.00
BOTTLE,GIN,CYLINDER YEAR 1780,FREE BLOWN,BLACK............. 25.00
BOTTLE,GIN,HAND-TWISTED NECK,OLIVE GREEN.................. 4.75
BOTTLE,GINGER ALE,CANADIAN,ORANGE,CARNIVAL GLASS........... 9.00
BOTTLE,GINGER ALE,G.EBBERWEIN,AMBER....................... 22.00
BOTTLE,GINGER BEER,BRIGGS,WATERTOWN,N.Y.,CROCKERY......... 4.00
BOTTLE,GINGER BEER,POTTERY................................ 3.50
BOTTLE,GLOVER'S IMPERIAL MANGE MEDICINE,6 1/2 FL.OZ.,AMBER.. 3.00
BOTTLE,GLOBER'S MANGE REMEDY,AMBER........................ 3.00
BOTTLE,GOLDEN APPLE....................................... 9.00
BOTTLE,GORDON'S GIN,LONDON................................ 3.00
BOTTLE,GORDON'S GIN,SQUARE,LIGHT GREEN.................... 5.00
BOTTLE,GRAEFENBERG CO.SARSAPARILLA COMPOUND,LABEL,CONTENTS,
  AQUA,7 IN.................................................. 25.00
BOTTLE,GRANT'S SAND FAST,THREE-SIDED,PAISLEY,SCOTLAND....... 4.00
BOTTLE,GREEN'S AUGUST FLOWER FOR DYSPEPSIA................. 4.00
BOTTLE,GROUND PONTIL,FLARING NECK,CUT BEVELED LIP,COBALT
  BLUE,FLINT................................................ 23.00
BOTTLE,GUILFORD MINERAL SPRING WATER,GUILFORD,VT.,BUBBLES,
  GREEN,QUART............................................... 32.00
BOTTLE,GUILFORD SPRINGS MINERAL WATER,9 1/2 IN............. 19.50
BOTTLE,GUITAR SHAPE,HARMONY WINE,LABEL,SPAIN,AMBER......... 7.50
BOTTLE,H.A.SMITH,WINE MERCHANT,NEWPORT.................... 50.00
BOTTLE,H.G.CO.,BEEHIVE,AQUA............................... 3.00
BOTTLE,H.J.HEINZ,PAT.1890 ON BASE,EIGHT SIDES,KEY IN SHIELD. 8.00
BOTTLE,H.LAKE INDIAN SPECIFIC,RAISED PANELS,NECK BULGE,AQUA,
  8 1/2 IN.................................................. 90.00
BOTTLE,HACK & SIMON,VINCENNES,IND.,GREEN.................. 2.50
BOTTLE,HAIG & HAIG,STERLING SILVER,BAMBOO OVERLAY.......... 32.00
BOTTLE,HAIR PRESERVATIVE & BEAUTIFIER,N.Y.,PONTIL,AQUA,7 IN. 15.00
BOTTLE,HAMLIN'S WIZARD OIL,TEAL BLUE,6 IN................. 7.00
BOTTLE,HARDEN'S HAND GRENADE,STAR,BLUE................... 15.00
BOTTLE,HARVARD RYE,SELECT STOCK,KLEIN BROS.,CIN.,O.,CIRCA
  1895...................................................... 9.00
BOTTLE,HASKINS NEVINE,LABEL............................... 6.50
BOTTLE,HATTIE & MYLIUS EPIDERMA FOR THE SKIN.............. 12.00
BOTTLE,HAWTHORN,EMERALD,PINT.............................. 16.00
BOTTLE,HAYNER WHISKEY DISTILLERY,TROY,OHIO,1897,BIMAL...... 8.00
BOTTLE,HAYNES,AMETHYST,PINT............................... 35.00
BOTTLE,HAYWARD HAND GRENADE,AQUA.......................... 20.00
BOTTLE,HEART,EMBOSSED NECKLACE,STOPPER,MASON,AMBER......... 8.00
BOTTLE,HIAWATHA SPRING WATER,APPLIED HANDLE,CERAMIC BAIL
  TOP,1883,AMBER............................................ 13.50
BOTTLE,HIPPIE,FLOWER GIRL,PAIR............................ 9.90
BOTTLE,HIRES EXTRACT,EMBOSSED LETTERS SAY FOR BREWING ROOT
  BEER AT HOME.............................................. 5.50
BOTTLE,HIRES,AMBER........................................ 25.00
BOTTLE,HOCK WINE,AMBER.................................... 3.00
BOTTLE,HOCK WINE,BLUE,QUART............................... 5.00
BOTTLE,HOLLYWOOD WHISKEY,AMBER,QUART...................... 5.00
BOTTLE,HOOD'S SARSAPARILLA....................... 3.00 TO 6.00

BOTTLE,HORLICK'S MALTED MILK,TIN LID,5 IN................... 3.50
BOTTLE,HOSTETTER'S BITTERS,APPLIED TOP,G.CO. ON BOTTOM...... 8.50
BOTTLE,HOURGLASS SHAPE,NU GRAPE,GREEN....................... 2.00
BOTTLE,HUDSON BAY,FLAT,MINATURE............................. 2.50
BOTTLE,HYG WILD CHERRY PHOSPHATE............................ 18.00
BOTTLE,I.GOLDBERG,EIGHT SIDES,APPLIED LIP,AMBER,QUART....... 7.00
BOTTLE,I.W.HARPER,MAN...................................... 65.00
BOTTLE,INK,AQUA CONE....................................... 2.50
BOTTLE,INK,AQUA UMBRELLA................................... 5.00
BOTTLE,INK,BARNACLES,POTTERY,PINT,1860..................... 10.00
BOTTLE,INK,CARTER,AMBER.................................... 12.00
BOTTLE,INK,CARTER'S,GREEN CONE............................. 6.00
BOTTLE,INK,CROCK,SANFORD,LABEL............................. 7.00
BOTTLE,INK,CUBE,CRYSTAL,HINGED STERLING SILVER TOP,INITIAL
   R.......................................................  5.00
BOTTLE,INK,DEEP BLUE,CARTERS CATHEDRAL..................... 32.00
BOTTLE,INK,DENBY,POURING SPOUT............................. 3.00
BOTTLE,INK,EIGHT FLAT SIDES,EMBOSSED PENN.MFG.WORKS,
   PHILADELPHIA,WHITE..................................... 145.00
BOTTLE,INK,EMBOSSED PENN.MFG.WORKS,PHILA.,MILK GLASS....... 145.00
BOTTLE,INK,MASTER,THREE MOLD,OLIVER AMBER,QUART............ 20.00
BOTTLE,INK,MR. & MRS. CARTER,DATED,PAIR................... 38.00
BOTTLE,INK,OCTAGON MUSHROOM SHAPE,PONTIL,AQUA.............. 32.00
BOTTLE,INK,PALE BLUE,OCTAGON PANELS,WIDE BASE,NARROW NECK,
   2 3/4 IN.TALL..........................................  6.00
BOTTLE,INK,PATENT 1886,AMBER,QUART......................... 6.00
BOTTLE,INK,ROUGH PONTIL,FULL LABEL,MAYNARD & NOYES,BOSTON... 70.00
BOTTLE,INK,ROUND TOP,NECK STICKING UP ON ONE SIDE,GROUND
   MOUTH,1 3/4 IN.........................................  7.00
BOTTLE,INK,SHAPE OF LADY'S SHOE,EMBOSSED DESIGN,ROUGH PONTIL 35.00
BOTTLE,INK,SLENDER,HANDLE,MARKED C NO.22,CROCKERY.......... 7.00
BOTTLE,INK,SQUARE,COBALT................................... 3.00
BOTTLE,INK,STAFFORD'S,MASTER POURING,AQUA,QUART............ 20.00
BOTTLE,INK,TAN,POTTERY..................................... 3.00
BOTTLE,INK,UMBRELLA,AQUA................................... 7.50
BOTTLE,INK,UMBRELLA,GOLDEN,OLIVE-AMBER TUBULAR PONTIL,BLOWN,
   NEW ENGLAND............................................ 45.00
BOTTLE,INK,UMBRELLA,OLIVE AMBER............................ 60.00
BOTTLE,INK,YELLOW AMBER CONE............................... 7.00
BOTTLE,IRISH SOLDIER....................................... 15.00
BOTTLE,IRISHMAN ON BARREL,CLEAR............................ 30.00
BOTTLE,J.R.WATKINS,8 1/2 IN................................ 2.00
BOTTLE,JACQUIN,FIGURAL,BUST OF WASHINGTON,BLUE............. 9.00
BOTTLE,JAR,A 10-CENT CIGAR FOR 5 CENTS,AMBER............... 30.00
BOTTLE,JAR,ALARM CLOCK FACE ON SIDE........................ 5.00
BOTTLE,JAR,APOTHECARY,CLEAR,GROUND STOPPER,12 IN.HIGH...... 9.50
BOTTLE,JAR,APOTHECARY,LID INVERTED IN MEASURING CUP,AMBER... 11.50
BOTTLE,JAR,APOTHECARY,PORCELAIN,FRANCE,10 1/2 IN.HIGH,PAIR.. 125.00
BOTTLE,JAR,APOTHECARY,STATUE OF LIBERTY.................... 50.00
BOTTLE,JAR,APOTHECARY,THUMBPRINT,GROUND PONTIL,BLOWN,
   MUSHROOM STOPPER.......................................  6.50
BOTTLE,JAR,BARBASOL,EIGHT-SIDED............................ 3.00
BOTTLE,JAR,EMBOSSED HORLICK'S MALTED MILK,CLEAR,LID,
   3 1/4 IN.TALL..........................................  2.00
BOTTLE,JAR,EMBOSSED OLD JUDGE COFFEE,OWL,LID,GALLON........ 6.50
BOTTLE,JAR,HONEY,FOOTED,COVER,WATERFORD CRYSTAL,
   7 1/2 IN.HIGH.......................................... 45.00
BOTTLE,JAR,KISS ME GUM,1/2 GALLON.......................... 18.00
BOTTLE,JAR,LIGHTNING,GLASS TOP,QUART....................... 2.50
BOTTLE,JAR,MR.PEANUT,EMBOSSED FIGURE,5-CENT SIGN,COVER..... 23.50
BOTTLE,JAR,NEWMAN'S PURE GOLD BAKING POWDER,FAIRPORT,N.Y.,
   TIN LID,AQUA...........................................  8.50
BOTTLE,JAR,PICKLE,ARMOUR,PANELED........................... 6.00
BOTTLE,JAR,PICKLE,GRAPES,12 1/2 IN.TALL.................... 15.00
BOTTLE,JAR,PICKLE,PARROTS,9 1/2 IN.TALL.................... 12.00
BOTTLE,JAR,PLANTERS PEANUT,PEANUT ON LID,10
   IN.HIGH......................................... 12.00 TO 17.50
BOTTLE,JAR,PLANTERS PEANUT,HEXAGON,EMBOSSED COVER,PEANUT
   FINIAL................................................. 12.50
BOTTLE,JAR,PLANTERS PEANUT,PAPER LABLE..................... 16.00
BOTTLE,JAR,PLANTERS PEANUT,SQUARE,EMBOSSED PLANTERS,COVER... 14.50
BOTTLE,JAR,POMADE,DR.L.C.DALE'S PATENT 1850,COBALT,PEWTER
   COVER.................................................. 37.00
BOTTLE,JAR,POWDER,BASE HAS STRETCH BARS,HAND-PAINTED,FOOTED,
   M.Z.,AUSTRIA........................................... 12.50
BOTTLE,JAR,POWDER,WHITE INSIDE,PEACH OVERLAY,SWIRL PATTERN,
   5 IN.TALL.............................................. 30.00
BOTTLE,JAR,RAISED PEANUTS ON FRONT & SIDES,MARKED A.H.,
   1 1/2 PINT.............................................  2.50
BOTTLE,JAR,SNUFF,MACCOBY................................... 6.00
BOTTLE,JAR,SNUFF,ORIGINAL LID,MARKED URJMAN................ 5.50

```
BOTTLE,JAR,SNUFF,P.LORILLARD.................................   8.00
BOTTLE,JAR,STORE,PEANUT,SQUIRREL,LABEL FRONT,TIN COVER,BAIL,
  WOODEN KNOB..............................................   8.50
BOTTLE,JAR,THE PEARL,SAYS PATD.AUG.23,70 & FEB.7,71,AQUA,
  PINT....................................................  20.00
BOTTLE,JAR,WESTERN ELECTRIC BATTERY,GROUND LIP..............   5.00
BOTTLE,JASBO-JIM,DANCER ON ROOF............................  25.00
BOTTLE,JENNY LIND,REVERSE GLASS FACTORY............ILLUS..  25.00
BOTTLE,JOHN RYAN 1866 CO.,BLUE.............................  25.00
BOTTLE,JOHN WYETH & BRO.,MEASURE,COBALT....................   7.75
BOTTLE,JOHN WYETH,DOSE CAP,COBALT..........................   5.00
BOTTLE,JOHNSON'S AMERICAN ANODYNE LINIMENT.................   5.00
BOTTLE,JUG,HANDLE,BOTTOM EMBOSSED MACY & JENKENS,N.Y.,AMBER.  25.00
BOTTLE,JUG,MEASURE MARKER,29-7 ATLAS HOCKING 5,BROWN,GALLON.   5.00
BOTTLE,JUG,WHISKEY,ORENE PARKER CO.,AMETHYST,GALLON........  20.00
BOTTLE,K. & L. WARNERS SAFE,PAPER LABEL....................  18.50
BOTTLE,KAHLUA TIKI GOD,BLACK...............................  12.50
```

JENNY LIND BOTTLE

```
BOTTLE,KALOPEAN HAIR DYE,NO.2,OPEN PONTIL...................   8.00
BOTTLE,KATSUP,REIF'S SPECIAL,AMBER.........................   4.00
BOTTLE,KENDELL SPAVIN CURE,AMBER...........................   5.00
BOTTLE,KIKUKAWA-UTA-HARU-HIRU..............................  12.50
BOTTLE,KILMER'S SWAMP ROOT,KIDNEY,LIVER & BLADDER CURE......   3.50
BOTTLE,KIOSK,MARIE BRIZARD.................................   8.95
BOTTLE,L.ROSE & CO.,VINE-COVERED,AQUA......................  17.50
BOTTLE,LANGLEYS,BACKWARD 9S,OPEN PONTIL....................  37.50
BOTTLE,LARKIN SOAP CO.,EMERALD GREEN,STOPPER...............   8.00
BOTTLE,LAST CHANCE JOE,CAMEO...............................  16.50
BOTTLE,LEG,LADY'S,AMBER....................................  100.00
BOTTLE,LEG,LADY'S,GREEN....................................  100.00
BOTTLE,LEIMAN BEER,BLOB TOP................................   4.00
BOTTLE,LEPRECHAUN,SAYS PLEASE GOD..........................   9.90
BOTTLE,LIME,ROSE DESIGN....................................  10.00
BOTTLE,LINCOLN,BANK........................................   2.00
BOTTLE,LION MAN............................................  29.50
BOTTLE,LIPPIZANER VETERINARY,EMBOSSED MAN,SADDLE,WHIP,GREEN,
  11 1/4 IN...............................................  20.00
BOTTLE,LIQUOZONE,PINT,BIMAL BROWN..........................   2.50
BOTTLE,LITTLE BO-PEEP AMMONIA,CLEAR........................   7.00
BOTTLE,LOCKPORT,GARGLING OIL,GREEN,LABEL...................   7.00
BOTTLE,LOG CABIN COUGH & CONSUMPTION REMEDY,AMBER..........  90.00
BOTTLE,LORILLARD,HELMET ON LID,AMBER.......................   8.50
BOTTLE,LUCKY IDOL,HAND-PAINTED,KAMOTSURU,PORCELAIN,JAPAN....  12.95
BOTTLE,LUXARDO,ALABASTER FISH,1960.................ILLUS..  40.00
BOTTLE,LUXARDO,CALYPSO GIRL................................  15.00
BOTTLE,LUXARDO,COFFEE CARAFE...............................  15.50
BOTTLE,LUXARDO,NUBIAN SLAVE................................  10.50
BOTTLE,LYON'S KATHAIRON FOR THE HAIR,OPEN PONTIL...........  11.00
BOTTLE,MALLET SHAPE,ENGRAVED FATHER TIME,CUT GLASS,CIRCA
  1840....................................................  120.00
BOTTLE,MAN,BLACK DERBY,HUGH POCKETS,CERAMIC,GERMANY........   6.50
BOTTLE,MAN,CHRISTMAS TREE,TOYS,BROWN,HANDLE,STOPPER,
  PORCELAIN,GERMANY.......................................  37.50
BOTTLE,MAN IN BLACK CAPE,ROYAL DOULTON.....................  35.00
BOTTLE,MAN IN BLACK CAPE,WADE,ENGLAND,8 IN.................  40.00
BOTTLE,MAN WITH HANDS IN BACK AGAINST STUMP OF TREE,12 IN...  12.00
BOTTLE,MALARIAL CHILL REMEDY...............................   3.00
BOTTLE,MARQUIS DE MONTESQUIO,MINIATURE.....................   9.00
BOTTLE,MASK,LAMP BASE......................................  18.50
BOTTLE,MASON,BLUE,QUART............................ILLUS..   6.00
BOTTLE,MAVRODAPHNE,A GREEK WINE,MINIATURE..................   2.50
```

LUXARDO BOTTLE, ALABASTER FISH

```
BOTTLE,MAVRODAPHNE,MINIATURE.............................       2.50
BOTTLE,MC ELREES WINE OF CARDUI,GREEN BIMAL.................     2.50
BOTTLE,MC CORMICK,PLATTE VALLEY............................      2.50
BOTTLE,MEDICINE,AQUA,HAND-BLOWN,5 IN.HIGH..................      1.00
BOTTLE,MEDICINE,BEVEL CORNERS,WIDE MOUTH,OPEN PONTIL,
    EMBOSSED IA,SQUARE......................................    10.95
BOTTLE,MEDICINE,CALCINED MAGNESIA,SQUARE,WIDE MOUTH,PONTIL,
    WHITTLED...............................................     12.00
BOTTLE,MEDICINE,FOR 40 ISACEN TABLETS,BRASS SCREW CAP,LABEL,
    AMETHYST...............................................     15.00
BOTTLE,MEDICINE,LONG NECK,GREEN KICK-UP & PONTIL,9 IN.TALL..    18.95
BOTTLE,MEDICINE,REVOLUTIONARY WAR,MARKED BRITISH BROAD
    ARROW,BLOWN............................................     25.00
BOTTLE,MEDICINE,TREATMENT OF CHOLERA,1832,PHOENIX,WOODEN
    BOX,13.................................................    130.00
BOTTLE,MERMAID,ROCKINGHAM TYPE.............................     47.50
BOTTLE,MEXICAN MUSTANG LINIMENT,OPEN PONTIL................     10.00
BOTTLE,MICROBE KILLER,AMBER,QUART..........................     50.00
BOTTLE,MILK OF MAGNESIA,U.S.PAT. AUGUST 21,1906,COBALT......     2.50
BOTTLE,MILK,ALTAMONT CREAMERY,ALTAMONT,ILL.,CLEAR..........      2.50
BOTTLE,MILK,AMBER......................................2.50 TO     8.00
BOTTLE,MILK,TIN CAP & HANDLE,PAT.1898,QUART................     10.00
BOTTLE,MILK,TIN HOLDER.....................................     35.00
BOTTLE,MILKS EMULSION,LARGE MOUTH,BROWN....................      3.50
BOTTLE,MINERAL SPRING,CONGRESS & EMPIRE SPRING CO.,WHITTLED,
    GREEN,QUART............................................     22.50
BOTTLE,MINERAL SPRING,GETTYSBURG KATALYSINE WATER,OLIVE
    GREEN,QUART............................................     30.00
BOTTLE,MINERAL WATER,CLARKE & WHITE,OLIVE GREEN,QUART.......    26.00
BOTTLE,MINERAL WATER,CONGRESS & EMPIRE SPRING CO.,GREEN,
    QUART..................................................     24.00
BOTTLE,MINERAL WATER,CONGRESS & EMPIRE SPRINGS,GREEN,PINT...     2.00
BOTTLE,MINERAL WATER,GETTYSBURG KATALYSINE,GREEN,QUART......    35.00
BOTTLE,MINERAL WATER,HATHORN SPRINGS,BROWN,PINT............     20.00
BOTTLE,MINERAL WATER,JOHN RYAN,GROUND PONTIL,COBALT........     24.00
BOTTLE,MINERAL WATER,MISSISQUOI SPRINGS,AMBER,QUART........     30.00
BOTTLE,MINERAL WATER,T.LAUGHTON SCARBOROUGH,CROWN INSIDE
    THREAD,GREEN...........................................      6.50
BOTTLE,MINERAL,GUILFORD...................................      30.00
BOTTLE,MINIATURE,HOUSE OF KOSHU,RAINBOW...................       3.50
BOTTLE,MINIATURE,RAILROAD,GIN,CONTINENTAL,PHILA...........       4.75
BOTTLE,MINIATURE,SAN MIGUEL BEER,MANILA,PHILIPPINES........      2.00
BOTTLE,MISSION DRY,BLACK...................................      7.50
BOTTLE,MOSES,AQUA.........................................      59.95
BOTTLE,MOSES,CLEAR,RICKER & SONS..........................      60.00
BOTTLE,MOXIE NERVE FOOD,BLUE-AQUA,ROUND,10 1/2 IN...........     8.50
BOTTLE,MR.BOSTON,THIN MAN,MINIATURE.......................       2.50
BOTTLE,MULFORD'S DIGESTIVE MALT EXTRACT,EMBOSSED,AMBER......     8.00
BOTTLE,MUSTANG LINIMENT FOR MAN AND BEAST.................       3.00
BOTTLE,MUSTARD PICKLE,AQUA,8 IN...........................       1.75
BOTTLE,MYAL QUALITY,BUBBLES,AMBER.........................       6.00
BOTTLE,MYERS ROCK ROSE,NEW HAVEN,COLLARED MOUTH,IRON PONTIL.    30.00
BOTTLE,NORTH OF ENGLAND SAUCE,AQUA,WOODEN PEG..............     32.00
BOTTLE,NULINESS,JOHN F.KENNEDY,IRIDESCENT BLUE.............     10.00
BOTTLE,NURSER,LAYS FLAT,TURNED UP STRETCHED TOP,THE SEASIDE.     6.50
```

```
BOTTLE,NURSING,BLUE & WHITE POTTERY.........................   35.00
BOTTLE,NURSING,MOTHER,BABY,ROCKING CHAIR,EMBOSSED MOTHER'S
  PET,GREEN..................................................   35.00
BOTTLE,NURSING,OVAL,ONE SIDE IS FLAT,OUNCE SCALE,EIGHT-POINT
  STAR,ACME.................................................     9.00
BOTTLE,NURSING,RAISED NECK,OVAL,H.WOOD & SONS...............     9.00
BOTTLE,NURSING,SUNNY BABE,SPRAWLED ON LENGTH OF ONE SIDE,
  EMBOSSED,8 OZ.............................................     7.00
BOTTLE,NURSING,THE JEWEL FEEDING BOTTLE,GOOSE NECK,AQUA.....     6.00
BOTTLE,NURSING,VIOLIN SHAPE,BURRS PAT.1872,AQUA,6 IN........    20.00
BOTTLE,OAKLAND CANADIAN MALT,LABEL,CLEAR....................     6.50
BOTTLE,OAKLAND CHEMICAL CO.,BROWN,4 IN......................     3.00
BOTTLE,OLD BUSHMILLS DISTILLERY,EMBOSSED FACTORY,DATED 1784,
  QUART....................................................      9.50
BOTTLE,OLD CASE,GIN,BUBBLES,IRON PONTIL,GREEN...............    18.00
BOTTLE,OLD DRUM WHISKEY.....................................     5.00
BOTTLE,OLD SACHEM........................110.00 TO   125.00
BOTTLE,OLNEY SODA WATER,OLNEY,ILL.,CLEAR...................      2.50
BOTTLE,ON THE TERRACE......................................     10.00
BOTTLE,ON THE TRAIL........................................      5.00
BOTTLE,ONION,BLACK.........................................    125.00
BOTTLE,ONION,BLACK,CIRCA 1700..............................     65.00
BOTTLE,ORANGE CRUSH,29 RIDGES,CLEAR........................      2.50
BOTTLE,OWL DRUG,CLEAR,4 1/4 IN.,ORANGE LABEL...............      3.75
BOTTLE,OWL,CLEAR...........................................      3.50
BOTTLE,OWL,RED,GLASS EYES..................................     12.00
BOTTLE,PALMER'S,GREEN,5 IN.................................      5.00
BOTTLE,PANELED,SAYS SMILE,DATED 1922,18 IN.HIGH............     45.00
BOTTLE,PAPER LABEL,NICE OLD PORT,BOSTON,AMBER,QUART........      5.00
BOTTLE,PAPER LABEL,OLD WAVERLY PROCESS,AMBER,QUART.........      5.00
BOTTLE,PAYNE CELERY COMPOUND,SQUARE,AMBER..................      5.00
BOTTLE,PEASANT WOMAN.......................................     10.00
BOTTLE,PEORIA,12-SIDED,WAX SEALER,POTTERY,BROWN,1/2 GALLON..     8.00
BOTTLE,PEPSI,BIRMINGHAM,AMBER..............................     15.00
BOTTLE,PEPTENZYME,CONTENTS,LABEL,8 OZ......................      9.50
BOTTLE,PERFUME,BALL SHAPE,HARVARD CUT,EMBOSSED SILVER CAP,
  CUT GLASS................................................     16.00
BOTTLE,PERFUME,BELL SHAPE,FLARED BASE,HANDLE,CORK,NICKEL
  CAP,6 IN.TALL............................................      9.00
BOTTLE,PERFUME,BLACK AMETHYST,CUBE SHAPE,MARKED QUERLAIN,
  PARIS,FRANCE.............................................     10.00
BOTTLE,PERFUME,BULBOUS,STERLING SILVER OVERLAY,STOPPER,
  7 IN.HIGH................................................     60.00
BOTTLE,PERFUME,CREAMY GROUND,MAROON FLORAL,METAL RIM,SIGNED
  RICHARD..................................................    150.00
BOTTLE,PERFUME,CRYSTAL,SILVER OVERLAY,FLORAL,BIRD,PANELS,
  GORHAM...................................................     59.50
BOTTLE,PERFUME,CUT CRYSTAL,GOLD TOP,BIRD,LEATHER CASE,
  3 3/4 IN.HIGH............................................     95.00
BOTTLE,PERFUME,DIAMONDS,SUNBURSTS,BALL STOPPER,CUT GLASS,SET
  OF FOUR..................................................     21.00
BOTTLE,PERFUME,DISK-SHAPED BODY,STOPPER,DABBER,AMBERINA,
  LALIQUE,WORTH............................................     32.00
BOTTLE,PERFUME,FLOWERS,2 DANCING FIGURES MAKE GLASS STOPPER,
  SATIN GLASS..............................................     60.00
BOTTLE,PERFUME,GLASS STOPPER,STERLING SILVER OVERLAY,CHASED
  DESIGN...................................................     24.00
BOTTLE,PERFUME,GOLD ORMOLU FRAME,PAIR......................     10.00
BOTTLE,PERFUME,GREEN,4-FOOTED ORMOLU HOLDER,40 STONES ON
  BASE,STOPPER.............................................     55.00
BOTTLE,PERFUME,HEAVY RIBBING,CLEAR CRYSTAL,STOPPER,
  PAIRPOINT,7 1/4 IN.......................................     15.00
BOTTLE,PERFUME,MINIATURE,NUDES,PORCELAIN,GERMANY,MARKED,PAIR   20.00
BOTTLE,PERFUME,OPALESCENT,HOBNAIL,STOPPER IS SMALL VASE.....     6.50
BOTTLE,PERFUME,OVAL,INVERTED RIBBING,EMBOSSED FLORAL,
  CRYSTAL,SILVER LID.......................................     13.00
BOTTLE,PERFUME,OVERALL HARVARD CUT,CUT GLASS,SILVER TOP,
  FACETED STOPPER..........................................     15.00
BOTTLE,PERFUME,PEDESTAL BASE,SWIRLED BLUE ON CLEAR,GOLD
  STOPPER,LUTZ.............................................     20.00
BOTTLE,PERFUME,PELICAN,GERMANY,MARKED,PORCELAIN............     10.00
BOTTLE,PERFUME,PINK ROSE IN BOTTLE & STOPPER,PAPERWEIGHT,
  WHITTEMORE...............................................    160.00
BOTTLE,PERFUME,PINK,BLUE,CUPID,RICKSECKER PERFUMER,N.Y.,
  PORCELAIN................................................     30.00
BOTTLE,PERFUME,RECTANGULAR,LALIQUE,3 IN. TALL..............     25.00
BOTTLE,PERFUME,SILVER FILIGREE,3 1/2 IN.TALL...............     12.50
BOTTLE,PERFUME,STERLING SILVER OVERLAY,LEAF DECOR,BALL
  STOPPER,2 3/4 IN.........................................     12.00
BOTTLE,PERFUME,STERLING SILVER OVERLAY,MONOGRAM,PAIR.......     27.50
BOTTLE,PERFUME,STOPPER,DAISY & BUTTON,PRESSED GLASS,
```

```
        5 1/2 IN.HIGH,PAIR.........................................    15.00
BOTTLE,PERFUME,THOUSAND-EYE,BULBOUS,5 1/2 IN.TALL...........    12.50
BOTTLE,PERFUME,YELLOW ROSES,PAPERWEIGHT,STOPPER,WHITTEMORE..   150.00
BOTTLE,PERRINE'S APPLE GINGER,CABIN........................    78.00
BOTTLE,PERSIAN SADDLE,BLUE-GREEN...........................    13.00
BOTTLE,PERUNA..............................................     4.00
BOTTLE,PETT'S BALD EAGLE WHISKEY,BOSTON,MASS...............     3.50
BOTTLE,PICKLE,CATHEDRAL,FOUR DOORS,I.G.CO.,AQUA,WOODEN PEG,
        8 3/4 IN...........................................    10.00
BOTTLE,PICNIC FLASK,SMALL BIMAL............................     3.00
BOTTLE,PIG SHAPE,READS AMERICAN BITTERS,AMBER..............     8.00
BOTTLE,PIG,SUFFOLK'S BITTERS,AMBER.........................   135.00
BOTTLE,PIKES PEAK,OLD RYE,PITTSBURGH,1/2 PINT..............    45.00
BOTTLE,PINE TREE TAR CORDIAL,GREEN.........................    35.00
BOTTLE,PIONEER SODA WORKS,RENO,NEVADA,LIGHT GREEN..........     5.00
BOTTLE,PLATTE VALLEY MISSOURI STRAIGHT CORN WHISKEY,PINT,
        POTTERY............................................     6.00
BOTTLE,POISON,AMBER........................................     5.00
BOTTLE,POISON,BROWN,3-SIDED................................     2.00
BOTTLE,POISON,COBALT BLUE,SQUARE,CORRUGATED ON TWO SIDES,
        2 1/4 IN.HIGH......................................     4.00
BOTTLE,POISON,EMBOSSED,HEXAGONAL,GROUND STOPPER,COBALT,
        5 3/4 IN.TALL......................................    17.50
BOTTLE,POISON,LATTICE,POINTS, USPHS,  BUBBLES,COBALT,
        1/2 GALLON.........................................    90.00
BOTTLE,POISON,OWL,COBALT,2 3/4 IN..........................    12.50
BOTTLE,POISON,THREE-SIDED,AMBER............................     2.50
BOTTLE,POISON,VAPO CRESOLENE,S IS REVERSED,DATED JULY 23,
        1894,4 IN.HIGH.....................................     4.50
BOTTLE,POISON,WYETH,COBALT,1 1/2 IN.DIAMETER,2 1/2 IN.HIGH..     3.75
BOTTLE,POLAND SPRINGS,MOSES,CLEAR..........................    35.00
BOTTLE,POLAND WATER,CLEAR,AMETHYST,H.RICKER & SONS,
        PROPRIETORS,AT BASE................................    80.00
BOTTLE,POP,AGATE SEALER....................................    15.00
BOTTLE,POP,PALMER COX BROWNIE..............................     6.50
BOTTLE,POP,RUBBER GASKET & WIRE LOOP INSIDE NECK,HAND BLOWN,
        HUTCHINSON.........................................     4.00
BOTTLE,POP,WIRE LOOP CONTROLLED RUBBER GASKET IN NECK,
        HUTCHINSON,AQUA....................................     4.00
BOTTLE,POP,WORD SMILE ON TWO SIDES,MESH-DESIGNED PANELS,
        PAT.7-11-1922......................................     3.50
BOTTLE,PORTER,LONG LADY'S LEG TYPE NECK,LATE 18TH CENTURY...   125.00
BOTTLE,PORTER,LONG NECK,OPEN PONTIL,FREE BLOWN,BLACK GLASS,
        CIRCA 1750.........................................    38.00
BOTTLE,PORTRAIT,WHITE,PORCELAIN,2 IN.,PAIR.................     3.00
BOTTLE,POWDER HORN,GROUND MOUTH,CLEAR,PEWTER TOP...........    16.00
BOTTLE,POWDER HORN,PRESSED GLASS,HANG UP...................     8.00
BOTTLE,PRICKLY ASH BITTERS,MACHINE.........................    15.00
BOTTLE,PURE FOOD SODA WATER CENTRALIA,ILL.,CLEAR...........     2.50
BOTTLE,PURE FOOD SODA WATER,CENTRALIA,ILL..................     2.00
BOTTLE,QUALITY BEVERAGE,MURPHYBORO,ILL.,CLEAR..............     2.50
BOTTLE,QUININE,GROUND STOPPER,COBALT.......................     7.50
BOTTLE,RADWAYS SARSAPARILLIAN,ENTD.ACCORD TO ACT OF
        CONGRESS,1/2 PINT..................................    12.00
BOTTLE,RAINEY'S CHILL REMEDY...............................     2.00
BOTTLE,RAVEN,BLACK.........................................    29.95
BOTTLE,RETONGA TONIC.......................................     3.00
BOTTLE,REVOLVER,TIN SCREW CAP,AMBER,9 1/2 IN...............    22.00
BOTTLE,ROLLING PIN,CORK....................................     9.00
BOTTLE,ROLLING PIN,SCREW CAP...............................     5.50
BOTTLE,ROSES LIME JUICE,14 IN..............................    10.50
BOTTLE,ROUND THE WORLD,STRATOSPHERE BALLOON,P.LUX,D.SHERMAN
        CORP...............................................    16.50
BOTTLE,ROYAL RUBY RED,QUART................................     7.50
BOTTLE,ROYAL RUBY SCHLITZ,LABEL,7 OZ.......................    25.00
BOTTLE,RUM,IMPRESSED OBER-SELTENS,NASSAU,HANDLE,LABEL,
        EARTHENWARE........................................    12.00
BOTTLE,RUMFORD,EMBOSSED,BLUE,4 1/2 IN......................     4.00
BOTTLE,RUMFORD,GREEN,EMBOSSED,4 1/2 IN.....................     4.00
BOTTLE,RUSHS BUCHU & IRON,A.H.FLANDERS,M.D.,NEW YORK,AQUA,
        PINT...............................................    15.00
BOTTLE,S.CLAY MILLER,UNION OVAL,LIGHT GOLD-AMBER...........    18.00
BOTTLE,S.O.DUNBAR,HALF PINT,AQUA...........................     9.50
BOTTLE,SAKE JUG,PINCHED SIDES,APPLIED DANCING FIGURE,1850,
        BIZENWARE..........................................    38.00
BOTTLE,SALLIANO,FIGURAL,SOLDIER,FIFTH......................     8.00
BOTTLE,SALT SAUCE,ROUGH PONTIL,INITIALS H.C.K.,AQUA........    35.00
BOTTLE,SARATOGA LINCOLN WATER,AMBER,PORCELAIN STOPPER......    20.00
BOTTLE,SARATOGA STAR SPRING,AMBER,QUART....................    20.00
BOTTLE,SARATOGA,BLOP TOP,CONGRESS & EMPIRE SPRING CO.,
        EMERALD GREEN,PINT.................................    22.50
```

```
BOTTLE,SARATOGA,CONGRESS & EMPIRE SPRINGS,EMPIRE WATER......     18.00
BOTTLE,SARATOGA,DARK GREEN,C.W.WESTON & CO.,PINT............     27.00
BOTTLE,SARSAPARILLA,AYER'S..................................     50.00
BOTTLE,SAXLEHNER BITTERQUELLE...............................     10.50
BOTTLE,SCENT,BLUE,ELONGATED ROSETTE DESIGN,SANDWICH GLASS,
  2 3/4 IN.................................................      44.00
BOTTLE,SCENT,DUCK-BILL,CARVED,WHITE OVER CITRON,LAY-DOWN,
  CAMEO,ENGLAND...........................................      450.00
BOTTLE,SCENT,OPAQUE,STEIGEL.................................     25.00
BOTTLE,SCENT,WHITE FLOWER,ACORN,SILVER BALL-SHAPED TOP,5 IN.    300.00
BOTTLE,SCHERAZADE,WITH BOX..................................     65.00
BOTTLE,SCOTCH,HAND-DECORATED,IRIS,FLORAL,GOLD,HANDLE,
  STOPPER,PORCELAIN.......................................       24.00
BOTTLE,SCOTT'S EMULSION,COD LIVER OIL,FISHERMAN WITH FISH,
  OVAL,AQUA...............................................        2.75
BOTTLE,SCOTT'S EMULSION COD LIVER OIL,WITH LIME & SODA,AQUA.      4.00
BOTTLE,SEAL,BLACK,A.S.C.R..................................      75.00
BOTTLE,SELTZER,BLUE-GREEN...................................      3.00
BOTTLE,SELTZER,DR.PEPPER,HEX-SIDED,BROWN....................     13.00
BOTTLE,SELTZER,MAE WEST,BLUE,SIPHON TUBE,PEWTER TOP,
  12 IN.TALL.............................................        15.00
BOTTLE,SELTZER,METAL CASINGS,SIPHON.........................      7.50
BOTTLE,SHAMPOODLE,COBALT....................................     14.00
BOTTLE,SHEEHAN'S MALT WHISKEY,CLEAR.........................      5.00
BOTTLE,SHOE-SHAPED,CURLED TOE,CLEAR,EMBOSSED PHALON & SON,
  N.Y.,5 IN..............................................        10.00
BOTTLE,SHOOFLY,CLEAR,QUART..................................     12.00
BOTTLE,SHOOFLY,EMBOSSED STAR,AMBER..........................      8.00
BOTTLE,SHOOFLY FLASK,BIMAL..................................      3.00
BOTTLE,SHOOFLY,TEAL BLUE,QUART..............................     15.00
BOTTLE,SICILIAN SOLDIER,GOLD COLOR..........................     15.00
BOTTLE,SILVER DOLLAR WHISKEY,CAP IS COLLAPSIBLE SHOT GLASS,
  PINT...................................................         6.00
BOTTLE,SIPHON,COMPLETELY FLUTED,CLEAR,CZECHOSLOVAKIA........      5.75
BOTTLE,SIPHON,ETCHED WESTERN SODA WORKS.....................      5.00
BOTTLE,SIPHON,MAE WEST,TAPERED,DARK BLUE....................     15.00
BOTTLE,SIPHON,SIPHON TUBE,PEWTER TOP,BOTTLER'S NAME IN
  RAISED LETTERS.........................................         5.00
BOTTLE,SITTING BEAR........................................       3.00
BOTTLE,SMELLING SALTS,STERLING SILVER OVERLAY & TOP,GREEN
  GLASS..................................................         6.50
BOTTLE,SMELLING,STIEGEL-TYPE................................     45.00
BOTTLE,SMELLING,STIEGEL-TYPE,DIAMOND DESIGN,SHEARED LIP,
  ROUGH PONTIL...........................................        65.00
BOTTLE,SNUFF,AGATE,FISH FORM,BROWN,MALACHITE STOPPER,CHIEN
  LUNG MARK..............................................        70.00
BOTTLE,SNUFF,AMBER,CARVED,WOMAN HOLDING FAN,ATTENDANTS,
  TREES,CHINA............................................       130.00
BOTTLE,SNUFF,BLUE OVERLAY,PAINTED SCENES INSIDE,GREEN TOP...     30.00
BOTTLE,SNUFF,BLUE,PAINTED INSIDE,ORIENTAL MAN & WOMAN,MARKED
  CHINA..................................................        27.50
BOTTLE,SNUFF,BLUE,WHITE,PORCELAIN,2 3/4 IN..................     80.00
BOTTLE,SNUFF,CHINESE CHARACTER WRITING & CARVING,IVORY,
  2 3/4 IN...............................................        21.50
BOTTLE,SNUFF,CHLOROMELANITE,FORM OF CUCUMBER,CORAL TOAD
  STOPPER,CHINA..........................................        40.00
BOTTLE,SNUFF,CORAL,CARVED,TWO BOYS,BATS,CORAL STOPPER.......    150.00
BOTTLE,SNUFF,CORAL,DRAGON & PHOENIX HANDLES,BOYS,FLORAL,FU
  LION STOPPER...........................................       230.00
BOTTLE,SNUFF,CRYSTALLINE GREEN CORUNDUM,RUBY & BLACK MOTTLE.    275.00
BOTTLE,SNUFF,DEEP RED,CYLINDRICAL,JADE STOPPER,2 IN.........     50.00
BOTTLE,SNUFF,DOUBLE BOTTLE OF MALACHITE & SILVER WITH INLAID
  STONES.................................................        90.00
BOTTLE,SNUFF,FIGURAL,MONKEY,PEACH TREE ON SIDE,HORN,STOPPER,
  CHINA..................................................       100.00
BOTTLE,SNUFF,FISH,SHELL,WAVES,CARVED,AMETHYST,BUBBLE STOPPER    135.00
BOTTLE,SNUFF,FRUIT-FORM.19TH CENTURY,AMBER..................    575.00
BOTTLE,SNUFF,GILDED METAL,18TH-19TH CENTURY................     475.00
BOTTLE,SNUFF,HELMES RAILROAD MILLS..........................     11.00
BOTTLE,SNUFF,INSIDE LANDSCAPE,PEKING GLASS,3 1/4 IN.........     19.50
BOTTLE,SNUFF,IVORY,CARVED MAN,TREE,ETCHED DEER,BIRD,TEAK
  STAND,2 3/4 IN.........................................        37.50
BOTTLE,SNUFF,JADE,MUTTONFAT,3 IN............................    125.00
BOTTLE,SNUFF,JAPANESE,LACQUE-BURGAUTE.......................    525.00
BOTTLE,SNUFF,LAPIS LAZULI,BLUE,GRAY & GOLD FLECKS,TURQUOISE
  STOPPER................................................       185.00
BOTTLE,SNUFF,LAPIS LAZULI,CARVED,CORAL STOPPER.......ILLUS..    300.00
BOTTLE,SNUFF,LAPIS LAZULI,HEART SHAPE,BLUE,TURQUOISE STOPPER    160.00
BOTTLE,SNUFF,LAQUE BURGUATE,MOTHER-OF-PEARL INLAY,HEXAGONAL,
  STAND..................................................       180.00
BOTTLE,SNUFF,MALACHITE.....................................     250.00
```

```
BOTTLE,SNUFF,MAN,LADY,CARVED,CHINA,PAIR....................  145.00
BOTTLE,SNUFF,MOSS AGATE,AVENTURINE STOPPER,PEKING GLASS.....   45.00
BOTTLE,SNUFF,MOTHER-OF-PEARL,19TH CENTURY..................  400.00
BOTTLE,SNUFF,MOTHER-OF-PEARL,CARVED DRAGONS................  145.00
BOTTLE,SNUFF,MOTHER-OF-PEARL,CARVED INSECT DECOR...........   95.00
BOTTLE,SNUFF,MOTHER-OF-PEARL,EIGHTEEN LOHAN FIGURES,DRAGON,
  CARVED..................................................   60.00
BOTTLE,SNUFF,MOTHER-OF-PEARL,GOLD,SILVER INLAY,JADE STOPPER,
  CHIEN LUNG..............................................  175.00
BOTTLE,SNUFF,MOTTLED GREEN-BEIGE JADE,JADE STOPPER,2 3/4 IN.  250.00
BOTTLE,SNUFF,MOUNTAIN SCENE ON ONE SIDE,BIRD,BRANCH ON
  OTHER,CHINA.............................................   35.00
BOTTLE,SNUFF,OPAL,BAT,CLOUD MOTIFS,CARVED,CORAL STOPPER,
  WOODEN STAND............................................  250.00
BOTTLE,SNUFF,OPAL,FIGURES,LIONS,CORAL STOPPER........ILLUS..  475.00
BOTTLE,SNUFF,OPAL,VARIEGATED,PREDOMINATE GREEN,CARVED
  DRAGONS,LAPIS TOP.......................................  400.00
BOTTLE,SNUFF,OPAL,WOMAN,BRIDGE,HOUSE,CORAL STOPPER...ILLUS..  625.00
BOTTLE,SNUFF,OPEN PONTIL,FREE-BLOWN,OLIVE GREEN............   45.00
BOTTLE,SNUFF,PAINTED INSIDE................................   32.00
BOTTLE,SNUFF,PEKING ENAMEL,RESERVES OF WOMEN IN GARDEN,
  YELLOW GROUND...........................................   90.00
BOTTLE,SNUFF,PEKING GLASS,RED,WHITE,TIGER'S-EYE STOPPER.....  150.00
BOTTLE,SNUFF,PINK,URN SHAPE,GREEN STOPPER..................   30.00
BOTTLE,SNUFF,ROBED LADIES,SCENERY,PAGODA,CARVED,IVORY,SIGNED   20.00
BOTTLE,SNUFF,ROCK CRYSTAL,INTERIOR-PAINTED.................  700.00
BOTTLE,SNUFF,ROCK CRYSTAL,QUARTZ STOPPER...................  150.00
BOTTLE,SNUFF,ROSE TOURMALINE,1850-1920.....................  700.00
BOTTLE,SNUFF,RUBY MATRIX,1800-1900.........................  750.00
```

LAPIS LAZULI SNUFF BOTTLE     OPAL SNUFF BOTTLE, LIONS     OPAL SNUFF BOTTLE,
                                                                WOMAN

```
BOTTLE,SNUFF,SAPPHIRE MATRIX,AMETHYSTINE QUARTZ STOPPER.....  125.00
BOTTLE,SNUFF,SHADES OF BLUE,BROWN,GOLD,CLOISONNE...........   75.00
BOTTLE,SNUFF,SILVER INLAY OF DRAGON AMONG CLOUDS,STOPPER,
  2 3/4 IN.HIGH...........................................   99.50
BOTTLE,SNUFF,SMOKE CRYSTAL,INTERIOR-PAINTED...............  350.00
BOTTLE,SNUFF,TAO KUANG,FIGURES IN FAMILLE ROSE,AGATE
  STOPPER,PORCELAIN.......................................  200.00
BOTTLE,SNUFF,TURQUOISE,FISH FORM,SCROLLING WAVES,MATCHING
  STOPPER.................................................  130.00
BOTTLE,SNUFF,TURQUOISE,FLATTENED HEART SHAPE,CORAL STOPPER..  100.00
BOTTLE,SNUFF,WHITE JADE,CARVED BOTH SIDES,CARNELIAN TOP,
  STAND,3 3/4 IN..........................................  265.00
BOTTLE,SNUFF,WHITE JADE,CARVED,TWO PEACHES,CORAL STOPPER,
  2 1/4 IN................................................  160.00
BOTTLE,SODA,BLOB,AMOS GORDON,TANNERSVILLE,N.Y.,WIRE PLUNGER,
  CLAMP...................................................    4.00
BOTTLE,SODA,BRIDGETON GLASS WORKS,N.J.,AQUA...............   12.00
BOTTLE,SODA,CANADA DRY,RED,GOLD,BEADED,CARNIVAL GLASS.......   10.00
BOTTLE,SODA,HENRY KUCK,CIRCLE SLUGPLATE,GREEN.............   22.00
BOTTLE,SODA,HUTCHINSON,WIRE LOOP CONTROLS RUBBER GASKET
  INSIDE NECK,AQUA........................................    4.00
BOTTLE,SODA,JOHN RYAN,1866,COBALT.........................   14.00
BOTTLE,SODA,MISSION,BLACK GLASS...........................    4.00
BOTTLE,SODA,RUSSELL,AQUA..................................    8.00
BOTTLE,SODA,SAYS SMILE,LIGHT BLUE,DATED 1922,20 IN...........   32.00
BOTTLE,SODA,THOMAS MAHER,DYOTTVILLE GLASS WORKS,SQUAT,GREEN.   35.00
BOTTLE,SODA,TORPEDO,BLOB TOP,AQUA.........................    3.00
BOTTLE,SODA,VON HARTEN & GROGEN,GREEN.....................   14.00
BOTTLE,SODA,W.EAGLE VESTRY,VARICK & CANAL STS.,PREMM SODA
  WATER,1840..............................................   10.00
BOTTLE,SODA WATER,EMBOSSED STAR,PINCHED NECK,MARBLE STOPPER
```

```
    INSIDE NECK......................................................  6.00
BOTTLE,SODA WATER,GLASS MARBLE STOPPER INSIDE NECK,EMBOSSED
    STAR,AQUA.......................................................  6.00
BOTTLE,SODA WATER,RUBBER GASKET,WIRE LOOP INSIDE NECK,
    HUTCHINSON,AQUA.................................................  4.00
BOTTLE,SODA WATER,SUNKEN & PINCHED NECK,GLASS MARBLE
    STOPPER,AQUA....................................................  6.00
BOTTLE,SPARK PLUG...................................................  8.00
BOTTLE,SPARKS,MINER................................................. 12.50
BOTTLE,SPIRIT,FOUR PARTS BLOWN INTO ONE............................. 35.00
BOTTLE,SPIRITS,FOUR PARTS,FRANCE.................................... 44.00
BOTTLE,SPRING WATER,CLYSMIC,LABEL,BLOB TOP,GREEN,ONE QUART.. 12.00
BOTTLE,SQUARE SHAPE,SAYS JAMES FOLSOM,SHIP'S APOTHECARY,
    BOSTON,1880.....................................................  9.50
BOTTLE,SQUARE,OLD EYE,STOPPER IS EYECUP MARKED WYETH CO.,
    COBALT BLUE.....................................................  5.00
BOTTLE,STEIGEL TYPE,ENAMEL,18TH CENTURY............................. 75.00
BOTTLE,STONEWARE GINGER BEER,SIGNED J C IN COBALT..............  8.00
BOTTLE,STRIKOW,FERTILITY GODDESS.................................... 17.50
BOTTLE,STRIKOW,TOTEM POLE........................................... 15.90
BOTTLE,STRIKOW,WATER JUG............................................ 24.90
BOTTLE,SWIRLED WHITE ON CLEAR STRIPES,POLISHED PONTIL,BLOWN,
    12 1/4 IN....................................................... 38.00
BOTTLE,SYPHON,ETCHED WESTERN SODA WORKS.............................  5.00
BOTTLE,SYRUP,OCTAGON,PULMONIC SYRUP WRITTEN IN RELIEF,CIRCA
    1800............................................................ 45.00
BOTTLE,TAYLOR CASTLE.......................................... 8.50 TO 12.00
BOTTLE,TEAPOT,ENGLISH RUM,PRESSED GLASS,5 1/2 IN................... 50.00
BOTTLE,TEAR,PRESSED SWIRL DESIGN,CUT NOTCHES ON SIDES,ENAMEL
    DECOR........................................................... 18.00
BOTTLE,TENILINE FOR SORE THROATS,GIRAFFE FRONT,AQUA.........  5.00
BOTTLE,THE CUTICURA SYSTEM OF CURING CONSTITUTIONAL HUMORS..  6.00
BOTTLE,THE GREAT DR.KILMERS SWAMP ROOT.......................  6.00
BOTTLE,THE HERO,QUART.............................................. 12.00
BOTTLE,THE OLD BUSH MILL EST.1784.................................. 15.00
BOTTLE,THOMAS ELECTRIC OIL,INTERNAL & EXTERNAL.................  3.00
BOTTLE,THOMPSONS BEEF,WINE & IRON,LABEL..........................  9.00
BOTTLE,THOMPSONS WILD CHERRY PHOSPHATE,AQUA...................  7.50
BOTTLE,THREAD MEDICINE BOTTLE,EMBOSSED PAT.DATE,LABEL,AMBER.  7.50
BOTTLE,THREE-PIECE MOLD,BLACK GLASS,PINT.........................  3.00
BOTTLE,THREE-PIECE MOLD,BLACK GLASS,QUART........................  5.00
BOTTLE,TIDDLE,COBALT,PAIR.........................................  5.00
BOTTLE,TOMPKINS CHEMISTS,271 WASHINGTON ST.,BOSTON,MILK
    GLASS,7 1/2 IN.................................................. 18.00
BOTTLE,TONIC,KKK................................................... 15.00
BOTTLE,TORPEDO,BLOB TOP............................................  5.00
BOTTLE,TREE OF LIFE,FITZGERALD....................................  6.00
BOTTLE,TSUNDURU,RED BUCKET......................................... 17.50
BOTTLE,TSUNDURU,RED BUCKET,MINIATURE.............................. 10.00
BOTTLE,TURLINGTON,BALSAM OF LIFE..................................  5.00
BOTTLE,TURTLE, MERRY CHRISTMAS  ON STOMACH,TIN SCREW CAP,
    5 1/2 IN....................................................... 10.00
BOTTLE,TURTLE,CLEAR,5 1/2 X 4 IN.................................. 20.00
BOTTLE,TURTLE,HEAD IS STOPPER,AMBER,4 1/2 X 2 1/2 IN........ 40.00
BOTTLE,TWO-MOLD TOP,THREE-MOLD BASE,OLIVE-AMBER,10 IN....... 10.00
BOTTLE,UNDERREINER,EFFINGHAM,ILL.,GREEN..........................  2.00
BOTTLE,UNION BOTTLING WORKS,CENTRALIA,ILL.,GREEN.............  2.50
BOTTLE,UNION EAGLE,AQUA,1/2 PINT.................................. 35.00
BOTTLE,UNION,HANDS & EAGLE,BLUE................................... 45.00
BOTTLE,VALALPHO WOLFE'S AROMATIC SCHNAPPS,HONEY AMBER.......  8.00
BOTTLE,VANDENBURG,BLOB & PAPER SEAL............................... 60.00
BOTTLE,VAUGHNS VEGETABLE LITHONTRIPTIC MIXTURE,BUFFALO,AQUA,
    PINT........................................................... 25.00
BOTTLE,VAUGHNS VEGETABLE LITHONTRIPTIC MIXTURE,BUFFALO,AQUA,
    QUART.......................................................... 18.00
BOTTLE,VIARENGO,CHICKEN ON NEST.................................. 12.00
BOTTLE,VIARENGO,CLOWN............................................  8.50
BOTTLE,VIARENGO,SKIER............................................  8.50
BOTTLE,VICENTE BOSCH,BADALONA,MINIATURE..........................  4.00
BOTTLE,VINAIGRETTE,CHASED SPIRALS ON BODY,GREEK KEY BORDER,
    OVAL,GOLD......................................................120.00
BOTTLE,VINEGAR WINE..............................................  5.00
BOTTLE,VINEGAR,CLEAR,HEISEY,SIGNED,5 IN.......................... 10.00
BOTTLE,VINEGAR,ETCHED,DATED...................................... 12.00
BOTTLE,VIOLIN,AMBER,6 IN......................................... 10.00
BOTTLE,VIOLIN,CLEAR,6 IN.........................................  8.00
BOTTLE,VIOLIN,COBALT.............................................  2.50
BOTTLE,VIOLIN,COBALT BLUE........................................  5.00
BOTTLE,VIOLIN,COBALT,10 IN....................................... 15.00
BOTTLE,VIOLIN,COBALT,8 IN,HIGH,PAIR..............................  7.00
BOTTLE,VIOLIN,PALE BLUE,BRACKET,MUSIC SCALE ON BACK,10 IN... 20.00
```

BOTTLE,WARES FISCH BITTERS.............................................. 150.00
BOTTLE,WARNERS COMPOUND A DIURETIC,LABEL,CONTENTS,AMBER,
7 IN............................................................. 20.00
BOTTLE,WARNERS K & L REMEDY,BLOB LIP,16 OZ.......... 9.00 TO 18.00
BOTTLE,WARNERS KIDNEY & LIVER CURE,HONEY AMBER...... 8.50 TO 15.00
BOTTLE,WARNERS SAFE CURE,LABEL............................... 12.00
BOTTLE,WARNERS SAFE CURE,ROCHESTER,N.Y.,ENGLAND,CANADA,AMBER 60.00
BOTTLE,WARNERS SAFE KIDNEY & LIVER CURE,SAFE HINGES ON LEFT
SIDE............................................................. 35.00
BOTTLE,WARNERS SAFE REMEDIES,AQUA............................ 17.00
BOTTLE,WARNERS SAFE RHEUMATIC CURE.......................... 34.00
BOTTLE,WASHINGTON CENTENNIAL,CLEAR CALABASH,1932............ 6.50
BOTTLE,WATER,MINERAL,POLAND SPRINGS,MAINE,HIRIAM RICKER..... 35.00
BOTTLE,WATER,SARATOGA CONGRESS.............................. 24.00
BOTTLE,WATER,STRAWBERRY,DIAMOND,FAN,CUT GLASS............... 22.50
BOTTLE,WEDDERBURN RYE,LABEL,EMBOSSED,AMBER.................. 7.00
BOTTLE,WHISKEY,AMBER,GLASS SCREW TOP,PAT.1861,PINT.......... 6.00
BOTTLE,WHISKEY,BELL,GOLDEN WEDDING,MARIGOLD,PINT............ 12.00
BOTTLE,WHISKEY,BELLE OF ANDERSON,EMBOSSED FIVE-POINT STAR,
MILK GLASS....................................................... 36.50
BOTTLE,WHISKEY,BRUNSING,TOLLE & POSTEL,INC.,QUART,AMBER..... 20.00
BOTTLE,WHISKEY,DUFF'S MALT,AMBER............................ 5.75
BOTTLE,WHISKEY,DUFFY MALT,AMBER............................. 1.00
BOTTLE,WHISKEY,DUFFY'S MALT,ROCHESTER,N.Y.,PATENT 1886,
AMBER,10 IN.HIGH................................................. 4.95
BOTTLE,WHISKEY,DUFFY'S MALT,1886,AMBER...................... 12.00
BOTTLE,WHISKEY,EMBOSSED HOLLYWOOD WHISKEY,AMBER,QUART....... 8.50
BOTTLE,WHISKEY,GOLD & WHITE DECOR,ENAMEL,BLOWN,FLINT,HANDLE,
GREEN............................................................ 65.00
BOTTLE,WHISKEY,GOLDEN WEDDING,CLEAR,EMBOSSED,PINT.......... 7.50
BOTTLE,WHISKEY,I.E.GOLDBERG,NEW YORK,N.Y.,AMBER............. 8.00
BOTTLE,WHISKEY,KEYSTONE,SAN JOSE,CALIFORNIA................. 32.50
BOTTLE,WHISKEY,KUMMEL BEAR,GREEN,LABEL IN RUSSIAN WRITING... 50.00
BOTTLE,WHISKEY,LABELS,CUSHING PROCESS,BOSTON,LIGHTHOUSE,
AMBER,QUART...................................................... 5.00
BOTTLE,WHISKEY,OLD LEXINGTON CLUB,EMBOSSED,AMBER............ 22.50
BOTTLE,WHISKEY,ROTH & CUTTER................................ 8.00
BOTTLE,WHISKEY,RUTHERFORD & KAY,AMBER....................... 6.00
BOTTLE,WHISKEY,S.C.BOEHM & CO.,SHEAF OF WHEAT & 1876 IN
SHIELD........................................................... 8.00
BOTTLE,WHISKEY,SAYS FELS WHISKEY,KANSAS CITY,INSIDE IS WELL,
ROPE,BUCKET...................................................... 30.00
BOTTLE,WHISKEY,SILVER DOLLAR,CLEAR,EMBOSSED,PINT........... 7.50
BOTTLE,WHISKEY,THREE-MOLD,BROWN............................. 4.00
BOTTLE,WHISKEY,THREE-MOLD,GREEN............................. 4.00
BOTTLE,WHISKEY,TWO-MOLD,DOUBLE COLLAR NECK,WHITTLED,
BLUE-GREEN....................................................... 10.00
BOTTLE,WHISKEY,UDOLPHO WOLFE SCHNAPPS,HONEY-AMBER,QUART..... 7.00
BOTTLE,WHISKEY,VIOLIN SHAPE,AMBER........................... 10.00
BOTTLE,WHISKEY,WALKER'S KILMARROCK,CORKER,AQUA,10 1/2 IN.... 17.50
BOTTLE,WHITEHOUSE VINEGAR,LID............................... 6.00
BOTTLE,WHITTLE,BUBBLES,GRAPHITE PONTIL,THREE-MOLD,OLIVE
AMBER,11 IN.HIGH................................................. 20.00
BOTTLE,WHITTLED,CYLINDRICAL,CONGRESS SPRING CO.,SARATOGA
SPRINGS,N.Y...................................................... 14.00
BOTTLE,WINE HOCK,BROKEN OUTSIDE BUBBLE,IMPROVED PONTIL,
FREE-BLOWN,AMBER................................................. 23.50
BOTTLE,WINE HOCK,COBALT..................................... 30.00
BOTTLE,WINE,BULBOUS PEAR-SHAPED,RED,CLEAR,SUNK HONEYCOMB,
D.D.ACKERMAN..................................................... 39.50
BOTTLE,WINE,BUNCH OF GRAPES SHAPE,CLEAR..................... 5.00
BOTTLE,WINE,EMBOSSED,APPLIED HANDLES,CROCKERY,GERMANY....... 4.00
BOTTLE,WINE,FIGURAL,BUNCH OF GRAPES,PURPLE,CLEAR STOPPER,
PAIR............................................................. 22.50
BOTTLE,WINE,FLINTLOCK PISTOL,PORCELAIN,16 IN.LONG.......... 8.50
BOTTLE,WINE,FOUR COLUMNS,HAND-BLOWN......................... 16.50
BOTTLE,WINE,HONEY AMBER,EARLY 18TH CENTURY,6 IN.TALL....... 35.00
BOTTLE,WINE,MINIATURE,THIN NECK,BLUE-GREEN,4 IN............. 2.50
BOTTLE,WINE,MONKEY AROUND,GREEN............................. 5.00
BOTTLE,WINE,ROUGH PONTIL,EARLY 18TH CENTURY................ 45.00
BOTTLE,WINE,ROUGH PONTIL,OLIVE GREEN,ELLENVILLE,N.Y.,PINT.. 22.00
BOTTLE,WINSLOWS SOOTHING SYRUP,OPEN PONTIL.................. 10.00
BOTTLE,WISTAR,OLIVE GREEN,CIRCA 1730,7 1/4 IN............... 95.00
BOTTLE,WM.RADAM MICROBE KILLER,EMBOSSED MAN,SKELETON,AMBER,
QUART............................................................ 40.00
BOTTLE,WOLFS MT.CARMEL BOTTLING,MT.CARMEL,ILL.,CLEAR........ 2.50
BOTTLE,WYETH DOSE,LABEL,CONTENTS............................ 7.00
BOTTLE,WYETH,MEASURE,STOPPER,COBALT......................... 9.00
BOTTLE,YERBA BUENA,PINT..................................... 60.00
BOTTLE,ZIMMERMAN,HAT........................................ 15.00

BOW FIGURAL CANDLESTICKS, C. 1755

```
BOW,CANDLESTICK,PAIR,FIGURAL,CIRCA 1755...............ILLUS..1,250.00
BOW,GARNITURE,3-PIECE,FLOWER-ENCRUSTED,CIRCA 1760...........1,550.00
BOW,STAND,SWEETMEAT,MONKEY,CIRCA 1755-60,5 1/4 IN. HIGH.....1,050.00
BOW,VASE,RETICULATED RIM,CIRCA 1760.........................  50.00
```

```
        BOXES OF ALL KINDS ARE COLLECTED. THEY WERE MADE OF
    THIN STRIPS OF INLAID WOOD,METAL,TORTOISESHELL,
    EMBROIDERY,OR OTHER MATERIAL.
BOX,SEE ALSO,STORE,TIN,SNUFF
BOX,ALMS,CARVED LID,FIGURES,SILVER MALTESE CROSS,1840,
    MAHOGANY........................................................  89.50
BOX,BAYUK PHILLIES PERFECTO,TIN,7 1/4 X 5 1/2 X 3 IN........   4.00
BOX,BIBLE,INCISED CHAIN OF ELONGATED OVALS,HINGE,OAK,26 X
    8 IN.HIGH...................................................... 200.00
BOX,BIRD,SINGING,ENAMEL SCENES,PEASANTS,LANDSCAPES,GILT
    METAL,4 IN.................................................... 250.00
BOX,BIRD,SINGING,ENAMEL,FLORAL,FRUIT,LANDSCAPE,CIRCA 1900,
    SILVER GILT................................................... 350.00
BOX,BIRD,SINGING,ENAMEL,LANDSCAPES,PANELS,CIRCA 1900,SILVER
    GILT,4 IN..................................................... 350.00
BOX,BLUE,SCENE,WATER,TREE,MAN,BOAT,SIGNED PARIS,PORCELAIN,
    4 X 2 IN......................................................  35.00
BOX,BRASS-BOUND ROSEWOOD,TRAVELING WRITING,19TH CENTURY,
    24 IN. LONG...................................................  75.00
BOX,BRIDE'S,BRIDE,GROOM,ELABORATE DRESS,TULIPS,CHERRIES,
    PENNA.,19 IN.................................................. 750.00
BOX,BURL WALNUT,BRASS HANDLE,6 IN. X 9 IN.....................  25.00
BOX,BURNT WOOD TECHNIQUE,FLAPPER GIRL,POLO HORSES,FRANCE,
    WOODEN........................................................  10.00
BOX,CAKE,LEAVITT & PIERCE,TIN,4 1/2 X 3 1/2 X 2 1/4 IN.......   3.00
BOX,CHERUBS IN BRASS RELIEF,METAL,HINGED LID,FRANCE,3 IN. X
    1 3/4 IN......................................................  60.00
BOX,CIGARETTE,ENAMEL,CASE,RUSSIA............................. 350.00
BOX,DOCUMENT,PRIMITIVE,COFFIN SHAPE,DOME TOP,DOVETAILED,
    PINE,1825,SIGNED..............................................  65.00
BOX,ENAMEL DECOR,FLORAL,FOLIAGE,DOME LID,GILT METAL,
    2 1/4 IN.DIAMETER............................................. 125.00
BOX,FLORAL,LANDSCAPE ON INTERIOR OF LID,MENNECY PORCELAIN,
    2 3/4 IN.LONG................................................. 450.00
BOX,INCENSE,FORM OF FOO DOG HEAD,SIGNED,3 1/2 IN.LONG.......   18.00
BOX,INLAID,COMPARTMENT INSIDE,LEGS,MAHOGANY,8 IN. X 14 IN...   35.00
BOX,JEWEL,GOLD-PLATED METAL,GREEN TAFFETA LINING............   11.00
BOX,JEWEL,MAN'S,DOGHOUSE,ROSEWOOD,BRASS DOG IN DOORWAY,BRASS
    FITTINGS......................................................  38.50
BOX,JEWEL,SPUN SILVER,RELIEF SNAILS TURNED OUTWARD FEET,CUT
    GLASS COVER...................................................  25.00
BOX,JEWELRY,EGG-SHAPED,FILIGREE BASE & TRIM,GOLD-RUBBED CUT
    DESIGN........................................................ 175.00
BOX,LACE,CROSS BAND COVER,BRASS RING HANDLE,SHERATON,
    MAHOGANY...................................................... 110.00
BOX,LACQUER,GOLD GROUND,SILVER DECOR,ALLOVER FLORAL,LEAVES,
    FOUR SECTIONS.................................................  65.00
BOX,LACQUER,TROIKA,HORSEMEN,PEASANT GIRLS,INSECTS,BIRDS,
```

RUSSIA, SET OF 4.......................................... 229.50
BOX, LACQUER, WHITE EGGSHELL COLOR, RAISED GOLD DECOR, HERON,
FLORAL, 4 IN.............................................. 28.00
BOX, LACQUERED SEA CREATURES, SEAWEED, MOTHER-OF-PEARL, 1800,
5 1/2 IN. ROUND........................................... 60.00
BOX, LANDSCAPE ON LID, HORSES PULLING TROIKA, LACQUERED, RUSSIA,
4 X 3 IN.................................................. 35.00
BOX, MINIATURE OF NOBLEMAN, DIAMOND SPRAYS, ENAMEL GROUND, GOLD,
SWISS, 1840............................................2,100.00
BOX, MUSIC, PORCELAIN, WOODEN PLINTH, HEAD OF WOMAN,
9 1/2 IN. HIGH............................................ 20.00
BOX, MUSIC, SWISS, 10 TUNES............................... 225.00
BOX, PAINTED LANDSCAPE ON LID, TORTOISESHELL, GOLD-MOUNTED,
PARIS, 1820............................................... 150.00
BOX, PAINTING ON IVORY LID, SCENE, INSIDE PAINTING, SILVER BASE,
3 IN...................................................... 275.00
BOX, PATCH, ENAMEL DECOR, BIRMINGHAM, 1 3/4 IN.........ILLUS.. 500.00
BOX, PATCH, ENAMEL, PORTRAIT OF FREDERICK THE GREAT, ROCOCO
SCROLLING, 1765........................................... 225.00
BOX, PATCH, FILIGREE TOP SET WITH PEARLS & BLUE STONES, BRASS,
2 IN. DIAMETER............................................ 15.00
BOX, PILL, GLASS, EMBOSSED FLOWERS, STERLING LID.......... 9.50
BOX, PINK ROSES, GOLD SCROLLS, HINGED, HAND-PAINTED, PORCELAIN,
4 X 5 IN.................................................. 26.00
BOX, POMADE, TERRA-COTTA & CREAM ORIENTAL DECOR, CERAMIC, BRASS
RIMS, HINGE............................................... 17.00
BOX, PORTRAIT, ENAMELED BEADING, HINGED LID, 4 1/2 IN. ROUND..... 50.00
BOX, POUNCE, BULBOUS BASE, BROAD DISH-SHAPED TOP, HOLES IN STAR

ENAMEL DECORATED PATCH BOX, BIRMINGHAM

DESIGN, MAPLE............................................. 7.50
BOX, POWDER, FLORAL, HAND-PAINTED, LID, 4 1/2 IN. DIAMETER........ 7.50
BOX, POWDER, ROSES INSIDE & OUTSIDE, HAND-PAINTED, DATED 1917,
SIGNED, 6 IN.............................................. 35.00
BOX, POWDER, SATIN FINISH, CLEAR, HEXAGONAL, HAND-PAINTED FLORAL,
HINGED LID................................................ 37.50
BOX, POWDER, WHITE GROUND, ORANGE POPPY DECOR, GOLD, COVER,
3 1/2 IN. DIAMETER........................................ 6.50
BOX, PURPLE GLASS, BRASS FILIGREE DECOR AROUND MIDRIFF, HINGED,
5 X 4 IN.................................................. 40.00
BOX, SCENE, CHAIN PIER, MARINE PARADE, BRIGHTON, REGENCY,
4 IN. HIGH................................................ 50.00
BOX, SEWING, MOTHER-OF-PEARL, SECTIONS, BRASS TRIM, 6 IN......... 75.00
BOX, SILVER & TORTOISESHELL, JOHN OBRISSET, 18TH CENTURY....... 100.00
BOX, SNUFF, AUSTRIAN SILVER, ENAMEL DRAGON, GERMAN SILVER, TWO
PIECES.................................................... 50.00
BOX, SNUFF, CLASSICAL FIGURES, ROCOCO CARTOUCHE, SCROLLS, FLORAL,
SILVER GILT............................................... 175.00
BOX, SNUFF, SCENE, ENAMELED, SILVER, GOLD WASH, FRANCE........... 95.00
BOX, SNUFF, PAINTED DESIGNS, PENNSYLVANIA DUTCH, WOODEN....... 22.00
BOX, SNUFF, RECTANGULAR, ROUNDED SIDES, ENDS, REEDED, FLORAL,
CHASED, GOLD.............................................. 625.00
BOX, SNUFF, SHOE, PAPIER-MACHE, HINGED LID, 3 IN.............. 10.00
BOX, SNUFF, STRIATED PINK AGATE, IVORY COVER, CARVED FEMALE
FIGURE, 3 1/4 IN.......................................... 150.00
BOX, SNUFF, TORTOISESHELL, 2 1/4 IN. X 1 3/4 IN............. 12.00
BOX, SPICE, CAROUCHE SHAPE, HINGED COVER, GERMANY, SILVER GILT... 250.00
BOX, TORTOISESHELL, SILVER SIDES, MOTHER-OF-PEARL PLAQUE, 1730,
3 1/4 IN.................................................. 20.00
BOX, TRINKET, ORANGE IRIDESCENT, BLACK, WHITE & GOLD ENAMEL ON
LID....................................................... 95.00
BOX, VENETIAN PAINTED WOOD BALLOT, 18TH CENTURY.............. 30.00
BOX, VIOLETS ON LID, LUSTERLESS WHITE, SIGNED BELLE WARE,
HINGED, 3 1/2 IN.......................................... 85.00

BOX,WOOD,CAMPHOR,NATURAL FINISH,BRASS TRIM,11 1/4 IN. X
  5 IN.WIDE...................................................... 15.00
BOX,YUKON GOLD RUSH SCENES,TRAPPERS,MOUNTAINS,INDIANS,
  HAND-PAINTED,8 IN.............................................. 94.50


     BRASS HAS BEEN USED FOR DECORATIVE PIECES AND USEFUL
     TABLEWARES SINCE ANCIENT TIMES. IT IS AN ALLOY OF
     COPPER,ZINC,AND OTHER METALS.
     BRASS,SEE ALSO BELLS,BRONZE,MINIATURE,TOOLS,TRIVET,ETC.
BRASS,ANCHOR LIGHT,HANDLE,SCOTLAND,12 1/2 IN. X
  9 IN.DIAMETER................................................. 145.00
BRASS,ANDIRONS,CIRCA 1840,TWO FEET HIGH........................ 38.00
BRASS,ANDIRONS,HEXAGONAL STANDARD,STEEPLE FINIAL,RICHARD
  WITTINGHAM.................................................... 600.00
BRASS,ANDIRONS,URN TOP,KNOPPED STANDARD,SPURRED ARCH
  SUPPORTS,18 1/2 IN............................................ 120.00
BRASS,ASHTRAY,ALADDIN LAMP SHAPE,INDIA......................... 1.50
BRASS,ASHTRAY,CENTER FIGURE UPRIGHT BRUSSELS BOY............... 4.50
BRASS,ASHTRAY,FLOWERS & LEAVES,MARKED CHINA,SET OF 4,NESTED. 3.95
BRASS,ASHTRAY,MARKED CHINA,4 IN.DIAMETER....................... 2.75
BRASS,BED WARMER,FORGED IRON HANDLE............................ 25.00
BRASS,BED WARMER,MAPLE HANDLE,39 1/2 IN........................ 110.00
BRASS,BED WARMER,TURNED WOODEN HANDLE,EAGLE DESIGN ON COVER. 95.00
BRASS,BED WARMER,WOODEN HANDLE,9 1/2 IN.DIAMETER.............. 42.50
BRASS,BIRDCAGE,POLISHED & LACQUERED............................ 18.00
BRASS,BIRDCAGE,SINGING CANARY,FRANCE........................... 150.00
BRASS,BOOK RACK,TWO LADIES' HEADS ON EACH END.................. 14.50
BRASS,BOOKEND,CUTOUT WHITE JADE OVAL PANELS,FRAME,MARKED
  CHINA,PAIR................................................... 30.00
BRASS,BOOKEND,EXTENSION,EMBOSSED & CUT OUT DESIGN,DAISIES,
  PAIR......................................................... 18.00
BRASS,BOOKEND,INDIAN,FULL FACE,HEADDRESS,PAIR.................. 17.50
BRASS,BOOKEND,ORNATE,OWLS,SLIDING,PAIR......................... 15.00
BRASS,BOOKEND,SLIDING,EXTENDS TO 22 IN.,CUTOUT FIGURE OF
  SCHOLAR,BOOKS................................................ 6.95
BRASS,BOOKSTAND,OWL,EXTENDS FROM 8 IN. TO 14 1/2 IN........... 15.00
BRASS,BOOT SCRAPER,SCROLL DESIGN,PEDESTAL,SAYS 1877 ACROSS
  BAR,6 1/2 IN................................................. 22.50
BRASS,BOWL,CANDY MAKING,U-SHAPE WROUGHT IRON HANDLES,
  10-IN.DIAMETER............................................... 19.50
BRASS,BOWL,EMBOSSED DRAGON,CALLIGRAPHY MEDALLIONS,CHINA..... 18.50
BRASS,BOWL,ENGRAVED DRAGON DESIGN,FOOTED,INCISED CHINA,
  6 3/4-IN.DIAMETER............................................ 17.50
BRASS,BOWL,ENGRAVED INTERIOR,DRAGONS,CHINESE MOTIF,TEAK
  STAND,CHINA.................................................. 19.50
BRASS,BOWL,GOOD LUCK,LONG LIFE OMENS,APPLIED DRAGON,
  5 IN.DIAMETER................................................ 14.00
BRASS,BOWL,HEAVY ETCHING,DRAGON,MARKED MADE IN CHINA........ 14.00
BRASS,BOWL,INCISED DRAGON,CHINESE DECOR,PEDESTAL BASE,10 IN. 17.00
BRASS,BOWL,RICE,ABSTRACT ENGRAVING,MOUNTAINS,TREES,INCISED
  CHINA,3...................................................... 19.50
BRASS,BOWL,ROUND BASE,MARKED CHINA,6-IN.DIAMETER............. 3.95
BRASS,BOX,APPLIED FLORAL PLAQUES,RUSSIAN BIRD MARK,1 1/2 X
  3/4 IN.TALL.................................................. 30.00
BRASS,BOX,BELT,FOR LETTERS,SCENE OF 1821 BATTLE.............. 15.00
BRASS,BOX,BLUE,ENAMELED PLAQUES,SHEPHERD,FLORAL,
  6 1/2-IN.DIAMETER............................................ 25.00
BRASS,BOX,BOOK SHAPE,ETCHED HINGE COVER,COMPOTE OF FRUIT &
  SCROLLS...................................................... 3.50
BRASS,BOX,CIGARETTE,APPLIED ENAMEL IN MULTICOLORS,MARKED
  CHINA,COVER.................................................. 4.95
BRASS,BOX,CIGARETTE,DRAGON DESIGN ON HINGED COVER,MARKED
  CHINA,4 IN.LONG.............................................. 6.95
BRASS,BOX,CIGARETTE,ENGRAVED WITH HAPPINESS SYMBOL,MATCH
  BOX,SET...................................................... 17.50
BRASS,BOX,CIGARETTE,JADE INSET................................. 25.00
BRASS,BOX,ENGRAVED,JADE LID,FLORAL SET WITH CORAL,TURQUOISE,
  IVORY,CHINA.................................................. 85.00
BRASS,BOX,FILIGREE,CARVED WHITE JADE LID,SEMIPRECIOUS
  STONES,CHINA................................................. 75.00
BRASS,BOX,FOR WAX TAPERS & VISTA LIGHTS,ENGRAVED,THE ROYAL
  SAFETY BOX................................................... 25.00
BRASS,BOX,INLAID SILVER DESIGN,HINGED LID,7 IN. X 4 IN...... 25.00
BRASS,BOX,LAUREL WREATH,GLASS DOME INSERT,PORTRAIT ON IVORY,
  FRANCE....................................................... 125.00
BRASS,BOX,QUEEN OF ENGLAND,CHRISTMAS,1914,NAMES OF BRITISH
  ALLIES ON LID................................................ 3.75
BRASS,BOX,SNUFF,TWO DIALS,CLOCK FACES,INDICATOR,TIME TO
  TAKE,TIME TAKEN.............................................. 25.00
BRASS,BOX,STAMP,COVER HAS OWL PERCHED ON AN OPEN BOOK....... 15.00

BRASS,BOX,STAMP,YELLOW & GREEN ENAMEL POPPY ON LID,
COMPARTMENTS,AUSTRIA............................................. 20.00
BRASS,BOX,TO ATTACH TO SURVEYOR'S BELT,HINGED LID,18TH
CENTURY......................................................... 30.00
BRASS,BOX,WOOD-LINED,CHINA,6 IN. X 3 1/2 IN. X 1 3/4 IN..... 5.98
BRASS,BREAD CRUMB SET,ORNATE,ROSES.............................. 12.50
BRASS,BRIDLE ROSETTE,PRESSED DESIGN,HORSE'S HEAD,WORLD WAR I 5.00
BRASS,BUCKET,COAL............................................... 65.00
BRASS,BUCKET,JELLY,15 IN.ACROSS,7 IN.DEEP...................... 20.00
BRASS,CANDELABRUM,ALTAR,TWELVE-CANDLE........................... 18.00
BRASS,CANDELABRUM,CARVED GREEN JADE MEDALLION,FIVE-CANDLE,
CHINA,PAIR...................................................... 87.50
BRASS,CANDELABRUM,SEVEN ARMS,POLISHED,MARKED CHINA.......... 18.50
BRASS,CANDELABRUM,THREE ARMS,TURNED SHANKS,CIRCA 1850,
11 1/2 IN.,PAIR................................................. 45.00
BRASS,CANDELABRUM,THREE-BRANCH,SIGNED JARVIE,ART NOUVEAU,
11 IN........................................................... 45.00
BRASS,CANDELABRUM,THREE-CANDLE,CHINA,8 1/2 IN.HIGH,PAIR..... 15.00
BRASS,CANDELABRUM,THREE HOLES,BRITISH RAMPANT LION,15 X
9 IN.,PAIR...................................................... 75.00
BRASS,CANDLEHOLDER,BASE IS TURTLE WITH FROG,MOUTH HOLDS
CANDLE.......................................................... 10.00
BRASS,CANDLEHOLDER,BASES ARE TURTLES,HEADS UP,2 1/2 IN.HIGH,
PAIR............................................................ 9.50
BRASS,CANDLEHOLDER,CLAMP-TYPE HOLDER,PATENT DATE 1887....... 15.00
BRASS,CANDLEHOLDER,PUSH-UP SAUCER TYPE,6-IN.DIAMETER BASE... 16.50
BRASS,CANDLEHOLDER,SAUCER TYPE,FOOTED........................... 12.50
BRASS,CANDLEHOLDER,SEVEN-PRONG,FLORAL DESIGN AROUND BASE.... 18.00
BRASS,CANDLEHOLDER,SPIRAL CENTERS,ENGLAND,20 IN.TALL,PAIR... 60.00
BRASS,CANDLEHOLDER,STAMP BOX,INKWELL,LETTER OPENER,ENAMELED
ROCOCO.......................................................... 185.00
BRASS,CANDLEHOLDER,SWIRLED STEM,19 IN.HIGH,PAIR.............. 65.00
BRASS,CANDLESNUFFER SCISSORS.................................... 4.00
BRASS,CANDLESNUFFER,ANGEL AT TOP, FIGURED HANDLE............ 15.00
BRASS,CANDLESNUFFER,SCISSOR TYPE,FOOTED........................ 12.75
BRASS,CANDLESNUFFER,TRAY,HAND-POLISHED.......................... 32.50
BRASS,CANDLESNUFFER,TRAY,9 1/2 IN.LONG.......................... 35.00
BRASS,CANDLESNUFFER,6 IN.LONG................................... 9.50
BRASS,CANDLESTICK,5 IN.HIGH,PAIR................................ 15.00
BRASS,CANDLESTICK,8 1/2 IN.TALL,PAIR............................ 12.00
BRASS,CANDLESTICK,ALLOVER EMBOSSING,FILAGREE CROSS ON BASE,
24 IN........................................................... 40.00
BRASS,CANDLESTICK,BALUSTER SHAPE,HAND-POLISHED,
11 1/2 IN.TALL,PAIR............................................. 40.00
BRASS,CANDLESTICK,BASE IS THREE TRIANGLES,CLAW FEET,CROSSES,
24 IN.,PAIR..................................................... 100.00
BRASS,CANDLESTICK,BEEHIVE & DIAMOND PRINCESS,10 3/4 IN.,PAIR 35.00
BRASS,CANDLESTICK,BEEHIVE,PUSH-UP,8 IN.HIGH,PAIR............. 23.50
BRASS,CANDLESTICK,BUTTERFLY SHADE ON ADJUSTABLE ROD,CHINA,
16 IN.,PAIR..................................................... 59.50
BRASS,CANDLESTICK,CAPSTAN BASE,FLEMISH,15TH CENTURY,
5 1/2 IN........................................................ 70.00
BRASS,CANDLESTICK,CENTER PUSH-UP,BEEHIVE,DIAMOND DESIGN,
10 IN.HIGH,PAIR................................................. 29.75
BRASS,CANDLESTICK,CENTER PUSH-UP,SQUARE BASE,5 IN.HIGH..... 9.95
BRASS,CANDLESTICK,CENTER PUSH-UP,SQUARE BASE,8 3/4 IN.HIGH.. 9.95
BRASS,CANDLESTICK,CIRCA 1840,10 IN.HIGH,PAIR................. 20.00
BRASS,CANDLESTICK,CLASSIC LINES,CANDLE EJECTOR,9
IN.,PAIR........................................ 19.50 TO 22.50
BRASS,CANDLESTICK,CUT PRISMS,MARBLE BASE,ENGLAND,13 IN.HIGH,
PAIR............................................................ 150.00
BRASS,CANDLESTICK,DIAMOND DESIGN,PUSH-UP,11 IN.HIGH,PAIR.... 38.00
BRASS,CANDLESTICK,DRAGONFLIES,CHINA,5 IN.HIGH,PAIR.......... 12.00
BRASS,CANDLESTICK,EMBOSSED,HOLY FAMILY AT BASE,31 IN........ 45.00
BRASS,CANDLESTICK,FLAT BASE,BUTTERFLY SHAPE,DECOR,3 IN.HIGH,
PAIR............................................................ 7.50
BRASS,CANDLESTICK,FOUR TIERS,PRISMS,CABRIOLE LEGS,CLAW FEET. 35.00
BRASS,CANDLESTICK,GIRL & BOY,FENCE,GRAPE DESIGN,PRISMS,
MARBLE BASE,PAIR................................................ 65.00
BRASS,CANDLESTICK,MAPLE LEAF,RING HANDLE,5 X 5 X 2 IN.TALL,
PAIR............................................................ 7.50
BRASS,CANDLESTICK,MENORAH,SAYS AMOS LODGE B'NAI B'RITH,
1868-1928....................................................... 8.75
BRASS,CANDLESTICK,MINIATURE,4 IN.HIGH,PAIR.................... 10.00
BRASS,CANDLESTICK,PUSH-UP,BULBOUS TURNINGS,9 IN.TALL,PAIR... 30.00
BRASS,CANDLESTICK,QUEEN ANNE,18TH CENTURY...................... 33.00
BRASS,CANDLESTICK,QUEEN OF DIAMONDS,11 IN.TALL,PAIR......... 55.00
BRASS,CANDLESTICK,RAISED MASQUE FACES,HAND-CHASED DECOR,
6 IN.,PAIR...................................................... 47.50
BRASS,CANDLESTICK,ROUND BASE,MARKED CHINA,5 IN.HIGH,PAIR.... 5.75
BRASS,CANDLESTICK,ROUND BASE,MARKED CHINA,3 IN.HIGH......... 4.75

```
BRASS,CANDLESTICK,SAUCER TYPE,PUSH-UP,HANDLE,DATED 1853.....    16.00
BRASS,CANDLESTICK,SHAPE OF WINGED DRAGONS,5 1/2 IN. HIGH,
  PAIR....................................................    14.75
BRASS,CANDLESTICK,SPIRAL STANDARD,CLAW FEET,ENGLAND,26 IN.,
  PAIR....................................................   300.00
BRASS,CANDLESTICK,SQUARE BASE,SQUARE RIDGES,10 IN.HIGH,PAIR.    22.50
BRASS,CANDLESTICK,WINGED DRAGON,6 1/2 IN.HIGH,PAIR..........    35.00
BRASS,CASH REGISTER,STICKER SAYS SOLD TO W.E.CARR,
  WAYNESVILLE,IND.,1905...................................    50.00
BRASS,CHAMBERSTICK,FLAT THUMB  REST ON HANDLE TOP,SAUCES
  4 IN.DIAMETER...........................................    22.50
BRASS,CHANDELIER,HOLDS 16 CANDLES,TWO TIERS,30 IN.HIGH,
  28 IN.DIAMETER..........................................   185.00
BRASS,CHANDELIER,THREE-TIERED,225 PRISMS,HANGS DOWN 45 IN.,
  30 IN.ACROSS............................................   750.00
BRASS,COAL SCUTTLE,ENGRAVED DESIGNS,MARKED CHINA...........     8.00
BRASS,COLUMN,FLUTED,EAGLE-TOPPED,IRON BASE,PAIR............    60.00
BRASS,COMPASS,SHIP,FRAME,DATED 1876,8 1/2 IN.DIAMETER......    85.00
BRASS,COMPASS,SURVEYOR'S,SILVERED DIAL MARKED THOS.WHITNEY,
  MAKER,PHILA.............................................    85.00
BRASS,CORN HUSKER,MARKED UNIVERSAL HUSKER,PAT.FEB.21,1882,
  5 IN...................................................     8.00
BRASS,CUP,COLLAPSIBLE,COUPLE RIDING BICYCLE BUILT FOR TWO,
  1897...................................................     3.95
BRASS,CUP,MARRIAGE,ORNATE,19TH CENTURY,6 1/2 IN............    25.00
BRASS,CUSPIDOR,3 IN.HIGH,9 IN.ACROSS......................    28.00
BRASS,CUSPIDOR,8 IN.HIGH,9-IN.DIAMETER BASE...............    32.50
BRASS,CUSPIDOR,COPPER-COATED,12 IN.HIGH,10-IN.DIAMETER.....    32.00
BRASS,CUSPIDOR,HEAVY BOTTOM,12 IN.TALL,10 IN.WIDE..........    50.00
BRASS,DESK SET,CALENDAR CLOCK,CUT GLASS INKWELL,HINGED
  COLLAR,STAND...........................................    50.00
BRASS,DIPPER,ENAMELED,DRAGON MOTIF,BLUE HANDLE,MARKED MADE
  IN CHINA...............................................    12.00
BRASS,DISH,LEAF DESIGN,MARKED CHINA,FOOTED,6 1/2-IN.DIAMETER     3.95
BRASS,DISH,RAISED CENTER DESIGN OF WOMAN GOLFER,2 1/4 X
  3 3/8 IN.LONG..........................................     2.50
BRASS,DISH,THREE-CORNERED,RAISED ROSE IN CENTER,
  5 1/2 IN.ACROSS........................................     4.75
BRASS,DISH,WOODEN HANDLES,COVER,10-IN.DIAMETER............     8.50
BRASS,EAGLE,AMERICAN,THREE-DIMENSIONAL,HAND-WROUGHT,
  11-IN.WINGSPREAD.......................................    48.00
BRASS,EASEL FRAME,GOLD FINISH,OVAL-SHAPED,5 1/2 IN.HIGH X
  4 3/8 IN.WIDE..........................................     3.75
BRASS,EASEL FRAME,RECTANGLE,7 1/2 IN.HIGH X 4 1/2 IN.WIDE...     3.75
BRASS,EWER,MELON RIB PORCELAIN CENTER,APPLE BLOSSOMS ON
  BASE,PAIR..............................................    35.00
BRASS,FIGURINE,FIGHTING COCK,CHINA,9 1/2 IN.,PAIR..........   275.00
BRASS,FIGURINE,MISS LIBERTY,HOLDS TWO 3-ARMED TORCHES,
  4 1/2 FT...............................................   495.00
BRASS,FIGURINE,SCULPTURE OF ABRAHAM LINCOLN,NINOMIYA
  KINJIRO,9 1/2 IN.......................................    75.00
BRASS,FIREPLACE ORNAMENT,STANDING HORSE,ENGLAND,
  7 1/2 IN.TALL,PAIR.....................................    40.00
BRASS,FOX,EGYPTIAN DECOR,BALL FEET,HINGED TOP,EDUSCHO,
  KAFFEE-TEE,GERMANY.....................................     8.50
BRASS,FRAME,EASEL,CUTOUT BORDER OF LEAVES & FLOWERS,8 X
  5 IN..................................................     3.95
BRASS,FRAME,EASEL,LACY CROWN AT TOP......................    25.00
BRASS,FRAME,EASEL,RECTANGULAR SHAPE,5 1/2 IN.HIGH,4 IN.WIDE.     3.75
BRASS,HAND-CUT OPENWORK NEAR TOP,ORIENTAL,5-IN.DIAMETER....    22.50
BRASS,HEARTH ORNAMENT,LION COUCHANT,SIGNED B.H.LOWE,7 IN. X
  4 IN..................................................    13.00
BRASS,HOLDER,STRING,BALL SHAPE,EMBOSSED,SCREWS APART IN
  CENTER................................................    18.00
BRASS,HOLDER,WATCH,SHELL SHAPE,ROUND TRAY.................    22.50
BRASS,HUMIDOR,FOUR RAISED INDIAN HEADS ON SIDES...........    35.00
BRASS,HUMIDOR,MARKED BENEDICT KORNAK BRASS 622............     9.00
BRASS,HUMIDOR,TOBACCO,SHAPE OF WORLD WAR I ARTILLERY SHELL,
  PLATED................................................     4.00
BRASS,INCENSE BURNER,BIRDS,FLOWERS,SEA ANIMALS,ELEPHANT HEAD
  HANDLES...............................................    45.00
BRASS,INCENSE BURNER,CHINA...............................    10.00
BRASS,INCENSE BURNER,FOO DOG FINIAL,FOOTED,6 IN.HIGH......    20.00
BRASS,INKWELL,BLUE,WHITE,HINGED COVER,6 IN.SQUARE TRAY,
  OPENWORK DESIGN........................................    35.00
BRASS,INKWELL,FOUR-LEAF CLOVER,SUNBONNET GIRL COVER,COPPER
  LINING................................................    13.00
BRASS,INKWELL,HINGED COVER,LEAF-SHAPED TRAY,ART NOUVEAU
  DESIGN................................................     7.50
BRASS,INKWELL,HINGED TOP,EMBOSSED,GLASS INSERT...........    18.00
BRASS,INKWELL,MEPHISTOPHELES,6 IN........................    18.00
```

BRASS,INKWELL,TURTLE SHAPE,CHILD RIDING ATOP FORMING COVER,
  CLEAR INSERT................................................. 22.50
BRASS,IRON,FLAT,CHARCOAL,8 IN.LONG.............................. 18.00
BRASS,JARDINIERE,LION HEAD HANDLES,RINGS IN MOUTH,FOOTED,
  ENGLAND,9 IN................................................. 35.00
BRASS,JARDINIERE,PANELS,EMBOSSED FLORAL,PEDESTAL,14 1/2 IN.
  X 40 IN.TALL................................................. 79.50
BRASS,JARDINIERE,THREE CLAW FEET,HAMMERED,SIGNED KARNLOFF
  BROS.,RUSSIA................................................. 20.00
BRASS,JUG,MARKED DELARUE MAKER GUERNSEY,9 IN................ 35.00
BRASS,KETTLE,BAIL,9 IN.HIGH,12 IN.DIAMETER..................... 25.00
BRASS,KETTLE,HANDLE ON EACH SIDE,8 1/2 IN.DIAMETER,4 IN.DEEP 12.50
BRASS,KETTLE,IRON BAIL HANDLE,12 IN.DIAMETER,5 1/2 IN.DEEP.. 12.50
BRASS,KETTLE,IRON BAIL HANDLE,13 IN.DIAMETER,6 IN.DEEP...... 14.50
BRASS,KETTLE,JELLY,IRON HANDLE,10 1/2 IN.DIAMETER,
  4 1/2 IN.HIGH............................................... 25.00
BRASS,LADLE,IRON HANDLE,15 IN.LONG,6 IN.DIAMETER............. 25.00
BRASS,LAMP,STUDENT,OIL CONTAINER,WHITE SHADE................. 75.00
BRASS,LAMP,TABLE,HANGING PAGODA WITH BELLS AT CORNERS,HOLDS
  BULB........................................................ 10.00
BRASS,LANTERN,CLEAR GLOBE,RAYO,U.S.A.......................... 10.00
BRASS,LANTERN,RED GLOBE....................................... 20.00
BRASS,LETTER OPENER,DUTCH BOY,HOLLAND......................... 7.50
BRASS,LETTER OPENER,HANDLE IN SHAPE OF WOMAN,5 3/4 IN.LONG.. 2.75
BRASS,LETTER OPENER,TURKEY CLAW............................... 9.00
BRASS,LETTER OPENER,WINDMILL,HOLLAND.......................... 7.50
BRASS,LIGHTER,CIGARETTE,COIN OF QUEEN VICTORIA,COIN OF KING
  GEORGE...................................................... 6.00
BRASS,MATCH HOLDER,UNPOLISHED,FROM TRAIN COACH,2 1/2 X
  4 1/2 IN.................................................... 5.00
BRASS,MATCH SAFE,A.BUSCH...................................... 9.00
BRASS,MATCH SAFE,POCKET,ROYAL CLUB,41 W.28 ST.,N.Y.,
  1886 INDIAN PENNIES......................................... 5.50
BRASS,MINE INSTRUMENT,HOOK,WET & DRY,LONDON,LEATHER CASE,
  8 IN........................................................ 15.00
BRASS,MIRROR,HANGING,BEVEL GLASS,EAGLE,PORTRAIT,ORNATE,35 X
  20 IN....................................................... 350.00
BRASS,MONSTER IN WHITE METAL TRIM,ANGELS,GRAPES,VINES........ 45.00
BRASS,MORTAR & PESTLE......................................... 15.00
BRASS,MORTAR & PESTLE,3 1/4 IN.HIGH........................... 18.50
BRASS,MORTAR & PESTLE,5 1/4 IN.HIGH........................... 25.00
BRASS,MORTAR,GLASS PESTLE..................................... 18.50
BRASS,MUG,BEER,CIRCA 1830,ENGLAND,ONE PINT.................... 10.00
BRASS,NUTCRACKER,DOG,11 1/2 IN.LONG........................... 20.00
BRASS,NUTCRACKER,EAGLE HEAD................................... 8.50
BRASS,NUTCRACKER,PARROT....................................... 15.00
BRASS,NUTCRACKER,ROOSTER........................... 8.00 TO 9.00
BRASS,NUTCRACKER,ROOSTER HEAD................................. 8.50
BRASS,NUTCRACKER,SHAPE HEAD OF COURT JESTER,6 3/4 IN.LONG... 6.95
BRASS,PAIL,BURNISHED,IRON HANDLE,10 1/2 IN.DIAMETER,
  9 IN.TALL................................................... 45.00
BRASS,PAIL,HALLMARKED,IRON HANDLE,18 1/2 X 12 IN.TALL........ 59.00
BRASS,PAN,2 1/4 IN.DEEP,5 1/2-IN.DIAMETER,7 1/2-IN.IRON
  HANDLE...................................................... 12.50
BRASS,PAN,2 1/2 IN.DEEP,6-IN.DIAMETER,6 1/2-IN.IRON HANDLE.. 12.50
BRASS,PAN,7-IN.LONG HANDLE,3 IN.DEEP,6-IN.DIAMETER........... 12.50
BRASS,PAN,11 1/2-IN.DIAMETER,5 1/2 IN.DEEP,11-IN.IRON HANDLE 14.50
BRASS,PAN,BREAD,TIN-LINED,RUSSIAN MARK,15 IN................. 28.00
BRASS,PAN,WARMING,PIERCED & ENGRAVED COVER,WOODEN HANDLE,
  42 IN.LONG.................................................. 65.00
BRASS,PASTRY MARKER,WHEEL,CIRCA 1800.......................... 8.00
BRASS,PENCIL SHARPENER........................................ 5.00
BRASS,PESTLE,18TH CENTURY,10 IN.LONG.......................... 15.00
BRASS,PISTOL,OCTAGON BARREL,PEARL HANDLE,MARKED AUSTRIA,
  1 1/2 IN.................................................... 9.00
BRASS,PITCHER,MINIATURE,ALE TYPE,CHINA........................ 6.50
BRASS,PLANTER,LION HEADS ON SIDES,FOOTED,5 IN.HIGH X
  5 1/2-IN.DIAMETER........................................... 18.50
BRASS,POST,NEWEL,CIRCA 1840,11 IN.AROUND,PAIR............... 38.00
BRASS,POT,BEAN,HEAVY BAIL & LID,FOOTED,ONE QUART............ 15.00
BRASS,PUMP,BEER KEG........................................... 20.00
BRASS,SAMOVAR,BURNISHED ROSE BRASS,REPEWTERED INSIDE,RUSSIA. 250.00
BRASS,SAMOVAR,BURNISHED,RUSSIAN............................... 110.00
BRASS,SAMOVAR,RUSSIA,SIGNED,EAGLE MARK,14 IN.HIGH,9 IN.WIDE. 90.00
BRASS,SAMOVAR,SQUARE BASE,SIDE HANDLES,DETACHABLE FUNNEL,
  RUSSIA,16 IN................................................ 125.00
BRASS,SCARIFICATOR,DOCTOR'S,MECHANICAL........................ 20.00
BRASS,SCONCE,WALL,EMBOSSED FRUIT,FLORAL,CANDLE ARMS,
  BOBECHES,ENGLAND............................................ 45.00
BRASS,SCOOP,HANDLE,PATENT 1868,8 IN.LONG...................... 7.75
BRASS,SERVER,DEMITASSE,MATCHING SUGAR......................... 12.00

```
BRASS,SEWING BIRD,FIGURED........................................     17.50
BRASS,SEWING BIRD,FOR OFFSET TABLE.............................     18.00
BRASS,SEWING BIRD,FOR STRAIGHT TABLE...........................     16.00
BRASS,SEWING BIRD,ORNATE,VELVET PINCUSHION.....................     25.00
BRASS,SEWING DOG...............................................     28.00
BRASS,SEXTANT,LENSES,TELESCOPE,NORIE & WILSON..............    165.00
BRASS,SHIPS TAFFRAIL LOG,DATED 1892,SPINNERS,ROPE...........    179.50
BRASS,SIFTER,SET OF EIGHT,NESTING ONE INSIDE THE OTHER......     28.00
BRASS,SILENT BUTLER,APPLIED ENAMEL DECOR,MARKED CHINA.......      4.95
BRASS,SKIMMER,IRON HANDLE,SIGNED F.B.S.,CANTON,OHIO,
    PAT.JAN.28,'86.............................................     28.00
BRASS,SLIPPER,LADY'S,BASE,3 IN. X 4 1/2 IN...................     20.00
BRASS,SPITTOON,9 IN...................................ILLUS..     18.00
BRASS,STIRRUPS,SPURS,CIRCA BEFORE 1830.......................     12.00
BRASS,SURVEYOR'S LEVEL,TRIPOD,MICROMETER ADJUSTMENTS,CLAMPS,
    1850.......................................................     35.00
BRASS,SURVEYOR'S TRANSIT,COMPASS,TELESCOPE,MAKER PATTRICK,
    LONDON,1800................................................     75.00
BRASS,SURVEYOR'S TRANSIT,TELESCOPE,STADIA,KEUFFEL & ESSER,
    MODEL NO.2.................................................    160.00
BRASS,TEA CADDY,DOME LID,5 1/2 IN.HIGH.......................     20.00
BRASS,TEAKETTLE,AMBER GLASS HANDLE,FOUR BUTTON FEET,MAKER
    J.C.B......................................................     47.00
BRASS,TEAKETTLE,ON CRADLE,ALCOHOL BURNER,WOODEN HANDLE &
    KNOB ON LID................................................     48.50
BRASS,TEAKETTLE,OPENWORK,COPPER BASE,ALCOHOL BURNER,
    PENNSYLVANIA DUTCH.........................................    135.00
```

BRASS SPITTOON

```
BRASS,TEAKETTLE,WITH COPPER,MADE TO SIT DOWN IN STOVE,
    GERMANY....................................................    125.00
BRASS,TEAKETTLE,WROUGHT IRON FRAME,ALCOHOL BURNER,BUFFALO
    MFG.CO.....................................................     50.00
BRASS,TEAPOT,BLOCK WOODEN HANDLE,STANDARD,ALCOHOL BURNER,
    14 IN.HIGH.................................................     42.50
BRASS,TEAPOT,HAMMERED NECK & SPOUT,PEWTER-LINED,FINIAL,
    12 IN......................................................     27.50
BRASS,TELEPHONE,POLISHED,DATED 1915..........................     45.00
BRASS,TELESCOPE,EXTENDS TO 36 IN.,ENGRAVED PARRY MASON &
    CO.,BOSTON.................................................     65.00
BRASS,TELESCOPE,SHIP CAPTAIN,SIGNED OSBORNE DAY OR NIGHT,
    LONDON.....................................................     75.00
BRASS,THIMBLE,GOLD-PLATED.....................................      6.50
BRASS,TIEBACK,CURTAIN,CENTER BUTTON,EMBOSSED BAND,IRON
    SCREWS,PAIR................................................      7.50
BRASS,TIMEPIECE,SUBSIDIARY SECONDS DIAL,WOODEN CASE,JOHN
    BILLE,LONDON...............................................     75.00
BRASS,TODDY WARMER,ALLOVER PIERCED,POLISHED,BURNER,HANDLE...     18.50
BRASS,TODDY WARMER,PIERCED,HANDLE,BURNER,SQUARE,FOOTED,
    POLISHED...................................................     12.00
BRASS,TODDY WARMER,PIERCED,POLISHED..........................     15.00
BRASS,TRAY,BREAD,SOUVENIR,SESQUICENTENNIAL,PHILADELPHIA,
    1776-1926..................................................     10.00
BRASS,TRAY,ENGRAVED CLASSICAL FIGURES,BURNISHED,HANDLES,
    9 1/2 X 15 IN..............................................     25.00
BRASS,TRAY,ENGRAVED DRAGON,PEACOCK,CHINA,14 IN.LONG X
    6 IN.WIDE..................................................     11.00
BRASS,TRAY,HAMMERED,RUSSIAN FACTORY MARK & ROMANOFF IMPERIAL
    EAGLE......................................................     25.00
BRASS,TRAY,HAND-HAMMERED,HANDLES,MARKED RUSSIA,10 IN.LONG X
    7 IN.WIDE..................................................      8.75
BRASS,TRAY,HAND-HAMMERED,OPEN HANDLES,COPPER RIVETS,
```

```
  13 1/2 IN.DIAMETER.....................................    12.00
BRASS,TRAY,MARKED MADE IN CHINA,8 IN.DIAMETER..............     6.50
BRASS,TRAY,MARKED RUSSIA,14 1/2 IN.DIAMETER................    14.75
BRASS,TRAY,OIL PRINTING OF ST.BERNARD DOG.................     10.00
BRASS,TRAY,ORNATE APPLIED HANDLES,ROUND,HAMMERED,RUSSIAN,
  13 IN...................................................    12.50
BRASS,TRAY,OVAL,MARKED,RUSSIA,8 1/4 IN....................      7.50
BRASS,TRAY,ROBERT BURNS,HOTEL.............................      4.00
BRASS,TRAY,SCENE,CHINESE MAN & WOMAN IN GARDEN,CHINA,
  12 IN.LONG..............................................      6.75
BRASS,TRAY,SCENE,WOMEN IN GARDEN,CRIMPED,MARKED CHINA,
  14-IN.DIAMETER..........................................    14.75
BRASS,TRAY,SERVING,HANDLE,18 IN. X 12 IN..................    18.00
BRASS,TRAY,TWO HANDLES,HAMMERED,SIGNED,RUSSIA,
  13 1/2-IN.DIAMETER......................................    15.00
BRASS,TRIVET,FIREPLACE,HORSE CENTER,10 1/2 IN.HIGH,
  8-IN.DIAMETER...........................................    36.00
BRASS,TRIVET,OPENWORK CENTER,FLORAL BORDER,MARKED CHINA,
  FOOTED.................................................      3.75
BRASS,TRIVET,TEA,TUDOR ROSE,OPENWORK DESIGN,ENGLAND.......      7.50
BRASS,TRIVET,TUDOR ROSE DESIGN,ENGLAND....................      7.50
BRASS,VASE,DRAGON WRAPPED AROUND NECK,CHINESE SIGNATURE,
  10 IN.HIGH..............................................    80.00
BRASS,VASE,ENGRAVED BLOSSOM & FOLIAGE DESIGN,URN SHAPE,
  CHINA,8 IN.HIGH.........................................    31.50
BRASS,VASE,ENGRAVED FLORAL,BULBOUS,FLARED TOP,CHINA,
  7 IN.HIGH...............................................    25.50
BRASS,VASE,MARKED CHINA,6 IN.HIGH.........................      3.95
BRASS,VASE,RUSSIAN,COPPER BANDS,HAMMERED,WEIGHTED,MARKED,
  14 1/2 IN...............................................    37.50
BRASS,WALL HOOK,END SHAPE OF SUN-GOD'S HEAD,EXTENDS
  6 1/4 IN.,SCREW-IN......................................      3.75
BRASS,WEIGHTS,NESTED IN A HINGED LID BUCKET CONTAINER......    45.00
BREAD TRAY,SEE PRESSED GLASS,BREAD TRAY
```

      BRIDES' BASKETS OF GLASS WERE USUALLY ONE-OF-A-KIND
      NOVELTIES MADE IN ANY OF THE AMERICAN AND IN SOME
      EUROPEAN GLASS FACTORIES. THEY WERE ESPECIALLY POPULAR
      ABOUT 1880 WHEN THE DECORATED BASKET WAS OFTEN GIVEN
      AS A WEDDING GIFT. CUT-GLASS BASKETS WERE POPULAR AFTER
      1890. ALL BRIDES' BASKETS LOST FAVOR ABOUT 1905.

```
BRIDE'S BASKET,BLUE OVERLAY,SCALLOPS WITHIN RUFFLES,INNER
  DECOR,10 IN.............................................    49.00
BRIDE'S BASKET,CASED GREEN OVERLAY,RUFFLES,SWIRLS,SILVER
  FRAME,6 3/4 IN..........................................    47.50
BRIDE'S BASKET,CASED PINK & WHITE GLASS,THORN HANDLE,
  VICTORIAN...............................................    25.00
BRIDE'S BASKET,CHARTREUSE,WHITE LINING,SATIN GLASS,BRASS
  FRAME..................................................    250.00
BRIDE'S BASKET,CLEAR TO THREADED AMBER,GREEN JEWELS,SILVER
  FRAME,5 IN..............................................    35.00
BRIDE'S BASKET,CRANBERRY,ENAMEL FLORAL,SILVER HOLDER,PANSIES
  ON HANDLE...............................................   158.00
BRIDE'S BASKET,CRANBERRY,SATIN,WHITE ENAMEL FLORAL,
  RESILVERED FRAME........................................   115.00
BRIDE'S BASKET,CRANBERRY OPALESCENT HOBNAIL,GOLD FLECK
  BOTTOM,NO HOLDER........................................    95.00
BRIDE'S BASKET,CRANBERRY TO LEMON-WHITE,FLUTED,SILVER PLATE
  HOLDER..................................................    65.00
BRIDE'S BASKET,CRANBERRY TO PINK,SCROLLED,BEADED,SILVER
  PLATE HOLDER............................................    67.50
BRIDE'S BASKET,CRIMPED AMBER RIBBON EDGE,WILD ROSE COLOR
  INSIDE,FLORAL...........................................    95.00
BRIDE'S BASKET,CRIMPED CLEAR EDGE,RUFFLED,ENAMELED FLORAL,
  SILVER FRAME............................................    60.00
BRIDE'S BASKET,CUT INSERT,DIAMONDS,STRAWBERRY FAN,FRAME,
  FOOTED,HANDLE...........................................   115.00
BRIDE'S BASKET,DARK TO LIGHT PINK,CLEAR APPLIED BORDER,
  RUFFLED,NO HOLDER.......................................    35.00
BRIDE'S BASKET,GREEN,GOLD DECOR,SCALLOPED,MINIATURE,SILVER
  HOLDER,FOOTED...........................................    19.50
BRIDE'S BASKET,MOTHER-OF-PEARL,BLUE,SILVER
  JACK-IN-THE-PULPIT FRAME................................   150.00
BRIDE'S BASKET,OPAQUE CREAM COLOR,APPLE BLOSSOMS,AMBER
  LEAVES,HANDLE...........................................   175.00
BRIDE'S BASKET,PINK,CAMPHOR OVERLAY,FOOTED,HANDLED,SATIN
  GLASS..................................................   110.00
BRIDE'S BASKET,PINK OVERLAY BOWL,CLEAR RIM,ORNATE HOLDER,
  FOOTED,HANDLE...........................................    67.00
BRIDE'S BASKET,PINK OVERLAY,CLEAR RIM,YELLOW ENAMEL BIRD,
```

SCROLLS,HOLDER......................................... 65.00
BRIDE'S BASKET,PINK SHADING,RUFFLED EDGE,SILVER FRAME,JAMES
W.TUFTS............................................... 75.00
BRIDE'S BASKET,PINK TO MAUVE,SATIN GLASS,NO HOLDER,10 IN. X
10 IN................................................. 75.00
BRIDE'S BASKET,PURPLE FLORAL,PINK LUSTER INSIDE,RUFFLED,MILK
GLASS................................................. 42.50
BRIDE'S BASKET,RAINBOW SATIN OVERLAY,MT.WASHINGTON......... 825.00
BRIDE'S BASKET,ROSE COLOR,ENAMELED PORTRAIT,BRISTOL,
10 1/2 IN.DIAMETER.................................... 225.00
BRIDE'S BASKET,ROSE COLOR INSIDE,AMBER EDGE,ORNATE
RESILVERED HOLDER..................................... 65.00
BRIDE'S BASKET,ROSE TO PINK,APPLIED AMBER FEET & HANDLE,BLUE
GRAPES................................................ 35.00
BRIDE'S BASKET,RUFFLED,PLEATED FLUTINGS,FLORAL,CRANBERRY,
FOOTED,11 IN.......................................... 150.00
BRIDE'S BASKET,SATIN GLASS,APPLIED DECOR,SILVER BASE,STEVENS
& WILLIAMS............................................ 250.00
BRIDE'S BASKET,SCALLOPED EDGE,PINK OVERLAY,HAND-BLOWN,
9 3/4 IN.DIAMETER..................................... 32.50
BRIDE'S BASKET,SILVER HOLDER ROBIN DISH,3 IN.HIGH,
6 3/4 IN.WIDE......................................... 65.00
BRIDE'S BASKET,SWIRL EMBOSSED,CASED,GREEN OVERLAY,SILVER
FRAME,6 3/4 IN........................................ 47.50
BRIDE'S BASKET,SWIRLED BLUE OPALESCENT,FRAME.............. 75.00
BRIDE'S BASKET,WHITE,DEEP ROSE LINING,AMBER RIM,RUFFLED,NO
HOLDER................................................ 85.00
BRIDE'S BASKET,WHITE,FLORAL,CREAMY LINING,SILVER PLATE FRAME 53.50
BRIDE'S BASKET,WHITE OVERLAY,PINK INSIDE,EDGED WITH AMBER,
12 1/2 IN.WIDE........................................ 65.00
BRIDE'S BASKET,WHITE TO DEEP PINK,ENAMEL FLORAL,SILVER
HOLDER,HANDLE......................................... 95.00
BRIDE'S BASKET,YELLOW TO PINK,BLUE-ENAMELED FLORAL,SILVER
FRAME,15 IN........................................... 195.00
BRIDE'S BOWL,BLUE SATIN,HONEYSUCKLE DECOR,SILVER HANDLE &
HOLDER................................................ 125.00
BRIDE'S BOWL,CASED,WHITE OUTSIDE,PINK INSIDE,ENAMELED,
CRIMPED,RUFFLED....................................... 65.00
BRIDE'S BOWL,CASED,WHITE,PINK TO BUTTERSCOTCH INSIDE,TAUTON
PLATE STAND........................................... 70.00
BRIDE'S BOWL,CRANBERRY TO PINK,GOLD DESIGN,CASED,13 IN.WIDE. 150.00
BRIDE'S BOWL,CREAMY GROUND,ROSE LINING,AMBER-EDGED TOP,
POINTED HOBNAIL....................................... 95.00
BRIDE'S BOWL,CRIMSON STRIPES,YELLOW,FRILLY,7 1/4 IN........ 35.00
BRIDE'S BOWL,HOBNAIL,OPALESCENT,FLUTED,RUFFLED,BLOWN,
CRANBERRY............................................. 135.00
BRIDE'S BOWL,LIGHT TO DARK BLUE,BLUE OVERLAY,FLEUR-DE-LIS,
ENAMEL FLORAL......................................... 45.00
BRIDE'S BOWL,PALE TO DEEP BLUE,ENAMELED ORCHID FLOWER,SILVER
HOLDER................................................ 88.50
BRIDE'S BOWL,ROSE TO WHITE INSIDE,WHITE OUTSIDE,FLOWERS..... 65.00
BRIDE'S BOWL,SKIRTED,GREEN OVERLAY,APPLIED CLEAR RIM,SILVER
HOLDER................................................ 47.00
BRIDE'S BOWL,WHITE,ENAMELED YELLOW LILIES,PINK EDGE,SILVER
HOLDER................................................ 85.00
BRIDE'S DISH,PINK,OPALESCENT,FLUTED RIM,9 IN.DIAMETER....... 42.00
BRIDLE,BRASS,MARTINGALE.................................... 6.00
BRIDLE,BUTTON,ANIMAL PICTURE INSIDE,PAIR................... 8.00
BRIDLE,BUTTON,LIKE PAPERWEIGHT............................. 7.50
BRIDLE,HAME,KNOB TOP,BRASS,PAIR,ROSETTE,BRASS,PAIR,ENGLAND.. 18.00
BRIDLE,HITCHING POST,HORSE HEAD,FLUTED,LIONS' HEADS ON BASE,
1880,56 IN............................................ 95.00
BRIDLE,HITCHING WEIGHT,IRON............................... 5.00
BRIDLE,HORSE BRASS ON LEATHER,FIVE PIECES................. 10.00
BRIDLE,HORSE BRASS ON LEATHER,FOUR PIECES................. 9.00
BRIDLE,HORSE BRASS ON LEATHER,SIX PIECES.................. 11.00
BRIDLE,HORSE COLLAR....................................... 3.50
BRIDLE,ROSETTE,BLUE GROUND,FLORAL,BRASS BACK.............. 2.95
BRIDLE,ROSETTE,BRASS BACK,EAGLE & FLAG ON BLUE GROUND ON
FRONT................................................. 2.95
BRIDLE,ROSETTE,BRASS BACK,FRONT DESIGN OF FLOWERS,BLUE
GROUND................................................ 3.50
BRIDLE,ROSETTE,EMBOSSED LETTERS SAY NEW YORK,BRASS......... 7.50
BRIDLE,ROSETTE,HEART,DOUBLE,BRASS......................... 5.00
BRIDLE,ROSETTE,HUNTING DOGS,2 IN.DIAMETER,PAIR............ 40.00
BRIDLE,ROSETTE,LEATHER,INITIAL M.,PAIR.................... 4.75
BRIDLE,ROSETTE,SHIELD & 13 STARS,BRASS.................... 7.50
BRIDLE,ROSETTES,BRASS BACK,FRONT DESIGN OF FLOWERS,BLUE
GROUND,PAIR........................................... 6.75
BRIDLE,ROSETTES,HEART DESIGN,BRASS,PAIR................... 4.95
BRIDLE,ROSETTES,INITIAL M.,BRASS & LEATHER,PAIR.......... 4.75

```
BRIDLE,ROSETTES,U.S.CAVALRY,BRASS,PAIR......................    6.00
BRIDLE,SADDLEBAG,HAND-TOOLED,LEATHER,CIRCA 1920.............   15.00
BRIDLE,SADDLEBAG,LEATHER,CIRCA 1870.........................   15.00
BRIDLE,SADDLE,CALVARY OFFICER,WORLD WAR I...................   40.00
BRIDLE,SADDLE,PACK,SPANISH-AMERICAN WAR.....................   45.00
BRIDLE,SADDLE,RACING TYPE,BROWN LEATHER.....................   25.00
BRIDLE,SADDLE,SIDE,PLUSH-COVERED SEAT.......................   30.00
```

```
       BRISTOL GLASS WAS MADE IN BRISTOL,ENGLAND,AFTER THE
       1700S. THE BRISTOL GLASS MOST OFTEN SEEN TODAY IS A
       VICTORIAN,LIGHT-WEIGHT OPAQUE GLASS THAT IS OFTEN BLUE.
       SOME OF THE GLASS WAS DECORATED WITH ENAMELS.
BRISTOL,ATOMIZER,PINK,ENAMELED FLOWERS......................    8.00
BRISTOL,BASKET,BLUE,BLACK RIM & HANDLE......................   27.50
BRISTOL,BASKET,CLEAR,YELLOW THREADING.......................   37.50
BRISTOL,BOTTLE,DRESSER,GOLD LEAVES,WHITE GRAPES,CUP-SHAPE
  STOPPER...................................................   12.50
BRISTOL,BOWL,CASED,PINK OVER WHITE,SCALLOPED,FLORAL INSIDE &
  OUTSIDE...................................................   53.00
BRISTOL,BOWL,FINGER,BLUE,CIRCA 1830.........................   20.00
BRISTOL,BOWL,FINGER,CRANBERRY GLASS,3 IN.HIGH,4 3/4 IN.WIDE,
  SET OF 7..................................................   30.00
BRISTOL,BOWL,FLUTED EDGE,FOOTED,5 IN.HIGH,12-IN.DIAMETER....   29.00
BRISTOL,BOWL,ROSE,PORTRAIT,CHILD,BROWN EYES,CURLS,YELLOW,
  WHITE TOP.................................................   35.00
BRISTOL,BOWL,WASH,PITCHER,ROSES,FLORAL......................   40.00
BRISTOL,BOX,POWDER,BLUE,WATER,MOUNTAINS,BIRD,BRASS RIM &
  HINGE....................................................   36.00
BRISTOL,BOX,POWDER,ROUND,DOME LID,GOLD BAND OF GAMBOLING
  CHILDREN,1825............................................   48.00
BRISTOL,BOX,POWDER,SATIN FINISH,DECORATED,FOOTED,HINGED
  COVER....................................................   65.00
BRISTOL,COOKIE JAR,SATIN FINISH,FLORAL,SILVER PLATE.........   38.00
BRISTOL,DRESSER SET,PAIR COLOGNE BOTTLES,POWDER BOX,FLORAL,
  HAND-PAINTED.............................................   25.50
BRISTOL,DRESSER SET,POWDER BOX,TWO PERFUME BOTTLES,ENAMEL
  DECOR....................................................   32.50
BRISTOL,EWER,ALLOVER DECOR,GOLD & YELLOW ENAMEL,POLISHED
  PONTIL,BLUE..............................................   29.00
BRISTOL,EWER,ALLOVER YELLOW & GOLD ENAMEL,APPLIED HANDLE,
  BLUE,6 7/8 IN............................................   29.00
BRISTOL,EWER,MANTEL DECOR,WHITE GROUND,WILD ROSE PATTERN,
  14 IN.TALL,PAIR..........................................   38.00
BRISTOL,JAR,APOTHECARY,WHITE & PALE GREEN,HAND-PAINTED
  FLORAL,COVER.............................................   69.50
BRISTOL,JAR,BISCUIT,BLUE,ENAMELED CRANES,RUSHES,FLORAL,
  SILVER COVER.............................................   45.00
BRISTOL,JAR,JAM,FLORAL DECOR,SILVER-PLATED COVER & HANDLE...   18.00
BRISTOL,LAMP,BLUE OPAQUE,ENAMELED PINK,YELLOW,WHITE LILIES,
  GREEN LEAVES.............................................  110.00
BRISTOL,LAMP,ENAMELED,LILIES,PINK,YELLOW,WHITE,BLUE OPAQUE,
  8 1/2 IN.HIGH............................................  125.00
BRISTOL,LAMP,HANGING,WHITE,RUSSET COLOR FLORAL,BRASS CHAIN..   75.00
BRISTOL,MANTEL SET,URN & TWO VASES,MUSTARD WITH GREEN ENAMEL
  DECOR....................................................  125.00
BRISTOL,PLATE,YELLOW IRIS DECOR,POLISHED PONTIL,
  HAND-PAINTED,12 IN.......................................   12.50
BRISTOL,PLATTER,MULBERRY COLOR,BIRD PARADISE PATTERN,
  MATCHING DISH,COVER......................................   27.50
BRISTOL,SHADE FOR HANGING LAMP,PINK LILIES,GREEN LEAVES,
  14 IN....................................................   50.00
BRISTOL,SHADE,LAMP,ASTRAL TYPE,LAVENDER SHADING,ROSE & GREEN
  FLORAL...................................................   37.50
BRISTOL,SHAKER,SUGAR,BLUE,OPAQUE,SILVER PLATE TOP,6 IN.TALL.   20.00
BRISTOL,SHAKER,SUGAR,VASELINE,SILVER PLATE TOP,6 IN.........   20.00
BRISTOL,SMOKEBELL,WHITE,APPLIED BLUE BAND,CRIMPED RIM,
  8 1/2 IN.HIGH............................................   15.00
BRISTOL,SMOKEBELL,APPLIED RUBY RIM,SELF RING ON TOP,BRASS
  CHAIN,7 IN.TALL..........................................   12.50
BRISTOL,SPOONER,SCALLOPED EDGE,PINK FLORAL,GOLD LEAVES,GOLD
  TRIM.....................................................    7.00
BRISTOL,TOOTHPICK,GREEN,PUFFED RECTANGULAR PANELS...........   18.00
BRISTOL,URN,LEAF,BIRD,BUTTERFLY,FLOWER DECOR,COVER,TWO VASES  135.00
BRISTOL,VASE,ASTER & LEAF DECOR,9 IN.HIGH...................   18.50
BRISTOL,VASE,BEIGE,ENAMELED BOAT,6 1/2 IN...................    6.00
BRISTOL,VASE,BLUE,8 IN.TALL.................................    7.50
BRISTOL,VASE,BLUE,10 1/2 IN.................................   45.00
BRISTOL,VASE,BLUE,ENAMELED DECOR,BUTTERFLIES,11 1/2 IN.HIGH,
  PAIR.....................................................   85.00
BRISTOL,VASE,BLUE,ENAMELED FIRS,FUNNEL SHAPE ON ROUND BASE,
```

```
    6 3/4 IN.............................................   18.00
BRISTOL,VASE,BLUE,ENAMELED FLORAL,BIRD ON LIMB,9 IN.........   10.00
BRISTOL,VASE,BLUE,HAND-PAINTED PORTRAIT,MEDALLION OF GIRL,
    12 1/4 IN..........................................   39.00
BRISTOL,VASE,BLUE TO WHITE,MARSH SCENE,BIRDS,FLOWERS,
    10 1/2 IN.HIGH.....................................   19.00
BRISTOL,VASE,BROWN THISTLES,WHITE SATIN,SLENDER NECK,
    16 1/2 IN.TALL.....................................   35.00
BRISTOL,VASE,BULBOUS,BROWN GROUND,HAND-PAINTED FLORAL,
    8 IN.TALL..........................................   30.00
BRISTOL,VASE,CAFE AU LAIT,HEAVY ENAMEL DECORATION,11 IN.....   15.00
BRISTOL,VASE,CAMPHOR,SATIN,ENAMEL FLORAL,LEAF,BLOWN,CIRCA
    1880,11 IN.........................................   15.00
BRISTOL,VASE,CHILDREN,HAND-PAINTED,10 1/2 IN.TALL,PAIR......   75.00
BRISTOL,VASE,CHILDREN,HAND-PAINTED,11 IN.HIGH,PAIR.........   60.00
BRISTOL,VASE,CREAM,HAND-PAINTED FLOWERS,8 IN...............    9.50
BRISTOL,VASE,CUPIDS PLAYING AMONG CLOUDS,FLUTED TOP,10 IN...   27.50
BRISTOL,VASE,ENAMEL FLORAL DECOR,CUSTARD GLASS,9 1/2 IN....   15.00
BRISTOL,VASE,ENAMEL FLOWERS,RED,BROWN,SCALLOPED,GILT TOP,
    BLOWN,PAIR.........................................   55.00
BRISTOL,VASE,ENAMELED,BLUE,5 1/2 X 4 1/2 IN.,PAIR.........    6.75
BRISTOL,VASE,ENAMELED BLUE & PINK FLORAL,LEAVES,GOLD,
    13 1/4 IN.HIGH,PAIR................................  100.00
BRISTOL,VASE,ENAMELED FLORAL,GOLD LEAVES,FROSTED,10 IN.HIGH.   13.50
BRISTOL,VASE,ENAMELED FORGET-ME-NOTS,8 IN.................    8.00
BRISTOL,VASE,ENAMELED STORKS IN WATER,GREEN FERN,
    11 3/4 IN.TALL,PAIR................................   55.00
BRISTOL,VASE,FLOWER BOUQUET ON EACH SIDE,PEDESTAL BASE,
    11 1/2 IN.,PAIR....................................   25.00
BRISTOL,VASE,FLOWERS,BULBOUS,ROUGH PONTIL MARK,9 IN........   20.00
BRISTOL,VASE,FROSTED OFF-WHITE,RED BIRD ON RED BRANCH,
    11 3/4 IN.,PAIR....................................   38.00
BRISTOL,VASE,FROSTED,FLORAL,8 IN.HIGH,PAIR................   30.00
BRISTOL,VASE,GOLD ENAMEL,FLORAL,BULBOUS,SLENDER NECK.......    6.50
BRISTOL,VASE,GRAY-GREEN,ENAMELED FLOWERS,6 1/2 IN.TALL.....   10.00
BRISTOL,VASE,GRAY,WHITE & GOLD TRIM,FLUTED TOP,12 IN.HIGH,
    PAIR...............................................   38.00
BRISTOL,VASE,GRECIAN-DRAPED NYMPHS,WHITE MORNING GLORIES,
    FLORAL,13 IN.HIGH..................................   55.00
BRISTOL,VASE,GREEN SHADING TO CREAM COLOR,FLORAL ENAMEL
    TRIM,12 IN.TALL....................................   28.00
BRISTOL,VASE,GREEN,DAISY WREATH,PORTRAIT OF GIRLS,COVER,
    20 IN.,PAIR........................................  147.50
BRISTOL,VASE,GREEN,ENAMELED FLOWER DECOR,BULBOUS,RUFFLED,
    6 1/2 IN.,PAIR.....................................   22.00
BRISTOL,VASE,GREEN,FLUTED,GIRL,FLORAL,7 1/2 IN............   35.00
BRISTOL,VASE,HAND HOLDING,MILKY,HAND-PAINTED FLOWERS,LEAVES,
    PAIR...............................................   58.00
BRISTOL,VASE,HAND-DECORATED IN ENAMELS & OILS,11 1/2 IN.HIGH   14.50
BRISTOL,VASE,HAND-PAINTED ENAMEL FLORAL DECOR,OPAQUE WHITE
    SATIN,PAIR.........................................   25.00
BRISTOL,VASE,INSECTS,FLOWERS,HAND-PAINTED,PAIR............   50.00
BRISTOL,VASE,MULTICOLORED FLOWER DECOR,WHITE GROUND,PAIR....   30.00
BRISTOL,VASE,OPALESCENT,CRIMPED RIM,BLUE,BLOWN,7 IN.HIGH....   18.00
BRISTOL,VASE,OPAQUE,ENAMELED FLOWERS,FLUTED TOP,9 IN.,PAIR..   27.50
BRISTOL,VASE,OPAQUE,RUFFLED TOP..........................   10.00
BRISTOL,VASE,OVERLAY,WHITE,BULBOUS,PINK RUFFLED TOP,BLOWN...   15.50
BRISTOL,VASE,PALE GREEN,MULTICOLOR FLORAL,PAIR.............   35.00
BRISTOL,VASE,PINK OVERLAY ON WHITE,ENAMEL BIRD ON BRANCH,
    5 1/2 IN...........................................   15.00
BRISTOL,VASE,PINK,CRANE,REEDS,5 1/2 IN....................   16.50
BRISTOL,VASE,PINK,ENAMELED FLORAL,CASED,5 1/2 IN..........    8.00
BRISTOL,VASE,PINK,ENAMELED ROSES,BLUE,PINK FOLIAGE,WHITE
    LINING,PAIR........................................   25.00
BRISTOL,VASE,PINK,WHITE CASING,ENAMEL WHITE FLORAL,CIRCULAR
    FOOT,11 IN.........................................   55.00
BRISTOL,VASE,PINK,WHITE CASING,ENAMELED,BULBOUS,6 IN.......    8.00
BRISTOL,VASE,PORTRAIT,ENAMELING,SIGNED STAHL,10 IN.........   16.50
BRISTOL,VASE,POWDER BLUE,BLOWN,3 1/4 IN.DIAMETER AT LIP,
    4 1/4 IN.HIGH......................................   12.00
BRISTOL,VASE,ROBINS-EGG BLUE,HAND-PAINTED,10 IN...........   18.50
BRISTOL,VASE,TURQUOISE ENAMEL FLOWERS,GREEN LEAVES,BULBOUS,
    11 IN.HIGH.........................................   21.00
BRISTOL,VASE,TURQUOISE,OVERALL FLORAL SPRAYS,GOLD-BEADED
    TRIM,1880..........................................   25.00
BRISTOL,VASE,VINE DECOR,BLUE & GOLD LEAVES,BLUEBIRD,
    10 1/4 IN.,PAIR....................................   37.50
BRISTOL,VASE,WHITE,ENAMEL FLORAL DECOR,STRAWBERRIES,CRIMPTED
    TOP................................................   12.00
BRISTOL,VASE,WHITE,FROSTED,ENAMEL DECOR,10 IN.............   17.50
BRISTOL,VASE,WHITE,GOLD COLOR FLOWERS,SCALLOPED,FLUTED,
```

```
        8 IN.,PAIR.................................................    28.75
BRISTOL,VASE,WHITE ENAMEL FLORAL,YELLOW LEAVES,TWO RED
        BERRIES,7 1/4 IN..........................................    25.00
BRISTOL,VASE,WHITE GROUND,SCENE,COLONIAL LADY,MAN,
        HAND-PAINTED,8 IN.........................................    15.00
BRISTOL,VASE,WHITE OPAQUE,BIRDS,RED & GOLD FOLIAGE,ROUGH
        PONTIL,PAIR...............................................    31.00
BRISTOL,VASE,WHITE SHADING TO ROSE,RUFFLED TOP,9 3/4 IN.....    15.00
BRISTOL,VASE,WHITE TO BLUE,PINK FLUTED TOP,OVERLAY FLORAL,
        FROSTED,12 IN.............................................    60.00
BRISTOL,VASE,WHITE TOP,CASED WITH BLUE,RUFFLED,6 1/4 IN.,
        PAIR......................................................    30.00
BRISTOL,VASE,WHITE-FROSTED,ENAMELED FLORAL,PINK-CASED FLUTED
        TOP,11 IN.................................................    45.00
BRONZE,SEE ALSO,LISTING UNDER ARTIST NAME
BRONZE,ASHTRAY-MATCH HOLDER,CURVILINEAR,SPREAD-WINGED OWL,
        GORHAM....................................................    46.00
BRONZE,ASHTRAY,ADVERTISING,SANFORD'S INK,SHOWS BOTTLE.......     5.00
BRONZE,BISON,CHARGING,SIGNED ROGERS,11 IN.LONG,7 IN.HIGH....   195.00
BRONZE,BOOKEND,CHERUB,FROG,BUTTERFLY,SIGNED,DATED,6 1/2 IN.,
        PAIR......................................................    45.00
BRONZE,BOOKEND,KNIGHT,MARBLE BASE,7 IN.,PAIR.................    35.00
BRONZE,BOOKEND,LINDBERGH,PAIR..............................    17.50
BRONZE,BOOKEND,LINDBERGH,PLANE & EAGLE,MARKED & DATED,PAIR..    20.00
BRONZE,BOOKEND,PARTIALLY OPEN BOOK,PARROT,EDGAR A.POE POEMS,
        ENAMEL,PAIR...............................................    23.00
BRONZE,BOOKEND,THE THINKER,PAIR............................    25.00
BRONZE,BOWL,MOTTLED GREEN ENAMEL,SIGNED CARL SORENSEN,ART
        NOUVEAU PERIOD............................................    30.00
BRONZE,BOX,JEWEL,EBONY,JADE POSTS,PLAQUES,MYTHICAL SCENES,
        18TH CENTURY..............................................   750.00
BRONZE,BOX,JEWEL,GOLD-WASHED,LID HAS SEMIPRECIOUS STONES,
        AUSTRIA...................................................   125.00
BRONZE,BUST OF BEETHOVEN,MARBLE PEDESTAL,SIGNED H.MULLER....    65.00
BRONZE,BUST,FRENCH,GILDED,NYMPH,MAURICE BOUVAL,1920.........   225.00
BRONZE,BUST,FRENCH,INNOCENCE,GEORGES VERON,18 IN. TALL......    90.00
BRONZE,BUST,FRENCH,NYMPH,G.GODET,8 3/4 IN. HIGH.............    90.00
BRONZE,BUST,FRENCH,ONDINE,HENRI JACOBS,20 1/4 IN. HIGH......   200.00
BRONZE,BUST,GEORGE WASHINGTON,MARBLE BASE,4 IN.............    15.75
BRONZE,BUST,GERMAN,YOUNG GIRL,ERNEST WAUTE,5 1/2 IN. HIGH...    60.00
BRONZE,BUST,GERMAN,8 1/4 IN. HIGH..........................    90.00
BRONZE,BUST,LONGFELLOW,MOUNTED ON WOODEN PLAQUE,METAL
        PRODUCTS CO.,1913.........................................    20.00
BRONZE,CANDLESTICK,COBRA,CHINA,PAIR........................    35.00
BRONZE,CANDLESTICK,FIGURE OF CHILD,SUPPORTS SOCKET,MARBLE
        PEDESTAL,PAIR.............................................   175.00
BRONZE,CANDLESTICK,FLEUR-DE-LIS MOTIF,25 IN.,PAIR............   125.00
BRONZE,CANDLESTICK,FRENCH,SILVERED,GEORGES DE DEURE,
        1868-1928.................................................   130.00
BRONZE,CANDLESTICK,LOUIS PHILIPPE,10 1/2 IN.TALL,PAIR.......    95.00
BRONZE,CANDLESTICK,ORNAMENTED,FOOTED FLEUR-DE-LIS BASE,
        25 IN.,PAIR...............................................   165.00
BRONZE,CANNON,MINIATURE....................................    10.00
BRONZE,CANNON,MINIATURE,FRANCE.............................    15.00
BRONZE,CHAMBER STICK,LILY PAD,FLOWER,FROG HANDLE,BARYE,
        4 IN.,PAIR................................................   425.00
BRONZE,CIGAR LIGHTER,HALF-MOON FACE SHAPE...................    75.00
BRONZE,CLOCK,GIRL,FOUNTAIN,MARBLE BASE,SIGNED,PAIR MATCHING
        URNS......................................................   400.00
BRONZE,DESK SET,BULL FIGHTING BEAR,GREEN ONYX BASE.........   160.00
BRONZE,DOG,SIGNED BARYE,5 IN.LONG,3 IN.HIGH................   225.00
BRONZE,DOORSTOP,SHIP,MAYFLOWER,11 1/2 IN.HIGH X 13 IN.ACROSS    18.00
BRONZE,EPERGNE,GESCHUTZE BIRDS ON SILVER BOWL EDGE,GLASS
        VASE,AUSTRIAN.............................................   100.00
BRONZE,FIGURE,A TARTAR,SIGNED & DATED 1871,TIFFANY & CO.....   325.00
BRONZE,FIGURE,MISS LIBERTY,HOLDS TWO THREE-ARMED TORCHES,
        WIRED,4 1/2 FT............................................   495.00
BRONZE,FIGURINE,ADAM & EVE EATING APPLE,SIGNED KORSCHA,DATED
        IVIV,5 IN.................................................   250.00
BRONZE,FIGURINE,ANTLERED DEER IN FOREST,SIGNED P.J.MENE.....   250.00
BRONZE,FIGURINE,APOLLO,SIGNED SOBRE,28 IN.HIGH.............   325.00
BRONZE,FIGURINE,ARAB MONEYLENDER SITTING ON RUG,POLYCHROMED,
        VIENNA....................................................    55.00
BRONZE,FIGURINE,ARAB ON CAMEL,VIENNA,5 IN.HIGH,5 IN.LONG....    75.00
BRONZE,FIGURINE,ARAB RIDER,GUN,SIGNED DUBUCAND,19 IN.LONG,
        20 IN.HIGH................................................   325.00
BRONZE,FIGURINE,ARAB SCRIBE SITTING ON CARPET,LEGS CROSSED,
        AUSTRIA...................................................    60.00
BRONZE,FIGURINE,ARAB STALLION & MARE,SILVER FINISH,SIGNED
        MENE,5 IN.LONG............................................   200.00
BRONZE,FIGURINE,BASKETBALL PLAYER,CIRCA 1920,5 IN..........     3.50
```

BRONZE,FIGURINE,BEAR STANDING UPRIGHT,MALACHITE ROCK,
27 IN.HIGH................................................ 450.00
BRONZE,FIGURINE,BEAR,ON MARBLE BALL,MARBLE BASE,
6 3/4 IN.HIGH............................................. 115.00
BRONZE,FIGURINE,BEAR,VIENNA,3 IN.HIGH X 6 IN.LONG.......... 85.00
BRONZE,FIGURINE,BIRD HOLDING FISH IN BEAK,SIGNED DE
LABRIERRE,5 IN.HIGH....................................... 175.00
BRONZE,FIGURINE,BIRD WITH FISH IN BEAK,SIGNED DE LABRIERRE,
6 1/2 IN.LONG............................................. 135.00
BRONZE,FIGURINE,BIRD,ON TREE STUMP,SIGNED L.CARVIN,
5 IN.HIGH,PAIR............................................ 125.00
BRONZE,FIGURINE,BIRD,SIGNED PAUTROT,7 IN.LONG X 5 IN.HIGH... 175.00
BRONZE,FIGURINE,BIRDS BATTLING,SIGNED DE LABRIERRE,9 1/2 X
12 IN.HIGH................................................ 365.00
BRONZE,FIGURINE,BLOODHOUND,SIGNED FREMIET,6 IN.LONG,
6 IN.HIGH................................................. 200.00
BRONZE,FIGURINE,BOXER,CIRCA,5 IN......................... 3.50
BRONZE,FIGURINE,BOY HOLDING FLOWERS,8 IN.HIGH............. 45.00
BRONZE,FIGURINE,BOY RIDING PIG,SIGNED,VIENNA,2 5/8 X 3 X
6 IN.HIGH................................................. 135.00
BRONZE,FIGURINE,BOY WITH TWO PIGS UNDER ARMS,3 1/2 IN.HIGH.. 32.00
BRONZE,FIGURINE,BOY,DUTCH,SEATED,IVORY FACE,SIGNED
P.TENEYZIZUK.............................................. 50.00
BRONZE,FIGURINE,BOY,GIRL,SIGNED PECHEUSE,11 IN.HIGH,PAIR.... 50.00
BRONZE,FIGURINE,BOY,KNICKERS,STRAW HAT,SAYS MENTION AU
SALON,BOURET.............................................. 110.00
BRONZE,FIGURINE,BOY,PAGE,PLUME,BUCKLE SHOES,FLOWING GARMENT,
4 1/2 IN.................................................. 32.00
BRONZE,FIGURINE,BUFFALO,ENAMEL,WHITE MARBLE BASE,8 IN.HIGH,
11 IN.LONG................................................ 75.00
BRONZE,FIGURINE,BUFFALO,SIGNED HAWKINS,1842,17 IN.LONG,
11 IN.HIGH,PAIR........................................... 550.00
BRONZE,FIGURINE,BULL,BY C.CLESINGER,ROME 1858,18 1/2 X
17 IN.HIGH................................................ 450.00
BRONZE,FIGURINE,BULL,SIGNED BARYE,4 1/2 IN. X 3 IN......... 250.00
BRONZE,FIGURINE,BULL,SIGNED BARYE,7 IN.LONG,6 IN.HIGH...... 350.00
BRONZE,FIGURINE,BULL,SIGNED GATTI,16 IN.LONG.............. 300.00
BRONZE,FIGURINE,BULL,SIGNED I.BONHEUR,5 IN. X 4 IN........ 235.00
BRONZE,FIGURINE,BULL,SIGNED ROSA B,13 IN.................. 500.00
BRONZE,FIGURINE,BUST,ARAB CHIEF,MOUNTED ON MARBLE BASE,
GIEDECKE,37 IN............................................ 750.00
BRONZE,FIGURINE,BUST,WOMAN,18 IN.HIGH,JEF LAMBEAUX,6 IN.HIGH
MARBLE...................................................1,200.00
BRONZE,FIGURINE,BUST DIANA,SIGNED PARIJS,20 IN.HIGH....... 300.00
BRONZE,FIGURINE,BUST OF ADIA,SIGNED DILLEY,1880,
4 1/2 IN.HIGH............................................. 75.00
BRONZE,FIGURINE,BUST OF GREEK WOMAN,SIGNED E.VILLANIS,
22 IN.HIGH................................................ 325.00
BRONZE,FIGURINE,CAMEL,LYING WITH FOLDED LEGS,2 1/4 X
1 3/4 IN.HIGH............................................. 22.00
BRONZE,FIGURINE,CAMEL,SIGNED A.BARYE,5 IN.LONG,5 IN.HIGH.... 175.00
BRONZE,FIGURINE,CAMEL,VIENNA,2 1/2 IN. X 3 IN.LONG......... 35.00
BRONZE,FIGURINE,CAMEL,9 IN.HIGH,10 IN.LONG................ 132.00
BRONZE,FIGURINE,CAT & TRAP,4 IN.LONG,SEPARATE MOUSE,VIENNA.. 75.00
BRONZE,FIGURINE,CAT,BEATING WASHTUB DRUM,VIENNA,
4 1/2 IN.HIGH............................................. 90.00
BRONZE,FIGURINE,CAT,COOKING,MOUSE IN PAN,VIENNA,
4 1/2 IN.LONG............................................. 90.00
BRONZE,FIGURINE,CAT,FALLEN BIRD,BASE FLOOR OUTLINED LIKE
TIER,P.J.MENE............................................. 110.00
BRONZE,FIGURINE,CAT,SIGNED GARDET,4 1/2 IN.LONG,
3 1/2 IN.HIGH............................................. 150.00
BRONZE,FIGURINE,CAT,TIPSY,HOLDS BOTTLE,VIENNA,2 IN.HIGH.... 35.00
BRONZE,FIGURINE,CHILDREN HOLDING INSTRUMENTS,DANCING,MARBLE
BASE,9 IN................................................. 210.00
BRONZE,FIGURINE,CHINESE WOMAN,SIGNED WITH CHINESE
CHARACTERS,25 IN.HIGH..................................... 500.00
BRONZE,FIGURINE,CLASSICAL WOMAN,SIGNED CLESINGER &
BARBEDIENNE............................................... 90.00
BRONZE,FIGURINE,COSSACK & GIRL ON HORSE,RUSSIA,SIGNED
A.M.BONOGUY,11 IN......................................... 525.00
BRONZE,FIGURINE,COW & CALF,P.J.MENE,14 IN.LONG X 11 IN.HIGH. 550.00
BRONZE,FIGURINE,CROUCHED JAGUAR,SIGNED BARYE,7 IN.LONG,
3 1/2 IN.HIGH............................................. 250.00
BRONZE,FIGURINE,CROUCHING VENUS,18TH CENTURY,SIGNED
SCARPANI,21 X 31 IN....................................... 550.00
BRONZE,FIGURINE,DACHSHUND,10 IN.LONG,5 1/4 IN.HIGH......... 107.00
BRONZE,FIGURINE,DANCER,CREATION BALL,SWORD,SCHMIDTHOFER,17TH
CENTURY................................................... 275.00
BRONZE,FIGURINE,DANCER,EMIL KIEMLEN,1869,12 1/2 IN. HIGH.... 300.00
BRONZE,FIGURINE,DANCING NUDE HOLDING TAMBOURINE,SIGNED

```
         V.SEIFERT,VIENNA.........................................   125.00
BRONZE,FIGURINE,DANTE,ARM RESTING ON VOLUME OF  DIVINE
  COMEDY.................................................... 175.00
BRONZE,FIGURINE,DARKY RIDING PIG,VIENNA,1 1/4 X
  1 1/2 IN.HIGH............................................    45.00
BRONZE,FIGURINE,DEER MUNCHING LEAVES,SIGNED P.J.MENE,7 IN. X
  7 IN.HIGH................................................  .385.00
BRONZE,FIGURINE,DESDEMONA,HIPPOLYTE,1863-1920,21 IN. HIGH...  175.00
BRONZE,FIGURINE,DIANA AND DEER,23 IN.HIGH..................  325.00
BRONZE,FIGURINE,DISCUS THROWER,CIRCA 1920,5 IN.............    3.50
BRONZE,FIGURINE,DOG,FERDINAND PAUTROT,FRENCH...............  300.00
BRONZE,FIGURINE,DOG,ORIENTAL,WINGED FEET,18 IN.LONG,PAIR....  500.00
BRONZE,FIGURINE,DOG,SIGNED MENE,12 IN.LONG X 8 IN.HIGH.....  300.00
BRONZE,FIGURINE,DOG,SIGNED MOIGNIEZ,8 1/2 IN.LONG,5 IN.HIGH.  225.00
BRONZE,FIGURINE,DOG,SIGNED PAUTROT,1/ IN.LONG X 9 IN.HIGH...  300.00
BRONZE,FIGURINE,DOG & BALL ON FIGURAL CARPET,SIGNED P.J.MENE  135.00
BRONZE,FIGURINE,DOG CHAINED TO FENCE,SIGNED VALLON,
  10 IN.HIGH...............................................  325.00
BRONZE,FIGURINE,DOG ON FIGURAL CARPET,SIGNED BARYE.........  150.00
BRONZE,FIGURINE,DOGS ATTACKING A BOAR,SIGNED P.J.MENE,18 X
  12 IN.HIGH................................................  600.00
BRONZE,FIGURINE,DOGS,CHAINED TO POST,R.WINDER 1892,4 1/2 X
  5 X 3 IN.HIGH.............................................   45.00
BRONZE,FIGURINE,DUTCH WORKMAN,HEIDKEHR,SIGNED F.RICHTPRJEC,
  8 1/2 IN.TALL............................................  125.00
BRONZE,FIGURINE,EAGLE ON CALCIDE ROCK,7 IN.WINGSPREAD......   35.50
BRONZE,FIGURINE,ELEPHANT,IVORY TUSKS,ONYX BASE,AUSTRIA,5 X
  6 IN.HIGH.................................................   55.00
BRONZE,FIGURINE,ELEPHANT,IVORY TUSKS,TEAK STAND,9 IN.HIGH...  220.00
BRONZE,FIGURINE,ELEPHANT,RUNNING,SIGNED BARYE,10 IN.LONG,
  6 IN.HIGH.................................................  375.00
BRONZE,FIGURINE,ELEPHANT,TRUNK DOWN,SIGNED BARYE,5 1/2 IN. X
  8 IN.....................................................  350.00
BRONZE,FIGURINE,ELEPHANT WITH CALF,CHINA,17 IN.LONG.......  165.00
BRONZE,FIGURINE,FARM HORSES PULLING DRAG,SIGNED F.CORNIE,
  24 IN.LONG...............................................  550.00
BRONZE,FIGURINE,FEMALE WITH CHILD,BY A.CEYZOVOX,DATED 1710,
  22 IN.HIGH...............................................  160.00
BRONZE,FIGURINE,FIGHTING LION,SIGNED BARYE,8 1/4 IN.LONG X
  4 IN.HIGH................................................  350.00
BRONZE,FIGURINE,FISHERBOY,SIGNED A.BOFILL,18 IN.HIGH.......  275.00
BRONZE,FIGURINE,FOO DOG,MOTHER,PUP,1820,MOTHER IS 5 IN.TALL,
  PAIR....................................................  110.00
BRONZE,FIGURINE,FOO DOG,ON BASE,18TH CENTURY,5 1/8 IN.TALL..   65.00
BRONZE,FIGURINE,FOX,SEATED,BROWN,BLACK,VIENNA,2 IN.........   24.00
BRONZE,FIGURINE,FRENCH FARMER COUPLE,L'ANGELUS,27 IN.HIGH...  275.00
BRONZE,FIGURINE,GALLOPING ELEPHANT,SIGNED BARYE,7 1/2 X
  5 IN.HIGH................................................  425.00
BRONZE,FIGURINE,GEISHA,CARRIES TRAY,VIENNA,3 IN.HIGH.......   50.00
BRONZE,FIGURINE,GIRL HOLDS BASKET,SUNBONNET,MARBLE BASE,
  7 1/2 X K IN.............................................   90.00
BRONZE,FIGURINE,GIRL ON BASKET,MARBLE BASE,JOSEPH CHERE,
  1830,18 IN...............................................  395.00
BRONZE,FIGURINE,GIRL,DUTCH,BONNET,WOODEN SHOES,MARBLE BASE,
  KECK.....................................................   32.00
BRONZE,FIGURINE,GIRL,NUDE,BENDING OVER,SIGNED V.H.SEIFERT,
  22 IN.HIGH...............................................  400.00
BRONZE,FIGURINE,GIRL,SKATES,COAT,FURS,MUFF,MARBLE BASE,
  SIGNED H.KECK............................................   32.00
BRONZE,FIGURINE,GOAT WITH SUCKLING KID,SIGNED PARMENTIER,
  8 1/2 IN.LONG............................................  250.00
BRONZE,FIGURINE,GOOSE,SPREAD WINGS,REED BASE,SIGNED
  L.V.PAGELLI.............................................   75.00
BRONZE,FIGURINE,GRAZING EWE,SIGNED ROSA B.,8 IN.LONG X
  6 IN.HIGH................................................  500.00
BRONZE,FIGURINE,GREEK WOMAN,OPHELIA,SIGNED A.P.MOREAU,
  18 IN.HIGH...............................................  300.00
BRONZE,FIGURINE,GREEK WOMAN,SIGNED BRONZES D'ART,BRUXELLES,
  27 IN.HIGH...............................................  285.00
BRONZE,FIGURINE,GREEK WOMAN,SIGNED H.DUMAIGE,17 IN.HIGH,PAIR  250.00
BRONZE,FIGURINE,HARLEQUIN,MARBLE BASE,SIGNED SCHMIDT-HOFER,
  10 1/2 IN................................................  145.00
BRONZE,FIGURINE,HORSE,CHRISTOPHE FRATIN,1800-65......ILLUS..  800.00
BRONZE,FIGURINE,HORSE,SIGNED P.J.MENE,16 IN.LONG X
  11 1/2 IN.HIGH...........................................  650.00
BRONZE,FIGURINE,HORSE,STANDING,SIGNED VALLON,10 IN.LONG.....  350.00
BRONZE,FIGURINE,HUNTER WITH DOG,SIGNED H.MILLER,25 IN.HIGH..  450.00
BRONZE,FIGURINE,HUNTING DOGS,PIERRE JULES MENE,1810-79......  375.00
BRONZE,FIGURINE,INDIAN CHIEF,BOW,ARROW,POLYCHROME,MARBLE
  BASE,C.KAUBA.............................................  375.00
BRONZE,FIGURINE,INDIAN STANDING BY CANOE,VIENNA,7 IN. X
```

```
    9 IN.LONG.............................................. 350.00
BRONZE,FIGURINE,INDIAN,HORSE, APPEAL TO THE GREAT SPIRIT,
    CYRUS DALLIN......................................... 750.00
BRONZE,FIGURINE,INDIAN,MOUNTAIN LION,E.DEEMING,ROMAN BRONZE
    WORKS,N.Y............................................ 800.00
BRONZE,FIGURINE,INFANT IN HIGHCHAIR,BY JUAN CLARA,GILTEC,
    9 3/4 IN.HIGH........................................ 375.00
BRONZE,FIGURINE,JAGUAR CLUTCHING HERON,SIGNED BARYE,4 1/2 X
    3 1/4 IN............................................. 210.00
BRONZE,FIGURINE,JAGUAR HOLDING PHEASANT,SIGNED BARYE,3 1/2 X
    5 IN.LONG............................................ 250.00
BRONZE,FIGURINE,JAGUAR RESTING,SIGNED BARYE,7 IN.LONG X
    3 1/2 IN.HIGH........................................ 250.00
BRONZE,FIGURINE,JASON OF GOLDEN FLEECE,SIGNED E.BARBEDIENNE,
    24 IN.HIGH........................................... 225.00
BRONZE,FIGURINE,LADY,FLOWING GARMENT,SEATED,HOLDS VASE,
    SIGNED MOREAU........................................ 350.00
BRONZE,FIGURINE,LEOPARD,STALKING,12 IN.LONG,4 1/2 IN.HIGH... 75.00
BRONZE,FIGURINE,LION,EATING,SIGNED BARYE,8 IN.LONG,4 IN.HIGH 350.00
BRONZE,FIGURINE,LION FIGHTING OFF SNAKE,SIGNED BARYE,
    9 IN.HIGH............................................ 450.00
BRONZE,FIGURINE,LION,ROARING,SIGNED BARYE,5 IN. HIGH,
    8 IN.LONG............................................ 250.00
BRONZE,FIGURINE,LION,SIGNED BARYE,R.BARBEDIENNE,FONDEUR,
    PARIS,10 IN.LONG..................................... 85.00
BRONZE,FIGURINE,LION,STRETCHED,YAWNING,SIGNED NYATT ANNAV,
    GORHAM & CO.......................................... 100.00
BRONZE,FIGURINE,LION,STRIDING,9 1/4 IN.LONG,5 3/4 IN.HIGH... 75.00
BRONZE,FIGURINE,LIONESS,BARYE.......................ILLUS.. 650.00
BRONZE,FIGURINE,LITTLE GIRL,STANDING ON STOOL,ONE SHOE OFF &
    IN HER HAND.......................................... 85.00
BRONZE,FIGURINE,MAKING LOVE,SIGNED R.MALLORY................ 450.00
BRONZE,FIGURINE,MAN CARRIES TOOL CASE,MARBLE BASE,6 IN.HIGH. 90.00
BRONZE,FIGURINE,MAN WITH HORSE,WOODEN BASE,EMBOSSED FRANCE,
    PAIR................................................. 57.50
```

BARYE BRONZE LIONESS

BRONZE HORSE STATUETTE, CHRISTOPHE FRATIN

BRONZE,FIGURINE,MARQUIS DE LAFAYETTE,AIME-JULES DALOU,
  1838-1902................................................... 750.00
BRONZE,FIGURINE,MERCURY,BROWN PATINA,SIGNED F.BARBEDIENNE,
  32 1/2 IN.HIGH.............................................. 180.00
BRONZE,FIGURINE,MERCURY,MARBLE BASE,SIGNED DE BALANGE,
  19 IN.HIGH................................................. 100.00
BRONZE,FIGURINE,MERCURY,SIGNED SOBRE,28 IN.HIGH.............. 325.00
BRONZE,FIGURINE,MINIATURE,NEGRO BOY ON RED SLED,VIENNA,
  1/2 IN.TALL................................................ 15.00
BRONZE,FIGURINE,MINIATURE,NEGRO CHILDREN,RED UMBRELLA,
  VIENNA,1/2 IN.TALL......................................... 15.00
BRONZE,FIGURINE,MONKEY ON ROCK,THUMBING NOSE,VIENNA,
  2 1/2 IN.HIGH.............................................. 45.00
BRONZE,FIGURINE,MONKEY SCRATCHING LEG,SIGNED JACMARDE,
  4 IN.LONG.................................................. 125.00
BRONZE,FIGURINE,MOOSE,EATING,MARBLE BASE,SIGNED MASON,
  4 IN.LONG.................................................. 125.00
BRONZE,FIGURINE,MOUSE EATING CHEESE,MARBLE BASE,SIGNED
  MASSON,4 X 4 IN............................................ 125.00
BRONZE,FIGURINE,MUSICIANS,DRUM,CYMBALS,LEADER,BASS,RED
  DEVIL,9 PIECES............................................. 90.00
BRONZE,FIGURINE,NAPOLEON ON HORSE,WHITE ROCK BASE,5 IN. X
  6 IN.HIGH.................................................. 130.00
BRONZE,FIGURINE,NAPOLEON,10 IN.HIGH......................... 215.00
BRONZE,FIGURINE,NEWSBOY,RUNNING,NATURAL STONE BASE,SIGNED
  D.A.PONZO.................................................. 225.00
BRONZE,FIGURINE,NOBLE IN CHAIN MAIL ON HORSE,SIGNED
  A.LANCERAY,RUSSIA.......................................... 650.00
BRONZE,FIGURINE,NUDE CHILD,STANDING,SIGNED J.VIERTHALER,
  13 IN.TALL................................................. 135.00
BRONZE,FIGURINE,NUDE GOLFER,SIGNED A.A.WEINMAN,18 IN.HIGH... 350.00
BRONZE,FIGURINE,NUDE WOMAN,LOOKS INTO HAND MIRROR,MARBLE
  BASE,E.WINKLER............................................. 550.00
BRONZE,FIGURINE,NUDE,HOLDS CASTANETS,SIGNED P.HOFFMAN,
  9 1/2 IN.TALL.............................................. 75.00
BRONZE,FIGURINE,NUDE,SIGNED J.BENK,9 IN.HIGH................ 180.00
BRONZE,FIGURINE,OWL PERCHED ON DOME,BASE,SIGNED M.SIX,
  6 IN.HIGH.................................................. 60.00
BRONZE,FIGURINE,PAIR OF CAMELS IN CARAVAN,ARAB LEADING,
  AUSTRIA.................................................... 38.00
BRONZE,FIGURINE,PAIR RELAY RUNNERS,CIRCA 1920,5 IN.......... 10.00
BRONZE,FIGURINE,PAN BLOWING HIS PIPES,1850,5 1/4 IN.TALL.... 50.00
BRONZE,FIGURINE,PAN,RECLINING,TWO BEAR CUBS,SIGNED
  E.FREMIET,FRANCE........................................... 215.00
BRONZE,FIGURINE,PANTHER STALKING TWO RABBITS,SIGNED
  DELABRIERRE,7 IN........................................... 135.00
BRONZE,FIGURINE,PANTHER,CROUCHING,SIGNED L.BUREAU,17 IN.LONG 110.00
BRONZE,FIGURINE,PANTHER,SELF BASE,SIGNED BARYE,7 3/4 IN. X
  4 1/2 IN.HIGH.............................................. 150.00
BRONZE,FIGURINE,PARROT ON PERCH,RED,GREEN,BLUE,VIENNA,
  6 IN.HIGH.................................................. 75.00
BRONZE,FIGURINE,PARTRIDGE,SIGNED MOIGNIEZ,10 1/2 IN.LONG X
  10 IN.HIGH................................................. 350.00
BRONZE,FIGURINE,PEKINESE STANDING WITH TILTED HEAD,VIENNA,
  3 1/2 IN.LONG.............................................. 75.00
BRONZE,FIGURINE,PHEASANT,REALISTIC FEATHERS,SIGNED,
  F.PAUTROT,13 IN.HIGH....................................... 200.00
BRONZE,FIGURINE,PHEASANT,SIGNED MOIGNIEZ,10 IN.LONG,
  14 IN.HIGH................................................. 225.00
BRONZE,FIGURINE,PHEASANT,SIGNED PAUTROT,9 IN.HIGH X
  5 1/2 IN.LONG.............................................. 185.00
BRONZE,FIGURINE,POLAR BEAR,SEATED,VIENNA,3 IN. X 3 IN....... 75.00
BRONZE,FIGURINE,RABBIT,RUNNING,WOOD BASE,VIENNA,
  9 1/2 IN.LONG.............................................. 75.00
BRONZE,FIGURINE,RACE RUNNER,CIRCA 1920,5 IN................. 3.50
BRONZE,FIGURINE,RECLINING GOAT,SIGNED POUTROT,5 IN.LONG,
  3 IN.HIGH.................................................. 125.00
BRONZE,FIGURINE,REINDEER BUCK WITH DOE,P.J.MENE............. 225.00
BRONZE,FIGURINE,RIFLEMAN,CIRCA 1920,3 X 5 IN................ 3.50
BRONZE,FIGURINE,RIFLEMAN,CIRCA 1920,5 IN.................... 3.50
BRONZE,FIGURINE,ROARING LION FIGHTING OFF SNAKE,SIGNED
  BARYE,6 IN.HIGH............................................ 450.00
BRONZE,FIGURINE,ROARING LION,SIGNED BARYE,6 1/2 X 11 IN.LONG 250.00
BRONZE,FIGURINE,ROBIN,AUSTRIA,5 3/4 IN..................... 40.00
BRONZE,FIGURINE,ROMULUS,REMUS,SHE-WOLF,SIGNED NELLI ROMA,
  2 1/2 IN.TALL.............................................. 45.00
BRONZE,FIGURINE,RUBENS THE PAINTER,SIGNED KAUBA,20 IN.HIGH.. 650.00
BRONZE,FIGURINE,RUNNING ELEPHANT,SIGNED BARYE, 5 X
  7 1/2 IN.LONG.............................................. 425.00
BRONZE,FIGURINE,RUSSIAN WOLFHOUND,WOODEN BASE,PAIR.......... 100.00
BRONZE,FIGURINE,SALOME,G.FLAMAND,8 1/2 IN.................. 175.00

```
BRONZE,FIGURINE,SAMAURAI WARRIOR,HOLDS SWORD,BOW,
  26 1/4 IN.HIGH......................................................   450.00
BRONZE,FIGURINE,SATYR,WOMAN,CHILD,SIGNED CLODION,18 IN.HIGH.   450.00
BRONZE,FIGURINE,SCOTTIE ON HIND LEGS,BEGGING,SIGNED
  MARGUERITE KIRMSE.................................................   110.00
BRONZE,FIGURINE,SEAL ON ROCKS,SIGNED E.ANGELA,1917,GORHAM,
  5 IN.HIGH.........................................................    83.00
BRONZE,FIGURINE,SEATED LION,COILED TAIL,SIGNED BARYE,5 1/2 X
  7 IN.HIGH.........................................................   175.00
BRONZE,FIGURINE,SETTER AT POINT,MAKER JOE CUMMING,ANTONIO
  PICCIOLA,9 IN.....................................................   250.00
BRONZE,FIGURINE,SETTER,BASE,SIGNED P.J.MENE,11 1/4 X
  5 3/4 IN.HIGH.....................................................   150.00
BRONZE,FIGURINE,SHEPHERD DOG,2 1/2 IN.TALL,3 IN.LONG..........    12.00
BRONZE,FIGURINE,SISTER APOLLO,SIGNED SOBRE,17 IN.HIGH.......   210.00
BRONZE,FIGURINE,SNAKE,BLACK,COILED,J.MUNK,1901,REED &
  BARTON,4 IN.HIGH..................................................   300.00
BRONZE,FIGURINE,SOLDIER ON HORSE,EMBEDDED JEWELS,ORIENTAL...   190.00
BRONZE,FIGURINE,SOLDIER WEARING CHAIN MAIL,SIGNED
  A.LANCERAY,RUSSIA.................................................   625.00
BRONZE,FIGURINE,SOLDIER,WOMAN ON HORSE,SIGNED WOLF,RUSSIA,
  12 IN.HIGH........................................................   550.00
BRONZE,FIGURINE,STAG,VIENNA,2 1/2 IN. X 5 IN...................    55.00
BRONZE,FIGURINE,STANDING LION,ROARING,SIGNED BARYE,6 1/2 X
  11 IN.LONG........................................................   225.00
BRONZE,FIGURINE,STANDING LION,SIGNED MOIGNIEZ,5 IN.LONG,
  3 IN.HIGH.........................................................   155.00
BRONZE,FIGURINE,STORK,GARDEN ORNAMENT,LIGHT FIXTURE ON TOP,
  33 IN.HIGH........................................................   125.00
BRONZE,FIGURINE,SUCKING KID AND GOAT,SIGNED PARMENTIER,
  8 1/2 X 8 IN.LONG.................................................   250.00
BRONZE,FIGURINE,SWIMMER,CIRCA 1920,5 IN.......................     3.50
BRONZE,FIGURINE,TENNIS PLAYER,CIRCA 1920,5 IN.................     3.50
BRONZE,FIGURINE,THREE DOGS BURROWING,BROWN PATINA,P.J.MENE,
  14 IN.LONG........................................................   300.00
BRONZE,FIGURINE,TIGER STANDING,SIGNED LEGOEDEL,6 IN.LONG,
  4 IN.HIGH.........................................................   100.00
BRONZE,FIGURINE,TROIKA,RUSSIA,SIGNED GRETCHOFF,6 1/2 X
  10 1/2 IN.LONG....................................................   650.00
BRONZE,FIGURINE,TWO CHICKS,BASE,C.H.VIRION,5 X 5 1/4 IN.TALL   125.00
BRONZE,FIGURINE,TWO ELEPHANTS,MARBLE ASHTRAY BASE............    90.00
BRONZE,FIGURINE,TWO KITTENS PLAYING,VIENNA,1 IN.X 1 1/4 IN..    35.00
BRONZE,FIGURINE,TWO LOVING CATS SITTING ON BENCH,VIENNA,2 X
  2 IN..............................................................    65.00
BRONZE,FIGURINE,VENUS,CHARLES LOUCHET CO.,14 1/2 IN. HIGH...   140.00
BRONZE,FIGURINE,WALKING TIGER,SIGNED BARYE,15 IN.LONG X
  8 IN.HIGH.........................................................   450.00
BRONZE,FIGURINE,WARRIOR,SIGNED HONOR PATRIA E.PICAULT,20
  IN.HIGH...........................................................   250.00
BRONZE,FIGURINE,WARRIOR,SIGNED KOWALEWSKI,16 IN.HIGH........   250.00
BRONZE,FIGURINE,WILD CANARY ON BRANCH,AUSTRIA,6 IN. X 5 IN..    49.00
BRONZE,FIGURINE,WINGED MERCURY,SIGNED DE BOLOGNE,MARBLE
  BASE,19 IN.HIGH...................................................   110.00
BRONZE,FIGURINE,WINGED VICTORY,MOUNTED ON WHITE BARBLE BASE,
  10 1/2 IN.........................................................    35.00
BRONZE,FIGURINE,WOLF SEATED ON HAUNCHES,HEAD TILTED
  DOWNWARD,DORE,2 IN................................................    32.50
BRONZE,FIGURINE,WOLFHOUND,VIENNA..............................    80.00
BRONZE,FIGURINE,WOMAN HOLDING CHILD,BRAZIER,SIGNED
  SAUVAGEAU,16 IN.TALL..............................................   350.00
BRONZE,FIGURINE,WOMAN,CHILD,HOLDS JUG,SIGNED SAUVAGEAU,
  16 IN.TALL........................................................   350.00
BRONZE,FIGURINE,WOMAN,FROG,LILY PAD,MARBLE BASE,SIGNED,
  10 1/2 IN.HIGH....................................................   250.00
BRONZE,FIGURINE,WOMAN,GAY 90 TYPE,1890 ERA,SIGNED ZACK,
  VIENNA............................................................   275.00
BRONZE,FIGURINE,WOMAN,GLANEUSE,SIGNED AUG.MOREAU,20 IN.HIGH.    48.00
BRONZE,FIGURINE,WOMAN,SEATED,SIGNED CA,2 IN.HIGH.............    10.00
BRONZE,FIGURINE,WOODPECKER,AUSTRIA,5 3/4 IN..................    40.00
BRONZE,FIGURINE,WORLD WAR I DOUGHBOY,SIGNED ROMAN BRONZE
  WORKS,12 IN.......................................................    85.00
BRONZE,FRAME,ENAMELED BORDER,OVAL SHAPE,10 X 14 IN...........    90.00
BRONZE,FRAME,ENAMELED,JEWELED,7 X 10 IN.......................    30.00
BRONZE,FRAME,MOTHS,SIGNED R.GANDOLFI,BEVELED GLASS,
  8 1/2 IN.DIAMETER.................................................    56.00
BRONZE,GROUP,ANIMAL,A.JACQUEMART,1824-96.............ILLUS..   525.00
BRONZE,GROUP,ANIMAL,CHRISTOPHE FRATIN,1800-64................   650.00
BRONZE,GROUP,BIRD,6 1/2 IN. HIGH..............................   225.00
BRONZE,GROUP,EQUESTRIAN,SIGNED,4 IN. HIGH,9 IN. WIDE........   525.00
BRONZE,INCENSE BURNER,KETTLE FORM,RAISED DECOR,MUSHROOM
  FINIAL,FOOTED.....................................................    28.00
```

BRONZE, INCENSE BURNER, RAISED FIGURES OF BIRDS & DRAGON, DOG
FINIAL.................................................... 95.00
BRONZE, INCENSE BURNER, RAISED SCROLL DESIGN, DOG FINIAL,
12 1/2 IN. HIGH.......................................... 145.00
BRONZE, INKSTAND, WILD BOAR, TREE STUMPS, FIGURAL MOUSE LIDS,
11 IN. LONG.............................................. 175.00
BRONZE, INKWELL, NIELLO DECOR, FLORAL, BATS, SCALLOPED SIDES,
CHINA.................................................... 22.00
BRONZE, INKWELL, PEN TRAY, PHEASANT STANDING ON SIDE, AUSTRIA, 11
IN. LONG................................................. 70.00
BRONZE, INKWELL, PHEASANT, PEN TRAY, MARKED AUSTRIA, 11 IN. LONG,
7 IN. WIDE............................................... 70.00
BRONZE, LAMP, DRAGON ON BASE, LEADED SHADE, FILIGREE, FAN SHAPE
FLORAL DECOR............................................. 275.00
BRONZE, LAMP, FRENCH, FIGURAL, 25 IN. HIGH................... 70.00
BRONZE, LAMP, TABLE, STAINED-GLASS, 17 1/2 IN. HIGH......... 100.00
BRONZE, LETTER OPENER, HANDLE IS HEAD OF A LINCOLN, 8 IN.... 6.95
BRONZE, MATCH HOLDER, AFRICAN IN HIGH HAT HOLDS PACK ON BACK,
VIENNA................................................... 37.50
BRONZE, MATCH HOLDER, BOY ON LOG HOLDING DOG, 5 3/4 IN. HIGH.... 42.00
BRONZE, MIRROR, DRAGONS, IDEOGRAPHS, BIRDS, ANIMALS, HAN DYNASTY,

BRONZE ANIMAL GROUP,
A. JACQUEMART

BRONZE DOG STATUETTE,
FERDINAND PAUTROT

7 1/4 IN................................................. 150.00
BRONZE, MIRROR, EASEL, FRENCH, AUGUST FERLET, 1867, 17 1/2 IN.
HIGH..................................................... 250.00
BRONZE, OFFICER, COLONIAL GENERAL, RIFLE, 10 1/2 IN. HIGH,
7 1/2 IN. WIDE........................................... 325.00
BRONZE, PAPERWEIGHT, ADVERTISING, COIN SHAPE, U.S.F. & G.
INS. CO, 1896-1946....................................... 6.00
BRONZE, PAPERWEIGHT, SALAMANDER, 3 1/2 IN. LONG............. 10.00
BRONZE, PERFUME BURNER, GOTHIC SHAPE, ORIENTAL............. 95.00
BRONZE, PLANTER, CYLINDER SHAPE, FOOTED, 10 IN. LONG,
3 IN. DIAMETER........................................... 10.00
BRONZE, PLANTER, MOUNTED ROMAN SOLDIERS, SIGNED W. HENNING, 1817,
GORHAM................................................... 33.00
BRONZE, PLAQUE, INDIAN, ARTIST-SIGNED, DATED, 7 1/2 IN. X
4 3/4 IN................................................. 110.00
BRONZE, PLAQUE, LINCOLN BUST, V.D. BREMMER, 1907, 7 X 9 1/4 IN.... 110.00
BRONZE, PLAQUE, MOZART, BIRDSEYE MAPLE EASEL............... 40.00
BRONZE, PLAQUE, RUSSIAN WOLFHOUND, SIGNED E. DRIPPE, OAK FRAME,
10 1/2 IN. HIGH.......................................... 145.00
BRONZE, PLAQUE, SHEPHERD, SHEPHERDESS, SHEEP, 10 3/4 X
12 IN. HIGH, FRANCE, PAIR................................ 75.00
BRONZE, PLAQUE, THEODORE ROOSEVELT IN RELIEF, BY JAMES FRASER,
1902, 13 IN.............................................. 65.00
BRONZE, RECEPTACLE, GIRL FEEDING KITTENS, OPEN, OVAL, SIGNED
P. TENEYZIZUK............................................ 45.00
BRONZE, RUSSIAN, FIGURE, HUNTER, ROCK-CRYSTAL BASE, 19TH CENTURY. 225.00
BRONZE, RUSSIAN, FIGURE, MONGOL, ROCK-CRYSTAL BASE, 19TH CENTURY. 175.00
BRONZE, RUSSIAN, ORMOLU, BEAR, ROCK-CRYSTAL BASE, 19TH CENTURY... 110.00
BRONZE, SEAL, NUDE WOMAN HOLDING DRAPERY, SCULPTURED, MONOGRAM,
3 1/2 IN. HIGH........................................... 35.00
BRONZE, STAG MUNCHING LEAVES, SIGNED P. J. MENE, 14 1/2 IN. HIGH,
15 IN. LONG.............................................. 325.00
BRONZE, STAND, MUSIC, CHERUB WITH VIOLIN, BIRDCAGE, DOLPHIN,
ROCOCO................................................... 47.50
BRONZE, STATUE, MISS LIBERTY, HOLDS THREE-ARM ELECTRIC TORCHES,
4 1/2 FEET............................................... 495.00
BRONZE, SUNDIAL, SAYS TIME TAKES ALL BUT MEMORIES,
10-IN. DIAMETER, 8 POUNDS................................ 50.00
BRONZE, TICKER TAPE MACHINE, BLACK IRON BASE, GLASS DOME COVER,
TAPE..................................................... 250.00

BRONZE,URN,ZIGZAG FLORAL BAND,BIRD MEDALLIONS,ROOSTER HEAD
  FINIAL,CHINA.................................................... 65.00
BRONZE,VASE,BIRDS IN FLOWERING TREES,ANIMAL HEAD HANDLE,
  CHINA,PAIR..................................................... 70.00
BRONZE,VASE,FLOWER-ARRANGEMENT,TWO SECTIONS,WAVES,SILVER
  INLAY,JAPAN.................................................... 75.00
BRONZE,VASE,FLOWER-ARRANGEMENT,TWO SECTIONS,FIGURINES,LEGS,
  JAPAN,13 IN................................................... 175.00
BRONZE,VASE,FRENCH,J.GARNIER,1880,6 IN........................... 60.00
BRONZE,VASE,INLAID ENAMEL,BRASS DECOR,PANELS,ELEPHANT HEAD
  HANDLES,CHINA................................................. 18.00
BRONZE,VASE,LEAVES FORM FOUNTAIN,NUDE WOMEN,C.KAUBA,4890,
  GESCHUTZ..................................................... 330.00
BRONZE,VASE,MOLDED CHERUBS,DRAGONFLY,BUTTERFLIES,5 1/4 IN.,
  PAIR.......................................................... 42.00
BRONZE,VASE,ORIENTAL MOTIF,EMBOSSED GILT BAT DECOR,
  9 1/2 IN.HIGH................................................ 125.00
BRONZE,VASE,RED,BLUE,GREEN,BROWN PORCELAIN INLAY,FOUR
  HANDLES,12 IN.HIGH.......................................... 195.00
BRONZE,VASE,WOMAN'S HEAD AT RIM,8 IN.HIGH,2 1/2-IN.DIAMETER
  BASE,PAIR..................................................... 45.00
BRONZE,WALL PANEL,WOMAN IN FLOWING ROBE,PITCHER,SIGNED
  F.BARBEDIENNE................................................ 110.00
BRONZE,WATCH FOB,PICTURES FIRE WAGON,MARKED CITIZEN HOSE,
  BRADFORD,PA.................................................... 7.00


      BUFFALO POTTERY WAS MADE IN BUFFALO,NEW YORK,AFTER
    1901. THE FIRM MARKED ITS WARES WITH A PICTURE OF A
    BUFFALO AND THE DATE OF MANUFACTURE. DELDARE WARE,THE
    KHAKI-BROWN POTTERY,DECORATED WITH HUNTING SCENES,IS
    THE MOST FAMOUS PRODUCT OF THE FACTORY.
BUFFALO POTTERY,BOTTLE,GIRL AT WELL,EMBOSSED................ 12.00
BUFFALO POTTERY,BUTTER PAT,BLUE,FLORAL BORDER,GOLD BAND,
  BUFFALO MARK,6................................................ 6.00
BUFFALO POTTERY,CHAMBER POT,GREEN CHRYSANTHEMUM DECOR....... 22.50
BUFFALO POTTERY,CREAMER & SUGAR,WHITE,LAVENDER CLOVER
  BLOSSOMS,1918................................................ 17.50
BUFFALO POTTERY,CREAMER,DELDARE,VILLAGE SCENES,1909......... 62.00
BUFFALO POTTERY,CREAMER,YE VILLAGE SCENES,DELDARE........... 90.00
BUFFALO POTTERY,DELDARE,BOWL,PUNCH,FALLOWFIELD HUNT,SIGNED
  J.I.STREUSEL................................................ 285.00
BUFFALO POTTERY,DELDARE,BOWL,YE LION INN,ARTIST-SIGNED,1909. 55.00
BUFFALO POTTERY,DELDARE,BOWL,YE VILLAGE TAVERN,9 IN......... 75.00
BUFFALO POTTERY,DELDARE,BOWL,YE VILLAGE TAVERN,
  9 1/8-IN.DIAMETER........................................... 175.00
BUFFALO POTTERY,DELDARE,CANDLESTICK,COLONIAL FIGURE,SIGNED,
  9 IN.,PAIR.................................................. 145.00
BUFFALO POTTERY,DELDARE,CANDLESTICK,VILLAGE SCENES,
  9 1/2 IN.HIGH,PAIR.......................................... 135.00
BUFFALO POTTERY,DELDARE,CREAMER............................. 65.00
BUFFALO POTTERY,DELDARE,CREAMER,SUGAR,VILLAGE LIFE IN YE
  OLDEN DAYS,1908............................................. 100.00
BUFFALO POTTERY,DELDARE,CUP & SAUCER,FALLOWFIELD HUNT,1908.. 110.00
BUFFALO POTTERY,DELDARE,CUP & SAUCER,YE OLDEN
  DAYS,1908........................................ 75.00 TO 110.00
BUFFALO POTTERY,DELDARE,HAIR RECEIVER,ARTIST-SIGNED......... 85.00
BUFFALO POTTERY,DELDARE,HAIR RECEIVER,YE VILLAGE STREET..... 95.00
BUFFALO POTTERY,DELDARE,PITCHER,FALLOWFIELD HUNT,7 IN....... 135.00
BUFFALO POTTERY,DELDARE,PITCHER,THEIR MANNER OF TELLING
  STORIES,6 IN................................................ 100.00
BUFFALO POTTERY,DELDARE,PITCHER,TO DEMAND MY ANNUAL RENT,
  8 IN.HIGH................................................... 145.00
BUFFALO POTTERY,DELDARE,PITCHER,WELCOME ME WITH MOST CORDIAL
  HOSPITALITY................................................. 150.00
BUFFALO POTTERY,DELDARE,PLATE,6 1/4 IN...............ILLUS.. 45.00
BUFFALO POTTERY,DELDARE,PLATE,AT YE LION INN,
  6 1/4 IN.DIAMETER........................................... 45.00
BUFFALO POTTERY,DELDARE,PLATE,FALLOWFIELD HUNT,6 3/8 IN..... 32.00
BUFFALO POTTERY,DELDARE,PLATE,FALLOWFIELD HUNT,9 1/2 IN..... 67.50
BUFFALO POTTERY,DELDARE,PLATE,FALLOWFIELD HUNT,THE START,
  1908,9 1/2 IN............................................... 57.50
BUFFALO POTTERY,DELDARE,PLATE,FALLOWFIELD HUNT,THE DEATH,
  B.WILLOW,1909............................................... 60.00
BUFFALO POTTERY,DELDARE,PLATE,FALLOWFIELD HUNT,THE START,
  13 1/2 IN................................................... 130.00
BUFFALO POTTERY,DELDARE,PLATE,SOUP,FALLOWFIELD HUNT,BREAKING
  COVER,9 IN.................................................. 75.00
BUFFALO POTTERY,DELDARE,PLATE,WHITE DOVES,BY R.STUART,1911,
  9 1/4 IN.................................................... 20.00
BUFFALO POTTERY,DELDARE,PLATE,YE OLDEN TIMES,

BUFFALO POTTERY,
DELDARE PLATE

```
    9 1/2 IN.DIAMETER.........................................    75.00
BUFFALO POTTERY,DELDARE,PLATE,YE TOWNE CRIER,8 1/2 IN.......    62.50
BUFFALO POTTERY,DELDARE,PLATE,YE VILLAGE GOSSIPS,
    10 IN.DIAMETER...........................................    80.00
BUFFALO POTTERY,DELDARE,PLATE,YE VILLAGE STREET,
    7 1/4 IN.DIAMETER........................................    65.00
BUFFALO POTTERY,DELDARE,SAUCER,THE VILLAGE STREET...........    24.50
BUFFALO POTTERY,DELDARE,TEAPOT,VILLAGE LIFE IN YE OLDEN
    DAYS,KUTH,1908...........................................    95.00
BUFFALO POTTERY,DELDARE,TRAY,CALLING CARD,FALLOWFIELD HUNT,
    SIGNED...................................................    85.00
BUFFALO POTTERY,DELDARE,TRAY,CALLING CARD,YE LION INN,SIGNED
    R.WASE...................................................    70.00
BUFFALO POTTERY,DELDARE,TRAY,PIN,YE OLDEN DAYS..............    50.00
BUFFALO POTTERY,DELDARE,TRIVET,TRAVELING IN YE OLDEN DAYS,
    6 IN.DIAMETER............................................    65.00
BUFFALO POTTERY,DELDARE,VASE,VILLAGE SCENES,9 IN.HIGH.......   100.00
BUFFALO POTTERY,DISH,FEEDING,CHILD'S,BOY & GIRL IN CENTER,
    SIGNED DRAYTON...........................................    10.00
BUFFALO POTTERY,DISH,RELISH,DELDARE,1908....................    92.00
BUFFALO POTTERY,DISH,SAUCE,ABINO WARE,1912..................   115.00
BUFFALO POTTERY,DISH,VEGETABLE,WILLOW WARE,HANDLES,COVER,
    8 1/2 IN.................................................    12.00
BUFFALO POTTERY,FISH SET,SIX PLATES,BASS,PIKE,SALMON,SIGNED
    R.K.BECK.................................................    42.50
BUFFALO POTTERY,GRAVY BOAT,LA FRANCE ROSE...................    10.00
BUFFALO POTTERY,JUG,GEORGE WASHINGTON ON HORSE,MT.VERNON,
    BLUE & WHITE.............................................    82.50
BUFFALO POTTERY,JUG,SQUATTY,WOMEN SEWING,CHILDREN,1907,
    HOLLAND,6 IN.............................................    50.00
BUFFALO POTTERY,MUG,MONK PICTURE,ADVERTISING BING & NATHAN..    14.00
BUFFALO POTTERY,MUSTARD,SEMIVITREOUS,1916...................    10.00
BUFFALO POTTERY,PITCHER,BEARS,ROOSEVELT..............ILLUS..   150.00
BUFFALO POTTERY,PITCHER,BLUE & WHITE WILLOW DESIGN,6 1/2 IN.    15.00
BUFFALO POTTERY,PITCHER,BLUE BIRD DECOR,9 IN.HIGH...........    12.00
BUFFALO POTTERY,PITCHER,BLUE,WHITE,GENERAL GEORGE
    WASHINGTON,MT.VERNON.....................................    76.00
BUFFALO POTTERY,PITCHER,CHINESE MOTIF ACCENTED WITH GOLD,
    1907,5 1/2 IN............................................    19.00
BUFFALO POTTERY,PITCHER,FOLD IN FRONT FORMS SPOUT,WOMAN,
    FLORAL,1907..............................................    45.00
BUFFALO POTTERY,PITCHER,WILLOW,BLUE ON WHITE,TAPERED
    CYLINDRICAL,1908.........................................    22.00
BUFFALO POTTERY,PLATE,ABINO WARE,9 IN.,1912.................   125.00
BUFFALO POTTERY,PLATE,B.P.O.E.,ELK HEAD,LEGEND.............    10.00
BUFFALO POTTERY,PLATE,BIRD,TEAL BLUE,GOLD EDGE,DATED 1907...    18.50
BUFFALO POTTERY,PLATE,BLUE WILLOW,DATED 1908,9 1/4 IN., SET
    OF 4.....................................................    24.60
BUFFALO POTTERY,PLATE,BLUE WILLOW,1915,10 IN................     8.50
BUFFALO POTTERY,PLATE,BLUE,U.S.CAPITOL,WASHINGTON,D.C.,
    10 1/2 IN................................................    10.00
```

BUFFALO POTTERY, PITCHER,
ROOSEVELT, BEARS

| | |
|---|---:|
| BUFFALO POTTERY,PLATE,CHOP,WILLOW WARE,1906,DEEP, 13 IN.DIAMETER.......... | 12.00 |
| BUFFALO POTTERY,PLATE,COMMEMORATION,FANEUIL HALL........... | 12.00 |
| BUFFALO POTTERY,PLATE,COMMEMORATION,INDEPENDENCE HALL....... | 12.00 |
| BUFFALO POTTERY,PLATE,DELDARE,1909,8 1/2 IN.......... | 65.00 |
| BUFFALO POTTERY,PLATE,DINNER,BLUE WILLOW,DATED 1909......... | 8.50 |
| BUFFALO POTTERY,PLATE,FEEDING,BABY'S,CAMPBELL KIDS.......... | 15.00 |
| BUFFALO POTTERY,PLATE,FISH,SCENE,R.K.BECK,9 1/2 IN. DIAMETER | 15.00 |
| BUFFALO POTTERY,PLATE,HUNTING SCENE CALLED THE GUNNER,DATED 1907,9 IN.......... | 15.00 |
| BUFFALO POTTERY,PLATE,LION'S INN,CLOSED HANDLES,7 IN........ | 75.00 |
| BUFFALO POTTERY,PLATE,MT.VERNON,10 IN.......... | 10.00 |
| BUFFALO POTTERY,PLATE,NIAGARA FALLS,BLUE & WHITE FLORAL BORDER.......... | 12.00 |
| BUFFALO POTTERY,PLATE,OLD HOME WEEK 1910,THE LOCKS,LOCKPORT, N.Y.......... | 12.00 |
| BUFFALO POTTERY,PLATE,SHADED DARK BLUE,FULL FIGURE BUFFALO, 1911.......... | 20.00 |
| BUFFALO POTTERY,PLATE,THE GUNNER,HUNTER & DOG,GREEN GROUND, 8 IN.......... | 18.00 |
| BUFFALO POTTERY,PLATE,TRAIN,NEW HAVEN TRAIN CROSSING,U.S.MAP OUTLINE.......... | 17.50 |
| BUFFALO POTTERY,PLATE,VILLAGE GOSSIPS,DELDARE,10 IN......... | 65.00 |
| BUFFALO POTTERY,PLATE,WILD DUCKS,GREEN GROUND,GOLD BORDER, DATED 1907.......... | 18.50 |
| BUFFALO POTTERY,PLATE,WILLOW WARE,1911,9 1/4 IN............. | 6.00 |
| BUFFALO POTTERY,PLATE,YE TOWN CRIER,DELDARE,8 1/4 IN........ | 67.50 |
| BUFFALO POTTERY,PLATTER,BLUE WILLOW,DATED 1908,14 1/4 IN. X 11 IN.......... | 40.00 |
| BUFFALO POTTERY,PLATTER,DEER & DOE AT STREAM,SIGNED R.K.BECK,15 IN.LONG.......... | 29.00 |
| BUFFALO POTTERY,PLATTER,GREEN FLOWERS,11 IN.......... | 6.50 |
| BUFFALO POTTERY,PLATTER,SENECA PATTERN,GREEN ON WHITE,OVAL, 15 X 11 IN.......... | 12.50 |
| BUFFALO POTTERY,PLATTER,WILLOW PATTERN,MULTICOLORED,9 X 12 IN.......... | 17.50 |
| BUFFALO POTTERY,TEA TILE,DELDARE,1924,6 IN.......... | 40.00 |
| BUFFALO POTTERY,TEAPOT,BLUE,WHITE,ARGYLE PATTERN,BULBOUS, 1914.......... | 22.50 |
| BUFFALO POTTERY,TILE,HANDLES,YE LION INN,L.STREISSEL, DELDARE,7 IN.......... | 72.50 |
| BUGGY,BABY,WICKER,PARASOL.......... | 100.00 |

BURMESE GLASS WAS DEVELOPED BY FREDERICK SHIRLEY AT THE
MT.WASHINGTON GLASS WORKS IN NEW BEDFORD,MASSACHUSETTS,
IN 1885. IT IS A TWO-TONE GLASS,SHADING FROM PEACH TO
YELLOW. SOME HAVE A PATTERN MOLD DESIGN. A FEW BURMESE
PIECES WERE DECORATED WITH PICTURES OR APPLIED GLASS
FLOWERS OF COLORED BURMESE GLASS.
BURMESE,WEBB,SEE WEBB

```
BURMESE,BASKET,SALMON COLOR TO YELLOW,7 1/2 IN.............      50.00
BURMESE,BOWL,DIAMOND PATTERN,SQUATTY,MT.WASHINGTON,3 IN.
   HIGH....................................................     250.00
BURMESE,BOWL,FINGER,ACID FINISH,YELLOW COLOR NEAR BOTTOM....     185.00
BURMESE,BOWL,MT.WASHINGTON,SCALLOPED,6 IN..................     200.00
BURMESE,BOWL,ROSE,BERRY PONTIL,LEMON TO PINK,WHITE RING
   DECOR AT TOP...........................................      50.00
BURMESE,BOWL,ROSE,CRIMPED TOP.............................     233.00
BURMESE,BOWL,ROSE,MINATURE,ACID CUT,2 3/4 IN. X
   2 1/2 IN.HIGH..........................................     185.00
BURMESE,BOWL,ROSE,MINIATURE...............................     220.00
BURMESE,BOWL,ROSE,MT.WASHINGTON...........................     230.00
BURMESE,BOWL,ROSE,PINK TO YELLOW,3 1/2 IN.TALL,
   3 1/4 IN.ACROSS TOP....................................      35.00
BURMESE,BOWL,RUFFLED TOP,THREE REED FEET,6 1/2 IN.HIGH X
   8 IN. ACROSS...........................................     225.00
BURMESE,BRIDE'S BASKET,SHINY,SILVER HOLDER,9 IN.DIAMETER....1,000.00
BURMESE,CASTOR SET,CRUET,SALT,PEPPER,PAIRPOINT BASE........     425.00
BURMESE,CONDIMENT SET,THREE PIECES,PAIRPOINT HOLDER,NEEDS
   RESILVERING...........................................     350.00
BURMESE,CREAMER,ACID FINISH,WHITE LINING,2 1/2 IN.TALL......      45.00
BURMESE,CREAMER,GUNDERSON,DIAMOND-QUILTED,SALMON PINK TO
   YELLOW...............................................     225.00
BURMESE,CRUET,APPLIED VASELINE RIBBED HANDLE,ACID FINISH,
   STOPPER,8 IN..........................................     320.00
BURMESE,CRUET,MT.WASHINGTON,ACID CUT,STOPPER,6 1/2 IN......     595.00
BURMESE,DISH,PRESERVE,SHELL-LIKE YELLOW WAIST,SILVER STAND,
   SPOON................................................     260.00
BURMESE,EPERGNE,SIGNED...................................2,000.00
BURMESE,JAR,COOKIE,ACORNS,OAK LEAVES,P IN DIAMOND MARK,
   MT.WASHINGTON.........................................     650.00
BURMESE,LAMP,FAIRY.......................................     125.00
BURMESE,LAMP,FAIRY,CLARKE CLEAR GLASS BASE,SIGNED.........      75.00
BURMESE,LAMP,FAIRY,PINK,SQUARE-SIDED.....................     500.00
BURMESE,LAMP,FAIRY,SIGNED,CLARKE BASE,SIGNED.............     625.00
BURMESE,LAMP,HANGING,FIVE MT.WASHINGTON PINK SHADES,BRASS
   FIXTURE...............................................     200.00
BURMESE,PAPERWEIGHT,EGG SHAPE,WEIGHS 1 1/2 POUNDS.........     395.00
BURMESE,PERFUME,RIBBED,GLOSSY,SILVER TOP & STOPPER.......     225.00
BURMESE,PITCHER,CANARY SHADING TO PINK,CRIMPED TOP,SATIN
   FINISH,5 IN...........................................     275.00
BURMESE,PITCHER,MT.WASHINGTON,SALMON PINK TO YELLOW,ACID,
   7 IN.HIGH.............................................     750.00
BURMESE,PITCHER,WATER,SALMON PINK,YELLOW HANDLE,ACID CUT,
   MT.WASHINGTON.........................................     750.00
BURMESE,SALT & PEPPER,MT.WASHINGTON,RIBBED,AGITATOR,DUSTY
   ROSE TO LEMON.........................................     165.00
BURMESE,SALT,PEPPER,VINEGAR,PAIRPOINT METAL HOLDER.......     425.00
BURMESE,SHADE,GAS,MT.WASHINGTON,PINK TO YELLOW,PINK LINING,
   GLOSSY................................................     125.00
BURMESE,SHADE,LAMP,RUFFLED TOP,MT.WASHINGTON,4 1/2 IN.TALL..      95.00
BURMESE,SHAKER,SALT & PEPPER,MT.WASHINGTON,RIBBED.........     185.00
BURMESE,SHAKER,SALT,RIBBED,MT.WASHINGTON.................     135.00
BURMESE,TOOTHPICK,DIAMOND-QUILTED,PINK TOP SHADING TO YELLOW   175.00
BURMESE,TOOTHPICK,FOUR-SIDED TOP,ROUND BOTTOM,BEADING,
   ALLOVER FLORAL........................................     225.00
BURMESE,TOOTHPICK,MT.WASHINGTON,DIAMOND-QUILTED,ACID FINISH,
   SQUARE................................................     195.00
BURMESE,TOOTHPICK,MT.WASHINGTON,ENAMELED DAISIES,SQUARE TOP.   325.00
BURMESE,TOOTHPICK,MT.WASHINGTON,YELLOW,PINK,WHITE DOT ENAMEL
   FLORAL................................................     280.00
BURMESE,TOOTHPICK,QUILTED TRICORNE TOP,BITTERSWEET DECOR,
   MT.WASHINGTON.........................................     265.00
BURMESE,TUMBLER,MT.WASHINGTON............................     150.00
BURMESE,TUMBLER,MT.WASHINGTON,SALMON PINK,YELLOW EDGE RIM,
   ACID CUT..............................................     180.00
BURMESE,VASE,APPLIED STRAWBERRY PONTIL,PICTURED R.W.LEE,
   MT.WASHINGTON.........................................     500.00
BURMESE,VASE,BERRY PONTIL,BULBOUS BOTTOM,LEMON TO PINK,
   8 1/2 IN.TALL.........................................      50.00
BURMESE,VASE,BULBOUS BASE,FLAT FLARING TOP,4 X
   10 1/2 IN.HIGH,PAIR...................................     425.00
BURMESE,VASE,CABINET,PINK TOP,SHADING TO YELLOW,TWO HANDLES,
   4 IN..................................................      45.00
BURMESE,VASE,DEEP PINK TO BRILLIANT YELLOW,ACID FINISH,
   4 IN.TALL.............................................     210.00
BURMESE,VASE,FLARED TOP,PETAL STYLE,DECORATED,PAIR.........     300.00
BURMESE,VASE,FLORIFORM,POINTED PETAL MOUTH,2 1/2 X
   2 1/4 IN.HIGH.........................................     210.00
BURMESE,VASE,JACK-IN-THE-PULPIT,SALMON PINK,YELLOW RUFFLED
   EDGE,10 IN............................................     225.00
```

BURMESE,VASE,LILY,HAND-CRAFTED REPOUSSE BASE,12 IN.HIGH..... 220.00
BURMESE,VASE,MT.WASHINGTON,ACID CUT,RUFFLED TOP,4 IN. X
   4 IN.TALL................................................ 225.00
BURMESE,VASE,MT.WASHINGTON,ENAMELED ROSE DECOR,HOOD VERSE... 950.00
BURMESE,VASE,MT.WASHINGTON,SATIN,PINK,YELLOW,TRUMPET SHAPE,
   24 IN.,PAIR...........................................2,800.00
BURMESE,VASE,OGEE SHAPE,TURNED-IN PETAL MOUTH,2 1/2 X
   3 3/4 IN.HIGH........................................... 210.00
BURMESE,VASE,RIBBING,5 IN.TALL............................. 250.00
BURMESE,VASE,STICK,MT.WASHINGTON,7 IN..................... 225.00
BURMESE,WEBB,LAMP,PYRAMID SHAPE,SALMON TO YELLOW SHADE,
   3 3/4 IN.TALL.......................................... 110.00
BURMESE,WEBB,LAMP,PYRAMID SHAPE,SALMON TO YELLOW SHADE,
   5 1/4 IN.TALL.......................................... 165.00


      BUTTER CHIPS OR BUTTER PATS WERE SMALL INDIVIDUAL
      DISHES FOR BUTTER. THEY WERE IN THE HEIGHT OF FASHION
      FROM 1880 TO 1910. EARLIER,AS WELL AS LATER,EXAMPLES
      ARE KNOWN.
BUTTER CHIP,GREEN,WHITE,ABBOTT PATTERN,JOHN MADDOCK,ENGLAND,
   SET OF 8................................................ 6.50
BUTTER CHIP,HAVILAND,MADE FOR H.WATSON CO.,LIMOGES.......... 1.00
BUTTERMILK GLASS,SEE CUSTARD


      BUTTONS HAVE BEEN KNOWN THROUGH THE CENTURIES,AND
      THERE ARE MILLIONS OF STYLES. ONLY A FEW OF THE MOST
      COMMON TYPES ARE LISTED FOR COMPARISON.
BUTTON,AMBER.............................................. 3.00
BUTTON,BIRD EATING GRAPES,METAL PICTURE,BRASS FRAMED,
   1 1/2 IN............................................... 8.50
BUTTON,BLUE FLORAL,VIOLETS,GOLD TRIM,HAND-PAINTED,PORCELAIN. 2.75
BUTTON,CARNELIAN.......................................... 3.00
BUTTON,CARVED JADE,CHINA.................................. 6.00
BUTTON,CINNABAR,CARVED.................................... 4.00
BUTTON,ENAMEL,CUTOUT STAR CENTER,SCALLOPS,BLUE,WHITE,BRASS,
   5/8 IN.,PAIR........................................... 6.00
BUTTON,ENAMELED SCROLL,ROSES,MARCASITE,SCALLOPED,FRANCE,
   1 1/4 IN............................................... 4.00
BUTTON,FOR DOLL CLOTHES,BOX OF 200....................... 3.50
BUTTON,GLASS,METAL PICTURE,LOT OF 30..................... 3.00
BUTTON,IVORY,CARVED RELIEF FIGURES UNDER TREES,SELF SHANK,
   CHINA,1 INCH........................................... 18.00
BUTTON,JADE,CARVED,MANDARIN,CHINA........................ 6.00
BUTTON,LADY'S HEAD,FLOWING HAIR,RELIEF,MARKED STERLING
   SILVER,1 1/4 IN........................................ 5.00
BUTTON,LITTLE RED SCHOOL HOUSE,TREE,RED GLASS,5/8 IN....... 8.50
BUTTON,MINERVA'S HEAD,CARAMEL OPAQUE GLASS,BRASS HEART
   BORDER,3/4 IN.......................................... 5.00
BUTTON,MOTHER-OF-PEARL,STERLING SILVER EARLY AUTOMOBILE
   OVERLAY................................................ 25.00
BUTTON,NEW HAMPSHIRE MILITARY,BRASS,7/8 IN.,SET OF 4........ 1.00
BUTTON,PAINTED,LAVENDER,1/4 IN.,SET OF 24................. 2.00
BUTTON,PAISLEY DESIGN,RED GLASS,3/4 IN................... 3.00
BUTTON,PAPERWEIGHT,GOLD SNAKE............................ 9.50
BUTTON,PAPERWEIGHT,GOLDSTONE ON ROSE GROUND,3/4-IN.DIAMETER. 8.00
BUTTON,PICTURE,PEWTER CAT,BIRD ON FENCE,PEWTER RIM,1 1/2 IN. 15.00
BUTTON,PICTURE,RUMPELSTILZCHEN,BRASS,1 1/8 IN.............. 9.50
BUTTON,RED,GREEN,YELLOW,STYLIZED DESIGN ON BLACK,CLOISONNE,
   3/4 IN.,5.............................................. 15.00
BUTTON,RELIEF,STAMPED THE JAUNTING CART,BRASS,1 1/8 IN...... 12.00
BUTTON,STRING,PICTURES,RED GLASS,OTHERS,1875-1918,11 FEET
   5 IN.LONG.............................................. 100.00
BUTTON,TOURING CAR,BRASS................................. 4.00
BUTTON,WHITE,GOLD CLOISONNES,ENAMEL PEONIES,CONVEX,ORNATE
   BACK,1 1/4 IN.......................................... 12.00


      CALCITE GLASS WAS MADE BY THE STEUBEN FACTORY TO BE
      USED WITH COLORED AURENE GLASS. IT WAS USUALLY USED AS
      THE LINER,SEE STEUBEN.
   CALCITE,SEE ALSO,STEUBEN
CALCITE,BOWL,FRUIT,5 7/8-IN.DIAMETER,1 1/8 IN.DEEP,
   1-IN.FLANGE............................................ 45.00
CALCITE,BOWL,12-IN.DIAMETER,3 IN.DEEP.................... 175.00
CALCITE,COMPOTE,GOLD..................................... 275.00
CALCITE,COMPOTE,GOLD COLOR,6-IN.DIAMETER................. 80.00
CALCITE,SHERBET,GOLD DECOR,UNDERPLATE.................... 80.00

CALENDAR PLATES WERE MADE IN THE UNITED STATES FROM
1906 TO 1929. A FEW WERE PRODUCED IN THE YEARS SINCE
THEN. A CALENDAR, THE NAME OF A STORE, A PICTURE OF
FLOWERS, A GIRL OR A SCENE WAS FEATURED ON THE PLATE.

| | |
|---|---|
| CALENDAR PLATE, 1895, FLORAL BORDER, NO ADVERTISING............ | 22.50 |
| CALENDAR PLATE, 1905, PORTRAIT OF THEODORE ROOSEVELT, TIN...... | 42.00 |
| CALENDAR PLATE, 1907, GIRL, TIN............................... | 25.00 |
| CALENDAR PLATE, 1908, GRAPES................................. | 16.00 |
| CALENDAR PLATE, 1908, LADY, FLOWING GOWN, STERLING CROWN CHINA.. | 48.00 |
| CALENDAR PLATE, 1909, BIRD IN FLIGHT, BANNER IN BEAK, SCALLOPED, ADVERTISING............................................... | 25.00 |
| CALENDAR PLATE, 1909, CENTER PICTURE, FROM DODGE, NEBRASKA..... | 12.50 |
| CALENDAR PLATE, 1909, CHRISTMAS DECOR, HOLLY, BERRIES, ADVERTISING............................................... | 9.50 |
| CALENDAR PLATE, 1909, CHRISTMAS DECOR, SANTA, REINDEER, MONTICELLO, MINNESOTA..................................... | 58.00 |
| CALENDAR PLATE, 1909, COMPLIMENTS DODGE, NEBRASKA, FLAGS, PIERCED, 7 1/2 IN.......................................... | 9.50 |
| CALENDAR PLATE, 1909, FLAG IN CENTER, COURTLAND, KANSAS, 9 IN.... | 15.00 |
| CALENDAR PLATE, 1909, FRUIT & FLORAL BORDER WITH MONTHS, WILLIAM H. TAFT............................................ | 12.00 |
| CALENDAR PLATE, 1909, GIRL, HOLLY TRIM...................... | 14.00 |
| CALENDAR PLATE, 1909, HOLLY & BERRIES, GREEN SHADING, POPE GOSSER MARK............................................... | 27.50 |
| CALENDAR PLATE, 1909, HOLLY, BERRIES, THE GOLDEN RULE MERCANTILE CO., IOWA.................................................. | 25.00 |
| CALENDAR PLATE, 1909, HOLLY, POPE GOSSER MARK, GOLDEN RULE MERCANTILE CO.............................................. | 25.00 |
| CALENDAR PLATE, 1909, HOLLY, 8 IN............................ | 25.00 |
| CALENDAR PLATE, 1909, LOVERS, SCENE, CALENDAR BORDER, SEVRES..... | 19.50 |
| CALENDAR PLATE, 1909, PICTURE CENTER, HEAD OF HUNTING DOG, 9 IN. | 12.00 |
| CALENDAR PLATE, 1909, PINK ROSE CENTER, HOLLY BORDER, 9 1/2 IN. DIAMETER........................................ | 18.50 |
| CALENDAR PLATE, 1909, PORTRAIT CENTER, SPRING VALLEY, WISCONSIN, 8 IN....................................................... | 15.00 |
| CALENDAR PLATE, 1909, PORTRAIT, GIRL CARRYING APPLE BLOSSOM BRANCH................................................... | 25.00 |
| CALENDAR PLATE, 1909, ROSE DECOR............................ | 14.00 |
| CALENDAR PLATE, 1909, ROSES................................. | 10.00 |
| CALENDAR PLATE, 1909, RUSTIC SCENE, HOUSE, BRIDGE, WATER, IMPERIAL CHINA................................................... | 29.00 |
| CALENDAR PLATE, 1909, SCENE WITH MONTHS AROUND IT............. | 10.00 |
| CALENDAR PLATE, 1909, SCENES & CALENDAR AROUND BORDER, PINK ROSE CENTER............................................... | 12.50 |
| CALENDAR PLATE, 1909, WATER LILY............................ | 10.00 |
| CALENDAR PLATE, 1910, ANGELS RINGING BELL, YE 1910 NEW YEAR, FORGET-ME-NOTS........................................... | 32.50 |
| CALENDAR PLATE, 1910, APPLES................................ | 10.00 |
| CALENDAR PLATE, 1910, BETSY ROSS, AMERICAN FLAG.............. | 11.00 |
| CALENDAR PLATE, 1910, BOUQUET OF ROSES CENTER, GARLAND BORDER, ADVERTISEMENT............................................. | 9.75 |
| CALENDAR PLATE, 1910, BULLDOG CENTER........................ | 13.50 |
| CALENDAR PLATE, 1910, CALENDARS AROUND PLATE, HAROLD, S.D., 8IN.. | 10.00 |
| CALENDAR PLATE, 1910, CHERUBS............................... | 13.00 |
| CALENDAR PLATE, 1910, CHERUBS RINGING BELL.................. | 15.00 |
| CALENDAR PLATE, 1910, CUPID DECOR........................... | 12.50 |
| CALENDAR PLATE, 1910, FRUIT CLUSTER CENTER, ROSES AROUND CALENDAR MONTHS.......................................... | 12.00 |
| CALENDAR PLATE, 1910, GIBSON GIRL, HOLLY, FRUITS, CARNATION MC NICOL MARK............................................... | 32.00 |
| CALENDAR PLATE, 1910, GIRL ON PIER CENTER, CALENDAR BORDER, 9 IN....................................................... | 15.00 |
| CALENDAR PLATE, 1910, GIRL SKATING......................... | 9.00 |
| CALENDAR PLATE, 1910, GOLD CIRCLE RIM, ROSES OVER CALENDAR..... | 10.00 |
| CALENDAR PLATE, 1910, HOLLY, ADVERTISEMENT.................. | 6.50 |
| CALENDAR PLATE, 1910, HOLLY, GOLD, 7 1/2 IN.................. | 8.00 |
| CALENDAR PLATE, 1910, HORSESHOE IN CENTER, 7 IN.............. | 15.00 |
| CALENDAR PLATE, 1910, LADY IN CENTER........................ | 14.00 |
| CALENDAR PLATE, 1910, LILACS, POPPIES, APPLE BLOSSOMS, HOLLY, BERRIES.................................................. | 12.75 |
| CALENDAR PLATE, 1910, MARKED STEUBENVILLE CHINA.............. | 22.00 |
| CALENDAR PLATE, 1910, NIAGARA FALLS, 8 1/2 IN................ | 7.00 |
| CALENDAR PLATE, 1910, PORTRAIT, LADY'S HEAD, WHITE FUR HAT, RED COAT..................................................... | 27.50 |
| CALENDAR PLATE, 1910, SCENE, WATER LILY CENTER, RIBBON & SCROLLS, ADVERTISING..................................... | 22.00 |
| CALENDAR PLATE, 1911, CHERUBS LIGHTING CANDLE............... | 12.00 |
| CALENDAR PLATE, 1911, DUCKS................................. | 8.50 |
| CALENDAR PLATE, 1911, FLORAL DECOR, SPRING VALLEY, WISCONSIN, | |

```
  8 IN................................................. 17.00
CALENDAR PLATE,1911,GIBSON GIRL.......................  9.50
CALENDAR PLATE,1911,HEN & CHICKS...................... 12.00
CALENDAR PLATE,1911,HEN WITH CHICKS,7 1/2 IN.DIAMETER. 12.50
CALENDAR PLATE,1911,LINCOLN PORTRAIT.................. 23.00
CALENDAR PLATE,1911,LINCOLN PORTRAIT,8 1/2 IN......... 32.00
CALENDAR PLATE,1911,MALLARD DUCKS,WATER,CATTAIL DECOR.  8.00
CALENDAR PLATE,1911,RURAL SCENE CENTER,ADVERTISING GAY
  HUDSON FALLS,N.Y....................................  9.00
CALENDAR PLATE,1911,SHOULD OLD ACQUAINTANCE BE FORGOT,DAILY
  PRESS,7 IN......................................... 15.00
CALENDAR PLATE,1911,VIOLETS,21 CLOCK FACES............ 11.50
CALENDAR PLATE,1911-12,SUNSET......................... 15.00
CALENDAR PLATE,1912,CUPID BORDER,BOUQUET OF YELLOW & PINK
  ROSES CENTER....................................... 12.00
CALENDAR PLATE,1912,FIVE DIFFERENT FRUITS,7 1/2 IN....  9.50
CALENDAR PLATE,1912,FLOWERS,SIGNED....................  8.50
CALENDAR PLATE,1912,GIRL.............................. 15.00
CALENDAR PLATE,1912,GIRL WITH BASKET OF FRUIT & FLOWERS,
  8 IN...............................................  8.00
CALENDAR PLATE,1912,HUNTER,PHEASANT,GUN............... 10.00
CALENDAR PLATE,1912,LARGE ROSES IN POT................  9.50
CALENDAR PLATE,1912,OUR MARTYRS,BUSTS OF LINCOLN,GARFIELD,
  MCKINLEY,FLAGS..................................... 25.00
CALENDAR PLATE,1912,OWL,GEO.B.WALLACE,GENERAL MERCHANDISE,
  E.RYEGATE,VT....................................... 32.00
CALENDAR PLATE,1912,OWL,OPEN BOOK,SCENE,GILT BORDER,
  A.HEITING & CO..................................... 18.00
CALENDAR PLATE,1912,PLUMS,FOLIAGE,SCALLOPED BORDER,
  ADVERTISING........................................ 20.00
CALENDAR PLATE,1912,PORTRAIT,GIRL,PINK DRESS,WATER,BOATS,
  RACQUET,GUN........................................ 25.00
CALENDAR PLATE,1912,WILD DUCKS........................ 12.50
CALENDAR PLATE,1912,WILD TURKEY,FORD & CLARKE,DRUGGISTS,
  CUMBERLAND,MD...................................... 35.00
CALENDAR PLATE,1913,BLACK SWANS,8 1/4 IN.............. 14.00
CALENDAR PLATE,1913,HORSESHOE,HORSES' HEADS,ARROW & BOW MARK
  ON BACK............................................ 25.00
CALENDAR PLATE,1913,ROBIN IN HEART OF LEAVES AND FLOWERS.  8.50
CALENDAR PLATE,1914,COUPLE RIDING HORSES IN COUNTRY... 15.00
CALENDAR PLATE,1914,FOUR-LEAF CLOVER,8 1/4 IN......... 14.00
CALENDAR PLATE,1914,SMALL BOY,MARKED DRESDEN,7 1/2 IN. 15.00
CALENDAR PLATE,1915,MAP OF PANAMA CANAL...............  8.50
CALENDAR PLATE,1915,PANAMA CANAL MAP,6 IN.DIAMETER....  6.50
CALENDAR PLATE,1915,PANAMA CANAL,7 1/4 IN............. 15.00
CALENDAR PLATE,1915,PANAMA CANAL,8 IN................. 15.00
CALENDAR PLATE,1916,BLUEBIRD BETWEEN EACH CALENDAR,BIRDS,
  MARSHES............................................ 25.00
CALENDAR PLATE,1916,GAME,SIGNED BY EDWIN MEERGIE,PALM
  FECHTELER & CO..................................... 45.00
CALENDAR PLATE,1916,INDIAN IN CANOE,SIGNED H SOULE,ELMWOOD,
  WISCONSIN.......................................... 17.00
CALENDAR PLATE,1916,INDIAN'S HEAD,AURORA DRUG & SUPPLY CO.,
  AURORA,N.Y......................................... 26.00
CALENDAR PLATE,1917,BASKET OF VIOLETS................. 22.00
CALENDAR PLATE,1917,WICKER BASKET TURNED OVER,VIOLETS
  POURING OUT........................................ 25.00
CALENDAR PLATE,1919,FLAG IN CENTER,LORRAINE,KANSAS,9 IN. 15.00
CALENDAR PLATE,1920,FLAG CENTER,BORDER HAS WWI INSIGNIA,
  EAGLE,VICTORY...................................... 20.00
CALENDAR PLATE,1920,FLAG CENTER,PEACE,7 1/8 IN........ 17.00
CALENDAR PLATE,1920,VICTORY DECOR,ALLIED FLAGS,DATED PEACE,
  JUNE 28,1919....................................... 15.00
CALENDAR PLATE,1921,GAME BIRDS........................ 25.00
CALENDAR PLATE,1924,FRUIT & FLOWERS................... 25.00
CALENDAR PLATE,1924,FRUIT DECOR,HAPPY NEW YEAR,S.F.FURNITURE
  STORE.............................................. 15.00
CALENDAR PLATE,1925,PINK & GREEN SHADINGS,DEPICTS THE
  STEEPLECHASE....................................... 12.00
CALENDAR PLATE,1926.............................ILLUS.. 15.00
CALENDAR PLATE,1928,LARGE DOG........................ 24.00
CALENDAR PLATE,1928,ROSES............................ 28.00
CALENDAR PLATE,1951,GOLD DECOR,10 IN..................  3.50
CALENDAR PLATE,1953,GOLD DECOR,10 IN..................  3.00
CALENDAR PLATE,1954,IVORY COLOR,GOLD DECOR,10 IN......  3.00
CALENDAR PLATE,1956 ON FACE,1955 ON REVERSE SIDE,TIN..  7.50
CALENDAR PLATE,GIBSON GIRL,COMPLIMENTS,KREBS COFFEE CO.,
  BLOOMINGTON........................................ 30.00
CALENDAR PLATE,GIBSON GIRL,HORSE,PIERCED BACK FOR HANGING,
```

CALENDAR PLATE, 1926

```
    9 1/2 IN................................................  12.50
CALENDAR PLATE,UNDATED,FLORAL,FLAG,CALENDAR BORDER,
   CHAS.MRECH,IOWA..........................................  35.00
```

```
    THE CAMBRIDGE GLASS COMPANY MADE PRESSED GLASS IN
    CAMBRIDGE,OHIO. IT WAS MARKED WITH A C IN A TRIANGLE
    ABOUT 1902.THE WORDS NEAR-CUT WERE USED AFTER 1906.
CAMBRIDGE,BOWL,PUNCH,PINK,STAND,EIGHT CUPS..................  55.00
CAMBRIDGE,BOWL,ROSE,COBALT,CLEAR FOOT......................  24.50
CAMBRIDGE,BOWL,ROYAL AMETHYST,MARK,11 IN.DIAMETER...........   8.50
CAMBRIDGE,BOX,STAMP,STERLING SILVER ON BRONZE,MARKED........  16.50
CAMBRIDGE,CONSOLE SET,BOWL WITH FLOWER HOLDER,NUDE,GREEN,
   CANDLEHOLDERS...........................................  41.50
CAMBRIDGE,CREAMER & SUGAR,PINK,MARKED WITH C IN TRIANGLE....  11.00
CAMBRIDGE,CREAMER & SUGAR,SHAPED LIKE FLOWER,PALE BLUE,
   SIGNED..................................................  16.00
CAMBRIDGE,CUP & SAUCER,BLACK SCALLOPED SAUCER,WHITE CUP,
   SIGNED C-4..............................................   3.50
CAMBRIDGE,CUP & SAUCER,ETCHED CRYSTAL,PINK,MARKED,SET OF SIX  24.00
CAMBRIDGE,DISH,CANDY,PINK,SCROLL HANDLES,ETCHED,MARKED,
   5 IN.DIAMETER...........................................  13.50
CAMBRIDGE,PLATE,AMBER,COIN TRIANGLE,8 IN....................   2.00
CAMBRIDGE,WINE SET,PAPER LABEL,AMETHYST,FIVE GLASSES........  27.50
CAMBRIDGE,WINE,AZURE-BLUE,WIDE-RINGED STEM,4 1/2 IN.TALL....  38.50
```

```
    CAMEO GLASS WAS MADE IN LAYERS IN MUCH THE SAME MANNER
    AS A CAMEO IN JEWELRY. PART OF THE TOP LAYER OF GLASS
    WAS CUT AWAY TO REVEAL A DIFFERENTLY COLORED GLASS
    BENEATH. THE MOST FAMOUS CAMEO GLASS WAS MADE DURING
    THE NINETEENTH CENTURY.
CAMEO,SEE ALSO,LISTING UNDER ARTIST'S NAME
CAMEO,ATOMIZER,JEWEL BOX,FUCHSIA CUT TO GOLD,CRISTALLERIE DE
   PANTIN MARK............................................. 275.00
CAMEO,ATOMIZER,ORANGE GROUND,AMBER FLORAL,TASSEL,SIGNED
   PARADI,8 IN.TALL........................................ 115.00
CAMEO,BOTTLE,PERFUME,SHADED WHITE FLORAL,YELLOW BASE,SILVER
   LID,ENGLAND............................................. 650.00
CAMEO,BOTTLE,SCENT,PINK GROUND,PURPLE VIOLETS,SIGNED
   E.RASPILLAR,FRANCE......................................  90.00
CAMEO,BOTTLE,SNUFF,OPAQUE PINK,CARVED OVERLAY OF FOO DOGS,
   CHINA................................................... 125.00
CAMEO,BOTTLE,SNUFF,OPAQUE WHITE,GREEN INCLUSIONS,FOO DOGS,
   CHINA...................................................  55.00
CAMEO,BOTTLE,SNUFF,TRANSLUCENT RED FISH,CARVED,GRAY JADE
   STOPPER,CHINA...........................................  65.00
CAMEO,BOWL,GREEN,BROWN BERRY,ACID CUT,OVAL,SIGNED RICHARD,
   6 1/4 X 3 IN............................................ 125.00
CAMEO,BOX,SNUFF,GEOMETRIC DESIGN,RED,WHITE,LION FACES ON
   SIDES,CHINA.............................................  45.00
CAMEO,BOX,SNUFF,SIX-COLORED FLORAL,FROG,BAT,WHITE GROUND,
   CHINA................................................... 150.00
CAMEO,CASTOR,PICKLE,CRUSHED STRAWBERRY COLOR FLORENTINE,
   HOLDER,TONGS............................................ 175.00
CAMEO,ICE BUCKET,FROSTED,APPLIED COBALT LEAVES,FOOTED,BRASS
   COLLAR.................................................. 350.00
CAMEO,PERFUME,RED CARVED FLOWERS,YELLOW FROSTED GROUND,
   ATOMIZER,BR MARK........................................  73.00
CAMEO,SHADE,LAMP,PASTEL,SIGNED MULLER FRERES,LUNEVILLE,
   6 IN.TALL,4............................................. 150.00
CAMEO,TOOTHPICK,GREEN FLORAL OVER PINK,SIGNED DESSIERE,
   NANCY,FRANCE............................................  85.00
CAMEO,TUMBLER,HIGHBALL,CRANBERRY CUT TO VASELINE,FROSTED
   SCENES..................................................  85.00
```

CAMEO,VASE,BLUE GROUND,WHITE ACORN & LEAF DESIGN,ENGLAND,
    7 1/2 IN.HIGH................................................ 375.00
CAMEO,VASE,BOWL,GREEN,RUFFLED,GILT,FLORAL ENAMEL,SIGNED MONT
    JOYE....................................................... 100.00
CAMEO,VASE,BUD,YELLOW GROUND,COBALT FLOWERS,SIGNED RICHARD,
    6 IN.TALL...................................................  90.00
CAMEO,VASE,CRANBERRY TO WHITE,MARKED DEPOSE,11 IN........... 250.00
CAMEO,VASE,CROISMARE NANCY,BLUE GROUND,PURPLE FLORAL,
    POLISHED,10 1/4 IN..........................................  80.00
CAMEO,VASE,DARK APRICOT SATIN GROUND,WHITE FLORAL,FLORENTINE  45.00
CAMEO,VASE,FROSTED GROUND,AMBER LEAVES & FLOWERS,GILT,SIGNED
    HONESDALE.................................................. 120.00
CAMEO,VASE,GOLD DECOR,HOLLY DESIGN,GREEN TO CLEAR,HONESDALE,
    12 1/4 IN................................................. 145.00
CAMEO,VASE,GREEN,GOLD,CARVED,SIGNED HONESDALE,8 1/2 IN.TALL,
    5 IN.WIDE................................................. 150.00
CAMEO,VASE,GREEN LILY & LEAVES,SIGNED ERISBACH,3 1/2 IN.
    HIGH......................................................  65.00
CAMEO,VASE,HONESDALE,CARVED,GREEN,GOLD,9 X 4 1/2 IN......... 150.00
CAMEO,VASE,MAROON FLORAL,LEAVES,MOTTLED ORANGE GROUND,
    RICHARD,5 1/2 IN.......................................... 158.00
CAMEO,VASE,MAROON LEAVES,STEMS,ORANGE GROUND,SIGNED RICHARD,
    5 1/2 IN................................................. 175.00
CAMEO,VASE,MINIATURE,RED GROUND,FLORAL DECOR,ENGLAND,
    3 1/2 IN.HIGH............................................ 550.00
CAMEO,VASE,OPAQUE ORANGE SATIN GROUND,BROWN ACORNS,PINE
    NEEDLES.................................................. 135.00
CAMEO,VASE,OPAQUE WHITE SATIN GROUND,PURPLE BLEEDING HEARTS,
    SIGNED................................................... 175.00
CAMEO,VASE,PALE BLUE FLORAL,LEAVES,PINK-ORCHID GROUND,
    7 IN.TALL................................................ 115.00
CAMEO GLASS,VASE,RICHARD,IVORY GROUND,BROWN IRIS PATTERN,
    BEE,BUTTERFLY............................................ 130.00
CAMEO,VASE,ST.DENIS........................................ 185.00
CAMEO,VASE,STICK,MANDARIN YELLOW,CARVED RED OVERLAY,FOO
    DOGS,PEKING,PAIR......................................... 800.00
CAMEO,VASE,STICK,SCENIC,WOODLAND LAKE,FLORAL,RICHARD,
    8 3/4 IN.HIGH............................................ 250.00
CAMEO,VASE,TURQUOISE GROUND,WHITE BIRD,FLORAL,BUTTERFLY,
    12 1/4 IN.TALL........................................... 145.00
CAMEO,VASE,YELLOW GROUND,BROWN TRUMPET VINE,FLORAL,SIGNED
    RICHARD,12 IN............................................ 150.00
CAMEO,WEBB,SEE WEBB
CAMPAIGN,SEE POLITICAL CAMPAIGN
CAMPBELL KIDS,PLATE,SOUP,WHITE,RED RIM,MARKED PORSGRUNN
    NORGE......................................................   6.50
CAMPBELL SOUP,SPOON,BOY,GIRLS.............................    4.50


        CAMPHOR GLASS IS A CLOUDY WHITE GLASS THAT HAS BEEN
    BLOWN OR PRESSED. IT WAS MADE BY MANY FACTORIES IN THE
    MIDWEST DURING THE MID-NINETEENTH CENTURY.
    CAMPHOR,SEE ALSO,PRESSED GLASS
CAMPHOR GLASS,BOTTLE,FIGURINE,CAT,JASMAN,2 1/2 IN.HIGH......    9.00
CAMPHOR GLASS,BOTTLE,SHAPE OF CAT,2 1/2 IN.HIGH............   11.00
CAMPHOR GLASS,BOWL,ALLOVER RAISED FLOWERS,DOVES FORM FINIAL
    ON COVER..................................................   18.00
CAMPHOR GLASS,BOWL,BERRY,SUNBURST CENTER,RUBY NOTCHED EDGE,
    SILVER HOLDER............................................   32.50
CAMPHOR GLASS,BOWL,CONSOLE,FLARED SHAPE,OPENWORK RIM,YELLOW,
    10 IN.TOP................................................   20.00
CAMPHOR GLASS,BOWL,QUILTED,PINK,BUTTON BASE,HANDLED,8 IN....   15.00
CAMPHOR GLASS,BOWL,ROSE,CRIMPED TOP,3 1/2 IN.HIGH..........   12.00
CAMPHOR GLASS,BOWL,ROSE,DEEP,9 IN.........................    7.00
CAMPHOR GLASS,CANDLEHOLDER,SILVER OVERLAY,IVY & GRAPE
    DESIGN,5 1/4 IN..........................................   35.00
CAMPHOR GLASS,CHAMBER STICK,FOOTED........................   17.50
CAMPHOR GLASS,COLOGNE,BELL SHAPE,GOLD ENAMEL DECOR,APPLIED
    COLORED DOTS.............................................   20.00
CAMPHOR GLASS,COMPOTE,FROSTED CLEAR FOOT & STEM,GREEN BOWL,
    7 3/4 IN.HIGH...........................................   15.00
CAMPHOR GLASS,COMPOTE,OPEN,6 IN.TALL,6-IN.DIAMETER........   26.00
CAMPHOR GLASS,CRUET,BLOSSOMS,GREEN HANDLE & STOPPER,PEAR
    SHAPE,GREEN.............................................   39.00
CAMPHOR GLASS,CRUET,MILLEFIORE,STOPPER,HANDLE.............   55.00
CAMPHOR GLASS,DISH,COVER,WILD BOAR FINIAL,BLUE,SANDWICH
    GLASS,8 1/2 IN.......................................... 175.00
CAMPHOR GLASS,DISH,FLEUR-DE-LIS,WATER SCENE,GOLD BAND,7 IN..    4.50
CAMPHOR GLASS,FIGURINE,GIRL WITH TWO GEESE,5 1/2 IN.HIGH....   25.00
CAMPHOR GLASS,JAR,POWDER,PINK,THREADED SILVER OVERLAY,SILVER
    LID.....................................................    5.00

CAMPHOR GLASS,JAR,POWDER,ROW OF ELEPHANTS,ELEPHANT FINIAL,
 FOOTED,PINK.................................................. 7.50
CAMPHOR GLASS,LAMP,MINIATURE,ALLOVER PATTERN,EMBOSSED
 PANSIES,SCROLL............................................... 65.00
CAMPHOR GLASS,LAMP,NITE,CANDLE,WHITE........................... 35.00
CAMPHOR GLASS,MATCH HOLDER,PIPE SHAPE,SOUVENIR................. 8.50
CAMPHOR GLASS,MUG,RED ROSE IN GOLD SHIELD,AMERICAN FLAG........ 16.00
CAMPHOR GLASS,PLATE,ROSE,HANDLES,12 1/2 IN..................... 7.00
CAMPHOR GLASS,SHOE,BUTTON,4 1/2 IN.HIGH....................... 12.00
CAMPHOR GLASS,SHOE,SOUVENIR,CENTENNIAL EXPOSITION,MARKED
 GILLINDER.................................................... 9.00
CAMPHOR GLASS,SHOE,7 IN....................................... 18.00
CAMPHOR GLASS,TOOTHPICK,CHILD RESTING AGAINST BUCKET,3 X
 5 IN.LONG................................................... 35.00
CAMPHOR GLASS,TOOTHPICK,HEART SHAPE,CHOCOLATE................. 5.00
CAMPHOR GLASS,TOOTHPICK,INDIVIDUAL SALT,THREE FACES........... 14.50
CAMPHOR GLASS,TRAY,DRESSER,POWDER JAR,LID,TWO COVERED JARS,
 WHITE....................................................... 15.00
CAMPHOR GLASS,TRAY,OVAL,SCALLOPED BORDER,SHELL,SCROLLS,11 X
 9 IN....................................................... 6.50
CAMPHOR GLASS,VASE,RELIEF FLORAL,BULBOUS,TIFFIN,OHIO,
 9 1/2 IN................................................... 28.50
CAMPHOR GLASS,VASE,RIBBED,VERTICAL BRASS BANDS,8 IN.HIGH.... 25.00
CANARY GLASS,SEE VASELINE GLASS
CANDELABRA,CUT GLASS,GILT METAL,GEORGE III,PAIR.....ILLUS.. 500.00
CANDELABRA,FRENCH ORMOLU FIGURAL,5-LIGHT,19TH CENTURY,PAIR. 450.00
CANDLEHOLDER,HOLDS THREE CANDLES,TWO VASES ON SIDES,CLEAR
 PRISMS,GLASS............................................... 35.00
CANDLESTICK,SEE ALSO,BRASS,CANDLEHOLDER,PEWTER,PRESSED
 GLASS
CANDLESTICK,CARVED STANDARD,FOLIAGE,TRIPOD BASE,GILT,ITALY,
 24 IN.,PAIR............................................... 85.00

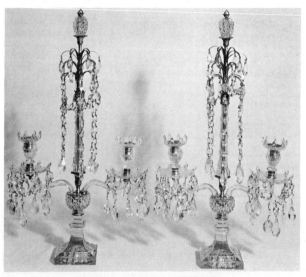

GEORGE III CUT GLASS CANDELABRA

CANDLESTICK,HOG SCRAPER,SIDE PUSH-UP,HANGING LIP,SIGNED,
 5 IN.LONG.................................................. 17.50
CANDLESTICK,SILVERED COPPER,CHERUBS,REPOUSSE STANDARD,ITALY,
 33 IN.,PAIR............................................... 130.00
CANDLESTICK,SILVERED COPPER,REPOUSSE STANDARD,ITALY,1780,
 33 IN.,PAIR............................................... 80.00


    CANDY CONTAINERS,ESPECIALLY THOSE MADE OF GLASS,WERE
    POPULAR DURING THE LATE VICTORIAN ERA.
CANDY CONTAINER,AIRPLANE...................................... 5.00
CANDY CONTAINER,AIRPLANE,TIN WINGS........................... 18.50
CANDY CONTAINER,AIRPLANE,TIN WINGS,ORIGINAL CANDY........... 9.00
CANDY CONTAINER,AMOS & ANDY IN AUTO.......................... 8.50
CANDY CONTAINER,ARMY HAT,EAGLE ON FRONT,AMBER................ 15.00
CANDY CONTAINER,ARMY TANK.................................... 6.00
CANDY CONTAINER,ARMY TANK,CANDY............................. 4.50
CANDY CONTAINER,AUTO........................................ 5.50
CANDY CONTAINER,AUTO,ELECTRIC COUPE,PAT.FEB.18,1913,EMBOSSED

```
   GUARANTEE.............................................  35.00
CANDY CONTAINER,AUTOMOBILE,COUPE,LONG HOOD..................  12.50
CANDY CONTAINER,BATTLESHIP,CONTENTS,CARDBOARD BOTTOM,VICTORY
   GLASS,INC.............................................  22.50
CANDY CONTAINER,BEAR.......................................   2.00
CANDY CONTAINER,BOOT,SANTA CLAUS,MERRY CHRISTMAS...........  15.00
CANDY CONTAINER,BOOT,SANTA'S,GREEN.........................  12.00
CANDY CONTAINER,BUCKET,HANDLE..............................   7.50
CANDY CONTAINER,BULLDOG,BROWN,CLOSURE......................  18.00
CANDY CONTAINER,BULLDOG,ON ROUND BASE,PAINTED,4 1/4 IN.....  16.00
CANDY CONTAINER,BULLDOG,SITTING,COLLAR,NO CLOSURE..........   6.50
CANDY CONTAINER,BULLDOG,STANDING ON ROUND BASE,PAINT,
   4 1/2 IN..............................................  18.00
CANDY CONTAINER,BULLDOG,6 IN...............................  45.00
CANDY CONTAINER,BUS........................................   8.50
CANDY CONTAINER,CABIN CRUISER,OPEN BOTTOM..................   6.00
CANDY CONTAINER,CAP,MILITARY STYLE,1942...................  10.00
CANDY CONTAINER,CHARLIE CHAPLIN,BORGFELDT..................  35.00
CANDY CONTAINER,CHICKEN....................................  12.50
CANDY CONTAINER,CHICKEN ON NEST.................... 4.00 TO   6.00
CANDY CONTAINER,CHICKEN ON SAGGING BASKET..................  15.00
CANDY CONTAINER,CHICKEN ON SAGGING BASKET,GREEN HEAD &
   BASKET,CLEAR..........................................  22.00
CANDY CONTAINER,CLOCK,ALARM,PEWTER CLOSURE.................  25.00
CANDY CONTAINER,CLOCK,MILK GLASS, GOLD DECOR,SLIDING TIN
   BASE..................................................  15.50
CANDY CONTAINER,CLOCK,TIN BOTTOM,GILT,MILK GLASS,SOUVENIR...  12.00
CANDY CONTAINER,DOG........................................   4.50
CANDY CONTAINER,DOG,CROSSETT...............................   2.50
CANDY CONTAINER,DOG,OPEN BOTTOM............................   6.00
CANDY CONTAINER,DOG,ORIGINAL CANDY.........................   7.50
CANDY CONTAINER,DOG,SCOTTY,SEATED..........................   6.00
CANDY CONTAINER,DONKEY & CART..............................  10.00
CANDY CONTAINER,DONKEY & CART,NO CLOSURE...................   7.00
CANDY CONTAINER,DONKEY PULLING BARREL......................  24.00
CANDY CONTAINER,ELECTRIC COUPE,PAT.FEB.18,1913,GUARANTEED BY
   VALE BROS.............................................  35.00
CANDY CONTAINER,ELECTRIC IRON WITH CORD....................   7.50
CANDY CONTAINER,ENGINE,CLEAR,ORIGINAL CANDY & LITHO TIN
   CLOSURE...............................................  15.00
CANDY CONTAINER,FIRE ENGINE....................... 5.50 TO  12.00
CANDY CONTAINER,FIRE ENGINE,ALL GLASS,NO CLOSURE...........   6.50
CANDY CONTAINER,FIRE ENGINE,CLEAR..........................   6.00
CANDY CONTAINER,FIRE ENGINE,ENCLOSURE,CANDY................   7.50
CANDY CONTAINER,FIRE ENGINE,METAL BASE.....................   8.50
CANDY CONTAINER,FIRE ENGINE,NO.11,CANDY....................   8.00
CANDY CONTAINER,FIRE ENGINE,TIN WHEELS,CLOSURE.............  14.50
CANDY CONTAINER,FIRE TRUCK,THREE DOT,USA,S IS BACKWARDS.....  35.00
CANDY CONTAINER,FISH,EMBOSSED FEATURES,CLEAR,8 1/2 X
   2 1/2 IN..............................................  18.00
CANDY CONTAINER,FISH,ORANGE PAINT,CAP,9 IN.LONG............  25.00
CANDY CONTAINER,FLASK,U.S. ON SIDE.........................   8.00
CANDY CONTAINER,GUN,STOUGHS THREE DOT,ORIGINAL CANDY.......   4.50
CANDY CONTAINER,GUN,4 IN...................................   5.50
CANDY CONTAINER,GUN,8 IN...................................  14.00
CANDY CONTAINER,HEARSE,NO.2................................  35.00
CANDY CONTAINER,HELICOPTER,BLUE TIN BLADE,SCREW CAP........  12.00
CANDY CONTAINER,HEN ON NEST....................... 5.00 TO   7.50
CANDY CONTAINER,HEN ON NEST,CLEAR,OPEN BOTTOM..............   5.00
CANDY CONTAINER,HEN ON NEST,NO CLOSURE.....................   7.00
CANDY CONTAINER,HEN ON NEST,5 IN.LONG......................   4.95
CANDY CONTAINER,HORSE & CART...................... 8.00 TO  12.00
CANDY CONTAINER,HOUND DOG,SITTING UP,SCREW-ON TOP..........   5.00
CANDY CONTAINER,HOUND PUPPY,STIPPLED HAT...................   6.00
CANDY CONTAINER,IRON WITH CORD,CARDBOARD CLOSURE...........   9.50
CANDY CONTAINER,JEEP.............................. 5.00 TO   9.50
CANDY CONTAINER,KIDDIE KAR.................................  18.50
CANDY CONTAINER,LADY'S LEG,FROSTED STOCKING,RED GARTER.....  13.00
CANDY CONTAINER,LAMP,CLEAR GLASS,6 IN......................   5.00
CANDY CONTAINER,LAMP,GLASS,RED CHIMNEY.....................   4.00
CANDY CONTAINER,LAMP,GONE WITH THE WIND,MILK GLASS.........  35.00
CANDY CONTAINER,LANTERN........................... 5.00 TO   5.50
CANDY CONTAINER,LANTERN,BAIL,CAP...........................  18.00
CANDY CONTAINER,LANTERN,BARN TYPE..........................  25.00
CANDY CONTAINER,LANTERN,BEVELED PANEL,SQUARE...............  38.00
CANDY CONTAINER,LANTERN,ELECTRIC,BOND......................  15.00
CANDY CONTAINER,LANTERN,GREEN GLASS........................  12.50
CANDY CONTAINER,LANTERN,GREEN GLASS,METAL..................   7.50
CANDY CONTAINER,LANTERN,METAL,GREEN GLOBE..................   6.50
CANDY CONTAINER,LANTERN,RED GLASS,TIN SHADE,BASE,HANDLE,
   5 3/4 IN..............................................   3.00
```

```
CANDY CONTAINER,LIBERTY BELL,AMBER,TIN SCREW CLOSURE........     25.00
CANDY CONTAINER,LIBERTY BELL,BLUE,TIN CLOSURE...............     20.00
CANDY CONTAINER,LIBERTY BELL,GREEN.........................     18.00
CANDY CONTAINER,LIBERTY BELL,3 1/4 IN.HIGH.................      8.75
CANDY CONTAINER,LIGHT BULB,BLUE............................     35.00
CANDY CONTAINER,LIGHTHOUSE.................................     10.00
CANDY CONTAINER,LITTLE BOILER NO.1.........................     25.00
CANDY CONTAINER,LOCOMOTIVE.................... 6.50 TO          30.00
CANDY CONTAINER,LOCOMOTIVE,BOTTOM OPENING,5 1/8............      6.00
CANDY CONTAINER,LOCOMOTIVE,CORK,NUMBER ON SIDE,PATENTED,
  3 1/2 IN................................................      9.00
CANDY CONTAINER,LOCOMOTIVE,FRONT OPENING,3 7/8 X 1 5/8 IN...     4.50
CANDY CONTAINER,LOCOMOTIVE,LITHOGRAPHED CLOSURE,4 3/16 X
  3 7/8 IN...............................................      8.50
CANDY CONTAINER,LOCOMOTIVE,NO CLOSURE......................      5.50
CANDY CONTAINER,LOCOMOTIVE,PAINTED WHEELS,4 7/8 X 2 1/8 IN..     6.00
CANDY CONTAINER,LOCOMOTIVE,TIN CLOSURE,6 1/2 X 3 3/4 IN.....    10.00
CANDY CONTAINER,MONKEY,7 3/4 IN............................     45.00
CANDY CONTAINER,MULE PULLING TWO-WHEELED BARREL............     30.00
CANDY CONTAINER,MULE PULLING TWO-WHEELED BARREL WITH DRIVER.    38.00
CANDY CONTAINER,NURSING BOTTLE WITH NIPPLE.................      3.50
CANDY CONTAINER,NURSING BOTTLE,RUBBER NIPPLE...............      2.50
CANDY CONTAINER,OFFICER'S CAP,MILITARY.....................      8.00
CANDY CONTAINER,OLD OAKEN BUCKET,GLASS BOTTOM,TIN TOP.......    15.00
CANDY CONTAINER,PETER RABBIT,6 IN..........................     12.00
CANDY CONTAINER,PIG,PAPIER-MACHE,GOLD,GERMAN,6 IN.LONG......     4.00
CANDY CONTAINER,PISTOL............................ 6.50 TO      9.50
CANDY CONTAINER,PISTOL,CLEAR,TIN CLOSURE...................     12.00
CANDY CONTAINER,PISTOL,DUELING,DOUBLE-BARRELED,13 IN.LONG,
  PAIR..................................................     35.00
CANDY CONTAINER,PISTOL,MERCURY-LINED.......................     15.00
CANDY CONTAINER,PISTOL,11 IN...............................     11.50
CANDY CONTAINER,POWDER HORN,EMBOSSED PAT.APPLIED FOR,TIN
  LID,GROUND LIP.........................................      8.00
CANDY CONTAINER,POWDER HORN,METAL CAP,5 IN.................      6.50
CANDY CONTAINER,PT BOAT....................................      9.00
CANDY CONTAINER,PUPPY,CLEAR................................      3.50
CANDY CONTAINER,PUPPY,SITTING..............................      2.75
CANDY CONTAINER,RABBIT............................. 6.50 TO      7.00
CANDY CONTAINER,RABBIT EATING CARROT.............. 9.50 TO     12.50
CANDY CONTAINER,RABBIT IN EGGSHELL,ORIGINAL TIN CLOSURE,GILT
  DECOR.................................................     13.50
CANDY CONTAINER,RABBIT IN EGGSHELL,PAINT...................     35.00
CANDY CONTAINER,RABBIT,BY STOUGH...........................     15.00
CANDY CONTAINER,RABBIT,PAPIER-MACHE,3 IN.HIGH,3 1/4 IN.BASE.     7.50
CANDY CONTAINER,RABBIT,RUNNING ON LOG,TIN CLOSURE..........     22.00
CANDY CONTAINER,RABBIT,SITTING.................... 6.50 TO      8.00
CANDY CONTAINER,REINDEER,FELT-COVERED......................     18.50
CANDY CONTAINER,REVOLVER...................................      8.00
CANDY CONTAINER,REVOLVER,AMBER,PLATED BRASS CAP ON BARREL,
  C.P.CO.,8 IN...........................................     16.50
CANDY CONTAINER,REVOLVER,AQUA,SCREW TOP,4 1/2 IN............     8.75
CANDY CONTAINER,REVOLVER,CLEAR.............................     10.00
CANDY CONTAINER,REVOLVER,TIN SCREW CAP.....................      8.50
CANDY CONTAINER,REVOLVER,7 1/2 IN..........................     12.00
CANDY CONTAINER,SANTA BOOT.................................      4.00
CANDY CONTAINER,SANTA BY SQUARE CHIMNEY,CLEAR..............     20.00
CANDY CONTAINER,SANTA CLAUS....................... 18.00 TO     25.00
CANDY CONTAINER,SANTA CLAUS AT CHIMNEY.....................     28.00
CANDY CONTAINER,SANTA CLAUS BOOT,CLEAR,ORIGINAL CANDY.......     7.50
CANDY CONTAINER,SANTA CLAUS BOOT,GREEN,COBALT..............      7.50
CANDY CONTAINER,SANTA CLAUS,STANDING,PAINTED...............     10.00
CANDY CONTAINER,SANTA CLAUS,TIN HEAD WITH BEARD FORMS TOP,
  PAINTED BODY...........................................     15.00
CANDY CONTAINER,SATCHEL,WIRE HANDLE,TIN SLIDING BASE........    10.00
CANDY CONTAINER,SCOTTIE............................ 3.00 TO      8.50
CANDY CONTAINER,SCOTTIE,OPEN TOP...........................      6.00
CANDY CONTAINER,SCOTTIE DOG,PAIR...........................      6.50
CANDY CONTAINER,SCOTTIE DOG,SAYS NIAGARA FALLS.............     40.00
CANDY CONTAINER,SCOUT CAR,ENCLOSURE,CANDY..................      7.50
CANDY CONTAINER,SEDAN......................................      7.00
CANDY CONTAINER,SHIP.......................................      5.50
CANDY CONTAINER,SITTING RABBIT.............................      5.00
CANDY CONTAINER,SKATING LANTERN............................      8.00
CANDY CONTAINER,SPARK PLUG,1923............................     35.00
CANDY CONTAINER,SPIRIT OF GOODWILL.........................     35.00
CANDY CONTAINER,STATUE OF LIBERTY..........................      5.00
CANDY CONTAINER,SUITCASE...................................     20.00
CANDY CONTAINER,SUITCASE,CLEAR,HANDLE,TIN CLOSURE..........     16.50
CANDY CONTAINER,SUITCASE,CLEAR,TIN COVER...................     12.00
CANDY CONTAINER,SUITCASE,FEB.1,1906........................     18.00
```

```
CANDY CONTAINER,SUITCASE,SOUVENIR,GOLD LETTERS,BEARS,MILK
  GLASS....................................................  42.50
CANDY CONTAINER,TANK,CONTENTS,COVER.........................   7.00
CANDY CONTAINER,TANK,OLIVE DRAB GREEN PAINT.................  25.00
CANDY CONTAINER,TELEPHONE...................................   4.00
CANDY CONTAINER,TELEPHONE,FRENCH............................   2.50
CANDY CONTAINER,TELEPHONE,FRENCH,METAL ARM..................   9.50
CANDY CONTAINER,TELEPHONE,RAISED DIAL.......................  11.00
CANDY CONTAINER,TELEPHONE,WITH CANDY........................  12.00
CANDY CONTAINER,TELEPHONE,WOOD RECEIVER,GREEN PAINT.........  15.00
CANDY CONTAINER,TELEPHONE,WOODEN HANDLE.....................  15.00
CANDY CONTAINER,TRAIN..............................5.50 TO    8.00
CANDY CONTAINER,TRAIN ENGINE,NO.1028,5 IN.LONG..............  11.00
CANDY CONTAINER,TRAIN ENGINE,SAYS 1028......................   4.50
CANDY CONTAINER,TRAIN,ENGINE,COAL CAR,TWO PASSENGER CARS,TIN
  WHEELS,SET...............................................  50.00
CANDY CONTAINER,TRAIN,LITHOGRAPHED CLOSURE..................  35.00
CANDY CONTAINER,TRAIN,TIN CLOSURE...........................  16.00
CANDY CONTAINER,TRUNK,MILK GLASS............................  12.50
CANDY CONTAINER,TURKEY,PAPIER-MACHE.........................   9.00
CANDY CONTAINER,VICTORY BUS.................................  15.00
CANDY CONTAINER,WINDMILL....................................  25.00
CANDY CONTAINER,WINDMILL,TIN WHEEL,NO BOTTOM................  12.50


      CANTON CHINA IS A BLUE-AND-WHITE WARE MADE NEAR CANTON,
  CHINA,FROM ABOUT 1785 TO 1895. IT HAS A HAND-DECORATED
  CHINESE SCENE.
CANTON,BOWL & DISH,OCTAGONAL,BLUE & WHITE,19TH CENTURY...... 175.00
CANTON,BOWL & PITCHER,MINIATURE,BROWN,RED & PINK FLOWERS....   8.50
CANTON,BOWL & STAND,FRUIT,RETICULATED BLUE & WHITE,19TH
  CENTURY.................................................. 200.00
CANTON,BOWL,BLUE & WHITE MUMS,8 1/2 IN......................  27.50
CANTON,BOWL,FISH,BLUE & WHITE,STAND,19TH CENTURY,13 IN. HIGH 750.00
CANTON,BOWL,RICE,BLUE,WHITE,COVER,PLATE.....................  26.00
CANTON,BOWL,ROSE,BLUE,WHITE PRUNUS BLOSSOMS,TWO RINGS IN
  BASE,COVER...............................................  23.00
CANTON,BOWL,ROSE,BLUE,WHITE PRUNUS FLOWERS,COVER............  21.00
CANTON,BOWL,SCENE INSIDE,1/2 SUN OUTSIDE,SIGNED,
  12 IN.DIAMETER...........................................  65.00
CANTON,BOX,BLUE,WHITE,CIRCA 1840,4 1/2 IN.HIGH,4 IN.SQUARE.. 200.00
CANTON,BUTTER PAT,BLUE......................................  10.00
CANTON,BUTTER PAT,MOUNTAIN,LAKE,TREE,BIRDS,FLORAL,BLUE,WHITE   3.00
CANTON,CUP & SAUCER,BLUE,WHITE,HANDLELESS...................  18.00
CANTON,CUP & SAUCER,DEMITASSE,BLUE,SET OF 6.................  65.00
CANTON,CUP,BLUE FIGURALS,HANDLELESS.........................  10.00
CANTON,DISH,FISH SHAPE,BLUE,WHITE....................ILLUS..  22.50
CANTON,DISH,LEAF,OPEN-HANDLED END,11 X 8 IN.................  60.00
```

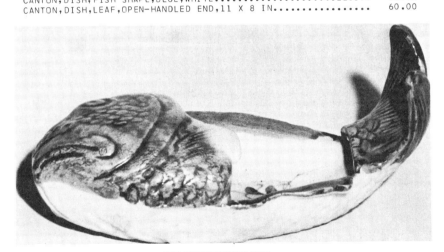

FISH SHAPE CANTON DISH

```
CANTON,DISH,LIGHT BLUE,HAND-PAINTED,PIERCED RIM,8 IN........  38.00
CANTON,DISH,VEGETABLE,BLUE,WHITE,BOAR'S TAIL HANDLES,
  LATTICE,KNOBBED LID...................................... 125.00
CANTON,DISH,VEGETABLE,BLUE,WHITE,COVER,8 IN.LONG X 7 IN.WIDE  95.00
CANTON,JAR,GINGER,BLUE FLEUR-DE-LIS,LID,SIGNED RIETI........  15.00
CANTON,JAR,GINGER,BLUE HAWTHORNE,DOUBLE RING,5 1/2 IN.......  24.50
CANTON,JAR,GINGER,DARK BLUE,WHITE BLOSSOMS,COVER,5 IN. X
```

```
     6 IN.TALL..............................................    25.00
CANTON,JAR,ROSE,PRUNUS FLOWERS,BLUE,RINGS IN BOTTOM,COVER...    21.00
CANTON,JAR,ROSE,WHITE PRUNUS BLOSSOMS,DARK BLUE GROUND,BLUE
     RING BASE.............................................    26.00
CANTON,LAMP,PAINTED SHADE,WIRED.............................    60.00
CANTON,PITCHER,CHINESE BLUE,WHITE,CIRCA 1840,4 7/8 IN.......    85.00
CANTON,PITCHER,MILK,BLUE,WHITE,CIRCA 1840,5 IN..............    85.00
CANTON,PITCHER,MILK,CHINESE BLUE & WHITE,CIRCA 1840,
     7 IN.HIGH............................................   200.00
CANTON,PITCHER,WATER,BLUE,WHITE,10 IN.TALL..................   225.00
CANTON,PLATE,BLUE,WHITE,OPEN LATTICE EDGE,OVAL,8 1/2 X
     9 1/2 IN.............................................    40.00
CANTON,PLATE,BLUE,WHITE,OPEN LATTICE EDGE,OVAL,9 1/2 X
     10 1/2 IN............................................    45.00
CANTON,PLATE,BLUE,WHITE,10 IN..............................    28.00
CANTON,PLATE,MANDARIN,ENAMEL,GOLD EMBELLISHMENTS,9 1/2 IN...    38.00
CANTON,PLATE,MEDALLION,9 3/4 IN.DIAMETER...................    25.00
CANTON,PLATE,6,BLUE & WHITE,8 1/2 IN. DIAM.................    50.00
CANTON,PLATTER,BLUE,RECTANGLE,12 1/4 IN.LONG...............    45.00
CANTON,PLATTER,CUT CORNERS,CIRCA 1780,19 3/4 X 16 1/4 IN....   175.00
CANTON,PLATTER,PAIR OF SPILL VASES & PLATE,BLUE & WHITE,
     16 IN. LONG..........................................    50.00
CANTON,PLATTER,PIERCED RIM,OVAL,11 IN. X 10 IN.............    65.00
CANTON,PLATTER,WELL & TREE,TWO OVAL FEET,13 1/4 IN. X
     16 1/4 IN.LONG........................................   130.00
CANTON,PLATTER,WILLOW PATTERN,BLUE,CHINA,9 IN. X 14 IN......    22.50
CANTON,POTS-DE-CREME,4,BLUE & WHITE,CIRCA 1825.............   300.00
CANTON,SALT,TRENCHER......................................    70.00
CANTON,SOUP,BLUE,WHITE,8 1/4 IN.DIAMETER..................    22.00
CANTON,TEAPOT,BLUE,METAL LID,6 IN.TALL,4 1/2 IN.DIAMETER....    50.00
CANTON,TEAPOT,BLUE,WHITE,GOLD LINES,STRAIGHT SPOUT.........    75.00
CANTON,TUREEN & STAND,COVERED,BLUE & WHITE,19TH CENTURY.....   150.00
CANTON,VEGETABLE,BLUE & WHITE,BLUE FINIAL ON COVER.........    95.00
```

```
          CAPO-DI-MONTE PORCELAIN WAS FIRST MADE IN NAPLES,ITALY,
          FROM 1743 TO 1759. THE FACTORY MOVED NEAR MADRID,SPAIN,
          AND REOPENED IN 1771 AND WORKED TO 1834. SINCE THAT
          TIME THE DOCCIA FACTORY OF ITALY ACQUIRED THE MOLDS AND
          STYLE,EVEN USING THE N AND CROWN MARK WHICH WAS MADE
          FAMOUS BY THE FACTORY.
CAPO-DI-MONTE,BELL,DINNER,BLUE CROWN MARK..................    27.50
CAPO-DI-MONTE,BOWL,CONSOLE,FOOTED,SIGNED,13 IN.............    65.00
CAPO-DI-MONTE,BOWL,ENAMELED MYTHOLOGICAL FIGURES,GINORI,
     1820,COVER...........................................   175.00
CAPO-DI-MONTE,BOWL,PUNCH,18TH-CENTURY FAIENCE,NUDE REVELERS,
     DOLPHINS.............................................   235.00
CAPO-DI-MONTE,COMPOTE,SQUARE BASE,FOUR CHERUBS,SIGNED,ITALY,
     13 1/2 IN............................................    42.50
CAPO-DI-MONTE,CUP & SAUCER,FARM SCENE,PEOPLE,ANIMALS,BLUE N
     & CROWN MARK.........................................    49.50
CAPO-DI-MONTE,CUP & SAUCER,MARKED BLUE N UNDER CROWN.......    45.00
CAPO-DI-MONTE,FIGURINE,COUPLE CARRYING WATER BUCKETS,CROWN
     MARK,3 IN............................................    35.00
CAPO-DI-MONTE,FIGURINE,LADY,SITTING,HOLDS BASKET OF FLOWERS,
     SIGNED..............................................    55.00
CAPO-DI-MONTE,FIGURINE,PEASANT COUPLE CARRYING WATER
     BUCKETS,3 IN.........................................    35.00
CAPO-DI-MONTE,FIGURINE,SKULL RESTING ON AN OPEN BOOK,9 X
     8 IN.HIGH............................................   125.00
CAPO-DI-MONTE,FIGURINE,SOLDIER,RED COAT,BLOWING GOLD BUGLE,
     WHITE HORSE..........................................    57.50
CAPO-DI-MONTE,FIGURINE,7 IN.,PAIR,IN GLASS DOME,WALNUT
     FOOTED BASE..........................................   115.00
CAPO-DI-MONTE,LAMP,SWIRLED PINK RIBS,CHERUBS,GILT,BRASS
     BASE,FOOTED,PAIR.....................................    69.50
CAPO-DI-MONTE,PLAQUE,CLASSICAL FIGURES,MARKED BLUE N,CROWN,
     6 1/2 IN.............................................    45.50
CAPO-DI-MONTE,PLAQUE,BATTLE SCENE,MEN.HORSES,CANNON,SABERS,
     CASTLE,FRAME.........................................   225.00
CAPO-DI-MONTE,PLATE,CHERUBS IN CENTER & ON BORDER,1800,
     SIGNED,13 IN.........................................   200.00
CAPO-DI-MONTE,SKULL RESTING ON OPEN BOOK,SIGNED,8 IN.HIGH,
     9 IN.LONG............................................   125.00
CAPO-DI-MONTE,STEIN,11 IN. HIGH...........................   500.00
CAPO-DI-MONTE,STEIN,UNHINGED LID,11 IN.HIGH...............   300.00
CAPO-DI-MONTE,TEAPOT,CREAMER,SUGAR,6 CUPS & SAUCERS,ITALY...    80.00
CAPO-DI-MONTE,URN,CHERUBS,LIONS' HEADS,COVER,MARKED,11 IN...    55.00
CAR,TRUNK,FITTED WITH THREE SUITCASES,BLACK,NICKEL TRIM,FOR
     1936 PACKARD.........................................    75.00
CAR,VASE,PELICAN DESIGN,ROSE AMBER........................     5.00
```

```
     CARAMEL SLAG,SEE SLAG
     CARD,ADVERTISING,PRICES RANGE FROM $.05 UP. SEE ILLUSTRATI
CARD,ADVERTISING,A & P BAKING POWDER,BASEBALL........ILLUS..     .30
CARD,ADVERTISING,BUCKINGHAM DYE FOR WHISKERS.........ILLUS..     .60
CARD,ADVERTISING,R.S.V.P. TABLE SALT.................ILLUS..    1.00
CARD,VALENTINE,10 IN. X 7 IN.,7 IN. X 6 IN.,10.............    25.00
CARDS,PLAYING,ADVERTISING,OLYMPIAN & HIAWATHA..............     1.00
CARDS,PLAYING,ADVERTISING,MILWAUKEE ROAD..................     1.00
CARDS,PLAYING,CENTURY OF PROGRESS,1934,ONE DECK.............     3.00
CARDS,PLAYING,DISCUS,ROUND,BOX.............................    10.00
```

BASEBALL CARD

ADVERTISING CARD, BUCKINGHAM
DYE FOR WHISKERS

ADVERTISING CARD, R.S.V.P. TABLE SALT

CARDS,PLAYING,DRAGONFLY DESIGN,GILT EDGES,REG.1881,ALLIGATOR
    SKIN CASE.............................................     6.50
CARDS,PLAYING,PAN-AMERICAN................................    12.00
CARDS,PLAYING,SCENIC,EACH CARD DIFFERENT,PACIFIC NORTHWEST,
    CANADA,1905..........................................     7.50
CARDS,PLAYING,SOUVENIR,AMONG THE WHITE MOUNTAINS,52 VIEWS...     5.00
CARDS,PLAYING,SOUVENIR,HISTORIC BOSTON,52 VIEWS............     5.00
CARDS,PLAYING,SOUVENIR,WESTERN PACIFIC,BOX................     6.00
CARDS,PLAYING,SOUVENIR,52 VIEWS ON GRAND TRUNK RAILWAY
    SYSTEM,BOX...........................................     7.00
CARDS,PLAYING,VIEWS OF OREGON,CROWN POINT,MT.WAUNA,LEATHER
    CASE.................................................     4.75
CARDS,PLAYING,WORLD'S FAIR,1933,CHICAGO,HALL OF SCIENCE.....     7.50


        CARLSBAD,GERMANY IS A MARK FOUND ON CHINA MADE BY
        SEVERAL FACTORIES IN GERMANY. MOST OF THE PIECES
        AVAILABLE TODAY WERE MADE AFTER 1891.
CARLSBAD,CREAMER,FLAG ON ONE SIDE,OLD GLORY WORDS ON OTHER,
    AUSTRIA..............................................     4.75
CARLSBAD,DISH,VEGETABLE,TWO HANDLES,COVER,ROSE & BLUE
    FLORAL,AUSTRIA.......................................    18.00
CARLSBAD,JAR,CRACKER,WHITE LUSTER,PINK FLOWERS,AUSTRIA.....    25.00
CARLSBAD,PITCHER,HAND-PAINTED,GOLD DRAGON HANDLE,AUSTRIA,
    4 IN.................................................    10.00
CARLSBAD,PLATE,CUPIDS IN CENTER,BLUE BORDER WITH GOLD DECOR,
    10 IN................................................    15.00
CARLSBAD,PLATE,DESSERT,WHITE GROUND,GOLD FLORAL,7 1/2 IN.,
    SET OF 4.............................................    12.50
CARLSBAD,PLATE,MAROON BAND EDGE,GOLD FILIGREE,BIRD & FLORAL
    IN CENTER............................................    10.00
CARLSBAD,PLATE,PINK APPLE BLOSSOMS,SWIRL & FLUTE BORDER,
    MARK,8 IN............................................     5.00
CARLSBAD,PLATE,SCALLOPED GILT EDGE,PINK & RED FLORAL,6 IN.,
    SET OF 10............................................    45.00
CARLSBAD,PLATE,WHITE,ORANGE POPPIES,GOLD RIM,VICTORIAN,
    AUSTRIA,10 1/2 IN....................................    17.00
CARLSBAD,PLATTER,ICE CREAM,WHITE GROUND,FLORAL DESIGN,
    AUSTRIA..............................................    12.00
CARLSBAD,PLATTER,POPPIES,SHEAF OF WHEAT,TEN MATCHING SOUPS,
    MARKED...............................................    59.00
CARLSBAD,PLATTER,TAUPE LEAVES & FLOWERS SHADED WITH YELLOW,
    PINK.................................................    24.00
CARLSBAD,TEA SET,FLORAL DECOR,TEAPOT,CREAMER,SUGAR,BEFORE
    1891.................................................    75.00
CARLSBAD,TUREEN,SOUP,PINK ROSES,BLUE GARLANDS..............    27.50


        CARNIVAL OR TAFFETA GLASS WAS AN INEXPENSIVE,PRESSED,
        IRIDESCENT GLASS MADE ABOUT 1900 TO 1920. CARNIVAL
        GLASS IS CURRENTLY BEING REPRODUCED. OVER 200 DIFFERENT
        PATTERNS ARE KNOWN.
CARNIVAL GLASS,SEE ALSO NORTHWOOD
CARNIVAL GLASS,ATOMIZER,BLUE,LA VERNE PATTERN..............     6.00
CARNIVAL GLASS,BANANA BOAT,GREEN,GRAPE & CABLE............   135.00
CARNIVAL GLASS,BANANA BOAT,MARIGOLD,GRAPE & CABLE.. 54.00 TO    85.00
CARNIVAL GLASS,BANANA BOAT,MARIGOLD,PEACHES,PEARS,RUFFLED,
    12 3/4 IN............................................    40.00
CARNIVAL GLASS,BANANA BOAT,MARIGOLD,PEACH & PEAR...........    40.00
CARNIVAL GLASS,BANANA BOAT,MARIGOLD,THISTLE,FOOTED,FENTON..    35.00
CARNIVAL GLASS,BANANA BOAT,PURPLE,GRAPE & CABLE...........    90.00
CARNIVAL GLASS,BANANA BOAT,PURPLE,CHERRY WREATH.... 75.00 TO    80.00
CARNIVAL GLASS,BANANA BOAT,RED,WREATHED CHERRY............   225.00
CARNIVAL GLASS,BANANA BOAT,WHITE,WREATHED CHERRY..........   250.00
CARNIVAL GLASS,BANK,MARIGOLD,BELL.........................     5.00
CARNIVAL GLASS,BANK,MARIGOLD,OWL.............. 12.00 TO    16.00
CARNIVAL GLASS,BASKET,AMETHYST,BEADED.....................    25.00
CARNIVAL GLASS,BASKET,BLUE,PERIWINKLE,FENTON,LACY EDGE.....    27.50
CARNIVAL GLASS,BASKET,BUSHEL,AQUA,NORTHWOOD................    65.00
CARNIVAL GLASS,BASKET,BUSHEL,PURPLE,N MARK................    35.00
CARNIVAL GLASS,BASKET,GREEN,MARKED N......................    38.00
CARNIVAL GLASS,BASKET,MARIGOLD,BASKET WEAVE,CLEAR HANDLE,
    5 X 7 IN.HIGH........................................    14.00
CARNIVAL GLASS,BASKET,MARIGOLD,BASKET WEAVE,TWO-HANDLED.....    15.00
CARNIVAL GLASS,BASKET,MARIGOLD,BASKET WEAVE...............    22.50
CARNIVAL GLASS,BASKET,MARIGOLD,TREE OF LIFE,SMALL.........    12.00
CARNIVAL GLASS,BASKET,PURPLE,STIPPLED RAYS,BANANA SHAPE,TWO
    HANDLES..............................................    14.50
CARNIVAL GLASS,BERRY SET,GREEN,IMPERIAL GRAPE,7 PIECES.....    45.00
CARNIVAL GLASS,BERRY SET,MARIGOLD,GRAPE,7 PIECES... 60.00 TO    65.00
CARNIVAL GLASS,BERRY SET,PURPLE,BEADED SHELL,SIX PIECES.....   225.00

```
CARNIVAL GLASS,BERRY SET,PURPLE,THREE FRUITS,N MARK, SIX
  PIECES........................................................   90.00
CARNIVAL GLASS,BONBON,BLUE,PERSIAN MEDALLION,GOLDEN
  IRIDESCENT....................................................   32.50
CARNIVAL GLASS,BONBON,BLUE,PERSIAN MEDALLION,TWO HANDLES....      20.00
CARNIVAL GLASS,BONBON,BLUE,POND LILY,METALLIC BLUE
  IRIDESCENT....................................................   37.50
CARNIVAL GLASS,BONBON,GREEN,PANELED HOLLY,N MARK............      28.00
CARNIVAL GLASS,BONBON,GREEN,PERSIAN MEDALLION,PEDESTAL,
  7-IN.DIAMETER.................................................   40.00
CARNIVAL GLASS,BONBON,MARIGOLD,LOTUS,GRAPE..................      14.00
CARNIVAL GLASS,BONBON,MARIGOLD,THREE FRUIT,BASKET WEAVE,PAIR      14.00
CARNIVAL GLASS,BONBON,PURPLE,QUESTION MARK PATTERN,TWO
  HANDLES,PEDESTAL..............................................   27.50
CARNIVAL GLASS,BONBON,PURPLE,THREE FRUITS,STEMMED...........      25.00
CARNIVAL GLASS,BONBON,WHITE,EMBROIDERED MUMS................      35.00
CARNIVAL GLASS,BOTTLE,BARBER,MARIGOLD......................      17.50
CARNIVAL GLASS,BOTTLE,COLOGNE,BLUE,ICE,GRAPE & CABLE........     250.00
CARNIVAL GLASS,BOTTLE,MARIGOLD,CANADA DRY,LABELS...........      12.00
CARNIVAL GLASS,BOTTLE,MARIGOLD,ILLINOIS DAISY..............      10.00
CARNIVAL GLASS,BOTTLE,MARIGOLD,PALE,HORN OF PLENTY.........      10.00
CARNIVAL GLASS,BOTTLE,MARIGOLD,POP,9 1/2 IN.TALL...........      10.00
CARNIVAL GLASS,BOTTLE,PURPLE,RAISED GRAPE DESIGN,STOPPER....      65.00
CARNIVAL GLASS,BOTTLE,TOILET WATER,ORANGE,GOLD LETTERING,
  STOPPER,PAIR..................................................   35.00
CARNIVAL GLASS,BOTTLE,WATER,GREEN,IMPERIAL GRAPE...........      40.00
CARNIVAL GLASS,BOTTLE,WHISKEY,MARIGOLD,GOLDEN WEDDING.......       5.75
CARNIVAL GLASS,BOTTLE,WHISKEY,MARIGOLD,JACKMAN WHISKEY......       9.00
CARNIVAL GLASS,BOTTLE,WINE,MARIGOLD,N.E.WINE CO............      15.00
CARNIVAL GLASS,BOWL,AMBER,PANSY SPRAY......................      35.00
CARNIVAL GLASS,BOWL,AMETHYST,APPLE BLOSSOMS,5 1/2 IN........      17.50
CARNIVAL GLASS,BOWL,AMETHYST,CABLE GRAPE,FOOTED,
  8-IN.DIAMETER.................................................   28.00
CARNIVAL GLASS,BOWL,AMETHYST,CAPTIVE ROSE,RUFFLE,
  8 1/4-IN.DIAMETER.............................................   27.50
CARNIVAL GLASS,BOWL,AMETHYST,CHRYSANTHEMUM,DUTCH WINDMILL,
  9 IN.........................................................   37.50
CARNIVAL GLASS,BOWL,AMETHYST,COSMOS,FLUTED,MILLERSBURG,
  10-IN.DIAMETER................................................   30.00
CARNIVAL GLASS,BOWL,AMETHYST,DRAGON & LOTUS,FOOTED,8 IN.....      45.00
CARNIVAL GLASS,BOWL,AMETHYST,GRAPE & CABLE,FOOTED,
  7 3/4-IN.DIAMETER.............................................   27.50
CARNIVAL GLASS,BOWL,AMETHYST,GRAPE & CABLE,FLUTED,FOOTED,
  8-IN.DIAMETER.................................................   25.00
CARNIVAL GLASS,BOWL,AMETHYST,GRAPES,MARKED N,8 IN..........      25.00
CARNIVAL GLASS,BOWL,AMETHYST,HOLLY,8 1/4-IN.DIAMETER........      25.00
CARNIVAL GLASS,BOWL,AMETHYST,HOLLY,FLUTED,MILLERSBURG,
  9 1/2-IN.DIAMETER.............................................   30.00
CARNIVAL GLASS,BOWL,AMETHYST,LOUISA,FOOTED,8 1/4-IN.DIAMETER      18.00
CARNIVAL GLASS,BOWL,AMETHYST,PEACOCK & GRAPE,FLUTED,
  SPATULA-FOOTED...............................................   42.50
CARNIVAL GLASS,BOWL,AMETHYST,PEACOCK & GRAPE,FOOTED,8 IN....      20.00
CARNIVAL GLASS,BOWL,AMETHYST,ROSE,DOUBLE STEMS,FOOTED,
  8 1/4 IN.....................................................   20.00
CARNIVAL GLASS,BOWL,AMETHYST,ROSE,LOOPS,FOOTED,FLUTED,
  8 1/2-IN.DIAMETER.............................................   25.00
CARNIVAL GLASS,BOWL,AMETHYST,RUFFLED,STRAWBERRY,MILLERSBURG.      27.50
CARNIVAL GLASS,BOWL,AMETHYST,STIPPLED RAYS & RIBBONS,
  MILLERSBURG..................................................   27.50
CARNIVAL GLASS,BOWL,AMETHYST,STRAWBERRY,N SIGNED,5 IN.......      16.00
CARNIVAL GLASS,BOWL,AMETHYST,THREE FRUITS,SUNFLOWER VARIANT
  EXTERIOR.....................................................   50.00
CARNIVAL GLASS,BOWL,AMETHYST,TREE OF LIFE,FOOTED,FOUR FOOTED
  DESSERTS.....................................................  185.00
CARNIVAL GLASS,BOWL,AMETHYST,VINTAGE GRAPE,RUFFLED,
  8 1/2-IN.DIAMETER.............................................   25.00
CARNIVAL GLASS,BOWL,BANANA,MARIGOLD,GRAPE & CABLE..........      40.00
CARNIVAL GLASS,BOWL,BANANA,MARIGOLD,GRAPE & CABLE,FOOTED,7 X
  12 IN........................................................   35.00
CARNIVAL GLASS,BOWL,BANANA,PURPLE,WREATHED CHERRY..........     100.00
CARNIVAL GLASS,BOWL,BANANA,WHITE,WREATHED CHERRIES.........      95.00
CARNIVAL GLASS,BOWL,BERRY,AMETHYST,PEACOCK AT FOUNTAIN.....      17.00
CARNIVAL GLASS,BOWL,BERRY,GREEN,FLORAL,MILLERSBURG,5 1/2 IN.      20.00
CARNIVAL GLASS,BOWL,BERRY,GREEN,GRAPE,CABLE,MARK N,11 X
  3 IN.........................................................   60.00
CARNIVAL GLASS,BOWL,BERRY,GREEN,GRAPE,4 1/2 IN. X
  10-IN.DIAMETER................................................   35.00
CARNIVAL GLASS,BOWL,BERRY,MARIGOLD,ADVERTISING FURNITURE,
  MILLER.......................................................   25.00
CARNIVAL GLASS,BOWL,BERRY,MARIGOLD,BUTTERFLY & BERRY,FOOTED,
  9 1/2 IN.....................................................   25.00
```

```
CARNIVAL GLASS,BOWL,BERRY,MARIGOLD,PANTHER,FOOTED...........   35.00
CARNIVAL GLASS,BOWL,BERRY,MARIGOLD,WATER LILY,CATTAIL.......    7.50
CARNIVAL GLASS,BOWL,BERRY,ORANGE,LEAF TIERS,FOOTED,
  8 1/4-IN.DIAMETER.......................................   38.00
CARNIVAL GLASS,BOWL,BERRY,ORANGE,RIBBED,9 IN.,SIX SHERBETS..   25.00
CARNIVAL GLASS,BOWL,BERRY,PURPLE,LITTLE FLOWERS............   20.00
CARNIVAL GLASS,BOWL,BERRY,PURPLE,VINTAGE GRAPE,5 1/2 IN.....   12.00
CARNIVAL GLASS,BOWL,BERRY,RED,LACY EDGE...................   85.00
CARNIVAL GLASS,BOWL,BERRY,RED,WREATHED CHERRY,SCALLOPED,
  4 SERVERS.............................................   500.00
CARNIVAL GLASS,BOWL,BERRY,WHITE,DAHLIA,FOOTED.............   125.00
CARNIVAL GLASS,BOWL,BLUE,ACORN PATTERN,7 1/2 IN...........   15.00
CARNIVAL GLASS,BOWL,BLUE,BERRY INSIDE,BASKET WEAVE OUTSIDE,
  LACY EDGE.............................................   20.00
CARNIVAL GLASS,BOWL,BLUE,CHRYSANTHEMUM,WINDMILL,FOOTED,
  10 IN................................................   49.50
CARNIVAL GLASS,BOWL,BLUE,DAISY PINWHEEL & CABLE,
  8 1/4-IN.DIAMETER.....................................   25.00
CARNIVAL GLASS,BOWL,BLUE,DOUBLE-STEMMED ROSE,FOOTED,9 IN....   28.00
CARNIVAL GLASS,BOWL,BLUE,DRAGON & LOTUS,
  8-IN.DIAMETER............................... 20.00 TO   25.00
CARNIVAL GLASS,BOWL,BLUE,DRAGON & LOTUS,7 1/2-IN.DIAMETER...   25.00
CARNIVAL GLASS,BOWL,BLUE,DRAGON & LOTUS,FOOTED,
  7 1/2-IN.DIAMETER.....................................   27.50
CARNIVAL GLASS,BOWL,BLUE,DRAGON & LOTUS,SHALLOW,8 IN........   20.00
CARNIVAL GLASS,BOWL,BLUE,DRAGON & LOTUS,SHALLOW,9 IN........   24.00
CARNIVAL GLASS,BOWL,BLUE,ELECTRIC,THREE FRUIT,STIPPLED,
  RUFFLED,FOOTED........................................   55.00
CARNIVAL GLASS,BOWL,BLUE,FLUTED,GRAPE DESIGN,LOW..........   12.50
CARNIVAL GLASS,BOWL,BLUE,FLUTED,HEARTS & FLOWERS,8 1/2 IN...   50.00
CARNIVAL GLASS,BOWL,BLUE,FOOTED,8 7/8 X 3 1/4 IN...........   32.50
CARNIVAL GLASS,BOWL,BLUE,FRUITS,FLOWERS,RUFFLED,N MARK,
  7 1/2 IN.............................................   21.00
CARNIVAL GLASS,BOWL,BLUE,GOOD LUCK......................   60.00
CARNIVAL GLASS,BOWL,BLUE,GRAPE & CABLE,FOOTED,
  7 3/4-IN.DIAMETER.....................................   25.00
CARNIVAL GLASS,BOWL,BLUE,GRAPE & CABLE,FLUTED,
  7 1/2-IN.DIAMETER.....................................   20.00
CARNIVAL GLASS,BOWL,BLUE,GRAPE & CABLE,FLUTED,FOOTED,
  AUSTRALIA,8 IN........................................   30.00
CARNIVAL GLASS,BOWL,BLUE,GRAPE & CABLE OUTSIDE,MILLERSBURG
  LACE INSIDE...........................................   50.00
CARNIVAL GLASS,BOWL,BLUE,HEART & VINE...................   25.00
CARNIVAL GLASS,BOWL,BLUE,HEART & VINE,EIGHT GROUPS OF
  RUFFLES ON EDGE.......................................   30.00
CARNIVAL GLASS,BOWL,BLUE,HOLLY & BERRY,FLUTED,9-IN.DIAMETER.   25.00
CARNIVAL GLASS,BOWL,BLUE,HOLLY PATTERN,9 IN..............   27.50
CARNIVAL GLASS,BOWL,BLUE,HORSES' HEADS,FOOTED............   68.00
CARNIVAL GLASS,BOWL,BLUE,ICE,HEARTS & FLOWERS,FLUTED,
  8 1/2 IN.DIAMETER.....................................   75.00
CARNIVAL GLASS,BOWL,BLUE,LOTUS & GRAPE..................   30.00
CARNIVAL GLASS,BOWL,BLUE,ORANGE TREE,FOOTED,10-IN.DIAMETER..   60.00
CARNIVAL GLASS,BOWL,BLUE,PASTEL,VINTAGE,BUTTERSCOTCH
  OVERLAY,FOOTED........................................   36.00
CARNIVAL GLASS,BOWL,BLUE,PEACOCK & GRAPE,7 1/2-IN.DIAMETER,
  3 IN.HIGH............................................   25.00
CARNIVAL GLASS,BOWL,BLUE,PEACOCK AT FOUNTAIN,8 IN..........   35.00
CARNIVAL GLASS,BOWL,BLUE,PEACOCK AT URN,SHALLOW,9 IN.......   45.00
CARNIVAL GLASS,BOWL,BLUE,PEACOCK TAIL,SHALLOW,9 IN........   60.00
CARNIVAL GLASS,BOWL,BLUE,PERSIAN MEDALLION,6 3/4-IN.DIAMETER   20.00
CARNIVAL GLASS,BOWL,BLUE,PERSIAN MEDALLION,GREEN-YELLOW
  IRIDESCENT............................................   19.00
CARNIVAL GLASS,BOWL,BLUE-PURPLE,IMPERIAL PANSY,LOW,
  9-IN.DIAMETER.........................................   28.50
CARNIVAL GLASS,BOWL,BLUE,STAG & HOLLY,10 IN..............   65.00
CARNIVAL GLASS,BOWL,BLUE,STAG & HOLLY,FOOTED,8 IN.........   45.00
CARNIVAL GLASS,BOWL,BLUE,STRAWBERRIES,PEACOCK & GRAPE
  INSIDE,SHALLOW........................................   23.00
CARNIVAL GLASS,BOWL,BUTTER,AMETHYST,CABLE,THUMBPRINT,N MARK.  135.00
CARNIVAL GLASS,BOWL,BUTTER,GREEN,GRAPE & CABLE,THUMBPRINT...  125.00
CARNIVAL GLASS,BOWL,CANDY,PURPLE,FINECUT & ROSES,FOOTED,N
  MARK................................................   22.00
CARNIVAL GLASS,BOWL,CANDY,WHITE,BASKET WEAVE,N MARK........   45.00
CARNIVAL GLASS,BOWL,CENTERPIECE,MARIGOLD,DOUBLE SCROLL,OVAL.   15.00
CARNIVAL GLASS,BOWL,CENTERPIECE,MARIGOLD,WIDE PANEL,
  UNDERPLATE............................................   30.00
CARNIVAL GLASS,BOWL,CEREAL,MARIGOLD,BOUQUET & LATTICE,
  6 1/2 IN.............................................    1.75
CARNIVAL GLASS,BOWL,FRUIT,BLUE,FENTON GRAPE,PERSIAN
  MEDALLION INSIDE......................................   97.50
CARNIVAL GLASS,BOWL,FRUIT,BLUE,ICE,GRAPE & CABLE..........  250.00
```

```
CARNIVAL GLASS,BOWL,FRUIT,GREEN,ICE,PANEL,FLORAL,SWAGS,
  IMPERIAL JEWELS.....................................................  14.00
CARNIVAL GLASS,BOWL,FRUIT,MARIGOLD,BUTTERFLY & TULIP........ 145.00
CARNIVAL GLASS,BOWL,FRUIT,MARIGOLD,MEMPHIS,
  11 1/4-IN.DIAMETER..................................................  40.00
CARNIVAL GLASS,BOWL,FRUIT,MARIGOLD,ORANGE TREE,FOOTED,
  10-IN.DIAMETER.....................................................  37.50
CARNIVAL GLASS,BOWL,FRUIT,PEACH,SKI STAR...................  38.00
CARNIVAL GLASS,BOWL,FRUIT,PURPLE,SKI STAR...................  85.00
CARNIVAL GLASS,BOWL,FRUIT,RED,IMPERIAL JEWEL................  69.00
CARNIVAL GLASS,BOWL,GREEN,BLACKBERRY WREATH,9 IN...........  32.50
CARNIVAL GLASS,BOWL,GREEN,BOW LEAF,CROSS-HATCHING,CRIMPED
  EDGE...............................................................  28.00
CARNIVAL GLASS,BOWL,GREEN,CABLE GRAPE,FOOTED,8-IN.DIAMETER..  23.00
CARNIVAL GLASS,BOWL,GREEN,CAPTIVE ROSE,FLUTED,
  8 3/4-IN.DIAMETER..................................................  27.50
CARNIVAL GLASS,BOWL,GREEN,CHERRY,MILLERSBURG,7-IN.DIAMETER..  20.00
CARNIVAL GLASS,BOWL,GREEN,DAHLIA,RUFFLED,FOOTED,NORTHWOOD...  22.00
CARNIVAL GLASS,BOWL,GREEN,DAISY & PLUME,FOOTED,FLAT,
  8 1/4 IN...........................................................  32.00
CARNIVAL GLASS,BOWL,GREEN,DAISY PINWHEEL & CABLE,
  8-IN.DIAMETER......................................................  25.00
CARNIVAL GLASS,BOWL,GREEN,DRAGON & LOTUS,RUFFLED,
  8 1/4-IN.DIAMETER..................................................  25.00
CARNIVAL GLASS,BOWL,GREEN,DRAGON & LOTUS,FOOTED,9 IN........  35.00
CARNIVAL GLASS,BOWL,GREEN,ELK.............................. 250.00
CARNIVAL GLASS,BOWL,GREEN,EMBOSSED SCROLL,8 IN.............  18.00
CARNIVAL GLASS,BOWL,GREEN,FLOWER,SCROLL,RUFFLED,LUSTER
  LINING.............................................................  22.00
CARNIVAL GLASS,BOWL,GREEN,FLUTED,SUNFLOWER,FOOTED,
  8 1/4-IN.DIAMETER..................................................  25.00
CARNIVAL GLASS,BOWL,GREEN,FOUR FLOWERS,8 X 2 1/4 IN.........  27.50
CARNIVAL GLASS,BOWL,GREEN,GOOD LUCK,RUFFLED,
  8 1/2-IN.DIAMETER..................................................  60.00
CARNIVAL GLASS,BOWL,GREEN,GRAPE & CABLE....................  32.00
CARNIVAL GLASS,BOWL,GREEN,GRAPE & CABLE,3-FOOTED,7 1/2 IN...  25.00
CARNIVAL GLASS,BOWL,GREEN,GRAPE & CABLE,8 1/2 IN...........  42.50
CARNIVAL GLASS,BOWL,GREEN,GRAPE & CABLE,FLUTED,
  8 1/2-IN.DIAMETER..................................................  27.50
CARNIVAL GLASS,BOWL,GREEN,GRAPE & CABLE,FOOTED.............  40.00
CARNIVAL GLASS,BOWL,GREEN,GRAPE & CABLE,MARKED N,8 1/2 X
  2 1/2 IN...........................................................  25.00
CARNIVAL GLASS,BOWL,GREEN,GRAPE & CABLE,SPATULA-FOOTED,
  8 3/4 X 3 IN.......................................................  35.00
CARNIVAL GLASS,BOWL,GREEN,HEART & VINE,8 IN................  30.00
CARNIVAL GLASS,BOWL,GREEN,HOLLY & BERRY,FLUTED,9-IN.DIAMETER  25.00
CARNIVAL GLASS,BOWL,GREEN,HOLLY SPRIG,BASKET SHAPE,SIDE
  HANDLES............................................................  35.00
CARNIVAL GLASS,BOWL,GREEN,HOLLY,MILLERSBURG,8 X 2 1/2 IN....  25.00
CARNIVAL GLASS,BOWL,GREEN,HOLLY,9 X 2 1/2 IN...............  35.00
CARNIVAL GLASS,BOWL,GREEN,HORSE MEDALLION,THREE SCROLLED
  FEET,7 1/2 IN......................................................  37.50
CARNIVAL GLASS,BOWL,GREEN,ICE,GRAPE,CABLE,FOOTED,N MARK,
  9 1/2 IN........................................................... 150.00
CARNIVAL GLASS,BOWL,GREEN,IMPERIAL GRAPE,8 3/4 X 2 1/4 IN...  20.00
CARNIVAL GLASS,BOWL,GREEN,IMPERIAL PANSY,9 IN. X 2. 22.00 TO  22.50
CARNIVAL GLASS,BOWL,GREEN,INVERTED STRAWBERRY,MARKED
  NEARCUT,STRAWMARK..................................................  16.00
CARNIVAL GLASS,BOWL,GREEN,LEAF & BEADS,MARKED N,9 IN.......  19.00
CARNIVAL GLASS,BOWL,GREEN,LIGHT,IMPERIAL,STRETCH,CUT STRIPES
  EXTERIOR...........................................................  18.00
CARNIVAL GLASS,BOWL,GREEN,LITTLE FLOWERS,10 1/2 IN.........  25.00
CARNIVAL GLASS,BOWL,GREEN,MILLERSBURG HOLLY,7 IN...........  18.00
CARNIVAL GLASS,BOWL,GREEN,MILLERSBURG RAYS & RIBBONS,
  9 1/4 IN...........................................................  22.00
CARNIVAL GLASS,BOWL,GREEN,NESTING SWAN,MILLERSBURG,10 IN.... 155.00
CARNIVAL GLASS,BOWL,GREEN,PANSY SPRAY,9 IN........ 15.00 TO  24.00
CARNIVAL GLASS,BOWL,GREEN,PEACOCK & GRAPES,SHALLOW,9 IN.....  24.00
CARNIVAL GLASS,BOWL,GREEN,PEACOCK AT URN,FLUTED,
  8-IN.DIAMETER......................................................  35.00
CARNIVAL GLASS,BOWL,GREEN,PEACOCK AT URN,RUFFLED,
  8 1/2-IN.DIAMETER..................................................  35.00
CARNIVAL GLASS,BOWL,GREEN,PEACOCK TAIL,8 3/8 X 3 IN........  26.50
CARNIVAL GLASS,BOWL,GREEN,PEACOCK,GRAPE,FLUTED,FOOTED,
  7 1/4-IN.DIAMETER..................................................  25.00
CARNIVAL GLASS,BOWL,GREEN,PEACOCK,GRAPE,SPATULA,FOOTED,8 X
  3 1/4 IN...........................................................  30.00
CARNIVAL GLASS,BOWL,GREEN,PEACOCK,GRAPE,FOOTED.............  27.50
CARNIVAL GLASS,BOWL,GREEN,PRIMROSE,FLUTED,MILLERSBURG,
  9 1/4 IN.DIAMETER..................................................  30.00
CARNIVAL GLASS,BOWL,GREEN,RIBBED PATTERN,MARKED N,8 IN......  15.00
```

```
CARNIVAL GLASS,BOWL,GREEN,RUFFLED,RIB,8 1/2 IN...............   14.00
CARNIVAL GLASS,BOWL,GREEN,SAILBOATS,ORANGE TREE EXTERIOR,
  6 1/2 IN...................................................   16.50
CARNIVAL GLASS,BOWL,GREEN,STAR OF DAVID,BOWS,FOOTED,
  8 1/4 IN.DIAMETER..........................................   25.00
CARNIVAL GLASS,BOWL,GREEN,STIPPLED DOTS,8 IN................   15.00
CARNIVAL GLASS,BOWL,GREEN,STIPPLED RAYS,6 IN................    7.00
CARNIVAL GLASS,BOWL,GREEN,STRAWBERRY,FLUTED,NORTHWOOD,
  8 3/4-IN.DIAMETER..........................................   27.50
CARNIVAL GLASS,BOWL,GREEN,SWIRLING LEAVES,TRICORNERED,
  MILLERSBURG,9 IN...........................................   32.50
CARNIVAL GLASS,BOWL,GREEN,THISTLE PATTERN,8 IN..............   25.00
CARNIVAL GLASS,BOWL,GREEN,THISTLE PATTERN,7 1/2 IN..........   20.00
CARNIVAL GLASS,BOWL,GREEN,THREE FRUITS,DOME,FOOTED,8 1/2 IN.   25.00
CARNIVAL GLASS,BOWL,GREEN,WHIRLING LEAVES,MILLERSBURG,
  9 1/2 IN..................................................   25.00
CARNIVAL GLASS,BOWL,GREEN,WILD ROSE,GRAPE LEAVES INSIDE,N
  MARK,9 IN.................................................   28.00
CARNIVAL GLASS,BOWL,GREEN,WILD ROSE,HEART RIM,FOOTED........   20.00
CARNIVAL GLASS,BOWL,GREEN,WILD ROSE,LACY OPEN EDGE,FOOTED,
  MARK N....................................................   25.00
CARNIVAL GLASS,BOWL,GREEN,WILD ROSE,OPENWORK HEART EDGE,
  6-IN.DIAMETER.............................................   35.00
CARNIVAL GLASS,BOWL,GREEN,WILD ROSE,OPEN HEART RIM,FOOTED,
  MARKED N..................................................   22.00
CARNIVAL GLASS,BOWL,GREEN,WISHBONE,FOOTED,MARK N,8 1/4 X
  2 3/4 IN..................................................   35.00
CARNIVAL GLASS,BOWL,ICE CREAM,BLUE,PEACOCK AT URN,BEE,
  11-IN.DIAMETER............................................   50.00
CARNIVAL GLASS,BOWL,ICE CREAM,GREEN,CHERRIES,MILLERSBURG,
  10 IN.....................................................   40.00
CARNIVAL GLASS,BOWL,ICE CREAM,MARIGOLD,PEACOCK,URN,
  MILLERSBURG,9 1/2 IN......................................   45.00
CARNIVAL GLASS,BOWL,ICE CREAM,PURPLE,PEACOCK AT URN,10 IN...   65.00
CARNIVAL GLASS,BOWL,ICE CREAM,WHITE,PEACOCK & URN,N MARK....  128.00
CARNIVAL GLASS,BOWL,MARIGOLD,ACORN.........................    9.00
CARNIVAL GLASS,BOWL,MARIGOLD,ACORN,DARK SATIN FINISH,
  7 1/2 IN..................................................   10.00
CARNIVAL GLASS,BOWL,MARIGOLD,ADVERTISING,GOOD WILL TOUR,
  BELLAIRE,OHIO.............................................   60.00
CARNIVAL GLASS,BOWL,MARIGOLD,AUSTRALIAN SWAN,5 5/8 IN.......   49.00
CARNIVAL GLASS,BOWL,MARIGOLD,BLACKBERRY,HAT SHAPE,
  MILLERSBURG...............................................   15.00
CARNIVAL GLASS,BOWL,MARIGOLD,BLACKBERRY SPRAY,FLARED,
  MILLERSBURG,7 IN..........................................   18.00
CARNIVAL GLASS,BOWL,MARIGOLD,BLACKBERRY WREATH,9 IN.........   20.00
CARNIVAL GLASS,BOWL,MARIGOLD,BLAZING CORNICOPIA VARIANT,9 X
  7 IN......................................................   15.00
CARNIVAL GLASS,BOWL,MARIGOLD,BUTTERFLY,BERRY,FOOTED.........    7.50
CARNIVAL GLASS,BOWL,MARIGOLD,BUTTERFLY,BOWER,AUSTRALIA,4 IN.   30.00
CARNIVAL GLASS,BOWL,MARIGOLD,BUTTERFLY,BOWER,AUSTRALIA,
  6 1/2 IN..................................................   30.00
CARNIVAL GLASS,BOWL,MARIGOLD,BUTTERFLY,TULIP,AUSTRALIA,9 IN.   40.00
CARNIVAL GLASS,BOWL,MARIGOLD,BUTTERFLY,TULIP,4-FOOTED,
  11 1/2 IN.................................................   45.00
CARNIVAL GLASS,BOWL,MARIGOLD,CHERRIES,FOOTED,10 IN..........   28.00
CARNIVAL GLASS,BOWL,MARIGOLD,CHERRY,MILLERSBURG,10 IN.......   30.00
CARNIVAL GLASS,BOWL,MARIGOLD,CHRYSANTHEMUM,FOOTED,11 IN.....   25.00
CARNIVAL GLASS,BOWL,MARIGOLD,COSMOS,MILLERSBURG,9
  1/2......................................... 10.00 TO       15.00
CARNIVAL GLASS,BOWL,MARIGOLD,CRIMPED EDGE,COMET PATTERN.....   22.50
CARNIVAL GLASS,BOWL,MARIGOLD,DIAMOND LACE..................    6.00
CARNIVAL GLASS,BOWL,MARIGOLD,DOGWOOD SPRAYS,LEAF TIERS
  EXTEND OVER TOP...........................................   22.00
CARNIVAL GLASS,BOWL,MARIGOLD,DRAGON & LOTUS,BLUE FEET,
  6 1/2 IN..................................................   25.00
CARNIVAL GLASS,BOWL,MARIGOLD,DRAGON & LOTUS................   17.50
CARNIVAL GLASS,BOWL,MARIGOLD,DRAGON & LOTUS,
  8 1/2-IN.DIAMETER.........................................   15.00
CARNIVAL GLASS,BOWL,MARIGOLD,DRAGON & LOTUS,
  9-IN.DIAMETER................................ 18.00 TO       20.00
CARNIVAL GLASS,BOWL,MARIGOLD,EGGNOG IN WHITE ENAMEL,COSMOS
  BASE,8 CUPS...............................................   25.00
CARNIVAL GLASS,BOWL,MARIGOLD,EMBOSSED GRAPES,10 IN.DIAMETER,
  4 IN.DEEP.................................................   16.00
CARNIVAL GLASS,BOWL,MARIGOLD,EMBOSSED GRAPES,SCALLOPS,
  9 1/2 IN.DIAMETER.........................................   28.00
CARNIVAL GLASS,BOWL,MARIGOLD,EMU,AUSTRALIA,5 IN.............   30.00
CARNIVAL GLASS,BOWL,MARIGOLD,FEATHER SCROLL,GRAPE ARBOR
  INSIDE,9 3/4 IN...........................................   27.50
CARNIVAL GLASS,BOWL,MARIGOLD,FEATHERED SERPENT INTERIOR,
```

HONEYCOMB,CLOVER......................................... 25.00
CARNIVAL GLASS,BOWL,MARIGOLD,FLUTED,AUSTRALIA,9 3/4 IN. X
4 1/4 IN................................................ 100.00
CARNIVAL GLASS,BOWL,MARIGOLD,FLUTED,MILLERSBURG SWIRLING
LEAVES,10 IN............................................ 20.00
CARNIVAL GLASS,BOWL,MARIGOLD,FROSTED BLOCK,8 IN........... 6.50
CARNIVAL GLASS,BOWL,MARIGOLD,GOOD LUCK,PINK HIGHLIGHTS...... 40.00
CARNIVAL GLASS,BOWL,MARIGOLD,GOOD LUCK,SHALLOW,9 IN.......... 28.00
CARNIVAL GLASS,BOWL,MARIGOLD,GOOD LUCK,8 3/4 IN............ 32.00
CARNIVAL GLASS,BOWL,MARIGOLD,GOOSEBERRY OUTSIDE,ORANGE TREE
INSIDE................................................. 22.00
CARNIVAL GLASS,BOWL,MARIGOLD,GRAPE & CABLE,3-FOOTED,
7 1/2 IN............................................... 15.00
CARNIVAL GLASS,BOWL,MARIGOLD,GRAPE & CABLE,6 1/2 IN......... 7.00
CARNIVAL GLASS,BOWL,MARIGOLD,GRAPE & CABLE,PERSIAN
MEDALLION,3 FEET........................................ 45.00
CARNIVAL GLASS,BOWL,MARIGOLD,GRAPE & CABLE,RUFFLED,
8 1/2-IN.DIAMETER...................................... 18.00
CARNIVAL GLASS,BOWL,MARIGOLD,GRAPE & CABLE,RUFFLED,FENTON,
SPATULA-FOOTED......................................... 18.00
CARNIVAL GLASS,BOWL,MARIGOLD,GRAPE CLUSTERS INSIDE,BASKET
WEAVE OUTSIDE.......................................... 15.00
CARNIVAL GLASS,BOWL,MARIGOLD,GRAPE,GOTHIC ARCH............. 7.00
CARNIVAL GLASS,BOWL,MARIGOLD,GRAPE,SCALLOPED.............. 30.00
CARNIVAL GLASS,BOWL,MARIGOLD,GRAPE,VINE,FLUTED,
9-IN.DIAMETER,2 IN.HIGH................................ 22.00
CARNIVAL GLASS,BOWL,MARIGOLD,HERON IN RUSHES,9 1/2 IN....... 35.00
CARNIVAL GLASS,BOWL,MARIGOLD,HOLLY & BERRY,9 IN........... 12.00
CARNIVAL GLASS,BOWL,MARIGOLD,HOLLY & STAG,FOOTED,7 1/2 IN... 30.00
CARNIVAL GLASS,BOWL,MARIGOLD,HOLLY,9 IN........... 14.00 TO 15.00
CARNIVAL GLASS,BOWL,MARIGOLD,HOLLY BERRY,FLEUR-DE-LIS EDGE,
9 IN................................................... 18.00
CARNIVAL GLASS,BOWL,MARIGOLD,HOLLY,HAT SHAPE.............. 7.50
CARNIVAL GLASS,BOWL,MARIGOLD,HOLLY,RUFFLED............... 12.50
CARNIVAL GLASS,BOWL,MARIGOLD,HORSE MEDALLION,6 1/2. 25.00 TO 27.50
CARNIVAL GLASS,BOWL,MARIGOLD,HORSE'S HEAD,FOOTED.......... 25.00
CARNIVAL GLASS,BOWL,MARIGOLD,HORSE'S HEAD,ONE SIDE TURNED
UP,ONE DOWN............................................ 42.50
CARNIVAL GLASS,BOWL,MARIGOLD,HORSES' HEADS IN MEDALLIONS,
6 1/2 IN............................................... 39.00
CARNIVAL GLASS,BOWL,MARIGOLD,IMPERIAL GRAPE DESIGN INSIDE &
OUTSIDE................................................ 10.00
CARNIVAL GLASS,BOWL,MARIGOLD,IMPERIAL JEWELS,SHORT PEDESTAL
BASE................................................... 25.00
CARNIVAL GLASS,BOWL,MARIGOLD,IRIS,HERRINGBONE,RUFFLED,11 IN. 6.50
CARNIVAL GLASS,BOWL,MARIGOLD,KANGAROO,AUSTRALIA,5 IN........ 30.00
CARNIVAL GLASS,BOWL,MARIGOLD,KANGAROO,9 IN. X 3 1/2 IN...... 85.00
CARNIVAL GLASS,BOWL,MARIGOLD,KINGFISHER,AUSTRALIA,5 IN...... 30.00
CARNIVAL GLASS,BOWL,MARIGOLD,KINGFISHER,AUSTRALIA,9 IN...... 80.00
CARNIVAL GLASS,BOWL,MARIGOLD,KIWI BIRDS,5 1/2 IN........... 49.00
CARNIVAL GLASS,BOWL,MARIGOLD,KOOKABURRA,AUSTRALIA,5 IN...... 30.00
CARNIVAL GLASS,BOWL,MARIGOLD,LEE PATTERN,FOOTED,5
1/2..................................................... 6.00 TO 7.00
CARNIVAL GLASS,BOWL,MARIGOLD,LIGHT,ALMOST WHITE,ROSES &
RUFFLES,FOOTED......................................... 14.00
CARNIVAL GLASS,BOWL,MARIGOLD,LION,7 1/2 IN................ 45.00
CARNIVAL GLASS,BOWL,MARIGOLD,LITTLE FISHES,FOOTED,AUSTRALIA,
9 IN................................................... 40.00
CARNIVAL GLASS,BOWL,MARIGOLD,LITTLE FISHES,RUFFLED,FOOTED,
5 3/4 IN............................................... 32.50
CARNIVAL GLASS,BOWL,MARIGOLD,LITTLE FLOWERS,TWIG FEET,FENTON 25.00
CARNIVAL GLASS,BOWL,MARIGOLD,LUSTER ROSE,8 IN............. 6.50
CARNIVAL GLASS,BOWL,MARIGOLD,MAGPIE,AUSTRALIA,9 IN......... 80.00
CARNIVAL GLASS,BOWL,MARIGOLD,MAGPIE,9 5/8 IN.............. 79.00
CARNIVAL GLASS,BOWL,MARIGOLD,MILLERSBURG HOLLY,FLUTED,8 IN.. 15.00
CARNIVAL GLASS,BOWL,MARIGOLD,MILLERSBURG CHERRY,9
1/4..................................................... 18.00 TO 20.00
CARNIVAL GLASS,BOWL,MARIGOLD,NORTHWOOD CHERRY,OPAL WHITE ON
UNDERSIDE.............................................. 20.00
CARNIVAL GLASS,BOWL,MARIGOLD,ORANGE TREE INTERIOR,BEARDED
BERRY EXTERIOR......................................... 25.00
CARNIVAL GLASS,BOWL,MARIGOLD,ORANGE TREE,FOOTED,10 IN....... 16.00
CARNIVAL GLASS,BOWL,MARIGOLD,OSTRICH,10 IN.X 3 1/2 IN....... 90.00
CARNIVAL GLASS,BOWL,MARIGOLD,PANSY ROSETTE,8 IN........... 37.50
CARNIVAL GLASS,BOWL,MARIGOLD,PANTHER,BLEEDING HEARTS,
BUTTERFLIES,FOOTED..................................... 85.00
CARNIVAL GLASS,BOWL,MARIGOLD,PANTHER,FOOTED.............. 35.00
CARNIVAL GLASS,BOWL,MARIGOLD,PANTHER,FOOTED,5 1/2 IN........ 19.00
CARNIVAL GLASS,BOWL,MARIGOLD,PASTEL,ACORNS,7 IN........... 14.50
CARNIVAL GLASS,BOWL,MARIGOLD,PEACOCK & DAHLIA,7 1/2 IN...... 11.00
CARNIVAL GLASS,BOWL,MARIGOLD,PEACOCK & GRAPE,BEARDED BERRY

| | |
|---|---|
| EXTERIOR.................................................. | 16.00 |
| CARNIVAL GLASS,BOWL,MARIGOLD,PEACOCK AT FOUNTAIN,8 IN....... | 21.00 |
| CARNIVAL GLASS,BOWL,MARIGOLD,PEACOCK AT URN,FLUTED, | |
| 8 3/4-IN.DIAMETER......................................... | 25.00 |
| CARNIVAL GLASS,BOWL,MARIGOLD,PEACOCK AT URN,SHALLOW,9 IN.... | 28.00 |
| CARNIVAL GLASS,BOWL,MARIGOLD,PEACOCK AT FOUNTAIN,9 IN. X | |
| 3 3/8 IN.................................................. | 42.50 |
| CARNIVAL GLASS,BOWL,MARIGOLD,PEACOCK EYE,9 IN.............. | 9.00 |
| CARNIVAL GLASS,BOWL,MARIGOLD,PEACOCK ON FENCE,9 IN......... | 35.00 |
| CARNIVAL GLASS,BOWL,MARIGOLD,PEACOCK ON FENCE,NORTHWOOD, | |
| 8 3/4 IN.................................................. | 37.00 |
| CARNIVAL GLASS,BOWL,MARIGOLD,PEACOCK TAIL,FLARED,SHALLOW, | |
| 7 IN...................................................... | 9.00 |
| CARNIVAL GLASS,BOWL,MARIGOLD,PERSIAN MEDALLION,9 IN......... | 17.50 |
| CARNIVAL GLASS,BOWL,MARIGOLD,PERSIAN MEDALLION,GRAPE,CABLE, | |
| 10 1/2 IN................................................. | 75.00 |
| CARNIVAL GLASS,BOWL,MARIGOLD,PINEAPPLE PATTERN,7 | |
| 1/2........................................... 7.00 TO | 8.00 |
| CARNIVAL GLASS,BOWL,MARIGOLD,PONY.......................... | 40.00 |
| CARNIVAL GLASS,BOWL,MARIGOLD,PONY,8 IN..................... | 45.00 |
| CARNIVAL GLASS,BOWL,MARIGOLD,RAINDROPS,KEYHOLE EXTERIOR, | |
| DOME-FOOTED............................................... | 18.00 |
| CARNIVAL GLASS,BOWL,MARIGOLD,RIBBED,RAISED FLORAL,CLOVER | |
| DECOR ON BASE............................................. | 28.50 |
| CARNIVAL GLASS,BOWL,MARIGOLD,ROSE SHOW..................... | 55.00 |
| CARNIVAL GLASS,BOWL,MARIGOLD,ROSES & RUFFLES,8 IN.......... | 10.00 |
| CARNIVAL GLASS,BOWL,MARIGOLD,ROSES & RUFFLES,FOOTED, | |
| 7 1/2 IN.................................................. | 25.00 |
| CARNIVAL GLASS,BOWL,MARIGOLD,ROSES & RUFFLES,FOOTED,8 IN.... | 14.00 |
| CARNIVAL GLASS,BOWL,MARIGOLD,ROSES & RUFFLES,FOOTED,11 IN... | 11.00 |
| CARNIVAL GLASS,BOWL,MARIGOLD,RUFFLED,MILLERSBURG STRAWBERRY, | |
| 6 1/4 IN.................................................. | 12.50 |
| CARNIVAL GLASS,BOWL,MARIGOLD,SCROLL EMBOSSED INTERIOR,FILE | |
| EXTERIOR.................................................. | 20.00 |
| CARNIVAL GLASS,BOWL,MARIGOLD,SHELL,WILD ROSE,OPEN HEART | |
| EDGE,FOOTED............................................... | 12.00 |
| CARNIVAL GLASS,BOWL,MARIGOLD,SINGLE FLOWER,OPAL WHITE ON | |
| UNDERSIDE,9 IN............................................ | 14.00 |
| CARNIVAL GLASS,BOWL,MARIGOLD,STAG & HOLLY,10 IN............ | 35.00 |
| CARNIVAL GLASS,BOWL,MARIGOLD,STAG & HOLLY,FOOTED........... | 30.00 |
| CARNIVAL GLASS,BOWL,MARIGOLD,STAG & HOLLY,FOOTED,8 IN...... | 25.00 |
| CARNIVAL GLASS,BOWL,MARIGOLD,STAG & HOLLY,FOOTED,11 IN...... | 45.00 |
| CARNIVAL GLASS,BOWL,MARIGOLD,STAG & HOLLY,FOOTED,FLUTED, | |
| 8-IN.DIAMETER............................................. | 27.50 |
| CARNIVAL GLASS,BOWL,MARIGOLD,STAG & HOLLY,FLAT,10 1/2 IN.... | 30.00 |
| CARNIVAL GLASS,BOWL,MARIGOLD,STAG & HOLLY,FLUTED,FOOTED, | |
| 7 3/4 IN.................................................. | 27.50 |
| CARNIVAL GLASS,BOWL,MARIGOLD,STAG & HOLLY,RUFFLED,FOOTED, | |
| 11 IN..................................................... | 55.00 |
| CARNIVAL GLASS,BOWL,MARIGOLD,STAR & FILE PATTERN, | |
| 6 1/2-IN.DIAMETER......................................... | 7.95 |
| CARNIVAL GLASS,BOWL,MARIGOLD,STAR MEDALLION,7 1/2 IN........ | 10.00 |
| CARNIVAL GLASS,BOWL,MARIGOLD,STIPPLED RAY,COLLAR,N MARK..... | 18.00 |
| CARNIVAL GLASS,BOWL,MARIGOLD,STIPPLED RAY,MARKED N, | |
| 10 1/2 IN................................................. | 8.00 |
| CARNIVAL GLASS,BOWL,MARIGOLD,STIPPLED RAY,MARKED N,10 IN.... | 12.00 |
| CARNIVAL GLASS,BOWL,MARIGOLD,STIPPLED RAY,RIBBONS, | |
| MILLERSBURG,9 IN.......................................... | 18.00 |
| CARNIVAL GLASS,BOWL,MARIGOLD,STIPPLED STRAWBERRY,FLUTED, | |
| NORTHWOOD................................................. | 20.00 |
| CARNIVAL GLASS,BOWL,MARIGOLD,STORK,RUSHES,10 IN............ | 35.00 |
| CARNIVAL GLASS,BOWL,MARIGOLD,STRAWBERRY,FLUTED,NORTHWOOD, | |
| 8 1/2 IN.................................................. | 18.00 |
| CARNIVAL GLASS,BOWL,MARIGOLD,STRAWBERRY,NORTHWOOD,8 1/2 IN.. | 22.00 |
| CARNIVAL GLASS,BOWL,MARIGOLD,STRAWBERRY,8 1/2 IN........... | 22.50 |
| CARNIVAL GLASS,BOWL,MARIGOLD,SUNFLOWER,THREE SPATULATE FEET. | 20.00 |
| CARNIVAL GLASS,BOWL,MARIGOLD,SWAN,AUSTRALIA,5 IN........... | 30.00 |
| CARNIVAL GLASS,BOWL,MARIGOLD,SWAN,AUSTRALIA,9 IN........... | 80.00 |
| CARNIVAL GLASS,BOWL,MARIGOLD,THISTLE,7 3/4-IN.DIAMETER...... | 12.50 |
| CARNIVAL GLASS,BOWL,MARIGOLD,THISTLE & THORN,FLAT,FOOTED, | |
| 9 IN...................................................... | 12.50 |
| CARNIVAL GLASS,BOWL,MARIGOLD,THISTLE & THORN,DEEP,FOOTED.... | 9.00 |
| CARNIVAL GLASS,BOWL,MARIGOLD,THISTLE & THORN,FOOTED,8 IN.... | 9.00 |
| CARNIVAL GLASS,BOWL,MARIGOLD,THREE ROSE DESIGN,FOOTED....... | 25.00 |
| CARNIVAL GLASS,BOWL,MARIGOLD,THUNDERBIRD,5 1/2 IN.......... | 50.00 |
| CARNIVAL GLASS,BOWL,MARIGOLD,THUNDERBIRD,AUSTRALIA,9 IN..... | 80.00 |
| CARNIVAL GLASS,BOWL,MARIGOLD,TREE OF LIFE,PLAIN INTERIOR, | |
| SHALLOW................................................... | 6.00 |
| CARNIVAL GLASS,BOWL,MARIGOLD,TWO FLOWERS,FOOTED,6 IN........ | 7.00 |
| CARNIVAL GLASS,BOWL,MARIGOLD,TWO FLOWERS,RUFFLED,FOOTED, | |
| 9 3/4 IN.................................................. | 15.00 |

```
CARNIVAL GLASS,BOWL,MARIGOLD,WILD DAISY & LOTUS,FOOTED,
  FENTON.............................................         20.00
CARNIVAL GLASS,BOWL,MARIGOLD,WINDMILL & FLORAL PATTERN,7 IN.     18.00
CARNIVAL GLASS,BOWL,MARIGOLD,WINDMILL,7 IN.DIAMETER........      18.50
CARNIVAL GLASS,BOWL,NUT,BLUE,GRAPE,FOOTED.;..............        24.00
CARNIVAL GLASS,BOWL,NUT,BLUE,VINTAGE,RED-GOLD IRIDESCENT,
  FOOTED.............................................          57.50
CARNIVAL GLASS,BOWL,NUT,MARIGOLD,VINTAGE,FOOTED.............     15.00
CARNIVAL GLASS,BOWL,NUT,PURPLE,LOUISA,FOOTED...............      18.00
CARNIVAL GLASS,BOWL,ORANGE,EMBOSSED GRAPE,9 IN..... 25.00 TO    35.00
CARNIVAL GLASS,BOWL,ORANGE,HOLLY,8 1/2 IN.................      15.00
CARNIVAL GLASS,BOWL,ORANGE,ROSES,RUFFLES.................       14.00
CARNIVAL GLASS,BOWL,PEACH,CRIMPED EDGE,CAROLINE,7 1/4 IN....     20.00
CARNIVAL GLASS,BOWL,PEACH,DRAGON & LOTUS..................      23.00
CARNIVAL GLASS,BOWL,POPPY,GREEN,NORTHWOOD.................       10.00
CARNIVAL GLASS,BOWL,PUNCH,BLUE,ORANGE TREE,11 X 10 IN.HIGH,
  5 CUPS.............................................         170.00
CARNIVAL GLASS,BOWL,PUNCH,BLUE,ORANGE TREE,
  TWO-PIECE.................................135.00 TO        175.00
CARNIVAL GLASS,BOWL,PUNCH,GREEN,GRAPE,VINE,LABELLE ROSE,
  TWO-PIECE..........................................        175.00
CARNIVAL GLASS,BOWL,PUNCH,GREEN,MEMPHIS,BASE,OPALESCENT LOOK
  AT EDGES...........................................        145.00
CARNIVAL GLASS,BOWL,PUNCH,MARIGOLD,FASHION,TWO-PIECE,6 CUPS.     95.00
CARNIVAL GLASS,BOWL,PUNCH,MARIGOLD,GRAPE,RUFFLED,TWO-PIECE..     75.00
CARNIVAL GLASS,BOWL,PUNCH,MARIGOLD,IMPERIAL HOBSTAR,
  TWO-PIECE,11 CUPS..................................        180.00
CARNIVAL GLASS,BOWL,PUNCH,MARIGOLD,MANY FRUITS.............     165.00
CARNIVAL GLASS,BOWL,PUNCH,MARIGOLD,ORANGE TREE,BASE,2 CUPS..     60.00
CARNIVAL GLASS,BOWL,PUNCH,MARIGOLD,PEACOCK AT FOUNTAIN,N
  MARK,TWO-PIECE.....................................        110.00
CARNIVAL GLASS,BOWL,PUNCH,MARIGOLD,PEACOCK AT FOUNTAIN,
  TWO-PIECE..........................................         55.00
CARNIVAL GLASS,BOWL,PUNCH,MARIGOLD,WREATH OF ROSES,SIX CUPS.    120.00
CARNIVAL GLASS,BOWL,PUNCH,PURPLE,CHERRIES,LEAVES,GRAPES,
  BASE,4 CUPS........................................        375.00
CARNIVAL GLASS,BOWL,PUNCH,PURPLE,GRAPE & CABLE,10 IN.,BASE,
  FOUR CUPS..........................................        219.00
CARNIVAL GLASS,BOWL,PUNCH,PURPLE,GRAPE & CABLE,BASE,SIX CUPS    295.00
CARNIVAL GLASS,BOWL,PUNCH,PURPLE,GRAPE,MARKED N..........        32.50
CARNIVAL GLASS,BOWL,PUNCH,PURPLE,ROSE,PERSIAN MEDALLION,BASE    200.00
CARNIVAL GLASS,BOWL,PURPLE,BASKET WEAVE,GRAPE & CABLE
  INSIDE,N MARK......................................         19.00
CARNIVAL GLASS,BOWL,PURPLE,BASKET WEAVE,STRAWBERRY INSIDE,N
  MARK,6 IN..........................................         15.00
CARNIVAL GLASS,BOWL,PURPLE,BASKET WEAVE,STRAWBERRY INSIDE,N
  MARK,9 IN..........................................         35.00
CARNIVAL GLASS,BOWL,PURPLE,BLACKBERRIES,7 IN..............       12.50
CARNIVAL GLASS,BOWL,PURPLE,BLACKBERRY WREATH,RUFFLED,
  MILLERSBURG,9 IN...................................         32.50
CARNIVAL GLASS,BOWL,PURPLE,BULL'S-EYE,THREE DOLPHIN FEET,
  8 1/2 IN...........................................         35.00
CARNIVAL GLASS,BOWL,PURPLE,BUTTERFLY,BOWER,RUFFLED,AUSTRALIA     50.00
CARNIVAL GLASS,BOWL,PURPLE,CAPTIVE ROSE,RUFFLED EDGE,
  8 1/4 IN...........................................         18.00
CARNIVAL GLASS,BOWL,PURPLE,COIN DOT,2 1/2 IN. X 6 IN........     10.00
CARNIVAL GLASS,BOWL,PURPLE,DAISY PINWHEEL,CABLE,FLUTED,
  8 3/4-IN.DIAMETER..................................         25.00
CARNIVAL GLASS,BOWL,PURPLE,DRAGON & LOTUS,9 IN...........        32.00
CARNIVAL GLASS,BOWL,PURPLE,DRAGON & LOTUS,FLUTED,FOOTED,
  7 3/4 IN...........................................         25.00
CARNIVAL GLASS,BOWL,PURPLE,DRAGON & LOTUS,THREE-FOOTED,8 IN.     35.00
CARNIVAL GLASS,BOWL,PURPLE,EMBOSSED SCROLLS,7 7/8 IN........     23.00
CARNIVAL GLASS,BOWL,PURPLE,EMU,AUSTRALIA,5 IN.............       60.00
CARNIVAL GLASS,BOWL,PURPLE,EMU,FLUTED,AUSTRALIA,9 1/4 X
  4 1/4 IN...........................................        140.00
CARNIVAL GLASS,BOWL,PURPLE,FEATHERED SERPENT,9 IN............    29.00
CARNIVAL GLASS,BOWL,PURPLE,FLAT,IMPERIAL JEWELS,11 IN.......     18.00
CARNIVAL GLASS,BOWL,PURPLE,FLOWERS,FRAMES,PANSY SHAPE,
  8 1/2 IN...........................................         27.00
CARNIVAL GLASS,BOWL,PURPLE,FLOWERS,POURED-ON GOLD LOOK,
  MILLERSBURG........................................         75.00
CARNIVAL GLASS,BOWL,PURPLE,FLUTED EXTERIOR,SHALLOW,
  8 IN.DIAMETER......................................         15.00
CARNIVAL GLASS,BOWL,PURPLE,FLUTED TOP,FOOTED,10 3/4 X
  5 1/8 IN...........................................         79.50
CARNIVAL GLASS,BOWL,PURPLE,FLUTED,PEACOCK EYE INSIDE,ZIPPER
  OUTSIDE............................................         25.00
CARNIVAL GLASS,BOWL,PURPLE,FRUITS,RUFFLED,MARKED N,
  8 3/4 IN.DIAMETER..................................         30.00
CARNIVAL GLASS,BOWL,PURPLE,GOLD IRIDESCENT,SHALLOW,APPLE
```

```
    BLOSSOM,TWIGS..............................................    28.00
CARNIVAL GLASS,BOWL,PURPLE,GOOD LUCK...........................    65.00
CARNIVAL GLASS,BOWL,PURPLE,GOOD LUCK,SHALLOW,9 IN............    65.00
CARNIVAL GLASS,BOWL,PURPLE,GRAPE & CABLE,FLUTED.............   100.00
CARNIVAL GLASS,BOWL,PURPLE,GRAPE & CABLE,FLUTED,FOOTED,
    7 1/2 IN...................................................    25.00
CARNIVAL GLASS,BOWL,PURPLE,GRAPE & CABLE,FOOTED,8 IN. X
    3 1/2 IN.HIGH..............................................    25.00
CARNIVAL GLASS,BOWL,PURPLE,GRAPE & CABLE,RUFFLED,MARKED N,
    9 3/4 IN...................................................    30.00
CARNIVAL GLASS,BOWL,PURPLE,GRAPE DELIGHT,FOOTED.............    65.00
CARNIVAL GLASS,BOWL,PURPLE,GRAPE LEAVES,MARKED N,8 3/4 IN...    29.50
CARNIVAL GLASS,BOWL,PURPLE,GRAPE,THUMBPRINT,MARKED N,5 IN...    15.00
CARNIVAL GLASS,BOWL,PURPLE,HATTIE,RUFFLED,9 IN..............    45.00
CARNIVAL GLASS,BOWL,PURPLE,HOLLY SPRIG,FLUTED,8-IN.DIAMETER.    30.00
CARNIVAL GLASS,BOWL,PURPLE,HONEYCOMB,RIBBON RIM,6 IN........    12.00
CARNIVAL GLASS,BOWL,PURPLE,IMPERIAL PANSY..................    30.00
CARNIVAL GLASS,BOWL,PURPLE,IMPERIAL PANSY,OVERLAPPING ARCS
    OUTSIDE,9 IN...............................................    22.00
CARNIVAL GLASS,BOWL,PURPLE,IMPERIAL PANSY,RUFFLED,
    9-IN.DIAMETER..............................................    28.50
CARNIVAL GLASS,BOWL,PURPLE,KANGAROO,AUSTRALIA,5 IN..........    60.00
CARNIVAL GLASS,BOWL,PURPLE,KANGAROO,AUSTRALIA,9 IN..........   150.00
CARNIVAL GLASS,BOWL,PURPLE,KINGFISHER,AUSTRALIA,5 IN........    50.00
CARNIVAL GLASS,BOWL,PURPLE,KINGFISHER,AUSTRALIA,9 IN........   125.00
CARNIVAL GLASS,BOWL,PURPLE,KINGFISH,FLUTED,AUSTRALIA,9 1/4 X
    4 1/4 IN...................................................   140.00
CARNIVAL GLASS,BOWL,PURPLE,KINGFISHER,5 1/4 IN..............    85.00
CARNIVAL GLASS,BOWL,PURPLE,KINGFISHER,9 1/2 IN..............   125.00
CARNIVAL GLASS,BOWL,PURPLE,KOOKABURRA,AUSTRALIA,5 IN........    50.00
CARNIVAL GLASS,BOWL,PURPLE,LITTLE FISHES,FOOTED,AUSTRALIA,
    9 IN.......................................................    65.00
CARNIVAL GLASS,BOWL,PURPLE,LOTUS & DRAGON,8 IN..............    32.50
CARNIVAL GLASS,BOWL,PURPLE,LUSTER ROSE,THREE SCROLLED FEET,
    11 IN......................................................    85.00
CARNIVAL GLASS,BOWL,PURPLE,MAGPIE,AUSTRALIA,5 IN............    50.00
CARNIVAL GLASS,BOWL,PURPLE,MAGPIE,AUSTRALIA,9 IN............   130.00
CARNIVAL GLASS,BOWL,PURPLE,MAGPIE,FLUTED,AUSTRIALIA,9 1/4 X
    4 1/4 IN...................................................   140.00
CARNIVAL GLASS,BOWL,PURPLE,MALAGA GRAPE,FENTON.............    27.50
CARNIVAL GLASS,BOWL,PURPLE,PANSY SPRAY,SHALLOW,9 IN.........    28.00
CARNIVAL GLASS,BOWL,PURPLE,PEACOCK AT URN,8 IN.............    34.00
CARNIVAL GLASS,BOWL,PURPLE,PEACOCK AT URN,FLUTED,
    8 3/4-IN.DIAMETER..........................................    58.00
CARNIVAL GLASS,BOWL,PURPLE,PEACOCK ON FENCE................    75.00
CARNIVAL GLASS,BOWL,PURPLE,PEACOCK ON FENCE,SHALLOW,9 IN....    55.00
CARNIVAL GLASS,BOWL,PURPLE,PEACOCK TAIL,SCALLOPS TURN BACK,
    7 IN.......................................................    14.00
CARNIVAL GLASS,BOWL,PURPLE,PEACOCK TAIL,SHALLOW,9 IN........    29.00
CARNIVAL GLASS,BOWL,PURPLE,PERSIAN MEDALLION,FLUTED,COPPER
    TONES,8 IN.................................................    28.00
CARNIVAL GLASS,BOWL,PURPLE,PINEAPPLE PATTERN,6 1/2 IN.......    15.00
CARNIVAL GLASS,BOWL,PURPLE,PINK IMPERIAL JEWELS,DOLPHINS,
    8 1/2 IN...................................................    55.00
CARNIVAL GLASS,BOWL,PURPLE,PONY............................   135.00
CARNIVAL GLASS,BOWL,PURPLE,RAINDROP PATTERN,SCALLOPED,
    7-IN.DIAMETER..............................................     8.50
CARNIVAL GLASS,BOWL,PURPLE,ROSE & RUFFLES,7-IN.DIAMETER.....    35.00
CARNIVAL GLASS,BOWL,PURPLE,ROSE,FOOTED,7 IN................    32.00
CARNIVAL GLASS,BOWL,PURPLE,RUFFLED,6 PETALS,SHALLOW,
    8 1/2 IN...................................................    18.00
CARNIVAL GLASS,BOWL,PURPLE,SCROLL EMBOSSED,7 IN. X 2 1/2 IN.    18.50
CARNIVAL GLASS,BOWL,PURPLE,SHELL,WILDROSE,OPEN HEART RIM,
    FOOTED,MARKED N............................................    23.50
CARNIVAL GLASS,BOWL,PURPLE,SKI STAR........................    15.00
CARNIVAL GLASS,BOWL,PURPLE,STAG & HOLLY,SHALLOW,3-FOOTED,
    11-IN.DIAMETER.............................................    65.00
CARNIVAL GLASS,BOWL,PURPLE,STAR OF DAVID,BOWS & GRAPE
    OUTSIDE,FOOTED.............................................    30.00
CARNIVAL GLASS,BOWL,PURPLE,STAR OF DAVID,BOWS,VINTAGE,DOME
    PEDESTAL...................................................    35.00
CARNIVAL GLASS,BOWL,PURPLE,STAR OF DAVID,FLORAL,GRAPES,VINE,
    LEAVES.....................................................    24.00
CARNIVAL GLASS,BOWL,PURPLE,STAR OF DAVID,RIM BASE,VINTAGE
    PATTERN INSIDE.............................................    47.50
CARNIVAL GLASS,BOWL,PURPLE,STIPPLED POSY & PODS,RUFFLED,
    10 IN......................................................    26.00
CARNIVAL GLASS,BOWL,PURPLE,STIPPLED RAY & RIBBONS,FLUTED,
    MILLERSBURG................................................    30.00
CARNIVAL GLASS,BOWL,PURPLE,STIPPLED RAY,9 1/2 IN.WIDE.......    24.00
CARNIVAL GLASS,BOWL,PURPLE,STRAWBERRY,MILLERSBURG,10 IN.X
```

```
  3 1/2 IN.................................................  60.00
CARNIVAL GLASS,BOWL,PURPLE,STRUTTING PEACOCK,RUFFLED EDGE,
  8 1/2 IN...............................................  45.00
CARNIVAL GLASS,BOWL,PURPLE,SWAN,AUSTRALIA,5 IN..............  50.00
CARNIVAL GLASS,BOWL,PURPLE,SWAN,AUSTRALIA,9 IN............. 130.00
CARNIVAL GLASS,BOWL,PURPLE,SWAN,FLUTED,AUSTRALIA,9 1/4 X
  4 1/4 IN............................................... 140.00
CARNIVAL GLASS,BOWL,PURPLE,THISTLE,SHALLOW,9 IN............  45.00
CARNIVAL GLASS,BOWL,PURPLE,THREE FRUITS,N MARK,8 1/2 IN....  29.00
CARNIVAL GLASS,BOWL,PURPLE,THUNDERBIRD,AUSTRALIA,9 IN...... 130.00
CARNIVAL GLASS,BOWL,PURPLE,THUNDERBIRD,AUSTRALIA,5 IN......  50.00
CARNIVAL GLASS,BOWL,PURPLE,THUNDERBIRD,FLUTED,AUSTRALIA,
  9 1/4 IN............................................... 140.00
CARNIVAL GLASS,BOWL,PURPLE,TWO PEACOCKS ON FENCE,9 IN......  65.00
CARNIVAL GLASS,BOWL,PURPLE,VINTAGE GRAPE,RUFFLED,9 IN......  20.00
CARNIVAL GLASS,BOWL,PURPLE,VINTAGE,LOW PEDESTAL,8 IN.......  38.00
CARNIVAL GLASS,BOWL,PURPLE,VINTAGE,NORTHWOOD,8 IN..........  23.00
CARNIVAL GLASS,BOWL,PURPLE,WILD ROSE,GRAPE LEAVES,FLARED
  EDGE,N MARK...........................................  28.00
CARNIVAL GLASS,BOWL,PURPLE,WILD ROSE,LACY OPEN EDGE,FOOTED,
  MARK N................................................  25.00
CARNIVAL GLASS,BOWL,PURPLE,WINDFLOWER,8 1/2 IN.............  25.00
CARNIVAL GLASS,BOWL,PURPLE,WISHBONE,FOOTED,8 IN............  27.00
CARNIVAL GLASS,BOWL,PURPLE,2 FLOWERS,FOOTED,7 1/2 IN.......  18.00
CARNIVAL GLASS,BOWL,RED,DRAGON & LOTUS,9 IN............... 185.00
CARNIVAL GLASS,BOWL,ROSE,AMBER OVER GREEN,LEAF & BEADS,
  FOOTED,N MARK.........................................  32.00
CARNIVAL GLASS,BOWL,ROSE,BLUE-GREEN-BUTTERSCOTCH,LEAF BEADS. 38.00
CARNIVAL GLASS,BOWL,ROSE,BLUE,BEADED CABLE,FOOTED..........  35.00
CARNIVAL GLASS,BOWL,ROSE,BLUE,GARLANDS....................  33.75
CARNIVAL GLASS,BOWL,ROSE,BLUE,GRAPE & LEAF,SIX-FOOTED.....  55.00
CARNIVAL GLASS,BOWL,ROSE,BLUE,ICE,FINE CUT & ROSES........  79.00
CARNIVAL GLASS,BOWL,ROSE,GREEN,LEAF & BEADS,FLARED,OPEN....  18.00
CARNIVAL GLASS,BOWL,ROSE,GREEN,LEAF & BEADS,FOOTED.........  38.50
CARNIVAL GLASS,BOWL,ROSE,GREEN,LOUISA.....................  27.50
CARNIVAL GLASS,BOWL,ROSE,GREEN,LOUISA,FOOTED..............  35.00
CARNIVAL GLASS,BOWL,ROSE,MARIGOLD,BEADED CABLE............  20.00
CARNIVAL GLASS,BOWL,ROSE,MARIGOLD,FINE CUT & ROSES........  20.00
CARNIVAL GLASS,BOWL,ROSE,MARIGOLD,GARLAND,FOOTED..........  25.00
CARNIVAL GLASS,BOWL,ROSE,MARIGOLD,GARLAND.................  25.00
CARNIVAL GLASS,BOWL,ROSE,MARIGOLD,GOLDEN GRAPES...........  45.00
CARNIVAL GLASS,BOWL,ROSE,MARIGOLD,GRAPE,FOOTED............  30.00
CARNIVAL GLASS,BOWL,ROSE,MARIGOLD,HONEYCOMB...............  75.00
CARNIVAL GLASS,BOWL,ROSE,MARIGOLD,LEAF & BEADS,FOOTED......  25.00
CARNIVAL GLASS,BOWL,ROSE,MARIGOLD,PERSIAN
  MEDALLION.................................... 25.00 TO   42.00
CARNIVAL GLASS,BOWL,ROSE,MARIGOLD,STAR & FILE.............  10.00
CARNIVAL GLASS,BOWL,ROSE,MARIGOLD,WIDE PANEL..............  30.00
CARNIVAL GLASS,BOWL,ROSE,MARIGOLD,WREATH OF ROSES.. 13.00 TO  15.00
CARNIVAL GLASS,BOWL,ROSE,ORANGE,DAISY & PLUME,BLACKBERRY
  INSIDE,FOOTED.........................................  35.00
CARNIVAL GLASS,BOWL,ROSE,PEACH COLOR,HONEYCOMB PATTERN,
  MILLERSBURG...........................................  48.00
CARNIVAL GLASS,BOWL,ROSE,PURPLE,BEADED CABLE,FOOTED,N MARK..  50.00
CARNIVAL GLASS,BOWL,ROSE,PURPLE,CABLE,CRIMPED EDGE,N MARK...  30.00
CARNIVAL GLASS,BOWL,ROSE,PURPLE,DAISY & PLUME,BLACKBERRY
  INSIDE,FOOTED.........................................  39.00
CARNIVAL GLASS,BOWL,ROSE,PURPLE,DRAPERY,N MARK............  35.00
CARNIVAL GLASS,BOWL,ROSE,PURPLE,DRAPERY,N MARK,GOLD & BRONZE
  IRIDESCENT............................................  65.00
CARNIVAL GLASS,BOWL,ROSE,PURPLE,FINE CUT & ROSES..........  31.00
CARNIVAL GLASS,BOWL,ROSE,PURPLE,FINE CUT & ROSES,SIGNED N...  40.00
CARNIVAL GLASS,BOWL,ROSE,PURPLE,GRAPE....................  48.00
CARNIVAL GLASS,BOWL,ROSE,PURPLE,LEAF & BEADS,THREE TWIG FEET  45.00
CARNIVAL GLASS,BOWL,ROSE,PURPLE,LEAF & BEADS,FOOTED,N MARK..  35.00
CARNIVAL GLASS,BOWL,ROSE,PURPLE,LOUISA,FOOTED.............  26.00
CARNIVAL GLASS,BOWL,ROSE,PURPLE,RASPBERRIES & MAYFLOWER.....  40.00
CARNIVAL GLASS,BOWL,ROSE,PURPLE,VINTAGE............ 47.00 TO  53.00
CARNIVAL GLASS,BOWL,ROSE,WHITE,DAISY & PLUME,BERRIES INSIDE,
  FOOTED................................................  65.00
CARNIVAL GLASS,BOWL,ROSE,WHITE,LEAF & BEADS,FOOTED..........  60.00
CARNIVAL GLASS,BOWL,SUGAR,GREEN,LUSTER FLUTED,HANDLED.......  18.00
CARNIVAL GLASS,BOWL,SUGAR,MARIGOLD,FOOTED,STIPPLED RAYS.....   7.50
CARNIVAL GLASS,BOWL,SUGAR,MARIGOLD,PEACOCK AT FOUNTAIN,COVER  32.00
CARNIVAL GLASS,BOWL,SUGAR,PURPLE,ORANGE TREE...............  17.00
CARNIVAL GLASS,BOWL,SUGAR,PURPLE,STRUTTING
  PEACOCK,COVER................................ 28.00 TO   35.00
CARNIVAL GLASS,BOWL,TURQUOISE,GRAPE & CABLE,SHALLOW,9 IN....  40.00
CARNIVAL GLASS,BOWL,WHITE,DAISY PINWHEEL,7 IN.............  45.00
CARNIVAL GLASS,BOWL,WHITE,FROSTED BLOCK,6 3/4 IN...........  15.00
CARNIVAL GLASS,BOWL,WHITE,HEARTS & FLOWERS,9 IN...........  30.00
```

```
CARNIVAL GLASS,BOWL,WHITE,HEARTS & FLOWERS,SERRATED RIM,
  8 3/4 IN.................................................  65.00
CARNIVAL GLASS,BOWL,WHITE,HOLLY,9 1/2 IN. X 2 3/4 IN........  37.50
CARNIVAL GLASS,BOWL,WHITE,ORANGE TREE.......................  60.00
CARNIVAL GLASS,BOWL,WHITE,PEACOCKS ON FENCE,FLUTED,SHALLOW..  85.00
CARNIVAL GLASS,BOWL,WHITE,WISHBONE,RUFFLED,9-IN.DIAMETER....  67.50
CARNIVAL GLASS,BOWL,WHITE,WREATHED CHERRIES,OVAL............  95.00
CARNIVAL GLASS,BOX,ORANGE,FIGURE OF DOG ON TOP,5 1/2 X
  3 1/2 IN.DIAMETER.......................................  12.00
CARNIVAL GLASS,BOX,POWDER,BLUE,ORANGE TREE,GOLD IRIDESCENT..  49.50
CARNIVAL GLASS,BUTTER,BLUE,FLUTED,N MARK...................  55.00
CARNIVAL GLASS,BUTTER,GREEN,GOLD TRIM,SIGNED NORTHWOOD......  43.50
CARNIVAL GLASS,BUTTER,MARIGOLD,FOOTED,WIDE PANEL,
  1 3/4 IN.HIGH..........................................  15.00
CARNIVAL GLASS,BUTTER,MARIGOLD,ORANGE TREE,FOOTED..........  45.00
CARNIVAL GLASS,BUTTER,MARIGOLD,STORK & RUSHES,COVER........  35.00
CARNIVAL GLASS,BUTTER,MARIGOLD,WATER LILY,CATTAIL,COVER.....  45.00
CARNIVAL GLASS,BUTTER,PURPLE,ACORN & BURR,COVER............. 135.00
CARNIVAL GLASS,BUTTER,SUGAR,CREAMER,SPOONER,MARIGOLD,
  BUTTERFLY,BERRY........................................  90.00
CARNIVAL GLASS,BUTTER,WHITE,COSMOS & CANE,COVER............  25.00
CARNIVAL GLASS,CAKE STAND,MARIGOLD,BUTTERFLY,BUSH,
  FLANNELFLOWER.......................................... 150.00
CARNIVAL GLASS,CAKE STAND,PURPLE,BUTTERFLY,AUSTRALIA....... 175.00
CARNIVAL GLASS,CANDLEHOLDER,MARIGOLD,LIGHT,BARBER POLE.....   8.50
CARNIVAL GLASS,CANDLESTICK,BLUE,ICE,8 1/2 IN.,PAIR........  45.00
CARNIVAL GLASS,CANDLESTICK,MARIGOLD,DOUBLE SCROLL,PAIR.....  20.00
CARNIVAL GLASS,CANDLESTICK,MARIGOLD,WIDE PANEL,6 1/2 IN.,
  PAIR...................................................  45.00
CARNIVAL GLASS,CANDLESTICK,PURPLE,GRAPE,N MARK,5 1/2 IN.....  50.00
CARNIVAL GLASS,CANDLESTICK,PURPLE,PANELED,BRONZE IRIDESCENT,
  PAIR...................................................  95.00
CARNIVAL GLASS,CANDLESTICK,WHITE,CORNUCOPIA,PAIR... 35.00 TO  75.00
CARNIVAL GLASS,CANDLESTICK,WHITE,DOMED FOOT,7 3/4 IN.HIGH...  18.00
CARNIVAL GLASS,CANDY,GREEN,LUSTER FLUTED,TWO HANDLES,N MARK.  16.00
CARNIVAL GLASS,CARAFE,PURPLE,GRAPE........................  85.00
CARNIVAL GLASS,CARAFE,WATER,GREEN,GRAPE,9 IN.TALL.........  22.00
CARNIVAL GLASS,CHALICE,GREEN,DOUBLE LOOP,3 7/8 IN.HIGH......  25.00
CARNIVAL GLASS,CHAMPAGNE,WHITE,SHRINER,1911...............  38.00
CARNIVAL GLASS,COLOGNE,MARIGOLD,GRAPE,CABLE,STOPPER........  70.00
CARNIVAL GLASS,COMPOTE,AMETHYST,DAISY & PLUME,N MARK.......  25.00
CARNIVAL GLASS,COMPOTE,AMETHYST,EMBOSSED SCROLL...........  20.00
CARNIVAL GLASS,COMPOTE,AMETHYST,PETALS,NORTHWOOD..........  40.00
CARNIVAL GLASS,COMPOTE,BLUE,MIKADO....................... 100.00
CARNIVAL GLASS,COMPOTE,BLUE,SCOTCH THISTLE,RUFFLED........  36.00
CARNIVAL GLASS,COMPOTE,CANDY,GREEN,IMPERIAL JEWELS,COVER,
  FOOTED,FINIAL..........................................  18.00
CARNIVAL GLASS,COMPOTE,CANDY,MARIGOLD,NAUTILIS............  95.00
CARNIVAL GLASS,COMPOTE,GREEN STAND,AMETHYST BODY,FLUTED
  EDGE,N MARK............................................  40.00
CARNIVAL GLASS,COMPOTE,GREEN,BLACKBERRY SPRAY,RUFFLED,
  PEDESTAL,6 1/2 IN......................................  18.00
CARNIVAL GLASS,COMPOTE,GREEN,GREEK KEY,N MARK,6 3/4 X
  4 1/2 IN.HIGH..........................................  25.00
CARNIVAL GLASS,COMPOTE,GREEN,LITTLE FLOWERS...............  24.00
CARNIVAL GLASS,COMPOTE,GREEN,PEACOCK EYE..................  17.00
CARNIVAL GLASS,COMPOTE,GREEN,SCROLL EMBOSSED,PAIR..........  32.00
CARNIVAL GLASS,COMPOTE,GREEN,SCROLL,EMBOSSED,
  6 1/4 IN.DIAMETER,PAIR.................................  25.00
CARNIVAL GLASS,COMPOTE,GREEN,THISTLE PATTERN.............  19.00
CARNIVAL GLASS,COMPOTE,JELLY,GREEN,IRIS,7 IN.............  25.00
CARNIVAL GLASS,COMPOTE,JELLY,MARIGOLD,PEACOCK &
  URN,FENTON.................................... 14.00 TO  20.00
CARNIVAL GLASS,COMPOTE,JELLY,MARIGOLD,PLAIN,CLEAR STEM.....  10.00
CARNIVAL GLASS,COMPOTE,JELLY,MARIGOLD,SMOOTH RAYS,CLEAR STEM   8.00
CARNIVAL GLASS,COMPOTE,JELLY,PURPLE,BRONZE IRIDESCENT,N MARK  12.50
CARNIVAL GLASS,COMPOTE,JELLY,PURPLE,PLAIN,N MARK..........  20.00
CARNIVAL GLASS,COMPOTE,MARIGOLD,5 X 3 X 3 IN.TALL.........  15.00
CARNIVAL GLASS,COMPOTE,MARIGOLD,BEADED PANEL,OPAL WHITE ON
  UNDERSIDE..............................................  15.00
CARNIVAL GLASS,COMPOTE,MARIGOLD,BUTTERFLY,WARATAH,ROLLED
  EDGE,AUSTRALIA.........................................  75.00
CARNIVAL GLASS,COMPOTE,MARIGOLD,BUTTERFLY,WARATAH,FLUTED
  EDGE,AUSTRALIA.........................................  75.00
CARNIVAL GLASS,COMPOTE,MARIGOLD,CATHEDRAL PATTERN.........   8.00
CARNIVAL GLASS,COMPOTE,MARIGOLD,EASTERN STAR,
  SCROLL........................................ 12.50 TO  15.00
CARNIVAL GLASS,COMPOTE,MARIGOLD,EMU,AUSTRALIA............. 150.00
CARNIVAL GLASS,COMPOTE,MARIGOLD,FLORAL,WHEAT,HANDLE.......  14.00
CARNIVAL GLASS,COMPOTE,MARIGOLD,HOLLY,BERRY...............   8.00
CARNIVAL GLASS,COMPOTE,MARIGOLD,IMPERIAL ARCS,6 3/4 X
```

```
    4 IN.HIGH.........................................     11.00
CARNIVAL GLASS,COMPOTE,MARIGOLD,IMPERIAL GRAPE,6 IN.........      8.50
CARNIVAL GLASS,COMPOTE,MARIGOLD,LINED BEADS PATTERN,OPAL
    WHITE UNDER.......................................     15.00
CARNIVAL GLASS,COMPOTE,MARIGOLD,MIKADO.....................     45.00
CARNIVAL GLASS,COMPOTE,MARIGOLD,OCTAGON,7 3/4 IN.DIAMETER,
    7 1/4 IN.HIGH.....................................     20.00
CARNIVAL GLASS,COMPOTE,MARIGOLD,OSTRICH,RAISED PATTERN,
    AUSTRALIA.........................................    150.00
CARNIVAL GLASS,COMPOTE,MARIGOLD,PEACOCK & URN..............     14.00
CARNIVAL GLASS,COMPOTE,MARIGOLD,PEACOCK & URN,6 IN.........     14.00
CARNIVAL GLASS,COMPOTE,MARIGOLD,PEACOCK & URN,CLEAR STEM,
    5 1/2 IN..........................................     18.00
CARNIVAL GLASS,COMPOTE,MARIGOLD,PEACOCK & URN,RUFFLED,6 IN..     25.00
CARNIVAL GLASS,COMPOTE,MARIGOLD,PROPELLER..................      8.00
CARNIVAL GLASS,COMPOTE,MARIGOLD,QUESTION MARK TOP,FRUIT
    PATTERN UNDER.....................................     12.50
CARNIVAL GLASS,COMPOTE,MARIGOLD,SPIRALED DIAMOND POINT,
    5 1/2 X 5 IN......................................      8.00
CARNIVAL GLASS,COMPOTE,MARIGOLD,STAR MEDALLION.............     15.00
CARNIVAL GLASS,COMPOTE,MARIGOLD,STRAWFLOWER,BUTTERFLY,BUSH,
    AUSTRALIA.........................................     75.00
CARNIVAL GLASS,COMPOTE,ORANGE,FIVE HEARTS,7 1/2 IN. X
    3 1/2 IN..........................................     23.00
CARNIVAL GLASS,COMPOTE,PURPLE,BASKET WEAVE,STEM,N MARK,
    7-IN.DIAMETER.....................................     25.00
CARNIVAL GLASS,COMPOTE,PURPLE,BLACKBERRY PATTERN,7 IN......     18.00
CARNIVAL GLASS,COMPOTE,PURPLE,BUTTERFLY,BUSH,AUSTRALIA,
    6 1/4 IN.HIGH.....................................    100.00
CARNIVAL GLASS,COMPOTE,PURPLE,BUTTERFLY,BUSH,AUSTRALIA,
    9 1/4 IN.WIDE.....................................    120.00
CARNIVAL GLASS,COMPOTE,PURPLE,BUTTERFLY,BUSH,AUSTRALIA,
    7 1/2 X 4 IN.HIGH.................................     80.00
CARNIVAL GLASS,COMPOTE,PURPLE,EMU,AUSTRALIA................    175.00
CARNIVAL GLASS,COMPOTE,PURPLE,HARVEST POPPY,7 IN...........     20.00
CARNIVAL GLASS,COMPOTE,PURPLE,HOBNAIL,AUSTRALIA,9 X
    6 1/2 IN.HIGH.....................................    100.00
CARNIVAL GLASS,COMPOTE,PURPLE,LUSTER LINING,N MARK,
    6 1/4-IN.DIAMETER.................................     35.00
CARNIVAL GLASS,COMPOTE,PURPLE,N IN CIRCLE,5 IN. X 6 IN.....     15.00
CARNIVAL GLASS,COMPOTE,PURPLE,OSTRICH,RAISED PATTERN,
    AUSTRALIA.........................................    225.00
CARNIVAL GLASS,COMPOTE,PURPLE,QUESTION MARK,TWO HANDLES,
    FOOTED............................................     16.00
CARNIVAL GLASS,COMPOTE,PURPLE,QUESTION MARK TOP,FRUIT
    PATTERN UNDER.....................................     20.00
CARNIVAL GLASS,COMPOTE,PURPLE,S-REPEAT,PLAIN INSIDE,
    AUSTRALIA.........................................     70.00
CARNIVAL GLASS,COMPOTE,PURPLE,THUMBPRINT,COLUMN,5 1/2 X
    5 IN. HIGH........................................     17.50
CARNIVAL GLASS,COMPOTE,PURPLE,TREE OF LIFE..........ILLUS..     60.00
CARNIVAL GLASS,COMPOTE,PURPLE,WREATH OF ROSES,6-IN.DIAMETER.    18.00
CARNIVAL GLASS,COMPOTE,WHITE,CONSTELLATION & SEA FOAM......     35.00
CARNIVAL GLASS,COMPOTE,WHITE,FLORAL,WHEAT,TURNED-DOWN RIM,
    TWO HANDLES.......................................    110.00
CARNIVAL GLASS,COMPOTE,WHITE,S REPEAT,5 1/2 IN.............     30.00
CARNIVAL GLASS,CREAMER & SUGAR,AMETHYST,PEACOCK AT FOUNTAIN,
    OPEN..............................................     85.00
CARNIVAL GLASS,CREAMER & SUGAR,BLUE,ORANGE TREE,OPEN.......     45.00
CARNIVAL GLASS,CREAMER & SUGAR,GREEN,GOLD TRIM,SIGNED
    NORTHWOOD.........................................     70.00
```

PURPLE TREE OF LIFE CARNIVAL GLASS COMPOTE

```
CARNIVAL GLASS,CREAMER & SUGAR,GREEN,GRAPE,CABLE.............    160.00
CARNIVAL GLASS,CREAMER & SUGAR,GREEN,LUSTER FLUTED. 24.00 TO      25.00
CARNIVAL GLASS,CREAMER & SUGAR,MARIGOLD,MILLERSBURG CHERRIES      38.00
CARNIVAL GLASS,CREAMER & SUGAR,MARIGOLD,PANSY SPRAY.........      18.50
CARNIVAL GLASS,CREAMER & SUGAR,MARIGOLD,PINEAPPLE,DOME FOOT,
  AUSTRALIA..............................................        60.00
CARNIVAL GLASS,CREAMER & SUGAR,MARIGOLD,SINGING BIRD........      40.00
CARNIVAL GLASS,CREAMER,GREEN,STIPPLED RAY...................      12.50
CARNIVAL GLASS,CREAMER,MARIGOLD,ACORN BURRS.................      27.50
CARNIVAL GLASS,CREAMER,MARIGOLD,IRIS,HERRINGBONE............       5.00
CARNIVAL GLASS,CREAMER,MARIGOLD,LEAF TIERS..................      22.00
CARNIVAL GLASS,CREAMER,MARIGOLD,LUSTER ROSE.................      18.00
CARNIVAL GLASS,CREAMER,MARIGOLD,PALE,STAR & FILE............      10.00
CARNIVAL GLASS,CREAMER,MARIGOLD,PANSY SPRAY.................      10.00
CARNIVAL GLASS,CREAMER,MARIGOLD,STAR MEDALLION,5 1/2 IN.HIGH      14.00
CARNIVAL GLASS,CREAMER,MARIGOLD,THISTLE & THORN.............      15.00
CARNIVAL GLASS,CREAMER,MARIGOLD,THISTLE & THORN,FOOTED......      12.00
CARNIVAL GLASS,CREAMER,PURPLE,PEACOCK AT FOUNTAIN...........      35.00
CARNIVAL GLASS,CREAMER,PURPLE,STIPPLED RAY..................      15.00
CARNIVAL GLASS,CREAMER,PURPLE,STRUTTING PEACOCK,
  COVER.................................... 20.00 TO           22.50
CARNIVAL GLASS,CREAMER,WHITE,ORANGE TREE....................      32.00
CARNIVAL GLASS,CUP & SAUCER,MARIGOLD,BOUQUET & LATTICE
  PATTERN................................................         2.50
CARNIVAL GLASS,CUP,LOVING,MARIGOLD,CORDELIA.................      32.00
CARNIVAL GLASS,CUP,LOVING,PURPLE,ORANGE TREE................      85.00
CARNIVAL GLASS,CUP,PUNCH,AMETHYST,GRAPE & CABLE,SIGNED......      17.50
CARNIVAL GLASS,CUP,PUNCH,AMETHYST,MEMPHIS...................      12.00
CARNIVAL GLASS,CUP,PUNCH,BLUE,ICE,GRAPE & CABLE.............      25.00
CARNIVAL GLASS,CUP,PUNCH,GREEN,ACORN BURR...................      16.00
CARNIVAL GLASS,CUP,PUNCH,GREEN,ACORN BURR,COPPER IRIDESCENT,
  MARKED N...............................................        16.00
CARNIVAL GLASS,CUP,PUNCH,GREEN,GRAPE & CABLE,MARKED N.......       8.00
CARNIVAL GLASS,CUP,PUNCH,GREEN,MEMPHIS.....................      12.00
CARNIVAL GLASS,CUP,PUNCH,GREEN,MEMPHIS,MARKED N.... 10.50 TO     12.00
CARNIVAL GLASS,CUP,PUNCH,MARIGOLD,ACORN BURR,N MARK.........     10.00
CARNIVAL GLASS,CUP,PUNCH,MARIGOLD,BUZZ STAR......... 6.00 TO      7.00
CARNIVAL GLASS,CUP,PUNCH,MARIGOLD,IMPERIAL GRAPE,SET OF 4...     26.00
CARNIVAL GLASS,CUP,PUNCH,MARIGOLD,STORK IN RUSHES...........      7.00
CARNIVAL GLASS,CUP,PUNCH,MARIGOLD,VINTAGE........... 6.25 TO      7.00
CARNIVAL GLASS,CUP,PUNCH,PURPLE,GRAPE & CABLE,
  MARKED................................... 12.00 TO          15.00
CARNIVAL GLASS,CUP,PUNCH,PURPLE,MANY FRUITS.................       9.00
CARNIVAL GLASS,CUP,PUNCH,PURPLE,MEMPHIS............. 10.00 TO     12.00
CARNIVAL GLASS,CUP,PUNCH,WHITE,ORANGE TREE..................      15.00
CARNIVAL GLASS,CUSPIDOR,LADY'S,MARIGOLD,4 IN.HIGH,7 IN.WIDE.     40.00
CARNIVAL GLASS,CUSPIDOR,ORANGE.............................      10.00
CARNIVAL GLASS,DECANTER,MARIGOLD,GOLDEN HARVEST PATTERN,
  STOPPER...............................................        45.00
CARNIVAL GLASS,DECANTER,MARIGOLD,GRAPE CLUSTERS,STOPPER.....     45.00
CARNIVAL GLASS,DECANTER,MARIGOLD,IMPERIAL GRAPE.............     35.00
CARNIVAL GLASS,DECANTER,MARIGOLD,IMPERIAL GRAPE,MUSHROOM
  STOPPER...............................................        20.00
CARNIVAL GLASS,DECANTER,MARIGOLD,IMPERIAL GRAPE,STOPPER,
  11 1/2 IN.TALL.........................................       45.00
CARNIVAL GLASS,DECANTER,MARIGOLD,IMPERIAL GRAPE,STOPPER.....     30.00
CARNIVAL GLASS,DECANTER,PURPLE,IMPERIAL GRAPE,STOPPER.......    110.00
CARNIVAL GLASS,DECANTER,WINE,GREEN,IMPERIAL GRAPE,NO STOPPER     25.00
CARNIVAL GLASS,DECANTER,WINE,MARIGOLD,IMPERIAL GRAPE,STOPPER     28.00
CARNIVAL GLASS,DECANTER,WINE,MARIGOLD,OCTAGON,STOPPER.......     32.50
CARNIVAL GLASS,DECANTER,WINE,PURPLE,GRAPES.................      87.50
CARNIVAL GLASS,DESSERT,MARIGOLD,RIBBED,CLEAR STEM,MATCHING
  PLATE.................................................         3.50
CARNIVAL GLASS,DISH,AMETHYST,FLUTED,PANELED RAYS,SILVER
  SHEEN,N MARK..........................................        20.00
CARNIVAL GLASS,DISH,AMETHYST,THREE FRUITS,TWO HANDLES,
  NORTHWOOD.............................................        28.00
CARNIVAL GLASS,DISH,BERRY,PURPLE,GRAPE & CABLE,N MARK.......     11.50
CARNIVAL GLASS,DISH,BERRY,PURPLE,PEACOCK,URN,MILLERSBURG,
  5 IN..................................................        25.00
CARNIVAL GLASS,DISH,BUTTER,AMETHYST,BOTH PIECES MARKED N....    100.00
CARNIVAL GLASS,DISH,BUTTER,MARIGOLD,GRAPE,CABLE,TWO PIECES,
  SIGNED N..............................................        55.00
CARNIVAL GLASS,DISH,BUTTER,PURPLE,GRAPE & CABLE.............    165.00
CARNIVAL GLASS,DISH,BUTTER,PURPLE,GRAPE & CABLE,COVER,N MARK     95.00
CARNIVAL GLASS,DISH,BUTTER,PURPLE,MAPLE LEAF...............     100.00
CARNIVAL GLASS,DISH,CANDY,AMETHYST,QUESTION MARK,TWO
  HANDLES,STEM.........................................         20.00
CARNIVAL GLASS,DISH,CANDY,AQUA,BASKET WEAVE................      15.00
CARNIVAL GLASS,DISH,CANDY,BLUE,ARABIC,TWO HANDLES,
  8-IN.DIAMETER........................................         18.00
```

```
CARNIVAL GLASS,DISH,CANDY,BLUE,FINE CUT & ROSES,FOOTED,8 IN.     40.00
CARNIVAL GLASS,DISH,CANDY,BLUE,ICE,LACY RIM..............        20.00
CARNIVAL GLASS,DISH,CANDY,BLUE,PERSIAN MEDALLION,TWO
  HANDLES,RUFFLED.....................................           20.00
CARNIVAL GLASS,DISH,CANDY,BUTTERFLY,TWO HANDLES,FENTON,
  7-IN.DIAMETER......................................            18.00
CARNIVAL GLASS,DISH,CANDY,GREEN,HOLLY,MILLERSBURG,2 HANDLES.     18.00
CARNIVAL GLASS,DISH,CANDY,GREEN,WREATH OF ROSES,PANELS,
  HANDLES...........................................             20.00
CARNIVAL GLASS,DISH,CANDY,ICE-GREEN,LACY TOP,BASKET WEAVE
  UNDER.............................................             18.00
CARNIVAL GLASS,DISH,CANDY,MARIGOLD,LACY RIM,BASKET WEAVE
  UNDER.............................................              8.00
CARNIVAL GLASS,DISH,CANDY,MARIGOLD,PERSIAN MEDALLION........      7.50
CARNIVAL GLASS,DISH,CANDY,MARIGOLD,STIPPLED RAYS,TWO HANDLES     9.00
CARNIVAL GLASS,DISH,CANDY,MARIGOLD,SWIRLED,COVER,STEEPLE
  FINIAL............................................             7.50
CARNIVAL GLASS,DISH,CANDY,PURPLE,LACY RIM..............         12.00
CARNIVAL GLASS,DISH,CANDY,PURPLE,SWIRL STAND,FLARED RIM,N
  MARK,PAIR.........................................            18.50
CARNIVAL GLASS,DISH,CANDY,RED,BLACKBERRY PATTERN,6 IN.......    80.00
CARNIVAL GLASS,DISH,CANDY,WHITE,DRAPERY,THREE-CORNERED,
  IRIDESCENT........................................            40.00
CARNIVAL GLASS,DISH,CANDY,WHITE,LEAF RAYS PATTERN,HANDLED,
  6 IN.............................................            22.00
CARNIVAL GLASS,DISH,CELERY,AMBER,PANSY SPRAY...........        35.00
CARNIVAL GLASS,DISH,FRUIT,AQUA,PASTEL,GRAPE & CABLE,SAWTOOTH
  RIM,N MARK........................................           57.00
CARNIVAL GLASS,DISH,GREEN,BLACKBERRY PATTERN,FLARED RIM,
  FOOTED,5 IN.......................................           12.50
CARNIVAL GLASS,DISH,GREEN,COSMOS,MILLERSBURG,
  5 3/4 IN.DIAMETER.................................           20.00
CARNIVAL GLASS,DISH,GREEN,GRAPE,RUFFLED,6 1/2 IN.......        23.00
CARNIVAL GLASS,DISH,GREEN,PASTEL,THREE FRUITS,RUFFLED,N
  MARK,8 1/2 IN.....................................           23.75
CARNIVAL GLASS,DISH,GREEN,RAYS,RUFFLED,N MARK,8 1/2 IN......    12.00
CARNIVAL GLASS,DISH,GREEN,VINTAGE,RUFFLED,BRONZE HIGHLIGHTS,
  N MARK...........................................            30.00
CARNIVAL GLASS,DISH,ICE CREAM,BLUE,ICE,PEACOCK,URN,N MARK...    45.00
CARNIVAL GLASS,DISH,ICE CREAM,MARIGOLD,PEACOCK AT URN,10 IN.    38.00
CARNIVAL GLASS,DISH,MARIGOLD,ADVERTISING,BASKET WEAVE,OPEN
  LACEWORK.........................................            35.00
CARNIVAL GLASS,DISH,MARIGOLD,BASKET WEAVE,WILMINGTON
  FURNITURE STORE..................................            25.00
CARNIVAL GLASS,DISH,MARIGOLD,BEADED CABLE,FOOTED,7 1/2 IN...    13.00
CARNIVAL GLASS,DISH,MARIGOLD,FLORAL & WHEAT,FOOTED.........     12.00
CARNIVAL GLASS,DISH,MARIGOLD,FLORAL & WHEAT,HANDLED.........    15.00
CARNIVAL GLASS,DISH,MARIGOLD,FLUTED,ADVERTISING MILLERS
  FURNITURE CO.....................................            40.00
CARNIVAL GLASS,DISH,MARIGOLD,HOLLY,FLOPPY HAT SHAPE.........     8.00
CARNIVAL GLASS,DISH,MARIGOLD,HOLLY,RUFFLED,6 3/4 IN.ROUND...    12.00
CARNIVAL GLASS,DISH,MARIGOLD,LEE PATTERN,HANDLE..........       6.00
CARNIVAL GLASS,DISH,MARIGOLD,LEE PATTERN,TWO-HANDLED........     7.00
CARNIVAL GLASS,DISH,MARIGOLD,LOTUS & GRAPE,6 IN..........       9.00
CARNIVAL GLASS,DISH,MARIGOLD,SAILBOAT & ORANGE TREE,RUFFLED,
  6 IN.............................................             9.00
CARNIVAL GLASS,DISH,MARIGOLD,SAYS FELDSMAN BROS,FURNITURE,
  SALISBURY,MD.....................................            30.00
CARNIVAL GLASS,DISH,MARIGOLD,SAYS JOHN H.BRAND CO.,
  FURNITURE,WILMINGTON.............................            35.00
CARNIVAL GLASS,DISH,MARIGOLD,SPRINGTIME,4 1/2 IN.......         9.00
CARNIVAL GLASS,DISH,MARIGOLD,SUNFLOWER,FOOTED,9 IN......       24.00
CARNIVAL GLASS,DISH,MARIGOLD,THISTLE THORN,FOOTED,8 1/2 IN..    10.00
CARNIVAL GLASS,DISH,NUT,PURPLE,GRAPE,SIX-FOOTED............     37.50
CARNIVAL GLASS,DISH,ORANGE,BAMBI,COVER................         15.00
CARNIVAL GLASS,DISH,ORANGE,GRAPE & LEAF,FLUTED EDGE,7 IN....    10.00
CARNIVAL GLASS,DISH,PICKLE,MARIGOLD,IMPERIAL PANSY,QUILTED..    16.50
CARNIVAL GLASS,DISH,PICKLE,MARIGOLD,PANSY,OBLONG...........     10.00
CARNIVAL GLASS,DISH,PURPLE,BEADED CABLE,FLUTED,FOOTED,
  7 3/4-IN.DIAMETER................................            27.50
CARNIVAL GLASS,DISH,PURPLE,GRAPE,CABLE,SCALLOPED,7 IN.......    12.00
CARNIVAL GLASS,DISH,RELISH,GREEN,WINDMILL,OVAL...........      22.50
CARNIVAL GLASS,DISH,RELISH,MARIGOLD,DIAMOND QUILTING,PANSY
  SPRAY............................................            14.00
CARNIVAL GLASS,DISH,SAUCE,BLUE,GRAPE & GOTHIC ARCH.........      9.00
CARNIVAL GLASS,DISH,SAUCE,GREEN,SINGING BIRD,4 1/2 IN......     38.00
CARNIVAL GLASS,DISH,SAUCE,MARIGOLD,BUTTERFLY AND BERRY......     7.50
CARNIVAL GLASS,DISH,SAUCE,MARIGOLD,PANTHER,BALL &
  CLAW............................................ 12.50 TO    14.00
CARNIVAL GLASS,DISH,SAUCE,MARIGOLD,TREE OF LIFE...........      2.00
CARNIVAL GLASS,DISH,SAUCE,PURPLE,ACORN & BURR...........       15.00
```

```
CARNIVAL GLASS,DISH,SAUCE,PURPLE,NORTHWOOD FLUTE............    10.00
CARNIVAL GLASS,DISH,SAUCE,PURPLE,PANTHER,FOOTED,6 IN........    30.00
CARNIVAL GLASS,DISH,SUNDAE,MARIGOLD,CLEAR STEM,NORTHWOOD....    24.00
CARNIVAL GLASS,DISH,VEGETABLE,MARIGOLD,OPEN,BOUQUET &
  LATTICE,10 3/8 IN....................................         3.75
CARNIVAL GLASS,DISH,WHITE,COSMOS & CANE,9 1/2 IN...........    58.00
CARNIVAL GLASS,DISH,WHITE,GRAPEVINE LATTICE,RUFFLED,6 3/4 X
  1 1/2 IN................................................     20.00
CARNIVAL GLASS,DOUGHNUT STAND,WHITE,QUESTION MARK,INTAGLIO
  PEACH PATTERN...........................................     30.00
CARNIVAL GLASS,DUCK,MARIGOLD..............................     12.00
CARNIVAL GLASS,DUCK,MARIGOLD,COVER........................     15.00
CARNIVAL GLASS,EPERGNE,MARIGOLD,FOUR LILIES...............    225.00
CARNIVAL GLASS,EPERGNE,PURPLE,SINGLE LILY,GRAPE PATTERN,
  MILLERSBURG.............................................     50.00
CARNIVAL GLASS,EPERGNE,PURPLE,VINTAGE.....................     85.00
CARNIVAL GLASS,EPERGNE,WHITE,TWO PARTS,LILY VASE,BOWL,
  WISHBONE,NORTHWOOD......................................    170.00
CARNIVAL GLASS,EYECUP,MARIGOLD............................      9.00
CARNIVAL GLASS,FERNERY,GREEN,LUSTER ROSE,FOOTED...........     18.00
CARNIVAL GLASS,FERNERY,GREEN,VINTAGE GRAPE,FOOTED.........     27.50
CARNIVAL GLASS,FERNERY,MARIGOLD,GRAPE VARIANT,FOOTED......     14.00
CARNIVAL GLASS,GOBLET,MARIGOLD,DAISY & PALM,CLEAR STEM,N
  MARK..................................................       22.00
CARNIVAL GLASS,GOBLET,MARIGOLD,IMPERIAL GRAPE,6 IN.HIGH...     20.00
CARNIVAL GLASS,GOBLET,MARIGOLD,ORANGE TREE..........  9.00 TO 10.00
CARNIVAL GLASS,GOBLET,WINE,BLUE,ORANGE TREE...............     35.00
CARNIVAL GLASS,GOBLET,WINE,MARIGOLD,FLUTE,ADVERTISING SPRING
  VALLEY,WIS.............................................       22.00
CARNIVAL GLASS,HAT,BLUE-GREEN,PALE,PINK-LAVENDER BRIM,
  4 1/4 IN.HIGH..........................................       45.00
CARNIVAL GLASS,HAT,BLUE-GREEN,PALE,PINK-LAVENDER BRIM,
  7 IN.HIGH..............................................       65.00
CARNIVAL GLASS,HAT,BLUE,BLACKBERRY........................     10.00
CARNIVAL GLASS,HAT,BLUE,BLACKBERRY,BANDED.................     13.50
CARNIVAL GLASS,HAT,BLUE,FRENCH KNOTS......................     20.00
CARNIVAL GLASS,HAT,BLUE,HOLLY.............................     18.00
CARNIVAL GLASS,HAT,GREEN,FLOWERING DILL...................     19.50
CARNIVAL GLASS,HAT,GREEN,HOLLY............................     18.00
CARNIVAL GLASS,HAT,MARIGOLD,LACY,JOHN BRAND FURNITURE AD
  INSIDE.................................................       28.00
CARNIVAL GLASS,HAT,MARIGOLD,STORK & RUSHES................     12.00
CARNIVAL GLASS,HAT,MARIGOLD,4 1/2 IN. HIGH................      5.00
CARNIVAL GLASS,HAT,PURPLE,RUFFLED RIM,RIBBED DESIGN,MARKED N   20.00
CARNIVAL GLASS,HAT,RED,BLACKBERRY SPRAY,6 IN..............     85.00
CARNIVAL GLASS,HAT,RED,BLACKBERRY,5 IN....................    100.00
CARNIVAL GLASS,HATPIN HOLDER,GREEN,GRAPE & CABLE..........     75.00
CARNIVAL GLASS,HATPIN HOLDER,GREEN,GRAPE & CABLE,FOOTED,
  NORTHWOOD..............................................       65.00
CARNIVAL GLASS,HATPIN HOLDER,GREEN,GRAPE & CABLE,N MARK.....    95.00
CARNIVAL GLASS,HATPIN HOLDER,MARIGOLD,GRAPE & CABLE.......     65.00
CARNIVAL GLASS,HATPIN HOLDER,MARIGOLD,ORANGE TREE PATTERN...    60.00
CARNIVAL GLASS,HATPIN HOLDER,PURPLE,GRAPE & CABLE.. 58.00 TO 65.00
CARNIVAL GLASS,HATPIN HOLDER,PURPLE,GRAPE & CABLE, N MARK...    95.00
CARNIVAL GLASS,HATPIN HOLDER,PURPLE,GRAPE PATTERN,7 IN.TALL.    38.00
CARNIVAL GLASS,HATPIN,PURPLE,BUMBLEBEE............. 15.00 TO  16.00
CARNIVAL GLASS,HATPIN,PURPLE,BUMBLEBEE,SLEEVE BACK,5 3/4 IN.   20.00
CARNIVAL GLASS,HATPIN,PURPLE,BUTTERFLY....................     15.00
CARNIVAL GLASS,HATPIN,PURPLE,BUTTERFLY,SLEEVE BACK,5 3/4 IN.   20.00
CARNIVAL GLASS,HATPIN,PURPLE,FLYING BAT...................     18.00
CARNIVAL GLASS,HATPIN,PURPLE,FLYING BAT,SLEEVE BACK,
  5 3/4 IN..............................................       25.00
CARNIVAL GLASS,HATPIN,PURPLE,PLUM & STEM,SLEEVE BACK,
  5 3/4 IN..............................................       15.00
CARNIVAL GLASS,HATPIN,PURPLE,PLUMS & STEMS,5 3/4 IN.......     12.00
CARNIVAL GLASS,HEN ON NEST,MARIGOLD.......................     85.00
CARNIVAL GLASS,HOLDER,HATPIN,BLUE,ORANGE TREE.............     53.50
CARNIVAL GLASS,HOLDER,MATCH,BLUE,CRANE,CATTAILS ON TOP,FISH
  ON BOTTOM..............................................       10.00
CARNIVAL GLASS,INSULATOR,MARIGOLD.........................      8.50
CARNIVAL GLASS,INSULATOR,MARIGOLD,CORNING PYREX.... 14.00 TO 18.00
CARNIVAL GLASS,INSULATOR,MARIGOLD,LARGE...................     55.00
CARNIVAL GLASS,JACK-IN-THE-PULPIT VASE,MARIGOLD,11 IN......      9.00
CARNIVAL GLASS,JAR,BLUE,TREE DECOR,BEADED,COVER,3 X
  3 1/2 IN..............................................       45.00
CARNIVAL GLASS,JAR,CANDY,MARIGOLD,COVER,8 IN..............      7.50
CARNIVAL GLASS,JAR,CANDY,MARIGOLD,CRINKLED,LID,PEDESTAL.....    32.00
CARNIVAL GLASS,JAR,COOKIE,MARIGOLD,HOURGLASS & DAISY
  PATTERN,COVER.........................................       35.00
CARNIVAL GLASS,JAR,COOKIE,WHITE,GRAPE,THUMBPRINT,COVER,
  SIGNED N..............................................      185.00
```

```
CARNIVAL GLASS,JAR,CRACKER,GREEN,INVERTED FEATHER & HOBSTAR.        85.00
CARNIVAL GLASS,JAR,CRACKER,PURPLE,GRAPE & CABLE..............      275.00
CARNIVAL GLASS,JAR,PICKLE,MARIGOLD,GOLDEN FLOWERS...........        10.00
CARNIVAL GLASS,JAR,POWDER,BLUE,ORANGE TREE,COVER............        35.00
CARNIVAL GLASS,JAR,POWDER,GREEN,STRAWBERRY,LID..............        32.00
CARNIVAL GLASS,JAR,POWDER,MARIGOLD,BAMBI...................          4.00
CARNIVAL GLASS,JAR,POWDER,MARIGOLD,ORANGE TREE,COVER........        25.00
CARNIVAL GLASS,JAR,POWDER,MARIGOLD,VINTAGE,COVER............        19.00
CARNIVAL GLASS,JAR,POWDER,PURPLE,ORANGE TREE...............         30.00
CARNIVAL GLASS,JAR,TOBACCO,MARIGOLD,PALE,ILLINOIS DAISY,
  COVER.................................................            28.00
CARNIVAL GLASS,JAR,TOBACCO,MARIGOLD,SIGNED I.G.............         10.50
CARNIVAL GLASS,LADLE,MARIGOLD,CURVED HANDLE,5 IN...........         22.00
CARNIVAL GLASS,LAMP,MARIGOLD,METAL HOLDER.................          37.50
CARNIVAL GLASS,LAMP,MARIGOLD,ZIPPER,LOOP,NO.2 BURNER,
  7 IN.TALL.............................................           150.00
CARNIVAL GLASS,MUG,AMETHYST,FISH & CATTAIL.................         55.00
CARNIVAL GLASS,MUG,BLUE,ICE,HOLLY PATTERN.................           7.50
CARNIVAL GLASS,MUG,BLUE,ORANGE TREE.............. 15.00 TO          17.50
CARNIVAL GLASS,MUG,BLUE,STORK.............................          37.00
CARNIVAL GLASS,MUG,MARIGOLD,FISHERMAN.....................          85.00
CARNIVAL GLASS,MUG,MARIGOLD,LITTLE BO PEEP,3 IN.HIGH......          22.50
CARNIVAL GLASS,MUG,MARIGOLD,ORANGE TREE............. 8.00 TO        12.00
CARNIVAL GLASS,MUG,MARIGOLD,ROBIN RED BREAST..............          25.00
CARNIVAL GLASS,MUG,MARIGOLD,SINGING BIRDS,FLOWERS..........         15.00
CARNIVAL GLASS,MUG,MARIGOLD,SINGING BIRD,MARKED N.........           6.00
CARNIVAL GLASS,MUG,MARIGOLD,SINGING BIRD......... 15.00 TO          18.00
CARNIVAL GLASS,MUG,MARIGOLD,SINGING BIRD,MARKED N.........          18.00
CARNIVAL GLASS,MUG,MARIGOLD,STORK,RUSHES..................          17.00
CARNIVAL GLASS,MUG,MARIGOLD,VINTAGE BANDED................           5.50
CARNIVAL GLASS,MUG,PURPLE,FISHERMAN.......................          55.00
CARNIVAL GLASS,MUG,PURPLE,SINGING BIRD............ 23.00 TO         37.00
CARNIVAL GLASS,MUG,PURPLE,SINGING BIRD,N MARK...... 22.00 TO        23.00
CARNIVAL GLASS,MUG,SHAVING,MARIGOLD,ROBIN.................          23.75
CARNIVAL GLASS,NAPPIE,GREEN,LUSTER FLUTE,HANDLE...........          15.00
CARNIVAL GLASS,NAPPIE,GREEN,STIPPLED RAY,MARKED N.........          15.00
CARNIVAL GLASS,NAPPIE,MARIGOLD,LEAF RAYS..................           8.00
CARNIVAL GLASS,NAPPIE,MARIGOLD,LEAF RAYS,HANDLE...........          11.00
CARNIVAL GLASS,NAPPIE,MARIGOLD,QUESTION MARK..............           8.00
CARNIVAL GLASS,NAPPIE,PURPLE,BUTTERFLY,MARKED N...........          35.00
CARNIVAL GLASS,NAPPIE,PURPLE,BUTTERFLY,NORTHWOOD..........          30.00
CARNIVAL GLASS,NAPPIE,PURPLE,FANTASY PATTERN,TWO HANDLES,
  FOOTED................................................            22.50
CARNIVAL GLASS,NAPPIE,PURPLE,OLIVE BRANCH & INDIA-TYPE
  DECOR,MARKED..........................................            22.50
CARNIVAL GLASS,NAPPIE,WHITE,STAR MEDALLION IN CENTER,
  6 IN.WIDE,PAIR........................................            15.00
CARNIVAL GLASS,ORANGE BOWL,MARIGOLD,GRAPE & CABLE..........         40.00
CARNIVAL GLASS,PARFAIT,GREEN,FLUTE PATTERN,5 1/4 X 5 1/4 IN.
  HIGH..................................................            10.00
CARNIVAL GLASS,PITCHER,AMETHYST,GRAPE,FLUTED RIM,BULBOUS,SIX
  TUMBLERS..............................................           145.00
CARNIVAL GLASS,PITCHER,BLUE,ENAMELED CHERRY,8 TUMBLERS......       100.00
CARNIVAL GLASS,PITCHER,BLUE,ICE,RASPBERRY,BASKET WEAVE......       125.00
CARNIVAL GLASS,PITCHER,BLUE,IMPERIAL GRAPE.................         75.00
CARNIVAL GLASS,PITCHER,GREEN,IMPERIAL GRAPE,TWO TUMBLERS....        65.00
CARNIVAL GLASS,PITCHER,GREEN,PEACH PATTERN,GILT,N MARK,FOUR
  TUMBLERS..............................................            70.00
CARNIVAL GLASS,PITCHER,MARIGOLD,APPLE TREE,FIVE TUMBLERS....        85.00
CARNIVAL GLASS,PITCHER,MARIGOLD,BUTTERFLY & BERRY,6 TUMBLERS        70.00
CARNIVAL GLASS,PITCHER,MARIGOLD,FLORAL & GRAPE,SIX TUMBLERS.        85.00
CARNIVAL GLASS,PITCHER,MARIGOLD,GRAPE & CABLE..............         79.00
CARNIVAL GLASS,PITCHER,MARIGOLD,GRAPE & LATTICE,TANKARD,
  4 TUMBLERS............................................            75.00
CARNIVAL GLASS,PITCHER,MARIGOLD,LATTICE & GRAPE,6 TUMBLERS..        75.00
CARNIVAL GLASS,PITCHER,MARIGOLD,POINSETTIA......... 15.00 TO        24.00
CARNIVAL GLASS,PITCHER,MARIGOLD,RASPBERRY,NORTHWOOD,
  4 TUMBLERS............................................            75.00
CARNIVAL GLASS,PITCHER,MARIGOLD,ROSE PATTERN,SIX TUMBLERS...        67.50
CARNIVAL GLASS,PITCHER,MARIGOLD,SINGING BIRD...............         79.00
CARNIVAL GLASS,PITCHER,MARIGOLD,TIGER LILY,2 TUMBLERS.......        55.00
CARNIVAL GLASS,PITCHER,MARIGOLD,WINDMILL..................          40.00
CARNIVAL GLASS,PITCHER,MILK,GREEN,RASPBERRY,NORTHWOOD.......        50.00
CARNIVAL GLASS,PITCHER,MILK,MARIGOLD,POINSETTIA.... 25.00 TO        27.50
CARNIVAL GLASS,PITCHER,MILK,MARIGOLD,STAR MEDALLION,
  6 IN.HIGH............................................            15.00
CARNIVAL GLASS,PITCHER,MILK,MARIGOLD,WINDMILL.............          17.50
CARNIVAL GLASS,PITCHER,MILK,PURPLE,BLACKBERRY,BASKET WEAVE..        60.00
CARNIVAL GLASS,PITCHER,MILK,PURPLE,RASPBERRY,MARKED N.......        45.00
CARNIVAL GLASS,PITCHER,PURPLE,BULBOUS,HAND-PAINTED,TWO
  TUMBLERS..............................................            50.00
```

CARNIVAL GLASS,PITCHER,PURPLE,DIAMOND PATTERN............... 48.00
CARNIVAL GLASS,PITCHER,PURPLE,GRAPE & CABLE,SIX TUMBLERS,N
MARK....................................................... 225.00
CARNIVAL GLASS,PITCHER,PURPLE,GRAPE & CABLE,THUMBPRINT,
4 TUMBLERS................................................. 148.50
CARNIVAL GLASS,PITCHER,PURPLE,IMPERIAL GRAPE,6 TUMBLERS..... 225.00
CARNIVAL GLASS,PITCHER,TANKARD,MARIGOLD,GRAPE & LATTICE..... 47.00
CARNIVAL GLASS,PITCHER,TANKARD,MARIGOLD,TEN MUMS............ 75.00
CARNIVAL GLASS,PITCHER,WATER,AMETHYST,GRAPE PATTERN,
6 TUMBLERS................................................. 145.00
CARNIVAL GLASS,PITCHER,WATER,BLUE,ICE,PEACOCK AT FOUNTAIN,N
MARK....................................................... 210.00
CARNIVAL GLASS,PITCHER,WATER,BLUE,PAINTED CHERRIES,
12 TUMBLERS................................................ 115.00
CARNIVAL GLASS,PITCHER,WATER,BLUE,PEACOCK AT FOUNTAIN,FIVE
TUMBLERS................................................... 225.00
CARNIVAL GLASS,PITCHER,WATER,GREEN,DIAMOND,MILLERSBURG..... 74.00
CARNIVAL GLASS,PITCHER,WATER,GREEN,RASPBERRY,N MARK........ 85.00
CARNIVAL GLASS,PITCHER,WATER,GREEN,TANKARD,SWIRL RIB....... 125.00
CARNIVAL GLASS,PITCHER,WATER,MARIGOLD,BUTTERFLY & BERRY.... 30.00
CARNIVAL GLASS,PITCHER,WATER,MARIGOLD,COLONIAL PATTERN,RIB
SWIRL INSIDE............................................... 32.00
CARNIVAL GLASS,PITCHER,WATER,MARIGOLD,GRAPE,GOTHIC ARCHES,
6 TUMBLERS................................................. 75.00
CARNIVAL GLASS,PITCHER,WATER,MARIGOLD,GRAPE & CABLE........ 95.00
CARNIVAL GLASS,PITCHER,WATER,MARIGOLD,IMPERIAL GRAPE,
6 TUMBLERS................................................. 80.00
CARNIVAL GLASS,PITCHER,WATER,MARIGOLD,MAPLE LEAF,NORTHWOOD,
4 TUMBLERS................................................. 60.00
CARNIVAL GLASS,PITCHER,WATER,MARIGOLD,NESTING PEACOCK...... 65.00
CARNIVAL GLASS,PITCHER,WATER,MARIGOLD,ORANGE TREE,FOOTED... 35.00
CARNIVAL GLASS,PITCHER,WATER,MARIGOLD,ROBIN............... 89.00
CARNIVAL GLASS,PITCHER,WATER,MARIGOLD,SINGING BIRD......... 95.00
CARNIVAL GLASS,PITCHER,WATER,MARIGOLD,TREE BARK PATTERN,
6 TUMBLERS................................................. 25.00
CARNIVAL GLASS,PITCHER,WATER,MARIGOLD,VINEYARD............ 29.00
CARNIVAL GLASS,PITCHER,WATER,PURPLE,DIAMOND LACE,6 TUMBLERS. 195.00
CARNIVAL GLASS,PITCHER,WATER,PURPLE,DIAMOND LACE.......... 100.00
CARNIVAL GLASS,PITCHER,WATER,PURPLE,GRAPE,N MARK,6 TUMBLERS. 189.50
CARNIVAL GLASS,PITCHER,WATER,PURPLE,GRAPE & CABLE,
6.....................................................150.00 TO 235.00
CARNIVAL GLASS,PITCHER,WATER,PURPLE,IMPERIAL GRAPE......... 75.00
CARNIVAL GLASS,PITCHER,WATER,WHITE,PEACOCK AT FOUNTAIN..... 225.00
CARNIVAL GLASS,PITCHER,WATER,WHITE,RIBBED................. 95.00
CARNIVAL GLASS,PLATE,AMETHYST,THREE FRUITS,9-IN.DIAMETER.... 35.00
CARNIVAL GLASS,PLATE,BLUE-PURPLE,IMPERIAL ROSE,BASKET WEAVE,
9 1/2 IN................................................... 30.00
CARNIVAL GLASS,PLATE,BLUE,GRAPE & CABLE,FOOTED,
8-IN.DIAMETER,3 IN.HIGH.................................... 40.00
CARNIVAL GLASS,PLATE,BLUE,GRAPE & CABLE,FOOTED,9-IN.DIAMETER 65.00
CARNIVAL GLASS,PLATE,BLUE,HOLLY........................... 65.00
CARNIVAL GLASS,PLATE,BLUE,PERSIAN MEDALLION,9 IN........... 50.00
CARNIVAL GLASS,PLATE,BLUE,THREE FRUITS,AUSTRALIA,7 1/2 IN... 30.00
CARNIVAL GLASS,PLATE,CAKE,ORANGE,GRAPE EDGE,CLEAR,CENTER
HANDLE..................................................... 18.00
CARNIVAL GLASS,PLATE,CAKE,PURPLE,BUTTERFLY,BUSH,AUSTRALIA... 200.00
CARNIVAL GLASS,PLATE,CAKE,WATER LILIES.................... 50.00
CARNIVAL GLASS,PLATE,CHOP,GREEN,HEAVY GRAPE,12 IN.......... 80.00
CARNIVAL GLASS,PLATE,CHOP,MARIGOLD,GRAPE,FENTON,11 1/4 IN... 60.00
CARNIVAL GLASS,PLATE,GREEN,ADVERTISING ROSE WINES & LIQUORS. 65.00
CARNIVAL GLASS,PLATE,GREEN,GRAPE & CABLE,STIPPLED,9 IN...... 35.00
CARNIVAL GLASS,PLATE,GREEN,HEAVY GRAPE,8-IN.DIAMETER........ 22.50
CARNIVAL GLASS,PLATE,GREEN,ICE,GRAPE & CABLE,FOOTED,
9-IN.DIAMETER.............................................. 80.00
CARNIVAL GLASS,PLATE,GREEN,ICE,PEACOCK ON FENCE,SCALLOPED,
RAYS,9 IN.................................................. 95.00
CARNIVAL GLASS,PLATE,GREEN,PASTEL,PEACOCK PATTERN,N MARK,
9 IN....................................................... 90.00
CARNIVAL GLASS,PLATE,GREEN,STRAWBERRY..................... 45.00
CARNIVAL GLASS,PLATE,GREEN,STRAWBERRY,N MARK,9 IN.......... 55.00
CARNIVAL GLASS,PLATE,GREEN,STRAWBERRY,9 IN................ 38.00
CARNIVAL GLASS,PLATE,GREEN,VINTAGE GRAPE,7 1/4-IN.DIAMETER.. 27.50
CARNIVAL GLASS,PLATE,GREEN,WILD STRAWBERRY,N MARK,7 1/2 IN.. 43.00
CARNIVAL GLASS,PLATE,MARIGOLD,APPLE BLOSSOM TWIGS,SATIN
FINISH,9 IN................................................ 20.00
CARNIVAL GLASS,PLATE,MARIGOLD,GRAPE & CABLE............... 22.00
CARNIVAL GLASS,PLATE,MARIGOLD,HEAVY GRAPE,7 1/2-IN.DIAMETER. 18.00
CARNIVAL GLASS,PLATE,MARIGOLD,HOLLY & BERRY,FOOTED,9 1/2 IN. 24.00
CARNIVAL GLASS,PLATE,MARIGOLD,HOLLY,10 IN................. 20.00
CARNIVAL GLASS,PLATE,MARIGOLD,HOMESTEAD,SIGNED NU ART....... 395.00
CARNIVAL GLASS,PLATE,MARIGOLD,IMPERIAL GRAPE,6 1/2 IN....... 6.00

```
CARNIVAL GLASS,PLATE,MARIGOLD,LUSTER,ROSE,9 IN..............    18.00
CARNIVAL GLASS,PLATE,MARIGOLD,PEARS,PEACHES,CHERRIES,BASKET
   WEAVE,N MARK............................................    24.00
CARNIVAL GLASS,PLATE,MARIGOLD,SODA GOLD,TREE OF LIFE,8 IN...     6.50
CARNIVAL GLASS,PLATE,MARIGOLD,SPECTORS DEPARTMENT STORE,
   9 1/2 IN...............................................     70.00
CARNIVAL GLASS,PLATE,MARIGOLD,STRAWBERRY BASKET WEAVE.......    25.00
CARNIVAL GLASS,PLATE,MARIGOLD,THREE FRUITS.................     25.00
CARNIVAL GLASS,PLATE,MARIGOLD,WINDFLOWER,9 IN...............    35.00
CARNIVAL GLASS,PLATE,PURPLE,GRAPE & CABLE,FOOTED............    65.00
CARNIVAL GLASS,PLATE,PURPLE,GRAPE & CABLE,BASKETWEAVE BACK,
   9 IN....................................................    40.00
CARNIVAL GLASS,PLATE,PURPLE,HONEYCOMB,RIBBON RIM,6 IN.......    17.00
CARNIVAL GLASS,PLATE,PURPLE,THREE FRUITS,N MARK,9 1/2 IN....    40.00
CARNIVAL GLASS,PLATE,PURPLE,THREE FRUITS,SAWTOOTH RIM,MARKED
   N......................................................     35.00
CARNIVAL GLASS,PLATE,PURPLE,THREE FRUITS,9 IN. X 1 1/2 IN...    42.50
CARNIVAL GLASS,PLATE,PURPLE,THREE FRUITS........... 32.00 TO    35.00
CARNIVAL GLASS,PLATE,RED-ORANGE,ROSES SPRAYS IN CENTER,
   9 1/4 IN................................................    25.00
CARNIVAL GLASS,PLATE,WALL,MARIGOLD,PANELS,15 IN.............    17.00
CARNIVAL GLASS,PLATE,WHITE,IMPERIAL JEWEL,STRETCH
   GLASS............................................ 14.00 TO    15.00
CARNIVAL GLASS,PLATE,WHITE,PEACOCK AT URN..................     75.00
CARNIVAL GLASS,PLATE,WHITE,PEACOCK ON FENCE,PANELS,
   SCALLOPED,9 1/4 IN......................................    52.50
CARNIVAL GLASS,PLATE,WHITE,PEACOCK ON THE FENCE............    120.00
CARNIVAL GLASS,PLATE,WHITE,THREE FRUITS,1 1/2 X 10 IN.......    50.00
CARNIVAL GLASS,PLATTER,MARIGOLD,OVAL,BOUQUET & LATTICE,
   12 IN.LONG..............................................     3.75
CARNIVAL GLASS,POWDER,MARIGOLD,VINTAGE,COVER...............     32.00
CARNIVAL GLASS,PUNCH BOWL,PURPLE,ORANGE TREE.........ILLUS..   185.00
CARNIVAL GLASS,PUNCH SET,PURPLE,MANY FRUITS,BOWL,BASE,SIX
   CUPS...................................................    290.00
```

ORANGE TREE CARNIVAL GLASS PUNCH BOWL

```
CARNIVAL GLASS,PURPLE,STRAWBERRY PATTERN,MARKED N,8 1/2 IN..    25.00
CARNIVAL GLASS,RELISH,MARIGOLD,IMPERIAL PANSY,OVAL.........     30.00
CARNIVAL GLASS,SALT,GREEN,SWAN............................     16.00
CARNIVAL GLASS,SALT,MASTER,BLUE,PASTEL,SWAN...............     25.00
CARNIVAL GLASS,SAUCE,BLUE,PASTEL,PEACOCK AT FOUNTAIN,N MARK.    22.50
CARNIVAL GLASS,SAUCE,CHERRY,FENTON,5 1/2 IN................     10.00
CARNIVAL GLASS,SAUCE,GREEN,COSMOS,MILLERSBURG.............     18.00
CARNIVAL GLASS,SAUCE,MARIGOLD,ACORN BURR,N MARK...........     12.00
CARNIVAL GLASS,SAUCE,MARIGOLD,BUTTERFLY & BERRY,FOOTED.....     6.50
CARNIVAL GLASS,SAUCE,MARIGOLD,CHERRY CIRCLES,ORANGE TREE
   EXTERIOR,5 IN...........................................    10.00
CARNIVAL GLASS,SAUCE,MARIGOLD,LUSTER ROSE.................      3.00
CARNIVAL GLASS,SAUCE,MARIGOLD,LUSTER ROSE,RUFFLED..........     6.00
CARNIVAL GLASS,SAUCE,MARIGOLD,PANTHER,6 IN................     16.00
CARNIVAL GLASS,SAUCE,PURPLE,EMBOSSED GRAPE,5 IN...........     19.00
CARNIVAL GLASS,SAUCE,PURPLE,GRAPE & THUMBPRINT,MARKED N,
   5 IN....................................................    15.00
CARNIVAL GLASS,SAUCEBOAT,PURPLE,FAN.......................     45.00
CARNIVAL GLASS,SAUCER,MARIGOLD,KITTEN.....................     32.00
CARNIVAL GLASS,SAUCER,MARIGOLD,THREE KITTENS,AUSTRALIA,
   4 1/2 IN................................................    30.00
CARNIVAL GLASS,SHADE,GAS,MARIGOLD,MAYFLOWER,PAIR..........     20.00
CARNIVAL GLASS,SHADE,LIGHT,MARIGOLD,SIGNED NU ART,PAIR.....    18.50
CARNIVAL GLASS,SHADE,LIGHT,WHITE..........................     1.50
CARNIVAL GLASS,SHADE,LIGHT,WHITE,QUILTED,5 IN.HIGH,PAIR....    12.00
CARNIVAL GLASS,SHAKER,SALT,BLUE,TREE OF LIFE..............     55.00
CARNIVAL GLASS,SHELL,WHITE................................    325.00
CARNIVAL GLASS,SHERBET,GREEN,LIME,FLUTED,N MARK...........     15.00
CARNIVAL GLASS,SHERBET,MARIGOLD,BOUQUET & LATTICE,PEDESTAL
```

```
STEM,SET OF 7.....................................    15.00
CARNIVAL GLASS,SHERBET,MARIGOLD,BOUQUET & LATTICE PATTERN,
  FOOTED..........................................     1.50
CARNIVAL GLASS,SHERBET,MARIGOLD,HOLLY..............     6.00
CARNIVAL GLASS,SHERBET,MARIGOLD,HOLLY & BERRY......     8.00
CARNIVAL GLASS,SHERBET,MARIGOLD,HOLLY,LIGHT GREEN STEM &
  BASE............................................    11.00
CARNIVAL GLASS,SHERBET,MARIGOLD,IRIS,HERRINGBONE,FOOTED.....     3.50
CARNIVAL GLASS,SHERBET,MARIGOLD,ORANGE TREE,STEMMED.........     8.00
CARNIVAL GLASS,SHERBET,MARIGOLD,STIPPLED.MATCHING SAUCER,SET
  OF 4............................................    40.00
CARNIVAL GLASS,SPOONER,AMETHYST,MARK N.............    45.00
CARNIVAL GLASS,SPOONER,GREEN,LUSTER ROSE...........    20.00
CARNIVAL GLASS,SPOONER,MARIGOLD,BUTTERFLY & BERRY,THREE BALL
  & CLAW FEET......................................    26.50
CARNIVAL GLASS,SPOONER,MARIGOLD,BUTTERFLY & BERRY..    12.50
CARNIVAL GLASS,SPOONER,MARIGOLD,HOBSTAR............    15.00
CARNIVAL GLASS,SPOONER,MARIGOLD,KITTEN.............    38.00
CARNIVAL GLASS,SPOONER,MARIGOLD,KITTENS,2 1/2 IN...    55.00
CARNIVAL GLASS,SPOONER,MARIGOLD,PEACOCK AT FOUNTAIN    25.00
CARNIVAL GLASS,SPOONER,ORANGE,BUTTERFLY & BERRY....    18.00
CARNIVAL GLASS,SPOONER,PURPLE,ACORN & BURR.........  35.00 TO   50.00
CARNIVAL GLASS,SPOONER,PURPLE,GRAPE & CABLE,N MARK.    60.00
CARNIVAL GLASS,SPOONER,PURPLE,LUSTER ROSE,2-HANDLED    20.00
CARNIVAL GLASS,SUGAR & CREAMER,MARIGOLD,MILLERSBURG CHERRIES    40.00
CARNIVAL GLASS,SUGAR,GREEN,DARK,IMPERIAL PANSY.....    15.00
CARNIVAL GLASS,SUGAR,GREEN,LUSTER FLUTE,HANDLE.....    15.00
CARNIVAL GLASS,SUGAR,GREEN,SHELL & JEWEL,COVER,5 1/2 IN.TALL    20.00
CARNIVAL GLASS,SUGAR,MARIGOLD,STAR & FILE..........    10.00
CARNIVAL GLASS,SUGAR,PURPLE,ACORN & BURR,COVER.....    85.00
CARNIVAL GLASS,SUGAR,PURPLE,ACORN & BURR,OVAL SHAPE,MARKED N    35.00
CARNIVAL GLASS,SUGAR,PURPLE,GRAPE,CABLE,COVER......    45.00
CARNIVAL GLASS,SUGAR,PURPLE,LUSTER FLUTE,N MARK....    12.00
CARNIVAL GLASS,SWAN,BLUE,PASTEL....................    18.00
CARNIVAL GLASS,SWAN,GREEN,PASTEL...................    15.00
CARNIVAL GLASS,SWAN,MARIGOLD,AUSTRALIA,9 1/2 IN....    73.00
CARNIVAL GLASS,SWAN,PURPLE,MILLERSBURG.............    95.00
CARNIVAL GLASS,SWEETMEAT,PURPLE,GRAPE,CABLE........   120.00
  CARNIVAL GLASS,TOOTHPICK HOLDER,SEE TOOTHPICK
CARNIVAL GLASS,TRAY,DRESSER,MARIGOLD,GRAPE,CABLE...    37.50
CARNIVAL GLASS,TRAY,MARIGOLD,GRAPE,CENTER HANDLE,10 IN......    16.50
CARNIVAL GLASS,TRAY,PIN,MARIGOLD,GRAPE,CABLE,SCALLOPED......    40.00
CARNIVAL GLASS,TRAY,PIN,PURPLE,GRAPE,CABLE.........    80.00
CARNIVAL GLASS,TRAY,PIN,WHITE,BUTTERFLY,FOOTED.....    48.00
CARNIVAL GLASS,TUMBLER,BLUE,BUTTERFLY & BERRY......  15.00 TO   26.00
CARNIVAL GLASS,TUMBLER,BLUE,ELECTRIC,PEACOCK AT THE FOUNTAIN    25.00
CARNIVAL GLASS,TUMBLER,BLUE,ENAMELED CHERRIES......    13.50
CARNIVAL GLASS,TUMBLER,BLUE,FLORAL & GRAPE.........    15.00
CARNIVAL GLASS,TUMBLER,BLUE,GRAPE & GOTHIC ARCHES..    14.00
CARNIVAL GLASS,TUMBLER,BLUE,LATTICE & GRAPE........    15.00
CARNIVAL GLASS,TUMBLER,BLUE,ORANGE TREE,FOOTED.....   155.00
CARNIVAL GLASS,TUMBLER,BLUE,PEACOCK AT FOUNTAIN....    20.00
CARNIVAL GLASS,TUMBLER,BLUE,STORK IN RUSHES........  15.00 TO   17.00
CARNIVAL GLASS,TUMBLER,GREEN,DAISY,PANELED.........    12.50
CARNIVAL GLASS,TUMBLER,GREEN,DANDELION,N MARK......    20.00
CARNIVAL GLASS,TUMBLER,GREEN,IMPERIAL GRAPE........    14.00
CARNIVAL GLASS,TUMBLER,GREEN,MORNING GLORY.........   185.00
CARNIVAL GLASS,TUMBLER,GREEN,ORIENTAL POPPY........  15.00 TO   20.00
CARNIVAL GLASS,TUMBLER,GREEN,PANELED DANDELION,SET OF 6.....    90.00
CARNIVAL GLASS,TUMBLER,GREEN,SINGING BIRD,N MARK...    17.50
CARNIVAL GLASS,TUMBLER,GREEN,THUMBPRINT & DIAMOND..    15.00
CARNIVAL GLASS,TUMBLER,GREEN,TIGER LILY............    15.00
CARNIVAL GLASS,TUMBLER,MARIGOLD,APPLE TREE.........  8.00 TO    9.00
CARNIVAL GLASS,TUMBLER,MARIGOLD,BUTTERFLY & BERRY..     7.50
CARNIVAL GLASS,TUMBLER,MARIGOLD,CRAB APPLE PATTERN.     7.00
CARNIVAL GLASS,TUMBLER,MARIGOLD,FLORAL & GRAPE.....     7.50
CARNIVAL GLASS,TUMBLER,MARIGOLD,FLORAL,GRAPEVINE...     6.00
CARNIVAL GLASS,TUMBLER,MARIGOLD,GRAPE..............     7.50
CARNIVAL GLASS,TUMBLER,MARIGOLD,GRAPE & CABLE......    10.00
CARNIVAL GLASS,TUMBLER,MARIGOLD,GRAPE ARBOR........    10.00
CARNIVAL GLASS,TUMBLER,MARIGOLD,GRAPES,MAPLE LEAVES,N MARK..    16.00
CARNIVAL GLASS,TUMBLER,MARIGOLD,GRAPEVINE & LATTICE    6.00
CARNIVAL GLASS,TUMBLER,MARIGOLD,IMPERIAL GRAPE,N MARK.......    15.00
CARNIVAL GLASS,TUMBLER,MARIGOLD,IMPERIAL GRAPE.....     8.00
CARNIVAL GLASS,TUMBLER,MARIGOLD,IRIS & HERRINGBONE,FOOTED,
  6 IN.,SET OF 4..................................    10.00
CARNIVAL GLASS,TUMBLER,MARIGOLD,MAPLE LEAF.........     7.50
CARNIVAL GLASS,TUMBLER,MARIGOLD,MILLERSBURG DIAMOND BAND....    10.00
CARNIVAL GLASS,TUMBLER,MARIGOLD,MUMS...............     8.50
CARNIVAL GLASS,TUMBLER,MARIGOLD,ORANGE TREE,FOOTED.    14.00
CARNIVAL GLASS,TUMBLER,MARIGOLD,PASTEL,LATTICE,DAISY.......     6.00
```

```
CARNIVAL GLASS,TUMBLER,MARIGOLD,RAMBLER ROSE...............        10.00
CARNIVAL GLASS,TUMBLER,MARIGOLD,RASPBERRY,N MARK...........        15.00
CARNIVAL GLASS,TUMBLER,MARIGOLD,ROBIN.....................        28.00
CARNIVAL GLASS,TUMBLER,MARIGOLD,STAR MEDALLION PATTERN,SET
   OF FIVE...........................................        30.00
CARNIVAL GLASS,TUMBLER,MARIGOLD,STORK IN RUSHES..... 5.00 TO       10.00
CARNIVAL GLASS,TUMBLER,MARIGOLD,VINEYARD,SET OF 6.........        55.00
CARNIVAL GLASS,TUMBLER,MARIGOLD,WATER LILY & CATTAIL........        8.00
CARNIVAL GLASS,TUMBLER,MARIGOLD,WATER LILY & CATTAILS,N MARK       16.00
CARNIVAL GLASS,TUMBLER,MARIGOLD,5 IN.....................         1.75
CARNIVAL GLASS,TUMBLER,ORANGE,FLORAL,GRAPEVINE..............        8.50
CARNIVAL GLASS,TUMBLER,PURPLE,PEACOCK AT FOUNTAIN....ILLUS..       15.00
CARNIVAL GLASS,TUMBLER,PURPLE,ACORN BURR.................        30.00
CARNIVAL GLASS,TUMBLER,PURPLE,BUTTERFLY,PLUME.............        20.00
CARNIVAL GLASS,TUMBLER,PURPLE,DAISY,PANELED..............        12.50
CARNIVAL GLASS,TUMBLER,PURPLE,DIAMOND LACE...............        12.50
CARNIVAL GLASS,TUMBLER,PURPLE,FLORAL,GRAPEVINE..............       11.00
CARNIVAL GLASS,TUMBLER,PURPLE,GRAPE & CABLE........ 13.00 TO       15.00
CARNIVAL GLASS,TUMBLER,PURPLE,GRAPE & CABLE,MARKED. 12.00 TO       15.00
CARNIVAL GLASS,TUMBLER,PURPLE,GRAPE & CABLE,SET OF 6.........       95.00
CARNIVAL GLASS,TUMBLER,PURPLE,GRAPE PATTERN,SIGNED.........       14.00
CARNIVAL GLASS,TUMBLER,PURPLE,MAPLE LEAF,SET OF 6...........      120.00
CARNIVAL GLASS,TUMBLER,PURPLE,MARILYN,MILLERSBURG...........       37.00
```

CARNIVAL GLASS TUMBLER, PEACOCK AT FOUNTAIN

```
CARNIVAL GLASS,TUMBLER,PURPLE,MILLERSBURG DIAMOND PATTERN...       15.00
CARNIVAL GLASS,TUMBLER,PURPLE,PEACOCK,N MARK................       22.00
CARNIVAL GLASS,TUMBLER,PURPLE,STORK IN BULLRUSHES...........       12.00
CARNIVAL GLASS,TUMBLER,PURPLE,THUMBPRINT & DIAMOND..........       15.00
CARNIVAL GLASS,TUMBLER,WHITE,BLUEBERRY....................        36.00
CARNIVAL GLASS,TUMBLER,WHITE,GRAPE & LATTICE...............        35.00
CARNIVAL GLASS,TUMBLER,WHITE,ORANGE TREE,FOOTED............        30.00
CARNIVAL GLASS,TUMBLER,WHITE,ORIENTAL POPPY...............        36.00
CARNIVAL GLASS,TUMBLER,WHITE,ORIENTAL POPPY,N MARK.........        40.00
CARNIVAL GLASS,TUMBLER,WHITE,PEACH PATTERN,PEACHES IN GOLD,
   MARKED N...........................................        30.00
CARNIVAL GLASS,TUMBLER,WHITE,WREATHED CHERRY..............        30.00
CARNIVAL GLASS,VASE,AMETHYST,DRAPERY,NORTHWOOD,8 3/4 IN.HIGH       14.00
CARNIVAL GLASS,VASE,AMETHYST,FLARED TOP,RIBBED INTERIOR,
   12 1/2 IN..........................................        13.00
CARNIVAL GLASS,VASE,AMETHYST,RIBBED,8 IN.HIGH,2-IN.DIAMETER.       20.00
CARNIVAL GLASS,VASE,AQUA,THIN RIB,PAIR....................        49.00
CARNIVAL GLASS,VASE,AUTO,BLUE,NO HOLDER..................        16.50
CARNIVAL GLASS,VASE,AUTO,MARIGOLD,MARKED BENZER.............        6.00
CARNIVAL GLASS,VASE,AUTO,MARIGOLD,TREE OF LIFE,NO BRACKET...        9.00
CARNIVAL GLASS,VASE,BLUE BOTTOM TO PURPLE TOP,WIDE PANELS,
   12 IN.............................................        14.00
CARNIVAL GLASS,VASE,BLUE,DIAMOND,RIB,10 IN................        12.00
CARNIVAL GLASS,VASE,BLUE,FINE RIB,11 IN..................         9.00
CARNIVAL GLASS,VASE,BLUE,GRAPES,N MARK,16 IN..............        32.50
CARNIVAL GLASS,VASE,FLOWER,AUTO,MARIGOLD.................        10.00
CARNIVAL GLASS,VASE,GREEN TO ORANGE RUFFLED TOP,SIGNED N,
   10 IN.............................................        18.00
CARNIVAL GLASS,VASE,GREEN,FEATHER PATTERN................        12.00
CARNIVAL GLASS,VASE,GREEN,ICE,CORN,N MARK................       100.00
CARNIVAL GLASS,VASE,GREEN,ICE,CORN,NORTHWOOD.............        92.00
CARNIVAL GLASS,VASE,GREEN,ROSE COLUMN...................       225.00
CARNIVAL GLASS,VASE,MARIGOLD,BEADED BULL'S-EYE,11 IN........       12.00
CARNIVAL GLASS,VASE,MARIGOLD,BUTTERFLY & BERRIES,9 IN.......       18.00
CARNIVAL GLASS,VASE,MARIGOLD,CLEAR AT BOTTOM,OLD IMPERIAL
   MARK,9 1/2 IN......................................        18.00
CARNIVAL GLASS,VASE,MARIGOLD,CORN,N MARK.................       125.00
```

```
CARNIVAL GLASS,VASE,MARIGOLD,CORNUCOPIA.....................    15.00
CARNIVAL GLASS,VASE,MARIGOLD,FAN,5 IN. HIGH.................     3.50
CARNIVAL GLASS,VASE,MARIGOLD,FINE RIB,N MARK................     9.00
CARNIVAL GLASS,VASE,MARIGOLD,FLUTED TOP,10 IN.HIGH..........    10.50
CARNIVAL GLASS,VASE,MARIGOLD,IMPERIAL MARK ON BOTTOM,
   9 1/2 IN.................................................    15.00
CARNIVAL GLASS,VASE,MARIGOLD,IRIS,HERRINGBONE,9 IN.HIGH.....     4.75
CARNIVAL GLASS,VASE,MARIGOLD,RIBBED,FLARING RIM,11 3/4 IN...     5.50
CARNIVAL GLASS,VASE,MARIGOLD,RIPPLE,17 IN...................    14.00
CARNIVAL GLASS,VASE,MARIGOLD,RIPPLE,9 1/2 IN................    12.00
CARNIVAL GLASS,VASE,MARIGOLD,ROCOCO.........................    15.00
CARNIVAL GLASS,VASE,MARIGOLD,TREE BARK PATTERN,8 IN.HIGH....     5.00
CARNIVAL GLASS,VASE,MARIGOLD,TWIN RIB PATTERN,11 1/2 IN.HIGH     4.75
CARNIVAL GLASS,VASE,PURPLE,BUTTERFLY,9 IN...................    12.00
CARNIVAL GLASS,VASE,PURPLE,CIRCLED SCROLL,7 IN..............    30.00
CARNIVAL GLASS,VASE,PURPLE,DIAMOND POINT,N MARK,8 IN........    18.00
CARNIVAL GLASS,VASE,PURPLE,DIAMOND POINT,SCALLOPS...........    20.00
CARNIVAL GLASS,VASE,PURPLE,GOLD IRIDESCENT,MARKED N,
   11 1/2 IN.HIGH,PAIR......................................    15.00
CARNIVAL GLASS,VASE,PURPLE,LATTICE & POINTS,FLOWER IN BASE,
   6 1/2 IN.................................................    12.50
CARNIVAL GLASS,VASE,PURPLE,LOGANBERRY.......................    95.00
CARNIVAL GLASS,VASE,PURPLE,PULLED LOOP,5 1/2 IN.............    15.00
CARNIVAL GLASS,VASE,PURPLE,RIPPLE,11 IN.....................    19.00
CARNIVAL GLASS,VASE,PURPLE,RIPPLE,11 1/2 IN.................    35.00
CARNIVAL GLASS,VASE,PURPLE,RIPPLED THREADS,8 IN.............    12.50
CARNIVAL GLASS,VASE,PURPLE,TARGET,10 1/2 IN.................    15.00
CARNIVAL GLASS,VASE,PURPLE,THIN RIB,N MARK,10 IN............    14.00
CARNIVAL GLASS,VASE,PURPLE,TORNADO,RIB TYPE.................    45.00
CARNIVAL GLASS,VASE,PURPLE,TWIG.............................    29.00
CARNIVAL GLASS,VASE,RED,KNOTTED BEADS,11 IN.................    75.00
CARNIVAL GLASS,VASE,RED,RIB PATTERN,10 1/2 IN.HIGH,PAIR.....   150.00
CARNIVAL GLASS,VASE,RED,THIN RIB...........................    85.00
CARNIVAL GLASS,VASE,WALL,MARIGOLD,BIRD & GRAPES.............    10.00
CARNIVAL GLASS,VASE,WALL,MARIGOLD,TREE OF LIFE..............     3.00
CARNIVAL GLASS,VASE,WHITE,DIAMOND & RIB,3 1/4 IN.BASE,
   10 IN.HIGH...............................................    22.50
CARNIVAL GLASS,VASE,WHITE,FROSTY,LINED LATTICE,10 IN........    22.00
CARNIVAL GLASS,VASE,WHITE,LINED LATTICE PATTERN,PAIR........    35.00
CARNIVAL GLASS,VASE,WHITE,THIN-RIBBED,N MARK,3 1/2-IN.BASE,
   11 IN.HIGH...............................................    25.00
CARNIVAL GLASS,WATER SET,BLUE,BUTTERFLY & BERRY.............   275.00
CARNIVAL GLASS,WATER SET,BLUE,GOD & HOME.................1,650.00
CARNIVAL GLASS,WATER SET,BLUE,PEACOCK AT FOUNTAIN,N MARK,
   SEVEN PIECES.............................................   250.00
CARNIVAL GLASS,WATER SET,MARIGOLD,PEACOCK AT THE FOUNTAIN,
   SEVEN PIECES.............................................   140.00
CARNIVAL GLASS,WATER SET,MARIGOLD,IMPERIAL GRAPE,7 PIECES...    60.00
CARNIVAL GLASS,WATER SET,MARIGOLD,VINEYEARD PATTERN,7 PIECES    85.00
CARNIVAL GLASS,WATER SET,PURPLE,GRAPE & CABLE,SEVEN PIECES..   190.00
CARNIVAL GLASS,WATER SET,WHITE,ENAMELED FLOWERS,THREE BANDS,
   SIX PIECES...............................................   185.00
CARNIVAL GLASS,WINE SET,MARIGOLD,OCTAGON,7 PIECES...........    60.00
CARNIVAL GLASS,WINE,BLUE,ORANGE TREE,SILVER IRIDESCENT,
   STEMMED..................................................    16.00
CARNIVAL GLASS,WINE,GREEN,ORANGE TREE......................    15.00
CARNIVAL GLASS,WINE,MARIGOLD,IMPERIAL GRAPE................     6.50
CARNIVAL GLASS,WINE,MARIGOLD,IMPERIAL GRAPE,FOOTED.........     7.50
CARNIVAL GLASS,WINE,MARIGOLD,IRIS PATTERN,SET OF 5.........    15.00
CARNIVAL GLASS,WINE,MARIGOLD,OCTAGON.......................    10.00
CARNIVAL GLASS,WINE,MARIGOLD,OCTAGON,PEDESTAL STEM.........    11.50
CARNIVAL GLASS,WINE,MARIGOLD,SAILBOATS,CABLE TWISTED FROSTY
   STEM.....................................................    15.00
CARNIVAL GLASS,WINE,MARIGOLD,VINTAGE,STEMMED...............    10.00
CAROUSEL HORSE,CARVED,WOODEN,LARGE.........................   190.00
CAROUSEL HORSE,CARVED,WOODEN,MEDIUM........................   160.00
CAROUSEL HORSE,CARVED,WOODEN,SMALL.........................   130.00
CAROUSEL HORSE,GRAY,RED & BROWN SADDLE,53 IN.LONG..........   110.00
CAROUSEL HORSE,PONY SIZE...................................   450.00
CAROUSEL HORSE,PRANCING POSITION,EARS COCKED FORWARD,PAINT.   575.00
CAROUSEL HORSE,PRANCING POSITION,EARS COCKED FORWARD,5 FEET
   X 5 FEET.................................................   625.00
CAROUSEL HORSE,THREE SIZES,PLATFORM,MIRRORS,MOTOR,THIRTY
   HORSES...............................................8,000.00
```

CASTLEFORD POTTERY OF CASTLEFORD,YORKSHIRE,ENGLAND,WAS
MADE BY THE DAVID DUNDERDALE & CO. FROM 1790 TO 1820.

```
CASTLEFORD,TEAPOT..........................................   135.00
CASTLEFORD,TEAPOT,RAISED DESIGN,BLUE & BROWN DECOR,HINGED
   LID......................................................   135.00
```

CASTOR SETS HAVE BEEN KNOWN AS EARLY AS 1705. MOST OF THOSE THAT HAVE BEEN FOUND TODAY DATE FROM THE VICTORIAN TIMES. A CASTOR SET USUALLY CONSISTS OF A SILVER-PLATED FRAME THAT HOLDS THREE TO SEVEN CONDIMENT BOTTLES. THE PICKLE CASTOR WAS A SINGLE GLASS JAR ABOUT SIX INCHES HIGH AND HELD IN A SILVER FRAME. A COVER AND TONGS WERE KEPT WITH THE JAR. THEY WERE POPULAR FROM 1890 TO 1900.

```
CASTOR,PICKLE,BIRDS,FLORAL,CRYSTAL PRISM INSERT,LID,FINIAL,
  FORK,SILVER.................................................    39.50
CASTOR,PICKLE,BLUE THREADING,WHITE LOOPINGS,LIZZARD HEADS ON
  BASE,SILVER................................................   125.00
CASTOR,PICKLE,CANE & SUNBURST,FRAME...................ILLUS..    27.50
CASTOR,PICKLE,CANE PATTERN INSERT...........................    24.00
CASTOR,PICKLE,CLEAR,INVERTED THUMBPRINT,ENAMEL FLORAL,SILVER
  HOLDER.....................................................    59.50
CASTOR,PICKLE,CLEAR,LACY SILVER HOLDER,EMBOSSED FEET,
  HANDLES,TONGS..............................................    69.00
CASTOR,PICKLE,CRANBERRY INSERT,SILVER,TONGS.................    47.50
CASTOR,PICKLE,CRANBERRY,SILVER-PLATED FRAME BY JAS.TUFTS OF
  BOSTON,TONGS...............................................    75.00
CASTOR,PICKLE,CRANBERRY,THUMBPRINT,HOLDER...................    65.00
CASTOR,PICKLE,CUPID & PSYCHE,CLEAR,SILVER HOLDER,COVER,TONGS    35.00
CASTOR,PICKLE,CUPID & PSYCHE,CLEAR,SILVER HOLDER,FOOTED,
  COVER,TONGS................................................    47.50
```

CANE AND SUNBURST PICKLE CASTOR FRAME

```
CASTOR,PICKLE,DAISY & BUTTON,V ORNAMENT,AMBER,FOOTED,FORK...    75.00
CASTOR,PICKLE,DIAMOND-EMBOSSED,CRANBERRY WIDE STRIPE,SILVER
  HOLDER,TONGS...............................................    46.50
CASTOR,PICKLE,ELK MEDALLION,SILVER FRAME,TONGS,ACME CO.,
  10 1/2 IN.HIGH.............................................    45.00
CASTOR,PICKLE,EMBOSSED LEAF CORNERS & TOP,CLEAR,SILVER
  FRAME,COVER,TONGS..........................................    45.00
CASTOR,PICKLE,EMERALD GREEN GLASS,FLEUR-DE-LIS,LEAVES,SILVER
  HOLDER.....................................................    63.50
CASTOR,PICKLE,FROSTED STORK,WATER,CATTAILS,EMBOSSED SILVER
  HOLDER,TONGS...............................................    39.50
CASTOR,PICKLE,GREEN,FINE CUT LOWER HALF,FLEUR-DE-LIS,SILVER
  HOLDER,TONGS...............................................    65.00
CASTOR,PICKLE,INVERTED THUMBPRINT,CRANBERRY,SILVER HOLDER,
  HANDLE,TONGS...............................................    61.50
CASTOR,PICKLE,INVERTED THUMBPRINT,FOOTED SILVER HOLDER,
  TONGS,CRANBERRY............................................    59.50
CASTOR,PICKLE,LOOPS,PRESSED GLASS INSERT,EMBOSSED LID,
  SILVER,MERIDEN.............................................    36.00
CASTOR,PICKLE,ORNATE SILVER FRAME,LID,TONGS,CLEAR INSERT,
  BLOCK PATTERN..............................................    65.00
CASTOR,PICKLE,RIBBED INSERT,RAYED BASE,SILVER PLATE HOLDER,
  FORK.......................................................    31.00
CASTOR,PICKLE,SILVER PLATE,TONGS,ORNATE.....................    20.00
CASTOR,PICKLE,SMALL THUMBPRINT,ENAMELED FLORAL,AMBER,FORK,
  11 IN......................................................    85.00
CASTOR,PICKLE,THUMBPRINT,CRANBERRY,RESILVERED FRAME & TONGS,
  13 IN......................................................   110.00
CASTOR SET,CRUET,SALT,PEPPER,TOOTHPICK,REVERSE 'S,GREEN,
  FOOTED TRAY................................................    45.00
```

CASTOR SET,FIVE BOTTLES,ETCHED FLORAL ON SILVER FRAME.......    65.00
CASTOR SET,FIVE BOTTLES,RUBY OVERLAY,ROSE PATTERN,SILVER
   FRAME,REVOLVING.............................................   65.00
CASTOR SET,FIVE BOTTLES,SILVER PLATE FRAME...........ILLUS..    35.00
CASTOR SET,FOUR BOTTLES,BELLFLOWER,PEWTER STAND.............    95.00
CASTOR SET,FOUR BOTTLES,CUT GLASS,PRISM CUT,MULTIFACETED
   STOPPERS,HOLDER.............................................   43.00
CASTOR SET,FOUR BOTTLES,MINIATURE,PEWTER HOLDER.............    25.00
CASTOR SET,FOUR BOTTLES,PRISM CUT,FACETED STOPPERS,SILVER
   PLATE HOLDER................................................   36.00
CASTOR SET,FOUR BOTTLES,SILVER PLATE HOLDER,ROTATES........    45.00
CASTOR SET,FOUR BOTTLES,STAR CUTTING,PUNTIES,SPLITS,SILVER
   PLATE FRAME.................................................   75.00
CASTOR SET,FOUR BOTTLES,WATERFORD CUT,SHEFFIELD SILVER
   HOLDER,BALL FEET............................................   45.00
CASTOR SET,MINIATURE,FRAME,4 BOTTLES.......................    30.00
CASTOR SET,OPENWORK,FOOTED,SILVER HOLDER,6 THUMBPRINT,
   CRANBERRY BOTTLES...........................................  125.00
CASTOR SET,SIX MATCHING CRUETS,SILVER PLATE................    90.00


        CAULDON IS AN ENGLISH POTTERY FACTORY WORKING AFTER
     1905.
CAULDON,BOWL,SOUP,TRELLIS & FLORAL,CLEAR CENTER,9 1/2 IN.,
   SET OF 3....................................................   12.00
CAULDON,PLATE,HUNTING & CASTLE SCENES,BEADED,SCALLOPED,SET
   OF 6........................................................   90.00
CAULDON,PLATE,HUNTING SCENE,10 1/2 IN......................    21.50
CAULDON,PLATE,INDIAN TREE,10 1/2 IN........................    14.00
CAULDON,PLATE,MESSINA,FLOW BLUE,CIRCA 1845,SIGNED,ENGLAND,
   10 IN.......................................................   30.00
CAULDON,PLATE,MULTICOLORED FLORAL,COBALT VASE IN CENTER,
   9 IN.,SET OF 3..............................................   15.00

FIVE BOTTLE CASTOR SET, SILVER PLATE FRAME


        CELADON IS A CHINESE PORCELAIN HAVING A VELVET-TEXTURED
     GREEN-GRAY GLAZE. JAPANESE AND KOREAN FACTORIES ALSO
     MADE A CELADON COLORED GLAZE.
CELADON,BASIN,WOMEN,CHILD,GARDEN,FAMILY COLORS,11 5/8 X
   3 7/8 IN.TALL...............................................  200.00
CELADON,BOWL,BULB,DIAMOND SHAPE PANELS,FLORETS,MING DYNASTY,
   11 1/4 IN...................................................  200.00
CELADON,BOWL,INTERIOR INCISED,FLORAL,COMBED DECOR,SUNG
   DYNASTY,5 1/2 IN............................................  275.00
CELADON,BOWL,RICE,DARK GREEN BRANCHES,WHITE FLOWERS.........     6.50
CELADON,BOX,WHITE,GREEN & BROWN GRASSES & FLORAL,GREEN,
   WHITE,ENGLAND...............................................   12.00
CELADON,CREAMER,SUGAR,BLUE,GREEN,WHITE CHRYSANTHEMUM,LEAVES,
   BRANCHES....................................................   50.00
CELADON,DISH,PLANTER,BLUE & WHITE FLORAL,8 IN. X 5 3/4 IN. X
   2 1/2 IN....................................................   17.95
CELADON,FIGURINE,SCHOLAR,ROBE,HAT,BOOK,SEATED,10 IN.HIGH....   125.00
CELADON,JARDINIERE,RAISED WHITE FLORAL,BLUE LEAVES,

HEXAGONAL,8 IN.......................................... 65.00
CELADON,MATCH SAFE,WALL,GREEN,MAPLE LEAF,BERRIES,GREEN
LEAVES................................................. 12.00
CELADON,PLATE,FAMILLE ROSE,ENAMELED,BIRDS,BUTTERFLIES,
FLORAL,10 IN........................................... 47.50
CELADON,UMBRELLA STAND,24 IN.HIGH,10 IN.DIAMETER........... 225.00
CELADON,UMBRELLA STAND,OPENWORK BAND TOP,FLOWER DECOR.... 250.00
CELADON,VASE,BRUSH FORM,ROSEWOOD STAND,4 IN.HIGH........ 285.00
CELADON,VASE,GREEN & WHITE DECOR,HEXAGONAL,11 IN.HIGH...... 25.00
CELADON,VASE,IRIS DECOR,CYLINDER,12 IN.TALL............. 32.00
CELADON,VASE,ORIENTAL,GRAY-GREEN,INCISED DESIGN,ROSEWOOD
STAND.................................................. 55.00
CENTENNIAL,PLATE,BALTIMORE & OHIO,1827-1927,SIGNED,LAMBERTON 10.00
CENTENNIAL,PLATE,CIVIL WAR,9 IN......................... 3.00


CHALKWARE IS REALLY PLASTER OF PARIS DECORATED WITH
WATERCOLORS. THE PIECES WERE MOLDED FROM KNOWN
STAFFORDSHIRE AND OTHER PORCELAIN MODELS AND PAINTED
AND SOLD AS INEXPENSIVE DECORATIONS. MOST OF THIS TYPE
OF CHALKWARE WAS MADE FROM ABOUT 1820 TO 1870.
CHALK,FIGURINE,BUST OF HIAWATHA,22 IN.HIGH............. 50.00
CHALK,FIGURINE,BUST OF INDIAN CHIEF,22 IN.HIGH.......... 60.00
CHALK,FIGURINE,CAT,SLEEPING,PAINT...................... 22.50
CHALK,INCENSE BURNER,INDIAN............................ 5.00
CHALK,INDIAN HEAD,FOR WALL,THREE DIMENSIONS,6 IN.WIDE,
9 IN.LONG.............................................. 10.00
CHALK,TOBY,KING HENRY VIII,LABEL READS MARSHAL TOPLOW,LONDON 22.00
CHALK,TOOTHPICK,DOG,WEARS COAT,SITS BESIDE BASKET........... 35.00
CHALKWARE,BANK,COCKER SPANIEL DOG,BLACK,BROWN GLASS EYES.... 20.00
CHALKWARE,BANK,TURKEY,NATURAL COLORS................... 17.50
CHALKWARE,BOOKEND,PIRATE,PAIR.......................... 10.00
CHALKWARE,CANDELABRUM,DECORATED,PENNSYLVANIA,19TH CENTURY... 160.00
CHALKWARE,FIGURINE,BUST OF ITALIAN MAIDEN,BLACK HAIR,
21 IN.TALL............................................. 59.00
CHALKWARE,FIGURINE,DEER,RECLINING,8 1/2 IN.LONG,10 IN.TALL.. 95.00
CHALKWARE,FIGURINE,DOG,SPANIEL,BLACK & RUST SPOTS,
10 3/4 IN.HIGH......................................... 60.00
CHALKWARE,FIGURINE,DOVE,YELLOW,PENNSYLVANIA............ 60.00
CHALKWARE,FIGURINE,ELEPHANT,15 IN. X 20 IN............. 35.00
CHALKWARE,FIGURINE,FROG,HOLLOW,10 IN. X 5 IN........... 30.00
CHALKWARE,FIGURINE,MOTHER AND LAMB,7 IN.HIGH........... 40.00
CHALKWARE,PIANO BABY,GIRL,SITTING,RUFFLED HAT,9 IN.HIGH.... 10.00
CHANTILLY,BOWL,KAKIEMON DECOR,SINGLE MOTH INTERIOR,HANDLES,
1740,7 IN.............................................. 550.00
CHANTILLY,TUREEN & STAND,SAUCE,COVERED,CIRCA 1725-35,
9 1/2 IN. LONG.........................................1,100.00


CHELSEA PORCELAIN WAS MADE IN THE CHELSEA AREA OF
LONDON FROM ABOUT 1745 TO 1784. RECENT COPIES OF THIS
WORK HAVE BEEN MADE FROM THE ORIGINAL MOLDS.
CHELSEA,BOTTLE,SCENT,CIRCA 1755,2 1/2 IN. HIGH.......ILLUS..1,100.00
CHELSEA,BOTTLE,SCENT,CIRCA 1775,DOVE IN TREE,2 3/4
IN.HIGH...............................................ILLUS..1,200.00
CHELSEA,BOTTLE,SCENT,FLUTE PLAYER,CIRCA 1760,6 1/2 IN. HIGH. 950.00
CHELSEA,BOTTLE,SCENT,FRUIT,CIRCA 1760,3 1/2 IN. HIGH........ 450.00
CHELSEA,BOTTLE,SCENT,THREE GRACES,CIRCA 1760,2 1/2 IN. HIGH. 400.00
CHELSEA,BOTTLE,SCENT,VASE,CIRCA 1760,3 1/2 IN. HIGH......... 350.00
CHELSEA,BOWL,OCTAGONAL,KAKIEMON DECORATION,RAISED ANCHOR
PERIOD................................................. 800.00
CHELSEA,CUP & SAUCER,WISHBONE HANDLE................... 12.50
CHELSEA,DISH,KAKIEMON DECORATION,RED ANCHOR PERIOD.......... 450.00
CHELSEA,DISH,OCTAGONAL,KAKIEMON DECORATION,CIRCA 1750....... 375.00
CHELSEA,DISH,RED ANCHOR PERIOD,OVAL,SCALLOPED EDGE.......... 60.00
CHELSEA,FIGURINE,ALLEGORICAL GROUP,CONTINENTS,MARK,
9 1/2 IN.HIGH,PAIR..................................... 600.00
CHELSEA,FIGURINE,COUNT BRUHL'S TAILOR,WIFE,DERBY.....ILLUS..1,000.00
CHELSEA,FIGURINE,LAMB,OVAL BASE,GOLD ANCHOR MARK,1 3/4 IN.,
PAIR................................................... 45.00
CHELSEA,FIGURINE,MARS,ALLEGORICAL,ROCKWORK BASE,MARK,
8 IN.HIGH.............................................. 60.00
CHELSEA,JUG,BLUE DECOR,THUMBPRINT BASE,GRAY,STONEWARE,
14 IN.HIGH............................................. 20.00
CHELSEA,PITCHER,DANIEL IN THE LIONS' DEN,LION HANDLES,6 IN.. 28.00
CHELSEA,PITCHER,MILK,WHITE,GOLD LUSTER BANDS,5 1/2 IN.TALL.. 15.00
CHELSEA,PLATE,PAINTED BIRDS,GOLD ANCHOR PERIOD.............. 350.00
CHELSEA,PLATE,PAIR,RED ANCHOR PERIOD,SCALLOPED EDGE,9 IN.
DIAM................................................... 175.00
CHELSEA,PLATE,THISTLE,BLUE SPRAYS ON WHITE GROUND,6 1/2 IN.,
SET OF 9............................................... 40.00
CHELSEA,PLATTER,PAINTED PEACOCK,PHEASANT,FLORAL,MARK,

CHELSEA SCENT BOTTLES, C. 1755

CHELSEA FIGURINE, COUNT BRUHL'S TAILOR, WIFE

```
     11 IN.LONG,PAIR................................................  225.00
CHELSEA,STATUETTE,ABUNDANCE,GOLD ANCHOR PERIOD.......ILLUS..  575.00
CHELSEA,STATUETTE GROUP,DERBY,CIRCA 1775,6 IN. HIGH.........  200.00
CHELSEA,TEAPOT,FLORAL,GOLD TRIM...............................   25.00
CHELSEA,VASE,BLUE,SHEPHERD,TWO HANDLES........................    3.00
```

     CHELSEA GRAPE PATTERN WAS MADE BEFORE 1840, PROBABLY
AT THE COALPORT FACTORY IN ENGLAND AND AT OTHER FIRMS.
A SMALL BUNCH OF GRAPES IN A RAISED DESIGN, COLORED
WITH PURPLE OR BLUE LUSTER, ARE ON THE BORDER OF THE
WHITE PLATE. MOST OF THE PIECES ARE UNMARKED. THE
PATTERN IS SOMETIMES CALLED AYNSELY OR GRANDMOTHER.

```
CHELSEA GRAPE,BOWL,SLOP,LUSTER..............................   14.00
CHELSEA GRAPE,COFFEEPOT,BLUE DECOR,BULBOUS,SLENDER NECK.....   75.00
CHELSEA GRAPE,CREAMER........................................    9.00
CHELSEA GRAPE,CUP & SAUCER..................... 9.00 TO  15.00
CHELSEA GRAPE,DISH,SAUCE,LUSTER.............................    3.00
CHELSEA GRAPE,PLATE,CAKE,COPPER LUSTER,9 1/2 IN.............   24.00
```

CHELSEA ABUNDANCE STATUETTE,
GOLD ANCHOR PERIOD

```
CHELSEA GRAPE,PLATE,CAKE,LUSTER,9 IN........................     8.50
CHELSEA GRAPE,PLATE,DESSERT,LUSTER..........................     7.50
CHELSEA GRAPE,PLATE,IMPRESSED MARK, CHALLINOR,10 IN.........     8.50
CHELSEA GRAPE,PLATE,IMPRESSED MARK,CHALLINOR,8 IN...........     5.00
CHELSEA GRAPE,PLATE,LEAF,RAISED PURPLE LUSTER,
   7 1/4-IN.DIAMETER........................................     9.00
CHESS SET,BONE,CARVED & TINTED,NATURAL & RED................    70.00
CHESS SET,BRASS,EQUADORIAN PLAYING BOARD BOX................   250.00
CHESS SET,GLASS,CLEAR AND AMBER.............................   275.00
CHESS SET,GLASS,FROSTED AND BLUE............................   140.00
CHESS SET,GLASS,VENETIAN,RED AND TURQUOISE BEADING..........   125.00
CHESS SET,IVORY,AFRICAN CARVED AND TINTED...................   275.00
CHESS SET,IVORY,INDIAN CARVED AND LACQUERED.........ILLUS..1,150.00
CHESS SET,JAPANESE CARVED AND TINTED........................   800.00
CHESS SET,LACQUERED,BLACK & RED.............................   260.00
CHESS SET,PAPIER-MACHE,BAVARIAN.............................   350.00
CHESS SET,SILVER & GILDED SILVER............................   475.00
CHESS SET,STEATITE,CARVED AND TINTED,GREEN & WHITE..........   110.00
```

```
        CHINESE EXPORT PORCELAIN IS ALL OF THE MANY KINDS OF
     PORCELAIN MADE IN CHINA FOR EXPORT TO AMERICA AND
     EUROPE IN THE 18TH AND 19TH CENTURIES. INCLUDED IN
     THIS CATEGORY ARE NANKING,CANTON,CHINESE LOWESTOFT,
     ARMORIAL,JESUIT,AND OTHER TYPES OF THE WARE.
        CHINESE EXPORT,SEE ALSO,CANTON,NANKING
CHINESE EXPORT,BELL,DINNER,LOTUS BLOSSOMS,WHITE ENAMEL ON
   METAL,MARKED.............................................    18.50
CHINESE EXPORT,BELL,ENAMELED,YELLOW,PASTEL FLORAL,MAN OF THE
   MOON HANDLE..............................................    37.50
CHINESE EXPORT,BOTTLE,ARMORIAL DECORATION,CIRCA 1760,9 IN.
   HIGH....................................................    450.00
CHINESE EXPORT,BOTTLE,CIRCA 1750,9 1/2 IN. HIGH.............   175.00
CHINESE EXPORT,BOWL,BLUE DRAGON,BAT,OVERALL PASTEL FLOWERS,
   PORCELAIN................................................    28.00
```

INDIAN IVORY CHESS SET

CHINESE EXPORT,BOWL,CAMILLE ROSE,SHALLOW,11-IN.DIAMETER,
  2 IN.HIGH.............................................................. 95.00
CHINESE EXPORT,BOWL,CIRCA 1750,10 1/4-IN.DIAMETER............ 200.00
CHINESE EXPORT,BOWL,CIRCA 1800,FOOTED,FAMILLE ROSE,
  9-IN.DIAMETER......................................................... 50.00
CHINESE EXPORT,BOWL,DRAGON,FLAMING PEARL,CHARACTERS INSIDE,
  BRASS,9 IN............................................................. 165.00
CHINESE EXPORT,BOWL,ENAMEL DECOR,LANDSCAPE & FIGURES,
  11-IN.DIAMETER........................................................ 95.00
CHINESE EXPORT,BOWL,EUROPEAN DECORATION,CIRCA 1765........... 600.00
CHINESE EXPORT,BOWL,FAMILLE ROSE LOTUS PETAL,CIRCA 1770..... 475.00
CHINESE EXPORT,BOWL,HUNT,BLACK DECORATION,CIRCA 1770,
  13-IN.DIAMETER........................................................ 250.00
CHINESE EXPORT,BOWL,OVAL,SWELLED BASE,1840,7 IN.,PAIR....... 45.00
CHINESE EXPORT,BOWL,PEONY & PHEASANT,CIRCA 1765,
  15 1/2-IN.DIAMETER................................................... 475.00
CHINESE EXPORT,BOWL,RED FITZHUGH PATTERN,MONTIETH,CIRCA
  1790...............................................................1,200.00
CHINESE EXPORT,BOWL,RICE,BLUE,WHITE DESIGN,DRAGON MOTIF,
  COVER,SIGNED.......................................................... 12.50
CHINESE EXPORT,BOWL,SAMSON,FOOTED,9 1/4-IN.DIAMETER......... 60.00
CHINESE EXPORT,BOWL,SCENES,CARP,UNDERSEA LIFE,COVER,
  PORCELAIN,9 IN........................................................ 125.00
CHINESE EXPORT,BOWL,SEPIA DECORATION,CIRCA 1785,
  5 1/2-IN.DIAMETER.................................................... 70.00
CHINESE EXPORT,BOWL,VIEW OF ABBEY AT ABERBROTHICK,CIRCA
  1775................................................................. 525.00
CHINESE EXPORT,BOX,GREEN LEAFY BACKGROUND,BUTTERFLIES,COVER,
  PORCELAIN............................................................. 17.50
CHINESE EXPORT,BOX,ROUGE,WHITE,WOMAN IN MEDALLION,BLUE
  FLORAL,COVER.......................................................... 32.50
CHINESE EXPORT,BOX,SCENE ON LID,GOLD-LACQUERED,CIRCA 1850,
  8 X 17 IN............................................................. 89.50
CHINESE EXPORT,BOX,SILVER & CARVED JADE,MARKED,3 1/2 IN. X
  1 1/2 IN.HIGH........................................................ 35.00
CHINESE EXPORT,CALLING CARD CASE,ORNATELY CARVED............ 12.50
CHINESE EXPORT,COMPOTE,DRAGON CENTER,PINK BORDER,FOOTED,
  6-IN.DIAMETER........................................................ 50.00
CHINESE EXPORT,CUP & SAUCER,RELIGIOUS DECORATION,CIRCA 1760.1,600.00
CHINESE EXPORT,DISH,ARMORIAL,CIRCA 1740,FAMILLE ROSE ILLUS.. 375.00
CHINESE EXPORT,DISH,FOR THE INDIAN MARKET,CIRCA 1780........ 80.00
CHINESE EXPORT,DISH,HOT-WATER,CIRCA 1800,ORIENTAL FIGURES... 125.00
CHINESE EXPORT,DISH,JESUIT DECORATION,18TH CENTURY...ILLUS.. 725.00
CHINESE EXPORT,DISH,MONOGRAMMED,CIRCA 1775,8 IN. LONG....... 260.00
CHINESE EXPORT,DISH,ORANGE PEEL,ENAMEL DECOR,CIRCA 1780,
  OCTAGONAL,8 IN........................................................ 150.00
CHINESE EXPORT,DISH,PARROT DECORATION,CIRCA 1770.....ILLUS.. 250.00
CHINESE EXPORT,DISH,VEINED LEAF SHAPE,FAMILLE ROSE COLOR
  DECOR,7 IN........................................................... 160.00
CHINESE EXPORT,FIGURE,MAIDEN IMMORTAL,CIRCA 1775,12 IN. HIGH 750.00
CHINESE EXPORT,FIGURINE,LADY,COSTUME,ENAMEL,PORCELAIN,PAIR.. 75.00
CHINESE EXPORT,FIGURINE,ORIENTAL MAN,PORCELAIN,9 IN.HIGH.... 45.00
CHINESE EXPORT,HOLDER,BRUSH,DEPICTS A DEITY,PORCELAIN,
  4 3/4 IN.TALL........................................................ 40.00
CHINESE EXPORT,HOLDER,BRUSH,RURAL SCENE,PORCELAIN,
  4 3/4 IN.TALL........................................................ 40.00
CHINESE EXPORT,INCENSE BURNER,FOO DOG,5 IN.................. 13.50
CHINESE EXPORT,IRON,SMOOTHING,BRONZE,RED CINNEBAR HANDLE,
  11 IN.LONG........................................................... 45.00
CHINESE EXPORT,JAR,GINGER,WHITE GROUND,GREEN,YELLOW DECOR,
  TEAK BASE............................................................ 65.00
CHINESE EXPORT,JUG,CREAM,ARMORIAL,CIRCA 1765............... 200.00
CHINESE EXPORT,JUG,MILK,COVERED,BLUE & GOLD,CIRCA 1790...... 60.00
CHINESE EXPORT,LAMP,CARVED JADE QUARTZ,ANIMAL,TEAK STAND,
  24 IN.,PAIR.......................................................... 250.00
CHINESE EXPORT,LAMP,FAIRY,BRASS,DECORATED WELL WITH GLASS
  DOME................................................................. 22.50
CHINESE EXPORT,MUG,MULTICOLOR MANDERIN FIGURES,DRAGON
  HANDLE,CIRCA 1750.................................................... 160.00
CHINESE EXPORT,PAINTING,NOBLE LADY,SERVANTS,1850,24 X
  30 IN.,PAIR.......................................................3,950.00
CHINESE EXPORT,PITCHER,HELMET,SEPIA FLOWER,EDGE TRIM........ 95.00
CHINESE EXPORT,PITCHER,SMALL FLORAL DECOR,HELMET SHAPE...... 95.00
CHINESE EXPORT,PLAQUE,LACQUER,MOTHER-OF-PEARL INLAY,FLORAL,
  BIRDS,PAIR........................................................... 125.00
CHINESE EXPORT,PLAQUE,TILE,BLUE,WHITE,LANDSCAPE,FRAME,12 X
  17 IN................................................................ 125.00
CHINESE EXPORT,PLATE,BASKET OF FLOWERS IN CENTER,GARLAND
  BORDER,9 IN.......................................................... 115.00
CHINESE EXPORT,PLATE,BLUE,WHITE,CIRCA 1720,8 IN.DIAMETER.... 85.00
CHINESE EXPORT,PLATE,CANTON BLUE,WHITE,CIRCA 1800,

```
    9 1/4-IN.DIAMETER,PAIR........................................   30.00
CHINESE EXPORT,PLATE,ENAMELED FLORAL & BIRDS,SIGNED.........    6.00
CHINESE EXPORT,PLATE,FAMILLE ROSE,ERMINE CLOAK,SPADE SHIELD,
    DOVES,1800..............................................................   62.00
CHINESE EXPORT,PLATE,FOR INDIAN MARKET,CIRCA 1770....ILLUS..  900.00
CHINESE EXPORT,PLATE,MEISSEN STYLE,CIRCA 1760,HARBOR SCENE..  300.00
CHINESE EXPORT,PLATE,PAIR,CIRCA 1750,EUROPEAN SCENES ILLUS..  850.00
CHINESE EXPORT,PLATE,PAIR,JESUIT DECORATION,CIRCA 1760......  325.00
CHINESE EXPORT,PLATE,POMPADOUR DECORATION...........ILLUS..  375.00
CHINESE EXPORT,PLATTER,ARMORIAL,CIRCA 1780,18 IN. LONG......  300.00
CHINESE EXPORT,PLATTER,CIRCA 1780,14 3/4 IN. LONG...........  100.00
CHINESE EXPORT,PLATTER,HOT-WATER,ARMORIAL,CIRCA 1795........  350.00
CHINESE EXPORT,PLATTER,IMPERIAL YELLOW,PINK FLORAL,PEACOCK..   75.00
CHINESE EXPORT,PLATTER,PAINTED WITH A CREST,CIRCA 1790......  250.00
CHINESE EXPORT,PLATTER,PAIR,CIRCA 1760,ARMORIAL,18 1/2 IN.
    LONG.....................................................................  575.00
CHINESE EXPORT,PLATTER,SWAG DECORATION,CIRCA 1780,14 1/2 IN.
    LONG.....................................................................  225.00
CHINESE EXPORT,POTS-DE-CREME,4,BLUE & WHITE,19TH CENTURY....  325.00
CHINESE EXPORT,POTS-DE CREME,4,CIRCA 1770.................1,200.00
CHINESE EXPORT,PUNCH BOWL,FAMILLE ROSE,CIRCA 1760-70,
    13 3/4-IN.DIAMETER.......................................................  300.00
```

CHINESE JESUIT DISH, 18TH CENTURY

CHINESE POMPADOUR PLATE

CHINESE PARROT DISH, C. 1770

CHINESE ARMORIAL DISH, C. 1740

CHINESE PLATES

C. 1750          C. 1770

CHINESE EXPORT,SAUCEBOAT,EUROPEAN DECORATION,CIRCA 1765,
8 1/2 IN.LONG........................................ 120.00
CHINESE EXPORT,SAUCEBOAT,FLORAL,CIRCA 1765,8 3/4 IN.LONG.... 100.00
CHINESE EXPORT,SAUCEBOAT,CIRCA 1750,9 IN.LONG,PAIR.......... 375.00
CHINESE EXPORT,SAUCER,EUROPEAN ALLEGORICAL DECORATION,CIRCA
1760................................................. 275.00
CHINESE EXPORT,SAUCER,EUROPEAN AMOUROUS DECORATION,CIRCA
1740................................................. 225.00
CHINESE EXPORT,SAUCER,EUROPEAN DECORATION,CIRCA 1760,
4 1/4-IN.DIAMETER.................................... 400.00
CHINESE EXPORT,STAND,WIG,BIRDS,PINK CHRYSANTHEMUM,PORCELAIN,
11 1/2 IN............................................ 80.00
CHINESE EXPORT,SUGAR,COVERED,CIRCA 1785,5 1/2 IN. HIGH...... 70.00
CHINESE EXPORT,SUGAR,COVERED,CIRCA 1810,5 IN. HIGH......... 50.00
CHINESE EXPORT,TEA CADDY,CIRCA 1770..................... 120.00
CHINESE EXPORT,TEA CADDY,CIRCA 1800,5 IN. HIGH........... 100.00
CHINESE EXPORT,TEA CADDY,LANDSCAPE,BLUE,WHITE,PORCELAIN,
PEWTER LID,1819...................................... 55.00
CHINESE EXPORT,TEA CADDY,PAGODA SCENES,LACQUERED,PEWTER
INSERTS,11 IN........................................ 195.00
CHINESE EXPORT,TEAPOT,CIRCA 1735........................ 225.00
CHINESE EXPORT,TEAPOT STAND,EUROPEAN FIGURES,CIRCA 1740,
5 IN. LONG........................................... 475.00
CHINESE EXPORT,TEA SERVICE,ARMORIAL,CIRCA 1790,29 PIECES....2,300.00
CHINESE EXPORT,TEA SERVICE,MINIATURE,CIRCA 1780,15 PIECES... 650.00
CHINESE EXPORT,TEAPOT,CIRCA 1780........................ 40.00
CHINESE EXPORT,TEAPOT,FAMILLE ROSE,CIRCA 1765,6 IN. HIGH.... 100.00
CHINESE EXPORT,TEAPOT,FIGURAL,CIRCA 1790,5 1/8 IN. HIGH..... 100.00
CHINESE EXPORT,TEAPOT,WHITE,MEDALLION,JLK IN SCRIPT,SUGAR
BOWL,SET............................................. 175.00
CHINESE EXPORT,TUREEN & STAND,BULL'S HEAD,
COMPAGNIE-DES-INDES,1765.............................4,250.00
CHINESE EXPORT,TUREEN & STAND,COVERED,CIRCA 1810,FAMILLE
ROSE................................................. 110.00
CHINESE EXPORT,TUREEN,BLUE,WHITE,LION FINIAL & HANDLES,13 X
9 IN................................................. 250.00
CHINESE EXPORT,TUREEN,BUTTERFLY DECORATION,CIRCA 1800....... 200.00
CHINESE EXPORT,TUREEN,CIRCA 1770,66 1/2 IN. LONG,OVAL....... 175.00
CHINESE EXPORT,TUREEN,PAIR,STANDS,CIRCA 1790,TRAY 14 1/2 IN.
LONG.................................................2,300.00
CHINESE EXPORT,TUREEN,PAIR,TOBACCO LEAF,CIRCA 1775,STANDS,
TRAY 7 IN............................................4,000.00
CHINESE EXPORT,URN,2,PISTOL HANDLE,CIRCA 1790........ILLUS.2,500.00
CHINESE EXPORT,URN,FAMILLE ROSE,CIRCA 1810.................. 725.00
CHINESE EXPORT,URN,PISTOL-HANDLED,SEPIA LANDSCAPES,CIRCA
1775.................................................1,200.00
CHINESE EXPORT,VASE,BLUE,LARGE FLOWERS ON SIDE,CHINESE
FIGURES & DECOR...................................... 40.00
CHINESE EXPORT,VASE,PAIR,FAMILLE ROSE,CIRCA 1770............ 750.00
CHINESE EXPORT,VASE,RED & PINK FLORAL,GOLD,SIDE HANDLE,EWER
SHAPE,MARK........................................... 10.00
CHINESE EXPORT,VASE,SCENE,PEOPLE,STORKS,ENAMEL,CHINESE
CHARACTER............................................ 17.50

CHINESE PISTOL HANDLE URN, C. 1790

```
CHOCOLATE POT,BROWN,GILT,PINECONE DECOR,HAND-PAINTED,GERMANY        20.00
CHOCOLATE POT,GEISHA GIRLS IN FLOWER GARDEN,ORIENTAL DECOR..        20.00
CHOCOLATE POT,GEISHA PORTRAIT,RED,GOLD,SIGNED...............        18.00
CHOCOLATE POT,GOLD COLOR GROUND,PURPLE & RED LILIES,GOLD
  BEADING........................................................   18.50
CHOCOLATE POT,KIMONA GIRLS,COBALT & GOLD TRIM...............        13.00
CHOCOLATE POT,OVERALL EMBOSSED,FLORAL,ORNATE HANDLE & LIP...        25.00
CHOCOLATE POT,THREE LARGE ROSES,LEAVES,GOLD ORNATE HANDLE,
  MARK 6144-2....................................................   18.00
CHOCOLATE SET,BEIGE,ROSES,ROCOCO-EDGED POT,TWIG HANDLE,
  6 CUPS & SAUCERS...............................................   85.00
CHOCOLATE SET,BLUE & GOLD,KIMONA...........................        60.00
CHOCOLATE SET,LILY DECOR,POT,4 CUPS,GERMANY................        22.50
CHOCOLATE SET,LILY DECOR,WHITE TO PALE PINK,POT,4 CUPS &
  SAUCERS,GERMANY................................................   50.00
CHOCOLATE SET,ORANGE POPPIES,GREEN LEAVES,GOLD,POT,6 CUPS &
  SAUCERS........................................................   45.00
CHOCOLATE SET,PINK,RED FLORAL,BIRDS,BLUE BORDER,4 CUPS,
  SAUCERS,POT,JAPAN..............................................   12.00
CHOCOLATE SET,POT,FIVE CUPS,HAND-PAINTED FLOWERS,JAPAN......        17.00
CHOCOLATE SET,ROSES,CREAM GROUND,GOLD DECOR,ARTIST-SIGNED,
  SCHWARZBURG....................................................  110.00
CHOCOLATE SET,WHITE,GREEN,APPLE DESIGN,POT,5 CUPS & SAUCERS,
  WEIMER.........................................................   95.00
CHRISTMAS LIGHT,CLUSTER OF GRAPES,GREEN,SILVER SHEEN,ART
  GLASS,4 IN.HIGH................................................   25.00


        CHRISTMAS PLATES WERE MADE BY SEVERAL FIRMS. THE MOST
        FAMOUS WERE MADE BY THE BING AND GROHNDAHL FACTORY OF
        DENMARK,AFTER 1895,AND THE ROYAL COPENHAGEN FACTORY,
        AFTER 1908. EACH PLATE HAS A BLUE-AND-WHITE GLAZE WITH
        A SCENE IN THE CENTER,THE DATE,AND THE WORD JULE.
CHRISTMAS PLATE,BAREUTHER,1967,BAVARIA......................        60.00
CHRISTMAS PLATE,BAREUTHER,1967,1968,1969,BAVARIAN,SET.......       100.00
CHRISTMAS PLATE,BING & GRONDAHL,1895..........................   2,000.00
CHRISTMAS PLATE,BING & GRONDAHL,1896..........................   1,000.00
CHRISTMAS PLATE,BING & GRONDAHL,1897........................       700.00
CHRISTMAS PLATE,BING & GRONDAHL,1898........................       850.00
CHRISTMAS PLATE,BING & GRONDAHL,1899........................       850.00
CHRISTMAS PLATE,BING & GRONDAHL,1900........................       450.00
CHRISTMAS PLATE,BING & GRONDAHL,1901........................       350.00
CHRISTMAS PLATE,BING & GRONDAHL,1901-1969,69 PLATES.........     2,500.00
CHRISTMAS PLATE,BING & GRONDAHL,1903........................       250.00
CHRISTMAS PLATE,BING & GRONDAHL,1904.................. 42.50 TO    150.00
CHRISTMAS PLATE,BING & GRONDAHL,1905.................. 72.00 TO    175.00
CHRISTMAS PLATE,BING & GRONDAHL,1906.................. 50.00 TO    125.00
CHRISTMAS PLATE,BING & GRONDAHL,1907.................. 53.00 TO    125.00
CHRISTMAS PLATE,BING & GRONDAHL,1908.................. 39.50 TO    100.00
CHRISTMAS PLATE,BING & GRONDAHL,1909.................. 48.00 TO    100.00
CHRISTMAS PLATE,BING & GRONDAHL,1910.................. 48.00 TO    100.00
CHRISTMAS PLATE,BING & GRONDAHL,1911........................       100.00
CHRISTMAS PLATE,BING & GRONDAHL,1912.................. 42.00 TO     90.00
CHRISTMAS PLATE,BING & GRONDAHL,1913.................. 42.00 TO     90.00
CHRISTMAS PLATE,BING & GRONDAHL,1914.................. 42.00 TO     90.00
CHRISTMAS PLATE,BING & GRONDAHL,1916.................. 39.50 TO     90.00
CHRISTMAS PLATE,BING & GRONDAHL,1917.................. 35.00 TO     42.00
CHRISTMAS PLATE,BING & GRONDAHL,1918.................. 35.00 TO     42.00
CHRISTMAS PLATE,BING & GRONDAHL,1919.................. 42.00 TO    100.00
CHRISTMAS PLATE,BING & GRONDAHL,1920.................. 34.00 TO     75.00
CHRISTMAS PLATE,BING & GRONDAHL,1921.................. 34.00 TO     75.00
CHRISTMAS PLATE,BING & GRONDAHL,1922.................. 34.00 TO     75.00
CHRISTMAS PLATE,BING & GRONDAHL,1923.................. 34.00 TO     75.00
CHRISTMAS PLATE,BING & GRONDAHL,1924.................. 34.00 TO     42.00
CHRISTMAS PLATE,BING & GRONDAHL,1925.................. 34.00 TO     75.00
CHRISTMAS PLATE,BING & GRONDAHL,1926.................. 34.00 TO     75.00
CHRISTMAS PLATE,BING & GRONDAHL,1927........................        34.00
CHRISTMAS PLATE,BING & GRONDAHL,1928.................. 34.00 TO     75.00
CHRISTMAS PLATE,BING & GRONDAHL,1929.................. 34.00 TO     42.00
CHRISTMAS PLATE,BING & GRONDAHL,1930........................       100.00
CHRISTMAS PLATE,BING & GRONDAHL,1931........................        95.00
CHRISTMAS PLATE,BING & GRONDAHL,1932........................        54.00
CHRISTMAS PLATE,BING & GRONDAHL,1933.................. 34.00 TO     75.00
CHRISTMAS PLATE,BING & GRONDAHL,1934.................. 34.00 TO     75.00
CHRISTMAS PLATE,BING & GRONDAHL,1935.................. 34.00 TO     75.00
CHRISTMAS PLATE,BING & GRONDAHL,1937.................. 57.00 TO     75.00
CHRISTMAS PLATE,BING & GRONDAHL,1939........................       200.00
CHRISTMAS PLATE,BING & GRONDAHL,1940........................       175.00
CHRISTMAS PLATE,BING & GRONDAHL,1941.................ILLUS..        250.00
CHRISTMAS PLATE,BING & GRONDAHL,1942.................. 80.00 TO    175.00
CHRISTMAS PLATE,BING & GRONDAHL,1944........................       150.00
```

BING AND GRONDAHL CHRISTMAS PLATE

```
CHRISTMAS PLATE,BING & GRONDAHL,1945........................    175.00
CHRISTMAS PLATE,BING & GRONDAHL,1946............... 37.50 TO    125.00
CHRISTMAS PLATE,BING & GRONDAHL,1947............... 70.00 TO    150.00
CHRISTMAS PLATE,BING & GRONDAHL,1948........................     90.00
CHRISTMAS PLATE,BING & GRONDAHL,1949............... 51.00 TO     90.00
CHRISTMAS PLATE,BING & GRONDAHL,1950........................    125.00
CHRISTMAS PLATE,BING & GRONDAHL,1951............... 39.50 TO    125.00
CHRISTMAS PLATE,BING & GRONDAHL,1952............... 54.00 TO    125.00
CHRISTMAS PLATE,BING & GRONDAHL,1953........................    125.00
CHRISTMAS PLATE,BING & GRONDAHL,1954............... 58.00 TO    125.00
CHRISTMAS PLATE,BING & GRONDAHL,1955............... 52.00 TO    125.00
CHRISTMAS PLATE,BING & GRONDAHL,1956........................    125.00
CHRISTMAS PLATE,BING & GRONDAHL,1957........................    125.00
CHRISTMAS PLATE,BING & GRONDAHL,1958........................    125.00
CHRISTMAS PLATE,BING & GRONDAHL,1959........................    175.00
CHRISTMAS PLATE,BING & GRONDAHL,1960........................    125.00
CHRISTMAS PLATE,BING & GRONDAHL,1961........................    100.00
CHRISTMAS PLATE,BING & GRONDAHL,1962........................     35.00
CHRISTMAS PLATE,BING & GRONDAHL,1963........................     40.00
CHRISTMAS PLATE,BING & GRONDAHL,1964........................     35.00
CHRISTMAS PLATE,BING & GRONDAHL,1965............... 28.00 TO     43.00
CHRISTMAS PLATE,BING & GRONDAHL,1966........................     14.00
CHRISTMAS PLATE,BING & GRONDAHL,1967............... 11.00 TO     27.00
CHRISTMAS PLATE,BING & GRONDAHL,1969........................     10.00
CHRISTMAS PLATE,FRANKOMA,1964,1965,1966,1967,SET OF 4.......    300.00
CHRISTMAS PLATE,FRANKOMA,1965.......................145.00 TO    150.00
CHRISTMAS PLATE,FRANKOMA,1965,1966,1967,1968,SET OF 4.......    275.00
CHRISTMAS PLATE,FRANKOMA,1966..............................     70.00
CHRISTMAS PLATE,FRANKOMA,1968..............................     11.00
CHRISTMAS PLATE,GORHAM,1925,ROMAN FIGURES GATHER GRAPES,
  EMBOSSED,BRONZE...........................................     65.00
CHRISTMAS PLATE,LALIQUE,1966...............................    250.00
CHRISTMAS PLATE,LALIQUE,1968...............................     90.00
CHRISTMAS PLATE,RORSTRAND SWEDISH,1969.....................     13.50
CHRISTMAS PLATE,RORSTRAND,1968,SWEDEN......................     82.00
CHRISTMAS PLATE,ROSENTHAL,1913.............................     37.50
CHRISTMAS PLATE,ROYAL COPENHAGEN,1910......................     72.50
CHRISTMAS PLATE,ROYAL COPENHAGEN,1913......................     86.00
CHRISTMAS PLATE,ROYAL COPENHAGEN,1915............... 67.50 TO     76.00
CHRISTMAS PLATE,ROYAL COPENHAGEN,1917............... 60.00 TO     74.00
CHRISTMAS PLATE,ROYAL COPENHAGEN,1918......................     58.00
CHRISTMAS PLATE,ROYAL COPENHAGEN,1919......................     65.00
CHRISTMAS PLATE,ROYAL COPENHAGEN,1920............... 39.00 TO     47.50
CHRISTMAS PLATE,ROYAL COPENHAGEN,1921............... 39.00 TO     45.00
CHRISTMAS PLATE,ROYAL COPENHAGEN,1922............... 38.50 TO     45.00
CHRISTMAS PLATE,ROYAL COPENHAGEN,1923............... 38.50 TO     50.00
CHRISTMAS PLATE,ROYAL COPENHAGEN,1924......................     38.50
CHRISTMAS PLATE,ROYAL COPENHAGEN,1925......................     38.50
CHRISTMAS PLATE,ROYAL COPENHAGEN,1926............... 38.50 TO     48.00
CHRISTMAS PLATE,ROYAL COPENHAGEN,1927......................     48.00
```

```
CHRISTMAS PLATE,ROYAL COPENHAGEN,1928........................    48.00
CHRISTMAS PLATE,ROYAL COPENHAGEN,1929........................    48.00
CHRISTMAS PLATE,ROYAL COPENHAGEN,1930........................    55.00
CHRISTMAS PLATE,ROYAL COPENHAGEN,1932........................    57.50
CHRISTMAS PLATE,ROYAL COPENHAGEN,1933........................    62.00
CHRISTMAS PLATE,ROYAL COPENHAGEN,1941........................   250.00
CHRISTMAS PLATE,ROYAL COPENHAGEN,1944........................   132.50
CHRISTMAS PLATE,ROYAL COPENHAGEN,1945........................   290.00
CHRISTMAS PLATE,ROYAL COPENHAGEN,1947........................   140.00
CHRISTMAS PLATE,ROYAL COPENHAGEN,1948........................    98.00
CHRISTMAS PLATE,ROYAL COPENHAGEN,1952........................    55.00
CHRISTMAS PLATE,ROYAL COPENHAGEN,1953........................    55.00
CHRISTMAS PLATE,ROYAL COPENHAGEN,1954........................   100.00
CHRISTMAS PLATE,ROYAL COPENHAGEN,1955........................   176.00
CHRISTMAS PLATE,ROYAL COPENHAGEN,1956........................   100.00
CHRISTMAS PLATE,ROYAL COPENHAGEN,1957.............. 67.00 TO    72.00
CHRISTMAS PLATE,ROYAL COPENHAGEN,1958.............. 54.00 TO    71.00
CHRISTMAS PLATE,ROYAL COPENHAGEN,1959.............. 67.00 TO    78.00
CHRISTMAS PLATE,ROYAL COPENHAGEN,1960.............. 49.50 TO    55.00
CHRISTMAS PLATE,ROYAL COPENHAGEN,1961........................    50.00
CHRISTMAS PLATE,ROYAL COPENHAGEN,1962.............. 63.00 TO    79.00
CHRISTMAS PLATE,ROYAL COPENHAGEN,1964........................    30.00
CHRISTMAS PLATE,ROYAL COPENHAGEN,1965........................    23.00
CHRISTMAS PLATE,ROYAL COPENHAGEN,1966.............. 14.00 TO    22.50
CHRISTMAS PLATE,ROYAL COPENHAGEN,1967.............. 12.00 TO    18.00
CHRISTMAS PLATE,WEDGWOOD,1969................................    23.00
CHRISTMAS TREE,CANDLEHOLDER,CLIP-ON..........................     1.00
     CIGAR STORE INDIAN,SEE WOODEN,CIGAR STORE INDIAN
```

```
       CINNABAR IS A VERMILION OR RED LACQUER. SOME PIECES ARE
       MADE WITH HUNDREDS OF THICKNESSES OF THE LACQUER THAT
       ARE LATER CARVED.
CINNABAR,BOTTLE,SNUFF,BROWN LACQUER,CH'IEN LUNG.............1,450.00
CINNABAR,BOTTLE,SNUFF,LACQUER,FLORAL,BIRDS,MATCHING STOPPER.    60.00
CINNABAR,BOTTLE,SNUFF,RED,WHITE JADE TOP....................   130.00
CINNABAR,BOWL,RED-BROWN,CARVED GARDENS,TEMPLE SCENES,TEAK
   STAND,CHINA..............................................    55.00
CINNABAR,BOX,CARVED FLORAL ON COVER,JADE MEDALLION,5 3/4 X
   3 3/4 IN.................................................    50.00
CINNABAR,BOX,RED,CARVING ON COVER & SIDES,4 1/2 IN. X 5 IN..    32.00
CINNABAR,BOX,TOP CARVED FLORAL,WHITE JADE MEDALLION,PIERCED
   DECOR...................................................    77.50
CINNABAR,BUTTON,LOTUS FLOWER DESIGN,CHINA,4/5-IN.DIAMETER,
   SET OF 5.................................................    10.00
CINNABAR,PLAQUE,RED,CARVED,BLACK & GOLD FRAME,6 1/2 X 7 IN..    25.00
CINNABAR,VASE,BRASS RIM ON TOP & BOTTOM,PAIR................    40.00
CINNABAR,VASE,CARVED EXTERIOR SCENE,TREES,MOUNTAINS,FIGURES,
   7 3/4 IN.................................................    72.50
CINNABAR,VASE,CARVED OVERALL FLORAL & FOLIAGE PATTERN,MARKED
   CHINA....................................................    49.50
CINNABAR,VASE,RESERVES ARE CARVED,FIGURES,LANDSCAPE,WIRED,
   11 1/2 IN................................................   265.00
```

```
       CIVIL WAR MEMENTOS ARE IMPORTANT COLLECTORS' ITEMS. MOST
       OF THE PIECES ARE MILITARY ITEMS USED FROM 1861 TO
       1865.
CIVIL WAR,BAYONET,SCABBARD,BELT & BUCKLE,CARTRIDGE BOX......    40.00
CIVIL WAR,BELT BUCKLE,U.S.,HOOKS,OVAL,BRASS.................    14.50
CIVIL WAR,BELT BUCKLE,UNION,E PLURIBUS UNUM,EAGLE...........    12.50
CIVIL WAR,BREASTPLATE,EAGLE HOLDING THREE ARROWS & OLIVE
   BRANCH,BRASS.............................................    14.50
CIVIL WAR,FLAG,HOMECOMING TYPE,ON STICK,PRINTED 36 STAR
   DESIGN,5 X 7 IN..........................................     4.50
CIVIL WAR,KNAPSACK..........................................     2.00
CIVIL WAR,SWORD,OFFICER'S,LEATHER BELT,BRASS BUCKLE,IVORY &
   BRASS HANDLE.............................................    85.00
```

```
       CLAMBROTH GLASS,POPULAR IN THE VICTORIAN ERA,IS A
       GRAYISH COLOR AND IS SEMIOPAQUE LIKE THE SOUP.
CLAMBROTH,BOTTLE,BARBER,WITCH HAZEL,STOPPER.................    15.00
CLAMBROTH,CANOE,SOUVENIR OF DODGE CITY,KANSAS,2 IN. X 6 IN..    10.00
CLAMBROTH,DISH,LACY,FOOTED,10 IN............................    12.50
CLAMBROTH,GOBLET,BUTTON ARCHES,SOUVENIR,FLORAL DECOR,
   6 IN.HIGH...............................................    16.00
CLAMBROTH,MUG,TWO BIRDS,SHEAF OF WHEAT,SANDWICH.............    30.00
CLAMBROTH,TOOTHPICK,SOUVENIR,NEWTON,KANSAS..................     8.00
CLAMBROTH,TUMBLER,BUTTON & ARCHES,SOUVENIR..................     8.00
CLAMBROTH,TUMBLER,SOUVENIR,BUTTON ARCHES....................    13.00
```

```
CLEWS,SEE ALSO FLOW BLUE
CLEWS,PLATE,BLUE,PEACE & PLENTY,IMPRESSED MARK,10 1/4 IN....    67.50
CLEWS,PLATE,FLORAL BORDER,HUNTING SCENE,IMPRESSED CIRCLED
   CROWN MARK...............................................    35.00
CLEWS,PLATE,LANDING OF LAFAYETTE,MARKED,10-IN.DIAMETER......    75.00
CLEWS,PLATTER,ALLOVER SCENIC,BLUE,SIGNED,17 IN.LONG.........    92.00
CLEWS,PLATTER,WELL & TREE,CIRCA 1819,18 IN. X 13 IN.........   115.00
CLOCK,ALARM,EIGHT-DAY,WOODEN CASE,TOP WOODEN HANDLE,NEW
   HAVEN,1908..............................................    18.00
CLOCK,ALARM,MUSICAL,HOME SWEET HOME.........................    65.00
CLOCK,ANSONIA,IRON,8 X 10 IN................................    18.50
CLOCK,ANSONIA,SHELF,EIGHT-DAY,STRIKING,MAHOGANY,14 IN.HIGH..    45.00
CLOCK,ANSONIA,STEEPLE,20 IN.TALL............................    70.00
CLOCK,ANSONIA,SWINGING ARM..................................   240.00
CLOCK,ARAB ON CAMEL,PORCELAIN,8 X 11 IN.....................    24.00
CLOCK,ATKINS & DOWNS,TWO WEIGHTS,WOODEN WORKS,33 IN.TALL,
   17 IN.WIDE..............................................   150.00
CLOCK,AUTOMOBILE,EIGHT-DAY,ELGIN............................    10.00
CLOCK,BANJO,AMERICAN,SIGNED TIFFANY & CO....................   125.00
CLOCK,BANJO,BRASS BEZELS,EAGLE ON TOP,PICTURES,EIGHT-DAY,NEW
   HAVEN...................................................    60.00
CLOCK,BANJO,DANIEL PRATT & SONS.............................   600.00
CLOCK,BANJO,EIGHT-DAY,INGRAHAM,33 IN.LONG...................    65.00
CLOCK,BANJO,ELMER STENNES...................................   300.00
CLOCK,BANJO,HOWARD..........................................   400.00
CLOCK,BANJO,MAHOGANY,EGLOMISE DECORATION,BOSTON,CIRCA 1825..1,400.00
CLOCK,BANJO,MINIATURE,EIGHT-DAY,REVERSE PAINTINGS,EAGLE,NEW
   HAVEN...................................................    33.00
CLOCK,BANJO,MINIATURE,EIGHT-DAY,STRIKE,NEW HAVEN,18 IN.HIGH.    68.00
CLOCK,BANJO,MINIATURE,NEW HAVEN.............................    38.00
CLOCK,BANJO,MINIATURE,SHIP ON DOOR,EAGLE TOP,NEW HAVEN,
   22 IN...................................................    68.00
CLOCK,BANJO,NEW HAVEN,REVERSE PAINTING ON DOOR GLASS,SHIPS,
   WALNUT,36 IN............................................   115.00
CLOCK,BANJO,PICTURE OF SHIPS IN BOX,EIGHT-DAY,STRIKES,NEW
   HAVEN,38 IN.............................................    90.00
CLOCK,BANJO,REVERSE PAINTING,CLIPPER,LIGHTHOUSE,WOOD,
   SESSIONS,36 IN..........................................    72.00
CLOCK,BANJO,ROSEWOOD,CIRCA 1850,HOWARD & DAVIS,BOSTON.......   350.00
CLOCK,BANJO,TIME & STRIKE,PENDULUM,EIGHT-DAY,GILBERT,
   36 IN.HIGH..............................................    77.00
CLOCK,BANJO,TIME & STRIKE,EIGHT-DAY,SESSIONS,28 IN.HIGH.....    58.00
CLOCK,BANJO,TWO BATTLESHIPS,U.S.FLAG,SHELF ON BOTTOM........1,000.00
CLOCK,BANJO,WEIGHT-DRIVEN,SIGNED EASTMAN....................1,025.00
CLOCK,BANJO,WEIGHT-DRIVEN,WALNUT CASE,SWAIN.................   750.00
CLOCK,BEEHIVE,30-HOUR,REVERSE PAINTINGS.....................    30.00
CLOCK,BEEHIVE,EIGHT-DAY,REVERSE PAINTINGS...................    60.00
CLOCK,BIGELOW,KENNARD,BOSTON,SHELF,PORCELAIN DIAL,INLAID
   CASE,PENDULUM...........................................    75.00
CLOCK,BIRD & FLOWERS ON FRONT,PORCELAIN,18 IN.TALL..........    75.00
CLOCK,BLACK MARBLE,TIME,BAROMETER,DAY OF MONTH & WEEK,12 X
   18 IN.HIGH..............................................   500.00
CLOCK,BLACK,LARGE ROSES,PORCELAIN,11 IN.....................    27.00
CLOCK,BOILER ROOM,30-HOUR,NICKELED BRASS CASE,SETH THOMAS...    44.00
CLOCK,BOUDOIR,CUT GLASS,HARVARD,INTAGLIO FLORAL,
   5 1/2 IN.HIGH,3 IN.WIDE.................................    55.00
CLOCK,BOUDOIR,MARBLE BASE,FLORAL & SCROLL DECOR,GILT METAL,
   5 1/4 IN.HIGH...........................................    50.00
CLOCK,BRACKET,DOUBLE FUSEE,CROWN WHEEL ESCAPMENT,T.WAGSTAFF,
   ENGLAND,1780............................................   325.00
CLOCK,BRACKET,EBONIZED,ANCHOR ESCAPEMENT,THOMAS MOSS,LONDON,
   16 IN.HIGH..............................................    90.00
CLOCK,BRACKET,EBONIZED,PEARWOOD CASE,FLAMBEAUX FINIALS,
   SWISS,20 1/2 IN.........................................   225.00
CLOCK,BRACKET,GEORGE III,JAMES BURTON,CIRCA 1800,
   14 3/4 IN.HIGH..........................................   175.00
CLOCK,BRACKET,GEORGE III,MAHOGANY,18TH CENTURY,11 IN. HIGH..   475.00
CLOCK,BRACKET,LOUIS XV,LACQUERED,ROCOCO,ORMOLU MOUNTS,FLORAL
   DECOR...................................................1,600.00
CLOCK,BRACKET,QUEEN ANNE,CALENDAR APERTURE,CHERUBS,PLAQUE,
   PEARWOOD CASE...........................................   850.00
CLOCK,BRASS DIAL,LONG CASE,ARCHED HOOD,HENRY WALLIS,
   MAHOGANY,105 IN.HIGH....................................   200.00
CLOCK,BRASS,SHELF,HOWARD & CO.,11 IN. HIGH..................   110.00
CLOCK,BRASS,TRAVELING,CHAS.FRODSHAM,19TH CENTURY,5 1/2 IN.
   HIGH....................................................   300.00
CLOCK,BRASS WORKS,GRADUATED BRASS BELL,QUARTER-HOUR STRIKE,
   1820....................................................   297.50
CLOCK,BRONZE & ORMOLU FIGURAL GARNITURE,19TH CENTURY,
   3 PIECES................................................   725.00
CLOCK,CALENDAR,DAVIS.......................................   115.00
```

```
CLOCK,CALENDAR,KITCHEN,STRIKING,OAK,INGRAHAM.................      52.00
CLOCK,CALENDAR,LONG DROP OCTAGON TOP,OAK CASE,INGRAHAM......      77.00
CLOCK,CALENDAR,PATENTED 1876,SETH THOMAS, 13 X 27 IN........     200.00
CLOCK,CALENDAR,REGULATOR,GOLD & BLACK DOOR,RED CALENDAR
   HAND,OAK....................................................      92.00
CLOCK,CAR,EIGHT-DAY,SILVER DIAL,SECOND HAND,WALTHAM.........      18.00
CLOCK,CARRIAGE,BRASS & GLASS,FRANCE........................      65.00
CLOCK,CARRIAGE,GLASS ON FOUR SIDES,FRANCE..................      75.00
CLOCK,CARRIAGE,GRAY & BROWN AGATE PANELS,ENAMEL DIAL,FRANCE,
   5 1/2 IN....................................................      70.00
CLOCK,CARRIAGE,MOSAIC INLAY PANELS,BLACK GROUND,KEY,1 7/8 X
   3 5/8 IN....................................................      50.00
CLOCK,CARRIAGE,MUSIC ALARM................................      30.00
CLOCK,CARRIAGE,MUSICAL....................................      25.00
CLOCK,CARRIAGE,OPEN ESCAPEMENT,EIGHT-DAY,MINIATURE,FRANCE...     150.00
CLOCK,CARRIAGE,QUADRANGULAR,BEVEL GLASS,FRANCE,4 1/2 IN.HIGH      40.00
CLOCK,CARRIAGE,REPEATER,CHIMES THE HOUR,PRESS BUTTON &
   REPEATS,BRASS..............................................     150.00
CLOCK,CARRIAGE,WITH REPEATER.....................  49.00 TO     55.00
CLOCK,CARVED GILT WOOD,WHITE ENAMEL DIAL,JUSTICE FIGURE,
   AUSTRIAN,37 IN..............................................     175.00
CLOCK,CHELSEA,SHIP'S BELL,BRASS CASE......................     120.00
CLOCK,CHELSEA,WEIGHT-DRIVEN REGULATOR.....................     135.00
CLOCK,CHIME,CARVED CHERUBS,MOON PHASES,OAK,ELLIOT,LONDON,
   8 FT.10 IN..............................................  1,600.00
CLOCK,CHIME,ENGRAVED FACE,MAHOGANY CASE,INLAY ON FRONT,
   GERMANY,15 IN..............................................      90.00
CLOCK,CLASSIC FIGURE,ANGEL,CLAW FEET,HARRISON,FRANCE,
   28 IN.HIGH.................................................     400.00
CLOCK,COMBINATION CLOCK-ALARM SAFE DEPOSIT BOX,1910.........      27.00
CLOCK,COTTAGE,MINIATURE,TIME,STRIKE,EIGHT-DAY,PAINTED GLASS,
   GILBERT....................................................      42.00
CLOCK,COTTAGE SHAPE,DELUX CLOCK CO.,NEW YORK...............       6.00
CLOCK,CUCKOO,CARVED BIRDS & LEAVES,GERMANY,10 IN. X 10 IN...      25.00
CLOCK,CUCKOO,HAND-CARVED EAGLE............................      95.00
CLOCK,CUCKOO,TWELVE-WEIGHT................................      27.50
CLOCK,CUPIDS & LUSTER DECOR,PORCELAIN,GERMANY,10 IN.HIGH....      37.50
CLOCK,DELUXE CLOCK CO.,NEW YORK,SHAPE OF COTTAGE...........       8.00
CLOCK,DOME UNDER GLASS,ORNATE FEET,EMBOSSED,BRASS,GILT,
   WELCH,6 1/2 IN.............................................      59.50
CLOCK,DOUBLE-STRIKE TAMBOUR,NEW HAVEN.....................      22.50
CLOCK,DOUBLE-WEIGHT WALL REGULATOR,ROLLING PINIONS,WELCH
   SPRING & CO................................................     215.00
CLOCK,DRESSER,ANSONIA,6 IN................................      35.00
CLOCK,DRESSER,NEW HAVEN,HAND-PAINTED FLOWERS,PORCELAIN,
   5 1/2 X 5 IN.TALL..........................................      14.00
CLOCK,DUTCH MARQUETRY,LONG CASE,18TH CENTURY..............     500.00
CLOCK,DUTCH MARQUETRY,MUSICAL,LONG CASE,18TH CENTURY,8 FEET
   HIGH.......................................................     450.00
CLOCK,EASEL,LAUREL-CHASED FRAME,BLACK ENAMEL DIAL,DORE,
   BRONZE,11 IN.HIGH..........................................     275.00
CLOCK,EIGHT DAY,DOUBLE FUSEE,ROSEWOOD CASE,STRIKES,C.JEROME,
   15 X 10 IN.................................................      75.00
CLOCK,EIGHT DAY,STRIKE,ROSEWOOD CASE,SETH THOMAS,NEW FACE...      60.00
CLOCK,EMPIRE ORMOLU PORTICO,19TH CENTURY..................     250.00
CLOCK,FATTORONI & SONS,AUTOMATIC ALARM,BRADFORD PATENT,11 X
   13 IN......................................................      32.50
CLOCK,FLORAL DECOR,PORCELAIN,WATERBURY....................      25.00
CLOCK,FOLIAGE WREATH ON DIAL,URN,FOLIAGE,DOME CASE,MCCABE,
   LONDON.....................................................     125.00
CLOCK,FOUR-BAR CHIME,BEVELED GLASS IN DOOR,31 IN..........      35.00
CLOCK,FRENCH CRYSTAL,MERCURY PENDULUM,SETH THOMAS.........      45.00
CLOCK,FRENCH ORMOLU FIGURAL,MANTEL,19TH CENTURY...........     275.00
CLOCK,FRENCH,ARCHED SWAN PENDULUM,SILVER DIAL,GILDED
   HARDWARE...................................................     150.00
CLOCK,GALLERY,DEEP GOLD,EIGHT-DAY,SPRING PENDULUM,21 IN.....     148.00
CLOCK,GALLERY,DOUBLE SPRING LEVER ACTION,SECOND HAND,SETH
   THOMAS.....................................................      45.00
CLOCK,GEORGIAN,EBONIZED,SHELF,T.LYNCH,19TH CENTURY.........     550.00
CLOCK,GILBERT,OCTAGON,SHORT DROP..........................      55.00
CLOCK,GILDED CAST IRON,SHELF,19TH CENTURY.................      70.00
CLOCK,GINGERBREAD,OAK,REFINISHED..........................      36.00
CLOCK,GOTHIC TYPE,ROSEWOOD CASE,GOLD LEAF TRIM,1880,30-HOUR,
   LABEL,JEROME...............................................      40.00
CLOCK,GRANDFATHER,BONNET TOP,EIGHT-DAY,BRASS DIAL,OAK,
   ENGLAND....................................................     400.00
CLOCK,GRANDFATHER,BRASS FACE,WEIGHTS,PENDULUM,GERMANY,
   6 FT.8 IN..................................................     250.00
CLOCK,GRANDFATHER,BRASS PENDULUM BALL,OAK,MISSION,72 IN.TALL      85.00
CLOCK,GRANDFATHER,BRASS WEIGHTS,PENDULUM,DOOR,OAK,
   GERMANY...........................................130.00 TO    145.00
```

```
CLOCK,GRANDFATHER,CHIMES,WESTMINISTER......................   450.00
CLOCK,GRANDFATHER,FENNEMORE & SONS,ENGLAND..................   235.00
CLOCK,GRANDFATHER,HEPPLEWHITE,CHERRY,8 FT. 8 IN......ILLUS..   425.00
CLOCK,GRANDFATHER,STRIKES HOUR & HALF HOUR,MAHOGANY-FINISHED
   PINE CASE...............................................   235.00
CLOCK,GRANDFATHER,STRIKING GONG,BRASS SPRING-DRIVEN,
   PENDULUM,AMERICAN........................................    22.00
CLOCK,GRANDFATHER,WEIGHT-DRIVEN,FLORAL & SEASHELL DIAL,1800,
   MAPLE...................................................   345.00
CLOCK,GRANDFATHER,WOODEN WORKS,CIRCA 1820,HOADLEY,PINE CASE.   285.00
CLOCK,GRANDFATHER,WOODEN WORKS,QUEEN ANNE,CHERRY...........   595.00
CLOCK,GRANDFATHER,7 FT.4 IN................................   150.00
CLOCK,HANGING,PORCELAIN DIAL,R.A.ON PENDULUM,FRANCE,
   25 IN.HIGH..............................................   100.00
CLOCK,INGRAHAM,STRIKE,PICTURE ON DOOR,STENCIL DESIGN IN
   NECK,WALNUT.............................................    75.00
CLOCK,IRON,BRASS WORKS,MADE BY F.KROEBER CO.,NEW YORK,19 IN.    30.00
CLOCK,ITHACA,GRANDFATHER,EIGHT-DAY SPRING,STRIKING,MAHOGANY.   250.00
CLOCK,JADE,GOLD,EIGHT DAY,19 JEWEL,WHITE ENAMEL AROUND FACE,
   CARTIER...............................................1,500.00
CLOCK,JEROME & CO.,STEEPLE,15 IN.TALL......................    70.00
CLOCK,JEWELED & FILIGREED EXTERIOR,MADE IN TURKEY..........   600.00
CLOCK,KITCHEN,ANSONIA,BLACK WALNUT.........................    55.00
```

HEPPLEWHITE GRANDFATHER CLOCK

```
CLOCK,KITCHEN,BLUE & WHITE CHECKERED DESIGN,PORCELAIN,
   10 1/2 IN.SQUARE........................................    22.50
CLOCK,KITCHEN,DECORATED DOOR GLASS,EIGHT-DAY,WELCH,OAK,
   14 3/4 X 25 IN..........................................    35.00
CLOCK,KITCHEN,GILBERT,GINGERBREAD..........................    40.00
CLOCK,KITCHEN,GINGERBREAD STYLE,EIGHT-DAY,STRIKING MOVEMENT.    28.00
CLOCK,KITCHEN,GINGERBREAD,OAK,LABEL,GILBERT................    40.00
CLOCK,KITCHEN,MISSION......................................    25.00
CLOCK,KITCHEN,OAK.........................................    40.00
CLOCK,LONG CASE,MAHOGANY,WALKER M.FENNEMORE,BIRMINGHAM,
   93 IN.TALL..............................................   175.00 ·
CLOCK,LONGCASE,DRUM SHAPE HOOD,DOOR ON TRUNK,BRACKET FEET,
   HOWDEN,78 IN............................................    75.00
CLOCK,LONGCASE,QUEEN ANNE,DOOR ON TRUNK,CHERUB SPANDRELS,
   JOHN PEPYS...........................................1,700.00
CLOCK,LOUIS XVI BRONZE & MARBLE,MANTEL,RAINGO FRES.........   525.00
CLOCK,LOWER GLASS DEPICTS BATTLE BETWEEN CONSTITUTION &
   GUERRIERE,STRIKE........................................   120.00
CLOCK,MANTEL,AMERICAN,BLACK................................    19.50
CLOCK,MANTEL,BLACK MARBLE,9 1/2 IN. HIGH,BALL,BLACK & CO....   150.00
CLOCK,MANTEL,BLACK,IRON STRIKING,ANSONIA..................    25.00
CLOCK,MANTEL,BRASS LIONS' HEADS,RINGS,BRASS DECOR,BLACK,SETH
   THOMAS..................................................    30.00
CLOCK,MANTEL,BRONZE DIAL,BRONZE & MARBLE BASE,FEMALE FIGURE,
   CHERUBS.................................................   185.00
CLOCK,MANTEL,BRONZE GILT,CIRCA 1832,JAPPY-FRERES...........   150.00
```

```
CLOCK,MANTEL,EMPIRE EBONIZED,19TH CENTURY,19 IN. HIGH.......    100.00
CLOCK,MANTEL,FOUR BLACK ENAMEL PILLARS,BRASS FACE &
    PENDULUM,FRANCE...............................................    175.00
CLOCK,MANTEL,FOUR POSTS,SPERRY & SHOW.......................     85.00
CLOCK,MANTEL,FRENCH BLACK MARBLE,PORCELAIN DIAL,STRIKING....     35.00
CLOCK,MANTEL,FRENCH WORKS...................................     24.50
CLOCK,MANTEL,FRENCH WORKS,MARKED FOURTEEN-DAY STRIKE,DAINTY
    BRASS TRIM...................................................     22.00
CLOCK,MANTEL,GILBERT,6 IN.WIDE,12 IN.TALL...................     47.50
CLOCK,MANTEL,GILDED METAL & MARBLE,TIFFANY & CO.,11 1/2 IN.
    HIGH........................................................    250.00
CLOCK,MANTEL,GILT BUFFALO HEADS ON EACH SIDE,GILT FEET,
    ANSONIA.....................................................    135.00
CLOCK,MANTEL,GINGERBREAD,WALNUT CASE........................     38.00
CLOCK,MANTEL,GOLD-WASHED ROCOCO,PIPER,BAGPIPES,MEDALLIONS,
    1853........................................................    179.50
CLOCK,MANTEL,LION HEADS ON SIDE,PATENT 1880,SETH THOMAS.....     32.00
CLOCK,MANTEL,LOUIS XV,WHITE ENAMEL DIAL,GIRL FIGURE,ORMOLU,
    CHEVALLIER..................................................    325.00
CLOCK,MANTEL,LOUIS XVI,FEMALE FIGURE,ORMOLU,BRONZE,MARTIN A
    PARIS,24 IN.................................................    350.00
CLOCK,MANTEL,LOUIS XVI,ORMOLU,19TH CENTURY..................1,400.00
CLOCK,MANTEL,LOUIS XVI STYLE,ORMOLU,MARBLE,P.SORMANI,PARIS,
    22 1/2 IN...................................................    650.00
CLOCK,MANTEL,LOUIS-PHILIPPE,ORMOLU,WOMAN,PETAL BORDER,GILT
    METAL,20 IN.................................................    100.00
CLOCK,MANTEL,MARBLE & ORMOLU,TIFFANY,YOUNG & ELLIS,
    18 IN.HIGH..................................................    375.00
CLOCK,MANTEL,MARBLE CASE,ORMOLU,THOMIRE ET CIE,PARIS,
    25 1/2 IN.HIGH..............................................    475.00
CLOCK,MANTEL,MERCURY PENDULUM,ANSONIA MOVEMENT,BRASS,GLASS
    SIDES.......................................................     75.00
CLOCK,MANTEL,METAL COWBOY & ROPE ON TOP,WOOD...............     20.00
CLOCK,MANTEL,MIRRORS ON SIDES,BRASS FIGURINE,EIGHT-DAY,NEW
    HAVEN,STRIKE................................................     75.00
CLOCK,MANTEL,MIRROR SIDES,ANGELS...........................    165.00
CLOCK,MANTEL,MISSION.......................................     35.00
CLOCK,MANTEL,NEW HAVEN,BLACK...............................     17.50
CLOCK,MANTEL,NEW HAVEN,MARBLE,IRON BASE,EIGHT-DAY,STRIKE,
    15 X 10 IN.TALL.............................................     41.00
CLOCK,MANTEL,ORMOLU TRIM,CIRCA 1754,VERNIS MARTIN..........    725.00
CLOCK,MANTEL,ORMOLU,EMPIRE,EUROPA ON BULL,DANCING NYMPHS,
    23 IN.HIGH..................................................    175.00
CLOCK,MANTEL,OUTSIDE ESCAPEMENT,BLACK,GILBERT....... 7.50 TO     17.50
CLOCK,MANTEL,PEAK TOP,BUTTON DECORATION,TABLET GLASS,COUPLE,
    LAMBS,WELCH.................................................     45.00
CLOCK,MANTEL,ROUNDED GOTHIC,WOOD INLAY CASE,SETH THOMAS,8 X
    13 IN.......................................................     22.50
CLOCK,MANTEL,SESSIONS......................................     19.50
CLOCK,MANTEL,SETH THOMAS,MARBELIZED BROWN FINISH,BRASS FEET,
    EIGHT-DAY...................................................     35.00
CLOCK,MANTEL,SHERATON,GILT METAL CLAW FEET,SATINWOOD,
    ROSEWOOD BORDERS............................................    180.00
CLOCK,MANTEL,SILVER FACE,BRASS SPANDRELS,CARVING ON TOP,
    SIDES,GERMANY...............................................     60.00
CLOCK,MANTEL,STRIKES ON CURLED GONGS,ADJUSTABLE FLY,
    WESTMINISTER,GERMANY........................................     48.00
CLOCK,MANTEL,WHITE MARBLE,LOUIS XVI,VENUS,CHERUBS,FLORAL
    SWAGS,14 IN.................................................1,000.00
CLOCK,MARBLE,16 IN.HIGH X 20 IN.LONG........................     47.50
CLOCK,MARBLE,FRENCH WORKS,GOLD DIAL........................     24.50
CLOCK,MARINE CHRONOMETER,56-HOUR UP & DOWN SCALE,BRASS CASE
    & HANDLES...................................................    290.00
CLOCK,MARINE,SECOND HAND,CHERRY CASE,E.HOWARD..............    175.00
CLOCK,MECHANICAL,BELL,HAMMER,TACHOMETER,MODEL A741,SETH
    THOMAS......................................................     35.00
CLOCK,MEDALLION,WHITE ENAMELED MYTHOLOGICAL FIGURES,
    A.KAUFFMANN.................................................    135.00
CLOCK,MERCURY PENDULUM,ENCASED IN BRASS & BEVELED GLASS,
    FRANCE,9 IN.................................................     90.00
CLOCK,MERCURY PENDULUM,GOLDEN OAK CASE,STANDARD ELECTRIC
    TIME CO.....................................................    250.00
CLOCK,NEW HAVEN,EIGHT-DAY REGULATOR,PENDULUM,CALENDAR DIAL,
    15 X 35 IN..................................................     60.00
CLOCK,NEW HAVEN,TWELVE-DAY,KEY WIND,WALNUT FRAME...........     25.00
CLOCK,ONE-BAR CHIME,28 IN..................................     29.00
CLOCK,O.G.WEIGHT,TABLET IN THE DOOR........................     32.00
CLOCK,OCTAGON LONG DROP CALENDAR DIAL,NEW HAVEN,OAK,
    34 IN.LONG..................................................    110.00
CLOCK,OCTAGON,CALENDAR DIAL,OAK,ADAMS REGULATOR,32 IN.LONG..    110.00
CLOCK,ONE BAR CHIME,28 IN..................................     29.00
```

CLOCK,PARLIAMENT,MAHOGANY CASE,5 FT........................  195.00
CLOCK,PARLOR,PANSY MODEL,EIGHT-DAY,STRIKE,DRAPE & TASSEL
    DESIGN,INGRAHAM...........................................   45.00
CLOCK,PENDULUM,KEY,EIGHT-DAY,CHIME,WALNUT CASE,SESSIONS
    NO.2779..................................................   20.00
CLOCK,PICTURE FRAME,BRASS INLAY,MARBLE DIAL,BLUE NUMERALS,
    FRANCE...................................................  125.00
CLOCK,PILLAR & SCROLL,BY TERRY,29 IN.HIGH X 16 IN.WIDE......  750.00
CLOCK,PILLAR & SCROLL,ELMER STENNES........................  250.00
CLOCK,PILLAR,SCROLL,EGLOMISE DECOR,SETH THOMAS,CIRCA 1825,
    30 1/2 IN.HIGH...........................................  550.00
CLOCK,PLATO,LANTERN,ONE-DAY MOVEMENT,1905..................   75.00
CLOCK,PORCELAIN,BLUE ORNAMENTATION,ENFUSED PLAQUES OF
    FLOWERS,14-DAY...........................................   76.00
CLOCK,PORCELAIN,BLUE,TRIMMED IN GOLD,9 IN.TALL..............   96.00
CLOCK,PORCELAIN,EIGHT-DAY,STRIKING,WATERBURY...............   40.00
CLOCK,PORCELAIN,OCTAGONAL SHAPE,FOUR ROLLED EDGES,
    HAND-PAINTED,FRANCE......................................  105.00
CLOCK,PORCELAIN DIAL & PENDULUM,WALNUT CASE,ORNATE FINIALS,
    VIENNA,31 IN.............................................   75.00
CLOCK,PORTICO SHAPE,ENAMEL COLUMNS,WREATH ORNAMENT,GILT,
    FRANCE,3 5/8 IN..........................................   90.00
CLOCK,POST OFFICE,CHAIN FUSEE,ENGLAND......................   75.00
CLOCK,PRENTISS,CALENDAR....................................    4.00
CLOCK,RAILROAD TYPE,WEIGHT,OAK CASE,SETH THOMAS,35 IN.LONG.   90.00
CLOCK,RAILROAD,WEIGHT,PENDULUM,ROSEWOOD CASE,32 IN.........   95.00
CLOCK,REGULATOR,BRASS WEIGHTS,PORCELAIN DIAL,CARVED WALNUT
    CASE,VIENNA..............................................  110.00
CLOCK,REGULATOR,CHERRY CASE,HOWARD,16-IN.DIAL..............  300.00
CLOCK,REGULATOR,CHERRY CASE,WEIGHT-DRIVEN,COLORED GLASS,
    BOSTON CLOCK CO..........................................  150.00
CLOCK,REGULATOR,E.HOWARD...................................  250.00
CLOCK,REGULATOR,INGRAM,30 IN...............................   55.00
CLOCK,REGULATOR,RED,BLACK & GOLD LOWER GLASS,SIGNED,HOWARD,
    MODEL 70.................................................  195.00
CLOCK,REGULATOR,SETH THOMAS NO.3...........................  350.00
CLOCK,REGULATOR,THREE-WEIGHT,CARVINGS,VIENNA...............  300.00
CLOCK,REGULATOR,WALNUT CASE,E.HOWARD,6 FT..................  390.00
CLOCK,REGULATOR,WEIGHT-DRIVEN,CHELSEA......................  135.00
CLOCK,REGULATOR,WEIGHT-DRIVEN,OCTAGONAL BEZEL,SETH THOMAS...  135.00
CLOCK,REGULATOR,WEIGHT-DRIVEN,30-DAY,ROSEWOOD CASE,ATKINS...  175.00
CLOCK,REPEATER,ENAMEL FACE & SIDES,6 IN.HIGH...............  525.00
CLOCK,ROOSEVELT,ANIMATED DIAL..............................   29.50
CLOCK,ROSEWOOD MARQUETRY,MANTEL,16 1/2 IN. HIGH............   80.00
CLOCK,ROUND TOP,SINGLE BRASS WEIGHT,OAK VENEER,SETH THOMAS,
    36 IN.LONG...............................................  142.00
CLOCK,SCHOOL,DOUBLE FUSEE,JEROME...........................  250.00
CLOCK,SCHOOL,DROP FRONT,TIME & STRIKE,EIGHT-DAY,MAHOGANY....   65.00
CLOCK,SCHOOL,REGULATOR,HOWARD..............................  250.00
CLOCK,SCHOOL,REGULATOR,SHORT DROP,INGRAHAM.................   68.00
CLOCK,SCHOOL,WALNUT,28 IN..................................   37.00
CLOCK,SCHOOL,WATERBURY,OAK CASE,DOOR HAS BEEN REMADE.......   75.00
CLOCK,SCHOOLHOUSE,28 IN....................................   47.00
CLOCK,SCHOOLHOUSE,EIGHT-DAY,OAK CASE.......................   59.00
CLOCK,SCHOOLHOUSE,ENGLISH TYPE DROP,NEW HAVEN,CHERRY.......   85.00
CLOCK,SCHOOLHOUSE,GILBERT,OAK,28 IN.LONG...................   85.00
CLOCK,SCHOOLHOUSE,IVORY INLAY,ENGLAND,REFINISHED...........   70.00
CLOCK,SCHOOLHOUSE,MINIATURE,EIGHT-DAY,DAINTIE NO.1,WATERBURY   75.00
CLOCK,SCHOOLHOUSE,OCTAGON,DARK OAK,9 IN.DIAL,REBUILT,14 X
    21 1/2 IN................................................   55.00
CLOCK,SCHOOLHOUSE,REGULATOR,DROP-PENDULUM PORT,GILBERT
    LABEL,OAK................................................   72.00
CLOCK,SCHOOLHOUSE,SETH THOMAS..............................   75.00
CLOCK,SELF-WINDING CLOCK COMPANY,NEW YORK,OAK CASE,
    48 IN.HIGH...............................................  138.00
CLOCK,SESSION,REVERSE PAINTING ON DOOR,SHIP,TIME ONLY,
    WALNUT,33 IN.............................................   90.00
CLOCK,SETH THOMAS,DOVER MODEL,SPRAY OF FLOWERS,MAHOGANY,
    18 3/4 IN.HIGH...........................................   33.00
CLOCK,SETH THOMAS,STRIKE,RAISED NUMERALS,FIFTEEN-DAY,SILVER
    DIAL,BRONZE..............................................   46.00
CLOCK,SHELF,30-HOUR,ROSEWOOD,JEROME & COMPANY..............   48.00
CLOCK,SHELF,BEVEL GLASS SIDES,BRASS FRAME,MERCURY PENDULUM,
    FRANCE...................................................   65.00
CLOCK,SHELF,BRASS WORKS,WEIGHT-DRIVEN,EAGLE ON GLASS,SETH
    THOMAS...................................................   65.00
CLOCK,SHELF,EIGHT-DAY,GLASS DOOR,STRIKES,WOOD,A.INGRAHAM,
    13 1/4 IN.HIGH...........................................   42.00
CLOCK,SHELF,INLAID MAHOGANY,C.1825.........................  700.00
CLOCK,SHELF,KITCHEN,CALENDAR,WALNUT........................   68.00
CLOCK,SHELF,MUSICAL,PORCELAIN FACE,ORNATE WOODEN CASE......   92.00

| | |
|---|---:|
| CLOCK,SHELF,OAK,28 X 8 IN. | 25.00 |
| CLOCK,SHELF,PUMEROY MOVEMENT,CALENDAR,ITHACA,WALNUT | 275.00 |
| CLOCK,SHELF,REVERSE PAINTED GLASS,MAHOGANY VENEER CASE,MAKER W.L.GILBERT. | 65.00 |
| CLOCK,SHELF,SHAPE OF CASTLE,PARAPET,FOOTED,LENAKIRCH,BRONZE, 16 IN. | 195.00 |
| CLOCK,SHELF,TIME,ALARM,STRIKE,EIGHT-DAY,JEROME | 35.00 |
| CLOCK,SHELF,WEIGHT-DRIVEN,EAGLE ON GLASS,SETH THOMAS,BRASS. | 65.00 |
| CLOCK,SHELF,WEIGHT,30-HOUR,GEORGE V.HOUSE,N.Y.,MAHOGANY,16 X 26 IN. | 60.00 |
| CLOCK,SHELF,WOOD MOVEMENT,30-HOUR,STRIKING,ELDRIDGE ATKINS, 31 IN.TALL | 75.00 |
| CLOCK,SHELF,WOODEN WORKS,PAINTING OF TWO GIRLS ON GLASS,ELI TERRY JR | 145.00 |
| CLOCK,SHIP SCENE,ANIMATED DIAL,SEAMAN,WHEEL,F.D.R.,MAN OF THE HOUR | 75.00 |
| CLOCK,SHIP,BELL,TIME & STRIKE,SETH THOMAS,6-IN.DIAL | 180.00 |
| CLOCK,SHIP,OCTAGON SHAPE,EIGHT-DAY,WOOD | 20.00 |
| CLOCK,SHIP,RINGS SHIP'S BELLS,WATERBURY,BRASS,9 1/2 IN.HIGH. | 175.00 |
| CLOCK,SHOWBOAT,ALARM | 25.00 |
| CLOCK,SILAS HOADLEY,GRANDFATHER,CALENDAR | 50.00 |
| CLOCK,SPINNING WHEEL,ALARM | 25.00 |
| CLOCK,SQUARE FACE,BROWN WOODEN EASEL,EIGHT-DAY,SETH THOMAS. | 20.00 |
| CLOCK,STATIONARY HAND,DIAL REVOLVES ON PLATFORM. | 27.00 |
| CLOCK,STEEPLE,EIGHT-DAY,STRIKE,20 IN.TALL. | 60.00 |
| CLOCK,STEEPLE,EIGHT-DAY,WILLIAM L.GILBERT CO.,20 IN | 65.00 |
| CLOCK,STEEPLE,EIGHT-DAY,WIND,BRISTOL,CONNECTICUT | 145.00 |
| CLOCK,STEEPLE,ONE-DAY,TERRY & ANDREWS,20 IN.TALL | 49.00 |
| CLOCK,STEEPLE,TIME & STRIKE,EIGHT DAY,SETH THOMAS | 55.00 |
| CLOCK,STEEPLE,TIME,STRIKE,ALARM,ROUND DIAL,30-HOUR, 17 IN.HIGH. | 64.00 |
| CLOCK,STEEPLE,30-HOUR,CONNECTICUT CLOCK COMPANY | 75.00 |
| CLOCK,STEEPLE,30-HOUR,NEW HAVEN. | 65.00 |
| CLOCK,STEEPLE,30-HOUR,STRIKE,BREWSTER & INGRAHAM. | 80.00 |
| CLOCK,STREET,TWO-FACED,WEIGHT-DRIVEN,BROWN STREET CLOCK CO., 14 FEET | 1,750.00 |
| CLOCK,SWINGING ARM,FRANCE,24 IN.HIGH X 12 IN.WIDE. | 850.00 |
| CLOCK,TALL CASE,BRACKET FEET,HEPPLEWHITE,INLAID WALNUT, 99 IN.HIGH. | 650.00 |
| CLOCK,THIRTY-DAY,OAK CASE,SETH THOMAS,24 IN.DIAMETER | 90.00 |
| CLOCK,THREE PILLARS,FLORAL,PORCELAIN,10 IN.HIGH. | 30.00 |
| CLOCK,TWO DIALS,CALENDAR,ITHACA,WALNUT. | 250.00 |
| CLOCK,VIENNA REGULATOR,TWO WEIGHTS,SECOND HAND,WALNUT CASE, FINIAL,48 IN. | 130.00 |
| CLOCK,W.L.GILBERT,TWO-BAR CHIME,30 IN. | 34.00 |
| CLOCK,WALL,CALENDAR DATES AROUND FACE,PENDULUM,OAK,SESSIONS. | 85.00 |
| CLOCK,WALL,CONNECTICUT,24 IN.LONG. | 45.00 |
| CLOCK,WALL,DOUBLE WEIGHT,NEW DIAL,WALNUT CASE,ANSONIA,54 IN. | 123.00 |
| CLOCK,WALL,FREE SWINGER,GERMANY. | 85.00 |
| CLOCK,WALL,GALLERY,ROUND,REFINISHED OAK,INGRAHAM,16 1/2 IN. | 30.00 |
| CLOCK,WALL,GLASS DOOR,BRASS PENDULUM,VIENNA REGULATOR, ENGLAND. | 65.00 |
| CLOCK,WALL,GLASS-COVERED FACE,BRASS MOVEMENT,PENDULUM,WOODEN FRAME. | 35.00 |
| CLOCK,WALL,LE ROY A PARIS,BRONZE,18 IN.HIGH,12 IN.WIDE. | 625.00 |
| CLOCK,WALL,MARINE,DOUBLE SPRING BALANCE WHEEL,BRASS CASE, WATERBURY. | 25.00 |
| CLOCK,WALL,MIRROR BACK,CARVED HEADPIECE,FINIALS,WALNUT INLAID,NEW HAVEN. | 75.00 |
| CLOCK,WALL,MISSION. | 45.00 |
| CLOCK,WALL,NEW BOTTOM GLASS,REVERSE GOLD BORDER,30-DAY,SETH THOMAS,OAK. | 175.00 |
| CLOCK,WALL,OCTAGONAL,DROP FRONT,SETH THOMAS,21 IN.HIGH. | 65.00 |
| CLOCK,WALL,OCTAGONALLY SHAPED,C.JEROME. | 32.00 |
| CLOCK,WALL,PEARL INLAY,EIGHT-DAY,WELSH. | 95.00 |
| CLOCK,WALL,PERPETUAL CALENDAR,WELCH. | 285.00 |
| CLOCK,WALL,REGULATOR,LONG,CALENDAR,OAK CASE. | 80.00 |
| CLOCK,WALL,REGULATOR,MUSICAL CHIME ON HOUR. | 65.00 |
| CLOCK,WALL,REGULATOR,8-DAY,BRASS WEIGHT,NEW DIAL,SECOND HAND,SETH THOMAS | 110.00 |
| CLOCK,WALL,ROUND TOP,V BOTTOM,EIGHT DAY,ANSONIA,31 IN.LONG. | 95.00 |
| CLOCK,WALL,SPRING DRIVE,BRASS PENDULUM,THERMOMETER, BAROMETER,60 IN. | 285.00 |
| CLOCK,WALL,SPRING-DRIVEN,43 IN. | 79.50 |
| CLOCK,WALL,SQUARE DIAL,BEVELED PLATE GLASS TABLET,CHIME BAR, GILBERT. | 50.00 |
| CLOCK,WALL,WEIGHT-DRIVEN,BRASS WORKS,EIGHT-DAY,O.GEE, WATERBURY,CONN. | 60.00 |
| CLOCK,WALTHAM,CHRONOMETER | 150.00 |
| CLOCK,WALTHAM,GRANDFATHER,WHITTINGTON,WESTMINSTER CHIMES, MOON PHASE | 1,250.00 |

```
CLOCK,WATERBURY,WEIGHT-DRIVEN REGULATOR,SECOND HAND,WALNUT,
  50 IN.LONG............................................    150.00
CLOCK,WEIGHT,BERGE PECK & CO.,BRISTOL,CONN.,PICTURE OF
  TRAIN,EIGHT-DAY......................................     110.00
CLOCK,WEIGHT,PILLAR,WOODEN WORKS,HENRY TERRY.............    125.00
CLOCK,WEIGHT,WOODEN WORKS,CHAUNCEY BOARDMAN.............     125.00
CLOCK,WHITE GROUND,SMALL FLOWERS AROUND BORDER,PORCELAIN,
  8 IN.................................................      13.00
CLOCK,WOODEN GEARS,WOOD,9 X 8 1/2 IN....................     12.00
CLOCK,WOODEN WORKS,EAGLE HANDS,THIRTY-HOUR,STENCILED SPLAT,
  ELI TERRY...........................................      450.00
CLOCK,WOODEN WORKS,JEROME & DARROW......................    100.00
CLOCK,WOODEN WORKS,MIRROR,DOOR,BELL STRIKES,BURR &
  CHITTENDEN..........................................       95.00
CLOCK,WOODEN WORKS,NEW GLASS IN BOTTOM,30 HOUR,ELI TERRY,
  34 IN.HIGH..........................................       95.00
CLOCK,WOODEN,MOUNTED IN BRASS,RUSSIA....................     38.00
CLOCK,400 DAY,BRASS,GERMANY.............................     25.00


     CLOISONNE ENAMEL WAS DEVELOPED DURING THE NINETEENTH
     CENTURY. A GLASS ENAMEL WAS APPLIED BETWEEN SMALL
     RIBBON-LIKE PIECES OF METAL ON A METAL BASE. MOST
     CLOISONNE IS JAPANESE.
CLOISONNE,ASHTRAY,ENAMELED,ATTACHED MATCHBOX HOLDER.........   29.00
CLOISONNE,ASHTRAY,RED COLORING,MARKED,4 1/2-IN.DIAMETER.....   14.00
CLOISONNE,ASHTRAY,TWO PARTS,REVOLVING TOP,GREEN,COPPER
  ACCENTS...............................................       8.00
CLOISONNE,BELT BUCKLE,BLUE FORAL PATTERN,1 3/4 IN.WIDE X
  2 3/4 IN.LONG..........................................     45.00
CLOISONNE,BIRD,CH'IEN LUNG PERIOD,5 IN.LONG X 4 IN.HIGH,PAIR1,000.00
CLOISONNE,BIRDS,CH'IEN LUNG,5 1/2 IN..................ILLUS..1,500.00
CLOISONNE,BIRDS,CH'IEN LUNG,COCK AND HEN,STAND.......ILLUS..1,500.00
CLOISONNE,BLOTTER,ROCKER TYPE...........................       7.50
CLOISONNE,BOTTLE,SNUFF,BLUE GROUND,AUTUMN FOLIAGE,STOPPER...  145.00
CLOISONNE,BOTTLE,SNUFF,BUDDHIST EMBLEMS,CLOUD MOTIFS,ENAMEL,
  BLUE...................................................    120.00
CLOISONNE,BOTTLE,SNUFF,GILDED METAL,ENAMEL..................  450.00
CLOISONNE,BOWL,ASHTRAY TYPE,BLACK GROUND,GOLDEN CLOISONNES,
  FLORAL.................................................     10.50
CLOISONNE,BOWL,BROWN GROUND,MULTICOLORED FLORAL,COBALT
  BOTTOM BORDER..........................................     37.50
CLOISONNE,BOWL,BROWN,DECOR,COVER,FLOWER FINIAL,FOOTED,4 IN..   30.00
```

CLOISONNE ENAMEL BIRDS,
CHIEN LUNG

CLOISONNE ENAMEL COCK AND
HEN, CHIEN LUNG

CLOISONNE,BOWL,DRAGONS,BIRDS,BUTTERFLIES,RED,GREEN,FOOTED,
   COVER,PAIR...................................................... 250.00
CLOISONNE,BOWL,FINGER,BLACK GROUND,RED & WHITE BLOSSOMS,
   GOLD,BLUE LINING.............................................. 19.00
CLOISONNE,BOWL,FINGER,RED TOP,YELLOW FLORAL,BLUE BASE,BLUE
   LINING........................................................ 19.00
CLOISONNE,BOWL,RICE,BLACK GROUND,FLORAL IN GREEN,BLUE,PINK,
   YELLOW,WHITE.................................................. 19.50
CLOISONNE,BOWL,RICE,MAROON & BLUE FLOWERS..................... 12.00
CLOISONNE,BOWL,RICE,RED & YELLOW FLORAL,GREEN GROUND,,
   4 1/2 IN.WIDE................................................. 6.50
CLOISONNE,BOWL,RUST-RED GROUND,FLORAL,COVER,2 1/2 IN.HIGH... 25.00
CLOISONNE,BOX & MATCHBOX HOLDER,GREEN,ALLOVER FLORAL DECOR,
   CHINA........................................................ 18.50
CLOISONNE,BOX,ALLOVER GEOMETRIC DESIGN,FLORAL,BLUE LINING,
   BRASS FEET................................................... 27.50
CLOISONNE,BOX,BLACK GROUND,VARIEGATED FLOWERS,COVER,3 X
   3 IN......................................................... 16.00
CLOISONNE,BOX,BLACK GROUND,YELLOW DRAGON,3-IN.DIAMETER...... 22.00
CLOISONNE,BOX,BLUE GROUND,FLORAL,LID,FOOTED,3 1/2 IN.LONG... 40.00
CLOISONNE,BOX,CIGAR,GREEN,RED,GOLD,COBALT,3-IN.DIAMETER..... 13.50
CLOISONNE,BOX,COLORFUL DRAGONS ON LID,CHINA 3 3/4 IN.LONG... 30.00
CLOISONNE,BOX,DRAGON DESIGN,BLUE,GREEN,GOLD,RED,COVER,CHINA,
   3 1/2 IN..................................................... 35.00
CLOISONNE,BOX,ENAMELED,COVER,4 IN.LONG....................... 43.00
CLOISONNE,BOX,GREEN GROUND,CHRYSANTHEMUMS,FOLIAGE,LINED BLUE
   ENAMEL,LID................................................... 13.50
CLOISONNE,BOX,GREEN GROUND,3 IN.............................. 18.00
CLOISONNE,BOX,GREEN GROUND,CHRYSANTHEMUM,PLUM BLOSSOMS,
   ENAMEL,LINING,LID............................................ 18.50
CLOISONNE,BOX,LADY ON LID,HINGED,5 3/4 IN.LONG............... 85.00
CLOISONNE,BOX,MELON RIB,FLORAL,BUTTERFLIES,BLUE LINING,
   FOOTED,COVER................................................. 35.00
CLOISONNE,BOX,PERIWINKLE BLUE,MANY TINY CLOISONNES,COVER,3 X
   3 IN......................................................... 17.00
CLOISONNE,BOX,RED-PURPLE GROUND,BLUE,PINK MORNING GLORIES,
   GREEN LINING................................................. 42.00
CLOISONNE,BOX,RED,GOLD WIRES,FLORAL,BLUE ENAMEL LINING,LID,
   SIGNED....................................................... 35.00
CLOISONNE,BOX,REPOUSSE,FIGURES IN RELIEF,RAISED MEDALLION ON
   COVER,LID.................................................... 13.50
CLOISONNE,BOX,TOBACCO,MULTICOLORED,BRASS FOO DOG FINIAL,6 X
   8 IN.HIGH.................................................... 18.00
CLOISONNE,BOX,TRINKET,BIRD OF PARADISE DESIGN,HINGED COVER,
   FOOTED....................................................... 18.00
CLOISONNE,BOX,WHITE,GREEN DESIGN,BLUE ENAMEL INTERIOR,MARKED
   CHINA,LID.................................................... 15.00
CLOISONNE,BOX,WHITE,GREEN DESIGN,BLUE INTERIOR,HINGED COVER,
   MARKED CHINA................................................. 15.00
CLOISONNE,BOX,WHITE,RED & BLUE FLORAL,FOO DOG FINIAL,
   5 1/2 IN.ROUND............................................... 35.00
CLOISONNE,BOX,YELLOW DRAGON,BLACK GROUND,BLUE ENAMEL INSIDE
   & BOTTOM..................................................... 45.00
CLOISONNE,BOX,YELLOW GROUND,CHRYSANTHEMUM,FOLIAGE,BLUE
   ENAMEL-LINED,LID............................................. 27.50
CLOISONNE,CANDLESTICK,BLACK,TURQUOISE DRAGON,6 IN.,PAIR..... 65.00
CLOISONNE,CUP,BLUE,MULTICOLOR CHARACTERS,BRASS,STERLING
   SILVER BODY.................................................. 85.00
CLOISONNE,DECANTER,OIL,WITH SAUCER,PAIR...................... 65.00
CLOISONNE,DESK BLOTTER,ROLLER TYPE,BLUE...................... 12.50
CLOISONNE,DISH,BLUE GROUND,LANDSCAPE,PANEL,FAN SHAPE,
   6 1/2 IN..................................................... 20.00
CLOISONNE,DISH,CANDY,THREE SECTIONS,GREEN GROUND,FLORAL,
   20 1/2 IN.................................................... 65.00
CLOISONNE,DISH,FLORAL DESIGN,STAND,4 1/2-IN.DIAMETER........ 17.50
CLOISONNE,DISH,SWEETMEAT,PEDESTAL,BRASS FINIAL,BANDS,MARKED
   CHINA,8 IN................................................... 24.00
CLOISONNE,FIGURINE,ELEPHANT,ALTAR,SEMI-PRECIOUS JEWELS,
   13 IN.HIGH,PAIR............................................2,000.00
CLOISONNE,FOOD WARMER,THREE COMPARTMENTS,BLUE LINING,BRASS
   TRIVET....................................................... 50.00
CLOISONNE,FRAME,GREEN,BUTTERFLIES,FLORAL,5 1/2 IN. X 7 IN... 30.00
CLOISONNE,HOLDER,BRUSH,FLORAL & GOLDSTONE DECOR,4 IN.TALL... 38.00
CLOISONNE,INCENSE BURNER,FOO DOG FINIAL,10 IN............... 75.00
CLOISONNE,JAR,FLOWERS,BUTTERFLIES,BULBOUS,FOOTED,COVER,
   4 IN.HIGH.................................................... 42.00
CLOISONNE,JAR,GINGER,BLUE GROUND,FLORAL DECOR,PAIR.......... 120.00
CLOISONNE,JAR,GINGER,GREEN,RED FLOWERS,COVER,4 IN........... 22.50
CLOISONNE,JAR,GINGER,RED GROUND,BLUE,WHITE,GREEN FLORAL..... 45.00
CLOISONNE,JAR,GINGER,WHITE GROUND,FLORAL,YELLOW BUDS,BLUE
   ENAMEL INSIDE................................................ 89.50

CLOISONNE,JAR,GINGER,WHITE GROUND,RED & BLUE FLORAL,TEAK
BASE,7 IN................................................ 85.00
CLOISONNE,JAR,ROSE,OVERALL FLORAL,BRASS CIRCLES,FLAT TOP,
TEAK BASE,PAIR........................................... 75.00
CLOISONNE,JAR,RUSTY-RED GROUND,FLORAL DECOR,COVER,7 1/2 IN.. 37.50
CLOISONNE,JAR,YELLOW GROUND,BLUE,RED,GREEN FLORAL,TEAK BASE,
9 IN.,PAIR............................................... 150.00
CLOISONNE,JARDINIERE,BLUE BAND,7 IN. X 5 1/2 IN.HIGH........ 65.00
CLOISONNE,LAMP,BLUE GROUND,FLORAL,VASES OF FLOWERS,WHITE
SHADE,8 1/2 IN........................................... 70.00
CLOISONNE,LAMP,TABLE,YELLOW,GREEN,BLUE,RED,FOOTED BRASS
BASE,2 SOCKETS........................................... 150.00
CLOISONNE,LETTER RACK,FLORAL MOTIF,BLUE-GREEN GROUND,TWO
SECTIONS................................................. 45.00
CLOISONNE,MATCH HOLDER,PENNY BOX,FLORAL.................... 6.50
CLOISONNE,MUSTARD POT,WHITE GROUND,BLUE & RED FLORAL,HINGED
COVER.................................................... 20.00
CLOISONNE,MUSTARD,BLACK GROUND,FLORAL...................... 6.00
CLOISONNE,NAPKIN RING,BLUE FLORAL PATTERN,SET OF 6......... 150.00
CLOISONNE,NAPKIN RING,BLUE GROUND,MAROON & YELLOW FLORAL,
MARKED CHINA............................................. 9.00
CLOISONNE,NAPKIN RING,DRAGON DECOR......................... 7.00
CLOISONNE,NAPKIN RING,FISHSCALE PATTERN.................... 8.50
CLOISONNE,NAPKIN RING,FLORAL............................... 8.00
CLOISONNE,NAPKIN RING,GREEN GROUND,PINK,BLUE,FLORAL,BUDS,
MARKED CHINA............................................. 9.00
CLOISONNE,NAPKIN RING,OVAL................................. 9.00
CLOISONNE,NAPKIN RING,TWO BUTTERFLIES,GREEN GROUND,BLUE DOT
BORDER................................................... 15.00
CLOISONNE,PILLBOX,ENAMEL,SILVER,ENGRAVED SCENE,BY FALLACI OF
FLORENCE................................................. 75.00
CLOISONNE,PITCHER,BLACK GROUND,PASTEL BUTTERFLIES,
5 3/4 IN.HIGH............................................ 65.00
CLOISONNE,PITCHER,MINIATURE,BLUE GROUND,RED,WHITE,GREEN
FLORAL,1 1/2 IN.......................................... 30.00
CLOISONNE,PLANTER,ENAMELED,5 IN.HIGH,3-IN.DIAMETER,PAIR..... 900.00
CLOISONNE,PLAQUE,BIRD DECOR,13 1/2-IN.DIAMETER............. 190.00
CLOISONNE,PLAQUE,BLACK GROUND,FLORAL,BIRDS,BUTTERFLIES,
12-IN.DIAMETER........................................... 55.00
CLOISONNE,PLAQUE,FLORAL DECOR,SCALLOPED RIM,15-IN.DIAMETER.. 350.00
CLOISONNE,PLAQUE,FLORAL DECOR,15-IN.DIAMETER............... 300.00
CLOISONNE,PLAQUE,WHEELBARROW WITH FLOWERS,SCALLOPED RIM,
12-IN.DIAMETER........................................... 95.00
CLOISONNE,PLATE,BIRDS,FLOWERS,BERRIES,BLUE GROUND,11 IN..... 84.00
CLOISONNE,PLATE,BLACK GROUND,BIRDS WINGING ACROSS BAMBOO,
14 1/2 IN................................................ 195.00
CLOISONNE,PLATE,BLUE GROUND,BIRD,PEONIES,9 1/4 IN........... 47.50
CLOISONNE,PLATE,BLUE,BUTTERFLIES,RAYED DECOR,FLORAL,
14-IN.DIAMETER........................................... 110.00
CLOISONNE,PLATE,BLUE,CHRYSANTHEMUM,BIRD,12 IN.,PAIR........ 290.00
CLOISONNE,PLATE,BLUE,QUAILS,REEDS,YELLOW BERRIES,12 IN...... 110.00
CLOISONNE,PLATE,BROWN GROUND,BUTTERFLIES,FANS,BLOSSOMS,
8 1/2 IN.,PAIR........................................... 259.50
CLOISONNE,PLATE,CHINESE SCENE,WATER,BOATS,MOUNTAINS,
6 3/4-IN.DIAMETER........................................ 19.00
CLOISONNE,PLATE,GREEN,PLUM TREE,PINK BUDS,WHITE BLOSSOMS,
ALSO BACK DECOR.......................................... 79.50
CLOISONNE,SHAKER,PEPPER,OPEN SALT,SPOON,FLORAL............. 14.00
CLOISONNE,TEAPOT,GREEN,BLUE,YELLOW........................ 47.50
CLOISONNE,TEAPOT,MINIATURE,RED,WHITE & GREEN FLORAL,
2 IN.HIGH................................................ 35.00
CLOISONNE,TEAPOT,MINIATURE,YELLOW GROUND,DRAGON,CANE HANDLE,
3 1/4 IN................................................. 55.00
CLOISONNE,TOOTHPICK,MULTICOLORED FLOWERS.................. 8.50
CLOISONNE,URN,BLUE GROUND,BRASS RIM,BASE,FINIAL,DOME COVER,
10 IN.HIGH............................................... 125.00
CLOISONNE,URN,BLUE,GILT,FLORAL,BRASS TRIM,TEAK STAND,CHINA,
8 IN.,PAIR............................................... 75.00
CLOISONNE,VASE,ALTERNATING PANELS,TURQUOISE,GOLD,FLORAL,
WIREWORK,6 IN............................................ 28.00
CLOISONNE,VASE,BEIGE GROUND,PANELS,BIRDS,FLORAL,FANS,
7 1/4 IN.HIGH,PAIR....................................... 159.50
CLOISONNE,VASE,BLACK GROUND,BLUE FLOWERS,6 IN.HIGH......... 22.50
CLOISONNE,VASE,BLACK GROUND,FLORAL,PINK,GREEN,BROWN,
BUTTERFLY,9 1/2 IN....................................... 65.00
CLOISONNE,VASE,BLACK GROUND,ORCHID,5 IN.HIGH.............. 65.00
CLOISONNE,VASE,BLACK GROUND,YELLOW DRAGONS,FLAMING PEARL,
CHINA,6 1/2 IN........................................... 27.50
CLOISONNE,VASE,BLUE,BUTTERFLIES,FLORAL,CARVED TEAK COVER,
12 IN.................................................... 185.00
CLOISONNE,VASE,BLUE,CHRYSANTHEMUM BRANCHES,FOLIAGE,TEAK

STAND,9 3/4 IN............................................ 79.50
CLOISONNE,VASE,BLUE,CRANELIKE BIRDS,PASTEL FLORAL SPRAYS,
12 IN.,PAIR.............................................. 295.00
CLOISONNE,VASE,BLUE,FLORA,10 IN.......................... 40.00
CLOISONNE,VASE,BLUE,GREEN,BROWN,GOLD,FLECKS,6 IN.HIGH...... 42.00
CLOISONNE,VASE,BLUE & GOLD DRAGON......................... 105.00
CLOISONNE,VASE,BLUE GROUND,BRASS CLOISONS OF TWO DRAGONS,
9 1/2 IN.,PAIR.......................................... 78.50
CLOISONNE,VASE,BLUE GROUND,FLORAL,BIRD,BUTTERFLY,5 X
10 IN.TALL.............................................. 95.00
CLOISONNE,VASE,BLUE GROUND,FLORAL,ON COPPER,CIRCA 1910,
8 IN.TALL............................................... 60.00
CLOISONNE,VASE,BLUE GROUND,FLORAL,STAND,MARKED CHINA,
9 1/2 IN.TALL,PAIR...................................... 125.00
CLOISONNE,VASE,BLUE GROUND,MULTICOLORED DRAGON,5 1/4 IN..... 38.00
CLOISONNE,VASE,BLUE GROUND,PEONIES,BIRDS,COVER,CHINA,
7 1/4 IN.HIGH........................................... 92.50
CLOISONNE,VASE,BROWN GROUND,FLORAL,ENAMELED,8 IN.HIGH,PAIR.. 125.00
CLOISONNE,VASE,BROWN-RED,FLORAL,6 IN...................... 22.50
CLOISONNE,VASE,BUTTERFLIES,FLOWERS,3 1/2 IN.HIGH,PAIR....... 33.00
CLOISONNE,VASE,COBALT GROUND,FLORAL DECOR,14 IN.HIGH....... 115.00
CLOISONNE,VASE,DARK BLUE GROUND,IRIS,5 3/4 IN.HIGH,PAIR..... 98.00
CLOISONNE,VASE,DARK RED,WHITE PLUM BLOSSOMS,GREEN BAMBOO,
TEAK STAND.............................................. 55.00
CLOISONNE,VASE,DEEP RED GROUND,WHITE BLOSSOMS,GREEN BAMBOO,
TEAK STAND.............................................. 60.00
CLOISONNE,VASE,ENAMELED,PIGEON BLOOD,6 IN.HIGH............ 60.00
CLOISONNE,VASE,FISH,UNDERSEA VEGETATION,10 IN.HIGH,PAIR..... 150.00
CLOISONNE,VASE,FISHSCALE,BLUE TO WHITE TO GREEN,FLORAL,BRASS
BASE & TOP.............................................. 22.00
CLOISONNE,VASE,FISHSCALE PATTERN,WHITE,ROSE COLOR,GREEN
BORDER,CHINA............................................ 39.50
CLOISONNE,VASE,FIVE-CLAW DRAGON DESIGN,9 IN.TALL,PAIR....... 125.00
CLOISONNE,VASE,FLORAL,BUTTERFLY,GOLDSTONE,8 1/2 IN......... 45.00
CLOISONNE,VASE,FLORAL,PINK,WHITE,STEMS,LEAVES,YELLOW LINING,
9 1/2 IN................................................ 52.00
CLOISONNE,VASE,FULL FIGURE SAMURAI WARRIOR,BUTTERFLY,
FLOWERS,10 IN........................................... 125.00
CLOISONNE,VASE,GOLDSTONE GROUND,BLOSSOMS,GREEN LINING,BRASS
BOUND,8 IN.............................................. 55.00
CLOISONNE,VASE,GOLDSTONE WITH BUTTERFLY DECOR,3 3/4 IN...... 10.00
CLOISONNE,VASE,GRAY,SHIELDLIKE PANELS,PHOENIX BIRD,CHINESE
DESIGN,PAIR............................................. 103.50
CLOISONNE,VASE,GREEN,MULTICOLORED BIRDS,9 3/4 IN.HIGH....... 225.00
CLOISONNE,VASE,GREEN,RED POINSETTIAS,GREEN LEAVES,
3 3/4 IN.TALL........................................... 12.50
CLOISONNE,VASE,GREEN,WHITE,ENAMELED,9 IN.HIGH,PAIR......... 95.00
CLOISONNE,VASE,MULTICOLOR DECOR,BUTTERFLIES,4 1/2 IN.HIGH... 17.50
CLOISONNE,VASE,MUSTARD GROUND,SPIDER MUMS,MULTICOLORED
FLORAL,BRASS BASE....................................... 38.00
CLOISONNE,VASE,RED,DAISY DESIGN,SILVER RIM AT TOP & BOTTOM.. 35.00
CLOISONNE,VASE,RED,SILVER ROSES,BAMBOO PATTERN ON BACK,
6 IN.,PAIR.............................................. 90.00
CLOISONNE,VASE,RED,TWO WHITE DRAGONS,FLAMING PEARL,CHINA,
8 1/4 IN.HIGH........................................... 45.00
CLOISONNE,VASE,RED GROUND,BIRDS,WISTERIA IN GREEN,WHITE,
GRAY,6 IN.,PAIR......................................... 95.00
CLOISONNE,VASE,RUST,PINK,YELLOW,CHINA,5 1/4 IN.HIGH......... 18.50
CLOISONNE,VASE,SILVER BIRDS & BAMBOO DESIGN,CRANBERRY,
15 IN.TALL.............................................. 175.00
CLOISONNE,VASE,TRANSLUCENT RED GROUND,PRUNUS TREE,4 1/2 IN.. 35.00
CLOISONNE,VASE,WHITE FRONT ON SHADED PINK GROUND,COPPER
COLLAR,BASE,PAIR........................................ 110.00
CLOISONNE,VASE,WILD GOOSE AMID FLOWERS,REEDS,SILVER
WIREWORK,PAIR........................................... 85.00
CLOISONNE,VASE,YELLOW GROUND,LAVENDER CHRYSANTHEMUMS,
4 1/2 IN.,PAIR.......................................... 67.50
CLOISONNE,VASE,YELLOW-GREEN GROUND,PLUM TREE,BLUE,PINK,RED
IN BLOSSOMS............................................. 43.50
CLOISONNE,VASE,YELLOW,BLUE GROUND,DRAGONS ON SIDES,TEARDROP
SHAPE,9 IN.............................................. 55.00
CLUTHRA,SEE,KIMBALL,STEUBEN


COALPORT WARE HAS BEEN MADE BY THE COALPORT PORCELAIN
WORKS OF ENGLAND FROM 1795 TO THE PRESENT TIME.
COALPORT,CHOCOLATE POT,INDIAN TREE,ROSES,GREEN FOLIAGE,
6 CUPS & SAUCERS........................................ 92.50
COALPORT,CUP & SAUCER,INDIAN TREE............... 12.50 TO 14.50
COALPORT,CUP,EGG,INDIAN TREE............................. 5.75
COALPORT,DISH,FLORAL DECOR,CIRCA 1820,9 1/4 IN.SQUARE...... 75.00

```
COALPORT,DISH,SAUCE,INDIAN TREE,6 IN.......................   6.50
COALPORT,HOLDER,LETTER,CIRCA 1820,PAIR..............ILLUS..   300.00
COALPORT,PLATE,CREAM COLOR,PICTURE OF BILL SIKES,BULLDOG,
  9 IN............................................................   8.00
COALPORT,PLATE,INDIAN TREE,SCALLOPED,7 1/2 IN.,SET OF 6.....   45.00
COALPORT,PLATE,INDIAN TREE,SIDE HANDLES,9 IN.SQUARE.........   18.50
COALPORT,PLATE,MUTED PINK GROUND,ROSE DECOR,HAND-PAINTED,
  12-IN.DIAMETER............................................   20.00
COALPORT,PLATE,PEMBROKE,CIRCA 1900,10 IN....................   10.00
COALPORT,SHOE,JEWELED,5 IN.LONG.............................   125.00
COALPORT,TEA SERVICE,BLUE BANDING,GILT LEAFAGE,PINK
  BLOSSOMS,30 PIECE..........................................   250.00
```

COBALT BLUE GLASS WAS MADE USING OXIDE OF COBALT. THE
CHARACTERISTIC BRIGHT DARK BLUE IDENTIFIES IT FOR THE
COLLECTOR. MOST COBALT GLASS FOUND TODAY WAS MADE AFTER
THE CIVIL WAR.
COBALT BLUE,SEE ALSO,SHIRLEY TEMPLE

COALPORT LETTER HOLDERS, C. 1820

```
COBALT BLUE,ATOMIZER,ENAMELED RED BERRIES,GREEN LEAVES,GOLD
  TRIM......................................................   12.00
COBALT BLUE,BANK,PIG........................................   4.50
COBALT BLUE,BERRY SET,KING'S 500,GOLD,SEVEN PIECES..........   115.00
COBALT BLUE,BONBONNIERE,EGG SHAPE,ENAMEL,COCK,HEN,LANDSCAPE,
  HINGED LID................................................   170.00
COBALT BLUE,BOTTLE,BARBER,ENAMEL DECOR......................   35.00
COBALT BLUE,BOTTLE,BARBER,ENAMELED DECOR,BLOWN..............   37.50
COBALT BLUE,BOTTLE,MAN,WOMAN,CHILD,STOPPERS ARE HEADS,SET OF
  3..........................................................   22.50
COBALT BLUE,BOTTLE,MASTER MILK,QUART........................   6.00
COBALT BLUE,BOTTLE,SCENT,PEWTER SCREW TOP...................   30.00
COBALT BLUE,BOTTLE,SMOOTHED PONTIL,FLARED NECK,BLOWN,1907,
  9 1/2 IN.HIGH.............................................   19.00
COBALT BLUE,BOTTLE,VIOLIN...................................   4.00
COBALT BLUE,BOWL,FRUIT,ROYAL LACE,10-IN.DIAMETER............   12.00
COBALT BLUE,BOWL,GRAPE & LEAF,10 1/4 IN.....................   18.00
COBALT BLUE,BOWL,INVERTED THUMBPRINT,3 X 5 IN...............   10.00
COBALT BLUE,BOWL,ROSE,ENAMELED FLOWER DECOR.................   10.00
COBALT BLUE,BOWL,ROSE,FLORAL DECOR,FITS IN BLACK METAL
  HOLDER....................................................   15.00
COBALT BLUE,BOWL,RUFFLED,2 1/2 IN.HIGH,11-IN.DIAMETER.......   30.00
COBALT BLUE,BOX,JEWEL,ENAMEL FLOWERS,BRASS COLLAR ON BOWL
  AND COVER.................................................   45.00
COBALT BLUE,BOX,PATCH,CLASSIC BEAUTY PORTRAIT ON HINGED
  COVER.....................................................   22.50
COBALT BLUE,BOX,POWDER,PORTRAIT COVER,WOMAN,ARTIST RENEAU,
  5-IN.DIAMETER.............................................   35.00
COBALT BLUE,CANDLESTICK,RIBBED PATTERN,HAND-BLOWN,7 IN.,PAIR   12.50
COBALT BLUE,CHRISTMAS LIGHT HOLDER,2 1/2-IN.DIAMETER,
  4 IN.TALL.................................................   15.00
COBALT BLUE,CHRISTMAS TREE ORNAMENT,DIAMOND-QUILTED.........   8.50
COBALT BLUE,COMPOTE,GOLD TRIM,7 IN.HIGH,7 1/2 IN.ACROSS TOP.   6.00
COBALT BLUE,CRUET,DOUBLE SNAIL VARIANT,STOPPER,SWIRL PATTERN   65.00
COBALT BLUE,CRUET,INVERTED THUMBPRINT.......................   15.00
COBALT BLUE,CRUET,INVERTED THUMBPRINT,CLEAR REED HANDLE,CUT
  STOPPER...................................................   36.00
COBALT BLUE,CUP & SAUCER,DEMITASSE,GOLD DECOR...............   17.50
COBALT BLUE,CUP & SAUCER,GOLD...............................   16.00
COBALT BLUE,CUP,PUNCH,PARROT,GOLD EYES......................   8.50
COBALT BLUE,CUP,SAUCER,GOLD OVERLAY,GOLD COLOR CUP BOWL,
```

PEDESTAL CUP............................................................. 35.00
COBALT BLUE,DECANTER,CLEAR APPLIED HANDLE,CLEAR BALL
STOPPER,9 1/2 IN.......................................................... 9.50
COBALT BLUE,DECANTER,SILVER DECOR,MUSHROOM STOPPER,5 LIQUOR
GLASSES................................................................. 18.50
COBALT BLUE,DECANTER,WINE,BARREL SHAPE,SILVER OVERLAY,SIX
GLASSES................................................................ 125.00
COBALT BLUE,DISH,BONBON,SILVER BASE,SILVER PARROT PEDESTAL,
6 IN.HIGH.............................................................. 150.00
COBALT BLUE,DISH,CANDY,BASKET WEAVE,LATTICE BORDER............ 5.00
COBALT BLUE,DISH,GOLD CROWN,SWAN WITH ARROW THROUGH BREAST,
FRANCE................................................................... 9.00
COBALT BLUE,DISH,HOBNAIL,TRIANGULAR,THREE-MOLD,FOOTED,
5 1/2 IN................................................................ 10.00
COBALT BLUE,DISH,PIE FLUTED RIM,RAISED CIRCLES ON UNDERSIDE,
FOOTED................................................................... 7.00
COBALT BLUE,EYECUP,EMBOSSED WYETH........................... 5.50
COBALT BLUE,EYECUP,PEDESTAL,NAME JOHN BULL ON BASE,DATED
1917..................................................................... 9.00
COBALT BLUE,FLASK,OVAL,ENCASED IN ORNATE WOOD FIBER......... 22.00
COBALT BLUE,FLASK,WHISKEY,SHEARED TOP,GRAPES,UNICORN,
1/2 PINT................................................................ 30.00
COBALT BLUE,HAT,BLUE COIN SPOTS,SOUTH JERSEY GLASS,3 1/2 X
8 IN.LONG............................................................... 45.00
COBALT BLUE,INKWELL......................................... 3.00
COBALT BLUE,INKWELL,CYLINDRICAL,SLOPING SHOULDERS,ROUGH
PONTIL................................................................. 100.00
COBALT BLUE,JAR,CRACKER,WHITE ENAMELED FLOWERS,SILVER LID... 55.00
COBALT BLUE,LAMP,BEADED,MINIATURE............................ 25.00
COBALT BLUE,LAMP,FAIRY,DIAMOND POINT,BASE MARKED S.CLARKE
FAIRY PYRAMID.......................................................... 26.50
COBALT BLUE,LAMP,NIGHT,EMBOSSED NUTMEG,BRASS HANDLE........ 30.00
COBALT BLUE,LAMP,PANELED,MILK GLASS SHADE,MARKED GLO-LAMP
PAT.1895............................................................... 20.00
COBALT BLUE,LAMP,SIDE HANDLE,3 3/4-IN.DIAMETER,2 IN.HIGH.... 18.00
COBALT BLUE,PAPERWEIGHT,TURTLE,CLEAR HEAD & FEET,PILGRIM
LABEL.................................................................. 12.50
COBALT BLUE,PERFUME,BUFF & GOLD ENAMEL LEAF DECOR,BLOWN,
STOPPER................................................................ 18.00
COBALT BLUE,PITCHER,APPLIED CLEAR HANDLE,THREE TUMBLERS..... 18.00
COBALT BLUE,PITCHER,JERSEY SWIRL,BLOWN...................... 10.00
COBALT BLUE,PITCHER,SILVER BAND AROUND MIDDLE,SIX TUMBLERS,
SILVER HOLDER.......................................................... 35.00
COBALT BLUE,PITCHER,WATER,BLOWN,8 TUMBLERS.................. 60.00
COBALT BLUE,PITCHER,WATER,CLEAR APPLIED HANDLE,BULBOUS...... 9.00
COBALT BLUE,PITCHER,WATER,HALL CHINA........................ 4.00
COBALT BLUE,PITCHER,WATER,THREADED PATTERN,CLEAR HANDLE,
5 TUMBLERS............................................................. 27.50
COBALT BLUE,PITCHER,WATER,9 IN.............................. 6.00
COBALT BLUE,PLATE,BRASS LOBSTER,CRAB MOUNTED ON PLATE,BRASS
RIM,FEET............................................................... 35.00
COBALT BLUE,PLATE,HOT,ORNATE PATTERN,SILVER PLATE FRAME,
FOOTED................................................................. 15.00
COBALT BLUE,PLATE,KINGS CROWN,8 IN.......................... 12.50
COBALT BLUE,RING TREE,2 COLOGNES,2 POWDER BOXES,TRAY,PIN
TRAY,GOLD............................................................. 175.00
COBALT BLUE,SALT DIP,AVENTURINE,SILVER RIM,INDIVIDUAL SPOON. 17.50
COBALT BLUE,SALT DIP,SILVER RIM,SPOON ADVENTURINE........... 17.50
COBALT BLUE,SALT,CHICKEN COVER.............................. 2.50
COBALT BLUE,SALT,MASTER,OVAL,ORNATE FOOTED SILVER HOLDER.... 10.00
COBALT BLUE,SALT,OPEN,SILVER HOLDER & SPOON,
1 3/4 IN.DIAMETER,PAIR................................................. 10.00
COBALT BLUE,SALT,ROUGH PONTIL,BLOWN......................... 25.00
COBALT BLUE,SHADE,FOR ELECTRIC LIGHT,5 IN.HIGH.............. 4.00
COBALT BLUE,SHAKER,SUGAR,FRUIT,METAL TOP.................... 25.00
COBALT BLUE,SHERBET,HOLLY,STEM.............................. 20.00
COBALT BLUE,SHOE,DAISY BUTTON............................... 3.00
COBALT BLUE,SHOE,FRENCH HEEL,BACK & SIDE STRAPS,SOUVENIR,
4 3/4 IN.LONG.......................................................... 25.00
COBALT BLUE,SHOE,LADY'S,SOUVENIR OF WAYNE GROCERY,5 IN...... 12.50
COBALT BLUE,SHOT GLASS,HANDLE............................... 3.50
COBALT BLUE,SPOONER,COLORADO................................ 48.00
COBALT BLUE,STEIN,DRINKING SCENE,LID,7 IN................... 26.00
COBALT BLUE,SUGAR,BUTTERFLY & BERRY,COVER................... 8.00
COBALT BLUE,SYRUP,TIN LID................................... 8.50
COBALT BLUE,TEAPOT,ADVERTISING SALADA TEA,S FINIAL ON LID,
TWO CUP................................................................ 4.00
COBALT BLUE,TOOTHPICK,COLORADO,GOLD TRIM.................... 22.00
COBALT BLUE,TOOTHPICK,HAT SHAPE,THREADED,SOUVENIR ST.CLOUD,
MINNESOTA.............................................................. 7.50
COBALT BLUE,TOOTHPICK,HAT,STIPPLED.......................... 10.00

```
COBALT BLUE,TOOTHPICK,TOP HAT,GOLD,OCEAN CITY,MARYLAND......     8.00
COBALT BLUE,TUMBLER,PAIRPOINT............................      4.50
COBALT BLUE,VASE,BUD,RIB.................................      7.50
COBALT BLUE,VASE,CLASSIC SHAPE,BLOWN,9 IN.TALL,PAIR.........    32.00
COBALT BLUE,VASE,FLORAL DECOR,ENAMEL,GOLD,7 1/4 IN..........    16.50
COBALT BLUE,VASE,FLOWERPOT SHAPE,PAIRPOINT,6 IN.TALL........    22.50
COBALT BLUE,VASE,HAND,CRIMPED TOP,9 IN.,PAIR..............     60.00
COBALT BLUE,VASE,HYACINTH................................      6.50
COBALT BLUE,VASE,INVERTED THUMBPRINT,5 1/2 IN.............     12.00
COBALT BLUE,VASE,LILIES OF THE VALLEY,BLUE LEAVES,1908,9 IN.   10.50
COBALT BLUE,VASE,PANELS,FLARING,10 IN....................     14.00
COBALT BLUE,VASE,PASTORAL SCENIC,12 IN.HIGH..............     18.50
COBALT BLUE,VASE,STERLING SILVER OVERLAY OF VINES,BERRIES,
   10 1/2 IN.HIGH.......................................     35.00
COBALT BLUE,VASE,SWIRLED PATTERN,OPEN PONTIL,BULBOUS,
   STIPPLED TOP,9 IN....................................     47.50
COBALT BLUE,VASE,WHITE HEART & VINE DECOR,ORANGE COLOR
   LINING,7 IN..........................................     85.00
COBALT BLUE,WHISKEY SHOT GLASS,HANDLE....................      3.50
COBALT BLUE,WHISKEY SNIFTER,ENAMEL FLORAL................      8.00


       COCA-COLA ADVERTISING ITEMS HAVE BECOME A SPECIAL FIELD
          FOR COLLECTORS.
COCA-COLA,BANK,RED,TIN............................... 6.50 TO    7.00
COCA-COLA,BOTTLE,AMBER............................... 10.00 TO  15.00
COCA-COLA,BOTTLE,COCA-COLA BOTTLING WORKS,VANDALIA,ILL.,
   CLEAR................................................      2.50
COCA-COLA,BOTTLE,CRYSTAL SODA WATER ON BOTTOM,CLEAR.........    2.50
COCA-COLA,BOTTLE,CIRCA 1900,AQUA.........................      4.50
COCA-COLA,BOTTLE,C IN CIRCLE,PURITY COCA-COLA BOTTLING,
   CENTRALIA,ILL.........................................     2.50
COCA-COLA,BOTTLE,CLEAR,20 IN.............................     25.00
COCA-COLA,BOTTLE,LIGHT BLUE..............................      6.00
COCA-COLA,BOTTLE,MINIATURE,MARKED,CAPPED,3 IN.TALL..........     .75
COCA-COLA,BOTTLE,SELTZER,10 SURFACES,SIPHON TUBE,PEWTER TOP,
   GREEN................................................     12.50
COCA-COLA,BOTTLE,SELTZER,SAYS COCA-COLA BOTTLING CO.,
   RICHMOND,INDIANA.....................................     22.00
COCA-COLA,BOTTLE,SELTZER,SIPHON TUBE,PEWTER TOP,INSCRIPTION,
   GREEN................................................     12.50
COCA-COLA,BOTTLE,SIPHON,TUBE,EMERALD GREEN,PEWTER TOP.......    17.50
COCA-COLA,BOTTLE,SODA WATER,SQUARE.......................      2.50
COCA-COLA,BOTTLE,SODA WATER,STAR,GREEN...................      2.50
COCA-COLA,BOTTLE,STRAIGHT SIDES,GREEN....................      2.50
COCA-COLA,BOTTLE,XMAS DEC.25,1923,PAT.DATE,AQUA,21 IN......    50.00
COCA-COLA,CARTON,WOODEN..................................      6.50
COCA-COLA,CASE,CIRCULAR COKE EMBLEM ON ENDS,WOODEN,
   10 IN.TALL,8 IN.WIDE.................................     25.00
COCA-COLA,CUT,COPPERPLATED,WOODEN BACK,5 X 6 IN..........      3.50
COCA-COLA,GIRL ON ICE SKATES,1941.......................      7.00
COCA-COLA,KEY CHAIN.....................................      2.00
COCA-COLA,MINIATURE,28 BOTTLES IN CASE,METAL,GOLD COLOR,
   1 IN.HIGH............................................     20.00
COCA-COLA,PENCIL SHARPENER,SHAPE OF BOTTLE...............      6.00
COCA-COLA,PLATE,YELLOW,COLOR TRANSFER,PORCELAIN,
   7 1/2-IN.DIAMETER....................................     16.50
COCA-COLA,PLAYING CARDS,WORLD WAR II.....................     12.00
COCA-COLA,POCKET KNIFE,SAYS COCA COLA BOTTLING CO.,3 IN.....    11.00
COCA-COLA,RADIO,SHAPED LIKE COOLER......................     95.00
COCA-COLA,SIGN,BROWN,TAN-RED,6 BOTTLES 25 CENTS,TIN,
   12 1/2 IN............................................      7.50
COCA-COLA,SIGN,ENAMEL ON TIN,GREEN,RED,WHITE,DRINK COCA
   COLA,11 X 30 IN......................................     22.00
COCA-COLA,SIGN,REVERSIBLE,RED CIRCLE WITH BOTTLE,21 IN.HIGH.   10.00
COCA-COLA,SIGN,THERMOMETER,RED,GOLD COLOR,TIN,DATED
   12/25/23,16 X 7 IN...................................     12.00
COCA-COLA,THERMOMETER,BOTTLE SHAPE,RED,16 1/2 IN.........      3.50
COCA-COLA,THERMOMETER,GOLD,BOTTLE SHAPE..................      4.00
COCA-COLA,THERMOMETER,GOLD COLOR BOTTLE,PATENT DEC.25,1912,
   16 X 7 IN............................................     14.00
COCA-COLA,THEROMETER,SHAPE OF BOTTLE,TIN.................     12.00
COCA-COLA,TRAY,BATHING BEAUTY,1934,RECTANGULAR...........     15.00
COCA-COLA,TRAY,CHANGE,GIRL,OVAL,DATED 1912...............     19.00
COCA-COLA,TRAY,CHANGE,1917,4 IN. X 6 IN..................     15.00
COCA-COLA,TRAY,COIN,LADY WITH BONNET,1904...............     35.00
COCA-COLA,TRAY,EVENING GOWN BEAUTY,1936..................     12.50
COCA-COLA,TRAY,GIRL FISHING OFF PIER,1940...............     15.00
COCA-COLA,TRAY,GIRL HOLDING BOTTLE......................      5.00
COCA-COLA,TRAY,GIRL IN BATHING SUIT,DATED 1939,SIGNED
   SUNDBLOM.............................................      6.00
```

COCA-COLA,TRAY,GIRL IN BLUE LEANING AGAINST DARK GREEN
   ROADSTER,1942.................................................. 10.50
COCA-COLA,TRAY,GIRL IN SWIMSUIT,1937.............................. 12.50
COCA-COLA,TRAY,GIRL WITH CHIN IN HAND,SPORTS OF SEASON ON
   BORDER....................................................... 8.00
COCA-COLA,TRAY,GIRL WITH YELLOW SCARF............................. 6.50
COCA-COLA,TRAY,GIRL,FOUR SEASONS,1930............................. 7.50
COCA-COLA,TRAY,GIRL,RED.......................................... 6.00
COCA-COLA,TRAY,LADY,CIRCA 1922................................... 16.50
COCA-COLA,TRAY,LADY,1923......................................... 17.50
COCA-COLA,TRAY,MOVIE STAR,1933................................... 10.00
COCA-COLA,TRAY,REDHEAD,1943...................................... 10.50
COCA-COLA,TRAY,THIRST KNOWS NO SEASON,GIRL'S
   PICTURE.................................... 3.50 TO 7.50
COCA-COLA,TRAY,TWO GIRLS,GREEN CAR,1942.......................... 7.00
COCA-COLA,TRAY,WOMAN IN FOX STOLE,1925........................... 17.50
COCA-COLA,TRAY,1938.............................................. 14.00
COCA-COLA,TUMBLER,GOLD COLOR,11 OUNCES........................... 10.00
COCA-COLA,TUMBLER,1920,6 OUNCES,SET OF 4......................... 8.00
COCA-COLA,WATCH FOB.............................................. 16.00


     COFFEE GRINDERS,HOME SIZE,WERE FIRST MADE ABOUT
     1894. THEY LOST FAVOR BY THE 1930S.
COFFEE GRINDER,20-INCH WHEELS.................................... 80.00
COFFEE GRINDER,ARCADE,IRON & GLASS............................... 20.00
COFFEE GRINDER,BOX TYPE,STOBRIDGE................................ 17.00
COFFEE GRINDER,BOX WITH DRAWER,6 X 6 IN.......................... 11.00
COFFEE GRINDER,DOVETAIL,ARCADE MFG. CO.,FREEPORT,ILL.,WOODEN
   & IRON...................................................... 17.50
COFFEE GRINDER,DOVETAIL,DRAWER,PINE,POLISHED BRASS CUP,IRON
   HANDLE,IDEAL................................................ 18.50
COFFEE GRINDER,DOVETAILED CORNERS,SQUARE,WOODEN,8 IN.HIGH... 20.00
COFFEE GRINDER,DOVETAILED,WALNUT,BRASS HOPPER.................... 35.00
COFFEE GRINDER,DRAWER,WOODEN BASE.....................ILLUS.. 18.00
COFFEE GRINDER,ENTERPRISE MFG. CO.,PAT.JULY 12,1898,IRON,
   8 1/2 IN.WHEELS............................................. 65.00
COFFEE GRINDER,GLASS CONTAINER,MARKED ENTERPIRSE,IRON....... 7.50
COFFEE GRINDER,IRON..................................ILLUS.. 22.00
COFFEE GRINDER,LAP TYPE,METAL,7 1/2 IN.HIGH X 6 IN.SQUARE... 12.50
COFFEE GRINDER,LAP TYPE,WOODEN,IRON DOME TOP..................... 14.00

COFFEE GRINDER, WOODEN BASE

IRON COFFEE GRINDER

COFFEE GRINDER,LAP,DOVETAILED WOOD,COVERED METAL HOPPER,
   PORCELAIN KNOB............................................. 15.00
COFFEE GRINDER,PAINT,IRON BASE,PATENT JULY 12,'98,ENTERPRISE
   MFG. CO.................................................... 135.00
COFFEE GRINDER,PAINT,WOODEN BASE,PATENT OCT.21,'73,
   ENTERPRISE MFG. CO......................................... 125.00
COFFEE GRINDER,PEWTER BIN,DOVETAILED,BRASS KNOB,SIGNED
   W.W.WEAVER................................................. 55.00
COFFEE GRINDER,PEWTER TOP........................................ 18.00
COFFEE GRINDER,SHAPE OF COFFEEPOT,HANDLE,SPOUT,THREE
   SETTINGS,30 IN............................................. 100.00
COFFEE GRINDER,SHORT,SQUATTY TYPE,PAINT,DATED 1886,IRON..... 14.00
COFFEE GRINDER,STORE TYPE,SIGNED ENTERPRISE MFG. CO.,1873,
   12 IN.HIGH................................................. 65.00
COFFEE GRINDER,STORE,DOUBLE WHEEL,DATED 1877,RED PAINT,
   FAIRBANKS MORSE............................................ 135.00
COFFEE GRINDER,STORE,EAGLE,KNOBS,FLOOR STAND,ENTERPRISE

```
            NO.9,1873........................................................   150.00
COFFEE GRINDER,TABLE MODEL,DRAWER,G.R.CO.,IRON & WOOD,
   6 1/2 IN.HIGH.................................................................    18.00
COFFEE GRINDER,TABLE MODEL,IRON HANDLE,DRAWER,LANDERS,FRARY,
   CLARK,TIN...................................................................    20.00
COFFEE GRINDER,TURN CRANK,DRAWER.............................................    25.00
COFFEE GRINDER,TWO WHEELS,PAINT,ENTERPRISE,9 1/2 IN. X
   7 1/2 IN.WIDE..............................................................    85.00
COFFEE GRINDER,TWO WHEELS,RED,COLE MFG.,PHILA.,
   10-IN.DIAMETER WHEELS......................................................    60.00
COFFEE GRINDER,WALL TYPE,BRASS MEDALLION.ATTACHED LID,IRON &
   TIN.......................................................................    14.00
COFFEE GRINDER,WALL TYPE,PORCELAIN,GERMANY,10 IN.TALL.......    17.50
COFFEE GRINDER,WALL,BOARD ATTACHED,IRON......................    8.00
COFFEE GRINDER,WALL,HIGBY.....................................   15.00
COFFEE GRINDER,WALL,IRON......................................    9.00
COFFEE GRINDER,WHITE IRON,PORCELAIN JAR,BLUE WINDMILL SCENE.    26.00
COFFEE MILL,DOVETAILED,BRASS TOP,DRAWER,BOX 4 1/2 IN........    14.50
COFFEE MILL,DRAWER,BRASS CUP,WOODEN...........................   18.00
COFFEE MILL,DRAWER,WOODEN,IRON CRANK..........................   12.50
COFFEE MILL,EMBOSSED TOP,IRON HANDLE & CRANK,WOOD,MARKED
   ARCADE MFG.CO..............................................................    16.75
COFFEE MILL,IRON CUP,NEW HANDLE & DRAWER,WOODEN...............   15.00
COFFEE MILL,TWO WHEELS,ENTERPRISE,PHILA.,12 1/2 IN.HIGH.....    60.00
COFFEE MILL,TWO WHEELS,SMALL..................................   38.50
COFFEE MILL,WALL TYPE,MARKED ENTERPRISE MFG.CO.,PHILA.,
   PA.NO.100,JAR..............................................................     8.50
COFFEE MILL,WALL,WHITE PORCELAIN,WOODEN LID,IRON GRINDER,
   WINDMILL DECOR.............................................................    25.00
COIN SILVER,SEE SILVER,AMERICAN AND SILVER,COIN
```

COMMEMORATION ITEMS HAVE BEEN PRODUCED TO HONOR A NEW
OR DECEASED MEMBER OF A ROYAL FAMILY. CORONATION CUPS
AND PLATES ARE PART OF THIS CATEGORY,AND THEY HAVE BEEN
MADE SINCE THE 1800S. SOME SOUVENIR SPOONS AND PLATES
ARE INCLUDED IN THIS CATEGORY.

```
COMMEMORATION,BEAKER,VICTORIA 1837-1897,ENAMEL ON TIN.......    22.50
COMMEMORATION,CUP & SAUCER,QUEEN VICTORIA JUBILEE,GRAY
   PORTRAIT,GERMANY..........................................................    17.50
COMMEMORATION,GOBLET,RMS QUEEN ELIZABETH'S LAST VOYAGE,
   DATED,ETCHED..............................................................    45.00
COMMEMORATION,MEDAL,CLEVELAND'S VISIT TO COLUMBIAN
   EXPOSITION................................................................     5.00
COMMEMORATION,MEDAL,DR.HUGO ECKNER,1929,FIRST AROUND THE
   WORLD,ZEPPELIN............................................................    12.00
COMMEMORATION,MEDAL,ROYAL VISIT OF KING EDWARD VII........    2.50
COMMEMORATION,MEDALLION,TORPEDOING LUSITANIA,1915,IRON......    35.00
COMMEMORATION,MUG,SILVER JUBILEE OF KING GEORGE V & QUEEN
   MARY,1935.................................................................    11.00
COMMEMORATION,PAPERWEIGHT,METROPOLITAN OPERA,RED LEATHER,
   GOLD PLAQUE...............................................................    75.00
COMMEMORATION,PITCHER,GEORGE V,SILVER JUBILEE,1935,PORTRAIT,
   CREAMWARE.................................................................    26.00
COMMEMORATION,PITCHER,JOHN PAUL JONES,BON HOMME RICHARD,
   SHIPS,DATED 1907.........................................................   125.00
COMMEMORATION,PITCHER,WATER,ADMIRAL DEWEY,9 IN..............    28.00
COMMEMORATION,PLAQUE,CHARLES LINDBERGH,SPIRIT OF ST.LOUIS,
   1927,COPPER..............................................................    25.00
COMMEMORATION,PLATE,1864 9 MAI 1914,HELGOLAND,SHOWS WARSHIP
   FIRING,8 IN...............................................................    40.00
COMMEMORATION,PLATE,1967,ISRAEL,FIRST EDITION,PAIR..........    25.00
COMMEMORATION,PLATE,ABRAHAM LINCOLN,WHITE,COLOR TRANSFER,
   CIRCA 1900................................................................    10.00
COMMEMORATION,PLATE,ADMIRAL DEWEY CENTER,MILK GLASS,
   7 1/2 IN..................................................................    10.50
COMMEMORATION,PLATE,ALLIED LIBERATION OF HOLLAND,1944,
   MAASTRICH,8 IN............................................................     6.50
COMMEMORATION,PLATE,B.P.O.E. ANNIVERSARY,PHILADELPHIA 1907,
   SCENE,TIN.................................................................    15.00
COMMEMORATION,PLATE,BREAD,ULYSSES S.GRANT...................    14.00
COMMEMORATION,PLATE,FATHER'S DAY,FIRST EDITION,1969,
   BARUETHER.................................................................    10.00
COMMEMORATION,PLATE,FRANKOMA,OKLA.,CENTENNIAL...............     5.00
COMMEMORATION,PLATE,GARFIELD MEMORIAL,CLEAR.................    11.00
COMMEMORATION,PLATE,HOME OF PRESIDENT COOLIDGE,ADAMS,IN BLUE
   & WHITE...................................................................    12.50
COMMEMORATION,PLATE,IOG.L.V.NAKSKOV,1898,THREE THISTLES,
   7 IN.DIAMETER.............................................................    30.00
COMMEMORATION,PLATE,ISRAELI,1967,TOWER OF DAVID.............    10.00
COMMEMORATION,PLATE,ISRAELI,1967,WAILING WALL...............    10.00
```

COMMEMORATION,PLATE,ISRAEL,1968.................................... 10.00
COMMEMORATION,PLATE,ISRAELI,1968,MASADA............................ 7.50
COMMEMORATION,PLATE,ISRAELI,1969,RACHEL'S TOMB.................... 6.50
COMMEMORATION,PLATE,KING GEORGE VII,QUEEN ELIZABETH,MAY,
  1939............................................................ 8.00
COMMEMORATION,PLATE,MOTHER'S DAY,1969,FIRST EDITION,
  BARUETHER...................................................... 10.00
COMMEMORATION,PLATE,OLD SOUTH CHURCH,BLUE,WHITE,FLORAL
  BORDER,WEDGWOOD............................................... 13.00
COMMEMORATION,PLATE,PILGRIM MONUMENT,PROVINCETOWN,MASS.,
  JONROTH,ENGLAND............................................... 8.00
COMMEMORATION,PLATE,PITTSBURGH 27TH TRIENNIAL 1898,COBALT
  BLUE BORDER................................................... 18.00
COMMEMORATION,PLATE,PRIMITIVE METHODIST CENTENARY,1807-1907,
  PORTRAIT...................................................... 15.00
COMMEMORATION,PLATE,QUEEN ELIZABETH II,7 1/2 IN................. 4.00
COMMEMORATION,PLATE,QUEEN VICTORIA JUBILEE,1887................. 22.50
COMMEMORATION,PLATE,QUEEN VICTORIA JUBILEE,PRESSED GLASS.... 12.00
COMMEMORATION,PLATE,SIBLEY HOUSE,HISTORY OF GENERAL SIBLEY,
  WEDGWOOD...................................................... 25.00
COMMEMORATION,PLATE,THE CAPITAL,SELESIA,10 IN.................. 12.00
COMMEMORATION,PLATE,THEODORE ROOSEVELT,ROLLED EDGE,BLUE,
  WHITE,10 IN................................................... 15.00
COMMEMORATION,PLATE,VALLEY FORGE,BLUE,ROLL EDGE,
  STAFFORDSHIRE................................................. 20.00
COMMEMORATION,PLATE,VIRGIN ISLANDS 1917-1967,7-IN.DIAMETER.. 30.00
COMMEMORATION,PLATE,WAR YEAR 1914,BLUE,VIENNA,8 1/4 IN...... 35.00
COMMEMORATION,PLATE,ZOOLOGIST,1859-1909 KOBENHAVN,ELEPHANTS,
  8 IN.......................................................... 40.00
COMMEMORATION,PLATTER,D.A.R.,WHITE PLAINS,FIRST CAPITOL OF
  N.Y.,ENGLAND.................................................. 30.00
COMMEMORATION,SALT,LIBERTY BELL,1776-1876 IN BASE,OVAL...... 8.50
COMMEMORATION,SPOON,SILVER-PLATE,PEACE,1918.................. 2.95
COMMEMORATION,SPOON,1898 CHICAGO PEACE JUBILEE,CAPTAIN
  HIGBEE PORTRAIT............................................... 5.50
COMMEMORATION,SUGAR & CREAMER,GEORGE & ELIZABETH............ 5.00
COMMEMORATION,TOKEN,PROHIBITION IN NEW YORK,1855............ 3.00
COMMEMORATION,TRAY,PIN,GEORGE VI,PORCELAIN.................. 5.00
COMMEMORATION,TUMBLER,F.D.ROOSEVELT,W.CHURCHILL............. 13.50
COMMEMORATION,TUMBLER,GEORGE WASHINGTON,1732-1932,GREEN,SET
  OF 8.......................................................... 12.00
COMMEMORATION,TUMBLER,VICTORIA JUBILEE,1837-1887,MOCHA ON
  CREAM,DOULTON................................................. 20.00


        W.T.COPELAND & SONS,LTD. RAN THE SPODE WORKS IN
        STAFFORDSHIRE,ENGLAND,FROM 1847 TO THE PRESENT.
        COPELAND & GARRET WAS THE FIRM NAME FROM 1833 TO 1847.
        COPELAND,SEE ALSO,SPODE
COPELAND,BOAT,GRAVY,HERON,PALM TREE,GILDED GRAPE LEAVES,
  1847,TRAY..................................................... 12.50
COPELAND,CHOCOLATE POT,INDIAN TREE,SIX CUPS & SCALLOPED
  SAUCERS....................................................... 92.50
COPELAND,CUP & SAUCER,CREAM GROUND,STORKS,PALM TREES,
  BUTTERFLIES,1847.............................................. 8.00
COPELAND,DISH,MAJOLICA,TWO LARGE LEAVES,GREEN,TWO HANDLES,
  12 X 8 IN..................................................... 12.00
COPELAND,DISH,VEGETABLE,HERON,PALM TREE,GILDED GRAPE LEAVES,
  1847,COVER.................................................... 22.00
COPELAND,EWER,ALLOVER BEADING,LEAVES,RING HANDLE WITH MASK,
  CIRCA 1870.................................................... 68.00
COPELAND,FIGURINE,MAIDEN HOLDS RABBIT,SIGNED
  F.M.MILLER-1873,16 1/4 IN.................................... 125.00
COPELAND,JAR,PICKLE,PINK,EMBOSSED HUNTING SCENE,SILVER FORK,
  APRIL,1889.................................................... 37.50
COPELAND,PITCHER,BLUE,WHITE RAISED FIGURES,CHERUBS,FLORAL,
  SPODE,7 IN.................................................... 45.00
COPELAND,PITCHER,CREAM GROUND,BLUE,WHITE FIGURES,
  5 1/2 IN.TALL................................................. 45.00
COPELAND,PLATE,BIRD,FLORAL,FLUTED RIM,GOLD,BRITISH REGISTRY,
  11/15/1879.................................................... 5.00
COPELAND,PLATE,BIRD'S NEST,BUTTERFLY,RUSHES IN CENTER,
  DAISIES ON BORDER............................................. 4.50
COPELAND,PLATE,BLUE,WHITE,SPODE.............................. 8.50
COPELAND,PLATE,FLORAL CENTER,HAND-PAINTED,MARKED,
  REGISTRATION MARK 1852........................................ 21.50
COPELAND,PLATE,GREEN HOLLY,RED BERRIES,SAYS A MERRY
  CHRISTMAS TO YOU.............................................. 35.00
COPELAND,PLATE,LYTTLE JOHN,10 1/4 IN......................... 12.50
COPELAND,PLATE,PEACOCK DESIGN,IMPRESSED MARK,CROWN,
  8 3/4-IN.DIAMETER............................................. 7.50

COPELAND,PLATE,TWO NYMPHS,FLORAL,HAND-PAINTED UNDER GLAZE,
STOKE-ON-TRENT.................................................... 12.50
COPELAND,PLATTER,CASTLE SCENE,FLOW BLUE,SPODE,MARKED,20 X
16 IN............................................................. 85.00
COPELAND,PLATTER,HERON,PALM TREE,GILDED GRAPE LEAVES,1847,
13 IN............................................................. 12.00
COPELAND,TEAPOT,WHITE,BIRDS,BAMBOO IN RELIEF,PEWTER LID,
PATENT 1874....................................................... 75.00
COPELAND,TRAY,BLUE COLUMBINE SPRAYS,BLUE & GREEN LEAVES,
11-IN.DIAMETER.................................................... 12.50
COPELAND,TUREEN,CREAM GROUND,STORKS,PALM TREES,BUTTERFLIES,
LADLE,TRAY........................................................ 25.00
COPELAND,TUREEN,HERON,PALM TREE,GILDED GRAPE LEAVES,1847,
LADLE,TRAY........................................................ 22.00
COPELAND SPODE,SEE ALSO,SPODE
COPELAND SPODE,GRAVY BOAT,UNDERPLATE,GAINSBOROUGH,SPRING
BOUQUET........................................................... 7.00
COPELAND SPODE,JUG,JASPER GROUND,APPLIED GRAPEVINE &
DRINKING SCENE.................................................... 67.00
COPELAND SPODE,PITCHER, SPODE TOWER,  SQUATTY,BLUE,4 IN.HIGH      9.50
COPELAND SPODE,PLATE,BLUE,PORTLAND,MAINE,LONGFELLOW HOME....      15.00
COPELAND SPODE,PLATE,BURGUNDY,BURNISHED GOLD,FISHSCALE
CENTER,PAIR....................................................... 75.00
COPELAND SPODE,PLATE,DUSTY ROSE COLOR,FLOWERED BORDER,
10 1/2 IN......................................................... 10.00
COPELAND SPODE,PLATE,MULTICOLORED BIRD IN CENTER,BORDER,
HAND-PAINTED...................................................... 12.50
COPELAND SPODE,PLATE,TWO BIRDS ON TREE,FLORAL BORDER,
8-IN.DIAMETER..................................................... 7.50
COPELAND SPODE,PLATE,WHITE,PHEASANT IN CENTER,FLORAL,VIENNA,
10 IN.,8.......................................................... 65.00
COPELAND SPODE,PLATE,WOODCOCK,NO.9,BLUE,WHITE..................    15.00
COPELAND SPODE,PLATTER,CREAMER,SUGAR,EIGHT SALAD PLATES,
REYNOLDS PATTERN.................................................. 70.00
COPELAND SPODE,TEAPOT,CREAMER,SUGAR,TRAY,FOUR CUPS,SAUCERS,
FLORAL............................................................ 139.00
COPELAND SPODE,TUREEN,WHITE,URN OF FLOWERS,ARTICHOKE FINIAL,
9 IN.SQUARE....................................................... 22.00
COPPER,BOOKEND,GALLEON SHIP,DATED 1880,PAIR...................    35.00
COPPER,BOWL,ROUND,PETALS AROUND SIDES,RUFFLED,SCALLOPED
EDGE.............................................................. 16.00
COPPER,BOX,SILVER COLOR PHOENIX ON LID,GEOMETRIC DECOR,
3 IN.LONG......................................................... 10.00
COPPER,BUCKET,BRASS EARS,HANDLE,BURNISHED,LACQUERED,12 IN. X
12 IN............................................................. 42.50
COPPER,BUCKET,COAL,HELMET TYPE.................................    40.00
COPPER,COAL HELMET,TWO DELFT HANDLES..........................    22.00
COPPER,COAL SCUTTLE,HAND-HAMMERED.............................    60.00
COPPER,COFFEE URN,FANCY DECOR,CABRIOLE LEGS,NICKEL-PLATED,
FRANCE,28 IN...................................................... 65.00
COPPER,COFFEEPOT,BURNISHED,10 1/2 IN..........................    18.00
COPPER,COFFEEPOT,CREAMER,SUGAR,TRAY,EMBOSSED FLORAL,
C.D.E.MARK........................................................ 42.50
COPPER,COFFEEPOT,TWO HANDLES,SPIGOT,ALCOHOL BURNER,
14 1/2 IN.HIGH.................................................... 32.50
COPPER,COFFEEPOT,7 1/2 IN.....................................    16.50
COPPER,CUSPIDOR,NICKELED,10-IN.DIAMETER.......................    10.00
COPPER,FIGURINE,FIGHTING COCKS,SILVER OVERLAY,10 IN.HIGH,
7 IN.WIDE......................................................... 150.00
COPPER,FIGURINE,PEGASUS,OPEN BACK,ZINC FINISH,25-IN.WINGSPAN     140.00
COPPER,FOOT WARMER,BRASS BAIL,12 X 8 1/2 IN...................    24.50
COPPER,FUNNEL,ZINC COLLAR,15 IN.HIGH X 10 1/2-IN.DIAMETER...      14.00
COPPER,FUNNEL,10 IN...........................................    11.50
COPPER,INKWELL FILLER,LONG SPOUT,BURNISHED....................    10.00
COPPER,INKWELL,PORCELAIN INSERT...............................    28.50
COPPER,JUG,CIRCA 1850.........................................    20.00
COPPER,KETTLE,CANDY,IRON HANDLES,19-IN.DIAMETER...............    45.00
COPPER,KETTLE,WATER,ENGLAND...................................    55.00
COPPER,LETTER OPENER,ADVERTISING..............................    4.00
COPPER,MATCH HOLDER,INDIAN,WALL...............................    22.00
COPPER,MEASURE,1 QT...........................................    22.00
COPPER,MOLD,EMBOSSED FRUIT ON BOTTOM,RING FOR HANGING,3 X
10-IN.DIAMETER.................................................... 22.00
COPPER,MOLD,SPONGE CAKE,9-IN.DIAMETER.........................    25.00
COPPER,PAIL,BEER,POLISHED,1 QUART.............................    14.00
COPPER,PAN,CANDY,2 HANDLES,16-IN.DIAMETER.....................    75.00
COPPER,PAN,STEW,BROAD HANDLE,DOVETAILED CONSTRUCTION,
HAND-POLISHED..................................................... 28.00
COPPER,PAN,WARMING,BLACK PAINT,ENGRAVED LID,WOOD HANDLE,
40 IN............................................................. 48.00
COPPER,PAN,WARMING,ETCHED DESIGN,MOLDED WOOD HANDLE.........      60.00

COPPER,PAPER CLIP,BULLDOG'S HEAD & PAWS IN RELIEF,HOLE FOR
    HANGING.......................................................... 14.00
COPPER,PERCOLATOR,COFFEE,ALCOHOL BURNER,STAND,BRASS SPIGOT,
    LACQUERED......................................................... 40.00
COPPER,PITCHER,BUFF DECORATED BAND,5 1/2 IN..................... 35.00
COPPER,PITCHER,FOUR TUMBLERS,SIGNED............................ 15.00
COPPER,PITCHER,GEORGIAN,BURNISHED,WOODEN HANDLE,5 IN. X
    6 1/2 IN.HIGH.................................................... 35.00
COPPER,PITCHER,GRAPE DESIGN,3 1/4 IN............................ 55.00
COPPER,PITCHER,RAISED FIGURES OF GIRL,CAT,BLUE BAND,CIRCA
    1820,3 1/2 IN................................................... 38.00
COPPER,PITCHER,TANKARD,HINGED COVER,8 1/2 IN.HIGH............... 20.00
COPPER,PITCHER,WHITE BAND WITH LUSTER,FLORALS,4 1/2 IN.HIGH.   32.00
COPPER,PITCHER,WINE,COVER,18TH CENTURY......................... 135.00
COPPER,POWDER FLASK,SIGNED CB BATTY 1847,CANNON,FLAGS,STARS,
    BRASS CAP....................................................... 65.00
COPPER,SAMOVAR,BRASS-FOOTED,19 IN.HIGH......................... 125.00
COPPER,SAMOVAR,TRAY,HEINRICHS,PARIS-N.Y.,13 IN................. 75.00
COPPER,SERVER,HAND-WORKED ROSETTES,FOUR LEGS,10 IN............ 20.00
COPPER,SKILLET,IRON HANDLE..................................... 32.00
COPPER,SKILLET,IRON HANDLE,16 IN.DIAMETER..................... 30.00
COPPER,STOMACH WARMER.......................................... 22.00
COPPER,TANKARD,HINGED COVER,8 1/2 IN.HIGH...................... 22.00
COPPER,TEAKETTLE,BEEHIVE SHAPE,WARMING STAND.................. 35.00
COPPER,TEAKETTLE,DOVETAILED,FINIAL ON COVER,SIGNED,ENGLAND..  85.00
COPPER,TEAKETTLE,DOVETAILED,GOOSENECK SPOUT,ACORN FINIAL,
    HANDLE,SIGNED.................................................. 125.00
COPPER,TEAPOT,DOVETAILED,COPPER & BRASS HANDLE,FINIAL,
    SIGNED,ENGLAND................................................. 85.00
COPPER,TEAPOT,PUFFY PANELED TOP & SIDES,8 1/4-IN.DIAMETER,
    2 1/2 IN.TALL.................................................. 18.00
COPPER,TEAPOT,RIB PANELED SIDES,RATTAN HANDLE,CHINA,
    7 3/4 IN.TALL................................................... 8.00
COPPER,TEAPOT,WOODEN HANDLE.................................... 17.50
COPPER,TRAY,CUTOUT FLORAL RIM,GLASS INSERT WITH DOILY,
    11-IN.ROUND................................................... 25.00
COPPER,WASH BASIN,POLISHED,HANGING RING....................... 22.00
COPPER,WASH BOILER,TIN TOP,WOODEN HANDLES.................... 17.50
CORAL,BOTTLE,SNUFF,18TH CENTURY,JADE STOPPER................1,100.00
CORAL,BOTTLE,SNUFF,CARVED,TREE TRUNK,BIRDS,LEAFAGE,BIRD FORM
    STOPPER...................................................... 200.00
CORAL,BOTTLE,SNUFF,TREE TRUNK FORM,BIRD,FRUIT,LEAFAGE,FRUIT
    FORM STOPPER................................................. 125.00
CORAL,FIGURINE,KUAN YIN,BIRD,DRAGON,WAVE SCROLLS,STAND,
    5 1/4 IN.HIGH................................................. 375.00
CORAL,FIGURINE,WOMAN,FLOWING ROBES,TWO BOYS AT HER FEET,
    8 IN.HIGH.................................................... 550.00
CORAL,GROUP,5 IN. HIGH,ROBED FIGURE OF BOY WITH JAR.......... 225.00
CORAL,GROUP,5 1/4 IN. HIGH,YOUNG WOMAN,BOY,WOOD STAND....... 250.00
CORAL,GROUP,6 1/4 IN. HIGH,YOUNG WOMAN,GIRL,WOOD STAND..... 450.00
CORAL,VASE,RED,BALUSTER SHAPE,TRUMPET NECK,STAND,
    10 1/2 IN.HIGH............................................... 225.00

        CORALENE GLASS WAS MADE BY FIRING MANY SMALL COLORED
        BEADS ON THE OUTSIDE OF GLASSWARE. IT WAS MADE IN MANY
        PATTERNS IN THE UNITED STATES AND EUROPE IN THE
        1880'S. REPRODUCTIONS ARE MADE TODAY.
CORALENE,TEAPOT,MEDALLION,MOUNTAINS & WATER SCENE,COVERED
    SUGAR,CREAMER................................................ 39.50
CORALENE,TUMBLER,CASED SATIN,DARK TO LIGHT PINK,GOLD
    BRANCHES,4 IN................................................ 75.00
CORALENE,TUMBLER,GRADUATED PINK,CASED,GOLD BRANCHES,4 IN....  150.00
CORALENE,TUMBLER,WHITE SATIN,BROWN OAK LEAVES,MT.WASHINGTON.   50.00
CORALENE,VASE,BLUE TO WHITE,CREAM CASING,YELLOW SEAWEED
    DECOR,8 IN.HIGH.............................................. 495.00
CORALENE,VASE,BLUE TO WHITE,SATIN,ALLOVER SEAWEED,
    MT.WASHINGTON,4 IN........................................... 260.00
CORALENE,VASE,CLEAR TO CRANBERRY,RUFFLED,CRIMPED TOP,
    BULBOUS,9 IN................................................. 450.00
CORALENE,VASE,CORAL BRANCH BEADING,OFF-WHITE CASING,
    4 1/2 IN.HIGH............................................... 365.00
CORALENE,VASE,MOTHER-OF-PEARL,RED TO PINK,ALLOVER BEADS,
    DIAMOND-QUILTED............................................. 475.00
CORALENE,VASE,PINK & WHITE IRIS,GREEN LEAVES,APPLIED TO
    PORCELAIN,7 IN.............................................. 225.00
CORALENE,VASE,PINK OVERLAY,RUFFLED TOP........................ 35.00
CORALENE,VASE,PINK TO RED,CORAL BRANCHES,GOLD RIM,WHITE
    CASING,5 IN.HIGH............................................ 285.00
CORALENE,VASE,RED BEADS,GARNET GEMS.......................... 490.00
CORALENE,VASE,WHEAT PATTERN,BRISTOL,12 IN.HIGH.............. 150.00

CORALENE,VASE,WHITE,PINK INNER CASING,BLUE SEAWEED DESIGN,
    RUFFLED,6 IN........................................... 150.00
CORALENE,VASE,YELLOW CORAL BRANCH BEADING,WHITE CASING,
    4 1/2 IN.HIGH......................................... 325.00
CORALENE,VASE,YELLOW SEAWEED,BLUE SATIN SHADES TO WHITE,
    7 IN.................................................. 160.00

      CORONATION CUPS HAVE BEEN MADE SINCE THE 1800S. PIECES
    OF POTTERY OR GLASS WITH A PICTURE OF THE MONARCH AND
    THE DATE HAVE BEEN MADE AS SOUVENIRS FOR MANY
    CORONATIONS.
CORONATION,BRANDY SNIFTER,KING EDWARD VIII,COAT OF ARMS,GILT   7.50
CORONATION,CUP & SAUCER,ELIZABETH & GEORGE VI............... 5.50
CORONATION,CUP & SAUCER,KING EDWARD VII,1902,RAISED ENAMEL,
    ORANGE,BLUE........................................... 15.00
CORONATION,CUP,KING EDWARD VII............................. 6.00
CORONATION,CUP,KING GEORGE VI,QUEEN ELIZABETH,1937.......... 6.00
CORONATION,GLOBE,EDWARD VIII,PORCELAIN..................... 15.00
CORONATION,HUMIDOR,CORONATION OF QUEEN ELIZABETH II,1953,
    SILVER PLATE.......................................... 3.95
CORONATION,MUG,EDWARD VII & ALEXANDRIA,1901,PORTRAITS,WHITE
    GROUND................................................ 15.00
CORONATION,MUG,ELIZABETH II,1953,COAT OF ARMS,GILT,PORCELAIN  8.50
CORONATION,MUG,GEORGE VI & ELIZABETH,1937.................. 8.00
CORONATION,MUG,KING EDWARD........................ILLUS.. 8.00
CORONATION,MUG,QUEEN ELIZABETH II,1953..................... 4.75
CORONATION,PITCHER,GEORGE V & MARY,1911,PORTRAITS,GREEN
    GROUND,7 IN........................................... 25.00

KING EDWARD CORONATION MUG

CORONATION,PLAQUE,EDWARD VII,ALEXANDRA,1902,PORTRAIT,ROYAL
    DOULTON,PAIR.......................................... 59.00
CORONATION,PLAQUE,EDWARD VII,1902,QUEEN ALEXANDRA,PAIR...... 65.00
CORONATION,PLATE,BREAD,ELIZABETH II,1953,ORNATE BEADING..... 11.00
CORONATION,PLATE,BREAD,GEORGE VI,1937,ORNATE BEADING........ 13.00
CORONATION,PLATE,CAKE,KING GEORGE & QUEEN ELIZABETH,CUP,
    SAUCER,BONE........................................... 10.00
CORONATION,PLATE,EDWARD VII,ROYAL DOULTON,8 1/4 IN.......... 25.00
CORONATION,PLATE,EDWARD VIII.............................. 5.50
CORONATION,PLATE,PORTRAIT OF EDWARD VIII,MAY 12,1937,9 IN... 3.50
CORONATION,PLATE,QUEEN ELIZABETH II,1953,8 1/2 IN... 4.75 TO  4.95
CORONATION,TEAPOT,ELIZABETH II,1953,ALLOVER GOLD,PORTRAIT,
    CREST................................................. 17.50
CORONATION,TOBY,GEORGE V,QUEEN MARY,1910,HAND-PAINTED,6 IN.,
    PAIR.................................................. 51.00
CORONATION,TUMBLER,ELIZABETH II,BLUE...................... 8.00

      COSMOS PATTERN GLASS IS A PATTERN OF PRESSED MILK GLASS
    WITH COLORED FLOWERS.
COSMOS,BUTTER,PINK BAND,COVER............................. 125.00

COSMOS,BUTTER,PINK BAND,MILK GLASS........................... 95.00
COSMOS,CASTOR SET,FOUR BOTTLES,PINK BAND..................... 350.00
COSMOS,CASTOR SET,SALT,PEPPER,MUSTARD,PINK BAND,MILK GLASS.. 350.00
COSMOS,DISH,BUTTER.......................................... 95.00
COSMOS,DISH,BUTTER,COVER.................................... 125.00
COSMOS,DISH,BUTTER,MILK GLASS................... 78.50 TO 145.00
COSMOS,DISH,BUTTER,PINK BAND.................... 75.00 TO 95.00
COSMOS,DISH,BUTTER,PINK BAND,COVER.......................... 100.00
COSMOS,JAR,CRACKER,APPLE BLOSSOM,SILVER LID & HANDLE,SATIN
    GLASS................................................... 80.00
COSMOS,LAMP,APPLE BLOSSOM,BLUE BAND,BURNER................... 55.00
COSMOS,LAMP,MINIATURE,CLEAR,UMBRELLA SHADE.................. 55.00
COSMOS,LAMP,PINK BAND,MILK GLASS............................ 85.00
COSMOS,LAMP,TABLE,DECOR,SHADE,16 IN.TALL.................... 145.00
COSMOS,LAMP,YELLOW BAND..................................... 190.00
COSMOS,NAPPIE,HANDLE,SAYS CLOVER-CGCO,CUT GLASS,
    6-IN.DIAMETER........................................... 20.00
COSMOS,PITCHER,WATER,PINK BAND,SIX TUMBLERS................. 275.00
COSMOS,SALT & PEPPER,PINK.................................. 45.00
COSMOS,SHAKER,SALT & PEPPER,APPLE BLOSSOM.................. 35.00
COSMOS,SHAKER,SALT,PINK BAND............................... 16.50
COSMOS,SHAKER,SALT,PINK,BLUE,YELLOW FLORAL,PINK BAND,MILK
    GLASS................................................... 25.00
COSMOS,SPOONER,CREAMER,COVERED SUGAR,COVERED BUTTER,PINK
    BAND.................................................... 325.00
COSMOS,SPOONER,PINK BORDER................................. 27.50
COSMOS,SUGAR,COVER......................................... 95.00
COSMOS,SYRUP,APPLE BLOSSOM,BLUE BAND,TIN SPRING TOP,APPLIED
    HANDLE.................................................. 45.00
COSMOS,SYRUP,PINK,BLUE,YELLOW FLOWERS,WHITE MILK GLASS...... 65.00
COSMOS,TUMBLER,PINK BAND................................... 28.00
    COUNTRY STORE,SEE STORE
    COVERLET,SEE LINEN,COVERLET
COWAN,CANDLESTICK,SHORT,PINK MOTTLED....................... 3.50
COWAN,FLOWER HOLDER,GIRL DANCING WITH SCARF,CREAM COLOR..... 25.00
COWAN,HEAD OF WOMAN,GRAY................................... 45.00
COWAN,VASE,YELLOW,ROUND.................................... 15.00


        CRACKLE GLASS WAS ORIGINALLY MADE BY THE VENETIANS BUT
    MOST OF THE WARE FOUND TODAY DATES FROM THE 1800S. THE
    GLASS WAS HEATED,COOLED,AND REFIRED SO THAT MANY SMALL
    LINES APPEARED INSIDE THE GLASS. IT WAS MADE IN MANY
    FACTORIES IN THE UNITED STATES AND EUROPE.
CRACKLE GLASS,BOWL,BLUE,WHITE,WALL OF TROY BORDER,
    8 1/4-IN.DIAMETER....................................... 250.00
CRACKLE GLASS,CHINESE WARRIORS,HORSES,RED,GREEN,BEIGE,
    6 1/4 IN................................................ 22.50
CRACKLE GLASS,JAR,PICKLE,HOURGLASS-SHAPED,BLUE,SILVER-PLATED 35.00
CRACKLE GLASS,JAR,SWEETMEAT,SAPPHIRE BLUE,RED STRAWBERRIES,
    AMBER EDGE.............................................. 350.00
CRACKLE GLASS,LEMONADE SET,BLUE,SMOOTH PONTIL,SEVEN PIECES.. 42.50
CRACKLE GLASS,PITCHER,APPLIED REEDED HANDLE,SMOOTH PONTIL,
    CLEAR................................................... 20.00
CRACKLE GLASS,PITCHER,BULBOUS,APPLIED HANDLE,AMBER,8 IN.TALL 32.00
CRACKLE GLASS,PITCHER,SCENE,STORKS IN WATER,ENAMEL,SQUATTY,
    AMBER,FRANCE............................................ 65.00
CRACKLE GLASS,SUGAR,PINK,ENAMEL FLORAL,SILVER COVER......... 35.00
CRACKLE GLASS,TOOTHPICK,MARINE GREEN....................... 12.50
CRACKLE GLASS,VASE,APPLIED BLUE GLASS BUTTONS,12 1/2 IN.TALL 25.00
CRACKLE GLASS,VASE,CHINESE DECOR,FLORAL,MONKEY HEAD HANDLES,
    13 1/2 IN............................................... 110.00
CRACKLE GLASS,VASE,GREEN,ENAMELED FISH & SEAWEED........... 45.00
CRACKLE GLASS,VASE,IRIDESCENT,SIGNED IMPERIAL.............. 120.00


        CRANBERRY GLASS IS AN ALMOST TRANSPARENT YELLOW-RED
    GLASS. IT RESEMBLES THE COLOR OF CRANBERRY JUICE.
    CRANBERRY GLASS,SEE ALSO CRUET,TOOTHPICK,RUBINA VERDE,
CRANBERRY GLASS,BANANA BOAT,DELAWARE PATTERN............... 65.00
CRANBERRY GLASS,BASE,PORTRAIT OF WOMAN ON PORCELAIN,GOLD
    ENAMEL,10 IN............................................ 125.00
CRANBERRY GLASS,BASKET,CLEAR APPLIED HANDLE & FEET,6 X
    6 1/2 IN.HIGH........................................... 35.00
CRANBERRY GLASS,BASKET,HOBNAIL,RUFFLED EDGE,CLEAR HANDLE,
    7 IN.................................................... 32.00
CRANBERRY GLASS,BASKET,THREADED,CRIMPED TOP,LOOPED CRYSTAL
    HANDLE,BLOWN............................................ 40.00
CRANBERRY GLASS,BELL,SILVER VINTAGE DECOR,INSCRIPTION,CLEAR
    PRISM HANDLE............................................ 21.00
CRANBERRY GLASS,BONBON,ENCIRCLED WITH APPLIED CLEAR PETALS.. 25.00

CRANBERRY GLASS,BOTTLE,BARBER,ENAMELING,8 IN.HIGH............ 35.00
CRANBERRY GLASS,BOTTLE,BARBER,HOBNAIL,BLOWN................. 65.00
CRANBERRY GLASS,BOTTLE,SCENT,PANELED,STERLING SILVER TOP,
  3 IN...................................................... 22.00
CRANBERRY GLASS,BOTTLE,WATER,INVERTED THUMBPRINT,ENAMELED
  FLORAL................................................... 30.00
CRANBERRY GLASS,BOWL,4-IN.DIAMETER,1 7/8 IN.DEEP............ 11.50
CRANBERRY GLASS,BOWL,BUTTER,FLUTED EDGE.................... 45.00
CRANBERRY GLASS,BOWL,ETCHED ROSES,APPLIED CLEAR FEET,
  8-IN.DIAMETER........................................... 20.00
CRANBERRY GLASS,BOWL,FINGER,BLOWN........................ 25.00
CRANBERRY GLASS,BOWL,FINGER,ENGRAVED ROSE & GRAPE,4 1/2 IN.. 25.00
CRANBERRY GLASS,BOWL,FINGER,INVERTED THUMBPRINT............ 25.00
CRANBERRY GLASS,BOWL,FINGER,PINCH PLEAT TOP,GROUND PONTIL,
  5-IN.DIAMETER........................................... 48.00
CRANBERRY GLASS,BOWL,FINGER,STAR CUTTING IN BASE........... 27.50
CRANBERRY GLASS,BOWL,GOLD DECOR WITH TOUCHES OF WHITE &
  TURQUOISE............................................... 30.00
CRANBERRY GLASS,BOWL,HOBNAIL,RUFFLED,GROUND PONTIL,SQUARE,
  9 IN.................................................... 145.00
CRANBERRY GLASS,BOWL,MAYONNAISE,FLUTED RIM,UNDERPLATE,
  PIECRUST RIM............................................ 35.00
CRANBERRY GLASS,BOWL,RELISH,FLUTED RIM,UNDERPLATE,PIECRUST
  RIM..................................................... 35.00
CRANBERRY GLASS,BOWL,ROSE,DAISY & FERN,CRIMPED RIM,
  4 1/2 IN.HIGH........................................... 35.00
CRANBERRY GLASS,BOWL,ROSE,ETCHED FLOWERS,FLASHED,BALL SHAPE. 12.00
CRANBERRY GLASS,BOWL,ROSE,FLAT DOTS,PLEATED & PINCHED TOP... 19.00
CRANBERRY GLASS,BOWL,ROSE,FLORAL,ENAMEL,PANELS,RUFFLED,BLOWN 48.00
CRANBERRY GLASS,BOWL,ROSE,OPALESCENT,HOBNAIL............... 65.00
CRANBERRY GLASS,BOWL,ROSE,STRETCHED COLLAR,4 IN........... 40.00
CRANBERRY GLASS,BOWL,ROSE,WHITE OVERLAY,CRIMPED TOP,4 IN.... 30.00
CRANBERRY GLASS,BOWL,SALAD,CUT BACK TO CLEAR.............. 20.00
CRANBERRY GLASS,BOX,HINGED TOP,BRASS,5 1/2 X 3 1/2 IN...... 70.00
CRANBERRY GLASS,BOX,TRINKET,ENAMELED,HINGED................ 85.00
CRANBERRY GLASS,BUTTER,ZIPPER,FLASHED,COVER............... 35.00
CRANBERRY GLASS,CANDLEHOLDER,FOOTED,MATCHING BOWL,DEER &
  TREE DESIGN............................................. 15.00
CRANBERRY GLASS,CANDLESTICK,CLEAR BALL,SPIRAL BUBBLES ABOVE
  FOOT,PAIR............................................... 95.00
CRANBERRY GLASS,CANDLESTICK,CRYSTAL KNOB IN CENTER,4 IN.,
  PAIR.................................................... 55.00
CRANBERRY GLASS,CANDLESTICK,DOUBLE-TWISTED STEM,BLENKO,
  7 1/4 IN.,PAIR.......................................... 65.00
CRANBERRY GLASS,CARAFE,CUT TO CLEAR,THUMBPRINT,STAR CUT
  BASE,TUMBLER............................................ 67.50
CRANBERRY GLASS,CARAFE,7 1/2 IN.,MATCHING TUMBLER.......... 45.00
CRANBERRY GLASS,CASTOR SET,FIVE BOTTLES,SILVER HOLDER,CENTER
  HANDLE,FEET............................................. 59.00
CRANBERRY GLASS,CASTOR,PICKLE,DOUBLE,BULBOUS PANELS,SILVER
  HOLDER,LIDS............................................. 150.00
CRANBERRY GLASS,CASTOR,PICKLE,GREEN ENAMEL PICKLE DECOR,
  SILVER FRAME............................................ 80.00
CRANBERRY GLASS,CASTOR,PICKLE,INVERTED THUMBPRINT,SIGNED N,
  SILVER HOLDER........................................... 85.00
CRANBERRY GLASS,CASTOR,PICKLE,INVERTED THUMBPRINT,ENAMEL,
  SILVER HOLDER........................................... 150.00
CRANBERRY GLASS,CASTOR,PICKLE,INVERTED THUMBPRINT,SILVER
  HOLDER,TONGS............................................ 65.00
CRANBERRY GLASS,CASTOR,PICKLE,OPALESCENT STRIPE,ORNATE
  SILVER FRAME............................................ 47.50
CRANBERRY GLASS,CLARET,SILVER HANDLE & TOP................ 65.00
CRANBERRY GLASS,COLOGNE,PORCELAIN PORTRAIT PLAQUE,GIRL,
  HAND-PAINTED............................................ 85.00
CRANBERRY GLASS,COLOGNE,WHITE OVERLAY,GOLD,STICK NECK,
  STOPPER,PAIR............................................ 225.00
CRANBERRY GLASS,COMPOTE,CLEAR STEM,OPEN,5 1/2 IN.HIGH,
  7-IN.DIAMETER........................................... 45.00
CRANBERRY GLASS,COMPOTE,CLEAR,PEDESTAL BASE,BLOWN STEM,
  5 1/2 IN.HIGH........................................... 40.00
CRANBERRY GLASS,COMPOTE,FEATHER PATTERN,OPAQUE WHITE RIM,
  GREEN BASE.............................................. 275.00
CRANBERRY GLASS,COMPOTE,FLUTED EDGE,CLEAR STEM,9-IN.DIAMETER 43.00
CRANBERRY GLASS,CREAMER,APPLIED CLEAR FEET & HANDLE......... 17.50
CRANBERRY GLASS,CREAMER,CLEAR,APPLIED HANDLE,FOOTED........ 30.00
CRANBERRY GLASS,CRUET,BULBOUS,PANELS,CLOVERLEAF SHAPE TOP,
  BLOWN,8 IN.............................................. 42.00
CRANBERRY GLASS,CRUET,DIAMOND PATTERN,REEDED HANDLE,FLUTED
  LIP,STOPPER............................................. 42.00
CRANBERRY GLASS,CRUET,INVERTED THUMBPRINT,CLEAR APPLIED
  HANDLE,STOPPER.......................................... 32.50

```
CRANBERRY GLASS,CRUET,INVERTED THUMBPRINT,CLEAR APPLIED
  HANDLE,7 IN.....................................................   43.00
CRANBERRY GLASS,CRUET,INVERTED THUMBPRINT,BALL SHAPE BASE,
  STOPPER.........................................................   35.00
CRANBERRY GLASS,CRUET,METAL CASTING,PAIR........................   65.00
CRANBERRY GLASS,CRUET,THREADED,SWIRLED,STOPPER.................   37.50
CRANBERRY GLASS,CRUET,VINE PATTERN,RIBBED,FLUTED..............   27.50
CRANBERRY GLASS,CRUET,VINEGAR,CLEAR HANDLE...................   40.00
CRANBERRY GLASS,CRUET,VINEGAR,HOBNAIL.......................   95.00
CRANBERRY GLASS,CUP,PUNCH,CLEAR APPLIED HANDLE,BLOWN........   12.50
CRANBERRY GLASS,CUP,PUNCH,CLEAR HANDLE......................   10.50
CRANBERRY GLASS,CUP,PUNCH,DELAWARE,GOLD.....................   14.00
CRANBERRY GLASS,DECANTER,CLEAR,APPLIED HANDLE,STOPPER,
  ENGLAND.........................................................   45.00
CRANBERRY GLASS,DECANTER,MELON RIB,TREFOIL SHAPE TOP,
  CLEAR-MOLDED HANDLE.............................................   22.50
CRANBERRY GLASS,DECANTER,OVOID BODY,BLOWN,HANDLE,CUT
  STOPPER,9 1/2 IN................................................   45.00
CRANBERRY GLASS,DECANTER,WINE,RIBBED,BLUE BLOSSOMS,GOLD,
  ENAMEL,9 IN.TALL................................................   42.00
CRANBERRY GLASS,DECANTER,WINE,WHITE ENAMELED FLEUR-DE-LIS...   35.00
CRANBERRY GLASS,DISH,CANDY,CUT FLORAL SPRAYS,CLEAR HANDLES,
  GOLD EDGE.......................................................   35.00
CRANBERRY GLASS,DISH,CANDY,PUFF PANELS,SCALLOPED RIM,6 IN...   15.00
CRANBERRY GLASS,DISH,CHEESE,WHITE OVERLAY PORTRAIT
  MEDALLION,GILT..................................................  225.00
CRANBERRY GLASS,DISH,CUT STARS,CLEAR KNOB ON LID............   12.50
CRANBERRY GLASS,DISH,JAM,SILVER-PLATED HOLDER,FOOTED,HANDLED   32.00
CRANBERRY GLASS,DISH,JELLY,FLUTED,CLEAR BASE,STERLING SILVER
  FRAME,SPOON.....................................................   60.00
CRANBERRY GLASS,DISH,SHELL,OVERSHOT,5 IN. X 3 3/4 IN........   19.00
CRANBERRY GLASS,EPERGNE,HEAVILY ENCRUSTED WITH GOLD.........  395.00
CRANBERRY GLASS,EPERGNE,HOLDER,MIRROR.......................   39.00
CRANBERRY GLASS,EPERGNE,LILY DECOR,CLEAR RIGAREE,BRASS
  FITTINGS,FLUTED.................................................  175.00
CRANBERRY GLASS,EPERGNE,RUFFLED BASE,CENTER LILY,TWO SIDE
  LILIES,21 IN....................................................  145.00
CRANBERRY GLASS,EPERGNE,THREE VASES,CLEAR GLASS RIGAREE,
  22 IN. HIGH.....................................................  250.00
CRANBERRY GLASS,EWER,GOLD,PASTEL ENAMELED FLORAL,7 IN.......   65.00
CRANBERRY GLASS,FERNERY,GOLD FLORAL,SPRAYS,GOLD WASH AROUND
  EDGES,5 IN......................................................  185.00
CRANBERRY GLASS,FIGURINE,HORSE,CLEAR APPLIED HEAD,LEGS,TAIL,
  SADDLE,PAIR.....................................................  225.00
CRANBERRY GLASS,FLASK,WHITE LOOPINGS,CORSET SHAPE,
  7 1/4 IN.TALL...................................................   85.00
CRANBERRY GLASS,GOBLET,CLEAR STEM & BASE,MATCHING FOOTED
  BOWLS,16 PIECES.................................................   95.00
CRANBERRY GLASS,GOBLET,PONTIL...............................   18.00
CRANBERRY GLASS,GOBLET,WATER,CONE SHAPE,SWIRLS,CLEAR BASE,
  BLOWN,7 IN......................................................   18.00
CRANBERRY GLASS,HAT,POLISHED PONTIL,BLOWN...................   35.00
CRANBERRY GLASS,JAR,BISCUIT,ENAMEL FLORAL,ACID CUT GROUND,
  6 IN.TALL.......................................................   70.00
CRANBERRY GLASS,JAR,BISCUIT,GOLD ENAMEL,FLORAL,SILVER COVER,
  BAIL............................................................   48.00
CRANBERRY GLASS,JAR,BISCUIT,THREADED,BLOWN,POLISHED PONTIL,
  SILVER COVER....................................................   50.00
CRANBERRY GLASS,JAR,CANDY,ALLOVER ENAMEL,4 IN.WIDE,6 IN.TALL   60.00
CRANBERRY GLASS,JAR,CRACKER,SILVER TOP & BAIL,
  6 1/2 IN.DIAMETER...............................................   75.00
CRANBERRY GLASS,JAR,JAM,APPLE-SHAPED,SILVER-PLATED COVER &
  HOLDER,PAIR.....................................................   45.00
CRANBERRY GLASS,JAR,JAM,BLOWN,SILVER COVER & BAIL,
  3 1/2 IN.HIGH...................................................   35.00
CRANBERRY GLASS,JAR,JAM,INVERTED THUMBPRINT,ENAMEL FLORAL,
  HOLDER,SPOON....................................................   87.50
CRANBERRY GLASS,JAR,MUSTARD,NICKEL SILVER HOLDER,BARBOUR
  SILVER CO.......................................................   35.00
CRANBERRY GLASS,KNIFE REST,PANELED CENTER BAR,FACETED BALL
  ENDS,3 IN.......................................................   42.00
CRANBERRY GLASS,LAMP,HALL,HANGING,HOBNAIL,BRASS CHAIN,21 X
  8 IN. HIGH......................................................   75.00
CRANBERRY GLASS,LAMP,HALL,HANGS,EGG-SHAPE GLOBE,BRASS FRAME,
  CHAIN,CANOPY....................................................   62.00
CRANBERRY GLASS,LAMP,HANGING,BULL'S-EYE.....................  350.00
CRANBERRY GLASS,LAMP,HANGING,HOBNAIL,BURNISHED BRASS FONT,
  PRISMS,WIRED....................................................  250.00
CRANBERRY GLASS,LAMP,MINIATURE,OPTIC,BULBOUS,BRASS COLLAR,
  FOOTED..........................................................   45.00
CRANBERRY GLASS,LAMP,OIL,CLEAR,SWIRL,HAND-BLOWN FONT,FENTON
```

GLASSWORKS.............................................. 13.00
CRANBERRY GLASS,LAMP,OIL,OPALESCENT STRIPE FONT,FENTON
GLASSWORKS.............................................. 13.50
CRANBERRY GLASS,MARMALADE,RIBBED,SILVER TOP & BAIL.......... 48.00
CRANBERRY GLASS,MUFFINEER,BULBOUS BOTTOM,SILVER LID......... 23.00
CRANBERRY GLASS,MUFFINEER,TOP MARKED EPNS.................. 28.00
CRANBERRY GLASS,MUFFINEER,PANELED,SILVER TOP....... 35.00 TO 42.50
CRANBERRY GLASS,MUFFINEER,PANELS.......................... 32.50
CRANBERRY GLASS,MUG,TOBY TYPE,FLASHED,7 IN.TALL........... 19.00
CRANBERRY GLASS,MUSTARD POT,SILVER-PLATED LACY HOLDER....... 35.00
CRANBERRY GLASS,PARFAIT,CLEAR BASE,SET OF 8................ 40.00
CRANBERRY GLASS,PERFUME,BRASS FILIGREE CASING,CHAIN,RING,
2 1/4 IN.HIGH.......................................... 20.00
CRANBERRY GLASS,PERFUME,ENAMEL FLOWER SPRAY,SILVER BAND,CUT
STOPPER................................................ 17.50
CRANBERRY GLASS,PERFUME,PURSE SIZE,HINGED SILVER COVER,
INSIDE STOPPER......................................... 22.50
CRANBERRY GLASS,PERFUME,QUILTED,ENAMEL FLOWER DECOR,
5 1/2 IN.HIGH.......................................... 32.00
CRANBERRY GLASS,PITCHER,ALMOND THUMBPRINT,ENAMELED
FORGET-ME-NOTS......................................... 95.00
CRANBERRY GLASS,PITCHER,APPLIED CLEAR HANDLE,7 IN.......... 45.00
CRANBERRY GLASS,PITCHER,APPLIED REEDED HANDLE,GROUND PONTIL,
TANKARD................................................ 37.50
CRANBERRY GLASS,PITCHER,BULBOUS,CLEAR HANDLE.............. 45.00
CRANBERRY GLASS,PITCHER,BULBOUS,CLEAR HANDLE,PLATFORM FOOT.. 24.00
CRANBERRY GLASS,PITCHER,CLEAR APPLIED HANDLE,PINCHED SPOUT,
GROUND PONTIL.......................................... 12.50
CRANBERRY GLASS,PITCHER,CLEAR APPLIED HANDLE,BLOWN,
7 1/2 IN.TALL.......................................... 35.00
CRANBERRY GLASS,PITCHER,CLEAR RIB,APPLIED HANDLE,7 IN. TALL. 60.00
CRANBERRY GLASS,PITCHER,CLEAR THREADED HANDLE,9 IN.......... 55.00
CRANBERRY GLASS,PITCHER,DAISY & FERN,PINK OVERLAY INSIDE
SPOUT,9 IN............................................. 67.50
CRANBERRY GLASS,PITCHER,GOLD & WHITE ENAMEL FLORAL,CRYSTAL
HANDLE,6 IN............................................ 38.00
CRANBERRY GLASS,PITCHER,GRADUATED HOBNAILS,WHITE NECK,CLEAR
HANDLE................................................. 60.00
CRANBERRY GLASS,PITCHER,INVERTED THUMBPRINT,POINTED
SCALLOPS,6 1/2 IN...................................... 45.00
CRANBERRY GLASS,PITCHER,INVERTED THUMBPRINT,RUFFLED TOP,
10 IN.................................................. 55.00
CRANBERRY GLASS,PITCHER,INVERTED THUMBPRINT,TANKARD SHAPE,
SIX TUMBLERS........................................... 90.00
CRANBERRY GLASS,PITCHER,LARGE THUMBPRINTS,FLUTED RIM,
BULBOUS,9 3/4 IN....................................... 75.00
CRANBERRY GLASS,PITCHER,LEMONADE,CLEAR,APPLIED HANDLE,SIX
TUMBLERS............................................... 90.00
CRANBERRY GLASS,PITCHER,LOOP PATTERN,CLEAR HANDLE,BULBOUS,
9 1/4 IN.HIGH.......................................... 110.00
CRANBERRY GLASS,PITCHER,MILK,TANKARD,APPLIED CLEAR HANDLE,
PONTIL,BLOWN........................................... 30.00
CRANBERRY GLASS,PITCHER,TANKARD,INVERTED THUMBPRINT INSIDE.. 33.00
CRANBERRY GLASS,PITCHER,TANKARD-SHAPED,INVERTED THUMBPRINT,
SIX TUMBLERS........................................... 90.00
CRANBERRY GLASS,PITCHER,WATER,DAISY & FERN................ 75.00
CRANBERRY GLASS,PITCHER,WATER,INVERTED THUMBPRINT,ENAMEL
DECOR,8 IN............................................. 68.00
CRANBERRY GLASS,PITCHER,WATER,LILY-OF-THE-VALLEY DECOR,
ENAMELED............................................... 95.00
CRANBERRY GLASS,PITCHER,WATER,MADE WITH GOLD,9 IN.TALL,
6 TUMBLERS............................................. 140.00
CRANBERRY GLASS,PITCHER,WATER,OVERSHOT,PEWTER LID.......... 65.00
CRANBERRY GLASS,PITCHER,WATER,PANEL,THUMBPRINT,DAISY,BUTTON. 135.00
CRANBERRY GLASS,PITCHER,WATER,RIBBED,BULBOUS,APPLIED CLEAR
HANDLE................................................. 65.00
CRANBERRY GLASS,PITCHER,WATER,RIBBED,OPALESCENT HERRINGBONE,
CLEAR HANDLE........................................... 55.00
CRANBERRY GLASS,PITCHER,WATER,SWIRL EFFECT,CLEAR REEDED
HANDLE,8 1/2 IN........................................ 65.00
CRANBERRY GLASS,PITCHER,WHITE CARNATIONS,ENAMEL,CUFF NECK,
6 1/2 IN.TALL.......................................... 65.00
CRANBERRY GLASS,SALT & PEPPER,PANELED,SILVER RIM,PAIR....... 18.00
CRANBERRY GLASS,SALT & PEPPER,ROYAL IVY,CRANBERRY TO CLEAR.. 40.00
CRANBERRY GLASS,SALT,CLEAR APPLIED DECOR,SILVER PLATE STAND. 16.00
CRANBERRY GLASS,SALT,MASTER,THREADED BORDER,APPLIED CLEAR
FEET................................................... 17.00
CRANBERRY GLASS,SALT,SILVER RIM,2 1/4-IN.DIAMETER.......... 20.00
CRANBERRY GLASS,SHADE,BULL'S-EYE,BRASS FONT,PRISMS TOP &
BOTTOM,HANGING......................................... 350.00
CRANBERRY GLASS,SHADE,HOBNAIL,14 IN....................... 175.00

CRANBERRY GLASS,SHADE,LAMP,HANGING,LARGE OPALESCENT COIN
  SPOTS,14 IN................................................ 200.00
CRANBERRY GLASS,SHAKER,SALT,ENAMELED FLORAL,CRANBERRY TO
  CLEAR...................................................... 14.00
CRANBERRY GLASS,SHAKER,SUGAR,BEVEL CUT,STAR,MOON,COVER...... 45.00
CRANBERRY GLASS,SHAKER,SUGAR,DIAMOND-QUILTED,BARREL SHAPE... 46.00
CRANBERRY GLASS,SHAKER,SUGAR,ENAMELED BLUE DAISIES,HOURGLASS
  SHAPE,LID.................................................. 45.00
CRANBERRY GLASS,SHAKER,SUGAR,LOW OVOID SHAPE,EMBOSSED BRASS
  TOP....................................................... 36.00
CRANBERRY GLASS,SHAKER,SUGAR,ORNATE SILVER TOP.............. 25.00
CRANBERRY GLASS,SHAKER,SUGAR,PANELED,SILVER TOP.... 22.50 TO 28.00
CRANBERRY GLASS,SHAKER,SUGAR,PANELED SIDES,BRASS TOP MARKED
  EPNS...................................................... 25.00
CRANBERRY GLASS,SHAKER,SUGAR,PANELS,SILVER-PLATED TOP....... 28.00
CRANBERRY GLASS,SHAKER,SUGAR,QUILTED DIAMOND IN MILKY WHITE. 30.00
CRANBERRY GLASS,SHAKER,SUGAR,ROYAL OAK,CRANBERRY TO CLEAR... 36.00
CRANBERRY GLASS,SHAKER,SUGAR,SILVER BAND,SILVER DOME COVER,
  CUTOUTS................................................... 44.50
CRANBERRY GLASS,SHAKER,SUGAR,SILVER-PLATED TOP,5 1/2 IN.TALL 25.00
CRANBERRY GLASS,SNIFTER,ETCHED FLORAL,CLEAR STEM & FOOT,
  ENGLAND,PAIR.............................................. 7.50
CRANBERRY GLASS,SUGAR SHAKER,PANELED,SILVER TOP............. 22.50
CRANBERRY GLASS,SYRUP,BULBOUS,HINGED ORNATE PEWTER COVER &
  HANDLE.................................................... 45.00
CRANBERRY GLASS,TOOTHPICK,CRIMPED TOP,CLEAR BAND & BASE OF
  THREE LEAVES.............................................. 25.00
CRANBERRY GLASS,TOOTHPICK,GREEN FLECKS..................... 38.50
CRANBERRY GLASS,TOOTHPICK,THREADED OVER OPALESCENT,FLUTED
  TOP,VASE SHAPE............................................ 30.00
CRANBERRY GLASS,TOOTHPICK,UMBRELLA LEAF.................... 30.00
CRANBERRY GLASS,TOOTHPICK,WHITE SPATTER,UMBRELLA LEAF...... 25.00
CRANBERRY GLASS,TUMBLER,BABY THUMBPRINT.................... 22.50
CRANBERRY GLASS,TUMBLER,DAISY & FERN,OPALESCENT............ 16.00
CRANBERRY GLASS,TUMBLER,DIAMOND PATTERN,PAIR............... 36.00
CRANBERRY GLASS,TUMBLER,DRAPE,WHITE LINING................. 27.50
CRANBERRY GLASS,TUMBLER,FROSTED TO CLEAR HOBNAIL........... 45.00
CRANBERRY GLASS,TUMBLER,JUICE SIZE,BLOWN.................... 12.00
CRANBERRY GLASS,TUMBLER,JUICE,ENAMELED..................... 10.00
CRANBERRY GLASS,TUMBLER,JUICE,POLISHED BOTTOM,BLOWN........ 9.00
CRANBERRY GLASS,TUMBLER,JUICE,SET OF 6..................... 36.00
CRANBERRY GLASS,TUMBLER,MELON RIBBON BODY.................. 12.50
CRANBERRY GLASS,TUMBLER,OPALESCENT SWIRL.................... 25.00
CRANBERRY GLASS,TUMBLER,QUILTED,CLEAR BASE................. 11.50
CRANBERRY GLASS,TUMBLER,SWIRL,OPALESCENT.................... 10.00
CRANBERRY GLASS,TUMBLER,THUMBPRINT......................... 20.00
CRANBERRY GLASS,TUMBLER,WHITE OPALESCENT STARS & STRIPES.... 27.50
CRANBERRY GLASS,TUMBLER,4 1/4 IN.HIGH...................... 11.00
CRANBERRY GLASS,VASE,BUD,WHITE OVERLAY,COIN SPOT,GOLD
  TRACERY,3 7/8 IN.......................................... 45.00
CRANBERRY GLASS,VASE,CLEAR BASE,ETCHED SPRAY OF FLOWERS,
  FLASHED,PAIR.............................................. 25.00
CRANBERRY GLASS,VASE,COIN GOLD FLORAL,GOLD LEAVES,VINES,
  CLOVERLEAF SHAPE.......................................... 35.00
CRANBERRY GLASS,VASE,CRUET TYPE,WHITE ENAMELED DAISIES,CLEAR
  STOPPER................................................... 59.00
CRANBERRY GLASS,VASE,ENAMELED BLUE FLOWERS,GOLD,11 IN.TALL.. 46.00
CRANBERRY GLASS,VASE,ENAMELED PANSIES,6 IN.HIGH X
  2 1/2-IN.DIAMETER......................................... 25.00
CRANBERRY GLASS,VASE,FLARED & CRIMPED TOP,CLEAR FEET,
  7 IN.TALL................................................. 35.00
CRANBERRY GLASS,VASE,FLUTED TOP,7 IN. HIGH................. 25.00
CRANBERRY GLASS,VASE,GOLD SCROLLS,BLUE FLORAL,BLOWN,
  8 IN.TALL................................................. 35.00
CRANBERRY GLASS,VASE,MELON SHAPE,RUFFLED EDGE,BULBOUS BASE,
  ENGLAND,6 IN.............................................. 18.50
CRANBERRY GLASS,VASE,OPALINE CASING,APPLIED CHERRIES,AMBER
  RUFFLED RIM............................................... 38.50
CRANBERRY GLASS,VASE,PORCELAIN MEDALLION,MAN HOLDS BASKET OF
  FLOWERS................................................... 105.00
CRANBERRY GLASS,VASE,PORCELAIN MEDALLION,WOMAN HOLDS DOG,
  HAND-PAINTED.............................................. 105.00
CRANBERRY GLASS,VASE,RIBBED,SHADED TO WHITE AT BOTTOM,
  FLUTED,CASED,8 IN......................................... 10.00
CRANBERRY GLASS,VASE,RUFFLED PIECRUST TOP,APPLIED CLEAR
  RIGAREE................................................... 21.00
CRANBERRY GLASS,VASE,RUFFLED RIM,CLEAR FOOT,10 1/4 IN.TALL.. 35.00
CRANBERRY GLASS,VASE,RUFFLED,GOLD DECOR,ENGLAND............ 46.00
CRANBERRY GLASS,VASE,TULIP,PIECRUST TOP,APPLIED CLEAR
  RIGAREE,12 IN............................................. 31.00
CRANBERRY GLASS,WATCH CASE,BRASS STAND..................... 37.50

CRANBERRY GLASS,WINE SET,CUT PANELED BASE,NECK,STOPPER,TRAY,
  SIX GLASSES...................................................... 69.50
CRANBERRY GLASS,WINE,CLEAR STEM & FOOT,BLOWN.................... 12.50
CRANBERRY GLASS,WINE,GOLD DECOR,CLEAR STEM,7 1/2 IN.HIGH,
  TWELVE......................................................... 600.00


    CREAMWARE OR QUEENSWARE WAS DEVELOPED BY JOSIAH
    WEDGWOOD ABOUT 1765. IT IS A CREAM-COLORED EARTHENWARE
    THAT HAS BEEN COPIED BY MANY FACTORIES.
CREAMWARE,BASKET & STAND,OPENWORK,CIRCA 1800................. 75.00
CREAMWARE,BASKET,OPENWORK,TWIG HANDLES,SCALLOPED,
  STAFFORDSHIRE,11 IN........................................... 120.00
CREAMWARE,FOOD WARMER,SPIRIT BURNER AT BASE,HANDLED BOWL ON
  TOP,1790...................................................... 100.00
CREAMWARE,PITCHER,BROWN & CREAM COLOR,SIGNED TURNER,CIRCA
  1784.......................................................... 150.00
CREAMWARE,PITCHER,BULBOUS,MEDALLION,CHARITY FIGURE,CHILDREN,
  COPPER........................................................ 85.00
CREAMWARE,PITCHER,ENAMELED,MARKED W.T.,1796,STAFFORDSHIRE,
  7 IN.HIGH..................................................... 50.00
CREAMWARE,PLATE,SET OF 6,FRENCH,10-IN.DIAMETER................ 80.00
CREAMWARE,PLATE,STAFFORDSHIRE,6,19TH CENTURY,MARINE
  DECORATION.................................................... 250.00
CREAMWARE,TEAPOT,CIRCA 1765,5 IN. HIGH........................ 100.00
CREAMWARE,TEAPOT,STAFFORDSHIRE,CIRCA 1780..................... 80.00
CREIL,TEA SERVICE,TRANSFER-DECORATED,MINIATURE,CIRCA 1825... 400.00


    CROESUS GLASS IS A SPECIAL PATTERN OF PRESSED GLASS
    MADE ABOUT 1897. IT WAS MADE IN CLEAR GLASS,EMERALD
    GREEN,OR AMETHYST. EACH PIECE WAS DECORATED WITH GOLD.
CROESUS,GREEN,BOWL,BERRY,GOLD,FOOTED......................... 25.00
CROESUS,GREEN,BOWL,BERRY,LARGE............................... 70.00
CROESUS,GREEN,BOWL,FRUIT..................................... 62.00
CROESUS,GREEN,BOWL,SUGAR,GOLD,COVER.......................... 67.50
CROESUS,GREEN,BUTTER,GOLD,COVER.................... 75.00 TO  85.00
CROESUS,GREEN,CASTOR,PICKLE,MATCHING TUMBLER................. 50.00
CROESUS,GREEN,CREAMER,COVERED SUGAR,COVERED BUTTER,SPOONER,
  GOLD.......................................................... 235.00
CROESUS,GREEN,CREAMER,COVERED SUGAR,SPOONER,TWO TUMBLERS.... 215.00
CROESUS,GREEN,CREAMER,INDIVIDUAL............................. 65.00
CROESUS,GREEN,CREAMER,SUGAR,BUTTER,SPOONER................... 200.00
CROESUS,GREEN,CREAMER & SUGAR,COVER.......................... 200.00
CROESUS,GREEN,DISH,PICKLE.................................... 30.00
CROESUS,GREEN,DISH,PICKLE,FLAT.............................. 15.00
CROESUS,GREEN,DISH,RELISH,OVAL.............................. 30.00
CROESUS,GREEN,DISH,SAUCE,GOLD..................... 20.00 TO  27.00
CROESUS,GREEN,PITCHER,WATER,GOLD................. 95.00 TO  175.00
CROESUS,GREEN,PITCHER,WATER,GOLD,SIX TUMBLERS............... 350.00
CROESUS,GREEN,SALT & PEPPER,GOLD.................. 65.00 TO  75.00
CROESUS,GREEN,SHAKER,SALT,GOLD.............................. 35.00
CROESUS,GREEN,SPOONER,FOOTED................................ 35.00
CROESUS,GREEN,SPOONER,GOLD.................................. 60.00
CROESUS,GREEN,SUGAR,COVER,GOLD.................... 65.00 TO  75.00
CROESUS,GREEN,SUGAR,GOLD,OPEN............................... 40.00
CROESUS,GREEN,TOOTHPICK,GOLD...................... 45.00 TO  69.00
CROESUS,GREEN,TUMBLER,GOLD........................ 32.50 TO  37.00
CROESUS,PURPLE,BOWL,BERRY,7 IN. DIAMETER.......... 72.50 TO  85.00
CROESUS,PURPLE,BUTTER,COVER................................. 135.00
CROESUS,PURPLE,CELERY...................................... 160.00
CROESUS,PURPLE,CREAMER...............................ILLUS.. 75.00
CROESUS,PURPLE,CREAMER & SUGAR,COVER.............. 175.00 TO 200.00
CROESUS,PURPLE,CRUET,VINEGAR,STOPPER....................... 175.00
CROESUS,PURPLE,DISH,PICKLE................................. 35.00
CROSEUS,PURPLE,DISH,SAUCE.................................. 35.00
CROESUS,PURPLE,DISH,SAUCE,FOOTED,GOLD TRIM........ 40.00 TO  50.00
CROESUS,PURPLE,JELLY,FOOTED................................ 67.50
CROESUS,PURPLE,RELISH..................................... 35.00
CROESUS,PURPLE,SALT & PEPPER,GOLD.......................... 47.50
CROESUS,PURPLE,SPOONER...............................ILLUS.. 75.00
CROESUS,PURPLE,SUGAR,COVERED.........................ILLUS.. 110.00
CROESUS,PURPLE,TOOTHPICK.......................... 65.00 TO  75.00
CROESUS,PURPLE,TRAY,GOLD,9 1/2 IN. X 3 3/4 IN............... 37.50
CROESUS,PURPLE,TUMBLER.................................... 58.50


    CROWN DERBY IS THE NICKNAME GIVEN TO THE WORKS OF THE
    ROYAL CROWN DERBY FACTORY,WHICH BEGAN WORKING IN
    ENGLAND IN 1859. AN EARLIER AND MORE FAMOUS ENGLISH
    DERBY FACTORY EXISTED FROM 1750 TO 1848. THE TWO
    FACTORIES WERE NOT RELATED. MOST OF THE PORCELAIN FOUND

CROESUS PURPLE CREAMER     CROESUS PURPLE SUGAR     CROESUS PURPLE SPOONER

```
        TODAY WITH THE DERBY MARK IS THE WORK OF THE LATER
        DERBY FACTORY.
CROWN DERBY,SEE ALSO,ROYAL CROWN DERBY
CROWN DERBY,BOWL & SAUCER,PINK LUSTER TYPE,RED STRIATIONS,
    GOLD BAND,1788.....................................         45.00
CROWN DERBY,CREAMER,FLORAL DECOR,GOLD,FLARING HANDLE,FOOTED,
    MARKED............................................         28.00
CROWN DERBY,CREAMER,SUGAR,IMARI PATTERN,CIRCA 1830..........    225.00
CROWN DERBY,CUP & SAUCER,DEMITASSE,FRUIT BRANCHES,CIRCA
    1880,SET OF 6......................................         75.00
CROWN DERBY,PLATE,BLACK GROUND,MULTICOLORED FLOWERS,GOLD,
    8 1/2 IN.,PAIR.....................................         38.00
CROWN DERBY,VASE,EAGLES,BIRDS,RING HANDLES,GOLD DECOR,
    7 3/4 IN.HIGH,PAIR.................................        300.00


        CROWN MILANO GLASS WAS MADE BY FREDERICK SHIRLEY ABOUT
        1890. IT HAD A PLAIN BISCUIT COLOR WITH A SATIN FINISH.
        IT WAS DECORATED WITH FLOWERS,AND OFTEN HAD LARGE GOLD
        SCROLLS.
CROWN MILANO,BASKET,BRIDE'S,ENAMELED PANSY DECOR,TRICORN,
    SIGNED............................................        750.00
CROWN MILANO,BOWL,MELON RIB,FLORAL DECOR,4 1/2 IN...........    182.00
CROWN MILANO,BOWL,ROSE,BISQUE FINISH EMULATING BURMESE,
    FLORAL,6 1/2 IN....................................        300.00
CROWN MILANO,BOWL,TAN,FLOWERS,PEWTER TOP & HANDLE..........    250.00
CROWN MILANO,BOX,JEWEL,FORGET-ME-NOT DECOR,GLOSSY FINISH,
    3 IN..............................................        150.00
CROWN MILANO,BOX,JEWEL,ORIGINAL LINING,MT. WASHINGTON.......    125.00
CROWN MILANO,BOX,MAGENTA RED SCROLLS,GOLD OUTLINE,FLORAL,
    COVER.............................................        325.00
CROWN MILANO,BOX,WHITE,YELLOW,QUEENS PATTERN,DAISY DECOR ON
    LID,LINING........................................        275.00
CROWN MILANO,COOKIE JAR,SIGNED,RESILVERED.............ILLUS.    350.00
CROWN MILANO,HUMIDOR,CREAM GROUND,PANSIES,SILVER PLATE LID,
    SIGNED M.W........................................        295.00
CROWN MILANO,JAR,BISCUIT,BLUE SHADING TO IVORY,ROSES,GOLD,
    MT.WASHINGTON.....................................        300.00
CROWN MILANO,JAR,CRACKER,APRICOT,APPLE BLOSSOM LIMBS &
    FLOWERS DECOR.....................................        275.00
CROWN MILANO,JAR,CRACKER,PANSY DECOR,MARK..................    250.00
CROWN MILANO,JAR,SWEETMEAT,AMETHYST JEWEL-LIKE BEADING,
    MEDALLIONS,COVER..................................        450.00
CROWN MILANO,JAR,SWEETMEAT,CHRYSANTHEMUM DECOR,
    GOLD-ENCRUSTED....................................        325.00
CROWN MILANO,SHADE,UMBRELLA,FLORAL,GOLD,BURMESE COLORING,
    10 1/2 IN.........................................        250.00
CROWN MILANO,SHAKER,GLOBULAR,PEWTER TOP,MT.WASHINGTON,PAIR..     30.00
CROWN MILANO,SUGAR,DIAMOND-QUILTED,WHITE TO YELLOW,PINK
    FLORAL,OPEN.......................................         65.00
CROWN MILANO,TUMBLER,MT.WASHINGTON,GOLD DECOR,SIGNED,CROWN,
    NUMBER............................................        300.00
CROWN MILANO,VASE,BEIGE GROUND,GOLD FERN,MT.WASHINGTON
    MEDALLIONS........................................        365.00
CROWN MILANO,VASE,MT.WASHINGTON,YELLOW TO PEACH GROUND,
    THISTLE DECOR.....................................        225.00
CROWN MILANO,VASE,SIGNED,8 IN.HIGH.........................    650.00
CROWN MILANO,VASE,WHITE SATIN GROUND,PINK SHADING,PANSIES,
    MARK,5 IN.TALL....................................        400.00
```

CROWN MILANO COOKIE JAR

CRUETS OF GLASS OR PORCELAIN WERE MADE TO HOLD VINEGAR
OR OIL. THEY WERE ESPECIALLY POPULAR DURING VICTORIAN
TIMES.

| | |
|---|---:|
| CRUET,SEE ALSO OTHER SECTIONS,AMBER,PRESSED GLASS,ETC. | |
| CRUET,AVOCADO GREEN,CLEAR SWIRL STOPPER,10 IN.............. | 35.00 |
| CRUET,BALL-SHAPED,INVERTED THUMBPRINT,CLEAR HANDLE,CRANBERRY | 45.00 |
| CRUET,BLUE,AMBER STOPPER & HANDLE,7 IN.HIGH................ | 37.50 |
| CRUET,BLUE,CLEAR APPLIED HANDLE & STOPPER.................. | 42.50 |
| CRUET,BULBOUS,PEDESTAL BASE,ORANGE & WHITE BLOSSOMS,STOPPER, | |
| 9 1/2 IN................................................ | 38.00 |
| CRUET,CHRYSANTHEMUM SPRIG,STOPPER,CUSTARD GLASS,5 IN........ | 65.00 |
| CRUET,COBALT OVERLAY CUT TO CLEAR,BRIDGETON ROSE PATTERN, | |
| STOPPER................................................. | 55.00 |
| CRUET,CUT GLASS,STOPPER,MARKED HAWKES ON BOTTOM............ | 65.00 |
| CRUET,EMERALD GREEN,GOLD COLOR ENAMEL OVERLAY,TINY JEWEL | |
| DECOR,9 IN.TALL......................................... | 39.50 |
| CRUET,EMERALD GREEN GROUND,WHITE ENAMEL LILY OF THE VALLEY, | |
| GOLD LEAVES............................................. | 35.00 |
| CRUET,ENAMELED FLORAL,LIGHT GREEN......................... | 17.50 |
| CRUET,GREEN GROUND,WHITE & GOLD ENAMEL FLORAL,CLEAR STOPPER, | |
| 10 IN.................................................. | 37.50 |
| CRUET,GREEN,DOUBLE S,PAINTED FACETED STOPPER............. | 16.00 |
| CRUET,GREEN,WHITE ENAMELED TASSELS,GOLD OVALS,STOPPER,HANDLE | 35.00 |
| CRUET,MILLEFIORI,CRANES,YELLOW,WHITE,BLUE,BROWN,CUT GLASS | |
| STOPPER................................................. | 110.00 |
| CRUET,MILLEFIORI,SATIN FINISH STOPPER,MURANO,7 IN........... | 26.00 |
| CRUET,OIL & VINEGAR,CLEAR,GROUND PONTIL,BUBBLE STOPPER, | |
| SILVER RIM,DOUBLE....................................... | 25.00 |
| CRUET,OIL & VINEGAR,ETCHED GLASS,STOPPER,GROUND PONTIL, | |
| 6 1/2 IN,HIGH........................................... | 8.00 |
| CRUET,PANELED THISTLE,PRISM STOPPER....................... | 10.00 |
| CRUET,PANELED,GROUND MOUTH,PONTIL,STOPPER,PANELS,EMERALD | |
| GREEN,BLOWN............................................. | 27.50 |
| CRUET,PANELS,FLARED BALL BASE,BLUE,WHITE ENAMELED FLORAL, | |
| STOPPER,AMBER........................................... | 35.00 |
| CRUET,PINK TO LAVENDER,PINK,BLUE APPLIED FLORAL,OPALESCENT | |
| PEDESTAL................................................ | 60.00 |
| CRUET,RAYED STAR BASE,BUZZ,RAYED STARS,NOTCHED HANDLE,CUT | |
| GLASS,7 IN.............................................. | 23.00 |
| CRUET,SALT,PEPPER,MUSTARD,VINEGAR,REVOLVES,4 IN.HIGH,CHILD'S | 47.50 |
| CRUET,STRAWBERRY,HOBNAIL,CLEAR APPLIED HANDLE & STOPPER, | |
| 7 1/2 IN.HIGH........................................... | 15.00 |
| CRUET,VASELINE TO PINK,HOBNAIL........................... | 30.00 |
| CRUET,VINEGAR,BEADED LOOP,FACETED STOPPER................. | 9.00 |
| CRUET,VINEGAR,CLEAR,STERLING SILVER DEPOSIT............... | 18.50 |
| CRUET,VINEGAR,FROSTED GLASS,GREEN ENAMEL DECOR............. | 25.00 |
| CRUET,VINEGAR,PORTRAIT,ARTIST-SIGNED,STOPPER,HANDLE, | |
| PORCELAIN............................................... | 38.00 |
| CRUET,YELLOW,AMBER HANDLE & STOPPER,PEACHBLOW,WHEELING...... | 450.00 |
| CRUET,ZIPPER EDGE ON RIBS & HANDLE,PONTIL MARK,NO STOPPER, | |
| 5 1/2 IN................................................ | 5.00 |

CUP PLATES ARE SMALL GLASS OR CHINA PLATES THAT HELD
THE CUP WHILE A GENTLEMAN OF THE MID-NINETEENTH

CENTURY DRANK HIS COFFEE OR TEA FROM THE SAUCER. THE
MOST FAMOUS CUP PLATES WERE MADE OF GLASS AT THE BOSTON
AND SANDWICH FACTORY LOCATED IN MASSACHUSETTS.

| | |
|---|---:|
| CUP PLATE,BLACK,WHITE,COW,SHEEP,BUILDING,3 3/4-IN.DIAMETER.. | 15.00 |
| CUP PLATE,BLUE & WHITE,CLEWS,1819. | 24.00 |
| CUP PLATE,BLUE,SCENE,BOSTON STATE HOUSE,ADAMS,10 IN......... | 55.00 |
| CUP PLATE,BROWN & WHITE,CENTER SCENE,BIRD & FLORAL BORDER, 3 3/4 IN...... | 15.00 |
| CUP PLATE,BROWN & WHITE,OCEAN SCENE CENTER,ROPE & SAILING VESSELS BORDER. | 15.00 |
| CUP PLATE,BROWN,EAGLE & FLORAL BORDER,CASTLES & BOAT CENTER, CLEWS..... | 12.00 |
| CUP PLATE,DARK BLUE,HALL'S SELECT VIEWS,BUILDING,BRIDGE, 4-IN.DIAMETER. | 35.00 |
| CUP PLATE,DARK BLUE,HALL'S SELECT VIEWS,CENTER SCENE,MARK 8 ON BOTTOM. | 35.00 |
| CUP PLATE,DARK BLUE,SHELL CENTER,SCROLL & FLORAL BORDER, ADAMS...... | 30.00 |
| CUP PLATE,DARK BLUE,VIEWS,PAIR...... | 50.00 |
| CUP PLATE,LIGHT BLUE,CENTER SCENE,ENGLAND,4 1/2-IN.DIAMETER. | 10.00 |
| CUP PLATE,LIGHT BLUE,FLORAL,THREE SMALL SCENES, 3 1/2-IN.DIAMETER. | 15.00 |
| CUP PLATE,SAILING SHIP,MEN IN ROWBOAT,SHIP BORDER,BROWN, STAFFORDSHIRE. | 12.00 |
| CUP PLATE,SCENE WITH HOUSE IN CENTER,MARK Z ON BOTTOM....... | 35.00 |

CURRIER AND IVES PRESSED GLASS PATTERN,SEE PRESSED GLASS


CURRIER AND IVES MADE THE FAMOUS AMERICAN LITHOGRAPHS
MARKED WITH THEIR NAME FROM 1857 TO 1907.

| | |
|---|---:|
| CURRIER,GEN.TAYLOR BEFORE BUENA VISTA,1847............... | 175.00 |
| CURRIER,JOHNSON SLAYS TECUMSEH,BATTLE OF THE THAMES 1813, 1841...... | 150.00 |
| CURRIER,READING THE SCRIPTURES,SMALL FOLIO,FRAME......... | 25.00 |
| CURRIER,SAVIOR OF WORLD,FRAME,16 1/2 IN. X 14 1/4 IN....... | 15.00 |
| CURRIER,THE LIFE AND AGE OF MAN,RESIST THE DEVIL,C.1850..... | 75.00 |
| CURRIER & IVES,ADMIRAL PORTER'S FLEET RUNNING THE REBEL BLOCKADE,FRAME. | 85.00 |
| CURRIER & IVES,AMERICAN BASEBALL,SCENE,LINEN,WALNUT FRAME... | 7.50 |
| CURRIER & IVES,AMERICAN RAILROAD,SCENE,LINEN,WALNUT FRAME... | 7.50 |
| CURRIER & IVES,AUTUMN. | 17.00 |
| CURRIER & IVES,BENJAMIN FRANKLIN. | 30.00 |
| CURRIER & IVES,BRIDGET,13 1/2 X 18 IN. | 22.50 |
| CURRIER & IVES,BURNING OF THE STEAMSHIP AUSTRIA,1858........ | 150.00 |
| CURRIER & IVES,CITY OF NEW YORK & ENVIRONS,FRAME. | 125.00 |
| CURRIER & IVES,FANNIE. | 15.00 |
| CURRIER & IVES,FIRST SMOKE-ALL RIGHT,FIRST SMOKE-ALL WRONG, PAIR...... | 50.00 |
| CURRIER & IVES,FOREST SCENE,SUMMER. | 35.00 |
| CURRIER & IVES,FOUR FLOWERS,ORNATE WALNUT FRAME. | 25.00 |
| CURRIER & IVES,FUTURITY OF THE RACE,COLOR,SIGNED MAURER, FRAME...... | 450.00 |
| CURRIER & IVES,GOING FOR A SHINE,DATED 1889. | 85.00 |
| CURRIER & IVES,HIAWATHA,WOOING,WEDDING,1858,FRAME,21 X 26 IN.,PAIR...... | 145.00 |
| CURRIER & IVES,LINCOLN,16 X 20 IN. | 75.00 |
| CURRIER & IVES,LITTLE ASTRONOMER,FRAME. | 35.00 |
| CURRIER & IVES,LITTLE BROTHERS,FRAME. | 45.00 |
| CURRIER & IVES,LITTLE SARAH,CHILD WITH KITTEN,PINE FRAME.... | 30.00 |
| CURRIER & IVES,LITTLE SISTER. | 22.00 |
| CURRIER & IVES,MARTHA. | 15.00 |
| CURRIER & IVES,MY DEAR LITTLE PET. | 75.00 |
| CURRIER & IVES,MY LITTLE FAVORITE,LINER,FRAME,1847,11 X 16 IN...... | 25.00 |
| CURRIER & IVES,NAPOLEON,FRAMED. | 15.00 |
| CURRIER & IVES,OLD FARM GATE,FRAME. | 25.00 |
| CURRIER & IVES,OLD SLEDGE,TWO CARD PLAYERS,FRAME. | 45.00 |
| CURRIER & IVES,PRINCE ALBERT,13 1/2 X 18 IN. | 32.00 |
| CURRIER & IVES,QUEEN OF THE BALL,FRAME. | 45.00 |
| CURRIER & IVES,QUEEN VICTORIA,13 1/2 X 18 IN. | 28.00 |
| CURRIER & IVES,REPRINTS,10 1/8 X 14 3/4 IN.,IN ALBUM,80..... | 15.00 |
| CURRIER & IVES,ROADSIDE MILL. | 12.00 |
| CURRIER & IVES,SCENERY OF UPPER MISSISSIPPI,INDIAN VILLAGES, FOLIO...... | 50.00 |
| CURRIER & IVES,SUMMER. | 17.00 |
| CURRIER & IVES,SUMMER IN THE COUNTRY,MAT,FRAME,21 X 17 IN... | 37.50 |
| CURRIER & IVES,THE ANGEL GABRIEL,FRAME. | 20.00 |
| CURRIER & IVES,THE BURNING OF CHICAGO,1871,LAKEFRONT VIEW... | 150.00 |
| CURRIER & IVES,THE CELEBRATED CLIPPER SHIP GRAPESHOT,SMALL FOLIO,FRAME...... | 75.00 |
| CURRIER & IVES,THE DECLARATION,MAHOGANY FRAME,16 1/2 X | |

```
     12 IN.............................................       24.00
CURRIER & IVES,THE DOCTOR....................................       25.00
CURRIER & IVES,THE FISHERMAN'S DOG,FRAME,17 X 12 IN.........       25.00
CURRIER & IVES,THE HUDSON AT PEEKSKILL,FRAME,13 1/2 X
     17 1/2 IN.............................................       28.00
CURRIER & IVES,THE KILLERIES,CONNEMARA,MAHOGANY FRAME,18 X
     14 IN.................................................       25.00
CURRIER & IVES,THE LOVE LETTER,FRAME.......................       15.00
CURRIER & IVES,THE MEMPHIS VX,THE JAMES HOWARD,1875........      275.00
CURRIER & IVES,THE MORNING PRAYER..........................       22.00
CURRIER & IVES,THE OLD HOMESTEAD,FRAME.....................       18.00
CURRIER & IVES,THE ROADSIDE MILL,FRAME.....................       35.00
CURRIER & IVES,THE SOUTHERN BELLE,FRAME....................       45.00
CURRIER & IVES,WASHINGTON RECEPTION BY THE LADIES,COPYRIGHT
     1889.................................................       28.00


        CUSTARD GLASS IS AN OPAQUE GLASS SOMETIMES KNOWN AS
        BUTTERMILK GLASS. IT WAS FIRST MADE AFTER 1886 AT THE
        LA BELLE GLASS WORKS,BRIDGEPORT,OHIO.
CUSTARD GLASS,ATOMIZER,BUTTERFLY,INTAGLIO & ENAMELED DECOR,
     8 IN.TALL............................................       50.00
CUSTARD GLASS,BANANA BOAT,ARGONAUT SHELL...........175.00 TO      180.00
CUSTARD GLASS,BANANA BOAT,CHERRY SPRIG,GOLD,SCRIPT ON BOTTOM      115.00
CUSTARD GLASS,BANANA BOAT,CHRYSANTHEMUM SPRIG......115.00 TO      165.00
CUSTARD GLASS,BANANA BOAT,CHRYSANTHEMUM SPRIG,
     SCRIPT................................100.00 TO      110.00
CUSTARD GLASS,BANANA BOAT,FOOTED,GOLD,LOUIS XV.............      140.00
CUSTARD GLASS,BANANA BOAT,GENEVA PATTERN,CREAMY GROUND......      125.00
CUSTARD GLASS,BANANA BOAT,GRAPE & CABLE,IRIDESCENT,FOOTED...      175.00
CUSTARD GLASS,BANANA BOAT,LOUIS XV,FOOTED..........110.00 TO      125.00
CUSTARD GLASS,BANANA BOAT,LOW CAKE STAND,SAUCE DISH.........      165.00
CUSTARD GLASS,BELL,ROSES,GOLD BANDING & LETTERING,SOUVENIR,
     HAND-PAINTED.........................................       60.00
CUSTARD GLASS,BERRY SET,INVERTED FAN & FEATHER.............      450.00
CUSTARD GLASS,BERRY SET,ROSES..............................      200.00
CUSTARD GLASS,BERRY SET,ROSES,GOLD TRIM,SOUVENIR,7 PIECES...      100.00
CUSTARD GLASS,BERRY,CHRYSANTHEMUM SPRIG,BLUE OPAQUE.........       60.00
CUSTARD GLASS,BOWL,BANANA,WINGED SCROLL....................      110.00
CUSTARD GLASS,BOWL,BERRY,ARGONAUT SHELL,SIGNED N,10 1/2 X
     6 IN.................................................       75.00
CUSTARD GLASS,BOWL,BERRY,ARGONAUT SHELL,SIGNED NORTHWOOD,SIX
     SAUCES...............................................      400.00
CUSTARD GLASS,BOWL,BERRY,CHRYSANTHEMUM SPRIG...............      145.00
CUSTARD GLASS,BOWL,BERRY,CHRYSANTHEMUM SPRIG,BLUE,OVAL,
     SIGNED...............................................      275.00
CUSTARD GLASS,BOWL,BERRY,CHRYSANTHEMUM SPRIG,SIGNED
     NORTHWOOD............................................      105.00
CUSTARD GLASS,BOWL,BERRY,CHRYSANTHEMUM SPRIG,BLUE,OVAL,
     SIGNED NORTHWOOD.....................................      250.00
CUSTARD GLASS,BOWL,BERRY,GENEVA,FOOTED.....................       90.00
CUSTARD GLASS,BOWL,BERRY,INDIVIDUAL FRUITS,IVORINA VERDE....      200.00
CUSTARD GLASS,BOWL,BERRY,INDIVIDUAL,LOUIS XV,GILT,OVAL,FOUR
     FEET.................................................       25.00
CUSTARD GLASS,BOWL,BERRY,INTAGLIO,FOOTED,7 1/2-IN.DIAMETER..      115.00
CUSTARD GLASS,BOWL,BERRY,INTAGLIO,FOOTED,9-IN.DIAMETER......      135.00
CUSTARD GLASS,BOWL,BERRY,INTAGLIO,GOLD,GREEN,SIX SAUCES.....      250.00
CUSTARD GLASS,BOWL,BERRY,INTAGLIO,7 1/2 IN.................      110.00
CUSTARD GLASS,BOWL,BERRY,INTAGLIO,9 IN.....................      125.00
CUSTARD GLASS,BOWL,BERRY,INVERTED FAN & FEATHER,GOLD.......      150.00
CUSTARD GLASS,BOWL,BERRY,IVORINA VERDE,FOUR SMALLER BOWLS,
     GOLD.................................................      125.00
CUSTARD GLASS,BOWL,BERRY,LARGE,BEADED CIRCLE,ENAMEL DECOR...      100.00
CUSTARD GLASS,BOWL,BERRY,LARGE,LITTLE GEM..................       65.00
CUSTARD GLASS,BOWL,BERRY,LARGE,WINGED SCROLL,GOLD..........       85.00
CUSTARD GLASS,BOWL,BERRY,LITTLE GEM........................       80.00
CUSTARD GLASS,BOWL,BERRY,RING BAND.........................      110.00
CUSTARD GLASS,BOWL,BLUEBIRDS,FLORAL IN GOLD,7 3/4 IN.......       35.00
CUSTARD GLASS,BOWL,CENTER,PAIR CANDLESTICKS,BLUE...........       60.00
CUSTARD GLASS,BOWL,CEREAL,SIGNED MC KEE,5 1/2 IN...........        2.50
CUSTARD GLASS,BOWL,DAISY & SCROLL,PEDESTAL,7 IN.LONG,
     3 3/4 IN.WIDE........................................       16.00
CUSTARD GLASS,BOWL,DAISY DESIGN,DEEP YELLOW,PEDESTAL.......       20.00
CUSTARD GLASS,BOWL,INDIVIDUAL FRUIT,WINGED SCROLL..........       23.00
CUSTARD GLASS,BOWL,INTAGLIO,ON PEDESTAL BASE,7 1/2 IN.WIDE..       85.00
CUSTARD GLASS,BOWL,MAIZE,OPAQUE WHITE,GREEN LEAVES,LIBBEY,
     9 IN.................................................       65.00
CUSTARD GLASS,BOWL,PIER & WAVE,2 3/8 IN.X 5 1/2 IN.........       15.00
CUSTARD GLASS,BOWL,PIER AND WAVE,FOOTED,5 1/2-IN.DIAMETER,
     2 1/2 IN.TALL........................................       22.00
CUSTARD GLASS,BOWL,RIBBED,FLORAL BORDER,REG.MARK 1878,
```

```
   3-IN.DIAMETER..........................................    20.00
CUSTARD GLASS,BOWL,SUGAR,CHRYSANTHEMUM SPRIG,COVER..........    85.00
CUSTARD GLASS,BOWL,SUGAR,COVER,LOUIS XV.....................    29.50
CUSTARD GLASS,BOWL,THREE FRUITS,SCALLOPED,11 IN.WIDE........    28.00
CUSTARD GLASS,BOX,POWDER,WINGED SCROLL,SOUVENIR,COVER.......    40.00
CUSTARD GLASS,BUTTER,GREEN DECOR,IVORINA VERDE,COVER........    45.00
CUSTARD GLASS,BUTTER,INVERTED FAN,FEATHER,ROSE-GOLD,COVER...   145.00
CUSTARD GLASS,BUTTER,LITTLE GEM PATTERN,COVER,FOOTED........    43.00
CUSTARD GLASS,BUTTER,LOUIS XV,COVER............... 85.00 TO   110.00
CUSTARD GLASS,BUTTER,MELON RIB,BEADED TRIM,FOOTED,COVER,
   FINIAL..................................................    85.00
CUSTARD GLASS,BUTTER,RING BAND WITH PAINTED ROSES,SIGNED,
   HEISEY.................................................     90.00
CUSTARD GLASS,BUTTER,RING BAND,COVER............... 80.00 TO    85.00
CUSTARD GLASS,BUTTER,WHITE,RED ROSE SPRAYS,RELIEF BEADING...    78.50
CUSTARD GLASS,BUTTER,WINGED SCROLL,COVER....................   125.00
CUSTARD GLASS,CANDLESTICK,OVAL BASE,4 IN. X 4 1/8 IN.TALL,
   PAIR....................................................    32.00
CUSTARD GLASS,CANISTER,MARKED COFFEE,WHITE METAL SCREW TOP,
   6 1/2 IN................................................     7.00
CUSTARD GLASS,CELERY,CHRYSANTHEMUM SPRIG,GOLD...............   145.00
CUSTARD GLASS,COMPOTE,ARGONAUT SHELL........................   100.00
CUSTARD GLASS,COMPOTE,CANDLESTICKS,BOWL,DISHES,COLONIAL,
   BLUE,16 PIECES..........................................   325.00
CUSTARD GLASS,COMPOTE,CHRYSANTHEMUM SPRIG,GOLD,7 IN.HIGH,
   4-IN.DIAMETER...........................................    48.00
CUSTARD GLASS,COMPOTE,CHRYSANTHEMUM SPRIG,OPALESCENT,
   4 1/2 IN................................................    57.50
CUSTARD GLASS,COMPOTE,CHRYSANTHEMUM SPRIG,GOLD,4 3/4 IN.HIGH    57.50
CUSTARD GLASS,COMPOTE,HEART PATTERN,SIGNED CLARK,8 IN.HIGH..    95.00
CUSTARD GLASS,COMPOTE,JELLY,ARGONAUT SHELL......... 78.00 TO   140.00
CUSTARD GLASS,COMPOTE,JELLY,CHRYSANTHEMUM SPRIG.... 38.00 TO    50.00
CUSTARD GLASS,COMPOTE,JELLY,INTAGLIO........................    55.00
CUSTARD GLASS,COMPOTE,JELLY,STRAWBERRY PATTERN,SCALLOPED,
   5 1/4 IN.HIGH...........................................    24.00
CUSTARD GLASS,COMPOTE,PIER AND WAVE,FOOTED..................    20.00
CUSTARD GLASS,COMPOTE,STRAWBERRY PATTERN,PEDESTAL,5 X
   5 IN.TALL...............................................    18.00
CUSTARD GLASS,COMPOTE,STRAWBERRY,FOOTED,5-IN.DIAMETER,
   5 IN.TALL...............................................    20.00
CUSTARD GLASS,CONDIMENT SET,FOOTED EPNS TRAY,SHAKERS,
   MUSTARD,SPOON...........................................    50.00
CUSTARD GLASS,CREAMER & SUGAR,LOUIS XV,SPOONER..............   145.00
CUSTARD GLASS,CREAMER & SUGAR,SPRAY OF RED ROSES,RELIEF
   BEADING,WHITE...........................................    75.00
CUSTARD GLASS,CREAMER,ARGONAUT SHELL............... 70.00 TO    85.00
CUSTARD GLASS,CREAMER,ARGONAUT SHELL,GOLD,SIGNED............    85.00
CUSTARD GLASS,CREAMER,ARGONAUT SHELL,SIGNED NORTHWOOD IN
   SCRIPT..................................................    70.00
CUSTARD GLASS,CREAMER,BLACKBERRY BAND,SIGNED MCK............    17.50
CUSTARD GLASS,CREAMER,CHRYSANTHEMUM SPRIG,BLUE,SIGNED.......   165.00
CUSTARD GLASS,CREAMER,CHRYSANTHEMUM SPRIG...................    70.00
CUSTARD GLASS,CREAMER,CHRYSANTHEMUM SPRIG,BLUE,SIGNED
   NORTHWOOD...............................................   165.00
CUSTARD GLASS,CREAMER,COVERED SUGAR,SPOON HOLDER,COVERED
   BUTTER,LOUIS XV.........................................   265.00
CUSTARD GLASS,CREAMER,FAN,NORTHWOOD.........................    30.00
CUSTARD GLASS,CREAMER,GOLD COLOR BUTTON BASE,RED ROSES......    26.00
CUSTARD GLASS,CREAMER,GOLD EDGE, H IN DIAMOND,SOUVENIR
   HOULTON,MAINE...........................................    10.00
CUSTARD GLASS,CREAMER,GRAPE,CABLE...........................    70.00
CUSTARD GLASS,CREAMER,GRAPE,THUMBPRINT,N IN CIRCLE MARK.....    60.00
CUSTARD GLASS,CREAMER,LITTLE GEM............................    22.00
CUSTARD GLASS,CREAMER,LOUIS XV..............................    60.00
CUSTARD GLASS,CREAMER,MAPLE LEAF............................    75.00
CUSTARD GLASS,CREAMER,RING BAND.............................    45.00
CUSTARD GLASS,CREAMER,SOUVENIR NIAGARA FALLS,N.Y............    12.00
CUSTARD GLASS,CREAMER,SOUVENIR,PINEAPPLE & FAN..............    18.00
CUSTARD GLASS,CREAMER,SUGAR,SPOONER,BUTTER,ARGONAUT SHELL,
   NORTHWOOD...............................................   350.00
CUSTARD GLASS,CREAMER,WHITE,RED ROSE SPRAYS,RELIEF BEADING..    35.00
CUSTARD GLASS,CREAMER,WINGED SCROLL.........................    45.00
CUSTARD GLASS,CRUET,ARGONAUT PATTERN,GOLD EMBOSSED SEAWEED
   TRIM,STOPPER............................................    75.00
CUSTARD GLASS,CRUET,CHRYSANTHEMUM SPRIG,NO STOPPER.........     60.00
CUSTARD GLASS,CRUET,CHRYSANTHEMUM SPRIG,STOPPER............    120.00
CUSTARD GLASS,CRUET,CHRYSANTHEMUM SPRIG,AMBER STOPPER WITH
   CUSTARD DECOR...........................................    95.00
CUSTARD GLASS,CRUET,LOUIS XV,NO STOPPER.....................    60.00
CUSTARD GLASS,CRUET,VINEGAR,ARGONAUT SHELL,STOPPER..........   145.00
CUSTARD GLASS,CRUET,VINEGAR,LOUIS XV,STOPPER................   120.00
```

CUSTARD GLASS,CRUET,WINGED SCROLL............................. 125.00
CUSTARD GLASS,CUP,PUNCH,SOUVENIR,CLINTONVILLE,WIS.,DIAMOND &
  PEG.......................................................... 17.00
CUSTARD GLASS,DISH,BANANA,CHRYSANTHEMUM SPRIG,GOLD.......... 185.00
CUSTARD GLASS,DISH,BANANA,CHRYSANTHEMUM SPRIG,SIGNED,
  NORTHWOOD.................................................. 185.00
CUSTARD GLASS,DISH,BANANA,LOUIS XV,GOLD..................... 150.00
CUSTARD GLASS,DISH,BERRY,SMALL,INVERTED FAN & FEATHER....... 85.00
CUSTARD GLASS,DISH,BRIM HAT,RUFFLED,BLACKBERRY PATTERN...... 25.00
CUSTARD GLASS,DISH,BUTTER,COVER,SQUARE...................... 7.00
CUSTARD GLASS,DISH,BUTTER,DECOR,GENEVA...................... 75.00
CUSTARD GLASS,DISH,BUTTER,GRAPE,GOTHIC ARCHES,GILT,
  IRIDESCENT................................................. 85.00
CUSTARD GLASS,DISH,BUTTER,GRAPE,THUMBPRINT,N IN CIRCLE MARK. 125.00
CUSTARD GLASS,DISH,BUTTER,MAPLE LEAF........................ 90.00
CUSTARD GLASS,DISH,BUTTER,SPRAY OF RED ROSES,RELIEF BEADING,
  WHITE..................................................... 75.00
CUSTARD GLASS,DISH,CHEESE,COVER............................. 27.50
CUSTARD GLASS,DISH,CHEESE,HOLLY BAND PATTERN,DOME COVER..... 15.00
CUSTARD GLASS,DISH,LOTUS,FENTON............................. 25.00
CUSTARD GLASS,DISH,POWDER,PICTURE,HIGHLAND COLLEGE,KANSAS,
  IVORINA VERDE............................................. 40.00
CUSTARD GLASS,DISH,POWDER,SOUVENIR,AMHERST,N.H.,LITTLE GEM.. 19.00
CUSTARD GLASS,DISH,PRAYER RUG PATTERN,FENTON................ 25.00
CUSTARD GLASS,DISH,SAUCE,CHRYSANTHEMUM SPRIG,SIGNED,
  NORTHWOOD,PAIR............................................ 65.00
CUSTARD GLASS,DISH,SAUCE,MAPLE LEAF,DIAMOND,OVAL,FOOTED,GILT 60.00
CUSTARD GLASS,DISH,SHELL SHAPE,FOOTED,SIGNED N.............. 28.50
CUSTARD GLASS,GLASS,WINE,FARMINGTON,N.H.,GOLD,4 1/2 IN.HIGH. 12.50
CUSTARD GLASS,GOBLET,JUICE,SIGNED MCKEE..................... 9.00
CUSTARD GLASS,GOBLET,LOOP,ARGUS,FLINT...................... 15.00
CUSTARD GLASS,GOBLET,PRESSED LEAF,1868..................... 15.00
CUSTARD GLASS,GOBLET,RIBS,STERLING SILVER OPENWORK,BIRD,
  BRANCH.................................................... 25.00
CUSTARD GLASS,HAIR RECEIVER,ROSES,BEADING................... 32.00
CUSTARD GLASS,HAT,GRAPE ARBOR,N MARK....................... 45.00
CUSTARD GLASS,HUMIDOR,NORTHWOOD............................. 275.00
CUSTARD GLASS,JAR,COFFEE,SIGNED MCKEE,LID,6 IN............. 5.00
CUSTARD GLASS,JAR,COOKIE,FLORAL BORDER,SILVER-PLATED COVER,
  BAIL HANDLE............................................... 55.00
CUSTARD GLASS,JAR,POWDER,SOUVENIR AMHERST,N.H.,COVER,FOOTED. 18.50
CUSTARD GLASS,JUICER,GREEN,6 IN. X 7 1/2 IN................. 18.50
CUSTARD GLASS,LAMP SHADE,TOP DIAMETER 1 3/4 IN.,BASE
  5-IN.DIAMETER,PAIR........................................ 18.00
CUSTARD GLASS,LAMP,MINIATURE,CHIMNEY,MELON RIB.............. 45.00
CUSTARD GLASS,MUG,EMBOSSED ROSE............................ 12.50
CUSTARD GLASS,MUG,MADISON,MAINE,PUNTY BAND PATTERN.......... 16.00
CUSTARD GLASS,MUG,OSHKOSH,BABY THUMBPRINT.................. 17.50
CUSTARD GLASS,MUG,SINGING BIRDS.................. 28.00 TO 30.00
CUSTARD GLASS,MUG,SOUVENIR,MARSHFIELD,VERMONT,GOLD TRIM,
  3 1/4 IN.................................................. 12.50
CUSTARD GLASS,MUG,SOUVENIR,PUNTY BAND PATTERN,
  MADISON,MAINE........................... 14.00 TO 15.00
CUSTARD GLASS,MUG,TOM & JERRY,SET OF 4...................... 20.00
CUSTARD GLASS,MUSTARD,LID,SPOON,SHAKER,OPEN SALT,TRAY,
  E.P.N.S.,ENGLAND.......................................... 35.00
CUSTARD GLASS,NAPKIN RING,RED ROSE,SOUVENIR................. 55.00
CUSTARD GLASS,NAPPIE,DIAMOND PEG........................... 16.00
CUSTARD GLASS,NAPPIE,LOTUS & GRAPE PATTERN,SCALLOPED,TWO
  HANDLES................................................... 24.00
CUSTARD GLASS,NAPPIE,PRAYER RUG............................ 19.00
CUSTARD GLASS,NAPPIE,PRAYER RUG BAND....................... 12.50
CUSTARD GLASS,NAPPIE,PRAYER RUG,TWO HANDLES................ 15.00
CUSTARD GLASS,NAPPIE,SATIN,TWO HANDLES..................... 18.50
CUSTARD GLASS,PITCHER,BERRY WREATH,4 IN.................... 25.00
CUSTARD GLASS,PITCHER,CHRYSANTHEMUM SPRIG,6 TUMBLERS....... 290.00
CUSTARD GLASS,PITCHER,CHRYSANTHEMUM SPRIG,SIGNED NORTHWOOD,
  4 TUMBLERS................................................ 275.00
CUSTARD GLASS,PITCHER,CREAMER,SUGAR,SPOONER,IVORINA VERDE,
  18 PIECES................................................. 595.00
CUSTARD GLASS,PITCHER,ENAMELED ROSE DECOR,SOUVENIR OF CONEY
  ISLAND,3 IN............................................... 12.00
CUSTARD GLASS,PITCHER,HONEYCOMB,FLOWER FLANGE,RED FLOWERS,
  7 IN.TALL................................................. 95.00
CUSTARD GLASS,PITCHER,INVERTED FAN & FEATHER............... 200.00
CUSTARD GLASS,PITCHER,MILK,DIAMOND WITH PEG,ROSES,CONEY
  ISLAND.................................................... 60.00
CUSTARD GLASS,PITCHER,MILK,DIAMOND WITH PEG................ 60.00
CUSTARD GLASS,PITCHER,MILK,ROSE DECOR,HELMET SPOUT,APPLIED
  HANDLE.................................................... 55.00
CUSTARD GLASS,PITCHER,RIBBED,BAND OF PEACOCKS,FLORAL,

REG.MARK 1878,2 IN.......................................... 22.50
CUSTARD GLASS,PITCHER,ROSES,GOLD,7 IN.TALL.................. 145.00
CUSTARD GLASS,PITCHER,SOUVENIR,CONNEAUT LAKE EXPOSITION,ROSE
DECOR...................................................... 18.00
CUSTARD GLASS,PITCHER,TANKARD,IVORINA VERDE................. 75.00
CUSTARD GLASS,PITCHER,WATER,ARGONAUT SHELL................. 150.00
CUSTARD GLASS,PITCHER,WATER,CHRYSANTHEMUM SPRIG............ 295.00
CUSTARD GLASS,PITCHER,WATER,CHRYSANTHEMUM SPRIG,
SIX.............................................315.00 TO 425.00
CUSTARD GLASS,PITCHER,WATER,CHRYSANTHEMUM SPRIG,GOLD,SIX
TUMBLERS,SIGNED............................................ 295.00
CUSTARD GLASS,PITCHER,WATER,DIAMOND WITH PEG,ROSES,SOUVENIR
SCENE...................................................... 85.00
CUSTARD GLASS,PITCHER,WATER,INTAGLIO,GREEN TRIM............ 110.00
CUSTARD GLASS,PITCHER,WATER,IVORINA VERDE.................. 100.00
CUSTARD GLASS,PITCHER,WATER,LOUIS XV............... 85.00 TO 115.00
CUSTARD GLASS,PITCHER,WATER,MAPLE LEAF..................... 145.00
CUSTARD GLASS,PITCHER,WATER,2 TUMBLERS,ARGONAUT SHELL...... 375.00
CUSTARD GLASS,PITCHER,WINGED SCROLL........................ 125.00
CUSTARD GLASS,PLATE,CAKE,PEACOCKS,STRAWBERRY DECOR,N MARK,
12-IN.DIAMETER............................................. 85.00
CUSTARD GLASS,PLATE,CAKE,11-IN.DIAMETER.................... 35.00
CUSTARD GLASS,PLATE,GRAPE & CABLE INSIDE,BASKET WEAVE
OUTSIDE,N MARK............................................. 25.00
CUSTARD GLASS,PLATE,NORTHWOOD TWIG,7-IN.DIAMETER........... 40.00
CUSTARD GLASS,PLATE,PRAYER RUG............................. 14.00
CUSTARD GLASS,PLATE,PRAYER RUG,7 IN........................ 16.00
CUSTARD GLASS,PLATE,PRAYER RUG,7 3/4-IN.DIAMETER........... 15.00
CUSTARD GLASS,PLATE,PRAYER RUG,8 1/4-IN.DIAMETER........... 17.50
CUSTARD GLASS,SALT & PEPPER SHAKERS,ARGONAUT SHELL......... 330.00
CUSTARD GLASS,SALT & PEPPER,CHRYSANTHEMUM SPRIG,PEWTER TOPS. 125.00
CUSTARD GLASS,SALT & PEPPER,CORN PATTERN................... 39.00
CUSTARD GLASS,SALT & PEPPER,DOUBLE TEARDROP BULGE,BLUE,TIN
TOPS....................................................... 60.00
CUSTARD GLASS,SALT & PEPPER,INTAGLIO,24K GOLD-PLATED TOPS... 75.00
CUSTARD GLASS,SALT,CHRYSANTHEMUM SPRIG,UNCOLORED........... 42.50
CUSTARD GLASS,SALT,CORN.................................... 12.50
CUSTARD GLASS,SALT,SUNSET.................................. 12.50
CUSTARD GLASS,SAUCE,ARGONAUT SHELL......................... 37.50
CUSTARD GLASS,SAUCE,ARGONAUT SHELL,SIGNED.................. 47.50
CUSTARD GLASS,SAUCE,CHRYSANTHEMUM SPRIG,BLUE,OVAL,SIGNED
NORTHWOOD.................................................. 85.00
CUSTARD GLASS,SAUCE,GRAPE & THUMBPRINT,SIGNED N............ 20.00
CUSTARD GLASS,SAUCE,TRAILING VINE,FLAT,GOLD................ 23.00
CUSTARD GLASS,SAUCE,WING SCROLL............................ 15.00
CUSTARD GLASS,SHADE,LAMP,ROPE,TASSEL,CUT GLASS PRISMS,GREEN. 85.00
CUSTARD GLASS,SHAKER,SALT & PEPPER,LOUIS XV................ 45.00
CUSTARD GLASS,SHAKER,SALT,INTAGLIO........................ 35.00
CUSTARD GLASS,SHAKER,SALT,INTAGLIO,GREEN,GOLD TRIM........ 40.00
CUSTARD GLASS,SHAKER,SALT,SOUVENIR,COW,BARN............... 8.50
CUSTARD GLASS,SHAKER,SALT,SOUVENIR,KRATKA,MINN.,FLORAL DECOR 5.00
CUSTARD GLASS,SHERBET,BLUE,N MARK.......................... 30.00
CUSTARD GLASS,SPOONER,BROWN DECOR,GRAPE,THUMBPRINT........ 30.00
CUSTARD GLASS,SPOONER,CHRYSANTHEMUM SPRIG.......... 39.00 TO 65.00
CUSTARD GLASS,SPOONER,GENEVA...................... 40.00 TO 60.00
CUSTARD GLASS,SPOONER,GENEVA,BROWN PAINT................... 30.00
CUSTARD GLASS,SPOONER,INTAGLIO............................. 60.00
CUSTARD GLASS,SPOONER,LOUIS XV.................... 45.00 TO 60.00
CUSTARD GLASS,SPOONER,WHITE,RED ROSE SPRAYS,RELIEF. 35.00 TO 55.00
CUSTARD GLASS,SPOONER,WINGED SCROLL.............. 40.00 TO 60.00
CUSTARD GLASS,SUGAR,CHRYSANTHEMUM SPRIG,NO COVER... 35.00 TO 40.00
CUSTARD GLASS,SUGAR,CHRYSANTHEMUM SPRIG,COVER...... 75.00 TO 80.00
CUSTARD GLASS,SUGAR,GRAPE,GOTHIC ARCHES,PEARLIZED,COVER..... 65.00
CUSTARD GLASS,SUGAR,INVERTED FAN & FEATHER,COVER........... 165.00
CUSTARD GLASS,SUGAR,IVORINA VERDE,GILT,BULBOUS,SCALLOPED,
OPEN....................................................... 55.00
CUSTARD GLASS,SUGAR,LOUIS XV,COVER......................... 75.00
CUSTARD GLASS,SUGAR,WHITE,RED ROSE SPRAYS,RELIEF BEADING.... 35.00
CUSTARD GLASS,SUGAR,WINGED SCROLL,COVER.................... 50.00
CUSTARD GLASS,SYRUP,IVORINA VERDE.......................... 150.00
CUSTARD GLASS,SYRUP,WINGED SCROLL,LID...................... 150.00
CUSTARD GLASS,TABLE SETTING,INVERTED FAN & FEATHER......... 520.00
CUSTARD GLASS,TOOTHPICK,ARGONAUT SHELL............. 85.00 TO 185.00
CUSTARD GLASS,TOOTHPICK,ARGONAUT SHELL,GOLD............... 165.00
CUSTARD GLASS,TOOTHPICK,CHRYSANTHEMUM SPRIG,BLUE OPAQUE.... 175.00
CUSTARD GLASS,TOOTHPICK,CHRYSANTHEMUM SPRIG,SIGNED NORTHWOOD 95.00
CUSTARD GLASS,TOOTHPICK,FLORAL AROUND TOP,FOOTED,VERMONT.... 45.00
CUSTARD GLASS,TOOTHPICK,FOOTED............................. 42.50
CUSTARD GLASS,TOOTHPICK,FOOTED,HONEYCOMB.................. 45.00
CUSTARD GLASS,TOOTHPICK,HONEYCOMB,FLOWER FLANGE,BLUE FEET,
PINK FLORAL................................................ 80.00

```
CUSTARD GLASS,TOOTHPICK,IVORINA VERDE,GOLD..................    75.00
CUSTARD GLASS,TOOTHPICK,OVALS ON BASE,SOUVENIR GREENVILLE,
   ILL.H.S...............................................    12.50
CUSTARD GLASS,TOOTHPICK,QUIXOTE.................... 18.00 TO   18.50
CUSTARD GLASS,TOOTHPICK,RED ASTORS,HAND-PAINTED,CRIMPED TOP,
   NOTCHED BASE...........................................    18.50
CUSTARD GLASS,TOOTHPICK,RING & BEADS............... 14.00 TO   15.00
CUSTARD GLASS,TOOTHPICK,SOUVENIR,CRESCENT PARK,RHODE ISLAND.    9.00
CUSTARD GLASS,TOOTHPICK,SPIRIT LAKE,IOWA...................    16.50
CUSTARD GLASS,TOOTHPICK,WINGED SCROLL,IVORINA VERDE.........   75.00
CUSTARD GLASS,TRAY,DRESSER,GRAPE & CABLE..................   175.00
CUSTARD GLASS,TRAY,PERFUME,SCROLLWORK,IREGULAR SHAPE,4 1/2 X
   9 IN.LONG..............................................    22.50
CUSTARD GLASS,TUMBLER,BLUE CHRYSANTHEMUM SPRIG.............   125.00
CUSTARD GLASS,TUMBLER,CHRYSANTHEMUM SPRIG,PINK,GREEN,GOLD...   30.00
CUSTARD GLASS,TUMBLER,CHRYSANTHEMUM SPRIG......... 24.00 TO   25.00
CUSTARD GLASS,TUMBLER,DELAWARE,BLUE TRIM ON LEAVES.........   17.00
CUSTARD GLASS,TUMBLER,DIAMOND WITH PEG,KRY-STOL...........    24.00
CUSTARD GLASS,TUMBLER,DIAMOND WITH PEG,SOUVENIR...........    28.00
CUSTARD GLASS,TUMBLER,GENEVA.........................ILLUS..   30.00
CUSTARD GLASS,TUMBLER,GOLD,IVORINA VERDE..................    25.00
CUSTARD GLASS,TUMBLER,HAND-PAINTED RED ROSES,SOUVENIR WEST
   LIBERTY,IOWA...........................................    15.50
CUSTARD GLASS,TUMBLER,HONEYCOMB & FLOWERS.................    22.00
CUSTARD GLASS,TUMBLER,HONEYCOMB,FLORAL RIM................    30.00
CUSTARD GLASS,TUMBLER,INTAGLIO...........................    30.00
CUSTARD GLASS,TUMBLER,INTAGLIO,BLUE,GOLD TRIM.............    32.00
CUSTARD GLASS,TUMBLER,INTAGLIO,GREEN TRIM................    35.00
CUSTARD GLASS,TUMBLER,IVORINA VERDE......................    30.00
CUSTARD GLASS,TUMBLER,LOUIS XV...........................    30.00
CUSTARD GLASS,TUMBLER,LOUIS XV,GILT......................    29.00
```

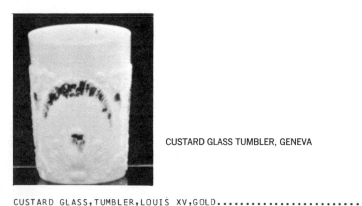

CUSTARD GLASS TUMBLER, GENEVA

```
CUSTARD GLASS,TUMBLER,LOUIS XV,GOLD......................    26.00
CUSTARD GLASS,TUMBLER,MAIZE,GREEN & BROWN LEAVES,LIBBEY.....   55.00
CUSTARD GLASS,TUMBLER,MAPLE LEAF,4 IN............. 25.00 TO   40.00
CUSTARD GLASS,TUMBLER,RAISED PURPLE GRAPES,GREEN LEAVES,N
   MARK..................................................    12.00
CUSTARD GLASS,TUMBLER,RIBBED DRAPE................. 24.00 TO   28.00
CUSTARD GLASS,TUMBLER,SIGNED MCKEE.......................    10.00
CUSTARD GLASS,TUMBLER,SOUVENIR,ALTON,N.H.................    10.00
CUSTARD GLASS,TUMBLER,SOUVENIR,BELMONT,N.H...............    10.00
CUSTARD GLASS,TUMBLER,SOUVENIR,DIAMOND WITH PEG..........    16.50
CUSTARD GLASS,TUMBLER,SOUVENIR,DIAMOND WITH PEG,LINCOLN PARK
   HIGH SCHOOL...........................................    25.00
CUSTARD GLASS,TUMBLER,SOUVENIR,DIAMOND WITH PEG,ROSES.......   28.00
CUSTARD GLASS,TUMBLER,SOUVENIR,HARPSWELL,MAINE...........    10.00
CUSTARD GLASS,TUMBLER,SOUVENIR,M.E.CHURCH OF AUBURN.......    15.00
CUSTARD GLASS,TUMBLER,SOUVENIR,POTLATCH,ID.,LARGEST SAWMILL
   IN THE WORLD..........................................    15.00
CUSTARD GLASS,TUMBLER,SOUVENIR,WHITEHALL,N.Y.............    10.50
CUSTARD GLASS,VASE,BLUE DRAGONFLY,ENAMELED FLORAL,FOLIAGE,
   RUFFLE,8 IN...........................................    45.00
CUSTARD GLASS,VASE,BUTTERFLY PATTERN,8 IN................    25.00
CUSTARD GLASS,VASE,BUTTERFLY,7 IN........................    16.00
CUSTARD GLASS,VASE,FLARED HAT,BLACKBERRY PATTERN,SILVER
   DECOR ON BERRIES......................................    17.50
CUSTARD GLASS,VASE,FLUTED TOP,HAND-PAINTED FLORAL,
   11 1/2 IN.TALL,PAIR...................................    85.00
CUSTARD GLASS,VASE,GOLD EDGE,RUFFLE,SOUVENIR,PEDESTAL,
   6 1/2 IN..............................................    17.50
CUSTARD GLASS,VASE,GRAND FORKS,N.D.,6 IN.................    25.00
CUSTARD GLASS,VASE,HENDRICKS,MINN.,6 IN..................    18.50
```

CUSTARD GLASS,VASE,JACK-IN-THE-PULPIT,PLEATED TOP,
CRYSTAL-CASED,8 IN............................................. 50.00
CUSTARD GLASS,VASE,SILVER LEAF & BERRY DECOR,HAT TYPE....... 12.00
CUSTARD GLASS,VASE,SOUVENIR,AMSTERDAM,N.Y.,FOOTED,SCALLOPED
TOP........................................................... 14.00
CUSTARD GLASS,VASE,SOUVENIR,CALUMET,MICH.,FOOTED,SCALLOPED
TOP........................................................... 14.00
CUSTARD GLASS,VASE,SOUVENIR,MELVILLE,N.D.,FOOTED,SCALLOPED
TOP........................................................... 14.00
CUSTARD GLASS,VASE,SOUVENIR,MILFORD,MASS.,FOOTED,SCALLOPED
TOP........................................................... 14.00
CUSTARD GLASS,VASE,SOUVENIR,PITTSFIELD,MAINE,ROSES.......... 14.00
CUSTARD GLASS,VASE,SOUVENIR,SCRANTON,PA.,FOOTED,SCALLOPED
TOP........................................................... 14.00
CUSTARD GLASS,VASE,STRAWBERRY,HAT TYPE...................... 15.00
CUSTARD GLASS,WATER SET,GENEVA,SEVEN PIECES................. 290.00
CUSTARD GLASS,WATER SET,HEISEY ROSE-DECORATED.............. 400.00
CUSTARD GLASS,WINE,DIAMOND PEG............................. 40.00
CUSTARD GLASS,WINE,SIGNED,FOOTED,4 1/2 IN.HIGH............. 10.00
CUSTARD,GOBLET,BELLFLOWER,DOUBLE VINE...................... 18.00

CUT GLASS HAS BEEN MADE SINCE ANCIENT TIMES,BUT THE
LARGE MAJORITY OF THE PIECES NOW FOR SALE DATE FROM
THE BRILLIANT PERIOD OF GLASS DESIGN,1880 TO 1905.
THESE PIECES HAD ELABORATE GEOMETRIC DESIGNS CUT WITH A
DEEP MITER CUT.
CUT GLASS,SEE ALSO,CRUET,TOOTHPICK,ETC.
CUT GLASS,APPLIQUE,WALL,ORMOLU BOWL,CANDLE ARMS,DROPS,WIRED,
24 IN.,4...................................................... 475.00
CUT GLASS,ASHTRAY,LACE PATTERN,2 IN.HIGH,6-IN.DIAMETER...... 35.00
CUT GLASS,ATOMIZER,FLORAL CUT,4 1/2 IN.HIGH................. 7.50
CUT GLASS,BANANA BOAT,ALTERNATING HARVARD & FLORAL,11 X
7 1/2 X 4 IN.................................................. 75.00
CUT GLASS,BANANA BOAT,HEAVY CUT,15 IN.LONG................. 75.00
CUT GLASS,BARREL,BISCUIT,DIAMOND CUT ARCHES,STAR CUT BASE,
SILVER LID................................................... 24.00
CUT GLASS,BASKET,ALLOVER CUT,CUT HANDLE,15 IN............. 130.00
CUT GLASS,BASKET,ALLOVER CUT,9 1/4 IN.WIDE,8 IN.HIGH TO TOP
OF HANDLE.................................................... 135.00
CUT GLASS,BASKET,ALLOVER FLORAL,NOTCHED HANDLE,8 IN.LONG,
4 IN.WIDE.................................................... 28.00
CUT GLASS,BASKET,FURIT,PAIR,GEORGE III,19TH CENTURY,9 IN.
LONG......................................................... 135.00
CUT GLASS,BASKET,HARVARD PATTERN,INTAGLIO FLORAL,10 IN. X
14 IN.HIGH................................................... 100.00
CUT GLASS,BASKET,HARVARD,FLORAL,6 IN. X 8 1/2 IN........... 39.50
CUT GLASS,BASKET,HARVARD,13 IN.HIGH,9 IN.WIDE............. 25.00
CUT GLASS,BASKET,HOBSTARS,7 IN. X 7 1/2 IN................ 95.00
CUT GLASS,BASKET,INTAGLIO CLEAR TO FROSTED FLORAL,CANE,
BUTTONS,14 IN................................................ 185.00
CUT GLASS,BASKET,INTAGLIO ROSE & LEAVES,FLARED TOP,HANDLE,
15 IN.HIGH................................................... 35.00
CUT GLASS,BASKET,OVERALL CUT,7 1/2 IN.LONG,6 1/2 IN.WIDE,
7 3/4 IN.HIGH................................................ 200.00
CUT GLASS,BASKET,SUNBURST,HOBSTARS,THUMBPRINT AROUND TOP
EDGE,OVAL.................................................... 59.00
CUT GLASS,BOAT,CELERY,FLAT,11 1/2 IN. X 4 1/2 IN........... 24.50
CUT GLASS,BONBON,ALLOVER LACELIKE CUTTING,CUT HANDLE,
6 1/4-IN.DIAMETER............................................ 37.50
CUT GLASS,BOTTLE,BITTERS,CANE,NOTCHED PRISM,LINEAR,PEDESTAL,
SILVER TOP................................................... 35.00
CUT GLASS,BOTTLE,CORNFLOWER,LEAF,10 X 6 IN.HIGH........... 31.00
CUT GLASS,BOTTLE,HARVARD PATTERN,CLEAR BUTTONS,CUT STOPPER,
8 IN.,PAIR................................................... 150.00
CUT GLASS,BOTTLE,LIQUOR,FLORAL,LEAVES,PANELED NECK,CUT STAR
BOTTOM....................................................... 24.50
CUT GLASS,BOTTLE,PERFUME,NOTCHED PRISM,HOBSTAR,7 3/4 IN.HIGH 65.00
CUT GLASS,BOTTLE,PERFUME,PINWHEEL,5 1/2 IN.HIGH,
11 1/2 IN.AROUND............................................. 27.00
CUT GLASS,BOTTLE,PERFUME,SQUARE,OVAL ALLOVER CUT STOPPER,
4 IN.TALL.................................................... 18.50
CUT GLASS,BOTTLE,SMELLING SALTS,ENAMEL RIM,CUT STOPPER...... 17.50
CUT GLASS,BOTTLE,SMELLING SALTS,STERLING SILVER LID,MONOGRAM 6.00
CUT GLASS,BOTTLE,WATER,CRANBERRY CUT TO CLEAR,FACETED
STOPPER,8 1/2 IN............................................. 85.00
CUT GLASS,BOTTLE,WATER,CRENELLATED NECK,HEXAGONAL & OVAL
FLUTES....................................................... 33.00
CUT GLASS,BOTTLE,WATER,DIAMOND,FAN,PANELED NECK,RAYED BASE.. 17.50
CUT GLASS,BOTTLE,WATER,RUSSIAN,8 IN.HIGH,5 1/2 IN.ACROSS
BOTTOM....................................................... 110.00

```
CUT GLASS,BOTTLE,WHISKEY,HARVARD,COSMOS,PRISM CUT TOP &
   STOPPER..............................................    90.00
CUT GLASS,BOTTLE,WINE,STRAWBERRY,FAN,18 IN. X 11 1/2 IN.HIGH   45.00
CUT GLASS,BOWL,3 3/4 IN.HIGH.......................ILLUS..    35.00
CUT GLASS,BOWL,ALLOVER CUT,COSMOS IN BASE,SIGNED HAWKES,
   5 3/4 IN..........................................    27.50
CUT GLASS,BOWL,ALLOVER CUT,FANS,DIAMOND,SAWTOOTH & SCALLOPED
   RIM,8 IN..........................................    35.00
CUT GLASS,BOWL,ALLOVER CUT,HOBSTAR,SCALLOPED TOP,
   8-IN.DIAMETER.....................................    45.00
CUT GLASS,BOWL,ALTERNATING HARVARD & FLORAL,OVAL,11 X
   7 1/2 X 4 IN......................................    75.00
CUT GLASS,BOWL,BANANA,10 1/4 IN....................ILLUS..    55.00
CUT GLASS,BOWL,BANANA,TRELLIS-SERRATED SIDES,HOBSTARS,
   11 3/4 X 3 IN.HIGH................................    42.00
CUT GLASS,BOWL,BANDS OF FEATHERS,HOBSTAR CUT HEX BUTTONS,
   SCALLOPED.........................................    46.50
CUT GLASS,BOWL,BERRY,FLOWERS,LEAVES,8-IN.DIAMETER..........    30.00
CUT GLASS,BOWL,BERRY,HOBSTAR,ALLOVER CUT,3 1/8 X
   8 1/4-IN.DIAMETER.................................    35.00
CUT GLASS,BOWL,BERRY,HOBSTARS,STRAWBERRY DIAMOND,INVERTED
   FAN...............................................    65.00
CUT GLASS,BOWL,BERRY,HOBSTARS,TEARDROP RADIALS,BLOCK MOTIF,
   NOTCHED PRISM.....................................    65.00
CUT GLASS,BOWL,CANARIA,VASELINE,PAIRPOINT,6-IN.DIAMETER.....    24.00
CUT GLASS,BOWL,CENTER,FLOWERS,GEOMETRICS,THREE SHELL FEET,
   LIBBEY............................................    88.00
CUT GLASS,BOWL,CENTER,HOBSTARS,GEOMETRICS,NOTCHED EDGE,
   SCALLOPS,9 IN.....................................    95.00
CUT GLASS,BOWL,CENTER,HOBSTARS,NOTCHED & SCALLOPED EDGE,
   FLARED............................................    95.00
```

CUT GLASS BOWL          CUT GLASS BOWL, BANANA

```
CUT GLASS,BOWL,CENTERPIECE,CLEAR BUTTONS,STEP CUTTING,STAR
   BASE,RUSSIA.......................................   300.00
CUT GLASS,BOWL,CENTERPIECE,FLOWERS,BUTTERFLIES,PRESSED
   LEAVES,FOOTED.....................................    40.00
CUT GLASS,BOWL,CHRYSANTHEMUM PATTERN,SIGNED HAWKES,
   8-IN.DIAMETER.....................................    40.00
CUT GLASS,BOWL,CLUSTER,EGGINTON,9 IN.WIDE,3 1/2 IN.WIDE.....   113.00
CUT GLASS,BOWL,CONSOLE,FLORAL,NOTCHED EDGE,SIGNED HAWKES,
   13 3/4 IN.........................................   250.00
CUT GLASS,BOWL,DAISY & BUTTON,8 IN.....................    50.00
CUT GLASS,BOWL,DIAMOND SHAPE,9 1/2 X 6 X 4 IN..........    39.00
CUT GLASS,BOWL,ETCHED FLOWERS,SIGNED CLARKE,9 IN...........    50.00
CUT GLASS,BOWL,FANS,DIAMONDS,HOBSTAR IN BASE,SAWTOOTH,
   SCALLOPED.........................................    47.50
CUT GLASS,BOWL,FANS,HOBSTARS,STRAWBERRY,DIAMONDS,STARS,
   TUTHILL,8 IN......................................    95.00
CUT GLASS,BOWL,FINGER,CLEAR TO AMETHYST,PAIRPOINT..........    22.00
CUT GLASS,BOWL,FINGER,DIAMOND & FAN,FULL STAR CUT BOTTOM....    15.00
CUT GLASS,BOWL,FINGER,FLUTE,MITER,VASELINE,
   4 1/2-IN.DIAMETER,PLATE...........................    50.00
CUT GLASS,BOWL,FINGER,RUSSIA..........................    48.50
CUT GLASS,BOWL,FINGER,SERRATED PRISM,MATCHING PLATE........    45.00
CUT GLASS,BOWL,FINGER,SIGNED HAWKES...................    18.50
CUT GLASS,BOWL,FLARED TOP,SHALLOW CUTTING,NOTCHED TOP,
   FOOTED,CAMBRIDGE..................................    30.00
CUT GLASS,BOWL,FLORAL & CUT,8 IN......................    22.00
CUT GLASS,BOWL,FOUR LARGE PINWHEELS,STARS,RAYED STAR BASE,
   7 1/2 IN..........................................    30.00
CUT GLASS,BOWL,FRUIT,CORINTHIAN PATTERN,20-POINT HOBSTAR
   BASE..............................................    61.00
CUT GLASS,BOWL,FRUIT,HOBSTAR CENTER,HOBSTARS,PINWHEELS,MITER
   CUT,FAN...........................................    45.00
CUT GLASS,BOWL,FRUIT,HOBSTARS,RIBBON CUT,DEEP MITER,STARS,
   CROSS HATCH.......................................    65.00
CUT GLASS,BOWL,FRUIT,SUNBURST PATTERN,PRISM & CANE RIBBONS,
   9 X 4 IN..........................................    65.00
CUT GLASS,BOWL,GERMAN BOHEMIAN,19TH CENTURY,2 PIECES,15 TO
   17 IN. HIGH.......................................   160.00
```

CUT GLASS,BOWL,HARVARD & FLOWERS,OBLONG..................... 30.00
CUT GLASS,BOWL,HEART-SHAPED,RUSSIAN PATTERN,CUT BUTTONS,8 X
   9 IN............................................................ 160.00
CUT GLASS,BOWL,HEAVY CUT,FOOTED,4 1/2 IN.HIGH,8 IN.DIAMETER. 48.00
CUT GLASS,BOWL,HOBSTAR & FAN,9 IN........................... 47.00
CUT GLASS,BOWL,HOBSTAR CROSSCUT,CHECKED DIAMOND,SPLIT
   VESICAS,SILVER RIM............................................. 95.00
CUT GLASS,BOWL,HOBSTAR,FAN,CROSSCUT,CANE,SCALLOPED,SIGNED
   BERGEN........................................................ 75.00
CUT GLASS,BOWL,HOBSTAR,PRISM,STANDARD,SIGNED CLARK,6 X
   6 1/2 IN.HIGH................................................. 82.00
CUT GLASS,BOWL,HOBSTAR,SMOOTH RIM,FOOTED.................... 42.00
CUT GLASS,BOWL,HOBSTAR,STRAWBERRY DIAMOND,FAN,STAR,STERLING
   SILVER RIM.................................................... 85.00
CUT GLASS,BOWL,HOBSTAR,8 IN................................. 42.00
CUT GLASS,BOWL,HOBSTARS,CANES,9-IN.DIAMETER,3 1/2 IN.DEEP... 55.00
CUT GLASS,BOWL,HOBSTARS,CROSS-HATCHED,AMBER,8 1/2 IN........ 59.00
CUT GLASS,BOWL,HOBSTARS,DIAMOND & FAN,HARVARD,GORHAM
   STERLING SILVER RIM........................................... 98.50
CUT GLASS,BOWL,HOBSTARS,DIAMOND CUT CENTER,3 3/4 IN.TALL,
   8 IN.DIAMETER................................................. 27.50
CUT GLASS,BOWL,MARKED LIBBEY,HOBSTAR,FAN,BULL'S-EYE,
   3 1/2 IN.HIGH................................................. 56.00
CUT GLASS,BOWL,MAYONNAISE,CUT INTAGLIO FLORAL,HOBSTARS,
   BLOCKS,UNDERPLATE............................................. 75.00
CUT GLASS,BOWL,MAYONNAISE,FLORENCE PATTERN,PLATE........... 55.00
CUT GLASS,BOWL,MAYONNAISE,IRIS PATTERN,PEDESTAL SHAPE,
   GRAVIC,HAWKES................................................ 50.00
CUT GLASS,BOWL,OVERALL CUT,COSMOS CUT IN BASE,SIGNED HAWKES,
   5 3/4 IN..................................................... 30.00
CUT GLASS,BOWL,OVERALL CUT,HOBSTAR,FAN,DIAMOND POINT,STAR,
   8 1/2 IN..................................................... 38.00
CUT GLASS,BOWL,OVERALL CUT,WRIGHT,8 X 3 IN................. 65.00
CUT GLASS,BOWL,PANELED,FLORAL & SCROLL,GILT BAND,SIGNED,
   5 3/4 IN..................................................... 50.00
CUT GLASS,BOWL,PANELS,HOBNAIL,FLORAL,LEAVES,OVAL,11 X
   7 1/2 X 5 1/2 IN............................................. 50.00
CUT GLASS,BOWL,PANELS,HOBSTAR,STARS,8 1/2 IN............... 55.00
CUT GLASS,BOWL,PINEAPPLE AND FAN,10 IN..................... 24.00
CUT GLASS,BOWL,PINWHEEL,8 IN. X 3 1/4 IN................... 50.00
CUT GLASS,BOWL,PINWHEELS,PRISM CUTS,8-IN.DIAMETER X
   3 1/2 IN.DEEP................................................ 32.00
CUT GLASS,BOWL,PINWHEELS,STARS,FANS,SCALLOPED,SIGNED WRIGHT,
   8 IN........................................................ 75.00
CUT GLASS,BOWL,PUNCH,BASE,ALLOVER SUNBURST PATTERN,11 1/4 X
   13 3/4 IN................................................... 475.00
CUT GLASS,BOWL,PUNCH,CORINTHIAN PATTERN,14 1/2 X 7 1/2 IN... 175.00
CUT GLASS,BOWL,PUNCH,DIAMOND POINT,STARS,FAN,ON STANDARD,
   12 X 12 IN.HIGH............................................. 375.00
CUT GLASS,BOWL,PUNCH,HOBSTAR,HARVARD,CANE,TWO PIECES,12 IN.
   X 13 IN.HIGH................................................ 375.00
CUT GLASS,BOWL,PUNCH,HOBSTAR,STRAWBERRY DIAMOND,BULL'S-EYE,
   PEDESTAL.................................................... 225.00
CUT GLASS,BOWL,PUNCH,HOBSTAR,STRAWBERRY,DIAMOND POINT,LADLE,
   BERGEN & CO................................................. 575.00
CUT GLASS,BOWL,PUNCH,OVERLAY RUBY,WOOD STAND,EIGHT CUPS,
   LADLE,SET................................................... 225.00
CUT GLASS,BOWL,PUNCH,PRISM CUT BORDER,DIAMONDS,STARS,CANE,
   SIGNED LIBBEY............................................... 350.00
CUT GLASS,BOWL,PUNCH,SIGNED HAWKES,8 1/2 IN.TALL,
   14 3/4-IN.DIAMETER.......................................... 250.00
CUT GLASS,BOWL,PUNCH,TWO PARTS,HOBSTARS,CANE,FANS,CROSSCUT,
   9 1/2 IN.HIGH............................................... 325.00
CUT GLASS,BOWL,PUNCH,TWO PIECES,HOBSTARS,FANS,STARS,
   STRAWBERRY,7 CUPS........................................... 420.00
CUT GLASS,BOWL,PUNCH,TWO PIECES,14-IN.DIAMETER,15 IN.HIGH... 525.00
CUT GLASS,BOWL,RAY CUT BASE,ROMAN KEY BORDER,S IN WREATH
   MARK....................................................... 29.00
CUT GLASS,BOWL,ROSE,CROSSCUT,DIAMOND,FAN,PEDESTAL FOOT,
   8 IN.HIGH.................................................. 85.00
CUT GLASS,BOWL,ROSE,DIAMOND & FANS,5 1/2-IN.DIAMETER,
   5 1/2 IN.HIGH.............................................. 35.00
CUT GLASS,BOWL,ROSE,DIAMOND POINT CUT,THREE BALL FEET,7 X
   7 1/4 IN.HIGH.............................................. 65.00
CUT GLASS,BOWL,ROSE,HOBSTAR BASE,STRAWBERRY,DIAMOND,FAN,
   OVERALL.................................................... 75.00
CUT GLASS,BOWL,ROSE,HOBSTAR CHAIN,NOTCHED PRISMS,NAILHEAD
   DIAMOND,FOOTED............................................. 67.00
CUT GLASS,BOWL,ROSE,HOBSTARS,FLASHED STARS,FANS,
   4 1/2-IN.DIAMETER.......................................... 35.00
CUT GLASS,BOWL,ROSE,HOBSTARS,HOBNAIL,PINWHEELS,DIAMOND POINT

```
FANS................................................  70.00
CUT GLASS,BOWL,ROSE,MARIGOLD,DAISY & PLUME...........  28.00
CUT GLASS,BOWL,ROSE,SIGNED LIBBEY,4 1/2 IN.HIGH X 6 IN.WIDE.  135.00
CUT GLASS,BOWL,ROSE,STRAWBERRY DIAMOND,CLEAR CUT PANELS.....  50.00
CUT GLASS,BOWL,ROSE,STRAWBERRY DIAMOND,FAN,DIAMOND POINT,
  NOTCHED RIM......................................  65.00
CUT GLASS,BOWL,ROSE,STRAWBERRY,DIAMOND,FAN,CROSSCUT,HAWKES,
  6-IN.DIAMETER....................................  125.00
CUT GLASS,BOWL,ROSE,7 IN.HIGH,25-IN.CIRCUMFERENCE,WEIGHS
  7 1/2 POUNDS.....................................  87.00
CUT GLASS,BOWL,ROYAL DESIGN,8-IN.DIAMETER............  175.00
CUT GLASS,BOWL,RUSSIA,CLEAR BUTTONS,8 IN.SQUARE......  97.50
CUT GLASS,BOWL,SALAD,HOBSTARS,STARS,FANS,STERLING SILVER
  GORHAM RIM.......................................  80.00
CUT GLASS,BOWL,SALAD,SUNBURSTS,LILIES,FLORAL,NOTCHED EDGE,
  CURVED FEET......................................  18.00
CUT GLASS,BOWL,SCALLOPED RIM,HOBSTARS,FANS,CROSSCUT,
  8 1/4-IN.DIAMETER................................  28.00
CUT GLASS,BOWL,SHALLOW,ALLOVER CUT,8-IN.DIAMETER.....  22.50
CUT GLASS,BOWL,SIGNED HAWKES,GRAVIC PATTERN BY LINDLEY,
  SILVER BASE......................................  250.00
CUT GLASS,BOWL,STAR IN DIAMOND BORDER & BOTTOM,ELITE,
  8-IN.DIAMETER....................................  42.50
CUT GLASS,BOWL,STAR,FAN,SILVER TOP,7-IN.TOP OPENING,
  2 IN.HIGH........................................  28.00
CUT GLASS,BOWL,STARS,DIAMONDS,ALLOVER CUT,10-IN.DIAMETER,
  5 IN.TALL........................................  85.00
CUT GLASS,BOWL,STRAWBERRY............................  50.00
CUT GLASS,BOWL,STRAWBERRY AND FAN,10-IN.DIAMETER,
  3 1/4 IN.DEEP....................................  40.00
CUT GLASS,BOWL,STRAWBERRY,DIAMOND,STAR,HOBSTAR,TRICORNERED,
  9 1/2 IN.........................................  75.00
CUT GLASS,BOWL,SUGAR,HOBSTARS,BEADED PANELS,NOTCHED HANDLES.  10.00
CUT GLASS,BOWL,SUNBURST,FANS,HOBSTAR,SCALLOPED RIM,8 1/4 IN.  38.00
CUT GLASS,BOWL,THREE LEGS,SIGNED HUNT,7 1/2 X 5 1/2 IN.HIGH.  72.00
CUT GLASS,BOWL,TRICORNERED,9-IN.DIAMETER.............  75.00
CUT GLASS,BOWL,TWELVE FAN PATTERN,8 1/4 IN...........  50.00
CUT GLASS,BOWL,TWO HANDLES,SHALLOW,8-IN.DIAMETER,2 IN.HIGH..  98.00
CUT GLASS,BOWL,TWO PARTS,ROSETTES,HOBSTARS,FANS,SCALLOPED,
  9 IN.............................................  130.00
CUT GLASS,BOWL,U.S.SHIELD MOTIF,10 X 4 1/2 IN.HIGH...  70.00
CUT GLASS,BOWL,VENETIAN PATTERN,HAWKES,JUNE 3,1890,
  12-IN.DIAMETER...................................  275.00
CUT GLASS,BOWL,VENETIAN PATTERN,8 IN................  67.00
CUT GLASS,BOWL,WEDDING,5 IN.HEARTS CUT IN HOBNAIL,BOWS,
  ARROWS,9 IN......................................  250.00
CUT GLASS,BOX,BULL'S-EYE,CROSSCUTTING BASE,STAR,HOBSTAR,FANS
  ON COVER.........................................  87.50
CUT GLASS,BOX,CIGARETTE,AMBER,CLEAR PANELS,PRISM CUT,
  LIFT-OFF TOP,HAWKES..............................  80.00
CUT GLASS,BOX,CIGARETTE,SIGNED,HAWKES................  22.00
CUT GLASS,BOX,COLLAR,LADY'S,MIRROR INSIDE LID,SILVER
  BINDINGS,1880....................................  175.00
CUT GLASS,BOX,COVER,HINGED,SILVER BAIL,6-IN.DIAMETER.  125.00
CUT GLASS,BOX,DIAMOND-TYPE CUTTING,HINGED & BOUND IN BRASS,
  4 X 3 IN.........................................  38.50
CUT GLASS,BOX,DRESSER,HARVARD,INTAGLIO FLORAL,STAR BOTTOM,
  SILVER RIM.......................................  200.00
CUT GLASS,BOX,FEATHER,CORNFLOWER,SILVER COVER,MARKED HAWKES,
  19 IN.WIDE.......................................  145.00
CUT GLASS,BOX,HEART-SHAPE,HARVARD,FLORAL,FOOTED,6 IN.  55.00
CUT GLASS,BOX,HEART-SHAPED,STERLING TOP,1 1/4 X 2 1/2 IN....  18.50
CUT GLASS,BOX,INTAGLIO CUT TOP,5 1/2-IN.DIAMETER.....  135.00
CUT GLASS,BOX,JEWEL,SERPENTINE,OVAL,HINGED...........  70.00
CUT GLASS,BOX,OVERALL CUT STAR & DIAMOND POINT,RAYED TOP &
  BASE,COVER.......................................  17.00
CUT GLASS,BOX,POWDER,DIAMOND,FAN,STERLING SILVER COVER,
  ROSES,DAISIES....................................  22.00
CUT GLASS,BOX,POWDER,HOBSTAR,FAN,STAR BASE,STERLING SILVER
  COVER,ENAMEL.....................................  40.00
CUT GLASS,BOX,POWDER,HOBSTARS,HINGED,6 IN............  85.00
CUT GLASS,BOX,POWDER,ROUND,SILVER LID................  22.00
CUT GLASS,BOX,POWDER,STRAWBERRY DIAMOND,FAN,SILVER TOP.....  25.00
CUT GLASS,BOX,RING,COBALT BLUE OVERLAY,BRASS RIM SET WITH
  PEARLS...........................................  45.00
CUT GLASS,BOX,STAR,FAN,SILVER RIM,3 1/2-IN.CIRCUMFERENCE....  145.00
CUT GLASS,BUCKET,DAISIES,STERLING SILVER BAND, HANDLE,
  RUSSIA,2 3/4 IN..................................  40.00
CUT GLASS,BUCKET,ICE,ALLOVER HARVARD.................  90.00
CUT GLASS,BUTTER,DAISY,CROSSCUT,HARVARD BORDER,STAR CUT
  KNOB,DOME........................................  85.00
```

CUT GLASS,BUTTER,FLORAL MOTIF,HARVARD BORDER,CUT KNOB FINIAL
ON COVER.................................................... 75.00
CUT GLASS,BUTTER,FLORALS,HARVARD,COVER......................... 60.00
CUT GLASS,BUTTER,ROSETTE FLOWERS,CUT KNOB FINIAL ON DOME LID   63.00
CUT GLASS,BUTTER PAT,HOBSTAR,STRAWBERRY,FAN,SIGNED HAWKES,
SET OF 4.................................................... 50.00
CUT GLASS,BUTTER PAT,HORSESHOE SHAPE,SET OF 6................ 25.00
CUT GLASS,BUTTER PAT,STRAWBERRY DIAMOND,FAN,SQUARE,SET OF 6.  65.00
CUT GLASS,CAKE STAND,BLOCK & FAN,10 IN...................... 17.50
CUT GLASS,CANDELABRA,TABLE,PAIR,GEORGE III,19TH CENTURY,
22 1/2 IN. HIGH........................................1,600.00
CUT GLASS,CANDELABRUM,OVAL DROP CHAINS,WEDGWOOD BASE,29 IN.,
PAIR...................................................1,900.00
CUT GLASS,CANDELABRUM,SOCLE,CANOPY,AMBER DROP CHAIN,
35 1/2 IN.,PAIR........................................2,000.00
CUT GLASS,CANDLESTICK,CAN BE COMPOTE IF REVERSED,HAWKES,
4 IN.,PAIR................................................. 175.00
CUT GLASS,CANDLESTICK,CURTAIN DRAPE,FIVE-PANELED,HOLLOW
STEM,8 IN.,PAIR............................................ 90.00
CUT GLASS,CANDLESTICK,DOME BASE,PEAR-SHAPED DROP CHAIN,
WIRED,12 IN.,PAIR.......................................... 190.00
CUT GLASS,CANDLESTICK,FACETED DROPS,BLUE & WHITE JASPERWARE
BASE,PAIR.................................................. 350.00
CUT GLASS,CANDLESTICK,FLORAL CUTTING,TEARDROPS,12 IN.,PAIR.. 145.00
CUT GLASS,CANDLESTICK,INTAGLIO,MARKED FRY,10 IN............. 25.00
CUT GLASS,CANDLESTICK,PAIR,GEORGE III,19TH CENTURY,
11 1/2 IN. HIGH............................................ 450.00
CUT GLASS,CANDLESTICK,SIGNED TUTHILL,8 IN.HIGH,PAIR........ 300.00
CUT GLASS,CANDLESTICK,SQUARE POST,NOTCHED CORNERS,
8 1/2 IN.TALL,PAIR......................................... 27.50
CUT GLASS,CANDLESTICK,TEARDROP INSIDE NOTCHED PRISM STEM,
7 3/4 IN.,PAIR............................................. 115.00
CUT GLASS,CANDLESTICK,TEARDROP STEM,PANEL,SERRATE EDGE,
LIBBEY,6 IN.,PAIR.......................................... 125.00
CUT GLASS,CANOE,HARVARD CUT,NOTCHED EDGE,5 X 11 1/2 IN.LONG. 75.00
CUT GLASS,CARAFE,ALLOVER CUT,HONEYCOMB THROAT,HAWKES........ 45.00
CUT GLASS,CARAFE,CROSSCUT DIAMONDS,FAN,SUNBURST BASE,PANELED
NECK....................................................... 25.00
CUT GLASS,CARAFE,HOBSTAR,FAN,DIAMOND,ALLOVER CUT............ 35.00
CUT GLASS,CARAFE,HOBSTARS,FANS,STRAWBERRY DIAMOND,BULBOUS
BASE,AMERICAN.............................................. 25.00
CUT GLASS,CARAFE,HOBSTARS,FANS,ZIPPER NECK.................. 22.00
CUT GLASS,CARAFE,HOBSTARS,PYRAMIDAL STAR COLUMNS,24-POINT
STAR BASE.................................................. 48.00
CUT GLASS,CARAFE,SARDIS PATTERN,BRILLIANT PERIOD,5 1/2 X
8 IN.HIGH.................................................. 24.00
CUT GLASS,CARAFE,SQUATTY SHAPE,DEEP CUT..................... 37.50
CUT GLASS,CARAFE,WATER,FANS,CROSS-HATCHING,TWENTY-FOUR-STAR
BASE....................................................... 45.00
CUT GLASS,CARAFE,WATER,HOBSTAR & FAN PATTERN,SIGNED CORNING,
8 1/4 IN................................................... 45.00
CUT GLASS,CARAFE,WATER,HOBSTARS............................. 26.50
CUT GLASS,CARAFE,WATER,HOBSTARS,FANS,PANEL CUT NECK,
8 1/2 IN.HIGH.............................................. 25.00
CUT GLASS,CARAFE,WATER,HOBSTARS,SPLIT VESICAS,STARS,FANS,
ALLOVER CUT................................................ 25.00
CUT GLASS,CARAFE,WATER,PINWHEEL PATTERN..................... 22.50
CUT GLASS,CARAFE,WATER,STAR CUT BUTTONS,ALLOVER CUT,RUSSIA,
6 1/2 IN.HIGH.............................................. 85.00
CUT GLASS,CARAFE,WATER,STAR MOTIF,FAN,FRINGE,RAYED BOTTOM,
NOTCHED NECK............................................... 20.00
CUT GLASS,CELERY BOAT,HOBSTARS,NAILHEAD,11 1/2 X 5 IN...... 32.50
CUT GLASS,CELERY,BUTTONS,POINTED ENDS,RUSSIA,11 IN.LONG,
4 3/4 IN.WIDE.............................................. 115.00
CUT GLASS,CELERY,FLAT,COMPLETELY CUT,11 1/2 IN. X 5 IN...... 28.50
CUT GLASS,CELERY,FLAT,HEAVY CUT,11 IN. X 5 IN.............. 24.50
CUT GLASS,CELERY,FLAT,ROSETTES,DIAMONDS,BEADING,STRAWBERRY,
LIBBEY..................................................... 65.00
CUT GLASS,CELERY,HOBSTAR,STRAWBERRY DIAMOND,FAN,NOTCHED &
SCALLOPED RIM.............................................. 30.00
CUT GLASS,CELERY,HOBSTAR,TURNED-IN SERRATED SIDES,11 3/4 IN. 32.00
CUT GLASS,CELERY,HOBSTARS,NAILHEAD,11 1/2 X 5 IN........... 32.50
CUT GLASS,CELERY,STAR,PRISM,HARVARD,11 X 4 1/2 IN.......... 45.00
CUT GLASS,CENTERPIECE,FIVE CANDY DISHES,RUSSIAN CUT &
HOBSTAR,HUNT............................................... 200.00
CUT GLASS,CHALICE,GREEN TO CLEAR,STARS,FAN,STRAWBERRY
DIAMOND,11 IN.HIGH......................................... 125.00
CUT GLASS,CHAMPAGNE TUB,BASKET WEAVE....................... 200.00
CUT GLASS,CHAMPAGNE,PANEL CUT STEM,STAR BASE,PLAIN BOWL,
HAWKES,PAIR................................................ 20.00
CUT GLASS,CHAMPAGNE,STRAWBERRY & FAN,STEM,SET OF 6......... 65.00

CUT GLASS,CHANDELIER,BALUSTER STEM,CANOPY,SIX ARMS,DROPS,
  39 IN.HIGH.......................................................   850.00
CUT GLASS,CHANDELIER,EMPIRE ORMOLU,19TH CENTURY..............1,400.00
CUT GLASS,CHANDELIER,FACETED DROP CHAINS,TWELVE CANDLE ARMS,
  41 IN.HIGH....................................................1,000.00
CUT GLASS,CLARET JUG,SILVER TRIM...................................    25.00
CUT GLASS,CLOCK,BOUDOIR,FLORALS & LEAVES,GEOMETRIC DESIGN...    38.00
CUT GLASS,CLOCK,BOUDOIR,HARVARD & FLORALS.....................    65.00
CUT GLASS,CLOCK,SIGNED SINCLAIRE..................................   135.00
CUT GLASS,COASTER,SILVER RIM,SET OF 5.........................    10.00
CUT GLASS,COLOGNE,PINEAPPLE & FAN.............................    10.00
CUT GLASS,COLOGNE,STRAWBERRY & FAN............................    10.00
CUT GLASS,COMPOTE,ALLOVER CUTTINGS,STEMMED,9 IN.TALL........    75.00
CUT GLASS,COMPOTE,CHECKERED DIAMOND,HOBSTAR,CAN BE INVERTED
  FOR VASE.....................................................   110.00
CUT GLASS,COMPOTE,COPPER WHEEL CUTTING,PAIRPOINT,6 1/4 X
  6 1/4 IN.HIGH................................................    29.50
CUT GLASS,COMPOTE,COSMOS-CUT,TEARDROP IN SIX-PANELED STEM,
  8 IN.TALL....................................................    38.50
CUT GLASS,COMPOTE,DEEP CUT,SIGNED WRIGHT,7 IN. X
  7 1/2 IN.HIGH................................................    52.00
CUT GLASS,COMPOTE,DEVONSHIRE PATTERN,TEARDROP STEM,STERLING
  SILVER RIM...................................................    80.00
CUT GLASS,COMPOTE,FLORAL,LEAVES,SIGNED HAWKES,7 IN.HIGH,PAIR    85.00
CUT GLASS,COMPOTE,FRUIT PATTERN,GRAVIC,SIGNED HAWKES........   150.00
CUT GLASS,COMPOTE,GRAPE PATTERN,SIGNED TUTHILL,
  6 1/2 IN.DIAMETER............................................    95.00
CUT GLASS,COMPOTE,GREEN CUT TO CLEAR,STAR,CROSS HATCHING,
  CLEAR STEM...................................................    65.00
CUT GLASS,COMPOTE,HOBSTAR CUT ON BOWL & FOOT,TEARDROP STEM,
  9 IN.TALL....................................................   225.00
CUT GLASS,COMPOTE,HOBSTAR,FLASHED FANS,SOLID HANDLE,STARRED
  BASE.........................................................    33.00
CUT GLASS,COMPOTE,HOBSTARS,CANE,FLARED BASE,SIGNED HOARE,
  7 IN.HIGH....................................................    85.00
CUT GLASS,COMPOTE,HOBSTARS,FANS,CROSS HATCH,PETTICOAT BASE,
  7 IN.HIGH....................................................    87.00
CUT GLASS,COMPOTE,HOBSTARS,FANS,HOBNAIL,RADIAL CUT BASE,
  9 1/4 IN.HIGH................................................    50.00
CUT GLASS,COMPOTE,HOBSTARS,TEARDROP IN PRISM CUT STEM,
  6-IN.DIAMETER................................................    65.00
CUT GLASS,COMPOTE,INTAGLIO,DIAMOND MOTIF,CORNFLOWER,SIGNED
  CLARKE,4 IN..................................................    79.00
CUT GLASS,COMPOTE,JELLY,CANE,DIAMOND POINT,FANS,TWO HANDLES.    55.00
CUT GLASS,COMPOTE,JELLY,HOBSTARS,CANE,DIAMOND POINT,NOTCHED
  STANDARD.....................................................    95.00
CUT GLASS,COMPOTE,JELLY,HOBSTARS,CANE,DIAMOND POINT,FANS,
  HOBSTAR BASE.................................................   110.00
CUT GLASS,COMPOTE,JELLY,HOBSTARS,ROSETTES,PANELED,FLARED,
  PEDESTAL.....................................................    70.00
CUT GLASS,COMPOTE,LOTUS PATTERN,TEARDROP STEM,9 1/4 IN.HIGH.    70.00
CUT GLASS,COMPOTE,LOZENGE & SLASH CUT,RAYED BASE,SIGNED
  STUART,ENGLAND...............................................    29.00
CUT GLASS,COMPOTE,MEDALLION,DIAMOND,SINCLAIRE,3 X 5 1/4 IN.,
  PAIR.........................................................   175.00
CUT GLASS,COMPOTE,PANELS,SCALLOPED EDGE,PEDESTAL,10 IN. X
  6 IN.HIGH....................................................    70.00
CUT GLASS,COMPOTE,PINWHEELS,FANS,CROSSCUT,NOTCHED STEM,STAR
  CUT BASE.....................................................    30.00
CUT GLASS,COMPOTE,PINWHEELS,HOBSTARS,STAR BASE,5 1/2 IN.HIGH    45.00
CUT GLASS,COMPOTE,RAYED-CUT BASE,SIX-SIDED STEM,NOTCHED
  CUTTING......................................................    58.00
CUT GLASS,COMPOTE,ROSETTE CUT BASE,RUFFLED,SERRATED,
  MEDALLIONS,8 1/2 IN..........................................    52.00
CUT GLASS,COMPOTE,RUFFLED BOWL,HEXAGONAL STEM,HOBSTAR
  ROSETTES,8 3/4 IN............................................    65.00
CUT GLASS,COMPOTE,SAWTOOTH EDGES,INTAGLIO ROSE CUT,8 1/2 IN.
  TALL.........................................................    35.00
CUT GLASS,COMPOTE,SERRATED,HOBSTAR BASE & BOWL,TEARDROP
  STEM,9 1/4 IN................................................    75.00
CUT GLASS,COMPOTE,SIGNED J.HOARE & CO.,CORNING,1853,5 X
  4 1/4 IN.HIGH................................................    75.00
CUT GLASS,COMPOTE,SNOWFLAKE,HOBSTAR,SIX-SIDED STEM,6 X
  10 IN.TALL...................................................    65.00
CUT GLASS,COMPOTE,STAR,FAN,8 IN.HIGH,PAIR.....................   155.00
CUT GLASS,COMPOTE,STARS,OCTAGON CUTTINGS,HOLLOW STEM,
  SUNBURST BASE................................................    31.00
CUT GLASS,COMPOTE,STEM.........................................    40.00
CUT GLASS,COMPOTE,STERLING SILVER STEM & BASE,BLOCK CUTTING,
  HAWKES.......................................................    47.50
CUT GLASS,COMPOTE,SUNBURST,TEARDROP IN STEM,5 1/2 X

```
     9 1/4 IN.HIGH.........................................   120.00
CUT GLASS,COMPOTE,TEARDROP IN STEM,5 3/4 X 8 IN.HIGH.......    40.00
CUT GLASS,COMPOTE,WILD ROSE PATTERN,STEM IN PRISM CUTTING,
     6-IN.DIAMETER........................................     65.00
CUT GLASS,CONDIMENT SET,SALT,PEPPER,MUSTARD,SILVER PLATE
     HOLDER...............................................     30.00
CUT GLASS,CORDIAL,FLORAL DESIGN,BLOWN CRYSTAL,TALL STEM,
     HAWKES,SET OF 8......................................    120.00
CUT GLASS,CORDIAL,HOBSTAR BUTTONS,RUSSIA,9 IN.HIGH........     85.00
CUT GLASS,CREAMER,BULBOUS,PINWHEELS,DIAMONDS,NOTCH-CUT
     HANDLE...............................................     15.00
CUT GLASS,CREAMER,FAN WITH DIAMONDS......................      12.00
CUT GLASS,CREAMER,HOBSTAR,FAN............................      17.00
CUT GLASS,CREAMER,PINWHEEL................... 11.00 TO        12.00
CUT GLASS,CREAMER,PINWHEEL PATTERN,BRILLIANT PERIOD........    18.00
CUT GLASS,CREAMER,SUGAR,CHAIN OF HOBSTARS & FAN,STAR BASE.    40.00
CUT GLASS,CREAMER,SUGAR,HOARE-CORNING,1853.........ILLUS..    55.00
CUT GLASS,CREAMER,SUGAR,HOBSTARS,CANES,CROSS HATCH,FANS,
     MITER,PEDESTAL.......................................    155.00
CUT GLASS,CREAMER,SUGAR,VENETIAN PATTERN,HARVARD BORDER,
     HONEYCOMB HANDLE.....................................     65.00
CUT GLASS,CREAMER & SUGAR,BIRD MOTIF,PEDESTAL.............    150.00
CUT GLASS,CREAMER & SUGAR,BRILLIANT PERIOD,SIGNED UNGER
     BROS.................................................     44.50
CUT GLASS,CREAMER & SUGAR,BUTTERFLY,FOLIAGE,PEDESTAL ON
     RAYED BASE...........................................     55.00
CUT GLASS,CREAMER & SUGAR,DAISIES,BUDS,LEAVES,,3 IN.HIGH..    36.50
CUT GLASS,CREAMER & SUGAR,DEEP CUT,SIGNED WRIGHT.........      75.00
CUT GLASS,CREAMER & SUGAR,ENTIRE BOTTOMS ARE CUT,CUT HANDLES  45.00
CUT GLASS,CREAMER & SUGAR,EXPANDING STAR,3 1/4 IN.TALL......   75.00
CUT GLASS,CREAMER & SUGAR,FLORAL,LEAVES,PEDESTAL...........    60.00
```

CUT GLASS CREAMER, SUGAR, CORNING 1853

```
CUT GLASS,CREAMER & SUGAR,FLORENCE PATTERN,STAR CUT BASE,
     NOTCHED HANDLE.......................................     35.00
CUT GLASS,CREAMER & SUGAR,FLOWERS,LEAVES,CUT BASES,TOPS,
     UNDERSPOUT...........................................     29.00
CUT GLASS,CREAMER & SUGAR,HOBSTAR........................      32.50
CUT GLASS,CREAMER & SUGAR,HOBSTAR,NOTCHED PRISM,HOBSTAR
     BASE,3 1/2 IN........................................     37.50
CUT GLASS,CREAMER & SUGAR,OVERALL CUT,RAYED STAR BASE,
     NOTCHED RIM..........................................     37.00
CUT GLASS,CREAMER & SUGAR,PINWHEEL.......................      35.00
CUT GLASS,CREAMER & SUGAR,PINWHEEL,SCALLOPED TOP.........      45.00
CUT GLASS,CREAMER & SUGAR,ROSE WITH HOBSTAR IN CENTER....      37.00
CUT GLASS,CREAMER & SUGAR,ROUND,ALLOVER CUT,HANDLED......      22.00
CUT GLASS,CREAMER & SUGAR,SIGNED  C  IN CLOVER LEAF......
CUT GLASS,CREAMER & SUGAR,SIGNED J.HOARE,CORNING.........      75.00
CUT GLASS,CREAMER & SUGAR,STAR,CRESCENT,SIGNED,EGGINGTON..     55.00
CUT GLASS,CREAMER & SUGAR,STAR,RAY,MEDALLION IN BOTTOM....     15.00
CUT GLASS,CRUET,ALLOVER CUT,FACETED STOPPER,SIGNED J.HORACE
     CORNING,DATE.........................................     35.00
CUT GLASS,CRUET,ALLOVER CUT,STOPPER,SIGNED F.M...........      45.00
CUT GLASS,CRUET,BLOCK PATTERN,JUG SHAPE,CUT HANDLE,CLOVER
     SHAPE TOP............................................     38.00
CUT GLASS,CRUET,BRILLIANT CUT,CUT STOPPER................      35.00
CUT GLASS,CRUET,CROSSCUT DIAMOND & FAN,SQUATTY...........      35.00
CUT GLASS,CRUET,DIAMOND-FACETED STOPPER,BOTH SIGNED HAWKES,
     7 IN.HIGH............................................     27.00
CUT GLASS,CRUET,DIAMOND,FAN,MATCHING STOPPER.............      25.00
CUT GLASS,CRUET,ENGRAVED OIL AND VINEGAR,FLORAL,SIGNED
     HAWKES,NO STOPPER....................................     22.00
CUT GLASS,CRUET,FACETED STOPPER,3 IN.DIAMETER,5 7/8 IN.HIGH.   16.00
CUT GLASS,CRUET,OIL & VINEGAR,12-POINT STAR CUT BASE,CUT
     STOPPER,PAIR.........................................     35.00
CUT GLASS,CRUET,OVERALL CUT,RAYED BASE,NOTCHED HANDLE,
     FACETED STOPPER......................................     28.00
CUT GLASS,CRUET,PINWHEEL,FAN,7 IN.HIGH,PAIR..............      49.00
CUT GLASS,CRUET,PYRAMID SHAPE,INTAGLIO DAISY,HARVARD BORDER,
     STOPPER,PAIR.........................................     55.00
CUT GLASS,CRUET,ROSE WITH HOBSTAR IN CENTER,7 IN.........      37.00
```

| | |
|---|---:|
| CUT GLASS,CRUET,SIGNED HUNT.......................... | 45.00 |
| CUT GLASS,CRUET,STOPPER,PEPPER,MUSTARD,SILVER LIDS, E.P.N.S.STAND.......................................... | 27.50 |
| CUT GLASS,CRUET,TASSO PATTERN........................ | 40.00 |
| CUT GLASS,CRUET,THUMBPRINT,FAN,HOBSTAR,RAYED BOTTOM,LAPIDARY CUT.................................................. | 14.50 |
| CUT GLASS,CRUET,VINEGAR & OIL,HAWKES,ENAMEL DECOR,STOPPERS, SIGNED................................................ | 35.00 |
| CUT GLASS,CRUET,VINEGAR,BUZZ SAW..................... | 21.50 |
| CUT GLASS,CRUET,VINEGAR,COSMOS....................... | 21.50 |
| CUT GLASS,CRUET,VINEGAR,DEEP CUT,STOPPER............. | 23.50 |
| CUT GLASS,CRUET,VINEGAR,SIGNED R IN RAMPANT LION..... | 32.00 |
| CUT GLASS,CRUET,VINEGAR,THUMBPRINT HANDLE,TWO-RING THROAT... | 26.00 |
| CUT GLASS,CUP & SAUCER,HOBSTARS,CANE,VESICAS,FANS,DIAMOND POINT................................................. | 65.00 |
| CUT GLASS,CUP,LOVING,PRISM PATTERN,THREE TRIPLE-NOTCHED HANDLES,HAWKES........................................ | 165.00 |
| CUT GLASS,CUP,MARRIAGE,OVERALL NOTCHED PRISM,RAYED BASE, THREE HANDLES........................................ | 35.00 |
| CUT GLASS,CUP,PUNCH,BULBOUS-SHAPED,2 1/2 IN.HIGH..... | 8.50 |
| CUT GLASS,CUP,PUNCH,CROSSCUT DIAMONDS & FANS,DIAMOND POINT, LIBBEY,6............................................. | 165.00 |
| CUT GLASS,CUP,PUNCH,HOBSTAR,MARIGOLD,SET OF 5........ | 25.00 |
| CUT GLASS,CUP,PUNCH,OVERALL CUT,CANE,FAN,STARS,16-RAYED BASE,PEDESTAL........................................ | 25.00 |
| CUT GLASS,CUP,PUNCH,STRAWBERRY,DIAMOND,FAN........... | 8.00 |
| CUT GLASS,DECANTER & BOTTLE,INTAGLIO FUCHSIAS,BLOWN STOPPERS,HAWKES....................................... | 225.00 |
| CUT GLASS,DECANTER,ALLOVER CUT,BUZZ SAW,FANS,UPSIDE DOWN HEART SHAPE.......................................... | 115.00 |
| CUT GLASS,DECANTER,ALLOVER CUT,FLAT APPLE SHAPE,STOPPER, 8 IN.TALL............................................ | 95.00 |
| CUT GLASS,DECANTER,ALLOVER CUT,HANDLE,CUT STOPPER, 14 IN.HIGH,1 QT....................................... | 100.00 |
| CUT GLASS,DECANTER,ALMOND CUT BASE,PANELED NECK,FACETED STOPPER,12 IN........................................ | 19.50 |
| CUT GLASS,DECANTER,BLUE CUT TO CLEAR,PANELS,CANE,COBALT BANDS,18 IN.HIGH..................................... | 75.00 |
| CUT GLASS,DECANTER,BRANDY,TRICORNER SPOUT,FACET CUT STOPPER. | 22.00 |
| CUT GLASS,DECANTER,CANE PATTERN,CANE TEARDROP STEEPLE STOPPER,PEDESTAL...................................... | 75.00 |
| CUT GLASS,DECANTER,CRANBERRY CUT TO CLEAR,LOW PEDESTAL, TEARDROP STOPPER..................................... | 125.00 |
| CUT GLASS,DECANTER,CRANBERRY TO CLEAR,PANEL CUT WITH PUNTIES,STOPPER...................................... | 85.00 |
| CUT GLASS,DECANTER,DIAMOND POINT & FANS,PANELED NECK, STOPPER,5 IN.HIGH.................................... | 30.00 |
| CUT GLASS,DECANTER,DORFLINGER'S MIDDLESEX PATTERN,BALL STOPPER,10 IN........................................ | 145.00 |
| CUT GLASS,DECANTER,ENGLAND,10 3/4 IN.HIGH............ | 47.00 |
| CUT GLASS,DECANTER,FLUTE CUTTING,CIRCA 1830-1880,11 IN.TALL. | 95.00 |
| CUT GLASS,DECANTER,HOBSTAR,FAN,CUT STOPPER,10 1/2 IN.TALL... | 115.00 |
| CUT GLASS,DECANTER,PANEL CUT SIDES,WINDOWS,STOPPER, 15 1/2 IN............................................ | 48.00 |
| CUT GLASS,DECANTER,PILLAR PATTERN,RUSSIA,13 IN.TALL......... | 295.00 |
| CUT GLASS,DECANTER,PINWHEEL & STAR,STEEPLE STOPPER.......... | 65.00 |
| CUT GLASS,DECANTER,PINWHEEL PATTERN,SQUARE,STOPPER, 11 IN.TALL.......................................... | 26.50 |
| CUT GLASS,DECANTER,PURPLE OVER CLEAR,OVERALL CUT,RAYED BASE, CUT STOPPER......................................... | 62.00 |
| CUT GLASS,DECANTER,SQUARE-SHAPED,HEAVY-CUT,MADE IN SCOTLAND ON BOTTOM........................................... | 25.00 |
| 'JT GLASS,DECANTER,STAR,FAN,STAR BASE,AMETHYST,STOPPER, 16 IN.TALL........................................... | 60.00 |
| CUT GLASS,DECANTER,STAR,TRIANGLE,PRISMATICS,STAR BASE,BLUE, 16 IN.TALL........................................... | 60.00 |
| CUT GLASS,DECANTER,VINTAGE DESIGN,CUT STOPPER,WATERFORD-TYPE | 68.00 |
| CUT GLASS,DECANTER,WATER,HOBSTAR,DIAMOND POINT,STEP CUT THROAT,HAWKES........................................ | 64.00 |
| CUT GLASS,DECANTER,WINE,DIAMOND CUTTING,FLAT MUSHROOM SHAPE STOPPER.............................................. | 59.00 |
| CUT GLASS,DECANTER,WINE,OVAL MITER,DIAMOND,FAN,STERLING SILVER NECK.......................................... | 65.00 |
| CUT GLASS,DESSERT,DIAGONAL CUT,SIGNED HAWKES................ | 20.00 |
| CUT GLASS,DISH,ALLOVER CUT,SIGNED HOARE,6 1/2-IN.DIAMETER... | 65.00 |
| CUT GLASS,DISH,ALLOVER CUT,STAR SHAPE...................... | 28.00 |
| CUT GLASS,DISH,BANANA,STRAWBERRY,DIAMOND,FAN,ENDS FLARE LOW. | 55.00 |
| CUT GLASS,DISH,BASKET-SHAPED,NO HANDLE,DAISIES,LEAVES, 7 1/2 IN.HIGH........................................ | 50.00 |
| CUT GLASS,DISH,BUTTER,ALLOVER CUT,MATCHING BASE............ | 125.00 |
| CUT GLASS,DISH,BUTTER,HARVARD,FLORALS,TWO PIECES........... | 77.50 |

```
CUT GLASS,DISH,CANDY,DIVIDED,TWO HANDLES,STRAWBERRY DIAMOND,
   HAWKES..............................................................    65.00
CUT GLASS,DISH,CANDY,FOOTED,SIGNED BIRKS.......... 28.00 TO    32.00
CUT GLASS,DISH,CANDY,HOBSTAR,FOUR SECTIONS,CUT HANDLES,
   10 IN...............................................................    51.00
CUT GLASS,DISH,CANDY,LACY-CUT HOBSTARS,DIVIDED,CUT HANDLES,
   9 IN................................................................    35.00
CUT GLASS,DISH,CANDY,PINWHEEL,FANS,NOTCH-CUT STEM,
   5-IN.DIAMETER.......................................................    22.00
CUT GLASS,DISH,CANDY,SCALLOPED,MARKED ELITE IN MAPLE LEAF,
   5 IN................................................................    20.00
CUT GLASS,DISH,CANDY,SIGNED BIRKS,6 IN...........................    28.00
CUT GLASS,DISH,CANDY,SIGNED ELITE & MAPLE LEAF,6 IN...........    28.00
CUT GLASS,DISH,CANDY,SIGNED ELITE,5 IN.ROUND...................    18.00
CUT GLASS,DISH,CANDY,STRAWBERRIES,SIGNED CLARKE,
   6-IN.DIAMETER.......................................................    23.00
CUT GLASS,DISH,CANOE SHAPE,STAR MOTIF,MARKED CLOVER-CGCO,
   14 IN.LONG..........................................................    35.00
CUT GLASS,DISH,CELERY,HOBSTAR & STAR CENTER,HOBSTAR BORDER,
   EGGINTON............................................................    56.00
CUT GLASS,DISH,CELERY,HOBSTAR,FAN,10 1/2 IN.LONG...............    37.50
CUT GLASS,DISH,CELERY,HOBSTARS WITH RUSSIAN PATTERN...........    39.50
CUT GLASS,DISH,CELERY,OVERALL CUT,HOBSTARS,DIAMOND POINT,
   10 1/2 IN...........................................................    30.00
CUT GLASS,DISH,CENTER STAR,STRAWBERRY,FAN,THREE-CORNER
   SHAPE,8 IN.WIDE.....................................................    35.00
CUT GLASS,DISH,CHEESE,DIAMONDS,FANS,MULTISTAR BOTTOM,SILVER
   PLATE DOME..........................................................    85.00
CUT GLASS,DISH,CHEESE,HOBSTARS,STRAWBERRY DIAMONDS,
   10 IN.DIAMETER......................................................   210.00
CUT GLASS,DISH,CHEESE,HORSESHOE,HARVARD,HOBNAIL,SPLIT
   VESICA,DOME LID.....................................................   125.00
CUT GLASS,DISH,COMET PATTERN,LIBBEY,8 IN........................    55.00
CUT GLASS,DISH,FERN,DEEP CUT,METAL LINER........................    55.00
CUT GLASS,DISH,FOUR SECTIONS,HARVARD,TWO NOTCHED HANDLES,
   8-IN.DIAMETER.......................................................    85.00
CUT GLASS,DISH,FOUR SECTIONS,HOBSTARS,CANE,FAN,HANDLES,
   SIGNED CLARK........................................................    68.00
CUT GLASS,DISH,FOUR SECTIONS,HOBSTARS,FAN,TWO CUT & NOTCHED
   HANDLES.............................................................    65.00
CUT GLASS,DISH,FOUR SECTIONS,TWO HANDLES,RUSSIA,11 1/2 IN. X
   2 IN.DEEP...........................................................   130.00
CUT GLASS,DISH,HOBSTAR,STRAWBERRY DIAMOND,HEART SHAPE,
   J.HOARE,1853........................................................    54.00
CUT GLASS,DISH,HOBSTARS,CROSSCUT,TWO HANDLES,NOTCHED,8 X
   11 IN...............................................................    75.00
CUT GLASS,DISH,HOBSTARS,ROSETTES,TWO LOOP HANDLES,8 3/4 IN..    31.00
CUT GLASS,DISH,ICE CREAM,STAR BUTTON,RUSSIA,6-IN.DIAMETER...    32.00
CUT GLASS,DISH,ICE CREAM,STRAWBERRY DIAMOND,SAWTOOTH &
   SCALLOP EDGE,4......................................................   120.00
CUT GLASS,DISH,LEAF SHAPE.......................................    28.00
CUT GLASS,DISH,LOW,SUNBURST CENTER,DIAMOND-CUT EDGE,LIBBEY,
   9 IN................................................................    38.00
CUT GLASS,DISH,NAPPIE,SIDE HANDLE,FLOWER SPRAYS,BUTTERFLIES.    17.50
CUT GLASS,DISH,OLIVE,CANE BOTTOM,SHELL SIDES,HOBSTARS,SIGNED
   CLARKE..............................................................    75.00
CUT GLASS,DISH,OLIVE,SIGNED BIRKS C.G.CO. IN CLOVERLEAF.....    25.00
CUT GLASS,DISH,PICKLE,FOLDS IN ON 2 SIDES,ALLOVER CUT,
   5 3/4 IN. X 3 IN....................................................    19.50
CUT GLASS,DISH,PICKLE,OVAL,SIGNED HAWKES,7 1/4 IN............    28.00
CUT GLASS,DISH,PIN,ALLOVER CUT,STAR-RAYED CENTER,
   4 3/4-IN.DIAMETER...................................................    15.00
CUT GLASS,DISH,RELISH,ALLOVER CUT,CURVED,HIGH SIDES,SIGNED
   CLARKE..............................................................    28.00
CUT GLASS,DISH,RELISH,DIAMOND,FAN,PAIR..........................    24.00
CUT GLASS,DISH,RELISH,HOBSTAR,4 3/4 IN. X 12 IN.LONG........    25.00
CUT GLASS,DISH,SAUCE,DIAMOND PATTERN,HAWKES,5 IN............    37.50
CUT GLASS,DISH,SHALLOW,OVERALL CUT,HOBSTARS,DIAMOND POINT,
   ROSETTES,6 IN.......................................................    18.00
CUT GLASS,DISH,SINGING BIRDS,PURPLE,TWO HANDLES...............    38.00
CUT GLASS,DISH,STRAWBERRY,FAN,STAR CENTER,THREE-CORNERED,
   8 IN.WIDE...........................................................    35.00
CUT GLASS,DISH,TRINKET,SAWTOOTH,DIAMOND,HEART SHAPE.........    15.00
CUT GLASS,DOORKNOB,AMBER........................................    10.00
CUT GLASS,EWER,DIAMOND,PANEL,CUT TO CLEAR,APPLIED CRANBERRY
   TRIM ON RIM.........................................................   160.00
CUT GLASS,FERNER,DEEP CUT,FOOTED,7 1/4 IN.......... 37.00 TO    37.50
CUT GLASS,FERNER,FOOTED.........................................    35.00
CUT GLASS,FERNER,HOBSTAR,FAN,FOOTED,7 1/2-IN.DIAMETER,
   4 3/4 IN.HIGH.......................................................    45.00
CUT GLASS,FERNER,MIXED PATTERNS,FOOTED,7 1/4 IN.............    37.50
```

CUT GLASS,FERNERY,COSMOS,MITERED LEAVES,HARVARD BAND,FOOTED,
   7 1/2 IN. .......................................................... 23.50
CUT GLASS,FERNERY,HOBSTAR MEDALLIONS,THREE FEET.............. 39.50
CUT GLASS,FERNERY,HOBSTARS,CANES,DAISY FIELDS,FOOTED,
   7 1/2 IN. .......................................................... 28.00
CUT GLASS,FERNERY,PANELS,HARVARD,HOBSTARS,KIMBERLY STAR
   BOTTOM,FOOTED. ..................................................... 95.00
CUT GLASS,FLASK,STERLING SILVER BASE IS A DRINKING PIECE,
   SCREW TOP. ......................................................... 25.00
CUT GLASS,FLASK,WHISKEY,FITS IN SILVER GILT BASE,MARKED,
   5 3/4 IN. .......................................................... 50.00
CUT GLASS,FLOWER CENTERPIECE,CARNATION PATTERN,SCALLOPED,
   GRAVIC,HAWKES. ..................................................... 235.00
CUT GLASS,GOBLET,BAND OF STRAWBERRIES,DIAMONDS AT RIM,STAR
   CUT BASE. .......................................................... 15.00
CUT GLASS,GOBLET,CROSSCUT DIAMOND & FAN,PINEAPPLE,SIGNED
   HAWKES. ............................................................ 28.50
CUT GLASS,GOBLET,DIAMOND,FLEUR-DE-LIS,INVERTED PYRAMID STEM,
   SET OF 8. .......................................................... 100.00
CUT GLASS,GOBLET,DIAMOND,RAY CUT FOOTBALL STEM,SET OF 4..... 72.00
CUT GLASS,GOBLET,FLUTE PATTERN,6 1/2 IN. TALL............... 15.00
CUT GLASS,GOBLET,HOBSTAR,DIAMOND POINT,FAN,RAYED BOTTOM,
   SERRATED STEM. ..................................................... 28.00
CUT GLASS,GOBLET,MILLICENT PATTERN,SIGNED HAWKES............ 27.50
CUT GLASS,GOBLET,NOTCHED PRISM,THUMBPRINTS,NOTCHED STEM..... 32.00
CUT GLASS,GOBLET,STRAWBERRY & FAN PATTERN.................. 28.75
CUT GLASS,GOBLET,WATER,PURPLE,ETCHED,PAIRPOINT,6 1/2 IN.,SET
   OF 10. ............................................................. 75.00
CUT GLASS,HAIR RECEIVER,BULL'S-EYE,FAN,CROSS-HATCHING,SILVER
   TOP. ............................................................... 22.50
CUT GLASS,HAIR RECEIVER,CANE,REPOUSSE SILVER TOP,1902,
   2 1/2 IN.HIGH. ..................................................... 12.00
CUT GLASS,HAIR RECEIVER,PINWHEEL,BULL'S-EYE,MATCHING POWDER
   BOX. ............................................................... 49.50
CUT GLASS,HUMIDOR,SILVER TOP................................ 150.00
CUT GLASS,ICE BUCKET,7 IN.HIGH X 6-IN.DIAMETER............. 110.00
CUT GLASS,ICE BUCKET,FLOWERS,CANE PATTERN,FAN,HANDLES,6 X
   4 1/2 IN. .......................................................... 52.00
CUT GLASS,ICE BUCKET,HOBSTARS,DIAMOND POINT,FAN TABS,
   4 3/4 IN.HIGH. ..................................................... 57.00
CUT GLASS,ICE BUCKET,PINWHEEL,HOBSTAR,SERRATED,5 IN.HIGH.... 43.00
CUT GLASS,ICE TUB,ALLOVER CUT,HOBSTAR,FANS,FERN,24-POINT
   STAR BASE,6 IN. .................................................... 85.00
CUT GLASS,INKWELL. ......................................... 21.00
CUT GLASS,INKWELL,MULTIRAYED BASE,SILVER PLATE TOP,DELFT
   MEDALLION. ......................................................... 38.00
CUT GLASS,INKWELL,SILVER LID,SILVER HOLDER,ORNATE FRAME,
   HOLDS PEN. ......................................................... 22.50
CUT GLASS,INKWELL,SWIRL RIB,DOME SHAPE BRASS LID,
   4 1/2 IN.HIGH. ..................................................... 38.00
CUT GLASS,INTAGLIO DAISIES,DRAPE,FAN,CUT STAR BASE,AMBER &
   CRYSTAL. ........................................................... 45.00
CUT GLASS,JAR,CANDY,HOBSTAR,NOTCHED PRISM,FAN,STERLING
   SILVER COVER. ...................................................... 45.00
CUT GLASS,JAR,COOKIE,DIAMOND,SILVER PLATE LID,HANDLE,
   ENGLAND,6 IN.TALL. ................................................. 45.00
CUT GLASS,JAR,COOKIE,SILVER HANDLE & COVER,ENGLAND.......... 17.50
CUT GLASS,JAR,CRACKER,LID,SIGNED LIBBEY.................... 195.00
CUT GLASS,JAR,DRESSER,ALLOVER CUT,ORNATE SILVER TOP,
   AMETHYST-TYPE STONE. ............................................... 22.00
CUT GLASS,JAR,DRESSER,ROSETTES,STOPPER,STERLING SILVER TOP,
   DATED 1895. ........................................................ 37.50
CUT GLASS,JAR,FLORAL DESIGN,URN SHAPE,COVER,HOARE & CO.,
   1853,5 IN.HIGH. .................................................... 42.50
CUT GLASS,JAR,HONEY,FOOTED,COVER,WATERFORD,7 1/2 IN.HIGH.... 35.00
CUT GLASS,JAR,HONEY,LID,THREE TINY FEET.................... 12.00
CUT GLASS,JAR,HORSERADISH,HOBSTARS,BULL'S-EYE,DIAMOND POINT,
   FANS,COVER. ........................................................ 39.50
CUT GLASS,JAR,JAM,CANE,FAN,STAR CUT BASE,STERLING SILVER
   BAIL,LID,HANDLE. ................................................... 50.00
CUT GLASS,JAR,MUSTARD,CANE,SUNBURSTS,SILVER TOP,COVER,
   HANDLE,SPOON. ...................................................... 12.50
CUT GLASS,JAR,MUSTARD,OVERALL DIAMOND POINT CUT,PLAIN BAND,
   COVER. ............................................................. 9.00
CUT GLASS,JAR,POWDER,DESIGN IN HIGH RELIEF,STERLING SILVER
   TOP. ............................................................... 15.00
CUT GLASS,JAR,POWDER,SILVER TOP HAS RAISED FIGURE OF WOMAN,
   FLOWING HAIR. ...................................................... 27.50
CUT GLASS,JAR,SQUARE BASE,SELF-COVERED,CUT KNOB FINIAL,
   4 IN.TALL. ......................................................... 28.50
CUT GLASS,JAR,SWEETMEAT,FLAT PRISM CUT SIDES,MUSHROOM

STOPPER,6 3/4 IN.................................................. 14.00
CUT GLASS,JAR,TOBACCO,PRISM,HOBSTAR,SILVER TOP,SPONGE HOLDER 75.00
CUT GLASS,JARDINIERE,CLEAR BUTTONS,TOP TURNS IN,
   RUSSIA.....................................225.00 TO  245.00
CUT GLASS,JARDINIERE,OVERALL CUT,FLORAL WITH CHAIR BOTTOM,
   FOOTED, 7 IN.................................................. 60.00
CUT GLASS,JARDINIERE,STARRED ROSETTE CLUSTERS,STRAWBERRY
   DIAMONDS..................................................... 235.00
CUT GLASS,JEWEL COFFER,LADY'S,STERLING SILVER BINDINGS,
   HINGE,CLASP,1880............................................. 175.00
CUT GLASS,JUG,CLARET,HOBSTARS,FANS,HARVARD,SIGNED HOARE,
   12 IN.HIGH................................................... 95.00
CUT GLASS,JUG,FLAT HOBNAIL,CLOVERLEAF-SHAPED TOP,STAR ON
   BOTTOM...................................................... 110.00
CUT GLASS,JUG,MILK,BARREL SHAPE,CUT BUTTONS,4 IN.HIGH....... 97.00
CUT GLASS,KNIFE REST,ALLOVER CUT CENTER,BALL ENDS,3 1/2 IN.. 28.00
CUT GLASS,KNIFE REST,ALLOVER CUT,5 IN...................... 17.50
CUT GLASS,KNIFE REST,BALL ENDS,FACET CUT,PRISMATIC CENTER,
   4 1/2 IN.................................................... 15.00
CUT GLASS,KNIFE REST,BALL ENDS,PINWHEEL,HOBSTAR,PRISMATIC
   CENTER..................................................... 17.00
CUT GLASS,KNIFE REST,BLOCK CUT ENDS,4 3/4 IN.LONG,PAIR...... 25.00
CUT GLASS,KNIFE REST,CUT BALL ENDS,3 IN.................... 19.50
CUT GLASS,KNIFE REST,CUT BALL ENDS,5 IN.LONG............... 16.00
CUT GLASS,KNIFE REST,DIAMOND & FANS........................ 22.00
CUT GLASS,KNIFE REST,DUMBBELL ENDS,SERRATED COLUMNS........ 10.00
CUT GLASS,KNIFE REST,DUMBBELL SHAPE,CONVEX DIAMOND,STAR,
   NOTCHING,4 IN.............................................. 16.50
CUT GLASS,KNIFE REST,FACET CUT BALL ENDS,4 1/2 IN.LONG,PAIR. 22.00
CUT GLASS,KNIFE REST,FACETED KNOB ENDS,VASELINE............ 45.00
CUT GLASS,KNIFE REST,LAPIDARY CUT BALL ENDS,4 1/2 IN.LONG,
   SET OF 6................................................... 55.00
CUT GLASS,KNIFE REST,LAPIDARY CUT,4 3/4 IN.LONG............ 12.00
CUT GLASS,KNIFE REST,NOTCHED PRISM PATTERN,4 1/2 IN.LONG.... 14.00
CUT GLASS,LAMP,BOUDOIR,FLORAL,HARVARD,ASTRAL TYPE DOME
   SHADE,17 IN.TALL........................................... 125.00
CUT GLASS,LAMP,BOUDOIR,TWO PIECES,PRISMS,12 1/2 IN......... 120.00
CUT GLASS,LAMP,BUZZ SAW,FANS,MUSHROOM-SHAPED,HANGING PRISMS,
   WIRED...................................................... 80.00
CUT GLASS,LAMP,ELECTRIC,SILVER MOUNT,25 IN. HIGH.....ILLUS.. 300.00
CUT GLASS,LAMP,FLOWER & LEAF,12 PRISMS,12 X 6-IN.DIAMETER,
   WIRED...................................................... 45.00
CUT GLASS,LAMP,FLOWERS,BUTTERFLIES,SILVER PLATE BASE,
   PEDESTAL,PRISMS............................................ 285.00
CUT GLASS,LAMP,HARVARD & FLORAL,PRISMS,16 IN. HIGH.......... 90.00
CUT GLASS,LAMP,HOBSTAR,MUSHROOM SHADE,ALLOVER CUT,TWO
   SOCKETS,21 IN.TALL......................................... 750.00
CUT GLASS,LAMP,MUSHROOM SHAPE,HANGING PRISMS,21 IN.HIGH X
   12-IN.DIAMETER............................................. 650.00

CUT GLASS ELECTRIC LAMP

CUT GLASS,LAMP,PINWHEELS,HOBSTARS,CUT PRISMS,PEDESTAL,WIRED,
  15 IN.TALL........................................................ 195.00
CUT GLASS,LIQUEUR,CANE PATTERN....................................... 12.50
CUT GLASS,LUSTRES,PRISMS,PURPLE,PAIR................................ 200.00
CUT GLASS,MAYONNAISE,HARVARD,FLORALS,TWO PIECES..................... 32.50
CUT GLASS,MAYONNAISE,NO.101 PATTERN,UNDERPLATE..................... 20.00
CUT GLASS,MAYONNAISE SET,HARVARD,FLORAL,NOTCHED & SCALLOPED
  RIM.............................................................. 45.00
CUT GLASS,MUFFINEER,CANE,DIAMOND POINT,FAN,SILVER TOP.......... 35.00
CUT GLASS,MUFFINEER,FLASHED STARS,CANE.............................. 43.00
CUT GLASS,MUFFINEER,FLORAL,STAR OPENINGS,STERLING SILVER TOP 38.00
CUT GLASS,MUFFINEER,HOBSTARS,DIAMOND POINT,FAN,SILVER PLATE
  TOP............................................................. 32.00
CUT GLASS,MUFFINEER,SILVER PLATE TOP,ENGLAND,6 1/2 IN....... 37.50
CUT GLASS,MUSTARD,BALL SHAPE,HINGED COVER,TWO HANDLES....... 20.00
CUT GLASS,MUSTARD,CANE PATTERN,BARREL SHAPE,COVER............ 15.00
CUT GLASS,MUSTARD,DIAMOND SHAPE,BLOCK PATTERN.............. 4.50
CUT GLASS,MUSTARD,PEDESTAL,COVER,SILVER PLATE SPOON......... 12.50
CUT GLASS,MUSTARD,PRISM CUT,STERLING SILVER SPOON,COLLAR,
  LID,HANDLE....................................................... 25.00
CUT GLASS,NAPKIN RING,DIAMOND PATTERN.............................. 9.50
CUT GLASS,NAPKIN RING,DOME SHAPE,DIAMOND PATTERN............. 9.50
CUT GLASS,NAPKIN RING,HEART SHAPE,DIAMOND PATTERN............ 9.50
CUT GLASS,NAPKIN RING,ROUND,DIAMOND PATTERN.................. 9.50
CUT GLASS,NAPPIE,BRILLIANT PERIOD,CUT HANDLE,7 1/2 IN....... 21.00
CUT GLASS,NAPPIE,BUZZ,DIAMOND POINT,FAN,RUFFLED RIM,
  7 1/2 IN........................................................ 14.00
CUT GLASS,NAPPIE,FOUR SECTIONS,HONEYCOMB HANDLES,10-IN.SIDE. 50.00
CUT GLASS,NAPPIE,HANDLED,SIGNED BIRKS.............................. 22.00
CUT GLASS,NAPPIE,HOBSTAR & FAN PATTERN,SCALLOPED,SAWTOOTH
  RIM,HANDLE....................................................... 20.00
CUT GLASS,NAPPIE,HOBSTAR,FAN,HANDLE,SIGNED TAYLOR,6 IN...... 45.00
CUT GLASS,NAPPIE,HOBSTAR,FAN,SCALLOPED SAWTOOTH RIM,HANDLE,
  6 IN............................................................ 25.00
CUT GLASS,NAPPIE,HOBSTAR,ROSETTE,HARVARD,LOOP HANDLE,
  7 5/8 IN........................................................ 22.00
CUT GLASS,NAPPIE,HOBSTARS,SIGNED HAWKES,6 IN................. 25.00
CUT GLASS,NAPPIE,HOBSTARS,STRAWBERRY DIAMOND & FAN,SIGNED
  LIBBEY,HANDLE................................................... 48.00
CUT GLASS,NAPPIE,HOOP CUT HANDLE.................................. 21.00
CUT GLASS,NAPPIE,OVERALL CUT,DIAMOND,STAR,FAN,NOTCHED &
  SCALLOPED RIM................................................... 23.00
CUT GLASS,NAPPIE,OVERALL FLORAL,NOTCHED & SCALLOPED RIM..... 12.00
CUT GLASS,NAPPIE,SIGNED BIRKS.................................... 30.00
CUT GLASS,NAPPIE,SIGNED EGGINGTON............................... 15.00
CUT GLASS,NAPPIE,SIGNED J.HOARE,CORNING,1853.................. 48.00
CUT GLASS,NAPPIE,STAR,FAN,LEAVES,ROSE,TWO HANDLES,7 IN.WIDE. 35.00
CUT GLASS,NAPPIE,WIDE STAR,LIBBEY,5 IN........................... 26.00
CUT GLASS,PAPERWEIGHT,CUT BOTTOM................................. 15.00
CUT GLASS,PAPERWEIGHT,HEART SHAPE,1/4 IN.THICK,2 IN.WIDE.... 13.50
CUT GLASS,PAPERWEIGHT,OVERALL CUT,SAYS J.A.Z.,MAY 23,1879,
  3 X 4 1/4 IN.................................................... 70.00
CUT GLASS,PAPERWEIGHT,SCORPIO,BEVELED,AMBER.................. 35.00
CUT GLASS,PERFUME,ALLOVER CUT,BULBOUS,STERLING SILVER
  STOPPER,6 IN.,PAIR............................................. 185.00
CUT GLASS,PERFUME,ALLOVER DIAMOND CUT,PAPERWEIGHT,5 IN.TALL. 17.50
CUT GLASS,PERFUME,ALLOVER HARVARD,STERLING SILVER CAP,2 X
  2 IN.HIGH....................................................... 45.00
CUT GLASS,PERFUME,BALL SHAPE,CUT STOPPER,STAR IN BASE,
  5 IN.TALL....................................................... 12.50
CUT GLASS,PERFUME,BALL,CANE PATTERN,STERLING SILVER TOP,
  1850,ENGLAND.................................................... 35.00
CUT GLASS,PERFUME,CANE,STOPPER,3 IN.SQUARE,6 IN.HIGH........ 45.00
CUT GLASS,PERFUME,CHATELAINE TYPE,SILVER FILIGREE HINGED
  CAP,CHAIN,HOOK.................................................. 15.00
CUT GLASS,PERFUME,CLEAR CROSSCUT STOPPER,5 1/2 IN.HIGH...... 22.00
CUT GLASS,PERFUME,CUT PANELS SLANTING INWARD FROM BASE TO
  TOP,STOPPER..................................................... 37.50
CUT GLASS,PERFUME,HARVARD PATTERN,PYRAMIDAL SHAPE,CUT
  STOPPERS,PAIR................................................... 35.00
CUT GLASS,PERFUME,INTAGLIO,STERLING SILVER TOP,3-IN.STOPPER. 25.00
CUT GLASS,PERFUME,JEWEL DECOR,NOTCHED PRISM,BLUE,
  CZECHOSLOVAKIA................................................... 14.50
CUT GLASS,PERFUME,NOTCHED PANEL & THROAT,CUT STOPPER,5 IN... 10.00
CUT GLASS,PERFUME,PRISM & BULL'S-EYE,SILVER STOPPER,
  5 IN.HIGH....................................................... 22.00
CUT GLASS,PERFUME,PRISMATIC CUT,BLUE OVERLAY,BALL STOPPER,
  5 1/2 IN.TALL................................................... 26.00
CUT GLASS,PERFUME,PRISMATIC CUT,BLUE OVERLAY,SPEAR STOPPER,
  7 1/2 IN........................................................ 30.00
CUT GLASS,PERFUME,PRISMATIC CUT,BLUE OVERLAY,BALL STOPPER,

```
  6 1/2 IN.TALL.........................................  30.00
CUT GLASS,PERFUME,STRAWBERRY DIAMOND,FAN,CYLINDER SHAPE,
  STOPPER,SET OF 3......................................  70.00
CUT GLASS,PERFUME,VINE,INTAGLIO FLORAL,PINK ENAMEL ON TOP,
  SILVER STOPPER.......................................  29.00
CUT GLASS,PITCHER,ALLOVER DEEP CUTTING,SIGNED LIBBEY,
  4 TUMBLERS........................................... 175.00
CUT GLASS,PITCHER,BULBOUS,NOTCHED HANDLE,7 IN.HIGH..........  75.00
CUT GLASS,PITCHER,BULL'S-EYE,HOBSTAR,FANS,NOTCHING,MITERS,
  TANKARD,10 IN.........................................  45.00
CUT GLASS,PITCHER,BUTTERMILK,SAMPLE,CANE,FEATHER,BULL'S-EYE,
  4 1/2 IN............................................. 110.00
CUT GLASS,PITCHER,CREAM,PINWHEEL PATTERN,BRILLIANT PERIOD...  18.00
CUT GLASS,PITCHER,DEEP HARVARD,FLORAL,HELMET TYPE,10 IN.,
  6 TUMBLERS........................................... 125.00
CUT GLASS,PITCHER,DEVONSHIRE PATTERN,7-IN.UNDERPLATE,1888... 135.00
CUT GLASS,PITCHER,ETCHED FLOWERS,10 IN...................  25.00
CUT GLASS,PITCHER,FINE CUT,TALL,SLENDER,10 IN.HIGH.........  37.50
CUT GLASS,PITCHER,FLASHED CRANBERRY TO CLEAR,GOLD TRIM,
  14 IN.HIGH........................................... 150.00
CUT GLASS,PITCHER,FLOWERS,LEAVES,10 1/4 IN.HIGH............  65.00
CUT GLASS,PITCHER,HELMET TYPE,PINWHEEL,9 1/2 IN.HIGH.......  50.00
CUT GLASS,PITCHER,HOBNAIL,WHEAT,8 TUMBLERS................ 212.00
CUT GLASS,PITCHER,HOBSTAR BASE,PINWHEEL CUT BODY.......... 200.00
CUT GLASS,PITCHER,HOBSTAR,STRAWBERRY DIAMOND,6 1/2 IN.BASE,
  8 IN.HIGH............................................  39.00
CUT GLASS,PITCHER,HOBSTARS,DOUBLE THUMBPRINT HANDLE,STAR
  BASE,10 IN.TALL......................................  68.00
CUT GLASS,PITCHER,HOBSTARS,MITERS,FANS,FLUTED LIP,STAR BASE,
  4 TUMBLERS...........................................  85.00
CUT GLASS,PITCHER,HOBSTARS,PINWHEEL,DIAMOND CUT & FAN,
  6 TUMBLERS...........................................  95.00
CUT GLASS,PITCHER,HOBSTARS,TANKARD,11 1/2 IN.HIGH..........  98.00
CUT GLASS,PITCHER,INTAGLIO DAISIES,NOTCHED HANDLE,J.HOARE,
  SIX TUMBLERS......................................... 127.50
CUT GLASS,PITCHER,MILK,HOBSTARS,DIAMOND POINT,CROSSCUT,FANS,
  TANKARD..............................................  50.00
CUT GLASS,PITCHER,MILK,HONEYCOMB,PRISMS,CIRCA 1820,7 IN.TALL  45.00
CUT GLASS,PITCHER,MILK,MAPLE LEAF,STAR CUT BASE,NOTCHED
  HANDLE,CLARK.........................................  75.00
CUT GLASS,PITCHER,MILK,NOTCHED PRISM,STAR BASE,3 1/2 X
  3 1/4 IN.............................................  22.00
CUT GLASS,PITCHER,MILK,SQUATTY,BULBOUS,NOTCHED HANDLE,SIGNED
  HAWKES...............................................  95.00
CUT GLASS,PITCHER,OVERALL CUT,HOBSTARS,CANE,ROSETTES,
  14-RAYED BOTTOM......................................  90.00
CUT GLASS,PITCHER,PINWHEEL PATTERN,TANKARD................  55.00
CUT GLASS,PITCHER,PINWHEEL,HELMET TYPE,9 1/2 IN............  45.00
CUT GLASS,PITCHER,PINWHEEL,THUMBPRINT HANDLE,9 1/2 IN.,SIX
  TUMBLERS.............................................  70.00
CUT GLASS,PITCHER,STARS,HOBSTARS,DIAMONDS,FLARES OUT AT
  BOTTOM,7 1/2 IN......................................  45.00
CUT GLASS,PITCHER,STRAWBERRY DIAMOND,FAN,HOBSTARS,
  SNOWFLAKES,10 1/2 IN.................................  60.00
CUT GLASS,PITCHER,STRAWBERRY DIAMOND,INTAGLIO CUT FLORAL,
  4 GLASSES............................................  65.00
CUT GLASS,PITCHER,SUNBURST PATTERN,CIRCA 1910............. 110.00
CUT GLASS,PITCHER,SUNBURST,7 3/4 IN.,CREAMER & SUGAR....... 200.00
CUT GLASS,PITCHER,TANKARD,INTAGLIO FLORAL PATTERN..........  95.00
CUT GLASS,PITCHER,WAFFLE DESIGN,RAYED BOTTOM,ENGLAND,
  5 1/2 IN.TALL........................................  35.00
CUT GLASS,PITCHER,WATER,ALLOVER CUT.......................  40.00
CUT GLASS,PITCHER,WATER,BELLFLOWER,RIBBED,DOUBLE VINE....... 110.00
CUT GLASS,PITCHER,WATER,BULBOUS,SIGNED LIBBEY,8 1/2 IN.TALL. 110.00
CUT GLASS,PITCHER,WATER,DAISIES,LEAVES,NOTCHED TOP,
  5 TUMBLERS...........................................  45.00
CUT GLASS,PITCHER,WATER,FIVE MATCHING TUMBLERS,SIGNED
  J.HOARE,CORNING...................................... 175.00
CUT GLASS,PITCHER,WATER,FLARED BASE,PINWHEELS,STAR IN BASE,
  CUT HANDLE...........................................  35.00
CUT GLASS,PITCHER,WATER,HELMET TYPE,HARVARD,FLORAL,SIX
  TUMBLERS............................................. 150.00
CUT GLASS,PITCHER,WATER,HOBSTARS,CROSS CUTTING,THUMBPRINT
  HANDLE...............................................  32.50
CUT GLASS,PITCHER,WATER,PINWHEEL DESIGN,TANKARD...........  52.50
CUT GLASS,PITCHER,WATER,PINWHEEL,SIX TUMBLERS............. 115.00
CUT GLASS,PITCHER,WATER,PINWHEELS,STARS,FANS,9 IN.TALL.....  47.50
CUT GLASS,PITCHER,WATER,SILVER BAND,TANKARD...............  65.00
CUT GLASS,PITCHER,WATER,STARS,GEOMETRICS,6 MATCHING TUMBLERS  95.00
CUT GLASS,PITCHER,WATER,SUNBURSTS,HOBSTARS,STRAWBERRY,FLARE
  BASE.................................................  38.00
```

CUT GLASS,PITCHER,WATER,TWO LARGE BUZZ STARS ON SIDES,
GEOMETRIC,DIAMONDS...................................... 48.00
CUT GLASS,PITCHER,9 1/2 IN.,6 TUMBLERS..................... 147.00
CUT GLASS,PLATE,6,SIGNED HAWKES.....................ILLUS.. 250.00
CUT GLASS,PLATE,CAKE,HOBSTAR,CANE,FEATHER,PAPERWEIGHT BASE,
PEDESTAL.................................................. 335.00
CUT GLASS,PLATE,CAKE,HOBSTAR,PEDESTAL,8 1/2 IN.HIGH......... 185.00
CUT GLASS,PLATE,CAKE,INTAGLIO CUT FLOWERS,ALLOVER CUT,
6 1/4-IN.DIAMETER....................................... 15.00
CUT GLASS,PLATE,CARNATION,FOLIAGE,BLACK ENAMEL RIM,8 IN..... 10.00
CUT GLASS,PLATE,CHAIN OF HOBSTARS & HOBNAILS AROUND RIM,
HOBSTAR CENTER.......................................... 65.00
CUT GLASS,PLATE,CHOP,CLEAR BUTTONS,DEEP-CUT PATTERN,
9 1/4-IN.DIAMETER....................................... 75.00
CUT GLASS,PLATE,CLEAR CENTER,DIAMOND & CROSS HATCH BORDER,
LIBBEY,6................................................ 180.00
CUT GLASS,PLATE,CRANBERRY CUT TO CLEAR,STRAWBERRY,FAN,
6 1/2-IN.DIAMETER....................................... 30.00
CUT GLASS,PLATE,DIAMOND,SIGNED LIBBEY,7 3/4-IN.DIAMETER.... 18.00
CUT GLASS,PLATE,HOBSTAR CENTER,DIAMONDS,CROSS-HATCHING,FANS,
HAWKES,6................................................ 250.00
CUT GLASS,PLATE,MOURNING,CARNATIONS,FOLIAGE,BLACK BAND
AROUND RIM,8 IN........................................ 10.00

CUT GLASS PLATE, SIGNED HAWKES

CUT GLASS,PLATE,SERVING,QUEENS PATTERN,SIGNED HAWKES,
10-IN.DIAMETER.......................................... 140.00
CUT GLASS,PLATE,STRAWBERRY DIAMOND & FAN,6 5/8 IN.......... 12.50
CUT GLASS,PLATE,STRAWBERRY DIAMOND,FAN,7 IN................ 25.00
CUT GLASS,PLATTER,HOBSTAR,MEDALLION,EDGES 1 1/4 IN.HIGH,
11 3/4 IN.............................................. 65.00
CUT GLASS,POT,PUFF,CANE PATTERN,SILVER PLATE COVER......... 15.00
CUT GLASS,RELISH,HARVARD PATTERN,6 IN..................... 20.00
CUT GLASS,RELISH,RAISED SIDES,SIGNED CLARKE............... 28.00
CUT GLASS,RING TREE,COBALT BLUE CUT TO CLEAR,4 IN.WIDE...... 35.00
CUT GLASS,SALT,FLORAL PATTERN,FOOTED..................... 6.50
CUT GLASS,SALT,HEX-STARRED BASE,SIX-SIDED PLUMES,SET OF 8... 45.00
CUT GLASS,SALT,INDIVIDUAL,FAN CUT........................ 2.50
CUT GLASS,SALT,INDIVIDUAL,FAN CUT,OPEN................... 3.00
CUT GLASS,SALT,INDIVIDUAL,HOBSTAR,FAN,SET OF 7............ 24.50
CUT GLASS,SALT,INDIVIDUAL,MULTIFACETED,RAYED BASE......... 2.75
CUT GLASS,SALT,INDIVIDUAL,PANELS,STARS,GEOMETRICS,STRAWBERRY
DIAMOND................................................ 10.00
CUT GLASS,SALT,INDIVIDUAL,PRISM CUT.............. 4.00 TO 4.50
CUT GLASS,SALT,MASTER,ALLOVER CUT WITH FLAT DIAMOND,NOTCHED
RIM.................................................... 7.00
CUT GLASS,SALT,MASTER,STRAWBERRY DIAMOND,FAN,RAYED BOTTOM,
FLUTED RIM............................................. 22.50
CUT GLASS,SALT,NOTCHED FLUTES,ROUND,SET OF 6.............. 36.00
CUT GLASS,SALT,NOTCHED PRISM,HOBSTARS.................... 10.75
CUT GLASS,SALT,STAR-RAYED HEXAGONAL BASE,OPEN,SET OF 4...... 42.00
CUT GLASS,SALT & PEPPER SHAKERS,HOBSTARS,PEWTER TOPS...... 25.00
CUT GLASS,SALT & PEPPER,HANDLED CUT TRAY,GLASS TOPS....... 20.00
CUT GLASS,SALT & PEPPER,HOBSTAR AND PRISM,PEWTER TOPS...... 20.00
CUT GLASS,SALT & PEPPER,OVERALL CUT,STERLING SILVER LIDS,
3 1/2 IN.TALL.......................................... 13.50
CUT GLASS,SALT & PEPPER,PRISM,ROSE DESIGN ON SILVER TOPS.... 20.00

```
CUT GLASS,SALT DIP,HOBSTAR,BULL'S-EYE,SIGNED,HAWKES,SET OF
   TWELVE.................................................   150.00
CUT GLASS,SALT DIP,INDIVIDUAL,LAPIDARY CUT SIDES,STAR CUT
   BASE,SET OF 6..........................................    15.00
CUT GLASS,SALT DIP,PRISM PATTERN,PAIR........................     5.00
CUT GLASS,SALT DIP,STERLING SILVER RIM.......................     9.50
CUT GLASS,SAUCE,SAWTOOTH,HOBSTARS,5 1/2 IN...................    12.50
CUT GLASS,SHAKER,SALT & PEPPER,SILVER TOP,PAIR...............     7.00
CUT GLASS,SHAKER,SUGAR,DIAMOND POINT,SILVER PLATE
   TOP......................................... 20.00 TO      25.00
CUT GLASS,SHAKER,SUGAR,FLORAL DESIGN,RESILVERED TOP,
   5 3/4 IN.HIGH..........................................    16.00
CUT GLASS,SHAKER,SUGAR,PRISMATIC CUT,SILVER TOP,
   5 1/2 IN.TALL..........................................    18.00
CUT GLASS,SHAKER,SUGAR,SILVER PLATE TOP,6 IN................    27.50
CUT GLASS,SHAKER,SUGAR,STAR-PIERCED DOME SILVER TOP,RAYED
   STAR BASE..............................................    65.00
CUT GLASS,SHERBET,HOBSTAR,FANS,CUT STEMS,STAR BOTTOM........    15.00
CUT GLASS,SHERBET,SIGNED LIBBEY,SET OF SIX..................    55.00
CUT GLASS,SHERRY,BELL SHAPE,SIGNED LIBBEY,SET OF 4..........    95.00
CUT GLASS,SPOONER,ALLOVER HARVARD...........................    30.00
CUT GLASS,SPOONER,HARVARD...................................    45.00
CUT GLASS,SPOONER,INTAGLIO CUT WILD ROSE,3 3/4 IN. X
   3 1/2-IN.DIAMETER......................................    22.00
CUT GLASS,SPOONER,STARS,CROSS-HATCHING,SPLITS,DOUBLE HANDLE.    24.00
CUT GLASS,SPOONER,TRELLIS-SERRATED TOP,OBLONG,5 IN..........    27.00
CUT GLASS,STAND,UMBRELLA,COBALT,COPPER PAN FOR BASE,8 IN. X
   24 IN.TALL.............................................   200.00
CUT GLASS,STEIN,PORCELAIN LID,BOY HOLDING FRUIT,HAND-PAINTED    40.00
CUT GLASS,SUGAR,LACY,CUT HANDLES,BASE.......................    15.50
CUT GLASS,SUGAR & CREAMER,DOUBLE HOBSTARS,STARS,NOTCHED
   HANDLES................................................    42.00
CUT GLASS,SUGAR SHAKER,6 1/4 IN.............................    20.00
CUT GLASS,SYRUP,ALLOVER CUT,ORNATE SILVER HANDLE,COLLAR,LID.    50.00
CUT GLASS,SYRUP,CROSSCUT DIAMOND,FAN,PRISM,STAR CUT BASE,
   SILVER LID.............................................    50.00
CUT GLASS,SYRUP,DORFINGER CUT,SILVER TOP....................    40.00
CUT GLASS,SYRUP,SIGNED BLACK,STARR & FROST,SILVER COVER,
   HANDLE,FEET............................................    65.00
CUT GLASS,SYRUP,SQUATTY,STERLING SILVER LID & HANDLE........    23.50
CUT GLASS,SYRUP,STRAWBERRY DIAMOND,OVERALL CUT,SILVER PLATE
   LID,HANDLE.............................................    75.00
CUT GLASS,SYRUP,STRAWBERRY DIAMOND,STAR,5 1/2 IN.HIGH.......    75.00
CUT GLASS,SYRUP,WEDGEMERE PATTERN,NOTCHED HANDLE,SILVER
   BAIL,LID,LIBBEY........................................    95.00
CUT GLASS,TANKARD,20-POINT HOBSTAR BASE,FANS,STERLING SILVER
   BAND...................................................   141.00
CUT GLASS,TANKARD,HARVARD,LEAVES,ROSETTE FLOWERS,CUT HANDLE,
   10 3/4 IN..............................................    49.00
CUT GLASS,TANKARD,HOBSTARS,PANELS OF CANE,CROSS HATCH,FANS,
   11 1/2 IN..............................................   135.00
CUT GLASS,TANKARD,STEP CUT UNDER SPOUT,CUT HANDLE,BASE,BOAT
   SHAPE..................................................    47.00
CUT GLASS,TEAPOT,BRILLIANT CUT,SINCLAIRE,COVER,6 1/2 IN.TALL   350.00
CUT GLASS,TOOTHPICK,ALLOVER HARVARD PATTERN,HOLE IN SILVER
   TOP,SQUARE.............................................    15.00
CUT GLASS,TOOTHPICK,BALL SHAPE,DIAMOND PATTERN..............    12.00
CUT GLASS,TOOTHPICK,BRONZED METAL BASE & FEET...............    37.50
CUT GLASS,TOOTHPICK,BULBOUS FACET BASE,CUP TOP,2 1/2 IN.HIGH     8.00
CUT GLASS,TOOTHPICK,DIAMOND & FAN,PAPERWEIGHT BASE..........    10.00
CUT GLASS,TOOTHPICK,DIAMOND PATTERN,PANELS,NOTCHED PRISM,
   SERRATED RIM...........................................     5.00
CUT GLASS,TOOTHPICK,EGG SHAPE,FOOTED........................    18.00
CUT GLASS,TOOTHPICK,FACETED BASE............................    12.00
CUT GLASS,TOOTHPICK,FLUTES,NOTCHED PRISM,2 IN.HIGH..........    12.50
CUT GLASS,TOOTHPICK,NOTCHED PRISM PATTERN...................    14.00
CUT GLASS,TOOTHPICK,PINWHEEL................................     8.50
CUT GLASS,TOOTHPICK,TUMBLER SHAPE,CANE CUTTING HALFWAY UP,
   STAR BASE..............................................     9.50
CUT GLASS,TRAY,ABERDEEN PATTERN,SIGNED HAWKES,10-IN.DIAMETER    85.00
CUT GLASS,TRAY,ACE OF SPADES,DIAMONDS,HEARTS,CLUBS,OVAL,
   SIGNED HAWKES..........................................    13.00
CUT GLASS,TRAY,ARCADIA PATTERN,ALLOVER CUT,OBLONG,13 X
   8 1/2 IN...............................................   125.00
CUT GLASS,TRAY,BREAD,HARVARD,HOBSTARS,VESICAS,
   11 3/4 IN.LONG,7 IN.WIDE...............................    85.00
CUT GLASS,TRAY,BREAD,HOBSTAR,DIAMOND,STRAWBERRY,FANS,12 X
   5 1/2 IN...............................................    55.00
CUT GLASS,TRAY,CELERY,ALLOVER DEEP CUT,HOBSTARS.............    37.00
CUT GLASS,TRAY,CELERY,WILD GRAPES CUT,11 X 4 1/2 IN.........    15.00
CUT GLASS,TRAY,CHEESE & CRACKER,TWO PARTS,DAISY,FERN,RAISED
```

```
CENTER TRAY................................................    65.00
CUT GLASS,TRAY,ICE CREAM,ALLOVER CUT.......................   125.00
CUT GLASS,TRAY,ICE CREAM,COSMOS PATTERN,DIAMOND SHAPE,14 IN.
  X 7 1/2 IN...............................................    32.50
CUT GLASS,TRAY,ICE CREAM,HOBSTAR,PINWHEEL,SERRATED,SCALLOPED   51.00
CUT GLASS,TRAY,ICE CREAM,HOBSTARS,FANS,14 IN.LONG,
  7 1/2 IN.WIDE............................................    65.00
CUT GLASS,TRAY,ICE CREAM,OVERALL CUT,HOBSTARS,NOTCHED,
  SCALLOPED RIM............................................    95.00
CUT GLASS,TRAY,ICE CREAM,SIGNED HAWKES.....................    65.00
CUT GLASS,TRAY,ICE CREAM,STRAWBERRY LEAVES,BLOSSOMS,BERRIES,
  LIBBEY..................................................     95.00
CUT GLASS,TRAY,MEDALLION,DIAMOND,ALLOVER CUT,13-IN.DIAMETER,
  2 IN.HIGH...............................................    200.00
CUT GLASS,TRAY,OVERALL CUT,HOBSTARS,HOBNAIL,FLASHED STARS,
  11 3/4 IN.LONG..........................................     75.00
CUT GLASS,TRAY,PIN,FLOWER,LEAF,OVAL,HAWKES.................     40.00
CUT GLASS,TRAY,RIBBED SIDES,CANE CORNERS,FLORAL BOTTOM,
  LIBBEY..................................................     25.00
CUT GLASS,TRAY,RING,POST IN CENTER.........................     7.50
CUT GLASS,TRAY,SERVING,RUSSIAN PATTERN,OVERALL CUT,CUT
  HANDLES,14 IN...........................................    295.00
CUT GLASS,TRAY,SHELL PATTERN,PINWHEEL HOBSTARS,
  12 1/4-IN.DIAMETER......................................     85.00
CUT GLASS,TRAY,SPOON,CANE,INTAGLIO FERNS,BOAT-SHAPE,SIGNED
  CLARKE..................................................     80.00
CUT GLASS,TRAY,STARS,BARS OF CANE,DIAMOND SHAPE,14 IN.LONG,
  7 IN.WIDE...............................................     95.00
CUT GLASS,TUMBLER,ALLOVER CUT,HEAVY........................     8.50
CUT GLASS,TUMBLER,ALLOVER CUT,HOBSTARS,CROSS-HATCHING,SIGNED
  EGGINTON,6..............................................    200.00
CUT GLASS,TUMBLER,BIRD IN FLIGHT,STRAW IN BEAK,WAVING LEAF
  SPRAYS..................................................     17.50
CUT GLASS,TUMBLER,BLOCK PATTERN,STAR BOTTOM,SET OF 5.......     70.00
CUT GLASS,TUMBLER,BUZZ & DIAMOND POINT OVERALL CUT,SET OF
  FOUR....................................................     31.00
CUT GLASS,TUMBLER,CRESCENT & STAR,SIGNED EGGINGTON.........     20.00
CUT GLASS,TUMBLER,CUT WITH PRISM,FANS,SPLITS,SET OF 6......     65.00
CUT GLASS,TUMBLER,CUTTING PATTERN DONE ON FINE METAL,SIGNED
  HOARE,6.................................................    120.00
CUT GLASS,TUMBLER,DIAMOND & FAN,SET OF 6...................     50.00
CUT GLASS,TUMBLER,DIAMOND SHAPE FIELD,RIBBON CUTTING,CROSS
  HATCH,LIBBEY............................................     20.00
CUT GLASS,TUMBLER,FANS,CROSS-HATCHING,TWENTY-FOUR-POINT STAR
  BASE....................................................     12.00
CUT GLASS,TUMBLER,FROSTED FLOWERS,STAR CUT CENTER,LEAVES,SET
  OF 5....................................................     30.00
CUT GLASS,TUMBLER,GEOMETRIC PATTERN........................      8.00
CUT GLASS,TUMBLER,HOBSTAR ROSETTES,NOTCHED PRISMS,STAR BASE,
  SET OF 5................................................     65.00
CUT GLASS,TUMBLER,HOBSTAR,NOTCHED PRISMS,FAN,SET OF 3......     37.00
CUT GLASS,TUMBLER,HOBSTARS,SPLIT VESICAS,SIGNED J.HOARE,
  8 1/2 IN.HIGH...........................................    125.00
CUT GLASS,TUMBLER,LEMONADE,CROSSCUT,DIAMOND,FAN,
  4 1/2 IN.HIGH,SET OF 4..................................     20.00
CUT GLASS,TUMBLER,MIDDLESEX PATTERN,SIGNED HAWKES,SET OF 4..     65.00
CUT GLASS,TUMBLER,PINWHEEL,SET OF 4........................     45.00
CUT GLASS,TUMBLER,RUSSIAN BUTTONS,FLORAL & LEAVES..........     20.00
CUT GLASS,TUMBLER,SATIN INTAGLIO LARGE WHEELS & GEOMETRICS,
  SIGNED HAWKES...........................................     17.50
CUT GLASS,TUMBLER,SCRIPT MONOGRAM,RUSSIA...................     28.50
CUT GLASS,TUMBLER,SIGNED CLARKE............................     20.00
CUT GLASS,TUMBLER,SIGNED HAWKES............................     20.00
CUT GLASS,VASE,ALLOVER CUT,NOTCHED CUTTING ON 6-SIDED STEM,
  FOOTED,6 IN.............................................     19.50
CUT GLASS,VASE,ALLOVER CUT,PAPERWEIGHT BOTTOM,V-SHAPED TOP,
  SQUARE BASE.............................................     25.00
CUT GLASS,VASE,ALLOVER HARVARD CUT PATTERN,STERLING SILVER
  BAND,3 IN...............................................     20.00
CUT GLASS,VASE,ALLOVER STARS,CUT STAR BASE,AMETHYST &
  CRYSTAL OVERLAY.........................................     45.00
CUT GLASS,VASE,BARREL SHAPE,INTAGLIO ROSES,SIGNED TUTHILL,
  8 1/4 IN................................................     55.00
CUT GLASS,VASE,BLUE CUT TO CLEAR,DORFLINGER,8 1/2 IN.TALL,
  PAIR....................................................     55.00
CUT GLASS,VASE,BRUNSWICK PATTERN,V SHAPE,PEDESTAL,HAWKES,
  12 IN.,PAIR.............................................    125.00
CUT GLASS,VASE,BUD,HEXAGON SHAPE BASE & STEM,SIGNED
  SINCLAIRE...............................................     50.00
CUT GLASS,VASE,BUD,HOBSTAR,STRAWBERRY DIAMOND,FAN,PEDESTAL,
  6 IN.TALL...............................................     22.00
```

CUT GLASS,VASE,BUD,INTAGLIO ROSES,NOTCHED RIM,TEARDROP STEM,
    LIBBEY............................................................... 64.00
CUT GLASS,VASE,BUD,PINWHEEL TOP,THUMBPRINT SIDES,8 IN....... 25.00
CUT GLASS,VASE,BULL'S-EYES ON BASE,FAN,THUMBPRINT,STAR-CUT
    BASE,RIBBING........................................................ 25.00
CUT GLASS,VASE,COPPER WHEEL ENGRAVING,RIBBONS,FLORAL,
    PEDESTAL,10 1/2 IN................................................ 35.00
CUT GLASS,VASE,CORSET SHAPE,SAWTOOTH TOP,CANES,HOBSTARS,
    BEADING,10 IN...................................................... 75.00
CUT GLASS,VASE,COSMOS,10 IN.................................... 40.00
CUT GLASS,VASE,CRYSTAL TO GREEN,FLORAL,SCROLL,
    DIAMOND-QUILTED,FAN SHAPE........................................ 45.00
CUT GLASS,VASE,DIAMOND,FLOWERS,POINSETTIA-LIKE PETALS,WHEEL
    CUT,9 IN........................................................... 30.00
CUT GLASS,VASE,DIAMOND,RAYED BASE,NOTCHED RIM,STUART,
    ENGLAND,5 IN...................................................... 28.00
CUT GLASS,VASE,FAN,STAR,BULL'S-EYE,NOTCHED PRISM,COLUMNS,
    15 IN.HIGH........................................................ 91.00
CUT GLASS,VASE,FAN,STRAWBERRY DIAMOND,STARS,BULL'S-EYES,
    PEDESTAL,19 IN................................................... 160.00
CUT GLASS,VASE,FANS,DIAMOND STRAWBERRY,STAR,POINTED TOP,
    12 1/4 IN.HIGH................................................... 50.00
CUT GLASS,VASE,FERN CUT WITH CUT LEAVES & FLORAL,13 IN.HIGH. 30.00
CUT GLASS,VASE,FLORAL,LEAVES,STAR & FILE AT TOP,12 IN.TALL.. 26.00
CUT GLASS,VASE,GARLAND PATTERN,PAIRPOINT,CYLINDRICAL,12 X
    4 1/2 IN.......................................................... 85.00
CUT GLASS,VASE,HARVARD,FROSTED FLOWER SPRAYS,FERN,FLARED,
    13 3/4 IN.TALL................................................... 75.00
CUT GLASS,VASE,HEART-SHAPED WREATHS,CHECKERBOARD DESIGN,
    FLORAL,HAWKES.................................................... 33.00
CUT GLASS,VASE,HOBSTAR ROWS,DIAMOND FIELD,PINWHEELS,STAR
    BASE,18 IN....................................................... 110.00
CUT GLASS,VASE,HOBSTAR,PANELS,THUMBPRINT,BULBOUS,MARKED
    CLARK,10 IN...................................................... 85.00
CUT GLASS,VASE,HOBSTAR,PRISMS,SIGNED HAWKES,14 IN.HIGH...... 96.00
CUT GLASS,VASE,HOBSTARS,HOBNAIL DIAMOND,STRAWBERRY,NOTCHED
    TOP,5 1/2 IN..................................................... 90.00
CUT GLASS,VASE,HOBSTARS,MITER,FAN,TWO NOTCHED HANDLES,
    12 1/2 IN.TALL.................................................. 325.00
CUT GLASS,VASE,INTAGLIO CUT DAISIES,CUT SWAG & THUMBPRINT,
    VASELINE......................................................... 48.00
CUT GLASS,VASE,INTAGLIO CUT,SIGNED LIBBEY,10 IN.HIGH........ 65.00
CUT GLASS,VASE,INTAGLIO DAISY,BUTTERFLY,10 IN.TALL.......... 55.00
CUT GLASS,VASE,INTAGLIO FLOWERS,DRAPE,RUFFLED EDGE,TUTHILL,
    6 IN.HIGH........................................................ 75.00
CUT GLASS,VASE,INTAGLIO LEAVES & FLOWERS,ALLOVER DESIGN,
    19 IN.HIGH....................................................... 22.00
CUT GLASS,VASE,INTALIO,14 IN.HIGH............................. 40.00
CUT GLASS,VASE,LARGE & SMALL DIAMONDS,NOTCHED RIM,SIGNED
    STUART,ENGLAND.................................................. 23.00
CUT GLASS,VASE,LILY-SHAPED,HOBSTARS,ALLOVER CUT,7 IN.HIGH... 18.00
CUT GLASS,VASE,MIDDLESEX,CYLINDER SHAPE,12 IN.HIGH.......... 125.00
CUT GLASS,VASE,NOTCH CUT RIM,INTAGLIO LILY OF VALLEY,
    FOLIAGE,LIBBEY.................................................. 60.00
CUT GLASS,VASE,PAIR,CAMEO-CUT CRANBERRY & CLEAR OVERLAY,
    9 1/2 IN. HIGH.................................................. 100.00
CUT GLASS,VASE,PANELED CUT,FLORAL & SCROLL,GILT BAND,
    TUBULAR,3 1/2 IN................................................ 35.00
CUT GLASS,VASE,PANELS IN ARCHES,DIAMOND POINT,NOTCHED
    THROAT,RUSSIA................................................... 73.00
CUT GLASS,VASE,PANELS,GILT BAND WITH FIGURAL DECOR,TUBULAR,
    AMETHYST......................................................... 65.00
CUT GLASS,VASE,POPPY DESIGN,DEEP INTAGLIO,MOUTH FLARES,
    SCALLOPING....................................................... 85.00
CUT GLASS,VASE,ROSE,HOBSTARS,STAR IN BASE,BULBOUS,TALL
    PEDESTAL......................................................... 42.50
CUT GLASS,VASE,ROSE,STAR MOTIF,HOBSTARS,BEADED STEM HAS
    BULL'S-EYE BAND................................................. 21.00
CUT GLASS,VASE,SIGNED HAWKES,9 IN.HIGH...................... 105.00
CUT GLASS,VASE,STAR,FAN,DIAMOND CUTTING,SERRATED THROAT,
    SCALLOPED,HAWKES................................................ 125.00
CUT GLASS,VASE,STAR,HOBNAIL,STRAWBERRY,SILVER TOP,
    5 1/4 IN.HIGH................................................... 52.00
CUT GLASS,VASE,STARS,FANS,PEDESTAL,SIGNED LIBBEY,5 X
    12 IN.TALL....................................................... 75.00
CUT GLASS,VASE,STARS,FLOWERS,LEAVES,MESH AT NECK,ALLOVER
    CUT,9 IN.TALL................................................... 300.00
CUT GLASS,VASE,STARS,THUMBPRINTS,ALLOVER CUT,SIGNED D & B,
    15 IN............................................................ 65.00
CUT GLASS,VASE,TEARDROP WITHIN,HOBSTARS,MEDALLIONS,FLORAL,
    PEDESTAL STEM................................................... 23.50

CUT GLASS,VASE,THREE VERTICAL ROWS,STRAWBERRY DIAMOND,
  BULL'S-EYE,HOBSTAR.......................................  60.00
CUT GLASS,VASE,TRUMPET SHAPE,CROSSCUT DIAMOND,FANS,FOOTED,
  14 IN.,PAIR.............................................  77.00
CUT GLASS,VASE,TRUMPET,PINWHEELS,DIAMOND POINT,SPLIT
  VESICAS,12 IN.HIGH......................................  45.00
CUT GLASS,VASE,TUTHILL,ETCHED FLOWERS,FLARED TOP,SCALLOPS,
  SIGNED,8 IN............................................. 125.00
CUT GLASS,WHISKEY,SIGNED LIBBEY,2 1/4 IN.HIGH.............  16.50
CUT GLASS,WHISKEY GLASS,WORLD'S FAIR,1893.................  10.00
CUT GLASS,WINE,CANE PATTERN,STEM,SET OF 13................  85.00
CUT GLASS,WINE,CANE PATTERN,STEM,4 3/4 IN.TALL............  12.50
CUT GLASS,WINE,CROSS HATCH,CANE,FAN,SET OF 11............. 165.00
CUT GLASS,WINE,CROSSCUT DIAMOND,FAN,PYRAMID DIAMONDS BETWEEN
  FANS,4..................................................  80.00
CUT GLASS,WINE,EMERALD GREEN,CUT TO CLEAR,DIAMOND,STRAWBERRY
  DIAMOND,3...............................................  75.00
CUT GLASS,WINE,HOBSTAR CHAIN,FANS,CROSS HATCH TRIANGLES,
  NOTCHED STEM............................................  30.00
CUT GLASS,WINE,HOBSTAR,STRAWBERRY DIAMOND,TEARDROP STEM,
  SIGNED LIBBEY...........................................  28.00
CUT GLASS,WINE,LIME GREEN BOWL,PRISM CUT PATTERN,TEARDROP
  STEM....................................................  38.50
CUT GLASS,WINE,MIDDLESEX PATTERN,FOOTED...................  20.00
CUT GLASS,WINE,PEDESTAL BASE,CONICAL,SIGNED HAWKES,SET OF 6.  75.00
CUT GLASS,WINE,STRAWBERRY DIAMOND,CUT STEM,RAYED BASE,SET OF
  7....................................................... 100.00
CUT GLASS,WINE,STRAWBERRY,FAN,SET OF 10................... 125.00
CUT GLASS,WINE,THISTLE PATTERN,16-RAY FOOT...............  25.00
CUT GLASS,WINE,TRIPLE FLOWER,FOLIAGE,BEADED CIRCLE,SIGNED
  HAWKES,5 IN.............................................  16.50

   CUT VELVET IS A SPECIAL TYPE OF ART GLASS MADE WITH
   TWO LAYERS OF BLOWN GLASS WHICH SHOWS A RAISED PATTERN.
   IT USUALLY HAD AN ACID FINISH OR VELVET-LIKE TEXTURE.
   IT WAS MADE BY MANY GLASS FACTORIES DURING THE LATE
   VICTORIAN YEARS.
CUT VELVET,CREAMER,COLLAR TOP,WHITE LINING & HANDLE,RIBBED,
  BLUE.................................................... 155.00
CUT VELVET,PITCHER,WATER,DEEP ROSE,DIAMOND-QUILTED,APPLIED
  HANDLE.................................................  95.00
CUT VELVET,TUMBLER,HONEYCOMB PATTERN,PINK.................  95.00
CUT VELVET,TUMBLER,SAPPHIRE BLUE,RIBBED TRAIN PATTERN.....  45.00
CUT VELVET,VASE,DEEP RASPBERRY PINK COLORING,GLOSSY,PAIR..  95.00
CUT VELVET,VASE,DIAMOND-QUILTED,BLUE,9 IN.HIGH............ 105.00
CUT VELVET,VASE,DIAMOND-QUILTED,ROSE COLOR,9 IN.HIGH...... 105.00
CUT VELVET,VASE,FLUTING AT TOP........................... 175.00
CUT VELVET,VASE,HERRINGBONE,ROSE TO PINK,ROUGH PONTIL,
  SANDWICH............................................... 135.00
CUT VELVET,VASE,PINK RIB,WHITE CASING,BULBOUS BASE,SLENDER
  NECK,6 IN.............................................. 125.00
CUT VELVET,VASE,ROYAL BLUE,RIBBED TRAIN PATTERN,WHITE
  CASING,5 IN.TALL....................................... 125.00
CUT VELVET,VASE,RUFFLED TOP,YELLOW & WHITE QUILTING,
  5 1/2 IN.TALL..........................................  85.00

   D'ARGENTAL WAS A FRENCH CAMEO GLASSMAKER OF THE LATE
   VICTORIAN PERIOD.
D'ARGENTAL,BOWL,YELLOW MATTE,RED ROSES,LEAVES,CARVED CAMEO,
  5 3/4 IN.HIGH.......................................... 300.00
D'ARGENTAL,VASE,AMETHYST MORNING GLORIES,CUSTARD GROUND,
  CAMEO,6 IN. WIDE....................................... 195.00
D'ARGENTAL,VASE,BUTTERSCOTCH GROUND,CHARCOAL GRAY FLORAL,
  CAMEO,5 1/2 IN......................................... 125.00
D'ARGENTAL,VASE,CAMEO,AMBER-ROSE GROUND,RED ROSES,THREE
  LAYER.................................................. 150.00
D'ARGENTAL,VASE,CAMEO,FROSTED GOLD COLOR GROUND,BROWN & RUST
  LEAVES................................................. 175.00
D'ARGENTAL,VASE,CAMEO,SIGNED,8 IN....................... 285.00
D'ARGENTAL,VASE,GRAPES,LEAVES,RED,ORANGE,BROWN,CARVED CAMEO,
  8 IN. HIGH............................................. 160.00
D'ARGENTAL,VASE,MIST,CHAMPAGNE & MAHOGANY COLORS,VINES,
  TRACERY,6 IN........................................... 100.00
DAGUERROTYPE,SEE ALBUM,PHOTOGRAPHY
DANISH CHRISTMAS PLATES,SEE CHRISTMAS PLATES
DANT,SEE BOTTLE,DANT

   DAUM,NANCY,IS THE MARK USED BY AUGUSTE AND ANTONIN
   DAUM ON PIECES OF FRENCH CAMEO GLASS MADE AFTER 1875.

```
DAUM NANCY,SEE ALSO,CAMEO GLASS
DAUM NANCY,ASHTRAY,HEART SHAPE,PAPERWEIGHT TYPE,FROSTED,
    JEWELED FLORAL ......................................        75.00
DAUM NANCY,BOTTLE,ACID CUT GROUND,ENAMEL SCENIC,MAN,
    WINDMILL,STOPPER ....................................       105.00
DAUM NANCY,BOWL,ALLOVER CUT OF RED IRIS FLORAL,CAMEO GLASS,
    SIGNED,7 1/2 IN 18500&'M &'NA&)GO1&H&2HGO1MA&+ZN)&-G&OB& &     185.00
DAUM NANCY,BOWL,BLEEDING HEART DESIGN,VINES,LEAVES,RED,
    GREEN,SIGNED .......................................        125.00
DAUM NANCY,BOWL,CAMEO,PEACHES,MOTTLED YELLOW & CAMPHOR SATIN
    GROUND .............................................        135.00
DAUM NANCY,BOWL,MOTTLED ORANGE & YELLOW,CINTRA TYPE,
    5 1/2-IN.DIAMETER ..................................         60.00
DAUM NANCY,BOWL,ORANGE MOTTLE,GOLD FOIL LAYERS,SIGNED,
    4-IN.DIAMETER ......................................         65.00
DAUM NANCY,BOWL,SILVERIA,ORANGE MOTTLE,LAYERS OF GOLD FOIL,
    SIGNED .............................................         65.00
DAUM NANCY,BOWL,YELLOW TO AMETHYST,ENAMELED FLORAL,2 1/2 X
    4 3/4 IN ...........................................        110.00
DAUM NANCY,BOWL,YELLOW,GREEN & RED GROJND,RED BERRIES,
    5-IN.DIAMETER ......................................        110.00
DAUM NANCY,BOWL,YELLOW,GREEN & RED GROUND,BLUE RASPBERRIES,
    CAMEO GLASS ........................................        110.00
DAUM NANCY,BOX,CARVED AMETHYST CROCUS,BLUE-GREEN GROUND,
    COVER,CAMEO ........................................        135.00
DAUM NANCY,BOX,FUCHSIA FLOWERS,MOTTLED WHITE MATTE GROUND,
    LID,6 IN ...........................................        250.00
DAUM NANCY,BOX,POWDER,SILVER TOP,SIGNED WITH CROSS OF
    LORRAINE ...........................................         45.00
DAUM NANCY,BOX,POWDER,YELLOW,GREEN GROUND,PINK MORNING
    GLORIES,SIGNED .....................................        145.00
DAUM NANCY,COMPOTE,YELLOW & BROWN GROUND,SPRIGS,LEAVES,
    FOOTED,CAMEO .......................................        325.00
DAUM NANCY,CUP & SAUCER,JADE GREEN,OPAQUE,SIGNED,LORRAINE
    CROSS ..............................................         48.00
DAUM NANCY,HONEY BOAT,CAMEO,CLOVER,BEE,SIGNED ...........        200.00
DAUM NANCY,JAR,CAMEO,COVER,SIGNED,6 IN. X 6 IN. X 3 1/2 IN..     155.00
DAUM NANCY,JAR,POMADE,CAMEO WINTER SCENE,STOPPER,3 IN. .....     110.00
DAUM NANCY,LAMP,AUTUMN SCENE,20 IN.TALL .................        675.00
DAUM NANCY,LAMP,CAMEO GLASS,SAILBOATS,SCENIC,GREEN,BLACK
    BASE,15 IN.HIGH ....................................        475.00
DAUM NANCY,LAMP,CAMEO,MOTTLED GROUND,CARVED,ENAMELED LEAF
    DECOR,FLORAL .......................................        275.00
DAUM NANCY,LAMP,CAMEO,YELLOW,BLACK,BROWN,TREES,WATER,SIGNED.     495.00
DAUM NANCY,LAMP,FISHING SAILBOATS ON SHADE & BASE,BLACK,
    GREEN,SIGNED .......................................        450.00
DAUM NANCY,LAMP,MINIATURE,CAMEO,SIGNED,WIRED ............        285.00
DAUM NANCY,PITCHER,HONESTY,TAN,YELLOW,FROST & GREEN SPATTER,
    12 IN.TALL .........................................        275.00
DAUM NANCY,PITCHER,MINIATURE,FROSTED GREEN GROUND,FLORAL,
    2 1/2 IN.HIGH ......................................        110.00
DAUM NANCY,TUMBLER,CAMEO,GOLD BERRIES,BLACK STEMS,LORRAINE
    CROSS ..............................................         85.00
DAUM NANCY,TUMBLER,CAMEO,YELLOW & ORANGE LEAVES,STEMS,ACID
    CUT ................................................        105.00
DAUM NANCY,TUMBLER,LORRAINE CROSS,VASELINE GROUND,ORANGE,
    BROWN MOTTLING .....................................         45.00
DAUM NANCY,TUMBLER,WHITE GROUND,SHADED RED,BLUE,GREEN
    FLORAL,SIGNED ......................................        225.00
DAUM NANCY,VASE,BIRCH TREES,ROCKS,STREAM,18 IN. ........        475.00
DAUM NANCY,VASE,BIRD,FOUR COLORS,RED FLOWERS,12 IN.HIGH....      140.00
DAUM NANCY,VASE,BLEEDING HEART,1 1/4 IN.WIDE AT TOP,
    4 IN.HIGH ..........................................         75.00
DAUM NANCY,VASE,BROWN,YELLOW & RUST LEAVES,DARK BOTTOM,
    FRANCE,16 IN .......................................        750.00
DAUM NANCY,VASE,CAMEO GLASS,18 3/4 IN. HIGH,SIGNED ......        135.00
DAUM NANCY,VASE,CAMEO,CARVED PEACHES,GRAY-PINK-YELLOW MATTE,
    BOWL SHAPE .........................................        225.00
DAUM NANCY,VASE,CAMEO,ENAMEL,FLORAL,MEDALLION BAND,FAN
    SHAPE,4 3/4 IN .....................................        135.00
DAUM NANCY,VASE,CAMEO,ENAMEL,FLORAL,MEDALLION BAND,FAN
    SHAPE,5 IN.HIGH ....................................        135.00
DAUM NANCY,VASE,CAMEO,FROSTED MOTTLED GOLD COLOR GROUND,LAKE
    SCENE ..............................................        195.00
DAUM NANCY,VASE,CAMEO,HONEY-GOLD GROUND,THISTLE CUTTING,
    4 1/2 IN.TALL ......................................         85.00
DAUM NANCY,VASE,CAMEO,RED CUT TO FROSTED LEAVES,SIGNED,
    15 1/4 IN.,PAIR ....................................        500.00
DAUM NANCY,VASE,CAMEO,SIX-COLOR SCENIC,SIGNED,FRANCE ......      145.00
DAUM NANCY,VASE,CAMEO,THREE-COLOR,PURPLE,BLUE,YELLOW,
    FLOWERS,GOLD .......................................        235.00
```

```
DAUM NANCY,VASE,CAMEO,YELLOW,GREEN,ORANGE GROUND,BLACK
   SAILBOAT.................................................   325.00
DAUM NANCY,VASE,CRACKLE FINISH BETWEEN 15 RIBS,SIX-SIDED
   TOP,FLINT,AMBER..........................................   134.00
DAUM NANCY,VASE,CROW & FOX,GREEN,GOLD,BLACK-FROSTED GROUND,
   8 IN.....................................................   250.00
DAUM NANCY,VASE,DAISIES CUT TO PALE BLUE & WHITE,GOLD,CAMEO,
   OVOID SHAPE..............................................   125.00
DAUM NANCY,VASE,DUTCH SCENE,BLUE,SAILBOATS,WINDMILL,WHITE
   GROUND,4 IN..............................................    95.00
DAUM NANCY,VASE,ENAMELED FLORAL,BAND OF MEDALLIONS,FAN
   SHAPE,CAMEO..............................................   115.00
DAUM NANCY,VASE,FLOWER-FORMED,5 IN.HIGH.....................   110.00
DAUM NANCY,VASE,FROSTED GROUND,CARVED SNAIL,LEAVES,BRANCES,
   8 IN.HIGH................................................   135.00
DAUM NANCY,VASE,GOLD-TEXTURED GROUND,ENAMELED RUST THISTLES,
   4 1/2 IN.................................................    90.00
DAUM NANCY,VASE,GREEN & YELLOW GROUND,MAPLE LEAVES,PODS,
   31 1/2 IN.HIGH...........................................   525.00
DAUM NANCY,VASE,GREEN BASE,MOTTLED BEIGE-GRAY GROUND,SWEET
   PEAS,SIGNED..............................................   150.00
DAUM NANCY,VASE,GREEN GROUND,BLACKBERRY BUSHES,OVAL,SIGNED,
   11 IN.HIGH...............................................   175.00
DAUM NANCY,VASE,GREEN GROUND,RED THISTLE,CAMEO,SIGNATURE,
   4 1/2 IN.HIGH............................................   135.00
DAUM NANCY,VASE,GREEN,ORANGE,BLUE,YELLOW,CUT BLUEBERRY
   DESIGN,SIGNED............................................   140.00
DAUM NANCY,VASE,LETTER HOLDER,BLUE,MOTTLED,SIGNED...........    80.00
DAUM NANCY,VASE,MAJORELLE,RIBBED,AVENTURINE,GREEN,SPATTER
   LINING,FRAME.............................................    99.00
DAUM NANCY,VASE,MINIATURE,MOTTLED GREEN & BLACK,SIGNED......    25.00
DAUM NANCY,VASE,MOTTLED ORANGE GROUND,PURPLE WISTERIA,CAMEO
   GLASS,7 IN...............................................   275.00
DAUM NANCY,VASE,MOTTLED ORANGE,YELLOW,SIGNED,2 1/4 X
   4 IN.TALL................................................    30.00
DAUM NANCY,VASE,RED FLOWER DECOR,CUT,ENAMELED,CAMEO,
   15 1/4 IN.TALL...........................................   160.00
DAUM NANCY,VASE,SCENIC,BLACK,GREEN,ORANGE,YELLOW,CAMPHOR
   GROUND,11 IN.............................................   325.00
DAUM NANCY,VASE,SCENIC,LANDSCAPE,SUMMER COLORS,4 IN.HIGH,
   2-IN.DIAMETER............................................   150.00
DAUM NANCY,VASE,SEMIFROSTED TRANSLUCENT GROUND,HONEYSUCKLE
   SPRAYS,CAMEO.............................................   175.00
DAUM NANCY,VASE,SERPENTINE SHAPE,FLORAL,LEAVES,GREEN,BLUE,
   ORANGE,7 IN..............................................   350.00
DAUM NANCY,VASE,SQUARE,AUTUMN LEAVES,YELLOW,ORANGE,GREEN,
   4 1/2 IN.HIGH............................................   135.00
DAUM NANCY,VASE,STICK,YELLOW,GREEN,BLACK,PEAR-SHAPED BASE,
   SIGNED...................................................    55.00
DAUM NANCY,VASE,SUMMER RAIN,6 IN.HIGH.......................   425.00
DAUM NANCY,VASE,SUMMER SCENE,SIGNED,6 IN. X 9 IN.HIGH.......   375.00
DAUM NANCY,VASE,SUMMER,8 IN.HIGH............................   350.00
DAUM NANCY,VASE,SUNSET COLORS,BLACK WOODLAND SCENE,AMBER,
   10 1/2 IN.HIGH...........................................   100.00
DAUM NANCY,VASE,SWIRLED YELLOW PANELS,PINK LOOPS,WHITE
   LINING,BLOWN.............................................    59.50
DAUM NANCY,VASE,TEXTURED GROUND,CLEAR PANSIES,GOLD DECOR,
   4 3/4 IN.HIGH............................................    95.00
DAUM NANCY,VASE,TWO-LAYER,THREE-COLOR WOODLAND SCENE,
   VILLAGE,11 1/2 IN........................................   295.00
DAUM NANCY,VASE,WINTER SCENE,SIGNED,3 IN.WIDE X 8 IN.HIGH...   375.00
DAUM NANCY,VASE,YELLOW TO BROWN,RED ENAMEL FLORAL,GOLD
   LEAVES,3 3/4 IN..........................................   165.00
```

DAVENPORT POTTERY AND PORCELAIN WERE MADE AT THE
DAVENPORT FACTORY IN LONGPORT,STAFFORDSHIRE,ENGLAND,
FROM 1793 TO 1887. EARTHENWARES,CREAMWARES,PORCELAINS,
IRONSTONE WARES,AND OTHER PRODUCTS WERE MADE. MOST OF
THE PIECES ARE MARKED WITH A FORM OF THE WORD
DAVENPORT.

```
DAVENPORT,COMPOTE,MAUVE GRAPE & LEAF DECOR ON BASE & EDGE,
   9 1/2 X 3 IN.............................................    35.00
DAVENPORT,CUP & SAUCER,DERBY COLORS & PATTERN,CIRCA 1810....    27.50
DAVENPORT,CUP & SAUCER,HANDLELESS,CYPRESS PATTERN,FLOW
   MULBERRY.................................................    22.50
DAVENPORT,DISH,SAUCE,AMOY,FLOW BLUE,IMPRESSED SIGNATURE &
   ANCHOR...................................................     9.50
DAVENPORT,DISH,VEGETABLE,BERRY PATTERN,PEAR FINIAL,IRONSTONE    37.00
DAVENPORT,DISH,VEGETABLE,CORN PATTERN,CORN HANDLES,CORN
   FINIAL,IRONSTONE.........................................    25.00
```

DAVENPORT,EWER,WHITE WITH BLUE MARBLING,CIRCA 1815......... 40.00
DAVENPORT,GRAVY BOAT,PEDESTAL,HANDLES,FLOWER FINIAL,TRAY,
  IRONSTONE.................................................. 42.00
DAVENPORT,PLATE,AMOY,FLOW BLUE,10 1/4 IN.................... 20.00
DAVENPORT,PLATE,BLUE,WHITE,CASTLE SCENE,MARKED,IRONSTONE.... 6.00
DAVENPORT,PLATE,IVY WREATH PATTERN,IMPRESSED ANCHOR,1227B IN
  RED....................................................... 25.00
DAVENPORT,PLATE,IVY WREATH,IMPRESSED MARK,9 1/2 IN.......... 23.00
DAVENPORT,PLATE,LANDSCAPE,GOLD STAR & BLUE BAND BORDER,CIRCA
  1820,PAIR................................................. 92.00
DAVENPORT,PLATE,RURAL SCENE,CIRCA 1820,IMPRESSED ANCHOR MARK 28.00
DAVENPORT,PLATTER,WHITE,BLUE BORDER,IMPRESSED ANCHOR MARK,
  18 IN.LONG................................................ 35.00


DE VEZ IS A NAME THAT APPEARS ON FRENCH ART NOUVEAU
  CAMEO GLASS.
DE VEZ,BOTTLE,SCENT,SCENIC,CAMEO,SIGNED,FRANCE,6 IN.HIGH.... 125.00
DE VEZ,BOTTLE,SCENT,SCENIC,GREEN,ORANGE,WHITE,CAMEO,SIGNED,
  7 IN.HIGH................................................. 125.00
DE VEZ,BOWL,ROSE,CAMEO,SCENIC,GREEN & PINK OVER CITRON
  GROUND,6 1/2 IN........................................... 275.00
DE VEZ,LAMP,CAMEO,LAKE,SKY,MOUNTAINS,BUILDINGS,MAN,BOAT,
  THREE LAYERS.............................................. 250.00
DE VEZ,LAMP,CAMEO,THREE-LAYER BASE,SHADE,BOAT,TREES,
  MOUNTAINS,11 IN.HIGH...................................... 250.00
DE VEZ,VASE,CAMEO,HAMMERED EFFECT,GREEN,FOX,GOAT,SCENE,
  FRANCE,8 1/2 IN........................................... 375.00
DE VEZ,VASE,CAMEO,SCENIC,RED & MAROON ON GOLD IRIDESCENT
  GROUND,10 IN.............................................. 235.00
DE VEZ,VASE,TREES,LAKE,ISLAND,MOUNTAINS,CAMEO,FOUR-LAYER,
  THREE-COLOR............................................... 225.00
DE VILBISS,ATOMIZER,CARNIVAL GLASS,MARIGOLD,SIGNED.......... 10.00
DE VILBISS,ATOMIZER,CASED ORANGE,STIPPLED GOLD,SIGNED,
  7 1/2 IN.................................................. 35.00
DE VILBISS,ATOMIZER,GOLD & MELON-COLORED PANELED SATIN
  GLASS,SIGNED.............................................. 22.50
DE VILBISS,BOTTLE,PERFUME,ETCHED FLORAL,LEAF,AMBER,
  7 1/2 IN.TALL............................................. 32.00
DE VILBISS,PERFUME,AMETHYST COLOR,GOLD-ENCRUSTED BODY,
  7 1/2 IN.TALL............................................. 32.00
DE VILBISS,PERFUME,ORANGE,IRIDESCENT,SIGNED DURAND.......... 73.00
DE VILBISS,VASE,SWIRL,PAPER LABEL,4 IN..................... 20.00


DECOYS ARE CARVED OR TURNED WOODEN COPIES OF BIRDS. THE
  DECOY WAS PLACED IN THE WATER TO LURE FLYING BIRDS TO
  THE POND FOR THE HUNTERS.
DECOY,BLACK & WHITE........................................ 9.00
DECOY,BLACK,15 IN.LONG..................................... 12.00
DECOY,BLUEBILL,BASSWOOD,BY J.SHEPHERD,ONTARIO,CANADA,CIRCA
  1950,SIGNED............................................... 25.00
DECOY,BROADBILL,PAIR,DETROIT............................... 80.00
DECOY,CANADA GOOSE,NEW ENGLAND ORIGIN...................... 50.00
DECOY,CANVAS,FLAT BILL,TURNED-UP TAIL,GLASS EYES,PAINTED,
  16 IN.LONG................................................ 12.00
DECOY,CANVASBACK DRAKE,DETROIT............................. 75.00
DECOY,CORK,COVERED WITH PAINTED CANVAS,PEKIN GLASS EYES,
  WEIGHT LOOP............................................... 22.00
DECOY,CROW,BLACK,GLASS EYES,16 1/2 IN...................... 10.00
DECOY,CROW,CHARLES PERDEW.................................. 325.00
DECOY,CURLEW,HUDSONIAN,NEW JERSEY.......................... 225.00
DECOY,DUCK,BLACK,GLASS EYES,HAND-CARVED,WOODEN,16 IN.LONG... 25.00
DECOY,DUCK,CANVASBACK DRAKE................................ 32.00
DECOY,DUCK,HAND-CARVED..................................... 14.50
DECOY,DUCK,HAND-CARVED,SIGNED H.T.,13 1/2 IN.LONG.......... 15.00
DECOY,DUCK,PAINTED,WOODEN,16 IN.LONG....................... 12.00
DECOY,DUCK,WHISTLER........................................ 38.00
DECOY,DUCK,WOODEN..................................8.50 TO 16.00
DECOY,GOLDENEYE,PINE,CARVED WINGS,ST.LAWRENCE RIVER AREA.... 22.00
DECOY,HERON,BLUE,SOUTH JERSEY.............................. 130.00
DECOY,MALLARD MALE & FEMALE,CANVAS,SEWN,GLASS EYES,PAIR..... 68.00
DECOY,MALLARD,WOODEN,PAINT................................. 16.00
DECOY,PLOVER,BLACK-BELLIED................................. 75.00
DECOY,PLOVER,WOODEN,PAINT.................................. 16.00
DECOY,REDHEAD,HAND-HEWN,PINE,NEW YORK THOUSAND ISLANDS,CIRCA
  1910...................................................... 55.00
DECOY,RUST COLOR........................................... 6.00
DECOY,SCOUP,SIGNED WARD BROS.,MADE IN 1967,PAIR............ 300.00
DECOY,SHORE BIRD,TIN,PAIR................................. 32.00
DECOY,SHORE BIRD,YELLOW LEGS,MOUNTED...................... 27.00

```
DECOY,SNIPE,BLACK-BREASTED PLOVER,METAL,WITHOUT STICK.......    22.00
DECOY,SNIPE,FOLDING STICK-UP TYPE,YELLOW LEGS,PATENT 1874,
  METAL,NO STICK.............................................    20.00
DECOY,SNIPE,SILHOUETTE,MOUNTED ON DRIFTWOOD BASE,PAINT,
  WOODEN....................................................    10.00
DECOY,SNIPE,TIN,PAIR.........................................    15.00
DECOY,SNOW GOOSE,BALSA,BY HERTER,INC.,MINNEAPOLIS,CIRCA
  1930......................................................    35.00
DECOY,YELLOW,GREEN,WHITE,BLACK..............................    11.50
```

THE DEDHAM POTTERY COMPANY OF DEDHAM,MASSACHUSETTS,
STARTED MAKING POTTERY IN 1866. IT WAS REORGANIZED AS
THE CHELSEA POTTERY COMPANY IN 1891,AND BECAME THE
DEDHAM POTTERY COMPANY IN 1895. THE FACTORY WAS FAMOUS
FOR ITS CRACKLEWARE DISHES,WHICH PICTURED BLUE
OUTLINES OF ANIMALS,FLOWERS,AND OTHER NATURAL MOTIFS.

```
DEDHAM POTTERY,BOWL & PLATE,RABBITS,MARKED..................    70.00
DEDHAM POTTERY,BOWL,MUSHROOMS,3 3/8-IN.DIAMETER,
  1 7/8 IN.TALL.............................................    55.00
DEDHAM POTTERY,BOWL,SWAN..............................ILLUS..    75.00
DEDHAM POTTERY,CREAMER,RABBIT,3 3/4 IN......................    30.00
DEDHAM POTTERY,CUP & SAUCER,RABBIT..........................    65.00
DEDHAM POTTERY,CUP & SAUCER,RABBIT BORDER,SIGNED WITH MARK..    68.00
DEDHAM POTTERY,PLATE,DUCKS AROUND BORDER,1902 MARK,6 IN.....    24.00
DEDHAM POTTERY,PLATE,HORSE CHESTNUT,8 1/2 IN................    35.00
DEDHAM POTTERY,PLATE,HORSE CHESTNUT,10 IN...................    65.00
DEDHAM POTTERY,PLATE,MAGNOLIA BORDER,8 1/4 IN.DIAMETER......    40.00
DEDHAM POTTERY,PLATE,POND LILY,HAS DEDHAM POTTERY WITH
  RABBIT MARK...............................................    25.00
DEDHAM POTTERY,PLATE,RABBIT,7 IN............................    25.00
DEDHAM POTTERY,PLATE,RABBIT,8 IN............................    35.00
DEDHAM POTTERY,PLATE,RABBIT,8 1/2-IN.DIAMETER...... 25.00 TO    40.00
DEDHAM POTTERY,PLATE,RABBIT,1896 MARK,6-IN.DIAMETER.........    18.00
DEDHAM POTTERY,PLATE,TURKEY,8 IN............................    85.00
DEDHAM POTTERY,PLATE,WATER LILY,7 IN........................    59.50
DEDHAM POTTERY,PLATE,WATER LILY PATTERN,IMPRESSED MARK,1895.    38.00
DEDHAM POTTERY,VASE,BROWN TO GREEN,MARKED,7 3/4 IN. HIGH....    67.50
DEGUE,VASE,OVOID,YELLOW BELLFLOWERS,WHITE CLUTHRA GROUND,
  11 IN.....................................................    90.00
DEGUE,VASE,SCENE,SIGNED,CAMEO GLASS.........................   165.00
DELATTE NANCY,VASE,BLUE GROUND,PURPLE IRIS DECOR,CAMEO
```

DEDHAM SWAN BOWL

```
  GLASS,8 1/2 IN............................................   300.00
DELATTE NANCY,VASE,PARROT BAND,CAMEO GLASS,16 IN.TALL,
  9-IN.DIAMETER.............................................   300.00
DELATTE,VASE,CAMEO,AQUA GROUND,SNOW,TREES,BULBOUS BOTTOM,
  SIGNED,8 IN...............................................   125.00
DELATTE,VASE,CAMEO,NANCY,BLUE GROUND,PURPLE IRIS DECOR,
  SIGNED,8 1/2 IN...........................................   300.00
DELATTE,VASE,CAMEO,NANCY,YELLOW GROUND,TREES,MOUNTAINS,
  BRIDGE,6 IN.HIGH..........................................   135.00
DELATTE,VASE,CAMEO,OPAQUE CHARTREUSE GROUND,BROWN TREE
  SCENE,ACID CUT............................................   165.00
DELATTE,VASE,CAMEO,OPAQUE LAVENDER-PINK GROUND,MAROON
  FLORAL,7 1/4 IN...........................................   150.00
DELATTE,VASE,CAMEO,PURPLE SHADING,BULBOUS,SIGNED,9 X
  18 1/2 IN.ROUND...........................................   175.00
DELATTE,VASE,CAMEO,WHITE GROUND,CARVED AMETHYST LEAVES,PINK
  CAMELLIA..................................................   295.00
DELATTE,VASE,COBALT & ORANGE SPATTER,SIGNED,15 1/2 IN. HIGH,
  9 LB......................................................    95.00
DELATTE,VASE,WHITE ACID GROUND,AMETHYST FLORAL SPRAY,SIGNED,
  7 3/4 IN..................................................    95.00
  DELAWARE,SEE PRESSED GLASS
  DELDARE,SEE BUFFALO POTTERY,DELAWARE
```

DELFT IS A TIN GLAZED POTTERY THAT HAS BEEN MADE SINCE
THE SEVENTEENTH CENTURY. IT IS DECORATED WITH BLUE ON
WHITE OR WITH COLORED DECORATIONS. MOST OF THE PIECES
SOLD TODAY WERE MADE AFTER 1891, AND THE NAME HOLLAND
APPEARS WITH THE DELFT FACTORY MARKS.

| | |
|---|---:|
| DELFT, BOTTLE, BLUE & WHITE, CIRCA 1730,9 1/4 IN. HIGH......... | 200.00 |
| DELFT, BOTTLE, TAN GROUND, BLUE SCENIC, FLORAL, THREE-SPOUT LIP, 8 1/2 IN................................................ | 27.00 |
| DELFT, CLOCK, DUTCH SCENE ON FACE.............................. | 15.00 |
| DELFT, CLOCK, KITCHEN, PENDANT TYPE, EIGHT-DAY, GERMAN MOVEMENT.. | 25.00 |
| DELFT, CREAMER, FOREFATHER'S ROCK, FOR MISS RICHBURN, PLYMOUTH, MASS., GERMANY.............................................. | 7.50 |
| DELFT, CREAMER, RECLINING COW, FARM SCENE, IMPRESSED GERMANY 1891...................................................... | 27.50 |
| DELFT, CUP & SAUCER, WINDMILL SCENE, SCALLOPED, FOOTED, MARK..... | 23.00 |
| DELFT, DISH, VEGETABLE, BLUE & WHITE WINDMILL SCENE, COVER, 11 IN. LONG............................................... | 22.00 |
| DELFT, FIGURE, BLUE, DUTCH BOY, GIRL, PAIR..................... | 20.00 |
| DELFT, FIGURINE, CAT, WHITE, BROWN, SIGNED, HOLLAND, CIRCA 1800, PAIR.................................................... | 129.50 |
| DELFT, FIGURINE, DUTCH BOY, GIRL, BLUE, WHITE, 4 IN. TALL, PAIR..... | 8.00 |
| DELFT, GARNITURE, BLUE & WHITE, 5-PIECE, 18TH CENTURY....ILLUS..2,000.00 | |
| DELFT, GARNITURE, FAIENCE, BLUE, CHRIST CHILD, THREE JARS, PAIR BEAKERS.................................................. | 475.00 |
| DELFT, INKWELL, COVER, SAUCER.................................. | 12.00 |
| DELFT, JAR, COVERED, CIRCA 1660, JAN SICKTIS VAN DEN HOUK, 12 IN. HIGH.................................................... | 50.00 |
| DELFT, JAR, GINGER, BLUE, WHITE, DOG FINIAL ON LID, 7 3/4 IN...... | 95.00 |
| DELFT, MUG, BLUE, WHITE, SAILBOAT SCENE, FLORALS, MARK, 4 1/4 IN. HIGH.......................................... | 25.00 |
| DELFT, MUG, PUZZLE............................................. | 45.00 |
| DELFT, PITCHER, STANDING COW, BLUE, 7 IN. LONG, 5 IN. HIGH......... | 32.00 |
| DELFT, PITCHER, WATER, BULBOUS, WHITE, BLUE FLOWERS & PEACOCK, CIRCA 1919.............................................. | 35.00 |

DELFT BLUE AND WHITE GARNITURE, 18TH CENTURY

| | |
|---|---:|
| DELFT, PITCHER, WHITE, BLUE SHIP, 4 1/4 IN...................... | 12.50 |
| DELFT, PLAQUE, BLUE, WHITE, WOMAN SEWING, SAILING VESSELS IN BACKGROUND.............................................. | 225.00 |
| DELFT, PLAQUE, POLYCHROME DECORATED, 18TH CENTURY, 13 1/4 IN. HIGH.................................................... | 300.00 |
| DELFT, PLAQUE, SCENE, CANAL, FARM, WINDMILLS, MARKED ROYAL SPHINX-MAASTRICHT....................................... | 27.50 |
| DELFT, PLAQUE, WINDMILL SCENE, BLUE........................... | 15.00 |
| DELFT, PLATE, BLUE & WHITE, ALLOVER FLORAL, WIRED TO HANG, 9 IN.. | 6.50 |
| DELFT, PLATE, BLUE ON WHITE, DUTCH SCENE, RIDGWAYS, ENGLAND, SET OF 4................................................... | 24.00 |
| DELFT, PLATE, BLUE, DUTCH WINDMILL & CANAL SCENE, PIERCED, 8 IN.. | 7.50 |
| DELFT, PLATE, BLUE, ORIENTAL POPPY, CHINA, 7 1/4 IN............. | 7.50 |
| DELFT, PLATE, BLUE, WHITE, WATERFRONT SCENE IN CENTER, PIERCED IN BACK, 12 IN............................................. | 15.00 |
| DELFT, PLATE, CHOP, BLUE, SUMMER DUTCH SCENE, 15 1/2 IN.......... | 17.50 |
| DELFT, PLATE, CHOP, BLUE, WINTER DUTCH SCENE, 15 1/2 IN.......... | 17.50 |
| DELFT, PLATE, CHOP, HOLLAND SCENE, FLOW BLUE, HAND-PAINTED, MARK, 16 IN................................................... | 20.00 |
| DELFT, PLATE, DUTCH SCENE, SIGNED, 9-IN. DIAMETER............... | 35.00 |
| DELFT, PLATE, FARM SCENE, MILL SCENE, SIGNED HAASTRITCH, PAIR.... | 37.50 |

```
DELFT,PLATE,SCENES,HOUSE,BOATS,TREES,COUNTRY ROAD,MAN,WOMAN,
DELFT,PLATE,SCENE,BARN,WELL,FARM,BLUE,PIERCED,12 1/4 IN.....    21.00
  PAIR.....................................................    25.00
DELFT,PLATE,WINDMILL SCENE,ARTIST-SIGNED,17-IN.DIAMETER.....    60.00
DELFT,PLATE,WINDMILL,GERMANY,8 IN..........................    20.00
DELFT,PLATE,WINDMILL,WAGON,HORSES,URN MARK,8 IN............    20.00
DELFT,SHOE,BASKET WEAVE,SHIP,4 1/2 IN.LONG.................    25.00
DELFT,STATUETTE,CAMEL,HOLLAND..............................    15.00
DELFT,STEIN,POLYCHROME,PEWTER,DATED 1721,10 1/2 IN.HIGH.....   295.00
DELFT,TILE,CIRCA 1750......................................    15.00
DELFT,TOBY,CREAMER,MAN STANDING,5 1/2 IN.TALL...............    22.00
DELFT,TOBY,JOLLY GOOD FELLOW...............................    85.00
DELFT,TOOTHPICK,BLUE SAILBOAT,ARTIST SIGNED................     8.00
DELFT,TRAY,BOAT & CHURCH SCENES,CROSSED PIPES,FLUTED SHELL
  EDGE,GERMANY.............................................    22.50
DELFT,VASE,BLUE,WHITE,CANAL SCENES,MARKED DELFT DEC.5,06,
  9 IN.,PAIR..............................................    47.50
DELFT,VASE,BLUE,WHITE,ROCOCO SCROLLS,VIGNETTE OF LOVERS,
  15 3/4 IN.,PAIR.........................................   250.00
DELFT,VASE,BUD,BLUE,FLORAL DESIGN,SQUARE,1800,6 IN.HIGH.....    18.00
```

DERBY PORCELAIN WAS MADE IN DERBY,ENGLAND,FROM 1756
TO THE PRESENT. THE FACTORY CHANGED NAMES AND MARKS
SEVERAL TIMES. CHELSEA DERBY (1770-1784),CROWN DERBY
(1784-1811) AND THE MODERN ROYAL CROWN DERBY ARE SOME
OF THE MOST FAMOUS PERIODS OF THE FACTORY.

```
DERBY,CUP,SAUCER,BLUE,GOLD,FLORAL,WITH GOLD LEAF BOWL,
  CHELSEA,CIRCA 1745......................................   120.00
DERBY,DINNER SERVICE,IMARI PATTERN,CROWN MARK,CIRCA 1820,
  59 PIECE................................................   600.00
DERBY,FIGURINE,DIANA,ROBE,DOE,FLOWERS,SCROLLWORK BASE,1755,
  12 IN.HIGH..............................................    75.00
DERBY,FIGURINE,FALSTAFF,GOLD SHIELD,BLOOR DERBY & CROWN
  MARK,9 IN.TALL..........................................    80.00
DERBY,FIGURINE,GODDESS OF WAR,HELMET,BREASTPLATE,LION AT
  FEET,11 IN.HIGH.........................................   125.00
DERBY,FIGURINE,PSYCHE,COMPANION,CUPID,CIRCA 1780,12 IN.HIGH.   175.00
DERBY,INKSTAND,BLUE & GOLD,CIRCA 1800.......................    60.00
DERBY,JAR,PAIR,FLOWER-ENCRUSTED,COVERED,CIRCA 1760..........   500.00
DERBY,JUG,CREAM,FLARED HANDLE,FLORAL,GILT,FOOTED,RED CROWN
  MARK....................................................    28.00
DERBY,MANTEL GARNITURE,PAIR PERFUME BURNERS,URN,FLORAL,GILT,
  8 & 10 IN...............................................   110.00
DERBY,PERFUME BURNER,MONSTER MASKS,CLAW FEET,IMARI DECOR,
  LID,PAIR................................................   150.00
DERBY,SAUCER & CUP,BLOOR,CIRCA 1825,CROWN & D IN RED MARK...    40.00
DERBY,STATUETTE,FLORA,CIRCA 1760....................ILLUS..   300.00
DERBY,STATUETTE,SHEPHERDESS,CIRCA 1770.....................   175.00
DERBY,TEAPOT,RIBBED,CHINOISERIE DECOR,COVER,CIRCA 1755......   100.00
DERBY,URN,INVERTED CAMPANA FORM,FLORAL,GILT,1800,
```

DERBY FLORA STATUETTE, C. 1760

```
    6 1/2 IN.HIGH,PAIR.............................................  130.00
DERBY,VASE,FLORAL,CIRCA 1810,11 IN. HIGH,FLORAL...............  150.00
DOCTOR'S,INSTRUMENT KIT,STETHESCOPE,HYPOS,TONGS,WALNUT CASE.   40.00
DOCTOR'S,MEDICAL APPARATUS,BATTERY-OPERATED BOX THAT CURED
    ILLS,APOLLO................................................   25.00
DOLL,AFRICAN,BISQUE HEAD,BRASS HOOP EARRINGS,GRASS SKIRT,
    HEUBAC K.,9 IN.............................................  145.00
DOLL,ALEXANDRIA,PRINCESS ELIZABETH,OPEN-SHUT EYES,24 IN.....   65.00
DOLL,ALICE IN WONDERLAND,WIMER FEET,DRESSED PARIAN,14 IN....  165.00
DOLL,ARMAND MARSEILLE,BALL-JOINTED,33 IN...................   125.00
DOLL,ARMAND MARSEILLE,BALL-JOINTED,SLEEP EYES,19 IN........   45.00
DOLL,AUTOMATION,HEAD & HANDS OF FIGURE MOVE,16 IN.HIGH......  300.00
DOLL,BABY,ALL BISQUE,PRISE,7 IN...........................    60.00
DOLL,BABY,BISQUE,ARMS,LEGS MOVE,KERR & HINZ,SANTA CLARA,
    CAL.,1900,4 IN.............................................    3.50
DOLL,BABY,BISQUE,COMPOSITION BODY,ROMPER SUIT,BOOTIES,A & M
    971,19 IN.................................................   65.00
DOLL,BABY,BISQUE,NEGRO,PIGTAILS,DIAPER,4 IN................    4.50
DOLL,BABY,BISQUE HEAD,COMPOSITION BODY,DIMPLES,DOUBLE CHIN,
    3-4 MARK..................................................   95.00
DOLL,BABY,BISQUE HEAD,COMPOSITION BODY,MARKED 3-4,KESTNER,
    15 1/2 IN.................................................   85.00
DOLL,BABY,BISQUE HEAD,CURLY WIG,DRESSED,KLEY & HAHN,
    19 IN.TALL................................................   95.00
DOLL,BABY,BISQUE HEAD,HOLES IN NOSTRILS,DRESSED,GERMANY,ABG
    13 61.....................................................   68.00
DOLL,BABY,BISQUE HEAD,MOVABLE TONGUE,COMPOSITION BODY,
    DRESSED,678-BP............................................   65.00
DOLL,BABY,BISQUE HEAD,PAPIER-MACHE BODY,KNIT JUMPER SUIT,
    9 IN......................................................   32.50
DOLL,BABY,BISQUE HEAD,PAPIER-MACHE BODY,DRESSED,
    J.D.K.NO.252,11 1/2 IN....................................   85.00
DOLL,BABY,BISQUE HEAD,WILD EYEBROWS,CURLY WIG,DRESSED,KLEY &
    KAHN,19 IN................................................   95.00
DOLL,BABY,BYE-LO,DRESSED IN PINK SATIN,PINK SATIN HOLDER,
    10 IN.....................................................  125.00
DOLL,BABY,CHARACTER,ARMAND MARSEILLES,DRESSED,FUR-TRIMMED
    CAPELET,24 IN.............................................  175.00
DOLL,BABY,CHARACTER,BISQUE,COMPOSITION BODY,DRESSED,K
    R-SIMON & HALBIG..........................................   50.00
DOLL,BABY,COLORED,COMPOSITION,JOINTED AT SHOULDERS & HIPS,
    MOLDED HAIR...............................................   12.00
DOLL,BABY,COMPOSITION HEAD,ARMS,LEGS,CLOTH BODY,PAINTED
    FEATURES,17 IN............................................   35.00
DOLL,BABY,DREAM,CLOTH BODY,BISQUE HANDS,DRESSED,MARKED AM
    GERMANY,10 IN.............................................   55.00
DOLL,BABY,DREAM,TIN HEAD,BLUE SLEEP EYES,12 IN.............   17.50
DOLL,BABY,GERMAN,AM971,12 1/2 IN......................ILLUS..   75.00
DOLL,BABY,GIRL,BISQUE HEAD,PAPERWEIGHT EYES,PIERCED EARS,
    FRANCE,21 IN..............................................  275.00
DOLL,BABY,KAMMER REINHARDT,15 IN......................ILLUS..  185.00
DOLL,BABY,KESTNER,NO.257,BLUE SLEEP EYES,OPEN MOUTH,WHITE
    ORGANDY DRESS.............................................   85.00
DOLL,BABY,MOLDED HAIR,PAINTED FEATURES,CLOTH BODY,DRESSED,
    HORSMAN...................................................   10.00
DOLL,BABY,MOLDED TONGUE,BROWN SLEEP EYES,BROWN WIG,DRESSED,
    14 IN.....................................................   47.50
DOLL,BABY,NEGRO,K STAR R KAISER,16 IN.....................   395.00
DOLL,BABY,RUBBER,MOSANDRA.................................    10.00
DOLL,BABY,TIN HEAD,COMPOSITION LEGS & ARMS,OPEN & CLOSE
    EYES,13 IN................................................   21.50
```

GERMAN BABY DOLL

KAMMER REINHARDT BABY DOLL

```
DOLL,BABY BUMPS,COMPOSITION,CLOTH BODY,DRESSED,12 IN........    40.00
DOLL,BABY BUMPS,NEGRO,COMPOSITION BODY,DRESSED,12 IN........    40.00
DOLL,BABY COO BY IDEAL....................................    35.00
DOLL,BALL-TURNED SHOULDER HEAD,KID BODY,BISQUE HANDS,MARKED
   639 11...............................................   185.00
DOLL,BELTON TYPE,BISQUE HEAD,PIERCED EARS,PAPIER-MACHE BODY,
   FRANCE...............................................   195.00
DOLL,BETSY ROSS,IN CHAIR SEWING FLAG,HANDMADE..............    15.00
DOLL,BETTY BOOP,BISQUE,JAPAN,7 IN.........................     5.50
DOLL,BETTY BOOP,CELLULOID,8 IN............................     7.50
DOLL,BISQUE,BABY,CLOTH BODY,NEGRO,OPEN NOSTRILS,ARTHUR
   GERLING,19 IN.........................................   150.00
DOLL,BISQUE,BABY,MOVABLE ARMS & LEGS,DRESSED,GERMANY,
   3 1/2 IN.............................................     2.15
DOLL,BISQUE,BALL-JOINTED,DRESSED,GEORGES,GERMANY,32 IN......   125.00
DOLL,BISQUE,BLONDE WIG,SLEEP EYES,8 IN.....................    22.00
DOLL,BISQUE,BROWN EYES,DRESSED,F.G.,24 IN..................   390.00
DOLL,BISQUE,BROWN FACE,PAINTED HAIR,SHOES,SOCKS,5 IN........    12.00
DOLL,BISQUE,BUTTERFLY BONNET,OLD STONE,18 IN...............   125.00
DOLL,BISQUE,EYES OPEN & CLOSE,VELVET COSTUME,GERMANY,
   6 IN.TALL............................................    12.50
DOLL,BISQUE,LONG HAIR,UNDRESSED,MARKED RUTH GERMANY,
   4 1/4 IN.............................................     6.50
DOLL,BISQUE,PAINTED EYES,HUMAN HAIR WIG,MOLDED SHOES &
   SOCKS,DRESSED........................................    27.50
DOLL,BISQUE,SLEEPING EYES,RED HAIR,CLOTH BODY,MARKED RUTH,
   DRESSED..............................................    25.00
DOLL,BISQUE,TINTED,DRESSED,MARKED UNIS-FRANCE,16 IN........   130.00
DOLL,BISQUE,WIRE-FASTENED ARMS & LEGS,BLONDE,MARKED JAPAN,
   5 IN.................................................    12.00
DOLL,BISQUE FACE,HUMAN HAIR WIG,COMPOSITION BODY,MARSEILLES,
   27 IN................................................    85.00
DOLL,BISQUE HANDS,HEAD,LEATHER BODY,DIMPLED,SLEEP EYES,
   DRESSED,A.M..........................................    55.00
DOLL,BISQUE HEAD,BALL-JOINTED COMPOSITION BODY,HUMAN HAIR
   WIG,GERMANY..........................................    85.00
DOLL,BISQUE HEAD,BLONDE WIG,COMPOSITION BODY,MARKED
   HANDWERCK,GERMANY....................................   105.00
DOLL,BISQUE HEAD,BLUE EYES,AUBURN HAIR,DRESSED,C.M.BERGMAN
   WALTERHOUSEN.........................................    47.50
DOLL,BISQUE HEAD,BLUE SLEEP EYES,BLONDE HAIR,DRESSED,SIMON
   HALBIG,25 IN.........................................    72.50
DOLL,BISQUE HEAD,BROWN EYES,BLONDE HAIR,DRESSED,C.M.BERGMAN
   WALTERHOUSEN.........................................    47.50
DOLL,BISQUE HEAD,BROWN HUMAN HAIR LONG CURLS,COMPOSITION
   BODY,H-2 295.........................................    65.00
DOLL,BISQUE HEAD,CLOTH BODY,CELLULOID HANDS,DRESSED,
   111 MARK,12 1/2 IN...................................   150.00
DOLL,BISQUE HEAD,CLOTH BODY,DREAM BABY,MARKED A.M.341,16 IN.   150.00
DOLL,BISQUE HEAD,CLOTH BODY,PAINTED EYES,SATIN DRESS & HAT,
   14 IN................................................   150.00
DOLL,BISQUE HEAD,COMPOSITION BODY,DRESS,UNDIES,COAT,GERMANY,
   28 IN................................................   125.00
DOLL,BISQUE HEAD,COMPOSITION BODY,JOINTED,DRESSED,SIMON
   HALBIG,25 IN.........................................    95.50
DOLL,BISQUE HEAD,COMPOSITION BODY,JOINTED,SILK DRESS,
   GERMANY,24 IN........................................    65.00
DOLL,BISQUE HEAD,COMPOSITION BODY,K STAR R SIMON HALBIG,
   26 IN................................................   125.00
DOLL,BISQUE HEAD,COMPOSITION BODY,LONG CURLY WIG,AM 390,
```

```
  HOLZE MASSE..................................................    65.00
DOLL,BISQUE HEAD,COMPOSITION BODY,MOHAIR WIG,DRESSED,
  GEBRUDER KNOCH...............................................    45.00
DOLL,BISQUE HEAD,COMPOSITION BODY,ORIGINAL CLOTHES,GERMANY..    25.00
DOLL,BISQUE HEAD,COMPOSITION HANDS & LEGS,SLEEP EYES,
  HEUBACH-KOOPELSDORF..........................................    38.00
DOLL,BISQUE HEAD,COMPOSITION JOINTED BODY,KESTNER,GERMANY,
  32 IN.......................................................   130.00
DOLL,BISQUE HEAD,CORD-STRUNG ARMS,LEGS,COMPOSITION SAWDUST
  BODY,DRESSED................................................    35.00
DOLL,BISQUE HEAD,DREAM BABY,CLOTH BODY,SOLID DOME,
  CHRISTENING DRESS...........................................    55.00
DOLL,BISQUE HEAD,DREAM BABY,OPEN MOUTH,SWIVEL HEAD,
  COMPOSITION BODY............................................    65.00
DOLL,BISQUE HEAD,DRESSED,MARK BEBE GESLAND,PARIS,1860,
  20 1/2 IN...................................................   250.00
DOLL,BISQUE HEAD,GINGHAM DRESS,MARK ARMAND MARSEILLE 390N
  GERMANY,25 IN...............................................    65.00
DOLL,BISQUE HEAD,HUMAN HAIR WIG & EYELASHES,BLUE EYES,
  DRESSED,GERMANY.............................................    55.00
DOLL,BISQUE HEAD,JOINTED BODY,FLORADORA,GERMANY,UNDRESSED,
  21 IN.......................................................    40.00
DOLL,BISQUE HEAD,JOINTED BODY,HANDWERCK,PIERCED EARS,
  GERMANY,NUDE,29 IN..........................................    40.00
DOLL,BISQUE HEAD,JOINTED BODY,NEW WIG,BROWN SLEEPING EYES,
  GERMANY,20 IN...............................................    40.00
DOLL,BISQUE HEAD,JOINTED BODY,VELVET & LACE DRESS,KESTNER,
  MARK,GERMANY................................................    85.00
DOLL,BISQUE HEAD,KID BODY,BLUE EYES,OPEN MOUTH,HEUBACH,
  17 IN.......................................................    60.00
DOLL,BISQUE HEAD,KID BODY,BROWN SLEEP EYES,JAPAN,1916,18 IN.   175.00
DOLL,BISQUE HEAD,KID BODY,FRENCH TAFFETA DRESS,PARASOL,
  11 IN.......................................................   200.00
DOLL,BISQUE HEAD,MARK GERMANY HEINRICH HANDWERCK SIMON
  HALBIG,26 IN................................................    85.00
DOLL,BISQUE HEAD,MARK GERMANY HEINRICH HANDWERCK SIMON
  HALBIG,28 1/2 IN............................................    85.00
DOLL,BISQUE HEAD,OPEN MOUTH,EYES MOVE,NEW WIG,SIMON &
  HALBIG,33 IN................................................    95.00
DOLL,BISQUE HEAD,PAPERWEIGHT EYES,DRESSED,MARK TETE JUMEAU,
  18 IN.......................................................   185.00
DOLL,BISQUE HEAD,PAPERWEIGHT EYES,HUMAN HAIR WIG,DRESSED,
  J.STEINER,PARIS.............................................   395.00
DOLL,BISQUE HEAD,PAPERWEIGHT EYES,KID BODY,BRU FASHION,
  DRESSED,21 IN...............................................   425.00
DOLL,BISQUE HEAD,PAPIER-MACHE BODY,BROWN SLEEP EYES,SIMON
  HALBIG,22 IN................................................   150.00
DOLL,BISQUE HEAD,PAPIER-MACHE BODY,PAINTED SHOES,CROCHETED
  DRESS.......................................................    45.00
DOLL,BISQUE HEAD,PAPIER-MACHE BODY,SCHOENAU HOFFMEISTER,DATE
  1909,20 IN..................................................   175.00
DOLL,BISQUE HEAD,REAL HAIR WIG,CLOSED MOUTH,DRESSED,BELTON,
  FRANCE,23 IN................................................   300.00
DOLL,BISQUE HEAD,SLEEP EYES,BROWN CURLS,KID BODY,DRESSED,
  M.B.JAPAN...................................................    55.00
DOLL,BISQUE HEAD,SLEEP EYES,OPEN MOUTH,COMPOSITION BODY,
  DRESSED,971-A.M.............................................    42.00
DOLL,BISQUE HEAD,SLEEPING EYES,COMPOSITION BODY,
  BALL-JOINTED,A.MARSEILLE....................................    42.50
DOLL,BISQUE HEAD,STICK TYPE COMPOSITION BODY,MARK FRANCE DL,
  13 1/2 IN...................................................   110.00
DOLL,BISQUE HEAD,THREE FACES,PAPIER-MACHE BODY,MARKED
  C.B.CASIMIR BRU.............................................   495.00
DOLL,BISQUE HEAD,TODDLER,PAPIER-MACHE BODY,MARKED L.W.C.,
  1916,19 1/2 IN..............................................   175.00
DOLL,BISQUE HEAD,TWO TEETH,MOLDED TONGUE,IMPRESSED PM 914,
  DRESSED,16 IN...............................................    95.00
DOLL,BISQUE HEAD & ARMS,KID BODY,BLONDE WIG,DRESSED,MARKED
  H.CH.O.H....................................................    65.50
DOLL,BISQUE HEAD & ARMS,KID BODY,CLOTH LEGS,OPEN MOUTH,
  DRESSED,GERMANY.............................................    45.00
DOLL,BISQUE HEAD & HANDS,CLOTH BODY,CLOSED MOUTH,DRESSED,
  22 IN.......................................................   125.00
DOLL,BISQUE HEAD & SHOULDERS,CLOTH BODY,DRESSED,PAINTED HIGH
  TOP SHOES...................................................    65.00
DOLL,BISQUE SHOULDER HEAD,KID BODY,RED RIDING HOOD OUTFIT,
  NO.154 MARK.................................................    65.00
DOLL,BISQUE SHOULDER HEAD,KID BODY,SLEEP EYES,HUMAN HAIR
  CURLS,KESTNER...............................................    65.00
DOLL,BISQUE SHOULDER HEAD,MOLDED HAIRDO,PAINTED EYES,KID
  BODY,DRESSED................................................   105.00
```

DOLL,BISQUE SHOULDER HEAD,PIERCED EARS,BLUE PAPERWEIGHT
EYES,DRESSED............................................. 85.00
DOLL,BISQUE SHOULDER HEAD,REAL HAIR WIG,KID BODY,DRESS,
19 IN.TALL............................................. 65.00
DOLL,BISQUE SHOULDER,SWIVEL HEAD,STITCHED LEATHER HANDS,
DRESSED,18 IN.......................................... 400.00
DOLL,BISQUE SOCKET HAND,FRENCH,25 IN................ILLUS.. 595.00
DOLL,BISQUE SOCKET HEAD,BROWN GLASS EYES,OPEN MOUTH,SIMON
HALBIG,42 IN........................................... 275.00
DOLL,BISQUE SOCKET HEAD,COMPOSITION BODY,DRESSED,S STAR WITH
PB H 1909.............................................. 85.00
DOLL,BISQUE SOCKET HEAD,COMPOSITION BODY,JOINTED,VELVET
DRESS,GERMANY.......................................... 65.00
DOLL,BISQUE SOCKET HEAD,COMPOSITION BODY,SLEEP EYES,DRESSED,
PANSY IV............................................... 75.00
DOLL,BISQUE SOCKET HEAD,JOINTED BODY,HUMAN HAIR,DRESSED,
KESTNER F-10 168....................................... 85.00
DOLL,BISQUE SOCKET HEAD,JOINTED STICK BODY,MARKED S PB H,
1909,GERMANY........................................... 32.50
DOLL,BLONDE MOHAIR,EYES BULGE,TETE JUMEAU,MEDAILLE D'OR,
20 IN.................................................. 285.00
DOLL,BOY,BABY,METAL,DRESSED,MARKED,PARSON JACKSON,11 IN..... 50.00
DOLL,BOY,BISQUE HEAD,INDENTED PAINTED EYES,ROMPER SUIT,MARK
20615.................................................. 65.00
DOLL,BOY,BISQUE HEAD,JOINTED BODY,SIMON HALBIG,GERMANY,
UNDRESSED,22 IN........................................ 45.00
DOLL,BOY,BISQUE HEAD,S.F.B.J.,NO.227,SOCKET NECK,COMPOSITION
BODY,14 IN............................................. 265.00
DOLL,BOY,BISQUE SOCKET HEAD,COMPOSITION BODY,DRESSED,ANCHOR
LC,17 IN............................................... 75.00
DOLL,BOY,BLUE EYES,BLONDE HAIR,EFFANBEE.................... 7.50
DOLL,BOY,CELLULOID SHOULDER HEAD,CLOTH BODY,COMPOSITION
ARMS,DRESSED........................................... 45.00
DOLL,BOY,CHARACTER,BISQUE HEAD,INSET BLUE EYES,DRESSED,
S.F.B.J............................................... 395.00
DOLL,BOY,CHINESE,LAUGHING,PAINTED FEATURES,CLOTH BODY,
DRESSED,18 IN.......................................... 75.00
DOLL,BOY,FROM COMIC STRIP,HENRY,WHITE SHIRT,RED PANTS,BLACK
SHOES,BISQUE........................................... 7.00
DOLL,BOY,GIRL,NEGRO,CARVED WOODEN HEADS,DRESSED,1860,
18 1/2 IN.,PAIR........................................ 450.00
DOLL,BOY,GOO-GOO EYES,MOLDED HAIR,DRESSED,MARKED A. & M.324,
6 1/2 IN............................................... 135.00
DOLL,BOY,MOLDED HAIR,EYELIDS,BISQUE,WOODEN BODY,DRESSED,
S.F.B.J.226............................................ 350.00
DOLL,BOY,STICK LEG BODY,STRIPED SUIT,VELVET TRIM,HAT,ANCHOR,
L C,FRANCE............................................. 85.00
DOLL,BOY,STUFFED BODY,CELLULOID HANDS,USED FOR 1908 PAIN
ADVERTISEMENT.......................................... 45.00
DOLL,BOY,SUN RUBBER,10 IN................................. 4.00
DOLL,BOY,TODDLER,BISQUE HEAD,DRESSED,MARK K STAR R SIMON &
HALBIG................................................. 65.00
DOLL,BOY,TODDLER,BLONDE WIG,SLEEP EYES,DRESSED IN OVERALLS,
FULPER,19 IN........................................... 95.00
DOLL,BOY,TODDLER,PAINTED HAIR,BISQUE HEAD,VELVET SUIT,
KESTNER,NO.151......................................... 125.00
DOLL,BRIDE,GROOM,JAPAN MOLDED FEATURES,CLOTHES,PAIR......... 15.00
DOLL,BROWN CURLS,STUFFED BODY,REWAXED HEAD,ARMS,HANDS,
DRESSED,29 IN.......................................... 200.00

FRENCH DOLL, BISQUE SOCKET HAND

DOLL,BROWN EYES,BROWN CURLS,FRENCH CHARACTER,MARKED 116,
  16 IN........................................................ 350.00
DOLL,BROWN EYES,TETE JUMEAU,17 IN.................................. 360.00
DOLL,BROWN SLEEP EYES,OPEN MOUTH,TEETH,BLONDE WIG,DRESSED,
  C.M.BERGMANN.................................................... 135.00
DOLL,BROWN WIG,BLUE EYES,OPEN MOUTH,KID BODY,ARMAND
  MARSEILLE,20 IN................................................ 40.00
DOLL,BROWN WIG,OPEN MOUTH,TEETH,KID BODY,ARMAND MARSEILLE,
  20 IN.......................................................... 68.00
DOLL,BROWN WIG,SLEEP EYES,WOODEN BODY,ARMAND MARSEILLE,
  13 1/2 IN...................................................... 38.00
DOLL,BUBBLES,1925,EFFANBEE,22 IN................................... 10.00
DOLL,BUSTER BROWN,BISQUE,5 IN...................................... 45.00
DOLL,BUTTERCUP BY E.I.HORSMAN,22 IN................................ 40.00
DOLL,BYE-LO,ALL BISQUE,JAPAN,5 IN.................................. 25.00
DOLL,BYE-LO,ALL BISQUE,MOLDED SHOES,SOCKS,GRACE S.PUTNAM,
  20-76 COPR..................................................... 135.00
DOLL,BYE-LO,BISQUE HEAD,DRESS,COPYRIGHT GRACE S.PUTNAM,
  GERMANY,12 IN.................................................. 175.00
DOLL,BYE-LO,RUBBER,SIGNED GRACE STOREY PUTNAM...................... 30.00
DOLL,BYE-LO,WAX OVER COMPOSITION,DREAM BABY BODY,15 IN............. 50.00
DOLL,CARNIVAL,COMPOSITION,JOINTED AT SHOULDERS,HUMAN HAIR,
  11 IN.......................................................... 10.00
DOLL,CELLULOID HEAD,BLONDE HAIR,BROWN GLASS EYES,K STAR R,
  23 IN.......................................................... 80.00
DOLL,CELLULOID,BOY,GOOGLE EYES,JOINTED ARMS,SIGNED IRWIN,
  6 IN.HIGH...................................................... 6.00
DOLL,CELLULOID,JOINTED LIMBS,PAINTED EYES,DRESSED,
  7 1/2 IN.HIGH.................................................. 6.00
DOLL,CELLULOID,PAINTED FEATURES,BROWN WIG,VELVET DRESS,
  INTERNATIONAL.................................................. 12.00
DOLL,CELLULOID,SLEEPS,MOVES LIMBS,3 IN............................. 3.00
DOLL,CHINESE,WOODEN STAND,PAPIER-MACHE FACE,ELABORATE
  COSTUME,14 IN.................................................. 8.50
DOLL,CLOWN,BISQUE HEAD,WOODEN BODY,MECHANICAL,HANDS HIT
  CYMBALS,GERMANY................................................ 55.00
DOLL,CLOWN,DRESSED IN CLOWN SUIT & HAT,LIMOGES,FRANCE,
  14 1/2 IN...................................................... 110.00
DOLL,COMPOSITION BODY,BROWN EYES,PIERCED EARS,DRESSED,1907,
  JUMEAU,30 IN................................................... 225.00
DOLL,COMPOSITION HEAD,COTTON-STUFFED BODY,DRESSED,HIGH-TOP
  SHOES,1915..................................................... 35.00
DOLL,COMPOSITION,GIRL,JOINTED LIMBS,BROWN WIG,PAINTED EYES.. 4.50
DOLL,COMPOSITION,MOLDED HAIRDO,PAINTED EYES,CLOTH BODY,
  GERMANY........................................................ 12.00
DOLL,CRECHE,HAND-CARVED,WOODEN,18TH CENTURY,FRANCE............ 90.00
DOLL,DIONNE QUINTUPLETS,COMPOSITION,WIGS,DRESSED,7 IN....... 150.00
DOLL,DIONNE QUINTUPLETS,DRESSED,7 IN............................... 115.00
DOLL,DOCTOR,IVORY,CARVED,NUDE,LACQUER LAP ROBE,
  MOTHER-OF-PEARL INLAY.......................................... 200.00
DOLL,DOCTOR,IVORY,CARVED........................................... 100.00
DOLL,DOLLEY MADISON,PARIAN SHOULDER HEAD,VELVET,TAFFETA &
  LACE DRESS..................................................... 165.00
DOLL,DOLLEY MADISON,PORCELAIN HEAD,MOLDED HAIRDO,RIBBON,BOW,
  20 IN.HIGH..................................................... 145.00
DOLL,DOME HEAD,PAINTED EYES,FRENCH FASHION,MARKED NO.3,
  14 1/2 IN...................................................... 275.00
DOLL,DREAM BABY,BISQUE HEAD,COMPOSITION HANDS,GERMANY,8 IN.. 70.00
DOLL,DREAM BABY,BISQUE HEAD,DRESSED,16 IN.......................... 85.00
DOLL,DUTCH BOY & GIRL,NORAH WELLINGTON,8 IN.,PAIR.................. 14.00
DOLL,EDEN BEBE,OPEN MOUTH,FRENCH CONFIRMATION OUTFIT........ 400.00
DOLL,EDEN BEBE,PAPIER-MACHE & WOODEN BODY,PAPERWEIGHT EYES,
  DRESSED........................................................ 245.00
DOLL,EFFANBEE,WALK,TALK,SLEEP,24 IN................................ 30.00
DOLL,EMMETT KELLY,DRESSED,HAND-CARVED,WOODEN,10 IN........... 12.00
DOLL,ESKIMO,WOODEN HEAD,WOOL BODY,IVORY KNIFE AT BELT,TRADE
  BEADS,1800..................................................... 75.00
DOLL,FLAPPER,BISQUE HEAD,BALL-JOINTED,SLEEP EYES,MARKED
  SIMON HALBIG................................................... 135.00
DOLL,FLAPPER,HAND-MADE ENTIRELY OF FELT,11 IN..................... 8.00
DOLL,FROZEN CHARLOTTE,BLUE GARTERS................................. 18.00
DOLL,FROZEN CHARLOTTE,CELLULOID,1 IN............................... 2.00
DOLL,FROZEN CHARLOTTE,CELLULOID,2 IN............................... 3.00
DOLL,FROZEN CHARLOTTE,WHISTLE,2 1/4 IN............................. 4.00
DOLL,FROZEN CHARLOTTE,BISQUE,3 IN.................................. 5.00
DOLL,GENTLEMAN,GREEK,GRECIAN COSTUME,PAPIER-MACHE,10 IN..... 6.00
DOLL,GIRL,BALL-JOINT BODY,DRESSED,S.F.B.J.,LIMOGES,22 IN... 195.00
DOLL,GIRL,BALL-JOINT BODY,HUMAN HAIR WIG,DRESSED,KESTNER,
  GERMANY 146.................................................... 95.00
DOLL,GIRL,BISQUE,BLUE PINAFORE,HOLDING CAT,12 IN.............. 20.00
DOLL,GIRL,BISQUE,MOVABLE ARMS,5 IN................................ 15.00

DOLL,GIRL,BISQUE,PINK,BLONDE WIG,ARMS & LEGS MOVE,DRESSED,
  5 IN.......................................................... 10.00
DOLL,GIRL,BISQUE,S.F.B.J.,15 1/2 IN........................... 95.00
DOLL,GIRL,BISQUE HEAD,BALL-JOINTED,COMPOSITION,S.GERMANY
  3 143,10 IN................................................... 50.00
DOLL,GIRL,BISQUE HEAD,BLONDE WIG,CLOSED MOUTH,MARKED TETE
  JUMEAU,15 IN.................................................. 325.00
DOLL,GIRL,BISQUE HEAD,MARKED HANDWERCK 119-13,COMPOSITION
  BODY,27 IN.................................................... 95.00
DOLL,GIRL,BISQUE HEAD,PAPERWEIGHT EYES,JOINTED BODY,DRESSED,
  JUMEAU....................................................... 325.00
DOLL,GIRL,BISQUE HEAD,SLEEP EYES,TEETH,BALL JOINT BODY,
  DRESS,A.B.& CO................................................ 57.50
DOLL,GIRL,BISQUE SHOULDER HEAD,KID BODY,DRESSED,MARKED A.M.,
  16 IN........................................................ 195.00
DOLL,GIRL,BISQUE SHOULDER HEAD,KID BODY,SILK & VELVET DRESS,
  18 IN........................................................ 60.00
DOLL,GIRL,BISQUE SOCKET HEAD,COMPOSITION JOINTED BODY,DRESS,
  MARKED A.M................................................... 55.00
DOLL,GIRL,BISQUE SWIVEL HEAD,GLASS EYES,FUR-TRIMMED DRESS,
  KESTNER...................................................... 65.00
DOLL,GIRL,BLUE PAPERWEIGHT EYES,DRESSED,MARKED JUMEAU,32 IN. 285.00
DOLL,GIRL,BLUE PAPERWEIGHT EYES,DRESSED,MARKED JUMEAU,CIRCA
  1907,20 IN................................................... 180.00
DOLL,GIRL,BROWN HAIR & EYES,DRESSED,S.F.B.J. 230 FRANCE,
  22 IN........................................................ 175.00
DOLL,GIRL,BROWN HAIR,BALL-JOINTED BODY,BISQUE COLORING,
  GERMANY,25 IN................................................ 75.00
DOLL,GIRL,BUNNY-TYPE,BODY COVERED WITH RABBIT FUR,BISQUE
  HEAD,11 1/2 IN............................................... 45.00
DOLL,GIRL,CELLULOID HEAD & HANDS,KID BODY,K STAR R 255,
  15 IN........................................................ 45.00
DOLL,GIRL,CELLULOID,SLEEP EYES,JOINTED LIMBS,6 1/2 IN.HIGH.. 3.00
DOLL,GIRL,CHUBBY,PAPERWEIGHT EYES,WHITE DRESS,JUMEAU,
  1907 MARK,31 IN.............................................. 375.00
DOLL,GIRL,CLOTH BODY,PORCELAIN HEAD,HANDS,FEET,DRESSED,
  18 1/2 IN.TALL............................................... 47.50
DOLL,GIRL,FRENCH CHARACTER,MARKED XI,16 IN.................. 350.00
DOLL,GIRL,HAIR WIG,OPEN MOUTH,S.F.B.J.,20 IN................ 145.00
DOLL,GIRL,HUMAN HAIR,BALL-JOINTED BODY,DRESSED,PIERCED EARS,
  29 IN........................................................ 135.00
DOLL,GIRL,KID BODY,BISQUE HEAD,DRESSED,MARKED LISSY,GERMANY,
  22 IN........................................................ 55.00
DOLL,GIRL,LIMOGES,FRANCE,11 1/2 IN.......................... 70.00
DOLL,GIRL,MABLE,KID BODY,BISQUE,BLONDE WIG,DRESSED,MARK
  GERMANY,18 IN................................................ 65.00
DOLL,GIRL,MARKED F.G.,13 1/2 IN............................. 275.00
DOLL,GIRL,MOHAIR WIG,COMPOSITION HEAD,DRESSED,MARKED A NASCO
  DOLL......................................................... 20.00
DOLL,GIRL,NEGRO,BISQUE HEAD,COMPOSITION BODY,MARK 11/0,
  10 IN........................................................ 50.00
DOLL,GIRL,ORIENTAL,BLACK MOHAIR WIG,PAINTED SOCKS & SHOES,
  BISQUE HEAD.................................................. 185.00
DOLL,GIRL,PAPERWEIGHT EYES,PIERCED EARS,PAPIER-MACHE & WOOD,
  JUMEAU....................................................... 365.00
DOLL,GIRL,PAPIER-MACHE & WOOD BODY,PAPERWEIGHT EYES,DRESSED,
  TETE JUMEAU.................................................. 275.00
DOLL,GIRL,PAPIER-MACHE,SOLID DOME SHOULDER HEAD,CLOTH BODY,
  DRESSED...................................................... 55.00
DOLL,GIRL,PARIAN,GLASS SET-IN EYES,MARK 1000XX6,17 IN...... 225.00
DOLL,GIRL,PIERCED EARS,BLUE EYES,UNMARKED JUMEAU,32 IN..... 225.00
DOLL,GIRL,PORCELAIN HEAD,BLACK HAIR,CLOTH BODY,HANDMADE
  DRESS,18 IN.................................................. 50.00
DOLL,GIRL,PORCELAIN HEAD,HANDS,DRESSED,INCISED NIPPON MARK,
  14 1/2 IN.................................................... 30.00
DOLL,GIRL,PORCELAIN SHOULDER HEAD,CLOTH BODY,PIERCED EYES,
  DRESSED...................................................... 45.00
DOLL,GIRL,SCHOENHUT,BLUE EYES,TEETH,BROWN WIG,DRESSED,19 IN. 75.00
DOLL,GIRL,SLEEP EYES,LONG LASHES,BALL-JOINTED BODY,LONG
  CURLS,MARKED S&H............................................. 57.50
DOLL,GRANDMOTHER,FOR DOLL HOUSE,MOLDED HAIRDO,5 3/4 IN.TALL. 32.50
DOLL,GRAY-BLUE EYES,RED WIG,COMPOSITION BODY,BALL JOINTS,
  JUMEAU,25 IN................................................. 225.00
DOLL,HANDWERCK,EARRINGS,DRESSED,32 IN...................... 195.00
DOLL,HANDWERCK,HEINRICH,BISQUE HEAD,KID BODY,CURLY WIG,
  DRESSED,16 IN................................................ 75.00
DOLL,HAPPY FAT,3 1/2 IN.HIGH,PAIR.......................... 175.00
DOLL,HEUBACH KOPPELSDORF,BISQUE HEAD,PAPIER-MACHE BODY,
  DRESSED,9 IN................................................. 65.00
DOLL,HEUBACH,KOPPELSDORF,BISQUE HEAD,KID BODY,DRESSED,16 IN. 70.00
DOLL,HOBO,OVERALLS,SHIRT,SOFT RUBBER,SIGNED,SEIDERSPIAN,

```
1948,16 1/2 IN.......................................      35.00
DOLL,HUMAN HAIR,EYES BULGE,OPEN MOUTH,L.C.PARIS,21 IN.......    260.00
DOLL,HUMAN HAIR,OPEN MOUTH,BEBE JUMEAU,DIPLOME D'HONNEUR,
   25 IN..............................................     250.00
DOLL,INDIAN,BISQUE HEAD,PAPERWEIGHT EYES,SWIVEL HEAD,SUIT,
   HEADPIECE..........................................     150.00
DOLL,JOEL ELLIS,DRESSED..............................      225.00
DOLL,JOINTED COMPOSITION BODY,OPEN MOUTH,PIERCED EARS,
   JUMEAU,20 IN........................................     165.00
DOLL,JUMEAU FASHION,WIG,GLASS EYES,DRESSED,23 IN.........    475.00
DOLL,K STAR R,S & H,JOINTED BODY,HUMAN HAIR WIG,WHITE DRESS,
   HAT,EARRINGS........................................     135.00
DOLL,KABUKI,LION DANCER,BROCADE ROBES,SILK FACE,COVERED
   STAND,15 1/2 IN.....................................      95.00
DOLL,KESTNER NO.171,BISQUE HEAD,PAPIER-MACHE BODY,LONG CURLY
   WIG,20 IN...........................................     125.00
DOLL,KESTNER,NO.3362,OPEN MOUTH,MOLDED BISQUE TEETH,JOINTED,
   22 IN..............................................      47.50
DOLL,KID BODY,BROWN WIG,GRAY EYES,WHITE KID SHOES,
   A.M.FLORADORA,29 IN.................................      65.00
DOLL,LADY,CLOTH,WIRE,COSTUMED CIRCA 1860,HAND-PAINTED FACE,
   PARIS,9 IN..........................................      32.50
DOLL,LADY,GREEK,GRECIAN COSTUME,PAPIER-MACHE,10 IN........      6.00
DOLL,LADY,PAINTED EYES,BISQUE HEAD,BLONDE MOHAIR WIG,KID
   BODY,DRESSED........................................     145.00
DOLL,LAMA,WAX,DRESSED IN COSTUME.....................       75.00
DOLL,LENCI,DRESSED...................................       25.00
DOLL,LENCI,GIRL POUTING & LOOKING SIDEWAYS,16 IN.........      35.00
DOLL,LIMOGES,BROWN HAIR,BLUE EYES,COMPOSITION BODY,DRESSED,
   20 IN..............................................     125.00
DOLL,LIMOGES,CLOWN SUIT,HAT,14 1/2 IN..................      55.00
DOLL,LINDA WILLIAMS,14 IN............................        7.50
DOLL,MADAME HENDREN,MARKED GRACE CORRY,PAINTED FEATURES,
   DRESSED,DUTCH.......................................      35.00
DOLL,MAGGE HEAD,NEGRO WOMAN,CERAMIC BISQUE,CLOTH BODY,19 IN.   65.00
DOLL,MAMMY,BEESWAX HEAD,VARGA,DRESSED IN SLAVE OUTFIT,CAPE,
   HOOD...............................................     150.00
DOLL,MAN,BISQUE HEAD,COMPOSITION BODY,MARK D.F.B,12 IN.....     55.00
DOLL,MAN,BISQUE HEAD,WIG,MUSTACHE,SUIT,WATCH,DERBY,SFBJ
   NO.60,24 IN.........................................     150.00
DOLL,MARGOT,DRESSED IN UNDERCLOTHES,MME.ALEXANDER,10 IN.....     14.00
DOLL,MECHANICAL,JESTER,BISQUE HEAD,HANDS PLAY SYMBOLS,
   10/0 MARK,14 IN.....................................      65.00
DOLL,MECHANICAL,KEY WIND,BISQUE HEAD TURNS,PAPIER-MACHE
   BODY,STEINER........................................     345.00
DOLL,MECHANICAL,TURNS HEAD,CRIES,WAVES ARMS,JUMEAU,24 IN....    175.00
DOLL,MICKEY MOUSE,RUBBER,10 IN.......................        7.00
DOLL,MINERVA,MOLDED FACE & HAIR,HAIR-STUFFED BODY,GERMANY,
   10 IN..............................................      22.50
DOLL,MINERVA,TIN HEAD,HUMAN HAIR WIG,PAPERWEIGHT EYES,
   GERMAMY,18 IN.......................................      37.50
DOLL,MINERVA,TIN HEAD,MOLDED HAIR,KID HANDS,HAIR-STUFFED
   BODY,26 IN..........................................      47.50
DOLL,MOLDED WAX,CURVED ARMS & LEGS,GLASS EYES,IN CRADLE,
   21 IN.LONG..........................................     500.00
DOLL,MUSICAL,STICK,BISQUE HEAD,BLUE EYES,BLONDE WIG,COSTUME,
   POUPARD.............................................      80.00
DOLL,NEGRO,FUR WIG,JOINTED BODY,PIERCED EARS,SIMON & HALBIG,
   1078,9 IN...........................................      65.00
DOLL,NEGRO,HUEBACH,8 1/2 IN.HIGH.....................      115.00
DOLL,OBLONG BROWN EYES,HUMAN HAIR,DRESSED,KESTNER,42 IN.....    495.00
DOLL,OILCLOTH,STUFFED HEAD & SHOULDERS...............        8.00
DOLL,OPEN MOUTH,DRESSED,S.F.B.J......................      180.00
DOLL,OPEN MOUTH,PORCELAIN TEETH,WIG,EARRINGS,DRESSED,A9T,
   21 IN..............................................     975.00
DOLL,OPEN MOUTH,WIG,BROWN EYES,DRESSED,TETE JUMEAU,28 IN....    290.00
DOLL,ORPHAN ANNIE,HEAVY OILCLOTH.....................        7.00
DOLL,PAPIER-MACHE & PLASTER HEAD,MOHAIR WIG,STRAW-FILLED
   BODY,DRESSED........................................      35.00
DOLL,PAPIER-MACHE HEAD,BLONDE MOLDED CURLS,PAINTED EYES,
   DRESSED,25 IN.......................................     150.00
DOLL,PAPIER-MACHE HEAD,BULGING EYES,COMPOSITION ARMS,LEGS,
   10 IN..............................................      35.00
DOLL,PAPIER-MACHE HEAD,BULGING GLASS EYES,STUFFED BODY,
   DRESSED,10 IN.......................................      45.00
DOLL,PAPIER-MACHE SHOULDERS,HEAD,CLOTH BODY,STRAW-STUFFED,
   COIN NECKLACE.......................................      65.00
DOLL,PAPIER-MACHE,GOLDEN SILK HAIR,MOURNING OUTFIT,CIRCA
   1850,10 IN..........................................     100.00
DOLL,PAPIER-MACHE,MOLDED HAIR,BLACK EYES,12 IN.HIGH.........     87.50
DOLL,PAPIER-MACHE,STRAW-FILLED BODY;WIG,PINK DRESS & BONNET,
```

15 IN.......................................................... 35.00
DOLL,PAPIER-MACHE SHOULDERS,HEAD,CLOTH BODY,STRAW-STUFFED,
COIN NECKLACE................................................. 65.00
DOLL,PARIAN HEAD,BLONDE,3 IN................................... 22.50
DOLL,PATRICIA,DRESSED,EFFANBEE,14 IN........................... 15.50
DOLL,PATSY-ANN,EFFANBEE,NOT DRESSED,20 IN...................... 24.00
DOLL,PENNY-WOODEN,HAND PAINTED,12 IN........................... 2.50
DOLL,PINCUSHION,BISQUE,REAL HAIR WIG,ARMS JOINTED AT
SHOULDERS,GERMANY............................................. 20.00
DOLL,PINCUSHION,BLONDE MOLDED HAIR,LAVENDER FABRIC DRESS,
HANDS HELD UP................................................. 15.00
DOLL,PORCELAIN FACE,BROWN EYES,KID BODY,HAIR WIG,DRESSED,
1909,13 1/2 IN................................................ 75.00
DOLL,PORCELAIN HEAD,ARMS,LEGS,STUFFED BODY,BLACK HAIR,
GERMANY,5 IN.................................................. 12.50
DOLL,PORCELAIN HEAD,DRESSED,BLONDE WIG,21 IN.TALL.............. 78.00
DOLL,PORCELAIN HEAD,KID BODY,CLOTH LEGS,OPEN MOUTH,DRESSED,
11 IN......................................................... 48.00
DOLL,PORCELAIN HEAD,KID BODY,DRESSED,HURET,FRANCE,18 IN....... 550.00
DOLL,PORCELAIN SHOULDER HEAD,CLOTH BODY,BLONDE CURLS,
DRESSED,11 1/2 IN............................................. 135.00
DOLL,PORCELAIN,OPEN MOUTH,LIMBACH,GERMANY...................... 180.00
DOLL,POURED WAX,BLONDE MOHAIR,COBALT EYES,PIERCED EARS,
DRESSED,1850.................................................. 75.00
DOLL,PRINCESS ELIZABETH,MARKED,15 IN........................... 15.00
DOLL,PRINCESS,JAPANESE,BROCADED COSTUME,FRAMED GLASS CASE,
21 IN......................................................... 200.00
DOLL,PRISCILLA ALDEN,JOHN,ARTIST MUR BRUYERE,PAIR............. 95.00
DOLL,QUEEN LOUISE,BLUE EYES,BLACK HUMAN HAIR WIG,BALL JOINT
BODY,DRESSED.................................................. 65.00
DOLL,RAG,ADVERTISING BLUE RIBBON MALT EXTRACT,COLORFUL LENA. 15.00
DOLL,ROYAL KESTNER,BLONDE WIG,BLUE EYES,KID BODY,DRESSED,
25 IN......................................................... 110.00
DOLL,RUBBER,BABEE-BEE,SUN...................................... 2.50
DOLL,RUBBER,GERBER............................................. 6.00
DOLL,RUBBER,RUTH NEWTON,8 IN................................... 3.50
DOLL,RUBBER,SO-WEE,SUN......................................... 2.50
DOLL,RUBBER,TOD-L-DEE,SUN...................................... 2.50
DOLL,SANTA CLAUS,COMPOSITION FACE & HANDS,PAPIER-MACHE,
OCCUPIED JAPAN................................................ 12.00
DOLL,SCARLETT O'HARA,BLUE TAFFETA OUTFIT,MME.ALEXANDER,
18 IN......................................................... 25.00
DOLL,SEATED,POTTERY,JAPAN,8 IN.HIGH............................ 100.00
DOLL,SHIRLEY TEMPLE,COMPOSITION,BLUE-FLOWERED DRESS,UNDIES,
SHOES,14 IN................................................... 75.00
DOLL,SHIRLEY TEMPLE,COMPOSITION,11 1/2 IN...................... 22.00
DOLL,SHIRLEY TEMPLE,DRESSED IN UNDERCLOTHES,IDEAL,12 IN....... 15.00
DOLL,SHIRLEY TEMPLE,IDEAL,11 IN................................ 20.00
DOLL,SHIRLEY TEMPLE,IDEAL,14 IN................................ 30.00
DOLL,SHIRLEY TEMPLE,SLEEP EYES................................. 55.00
DOLL,SHIRLEY TEMPLE,21 IN...................................... 35.00
DOLL,SIMON & HALBIG,BRAIDED BLONDE HAIR,SLEEPING EYES,29 IN. 150.00
DOLL,SIMON HALBIG,DRESSED IN VELVET & ERMINE,33 IN........... 250.00
DOLL,SMILING,DIMPLES,MARKED BEBE JUMEAU DIPLOME D'HONNEUR
224,13 IN.................................................... 350.00
DOLL,STEINER,CLOSED MOUTH,MARKED HEAD & BODY.................. 460.00
DOLL,STEINER,OPEN MOUTH,PIERCED EARS,FRANCE................... 375.00
DOLL,STOCKINET,BLONDE,DRESSED,MARKED CHASE,LABEL,16 IN....... 60.00
DOLL,SWISS COSTUME,GLASS SLEEP EYES,ORIGINAL DRESS,12 IN..... 15.00
DOLL,SWIVEL HEAD,KID BODY & HANDS,SILK SKIRT,VELVET TOP,
FRANCE,13 IN.................................................. 300.00
DOLL,TERRI LEE,DARK HAIR,DRESSED,16 IN......................... 11.50
DOLL,TERRI LEE,UNDRESSED,16 IN................................. 12.95
DOLL,TETE JUMEAU,HUMAN HAIR WIG,PIERCED EARS,PAPERWEIGHT
EYES.......................................................... 450.00
DOLL,TETE JUMEAU,OPEN MOUTH,PINK & WHITE EYELET OUTFIT,
SIGNED........................................................ 325.00
DOLL,THEODORA GEARHART,BLACK HAIR,CUSTOM-DRESSED,17 IN....... 85.00
DOLL,TIN FACE,ENAMELED,STUFFED KID BODY,DRESSED,SILK DRESS,
17 1/2 IN..................................................... 65.00
DOLL,TIN HEAD,MINERVA,MOLDED HAIR,HAIR-STUFFED,NUDE,GERMANY,
10 IN......................................................... 22.00
DOLL,TIN HEAD,MINERVA,MOLDED HAIR,KID HANDS,HAIR-STUFFED,
GERMANY,26 IN................................................. 50.00
DOLL,TIN SHOULDER HEAD,BLUE PAINTED EYES,MOLDED HAIR,CLOTH
BODY,DRESSED.................................................. 22.00
DOLL,TIN SHOULDER HEAD,MARKED K & W NICAPUT,GERMANY,DRESSED,
17 IN......................................................... 55.00
DOLL,TODDLER,AFRICAN,BISQUE HEAD,EARRINGS,GRASS SKIRT,
HEUBACH,10 IN................................................. 145.00
DOLL,TODDLER,BALL-JOINTED BODY,PARTY DRESS & HAT,GERMANY,

22 IN.................................................... 125.00
DOLL,TODDLER,BISQUE HEAD,BLONDE WIG,EYES MOVE,SIMON &
  HALBIG,27 IN........................................... 125.00
DOLL,TODDLER,BISQUE HEAD,PAPERWEIGHT EYES,MOLDED TEETH,WIG,
  FRANCE,14 IN........................................... 22.50
DOLL,TODDLER,BLONDE HAIR,BROWN EYES,P.M. 914,17 IN........ 75.00
DOLL,TODDLER,BOY,MOLDED HAIRLINE,F-1 MARK ON NECK,NUDE,
  FRANCE,10 IN........................................... 85.00
DOLL,TODDLER,COMPOSITION HEAD,SLEEP EYES,MOLDED HAIR,CLOTH
  BODY,DRESSED........................................... 15.00
DOLL,TODDLER,HERMANN STEINER,SLEEP EYES,HUMAN HAIR WIG,
  20 IN.................................................. 75.00
DOLL,TODDLER,INCISED GRETE,SLEEP EYES,HUMAN HAIR,16 IN...... 75.00
DOLL,TODDLER,LAUGHING,CLOSED MOUTH,BLUE SLEEP EYES,DRESSED,
  JUMEAU................................................. 250.00
DOLL,TODDLER,S.F.B.J.,NO.251,JOINTED BODY,BISQUE TONGUE &
  TEETH,20 IN............................................ 155.00
DOLL,TODDLER,SLEEPING EYES,GEBRUDER HEUBACH,13 IN.......... 50.00
DOLL,TODDLER,TIN HEAD,COMPOSITION BODY,MARK K & W NICAPUT
  42 GERMANY............................................. 35.00
DOLL,TURNED SHOULDER HEAD,KID BODY,BISQUE HANDS,MARKED O,
  GERMANY................................................ 125.00
DOLL,WALKING,PIERCED EARS,LONG CURL WIG,NUDE,TETE JUMEAU,
  15 1/2 IN.............................................. 395.00
DOLL,WALKING,TETE JUMEAU,HUMAN HAIR WIG,CLOSED MOUTH,NUDE,
  15 1/2 IN.............................................. 395.00
DOLL,WAX HEAD,BUST,LIMBS,CLOTH-STUFFED BODY,DRESSED,FRANCE,
  14 IN.................................................. 89.50
DOLL,WENDY,BLONDE HAIR,DRESSED IN PANTIES,MME.ALEXANDER,
  8 IN................................................... 10.50
DOLL,WINKIE,LABEL SAYS WINKIE COPYRIGHT 1919 BY MAX MERTEN,
  16 1/2 IN.............................................. 10.00
DOLL,WOODEN-JOINTED,LABEL ON CHEST READS JOY,COPYRIGHT,
  J.L.KALLUS,11 IN....................................... 35.00
DOORKNOB,PAPERWEIGHT,MILLEFIORI,CANES,CENTER PINK FLORETTE,
  1 13/16 IN............................................. 40.00
DOORKNOB,PAPERWEIGHT,ST.LOUIS,FLORAL,2 1/16 & 2 3/16 IN.,
  PAIR...............................................1,000.00
DOORKNOB,PAPERWEIGHT,ST.LOUIS,MILLEFIORI,POMPON,CANES,
  1 3/4-IN.DIAMETER...................................... 180.00
DOORSTOP,SEE IRON,DOORSTOP


    DOUGHTY BIRDS WERE MADE BY DOROTHY DOUGHTY FOR THE
    ROYAL WORCESTER PORCELAIN COMPANY OF ENGLAND FROM
    1936 TO 1962. THEY HAVE BECOME VERY COLLECTIBLE.
DOUGHTY,BLUEBIRD,MOUNTAIN,SPLEENWORT NIGER,9 1/4 &
  9 1/2 IN.,PAIR.....................................1,500.00
DOUGHTY,CARDINAL,COCK,VIRGINIAN,ORANGE-RED,ORANGE BLOSSOMS,
  11 1/2 IN..........................................1,250.00
DOUGHTY,CARDINAL,VIRGINIAN,ORANGE BLOSSOMS,11 1/2 IN.HIGH,
  PAIR...............................................3,750.00
DOUGHTY,CHIFFCHAFF AMID FLOWERING COW PARSLEY,REPAIRED,
  17 IN.HIGH............................................. 650.00
DOUGHTY,CHIFFCHAFF,FLOWERING COW PARSLEY & HOGWEED,
  17 IN.HIGH.........................................1,000.00
DOUGHTY,FLYCATCHER,SCISSOR TAIL,BISQUE,ROYAL WORCESTER MARK,
  24 IN.HIGH............................................. 500.00
DOUGHTY,FLYCATCHER,SCISSOR TAIL,TWO IN FLIGHT,BISQUE,
  24 IN.HIGH............................................. 450.00
DOUGHTY,GNATCATCHER,BLUE-GRAY,WHITE DOGWOOD,WOOD PLINTH,
  11 1/2 IN.,PAIR....................................2,200.00
DOUGHTY,GOLDFINCH,THISTLE,M.ALEX DICKENS,6 1/2 IN.,PAIR.....3,000.00
DOUGHTY,HUMMINGBIRD,RUBYTHROAT,FUCHSIA BLOSSOM,10 3/4 &
  11 1/2 IN.,PAIR....................................2,100.00
DOUGHTY,KINGLET,GOLDEN CROWN,NOBLE PINE,7 1/2 IN.HIGH,PAIR..2,000.00
DOUGHTY,LAZULI BUNTING,CHOKE CHERRY,WOODEN STAND,10 IN.HIGH,
  PAIR...............................................1,750.00
DOUGHTY,MYRTLE WARBLER,WEEPING CHERRY,9 1/4 IN.,PAIR........1,600.00
DOUGHTY,OWL,ELF,BLUE-GRAY,WHITE,SAGUARO,WOODEN PLINTH,
  11 IN.HIGH.........................................2,250.00
DOUGHTY,PARULA WARBLER,SWEET BAY,8 1/4 & 9 IN.,PAIR........2,200.00
DOUGHTY,PHOEBE,FLAME VINE,WOODEN PLINTH,9 3/4 IN.HIGH,PAIR..3,250.00
DOUGHTY,REDSTART,AMERICAN,IN HEMLOCK,7 1/2 & 8 1/2 IN.,PAIR.3,500.00
DOUGHTY,TANAGER,SCARLET,WHITE OAK SPRAYS,11 1/4 & 12 IN.,
  PAIR...............................................2,000.00
DOUGHTY,WARBLER,CERULEAN,RED MAPLE,WOODEN PLINTH,
  8 1/2 IN.HIGH,PAIR.................................2,500.00
DOUGHTY,WREN,CANYON,WILD LUPIN,WOODEN PLINTH,6 & 7 1/2 IN.,
  PAIR...............................................1,500.00
DOUGHTY,WREN,PRICKLY PEAR CACTUS,10 1/2 IN.,PAIR.....ILLUS..2,000.00

DOUGHTY, PRICKLY PEAR CACTUS, WRENS

```
DOUGHTY,YELLOWTHROAT,WATER HYACINTHS,11 1/4 & 12 1/4 IN.,
   PAIR.................................................2,100.00


      DOULTON POTTERY AND PORCELAIN WERE MADE BY DOULTON AND
         CO. OF BURSLEM,ENGLAND AFTER 1882. THE NAME ROYAL
         DOULTON APPEARED ON THEIR WARES AFTER 1902.
      DOULTON,SEE ALSO,ROYAL DOULTON
DOULTON,BOTTLE,INK,BROWN SLIPWARE FINISH,LAMBERT............    12.00
DOULTON,BOTTLE,OLD CROW....................................    80.00
DOULTON,BOWL,LILIES,BLUE,PINK,GOLD TRIM,ARTIST-SIGNED,
   BURSLEM.................................................    65.00
DOULTON,BOWL,WATTEAU PATTERN,FLOW BLUE,14 1/4 IN. X
   6 1/2 IN................................................    60.00
DOULTON,CHOCOLATE POT,BROWN,GOLD,BLUE,HENNA FLORAL,MARK WITH
   ASTERISK................................................    27.50
DOULTON,EWER,DARK BLUE SCROLLS,FLORAL DECOR,GILT,BURSLEM,
   8 IN.,PAIR..............................................    45.00
DOULTON,FOOTWARMER,TAN & BROWN STONEWARE,SATCHEL-SHAPED,
   LAMBETH.................................................    15.00
DOULTON,JAR,BISCUIT,BUFF GROUND,COW DECOR,ARTIST HANNAH
   BARLOW,1880.............................................   150.00
DOULTON,JAR,BISCUIT,GOLD ON CREAM COLOR,SILVER BAIL & COVER,
   BURSLEM.................................................    75.00
DOULTON,JAR,TAN,GREEN,BLUE FLORAL,IMPRESSED LAMBETH & NUMBER   12.00
DOULTON,JAR,TOBACCO,ALLOVER LEAF DECOR,TAN,GRAY,NATURAL
   FOLIAGE WARE............................................    43.00
DOULTON,JAR,TOBACCO,BROWN & TAN,DICKENSWARE,MARK...........    35.00
DOULTON,JARDINIERE,TAN,GRAY,BLUE,STONEWARE................   125.00
DOULTON,JUG,BLUE BODY,BROWN RIM & NECK,FLORAL,BEADING,SIGNED
   M.R. 1891...............................................    30.00
DOULTON,JUG,FOOL-THE-EYE,SEAMS,RIVETS,COPPER,8 1/2 IN.HIGH..   58.00
DOULTON,JUG,FOOL-THE-EYE,SEAMS,RIVETS,COPPER,7 IN.HIGH......   40.00
DOULTON,JUG,TAN,BROWN,RELIEF PATTERN OF WHITE FLORAL,
   5 1/2 IN.HIGH...........................................    30.00
DOULTON,MUG,DARK & LIGHT BROWN,THOSE WHO HAVE MONEY ARE
   TROUBLED................................................    25.00
DOULTON,MUG,SOUVENIR,LEWIS W.F.CAREY,JULY 2,1893,GREEN,BROWN
   EMBLEM..................................................    20.00
DOULTON,MUG,THE TRAPPER...................................    22.00
DOULTON,MUSTARD POT,BLUE,BROWN,1881.......................    36.00
DOULTON,PITCHER,BROWN TRANSFER PORTRAITS OF QUEEN VICTORIA,
   1847-1897...............................................    45.00
DOULTON,PITCHER,COMMEMORATION,CHARLES REX,1646,STONEWARE,
   LAMBETH,1830............................................   150.00
DOULTON,PITCHER,COMMEMORATIVE,S.AFRICA,1900,LORD ROBERTS,
   ANIMALS.................................................    47.50
DOULTON,PITCHER,HIGH RELIEF HUNTING FIGURES,TAN,BROWN,
   LAMBERT.................................................    35.00
DOULTON,PITCHER,HUNTING SCENE,BROWN TO TAN,LAMBETH,
   5 1/4 IN.HIGH...........................................    25.00
DOULTON,PITCHER,HUNTING SCENES,BROWN & TAN,BULBOUS,LAMBETH,
```

```
   6 IN.HIGH..............................................    20.00
DOULTON,PITCHER,ISTHMIAN GAMES,FLOW BLUE,BURSLEM,6 1/2 IN...    50.00
DOULTON,PITCHER,RIBBED DESIGN ON LOWER PART,GREEN BAND WITH
   FISH,SEAWEED..........................................     22.00
DOULTON,PITCHER,TAVERN SCENE IN HIGH RELIEF,BROWN,LAMBERT,
   4 1/2 IN.TALL.........................................     20.00
DOULTON,PITCHER,TAVERN SCENE IN HIGH RELIEF,BROWN,LAMBERT,
   5 1/2 IN.TALL.........................................     22.00
DOULTON,PLATE,PASTEL PINK,GOLD POPPIES,CIRCA 1880,9 IN.....    18.50
DOULTON,PLATE,WINDMILL MOTIF,BURSLEM,10 1/2 IN.DIAMETER.....    17.50
DOULTON,VASE,BLUE,GREEN,TAN,PURPLE FLORAL,FLARED,8 IN. TALL.   18.50
DOULTON,VASE,BROWN,BLUE,GRAY,ARTIST MARGARET AITKEN,1878,
   3 1/4 IN.,PAIR........................................     47.50
DOULTON,VASE,HAND-PAINTED,LADY IN GRECIAN GOWN,PLAYS FLUTE,
   11 1/2 IN.............................................     65.00
DOULTON,VASE,LAMBETH,GREEN,YELLOW,MARKED,11 3/4 IN..........    31.50
DOULTON,VASE,MOTTLED BLUE & GREEN,BLUE LINING,LAMBETH,
   ENGLAND,PAIR..........................................     29.50


      DRESDEN CHINA IS ANY CHINA MADE IN THE TOWN OF DRESDEN,
      GERMANY. THE MOST FAMOUS FACTORY IN DRESDEN IS THE
      MEISSEN FACTORY.
   DRESDEN,SEE ALSO,MEISSEN
DRESDEN,BOWL,FLOWERS,HAND-PAINTED,SCALLOPED RIM,
   8 1/2 IN.SQUARE.......................................     48.00
DRESDEN,BOWL,OPEN LATTICEWORK,APPLIED ROSES,OBLONG,
   9 IN.LONG,6 IN.WIDE...................................     55.00
DRESDEN,BOWL,PIERCED EDGE,FLORAL,OPEN HANDLES,OVAL,12 IN....    27.50
DRESDEN,BOWL,RED & PURPLE FLOWERS,GILT,RETICULATED SIDES,
   BAVARIA,8 IN..........................................     25.00
DRESDEN,BOWL,RED,YELLOW,PURPLE BUDS,GILT,ROPE PORCELAIN
   HANDLES,MEISSEN.......................................     35.00
DRESDEN,BOX,PATCH,FLORAL INSIDE & OUTSIDE,SILVER MOUNTS,
   1 1/2 X 1 IN..........................................     55.00
DRESDEN,BOX,SCENE,FORGET-ME-NOTS,SCENE INSIDE LID,ORMOLU
   TRIM,5 IN.WIDE........................................     45.00
DRESDEN,BOX,WHITE BIRD,WINGS SPREAD,GOLD & WHITE FLORAL,
   OVAL,COVER............................................     98.50
DRESDEN,BUST,SET OF 4 CHILDREN,9 IN. HIGH..............    375.00
DRESDEN,CANDLESTICK,CIRCA 1727,5 1/2 IN.TALL,PAIR......    150.00
DRESDEN,CHOCOLATE POT,AQUA,GOLD,FIVE CUPS,SAUCERS,PINK,AQUA,
   YELLOW,BLUE...........................................    175.00
DRESDEN,CHOCOLATE POT,COBALT,GOLD BORDER,MINIATURES AROUND
   CENTER................................................    225.00
DRESDEN,CHOCOLATE POT,FIVE CUPS,SAUCERS,DIFFERENT COLORS,
   FLORALS,GOLD..........................................    200.00
DRESDEN,CHOCOLATE POT,MULTICOLORED FLORAL,SCHUMAN,
   10 1/2 IN.HIGH........................................     25.00
DRESDEN,CHOCOLATE POT,TWO PORTRAITS,PAINTED AT MON BIJOU,
   SAXONY ELECTOR........................................     95.00
DRESDEN,COFFEEPOT,FLORAL PATTERN,SCHUMAN,11 IN.............    45.00
DRESDEN,COMPOTE,PAIR,RETICULATED,10 1/2 IN. HIGH...........    500.00
DRESDEN,COOLER,FRUIT,PAIR,8 IN. HIGH,CROSSED SWORDS MARK....   375.00
DRESDEN,CUP & SAUCER,ALLOVER FLORAL........................    27.50
DRESDEN,CUP,EGG,WHITE,BLUE FLOWERS,ATTACHED SAUCER.........    12.00
DRESDEN,DISH,BUTTER,FORGET-ME-NOTS,COVER,SCHUMAN..........    12.50
DRESDEN,FIGURINE,COACH,HORSES,DRIVER,LADY,FOOTMAN,16 IN.LONG   125.00
DRESDEN,FIGURINE,TAILOR RIDING RAM,FLORAL RELIEF BASE,1895,
   6 X 8 1/2 IN..........................................     85.00
DRESDEN,MIRROR,BLUE,PINK,WHITE,FLOWERS IN RELIEF,PORCELAIN..    75.00
DRESDEN,NAPKIN RING,FLORAL.................................     8.00
DRESDEN,PATCH BOX..........................................    25.00
DRESDEN,PITCHER,GRAPE PATTERN,SIX HANDLED MUGS.............    55.00
DRESDEN,PLACE-CARD HOLDER,FLAT,FLORAL BORDER,SPACE IN CENTER
   FOR NAME,12...........................................     60.00
DRESDEN,PLATE,BREAD & BUTTER,PANELED,SET OF 11 IN VARIOUS
   COLORS................................................    137.50
DRESDEN,PLATE,CAKE,FLORAL CENTER,LATTICE DECOR,GILT,
   18 SERVING PLATES.....................................    160.00
DRESDEN,PLATE,CAKE,PINK ROSES,BLUE FORGET-ME-NOTS,GOLD EDGE,
   HANDLES...............................................     12.00
DRESDEN,PLATE,CHIEF WOLF ROBE IN CENTER,SAYS HIGGANUM TRIBE,
   RUST BORDER...........................................     22.50
DRESDEN,PLATE,DEEP,RIBBED,BLUE DECOR,VILLEROY & BOCH,SET OF
   2.....................................................     10.00
DRESDEN,PLATE,FLORAL CENTER,NOSEGAYS,LATTICE BORDER,
   SCHUMAN BAVARIA,6.....................................     60.00
DRESDEN,PLATE,FLOWER LATTICE BORDER,MARKED,8 1/2 IN.........    50.00
DRESDEN,PLATE,FLOWER MOTIF,OPENWORK,BAVARIA SCHUMAN MARK,
   PAIR..................................................     20.00
```

```
DRESDEN,PLATE,PICTORIAL,SAILING CLOSE,GOLD BORDER,6 3/4 IN..      5.50
DRESDEN,PLATE,PICTORIAL,SIGNS OF A THAW,GOLD BORDER,
  PRATTSVILLE,N.Y.........................................         5.50
DRESDEN,SHOE,WHITE GROUND,LOVERS,WOODED AREA,GOLD,7 IN......     22.50
DRESDEN,TEA CADDY,ALLOVER FLORAL,GOLD,BLUE CROWN UNDER GLAZE     25.00
DRESDEN,TEA CADDY,HAND-PAINTED FLORAL,RK MARK..............      38.00
DRESDEN,TEAPOT,CHILD'S,CREAMER,SUGAR,FOUR CUPS,SAUCERS,
  PLATES,FLORAL..........................................        28.00
DRESDEN,URN,SCENES,MEN IN BATTLE,ARTIST HELEN WOLFSHOLM,
  14 1/2 IN.,PAIR........................................       595.00
DRESDEN,URN,YELLOW,GOLD,SCENE ON UPPER PORTION,4 IN.HIGH,
  PAIR...................................................       150.00
DRESDEN,VASE,PAINTED BIRD OF PARADISE,SIGNED,5 1/2 IN.HIGH..     35.00
DRESDEN,VASE,PORTRAIT,OVERLAY GOLD DECOR,TWO GOLD EARS,
  9 IN.HIGH..............................................       125.00
```

```
        DURAND GLASS WAS MADE BY VICTOR DURAND FROM 1879 TO
        1935 AT SEVERAL FACTORIES. MOST OF THE IRIDESCENT
        DURAND GLASS WAS MADE BY VICTOR DURAND,JR.,FROM 1912
        TO 1924 AT THE DURAND ART GLASS WORKS IN VINELAND,NEW
        JERSEY.
DURAND,BOWL,BLUE,SCALLOP,LABEL,VINELAND FLINT GLASS WORKS,
  NO.12 TUT BLUE.........................................       125.00
DURAND,BOWL,IRIDIZED GOLD & SILVER,STRETCHED,UNDULATING
  BORDER,SIGNED..........................................       220.00
DURAND,CHAMPAGNE,LAVENDER,ACID ETCH,ALLOVER LEAVES &
  BERRIES,PAIR...........................................        46.50
DURAND,COMPOTE,BLUE,FEATHER PATTERN,AMBER BASE,1 1/4 IN. X
  6 1/4 IN...............................................       150.00
DURAND,COMPOTE,BLUE,WHITE FEATHER PATTERN,AMBER BASE,6 X
  1 1/4 IN.HIGH..........................................       165.00
DURAND,COMPOTE,FEATHER PATTERN,BLUE,WHITE DECOR,AMBER BASE..    165.00
DURAND,DECANTER,CAPTAIN'S,BLUE IRIDESCENT,JUG SHAPE,SIGNED,
  6 IN.HIGH..............................................       495.00
DURAND,LAMP,BLUE WITH SILVER THREADING,WHITE SILK SHADE,
  12 IN..................................................       150.00
DURAND,PLATE,COBALT OVER CLEAR,PEACOCK FEATHER DESIGN,CUT
  FLOWERS,8 IN...........................................       185.00
DURAND,PLATE,PINK & WHITE FEATHER CENTER,CUT BORDER,
  CRANBERRY,8 IN.........................................       160.00
DURAND,SHADE,GAS,GOLD THREADING,GREEN HEARTS,GOLD COLOR
  CALCITE INSIDE.........................................        28.00
DURAND,SHADE,GAS,WHITE GROUND,GOLD & GREEN HEARTS,CALCITE
  INTERIOR...............................................        31.50
DURAND,SHADE,GAS,WHITE,GOLD & GREEN HEARTS,CALCITE INTERIOR.     31.50
DURAND,VASE,BLUE,PEDESTAL BASE,SIGNED,9 1/4 IN.HIGH,PAIR....    650.00
DURAND,VASE,BLUE,WHITE MARBLE-LIKE SWIRLS FROM TOP TO BOTTOM    175.00
DURAND,VASE,GOLD IRIDESCENT BASE,GREEN OVERLAY,PINK
  HIGHLIGHTS,9 3/4 IN....................................       225.00
DURAND,VASE,GOLDEN ORANGE IRIDESCENT,SILVER & BLUE
  HIGHLIGHTS,4 IN........................................       125.00
DURAND,VASE,GOLDEN-ORANGE IRIDESCENT,SILVER & BLUE
  HIGHLIGHTS,4 IN.HIGH...................................       125.00
DURAND,VASE,GREEN GROUND,SILVER IRIDESCENT PANELS,VERTICAL
  RIVULETS...............................................       500.00
DURAND,VASE,IRIDESCENT GREEN,PITTED IN IRREGULAR DESIGN,
  SIGNED,10 IN...........................................       300.00
DURAND,VASE,KING TUT PATTERN,PINK SWIRLS,LOOPS,GREEN-BLUE
  GROUND,8 IN............................................       225.00
DURAND,VASE,KING TUT,BLUE,SILVER IRIDESCENT,6 1/4 IN.HIGH...    250.00
DURAND,VASE,ORANGE GROUND,IRIDESCENT,GREEN LEAVES,VEINS,
  6 1/2 IN.TALL..........................................       350.00
DURAND,VASE,ORANGE,IRIDESCENT,BLUE HIGHLIGHTS,URN SHAPE,
  12 IN.TALL.............................................       150.00
DURAND,VASE,PEACOCK BLUE,SIGNED IN V 1722-6,5 1/4 IN.......     225.00
DURAND,VASE,SNOWFLAKING,BLUE IRIDESCENT,4 IN. X 6 1/2 IN....    425.00
DURAND,WINE GLASS,COBALT,WHITE FEATHERING,VASELINE FOOT &
  STEM,CUT BAND..........................................       120.00
```

```
ENAMEL,BASKET,HANDLE,ALLOVER ENAMEL,RUSSIA,5-IN.DIAMETER....1,300.00
ENAMEL,BOWL,CHAMPLEVE,RUSSIA,3 1/4-IN.DIAMETER,1 3/4 IN.HIGH    350.00
ENAMEL,BOX,HOLDS MATCHES,METAL,TOP CARVED WITH WHITE JADE,
  CHINA.................................................         20.00
ENAMEL,BOX,JEWEL,FROSTED GLASS ENAMELED FLOWERS & GOLD
  DECOR,COVER...........................................          6.00
ENAMEL,BOX,PATCH,COVER DEPICTS CHURCH & TREES,INSIDE MIRROR.     70.00
ENAMEL,BOX,SCENES,NUDE IN BATH WITH LADY ATTENDANT ON COVER,
  FRANCE................................................        115.00
ENAMEL,BRANDY TASTER,RUSSIAN,MARK.........................      195.00
ENAMEL,BUCKLE,BELT,TWO PARTS HELD BY DAGGER,SIGNED
```

| | |
|---|---|
| KOKOSHNIK,RUSSIA | 260.00 |
| ENAMEL,CIGARETTE CASE,RUSSIA | 325.00 TO 395.00 |
| ENAMEL,CREAMER,SUGAR BASKET,RUSSIA | 1,400.00 |
| ENAMEL,DISH,NUT,PEDESTAL,RUSSIA,3 1/4-IN.DIAMETER,2 IN.HIGH, PAIR | 1,200.00 |
| ENAMEL,EGG STAND,RUSSIA,5 3/4 IN.HIGH | 1,400.00 |
| ENAMEL,FORK,LEMON,CHAMPLEVE,RUSSIA | 100.00 |
| ENAMEL,FRENCH,SPOON,DEMITASSE,STERLING SILVER,GOLD WASH BOWL,SET OF 7 | 85.00 |
| ENAMEL,GERMAN,FRAME,FLORAL,CARMINE,WHITE,SIGNED STUPPE, BERLIN,5 X 7 IN | 68.00 |
| ENAMEL,GLASS HOLDER,RUSSIA,6 IN.HIGH | 450.00 |
| ENAMEL,HOLDER,CIGARETTE,PIPE SHAPE,IVORY MOUTHPIECE, MULTICOLOR,RUSSIA | 265.00 |
| ENAMEL,KOVSH CUP,RUSSIAN,YELLOW GROUND,FLORAL,ON SILVER, 6 1/4 IN | 750.00 |
| ENAMEL,LADLE,KOVSH TYPE,ALLOVER ENAMEL,RUSSIA,6 1/2 IN | 750.00 |
| ENAMEL,LIQUEUR,PEDESTAL,RUSSIA,3 1/2 IN.HIGH | 400.00 |
| ENAMEL,NAPKIN RING,RUSSIA | 150.00 |
| ENAMEL,PEN,RUSSIA,5 IN.LONG | 110.00 |
| ENAMEL,PLATE,RUSSIA,6-IN.DIAMETER | 600.00 |
| ENAMEL,SALT & SPOON,RUSSIA | 160.00 |
| ENAMEL,SCOOP,SUGAR,CHAMPLEVE,RUSSIA | 150.00 |
| ENAMEL,SPOON,DEMITASSE,RUSSIA,SET OF 12 | 450.00 |
| ENAMEL,SPOON,RUSSIA,3 1/2 IN.LONG | 600.00 |
| ENAMEL,SPOON,RUSSIA,5 1/2 IN.LONG,SET OF 6 | 375.00 |
| ENAMEL,TEASPOON,RUSSIAN,DESIGN | 30.00 |
| ENAMEL,TONGS,RUSSIA | 175.00 |
| ENAMEL,VASE,BLUE GROUND,RED HOLLY BERRIES,WHITE MISTLETOE, FRANCE,4 IN | 175.00 |
| ENAMEL,VASE,MAN WOOING LADY,SCROLLING,RED LINING,SIGNED R.TABOS,9 IN | 450.00 |
| ENAMEL,VASE,TIGER LILIES,BLUE & ORANGE GROUND,FRANCE, 7 IN.HIGH | 195.00 |
| ENAMEL,VODKA CUP,RUSSIAN,SIGNED | 430.00 |
| ENAMEL,WIG HOLDER,FRENCH GLASS,1715-30,8 IN. HIGH | 400.00 |

END OF DAY GLASS IS NOW AN OUT-OF-FASHION NAME FOR
SPATTERED GLASS. THE GLASS WAS MADE OF MANY BITS AND
PIECES OF COLORED GLASS. TRADITIONALLY,THE GLASS WAS
MADE BY WORKMEN FROM THE ODDS AND ENDS LEFT FROM THE
GLASS USED DURING THE DAY. ACTUALLY IT WAS A
DELIBERATELY MANUFACTURED PRODUCT POPULAR ABOUT 1880 TO
1900,AND SOME OF IT IS STILL BEING MADE.

| | |
|---|---|
| END OF DAY,BASKET,BROWN,WHITE,RED,CASED,RUFFLED,THORN HANDLE,FOOTED | 75.00 |
| END OF DAY,BASKET,GREEN,PINK RUFFLED TOP,FENTON | 15.00 |
| END OF DAY,BASKET,GREEN,RED,APPLIED CLEAR THORN HANDLE,BLOWN | 65.00 |
| END OF DAY,BASKET,PINK,YELLOW,WHITE,6 IN | 65.00 |
| END OF DAY,BOTTLE,BARBER,RED & WHITE,4 IN.SQUARE BASE, 12 IN.HIGH | 39.50 |
| END OF DAY,BOX,POWDER,CASED,RIGAREE TRIM,CLEAR FEET, 4-IN.DIAMETER | 45.00 |
| END OF DAY,CASTOR,PICKLE,BLUE,RED,BLACK,GREEN,WHITE-LINED, SILVER HOLDER | 75.50 |
| END OF DAY,CREAMER & SUGAR,PINK ROYAL IVY | 95.00 |
| END OF DAY,DARNER,PINK,YELLOW,ORANGE,STEUBEN | 25.00 |
| END OF DAY,DECANTER,BROWN SHADES,OVOID BODY,SLENDER NECK, TWISTED HANDLE | 28.50 |
| END OF DAY,DISH,JELLY,PINK,WHITE,SILVERED METAL COVER,SPOON OPENING | 20.00 |
| END OF DAY,LAMP,FAIRY,YELLOW,ROSE COLOR,CLARKE BASE | 40.00 |
| END OF DAY,LAMP,KEROSENE,BURNER,HANDLE,4 1/2-IN. X 4 1/4-IN.DIAMETER | 50.00 |
| END OF DAY,MUFFINEER,PINK PREDOMINATE | 20.00 |
| END OF DAY,PITCHER,MILK,DEEP YELLOW,WHITE CASING,SWIRL DESIGN | 65.00 |
| END OF DAY,PITCHER,MILK,YELLOW,SWIRLED,WHITE-CASED | 85.00 |
| END OF DAY,PITCHER,YELLOW,ORANGE,GREEN HANDLE,11 IN.HIGH | 40.00 |
| END OF DAY,TUMBLER,DEEP RED WITH WHITE | 15.00 |
| END OF DAY,TUMBLER,PINK & WHITE | 37.50 |
| END OF DAY,TUMBLER,PINK,BLUE,YELLOW MOTTLING,SILVER FLECKS | 27.50 |
| END OF DAY,TUMBLER,YELLOW,GOLD EMBOSSED,CASED,KAISERBRUM | 18.00 |
| END OF DAY,VASE,AMBER,WHITE,RUFFLED TOP,RIGAREE,6 IN.HIGH | 15.00 |
| END OF DAY,VASE,BLUE,BROWN,GREEN,FLUTED GOLD TOP,BULBOUS BOTTOM,11 IN | 30.00 |
| END OF DAY,VASE,BUD,DOUBLE-CASED,WHITE INSIDE,CLEAR OUTSIDE, 8 1/2 IN | 18.00 |
| END OF DAY,VASE,CASED GLASS,FLARED,CRIMPED,CLEAR TOP BORDER, 9 IN.TALL | 40.00 |

END OF DAY,VASE,CASED IN YELLOW & WHITE,GOLD,ENAMELED DECOR,
  10 IN.,PAIR..................................................  55.00
END OF DAY,VASE,CASED,CLEAR APPLIED HANDLE,LEAF,BULBOUS,
  RUFFLED.....................................................  55.00
END OF DAY,VASE,CLEAR LEAF DECOR,FORMS HANDLE,WHITE-LINED,
  PINK,TAN,WHITE..............................................  59.50
END OF DAY,VASE,FLUTED TOP,10 X 5 1/2 IN.HIGH................  45.00
END OF DAY,VASE,GREEN & CREAM COLOR,SPANGLED WITH SILVER....  25.00
END OF DAY,VASE,JACK-IN-THE-PULPIT,PINK,WHITE,CHARTREUSE,
  8 1/2 IN.HIGH...............................................  24.00
END OF DAY,VASE,PASTEL COLORS,OPAL LINING,RUFFLED TOP,
  7 1/4 IN....................................................  14.00
END OF DAY,VASE,PINK.CASED,9 IN..............................  57.00
END OF DAY,VASE,PINK,SWIRLS,WHITE LINING,5 1/2 IN. X
  3 1/2 IN.SQUARE.............................................  35.00
END OF DAY,VASE,PINK,WHITE,WINE-RED SPLOTCHES,BULBOUS,
  RIBBED,5 1/2 IN.............................................  22.00
END OF DAY,VASE,RED,GREEN,WHITE,BLUE,CASED IN WHITE,BLOWN,
  8 IN.,PAIR..................................................  50.00
END OF DAY,VASE,RED,WHITE,BLUE SWIRL,8 1/2 IN................  13.00
END OF DAY,VASE,ROSE COLOR & YELLOW,SCALLOPED FOLDS.........  25.00
END OF DAY,VASE,SATIN GLASS,SIGNED...........................  32.00
END OF DAY,VASE,VARIEGATED PINKS,RUFFLED TOP,8 3/4 IN.......  16.00
END OF DAY,VASE,YELLOW,PINK,RED,WHITE,5 IN. HIGH............  38.00
EZRA BROOKS,SEE BOTTLE,EZRA BROOKS


FABERGE,CARL GUSTAVOVICH,WAS A GOLDSMITH AND JEWELER TO
  THE RUSSIAN IMPERIAL COURT FROM ABOUT 1870 TO 1914.
FABERGE,ASHTRAY,ART NOUVEAU SILVER,CIRCA 1900...............  400.00
FABERGE,BELL-PUSH,GILDED SILVER & ENAMEL,CIRCA 1900.........1,300.00
FABERGE,CASKET,JEWEL,GILDED SILVER & ENAMEL,FEODOR RUCKERT..5,000.00
FABERGE,CIGARETTE CASE,WHITE ENAMEL.........................2,600.00
FABERGE,CLOCK,GILDED SILVER & TRANSLUCENT ENAMEL,TABLE,1913.2,100.00
FABERGE,DISH,CAVIAR,AGATE,ON STAND..........................3,750.00
FABERGE,FIGURE,ATLAS,LAPIS LAZULI & GILDED SILVER-MOUNTED,
  SMOKY TOPAZ.................................................3,700.00
FABERGE,FIGURE,ELEPHANT,CARVED GARNET.......................2,300.00
FABERGE,FIGURE,KIWI,CARVED AGATE & GOLD.....................8,000.00
FABERGE,FIGURE,PIG,AGATE,CARVED.............................2,500.00
FABERGE,FLOWER,WILD,GOLD,JADE & NEPHRITE,HENDRIK WIGSTROM...8,000.00
FABERGE,FRAME,ROSE DIAMONDS & STERLING RIBBON GARLAND,GOLD,
  3 1/2 IN.HIGH...............................................1,250.00
FABERGE,FRAME,TWO-COLOR GOLD & NEPHRITE,MICHAEL PERCHIN.....2,500.00
FABERGE,ICON,OUR LADY OF KAZAN..............................3,250.00
FABERGE,ICON,OUR LADY OF THE SIGN...........................3,000.00
FABERGE,KOVSH,SILVER-MOUNTED POTTERY,ANDERS NEVELAINEN......1,300.00
FABERGE,PEN HOLDER,SILVER,FEODOR AFANASSIEV.................  300.00
FABERGE,SERVING SET,FISH,THREE PIECES,ART NOUVEAU,CIRCA
  1900........................................................  225.00
FABERGE,SHADE,CANDLE,PAIR,SILVER-MOUNTED NEPHRITE,CIRCA
  1900........................................................  750.00
FAIENCE,BOX,SNUFF,PUCE LANDSCAPE,GILT SCROLLWORK,FLORAL,
  GERMANY,1780................................................  60.00
FAIENCE,CACHEPOT,PAIR,FRENCH POLYCHROME DECORATED,CIRCA
  1740........................................................  675.00
FAIENCE,DISH,BLUE,WHITE,ORIENTAL DECOR,PATTERN BORDER,PAIR..  125.00
FAIENCE,DISH,CIRCA 1760,12-IN.DIAMETER,BLUE STENCILED.......  40.00
FAIENCE,GROUP,5 IN. HIGH,BABY IN CRADLE.....................  50.00
FAIENCE,GROUP,LE FILS DE PAUL RUBENS,17TH-CENTURY CHILD,
  11 1/2 IN.HIGH..............................................  160.00
FAIENCE,JAR,BLUE,WHITE,LANDSCAPE,HANDLES,COVER,SAVONA,ITALY,
  18 IN.,PAIR.................................................  175.00
FAIENCE,JUG,TULIPS,ROSES,TIN GLAZE ENAMEL,FRANCE,1770.......  100.00
FAIENCE,PLATE,FLORAL,INSECTS,COAT OF ARMS,MOTTO,ARMORIAL,
  ITALIAN,PAIR................................................  175.00
FAIENCE,PLATE,FRENCH,CIRCA 1760.............................  120.00
FAIENCE,TEAPOT,GALLE,10 3/4 IN. HIGH,SIGNED.................  300.00
FAIENCE,TUREEN,PAIR,FRENCH,LETTUCE,CIRCA 1760..............  400.00
FAIENCE,VASE,GALLE,12 IN. HIGH,SIGNED.......................  85.00


FAIRINGS ARE SMALL SOUVENIR CHINA BOXES SOLD AT COUNTY
  FAIRS DURING THE NINETEENTH CENTURY.
FAIRING,FIGURINE,THE LAST TO BED TO PUT OUT THE LIGHT,
  GERMANY.....................................................  35.00
FAIRING,FIGURINE,WHEN A MAN IS MARRIED HIS TROUBLES BEGIN,
  GERMANY.....................................................  35.00
FAN,ADVERTISING,CAFE LAFAYETTE,HOTEL BREVOORT,N.Y.,PAPER....  6.50
FAN,ADVERTISING,DRUGSTORE...................................  1.00
FAN,BLACK LACE STICKS,FLORAL ON BLACK SATIN,OPENS TO 20 IN..  10.00

```
FAN,BLACK LACQUER STICKS,SILVER PAINTING ON BLACK,11 IN.....      3.00
FAN,BLACK LACQUER,ORIENTAL DESIGN ON RED PAPER,10 IN........      4.00
FAN,BULLFIGHT PICTURE,RECUERDO,PAPER......................       5.00
FAN,CARVED & PAINTED BLACK LACAUERED STICKS,FLORAL,BIRDS,
  PAPER..................................................       15.00
FAN,CARVED BAMBOO STICKS,PAINTED,TAN PARCHMENT,12 IN.......       5.00
FAN,CELLULOID FRAME,WHITE,CARVED FLORAL DECOR,6 IN.LONG....      12.50
FAN,CHIFFON,LACE-TRIMMED,HAND-PAINTED FLORAL,VINE,CARVED
  IVORY FRAME............................................        9.00
FAN,EIGHTEEN AMBER-COLORED RIBS,AMBER OSTRICH PLUMES........     11.00
FAN,ENGRAVED & PAINTED STICKS,BLOSSOMS & BUTTERFLIES ON RED
  SATIN,25 IN............................................       15.00
FAN,FEATHER,OSTRICH,BLACK.................................       10.00
FAN,FLORAL,PAPER,8 IN....................................        1.00
FAN,FLORAL,SINGER BUILDING,PAPER,8 IN.....................       3.00
FAN,FOLDING,CELLULOID FRAME,ORIENTAL SCENE,HAND PAINTED.....      2.50
FAN,GOLD DECOR,BLACK,CIRCA 1870..........................       18.00
FAN,HAND-PAINTED BIRDS ON CHIFFON,CARVED IVORY RIBS........       9.00
FAN,IVORY RIBS,CARVED,PIERCED,HAND-PAINTED BIRDS ON WHITE
  CHIFFON,14 IN..........................................       11.00
FAN,IVORY SPLATS,CHIFFON SEQUIN...........................        2.50
FAN,IVORY,PINK FLORAL,7 IN...............................        5.00
FAN,LACE & CHIFFON,LACE FLOWERS,IVORY FRAME................       8.00
FAN,LACE,BLACK,TORTOISESHELL STAYS,FRANCE,24 IN.LONG WHEN
  OPEN..................................................        35.00
FAN,LACE,MOTHER-OF-PEARL RIBS,FRANCE......................       27.50
FAN,LACY & COLORFUL,SANDELWOOD,5 IN.......................       10.00
FAN,MOTHER-OF-PEARL,LACE,FRANCE...........................       27.50
FAN,PINK FEATHERS,SILVER TRIM,PAINTED WOODEN FRAME,PINK
  RIBBON BOW.............................................        9.00
FAN,RED LACQUER PIERCED SANDLEWOOD,SPANISH VILLAS ON CLOTH
  TOP...................................................         6.50
FAN,SILK,BLACK LACQUER,PAINTED,FOLDING....................        4.50
FAN,SILK,BLACK,LACE EDGE,HAND-PAINTED DESIGN,CARVED STICKS,
  18 IN.OPEN............................................        28.00
FAN,SILK,RED,HAND-PAINTED FLOWERS,GRAINED WOODEN STICKS,
  12 X/4 IN.............................................        18.00
FAN,SILK,WHITE,BROWN OPENWORK STICKS......................        8.00
FAN,SPINDLE,BLACK PLUME FEATHERS,AMBER....................       15.00
FAN,TAPESTRY TYPE FABRIC,MAN,LADIES,COURT DRESS,BRASS ENDS,
  26 IN.OPEN............................................        37.50
FAN,TORTOISESHELL RIBS,SIX LONG,CURLING PINK OSTRICH PLUMES.     11.00
FAN,TORTOISESHELL,CASE,CHINA.............................        75.00
FAN,TORTOISE STICKS,BRASS KNOBS,FLORAL BORDER,RED CLOTH,
  PAT.6/22/80...........................................        15.00
FAN,TURKEY FEATHER,HAND-PAINTED DECOR,1860................        3.00
FAN,TURKEY FEATHERS,HAND-PAINTED,BLACK....................        4.00
FAN,WEDDING,IVORY STICKS,WHITE SHADING TO SMOKE FEATHERS....     45.00
FAN,WHITE LACQUER,SILVER DECOR,LACE INSERTS ON WHITE SILK,
  SEQUINS,FLORAL........................................        15.00
```

FINDLAY OR ONYX GLASS WAS MADE USING THREE LAYERS OF
GLASS. IT WAS MANUFACTURED BY THE DALZELL GILMORE
LEIGHTON COMPANY ABOUT 1889 IN FINDLAY,OHIO. THE
SILVER,RUBY,OR BLACK PATTERN WAS MOLDED INTO THE GLASS.
THE GLASS CAME IN SEVERAL COLORS,BUT WAS USUALLY WHITE
OR RUBY.

```
FINDLAY ONYX,BOWL,BERRY,8 IN.............................       400.00
FINDLAY ONYX,BOWL,CREAM COLOR,8 IN.......................       195.00
FINDLAY ONYX,DISH,COLLAR,COVERED,RED.....................       925.00
FINDLAY ONYX,DISH,COLLAR,COVERED,WHITE...................       425.00
FINDLAY ONYX,PITCHER.............................ILLUS..        450.00
FINDLAY ONYX,SHAKER,SUGAR,5 1/2 IN.HIGH..................       265.00
FINDLAY ONYX,SAUCE,4 1/2 IN..............................       125.00
FINDLAY ONYX,SPOONER CREAM & PLATINUM COLORS,4 1/4 IN.HIGH..    195.00
FIRE,BUCKET,GREEN PAINT,BLACK & GOLD DECOR,LEATHER,CIRCA
  1840..................................................        95.00
```

FIREGLOW GLASS RESEMBLES ENGLISH BRISTOL GLASS. BUT A
REDDISH-BROWN COLOR CAN BE SEEN WHEN THE PIECE IS HELD
TO THE LIGHT. IT IS A FORM OF ART GLASS MADE BY THE
BOSTON AND SANDWICH GLASS CO. OF MASSACHUSETTS,AND
OTHERS.

```
FIREGLOW,EWER,BROWN DECOR,REED HANDLE,PEDESTAL BASE,RUFFLE
  TOP,SANDWICH..........................................       225.00
FIREGLOW,TUMBLER,SATIN EXTERIOR,FLORAL DECOR,PEACH COLORING
  INSIDE................................................        60.00
FIREGLOW,VASE,DECOR,3 IN.................................        22.50
FIREGLOW,VASE,ENAMELED FLOWERS,GREEN,BROWN,PINK,WHITE,
```

FINDLAY ONYX PITCHER

```
    5 1/2 X 10 IN.TALL.........................................   110.00
FIREGLOW,VASE,FLORAL,HAND-PAINTED,BEIGE GROUND,SANDWICH
    GLASS,5 1/2 IN............................................    55.00
FIREGLOW,VASE,RAISED DECOR,9 IN..............................    69.00
```

HER END,HUNGARY,HAD A PORCELAIN FACTORY THAT WAS FOUNDED
IN 1839,AND IT HAS CONTINUED WORKING INTO THE TWENTIETH
CENTURY. THE FIRM WAS DIRECTED BY MORITZ FISCHER,AND
THE WARES ARE SOMETIMES CALLED FISCHER CHINA.

```
FISCHER,VASE,BEIGE,PINK,GREEN,BUDAPEST,12 1/4 IN.HIGH.......   150.00
FISCHER,VASE,HANDLED,GOLD RETICULATED,EMBOSSED FLOWER,
    BUDAPEST,12 IN...........................................    39.00
FISCHER,VASE,YELLOW SCROLLS,MEDALLION FRONT & BACK,ANIMAL
    DECOR HANDLE.............................................    65.00
```

FISH SETS WERE POPULAR DURING THE LATE VICTORIAN
PERIOD. A LARGE PLATTER WITH AT LEAST A DOZEN PLATES
MADE A SET. EACH PIECE OF THE POTTERY OR PORCELAIN WAS
USUALLY DECORATED WITH A DIFFERENT TYPE OF FISH.

```
FISH SET,HAND-PAINTED FISH,EMBOSSED GOLD NET,SAUCEBOAT,
    12 PLATES,BLUE...........................................    75.00
FISH SET,PEARL HANDLE,GOLD,SILVER,11 1/4-IN.FORK,
    13 1/4-IN.KNIFE..........................................    46.00
FISH SET,PLATTER,TEN PLATES,PAINTED TROUT,CARP,PIKE,GOLD
    RIMS,LIMOGES.............................................   135.00
FISH SET,PORCELAIN,SEASHELLS,LILY PADS,SIGNED,AUSTRIA,
    11 PIECES................................................   125.00
FISH SET,ROSES,VINES,HAND-PAINTED,PLATTER,EIGHT PLATES,
    AUSTRIA..................................................   100.00
FLAG,AMERICAN,THIRTEEN STARS,EIGHT STRIPES,26 IN.LONG.......   850.00
FLAG,BATTLE,T.ROOSEVELT,1912.................................    25.00
    FLINT,SEE,PRESSED GLASS
```

FLOW BLUE OR FLO BLUE WAS MADE IN ENGLAND ABOUT 1830 TO
1900. THE PLATES WERE PRINTED WITH DESIGNS USING A
COBALT BLUE COLORING. THE COLOR FLOWED FROM THE DESIGN
TO THE WHITE PLATE SO THE FINISHED PLATE HAD A SMEARED
BLUE DESIGN. THE PLATES WERE USUALLY MADE OF IRONSTONE
CHINA.

```
FLOW BLUE,BOWL,CONWAY PATTERN,ALLOVER FLORAL,SCROLLS,NEW
    WHARF....................................................    15.00
FLOW BLUE,BOWL,KESWICK,OBLONG,SHALLOW,12 IN. X 9 1/2 IN.....    20.00
FLOW BLUE,BOWL,SIGNED L O S ENGLAND,9-IN.DIAMETER............     4.50
FLOW BLUE,BOWL,SOBROAN.......................................    32.50
FLOW BLUE,BOWL,SOUP,MILAN PATTERN,9 IN.......................     6.00
FLOW BLUE,BOWL,SOUP,ROSE PATTERN.............................     8.00
FLOW BLUE,BOWL,TOURAINE,6-IN.DIAMETER........................    15.00
FLOW BLUE,BOWL,VEGETABLE,OPEN,FAIRY VILLAS,
    10 1/2-IN.DIAMETER.......................................    25.00
FLOW BLUE,BOWL,VEGETABLE,OPEN,10 IN.ACROSS...................    22.00
FLOW BLUE,BOWL,WASH,PITCHER..................................    75.00
FLOW BLUE,BUTTER PAT,BLUEBIRD IN CENTER......................     9.50
FLOW BLUE,BUTTER PAT,GOLD TRIM,SET OF 6......................    13.50
FLOW BLUE,BUTTER PAT,ONION PATTERN,BY ALLERTON...............     5.00
FLOW BLUE,BUTTER PAT,SET OF 3................................    10.00
```

```
FLOW BLUE,CANDLESTICK,POPPY PATTERN,6 1/2 IN.HIGH...........        24.50
FLOW BLUE,CELERY,ALLOVER FLOWERS,GOLD EDGE,SIGNED WARWICK,
  5 1/2 X 12 IN..................................................   35.00
FLOW BLUE,CHOCOLATE POT,BLUE,GOLD,SHORT SPOUT,LA BELLE......        65.00
FLOW BLUE,COFFEEPOT,CLEWS,CHRISTMAS EVE.............ILLUS..        290.00
FLOW BLUE,COMPOTE,FLORAL DECOR,PEDESTAL BASE,MOLDED LEAF
  HANDLES,COVER...............................................      40.00
FLOW BLUE,CREAMER,HADDON......................................      15.00
FLOW BLUE,CUP,CLEWS,CHRISTMAS EVE,PAIR...............ILLUS..       130.00
FLOW BLUE,CUP & SAUCER,DEMITASSE,LORNE........................      10.00
FLOW BLUE,CUP & SAUCER,OREGON,HANDLELESS......................      25.00
FLOW BLUE,CUP & SAUCER,OVANDO-MEAKIN PATTERN..................      16.50
FLOW BLUE,CUP & SAUCER,SCINDE.................................      28.00
FLOW BLUE,DISH,BONE,BLUE FLORAL SPRAY,GOLD TRIM,SET OF 7....        45.00
FLOW BLUE,DISH,KESWICK PATTERN,WOOD & SON,ENGLAND,1875,12 X
  2 IN.DEEP...................................................      12.50
FLOW BLUE,DISH,RELISH,SCINDE..................................      13.00
FLOW BLUE,DISH,SAUCE,VIRGINIA PATTERN,MADDOCK,5 1/4 IN., SET
  OF 6........................................................      27.50
FLOW BLUE,DISH,VEGETABLE,FAIRY VILLAS,COVER...................      45.00
FLOW BLUE,DISH,VEGETABLE,FAIRY VILLAS,ROUND,ADAMS,10 IN.....        30.00
FLOW BLUE,DISH,VEGETABLE,OPEN,ENGLAND,9 1/2 IN. X 7 1/2 IN..         8.00
FLOW BLUE,DISH,VEGETABLE,OPEN,12 1/2 IN..............ILLUS..       180.00
FLOW BLUE,DISH,VEGETABLE,OPEN,ESCAPE OF MOUSE........ILLUS..        45.00
FLOW BLUE,DISH,VEGETABLE,SCINDE,OPEN,FLAT RIM,9 1/2 X
  7 1/2 IN.DEEP..............................................      24.00
```

OPEN VEGETABLE DISH,
ESCAPE OF MOUSE

CLEWS COFFEEPOT,
CHRISTMAS EVE

OPEN VEGETABLE DISH

CLEWS CUPS, CHRISTMAS EVE

```
FLOW BLUE,DISH,VEGETABLE,SHELL,COVER..........................      45.00
FLOW BLUE,DISH,VEGETABLE,WINTER VIEW OF PITTSFIELD,MASS.,
  OPEN,CLEWS.................................................      95.00
FLOW BLUE,GRAVY BOAT,FLORIDA PATTERN,ENGLISH MARK...........       10.00
FLOW BLUE,GRAVY BOAT,OVANDO...................................      15.00
FLOW BLUE,GRAVY BOAT,SEVILLE,NEW WHARF........................      14.50
FLOW BLUE,GRAVY BOAT,WALDORF PATTERN..........................      16.00
FLOW BLUE,JAR,BISCUIT,BARREL SHAPE,ELKS,FLORAL,BASKET WEAVE,
  1890,MARK..................................................      35.00
FLOW BLUE,JARDINERE,SASKIA DECOR,GOLD EDGED,ENGLAND,8 X
  6 1/2 IN.TALL..............................................      17.50
FLOW BLUE,MUG,TOGO PATTERN....................................      13.00
FLOW BLUE,MUSTARD,COVER,PEPPER SHAKER,OPEN SALT,GOLD TRIM,
  SPOON,FRAME................................................      20.00
FLOW BLUE,PITCHER & BOWL,GILT,LA BELLE CHINA..................      85.00
FLOW BLUE,PITCHER,ALLOVER FLORAL,COBALT BAND & HANDLE,LA
  BELLE,TWO-QUART............................................      35.00
FLOW BLUE,PITCHER,GRAVY,LONIAL...............................      11.50
FLOW BLUE,PITCHER,MEDALLION,FLOWER,COPPER LUSTER TRIM,
  7 1/2 IN.HIGH.............................................      65.00
FLOW BLUE,PITCHER,WATER,CASHMERE,7 IN.TALL....................      65.00
FLOW BLUE,PLATE,ALMA,IRONSTONE,9 1/2 IN.......................      14.00
FLOW BLUE,PLATE,AMOY DAVENPORT,10 1/4-IN.DIAMETER.............      20.00
FLOW BLUE,PLATE,AMOY,10 IN....................................      15.00
FLOW BLUE,PLATE,BLACKBERRY,JOHNSON BROS.,ENGLAND,9 IN.......        15.00
FLOW BLUE,PLATE,BLUE DANUBE,9 IN..............................       8.00
FLOW BLUE,PLATE,BLUE DANUBE,10 IN.............................       9.00
FLOW BLUE,PLATE,BLUE DANUBE,JOHNSON BROTHERS,7 IN... 5.00 TO        7.00
FLOW BLUE,PLATE,CATHERINE,8 3/4 IN............................       6.00
FLOW BLUE,PLATE,CHAPOO PATTERN,8 1/2 IN.......................       8.50
FLOW BLUE,PLATE,CHOP,CASTRO PATTERN,14-IN.DIAMETER...........       20.00
FLOW BLUE,PLATE,COBURG PATTERN,8 1/4 IN.......................      18.00
FLOW BLUE,PLATE,COBURG,9 IN...................................      14.50
FLOW BLUE,PLATE,CONWAY PATTERN,ALLOVER FLORAL,SCROLLS,NEW
  WHARF,9 IN.................................................       8.00
```

FLOW BLUE,PLATE,DESSERT,TOURAINE,7 1/2 IN.................  12.50
FLOW BLUE,PLATE,ECLIPSE PATTERN,GOLD,JOHNSON BROS.,ENGLAND,
  9 IN..................................................  12.00
FLOW BLUE,PLATE,FAIRY VILLA,8 3/4 IN......................  11.00
FLOW BLUE,PLATE,FLEUR-DE-LIS,HANDLEY,9 IN.................  12.50
FLOW BLUE,PLATE,GOTHIC SCENE,9 1/4 IN.....................  15.00
FLOW BLUE,PLATE,GRINDLEY MELBOURNE,8 1/2 IN...............   8.00
FLOW BLUE,PLATE,LANDING OF LAFAYETTE,CLEWS,8 3/4 IN....... 100.00
FLOW BLUE,PLATE,LOIS PATTERN............................  12.50
FLOW BLUE,PLATE,LUCERNE,9 IN..............................   8.50
FLOW BLUE,PLATE,MADE FOR MASS.FURNITURE CO.,1880,
  BENJ.HARRISON,ENGLAND.................................. 150.00
FLOW BLUE,PLATE,MADRAS,10 IN..............................  11.00
FLOW BLUE,PLATE,MANILA PATTERN,7 1/2 IN...................  18.00
FLOW BLUE,PLATE,MARTHA WASHINGTON,ADVERTISING,SHAWMUT
  FURNITURE CO..........................................  25.00
FLOW BLUE,PLATE,MCKINLEY,9-IN.DIAMETER....................   8.00
FLOW BLUE,PLATE,OREGON,10 1/2 IN..........................  15.00
FLOW BLUE,PLATE,OREGON,7 1/2 IN...........................   9.50
FLOW BLUE,PLATE,ORIENTAL PATTERN,10 IN....................  12.00
FLOW BLUE,PLATE,OSBORNE,GRINDLEY,8 3/4-IN.DIAMETER........  10.50
FLOW BLUE,PLATE,PARIS,NEW WHARF...........................   7.50
FLOW BLUE,PLATE,PERSIAN PATTERN,10 IN.....................  12.00
FLOW BLUE,PLATE,PICTORIAL,WINDMILL,GOLD SEASHELL SCALLOPED
  EDGE..................................................  65.00
FLOW BLUE,PLATE,PICTORIAL,WINDSOR CASTLE,GOLD SEASHELL
  SCALLOPED EDGE........................................  65.00
FLOW BLUE,PLATE,POPPY PATTERN,10 IN.......................  10.00
FLOW BLUE,PLATE,SAILBOAT,ARTIST-INITIALED,9 IN.,PAIR......  15.00
FLOW BLUE,PLATE,SALAD,TOURAINE PATTERN,7 5/8 IN...........  10.00
FLOW BLUE,PLATE,SCENE,WINDSOR CASTLE,IRREGULAR SHELL EDGE...  65.00
FLOW BLUE,PLATE,SCINDE,7 1/4 IN...........................  14.00
FLOW BLUE,PLATE,SCINDE,9 IN...............................  14.50
FLOW BLUE,PLATE,SCINDE,9 3/8 IN...........................  18.00
FLOW BLUE,PLATE,SCINDE,ALCOCK,SUNKEN PANELS ON EDGE,
  9 1/2 IN..............................................  19.50
FLOW BLUE,PLATE,SOUP,DAINTY PATTERN.......................  16.00
FLOW BLUE,PLATE,SOUP,TOURAINE.............................  10.00
FLOW BLUE,PLATE,SOUP,TOURAINE PATTERN,GOLD EDGE,STANLEY CO.,
  ENGLAND,6.............................................  35.00
FLOW BLUE,PLATE,ST.PAUL SCHOOL,ADAMS......................  18.50
FLOW BLUE,PLATE,STATES,CLEWS,8 3/4 IN..................... 110.00
FLOW BLUE,PLATE,TEMPLE,7 7/8 IN...........................  12.00
FLOW BLUE,PLATE,THE VALENTINE,WILKIE,CLEWS,10 IN..........  88.00
FLOW BLUE,PLATE,TOURAINE,6 1/2 IN.........................   7.50
FLOW BLUE,PLATE,TOURAINE,8 1/2 IN.........................  12.00
FLOW BLUE,PLATE,TOURAINE,8 3/4 IN........... 12.00 TO     15.00
FLOW BLUE,PLATE,TOURAINE,9 IN.............................   9.00
FLOW BLUE,PLATE,UTOPIA....................................   7.50
FLOW BLUE,PLATE,WATTEAU,9 IN..............................   9.00
FLOW BLUE,PLATE,WHAMPOA,7 3/8 IN..........................  11.00
FLOW BLUE,PLATTER,ACORN & LEAF BORDER,10 1/2 IN. X 16 IN....  85.00
FLOW BLUE,PLATTER,ARGYLE..................................  38.00
FLOW BLUE,PLATTER,BLUE DANUBE,OVAL,10 1/2 IN. X 14 1/4 IN...  15.00
FLOW BLUE,PLATTER,BLUE GARDEN & CASTLE SCENE,FLORAL BORDER,
  SIGNED J.R............................................  45.00
FLOW BLUE,PLATTER,CASTLE RUINS SCENE,LEAF & ACORN BORDER,
  REG.MARK 1848......................................... 129.00
FLOW BLUE,PLATTER,CONWAY PATTERN,ALLOVER FLORAL,SCROLLS,NEW
  WHARF.................................................  15.00
FLOW BLUE,PLATTER,CUT CORNERS,MARKED BURGESS & LEIGH,
  BURLEIGH..............................................  20.00
FLOW BLUE,PLATTER,DELAMER PATTERN,HENRY ALCOCK,10 1/2 IN....  15.00
FLOW BLUE,PLATTER,FRUIT & FLOWER BORDER,SMALL CENTRAL VIEW,
  21 IN................................................. 125.00
FLOW BLUE,PLATTER,GOLD LEAVES,MARKED THE COLONIAL CO.,
  12 1/2 IN.............................................   7.00
FLOW BLUE,PLATTER,KHYBER,7 1/2 IN. X 10 IN................  17.50
FLOW BLUE,PLATTER,LACY PATTERN,BOOTE & CO.,11 IN..........  12.00
FLOW BLUE,PLATTER,MANILA,10 IN. X 13 IN...................  35.00
FLOW BLUE,PLATTER,MARKED KESWICK,WOOD & SONS,ENGLAND......  12.50
FLOW BLUE,PLATTER,MARKED MILAN,CROWN,ALFRED MEAKIN,LTD.,11 X
  16 IN.................................................  22.00
FLOW BLUE,PLATTER,NONPAREIL,13 1/4 X 11 IN................  30.00
FLOW BLUE,PLATTER,PITTSFIELD ELM,HANDLES,OVAL,CLEWS,8 IN.... 100.00
FLOW BLUE,PLATTER,SCALLOPED EDGE,KRONA,WOOD & SONS,16 X
  11 1/2 IN.............................................  45.00
FLOW BLUE,PLATTER,SCENIC,BURGESS & LEIGH NONPAREIL,13 X
  15 1/2 IN.LONG........................................  45.00
FLOW BLUE,PLATTER,SCINDE,13 1/2 IN. X 10 1/2 IN...........  37.50
FLOW BLUE,PLATTER,SHELL,SEAWEED,LUSTER COPPER TRIM,

```
    8 5/8 IN.SQUARE.................................................    18.50
FLOW BLUE,PLATTER,TOKYO PATTERN,12 1/2 IN.........................     7.50
FLOW BLUE,PLATTER,TONQUIN,OCTAGON,16 IN. X 12 IN..................    48.00
FLOW BLUE,PLATTER,TOURAINE........................................    25.00
FLOW BLUE,PLATTER,WILLOW PATTERN,CLEWS,CIRCA 1819,18 IN. X
    13 IN.........................................................   125.00
FLOW BLUE,RING TREE...............................................    12.50
FLOW BLUE,SAUCE,ARGYLE............................................     5.00
FLOW BLUE,SAUCE,LORNE PATTERN,SET OF 6............................     3.50
FLOW BLUE,SOUP,MEAKIN,10 IN.......................................     9.00
FLOW BLUE,SUGAR & CREAMER,CHILD'S,LA BELLE PATTERN................    15.00
FLOW BLUE,SYRUP,DARK BLUE FUSED THROUGHOUT,PEWTER HINGED
    TOP,LA BELLE..................................................    35.00
FLOW BLUE,TEAPOT,MARKED M.........................................    20.00
FLOW BLUE,TOOTHPICK,CHILD'S FACE IN HIGH RELIEF,SCALLOPED
    TOP,SHELLS...................................................    37.50
FLOW BLUE,TUREEN,FORGET-ME-NOT PATTERN,COVER,S.W.DEAN,
    ENGLAND,10 X 6 IN.............................................    35.00
FLOW BLUE,TUREEN,UNDERPLATE,LADLE,COVER,8 IN......................    38.50
FLOW BLUE,TUREEN,VEGETABLE,TOURAINE...............................    35.00
FLOW BLUE,TUREEN,WATTEAU,OPEN HANDLES,ROLLED EDGE,LOW
    PEDESTAL,DOULTON..............................................    55.00
FLOW BLUE,VASE,FLORAL,ENGLAND,8 IN.HIGH,5-IN.DIAMETER.............    22.50
FLOW BLUE,VEGETABLE,CONWAY,OPEN,9 IN.ROUND........................    12.50
FLOW BLUE,VEGETABLE,KESWICK,OPEN,OVAL,11 IN.......................    12.50
FLOW BLUE,VEGETABLE,LADAS PATTERN,RIDGWAY,COVER...................    30.00
FLOW BLUE,VEGETABLE,STERLING PATTERN,COVER,JOHNSON BROTHERS.......    20.00
FLOW BLUE,WASH SET,WASHBOWL,PITCHER,SMALL PITCHER,SOAP DISH,
    MUG,POT......................................................   145.00


    FOO DOGS ARE MYTHICAL CHINESE FIGURES,PART DOG AND
    PART LION. THEY WERE MADE OF POTTERY,PORCELAIN,CARVED
    STONE,AND WOOD.
FOO DOG,CHINESE ROOF TILE,TRANSPARENT GREEN GLAZE,CIRCA
    1767.........................................................   165.00
FOO DOG,INCENSE BURNER,FLARED HANDLES,FOOTED,1819,BRONZE,
    4 1/2 IN.TALL.................................................    30.00
FOO DOG,MALE,FEMALE,YELLOW,GREEN TRIM,BROWN BASE,CHINA,11
    IN.HIGH,PAIR.................................................    45.00
FOO DOG,PASTE WITH HIGH GLAZE,CHINA,6 1/2 IN......................    45.00
FOO DOG,PLAYS WITH BALL,CIRCA 1800,CHINESE,BRONZE,6 IN.LONG.      68.00
FOO DOG,PLAYS WITH BALL,KUTANI,11 IN.TALL.........................    60.00
FOO DOG,SEAL,RED,BLACK,GRAY STONES,CARVING,2 IN.TALL........      10.00


    FOSTORIA GLASS,MADE IN FOSTORIA,OHIO,IS A TWENTIETH-
    CENTURY PRODUCT.
FOSTORIA,BOWL,FROSTED,ETCHED GARLANDS & BOWS,AMBER,FOOTED,
    11 1/2 IN....................................................    12.50
FOSTORIA,BOWL,FRUIT,PRISCILLA PATTERN.............................    12.00
FOSTORIA,DISH,COLONIAL PATTERN,7 1/2-IN.DIAMETER,SET OF 6...      16.00
FOSTORIA,GOBLET,CHINTZ PATTERN,7 1/2 IN.HIGH,SET OF 4.......      16.00
FOSTORIA,TOOTHPICK,SUNBURST BASE,FLINT............................     8.50
FOSTORIA,TUMBLER,DIAMOND PATTERN,BLUE.............................     6.00
    FOVAL,SEE FRY
    FRAME,SEE FURNITURE,FRAME
    FRANCISWARE,SEE ALSO HOBNAIL
FRANCISWARE,BOWL,BERRY,FROSTED HOBNAIL,AMBER PLEATED TOP,
    7 1/2 IN.SQUARE..............................................    23.50
FRANCISWARE,BOWL,BERRY,FROSTED HOBNAIL,RUFFLED AMBER BAND,
    7 IN.SQUARE..................................................    65.00
FRANCISWARE,BOWL,CRIMPED TOP,AMBER,4-IN.DIAMETER,4 IN.HIGH..      35.00
FRANCISWARE,BOWL,SUGAR,COVER......................................    54.00
FRANCISWARE,BOWL,SUGAR,FROSTED HOBS,AMBER BAND & KNOB,COVER.      45.00
FRANCISWARE,CREAMER,GROUND PONTIL,4 X 4 IN........................    50.00
FRANCISWARE,DISH,BUTTER,COVER.....................................    68.00
FRANCISWARE,DISH,OVAL,5 1/2 IN. X 7 1/2 IN. X 2 IN. DEEP....      37.00
FRANCISWARE,SAUCE,FROSTED HOBNAIL,RUFFLED AMBER BAND,4 IN...      20.00
FRANCISWARE,SPOONER,GROUND PONTIL,4 IN. X 4 IN....................    42.50
FRANCISWARE,TOOTHPICK,FROSTED NOBNAIL............... 35.00 TO     55.00
FRANCISWARE,VASE,CELERY,FROSTED HOBNAIL,AMBER PLEATED TOP,
    6 1/2 IN.TALL................................................    45.00
FRANKENTHAL,CABARET,ALLEGORICAL DECORATION,CIRCA 1765.......     700.00
FRANKENTHAL,DISH,PUCE DECOR,MULTICOLOR BORDER...............     400.00
FRANKENTHAL,POT,BULB,CIRCA 1765,8 IN. LONG.................     225.00
FRANKENTHAL,STATUETTE GROUP,SHEEP SHEARING,1755-61,5 1/4 IN.
    HIGH.........................................................   550.00
FRANKENTHAL,STATUETTE,YOUTH SHEARING SHEEP,1765-69,5 1/4 IN.
    TALL.........................................................   425.00
FRANKENTHAL,COFFEEPOT,SCENIC,CIRCA 1780,MONOGRAM CARL
```

```
      THEODORE.............................................    75.00
FRANKOMA,PLAQUE,WILL ROGERS,SIGNED,1936 LABEL,5 X 6 IN......    22.00
```

FRY GLASS WAS MADE BY THE FAMOUS H.C. FRY GLASS COMPANY
OF ROCHESTER,PENNSYLVANIA. IT INCLUDES CUT GLASS,BUT
THE FAMOUS FRY GLASS TODAY IS THE FOVAL OR PEARL ART
GLASS. THIS IS AN OPAL WARE DECORATED WITH COLORED
TRIM. IT WAS MADE FROM 1922 TO 1933.

```
FRY,SEE ALSO CUT GLASS
FRY,BOWL,BLACK,CLEAR BALL STEM,6 IN.TALL,9-IN.DIAMETER......    45.00
FRY,BOWL,CUT GLASS,SIGNED,8-IN.DIAMETER.....................    60.00
FRY,BOWL,YELLOW,BLACK RIM,POLISHED PONTIL,9-IN.DIAMETER.....    25.00
FRY,COMPOTE,JELLY,STRATFORD PATTERN,NOTCHED STANDARD,
   10 1/2 IN.HIGH...........................................   165.00
FRY,CUP,CUSTARD.............................................    10.00
FRY,CUSTARD CUP,OVENWARE,OPALESCENT,DATED 1919..............     5.00
FRY,DISH,RELISH,COPPER WHEEL ENGRAVING,SIGNED..............     45.00
FRY,EPERGNE,SINGLE,INTAGLIO CUT,SIGNED......................    85.00
FRY,NAPPY,CUT GLASS,SIGNED,5 1/2 IN.DIAMETER...............     28.00
FRY,PAN,BAKING,OVAL,6 IN. X 1 1/2 IN.DEEP...................     8.00
FRY,PAN,BREAD,OPALESCENT,PATENT AND DATE MARK..............     8.00
FRY,PITCHER,OPALESCENT BLUE STRIPES OVER BLUE CRYSTAL,
   4 TUMBLERS...............................................    48.00
FRY,PITCHER,SAPPHIRE BLUE OPAL STRIPES,MARKED,FOUR TUMBLERS.   135.00
FRY,PLATE,CAKE,FLORAL DESIGN,OPALESCENT,10 1/2 IN..........     8.00
FRY,PLATE,MILKY BLUE,8 1/2-IN.DIAMETER......................    36.00
FRY,PLATE,OPALESCENT,FLUTED RIM,8 IN........................    12.75
FRY,PLATE,PIE,OVENWARE,SIGNED,9 IN..........................     8.00
FRY,PLATE,PIE,OVENWARE,10 IN................................    15.00
FRY,PLATE,PIE,OVENWARE,9 IN.................................    13.00
FRY,PLATE,PIE,8 IN..........................................    11.00
FRY,PLATE,PINK & SHADED COLORS,STEMMED SHERBET,SET.........     90.00
FRY,RAMEKIN,OVENWARE........................................     5.00
FRY,SHERBET,LIGHT BLUE STEM & BASE,SMOKY YELLOW BOWL.......     65.00
FRY,TRAY,CUT GLASS,10 X 9 IN................................   125.00
FRY,TRAY,FLORAL DECOR,OPALESCENT,FLUTED RIM,12 1/2 IN.LONG..    19.00
FRY,TUMBLER,LEMONADE,CRACKLE,APPLIED BLUE BERRIES AROUND
   BASE,5 3/4 IN............................................    10.00
FRY,VASE,APPLE GREEN LEAVES,CRACKLE GLASS,CLEAR,10 IN.TALL..    75.00
FRY,VASE,APPLIED BLUE ROSETTES,CRACKLE,7 1/4 IN.HIGH.......     28.00
FRY,VASE,CRACKLE,CRYSTAL,APPLIED BLUE PODS,8 3/4 IN........     25.00
FRY,VASE,GREEN DIAMOND DESIGN,JOHN WANAMAKER & FRY PAPER
   LABEL....................................................    38.00
FRY,VASE,THREE GREEN BLOWN BLOSSOMS APPLIED,CRACKLE GLASS,
   8 1/2 IN.................................................    45.00
FRY FOVAL,ATOMIZER,6 1/2 IN.TALL............................    18.00
FRY FOVAL,BOTTLE,BARBER,MILKY WHITE,FIERY OPALESCENT.......     45.00
FRY FOVAL,BOTTLE,PERFUME,PEARL..............................   150.00
FRY FOVAL,BOWL-VASE,MUSHROOM TOP,BLUE BASE,4 1/2 IN.HIGH....   115.00
FRY FOVAL,CANDLESTICK,BLUE AND WHITE,10 IN.................    175.00
FRY FOVAL,CANDLESTICK,BLUE,OPALESCENT,SPIRAL ON STEM,
   10 3/4 IN.,PAIR.....................................ILLUS ..  150.00
FRY FOVAL,CANDLESTICK,FIERY OPAL GLASS,BLUE WAFERS,DIAGONAL
   THREADS,PAIR ............................................   210.00
FRY FOVAL,CANDLESTICK,GREEN & WHITE.........................    80.00
FRY FOVAL,CANDLESTICK,PEARL,DELFT BUTTONS & STRIPES ON
   POSTS,10 IN.,PAIR .......................................   265.00
FRY FOVAL,COFFEEPOT,OPALESCENT,WHITE HANDLE,10 IN.HIGH......   275.00
FRY FOVAL,COMPOTE,CENTERPIECE,BLUE,FLARE DOME BASE,
   14-IN.DIAMETER...........................................   135.00
FRY FOVAL,COMPOTE,CREAM COLOR BASE,BOWL,BLUE STANDARD,
   9 1/4-IN.DIAMETER........................................   125.00
FRY FOVAL,CONSOLE SET,CENTER FOOTED BOWL,PAIR CANDLESTICKS,
   JADE,SILVER .............................................   295.00
FRY FOVAL,CREAMER,OPALESCENT,GREEN TRIM,UNDER TRAY..........    65.00
FRY FOVAL,CRUET,CLEAR,GREEN STOPPER & HANDLE................    10.00
FRY FOVAL,CUP & SAUCER,BLUE OPALINE HANDLE..................    50.00
FRY FOVAL,CUP & SAUCER,DEMITASSE,DELFT HANDLE,STERLING
   SILVER TRIM,4 ...........................................   200.00
FRY FOVAL,CUP & SAUCER,GREEN JADE HANDLE....................    50.00
FRY FOVAL,CUP & SAUCER,OPALESCENT,BLUE HANDLE..............     53.00
FRY FOVAL,CUP & SAUCER,OPALESCENT,GREEN TRIM...............     40.00
FRY FOVAL,LEMON SERVER,OPALESCENT,COBALT CENTER RING HANDLE,
   6 IN.....................................................    45.00
FRY FOVAL,PERCOLATOR,COFFEE,PALE BLUE.......................    75.00
FRY FOVAL,PITCHER,YELLOW,IRIDESCENT,COBALT HANDLE,FOUR
   TUMBLERS.................................................   170.00
FRY FOVAL,PLATE,SOUP BOWL,CUP & SAUCER,BLUE RIM,FOUR OF EACH   470.00
FRY FOVAL,TEAPOT,CREAMY OPALESCENT..........................   105.00
FRY FOVAL,TOOTHPICK,RUFFLED,KETTLE SHAPE,APPLIED BLUE
```

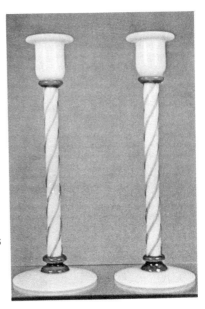

BLUE AND WHITE CANDLESTICKS

```
CRYSTAL HANDLES....................................................   40.00
FRY FOVAL,WINE,GREEN STEM,4 IN....................................   38.00


     FULPER IS THE MARK USED BY THE AMERICAN POTTERY
  COMPANY OF FLEMINGTON,NEW JERSEY.
FULPER,COMPOTE,BASE IS THREE GARGOYLES........................   35.00
FULPER,COMPOTE,THREE FIGURES,11-IN.DIAMETER...................   28.00
FULPER,JUG,BROWN,SESQUICENTENNIAL,PHILADELPHIA,1926,
  5 1/2 IN.....................................................   12.50
FULPER,LAMP,MUSHROOM SHADE,GLASS INSERTS,18-IN.DIAMETER,
  17 IN.TALL...................................................  425.00
FULPER,VASE,BLUE GLAZE,9 IN.TALL..............................   25.00
FULPER,VASE,BLUE SHADING,TWO HANDLES,INCISED MARK,8 3/4 IN..   10.00
FULPER,VASE,BROWN & GREEN,11 IN...............................   13.00
FULPER,VASE,BULBOUS,GREEN GLAZE,SILVER FLECKS,MOTTLED,
  HANDLES,BLACK MARK...........................................   12.00
FULPER,VASE,FAT BEEHIVE SHAPE,SPECKLED ON GREEN,HANDLE,6 IN.   12.50
FULPER,VASE,GRAY,GRECIAN FORM,16 IN...........................   20.00
FULPER,VASE,GREEN MATTE FINISH,BULBOUS,SIGNED,6 1/2 IN......    8.50
FULPER,VASE,GREEN TO DEEP ROSE,THREE HANDLES,SIGNED,
  6 1/4 IN.TALL................................................   25.00
FULPER,VASE,GREEN,SIGNED,9 1/2 IN.............................   10.00
FULPER,VASE,MAUVE ROSE COLOR,SLENDER,SIGNED,6 IN.............    6.50
FULPER,VASE,SILVERY BLUE-GREEN................................   25.00
FULPER,VASE,SILVERY BLUE-GREEN,HANDLES........................   35.00
FULPER,VASE,TORTOISESHELL,12 IN.HIGH..........................   13.00
FURNITURE,ALTAR,CHURCH,OAK,CARVED,BRASS LION HEADS,JEWEL
  BOOK HOLDER..................................................   87.00
FURNITURE,ARMCHAIR,BEAKER SHAPE SPLAT,CURVED ARMRESTS,
  MAHOGANY.....................................................  300.00
FURNITURE,ARMCHAIR,BIEDERMEIER,SQUARE BACK,GILT LION MASK,
  FRUITWOOD,PAIR...............................................  400.00
FURNITURE,ARMCHAIR,CARVED,GEORGE III,MAHOGANY,4......ILLUS..1,400.00
FURNITURE,ARMCHAIR,CHIPPENDALE,TALL BACK,PIERCED SPLAT,YEW
  WOOD.........................................................  350.00
FURNITURE,ARMCHAIR,CURULE,UPHOLSTERED BACKREST,SPANISH,
  CARVED,WALNUT................................................  275.00
FURNITURE,ARMCHAIR,DAMASK SEAT,CHIPPENDALE,CARVED MAHOGANY,
  RESTORED.....................................................  750.00
FURNITURE,ARMCHAIR,DECORATED,REGENCY,STRIPED MATERIAL SEAT,
  PAIR.........................................................  275.00
FURNITURE,ARMCHAIR,HEPPLEWHITE,MAHOGANY,WING,18TH CENTURY,
  AMERICAN...................................................1,100.00
FURNITURE,ARMCHAIR,MARTHA WASHINGTON,HEPPLEWHITE,MAHOGANY...2,000.00
FURNITURE,ARMCHAIR,NEEDLEPOINT SEAT,SHERATON,MAHOGANY,SET OF
  4............................................................  475.00
FURNITURE,ARMCHAIR,QUEEN ANNE,SPANISH FEET,MAPLE,AMERICAN...  750.00
FURNITURE,ARMCHAIR,QUEEN ANNE,WING,CANTED BACK,CLOSED SIDES,
```

GEORGE III MAHOGANY ARMCHAIRS

```
WALNUT...........................................................  800.00
FURNITURE,ARMCHAIR,QUEEN ANNE,WING,MAROON VELVET,FRINGE,
   WALNUT........................................................  550.00
FURNITURE,ARMCHAIR,RECTANGULAR BACKREST,VELVET SEAT,SPANISH,
   PAIR..........................................................  575.00
FURNITURE,ARMCHAIR,RED LACQUER,ALLOVER LANDSCAPE,FLORAL,
   FOLIAGE,CHINA.................................................  150.00
FURNITURE,ARMCHAIR,REGENCY,MAHOGANY,ENGLISH,19TH CENTURY....  275.00
FURNITURE,ARMCHAIR,REGENCY,ROSEWOOD,ENGLISH,19TH CENTURY....  375.00
FURNITURE,ARMCHAIR,SHERATON,CARVED MAHOGANY,18TH CENTURY,
   AMERICAN......................................................  325.00
FURNITURE,ARMCHAIR,SHERATON,MAHOGANY,ENGLISH,18TH CENTURY...  950.00
FURNITURE,ARMCHAIR,SHIELD-SHAPE BACK,CARVED,STUFFOVER SEAT,
   MAHOGANY......................................................  140.00
FURNITURE,ARMCHAIR,SLAT BACK,ARCHED SLATS,ONION FINIALS,RUSH
   SEAT,MAPLE....................................................  250.00
FURNITURE,ARMCHAIR,SLAT BACK,ONION FINIALS,RUSH SEAT,CURLY
   MAPLE.........................................................  575.00
FURNITURE,ARMCHAIR,VICTORIAN,19TH CENTURY,2 PIECES..........   90.00
FURNITURE,ARMCHAIR,VICTORIAN,CARVED ROSEWOOD,CIRCA 1850,
   AMERICAN......................................................  350.00
FURNITURE,ARMCHAIR,WINDSOR,BOW-BACK,18TH CENTURY,
   NEW.................................................120.00 TO  175.00
FURNITURE,ARMCHAIR,WINDSOR,BRACE-BACK,18TH CENTURY,NEW
   ENGLAND.......................................................  225.00
FURNITURE,ARMCHAIR,WINDSOR,WALNUT,19TH CENTURY..............  275.00
FURNITURE,ARMCHAIR,WINDSOR,YEW WOOD,SET OF 6.........ILLUS.1,600.00
FURNITURE,ARMCHAIR,WING,FLORAL DAMASK UPHOLSTERY,CARVED,
   WALNUT......................................................1,200.00
FURNITURE,ARMCHAIR,WING,PADDED ARMRESTS,FLAT STRETCHERS,
   NEEDLEPOINT...................................................  450.00
FURNITURE,ARMCHAIR,WING,SQUARE LEGS,H-SHAPED STRETCHER,
   NEEDLEPOINT...................................................  800.00
FURNITURE,ART NOUVEAU,ETAGERE,FRENCH MARQUETRY,53 IN. HIGH,
   SIGNED........................................................  200.00
FURNITURE,ART NOUVEAU,TABLE,OCCASIONAL,FRENCH MARQUETRY,
   EMILE GALLE...................................................  175.00
FURNITURE,ART NOUVEAU,TABLE,2-TIER OCCASIONAL,FRENCH
   MAHOGANY MARQUETRY............................................  500.00
FURNITURE,ART NOUVEAU,TORCHERE,FRENCH MAHOGANY MARQUETRY,
   EMILE GALLE...................................................  350.00
FURNITURE,ART NOUVEAU,WARDROBE,FRENCH CARVED WALNUT,6 FT.
   HIGH..........................................................  750.00
FURNITURE,ART NOUVEAU,WARDROBE,FRENCH MAHOGANY MARQUETRY,
   MAJORELLE.....................................................  400.00
FURNITURE,BACKBAR,WHITE MARBLE TOP,STAINED GLASS SIDES,
   MIRROR,10 FT.LONG.............................................  400.00
FURNITURE,BAR,ART GLASS PANELS,INSETS,THREE LAMPS,OAK,6 FT.
   X 13 FT.....................................................1,200.00
FURNITURE,BAR,MAHOGANY BACK,MARBLE TOP,STAINED GLASS SIDES,
   MIRROR,10 FT..................................................  500.00
FURNITURE,BAR,WHITE MARBLE TOP,MIRROR,WESTERN STYLE,MAPLE...  100.00
FURNITURE,BED JACK,FOR TIGHTENING ROPE BEDS,WOODEN,CARVED...    8.00
FURNITURE,BED STEP,THREE TREADS,SWIVEL DOOR,DRAWER,LEGS,
```

YEW WOOD WINDSOR ARMCHAIRS

```
  MAHOGANY.....................................................  425.00
FURNITURE,BED,BRASS,ORNATE,POLISHED..........................   75.00
FURNITURE,BED,CANOPY,DOUBLE SIZE,SHERATON,FLAT TESTER,
  MAHOGANY...................................................  795.00
FURNITURE,BED,CIRCULAR CANOPY,SHERATON,BIRCH,HANDMADE SPREAD
  & TRAPPINGS..............................................1,150.00
FURNITURE,BED,DAY,VICTORIAN UPHOLSTERED,19TH CENTURY,7 FEET
  LONG.......................................................  130.00
FURNITURE,BED,DOUBLE,SATIN FINISH,IRON SIDE RAILS,BRASS.....  100.00
FURNITURE,BED,MAPLE LOW HEADPOSTS,PINE HEADBOARD,28 1/2 X
  28 IN.WIDE.................................................   38.00
FURNITURE,BED,MAPLE ROPE,TURNED POST,FULL SIZE,REFINISHED...  135.00
FURNITURE,BED,MARQUETRY,LOUIS XV,KINGWOOD,66 X 82 X
  66 IN.WIDE.................................................  650.00
FURNITURE,BED,POSTER,BELL & BALL,MAPLE,POSTS ARE 43 IN.HIGH.   68.00
FURNITURE,BED,POSTER,TIGER STRIPE..........................  525.00
FURNITURE,BED,SLEIGH,FULL SIZE,MAHOGANY.....................   65.00
FURNITURE,BED,SPOOL,WALNUT..................................   65.00
FURNITURE,BED,SQUARE POSTS,FULL SIZE,BRASS..................   32.50
FURNITURE,BED,TRUNDLE,POSTERS,REFINISHED,CHERRY.............  125.00
FURNITURE,BEDSTEAD,FEDERAL,BRASS-INLAID MAHOGANY,19TH
  CENTURY...................................................  150.00
FURNITURE,BEDSTEAD,TESTER,PAIR,HEPPLEWHITE,CARVED MAHOGANY,
  18TH CENTURY..............................................  100.00
FURNITURE,BEDSTEAD,TESTER,SHERATON,CARVED MAHOGANY,19TH
  CENTURY...................................................  125.00
FURNITURE,BEDSTEAD,TESTER,SHERATON,MAHOGANY,19TH CENTURY,
  AMERICAN..................................................  950.00
FURNITURE,BELLOWS,FIREPLACE,20 IN.LONG,8 IN.SIDE............   16.00
FURNITURE,BELLOWS,LEATHER,28 IN.LONG........................   20.00
FURNITURE,BENCH,BOOTJACK ENDS,PINE,20 1/2 IN.HIGH,48 IN.LONG   18.00
FURNITURE,BENCH,DEACON,EIGHT LEGS...........................  145.00
FURNITURE,BENCH,DEACON,SPINDLE BACK,SOLID SEAT,CURVED ARMS,
  7 FEET LONG...............................................   85.00
FURNITURE,BENCH,DEACON,TURNED SPINDLES,BENT ARMS,STRETCHERS,
  EIGHT LEGS................................................  110.00
FURNITURE,BENCH,DEACON,7 FEET LONG..........................   68.00
FURNITURE,BENCH,EIGHT-SIDED HICKORY LEGS,CURLY MAPLE,
  11 1/2 X 29 1/2 IN........................................   40.00
FURNITURE,BENCH,FIREPLACE,SPLAYED LEGS,ONE-BOARD TOP,
  52 IN.LONG................................................   45.00
FURNITURE,BENCH,RAIL ON BALUSTER SUPPORTS,PAW FEET,ITALIAN,
  WALNUT,65 IN..............................................  225.00
FURNITURE,BENCH,WINDSOR,STENCILS,EIGHT LEGS,PENNSYLVANIA,
  7 FT. X 22 IN.............................................  265.00
FURNITURE,BERGERE A OREILLE,LOUIS XV,PROVINCIAL,RECLINING,
  CARVED OAK................................................  400.00
FURNITURE,BERGERE,LOUIS XVI,AUBUSSON TAPESTRY,GILT.700.00 TO  850.00
```

FURNITURE,BOOKCASE,BREAKFRONT,DOORS,DRAWERS,MAHOGANY,97 X
92 IN.WIDE..................................................2,200.00
FURNITURE,BOOKCASE,D SHAPE,SPINDLE-SUPPORTED SHELVES,
ROSEWOOD,36 1/2 IN........................................ 450.00
FURNITURE,BOOKCASE,DUTCH MARQUETRY,18TH CENTURY.............2,300.00
FURNITURE,BOOKSHELF,ON STAND,DRAWERS IN BASE,SHERATON,
MAHOGANY,48 IN........................................... 475.00
FURNITURE,BOOKSHELF,STANDING,CUPBOARD,GLASS PANELS,MAHOGANY,
52 IN.HIGH............................................... 150.00
FURNITURE,BOOKSHELF,STANDING,GEORGE IV,1800,MAHOGANY,18 X
37 IN.HIGH............................................... 225.00
FURNITURE,BOOKSTAND,INLAID WALNUT,REVOLVING,19TH CENTURY.... 210.00
FURNITURE,BOOKSTAND,VICTORIAN BLEACHED OAK,19TH CENTURY..... 300.00
FURNITURE,BOX,CANDLE,HANGING,TRIANGULAR HANGER TAB,PINE,
11 IN. X 15 IN........................................... 45.00
FURNITURE,BOX,COAL,MAHOGANY,TIN-LINED,BRASS SHOVEL IN
HOLDER,ENGLAND........................................... 50.00
FURNITURE,BOX,COAL,MIRROR,VICTORIAN........................ 125.00
FURNITURE,BOX,KNIFE CLEANING,SQUARE CUT NAILS,PINE,5 X 10 X
29 IN.LONG............................................... 35.00
FURNITURE,BREAKFRONT BOOKCASE,ADJUSTABLE SHELVES,FOUR DOORS,
107 X 93 IN...............................................1,700.00
FURNITURE,BREAKFRONT BOOKCASE,FOUR 13-PANELED DOORS,
MAHOGANY,99 X 98 IN.......................................1,400.00
FURNITURE,BUFFET,HEPPLEWHITE,D SHAPE,MAHOGANY.............. 365.00
FURNITURE,BUREAU,CENTRAL CUPBOARD,PIGEONHOLES,QUEEN ANNE,
WALNUT,41 IN............................................. 950.00
FURNITURE,BUREAU,CYLINDER,TAMBOUR SHUTTER,DUTCH MARQUETRY,
MAHOGANY................................................. 350.00
FURNITURE,BUREAU,CYLINDER,WRITING SURFACE,DRAWERS,INLAID
FRUITWOOD,ITALY.......................................... 700.00
FURNITURE,BUREAU,LEATHER WRITING SURFACE,THREE DRAWERS,BURL
YEW WOOD................................................. 700.00
FURNITURE,BUREAU,MINIATURE,INDO-DUTCH PADOUK,DRAWERS,
15 1/2 IN.HIGH........................................... 150.00
FURNITURE,BUREAU PLAT,LOUIS XV STYLE.................ILLUS..4,500.00
FURNITURE,BUREAU PLAT,PARQUETRY,LOUIS XV,KINGWOOD,64 IN.
WIDE......................................................2,600.00
FURNITURE,BUREAU PLAT,REGENCE STYLE,KINGWOOD & MAHOGANY,70 X
31 1/2 IN................................................ 850.00
FURNITURE,BUREAU BOOKCASE,CHIPPENDALE,MAHOGANY,17TH CENTURY,
ENGLAND...................................................1,275.00
FURNITURE,BUREAU BOOKCASE,QUEEN ANNE,WALNUT,81 IN....ILLUS..1,750.00
FURNITURE,BUTLER'S SEAT,UMBRELLA STAND,DRAWER,MIRROR,HOOKS,
MAHOGANY................................................. 750.00
FURNITURE,CABINET,BUTLER'S SECRETARY,VICTORIAN,MAHOGANY,
CIRCA 1840............................................... 225.00
FURNITURE,CABINET,CHIPPENDALE,CHERRYWOOD,18TH CENTURY,NEW
ENGLAND.................................................. 700.00
FURNITURE,CABINET,COIN,MINIATURE,MAHOGANY & WALNUT,
9 1/2 IN.HIGH............................................ 60.00
FURNITURE,CABINET,COROMANDEL,FIGURES,ROSE MOTIF,BROWN-BLACK,
CHINA,PAIR............................................... 695.00
FURNITURE,CABINET,CURIO,CARVED,18TH CENTURY,TEAK,36 IN. X
75 IN.HIGH............................................... 900.00
FURNITURE,CABINET,CURIO,CURVED GLASS IN DOOR & SIDES,BRASS
TRIM,FRANCE.............................................. 185.00
FURNITURE,CABINET,CURIO,RED-LACQUERED,LINED WITH TEA PAPER,
ROSEWOOD................................................. 150.00
FURNITURE,CABINET,CURIO,SEDAN CHAIR,INLAID,ORMULU,18TH
CENTURY,FRANCE........................................... 600.00
FURNITURE,CABINET,CURVED GLASS DOOR & PANELS,WALNUT FINISH,
56 IN.HIGH............................................... 125.00
FURNITURE,CABINET,FEDERAL,BRASS-INLAID ROSEWOOD,19TH CENTURY 100.00
FURNITURE,CABINET,GLASS DOORS,DRAWERS,BINS,COVERS,MAHOGANY,
54 X 70 IN................................................1,850.00
FURNITURE,CABINET,HUTCH,PINE,19TH CENTURY,AMERICAN......... 80.00
FURNITURE,CABINET,ON STAND,PORCELAIN,ORMOLU,89 IN....ILLUS.. 900.00
FURNITURE,CABINET,PADOUK,ON STAND,ORIENTAL GOTHIC,PIERCED
PANELS....................................................1,100.00
FURNITURE,CABINET,SEWING,THREE DRAWERS,REEDED LEGS,MAHOGANY,
28 IN.TALL............................................... 59.00
FURNITURE,CABINET,SIDE,LOUIS XV,VERDE ANTICO MARBLE TOP,
KINGWOOD,45 IN............................................1,000.00
FURNITURE,CABINET,SPICE,EIGHT DRAWERS,STENCILING........... 39.00
FURNITURE,CABINET,SPICE,EIGHT DRAWERS,PINE,5 IN. X 11 IN. X
18 IN.................................................... 20.00
FURNITURE,CABINET,SPICE,NINE SMALL DRAWERS,ONE LARGE DRAWER,
WALNUT................................................... 85.00
FURNITURE,CABINET,SPICE AND SEED,41 IN. HIGH.........ILLUS.. 800.00
FURNITURE,CABINET,SPOOL,FOUR DRAWERS,OAK.................. 35.00

LOUIS XV BUREAU PLAT

QUEEN ANNE WALNUT
BUREAU BOOKCASE

CABINET ON STAND

SPICE AND SEED CABINET

```
FURNITURE,CABINET,SPOOL,FOUR DRAWERS,WALNUT.................    35.00
FURNITURE,CABINET,SPOOL,SIX DRAWERS,END TABLE SIZE,
   REFINISHED.............................................    75.00
FURNITURE,CABINET,SPOOL,SIX DRAWERS,MERRICK'S SPOOL COTTON,
   OAK....................................................    98.00
FURNITURE,CABINET,SPOOL,TWO DRAWERS,BRASS PULLS,CHERRY......    24.00
```

FURNITURE,CABINET,SPOOL,TWO DRAWERS,WALNUT.................... 26.00
FURNITURE,CABINET,TOBACCO,OAK,PIPE RACK ON DOOR,ROYAL
DOULTON HUMIDOR.................................................. 48.00
FURNITURE,CABINET,VITRINE,LOUIS XV,MARBLE TOP,KINGWOOD,
70 IN.HIGH....................................................3,250.00
FURNITURE,CABINET,VITRINE,VICTORIAN,HALF ROUND FORM,DOORS,
SATIN BIRCH.................................................... 200.00
FURNITURE,CABINET,WALL,SECTIONS,GLASS DOOR,HONG KONG,TEAK,
33 1/2 IN...................................................... 199.00
FURNITURE,CADDY,TEA,MOTHER-OF-PEARL INLAID,BLACK,LACQUER,
11 IN.TALL..................................................... 145.00
FURNITURE,CADDY,TEA,TORTOISESHELL,REGENCY,SILVER BALL FEET,
FINIAL......................................................... 140.00
FURNITURE,CANDLE SHADE,CARVED WOODEN FRAME,BLACK SILK,FOOTED 15.00
FURNITURE,CANDLESTAND,CARVED TOP,CARVED LEAF PEDESTAL,LEGS,
MAPLE,31 IN.................................................... 55.00
FURNITURE,CANDLESTAND,CHIPPENDALE,CARVED MAHOGANY,19TH
CENTURY,AMERICAN.............................................. 150.00
FURNITURE,CANDLESTAND,CHIPPENDALE,CHERRYWOOD,18TH CENTURY,
AMERICAN...................................................... 125.00
FURNITURE,CANDLESTAND,HEPPLEWITHE,CHERRYWOOD,19TH CENTURY,
NEW ENGLAND................................................... 150.00
FURNITURE,CANDLESTAND,TRIPOD BASE,SNAKE FOOT,CHERRY,NEW
ENGLAND....................................................... 225.00
FURNITURE,CANTERBURY,FOUR DIVISIONS,BRASS CARRYING HANDLE,
MAHOGANY...................................................... 275.00
FURNITURE,CANTERBURY,FOUR DIVISIONS,GILT HANDLE,DRAWER,
BRACKET FEET................................................1,500.00
FURNITURE,CANTERBURY,THREE DIVISIONS,CONCAVE TOP RAILS,
MAHOGANY,19 IN................................................ 175.00
FURNITURE,CELLARETTE,LIFT TOP,TRIPLE BRASS BANDS,SHAPED
LEGS,MAHOGANY................................................. 400.00
FURNITURE,CHAIR,4,SHERATON,TURNED-WOOD,19TH CENTURY,AMERICAN 70.00
FURNITURE,CHAIR,4,VICTORIAN,SIDE,MAHOGANY,CIRCA 1850,
AMERICAN...................................................... 60.00
FURNITURE,CHAIR,4,VICTORIAN TURNED WALNUT,BALLROOM,19TH
CENTURY....................................................... 225.00
FURNITURE,CHAIR,9,VICTORIAN,CURLY MAPLE,SIDE,19TH CENTURY,
NEW ENGLAND................................................... 225.00
FURNITURE,CHAIR,14,DINING,VICTORIAN CARVED WALNUT,19TH
CENTURY....................................................... 200.00
FURNITURE,CHAIR,ALTAR,BACK HAS MARBLE INSET,BATS,MOON,CHINA,
TEAK,PAIR..................................................... 750.00
FURNITURE,CHAIR,ARM,CARVED TEAK,TWO TIGERS AT ENDS OF ARMS,
INDIA,1880..................................................1,250.00
FURNITURE,CHAIR,ARM,UPHOLSTERED SEAT & BACK CENTER,GOTHIC
DESIGN,WALNUT................................................. 28.50
FURNITURE,CHAIR,BALL & CLAW FEET,FINIALS ON BRASS ROD,OAK... 22.50
FURNITURE,CHAIR,BROAD CREST RAIL,PAINTED LANDSCAPE,CANE
SEAT,SABER LEGS............................................... 125.00
FURNITURE,CHAIR,CAPTAIN'S.............................ILLUS.. 20.00

CAPTAIN'S CHAIR

```
FURNITURE,CHAIR,CARVED DANTE HEAD ON BACK,SHIELD ON FRONT,
    UPHOLSTERED...............................................    90.00
FURNITURE,CHAIR,CHILD'S,PAINTED TO SIMULATE MAHOGANY,SPINDLE
    SPLATS...................................................    50.00
FURNITURE,CHAIR,CHILD'S,PLANK SEAT,STENCIL,ALPHABET, GOOD
    GIRL, SPLATS.............................................    18.00
FURNITURE,CHAIR,CHILD'S,LADDER-BACK,ARCHED SPLATS,RUSH SEAT,
    PAINTED..................................................    18.00
FURNITURE,CHAIR,CHILD'S,SLAT BACK,TURNED ARMS & LEGS,FRANCE,
    CIRCA 1820...............................................    55.00
FURNITURE,CHAIR,CHILD'S,VICTORIAN ROSEWOOD,CIRCA 1860,
    AMERICAN.................................................   180.00
FURNITURE,CHAIR,CHILD'S,WINDSOR,SIDE,18TH CENTURY............   375.00
FURNITURE,CHAIR,CORNER,AMERICAN COUNTRY,PAINTED......ILLUS..    90.00
FURNITURE,CHAIR,CORNER,CARVED MAHOGANY,GEORGE III....ILLUS..   550.00
FURNITURE,CHAIR,CORNER,CURVED BACKREST,SQUARE LEGS,VELVET
    SEAT COVER...............................................   275.00
FURNITURE,CHAIR,CORNER,EASTLAKE.............................    65.00
FURNITURE,CHAIR,CORNER,SPLIT RUSH SEAT,MAPLE,18TH CENTURY,
    REFINISHED...............................................   285.00
FURNITURE,CHAIR,DESK,GREEN LEATHER BACK,SEAT,SIDES,ORMOLU
    MOUNTS,ITALY.............................................   200.00
```

AMERICAN COUNTRY CORNER CHAIR

GEORGE III MAHOGANY CORNER CHAIR

```
FURNITURE,CHAIR,DESK,SWIVEL,ARMS,UPHOLSTERED SEAT & BACK
  CENTER,OAK...................................................   15.00
FURNITURE,CHAIR,DINING,BLACK LACQUER,VELVET SEAT,QUEEN ANNE,
  SET OF 8.................................................1,750.00
FURNITURE,CHAIR,DINING,LEATHER UPHOLSTERY,HEPPLEWHITE,
  MAHOGANY,SET OF 6..........................................  525.00
FURNITURE,CHAIR,DINING,MOLDED UPRIGHT,SHAPED TOP RAIL,
  MAHOGANY,SET OF 6..........................................  950.00
FURNITURE,CHAIR,DINING,PIERCED VASE FORM SPLAT,MAHOGANY,SET
  OF 5.......................................................  200.00
FURNITURE,CHAIR,DINING,REED UPRIGHT,LEATHER SEAT,1800,
  MAHOGANY,SET OF 7..........................................  500.00
FURNITURE,CHAIR,DINING,RUSH SEAT,SABER LEGS,FRUITWOOD,
  BEIDERMEIER,SIX............................................  300.00
FURNITURE,CHAIR,EXERCISE,SPRUNG SEAT,PULLOUT FOOTREST,
  MAHOGANY...................................................  225.00
FURNITURE,CHAIR,FIDDLEBACK,NEW CANE SEAT,CURLY MAPLE,SET OF
  6..........................................................  425.00
FURNITURE,CHAIR,FIDDLEBACK,CANE SEAT,REFINISHED,CURLY MAPLE.   25.00
FURNITURE,CHAIR,GENT'S,CARVED ROSES,MAHOGANY,NEW UPHOLSTERY.  185.00
FURNITURE,CHAIR,GEORGE I,MAHOGANY,17TH CENTURY,ENGLAND......  500.00
FURNITURE,CHAIR,HIGH,CHILD'S,RUSH SEAT,MAPLE...............   95.00
FURNITURE,CHAIR,ICE CREAM............................ILLUS.   12.00
FURNITURE,CHAIR,ICE CREAM,WHITE,VELVET SEAT,3 IN.HIGH.......    5.00
FURNITURE,CHAIR,LADDER-BACK,SAUSAGE TURNINGS,18TH CENTURY,
  MAPLE & ASH................................................  135.00
FURNITURE,CHAIR,LADY'S,TUFTED BACK,NEW GREEN VELVET COVER,
  WALNUT.....................................................  150.00
```

ICE CREAM CHAIR

```
FURNITURE,CHAIR,LION'S PAW FEET,RAM'S HORNS ON ARMS,WALNUT..   27.50
FURNITURE,CHAIR,OFFICE,HIGH CARVED BACK,SWIVEL,OAK.........   65.00
FURNITURE,CHAIR,PAINT & STENCIL,SHERATON,THREE SIDE & ONE
  ARM CHAIR..................................................  600.00
FURNITURE,CHAIR,PAIR,ENGLISH,HEPPLEWHITE,FRUITWOOD,SIDE,19TH
  CENTURY....................................................  350.00
FURNITURE,CHAIR,PAIR,SIDE,SHERATON,BAMBOO-TURNER,19TH
  CENTURY,AMERICAN...........................................  150.00
FURNITURE,CHAIR,PLANK SEAT,ARROW BACK,STENCIL,PAINTED,PAIR..   68.00
FURNITURE,CHAIR,PLANK SEAT,DOG-EAR TOP RAIL,PENNSYLVANIA,SET
  OF 6.......................................................  265.00
FURNITURE,CHAIR,PLUSH SEAT,DOG EAR TOP RAIL,PENNSYLVANIA,SET
  OF 6.......................................................  265.00
FURNITURE,CHAIR,QUEEN ANNE,RUSH SLIP SEAT,1882,MAHOGANY.....  750.00
FURNITURE,CHAIR,RABBIT EAR,PLANK SEAT,ARROW BACK...........   35.00
FURNITURE,CHAIR,ROCKING,LINCOLN,MAPLE......................   46.00
FURNITURE,CHAIR,ROCKING,WINDSOR,HOOPED BACK,PIERCED SPLAT,
  ASH........................................................  170.00
FURNITURE,CHAIR,ROCKING,WINDSOR,RABBIT EAR,STENCIL.........   45.00
FURNITURE,CHAIR,RUSH SEAT,DOUBLE RAIL IN BACK,WALNUT,MAPLE,
  OAK,4......................................................  125.00
FURNITURE,CHAIR,SHERATON,MAHOGANY,ENGLISH,18TH CENTURY......  160.00
FURNITURE,CHAIR,SIDE,BLACK HAIRCLOTH SEAT,HEPPLEWHITE,
  MAHOGANY................................................1,600.00
```

```
FURNITURE,CHAIR,SIDE,CAROLINE,CARVED,CANE SEAT & BACKREST,
  WALNUT...................................................    70.00
FURNITURE,CHAIR,SIDE,CARVED,FRANCE,WALNUT....................    45.00
FURNITURE,CHAIR,SIDE,CARVED,HOOP BACK,QUEEN ANNE,WALNUT,PAIR   700.00
FURNITURE,CHAIR,SIDE,CARVED,SATIN UPHOLSTERY,EMPIRE,
  MAHOGANY,PAIR...........................................    800.00
FURNITURE,CHAIR,SIDE,CARVED,VINES,TAPERED LEGS,FOLIAGE,
  MAHOGANY,PAIR...........................................    150.00
FURNITURE,CHAIR,SIDE,CHIPPENDALE,CHERRYWOOD,18TH CENTURY,NEW
  ENGLAND.................................................    125.00
FURNITURE,CHAIR,SIDE,FIDDLEBACK,EMPIRE,WALNUT,NEEDLEPOINT
  SEAT,PAIR...............................................    115.00
FURNITURE,CHAIR,SIDE,LADDER-BACK,RUSH SEAT,CARVED,YORKSHIRE,
  ASH,PAIR................................................    225.00
FURNITURE,CHAIR,SIDE,LADDER-BACK,SHIELD-SHAPE BACK,MAHOGANY,
  PAIR....................................................     85.00
FURNITURE,CHAIR,SIDE,LYRE BACK,GREEN VELVET SEAT,WALNUT,
  21 1/2 IN.HIGH..........................................     45.00
FURNITURE,CHAIR,SIDE,NAPOLEON III,PAIR,WITH PAIR CHAIRS SAME
  PERIOD,4................................................    150.00
FURNITURE,CHAIR,SIDE,PADOUK,NEEDLEWORK UPHOLSTERY,DUTCH,PAIR    60.00
FURNITURE,CHAIR,SIDE,QUEEN ANNE,LEATHER SEAT,ARCHED CREST
  RAIL,WALNUT...........................................1,000.00
FURNITURE,CHAIR,SIDE,QUEEN ANNE,TEXTURE FABRIC SEAT,WALNUT,
  PAIR................................................1,900.00
FURNITURE,CHAIR,SIDE,REGENCY,SPINDLE SPLATS,CANE SEAT,
  PAINTED,SET OF 6........................................    200.00
FURNITURE,CHAIR,SIDE,REGENCY,SPINDLE SPLATS,RUSH SEAT,
  PAINTED,SET OF 4........................................    110.00
FURNITURE,CHAIR,SIDE,ROSE,BASKET ON TOP RAIL,NEEDLEPOINT
  SEAT,WALNUT,4...........................................    350.00
FURNITURE,CHAIR,SIDE,SHIELD-SHAPE BACK,STUFFOVER SEAT,
  HEPPLEWHITE,PAIR........................................    450.00
FURNITURE,CHAIR,SIDE,SHIELD-SHAPE BACK,VASE-SHAPE SPLAT,
  FOLIAGE,PAIR............................................    450.00
FURNITURE,CHAIR,SIDE,TIGER MAPLE,CIRCA 1840.................     59.00
FURNITURE,CHAIR,SIDE,UPHOLSTERED BACK,STUFFOVER SEAT,
  MAHOGANY,SET OF 6.......................................    550.00
FURNITURE,CHAIR,SIDE,VICTORIAN,CURVED BACKREST,PAINTED
  BLACK,GILT,PAIR.........................................     80.00
FURNITURE,CHAIR,SIDE,WINDSOR,SEVEN SPINDLES,TWO-SPINDLE
  BRACE BACK,BLACK........................................    200.00
FURNITURE,CHAIR,SIDE,6,PAINTED MAPLE,SLAT-BACK,18TH CENTURY,
  AMERICAN................................................    125.00
FURNITURE,CHAIR,SIDE,6,VICTORIAN,MAHOGANY & CHERRYWOOD,19TH
  CENTURY.................................................    170.00
FURNITURE,CHAIR,SLAT-BACK,TURNED ARMS & LEGS,FRANCE,1840....     45.00
FURNITURE,CHAIR,SPINDLES IN BACK FRAME,CUSHIONED SEATS,
  CANED,OAK...............................................     18.00
FURNITURE,CHAIR,SPINDLE-BACK,CURVED STRETCHER,CANE SEAT,
  HONEY MAPLE,4...........................................    125.00
FURNITURE,CHAIR,TEAK,ORIENTAL........................ILLUS..    200.00
```

ORIENTAL TEAK CHAIR

FURNITURE,CHAIR,VICTORIAN,PAINT,LACQUER,MOTHER-OF-PEARL
    DECOR,PAIR.................................................. 75.00
FURNITURE,CHAIR,VICTORIAN,PAPIER-MACHE,LACQUER,
    MOTHER-OF-PEARL DECOR...................................... 150.00
FURNITURE,CHAIR,WEAVER,SPLIT BARK SEAT,CIRCA 1800........... 85.00
FURNITURE,CHAIR,WICKER.................................ILLUS.. 25.00
FURNITURE,CHAIR,WINDSOR,BIRDCAGE,SIGNED,DECORATED,SET OF 6.. 895.00
FURNITURE,CHAIR,WINDSOR,BIRDCAGE BACK....................... 150.00
FURNITURE,CHAIR,WINDSOR,BUTTERFLY,PENNA.,SET OF 6,ONE
    SLIPPER CHAIR............................................. 750.00
FURNITURE,CHAIR,WINDSOR,FANBACK,SEVEN SPINDLES,SADDLE SEAT,
    BLACK.................................................... 175.00
FURNITURE,CHAIR,WINDSOR,RABBIT EAR......................... 85.00
FURNITURE,CHAIR,WINDSOR,RABBIT EAR,SET OF 4................ 365.00
FURNITURE,CHAIR,WINDSOR,SADDLED PLANK SEATS,ARROW-BACK,GREEN
    PAINT,3.................................................. 120.00
FURNITURE,CHAIR,WINDSOR,STICK-BACK,SIX SPINDLES,PLANK SEAT,
    PAINTED,PAIR............................................. 65.00
FURNITURE,CHAIR,WING,CHIPPENDALE,MAHOGANY..................1,765.00
FURNITURE,CHAIR,WRITING,CURVED BACKREST,FAN-SHAPE SEAT,
    SQUARE LEGS.............................................. 175.00
FURNITURE,CHAIR-BED,FOLDING,1874 MODEL FOR PATENT
    APPLICATION.............................................. 35.00
FURNITURE,CHAISE LOUNGE,ORNATE WALNUT,VELVET COVER.......... 155.00
FURNITURE,CHAISE LOUNGE,REGENCY,UPHOLSTERED,BOLSTER,
    MAHOGANY,6 FEET LONG..................................... 150.00
FURNITURE,CHAISE LOUNGE,TEAKWOOD,CHINA...................... 350.00
FURNITURE,CHEST,APOTHECARY,BRACKET BASE,PANELED ENDS,
    15 DRAWERS,PINE.......................................... 325.00
FURNITURE,CHEST,APOTHECARY,TWO LONG DRAWERS,16 SMALL
    DRAWERS,PINE............................................. 365.00
FURNITURE,CHEST,BACHELOR,SOLID END,FOUR DRAWERS,WALNUT,
    30 IN.HIGH............................................... 225.00
FURNITURE,CHEST,BLANKET,CHERRY,REFINISHED.................. 75.00
FURNITURE,CHEST,BLANKET,CHIPPENDALE,TWO DRAWERS,BRACKET
    FOOT,40 IN.WIDE......................................... 285.00
FURNITURE,CHEST,BLANKET,LIFT TOP,PANELED DRAWER,PINE,44 X
    25 1/2 IN.HIGH.......................................... 200.00
FURNITURE,CHEST,BLANKET,OAK,17TH CENTURY................... 225.00
FURNITURE,CHEST,BLANKET,PINE,19TH CENTURY,AMERICAN......... 80.00
FURNITURE,CHEST,BLANKET,TWO DRAWERS,STENCIL,HEPPLEWHITE,
    CIRCA 1815.............................................. 235.00
FURNITURE,CHEST,BLANKET,TWO DRAWERS,LIFT TOP,PINE.......... 125.00
FURNITURE,CHEST,BLANKET,TWO DRAWERS,STIPPLED GREEN,RED TRIM,
    CHIPPENDALE............................................. 750.00
FURNITURE,CHEST,BLANKET,36 IN.HIGH,WALNUT & PINE.......... 110.00
FURNITURE,CHEST,BOW FRONT,FIVE DRAWERS,SPLAYED BRACKET FEET,
    MAHOGANY................................................ 350.00
FURNITURE,CHEST,BOW FRONT,TULIPWOOD EDGE,FOUR DRAWERS,
    MAHOGANY................................................ 800.00
FURNITURE,CHEST,BRIDE'S,PENN,PINE,1799..............ILLUS.. 325.00
FURNITURE,CHEST,BRIDE'S,PENNSYLVANIA,PINE,51 IN.....ILLUS..2,000.00
FURNITURE,CHEST,BUTLER'S SECRETARY,DRAWERS,CHIPPENDALE,
    MAHOGANY,43 IN..........................................1,300.00
FURNITURE,CHEST,CHIPPENDALE,FOUR DRAWERS,FRENCH FEET,CHERRY,
    42 IN.WIDE.............................................. 575.00
FURNITURE,CHEST,CUTLERY,BRASS HANDLES,TWO-TIER STAND,
    ENGLAND,MAHOGANY........................................ 100.00
FURNITURE,CHEST,DRESSING,SHERATON,INLAID MAHOGANY,19TH
    CENTURY................................................. 80.00
FURNITURE,CHEST,EIGHT DRAWERS,TURNED SHERATON FEET,1810,
    CHERRY.................................................. 650.00
FURNITURE,CHEST,FIGURES,FLORAL,IVORY,JADE,MOTHER-OF-PEARL,
    CHINA................................................... 650.00
FURNITURE,CHEST,FIVE DRAWERS,MAPLE,BRACKET BASE,BRASSES,
    36 IN.WIDE.............................................. 450.00
FURNITURE,CHEST,FIVE DRAWERS,MAPLE,BRACKET BASE TYPE,
    BRASSES,OLD VARNISH..................................... 395.00
FURNITURE,CHEST,FOUR DRAWERS,1815,NEEDS BRACKET BASE....... 115.00
FURNITURE,CHEST,FOUR DRAWERS,BOWFRONT,HEPPLEWHITE,MAHOGANY,
    PENNSYLVANIA............................................ 450.00
FURNITURE,CHEST,FOUR DRAWERS,CHIPPENDALE,MAHOGANY,RESTORED,
    30 1/2 IN............................................... 750.00
FURNITURE,CHEST,FOUR DRAWERS,CIRCA 1810,TIGER MAPLE........ 145.00
FURNITURE,CHEST,FOUR DRAWERS,CUTOUT BASE,WOODEN PULLS,1800,
    34 1/2 IN............................................... 235.00
FURNITURE,CHEST,FOUR DRAWERS,PANEL END,PINE,PAINTED,NEW
    ENGLAND................................................. 45.00
FURNITURE,CHEST,FOUR DRAWERS,PINE,SOLID END,NEW ENGLAND,39 X
    38 IN.HIGH.............................................. 110.00
FURNITURE,CHEST,FOUR DRAWERS,PLANK ENDS,DOVETAIL,CIRCA 1800,

WICKER CHAIR

BRIDE'S CHEST

PENNSYLVANIA PINE BRIDE'S CHEST

```
CHERRY.......................................................  400.00
FURNITURE,CHEST,FOUR DRAWERS,SOLID END,BIRCH,BRACKET BASE,
  37 X 35 IN..................................................  285.00
FURNITURE,CHEST,FOUR DRAWERS,SOLID END,BRACKET-TYPE BASE,
  PINE........................................................  225.00
FURNITURE,CHEST,FOUR DRAWERS,SOLID END,MAPLE,GOOD BRASSES,
  36 X 34 IN..................................................  295.00
FURNITURE,CHEST,FOUR DRAWERS,SOLID END,PINE,BRACKET BASE,
  36 X 38 IN.HIGH.............................................  265.00
FURNITURE,CHEST,FOUR GRADUATED DRAWERS,TWO SIDE BY SIDE,
  1800,CHERRY.................................................  400.00
FURNITURE,CHEST,HEPPLEWHITE,BOWFRONT,FOUR DRAWERS,INLAY,
  MAHOGANY,40 IN..............................................  475.00
FURNITURE,CHEST,HIGH,SHERATON,BRASSES,CHERRY.................  650.00
FURNITURE,CHEST,IMMIGRANT,DOVETAILED,OAK.....................  125.00
FURNITURE,CHEST,LEATHER GROUND,PAINTED DECOR,STAND,DUTCH,
  38 IN.HIGH..................................................  100.00
FURNITURE,CHEST,MINIATURE,FOUR DRAWERS,HEPPLEWHITE,MAHOGANY,
  11 1/2 IN...................................................  225.00
FURNITURE,CHEST,MINIATURE,FOUR DRAWERS,PAINTED,PINE,14 X
  13 1/2 IN.WIDE..............................................  170.00
FURNITURE,CHEST,NORWEGIAN,PAINTED,IRONWORK,DATED 1839,18 X
  20 X 40 IN..................................................  175.00
FURNITURE,CHEST OF DRAWERS,DUTCH,MAHOGANY,19TH CENTURY.......  425.00
FURNITURE,CHEST OF DRAWERS,HEPPLEWHITE,INLAID MAHOGANY,CIRCA
  1800........................................................  450.00
FURNITURE,CHEST OF DRAWERS,HEPPLEWHITE,MAHOGANY,
  BOWFRONT.........................................500.00 TO  650.00
FURNITURE,CHEST OF DRAWERS,HEPPLEWHITE,MAHOGANY & BIRD'S-EYE
  MAPLE.......................................................  200.00
FURNITURE,CHEST OF DRAWERS,HEPPLEWHITE,MAHOGANY,SWELL FRONT,
  AMERICAN....................................................  750.00
FURNITURE,CHEST OF DRAWERS,MINIATURE,MAHOGANY,BOWFRONT,19TH
  CENTURY.....................................................  300.00
FURNITURE,CHEST OF DRAWERS,PINE,19TH CENTURY,AMERICAN.......  225.00
FURNITURE,CHEST,OLIVEWOOD VENEER,C.1700.............ILLUS..2,000.00
FURNITURE,CHEST ON FRAME,WILLIAM & MARY,MATCHING TABLE,
  OYSTER BURL,1680.........................................1,990.00
FURNITURE,CHEST-ON-CHEST,CAMPAIGN,PAINTED BLACK,FIVE
  DRAWERS,ENGLAND.............................................  350.00
FURNITURE,CHEST-ON-CHEST,CHIPPENDALE,CARVED MAHOGANY,44 X
  98 IN.HIGH...............................................6,000.00
FURNITURE,CHEST,ON STAND,GILT HINGES,ESCUTCHEONS,FLORAL,
  LACQUER,62 IN............................................1,000.00
FURNITURE,CHEST,ON STAND,WILLIAM & MARY,WALNUT,38 1/2 X
  64 1/2 IN.HIGH.............................................  325.00
FURNITURE,CHEST,SIX DRAWERS,MAPLE,BRACKET BASE,GOOD BRASSES,
  36 X 52 IN..................................................  650.00
FURNITURE,CHEST,SIX DRAWERS,BRACKET BASE,TIGER MAPLE,
  CHIPPENDALE..............................................1,495.00
FURNITURE,CHEST,SIX DRAWERS,BRACKET BASE,CHIPPENDALE,
  54 IN.HIGH...............................................1,250.00
```

CHEST, OLIVEWOOD VENEER, C. 1700

```
FURNITURE,CHEST,STIPPLED,DOVETAILED,LOCK,PENNA.DUTCH,7 X
  14 X 6 1/2 IN........................................................   85.00
FURNITURE,CHEST,THREE DRAWERS,PINE,NEW ENGLAND,34 IN.WIDE,
  28 IN.HIGH..........................................................  400.00
FURNITURE,CHEST,VICTORIAN...............................................   65.00
FURNITURE,CLOCK,CASE,HEPPLEWHITE,CHERRYWOOD,CIRCA 1825.......  850.00
FURNITURE,CLOCK,TALL-CASE,CHIPPENDALE,MAHOGANY,C.1810.......  600.00
FURNITURE,CLOCK,TALL-CASE,HEPPLEWHITE,MAHOGANY,CIRCA 1815...  650.00
FURNITURE,COMB RACK,TOWEL BAR,MIRROR,OAK,VICTORIAN,
  REFINISHED.........................................................   22.00
FURNITURE,COMMODE,BEDSIDE,LIFT TOP,CIRCULAR PLINTH,DRAWER,
  WALNUT.............................................................   50.00
FURNITURE,COMMODE,BURL FRONT,THREE DRAWERS,ONE DOOR,
  BUTTERNUT TOP,WALNUT...............................................  150.00
FURNITURE,COMMODE,HALL,BACK SPLASH,STENCILED,MARBLE TOP,
  DRAWER,DOOR,PINE...................................................   48.00
FURNITURE,COMMODE,HALL,DOOR,DRAWER,MARBLE TOP,MAHOGANY,
  BLACK,17 X 20 IN...................................................   98.00
FURNITURE,COMMODE,LOUIS XVI MAHOGANY,18TH CENTURY,35 IN.
  HIGH...........................................................1,700.00
FURNITURE,COMMODE,LOUIS XVI,BY PAUL SORMANI,PARIS,MAHOGANY,
  57 IN.WIDE.....................................................2,100.00
FURNITURE,COMMODE,MARQUETRY,LOUIS XVI,40 IN.HIGH X 70 IN.
  WIDE...........................................................1,600.00
FURNITURE,COMMODE,MARQUETRY,SIGNED H.BIEDER.........ILLUS..2,200.00
FURNITURE,CRADLE,CURVED SIDES,PINE,12 IN.WIDE,36 IN.LONG....   32.00
FURNITURE,CRADLE,DOVETAILING,CHERRY,REFINISHED,15 X
  40 IN.LONG.........................................................   95.00
FURNITURE,CRADLE,HOOD,PINE.............................................  105.00
FURNITURE,CRADLE,1904..................................................   15.00
FURNITURE,CREDENZA,ITALIAN RENAISSANCE,CARVED,DRAWERS,DOORS,
  44 IN..............................................................  650.00
FURNITURE,CUPBOARD,BEDSIDE,GALLERY TOP,SINGLE DOOR,MAHOGANY,
  27 IN.,PAIR........................................................  350.00
FURNITURE,CUPBOARD,BEDSIDE,TRAY TOP,GRIPS,TAMBOUR SHUTTER,
  DRAWER,31 IN.......................................................  135.00
FURNITURE,CUPBOARD,BEDSIDE,6 PIECES,MARBLE TOP.............  130.00
FURNITURE,CUPBOARD,CHIPPENDALE,CHERRYWOOD,CORNER,18TH
  CENTURY........................................................1,850.00
FURNITURE,CUPBOARD,CORNER,CATHEDRAL DOORS,SHELL INTERIOR,
  PINE,7 FT.TALL.....................................................  950.00
FURNITURE,CUPBOARD,CORNER,HANGING,OPEN FRONT,THREE SHELVES,
  PINE,36 IN.........................................................   85.00
FURNITURE,CUPBOARD,CORNER,HANGING,PANEL DOOR,SHELF,DRAWER,
  BLACK WALNUT.......................................................  125.00
FURNITURE,CUPBOARD,CORNER,RAISED PANELS,PENNSYLVANIA,WALNUT.  300.00
FURNITURE,CUPBOARD,CORNER,TWO-PART,PANELED DOORS,DRAWER,PINE  550.00
FURNITURE,CUPBOARD,CORNER,TWO-PIECE,ARCHED DOOR,CIRCA 1780,
  PENNSYLVANIA...................................................1,650.00
FURNITURE,CUPBOARD,COURT,JACOBEAN,TWO DOORS,FOLIAGE INLAY,
  CARVED FRIEZE......................................................  600.00
FURNITURE,CUPBOARD,HANGING,GLASS DOORS,MAHOGANY FINISH,PINE,
  34 IN.HIGH.........................................................   32.50
```

MARQUETRY COMMODE,
SIGNED H. BIEDER

FURNITURE,CUPBOARD,HANGING,MAHOGANY,52 IN.WIDE X
  29 1/2 IN.HIGH.................................................... 195.00
FURNITURE,CUPBOARD,HUTCH,MOLDED REED CORNICE,DOORS,PINE,
  PENNSYLVANIA...............................................1,100.00
FURNITURE,CUPBOARD,LINEN,LOUIS XV,PROVINCIAL,FRUITWOOD,18TH
  CENTURY........................................................ 550.00
FURNITURE,CUPBOARD,LOUIS XV,PROVINCIAL,ARCHED DOORS,CARVED,
  FRUITWOOD...................................................... 425.00
FURNITURE,CUPBOARD,LOUIS XV,PROVINCIAL,DOORS,CARVED PANELS,
  OAK,49 IN...................................................... 250.00
FURNITURE,CUPBOARD,PAIR,EMPIRE MAHOGANY,PEDESTAL,19TH
  CENTURY........................................................ 400.00
FURNITURE,CUPBOARD,PIE,BOTTOM DRAWER,HEART CUTOUT BASE,
  WOODEN......................................................... 115.00
FURNITURE,CUPBOARD,PIE,TWO DOORS,PIERCED TIN PANELS,DRAWERS,
  PINE,PENNA..................................................... 350.00
FURNITURE,CUPBOARD,WALNUT,49 1/2 IN. X 7 1/2 FT......ILLUS.. 250.00
FURNITURE,CUTLERY BOX,CUTOUT CENTER HANDLE,DIVIDED,COVER,
  FRANCE,1820.................................................... 55.00
FURNITURE,CUTLERY BOX,SLANT LID,INLAID,IRELAND,MAHOGANY,
  13 1/2 IN.TALL................................................. 160.00
FURNITURE,DESK,BUTLER'S SECRETARY,FEDERAL,MAHOGANY,19TH
  CENTURY,AMERICAN............................................... 350.00
FURNITURE,DESK,CHIPPENDALE,MAHOGANY,KNEEHOLE,18TH CENTURY,
  AMERICAN....................................................... 700.00
FURNITURE,DESK,DAVENPORT,LEATHER WRITING SURFACE,DRAWERS,
  ROSEWOOD....................................................... 300.00

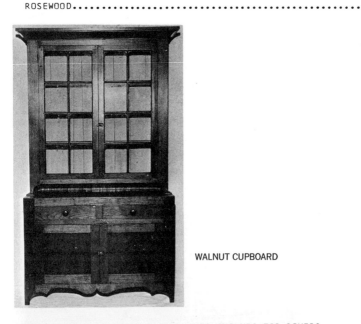

WALNUT CUPBOARD

FURNITURE,DESK,DRAWERS,PIGEONHOLES,SHELVES,TOP COVERS,
  CHERRY,1869.................................................... 265.00
FURNITURE,DESK,FLAT TOP,DRAWERS,LINCOLN MEDALLION,1880,
  MAHOGANY....................................................... 345.00
FURNITURE,DESK,GOVERNOR WINTHROP,DOUBLE STEP INTERIOR,MAPLE,
  38 IN.WIDE..................................................... 750.00
FURNITURE,DESK,HEPPLEWHITE,PINE,SLANT-FRONT,19TH CENTURY,
  AMERICAN....................................................... 300.00
FURNITURE,DESK,LADY'S,DRAWER,HAND-CARVED FRUIT HANDLE,BLACK
  WALNUT......................................................... 129.00
FURNITURE,DESK,LADY'S,OVAL TOP,DRAWER,WALNUT,19 X 30 X
  29 1/2 IN.HIGH................................................. 115.00
FURNITURE,DESK,PIGEONHOLES,FOUR DRAWERS,BRASS PULLS,MAPLE,
  36 IN.WIDE..................................................... 750.00
FURNITURE,DESK,PIGEONHOLES,LEDGER SPACES,DRAWERS,MAHOGANY,
  TWO-PIECE...................................................... 400.00
FURNITURE,DESK,POST OFFICE,RHODE ISLAND PINE,TURNED LEGS,
  CUBBYHOLES..................................................... 350.00
FURNITURE,DESK,QUAKER MEETING HOUSE,DOVETAILED,SPLIT LIFT
  LIDS,WALNUT.................................................... 375.00
FURNITURE,DESK,ROLLTOP,OAK...................................... 150.00
FURNITURE,DESK,ROLLTOP,WALNUT................................... 145.00
FURNITURE,DESK,SCHOOLMASTER-TYPE................................ 75.00

```
FURNITURE,DESK,SCHOOLMASTER,SLANT LIFT TOP,FILE BOX ON SIDE
    OF TOP,OAK.............................................   200.00
FURNITURE,DESK,SIX DRAWERS GALLERY,CENTER DOOR HAS OVAL
    PORCELAIN,FRANCE.......................................   700.00
FURNITURE,DESK,SLANT FRONT,BRACKET FEET,CHIPPENDALE,WALNUT,
    PENNSYLVANIA..........................................   900.00
FURNITURE,DESK,SLANT FRONT,CHIPPENDALE,INLAID,WALNUT,40 X
    42 1/2 IN.HIGH........................................   750.00
FURNITURE,DESK,SLANT FRONT,18TH CENTURY,CHERRY............   950.00
FURNITURE,DESK,SLANT TOP,CHIPPENDALE,BOOTJACK ENDS,PINE,
    24 IN.WIDE............................................   375.00
FURNITURE,DESK,VICTORIAN BLEACHED OAK,PEDESTAL,19TH CENTURY.  350.00
FURNITURE,DESK,WRITING,BLOCK FRONT,CHIPPENDALE,MAHOGANY,NEW
    ENGLAND............................................5,250.00
FURNITURE,DOUGH TROUGH,PINE,19TH CENTURY,AMERICAN..........    50.00
FURNITURE,DRESSER,WELSH,QUEEN ANNE,OAK,1720,78 IN.HIGH,
    72 IN.LONG.........................................1,545.00
FURNITURE,DRESSER,WHITE MARBLE TOP,TEN DRAWERS,CARVED PULLS,
    WALNUT...............................................   250.00
FURNITURE,DRESSER,WISHBONE,WALNUT.........................    90.00
FURNITURE,DRESSER,YORKSHIRE,QUEEN ANNE,OAK,77 IN.....ILLUS..1,600.00
FURNITURE,DRY SINK,PINE...................................    39.50
FURNITURE,ETAGERE,TWO-TIER,LOUIS XV,KINGWOOD,35 IN.HIGH,
    28-IN.DIAMETER.....................................1,100.00
FURNITURE,FENDER,PIERCED STEEL & BRASS,IMPLEMENT REST,
    63 IN.LONG...........................................   125.00
FURNITURE,FIREPLACE SCREEN,ORNATE SPOKES,CIRCLES,SCROLLS,
```

QUEEN ANNE OAK DRESSER,
YORKSHIRE

```
    BENTWOOD,1880........................................    65.00
FURNITURE,FIREPLACE TRAMMEL,SAW TEETH,IRON,30 IN.LONG......    65.00
FURNITURE,FIREPLACE,MARBLE,CIRCA 1800.....................   125.00
FURNITURE,FLAX WHEEL,AMERICAN.............................    55.00
FURNITURE,FOOT WARMER,CARPET-COVERED,DRAWER FOR CHARCOAL...     7.50
FURNITURE,FOOTSTOOL,CRICKET,RED...........................    18.00
FURNITURE,FOOTSTOOL,QUEEN ANNE,CARVED WALNUT,NEEDLEPOINT
    TOP,ROUND............................................    65.00
FURNITURE,FOOTSTOOL,SCROLL FORM,CARVED FLORAL,UPHOLSTERED,
    ROSEWOOD.............................................    45.00
FURNITURE,FOOTSTOOL,WALNUT,TAPESTRY TOP...................     4.00
FURNITURE,FRAME,PICTURE,EASEL-BACK,BRASS OVER IRON,ORNATE,
    5 X 7 IN.............................................     8.50
FURNITURE,GLOBE,MINIATURE,TERRESTRIAL,CELESTIAL,MALLEY,
    6 1/2 IN.,PAIR.......................................   230.00
FURNITURE,GLOBE,TERRESTRIAL,CELESTIAL,STAND,LEGS,T.HARRIS &
    SON,PAIR...........................................1,000.00
FURNITURE,HAT RACK,WALL,OAK,10 PORCELAIN-CAPPED PEGS,
    STRETCHES TO 48 IN...................................    21.00
FURNITURE,HIGHBOY,CHIPPENDALE,CURLY MAPLE,18TH CENTURY,RHODE
    ISLAND.............................................2,250.00
FURNITURE,HIGHBOY,QUEEN ANNE,CHERRYWOOD,18TH CENTURY,NEW
    ENGLAND............................................1,200.00
```

```
FURNITURE,HIGHBOY,QUEEN ANNE,WALNUT,18TH CENTURY,AMERICAN...2,800.00
FURNITURE,HIGHBOY,ROSETTES,MAPLE SIDES,HONDURAS MAHOGANY,
   CIRCA 1780.................................................8,500.00
FURNITURE,HIGHCHAIR,CHILD'S,RUSH SEAT.........................   75.00
FURNITURE,HIGHCHAIR,CHILD'S,WINDSOR TYPE,PLANK SEAT,SPLAYED
   LEGS......................................................   50.00
FURNITURE,HUNT BOARD,SHERATON.................................  950.00
FURNITURE,INSTRUMENT,ASTROLOGICAL,PAINTED WOOD,19TH CENTURY.   350.00
FURNITURE,KNEELING BENCH,NOTCHED DECOR ON ENDS,NEW ENGLAND,
   PINE,21 IN................................................   17.50
FURNITURE,LIBRARY STEPS/BERGERE,SEAT & BACK FOLD,LOOSE
   CUSHION,MAHOGANY..........................................  250.00
FURNITURE,LOOM,RUG............................................  125.00
FURNITURE,LOVE SEAT,GRAPE BACK,WALNUT,HORSEHAIR COVERING,
   48 IN.SEAT................................................  165.00
FURNITURE,LOVE SEAT,TUFTED MEDALLION BACK,ROSEWOOD,CIRCA
   1840......................................................  600.00
FURNITURE,LOVE SEAT,VICTORIAN,FINGER-CARVED,WALNUT...........  100.00
FURNITURE,LOWBOY,QUEEN ANNE,WALNUT,18TH CENTURY,NEW ENGLAND.4,250.00
FURNITURE,MANTEL,VITRUVIAN SCROLLS,CARRARA MARBLE,48 X
   73 IN. WIDE...............................................  425.00
FURNITURE,MIRROR,BRASS FRAME,CUTOUT FLORAL DECOR,OVAL,8 IN.
   X 10 IN...................................................   16.50
FURNITURE,MIRROR,DRESSING TABLE,DRAWERS,OGEE BRACKET FEET,
   MAHOGANY..................................................  100.00
FURNITURE,MIRROR,DRESSING TABLE,LOUIS XV BOULLE,19TH CENTURY  375.00
FURNITURE,MIRROR,DRESSING TABLE,MARQUETRY,DUTCH,WALNUT,
   25 1/2 IN.HIGH............................................  170.00
FURNITURE,MIRROR,DRESSING TABLE,SHIELD-SHAPE PLATE,DRAWERS,
   BRACKET FEET..............................................  125.00
FURNITURE,MIRROR,DRESSING,INLAID MAHOGANY,MIRROR MISSING,
   25 IN.HIGH................................................   80.00
FURNITURE,MIRROR,FEDERAL,CARVED & GILDED CONVEX,WALL,CIRCA
   1810......................................................  500.00
FURNITURE,MIRROR,GILT WOOD,ADAM STYLE,FLORAL SWAGS,CARVED
   EWERS,PAIR................................................  225.00
FURNITURE,MIRROR,GILT WOOD,C SCROLLS,FOLIAGE,CHIPPENDALE
   STYLE,PAIR................................................  275.00
FURNITURE,MIRROR,HAND,METAL,CLOISONNE-TYPE ENAMEL,CIRCA
   1880,CHINA................................................   45.00
FURNITURE,MIRROR,PHOENIX ON TOP CENTER,PARCEL-GILT MAHOGANY,
   58 IN.HIGH................................................4,000.00
FURNITURE,MIRROR,REVERSE PAINTING ON GLASS,MAHOGANY FRAME,
   12 X 20 IN................................................   79.00
FURNITURE,MIRROR,TRAVELING,FOLDING,THREE SECTIONS,MAHOGANY
   FRAME.....................................................   45.00
FURNITURE,MIRROR,WALL,FEDERAL,CARVED & PARCEL-GILT,CIRCA
   1800......................................................  450.00
FURNITURE,MIRROR,WALL,FEDERAL,GILDED,EGLOMISE DECORATION,
   CIRCA 1810................................................  275.00
FURNITURE,MIRROR,WALL,GILT GESSO,CARVED,QUEEN ANNE,22 1/2 X
   43 IN.HIGH................................................  250.00
FURNITURE,MIRROR,WALL,GILT WOOD,CARVED,TRELLIS,LEAF TIPS,
   FLORAL,52 IN..............................................  550.00
FURNITURE,MIRROR,WALL,SCROLL-CARVED,PARCEL-GILT,CHIPPENDALE,
   MAHOGANY..................................................  250.00
FURNITURE,MIRROR,WALL,SHERATON,INLAID MAHOGANY,18TH CENTURY.  525.00
FURNITURE,MUSIC STAND,ROCOCO,BRONZE FINISH,CHERUB,VIOLIN,
   BIRDCAGE..................................................   47.50
FURNITURE,NIGHT STAND,DRAWER,HEPPLEWHITE,MAHOGANY,22 X
   31 IN.HIGH................................................  250.00
FURNITURE,NIGHT STAND,ONE DRAWER,TOWEL RACKS,PINE,REFINISHED   20.00
FURNITURE,NIGHTSTAND,TWO DRAWERS,SHERATON,CURLY MAPLE &
   CHERRYWOOD................................................  150.00
FURNITURE,PANEL,SET OF 4,AUBUSSON TAPESTRY,12 FT. X 5 FT....  850.00
FURNITURE,PARLOR SET,HORSEHAIR,BLACK WALNUT,VICTORIAN,
   7 PIECES..................................................  295.00
FURNITURE,PEDESTAL,TERM FORM,TAPERED COLUMN,PANELS,MARBLE,
   51 IN.,PAIR...............................................  900.00
FURNITURE,RACK,DICTIONARY,PEDESTAL,BASE,CASTORS,IRON,WITH
   DICTIONARY................................................   95.00
FURNITURE,RING,TOWEL,WALL,CURLY MAPLE........................    5.00
FURNITURE,ROCKER,BOSTON......................................   55.00
FURNITURE,ROCKER,BOSTON,HICKORY SPINDLES,PAINTED BLACK,MAPLE   65.00
FURNITURE,ROCKER,BOSTON,LADY'S...............................   46.00
FURNITURE,ROCKER,BOSTON,STENCIL,REFINISHED...................  119.00
FURNITURE,ROCKER,GRAPE BACK,REUPHOLSTERED,WALNUT............   129.00
FURNITURE,ROCKER,PINE,REFINISHED & REUPHOLSTERED............   110.00
FURNITURE,ROCKER,PLATFORM,MAPLE..............................   35.00
FURNITURE,SCREEN,CHINESE INCISED LACQUER,EIGHT FOLDS,18TH
   CENTURY...................................................  550.00
```

FURNITURE,SCREEN,CHINESE,BLACK LACQUER,EIGHT FOLDS,19TH
  CENTURY..............................................................3,250.00
FURNITURE,SCREEN,EIGHT FOLDS,COROMANDEL,LACQUER,CHINA,
  85 IN.HIGH.......................................................... 170.00
FURNITURE,SCREEN,FIRE,CARTOUCHE SHAPE FRAME,NEEDLEWORK
  PANEL,WALNUT........................................................ 250.00
FURNITURE,SCREEN,FIRE,VICTORIAN STAINED GLASS & ROSEWOOD.... 325.00
FURNITURE,SCREEN,FOUR FOLDS,COROMANDEL,LACQUER,CHINESE,
  70 1/2 IN.HIGH..................................................... 550.00
FURNITURE,SCREEN,FOUR FOLDS,LACQUER,COROMANDEL,ORIENTAL
  MOTIF,72 IN.HIGH.................................................... 525.00
FURNITURE,SCREEN,FRENCH,PAINTED PAPER,THREE FOLDS,19TH
  CENTURY............................................................. 500.00
FURNITURE,SCREEN,PAINTED LEATHER,THREE FOLDS,POOR CONDITION,
  85 X 66 IN......................................................... 90.00
FURNITURE,SCREEN,POLE,NEEDLEWORK BANNER,TRIPOD LEGS,CARVED
  MAHOGANY............................................................ 350.00
FURNITURE,SCREEN,POLE,ROSEWOOD FRAME & BASE,NEEDLEPOINT,
  GIRL,BIRD,SCENE.................................................... 95.00
FURNITURE,SCREEN,SIX FOLDS,PAINTED CANVAS,ALLOVER SCENE,
  73 IN.HIGH......................................................... 200.00
FURNITURE,SCREEN,SIX FOLDS,MOUNTAINOUS LANDSCAPE,JAPAN,
  47 IN.HIGH......................................................... 40.00
FURNITURE,SCREEN,SNAKE FOOT,ADJUSTABLE SCREEN,QUEEN ANNE,
  55 IN.HIGH......................................................... 295.00
FURNITURE,SCREEN,THREE FOLDS,NAPOLEON III,TAPESTRY,GILT
  WOOD,61 IN.HIGH.................................................... 300.00
FURNITURE,SCREEN,THREE FOLDS,PAINTED CANVAS,PANELS,CASTERS,
  67 IN.HIGH......................................................... 100.00
FURNITURE,SEAT,SPRING WAGON,REFINISHED...................... 60.00
FURNITURE,SECRETARY-BOOKCASE,CHIPPENDALE,MAHOGANY,47 X
  95 IN.HIGH.........................................................2,750.00
FURNITURE,SECRETARY,BIEDERMEIER,DENTIL CORNICE,TAMBOUR
  CUPBOARD,WALNUT..................................................... 200.00
FURNITURE,SECRETARY,CABINET,ROLLTOP DESK,CARVED WALNUT,
  9 FEET TALL........................................................ 500.00
FURNITURE,SECRETARY,FALL FRONT,DRAWERS,PIGEONHOLES,DOORS,
  MAHOGANY............................................................ 500.00
FURNITURE,SERVING STAND,MARTHA WASHINGTON,MAHOGANY FINISH... 18.00
FURNITURE,SETTEE,BRUSSELS TAPESTRY,WALNUT,QUEEN ANNE,
  RESTORED,68 IN.LONG................................................ 350.00
FURNITURE,SETTEE,C.1830 AMERICAN,MAPLE,CHERRY........ILLUS..1,200.00
FURNITURE,SETTEE,CAMEO CARVED ON ARMS,UPHOLSTERY,TWO CHAIRS. 600.00
FURNITURE,SETTEE,CARVED,FLORAL SILK UPHOLSTERY,BEECHWOOD,
  56 IN.LONG......................................................... 400.00
FURNITURE,SETTEE,CHURCH,PINE,19TH CENTURY................... 150.00
FURNITURE,SETTEE,CURVED ARMRESTS,UPHOLSTERED,MAHOGANY,
  36 1/2 IN.LONG..................................................... 300.00
FURNITURE,SETTEE,GEORGE III,UPHOLSTERY,SPLAYED LEGS,
  MAHOGANY,5 FEET LONG............................................... 125.00
FURNITURE,SETTEE,NAPOLEON III,AUBUSSON TAPESTRY UPHOLSTERY,
  GILT WOOD.......................................................... 250.00
FURNITURE,SETTEE,NEEDLEWORK UPHOLSTER,GEORGE III STYLE,
  MAHOGANY............................................................ 250.00
FURNITURE,SETTEE,REGENCY,UPHOLSTERED,MAHOGANY,76 1/2 IN.LONG 200.00
FURNITURE,SETTEE,TWO-CHAIR BACK,PETIT POINT UPHOLSTERED
  SEAT,WALNUT........................................................ 575.00
FURNITURE,SETTEE,UPHOLSTERED,MAHOGANY FRAME................. 300.00

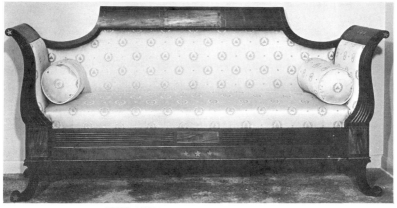

SETTEE, AMERICAN, MAPLE, CHERRY, C. 1830

```
FURNITURE,SETTEE,WINDSOR,BAMBOO-TURNED SPINDLES,PLANK SEAT,
  70 IN.LONG......................................................    900.00
FURNITURE,SETTEE,WINDSOR,DUCKBILL,BIRDCAGE,BAMBOO TURNINGS,
  6 FEET LONG....................................................    750.00
FURNITURE,SETTEE,WINDSOR,FOUR-CHAIR BACK,PLANK SEAT,
  78 IN.LONG.....................................................    950.00
FURNITURE,SEWING BOX,DIVIDED TOP DRAWER,HANDLE,3 DRAWERS,
  MULBERRY WOOD..................................................     19.50
FURNITURE,SEWING BOX,TWO TIERS,DRAWER FOR SPOOLS,MAHOGANY,
  5 1/2 X 7 IN...................................................     18.00
FURNITURE,SHELF,DRAWER,WOODEN,REFINISHED,31 IN.LONG,
  8 1/2 IN.HIGH..................................................     22.50
FURNITURE,SHELF,HANGING,REGENCY,PAINTED TO SIMULATE
  SATINWOOD,28 IN.WIDE...........................................    160.00
FURNITURE,SHELF,MIRROR BACK,WALNUT,28 IN.LONG X 56 IN.HIGH..      65.00
FURNITURE,SHELF,PAIR,CHIPPENDALE,MAHOGANY,HANGING,ENGLISH,
  18TH CENTURY.................................................2,200.00
FURNITURE,SHELF,PAPIER-MACHE,ORIENTAL DESIGNS,FOLDS FLAT,
  14 IN.HIGH.....................................................     15.00
FURNITURE,SIDEBOARD,ARCHED,TAMBOUR CUPBOARD,DRAWERS,
  MAHOGANY,54 IN.WIDE............................................    650.00
FURNITURE,SIDEBOARD,BOWED BREAKFRONT FORM,MAHOGANY,35 IN. X
  6 FEET WIDE....................................................    850.00
FURNITURE,SIDEBOARD,BOWFRONT CENTER SECTION,HEPPLEWHITE,
  MAHOGANY....................................................1,550.00
FURNITURE,SIDEBOARD,BRASS HANDLES,ENGLAND,OAK,22 1/2 IN. X
  44 IN.HIGH.....................................................    375.00
FURNITURE,SIDEBOARD,BREAKFRONT OUTLINE,CENTER DRAWER,
  MAHOGANY,36 IN.HIGH.........................................1,300.00
FURNITURE,SIDEBOARD,DRAWER ABOVE ARCHED RECESS,MAHOGANY,55 X
  35 IN.HIGH.....................................................    800.00
FURNITURE,SIDEBOARD,FEDERAL,MAHOGANY,CIRCA 1815......ILLUS..2,200.00
FURNITURE,SIDEBOARD,FIVE DRAWERS,MARBLE TOP,MIRROR BACK,
  WALNUT,78 IN...................................................    195.00
FURNITURE,SIDEBOARD,HEPPLEWHITE,INLAID MAHOGANY SERPENTINE..2,100.00
FURNITURE,SIDEBOARD,HEPPLEWHITE,INLAID,MAHOGANY,18TH CENTURY1,800.00
FURNITURE,SIDEBOARD,INLAID,HEPPLEWHITE,MAHOGANY......ILLUS..2,100.00
FURNITURE,SIDEBOARD,MIRROR-BACK TOP,CLAW FEET,OAK,
  52 IN.LONG,75 IN.HIGH..........................................     75.00
FURNITURE,SIDEBOARD,PINE.........................................    450.00
FURNITURE,SIDEBOARD,SERPENTINE,SILVER DRAWER,TWO DEEP
  DRAWERS,MAHOGANY...............................................    425.00
FURNITURE,SIDEBOARD,SHERATON,MAHOGANY,FRONT REEDING,48 IN...    550.00
FURNITURE,SIDEBOARD,SHERATON,MAHOGANY,MINIATURE,19TH CENTURY    275.00
FURNITURE,SINK CUPBOARD,TWO DOORS ABOVE WELL,SPICE DRAWERS,
  PENNSYLVANIA...................................................    225.00
FURNITURE,SOFA,CLAW & BALL FEET,CHIPPENDALE,CARVED MAHOGANY,
  72 1/2 IN...................................................1,700.00
FURNITURE,SOFA,FEDERAL,BRASS INLAID MAHOGANY,19TH CENTURY...    250.00
FURNITURE,SOFA,FEDERAL,CARVED MAHOGANY,CIRCA 1825,NEW YORK..    700.00
FURNITURE,SOFA,FEDERAL,SERPENTINE BACK,BROCADE BOLSTERS,
  82 IN.LONG.....................................................    200.00
```

FEDERAL MAHOGONY SIDEBOARD, C. 1815

```
FURNITURE,SOFA,GRAPE BACK,WALNUT,68 IN.,TWO SIDE CHAIRS,NEW
  UPHOLSTERING...........................................  545.00
FURNITURE,SOFA,REED FRAME,SHERATON,VELOUR,WALNUT,53 IN.LONG.1,200.00
FURNITURE,SOFA,STUFFED SIDES,OVERSCROLL,MAHOGANY,7 FEET LONG  150.00
FURNITURE,SOFA,VELOUR BACK,SIDES,SEAT,SHERATON,MAHOGANY,
  66 1/2 IN.LONG.......................................2,900.00
FURNITURE,SOFA,VICTORIAN,EBONIZED WOOD,1860,PAIR.....ILLUS..3,000.00
FURNITURE,SOFA,VICTORIAN UPHOLSTERED,RED LEATHER,19TH
  CENTURY..............................................  600.00
FURNITURE,SPICE BOX,WALL,EIGHT DRAWERS,PORCELAIN KNOBS,OAK..   45.00
FURNITURE,SPICE CABINET,NINE SMALL DRAWERS,ONE LARGE DRAWER,
  WALNUT...............................................   85.00
FURNITURE,SPINNING WHEEL............................ILLUS..   40.00
```

HEPPLEWHITE MAHOGANY SIDEBOARD

SPINNING WHEEL

```
FURNITURE,SPINNING WHEEL,DOUBLE HEADS,CHANGEABLE WHEELPOSTS.   48.00
FURNITURE,SPINNING WHEEL,MEDIUM SIZE......................   100.00
FURNITURE,SPINNING WHEEL,PAINTED ORANGE,SCANDINAVIAN,
  40 1/2 IN.HIGH......................................    45.00
FURNITURE,SPINNING WHEEL,RED PAINT,22 IN.WHEEL,36 IN.HIGH...   40.00
FURNITURE,SPINNING WHEEL,SPINDLE SPOKES,ORANGE PAINT,
  SCANDINAVIAN,36 IN..................................    35.00
FURNITURE,SPINNING WHEEL,TWIN SHUTTLES,FLAX DISTAFF,
  16-IN.WHEELS........................................    49.50
FURNITURE,SPINNING WHEEL,43-IN.DIAMETER WHEEL.............    35.00
FURNITURE,STAND,BAMBOO DESIGN,MARBLE TOP,ROSEWOOD,
  32 IN.HIGH,PAIR.....................................   250.00
FURNITURE,STAND,BLACKAMOOR,HOLDS TRAY,PAINTED,GILT,VENETIAN,
  57 IN.HIGH..........................................   225.00
FURNITURE,STAND,BRASS,LACY,ONYX TOP,SHELF,14 IN.SQUARE,
  10-IN.DIAMETER......................................    62.50
FURNITURE,STAND,CANDLE,PAINTED,HEPPLEWHITE................   115.00
FURNITURE,STAND,COUNTRY,ONE DRAWER,PINE,18 X 18 X 29 IN.HIGH   69.50
FURNITURE,STAND,DICTIONARY,IRON BASE,WOODEN WINGS,WITH
  DICTIONARY..........................................    48.00
FURNITURE,STAND,DRAWER,LYRE-SHAPE LEGS,BOTTOM SHELF,WALNUT,
  27 1/2 IN...........................................    62.50
FURNITURE,STAND,DROP LEAF,ONE DRAWER,PINE,28 1/2 IN.HIGH....   58.00
FURNITURE,STAND,LAMP,SPOOL-TURNED COLUMN,CIRCA 1810,
  AMERICAN,CHERRY.....................................   145.00
FURNITURE,STAND,NIGHT,HEPPLEWHITE,CIRCA 1810,AMERICAN.......  200.00
FURNITURE,STAND,NIGHT,PINE,19TH CENTURY,AMERICAN...........  125.00
FURNITURE,STAND,ONE DRAWER,CHERRY.........................    97.50
FURNITURE,STAND,ONE DRAWER,SQUARE TOP,CURLY MAPLE,21 X
  28 IN.HIGH..........................................   160.00
FURNITURE,STAND,ONE DRAWER,TAPERED LEGS,CHERRY,18 X 18 X
  26 IN.HIGH..........................................    75.00
FURNITURE,STAND,ONE DRAWER,TAPERED LEGS,CHERRY,REFINISHED,
  26 IN.HIGH..........................................    75.00
FURNITURE,STAND,SEWING,TWO DRAWERS,FEDERAL PERIOD,MAHOGANY..  275.00
FURNITURE,STAND,SEWING,VICTORIAN,WALNUT,ENGLISH,19TH CENTURY  140.00
FURNITURE,STAND,SINGLE DRAWER,STENCIL,MAPLE...............    28.00
FURNITURE,STAND,THREE-TIER,OAK,30 1/2 IN.HIGH.............    35.00
FURNITURE,STAND,UMBRELLA,WALNUT,BRASS PAN.................    28.00
```

VICTORIAN·EBONIZED WOOD SOFA C. 1860

FURNITURE,STAND,URN,OVAL TOP,UNDULATING GALLERY,TAPERED
LEGS,MAHOGANY ........................................................ 375.00
FURNITURE,STEP,BED,GEORGE III,LIFT TOPS,DRAWER FRONT,
MAHOGANY ............................................................. 200.00
FURNITURE,STOOL,JACOBEAN,CARVED,MOLDED TOP,PLAIN FRIEZE,OAK. 150.00
FURNITURE,STOOL,MILK,THREE LEGS,11 1/2 IN.HIGH,SEAT
16 IN.LONG,8 IN.WIDE ................................................ 16.50
FURNITURE,STOOL,MILKING,THREE MORTISED & WEDGED LEGS,HOLE
FOR HANGING .......................................................... 8.00
FURNITURE,STOOL,MILKING,THREE ROUND LEGS EXTEND THROUGH TOP,
BURL TOP ............................................................. 25.00
FURNITURE,STOOL,ORGAN,HIGH BACK ...................................... 38.00
FURNITURE,STOOL,PIANO,ADJUSTABLE,GLASS BALL FEET,NEEDS
REFINISHING .......................................................... 15.00
FURNITURE,STOOL,PIANO,CLAW & GLASS BALL FEET ......................... 18.00
FURNITURE,STOOL,PIANO,GEORGE III,UPHOLSTERED TOP,SCREW
SUPPORT,MAHOGANY ..................................................... 40.00
FURNITURE,STOOL,PIANO,ORNATE LEGS,BALL & CLAW FEET,
ADJUSTABLE,WALNUT .................................................... 27.50
FURNITURE,STOOL,PIANO,REVOLVING SEAT,SABER LEGS,REGENCY,
ROSEWOOD ............................................................. 150.00
FURNITURE,STOOL,PIANO,REVOLVING,RED LEATHER SEAT,FLUTED
LEGS,ROSEWOOD ........................................................ 190.00
FURNITURE,STOOL,PIANO,ROPE LEGS,CLAW & BALL FEET,MAHOGANY ... 25.00
FURNITURE,STOOL,PIANO,UPHOLSTERED,RATCHET ADJUSTMENT,PATENT
OTTOMAN,1880 ......................................................... 18.50
FURNITURE,STOOL,PIANO,WITH BACK,CLAW FEET ............................ 55.00
FURNITURE,STOOL,RECTANGULAR,STUFFOVER SEAT,NEEDLEPOINT,
SQUARE LEGS .......................................................... 210.00
FURNITURE,STOOL,WALNUT ............................................... 45.00
FURNITURE,TABLE SCREEN,SLATE,LANDSCAPE,CARVED,GILT FRAME,
19 IN .............................................................. 1,200.00
FURNITURE,TABLE,ALTAR,CARVED KEY & CLOUD DESIGN,SYMBOLS,
CHINA,TEAK ........................................................... 695.00
FURNITURE,TABLE,ARCHITECT,DRAWER,SPLIT FRONT LEGS,MAHOGANY,
31 IN.HIGH ........................................................... 375.00
FURNITURE,TABLE,BEDSIDE,GEORGE III,CUPBOARD DOOR,GALLERY
TOP,MAHOGANY ......................................................... 150.00
FURNITURE,TABLE,BEDSIDE,SHERATON,INLAID MAHOGANY,CIRCA 1800,
ENGLISH .............................................................. 190.00
FURNITURE,TABLE,BEDSIDE,SHERATON,MAHOGANY,KIDNEY-SHAPED,18TH
CENTURY .............................................................. 950.00
FURNITURE,TABLE,BIRDCAGE SUPPORT,SHAPED TRIPOD LEGS,CLUB
FEET,MAHOGANY ........................................................ 275.00
FURNITURE,TABLE,BRASS TRAY CENTER,ELEPHANT HEAD,IVORY TUSKS,
TEAKWOOD ............................................................. 350.00
FURNITURE,TABLE,BRASS,MARBLE TOP,18 1/2 IN.SQUARE X
34 1/2 IN.HIGH ....................................................... 190.00
FURNITURE,TABLE,BRASS,MARBLE TOP,18 1/2 X 18 1/2 X
35 1/2 IN ............................................................ 210.00
FURNITURE,TABLE,BREADBOARD ENDS,TAPERED LEGS,DRAWER,PINE
TOP,MAPLE BASE ....................................................... 110.00

```
FURNITURE,TABLE,BREAKFAST,DROP LEAF,DRAWER IN FRIEZE,
   MAHOGANY,28 IN............................................    125.00
FURNITURE,TABLE,BREAKFAST,TILT-TOP,BALUSTER-SHAPE SUPPORT,
   MAHOGANY.................................................    425.00
FURNITURE,TABLE,CARD,CONCERTINA,MAHOGANY,17TH CENTURY,
   ENGLAND..................................................    675.00
FURNITURE,TABLE,CARD,D-SHAPE,FOLDING TOP,SHERATON,MAHOGANY,
   WARPED,PAIR..............................................    500.00
FURNITURE,TABLE,CARD,DUTCH MARQUETRY,18TH CENTURY,29 1/2 IN.
   HIGH.....................................................    350.00
FURNITURE,TABLE,CARD,EBONIZED WOOD,BURL WALNUT,REGENCY STYLE    250.00
FURNITURE,TABLE,CARD,EMPIRE MAHOGANY,19TH CENTURY,AMERICAN.     350.00
FURNITURE,TABLE,CARD,FEDERAL MAHOGANY,19TH CENTURY,AMERICAN.    425.00
FURNITURE,TABLE,CARD,FOLDING,ALLOVER MOTIF,REGENCY,MAHOGANY,
   PAIR.....................................................    450.00
FURNITURE,TABLE,CARD,GEORGE III,FOLDING TOP,RECESSED WELLS,
   MAHOGANY.................................................    450.00
FURNITURE,TABLE,CARD,HEPPLEWHITE,INLAID MAHOGANY.....ILLUS..1,000.00
FURNITURE,TABLE,CARD,HEPPLEWHITE,INLAID MAHOGANY,18TH
   CENTURY..................................................    800.00
FURNITURE,TABLE,CARD,HEPPLEWHITE,INLAID,MAHOGANY,36 X
   29 1/2 IN.HIGH...........................................    375.00
FURNITURE,TABLE,CARD,HEPPLEWHITE,MAHOGANY,19TH CENTURY,
   AMERICAN.................................................    200.00
FURNITURE,TABLE,CARD,MAHOGANY MARQUETRY,FOLDING,19TH CENTURY    300.00
FURNITURE,TABLE,CARD,SATINWOOD & EBONY INLAY,MAHOGANY,
   HEPPLEWHITE..............................................    675.00
FURNITURE,TABLE,CARD,SATINWOOD BORDER,GREEN,BAIZE-LINED
   SURFACE,SHERATON.........................................    300.00
```

HEPPLEWHITE MAHOGANY
CARD TABLE

```
FURNITURE,TABLE,CARD,SERPENTINE SHAPE,ROPE LEGS,CIRCA 1830,
   MAHOGANY.................................................    159.00
FURNITURE,TABLE,CARD,SHERATON,CONNELLY-HAINES SCHOOL,1815,
   MAHOGANY................................................. 1,500.00
FURNITURE,TABLE,CARD,SHERATON,INLAID,MAHOGANY,36 X
   29 1/2 IN.HIGH...........................................    650.00
FURNITURE,TABLE,CARD,SHERATON,MAHOGANY,CIRCA 1820,AMERICAN..    125.00
FURNITURE,TABLE,CARVED PEDESTAL BASE,WALNUT,WHITE MARBLE
   TOP,29 IN.TALL...........................................     75.00
FURNITURE,TABLE,CARVED,EMBROIDERED PIECE ON TOP,GLASS COVER,
   CHINA,TEAK...............................................    175.00
FURNITURE,TABLE,CARVED,TEAKWOOD,CHINA......................    185.00
FURNITURE,TABLE,CENTER,BREAKFRONT FORM TOP,D-SHAPE ENDS,
   REGENCY,ROSEWOOD.........................................    300.00
FURNITURE,TABLE,CENTER,DRAWERS,REGENCY,MAHOGANY,47 X
   28 1/2 IN.HIGH...........................................    200.00
FURNITURE,TABLE,CENTER,LOUIS XV,SUNRAY PATTERN ON TOP,
   KINGWOOD,31 IN...........................................    425.00
FURNITURE,TABLE,CENTER,REMOVABLE TOP,THREE FRIEZE DRAWERS,
   WALNUT...................................................    500.00
FURNITURE,TABLE,CENTER,VICTORIAN,PAINTED,LACQUERED,31 X
   38 IN.HIGH...............................................    225.00
FURNITURE,TABLE,COFFEE,KEY DESIGN,TOP NEEDS REFINISHING,
```

| | |
|---|---|
| CHINA,TEAK..................................................... | 350.00 |
| FURNITURE,TABLE,COLONNETTE SUPPORTS,SPLAYED LEGS,MAHOGANY, NEST OF THREE..................................................... | 350.00 |
| FURNITURE,TABLE,CONSOLE,D-SHAPE TOP,REEDED EDGE,SIX LEGS, SHERATON,PAIR................................................... | 500.00 |
| FURNITURE,TABLE,CORNER,DROP LEAF,TRIANGULAR TOP,MAHOGANY, 28 IN.HIGH...................................................... | 275.00 |
| FURNITURE,TABLE,DINING,CHIPPENDALE,TIGER MAPLE............... | 235.00 |
| FURNITURE,TABLE,DINING,D END,DROP LEAF,GATELEGS ON SIDES, MAHOGANY....................................................... | 650.00 |
| FURNITURE,TABLE,DINING,DROP LEAF,CHERRYWOOD,19TH CENTURY, AMERICAN....................................................... | 100.00 |
| FURNITURE,TABLE,DINING,DROP LEAF,MAHOGANY,42 1/2 IN.EXTENDED | 300.00 |
| FURNITURE,TABLE,DINING,DROP LEAF,WALNUT,19TH CENTURY, AMERICAN....................................................... | 175.00 |
| FURNITURE,TABLE,DINING,DROP LEAF,TAPER LEGS,MAHOGANY, 61 1/2 IN.EXTENDED.............................................. | 700.00 |
| FURNITURE,TABLE,DINING,EXTENDING,CIRCULAR TOP,ONE LEAF, MAHOGANY....................................................... | 500.00 |
| FURNITURE,TABLE,DINING,EXTENDING,DROP LEAF,TWO LEAVES, MAHOGANY....................................................... | 675.00 |
| FURNITURE,TABLE,DINING,EXTENDING,VICTORIAN CARVED MAHOGANY, 19TH CENTURY................................................... | 300.00 |
| FURNITURE,TABLE,DINING,OVAL SERPENTINE TOP,PEDESTAL,ROCOCO LEGS,1860...................................................... | 295.00 |
| FURNITURE,TABLE,DRAW LEAF,RECTANGULAR TOP,BALUSTER LEGS,OAK, 31 IN.HIGH..................................................... | 600.00 |
| FURNITURE,TABLE,DRAWER,PLATFORM BETWEEN LEGS,ROPE LEGS,CLAW FEET,OAK....................................................... | 125.00 |
| FURNITURE,TABLE,DRESSING,GEORGE III,DRAWERS,SQUARE,TAPERED LEGS,MAHOGANY.................................................. | 400.00 |
| FURNITURE,TABLE,DRESSING,MAN'S,SATINWOOD TOP,SHERATON, MAHOGANY....................................................... | 500.00 |
| FURNITURE,TABLE,DRESSING,SHERATON,PINE,19TH CENTURY,AMERICAN | 100.00 |
| FURNITURE,TABLE,DROP LEAF,END DRAWERS,PEDESTAL BASE,20 IN. X 42 IN.LONG..................................................... | 95.00 |
| FURNITURE,TABLE,DROP LEAF,EXTENSION,THREE LEAVES,OVAL,BLACK WALNUT......................................................... | 75.00 |
| FURNITURE,TABLE,DROP LEAF,FEDERAL,MAHOGANY,CIRCA 1820, AMERICAN....................................................... | 350.00 |
| FURNITURE,TABLE,DROP LEAF,FEDERAL,MAHOGANY,CIRCA 1825,NEW YORK........................................................... | 350.00 |
| FURNITURE,TABLE,DROP LEAF,GEORGE III,MAHOGANY,56 IN.EXTENDED | 325.00 |
| FURNITURE,TABLE,DROP LEAF,RECTANGULAR TOP,TAPER LEGS, REFRAMED,28 IN.................................................. | 120.00 |
| FURNITURE,TABLE,DROP LEAF,SHERATON,CARVED,MAHOGANY,DUNCAN PHYFE,1815.................................................3,250.00 | |
| FURNITURE,TABLE,DROP LEAF,SHERATON,MAHOGANY,1815,45 X 30 IN.HIGH..................................................... | 275.00 |
| FURNITURE,TABLE,DROP LEAF,SIX LEGS,CHERRY,REFINISHED........ | 325.00 |
| FURNITURE,TABLE,DROP LEAF,SIX LEGS,LEAVES,TULIP POPLAR, PENNA.47 X 69 IN................................................ | 350.00 |
| FURNITURE,TABLE,DROP LEAF,SWING LEG,SHERATON,MAPLE,47 1/2 X 16 1/2 IN...................................................... | 125.00 |
| FURNITURE,TABLE,DROP LEAF,TAPERED LEGS,HEPPELWHITE,PINE TOP, MAPLE LEGS..................................................... | 38.50 |
| FURNITURE,TABLE,DROP LEAF,THREE-BOARD,WALNUT,45 IN. X 69 IN. | 300.00 |
| FURNITURE,TABLE,DRUM TOP,GREEN LEATHER,FOUR DRAWERS, RESTORED,29 IN.HIGH............................................. | 475.00 |
| FURNITURE,TABLE,DRUM,LEATHER TOP,FOUR DRAWERS,REGENCY, WALNUT,28 IN.HIGH............................................... | 200.00 |
| FURNITURE,TABLE,DUTCH MARQUETRY,CLAW FEET,30 IN.DIAMETER.... | 450.00 |
| FURNITURE,TABLE,GAME,CHESSBOARD TOP,SATINWOOD,ROSEWOOD, REGENCY,31 IN.................................................. | 350.00 |
| FURNITURE,TABLE,GAME,CHESSBOARD,CRIBBAGE MARKERS,SHERATON, OLIVEWOOD...................................................... | 550.00 |
| FURNITURE,TABLE,GAME,FELT,BRASSES,OPEN/CLOSE,CIRCA 1870, FRUITWOOD...................................................... | 245.00 |
| FURNITURE,TABLE,GAME,LOUIS XV,LACQUER,GILT,MOTHER-OF-PEARL FLORAL,30 IN.................................................... | 300.00 |
| FURNITURE,TABLE,GATELEG,CARVED OAK,CHARLES II,26 IN.HIGH.... | 500.00 |
| FURNITURE,TABLE,GEORGIAN,MAHOGANY,TILTING-TOP,BREAKFAST, ENGLISH........................................................ | 325.00 |
| FURNITURE,TABLE,HALF-MOON,HEPPLEWHITE,MAHOGANY.............. | 190.00 |
| FURNITURE,TABLE,HARVEST,TIGER MAPLE,5 FEET LONG............. | 550.00 |
| FURNITURE,TABLE,HEPPLEWHITE,DROP LEAF,PENNSYLVANIA,WALNUT, 52 1/2 IN.LONG.................................................. | 125.00 |
| FURNITURE,TABLE,HUTCH,CHIPPENDALE,PINE,MAPLE,3 X 5 FEET TOP, 30 IN.HIGH..................................................... | 325.00 |
| FURNITURE,TABLE,HUTCH,PINE,18TH CENTURY,AMERICAN............ | 200.00 |
| FURNITURE,TABLE,HUTCH,PINE,19TH CENTURY,AMERICAN............ | 200.00 |

```
FURNITURE,TABLE,HUTCH,PINE,34 X 60 IN.LONG,MAPLE CHAIR BASE,
   28 1/2 IN.......................................................  395.00
FURNITURE,TABLE,HUTCH,THREE-BOARD TOP,SEAT BASE,PEGGED,PINE,
   50 X 28 IN......................................................  310.00
FURNITURE,TABLE,JACOBEAN,DROP LEAF,BARLEY-SUGAR TWIST LEGS,
   CARVED,OAK......................................................  175.00
FURNITURE,TABLE,LIBRARY,BIRDS-EYE,CIRCA 1870.....................  485.00
FURNITURE,TABLE,LIBRARY,DRUM TOP,GEORGE III,MAHOGANY,
   ENGLISH,CIRCA 1800..............................................  750.00
FURNITURE,TABLE,LIBRARY,TWO DRAWERS,QUADRUPLE LEGS,MAHOGANY.  125.00
FURNITURE,TABLE,MARBLE INLAY TOP,HAND-CARVED,TEAKWOOD,22 X
   36 IN.HIGH......................................................  225.00
FURNITURE,TABLE,MARBLE TOP,FOUR LEGS,BRASS CASTERS,WALNUT,
   29 IN.HIGH......................................................  100.00
FURNITURE,TABLE,MARBLE TOP,OVAL,BRASS CASTERS,WALNUT,
   29 IN.HIGH......................................................  100.00
FURNITURE,TABLE,NEST,CARVED LATTICEWORK,TEAK,FOUR...........  235.00
FURNITURE,TABLE,OCCASIONAL,CIRCULAR,TILT-TOP,BIRDCAGE
   SUPPORT,MAHOGANY................................................  200.00
FURNITURE,TABLE,OCCASIONAL,CRESCENT SHAPE,INLAID AMBOYNA,
   29 1/2 IN.HIGH..................................................  375.00
FURNITURE,TABLE,OCCASIONAL,FRENCH MARQUETRY,19TH CENTURY....  400.00
FURNITURE,TABLE,OCCASIONAL,PAINTED,LACQUERED,TILT-TOP,18 X
   28 IN.HIGH......................................................   60.00
FURNITURE,TABLE,OVAL,FOUR LEGS,WALNUT,MARBLE TOP,BRASS
   CASTERS,29 IN...................................................  100.00
FURNITURE,TABLE,PEDESTAL,BLACK MARBLE TOP,LIONS' FEET,
   31 IN.TALL,FRANCE...............................................  125.00
FURNITURE,TABLE,PEDESTAL,EMPIRE,MAHOGANY,64 IN.SQUARE,
   5 LEAVES........................................................  395.00
FURNITURE,TABLE,PEMBROKE,DROP LEAF,DRAWER,MAHOGANY,34 X
   28 1/2 IN.HIGH..................................................  250.00
FURNITURE,TABLE,PEMBROOKE,INLAY,HEPPLEWHITE.................  265.00
FURNITURE,TABLE,PEMBROKE,SHERATON,MAHOGANY.........ILLUS..1,000.00
FURNITURE,TABLE,PIECRUST,PALMETTES,TRIPOD LEGS,TILT-TOP,
   MAHOGANY........................................................  375.00
FURNITURE,TABLE,PIER,PAINTED,FLORAL,FOLIAGE,GILT WOODEN
   LEGS,BLOCK TOES.................................................  650.00
FURNITURE,TABLE,READING,RECTANGULAR TOP,RATCHET SUPPORT,
   MAHOGANY........................................................  240.00
FURNITURE,TABLE,REFECTORY,TURNED LEG,SHELF,WALNUT,8 FEET
   LONG............................................................  265.00
FURNITURE,TABLE,RENT,DRUM TOP,LEATHER,DRAWERS,CUPBOARD BASE,
   MAHOGANY......................................................1,200.00
FURNITURE,TABLE,ROUND,EXTENSION,THREE LEAVES,PEDESTAL BASE,
   1882,MAHOGANY...................................................  500.00
FURNITURE,TABLE,SATINWOOD BANDING,TRESTLE FEET,ROSEWOOD,NEST
   OF THREE........................................................  300.00
FURNITURE,TABLE,SEWING,MAHOGANY,WITH TWO-TIER TABLE,MAHOGANY  125.00
```

SHERATON MAHOGANY
PEMBROKE TABLE

```
FURNITURE,TABLE,SHERATON,CURLY MAPLE,OCCASIONAL,19TH CENTURY    150.00
FURNITURE,TABLE,SIDE DRAWER,MAHOGANY,SHERATON PEMBROKE,20 X
   36 IN......................................................    295.00
FURNITURE,TABLE,SIDE,CONTINENTAL PARQUETRY,RESTORED,
   30 IN.HIGH.................................................    375.00
FURNITURE,TABLE,SIDE,DRAWER,BALUSTER-TURNED LEGS,BOX
   STRETCHER,WALNUT...........................................    225.00
FURNITURE,TABLE,SIDE,HEPPLEWHITE,MAHOGANY,18TH CENTURY,
   AMERICAN..................................................1,050.00
FURNITURE,TABLE,SIDE,RECTANGULAR TOP,MOLDED BORDER,QUEEN
   ANNE,OAK...................................................    275.00
FURNITURE,TABLE,SIDE,WILLIAM & MARY,DRAWER,BALUSTER LEGS,
   OAK,28 1/2 IN..............................................    125.00
FURNITURE,TABLE,SINGLE DROP BOARD,TURNED LEGS,CIRCA 1825,
   MAPLE,48 IN................................................    250.00
FURNITURE,TABLE,SOFA,BRASS INLAY,DRAWERS,OVERHANGING TOP,
   ROSEWOOD...................................................    475.00
FURNITURE,TABLE,SOFA,DROP LEAF,PLATFORM BASE,ROSEWOOD,
   57 IN.WIDE.................................................     75.00
FURNITURE,TABLE,SOFA,DROP LEAF,TWO DRAWERS,PILLARS ON BASE,
   MAHOGANY...................................................    350.00
FURNITURE,TABLE,SOFA,REGENCY,MAHOGANY,ENGLISH,19TH CENTURY..    450.00
FURNITURE,TABLE,STEP,BEDSIDE,DRAWER,WHITE KNOBS,REFINISHED,
   CHERRY,PAIR................................................    125.00
FURNITURE,TABLE,SWING-LEG,CHIPPENDALE,MAPLE,AMERICAN,43 X
   13 IN......................................................    495.00
FURNITURE,TABLE,TEA,CHIPPENDALE,CARVED MAHOGANY,CLAW & BALL
   FEET,1760................................................7,000.00
FURNITURE,TABLE,TILTING-TOP,HEPPLEWHITE,CHERRYWOOD,19TH
   CENTURY....................................................     70.00
FURNITURE,TABLE,TRIPOD,TILT-TOP,GEORGE II,MAHOGANY,REPAIRED,
   27 1/2 IN..................................................    140.00
FURNITURE,TABLE,VICTORIAN BLEACHED OAK,LIBRARY,19TH CENTURY.    225.00
FURNITURE,TABLE,VICTORIAN CARVED OAK,REFECTORY,19TH CENTURY.    350.00
FURNITURE,TABLE,WINE,PIECRUST TOP,FLUTED COLUMNAR SUPPORT,
   RESTORED...................................................    300.00
FURNITURE,TABLE,WRITING,GEORGE II,DRAWERS,CUPBOARD,DOOR,
   WALNUT-VENEERED............................................    650.00
FURNITURE,TABLE,WRITING,KIDNEY SHAPE,REEDED LEGS,GEORGE IV,
   MAHOGANY...................................................    625.00
FURNITURE,TABLE,WRITING,LADY'S,DRAWER,EBONY HANDLE,
   SATINWOOD,30 IN.HIGH.......................................    175.00
FURNITURE,TABLE,WRITING,LADY'S,DRAWER,TAPERED LEGS,PLATFORM
   STRETCHER..................................................    425.00
FURNITURE,TABLE,WRITING,PEDESTAL,LEATHER TOP,MAHOGANY,60 X
   30 IN.HIGH.................................................    450.00
FURNITURE,TABLE,WRITING,WILLIAM IV,PEDESTAL,AMBOYNA WOOD,
   60 X 30 1/2 IN...........................................5,750.0
FURNITURE,TALLBOY,CHINOISERIE,BLACK GROUND,17TH CENTURY,
   ENGLAND,50 IN............................................2,000.00
FURNITURE,TEA CADDY,FOOTED,HINGED COVER,LOCK,TEAK,15 IN. X
   10 IN.HIGH.................................................    350.00
FURNITURE,TEA CADDY,THREE PARTITIONS INSIDE,HINGED TOP,
   ROSEWOOD...................................................     35.00
FURNITURE,TEA CART,CURVED DROP LEAF SIDES,DRAWER,GLASS
   LIFT-OFF TOP...............................................     75.00
FURNITURE,TORCHERE,CARVED & GILDED WOOD,58 IN. HIGH.........    120.00
FURNITURE,TRAY ON STAND,BUTLER'S,GEORGIAN,MAHOGANY,ENGLISH,
   19TH CENTURY...............................................    240.00
FURNITURE,TRAY,BUTLER'S,RECTANGULAR,SHAPED GALLERY,HAND
   GRIPS,STAND................................................    600.00
FURNITURE,TRAY,TEA,GALLE,MARQUETRY,24 1/2 IN. LONG,SIGNED,
   OBLONG.....................................................    225.00
FURNITURE,TROUGH,DOUGH,REMOVABLE TOP,VALANCED APRON,SPLAYED
   LEGS,PINE..................................................    250.00
FURNITURE,VITRINE,LOUIS XV,ROUGE ROYALE MARBLE TOP,KINGWOOD,
   49 IN......................................................    900.00
FURNITURE,VITRINE,LOUIS XV,SERPENTINE OUTLINE,MARBLE TOP,
   KINGWOOD,62 IN...........................................1,050.00
FURNITURE,WALL HANGING,3-DIMENSIONAL,JADITE & QUARTZ FLORAL,
   FRAME,PAIR.................................................     45.00
FURNITURE,WALL RACK,SEVEN PEGS,PORCELAIN TIPS,FOLDING.......      5.00
FURNITURE,WARDROBE,ART NOUVEAU,FRENCH.................ILLUS..    750.00
FURNITURE,WARDROBE,GREEN PAINT,PINE,ONE DOOR REPAIRED,18 X
   44 X 72 IN.................................................     75.00
FURNITURE,WARDROBE,TWO PANELED DOORS,CUTOUT BASE,PINE,41 X
   15 X 78 IN.................................................     85.00
FURNITURE,WASHSTAND,EMPIRE,MAHOGANY,19TH CENTURY,AMERICAN,..    225.00
FURNITURE,WASHSTAND,ENCLOSED,GEORGE III,MAHOGANY,24 X
   32 IN.HIGH.................................................    180.00
FURNITURE,WASHSTAND,ONE DRAWER,YELLOW PAINT.................     49.00
```

FRENCH ART NOUVEAU WARDROBE

```
FURNITURE,WASHSTAND,PIERCED FRIEZE DECOR,MAHOGANY,
  30 1/2 IN.HIGH.......................................    130.00
FURNITURE,WASHSTAND,SPLASHBOARD,WALNUT,MARBLE TOP..........    100.00
FURNITURE,WATCH HOLDER,HEPPLEWHITE,INLAID MAHOGANY,18TH
  CENTURY............................................    175.00
FURNITURE,WHATNOT,CORNER,FLOOR,MADE OF SMALL SPOOLS,FOUR
  SHELVES............................................     45.00
FURNITURE,WHATNOT,FOUR-TIER,DRAWER IN BASE,MAHOGANY,
  47 1/2 IN.HIGH......................................    375.00
FURNITURE,WHATNOT,REGENCY,MAHOGANY,ENGLISH,19TH CENTURY.....    625.00
FURNITURE,WIG STAND,MAHOGANY,18TH CENTURY,AMERICAN..........    200.00
FURNITURE,WINDOW SEAT,CANE SEAT,SPINDLE STRETCHERS,MAHOGANY,
  29 IN.LONG.........................................    225.00
FURNITURE,WINDOW SEAT,YELLOW FLORAL SILK UPHOLSTERY,CARVED
  BEECHWOOD..........................................    450.00
FURNITURE,WINE COOLER,GEORGE III,LIFT TOP,COMPARTMENTS,
  MAHOGANY,24 IN......................................    550.00
FURNITURE,WINE COOLER,SARCOPHAGUS-SHAPE BODY,DOME COVER,
  SPLAYED LEGS.......................................    325.00
FURNITURE,WORKTABLE,FEDERAL,BRASS INLAID MAHOGANY,19TH
  CENTURY............................................    130.00
FURNITURE,WORKTABLE,FEDERAL,MAHOGANY,CIRCA 1825,AMERICAN....    475.00
FURNITURE,WORKTABLE,HEPPLEWHITE,BURLWOOD,ENGLISH,18TH
  CENTURY............................................    200.00
FURNITURE,WORKTABLE,HINGED TOP,COMPARTMENTED TRAYS,SHERATON,
  MAHOGANY.........................................2,750.00
FURNITURE,WORKTABLE,LYRE FORM,INLAID,SHERATON,MAHOGANY,
  BIRD'S-EYE MAPLE.................................2,500.00
FURSTENBURG,SAUCER,CIRCA 1765,TWO PIECES...................    100.00
FURSTENBERG,TEAPOT,WHITE,GOLD,VINES,GRAPE CLUSTERS,GOLD,
  CIRCA 1750.........................................    200.00
FURSTENBURG,BOWL,CIRCA 1760,6 3/4 IN. DIAM.................     50.00
FURSTENBURG,EWER,COVERED,CIRCA 1765,5 1/4 IN. HIGH.........    250.00


        GALLE GLASS WAS MADE BY THE GALLE FACTORY FOUNDED BY
        EMILE GALLE OF FRANCE. THE FIRM MADE CAMEO GLASS,
        FURNITURE,AND OTHER ART NOUVEAU ITEMS FROM 1879 TO
        1905.
   GALLE,SEE ALSO,CAMEO GLASS,FURNITURE
GALLE,ATOMIZER,CAMEO CUT,SIGNED..........................    135.00
GALLE,ATOMIZER,CAMEO GLASS,13 3/4 IN. HIGH,SIGNED..........    140.00
GALLE,ATOMIZER,CAMEO,SIGNED,FRANCE,8 IN.HIGH...............    125.00
GALLE,ATOMIZER,CAMEO,SIGNED,7 IN.HIGH.....................    130.00
GALLE,BOWL,BLUE FLORAL,CENTER SCENIC MEDALLION,LAKE,BOATS,
  GOLD,6 1/2 IN......................................    125.00
GALLE,BOWL,BURNT ORANGE TO WHITE GROUND,GREEN LEAVES,ACID
  CUT,CAMEO.........................................    250.00
GALLE,BOWL,CAMEO,PURPLE ON FROST,SWEET PEA,4 1/2-IN.DIAMETER    145.00
GALLE,BOWL,CAMEO,YELLOW,ORANGE,BROWN FLORAL,SIGNED,
  2 1/2 IN.HIGH.......................................    165.00
```

```
GALLE,BOWL,CENTERPIECE,ACID GROUND,LAVENDER & PINK FLORAL,
   OVAL......................................................  325.00
GALLE,BOWL,CLEAR TO GREEN,PURPLE LEAVES,1 IN. X 5 3/4 IN....  275.00
GALLE,BOWL,CRANBERRY & PUCE,SIGNED,4 1/2 IN.WIDE X
   1 3/4 IN.TALL.............................................   95.00
GALLE,BOWL,FLORAL BOUQUET,LAVENDER,PINK,RUFFLED TOP,6 IN. X
   4 IN.HIGH.................................................  325.00
GALLE,BOWL,FLOWER,CAMEO,PINK GROUND,MORNING GLORY VINES,
   CARVED,BLUE...............................................  235.00
GALLE,BOWL,GREEN,BROWN LEAF SPRAYS,GLOSSY,FOOTED,
   5 1/4-IN.DIAMETER.........................................  135.00
GALLE,BOWL,POTTERY,BROWN GLAZE,FISH........................  250.00
GALLE,BOWL,ROSE,CAMEO GLASS,6 1/2-IN.DIAMETER..............  150.00
BALLE,BOWL,ROSE,CAMEO,OVID,PINK TO FROST,SWEET PEAS,PURPLE,
   5 IN.TALL.................................................  165.00
GALLE,BOWL,ROSE,CAMEO,SCENIC,TREES,SHORE,MOUNTAINS,GOLDEN
   GROUND...................................................  165.00
GALLE,BOWL,ROSY-PEACH,AMETHYST ORCHID SPRAY,WHITE TOP,
   2 1/2 IN.HIGH............................................  130.00
GALLE,BOX,CAMEO,GREEN TREES,BIRD ON BRANCH,PINK-WHITE
   GROUND,COVER.............................................  155.00
GALLE,BOX,COVERED,CAMEO GLASS,6-IN.DIAMETER........150.00 TO  160.00
GALLE,BOX,FLORAL,GREEN,COVER...............................  175.00
GALLE,BOX,GLASS,COVERED,SIGNED,5 1/2-IN.DIAMETER...........  135.00
GALLE,BOX,MAUVE FLOWERS,YELLOW FROSTED GROUND,COVER,SIGNED,
   3 1/2 IN.HIGH............................................  150.00
GALLE,BOX,WHITE & GREEN GROUND,DRAGONFLIES,LILY PADS,LID,
   6-IN.DIAMETER............................................  250.00
GALLE,CANDELABRUM,FIGURAL,SIGNED E.GALLE,23 1/2 IN.HIGH,PAIR  250.00
GALLE,CHANDELIER,CAMEO GLASS,15 IN. HIGH,SIGNED............  350.00
GALLE,CRUET,BLUE,FLORAL,TWISTED HANDLE,HEART-SHAPE STOPPER,
   E.GALLE NANCY............................................  175.00
GALLE,CRUET,ENAMELED THISTLE,MAROON,BEIGE,PINK,APPLIED
   HANDLE,AMBER.............................................  275.00
GALLE,CUP & SAUCER,WHITE,GOLD & SILVER FLEUR-DE-LIS,SIGNED
   E.GALLE,1860.............................................  108.00
GALLE,DECANTER,TRAY,FOUR LIQUORS,AMBER,ENAMELED FLORAL,PINK,
   BROWN,BLUE...............................................  325.00
GALLE,DISH,BONBON,ENAMELED GLASS,8 3/4 IN.LONG,SIGNED......   75.00
GALLE,DISH,VIOLETS,GOLD EDGE,FIVE COMPARTMENTS,
   11-IN.DIAMETER...........................................  115.00
GALLE,GOBLET,WINE,PANELED AMBER,ENAMELED FLORAL,APPLIED
   CABOCHONS,SIGNED.........................................   95.00
GALLE,INKSTAND,FAIENCE,13 IN. LONG,SIGNED.................  375.00
GALLE,JAR,COVERED,CAMEO GLASS,10 IN. HIGH,SIGNED..........  175.00
GALLE,JARDINIERE,CAMEO GLASS,12 IN. LONG,SIGNED..........  150.00
GALLE,LAMP,BLUEBELLS DECOR,SIGNED,16 IN.HIGH..............  350.00
GALLE,LAMP,CAMEO GLASS & BRONZE,THREE GRACES,19 IN...ILLUS..1,300.00
GALLE,LAMP,CAMEO GLASS,TABLE,22 IN. HIGH,SIGNED...........  900.00
GALLE,LAMP,PERFUME,CAMEO,RASPBERRY COLOR,SHOOTING STAR
   DESIGN,SIGNED............................................  245.00
GALLE,LAMP,SCENT,CAMEO,YELLOW,ORANGE FLOWERS,METAL COLLAR,
   SNUFFER,7 IN.............................................  120.00
GALLE,LIQUEUR GLASS,CRYSTAL PANEL GROUND,ALLOVER ENAMEL
   FLORAL,MOTTO.............................................   40.00
GALLE,PERFUME,CAMEO,BROWN,CUT TO YELLOW GROUND,ATOMIZER.....  110.00
```

GALLE CAMEO GLASS AND BRONZE LAMP

GALLE,PERFUME,YELLOW,BROWN FLORAL,CAMEO GLASS,SIGNED,NEW
  ATOMIZER.................................................... 95.00
GALLE,PITCHER,CAMEO GLASS,8 1/2 IN. HIGH,SIGNED............. 230.00
GALLE,PITCHER,LUSTER,EMILE GALLE,NANCY,FRANCE,LORRAINE CROSS
  SIGNATURE.................................................. 175.00
GALLE,SERVICE,LIQUEUR,ENAMELED GLASS,12 PIECES,12-IN.TRAY... 550.00
GALLE,TOOTHPICK,MYSTIC COLOR DESIGNS,SIGNED,2 1/4 IN........  77.50
GALLE,TRAY,FLORAL,ENAMEL,PINK,BROWN,LAVENDER,AMBER GLASS,
  4 1/4 IN.SQUARE............................................  95.00
GALLE,TUMBLER,BLUE,ENAMELED CHRYSANTHEMUMS,SIGNED,RUFFLED
  FOOT......................................................  85.00
GALLE,TUMBLER,INVERTED COIN SPOT,VASELINE COLOR,GOLD ENAMEL
  BORDER....................................................  48.00
GALLE,VASE,7 IN.,SIGNED,CAMEO.........................ILLUS.. 200.00
GALLE,VASE,8 IN.HIGH,SIGNED,CAMEO.......................... 150.00
GALLE,VASE,10 1/2 IN.HIGH,SIGNED,CAMEO..................... 120.00
GALLE,VASE,12 IN.HIGH,SIGNED,CAMEO........................ 130.00
GALLE,VASE,AMETHYST,SIGNED,8 1/2 IN.,CAMEO................ 240.00
GALLE,VASE,AMETHYST ACID GROUND,AMETHYST FLORAL SPRAY,
  6 1/4 IN.HIGH............................................. 110.00
GALLE,VASE,AMETHYST FLOWER SPRAYS,DUSTY PINK GROUND,SIGNED,
  3 3/4 IN.HIGH............................................. 125.00
GALLE,VASE,BANJO SHAPE,YELLOW GROUND,BROWN FLOWERS,
  6 3/4 IN.,CAMEO.......................................... 130.00
GALLE,VASE,BLUE,ENAMELED FLORAL SPRAYS,MULTICOLORED DRAGON,
  CROWN,6 IN............................................... 265.00
GALLE,VASE,BLUE GROUND,BROWN FLORAL & LEAVES,6 1/2 IN.,CAMEO 150.00
GALLE,VASE,BUTTERSCOTCH GROUND,MOCHA LEAVES & FLOWERS,
  7 1/2 IN.,CAMEO.......................................... 200.00
GALLE,VASE,CABINET,4 1/4 IN.HIGH,CAMEO..................... 110.00
GALLE,VASE,CABINET,6 IN.HIGH,CAMEO....................ILLUS.. 110.00
GALLE,VASE,CAMPHOR GROUND,GOLD-ORANGE LEAF & FLORAL DECOR,
  4 IN.HIGH................................................ 145.00
GALLE,VASE,COLUMBINE MOTIF,CAMEO.......................... 235.00
GALLE,VASE,DARK GREEN,GINKGO TREE DECOR,WHITE,GOLD SHADING,
  CAMEO,27 IN.............................................. 325.00
GALLE,VASE,DARK RED,GREEN,CAMEO,SIGNED WITH STAR,12 IN.TALL.  90.00
GALLE,VASE,DEEP LAVENDER TO PALE YELLOW,WATER FLOWERS,
  13 IN.TALL,CAMEO......................................... 225.00
GALLE,VASE,DUSTY ORANGE NASTURTIUM,LEAVES,ACID CUT,SIGNED,
  4 IN.HIGH................................................  90.00
GALLE,VASE,DUSTY ORANGE POPPY ON WHITE & ORANGE GROUND,CUT
  ACID,SIGNED..............................................  95.00
GALLE,VASE,ENAMELED,BONHEUR AU NYMPH BLANC,6 1/2 IN. ILLUS.. 525.00
GALLE,VASE,ENAMELED,GREEN,FLUTED,PYRIFORM.............ILLUS.. 385.00
GALLE,VASE,ENAMELED FLOWERS & LEAVES,GOLD TRACERY,AMBER,
  SIGNED,5 IN.............................................. 110.00
GALLE,VASE,ENAMELED GLASS,BOTTLE-FORM,6 IN. HIGH,SIGNED..... 125.00
GALLE,VASE,ENAMELED GLASS,14 1/4 IN. HIGH,SIGNED.......... 200.00
GALLE,VASE,ENAMELED GLASS,7 1/4 IN. HIGH,SIGNED........... 225.00
GALLE,VASE,FLAT GOURD-SHAPED,CARVED BLOSSOMS,LEAVES,
  AMETHYST,CAMEO........................................... 225.00
GALLE,VASE,FLAT,GRASS,FLORAL,GREEN,YELLOW,ORANGE,APPLIED
  HANDLES.................................................. 250.00
GALLE,VASE,FLORIDA KEYS PATTERN,AMBER TO FROST,LEAVES,
  FOOTED,CAMEO............................................. 160.00

GALLE CAMEO VASE

GALLE CAMEO GLASS VASE

GALLE,VASE,FRANCE,SIGNED,4 IN.HIGH,CAMEO.................... 85.00
GALLE,VASE,FROSTED BLUE & CLEAR GROUND,AMBER WATER LILIES,
   LEAVES,CAMEO............................................ 195.00
GALLE,VASE,FROSTED GROUND,DEEP CUT GREEN & ORANGE DECOR,
   6 IN................................................... 165.00
GALLE,VASE,FROSTED GROUND,PURPLE FLORAL,SIGNED,
   8 1/2 IN.HIGH,CAMEO.................................... 250.00
GALLE,VASE,FROSTED GROUND,WINE FLORAL,CYLINDRICAL TOP,CAMEO
   GLASS,14 IN............................................ 250.00
GALLE,VASE,FROSTED GROUND,WISTERIA DECOR,SIGNED,4 IN........ 85.00
GALLE,VASE,FROSTY GROUND,CAMEO-CARVED LEAVES & FLORAL,
   SIGNED,FRANCE,1814..................................... 135.00
GALLE,VASE,FROSTY GROUND,PURPLE FLOWERS,SIGNED WITH STAR,
   CAMEO,4 1/2 IN......................................... 120.00
GALLE,VASE,FROSTY WHITE,LAVENDER,7 1/4 IN.TALL.............. 175.00
GALLE,VASE,GOLD,BROWN BERRIES & LEAVES,ACID FINISH,
   8 1/2 IN.TALL,CAMEO................................... 325.00
GALLE,VASE,GOLD & WHITE ACID GROUND,AMBER PINECONES,
   9 1/2 IN.TALL......................................... 190.00
GALLE,VASE,GOLD ACID GROUND,BROWN VIOLETS,SIGNED,2 1/2 X
   6 1/4 IN.HIGH......................................... 130.00
GALLE,VASE,GOLD SATIN GROUND,GREEN & BROWN PLUMS,
   3 3/4 IN.TALL,CAMEO................................... 160.00
GALLE,VASE,GREEN,LAKE SCENE,SIGNED,5 IN.TALL,CAMEO......... 150.00
GALLE,VASE,GREEN,ORANGE GROUND,GREEN FERN ON FROST,CAMEO,
   4 IN.HIGH............................................. 125.00
GALLE,VASE,GREEN,ROSE,BROWN,ACID CUT,9 IN.HIGH............. 155.00
GALLE,VASE,GREEN,YELLOW,SIGNED,14 IN.TALL,CAMEO............ 160.00
GALLE,VASE,GREEN & PINK LEAVES,CARVED,CAMEO,4-IN.DIAMETER
   BASE,6 IN.HIGH........................................ 159.00
GALLE,VASE,GREEN BASE,LILAC DESIGN ON STANDARD,LAYERS IN
   GREENS,23 IN.......................................... 250.00
GALLE,VASE,INLAID GLASS,8 IN. HIGH,SIGNED................. 250.00
GALLE,VASE,IRIS,CAMEO,ORIENTAL SIGNATURE,15 1/2 IN.HIGH.... 270.00
GALLE,VASE,LANDSCAPE,5 IN.HIGH,CAMEO...................... 125.00
GALLE,VASE,LANDSCAPE,7 3/4 IN.HIGH,SIGNED,CAMEO........... 200.00
GALLE,VASE,LANDSCAPE,15 1/2 IN.HIGH,SIGNED,CAMEO.......... 275.00
GALLE,VASE,LANDSCAPE,CABINET,6 1/2 IN.HIGH,CAMEO.......... 150.00
GALLE,VASE,MAHOGANY COLOR GROUND,POPPY LEAVES,DELPHINIUM,
   14 IN.TALL............................................ 200.00
GALLE,VASE,MAHOGANY COLOR,CHAMPAGNE & MISTY COLORATIONS,
   DECOR,18 IN.TALL...................................... 200.00
GALLE,VASE,MARQUETRY DE VERRE AND CAMEO GLASS,GREEN..ILLUS.1,600.00
GALLE,VASE,MOTTLED BROWN GROUND,GREEN LEAVES,7 IN.......... 175.00
GALLE,VASE,ORANGE BERRIES,LEAVES,CAMPHOR MATTE GROUND,
   4 1/2 IN.,CAMEO....................................... 125.00
GALLE,VASE,ORANGE FLOWERS CUT THROUGH TO WHITE GROUND,
   3 1/2 IN.,CAMEO........................................ 95.00
GALLE,VASE,ORANGE GROUND,FLORAL,SIGNED,3 1/2 IN............ 98.00
GALLE,VASE,PALE BLUE GROUND,BROWN FLORAL,LEAVES,BULBOUS,
   6 1/2 IN.,CAMEO....................................... 125.00
GALLE,VASE,PASTEL PINK,LAVENDER FLORAL DECOR,SIGNED,
   6 IN.TALL,CAMEO........................................ 85.00
GALLE,VASE,PEACH GROUND,AMETHYST ORCHID SPRAY,SIGNED,
   5 1/2 IN.HIGH......................................... 145.00

GALLE ENAMELED VASE    GALLE PYRIFORM ENAMELED VASE    GALLE MARQUETRY VASE

GALLE,VASE,PINK & FROSTED GROUND,LAVENDER DECOR,ACID CUT,
   6 1/2 IN.HIGH.....................................................   135.00
GALLE,VASE,PINK & GREEN,CAMEO,2 1/2 IN.HIGH X 4-IN.DIAMETER.          115.00
GALLE,VASE,PINK ACID GROUND,AMETHYST ORCHID SPRAY,2 IN. X
   4 3/4 IN.HIGH....................................................   125.00
GALLE,VASE,PINK FROSTED GROUND,LAVENDER FLOWERS,GREEN
   LEAVES,3 IN.,CAMEO................................................    82.00
GALLE,VASE,PINK GROUND,PURPLE & GREEN FLOWERS,MARKED,
   MINIATURE........................................................    80.00
GALLE,VASE,PINK NASTURTIUM ON WHITE-FROSTED GROUND,SIGNED,
   3 3/4 IN.HIGH....................................................    95.00
GALLE,VASE,PINK,BROWN,GREEN,FROSTED,CURRANT DESIGN,CAMEO,
   3 1/4 IN.........................................................   125.00
GALLE,VASE,PURPLE BLEEDING HEART,FROST GROUND,CAMEO,
   13 3/4 IN.HIGH...................................................   205.00
GALLE,VASE,PURPLE FLOWERS,4 IN....................................   105.00
GALLE,VASE,PURPLE,FLORAL,SIGNED,3 1/2 IN..........................    98.00
GALLE,VASE,SMOKY CRYSTAL SWIRL,ENAMEL FLORAL,GOLD COLOR
   LEAF,7 IN. HIGH..................................................   235.00
GALLE,VASE,STICK,BEIGE GROUND,RUSSET,WATER LILIES,CARVED,
   4 IN.HIGH........................................................   157.50
GALLE,VASE,STICK,CARVED,PASTEL GREEN,ORANGE LEAVES,
   11 IN.HIGH.......................................................   185.00
GALLE,VASE,STICK,PURPLE BLEEDING HEART,YELLOW,PURPLE GROUND,
   6 3/4 IN.........................................................   155.00
GALLE,VASE,STICK,PURPLE BLEEDING HEART,YELLOW,PURPLE GROUND,
   CAMEO,13 IN......................................................   215.00
GALLE,VASE,TAN,LAYERED BROWN DECOR,IRIS DESIGN,16 IN.TALL...         225.00
GALLE,VASE,TIGER LILY & LEAF DESIGN,DARK & LIGHT BROWN,
   14 IN.,CAMEO.....................................................   275.00
GALLE,VASE,WATER SCENIC,GREEN WATER LILIES,PINK TO LAVENDER
   SATIN GROUND.....................................................   175.00
GALLE,VASE,WHEEL CUT FLORAL,BLUE,AMETHYST,GREEN ON FROSTED
   GROUND,15 IN.....................................................   450.00
GALLE,VASE,WHITE GROUND,ORANGE NASTURTIUM,ACID CUT,4 IN.HIGH          85.00
GALLE,VASE,WHITE GROUND,TURQUOISE,ACID CUT,TRUMPET FLOWERS,
   12 1/2 IN........................................................   175.00
GALLE,VASE,WINE LEAF & BERRY SPRAYS,BLUE GROUND,SIGNED,
   3 1/2 IN.HIGH....................................................   125.00
GALLE,VASE,YELLOW ACID BACKGROUND,POLISHED BROWN FLORAL,
   5 1/2 IN.HIGH....................................................   145.00
GALLE,VASE,YELLOW BASE,FOUR CUTTINGS OF RED THROUGH PINK,
   11 1/2 IN........................................................   300.00
GALLE,VASE,YELLOW GROUND,BROWN FLOWERS & LEAVES,CAMEO,5 IN..         165.00
GALLE,VASE,YELLOW GROUND,PURPLE FLORAL,CAMEO,6 3/4 IN.HIGH.          165.00
GALLE,VASE,YELLOW-WHITE GROUND,CLEAR RED AT BOTTOM,SIGNED...         170.00
GALLE,VASE,YELLOW,ORANGE,WHITE,4 IN.HIGH..........................    85.00
GALLE,WALL SCONCE,CAMEO,BLUE,FROST,ORANGE FLORAL,
   9 1/2 IN.LONG,PAIR...............................................   600.00

         GAME PLATES ARE ANY TYPE OF PLATE DECORATED WITH
         PICTURES OF BIRDS,ANIMALS,OR FISH. THE GAME PLATES
         USUALLY CAME IN SETS CONSISTING OF TWELVE DISHES AND A
         SERVING PLATTER. THESE GAME PLATES WERE MOST POPULAR
         DURING THE 1880S.
GAME,JACKSTRAWS...................................................ILLUS..     8.00
GAME PLATE,BIRD,YELLOW,APRICOT GROUND,ROCOCO,SIGNED RENE,
   10 IN............................................................    39.00
GAME PLATE,BIRDS,HIGHLY COLORED PLUMAGE,OVAL,SIGNED BY
   ARTIST,LUC,FRANCE................................................    22.50
GAME PLATE,CARIBOU BUCKS & DOES,R.K.BECK,9-IN.DIAMETER......          15.00
GAME PLATE,CHINESE PHEASANT,GOLD & COBALT BORDER,STOKE &
   SON,9 IN.........................................................    22.00
GAME PLATE,DEER GRAZING,SIGNED R.K.BECKER,11 IN.............          49.00
GAME PLATE,DEER,DOE,SCENIC,FLORAL,GOLD EDGE,SIGNED R.K.BECK,
   12 7/8 IN........................................................    31.00
GAME PLATE,DEER,DOG,MOUNTAINS,HAND-PAINTED,SIGNED PRADET,
   LIMOGES..........................................................    39.00
GAME PLATE,DEER,R.K.BECK,9-IN.DIAMETER.............................    15.00
GAME PLATE,DOG,WILD DUCK,HAND-PAINTED,8 IN.........................    15.00
GAME PLATE,GOLD-SPLASHED PINK GROUND,CENTER BIRD,MANSARD,
   PARIS,SET OF 4...................................................   100.00
GAME PLATE,GROUSE,TREES,SKY,GOLD RIM,GERMAN MARK,PIERCED,
   11-IN.DIAMETER...................................................    50.00
GAME PLATE,HUNTER,TWO SETTERS,BIRD & FLORAL BORDER,
   STAFFORDSHIRE....................................................    25.00
GAME PLATE,MALLARD DUCK CENTER,GOLD ROCOCO BORDER,PASTEL
   GROUND,10 IN.....................................................    85.00
GAME PLATE,MOOSE,R.K.BECK,9-IN.DIAMETER............................    15.00
GAME PLATE,ONE PHEASANT,SCALLOPED EDGE,CHOISY LE ROI,9 IN...          25.00

JACKSTRAWS

| | |
|---|---|
| GAME PLATE,ONE ROOSTER,SCALLOPED EDGE,CHOISY LE ROI,9 IN.... | 25.00 |
| GAME PLATE,PHEASANT,CORONET........................... | 32.00 |
| GAME PLATE,QUAIL IN FLIGHT,SIGNED R.K.BECK,GLOBE CHINA CO., OHIO.................................................. | 15.00 |
| GAME PLATE,QUAIL,FLORAL,GREEN TREES,GILT EDGE,HAND-PAINTED, 13 1/2 IN............................................. | 45.00 |
| GAME PLATE,ROMAN KEY RIM,SCENE,BULL MOOSE,MARK SELB BAVARIA, 11 IN................................................ | 42.50 |
| GAME PLATE,SWIMMING DUCK,TURQUOISE SKY,PIERCED,J.S.BAVARIA, 9 IN................................................. | 26.00 |
| GAME PLATE,TURKEY,CORONET............................. | 32.00 |
| GAME PLATE,TWO BIRDS IN CENTER,PINK & WHITE SCALLOP, 7 1/8 IN.,PAIR..................................... | 12.50 |
| GAME PLATE,TWO GEESE,SCALLOPED EDGE,CHOISY LE ROI,9 IN..... | 25.00 |
| GAME PLATE,TWO LARGE DEER IN WOODS,WATER,GILT EDGE,MARKED NO.1301,10 IN.......................................... | 25.00 |
| GAME PLATE,TWO QUAIL,ROCOCO BORDER,SIGNED L.COUDERT, 9 1/2 IN.............................................. | 75.00 |
| GAME PLATE,TWO SEA GULLS IN FLIGHT,HAND-PAINTED,LIMOGES, FRANCE................................................ | 37.50 |
| GAME PLATE,WILD BIRDS,LIMOGES,8 1/2 IN.,PAIR.......... | 14.00 |
| GAME PLATE,WILD BOAR IN WOODS,HAND-PAINTED,NONTEREAU, 11 3/4 IN............................................. | 25.00 |
| GAME PLATE,WILD BOARS IN CENTER,HAND-PAINTED,AUSTRIA, 8 1/2 IN.............................................. | 25.00 |
| GAME PLATE,WILD DUCK,COIN GOLD TRIM,PIERCED,12-IN.DIAMETER.. | 69.50 |
| GAME,PLATTER,BIRDS,ROUND,SIGNED R.K. BECK................. | 30.00 |
| GAME PLATTER,PHEASANT IN WOOD SCENE,GREEN,RUST GROUND,OVAL, SCALLOPED............................................. | 28.00 |
| GAME SET,GREEN,GOLD RIM,WILD TURKEY,PLATTER,5 PLATES, FRANCAISE PORCELAIN................................... | 47.00 |
| GAME SET,PLATTER,SIX PLATES,HAND-PAINTED BIRDS,SIGNED ALFRED,HAVILAND.......................................... | 190.00 |

GAUDY DUTCH POTTERY WAS MADE IN ENGLAND FOR AMERICA FROM ABOUT 1810 TO 1820. IT IS A WHITE EARTHENWARE WITH IMARI-STYLE DECORATIONS OF RED,BLUE,GREEN, YELLOW AND BLACK.

| | |
|---|---|
| GAUDY DUTCH,BOWL,KING'S ROSE,13-IN.DIAMETER,5 IN.HIGH....... | 165.00 |
| GAUDY DUTCH,PLATE,KING'S ROSE PATTERN,VINE BORDER,ENAMEL, 5 1/2 IN.............................................. | 75.00 |
| GAUDY DUTCH,PLATE,9 3/4 IN.DIAM.,CORNATION PATTERN...ILLUS.. | 430.00 |
| GAUDY IRONSTONE,CUP & SAUCER,IMPRESSED SIGNATURE............ | 25.00 |
| GAUDY IRONSTONE,CUP & SAUCER,MULTICOLORED.................. | 22.50 |
| GAUDY IRONSTONE,CUP,SAUCER,CHINOISERIE DECOR,RUST,BLACK, GREEN,PINK,BEIGE..................................... | 17.50 |
| GAUDY IRONSTONE,GRAVY BOAT & DISH......................... | 36.00 |
| GAUDY IRONSTONE,PITCHER,COBALT & ORANGE ON WHITE GROUND, MASON,6 IN.HIGH...................................... | 30.00 |
| GAUDY IRONSTONE,PITCHER,DOLPHIN HANDLE,MASON'S PATENT, 3 3/4 IN............................................. | 30.00 |
| GAUDY IRONSTONE,PITCHER,OCTAGON SHAPE,SERPENT HANDLE, 6 IN.HIGH............................................ | 25.00 |
| GAUDY IRONSTONE,PITCHER,SNAKE HANDLE,MASON,3 IN.HIGH........ | 24.00 |
| GAUDY IRONSTONE,PITCHER,SNAKE HANDLE,7 IN................. | 40.00 |
| GAUDY IRONSTONE,PLATE,IMARI DECOR,ORANGE,BLACK,GOLD,MARKED | |

GAUDY DUTCH PLATE, CORONATION PATTERN

```
  ASHWORTH......................................................    12.50
GAUDY IRONSTONE,PLATE,SEEING EYE,5 IN.........................    35.00
GAUDY IRONSTONE,PLATE,URN PATTERN,DARK BLUE,9 1/2 IN..........    27.50
GAUDY IRONSTONE,PLATTER,ASHWORTH,MASON'S PATENT,11 IN.,
  13 IN.,18 IN.,3............................................    65.00
GAUDY IRONSTONE,PLATTER,FLORAL,COPELAND,10 1/2 IN.............    22.50
GAUDY IRONSTONE,SOUP,ASHWORTH,MASON'S PATENT,10 1/4 IN.WIDE,
  SET OF 11..................................................    90.00
```

```
      GAUDY WELSH IS AN IMARI DECORATED EARTHENWARE WITH RED,
      BLUE,GREEN,AND GOLD DECORATIONS. IT WAS MADE AFTER
      1820.
GAUDY WELSH,CUP & SAUCER,COBALT,HAND-PAINTED FLORAL,LUSTER
  TRIM......................................................      45.00
GAUDY WELSH,CUP & SAUCER,TULIP PATTERN............. 20.00 TO     24.00
GAUDY WELSH,CUP & SAUCER,WHITE GROUND,BLUE & PINK FLORAL,
  CIRCA 1850................................................      25.00
GAUDY WELSH,BOWL,OYSTER PATTERN,MARKED ALLERTON.............      25.00
GAUDY WELSH,BOWL,SUGAR,DAISY & CHAIN PATTERN,COVER..........      50.00
GAUDY WELSH,BOWL,SUGAR,SHANGHAI PATTERN,COVER...............      48.00
GAUDY WELSH,BOWL,WASTE,GRAPE PATTERN,3 IN.HIGH,5-IN.DIAMETER     35.00
GAUDY WELSH,CREAMER,DAISY & CHAIN PATTERN...................      40.00
GAUDY WELSH,CREAMER,OYSTER PATTERN................. 23.00 TO     42.00
GAUDY WELSH,CUP & SAUCER,CARNATION,COBALT TRIANGLES.........      28.00
GAUDY WELSH,CUP & SAUCER,DEMITASSE,WAGON WHEEL PATTERN......      25.00
GAUDY WELSH,CUP & SAUCER,OYSTER PATTERN.....................      32.50
GAUDY WELSH,CUP & SAUCER,SCALLOPED TOP......................      17.50
GAUDY WELSH,CUP & SAUCER,TULIP DECOR........................      25.00
GAUDY WELSH,CUP & SAUCER,TULIP PATTERN............. 15.00 TO     22.50
GAUDY WELSH,CUP & SAUCER,TULIP PATTERN,SET OF 6....150.00 TO    250.00
GAUDY WELSH,CUP,CHILD'S,COLORED DECOR,GOLD,PAIR.............      17.50
GAUDY WELSH,EWER,TULIP PATTERN,4 IN.........................      22.00
GAUDY WELSH,MUG,MINIATURE,THREE HANDLES,ATHERTON............      15.00
GAUDY WELSH,MUG,OYSTER PATTERN..............................      28.00
GAUDY WELSH,MUG,OYSTER PATTERN,3 IN.........................      23.00
GAUDY WELSH,MUG,SHAVING,COLORFUL DECOR......................      34.00
GAUDY WELSH,PITCHER,ATHERTON,5 IN.HIGH......................      32.00
GAUDY WELSH,PITCHER,MILK,OYSTER PATTERN.....................      55.00
GAUDY WELSH,PLATE,URN PATTERN,10 IN.........................      55.00
GAUDY WELSH,PLATE,WAGON WHEEL,7 1/2 IN......................      65.00
GAUDY WELSH,PLATE,WHITE GROUND,BLUE & PINK FLORAL,9 IN......      20.00
GAUDY WELSH,SAUCE,SHANGHAI PATTERN,6 IN.....................       8.00
GAUDY WELSH,SAUCER,TULIP PATTERN............................       9.00
GAUDY WELSH,TEAPOT,DAISY & CHAIN PATTERN....................      70.00
```

```
      GIBSON GIRL PLATES WERE MADE IN THE EARLY 1900S BY THE
      ROYAL DOULTON POTTERY AT LAMBETH,ENGLAND. THERE ARE
      TWENTY-FOUR DIFFERENT PLATES FEATURING A PICTURE OF THE
      GIBSON GIRL BY THE ARTIST CHARLES DANA GIBSON.
GIBSON GIRL,CALENDAR PLATE,1909.............................      15.00
GIBSON GIRL,EASEL,RIDING BICYCLE,WHITE,PAT.DATE 1896........      23.50
GIBSON GIRL,FIGURINE,WEARS BIG HAT,HOLDS PARASOL,BISQUE,
  10 IN.TALL...............................................      22.50
GIBSON GIRL,PLATE,BY CHARLES DANA GIBSON,1900,ROYAL DOULTON.      45.00
GIBSON GIRL,PLATE,DAY AFTER ARRIVING AT HER JOURNEY'S END,
```

```
     10 1/2 IN..........................................................  35.00
GIBSON GIRL,PLATE,FAILING TO FIND REST--SHE RETURNS HOME,
     ROYAL DOULTON.....................................................  42.50
GIBSON GIRL,PLATE,MESSAGE FROM OUTSIDE WORLD,ROYAL. 25.00 TO  35.00
GIBSON GIRL,PLATE,MISS BABBLES BRINGS A COPY....... 28.00 TO  32.50
GIBSON GIRL,PLATE,MISS BABBLES,THE AUTHORESS,READS ALOUD,
     SIGNED,1900.......................................................  35.00
GIBSON GIRL,PLATE,MRS.DIGGS IS ALARMED,ROYAL DOULTON........  33.50
GIBSON GIRL,PLATE,QUIET DINNER WITH DR.BOTTLES,ROYAL DOULTON  33.50
GIBSON GIRL,PLATE,SHE CONTEMPLATES THE CLOISTER..........  27.50
GIBSON GIRL,PLATE,SHE DECIDES TO DIE IN SPITE OF DR.BOTTLES.  35.00
GIBSON GIRL,PLATE,SHE GOES AS JULIET,10 1/2 IN...............  35.00
GIBSON GIRL,PLATE,SHE GOES INTO COLOR,ROYAL DOULTON..........  33.50
GIBSON GIRL,PLATE,SHE GOES TO FANCY DRESS BALL AS
     JULIET........................................... 25.00 TO  35.00
GIBSON GIRL,PLATE,SHE IS DISTURBED BY A VISION.............  27.50
GIBSON GIRL,PLATE,SHE IS THE SUBJECT OF MORE HOSTILE
     CRITICISM,DOULTON.................................................  35.00
GIBSON GIRL,PLATE,SHE LOOKS FOR RELIEF............. 28.00 TO  45.00
GIBSON GIRL,PLATE,SOME THINK THAT SHE HAS REMAINED,ROYAL
     DOULTON...........................................................  25.00
GIBSON GIRL,PLATE, THEY ALL GO SKATING,  10 1/4 IN..........  32.00
GIBSON GIRL,PLATE,WINNING NEW FRIENDS,ROYAL
     DOULTON.......................................... 35.00 TO  45.00
GIBSON GIRL,PRINT,A WORD TO THE WISE,1906,15 IN. X 10 IN....   7.00
GIBSON GIRL,PRINT,BIG GAME,1906,15 IN. X 10 IN.............   5.00
GIBSON GIRL,PRINT,STORY OF AN EMPTY SLEEVE,1906,15 IN. X
     10 IN.............................................................  15.00
GIBSON GIRL,PRINT,TWO IS COMPANY,THREE IS A CROWD,1906,
     15 IN. X 10 IN....................................................  10.00
GIBSON GIRL,VASE,PORTRAIT,MAROON GROUND,HANDLES,
     CZECHOSLOVAKIA,PAIR...............................................  15.00
```

     GILLINDER GLASS WAS MADE BY THE FIRMS FOUNDED BY JAMES
     GILLINDER AND HIS SONS IN 1860. THE ORIGINAL FIRM WAS
     THE FRANKLIN FLINT GLASS CO.,THEN CAME GILLINDER AND
     BENNET,AND FINALLY GILLINDER AND SONS. THE FIRMS MADE
     MANY PATTERNS OF PRESSED AND CUT GLASS UNTIL THE 1930S.

```
GILLINDER,PAPERWEIGHT,BUDDHA,RUBY GLASS,SIGNED,5 1/2 IN.TALL  65.00
GILLINDER,SLIPPER,CLEAR,SIGNED...............................  20.00
GILLINDER,SLIPPER,FROSTED,SIGNED.............................  22.50
GILLINDER,TUMBLER,ENGRAVED SAILING SHIP,BIRDS,SCRIPT
     SIGNATURE.........................................................  22.50
```

     GINGER JARS HAVE WIDE MOUTHS AND ROUNDED BODIES. IT IS
     BELIEVED THAT THE JAR ORIGINALLY HELD CANDIED FRUITS
     AND GINGER AND WAS GIVEN TO FRIENDS ON THE CHINESE NEW
     YEAR.

```
GINGER JAR,BLUE,WHITE,LANDSCAPE,RIVER,FIGURES,KANG HSI,CHINA  225.00
GINGER JAR,BLUE,WHITE,PRUNUS BLOSSOMS,KANG HSI,CHINA,
     10 IN.HIGH........................................................ 175.00
GINGER JAR,BLUE,WHITE,STAG,DOE,RIVER,TREES,COVER,KANG HSI,
     CHINA............................................................. 150.00
GINORI,PLATE,MEDALLION,WINGED CUPID RIDING DOLPHIN,COBALT,
     9 1/4 IN..........................................................  16.00
GINORI,TRAY,DRESSER,GOLD EDGE,YELLOW FLORAL,HAND-PAINTED,
     SIGNED............................................................  15.00
GIRANDOLE,CARTOUCHE-SHAPE PLATE,GILT WOODEN FRAME,ITALY,
     37 IN.,PAIR......................................................1,800.00
GIRANDOLE,GOLD LEAF,MARBLE BASE,PRISMS,MAN,WOMAN,BIRD,
     16 IN.TALL,PAIR...................................................  75.00
GIRANDOLE,INDIAN,FULL FIGURE,WITH SPEAR,THREE BRANCHES......  200.00
GIRANDOLE,INDIANS,BRONZE,MARBLE BASE,THREE PIECES...........  300.00
GIRANDOLE,MAN,WOMAN IN FRENCH ATTIRE,DOUBLE HANDLE,BRASS,
     PRISMS,PAIR.......................................................  80.00
GIRANDOLE,MAN,WOMAN,DOG,MARBLE BASE,PRISMS,BRASS,THREE
     CANDLES,SET OF 3..................................................  125.00
GIRANDOLE,THREE BRANCHES,SETTER DOG,MARBLE BASE,BOBECHES,
     PRISMS,BRASS......................................................  85.00
GIRANDOLE,THREE ORNATE ARMS,BRASS,PRISMS,MAN & WOMAN ON
     MARBLE BASE.......................................................  35.00
GOLD,CASE,PICTURE,CASTLE SCENE ON BACK,HOLDS 4 PICTURES,
     CIRCA 1850........................................................  75.00
GOLD,LORGNETTE,FOLDS,MARKED 14K..............................  27.50
GOLD,NUT PICK,AMETHYST SET IN TOP............................  10.00
GOLD,PURSE,MESH,CHAIN,AMETHYST ON CLASP,76 PENNYWEIGHT IN
     GOLD,14 KT........................................................ 225.00
GOLD,THIMBLE,BAND OF ENGRAVED FLOWERS,TREE IN TRIANGLE,
     SEPT.5,1918,10K...................................................  25.00
```

```
GOLD,THIMBLE,CHILD'S,EMBOSSED HEART & FLORAL BORDER,ENGRAVED
   NAME,1899......................................................    25.00
GOLD,THIMBLE,EMBOSSED AND ENGRAVED GRAPES AND VINES.........    25.00
GOLD,THIMBLE,GEM AMETHYST TOP,RELIEF GRAPE BORDER,BEADED,
   CIRCA 1850....................................................    25.00
GOLD,THIMBLE,SIZE 8.............................................    17.00
GOLD,THIMBLE,SIZE 9,ORNATE BORDER,INSCRIPTION,14K...........    20.00
GOLD,THIMBLE,SIZE 13,MARKED 10K..............................    15.00
GOLD,THIMBLE,10K................................................    15.00
GOLD,THIMBLE,14K................................................    11.50
```

```
      GOOFUS GLASS WAS MADE FROM ABOUT 1900 TO 1920 BY MANY
   AMERICAN FACTORIES.IT WAS ORIGINALLY PAINTED GOLD,RED,
   GREEN,BRONZE,PINK,PURPLE,AND OTHER BRIGHT COLORS.
GOOFUS GLASS,BOWL,BROWN,RED FLOWERS,9 1/2 IN..............     5.00
GOOFUS GLASS,BOWL,CLEAR,GILT FRUIT DECOR,10-IN.DIAMETER.....     7.00
GOOFUS GLASS,BOWL,DEEP,CARNATION WREATH,9 IN.................    12.00
GOOFUS GLASS,BOWL,DOGWOOD PATTERN,9 IN......................    10.50
GOOFUS GLASS,BOWL,FRUIT,RED OUTSIDE,SILVER COLOR INSIDE.....    15.00
GOOFUS GLASS,BOWL,GOLD COLOR,BURGUNDY MORNING GLORIES,
   9 3/4 IN......................................................    10.00
GOOFUS GLASS,BOWL,GREEN WITH RED FLOWERS,MARKED N..........     9.00
GOOFUS GLASS,BOWL,RED GRAPES,GILT.............................    10.00
GOOFUS GLASS,BOWL,RED MUMS,GOLD,9 IN.........................     6.00
GOOFUS GLASS,BOWL,ROSES,10 IN...................................    12.50
GOOFUS GLASS,BOWL,ROSES,SHALLOW,11 IN........................     5.00
GOOFUS GLASS,BOWL,ROSES,9 IN....................................     7.00
GOOFUS GLASS,COMPOTE,RED,GOLD OVER GREEN,OPEN,6-IN.DIAMETER.    10.00
GOOFUS GLASS,DISH,RUFFLED,GOLD & SHADED RED GROUND,RED
   ROSES,9 1/4 IN................................................    16.50
GOOFUS GLASS,JAR,PICKLE,FLORAL DESIGN,21 IN.HIGH............     8.00
GOOFUS GLASS,JAR,PICKLE,RAISED GRAPES AND LEAVES,ONE QUART..    10.00
GOOFUS GLASS,JAR,POWDER,ROSE PATTERN,BUST OF LADY ON COVER..    11.00
GOOFUS GLASS,LAMP BASE,PEACOCK,GREEN,RED,GOLD...............    25.00
GOOFUS GLASS,LAMP,GONE WITH THE WIND.........................    45.00
GOOFUS GLASS,PAINTED RED & GOLD,WILD ROSES,SCROLLS,9 X
   2 1/2 IN......................................................     9.50
GOOFUS GLASS,PLATE,CAKE,RED & GOLD...........................     4.75
GOOFUS GLASS,PLATE,IRIS DECOR,8 IN.............................     4.00
GOOFUS GLASS,PLATE,RED NARCISSUS IN CENTER,GOLD,
   3 1/2-IN.DIAMETER............................................     4.00
GOOFUS GLASS,PLATE,RED ROSES,GOLD,7 1/2-IN.DIAMETER........     5.00
GOOFUS GLASS,PLATE,SPRAYS OF RED ACORNS,GREEN LEAVES,GILT,
   11 1/4 IN.....................................................     7.50
GOOFUS GLASS,VASE,GRAPES,7 IN..................................     9.50
GOOFUS GLASS,VASE,LA BELLE POPPY,OPALESCENT,7 IN.HIGH.......    10.00
GOOFUS GLASS,VASE,LA BELLE ROSE,CLEAR,5 1/2 IN.HIGH.........     3.50
GOOFUS GLASS,VASE,LA BELLE ROSE,OPALESCENT,5 1/2 IN.HIGH....    10.00
GOOFUS GLASS,VASE,ROSES,7 IN....................................     9.50
```

```
      GRANITEWARE IS AN ENAMELED TINWARE THAT HAS BEEN USED
   IN THE KITCHEN FROM THE LATE NINETEENTH CENTURY TO THE
   PRESENT. EARLIER GRANITEWARE WAS GREEN OR TURQUOISE
   BLUE,WITH WHITE SPATTERS. THE LATER WARE WAS GRAY WITH
   WHITE SPATTERS. REPRODUCTIONS ARE BEING MADE IN ALL
   COLORS.
GRANITEWARE,BUTTER,PEWTER COLLAR,BAR HANDLES & FINIAL.......    37.50
GRANITEWARE,CAN,CREAM,SWIRL,BLUE,LID,BAIL...................     9.50
GRANITEWARE,COFFEEPOT,GRAY,8 IN.TALL.........................     2.00
GRANITEWARE,COFFEEPOT,GREEN & WHITE..........................     6.00
GRANITEWARE,COFFEEPOT,PEWTER FITTINGS,THUMB REST HANDLE,
   GREEN.........................................................    35.00
GRANITEWARE,LUNCH PAIL,GRAY,MINER'S.........................    12.50
GRANITEWARE,SHELF,HANGING,GRAY-MOTTLED,INSERTS MARKED ZAND,
   15 IN.LONG....................................................    28.00
GRANITEWARE,STRAINER,BROWN & WHITE SPECKLE..................     5.00
GRANITEWARE,TEAPOT,DOMED TIN LID,6 IN.HIGH...................     6.50
GRANITEWARE,WASH BASIN,WHITE EXTERIOR,BLUE & WHITE INTERIOR.     5.00
GREENTOWN, SEE ALSO PRESSED GLASS,SLAG,CARAMEL
GREENTOWN,MUG,TROUBADOR.......................................    15.00
GUN, SEE WEAPON, GUN
```

```
      GUNDERSON GLASS WAS MADE AT THE GUNDERSON PAIRPONT
   WORKS OF NEW BEDFORD,MASSACHUSETTS,FROM 1952 TO 1957.
   GUNDERSON PEACHBLOW IS ESPECIALLY FAMOUS.
   GUNDERSON, SEE ALSO PEACHBLOW
GUNDERSON,BURMESE,CREAMER,BELL BOTTOM,ACID FINISH...........   110.00
GUNDERSON,BURMESE,HAT,PINK TO YELLOW,DIAMOND QUILTED,PINK
```

```
    INSIDE....................................................  180.00
GUNDERSON,BURMESE,TUMBLER,PINK,YELLOW,ACID FINISH,4 IN.TALL.  118.50
GUNDERSON,CUP & SAUCER,RASPBERRY,WHITE HANDLE,PEDESTAL BASE.   85.00
GUNDERSON,NAPPIE,CRYSTAL HANDLE,4-IN.DIAMETER,LABEL.........   16.00
GUNDERSON,PEACHBLOW,CREAMER,SUGAR,DEEP RASPBERRY TO WHITE,
    PEDESTAL.................................................  195.00
GUNDERSON,PEACHBLOW,CUP & SAUCER.................115.00 TO    135.00
GUNDERSON,PEACHBLOW,DECANTER,BULBOUS,RASPBERRY TO WHITE,
    STOPPER.................................................  225.00
GUNDERSON,PEACHBLOW,GOBLET,DEEP PINK TO WHITE,WHITE BALUSTER
    STEM....................................................  150.00
GUNDERSON,PEACHBLOW,GOBLET,DULL FINISH.....................  150.00
GUNDERSON,PEACHBLOW,GOBLET,RASPBERRY TO WHITE,ACID FINISH,
    6 1/2 IN................................................  128.50
GUNDERSON,PEACHBLOW,PITCHER,WATER,ROSE TO WHITE,CRIMPED
    MOUTH...................................................  175.00
GUNDERSON,PEACHBLOW,TUMBLER,BLUE-WHITE TO PINK,DEEP
    RASPBERRY LINING........................................  110.00
GUNDERSON,PEACHBLOW,TUMBLER,ROSE TO WHITE,RASPBERRY LINING,
    4 IN.TALL...............................................  110.00
GUNDERSON,PEACHBLOW,VASE,BANJO SHAPE,6 3/4 IN.HIGH,PAIR....  175.00
GUNDERSON,PEACHBLOW,VASE,LILY,PINK SHADING INTO WHITE,
    9 1/4 IN.TALL...........................................  140.00
GUNDERSON,TOOTHPICK,PLUM COLOR,GLOSSY,BOX-PLEATED,CAMILLIA..  100.00
GUTTA PERCHA,SEE ALBUM,PHOTOGRAPHY


        HANDEL,PHILIP,WORKED IN MERIDEN,CONNECTICUT,ABOUT 1885
        AND IN NEW YORK CITY FROM ABOUT 1900 TO THE 1930S. HIS
        FIRM MADE ART GLASS AND OTHER TYPES OF LAMPS.
HANDEL,BOWL,MELON RIBS,RUST & GREEN GROUND,BRASS RIM,SIGNED.   30.00
HANDEL,BOX,VERDE FINISH, CHIPPED  GROUND,VIOLETS INSIDE,
    SIGNED RUNGE............................................  115.00
HANDEL,HUMIDOR,EMBOSSED SCROLL,DOG DECOR,GREEN & BROWN
    GROUND,SIGNED...........................................   85.00
HANDEL,HUMIDOR,GREEN,BROWN,BEAR IN A TREE,HAND-PAINTED,
    ARTIST-SIGNED...........................................  115.00
HANDEL,HUMIDOR,MELON RIB,AUTUMN SHADES OVER OPAQUE WHITE,
    SILVER COVER............................................   47.50
HANDEL,HUMIDOR,TOBACCO,GREEN & BROWN GROUND,DOG PORTRAIT,
    ARTIST RUNGE............................................   75.00
HANDEL,HUMIDOR,TOBACCO,RUST,GREEN GROUND,POINTER DOG,
    MOUNTAINS,BAUER.........................................  135.00
HANDEL,JAR,COOKIE,BLUE SHADING TO WHITE,TRANSFER PRINT DECOR
    OF DAISIES..............................................   70.00
HANDEL,JAR,TOBACCO,HUNTING DOGS,COVER,SIGNED,7 1/2 IN. TALL.   75.00
HANDEL,LAMP,BELL-SHAPE,YELLOW,RED ROSES,GREEN LEAVES,BRONZE
    BASE....................................................  145.00
HANDEL,LAMP,BLUE,PERSIAN EFFECT BAND,HAND-PAINTED,THREE
    LIGHTS,18 IN............................................  200.00
HANDEL,LAMP,BRONZE,BELL-SHAPE SHADE,GOLD IRIDESCENT,SIGNED,
    18 IN.HIGH..............................................  169.00
HANDEL,LAMP,DESK,BELL-SHAPE SHADE,PALM OVERLAY,LEADED,BRONZE
    BASE....................................................  195.00
HANDEL,LAMP,DESK,GREEN ART GLASS,BRONZE FEATHER OVERLAY,
    BRONZE BASE.............................................  500.00
HANDEL,LAMP,DESK,SWIVEL SHADE,LANDSCAPE SCENE,SUN,CLOUDS,
    SKY,BRONZE BASE.........................................  135.00
HANDEL,LAMP,FLOOR,SHADE SIGNED MOSSERINE HANDEL,57 IN.HIGH..  160.00
HANDEL,LAMP,FROSTED SHADE,RIPPLED SURFACE,BLUE,ORANGE
    FLORAL,SIGNED...........................................   80.00
HANDEL,LAMP,GREEN PANELS,FLORAL,LEAD OVERLAY,BRONZE BASE,
    22 1/2 IN.TALL..........................................  295.00
HANDEL,LAMP,MUSHROOM SHADE,GREEN,ACORNS & OAK LEAVES,SIGNED,
    10 IN...................................................   45.00
HANDEL,LAMP,PALM TREE TRUNK BASE,SHADE HAS RIVER SCENE,
    24 IN.HIGH..............................................  185.00
HANDEL,LAMP,PINK SHADE,ROBINS,TREES,APPLE BLOSSOMS,
    ARTIST-SIGNED,18 IN.....................................  225.00
HANDEL,LAMP,POND LILY,GREEN & WHITE SHADE..................  250.00
HANDEL,LAMP,SCENIC LANDSCAPE,BRONZE BASE...................  150.00
HANDEL,LAMP,YELLOW SHADE,HAND-PAINTED FLORAL BAND,TWO
    LIGHTS,15 IN.HIGH.......................................  185.00
HANDEL,SHADE,CREAM COLOR,LEAVES CONNECTED BY TENDRILS,TWO
    LIGHTS,14 IN............................................  100.00
HANDEL,SHADE,FROSTED WHITE,ENAMELED PINK APPLE BLOSSOMS,10
    IN.HIGH.................................................  115.00
HANDEL,TAZZA,ENAMEL GOLDENRODS,GREEN & WHITE GROUND,OPAL
    GLASS,7 3/4 IN..........................................   75.00
HANDEL,VASE,TREE SCENERY,SIGNED & NUMBERED,8 IN.HIGH.......   42.50
```

HATPIN HOLDERS WERE POPULAR ONLY DURING THE PERIOD OF
THE LARGE HAT HELD BY THE EQUALLY LARGE HATPIN. THE
HATPINS WERE ABOUT THREE TO SIX INCHES IN LENGTH. MOST
OF THE HOLDERS DATE FROM THE PERIOD FROM 1880 TO 1910.

| | |
|---|---|
| HATPIN HOLDER,AFFIXED TO TRAY,RING TREE EACH SIDE,SCROLLS, FLORAL,BEADING...................................... | 16.50 |
| HATPIN HOLDER,GILT DECOR,MARKED ZS & CO.,BAVARIA.......... | 10.00 |
| HATPIN HOLDER,GREEN-GOLD,ROSES,HAND-PAINTED,OVAL,AUSTRIA.... | 10.00 |
| HATPIN HOLDER,HAND-DECORATED,PORCELAIN..................... | 12.50 |
| HATPIN HOLDER,OPEN FERN NECK,TWO GREEN,ONE RED STONE,24K GOLD PLATE.............................................. | 22.50 |
| HATPIN HOLDER,PINK & WHITE FLOWERS,GOLD TRIM,MARK,ROYAL CARLSBAD............................................... | 8.00 |
| HATPIN HOLDER,SHADED GREEN,WHITE POPPIES................... | 18.00 |
| HATPIN HOLDER,WHITE GROUND,COBALT,RED,GREEN DECOR,GOLD, HANDLES,PORCELAIN...................................... | 13.50 |
| HATPIN HOLDER,WHITE,GOLD LEAVES,ANGELS,PORTRAIT............ | 18.00 |
| HATPIN,ADVERTISES ECONOMY STOVES,10 1/2 IN................ | 4.75 |
| HATPIN,GOLD PIQUE-INVERTED PEAR SHAPE,AMBER............... | 12.00 |
| HATPIN,JADE DROP IN 18K WHITE GOLD FITTING,TEAR-SHAPE DROP.. | 17.50 |
| HATPIN,PORCELAIN KNOB,BLUE ENAMEL,MEDALLION,FLORAL, HAND-PAINTED.......................................... | 15.00 |
| HATPIN,STERLING SILVER,FLOWER............................. | 7.00 |

HAVILAND CHINA HAS BEEN MADE IN LIMOGES,FRANCE,SINCE
1846. THE FACTORY WAS STARTED BY THE HAVILAND BROTHERS
OF NEW YORK CITY. OTHER FACTORIES WORKED IN THE TOWN OF
LIMOGES MAKING A SIMILAR CHINAWARE.

HAVILAND,SEE ALSO LIMOGES

| | |
|---|---|
| HAVILAND,BOWL,CHERRIES,GOLD,OVAL,SIGNED,MATCHING PLATE...... | 18.50 |
| HAVILAND,BOWL,SALAD,CHRYSANTHEMUM PATTERN.................. | 38.50 |
| HAVILAND,BOWL,STRAWBERRIES,LEAVES,BLOSSOMS,FLUTED,BEADED, GOLD RIM.............................................. | 35.00 |
| HAVILAND,BOX,JEWEL,GREEN GROUND,PINK MOSS ROSES ON TOP,BLUE VELVET-LINED......................................... | 25.00 |
| HAVILAND,BOX,POWDER,VIOLETS,GOLD LEAF,HINGED COVER, HAND-PAINTED.......................................... | 35.00 |
| HAVILAND,BUTTER CHIP,PINK & BLUE FLOWERS,SET OF 6.......... | 8.00 |
| HAVILAND,BUTTER PAT,PINK & WHITE ROSES,GARLANDS,GOLD,SET OF 4.................................................... | 11.00 |
| HAVILAND,BUTTER PAT,WHITE................................. | 1.00 |
| HAVILAND,CELERY,LAVENDER FLOWERS,GOLD,WASP-WAISTED,OPEN HANDLES,LIMOGES....................................... | 12.50 |
| HAVILAND,CHOCOLATE POT,BLUE,YELLOW,PINK,RED ROSES,GREEN LEAVES,GOLD TRIM...................................... | 20.00 |
| HAVILAND,CHOCOLATE POT,BUFF TO BROWN GROUND,YELLOW ROSES, GOLD HANDLE........................................... | 65.00 |
| HAVILAND,CHOCOLATE POT,CREAMER,SUGAR,ART NOUVEAU STYLING, FRANCE................................................ | 48.00 |
| HAVILAND,COFFEEPOT,CREAMER,SUGAR,SILVER WEDDING PATTERN..... | 55.00 |
| HAVILAND,CREAMER,PINK FLOWERS,GOLD TRIM................... | 15.00 |
| HAVILAND,CREAMER & SUGAR,BLUE FORGET-ME-NOTS,FRANCE,MARKED.. | 35.00 |
| HAVILAND,CREAMER & SUGAR,HAND-PAINTED LILY OF THE VALLEY, GOLD.................................................. | 47.50 |
| HAVILAND,CREAMER & SUGAR,LIGHT BLUE BACHELOR BUTTON,GOLD TRIM.................................................. | 35.00 |
| HAVILAND,CREAMER & SUGAR,ROSE DESIGN,LIMOGES............... | 19.00 |
| HAVILAND,CUP & SAUCER,DEMITASSE,APPLE BLOSSOM PATTERN,SET OF 6.................................................... | 65.00 |
| HAVILAND,CUP & SAUCER,DEMITASSE,SPRINGTIME................. | 7.00 |
| HAVILAND,CUP & SAUCER,DEMITASSE,WHITE,GOLD TRIM............ | 5.00 |
| HAVILAND,CUP & SAUCER,RED POPPY DECOR,FRANCE.............. | 12.50 |
| HAVILAND,DESSERT SET,12 CUPS & SAUCERS,12 PLATES,PINK ROSES. | 125.00 |
| HAVILAND,DISH,RELISH,MOSS ROSE,7 1/2 X 4 IN............... | 3.50 |
| HAVILAND,DISH,SAUCE,WHITE,RANSON PATTERN,PAIR............. | 4.50 |
| HAVILAND,DISH,VEGETABLE,FLEUR-DE-LIS PATTERN,1856.......... | 20.00 |
| HAVILAND,DISH,VEGETABLE,SMALL PINK ROSES,GOLD,ROUND,COVER... | 12.00 |
| HAVILAND,GRAVY BOAT ATTACHED TO TRAY,HANDLES,YELLOW & BROWN DECOR................................................. | 12.50 |
| HAVILAND,JAR,DRESSER,CREAM GROUND,TREE BRANCHES,BLUE FLORAL, GOLD,3................................................ | 55.00 |
| HAVILAND,MUG,SHAVING,APPLE BLOSSOMS,HAND-PAINTED,INITIALS... | 14.50 |
| HAVILAND,MUG,SHAVING,WHITE,NUMBER 36 IN GOLD.............. | 6.95 |
| HAVILAND,MUG,SHAVING,WHITE,NUMBER 71 IN GOLD.............. | 6.95 |
| HAVILAND,NAPKIN RING,HAND-PAINTED......................... | 10.00 |
| HAVILAND,PITCHER,BUNCH PURPLE GRAPES,VINES,GOLD HANDLE, SIGNED,9 1/4 IN....................................... | 15.50 |
| HAVILAND,PITCHER,MILK,HEAD IS COVER,MATCHING CREAMER....... | 125.00 |
| HAVILAND,PLATE,BREAD & BUTTER,AUTUMN LEAF................. | 6.00 |

```
HAVILAND,PLATE,CHOP,GRAPES,LEAVES,BROWN,GREEN,GOLD,
   12 1/2 IN.....................................................    32.50
HAVILAND,PLATE,CHOP,ROSES,VIOLETS,GOLD,13 IN.................    18.00
HAVILAND,PLATE,COIN GOLD RIM,BLUE TRIM,ROSES,HAND-PAINTED,
   SET OF 6....................................................    14.50
HAVILAND,PLATE,DESSERT,GOLD RIM,EACH DIFFERENT FLORAL,GOLD
   RIM,SET OF 6................................................    36.00
HAVILAND,PLATE,DESSERT,TROY PATTERN,6 1/4 IN.................     1.50
HAVILAND,PLATE,DINNER,AUTUMN LEAF.............................     8.00
HAVILAND,PLATE,FRUIT BLOSSOMS,BLACKBERRIES,RASPBERRIES,
   MARKED A.H.,1898............................................     4.00
HAVILAND,PLATE,HAND-PAINTED VIOLETS,LEAVES,STEMS,MARK,
   8 1/2 IN....................................................    18.00
HAVILAND,PLATE,HIGH RELIEF BEADED RIM,SIGNED,FRANCE,
   9 1/2 IN....................................................    25.00
HAVILAND,PLATE,MARTHA WASHINGTON,FIRST EDITION...............    35.00
HAVILAND,PLATE,OYSTER,PINK,LAVENDER MARSH FLOWERS,BUTTERFLY,
   FISH,GOLD...................................................    30.00
HAVILAND,PLATE,RED POPPIES,GOLD BORDER,ARTIST-SIGNED,
   12 3/4 IN...................................................    48.50
HAVILAND,PLATE,SHADED GROUND,PINK & ROSE COLOR PEONIES,
   11 1/4 IN...................................................    25.00
HAVILAND,PLATE,TINY ROSES,GILT,6 IN..........................     2.00
HAVILAND,PLATE,YELLOW ROSES,ARTIST-SIGNED IB,12 IN...........    25.00
HAVILAND,PLATTER,FLEUR-DE-LIS PATTERN,1876,15 IN.............    20.00
HAVILAND,PLATTER,FORGET-ME-NOTS,TOUCHES OF PINK,16 IN........    19.50
HAVILAND,PLATTER,PINK & GREEN FLORAL,NOTCHED CORNERS,
   14 1/2 IN...................................................    20.00
HAVILAND,PLATTER,SMALL PINK ROSES ON BORDER,11 1/4 IN. X
   8 IN.......................................................     5.00
HAVILAND,PLATTER,YELLOW GROUND,PINK FLORAL,LEAVES,ROSE
   BORDER,10 IN.LONG...........................................    17.50
HAVILAND,POT,CHOCOLATE,CREAM TO BLUE,ROSES,HANDLE,GOLD
   FINIAL,FRANCE...............................................    20.00
HAVILAND,SAUCE,BAND & LINE,FRANCE,5 1/2 IN...................     2.50
HAVILAND,SUGAR,MOSS ROSE,COVER,IMPRESSED REGISTRATION MARK,
   ROPE HANDLES................................................    18.00
HAVILAND,TABLE SETTING,RAJAH PATTERN,PORCELAIN,72 PIECES....   110.00
HAVILAND,TANKARD,YELLOW FLORAL,RIBBON HANDLE,GOLD,6 1/2 IN..    12.00
HAVILAND,TOOTHPICK,GOLD AURENE,PINCHED SIDES,SIGNED,
   2 1/4 IN...................................................   125.00
HAVILAND,TRAY,COIN GOLD RIM,RUST & GREEN FERN DESIGN,
   HAND-PAINTED................................................     9.00
HAVILAND,TRAY,DRESSER,WHITE GROUND,FLORAL,11 X 7 IN.,FRANCE.     8.00
HAVILAND,TRAY,DRESSER,YELLOW DAFFODILS,SCALLOPED,GOLD TRIM,
   SIGNED......................................................    12.50
HAVILAND,TUREEN,VEGETABLE,LAVENDER MORNING GLORIES,COVER....    25.00


        T.G.HAWKES & COMPANY OF CORNING,NEW YORK,WAS FOUNDED
        IN 1880. THE FIRM CUT GLASS MADE AT OTHER FIRMS UNTIL
        1962. MANY PIECES ARE MARKED WITH THE TRADEMARK,A
        TREFOIL RING ENCLOSING A FLEUR-DE-LIS AND TWO HAWKS.
HAWKES,BOTTLE,COLOGNE,HEAVY CUT,THUMBPRINT,SIGNED...........    65.00
HAWKES,BOTTLE,OIL & VINEGAR,ENGRAVED FLORAL,DOUBLE LIPS,
   SILVER STOPPER..............................................    37.50
HAWKES,BOTTLE,WORCESTERSHIRE,BRUNSWICK PATTERN,STOPPER,
   SIGNED, 8 IN................................................    85.00
HAWKES,BOWL,CLEAR,GOLD BAND AT TOP,YELLOW LINING,SIGNED,
   7-IN.DIAMETER...............................................    22.50
HAWKES,BOWL,FINGER,CARNATION PATTERN,GRAVIC GLASS,SIGNED....    75.00
HAWKES,BOWL,FINGER,CUT SWAGGED FLORAL PATTERN,5-IN.DIAMETER,
   SET OF 8....................................................    80.00
HAWKES,BOWL,FINGER,PLATE,ENGRAVED FESTOONS,FLORAL,BLOWN,
   QUATREFOIL MARK.............................................    25.00
HAWKES,BOWL,FINGER,PLATE,INTAGLIO CUT,SIGNED.................    25.00
HAWKES,BOX,INTAGLIO & CUT,SILVER HINGE,SIGNED,6-IN.DIAMETER.   155.00
HAWKES,BOX,IRIS PATTERN,SIGNED HAWKES GRAVIC GLASS,LID,
   6 1/2-IN.DIAMETER...........................................   195.00
HAWKES,CASTOR,BITTERS,CLEREMONT ENGRAVED DESIGN,DISC FOOT,
   SILVER CAP..................................................    36.00
HAWKES,COMPOTE,FLORAL DESIGN,COPPER WHEEL ETCHING,SIGNED,
   4 1/2 IN.HIGH...............................................    30.00
HAWKES,COMPOTE,FLORAL ETCHING,4 1/2 IN.HIGH,
   5 1/2-IN.DIAMETER...........................................    28.00
HAWKES,DISH,FRUIT,ETCHED,ROSE & SPRAY,BASKET SHAPE,SIGNED...    25.00
HAWKES,PERFUME CASTOR SET,SIX BOTTLES,GLASS CASTOR,SILVER
   RAIL,TOPS...................................................    69.50
HAWKES,PERFUME,DAISY,BUTTON,THUMBPRINT PANELS,PEDESTAL BASE,
   SIGNED......................................................    18.00
HAWKES,SHAKER,COCKTAIL,SHIP,COAT OF ARMS,ENAMEL,SILVER TOP,
```

| | |
|---|---|
| LA LONDE..................................................... | 50.00 |
| HAWKES,SHERBET,FLOWER & LEAF FESTOONS,FOOTED,3 IN.TALL,SET OF 4........................................................ | 38.00 |
| HAWKES,TRAY,DIAMOND-SHAPED FIELD,ENGRAVED BIRD,CROSSCUT DIAMONDS,OVAL................................................. | 150.00 |
| HAWKES,VASE,ENGRAVED BIRD & FLOWERS,LAVENDER,SIGNED,8 IN.... | 60.00 |
| HAWKES,VASE,FAN,ENGRAVED BERRIES,LEAVES,AMBER,9 1/2 IN.TALL. | 48.00 |
| HAWKES,VASE,INTAGLIO CUT LAUREL WREATH DECOR,CRYSTAL,SIGNED, 6 IN.TALL................................................... | 16.00 |
| HAWKES,VASE,SATIN CAMPHOR-LIKE GLASS,IRIDESCENT,ENGRAVED FLORAL,10 IN.................................................. | 55.00 |
| HAWKES,WHISKEY SHOT GLASS,MIDDLESEX PATTERN,2 1/2 IN.HIGH, SET OF 5.................................................... | 80.00 |
| HAWKES,WHISKEY,ALLOVER CUT,SIGNED,2 1/2 IN.HIGH............. | 6.50 |
| HAWKES,WINE,FLOWER SPRAY CUTTING,BLOWN,SIGNED,7 1/2 IN.HIGH. | 22.00 |

HEISEY GLASS WAS MADE FROM 1895 TO 1958 IN NEWARK, OHIO,BY A.H. HEISEY AND CO. INC.

| | |
|---|---|
| HEISEY,BASKET,BOWED,TWO HANDLES,MARK,6 1/2 IN.LONG, 4 IN.WIDE,3 IN.HIGH........................................... | 8.50 |
| HEISEY,BASKET,CUT & ETCHED FLORAL,BUTTERFLIES,HANDLE, 13 IN.TALL.................................................... | 38.50 |
| HEISEY,BASKET,CUT FLOWERS,SCALLOPED TOP,SIGNED.............. | 45.00 |
| HEISEY,BASKET,HAMMERED METAL HANDLE,SWIRL PANELS,MARKED..... | 20.00 |
| HEISEY,BASKET,ICE,BROAD SWIRL PANELS,AMBER,HAMMERED METAL HANDLE,MARK................................................. | 18.50 |
| HEISEY,BASKET,RIBBED PANELS,CLEAR,RECTANGULAR,SIGNED, 11 1/2 IN.HIGH.................................................. | 18.75 |
| HEISEY,BASKET,RIBBED PANELS,STAR BASE,11 IN.HIGH............ | 18.00 |
| HEISEY,BASKET,SQUARE SHAPE,SIGNED,12 IN.HIGH............... | 22.50 |
| HEISEY,BOWL,AMBER,GOLD,SIGNED.............................. | 12.50 |
| HEISEY,BOWL,BERRY,WILLIAMSBURG PATTERN,8 1/2-IN.DIAMETER.... | 8.00 |
| HEISEY,BOWL,CENTERPIECE,RIBBED,12 IN....................... | 15.00 |
| HEISEY,BOWL,FRUIT,LOW,TURNED EDGE,GOLD & BLUE BANDS,GRAPES, PEARS...................................................... | 30.00 |
| HEISEY,BOWL,FRUIT,PANEL PATTERN,INTAGLIO CUT DAISIES,DATED 4-15-13.................................................... | 12.00 |
| HEISEY,BOWL,FRUIT,SUNBURST,SIGNED H IN DIAMOND,13 X 9 1/2 IN.................................................... | 20.00 |
| HEISEY,BOWL,LOOP PATTERN,SIGNED,18-IN.DIAMETER............. | 17.50 |
| HEISEY,BOWL,ORANGE,BLACK-ENAMELED DECOR,HEAVY GOLD RIM...... | 18.00 |
| HEISEY,BOWL,PANELS,CUT CIRCLES,BOAT SHAPE,LOW STANDARD, SCALLOPED.................................................. | 15.00 |
| HEISEY,BOWL,PINWHEEL DESIGN,8 1/2 IN....................... | 15.00 |
| HEISEY,BOWL,PUNCH,RIBBED,TWO-PIECE,SIGNED, 14 1/2-IN.DIAMETER,13 IN.TALL............................... | 35.00 |
| HEISEY,BOWL,PUNCH,TWO PARTS,PANELED DESIGN,15 IN.WIDE, 10 IN.HIGH................................................. | 75.00 |
| HEISEY,BOWL,ROMAN KEY DESIGN,3 1/2 IN.DEEP X 8 1/2-IN.DIAMETER............................................ | 17.50 |
| HEISEY,BOWL,ROMAN KEY EDGE................................ | 25.00 |
| HEISEY,BOWL,ROSE,QUILTED,MARKED,7 IN.TALL,22 1/2 IN.AROUND.. | 13.00 |
| HEISEY,BOWL,SUGAR,CUSTARD RING BAND,GOLD FAIR,SIGNED........ | 45.00 |
| HEISEY,BOWL,SUGAR,STERLING OVERLAY,SIGNED.................. | 12.00 |
| HEISEY,BOWL,SWIRLED,GREEN,SIGNED,9 IN...................... | 12.50 |
| HEISEY,BOWL,3-IN.CENTER,2 1/2 IN.FLARE AROUND,STAR BOTTOM, MARKED..................................................... | 10.00 |
| HEISEY,BOX,CLEAR,PANELED,JEWELS SET IN OPENWORK GOLD METAL TOP,1910.................................................. | 18.00 |
| HEISEY,BOX,GREEN,DOLPHIN FINIAL ON COVER,OVAL,SIGNED, 6 1/2 IN.................................................... | 19.00 |
| HEISEY,BOX,POWDER,CLEAR,COVER,DATED 1910,5-IN.DIAMETER...... | 22.50 |
| HEISEY,BOX,RIBBED,RAYED SAWTOOTH EDGES,MARKED.............. | 6.00 |
| HEISEY,BUTTER PAT,CLEAR,SIGNED............................. | 2.00 |
| HEISEY,BUTTER TUB,ENGRAVED ROSES,MARKED.................... | 25.00 |
| HEISEY,CAKE STAND,CHAIN & LOCKET........................... | 37.50 |
| HEISEY,CANDLEHOLDER,HORN OF PLENTY,MARKED,PAIR............. | 12.50 |
| HEISEY,CANDLEHOLDER,RIBBED PATTERN,SIGNED,10 1/2 IN.TALL.... | 10.00 |
| HEISEY,CANDLEHOLDER,SAUCER BOBECHE,CUT PRISMS,ALLOVER RIB PATTERN,PAIR............................................... | 45.00 |
| HEISEY,CANDLESTICK,CUT EDGES,CRYSTAL,PAIR.................. | 50.00 |
| HEISEY,CANDLESTICK,PANELED,HEXAGON BASE,SIGNED,7 3/4 IN., PAIR....................................................... | 18.00 |
| HEISEY,CARAFE,COLONIAL,PAPER LABEL........................ | 28.50 |
| HEISEY,CELERY,ALLOVER PLEATED FLUTES,RUBY-FLASHED BAND AT TOP,GOLD,BLUE.............................................. | 15.00 |
| HEISEY,CELERY,GREEK KEY PATTERN,STAR IN BASE,12 IN.......... | 25.00 |
| HEISEY,CELERY,RIBBED,FOOTED,SIGNED........................ | 14.00 |
| HEISEY,CHAMBERSTICK,PINK,MATCHING LEAF-SHAPE DISH,13 IN.HIGH | 10.00 |
| HEISEY,COMPOTE,CANDY,PANELS,BAND OF FLOWERS,BUTTERFLIES, | |

| | |
|---|---|
| COVER,10 IN.HIGH.............................................. | 14.00 |
| HEISEY,COMPOTE,ETCHED PANELS,SILVER OVERLAY TRIM,SIGNED, 9 1/4 IN.HIGH............................................... | 18.50 |
| HEISEY,COMPOTE,JELLY,PINEAPPLE,FAN,GREEN,GOLD............... | 25.00 |
| HEISEY,COMPOTE,WIDE PANELS,OCTAGON-SHAPE BASE,SCALLOPED EDGE,8 3/4 IN.............................................. | 32.00 |
| HEISEY,CORDIAL,STEMMED,FLUTED................................ | 3.75 |
| HEISEY,CREAMER & SUGAR,CLEAR,SIGNED.......................... | 8.50 |
| HEISEY,CREAMER & SUGAR,PINK,PANELED,SIGNED................... | 14.00 |
| HEISEY,CREAMER & SUGAR,THUMBPRINT,AMETHYST,MARKED............ | 18.00 |
| HEISEY,CREAMER,BABY THUMBPRINT,CUSTARD GLASS,MARKED H....... | 12.00 |
| HEISEY,CREAMER,CLEAR WHIRLPOOL............................... | 7.50 |
| HEISEY,CREAMER,PANELS,BLACK ENAMEL EDGE,ROSES,FLORAL,GOLD, BASE DISH.................................................. | 25.00 |
| HEISEY,CREAMER,SUGAR,COVER,DIAMOND-QUILTED................... | 15.00 |
| HEISEY,CREAMER,SUGAR,MINIATURE,DEEP-RIBBED,ON 7- X 3 3/4-IN.TRAY............................................... | 15.00 |
| HEISEY,CREAMER,WHIRLPOOL PATTERN,CLEAR,SIGNED................ | 6.50 |
| HEISEY,CRUET,CLEAR,SIGNED.................................... | 10.50 |
| HEISEY,CRUET,EMBOSSED PINEAPPLES,PINEAPPLE STOPPER,BLOWN, SIGNED..................................................... | 18.00 |
| HEISEY,CRUET,ETCHED FLORAL,STOPPER,PONTIL,SIGNED............ | 18.00 |
| HEISEY,CRUET,FACETED STOPPER,SIGNED,3 1/2 IN.HIGH........... | 13.00 |
| HEISEY,CRUET,VINEGAR,ETCHED FLORAL DESIGN,STOPPER,8 IN.TALL. | 14.00 |
| HEISEY,CUP,PUNCH,CLEAR,STAR BASE............................ | 5.00 |
| HEISEY,CUSPIDOR,CLEAR,PANELED,LADY'S SIZE,4 IN.ACROSS, 3 IN.HIGH.................................................. | 11.00 |
| HEISEY,DISH,BONBON,PINK,SWIRLED PANELS,SIGNED,7 X 5 1/2 IN.. | 9.50 |
| HEISEY,DISH,BUTTER,COLONIAL................................. | 20.00 |
| HEISEY,DISH,BUTTER,ETCHED BERRY,CLEAR,COVER,MARKED.......... | 18.00 |
| HEISEY,DISH,CANDY,BUZZ STAR PATTERN,SPADE SHAPE,CLEAR, 6 1/2 IN.HIGH.............................................. | 10.00 |
| HEISEY,DISH,CANDY,CRYSTOLITE PATTERN,THREE SECTIONS,COVER, 7 IN...................................................... | 6.50 |
| HEISEY,DISH,CANDY,ETCHED,HANDLES,EMERALD GREEN,SIGNED, 6 1/2 X 6 3/4 IN........................................... | 10.00 |
| HEISEY,DISH,CANDY,GREEN,PEAKED,PEDESTAL,COVER............... | 15.00 |
| HEISEY,DISH,CANDY,PINK,TRICORNERED,MARKED,THREE HANDLES, 6 IN...................................................... | 13.50 |
| HEISEY,DISH,CANDY,SWIRLED PANELS,HANDLED,GREEN,SIGNED....... | 11.00 |
| HEISEY,DISH,CANDY,TRIANGLE,THREE HANDLES,SIGNED,AMBER....... | 8.50 |
| HEISEY,DISH,CELERY,GREEN KEY,SIGNED,12 X 4 IN............... | 17.50 |
| HEISEY,DISH,CELERY,SILVER OVERLAY,AMBER,OBLONG.............. | 10.00 |
| HEISEY,DISH,CELERY,SUNBURST,MARKED H........................ | 12.00 |
| HEISEY,DISH,CELERY,SUNBURST,12 IN........................... | 9.50 |
| HEISEY,DISH,CHEESE,PANELED,STAR BOTTOM,OVAL,SIGNED, 6 1/2 IN.ACROSS............................................ | 13.00 |
| HEISEY,DISH,CONSOLE,GREEK KEY PATTERN,SIGNED................ | 10.00 |
| HEISEY,DISH,CURVED ENDS,PANELS AT SIDE,SIGNED,9 1/2 X 3 1/4 IN. WIDE........................................... | 18.00 |
| HEISEY,DISH,ENAMELED FLOWERS,OVAL,MARKED,6 3/4 IN.X 5 1/2 IN................................................... | 9.50 |
| HEISEY,DISH,ETCHED FLOWERS,STAR BASE,TUB SHAPE,TURNED-UP HANDLES.................................................... | 7.00 |
| HEISEY,DISH,NUT,STERLING DEPOSIT ON GLASS,FOOTED, 2 3/4-IN.DIAMETER.......................................... | 7.00 |
| HEISEY,DISH,RELISH,LEAF SHAPE,SIGNED,10 IN.LONG............. | 8.00 |
| HEISEY,DISH,RELISH,RIBBED,SIGNED,6 1/2 X 10 1/2 IN.LONG..... | 6.50 |
| HEISEY,DISH,SAUCE,COLONIAL PATTERN,MARKED H IN DIAMOND, 5 3/4 X 4 1/2 IN........................................... | 3.50 |
| HEISEY,DISH,SAUCE,GREEK KEY,MARKED.......................... | 3.50 |
| HEISEY,DISH,SAUCE,PANELED,STAR-RAYED BOTTOM,SET OF 5........ | 12.00 |
| HEISEY,GOBLET,BLOCK PATTERN,MARKED.......................... | 9.00 |
| HEISEY,GOBLET,WINE,SOUVENIR BORTH,WIS.,CUSTARD GLASS, 3 1/2 IN.................................................. | 15.00 |
| HEISEY,HAIR RECEIVER,SILVER TOP............................. | 8.50 |
| HEISEY,HAIR RECEIVER,STAR BASE,COVER,SIGNED................. | 8.00 |
| HEISEY,HOLDER,SUGAR,DOMINO CUBE,CIRCA 1900,SIGNED & NO.355.. | 10.00 |
| HEISEY,JAR,COOKIE,FLUTE PATTERN,SIGNED,10 IN. X 6-IN.DIAMETER............................................. | 40.00 |
| HEISEY,JAR,POWDER,RAYED BASE,COVER,SIGNED,3 X 5 IN.......... | 11.00 |
| HEISEY,JAR,POWDER,SILVER TOP,FAN & DIAMOND,3 1/2 X 4 IN..... | 17.50 |
| HEISEY,JAR,TOBACCO,METAL INSERT FOR MOISTURE,SIGNED,DOMED TOP....................................................... | 35.00 |
| HEISEY,JUICE GLASS,COLONIAL PATTERN,MARKED.................. | 1.50 |
| HEISEY,MAYONNAISE SET,INTAGLIO CUT ROSES,SIGNED,3 PIECES.... | 35.00 |
| HEISEY,MUG,BABY THUMBPRINT,ADVERTISING,1901,CUSTARD......... | 12.00 |
| HEISEY,MUG,PANELED,SIGNED................................... | 5.00 |
| HEISEY,MUG,RUBY & CLEAR,THUMBPRINT,CAROLINE HILL,1902....... | 10.00 |
| HEISEY,MUSTARD,OLD WILLIAMSBURG,COVER,SIGNED................ | 8.50 |
| HEISEY,NAPPIE,GREEK KEY PATTERN,HANDLED,SIGNED,5-IN.DIAMETER | 13.50 |

HEISEY,NAPPIE,WILLIAMSBURG PATTERN,SIGNED,6 IN.WIDE,
  2 1/2 IN.HIGH.............................................. 11.00
HEISEY,PITCHER,COLONIAL,BULBOUS,8 1/4 IN.TALL................ 21.00
HEISEY,PITCHER,MELON SHAPE,SIGNED,1 QT...................... 23.00
HEISEY,PITCHER,PANEL & BLOCK,MARK.......................... 13.50
HEISEY,PITCHER,PRINCE OF WALES PATTERN,GOLD TRIM,9 IN.TALL,
  5 GLASSES................................................. 45.00
HEISEY,PITCHER,RIBBED,NOTCHED,HONEY AMBER,SIGNED,7 IN...... 17.50
HEISEY,PITCHER,WATER,CLEAR,SIGNED.......................... 16.00
HEISEY,PITCHER,WATER,OLD WILLIAMSBURG,6 1/2 IN............. 10.00
HEISEY,PITCHER,WATER,PANELED,APPLIED HANDLE,MARKED......... 10.00
HEISEY,PITCHER,WATER,PILLOW IN CIRCLE PATTERN,BULBOUS,
  SIGNED,8 IN.HIGH......................................... 18.00
HEISEY,PITCHER,WATER,ROMAN KEY............................. 45.00
HEISEY,PLATE,CAKE,COLONIAL,MARK,10 1/2 IN.................. 12.00
HEISEY,PLATE,FLAMINGO,OCTAGONAL,SANDWICH BEEHIVE PATTERN,
  8-IN.DIAMETER............................................ 75.00
HEISEY,PLATE,FLOWERS & SCROLL,6 IN......................... 1.75
HEISEY,PLATE,GREEK KEY PATTERN,SIGNED,5 IN................. 5.00
HEISEY,PLATE,OLD WILLIAMSBURG PATTERN,8 1/4-IN.DIAMETER.... 7.00
HEISEY,PLATE,PINK SWIRL,11-IN.DIAMETER..................... 3.50
HEISEY,PLATE,PINK,DIAGONAL PANEL BORDER,MARKED,
  7-IN.DIAMETER,SET OF 6................................... 27.00
HEISEY,PLATE,PINK,SIGNED,7 IN.SQUARE,SET OF 10............. 28.00
HEISEY,PLATE,QUEEN ANNE PATTERN,CLEAR,8-IN.DIAMETER........ 3.00
HEISEY,SALT,COLONIAL,GREEN,PEDESTAL....................... 2.50
HEISEY,SALT,FLAMINGO,SIGNED................................ 4.00
HEISEY,SALT,GREEK KEY PATTERN,FOOTED,SIGNED............... 12.50
HEISEY,SALT,ROMAN KEY,SHERBET SHAPE,STEMMED,1 3/4 IN.HIGH... 3.50
HEISEY,SAUCE BOAT,GREEN,TRAY,LADLE,SIGNED................. 20.00
HEISEY,SAUCE,COLONIAL PATTERN,SCALLOPED,MARKED............. 3.25
HEISEY,SAUCE,FLUTED,SIGNED................................. 3.50
HEISEY,SAUCE,OLD WILLIAMSBURG,SIGNED...................... 2.75
HEISEY,SAUCE,PUNTY & DIAMOND POINT,4 3/4 IN................ 4.50
HEISEY,SAUCE,WILLIAMSBURG PATTERN,4 1/4-IN.DIAMETER........ 20.00
HEISEY,SHERBERT,CLEAR,MARKED WITH H IN DIAMOND,SET OF 11.... 37.50
HEISEY,SHERBET,FLUTED,MARK................................. 3.50
HEISEY,SHERBET,GREEK KEY PATTERN,FOOTED,SIGNED............. 5.00
HEISEY,SHERBET,OLD WILLIAMSBURG,SIGNED..................... 4.00
HEISEY,SUGAR & CREAMER,INCISED ROUNDED PANELS,MARKED,PAIR... 8.00
HEISEY,SUGAR & CREAMER,TINY CUT FLOWERS,2 1/4 IN.......... 17.50
HEISEY,SUGAR,GREEK KEY,HANDLES,OPEN,DATED,SIGNED.......... 25.00
HEISEY,SUGAR,WILLIAMSBURG,COVER............................ 8.50
HEISEY,TOOTHPICK,DIAMOND-QUILTED,CLEAR,SIGNED.............. 6.50
HEISEY,TRAY,CUT & ETCHED ROSES,SILVER BORDER,SIGNED........ 35.00
HEISEY,TRAY,RELISH,1/2 IN.GOLD EDGE,HEXAGON SHAPE,9 X 4 IN.. 10.00
HEISEY,TRAY,SANDWICH,ETCHED CHRYSANTHEMUM,CREAMER & SUGAR,
  SIGNED................................................... 15.00
HEISEY,TUMBLER,FOOTED,CANARY GLASS,SIGNED................. 12.00
HEISEY,TUMBLER,PANEL & BLOCK PATTERN,HAND-FINISHED,SIGNED... 6.00
HEISEY,TUMBLER,SOUVENIR,WORLD'S FAIR,1904,PAINTED ROSE...... 30.00
HEISEY,WHISKEY,ETCHED,FORT WILLIAM HENRY,COAT OF ARMS,SIGNED 5.00
HEISEY,WINE,COLONIAL PATTERN,MARKED H IN DIAMOND,
  3 5/8-IN.DIAMETER........................................ 4.00
HEISEY,WINE,FLUTED,STEM,SIGNED............................. 12.00
HEISEY,WINE,PANELED,CLEAR,SIGNED,3 IN.HIGH................. 5.75
  HEREND,SEE FISCHER
HEREND,PLATE,WHITE,GREEN RIM,RIBBED,GOLD BAND,HUNGARY,
  11 IN.,SET OF 11......................................... 100.00
HEREND,URN,FRUIT,FLORAL,GOLD FEET & BANDING,ARMS OF HUNGARY,
  4 IN..................................................... 150.00
  HISTORIC BLUE,SEE STAFFORDSHIRE


    HOBNAIL GLASS IS A PATTERN OF PRESSED GLASS WITH BUMPS
    IN AN ALLOVER PATTERN. DOZENS OF HOBNAIL PATTERNS AND
    VARIANTS HAVE BEEN MADE. REPRODUCTIONS OF MANY TYPES OF
    HOBNAIL GLASS CAN BE FOUND.
  HOBNAIL,SEE ALSO FRANCISWARE
HOBNAIL,BASKET,OPALESCENT,BLUE,RUFFLED,CLEAR APPLIED HANDLE,
  9 IN.TALL................................................ 15.00
HOBNAIL,BASKET,OPALESCENT,CLEAR TO WHITE,BLUE TONES,RUFFLED,
  CLEAR HANDLE............................................. 12.50
HOBNAIL,BOTTLE,OPALESCENT,PAIR............................ 5.50
HOBNAIL,BOWL,BERRY,FAN TOP,AMBER,11-IN.DIAMETER........... 42.50
HOBNAIL,BOWL,BERRY,WHITE WITH BLUISH CAST,CIRCA
  1880.......................................... 30.00 TO 35.00
HOBNAIL,BOWL,OPALESCENT,CLEAR TO WHITE,BLUE TONES,RUFFLED,
  PLEATED................................................. 15.00
HOBNAIL,BOWL,ROSE,OPALESCENT,4 IN.HIGH.................... 10.00
HOBNAIL,BOX,POWDER,OPALESCENT,COVER,FINIAL,BLUE,COLOGNE

```
BOTTLE,STOPPER..............................................   25.00
HOBNAIL,BUTTER PAT,WHITE WITH BLUISH CAST,CIRCA 1880........    5.00
HOBNAIL,CREAMER,OPALESCENT,BLUE.............................   22.00
HOBNAIL,CREAMER,OPALESCENT,FRILLED TOP,3 IN.HIGH............   10.00
HOBNAIL,CREAMER & SUGAR,OPALESCENT,FRILLED TOPS.............   33.00
HOBNAIL,CREAMER & SUGAR,OPALESCENT,MINIATURE,BLUE...........   25.00
HOBNAIL,DISH,BUTTER,COVER,WHITE WITH BLUISH CAST,CIRCA 1880.   37.50
HOBNAIL,DISH,CANDY,OPALESCENT,HANDLES,COVER.................    5.75
HOBNAIL,DISH,PICKLE,OBLONG,WHITE WITH BLUISH CAST,CIRCA
   1880......................................................   15.00
HOBNAIL,DISH,SAUCE,WHITE WITH BLUISH CAST,CIRCA 1880........    5.50
HOBNAIL,PERFUME,OPALESCENT,STOPPER.........................   17.50
HOBNAIL,PITCHER,MILK,OPALESCENT,CLEAR TO WHITE,BLUE TONES,
   APPLIED HANDLE............................................   22.50
HOBNAIL,PITCHER,WATER,OPALESCENT,WHITE,SQUARE TOP..........   95.00
HOBNAIL,SALT,OPALESCENT,ROUND,SCALLOPED BORDER,PEDESTAL.....    6.50
HOBNAIL,SALT & PEPPER,WHITE WITH BLUISH CAST,CIRCA 1880.....   18.00
HOBNAIL,SHERBET,OPALESCENT,YELLOW..........................   10.00
HOBNAIL,SPOONER,OPALESCENT,BLUE............................   17.00
HOBNAIL,SPOONER,OPALESCENT,RUFFLED TOP.....................   16.00
HOBNAIL,SPOONER,WHITE WITH BLUISH CAST,CIRCA 1880..........   20.00
HOBNAIL,TUMBLER,OPALESCENT,POLISHED PONTIL.................   18.50
HOBNAIL,TUMBLER,OPALESCENT,THREE-MOLD,HAND-PULLED,4 IN.HIGH.   25.00
HOBNAIL,TUMBLER,WHITE WITH BLUISH CAST,CIRCA 1880..........   15.00
HOBNAIL,VASE,CELERY,WHITE WITH BLUISH CAST,CIRCA 1880.......   35.00
HOBNAIL,VASE,OPALESCENT,BLUE,FAN SHAPE,CRIMPED TOP..........   20.00
```

```
     HOCHST,OR HOECHST,PORCELAIN WAS MADE IN GERMANY FROM
     1746 TO 1796. IT WAS MARKED WITH A SIX-SPOKE WHEEL.
HOCHST,BOX,FRUITS,PUCE LANDSCAPE,PUTTO FINIAL ON COVER,1765,
   6 IN......................................................  120.00
HOCHST,CUP & SAUCER,CIRCA 1760.............................  175.00
HOCHST,FIGURINE,BOY,WHITE JACKET,PINK BREECHES,HOLDS BARREL,
   7 1/2 IN..................................................  275.00
HOCHST,GROUP,FAIENCE,CIRCA 1770,9 IN. HIGH.................  550.00
HOCHST,STATUETTE GROUP,ALLEGORICAL,CIRCA 1770,5 1/2 IN. HIGH  300.00
HOCHST,STATUETTE,CIRCA 1775,5 IN. HIGH,YOUNG BOY...........  300.00
HOCHST,STATUETTE,PAIR,8 IN. HIGH,WHEEL MARK IN BLUE........  100.00
HOCHST,STATUETTE,YOUNG GIRL,CIRCA 1775,6 IN. HIGH..........   60.00
HOCHST,SUGAR BOWL,COVERED,CIRCA 1760.......................  275.00
HOCHST,TRAY,FAIENCE,19TH CENTURY,8 IN. LONG................  100.00
```

```
     HOLLY AMBER OR GOLDEN AGATE GLASS WAS MADE BY THE
     INDIANA TUMBLER AND GOBLET COMPANY FROM JANUARY 1,
     1903,TO JUNE 13,1903. IT IS A PRESSED GLASS PATTERN
     FEATURING HOLLY LEAVES IN THE AMBER-SHADED GLASS.
HOLLY AMBER,DISH,BUTTER,COVERED.....................ILLUS..  150.00
HOLLY AMBER,DISH,PICKLE,HANDLES,9 IN. X 4 IN. X 1 IN.DEEP...  250.00
HOLLY AMBER,TOOTHPICK......................................  139.50
HONESDALE,VASE,CAMEO GLASS,10 3/4 IN. HIGH,SIGNED..........  125.00
HONESDALE,VASE,CAMEO GLASS,9 1/2 IN. HIGH,SIGNED...........  100.00
HULL POTTERY,BOWL..........................................    4.00
HULL POTTERY,CREAMER,SUGAR,PINK & BLUE BUTTERFLIES,
   FORGET-ME-NOTS,FOOTED.....................................    8.95
HULL POTTERY,HORN OF PLENTY................................    5.00
HULL POTTERY,PITCHER,DARK PINK BASE,HANDLE,7 IN............    6.50
```

HOLLY AMBER BUTTER DISH

HULL POTTERY,PLANTER,SWAN SHAPE,ARCHED NECK,CREAM COLOR,
CHARTREUSE.................................................... 20.00
HULL POTTERY,TEAPOT,CREAMER,SUGAR,PINK GLAZE,EMBOSSED BLUE
FLORAL........................................................ 30.00
HULL POTTERY,VASE,CREAM TO YELLOW,PINK FLORAL,CLOVER SHAPE,
HANDLES....................................................... 15.00
HULL POTTERY,VASE,GREEN,PINK POINSETTIA,TWO HANDLES,
5 1/2 IN...................................................... 6.00
HULL POTTERY,VASE,PINK TO IVORY TO GREEN,YELLOW FLORAL,TWO
HANDLES....................................................... 7.00
HULL,TEAPOT,YELLOW TO ROSE,PINK & YELLOW FLOWERS,CREAMER,
OPEN SUGAR.................................................... 18.50

ICON,GREEK,ON WOOD PANEL,18TH CENTURY,18 X 14 1/2 IN......... 285.00
ICON,RUSSIAN,WOODEN PANEL,18TH CENTURY,11 IN. X 8 1/4 IN.... 195.00


IMARI PATTERNS ARE NAMED FOR THE JAPANESE WARE
DECORATED WITH ORANGE AND BLUE STYLIZED FLOWERS. THE
DESIGN ON THE JAPANESE WARE BECAME SO CHARACTERISTIC
THAT THE NAME IMARI HAS COME TO MEAN ANY PATTERN OF
THIS TYPE. IT WAS COPIED BY THE EUROPEAN FACTORIES OF
THE EIGHTEENTH AND EARLY NINETEENTH CENTURIES.

IMARI,BOWL,ALLOVER DECOR IN RUST-RED,BLUE,SCALLOPED,
3 1/4 IN.HIGH................................................. 38.00
IMARI,BOWL,ALTERNATING DESIGN PANELS,RUST,BLUE,
7 1/2-IN.DIAMETER............................................. 25.00
IMARI,BOWL,BLUE & WHITE FLORAL,ENAMELED DECOR ON SIX PANELS,
4 3/4 IN...................................................... 30.00
IMARI,BOWL,BLUE & WHITE,COVER,9-IN.DIAMETER.................. 45.00
IMARI,BOWL,BLUE,TANGERINE,GREEN DECOR,BASKET OF FLOWERS IN
CENTER........................................................ 9.50
IMARI,BOWL,CLOVERLEAF SHAPE,PANELED POLYCHROME,9-IN.DIAMETER 25.00
IMARI,BOWL,COLORFUL MOTIF,SCALLOPED TOP,8 1/2-IN.DIAMETER X
3 IN.HIGH..................................................... 38.00
IMARI,BOWL,ELEPHANT MOTIF,DECOR INSIDE & OUTSIDE,
9 3/4-IN.DIAMETER............................................. 65.00
IMARI,BOWL,FLORAL PANELS INSIDE & OUTSIDE,BOWL OF FLOWERS IN
CENTER........................................................ 37.00
IMARI,BOWL,OCTAGON SHAPE,CARVED TEAK BASE,9 1/4 IN. X
7 1/4 IN.HIGH................................................. 150.00
IMARI,BOWL,ORANGE & BLUE DECOR,7 1/2-IN.DIAMETER............. 18.00
IMARI,BOWL,ORANGE,BLUE PANELS,FLORAL,LEAVES,RUFFLED,
7 3/8-IN.DIAMETER............................................. 34.50
IMARI,BOWL,PANELED SCENES,FLORAL,RED,COBALT,CHINA,
10-IN.DIAMETER................................................ 45.00
IMARI,BOWL,PANELS,FIVE COLORS,7 1/2-IN.DIAMETER,
2 3/4 IN.DEEP................................................. 25.00
IMARI,BOWL,POLYCHROME,7 1/4 X 3 1/2 IN.HIGH.................. 25.00
IMARI,BOWL,PUNCH,ALLOVER BITTERSWEET DESIGN,RED,BLUE........ 150.00
IMARI,BOWL,RED,AQUA,ORANGE,4 X 9 1/2 IN...................... 22.50
IMARI,BOWL,ROSE,SCENES,SAGES RIDING EGRETS & DOLPHINS,COVER,
CIRCA 1850.................................................... 20.00
IMARI,BOWL,THREE RESERVES,MYTHOLOGICAL ANIMALS,
6 1/2-IN.DIAMETER............................................. 35.00
IMARI,BOWL,UNDERGLAZE BLUE,PANELS,3 1/4 IN.HIGH,
8 3/4-IN.DIAMETER............................................. 20.00
IMARI,CHARGER,FLOWERPOT CENTER,18 IN......................... 65.00
IMARI,CHARGER,PEACOCK CENTER,ENAMEL,17 7/8-IN.DIAMETER...... 225.00
IMARI,CREAMER,DERBY,CIRCA 1820,MARKED,3 3/4 IN.HIGH......... 42.00
IMARI,CUP & SAUCER,DERBY,CIRCA 1820,MARKED.................. 30.00
IMARI,CUP & SAUCER,HANDLED CUP,FIVE COLORS,RUST
PREDOMINATING................................................. 22.00
IMARI,DISH,BLUE,WHITE,FISH SHAPE,7 IN.LONG.................. 40.00
IMARI,JAR,GINGER,FLOWERPOT PATTERN,TWO LIDS,CIRCA 1840,
7 IN.HIGH..................................................... 45.00
IMARI,LAMP,ORIENTAL TYPE,FRINGED SILK SHADE,20 1/2 IN.TALL.. 65.00
IMARI,PITCHER,ORIENTAL MOTIF,BURSLEM,7 1/2 IN............... 55.00
IMARI,PLAQUE,SCALLOPED BORDER,16-IN.DIAMETER............... 125.00
IMARI,PLATE,BLUE & GOLD DECOR,HANDMADE,18TH CENTURY,
10 1/2-IN.DIAMETER............................................ 45.00
IMARI,PLATE,BLUE & TANGERINE POT OF FLOWERS IN CENTER,
8 1/4 IN...................................................... 10.00
IMARI,PLATE,BLUE,ORANGE,GRAY,GOLD,CIRCA 1790,FLIGHT
WORCESTER,8 1/2 IN............................................ 50.00
IMARI,PLATE,BLUE,WHITE,GRASSHOPPER,8 1/4-IN.DIAMETER........ 28.00
IMARI,PLATE,CIRCA 1790,SPODE,9-IN.DIAMETER................. 35.00
IMARI,PLATE,DARK BLUE,TERRA COTTA,YELLOW FLOWERS,BIRDS,
CENTER FLOWER................................................. 45.00
IMARI,PLATE,DRAGON,MEDALLIONS,SCENES,CIRCA 1800,TEAK EASEL,
18 IN......................................................... 175.00

IMARI,PLATE,FAN PANELS........................................ 35.00
IMARI,PLATE,FLORAL & GEOMETRIC................................ 10.00
IMARI,PLATE,FLORAL,BUTTERFLIES,TANGERINE,BLACK,YELLOW,GOLD,
   GRAY,12 IN................................................. 32.50
IMARI,PLATE,FLOWERS ON BAMBOO TRELLIS,BLUE,WHITE,5 1/2 IN.,
   PAIR...................................................... 10.00
IMARI,PLATE,PANELS,FLORAL CENTER,GOLD,1889,11 IN............. 60.00
IMARI,PLATE,SCALLOPED BORDER,8 1/4-IN.DIAMETER.............. 22.50
IMARI,PLATE,SCENES,SAGES RIDING ON EGRETS & DOLPHINS,CIRCA
   1850...................................................... 20.00
IMARI,PLATE,WHIMSICAL FIGURES,POLYCHROME COLORS,
   14 1/2-IN.DIAMETER........................................ 95.00
IMARI,PLATTER,BLUE,RED,GOLD,COBALT DESIGN,SCALLOPS,ORIENTAL
   SIGNATURE................................................. 97.00
IMARI,PLATTER,COBALT & TANGERINE PATTERN,RED & GREEN FLORAL,
   BIRDS..................................................... 22.00
IMARI,PLATTER,LANDSCAPE,BIRDS,DRAGONS,12-IN.DIAMETER........ 45.00
IMPERIAL,TRAY,CANDLEWICK PATTERN,HANDLES,13 IN.............. 6.00
IMPERIAL,VASE,BLUE GROUND,WHITE DRAG LOOP,BLACK HANDLES &
   FOOT,10 IN................................................ 55.00
IMPERIAL,VASE,BULBOUS,FLARE,BLUE,GREEN,WHITE,IRIDESCENT BLUE
   INSIDE.................................................... 55.00
IMPERIAL,VASE,DEEP PURPLE IRIDESCENT & AMETHYST,BLACK
   SIGNATURE................................................. 60.00
IMPERIAL,VASE,FREE-HAND,BLUE & WHITE SWIRL,ORANGE INTERIOR,
   9 1/2 IN.................................................. 65.00
INDIAN TREE,SEE COALPORT
INKWELL,ALABASTER,SWING COVER............................... 10.00
INKWELL,ALLOVER FLORAL & GEOMETRIC DESIGN,BLUES
   PREDOMINATING,CLOISONNE................................... 65.00
INKWELL,BEVELED CUT BLOCKS,4 EACH SIDE,CUT GLASS............ 15.00
INKWELL,BLACK COAL,COVER,GLASS INSERT....................... 8.00
INKWELL,BLUE,IRIDESCENT,BRASS LID,HOLLY LEAVES,BERRIES,
   TIFFANY TYPE.............................................. 48.50
INKWELL,BRASS,GLASS LINER,MARBLE BASE,BRASS & MARBLE
   BLOTTER,TWO............................................... 55.00
INKWELL,BRASS,OPENWORK PANELS,LEAF DESIGN,STAINED GLASS,
   MARKED TIFFANY............................................ 45.00
INKWELL,CASKET SHAPE,PLATFORM,TWIN WELLS,WELL FOR BLOTTING
   POWDER,BRONZE............................................. 75.00
INKWELL,CHARACTER-SHAPED HEAD,METAL......................... 12.50
INKWELL,CIRCULAR AMETHYST BASE,HINGED BALL WELL,KNOB FINIAL,
   IRIDESCENT................................................ 25.00
INKWELL,COVERED CONTAINER,TWO LOVEBIRDS ON SIDE,FOOTED,
   BRASS,8 IN.LONG........................................... 25.00
INKWELL,CRANBERRY,BRONZE,FRANCE............................. 55.00
INKWELL,CRYSTAL PYRAMID,TWO,BRASS TRAY,FOOTED............... 25.00
INKWELL,CRYSTAL,INTAGLIO CUTS,SILVER TOP,GORHAM............. 59.00
INKWELL,CURLING STONE,METAL COVER,HANDLE,GRAY,
   3 1/8-IN.DIAMETER......................................... 15.00
INKWELL,CUT GLASS,BRASS BASE & HINGED LID,FOOTED........... 35.00
INKWELL,DEEP RED GLASS,CIRCULAR BASE,POLISHED BOTTOM,COVER,
   BALL FINIAL............................................... 25.00
INKWELL,DOME SHAPE,GREEN & PURPLE IRIDESCENT,HINGED BRASS
   LID,LINER................................................. 56.50
INKWELL,DOUBLE,TWO GLASS SNAILS IN IRON RACK,DATED JAN. 79.. 20.00
INKWELL,FAIENCE,CIRCA 1850,FRANCE........................... 30.00
INKWELL,FLOWER DECOR,HAND-PAINTED,PORCELAIN,TWO INSERTS &
   BLOTTER................................................... 28.50
INKWELL,FLOWER SHAPE,HINGED LID,IRON,MILK GLASS INSERT...... 10.00
INKWELL,GREEN BASE,CLEAR DOME TOP,TRIANGULAR SHAPE.......... 3.95
INKWELL,GREEN DOME,GREEN SQUARE BASE,JACOBUS............... 18.00
INKWELL,HAND-PAINTED BUTTERFLY,WILD FLOWERS,SQUARE BASE,LID,
   PORCELAIN................................................. 39.50
INKWELL,IGLOO TYPE,MARKED J. & I.E.M.,CLEAR............... 7.50
INKWELL,IRIDESCENT GLASS,RAINBOW HIGHLIGHTS,HINGED,4 IN.HIGH 16.00
INKWELL,IRON INKSTAND,BULLDOG,BRASS TOP,EXTENDED BRANCHES
   HOLDS PENS................................................ 22.50
INKWELL,IRON,GLASS BOTTLE................................... 12.50
INKWELL,LIFT-UP COVER,GLASS INSERT,SILVER PLATE,3 IN.SQUARE. 3.95
INKWELL,LIFT-UP COVER,TRAY FOR PENS OR PENCILS,TRAY,BRASS... 4.75
INKWELL,MADE FROM STAGHORN,HINGED BRASS LID................ 11.00
INKWELL,MINATURE,ENAMEL,RED GROUND,MULTICOLOR DECOR,FRANCE,
   2 1/2 IN.HIGH............................................. 75.00
INKWELL,NICKLE-PLATE OVER BRASS,ROMAN KEY DESIGN,SWIRL GLASS
   WELL,4 IN................................................. 6.95
INKWELL,ORMOLU,CHERUB,RED MARBLE BASE,ORMOLU FEET,FRANCE,10
   IN.LONG................................................... 135.00
INKWELL,PAPERWEIGHT TYPE,CLEAR,SQUARE,BEVELED,SILVER PLATE
   HINGED COVER.............................................. 7.00
INKWELL,PAPERWEIGHT,CONTROLLED AIR BUBBLE DESIGN,STERLING

```
SILVER LID.......................................  35.00
INKWELL,PEN RACK,DATED 1879,IRON & GLASS...................   8.75
INKWELL,PEN RACK,FOOTED BASE,NICKLE-PLATE OVER BRASS,CRYSTAL
  WELL...........................................   7.75
INKWELL,PEWTER,HOLES FOR QUILLS,COVER,ENGLAND..............  19.00
INKWELL,PEWTER,4 HOLES....................................  37.00
INKWELL,PORCELAIN,BLUE & WHITE,VIOLETS,PEN REST,COVER.......  14.00
INKWELL,RAISED TOP RIM,SOAPSTONE,SQUARE....................  25.00
INKWELL,RIBBED CLEAR GLASS,MOLDED,OVAL.....................   9.00
INKWELL,ROUND,BLUE-GREEN,EMBOSSED J.J.BUTLER,CINCINNATI,
  OHIO,CIRCA 1860................................   9.00
INKWELL,SAILOR WITH CLAY PIPE,COILED ROPE,BRONZE FINISH,
  PORCELAIN INSET...............................  34.50
INKWELL,SCHOOL DESK,BLACK BAKELITE TOP.....................   2.00
INKWELL,SCROLLED OPENWORK BASE,HINGED LID,GLASS INSET,
  PEWTER,FRANCE.................................   8.50
INKWELL,SHAPE OF LARGE CRAB,HINGED COVER,IRON..............  10.00
INKWELL,SLAB,HINGED TOP,TWO,MARBLE,GOLD PEN,9 IN. X 5 IN....  19.00
INKWELL,STAGHORN,TWO CRYSTAL INSERTS......................  35.00
INKWELL,STAND,PEN RACK,PAT.1912...........................   3.00
INKWELL,STAND,PEN REST,HINGED WELL,PATENTED BAROMETER,1883..  18.00
INKWELL,STANDS ON SIX HEART SHAPE PETALS,IRON,GLASS INSERT,
  TANNEWITZ.....................................  14.50
INKWELL,STENCIL,PLACE FOR PENS,WOODEN,4 IN.DIAMETER.........  10.00
INKWELL,SWIRL DESIGN,STAR BASE,COVER......................   5.00
INKWELL,TALAVERA DESIGN,SPANISH,1825......................  20.00
INKWELL,TEN-SIDED BASE,ROUND TOP,GROUND BOTTOM,GLASS.......   2.00
INKWELL,TRAVELING,CUBE SHAPE,BRASS HANDLE,GLASS INSERT,TIN,
  1 IN.SQUARE...................................   6.00
INKWELL,WAFFLE DESIGN ON COVER,SQUARE.....................   4.50
INKWELL,WHITE METAL,COOPER FINISH,MILK GLASS INSERT,3 X
  2 1/2 IN.TALL.................................   5.00
INKWELL,WOODEN,BROWN,GOLD DECOR,GLASS INSERT,HOLES FOR PENS,
  3 IN.HIGH.....................................  24.00


         INSULATORS OF GLASS OR POTTERY HAVE BEEN MADE FOR USE
         ON TELEGRAPH OR TELEPHONE POLES SINCE 1844.
INSULATOR,ARMSTRONG,DARK AMBER............................   9.00
INSULATOR,ARMSTRONG,DOME NO.2.............................   1.50
INSULATOR,ARMSTRONG,FLAT,TW...............................   1.50
INSULATOR,ARMSTRONG,NO.52,2U,DEEP AMBER...................   6.50
INSULATOR,ARMSTRONG T.S...................................   2.00
INSULATOR,B & O...........................................  20.00
INSULATOR,B.T.C. MONTREAL,AMETHYST........................  14.50
INSULATOR,B.T.CO.,CANADA,TOLL,ICE BLUE....................   5.00
INSULATOR,B.T.CO.OF CANADA,PONY,PURPLE....................   5.50
INSULATOR,BABY BEEHIVE,BROWN GLAZE........................   1.00
INSULATOR,BARCLAY PATENT SPIRAL GROOVE....................   5.00
INSULATOR,BEEHIVE,B.......................................   2.00
INSULATOR,BEEHIVE,STAR....................................   3.00
INSULATOR,BENNINGTON,BROWN,MOTTLED........................   5.00
INSULATOR,BROOKFIELD W.U.T.CO.,NO.55,PAT.FEB.22,1870,FULTON.  10.00
INSULATOR,BROOKFIELD,GREEN................................   5.00
INSULATOR,BROOKFIELD,HOOPSKIRT,OLIVE GREEN................   7.00
INSULATOR,BROOKFIELD,NO.X2,AQUA...........................   2.00
INSULATOR,BROOKFIELD,NO.45,CLIFF ST.,N.Y.,2883,BEEHIVE,AQUA.   4.00
INSULATOR,BROOKFIELD,NO.95,PAT.1870,B & O R.R.............   4.00
INSULATOR,BROOKFIELD,SIGNAL,EMERALD GREEN,DOUBLE PETTICOAT..   5.00
INSULATOR,BROOKFIELD,TOLL,GREEN...........................   4.50
INSULATOR,C.C.T. & CO.....................................  20.00
INSULATOR,C.D. & P.TEL.CO.................................  15.00
INSULATOR,C.G.U.CO.,AMETHYST PONY.........................   5.50
INSULATOR,CABLE,ROMAN HELMET,AQUA-GREEN...................  15.00
INSULATOR,CALIFORNIA,BABY SIGNAL,SCA......................  10.00
INSULATOR,CALIFORNIA,BABY SIGNAL,SMOKY....................   8.00
INSULATOR,CALIFORNIA,BEEHIVE,GREEN........................   7.00
INSULATOR,CALIFORNIA,BEEHIVE,PINK.........................  10.00
INSULATOR,CALIFORNIA,NO.A007,SMOKY GREEN..................  10.00
INSULATOR,CALIFORNIA,SIGNAL,AMETHYST......................   6.00
INSULATOR,CALIFORNIA,SIGNAL,AQUA...............  4.50 TO    5.00
INSULATOR,CALIFORNIA,SIGNAL,GRAY...............  4.50 TO    5.50
INSULATOR,CALIFORNIA,SMOKE GREEN SIGNAL...................   4.50
INSULATOR,CHICAGO INSULATING CO.EMBOSSED UNDER BASE........  42.50
INSULATOR,DIAMOND,BLACK GLASS PONY........................   5.00
INSULATOR,DIAMOND GROOVE OVER GROOVE,EMBOSSED,CHICAGO
  INSULATING CO.................................  35.00
INSULATOR,DIAMOND PONY,OLIVE GREEN........................   4.00
INSULATOR,EMBOSSED STAR AT BASE,GREEN.....................  50.00
INSULATOR,FAIRMOUNT-K.C.G.W.,EMBOSSED.....................  30.00
```

| | |
|---|---|
| INSULATOR,G I CERAMIC,WORLD WAR II........................ | 2.00 |
| INSULATOR,G.N.W.TEL.CO.,BEEHIVE,PURPLE.................... | 14.50 |
| INSULATOR,G.N.W.TEL.CO.,BEEHIVE,DEEP PURPLE,CANADA.......... | 10.00 |
| INSULATOR,GAYNER NO.48-400............................. | 16.25 |
| INSULATOR,GAYNER,NO.36-190,ICE BLUE SIGNAL............. | 5.50 |
| INSULATOR,GAYNER,NO.48-400,AQUA....................... | 6.50 |
| INSULATOR,GAYNER,NO.530,TRANSPOSITION.................. | 50.00 |
| INSULATOR,GREEN POTTERY.............................. | 3.50 |
| INSULATOR,H.G.CO.,AQUA,PETTICOAT SIGNAL,DOUBLE PETTICOAT.... | 4.50 |
| INSULATOR,H.G.CO.,AQUA,STANDARD SIGNAL,DOUBLE PETTICOAT..... | 4.00 |
| INSULATOR,H.G.CO.,BEEHIVE,AQUA........................ | 3.00 |
| INSULATOR,H.G.CO.,BLUE,PETTICOAT SIGNAL................ | 7.00 |
| INSULATOR,H.G.CO.,GREEN,PETTICOAT SIGNAL.............. | 5.00 |
| INSULATOR,H.G.CO.,PETTICOAT,AMBER.................... | 14.50 |
| INSULATOR,H.G.CO.TRANSPORTATION,PAT. 1893............. | 24.00 |
| INSULATOR,H.G.COMPANY,GREEN,MILK GLASS,BEEHIVE........... | 10.00 |
| INSULATOR,H.G.COMPANY,PATENT MAY 2,1893,PETTICOAT,COBALT.... | 50.00 |
| INSULATOR,HAWLEY,PENNSYLVANIA,AQUA,BEEHIVE............. | 8.00 |
| INSULATOR,HEMINGRAY,DOUBLE PETTICOAT BEEHIVE,AQUA.......... | 4.00 |
| INSULATOR,HEMINGRAY,DOUBLE,PURPLE..................... | 16.00 |
| INSULATOR,HEMINGRAY,NO.9,AQUA,PATENTED MAY 2,1893........... | 1.25 |
| INSULATOR,HEMINGRAY,NO.9,BLUE........................ | 35.00 |
| INSULATOR,HEMINGRAY,NO.9,CLEAR................ 1.00 TO | 35.00 |
| INSULATOR,HEMINGRAY,NO.10,TURQUOISE................... | 2.50 |
| INSULATOR,HEMINGRAY,NO.12,PURPLE..................... | 20.00 |
| INSULATOR,HEMINGRAY,NO.14,AQUA....................... | 4.00 |
| INSULATOR,HEMINGRAY,NO.14,AQUA,BABY SIGNAL,DOUBLE PETTICOAT. | 3.00 |
| INSULATOR,HEMINGRAY,NO.16,BLUE....................... | 3.50 |
| INSULATOR,HEMINGRAY,NO.19,AMBER.............. 10.00 TO | 14.50 |
| INSULATOR,HEMINGRAY,NO.19,AQUA....................... | 2.50 |
| INSULATOR,HEMINGRAY,NO. 19,BLUE...................... | 3.00 |
| INSULATOR,HEMINGRAY,NO.19,COBALT..................... | 20.00 |
| INSULATOR,HEMINGRAY,NO.19,COBALT BLUE,MADE IN U.S.A....... | 15.00 |
| INSULATOR,HEMINGRAY,NO.19,DEEP TURQUOISE.............. | 2.00 |
| INSULATOR,HEMINGRAY,NO.19,GREEN...................... | 7.50 |
| INSULATOR,HEMINGRAY,NO.20,DEEP TURQUOISE.............. | 2.00 |
| INSULATOR,HEMINGRAY,NO.20,TURQUOISE.................. | 4.00 |
| INSULATOR,HEMINGRAY,NO. 21,AQUA..................... | 4.50 |
| INSULATOR,HEMINGRAY,NO. 21,BLUE..................... | 6.50 |
| INSULATOR,HEMINGRAY,NO.23,BLUE...................... | 20.00 |
| INSULATOR,HEMINGRAY,NO.40,BLUE...................... | 25.00 |
| INSULATOR,HEMINGRAY,NO.40,DEEP TURQUOISE.............. | 2.00 |
| INSULATOR,HEMINGRAY,NO.42,AQUA...................... | 2.50 |
| INSULATOR,HEMINGRAY,NO.42,BLUE...................... | 1.00 |
| INSULATOR,HEMINGRAY,NO.42,TURQUOISE.................. | 2.50 |
| INSULATOR,HEMINGRAY,NO.43,AQUA...................... | 4.50 |
| INSULATOR,HEMINGRAY,NO.43,MINT GREEN................. | 9.00 |
| INSULATOR,HEMINGRAY,NO.56,CLEAR..................... | 2.25 |
| INSULATOR,HEMINGRAY,NO.62,AMBER..................... | 20.00 |
| INSULATOR,HEMINGRAY,NO.510,AMBER.................... | 11.00 |
| INSULATOR,HEMINGRAY,NO. 510,DARK OLIVE............... | 10.00 |
| INSULATOR,HEMINGRAY,NO.512,CLEAR.................... | 10.00 |
| INSULATOR,HEMINGRAY,NO.CD 151,PETTICOAT,DOUBLE ROW OF DRIP | |
| POINTS,AQUA...................................... | 4.50 |
| INSULATOR,HEMINGRAY,NO.D510......................... | 10.00 |
| INSULATOR,HEMINGRAY,NO.D510,BLACK AMBER............... | 10.00 |
| INSULATOR,HEMINGRAY,NO.D510,CARNIVAL GLASS........ 10.00 TO | 12.50 |
| INSULATOR,HEMINGRAY,NO.D510,RUBY AMBER................ | 12.00 |
| INSULATOR,HEMINGRAY,NO.D512......................... | 10.00 |
| INSULATOR,HEMINGRAY,NO.D512,CARNIVAL GLASS............. | 20.00 |
| INSULATOR,HEMINGRAY,NO.D512,HONEY AMBER............... | 20.00 |
| INSULATOR,HEMINGRAY,NO.D512,SMOKE AMBER............... | 15.00 |
| INSULATOR,HEMINGRAY,NO.E-1......................... | 60.00 |
| INSULATOR,HEMINGRAY,NO.E-2......................... | 60.00 |
| INSULATOR,HEMINGRAY,NO.E-3......................... | 60.00 |
| INSULATOR,HEMINGRAY,NO.E-3,BLUE.................... | 135.00 |
| INSULATOR,HEMINGRAY W.U.T. TS-2,CARNIVAL GLASS........... | 7.50 |
| INSULATOR,KNOWLES,NO.2,CABLE,GREEN.................... | 15.00 |
| INSULATOR,LOCKE,NO.21,GREEN......................... | 25.00 |
| INSULATOR,LYNCHBURG,NO.10,PONY,SMOKY,DOUBLE PETTICOAT....... | 6.00 |
| INSULATOR,LYNCHBURG,NO.31........................... | 3.00 |
| INSULATOR,LYNCHBURG,NO.44,ICE BLUE.................... | 7.50 |
| INSULATOR,MAYDWELL,NO.9............................ | 3.00 |
| INSULATOR,MAYDWELL,NO.9,PALE GREEN................... | 2.25 |
| INSULATOR,MAYDWELL,NO.20,MILK GLASS.................. | 10.00 |
| INSULATOR,MAYDWELL NO.42........................... | 1.50 |
| INSULATOR,MCLAUGHLIN,NO.16,EMERALD GREEN............. | 5.00 |
| INSULATOR,MCLAUGHLIN,NO.16,LIGHT GREEN............... | 2.00 |
| INSULATOR,MCLAUGHLIN,NO.20,EMERALD GREEN............. | 5.00 |
| INSULATOR,MC LAUGHLIN NO.42,AQUA.................... | 5.00 |
| INSULATOR,MC LAUGHLIN,NO.42,LIGHT GREEN.............. | 3.00 |

```
INSULATOR,MC LAUGHLIN,NO.42,SMOKE BLUE........................       3.50
INSULATOR,MCLAUGHLIN,NO.62,CABLE,LIGHT GREEN.................      12.00
INSULATOR,MILK GLASS................................. 8.00 TO      10.00
INSULATOR,MINE,CD 187,NOVEMBER 23,1886,AQUA..................      55.00
INSULATOR,MOANADA,CANADA OVER MONTREAL,ICE BLUE..............       7.50
INSULATOR,MUNCIE............................................      15.00
INSULATOR,MUNCIE,LARGE,WITH STAND...........................      45.00
INSULATOR,N.A.T.,COBALT.....................................      35.00
INSULATOR,N.A.T.CO.,POTTERY BEEHIVE.........................       3.00
INSULATOR,NO.D 512,CARNIVAL GLASS...........................      17.50
INSULATOR,NO.63,PYREX,CARNIVAL GLASS........................       8.00
INSULATOR,OAKMAN,ROMAN HELMET,AQUA..........................      35.00
INSULATOR,ONE STAR,BEEHIVE,AQUA.............................       4.50
INSULATOR,ONE STAR,SIGNAL,DEEP OLIVE GREEN,3 1/8 X 4 IN.....       3.50
INSULATOR,OPALINE,NO.E14-B..................................      75.00
INSULATOR,PASTEL SADDLE GROOVE,AQUA,DOUBLE PETTICOAT.........       6.00
INSULATOR,PENNSYLVANIA RAILROAD.............................       5.50
INSULATOR,PERU-K.C.G. CO....................................      35.00
INSULATOR,PLEATED SKIRT,BLUE................................      15.00
INSULATOR,PONY,VNM,MONTREAL,PURPLE..........................       6.00
INSULATOR,PORCELAIN,COBALT..................................       3.50
INSULATOR,PORCELAIN,WHITE...................................       1.25
INSULATOR,POSTAL BEEHIVE,AQUA...............................       7.00
INSULATOR,POSTAL BEEHIVE,PINK...............................      10.00
INSULATOR,POSTAL SADDLE GROOVE,AQUA................. 10.00 TO      11.00
INSULATOR,POSTAL,BEEHIVE,PURPLE.............................      12.50
INSULATOR,PYREX,CARNIVAL GLASS..............................      10.00
INSULATOR,PYREX,NO.171,CARNIVAL GLASS.......................      35.00
INSULATOR,PYREX,SAUCER SHAPE,CARNIVAL GLASS,10 IN.DIAMETER,
   4 IN.DOME...............................................      32.50
INSULATOR,PYREX,T.M.REG.,CARNIVAL GLASS.....................       6.50
INSULATOR,RAM'S HORN,BROOKS PAT.............................      25.00
INSULATOR,ROMAN HELMET,CABLE,AQUA...........................      22.50
INSULATOR,SAN FRANCISCO,PONY,AQUA...........................       3.00
INSULATOR,SAN FRANCISCO,PONY,GREEN..........................       5.00
INSULATOR,SPIRAL GROOVE,MISSPELLED PATNTED OCT.8,1907.......      10.00
INSULATOR,SPIRAL GROOVE,PATENT OCT.8,1907...................       3.00
INSULATOR,STAR BEEHIVE,AQUA.................................       3.00
INSULATOR,STAR BEEHIVE,OLIVE GREEN..........................       4.50
INSULATOR,THE ELECTRICAL SUPPLY CO.,CHICAGO.................      20.00
INSULATOR,THE ELECTRICAL SUPPLY COMPANY,CHICAGO,AQUA........      30.00
INSULATOR,THOMAS,IRONSTONE..................................       2.25
INSULATOR,THOMAS,SIGNAL,PORCELAIN,COBALT....................       3.00
INSULATOR,TOLL,B.T.C.,CANADA,ICE BLUE.......................       3.00
INSULATOR,TOLL,NM,CANADA,PURPLE.............................       7.00
INSULATOR,TS,NO.2,CARNIVAL GLASS............................       8.00
INSULATOR,V M R NAPOLI......................................      10.00
INSULATOR,V.G.CONVERSE,PROVO TYPE...........................      40.00
INSULATOR,VMR,NAPOLI,GREEN TOLL.............................       4.00
INSULATOR,W.BROOKFIELD,BEEHIVE,PURPLE.......................      14.50
INSULATOR,W.BROOKFIELD,45 CLIFF ST.,N.Y.,AQUA,BEEHIVE,MOLD
   LINE ON DOME...........................................       6.00
INSULATOR,W.E.MFG.CO.,AQUA,PAT.DEC.19,1871.................       8.50
INSULATOR,W.F.G.CO.,DENVER,COLO.,SIGNAL SCA................       5.00
INSULATOR,W.G.M.CO.,PURPLE TOLL............................      10.00
INSULATOR,WHITALL TATUM C.S.C.,LIGHT SILVER CAST TOLL......       4.00
INSULATOR,WHITALL TATUM CO.,NO.1,PURPLE............. 5.00 TO       6.00
INSULATOR,WHITALL TATUM,NO.1,DEEP PURPLE....................       5.00
INSULATOR,WHITALL TATUM,NO.512 U,AMBER,SADDLE GROOVE........       9.00
INSULATOR,WHITALL TATUM,NO.512U,DARK RUBY AMBER.............       7.00
INSULATOR,WHITALL TATUM,PURPLE..................... 4.50 TO      15.00
INSULATOR,WHITALL TATUM,NO.1,BLUE...........................       2.50
INSULATOR,WOOD CABLE........................................      10.00
```

```
       INVALID FEEDERS WERE MADE DURING THE EIGHTEENTH AND
   NINETEENTH CENTURIES. THE FEEDER IS A DISH HAVING A
   SPOUT OR BEAK THAT MADE IT EASIER FOR A SICK PERSON TO
   BE FED.
INVALID,FEEDER,PINK FLOWERS,PORCELAIN.......................       9.75
INVALID,FEEDER,WHITE,PORCELAIN..............................       4.00
   IRON,SEE ALSO,KITCHEN,TOOL,STORE
IRON,ANCHOR,35 IN.LONG,HOOK 24 IN.WIDE,WEIGHT 15 POUNDS.....      22.50
IRON,ANDIRON,PUNCH,JUDY,13 IN.,SHANK 17 1/2 IN..............      36.00
IRON,APPLE PEELER.................................... ILLUS..       8.00
IRON,BANK,BATTLESHIP MAINE,STILL............................      23.00
IRON,BED WARMER,PIERCED BRASS LID...........................      40.00
IRON,BETTY RACK,TWO MOUNTED HEARTS,FIGURE,SPIKES INTO WALL,
   16 IN.LONG..............................................      45.00
IRON,BOOK END,END OF TRAIL,PAINT,PAIR.......................       8.00
IRON,BOOK END,HORSE,IRON,PAIR...............................       5.00
```

IRON APPLE PEELER

```
IRON,BOOKEND,INDIAN HEAD,IRON,PAIR.........................    5.00
IRON,BOOKEND,PARROT,IRON,PAIR..............................    5.00
IRON,BOOKEND,SAILING SHIP,BRASS-FLASHED OVER IRON,
  5 1/2 IN.HIGH,PAIR.......................................    9.00
IRON,BOOKEND,SHAPE OF TWO FISH JUMPING OUT OF WATER,
  6 IN.HIGH,PAIR...........................................    6.95
IRON,BOOKEND,SHIP,IRON,PAIR................................    5.00
IRON,BOOTJACK,FOLDING,LADY'S,TRAVELING,8 IN.LONG...........   15.00
IRON,BOOTJACK,ADJUSTABLE PRONGS,PATENT 1873................   25.00
IRON,BOOTJACK,BEETLE.............................. 9.00 TO   10.00
IRON,BOOTJACK,BEETLE,10 IN.................................   15.00
IRON,BOOTJACK,BEETLE,9 1/2 IN..............................   15.00
IRON,BOOTJACK,HEART DESIGN.................................   11.50
IRON,BOOTJACK,LYRE TYPE,9 IN...............................   15.00
IRON,BOOTJACK,NAUGHTY NELLIE...................... 7.75 TO    9.75
IRON,BOOTJACK,NAUGHTY NELLY,10 IN.LONG.....................    1.75
IRON,BOOTJACK,OPENWORK,CROSS IN CENTER,DOUBLE-ENDED,
  12 IN.LONG...............................................    8.00
IRON,BOOTJACK,VINE DESIGN,11 IN............................   16.00
IRON,BOOTJACK,VINE DESIGN,12 IN............................   16.00
IRON,BOTTLE DECORKER,CLAMPS,MARKED HARTERS WILD CHERRY
  BITTERS,LEVER............................................   35.00
IRON,BOX,MATCH,SHAPE OF FOOTED STOVE,STAND OR HANGING,4 IN.
  X 3 3/4 IN...............................................    8.50
IRON,BOX,MATCH,SLOT IN COVER...............................    8.00
IRON,BRACKET,SLANT FRAME,SHELLS,FLEUR-DE-LIS,FRANCE,
  27 IN.LONG,PAIR..........................................   25.00
IRON,BUGGY STEP............................................    4.50
IRON,BUGGY STEP,FIVE.......................................   15.00
IRON,CANDLE & RUSH LIGHT HOLDER,ADJUSTABLE,TRIPOD BASE,
  37 IN.TALL...............................................  245.00
IRON,CANDLE & SPLINT HOLDER,FORGE-WELDED,LATE 17TH CENTURY..  165.00
IRON,CANDLE PRICKET,HOLDER,TWISTED STEM,CROWN BASE,
  17 IN.TALL...............................................  225.00
IRON,CANDLE TRIMMER,PAT.1854...............................   12.50
IRON,CANDLEHOLDER,DRAGON,REFINISHED,6 IN.HIGH..............    6.00
IRON,CANDLESNUFFER,FOOTED,SIGNED HOBDAY PATENT MECHANICAL...   24.00
IRON,CANDLESNUFFER,SCISSOR TYPE................... 9.00 TO    9.50
IRON,CANDLESTICK,HOG SCRAPER...............................    9.50
IRON,CANDLESTICK,HOG SCRAPER,BRASS RING,8 1/2 IN...........   37.50
IRON,CANDLESTICK,HOG SCRAPER,SHELL-SHAPE PUSH-UP HANDLE,
  7 IN.HIGH...............................................    15.00
IRON,CANDLESTICK,SHAPE OF HOLLY LEAVES & BERRIES,PATENT
  1921,PAIR................................................    3.75
IRON,CANDLESTICK,VICTORIAN CHAMBER-TYPE,LEAF DESIGN,
  4 1/4 IN.,PAIR...........................................    6.75
IRON,CHARCOAL.......................................ILLUS..    6.00
IRON,CHERRY PITTER..................................ILLUS..    9.00
IRON,CIGAR CUTTER,DONKEY,USED FOR LIGHTING CIGARS WITH GAS
  JET......................................................   27.50
IRON,CIRCUS WAGON,13 IN.LONG...............................    5.50
   IRON COFFEE GRINDER,SEE COFFEE GRINDER
IRON,CONTAINER,MATCH,SCROLL DESIGN,LIFT-UP COVER...........    8.75
IRON,CUSPIDOR,WHITE PORCELAIN INSIDE,FLANGED TOP,8 IN. X
  6 IN.TALL................................................   25.00
IRON,DISH,BIRDS ON BRANCH,LEAF SHAPE,FOOTED,9 IN.LONG......    5.75
IRON,DISH,OPENWORK BORDER,FLORAL,SCROLLS,GOLD FINISH,FOOTED,
  10 IN.SQUARE.............................................    6.75
IRON,DISH,SHAPE OF BAT,READING HARDWARE CO.,PACKARD & EVANS
  CO.,BOSTON...............................................    6.75
```

CHARCOAL IRON

IRON CHERRY PITTER

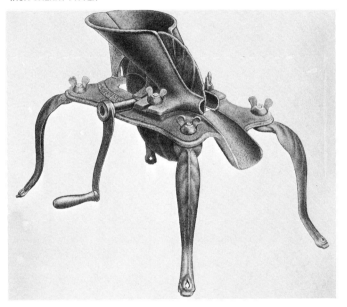

```
IRON,DISH,SHAPE OF LION'S HEAD,FOOTED,5 3/4 IN.LONG,
   5 1/4 IN.WIDE....................................................    4.75
IRON,DOOR KNOCKER,INVERTED HEART SHAPE,STEEL LOCK & KEY,TWO
   PIECES,8 IN..................................................  50.00
```

IRON DOORSTOPS HAVE BEEN MADE IN ALL TYPES OF
DESIGNS. THE VAST MAJORITY OF THE DOORSTOPS SOLD TODAY
ARE CAST IRON AND WERE MADE FROM ABOUT 1890 TO 1930.
MOST OF THEM ARE SHAPED LIKE PEOPLE,ANIMALS,FLOWERS,OR
SHIPS.

```
IRON,DOORSTOP,AIREDALE..........................................  12.00
IRON,DOORSTOP,AUNT JEMIMA,PAINTED................................  25.00
IRON,DOORSTOP,BASKET OF FLOWERS SHAPE............................   3.95
IRON,DOORSTOP,BLACK CAT,SEATED,8 1/4 POUNDS......................   8.75
IRON,DOORSTOP,BOOT,LADY'S,HIGH BUTTON,7 IN.HIGH..................  15.00
IRON,DOORSTOP,BOY WITH TEDDY BEAR................................  12.00
IRON,DOORSTOP,BULL,STANDING......................................  15.00
IRON,DOORSTOP,CAT,RECLINING,HEAD RAISED,PAINT....................  22.50
IRON,DOORSTOP,CAT,SITTING,7 3/4 IN...............................  10.00
IRON,DOORSTOP,DOG................................................   8.50
IRON,DOORSTOP,DOLLY DIMPLE WITH DOLL,SIGNED......................  12.00
IRON,DOORSTOP,ENGLISH CARRIAGE,7 IN.HIGH.........................   7.50
IRON,DOORSTOP,FLOWER BASKET,8 IN.................................   8.00
IRON,DOORSTOP,FROG...............................................  15.00
IRON,DOORSTOP,GERMAN SHEPHERD DOG,DAVISON CO.,14 IN. X
   13 IN.HIGH....................................................  22.50
IRON,DOORSTOP,GIRL,WEARS SUNBONNET,6 1/2 IN......................  10.00
IRON,DOORSTOP,LIGHTHOUSE OF GLOUCESTER,MASS.,1920,
```

```
    11 1/2 IN.HIGH...........................................    6.95
IRON,DOORSTOP,MR.MICAWBER AND FAMILY........................   14.50
IRON,DOORSTOP,OWL,BRASS-TINTED,10 IN.HIGH...................   22.50
IRON,DOORSTOP,PEACOCK,EMBOSSED,GREEN FEATHERS,9 1/2 IN.TALL,
    20 IN.LONG.............................................   27.50
IRON,DOORSTOP,REINDEER WITH ANTLERS,PAIR...................   17.50
IRON,DOORSTOP,SCOTTIE,5 1/2 IN.HIGH........................    7.50
IRON,DOORSTOP,SHAPE OF MAYFLOWER SHIP......................    4.75
IRON,DOORSTOP,SHAPE OF SPANISH GALLEON.....................    4.75
IRON,DOORSTOP,SHIP.........................................    9.00
IRON,DOORSTOP,SOUTHERN BELLE,5 TIERED DRESS,RUFFLES,BONNET,
    5 IN. TALL............................................   24.00
IRON,DOORSTOP,VIKING SHIP..................................    5.00
IRON,EASEL FRAME,GOLD FINISH,HAS MIRROR IN IT,OVAL.........    9.95
IRON,EASEL FRAME,OPENWORK BORDER,LEAVES,SCROLLS,MIRROR,GOLD
    FINISH................................................    7.95
IRON,FIGURINE,HALF FIGURES OF SHEEP & LAMB,4 1/8 IN.LONG X
    3 IN.HIGH.............................................    2.50
IRON,FIGURINE,LIZARD,CURLING TAIL,MARKED SHERWIN WILLIAMS
    CO.PAINT..............................................    6.75
IRON,FLIPPER,CAKE,SHORT HANDLE,KEYHOLE-SHAPED FLAT BLADE,
    8 1/2 IN.LONG.........................................   18.00
IRON,FLUTING IRON.................................ILLUS..   15.00
IRON,FOOT SCRAPER,ORNATE FENCE WITH POST AT EACH END,BLACK,
    6 1/2 IN.LONG.........................................   10.00
```

FLUTING IRON

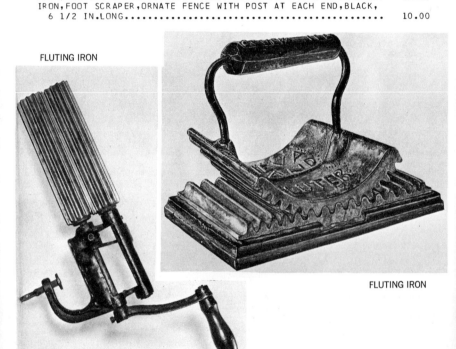

FLUTING IRON

```
IRON,FOOT SCRAPER,ORNATE FENCE,END POSTS,3 1/4 IN.HIGH,
    6 IN.LONG.............................................    8.50
IRON,FORGE,BLACKSMITH......................................   80.00
IRON,FORK,THREE FLAT TINES,6 1/2 IN.LONG,TWISTED HANDLE,
    25 1/4 IN.LONG........................................   22.50
IRON,FORK,TOASTING,THREE TINES,15 IN......................    4.00
IRON,FRAME,GOLD FINISH,OPENWORK BORDER,LEAVES & SCROLLS,9 X
    12 IN.HIGH............................................    7.95
IRON,FURNACE POKER,59 IN.LONG.............................    5.00
IRON,GRATE,FIRE,MEDALLION,URN,DRAPERY,WITH FLOOR LAMP ON
    TRIPOD LEGS...........................................   70.00
IRON,HARPOON,TOGGLE.......................................   65.00
IRON,HARPOON,WHALING,HAND-FORGED,EYE FOR CORD,SOCKET FOR
    HANDLE,59 IN..........................................   20.00
IRON,HITCHING POST,HORSE HEAD,RING IN MOUTH...............   90.00
IRON,HOLDER,MATCH,GRAPE DECOR,PAINT.......................    7.50
IRON,HOLDER,PENS & PENCILS,DIAMOND K,3 1/2 IN.LONG........    2.95
IRON,HOLDER,TWINE,6 IN.HIGH...............................   20.00
IRON,HORSE HANDLE,TRIBASE,7 IN.LONG,4 1/2 IN.HIGH.........   20.00
IRON,HORSE'S HEAD FOR HITCHING POST.......................   72.50
IRON,ICE TONGS..................................ILLUS..    5.00
```

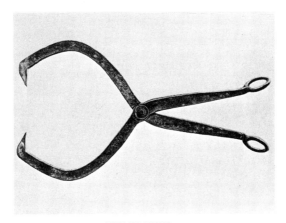

IRON ICE TONGS

```
IRON,INK STAND,EMBOSSED,PEN RACK,COVER,BACK RACK,5 X
   4 1/2 IN........................................................  15.00
IRON,INKWELL,MAN ON CARPET,4 3/4 IN.TALL X 9 IN.LONG.........  24.50
IRON,INKWELL,ONE INSERT.......................................  15.00
IRON,INKWELL,PERSIAN RUG SHAPE,FRINGE IS PENHOLDER,TURK
   HOLDS RUG.....................................................  27.50
IRON,KETTLE,BAIL,BLACK,FOUR-GALLON............................  12.50
IRON,KETTLE,BLACK,FOOTED,10 1/2 IN. X 13 IN...................  22.00
IRON,KETTLE,GYPSY,FOOTED,9 IN.HIGH,10 1/2 IN.ACROSS..........  10.00
IRON,KETTLE,PATENT MEDICINE,MARKED S.S.S.FOR THE BLOOD,
   FOOTED,6 IN.HIGH.............................................  22.00
IRON,LADLE,MELTING,POUR SPOUT,COB HANDLES,TO FILL BULLET
   MOLD,PAT.1877................................................   9.50
IRON,LADLE,PERFORATED,LARGE BOWL,HOOK END,21 IN.LONG........   8.00
IRON,LETTER RACK,HEAD OF BULLDOG ON BOTH SIDES...............   4.95
IRON,MAILBOX,WALL TYPE,NAME GRISWOLD,ERIE,PENNA.,13 IN.LONG.   8.50
IRON,MATCHBOX,FOR WALL,5 1/4 IN...............................   5.00
IRON,MATCHBOX,SCREWS ON WALL,SELF-CLOSING,PAT.NEW HAVEN,
   1864 ON COVER................................................   7.50
IRON,MATCHBOX,WALL TYPE,COVER,DATED 1864.....................  10.50
IRON,MATCHBOX,WALL,SHAPE DOUBLE HUNTER'S POUCH,HORN,RABBIT,
   BIRD,1870....................................................  12.75
IRON,MATCH CONTAINER,SCROLL DECOR,LIFT-UP COVER.............   8.75
IRON,MATCH CONTAINER,WALL,SCROLL DESIGN,LIFT-UP COVER.......   8.75
IRON,MATCH CONTAINER,WALL,URN DESIGN,PATENT 1867...........   9.75
IRON,MATCH HOLDER,HIGH BUTTON SHOE ON SCRATCH BASE.........  12.50
IRON,MATCH HOLDER,ORNATE SCROLL,PAINTED FLORAL,DATED JAN.15,
   1867,DOUBLE...................................................  12.00
IRON,MATCH HOLDER,SHOE...............................ILLUS.,   7.50
IRON,MATCH HOLDER,SHOE,LADY'S HIGH BUTTON,BASE.............  12.50
IRON,MATCH HOLDER,STAND-UP TYPE,SITTING DOG,IRON,3 1/4 X
   1 1/4 IN.HIGH................................................  10.00
IRON,MATCH HOLDER,WALL,ORNATE DECOR,ATTACHED BIN FOR USED
   MATCHES......................................................   9.00
IRON,MATCH HOLDER,WALL,TWO POCKETS,DATED.....................  15.00
IRON,MATCH SAFE,HANGING,HINGED LID,SCRATCHER,MARKED NV &
   CO.,PAT.1864.................................................   8.50
IRON,MATCH SAFE,WALL,TWO COMPARTMENT,7 IN...................   8.00
IRON,MOLD,BULLET,PINCERS-TYPE,HAND FORGED,AMERICAN.........   7.00
IRON,MOLD,LAMB,TWO PARTS......................................  22.50
IRON,MORTAR,6 IN.HIGH,PESTLE,8 3/4 IN........................  15.00
IRON,NUTCRACKER,DOG..................................ILLUS..  12.50
IRON,NUTCRACKER,DOG FIGURE,JAW CRACKS NUTS,MARKED
   L.A.ALTHOFF CO...............................................  15.00
IRON,NUTCRACKER,FORM OF CROCODILE,PAINT,11 3/4 IN.LONG......  11.00
IRON,NUTCRACKER,VISE TYPE,PERFECTION,PATENTED 1914..........   8.00
IRON,PLAQUE,TWO PHEASANTS,WALL................................   6.50
IRON,PLEATER,PAT.AUG.19,1879..................................  35.00
IRON,POT,RATTAIL HANDLE,THREE SPLAYED FEET,4 5/8 X
   5 1/2-IN.DIAMETER...........................................  12.50
IRON,POT,STEAM-VENTED,DOMED LID,2-GALLON.....................  13.00
IRON,POT,WITH SIDE GRIP.......................................   8.00
IRON,RACK,HAT,FOLDING,FIVE HOOKS,DATED 1864..................  20.00
IRON,RUSH LIGHT,WOODEN BASE,10 IN.HIGH.......................  94.50
IRON,SADIRON........................................ILLUS..   8.00
IRON,SADIRON,DETACHABLE HANDLE,MARKED BLESS & DRAKE,NEWARK,
```

IRON SHOE MATCH HOLDER

IRON NUTCRACKER

SADIRON

```
    N.J...................................................   3.75
IRON,SADIRON,FRANCE,1868..............................  17.50
IRON,SHELF BRACKET,LACY,8 X 6 IN.,PAIR................   3.95
IRON,SHOE LAST........................................   3.00
IRON,SLEIGH,8 IN.LONG.................................   3.50
IRON,SPOON,SPATULA,SPOON HAS BRASS SCOOP,SIGNED,PAIR..  75.00
IRON,STATUETTE,NEGRO BOY,GIRL,PAIR....................  17.50
IRON,STEAM PUMPER,TWO HORSES,LEATHER TRACES,DRIVER,ORIGINAL
    PAINT.............................................  65.00
IRON,STEPS,BUGGY,THREE................................   4.75
IRON,STOVE,COUNTRY,WARMING SHELVES,GRATES,SIX LEGS,5 1/2 X
    12 IN.LONG........................................  40.00
IRON,STOVE,POTBELLY...................................  40.00
IRON,TEAKETTLE.............................ILLUS..     25.00
IRON,TEAKETTLE,COVER,BLACK............................  15.00
IRON,TEAKETTLE,GOOSENECK,FLAT BASE....................  37.50
IRON,TEDDY ROOSEVELT ON HORSE,BRONZED,IMPRESSED 1898..  15.00
IRON,TOBACCO CUTTER,IMP THUMBING NOSE ON BLADE........  28.50
IRON,TOKEN,EAGLE FOUNDRY,BELLEVILLE,ILL.,EAGLE,G.D.KLEMME...  5.00
IRON,TONGS,BLACKSMITH.................................   6.50
IRON,TOOTHPICK,HIGH BUTTON SHOE.......................  17.50
IRON,TRAMMEL,RAISES OR LOWERS KETTLES IN FIREPLACE,
    40 IN.LONG CLOSED.................................  15.00
IRON,TRIVET,E P IN CENTER,ENTERPRISE,PHILA.AROUND EDGE,6 IN.   8.00
IRON,TRIVET,FIVE-POINTED STAR IN CENTER,HANDLE,
    5 1/4-IN.DIAMETER.................................   8.00
IRON,TRIVET,HAS H IN CENTER,WARNAK ON BOTTOM,5 3/4 IN.   8.00
```

IRON TEAKETTLE

```
IRON,TRIVET,HAS W IN CENTER,HANDLE..........................      8.00
IRON,TRIVET,HEART,WOODEN HANDLE,HAND-FORGED.................     60.00
IRON,TRIVET,HORSESHOE SHAPE,THREE-LEAF CLOVER IN CENTER,SAYS
   LUCK,6 IN...............................................     10.00
IRON,TRIVET,LACY,ROUND,CLAW FEET............................      7.50
IRON,TRIVET,POINTED END,MARKED VULCAN,7 IN..................      8.00
IRON,TRIVET,RECTANGULAR,TWELVE ONE-INCH SQUARES.............      8.00
IRON,TYPEWRITER,TINY,BLACK-ENAMELED,1900 LAMBERT,MADE IN
   N.Y.,CASE...............................................     12.00
IRON,WAFFLE IRON,CAMPFIRE GRUBSTAKE,PATENT 1889.............      7.00
IRON,WICK TRIMMER,SCISSORS TYPE,DATED 1854.................      9.50
```

```
         IRONSTONE CHINA WAS FIRST MADE IN 1813. IT GAINED ITS
      GREATEST POPULARITY DURING THE MID-NINETEENTH CENTURY.
      THE HEAVY,DURABLE,OFF-WHITE POTTERY WAS MADE IN WHITE
      OR WAS COLORED WITH ANY OF HUNDREDS OF PATTERNS. MUCH
      FLOW BLUE POTTERY WAS MADE OF IRONSTONE. SOME OF THE
      PIECES HAD RAISED DECORATIONS.
      IRONSTONE,SEE ALSO CHELSEA GRAPE
      IRONSTONE,SEE ALSO GAUDY IRONSTONE
IRONSTONE,BOWL,BOWKNOT,5 1/2 IN.DIAMETER,3 1/2 IN.DEEP......      8.50
IRONSTONE,BOWL,CHAMBER,RAISED WHITE RIM DESIGN,PANELED
   INSIDE,14 IN............................................      8.00
IRONSTONE,BOWL,CREAM GROUND,RED SCENE,MASON'S IRONSTONE
   CHINA,ENGLAND...........................................     20.00
IRONSTONE,BOWL,DEEP,ROUNDED PANEL,ROYAL,9 IN.SQUARE........      6.50
IRONSTONE,BOWL,HANDLES & FINIAL ARE FACES,COVER,MEAKIN,7 X
   6 1/2 IN.HIGH...........................................     17.50
IRONSTONE,BOWL,PITCHER,EMBOSSED RIB PANELS,WHITE...........     41.50
IRONSTONE,BOWL,SOUP,HARPERS FERRY FROM POTOMAC SIDE,BLUE,
   OPAQUE..................................................     30.00
IRONSTONE,BOWL,SUGAR,BULBOUS,LEAVES,NUTS OUTLINED IN PINK
   LUSTER,COVER............................................     27.50
IRONSTONE,BOWL,SUGAR,FLORAL DECOR,GOLD,JOHN EDWARDS........     15.00
IRONSTONE,BOWL,WHITE,PEDESTAL,BY GEORGE SCOTT,28 1/2 IN. X
   6 IN.HIGH...............................................     22.50
IRONSTONE,BOX,TRINKET,ROSE-COLORED,ENGLISH SCENE,COVER,
   MASON'S PATENT..........................................     12.50
IRONSTONE,BUTTER PAT,SET OF 4..............................      4.00
IRONSTONE,BUTTER PAT,SQUARE,ALEXANDRIA,SET OF 6............      9.00
IRONSTONE,CAKE STAND,PEDESTAL..............................     35.00
IRONSTONE,CANDLESTICK,DECOR,4 1/8 IN.TALL,PAIR.............     38.00
IRONSTONE,COFFEEPOT,S.B. & SON.............................     25.00
IRONSTONE,COMPOTE,RIBBED,IMPRESSED JAMES EDWARD DALEHALL,
   10 IN..................................................     15.00
IRONSTONE,COMPOTE,RIBBED,WHITE,FOOTED,IMPRESSED JAMES
   EDWARD,DALEHALL.........................................     16.00
IRONSTONE,CREAMER,WHITE,SIGNED EDWARD WALLET CO.,CIRCA 1850.     20.00
IRONSTONE,CUP & SAUCER,HANDLELESS,BROWN TRANSFER,MONKEY,BOY,
   1870...................................................     16.00
IRONSTONE,DINNER SERVICE,FLORAL,WITH EIGHT MASON PLATES,
   39 PIECES...............................................    900.00
IRONSTONE,DISH,BONE,WHITE,OVAL,LAMBERTON-SCHIMELL,7 1/2 X
   3 1/2 IN................................................      3.00
IRONSTONE,DISH,RELISH,OBLONG,JOHNSON BROTHERS,5 1/2 IN.....      2.50
IRONSTONE,DISH,SERVING,THREE SECTIONS,HANDLE,RAISED DECOR
   RIM,WM.ADAMS............................................     12.50
IRONSTONE,DISH,SOAP,BLACK TRANSFER,COVER,ENGLAND,4 1/2 X
   6 IN.WIDE...............................................      6.50
IRONSTONE,DISH,SOAP,GRAY GROUND,PINK ROSES,5-IN.DIAMETER....      6.50
IRONSTONE,DISH,SOAP,WHITE GROUND,PINK DECOR,THREE PIECES,
   1879...................................................      7.50
IRONSTONE,DISH,SOAP,WHITE,OVAL,OAK LEAVES,ACORN FINIAL......      8.00
```

```
IRONSTONE,DISH,SOUP,BISHOP & POWELL,8 5/8 IN..............         2.00
IRONSTONE,DISH,SOUP,WHEAT PATTERN,FLUTED,MEAKIN,9 1/2 IN....       3.50
IRONSTONE,DISH,VEGETABLE,COVER......................              6.50
IRONSTONE,DISH,VEGETABLE,LIGHT BLUE,MARKED  SIAM,CLEMENSTON,
   NO.14.............................................             20.00
IRONSTONE,DISH,VEGETABLE,LILY OF THE VALLEY,MEAKIN,9 IN.....      18.00
IRONSTONE,DISH,VEGETABLE,VIOLA PATTERN,TWO HANDLES,OPEN,
   J.G.MEAKIN........................................             7.50
IRONSTONE,FRUIT PIE SET,PEACHES,PEARS,APPLES,EUREKA,10
   PIECES...........................................             31.00
IRONSTONE,GRAVY BOAT,CABLE DECOR.....................            7.50
IRONSTONE,GRAVY BOAT,DARK BLUE TRANSFER,BOATS,CIRCA 1850....      9.00
IRONSTONE,GRAVY BOAT,WHITE,LADLE,DAVENPORT MARK...........       10.00
IRONSTONE,JUG,BLUE & WHITE DECOR,MARKED MASON PATENT,
   4 1/2 IN.........................................            29.50
IRONSTONE,JUG,CHINESE DECOR,MARKED MASON,6 1/4 IN........        25.00
IRONSTONE,JUG,CHINESE DECOR,MARKED MASON,5 1/4 IN........        20.00
IRONSTONE,JUG,FLORAL & GOLD DECOR,HOURGLASS SHAPE,1925,
   HANDLE,MASON.....................................            57.00
IRONSTONE,JUG,ORIENTAL DECOR,MARKED MASON PATENT............     23.50
IRONSTONE,LADLE,3-IN.BOWL,5-IN.HANDLE....................        6.50
IRONSTONE,MATCH HOLDER,CONE SHAPE,THREADED FOR STRIKING.....     4.50
IRONSTONE,MOLD,PUDDING,DESIGN IN BASE,5 1/2 IN.HIGH.......       8.50
IRONSTONE,MOLD,PUDDING,GRAIN SHEAF,8 IN. X 6 IN. X 3 1/2 IN.    12.00
IRONSTONE,MUG,TURQUOISE,TRANSFER,UNCLE..................        10.00
IRONSTONE,PITCHER & WASHBOWL,CHILD'S...................         20.00
IRONSTONE,PITCHER,APPLE BLOSSOM,GOLD,ENGLAND...........         22.50
IRONSTONE,PITCHER,BUTTERMILK,TWO BLUE BANDS,10 IN.HIGH....      12.50
IRONSTONE,PITCHER,COW,GREEN ON CREAMY GROUND,8 IN.HIGH.....     12.50
IRONSTONE,PITCHER,MARBELIZED DECOR.....................         6.50
IRONSTONE,PITCHER,MELON RIB,DAISIES & FERN ON SCALLOPED TOP,
   ENGLAND..........................................           12.00
IRONSTONE,PITCHER,MILK,EMBOSSED HANDLE,SQUARE SPOUT,MARKED
   EDWARDS..........................................          15.50
IRONSTONE,PITCHER,MILK,LILY OF THE VALLEY,BURGESS,BURSLEM,
   8 IN.HIGH........................................          16.00
IRONSTONE,PITCHER,PORTRAIT,GARFIELD,EAGLE SPOUT & HANDLE,
   8 1/2 IN.HIGH....................................         100.00
IRONSTONE,PITCHER,ROSE MOTIF,GOLD,ENGLAND..............        22.50
IRONSTONE,PITCHER,SHEAF OF WHEAT,WHITE,JOHNSON,6 IN........     15.00
IRONSTONE,PITCHER,WASH,EMBOSSED SCROLLS,ORNATE HANDLE,WHITE,
   SIGNED...........................................          15.00
IRONSTONE,PITCHER,WATER,WHEAT,RIBBED,MARK CERES-WILLIAM
   ADAMS,TUNSTALL...................................         45.00
IRONSTONE,PITCHER,WHITE,ALFRED MEAKIN,ENGLAND.............      35.00
IRONSTONE,PITCHER,WHITE,MARKED ROYAL PATENT,IRONSTONE,GEORGE
   JONES,6 IN.......................................          8.50
IRONSTONE,PITCHER,WHITE,WHEAT PATTERN,OLD ENGLISH MARK,BOWL.    45.00
IRONSTONE,PITCHER,WHITE,WHEAT PATTERN,SIGNED ANTHONY SHAW,
   PARIS,8 IN.......................................         14.50
IRONSTONE,PITCHER,6 IN.............................          4.75
IRONSTONE,PLATE,BLACK TRANSFER CENTER,HARPERS FERRY FROM
   POTOMAC SIDE.....................................          28.00
IRONSTONE,PLATE,BLUE & WHITE TRANSFER,VENUS,1840,PODMORE &
   WALKER..........................................          11.50
IRONSTONE,PLATE,BLUE ON WHITE,LUCERNE SCENIC,BY GOODFELLOW,
   ENGLAND,1845.....................................         10.50
IRONSTONE,PLATE,BLUE WILLOW PATTERN,MASON,10 1/2 IN.,SET OF
   8...............................................          47.00
IRONSTONE,PLATE,BLUE,WHITE,PORTLAND PATTERN,J.CLEMENTSON,
   9 1/2 IN........................................          8.50
IRONSTONE,PLATE,BROWN,CANELLA,8 1/2 IN.................       22.00
IRONSTONE,PLATE,CAKE,BLUE,WHITE,RURAL SCENIC,FLORAL DECOR,
   11 3/4 IN.......................................          25.00
IRONSTONE,PLATE,CORINTHIA,BLUE,WHITE,CHALLINOR,10 IN.....      15.00
IRONSTONE,PLATE,DARK BLUE,TONQUIN PATTERN,10 1/4 IN.......      21.00
IRONSTONE,PLATE,DINNER,LUSTER BAND,EMBOSSED EDGE...........     8.00
IRONSTONE,PLATE,FLORAL,1813,MARKED MASON'S PATENT IRONSTONE
   CHINA...........................................          50.00
IRONSTONE,PLATE,GREEN,CANELLA.........................        22.00
IRONSTONE,PLATE,OCTAGON,ROSE,AMERICAN MARINE,MASON,CIRCA
   1870............................................          8.00
IRONSTONE,PLATE,PARADISE,8 IN.........................        15.00
IRONSTONE,PLATE,PURPLE,CLEOPATRA,8 IN.................         15.00
IRONSTONE,PLATE,PURPLE,ZAMARRA,8 1/2 IN...............         20.00
IRONSTONE,PLATE,RED,ZAMARRA,9 1/2 IN..................         30.00
IRONSTONE,PLATE,TREE PATTERN,ORIENTAL,MASON,5 1/2 IN.......     6.00
IRONSTONE,PLATE,WHEAT,8 1/2 IN........................         6.00
IRONSTONE,PLATE,WHITE,WHEAT PATTERN,CLEMENTS & HANLEY,
   9 5/8 IN........................................          7.50
IRONSTONE,PLATE,WILLOW DESIGN,SCALLOPED RIM,MASON,10 1/2 IN.   17.00
```

```
IRONSTONE,PLATTER,ACORNS,OAK LEAVES,OVAL,MEAKIN BROS.,21 X
   14 1/2 IN.........................................        18.50
IRONSTONE,PLATTER,BLUE,SIAM PATTERN,CLEMENTSON BROS.,
   ENGLAND,14 X 11 IN..................................       17.50
IRONSTONE,PLATTER,LIGHT BLUE,RECTANGULAR CUTOUT CORNERS,
   CHALLINOR........................................         15.00
IRONSTONE,PLATTER,SYDENHAM SHAPE,BY T. & R.BOOTE,ENGLAND,
   WHITE,16 IN.......................................        18.00
IRONSTONE,PLATTER,TEA ROSE,ALFRED MEAKIN,ENGLAND,11 1/4 X
   15 1/2 IN.........................................        17.50
IRONSTONE,POT,CHAMBER,WHEAT PATTERN,ORNATE HANDLE,FINIAL,
   JOHNSON BROS......................................         9.00
IRONSTONE,RAMEKIN,WHITE,UNDERLINER,SET OF 4.............       20.00
IRONSTONE,SAUCE,WHEAT PATTERN..........................        1.00
IRONSTONE,SAUCEBOAT,WHEAT...............................        8.00
IRONSTONE,SOUP,EMBOSSED DECOR,WHITE FUCHSIA.............        8.00
IRONSTONE,SOUP,FLANGE RIM,MARKED POWELL & BISHOP,10 IN......    6.50
IRONSTONE,SQUEEZER,LEMON,IRON HOLDER...................        12.00
IRONSTONE,SUGAR,BULBOUS,LEAVES,NUTS,PINK LUSTER TRIM,LEAF &
   NUT FINIAL........................................        27.50
IRONSTONE,SUGAR,GOLD TRIM,TWO HANDLES..................        15.00
IRONSTONE,TEA LEAF,BOWL,SUGAR,COVER,ALFRED MEAKIN,ENGLAND...   24.50
IRONSTONE,TEA LEAF,BOWL & PITCHER......................        45.00
IRONSTONE,TEA LEAF,BUTTER,CHIP,SQUARE,MELLAR & TAYLOR,SET OF
   6.................................................         3.50
IRONSTONE,TEA LEAF,BUTTER PAT..........................        3.50
IRONSTONE,TEA LEAF,BOWL,VEGETABLE,MELLOR,TAYLOR & CO.,
   ENGLAND...........................................        22.50
IRONSTONE,TEA LEAF,BUTTER CHIP,ROUND,MEAKIN............        5.00
IRONSTONE,TEA LEAF,CUP & SAUCER,CHILD'S,HANDLELESS..........   12.50
IRONSTONE,TEA LEAF,CUP & SAUCER,HANDLELESS,WILKINSON.......    20.00
IRONSTONE,TEA LEAF,DISH,SAUCE,PAIR.....................       12.00
IRONSTONE,TEA LEAF,DISH,VEGETABLE,ALFRED MEAKIN,ENGLAND,
   8 IN.SQUARE.......................................         8.75
IRONSTONE,TEA LEAF,DISH,VEGETABLE,MELLAR & TAYLOR,8 1/2 X
   6 1/2 IN..........................................        12.50
IRONSTONE,TEA LEAF,DISH,VEGETABLE,MELLAR & TAYLOR,10 X 8 IN.   15.00
IRONSTONE,TEA LEAF,GRAVY BOAT,ANTHONY SHAW.............       18.00
IRONSTONE,TEA LEAF,PLATE,8 IN......................ILLUS..     4.50
IRONSTONE,TEA LEAF,PLATE,ANTHONY SHAW,8 IN.,SET OF 4........   17.50
```

TEA LEAF IRONSTONE PLATE

```
IRONSTONE,TEA LEAF,PLATE,LUSTER,MEAKIN,8 IN.................    8.00
IRONSTONE,TEA LEAF,PLATE,MARKED A.SHAW,5 1/2 IN.............    6.50
IRONSTONE,TEA LEAF,PLATE,MARKED ALFRED MEAKIN,ENGLAND,10 IN.   8.00
IRONSTONE,TEA LEAF,PLATTER,14 IN.LONG,11 IN.WIDE...........    14.00
IRONSTONE,TEA LEAF,PLATTER,ALFRED MEAKIN,12 3/4 IN. X
   9 1/4 IN..........................................        12.50
IRONSTONE,TEA LEAF,PLATTER,MARKED WEDGWOOD,8 X 11 IN........   20.00
IRONSTONE,TEA LEAF,PLATTER,MEAKIN,8 1/2 X 11 IN.........       8.25
IRONSTONE,TEA LEAF,PLATTER,MEAKIN,9 1/2 IN. X 13 IN.........    9.25
IRONSTONE,TEA LEAF,PLATTER,MELLAR & TAYLOR,10 IN. X
   10 1/2 IN.........................................        12.50
IRONSTONE,TEA LEAF,PLATTER,MELLAR & TAYLOR,12 IN.......       12.00
IRONSTONE,TEA LEAF,PLATTER,WHITE,MARKED ALFRED MEAKIN.......   21.50
IRONSTONE,TEA LEAF,PLATTER,WHITE,MELLAR & TAYLOR,ENGLAND....   18.00
IRONSTONE,TEA LEAF,POT,CHAMBER,BAMBOO HANDLES,MEAKIN.......    35.00
IRONSTONE,TEA LEAF,SAUCE,ROUND,ANTHONY SHAW,5 IN.............   5.00
IRONSTONE,TEA LEAF,SAUCE,SQUARE,WILKINSON,4 1/4 IN..........    6.00
IRONSTONE,TEA LEAF,SAUCER..............................        5.00
IRONSTONE,TEA LEAF,SAUCER,MARKED ALFRED MEAKIN,ENGLAND......    5.00
IRONSTONE,TEA LEAF,WASHBOWL,ENGLAND....................       35.00
```

```
IRONSTONE,TEAPOT,MELON RIB,WHEAT,BERRIES,WHITE,MAKER
  CLEMENTSON BROS.......................................    25.00
IRONSTONE,TEAPOT,PINK,WHITE,ENGLISH SCENES,FOOTED TRIVET,
  MASON'S PATENT.......................................    28.50
IRONSTONE,TEAPOT,WHITE,WHEAT,ELSMORE & FORSTER............    27.50
IRONSTONE,TRAY,PIN,ORIENTAL DECOR,MARKED MASON PATENT,5 IN..    11.50
IRONSTONE,TUREEN,GRAVY,WHITE,ROPE & BAR HANDLES & FINIAL,
  MARKED...............................................    10.00
IRONSTONE,TUREEN,MUSTARD,COVER,MINIATURE,ATTACHED TRAY......    25.00
IRONSTONE,TUREEN,SAUCE,COVER,TULIP SHAPE,TRAY,LADLE,SYDENHAM    55.00
IRONSTONE,TUREEN,SOUP,FLOWER FINIAL,LADLE,MAASTRICHT,HOLLAND    48.00
IRONSTONE,TUREEN,VEGETABLE,PEDESTAL FOOT,SIDE HANDLES,MAKER
  BURGESS..............................................    12.50
IRONSTONE,VASE,EIGHT-SIDED,JAPANESE SCENE,MASON'S PATENT
  IRONSTONE............................................    55.00
IRONSTONE,VASE,EIGHT-SIDED,RUST-RED,GREEN,BLACK,MASON'S
  PATENT,5 1/2 IN......................................    16.00
IRONSTONE,VASE,PINK GROUND,WHITE DAISIES,GILT,5 IN.........     5.00
IRONSTONE,VASE,RED FLOWERS,GREEN LEAVES,SOAP & CLOTH DISH,
  MASON,SET............................................    32.00
IRONSTONE,WASHBOWL,BLEEDING HEART DECOR,18-IN.DIAMETER......    17.50
IRONSTONE,WASHBOWL,BLUE & WHITE TRANSFER,GRECIAN MOTIF,
  CLEMENTSON...........................................    25.00
IRONSTONE,WASHBOWL & PITCHER,CHILD'S,WHITE.................    20.00
IVORY,SEE ALSO,BOTTLE,SNUFF,NETSUKE
IVORY,BALL,PUZZLE,DRAGONS,STAND,HEAD OF BEARDED MAN,CHINA,
  15 IN.HIGH...........................................    65.00
IVORY,BALL,PUZZLE,FLORAL,DIAPER DESIGN,STAND,CASE,25 IN.HIGH   750.00
IVORY,BALL,PUZZLE,FLOWER,STAND,BOY FIGURE,HOLDS VASE,CHINA,
  12 IN.HIGH...........................................    50.00
IVORY,BASKET OF FLOWERS,HANGING,CHINA,WOODEN STAND,
  11 1/2 IN.LONG.......................................    85.00
IVORY,BOAT,RIVER,FIGURES ON DECK,TWO MEN PLAYING GO,STAND,
  CHINA,10 IN..........................................    70.00
IVORY,BOAT,TREE,MONKEY,PEACH BRANCH,MAIDEN,ATTENDANT,CHINA,
  16 IN.LONG...........................................   750.00
IVORY,BOTTLE,POLYCHROME-CARVED,WOMAN RIDING CAMEL,HEAD IS
  STOPPER,3 IN.........................................    75.00
IVORY,BOTTLE,SNUFF,CARVED..................... 70.00 TO    95.00
IVORY,BOTTLE,SNUFF,FIGURES,HAND-CARVED,3 IN.TALL...........    45.00
IVORY,BOTTLE,SNUFF,GREEN DRAGON HANDLES,BLACK GROUND,TINTED,
  CHINA................................................   100.00
IVORY,BOTTLE,SNUFF,JAPANESE,TINTED,20TH CENTURY...........   250.00
IVORY,BOTTLE,SNUFF,LADIES,CHILDREN,GARDEN SCENE,CARVED,
  WOODEN STAND.........................................   115.00
IVORY,BOWL,INCENSE,ORIENTAL,CARVED,DRAGON TOP & HANDLES,
  9 IN.HIGH............................................   250.00
IVORY,BOX,THREE HAND-PAINTED MINIATURES ON LID,LADY IN PINK,
  3 IN.................................................    75.00
IVORY,BRUSH & COMB,BABY'S,HAND-PAINTED FLORAL,CASE.........     6.50
IVORY,BUST,HALF PORTRAIT OF MARIA DE MEDICI,BASE,GRIFFIN
  LEGS,6 IN.HIGH.......................................   275.00
IVORY,CALLING CARD CASE,NOTEBOOK,PENCIL,STAG,FOLIAGE,CARVED,
  SILK LINING..........................................    41.00
IVORY,CARVED TUSK,FIGURES,HOLLOW INSIDE,30 IN.LONG.........   400.00
IVORY,CARVED TUSK,PIERCED,GRAPE VINES,RODENTS,WOODEN STAND,
  CHINA,20 IN..........................................    90.00
IVORY,CARVING,KUAN YIN,ROBED,HOLDS SCROLLING,WITH TABLE
  SCREEN,SCENE.........................................   190.00
IVORY,CARVING,MAN,HOLDS FLY WHISK,SEATED BOY,RODENT,JAPAN,
  6 IN.HIGH............................................   100.00
IVORY,CARVING,MODEL OF TEMPLE,PINE TREES,CLIFF,FIGURES,
  GARDEN...............................................    70.00
IVORY,CARVING,RATS DEVOURING DAIKON,EYES INLAID IN HORN,
  WOODEN STAND.........................................    20.00
IVORY,CASE,CALLING CARD,CARVED PAGODAS,HUMAN FIGURES,1790,
  CHINA................................................   165.00
IVORY,CHESS SET,ELEPHANT TUSK.............................   250.00
IVORY,CHESS SET,OPPONENTS LACQUERED RED,FIGURES 3 1/2 &
  4 IN.TALL,CASE.......................................   350.00
IVORY,CHESS SET,RED,WHITE,SIZES FROM 1 1/2 IN. TO 2 3/4 IN.,
  WOODEN BOX...........................................    50.00
IVORY,COMB,ARCHED TOP,GRADUATED BALLS,YELLOW PATINA,
  5 IN.WIDE............................................    15.00
IVORY,COMB,CARVED FLORAL,BIRDS,3 3/4 IN. X 6 3/4 IN........    40.00
IVORY,COMB,CARVED,7 IN.HIGH...............................    30.00
IVORY,CROSS,PAINTING......................................    22.50
IVORY,CRUCIFIX,THE CORPUS,ELONGATED FIGURE,DIEPPE,
  10 1/2 IN.HIGH.......................................    75.00
IVORY,DISH,BONBON,SCALLOPED RIM,CENTER HANDLE,OHME,SILESIA,
  NO.16................................................    20.00
```

```
IVORY,DOCTOR'S DOLL,NUDE,RECLINING,ORIENTAL,8 IN.LONG.......      50.00
IVORY,ELEPHANT TUSK,WEIGHT 5 POUNDS,17 IN.,1902,PAIR.......      90.00
IVORY,FIGURINE,BEARDED MAN,HOLDS STAFF & PLANT,DRAPED ROBE,
  WOODEN BASE.....................................................      85.00
IVORY,FIGURINE,BIRDS,GNARLED BLOSSOMING TREE,ROCKWORK,WOODEN
  STAND,CHINA...................................................     100.00
IVORY,FIGURINE,BODHISATTVA,TEN ARMS HOLD VASE,GILT
  CHARACTERS,CHINA.............................................     350.00
IVORY,FIGURINE,BRIDGE OF FIVE GRADUATED ELEPHANTS,TEAK BASE,
  5 1/2 IN.......................................................      85.00
IVORY,FIGURINE,CARVED,BOY HOLDING FISHING NET & SHEAF OF
  WHEAT,4 IN.HIGH.............................................      32.00
IVORY,FIGURINE,CARVED,NUDE ORIENTAL WOMAN LYING ON BACK,
  1 IN. X 5 IN..................................................      25.00
IVORY,FIGURINE,CARVED,TWO MEN FIGHTING OVER SCROLL,4 X I
  IN.HIGH......................................................      65.00
IVORY,FIGURINE,CHINESE FISHERMAN,THREE FISHES,CARVED,SIGNED,
  10 IN.HIGH...................................................      75.00
IVORY,FIGURINE,DOG,SEATED,CARVED,BROWN FACE & EARS,1 IN.TALL       9.50
IVORY,FIGURINE,DRAGON,OPEN MOUTH,FLAME MOTIFS,JAPAN,
  29 1/2 IN.LONG..............................................     225.00
IVORY,FIGURINE,EGG WITH EMERGING CHICK,HAND-CARVED,SIGNED,
  4 IN.........................................................      35.00
IVORY,FIGURINE,ELEPHANT,CARVED,TURNED-UP TRUNK,TWO LARGE,ONE
  SMALL,3......................................................      45.00
IVORY,FIGURINE,ELEPHANT,STRIDING,UPRAISED TRUNK,WOODEN
  STAND,8 IN.LONG.............................................     100.00
IVORY,FIGURINE,FARMHOUSE,THATCHED ROOF,TREES,FARMER,PLOW,OX,
  JAPAN........................................................     150.00
IVORY,FIGURINE,FERTILITY GOD,HOLDS STAFF,FISH,CHILD AT SIDE,
  CARVED......................................................     150.00
IVORY,FIGURINE,FIGHTING COCK,CROUCHED,HAND-CARVED,
  2 1/2 IN.LONG,PAIR..........................................      35.00
IVORY,FIGURINE,FISHERMAN,BASKET,BOY HOLDS SEASHELL,JAPAN,
  12 3/4 IN....................................................     100.00
IVORY,FIGURINE,FISHERMEN IN BOATS,WATERFOWL,JAPAN,
  12 1/2 IN.LONG..............................................     200.00
IVORY,FIGURINE,FU LION,CHINA,10 1/4 IN.HIGH,PAIR.....ILLUS..     250.00
```

IVORY FIGURINES, FU LION, CHINA

```
IVORY,FIGURINE,FU LION,MALE,FEMALE,THREE CUBS,CHINA,
  4 1/4 IN.HIGH,PAIR..........................................     150.00
IVORY,FIGURINE,GODDESS OF MERCY,SEATED ON WOOD PLINTH,
  CARVED,6 1/2 IN.............................................      80.00
IVORY,FIGURINE,KABUKI DANCER,FACE TURNS,SIGNED..............      75.00
IVORY,FIGURINE,KAYAK,ESKIMO,WALRUS,HARPOONS,PADDLES,CARVED,
  10 IN. LONG.................................................     130.00
IVORY,FIGURINE,KWANNON,WEARS CROWN,PENDANTS,HOLDS BRANCH,
  VASE,JAPAN..................................................      70.00
IVORY,FIGURINE,LADY,CARVED,CHINA,4 1/4 IN...................      29.50
IVORY,FIGURINE,LI TIEH-KUAI,BEGGAR,CRUTCH,ROBED,WOODEN
  STAND,CHINA.................................................     175.00
IVORY,FIGURINE,MADONNA,GERMANY,12 IN.TALL..................      45.00
IVORY,FIGURINE,MAN CARRYS WICKER CREEL,SACK,POLE,BOY,JAPAN,
  17 1/4 IN...................................................     250.00
IVORY,FIGURINE,NOBLE,PORTERS,DOG,SIGNED,OKI-MONO,4 X 4 1/2 X
  2 IN........................................................      85.00
```

```
IVORY,FIGURINE,OFFICIAL FIGURE,HOLDS BANNER,ROCKWORK BASE,
    WOODEN STAND............................................................    225.00
IVORY,FIGURINE,OFFICIAL,ROBED,HAT,HOLDS HU TABLET,WOODEN
    STAND,CHINA.............................................................    120.00
IVORY,FIGURINE,ORIENTAL,FLOWING ROBE,CARVED,VELVET-LINED
    CASE,20 IN.............................................................    450.00
IVORY,FIGURINE,SAGE,BEARD,ROBED,HOLDS FAN,STAFF,WOODEN
    STAND,CHINA.............................................................     80.00
IVORY,FIGURINE,SHOU LAO,HOLDS CHILD,STAFF,ATTENDANTS,WOODEN
    STAND,CHINA.............................................................     70.00
IVORY,FIGURINE,TURTLE SHRINE,DRAGON HEAD,TABLET ON BACK,STEP
    BASE,CHINA.............................................................    190.00
IVORY,FIGURINE,WARRIOR,BEARD,MUSTACHE,WEARS HELMET,ARMOR,
    SWORD,CHINA............................................................    200.00
IVORY,FIGURINE,WARRIOR,CARVED,11 IN....................................     90.00
IVORY,FIGURINE,WARRIOR,WEARS HELMET,ARMOR,SWORD,DAGGER,HOLDS
    DRUM,JAPAN............................................................     70.00
IVORY,FIGURINE,WOMAN,HOLDS NEST,BIRD,CARVED,18 IN.HIGH......    450.00
IVORY,HOOK,BUTTON......................................................      3.00
IVORY,INCENSE BURNER,LOOSE RING HANDLES,DRAGONS,TREES,WOMEN,
    13 1/4 IN.............................................................    275.00
IVORY,LETTER OPENER,FLOWER & BOOK,CARVED,8 1/2 IN..............      4.00
IVORY,LETTER OPENER,PENHOLDER INSIDE SCREW HANDLE,9 IN......      6.00
IVORY,LETTER OPENER,STERLING HANDLE,MONOGRAM S.N.,8 1/2 IN..      6.50
IVORY,MEDICINE DOLL IN EARLY PREGNANCY,ON WOODEN COUCH,
    6 IN.LONG............................................................     85.00
IVORY,NAIL FILE.......................................................      3.00
IVORY,NAPKIN RING,CARVED....................................... 5.50 TO      9.00
IVORY,NAPKIN RING,CARVED,PAIR..........................................     10.00
IVORY,NAPKIN RING,CARVED,PEOPLE,TREES..................................      9.00
IVORY,NAPKIN RING,GOLD ENAMEL BIRDS & GRAPES...................      9.50
IVORY,NARWHALE TUSK,TWISTED SHAPE,29 IN.LONG...................     97.50
IVORY,NETSUKE,MAN,SEATED,HOLDS BOWL,MAN STANDS BEHIND HIM,
    1 1/8 IN.HIGH.........................................................     35.00
IVORY,NETSUKE,PEOPLE,ANIMALS,BUILDINGS,CARVED,2 IN.HIGH,SET
    OF 6..................................................................    200.00
IVORY,NETSUKE,THE WORRIERS,THREE MEN WITH CASK,SIGNED.......     40.00
IVORY,PARASOL HANDLE,GERMAN............................................    100.00
IVORY,PARASOL HANDLE,LOUIX XVI DESIGN,SILVER STUDS,GERMANY,
    1780..................................................................     70.00
IVORY,PLAQUE,TWO FEMALE FIGURES,HOLD SWORDS,BANNER,IN BOAT,
    CARVED FRAME..........................................................    225.00
IVORY,PORTRAIT,NAPOLEON,HAND PAINTED,BRASS FRAME,1 3/4 X
    2 IN..................................................................     25.00
IVORY,POT,INCENSE,THREE MONKEYS INSIDE COVER,CHINESE
    LETTERING,5 1/8 IN....................................................    100.00
IVORY,RULER,FOLDING,LAYERED,BRASS HINGES,12 1/4 IN..........      6.25
IVORY,SCREEN,TABLE,SIX FOLDS,ROSEWOOD FRAMES INLAID WITH
    SILVER WIRE...........................................................    325.00
IVORY,SHIP,TREASURE,SINGLE MAST,TAOIST FIGURES ON DECK,
    JAPAN,7 1/2 IN........................................................    160.00
IVORY,STATUE,KUAN YIN,CHINA,37 3/4 IN.HIGH...........ILLUS..1,700.00
IVORY,STATUE,SHOU LAO,CHINA,37 IN.HIGH................ILLUS..    650.00
IVORY,TOOTHBRUSH,CARVED HANDLE.........................................      3.00
IVORY,TOOTHPICK,EGG ON NEST,HAND-CARVED............................     19.50
IVORY,VASE,BALUSTER,LOOSE RING HANDLES,7 1/2 IN.HIGH,CHINA,
    PAIR..................................................................    225.00
IVORY,VASE,CARVED IN LOW RELIEF,DRAGON,BUDDHIST EMBLEMS,
    CHINA,12 1/4 IN.......................................................    250.00
IVORY,VASE,PIETRA DURA DECOR,STAND,JAPAN,18 IN.HIGH,PAIR....    700.00
IVORY,VASE,STAMFORD PATTERN,RACING DEER,SIGNATURE,10 IN.TALL    500.00
IVORY,WALKING STICK,35 IN..............................................     18.00
IVORY,WHALE,NEST OF SIX TRAYS,COFFIN LID SHAPE,PADOUK WOOD,
    GRADUATING............................................................    550.00
```

JACK-IN-THE-PULPIT VASES WERE NAMED FOR THEIR ODD
TRUMPET-LIKE SHAPE THAT RESEMBLES THE WILD PLANT
CALLED A JACK-IN-THE-PULPIT. THE DESIGN ORIGINATED IN
THE LATE VICTORIAN YEARS.

```
JACK-IN-THE-PULPIT,SEE ALSO,UNDER SPECIFIC ART GLASS
    HEADINGS
JACK-IN-THE-PULPIT,BOWL,ROSE,AMBER PANELED GLASS,APPLIED
    FLOWERS,COLLAR........................................................     44.50
JACK-IN-THE-PULPIT,CRANBERRY GLASS,ROUGH PONTIL,
    9 1/2 IN.HIGH.........................................................     38.00
JACK-IN-THE-PULPIT,CRANBERRY,OPAQUE WHITE LINING,GREEN BASE
    & FOOT................................................................     35.00
JACK-IN-THE-PULPIT,GREEN BOTTOM TO WHITE TOP,RIGAREE BAND,
    8 1/2 IN.HIGH.........................................................     27.50
JACK-IN-THE-PULPIT,VASE,AMBERINA,FUCHSIA,7 1/4 IN.HIGH......    165.00
```

IVORY STATUE,
KUAN YIN,
CHINA

IVORY STATUE,
SHOU LAO,
CHINA

```
JACK-IN-THE-PULPIT,VASE,AMETHYST TO CLEAR BASE,
    CHRYSANTHEMUMS,12 IN......................................    50.00
JACK-IN-THE-PULPIT,VASE,AURENE,GOLD IRIDESCENT,MINIATURE,
    SIGNED,6 IN...............................................   235.00
JACK-IN-THE-PULPIT,VASE,BLUE TUBULAR BODY,PINK TOP,
    4 3/4 IN.HIGH.............................................    25.00
JACK-IN-THE-PULPIT,VASE,CANARY OPALESCENT,8 IN. TALL........    29.50
JACK-IN-THE-PULPIT,VASE,CARNIVAL GLASS,MARIGOLD,RIBBED,PAIR.    40.00
JACK-IN-THE-PULPIT,VASE,COBALT,10 IN.......................    24.00
JACK-IN-THE-PULPIT,VASE,CRANBERRY GLASS,VASELINE BASE,BLOWN,
    13 IN.TALL...............................................    45.00
JACK-IN-THE-PULPIT,VASE,CRANBERRY TO CLEAR,STAR BASE,12 IN..    45.00
JACK-IN-THE-PULPIT,VASE,CRANBERRY,VASELINE EDGE,PINK OPAQUE
    LINING...................................................    35.00
JACK-IN-THE-PULPIT,VASE,CRYSTAL,PURPLE EDGING,CRYSTAL
    RIGAREE,8 1/2 IN.........................................    32.00
JACK-IN-THE-PULPIT,VASE,ENAMELED FLORAL,COBALT BLUE,
    7 IN.HIGH................................................    15.50
JACK-IN-THE-PULPIT,VASE,FLUTED RED EDGE,VASELINE GLASS,6 IN.    32.00
JACK-IN-THE-PULPIT,VASE,GREEN TO OPALESCENT,7 1/2 X
    10 1/2 IN.TALL...........................................    18.50
JACK-IN-THE-PULPIT,VASE,GREEN TRIM,RUFFLED TOP,MILK GLASS,
    7 IN.....................................................    12.50
JACK-IN-THE-PULPIT,VASE,GREEN,BLOWN,6 1/2 IN................    21.50
JACK-IN-THE-PULPIT,VASE,GREEN,PANELED STEM,OPALESCENT TOP,
    10 1/2 IN.HIGH...........................................    27.00
JACK-IN-THE-PULPIT,VASE,GREEN,6 IN.........................    21.00
JACK-IN-THE-PULPIT,VASE,MILK GLASS,BLUE,7 IN.TALL..........    20.00
JACK-IN-THE-PULPIT,VASE,MILK GLASS,BLUE,FENTON,7 IN.TALL....    24.00
JACK-IN-THE-PULPIT,VASE,MULTICOLORED HIGHLIGHTS,IRIDESCENT,
    RUFFLED..................................................    85.00
JACK-IN-THE-PULPIT,VASE,OPALESCENT CRANBERRY TO CLEAR BASE,
    RIGAREE,PAIR.............................................    70.00
JACK-IN-THE-PULPIT,VASE,PALE GREEN TO OPALESCENT TO PINK
    RUFFLED TOP..............................................    24.00
JACK-IN-THE-PULPIT,VASE,PALE GREEN,OPALESCENT,ROUGH PONTIL,
    6 1/2 IN.................................................    20.00
JACK-IN-THE-PULPIT,VASE,PEACHBLOW,ROSE-PINK TO PINK-WHITE,
    SANDWICH.................................................    87.50
JACK-IN-THE-PULPIT,VASE,PINK,CLEAR,BLOWN,10 1/2 IN.HIGH.....    20.00
JACK-IN-THE-PULPIT,VASE,QUEZAL,9 IN........................   450.00
JACK-IN-THE-PULPIT,VASE,ROSE TO YELLOW,BURMESE,8 X 8 IN.TALL   650.00
JACK-IN-THE-PULPIT,VASE,ROUGH PONTIL,LIGHT AMBER TO GREEN,
    7 1/2 IN.................................................    20.00
JACK-IN-THE-PULPIT,VASE,RUBINA,HOBNAIL,FROSTED,
    10 1/2 IN.TALL...........................................    59.50
```

JACK-IN-THE-PULPIT,VASE,TRANSPARENT RAINBOW,11 IN.TALL......    135.00
JACK-IN-THE-PULPIT,VASE,WHITE THREADING,RUFFLED,AMBER,BLOWN,
  6 IN.TALL.................................................     28.00
JACK-IN-THE-PULPIT,VASE,WHITE WITH PURPLE SLAG..............     16.00
JACK-IN-THE-PULPIT,VASE,WHITE,PINK CASING,DIMPLED BOTTOM,
  SATIN GLASS...............................................    125.00
JACK-IN-THE-PULPIT,VASE,WHITE,PINK LINING,BLUE SNAKE AROUND
  BODY.....................................................     45.00


        JACKFIELD WARE WAS ORIGINALLY A BLACK GLAZED POTTERY
        MADE IN JACKFIELD,ENGLAND,SINCE 1630. A YELLOW GLAZED
        WARE HAS ALSO BEEN CALLED JACKFIELD WARE. MOST OF THE
        PIECES REFERRED TO AS JACKFIELD ARE BLACK PIECES MADE
        DURING THE VICTORIAN ERA.
JACKFIELD,BOX,JEWEL,BLACK,ENAMELED ROSES ON COVER,BRASS
  FEET,5 1/4 IN.............................................     49.50
JACKFIELD,CREAMER,COW..................... 35.00 TO             48.00
JACKFIELD,DOG,BLACK,14 IN.TALL,PAIR........................     70.00
JACKFIELD,EWER,GOLD LEAVES & CLASSIC HEAD,BLACK GLAZE,
  11 1/2 IN.,PAIR...........................................     65.00
JACKFIELD,FIGURINE,DOG,BLACK,10 IN.,PAIR...................     37.50
JACKFIELD,FIGURINE,POODLE,BLACK,9 1/2 IN.HIGH,PAIR.........     55.00
JACKFIELD,FIGURINE,ROOSTER,BLACK,ENGLAND,11 1/4 IN.TALL,PAIR   140.00
JACKFIELD,JUG,OLIVE GREEN PANELS,GOLD LEAF,FORGET-ME-NOT
  DECOR,8 IN...............................................     35.00
JACKFIELD,PITCHER,BLACK,WHITE ENAMELED IVY,FROSTED LEAVES,
  7 3/4 IN.TALL.............................................     55.00
JACKFIELD,TEAPOT,BLACK.....................................     22.50
JADE,ASHTRAY,DARK GREEN,ELEPHANTS ON RIM,BROWN SOAPSTONE
  SEAL,BUDDHA...............................................     70.00
JADE,BELT AMULET,WHITE,TWO ROYAL CARP ENTWINED.............     70.00
JADE,BELT BUCKLE,WHITE WITH BROWN STREAKS,FORM OF FOO DOG,
  2 1/2 IN.LONG.............................................    185.00
JADE,BELT HOOK,GREEN WITH CARMINE,PLUMS & DRAGON HEAD ON
  HOOK.....................................................     45.00
JADE,BELT ORNAMENT,FISH,WHITE WITH GREEN INCLUSIONS........     60.00
JADE,BELT ORNAMENT,OPENWORK CARVING,WHITE-YELLOW...........     75.00
JADE,BELT ORNAMENT,RELIEF CARVING,WHITE-GRAY,ROUND.........     80.00
JADE,BOTTLE,SNUFF,BLACK & WHITE............................  1,200.00
JADE,BOTTLE,SNUFF,BLACK,HEART SHAPE,ROUNDED SHOULDERS,
  MALACHITE STOPPER.........................................     70.00
JADE,BOTTLE,SNUFF,BLACK,HEART SHAPE,ROUNDED SHOULDERS,CORAL
  STOPPER...................................................     80.00
JADE,BOTTLE,SNUFF,BURNT,1800-60............................    375.00
JADE,BOTTLE,SNUFF,FEI-TSUI,FLATTENED HEART SHAPE,MAN,HORSE,
  BRIDGE,TREE...............................................    160.00
JADE,BOTTLE,SNUFF,FISH FORM,GREEN,CARNELIAN AGATE STOPPER...     85.00
JADE,BOTTLE,SNUFF,GRAY,FLATTENED QUADRANGLE,CARNELIAN AGATE
  STOPPER...................................................    110.00
JADE,BOTTLE,SNUFF,LADY'S,WHITE,MOTTLED JADE TOP............     75.00
JADE,BOTTLE,SNUFF,LAVENDER,FEI-TSUE,FLATTENED OVOID.........    160.00
JADE,BOTTLE,SNUFF,MUTTON FAT,WHITE-GREEN,DOUBLE GOURD SHAPE.     85.00
JADE,BOTTLE,SNUFF,ONION GREEN,TIBETAN......................  1,300.00
JADE,BOTTLE,SNUFF,PINK-WHITE,YELLOW MOTTLING,MELON SHAPE,
  CARVED LEAVES.............................................    135.00
JADE,BOTTLE,SNUFF,QUADRANGULAR,PANEL CUT SIDES,LAVENDER,
  CROCIDOLITE TOP...........................................    160.00
JADE,BOTTLE,SNUFF,WHITE,BROWN MOTTLING,FORM OF A CICADA,
  CARVED...................................................    100.00
JADE,BOTTLE,SNUFF,WHITE,CORAL STOPPER......................    150.00
JADE,BOTTLE,SNUFF,WHITE,LAPIS LAZULI STOPPER...............    100.00
JADE,BOX,GREEN,BOUND IN BRASS,HINGED LID,3 IN. X 3 1/2 IN...    115.00
JADE,BUCKLE,WHITE,DRAGON,2 1/2 IN.LONG.....................     60.00
JADE,BUTTERFLY,IMPERIAL,OPENWORK CARVING,WHITE-GREEN.......     70.00
JADE,BUTTERFLY,WHITE,3 1/4 IN.WIDE,WOODEN STAND,SILK-LINED
  BOX.......................................................     60.00
JADE,BUTTONHOOK,DRAGON HEAD,WHITE-GREEN,2 1/2 IN...........     25.00
JADE,BUTTONHOOK,DRAGON ON TOP..............................     70.00
JADE,CANDLESTICK,SOME ALABASTER,GREEN,PAPER LABEL,8 IN.TALL.     75.00
JADE,CICADA,WHITE,1 1/8 IN. X 3/4 IN.......................     20.00
JADE,CORDIAL,LIGHT GREEN,SILK-COVERED STAND,SET OF 6........     75.00
JADE,COVER ON BOX,APPLIED FLORAL DECOR,5 IN.LONG X
  3 1/2 IN.WIDE.............................................     75.00
JADE,FIGURINE,BOY,CREAMY WHITE,CARVED,TEAK STAND,2 IN.HIGH..     60.00
JADE,FIGURINE,DRAGON,TREE,CARVED,BROWN-WHITE,STAND,1 1/2 IN.
  X 2 IN....................................................     60.00
JADE,FIGURINE,HORSE,HOOVES TUCKED UNDER,WHITE,CHINA.........     55.00
JADE,FIGURINE,MOUNTAIN,RIVER,BOAT,MEN,GREEN,1266 GRAMS OF
  NEPHRITE JADE.............................................    765.00
JADE,FIGURINE,TWO GOOD LUCK PEACHES,BAT,WHITE,TEAK STAND,

| | |
|---|---:|
| 1 1/2 IN.HIGH.......................................... | 52.50 |
| JADE,FIGURINE,WHITE,BOY HOLDS BRANCH,CARVED,FITTED ROSEWOOD STAND,3 IN............................................ | 75.00 |
| JADE,FIGURINE,WHITE,BOY,FRUITING BRANCH,UNDERCUT RETICULATION,1 5/8 IN............................... | 75.00 |
| JADE,FIGURINE,WHITE,CATFISH,WATER PLANTS,CARVED,2 1/8 IN. X 2 IN.................................................. | 75.00 |
| JADE,FIGURINE,WHITE,TWO LILIES,STEMS,FOLIAGE,CARVED,ROSEWOOD STAND,3 IN............................................ | 75.00 |
| JADE,FIGURINE,WOMAN,CARVED,TEAK STAND,9 1/2 IN.HIGH........ | 650.00 |
| JADE,FINGERING PIECE,TWO FRUIT & LEAVES,MUTTON-FAT,CARVED ON BOTH SIDES.................................... | 65.00 |
| JADE,FISH,MOUNTED ON TEAK STAND......................... | 60.00 |
| JADE,GRAPES,BUNCH....................................... | 25.75 |
| JADE,HANDLING PIECE,BUTTERFLY,CARVED,2 1/4 IN. X 3 1/2 IN... | 50.00 |
| JADE,JAR,DARK GREEN,LOTUS BLOSSOMS,RING HANDLES,COVER, 3 3/4 IN.HIGH........................................... | 250.00 |
| JADE,LOTUS LEAVES,PODS,CARVED,MUTTONFAT..................... | 60.00 |
| JADE,LOTUS,FOLDED,YELLOW SKIN OF JADE ON WHITE............. | 55.00 |
| JADE,MONKEY HOLDING BRANCH,BROWN STREAKING THROUGH MUTTONFAT | 65.00 |
| JADE,MUSHROOM AND LOTUS,MUTTONFAT......................... | 65.00 |
| JADE,NECKLACE,14 OVALS SET IN PRONGS,JOINED,MOTTLED,CARVED, GREEN,CHINA........................................... | 300.00 |
| JADE,NETSUKE,WHITE,TWO KITTENS,FLORAL SPRAY,CARVED, 1 5/8 IN.WIDE.......................................... | 125.00 |
| JADE,PENDANT,WHITE,CICADA,1 1/8 IN.LONG................... | 18.00 |
| JADE,SAUCER,PALE GREEN-WHITE............................. | 9.00 |
| JADE,SWORD ORNAMENT,BROWNISH-GRAY,DETAILED CARVING ON BACK.. | 80.00 |
| JADE,SWORD ORNAMENT,WHITE-GREEN,BLACK INCLUSIONS,CARVING ON BACK.................................................. | 75.00 |
| JADE,SWORD ORNAMENT,WHITE,DRAGON HEAD,CARVED.............. | 80.00 |
| JADE,TEAPOT,LIGHT GREEN,CARVED,COVER,FOUR SMALL FEET,TEAK STAND,4 IN............................................. | 250.00 |
| JADE,THUMB RINGS SET IN CHINESE SILVER TO MAKE SALT & PEPPER SHAKERS............................................... | 100.00 |
| JADE,TREE,CARNELIAN,ROSE QUARTZ & JADE FLOWERS,JADE LEAVES, TUB,11 IN............................................. | 175.00 |
| JADE,TREE,DIFFERENT COLORS OF HEAVY JADE ROSE QUARTZ, 10 1/2 IN.TALL........................................ | 225.00 |
| JADE,TREE,MULTICOLORED FLOWERS,5 IN...................... | 22.50 |
| JADE,TREE,SEMIPRECIOUS MULTICOLORED FLOWERS,24 IN......... | 210.00 |
| JADE,TREE,SIX SEMIPRECIOUS STONE BUDS,5 IN............... | 22.75 |
| JADE,TWO MYTHICAL ANIMALS,ORIENTAL CHARACTERS,WHITE,WOODEN STAND,BOX............................................. | 60.00 |
| JADE,VASE,GREEN,CARVED BIRDS,FLORAL,CH'IEN LUNG,1750,TEAK STAND,8 IN...........................................| 1,450.00 |

JASPERWARE IS A FINE-GRAINED POTTERY DEVELOPED BY
JOSIAH WEDGWOOD IN 1775. THE JASPER WAS MADE IN MANY
COLORS INCLUDING THE MOST FAMOUS,A LIGHT BLUE. IT IS
STILL BEING MADE.

| | |
|---|---:|
| JASPERWARE,ASHTRAY,INDIAN SMOKING PIPE,GREEN,GERMANY,6 X 4 7/8 IN.............................................. | 20.00 |
| JASPERWARE,BLUE,WHITE RELIEF HORSE-DRAWN COACH,WOMAN,MAN, WEDGWOOD.............................................. | 85.00 |
| JASPERWARE,BOTTLE,SNUFF,GREEN,RED,BIRD,BLOSSOMING TREE, ROCKWORK,CARVED....................................... | 90.00 |
| JASPERWARE,BOWL,SALAD,BLUE,WHITE,FIGURES,SILVER PLATE BAND, WEDGWOOD.............................................. | 110.00 |
| JASPERWARE,BOX,BLUE,LID HAS CHERUBS PLAYING INSTRUMENTS, 4 3/4 IN.LONG......................................... | 22.00 |
| JASPERWARE,BOX,DARK BLUE,WHITE CHARIOT,COVER,WEDGWOOD, ENGLAND,4 IN.SQ....................................... | 35.00 |
| JASPERWARE,BOX,GODDESS,CHERUB PLAYING HARP,HEART SHAPE, WEDGWOOD,BLUE......................................... | 40.00 |
| JASPERWARE,BOX,LADY WITH MIRROR,COVER.................... | 22.00 |
| JASPERWARE,BOX,OLIVE GREEN,CHERUBS,DOVES,PIANO SHAPE,BLACK & WHITE KEYS........................................... | 45.00 |
| JASPERWARE,BOX,POWDER,LADY WITH PLUMES,PARASOL ON COVER, GREEN................................................. | 20.00 |
| JASPERWARE,BOX,POWDER,WHITE,RAISED MAN & WOMAN IN PASTELS... | 15.00 |
| JASPERWARE,CANDLESTICK,BLUE,WHITE DECOR,HANDLE............ | 12.00 |
| JASPERWARE,CHOCOLATE POT,DARK GREEN,WHITE CLASSICAL FIGURES, WEDGWOOD.............................................. | 150.00 |
| JASPERWARE,CLOCK,GREEN,WHITE SCROLLS,FLORAL,CUPID PLAYING HARP,5 IN.TALL........................................ | 90.00 |
| JASPERWARE,CREAMER,DEEP BLUE,BARREL SHAPE,MYTHOLOGICAL FIGURES,MEDALLION..................................... | 18.50 |
| JASPERWARE,CREAMER,PALE BLUE,CLASSIC FIGURES,WEDGWOOD, ENGLAND............................................... | 12.00 |

JASPERWARE,CRUET,FOUR PIECES,SILVER PLATE STAND,8 IN........  40.00
JASPERWARE,CUP,DARK BLUE,THREE-HANDLED,WEDGWOOD,ENGLAND,
  4 1/2 IN.HIGH.............................................  40.00
JASPERWARE,DISH,WHITE MOUSE PERCHED ON EDGE,GREEN,OVAL......  12.00
JASPERWARE,FERNERY,BLUE,CLASSICAL FIGURES,FOOTED,ENGLAND,
  8-IN.DIAMETER.............................................  75.00
JASPERWARE,FIGURINE,WOMAN WEARING CAMISOLE,SITTING NEAR
  BASKET,GERMANY............................................  22.00
JASPERWARE,HAIR RECEIVER,GREEN & WHITE,3 1/4-IN.DIAMETER....  18.00
JASPERWARE,HAIR RECEIVER,GREEN,BOY & GIRL IN WHITE,ROSE
  GARLANDS.................................................  29.00
JASPERWARE,HOLDER,MATCH,GIRL SEATED AGAINST BASKET,GERMANY..  20.00
JASPERWARE,JAR,CRACKER,BLUE,WHITE CLASSIC FIGURES,SILVER
  BALL FEET,COVER..........................................  77.00
JASPERWARE,JAR,CRACKER,DARK BLUE,CLASSIC FIGURES,WEDGWOOD,
  ENGLAND..................................................  65.00
JASPERWARE,JAR,POWDER,GREEN,LACY BORDER,FLORAL,GIRL'S HEAD
  ON COVER.................................................  10.00
JASPERWARE,JAR,WHITE BISQUE CAMEO HEAD,CHERUBS,BLUE,COVER,
  WEDGWOOD.................................................  18.50
JASPERWARE,MATCH HOLDER,BLUE,ADAMS,TUNSTALL,ENGLAND........  18.00
JASPERWARE,PITCHER,APPLIED CLASSICAL WHITE FIGURES,BLUE,
  MARK,5 IN................................................  12.50
JASPERWARE,PITCHER,MILK,BLUE,WHITE MEDALLIONS,GODDESS,
  CHERUB,WREATHS...........................................  50.00
JASPERWARE,PITCHER,MINIATURE..............................  21.00
JASPERWARE,PITCHER,ROPE HANDLE,FIGURES,TANKARD,WEDGWOOD,
  5 1/2 IN.................................................  45.00
JASPERWARE,PITCHER,ROSE WREATHS OF ROSES,FIGURES,IMPRESSED
  1802.....................................................  16.00
JASPERWARE,PITCHER,WHITE CLASSIC FIGURES,ROPE HANDLE,BLUE,
  DUDSON,ENGLAND...........................................  25.00
JASPERWARE,PLAQUE,CHERUB,BIRD,LEAVES,VINES ON BORDER,
  4 1/2-IN.DIAMETER........................................  25.00
JASPERWARE,PLAQUE,FRANZ LISZT,DARK GREEN,OVAL,7 IN.HIGH,
  5 IN.ACROSS..............................................  22.50
JASPERWARE,PLAQUE,GREEN,CHERUB,DRAGONFLIES,SEMINUDE LADY,
  10 X 7 IN................................................ 145.00
JASPERWARE,PLAQUE,GREEN,CUPID WITH UMBRELLA,BIRD,4 1/2 IN...  12.50
JASPERWARE,PLAQUE,GREEN,LEAF SHAPE,APPLIED MAN IN WHITE
  COURT DRESS,OVAL.........................................  28.00
JASPERWARE,PLAQUE,GREEN,WHITE CUPID ON LIMB,GERMANY,6 IN....  25.00
JASPERWARE,PLAQUE,GREEN,WHITE FIGURES,INDIAN ON HORSE,
  BUFFALO,SIGNED...........................................  25.00
JASPERWARE,PLAQUE,GREEN,WHITE,INDIAN IN PROFILE SMOKING,
  ROCOCO EDGE..............................................  22.50
JASPERWARE,PLAQUE,INDIAN CHIEF,GREEN,6 IN. X 5 IN..........  35.00
JASPERWARE,PLAQUE,INDIAN HEAD IN WHITE CAMEO RELIEF,GREEN
  GROUND,5 IN..............................................  25.00
JASPERWARE,PLAQUE,INDIAN IN FEATHER HEADDRESS,GREEN,4 X
  5 IN.....................................................  22.50
JASPERWARE,PLAQUE,MERMAID & OLD MAN OF THE SEA.............  24.00
JASPERWARE,PLAQUE,WALL,VIOLET,WHITE STAGS & SCROLL DESIGN,
  4 X 5 IN.................................................  12.00
JASPERWARE,PLATE,INDIAN,HIGH HAWK,NO.32,6 IN...............  35.00
JASPERWARE,PORTRAIT MEDALLION,GREEN,WHITE,WELLINGTON,
  BONAPARTE,PAIR...........................................  45.00
JASPERWARE,POT,MUSTARD,WHITE,CUPIDS & CHILDREN,COVER,SPOON,
  WEDGWOOD.................................................  30.00
JASPERWARE,SHAKER,SUGAR,BLUE,WHITE,WEDGWOOD,ENGLAND........  35.00
JASPERWARE,SYRUP,BLUE,WHITE,CLASSICAL FIGURES,GRAPE,LEAF
  BORDER,WEDGWOOD..........................................  50.00
JASPERWARE,TEAPOT,CREAMER,SUGAR,LIGHT & DARK BLUE,WHITE
  FIGURES................................................. 125.00
JASPERWARE,TEAPOT,LIGHT BLUE,CLASSIC FIGURES,WEDGWOOD,
  ENGLAND..................................................  46.00
JASPERWARE,TOOTHPICK,BARREL SHAPE,ADAMS...................  12.00
JASPERWARE,TOOTHPICK,BLUE,ADAMS,TUNSTALL,ENGLAND,CROWN &
  SHIELD MARK..............................................  22.50
JASPERWARE,TRAY,GODDESS,BIRDS,CUPID,GREEN,ORCHID,WHITE,OVAL,
  6 1/2 IN.................................................  25.00
JASPERWARE,VASE,BLUE,BIRDS & DOG,2 HANDLED,SIGNED,5 IN.....  19.50
JASPERWARE,VASE,BLUE,WHITE,CHILDREN FIGURES,FLARED TOP,
  WEDGWOOD,5 IN............................................  38.00
JASPERWARE,VASE,CHILDREN AT PLAY,BLUE,WEDGWOOD,5 1/4 IN....  24.50
JASPERWARE,VASE,DARK BLUE,WHITE CLASSICAL FIGURES,MARKED
  WEDGWOOD,8 IN............................................  85.00
JASPERWARE,VASE,GERMAN,GREEN,DIP,9 IN...............ILLUS..  10.00
JASPERWARE,VASE,GREEN,GIRL PICKING GRAPES,CUPID,
  5 1/2 IN.TALL,PAIR.......................................  29.50
JASPERWARE,VASE,SIGNED ADAMS,ESTABLISHED 1657,TUNSTALL,

GERMAN JASPERWARE VASE

```
ENGLAND,BLUE.............................................    55.00
JASPERWARE,VASE,WALL,FAN,CLASSIC FIGURE,GREEN,7 1/2 IN.LONG.    11.00
JEWELRY,BANGLE,CROSSOVER MOUNT,FORM OF TWO HANDS,DIAMOND,
   ENAMEL FAN,GOLD.......................................   700.00
JEWELRY,BANGLE,DIAMOND & EMERALD STAR MOTIF,GOLD MOUNT,CIRCA
   1875................................................   500.00
JEWELRY,BANGLE,HALF PEARLS,TRANSLUCENT BLUE ENAMEL,SCROLL
   DESIGN,GOLD..........................................   325.00
JEWELRY,BANGLE,MINE & ROSE DIAMONDS IN ROPE TWIST PATTERN,
   GOLD,SILVER..........................................   550.00
JEWELRY,BANGLE,MINE & ROSE DIAMONDS,WEIGH 2.40 CARATS,GOLD,
   CIRCA 1880...........................................   650.00
JEWELRY,BANGLE,RUBY,EMERALD,SIX DIAMONDS,GOLD,CIRCA 1890....   225.00
JEWELRY,BANGLE,SNAKE,GREEN & YELLOW ENAMEL,MINE & ROSE
   DIAMONDS,GOLD......................................1,100.00
JEWELRY,BANGLE,TEXTURED GOLD SHANK,FLUTED FINIAL,GOLD,
   ENGLAND,PAIR.........................................   300.00
JEWELRY,BANGLE,THREE CORALS,TWELVE HALF PEARLS,GOLD.........   275.00
JEWELRY,BAR PIN,ENTWINED GOLD,SIX PEARLS BETWEEN EACH TWIST,
   1 1/4 IN.............................................    20.00
JEWELRY,BAR PIN,GOLD,PRONG-MOUNTED 1.83-CARAT DIAMOND,1 INCH
   LONG...............................................1,000.00
JEWELRY,BAR PIN,OVAL,BEIGE AGATE,GOLD NUGGET BORDER,MARKED
   DAWSON..............................................    25.00
JEWELRY,BEADS,CHERRY AMBER,15 1/2 IN......................    17.00
JEWELRY,BEADS,CHOKER,PEA-SIZE,POLISHED ROUND CORAL.........    25.00
JEWELRY,BEADS,GOLD VENETIAN GLASS,GRADUATED,21 IN.LONG......    45.00
JEWELRY,BEADS,HONEY AMBER,31 IN.LONG,PAIR.................    27.50
JEWELRY,BEADS,IVORY,BLACK SPACERS,32 IN..................     9.50
JEWELRY,BEADS,95 MATCHED DIAMOND-CUT RED AMBER,36 IN.LONG...   135.00
JEWELRY,BRACELET,ALLOVER CHASING,GUARD CHAIN,GOLD OVER
   SILVER..............................................    35.00
JEWELRY,BRACELET,BANGLE,JADE,PAIR.........................    95.00
JEWELRY,BRACELET,BANGLE,TWISTED GOLD......................    45.00
JEWELRY,BRACELET,BELT FORM,ENAMEL SLIDE,MINE DIAMONDS,GOLD,
   CIRCA 1850...........................................   500.00
JEWELRY,BRACELET,CHAIN LINKS,DOME CENTER SECTIONS,
   TURQUOISES,GOLD,SILVER...............................   325.00
JEWELRY,BRACELET,CHARMS,TORTOISESHELL.....................     8.50
JEWELRY,BRACELET,CINNABAR,BANGLE TYPE,FLOWERS,SCROLLS,RED,
   7/8 IN.WIDE..........................................     9.50
JEWELRY,BRACELET,DEPICTS PA HSEIN,TAOIST IMMORTALS,SILVER,
   ENAMEL,IVORY.........................................   130.00
JEWELRY,BRACELET,ENGRAVED FLORAL & LEAVES,GOLD,5/8 IN.WIDE..    18.00
JEWELRY,BRACELET,FLEXIBLE,ALTERNATING PEARLS & CORAL BEADS,
   THIN,GOLD............................................    27.00
JEWELRY,BRACELET,FLEXIBLE,CABOCHON GARNET,HALF PEARLS,BLUE
   ENAMEL,GOLD..........................................   275.00
JEWELRY,BRACELET,FLEXIBLE,ENAMEL,ROSE DIAMOND STAR DECOR,
   ENGLAND,1860.........................................   275.00
JEWELRY,BRACELET,FLEXIBLE,GOLD & ENAMEL LINKS,ROSE DIAMOND
   ORNAMENT.............................................   450.00
JEWELRY,BRACELET,GOLD MESH,FACETED AMETHYST,TASSELS,PAIR....   600.00
JEWELRY,BRACELET,GOLD ON SILVER,ALLOVER ENGRAVING,GUARD
   CHAIN...............................................    45.00
JEWELRY,BRACELET,JADE,PALE GREEN & BROWN..................   125.00
JEWELRY,BRACELET,LARGE LINKS,STERLING SILVER..............    10.00
JEWELRY,BRACELET,PRIESTS,BROWN TEAKWOOD,GOLD TRIM,CHINA,PAIR    12.00
JEWELRY,BRACELET,SCROLLS,ROSE DIAMONDS,BLACK ENAMEL,GOLD,
   3/4 IN.WIDE..........................................   600.00
JEWELRY,BRACELET,SEVEN CAMEOS,CLASSIC FIGURES,JOINED BY
   SILVER LINKS.........................................    45.00
```

```
JEWELRY,BRACELET,SEVEN GARNETS SET IN PRONGS,OPENWORK,GOLD..      65.00
JEWELRY,BRACELET,SILVER FILIGREE,10 BLUE LAPIS LAZULI
   STONES,RUSSIA.................................................   50.00
JEWELRY,BRACELET,SNAKE,FLEXIBLE,BLUE ENAMEL HEAD,HALF
   PEARLS,GOLD.................................................    150.00
JEWELRY,BRACELET,STIFF,ALLOVER BLACK ENAMEL,HINGE,
   3/16 IN.WIDE................................................     50.00
JEWELRY,BRACELET,STIFF,HINGED,STRAIGHT ROW OF GARNETS.......      45.00
JEWELRY,BRACELET,STRETCH,TORTOISESHELL,ETCHED FANS,
   1 3/4 IN.WIDE................................................      5.00
JEWELRY,BRACELET,TIERED SILVER DISCS,BLUE ENAMEL,30 GREEN
   EMERALDS....................................................    250.00
JEWELRY,BRACELET,44 ROSE DIAMONDS,SILVER TOP,GOLD BOTTOM,
   FLEXIBLE....................................................    400.00
JEWELRY,BROOCH,ABALONE SHELL,STERLING SILVER CLOVER........        5.00
JEWELRY,BROOCH,ACORN & LEAF DECOR,OBLONG,HOLLOWARE TYPE,
   3 1/2 IN....................................................     10.00
JEWELRY,BROOCH,AMETHYST,ETRUSCAN STYLE,GOLD,1 IN. X
   1 3/4 IN....................................................    225.00
JEWELRY,BROOCH,AMETHYST,SURROUNDED BY SEED PEARLS,SQUARE....       85.00
JEWELRY,BROOCH,BEETLE CENTER,STONE IN BODY,HAMMERED SILVER..       20.00
JEWELRY,BROOCH,BEETLE,EMERALDS,MINE DIAMONDS,GOLD MOUNT,
   ENGLAND.....................................................    375.00
JEWELRY,BROOCH,BIRD IN FLIGHT,DIAMOND DANGLES FROM MOUTH,
   1 1/2 IN....................................................     35.00
JEWELRY,BROOCH,BIRD,FLOWERS,LEAVES,CARVED,CORAL,GOLD,
   1 3/4 IN....................................................     65.00
JEWELRY,BROOCH,BLACK ENAMEL,HAIR LOCKET FRAMED IN GOLD
   CENTER,1836.................................................     15.00
JEWELRY,BROOCH,BLACK ENAMEL,THREE DROPS,MATCHING EARRINGS,
   PIERCED,GOLD................................................     75.00
JEWELRY,BROOCH,BUCKLE FORM,FOUR MINE DIAMONDS,RUBY,GOLD,
   ENGLAND.....................................................    225.00
JEWELRY,BROOCH,BUTTERFLY,MINE DIAMONDS,RUBIES,SAPPHIRES,
   TURQUOISES,GOLD.............................................    325.00
JEWELRY,BROOCH,BUTTERFLY,MINE DIAMONDS,SAPPHIRES,PEARLS,
   GREEN GARNET................................................    500.00
JEWELRY,BROOCH,BUTTERFLY,MINE DIAMONDS,TURQUOISES,GARNETS,
   GOLD,SILVER.................................................    225.00
JEWELRY,BROOCH,BUTTERFLY,ROSE DIAMONDS,EMERALD,RUBIES,
   SAPPHIRES,GOLD..............................................    650.00
JEWELRY,BROOCH,BUTTERFLY,THIRTY RUBIES,MINE & ROSE DIAMONDS,
   GOLD,SILVER.................................................    650.00
JEWELRY,BROOCH,BUTTERFLY,TREMBLANT,DIAMOND,EMERALD...ILLUS.1,400.00
JEWELRY,BROOCH,CAMEO,BROWN & WHITE SHELL,GOLD ETRUSCAN-STYLE
   FRAME.......................................................    225.00
JEWELRY,BROOCH,CAMEO,BROWN,WHITE,WOMAN,HOUSE,TREES,GOLD
   FRAME.......................................................     75.00
JEWELRY,BROOCH,CAMEO,BUST OF WOMAN,ELIZABETHAN DRESS,GOLD,
   PAIR........................................................    425.00
JEWELRY,BROOCH,CAMEO,CLASSICAL WOMAN,HALF PEARLS,OVAL GOLD
   MOUNT,1860..................................................    325.00
JEWELRY,BROOCH,CAMEO,GODDESS IN CHARIOT,TWO HORSES,14K GOLD.       44.00
JEWELRY,BROOCH,CAMEO,PEARLS FORM ACORNS,GOLD MOUNT...ILLUS..      275.00
JEWELRY,BROOCH,CAMEO,PEARLS,OPENWORK GOLD MOUNT......ILLUS..      275.00
```

BUTTERFLY BROOCH, TREMBLANT

CAMEO BROOCH, PEARLY
FORM ACORNS

CAMEO BROOCH, OPENWORK
GOLD MOUNT

| | |
|---|---:|
| JEWELRY,BROOCH,CAMEO,SHELL,LADY IN GARDEN,WIDE RIM.GOLD-PLATED,2 IN. | 18.50 |
| JEWELRY,BROOCH,CAMEO,WOMAN'S FACE,GOLD,BEADING,PAIR MATCHED EARRINGS | 200.00 |
| JEWELRY,BROOCH,CAMEO,10K GOLD MOUNT | 9.50 |
| JEWELRY,BROOCH,CARAMEL COLOR CAMEO,LADY,WOOD VINES,FLORAL GARLAND,BIRD | 150.00 |
| JEWELRY,BROOCH,CARVED AMBER,ENAMELED FRAME,OVAL | 45.00 |
| JEWELRY,BROOCH,CIRCLE,SWIRL DESIGN,EMERALDS,ROSE DIAMONDS, GOLD,SILVER | 300.00 |
| JEWELRY,BROOCH,CIRCULAR,ETRUSCAN STYLE,EMERALD,MINE DIAMONDS,TASSEL,GOLD | 200.00 |
| JEWELRY,BROOCH,CROWNED COAT OF ARMS,OPEN WORK,ENAMEL ON STERLING | 10.00 |
| JEWELRY,BROOCH,ENGRAVED FLORAL,SIX DIAMONDS,SIX EMERALDS, 18-KARAT GOLD | 500.00 |
| JEWELRY,BROOCH,ENGRAVED LEAVES,FLOWERS,TWO DIAMONDS, EMERALDS,18K GOLD | 500.00 |
| JEWELRY,BROOCH,FIERY OPAL,PINK MATRIX GROUND,GOLD FRAME, 1 1/2 X 3/4 IN. | 75.00 |
| JEWELRY,BROOCH,FOUR-LEAF CLOVER,GOLD,7/8 IN. | 25.00 |
| JEWELRY,BROOCH,GARNET,LARGE STONE IN CENTER,5/8 IN.WIDE, 2 1/4 IN.ACROSS | 26.50 |
| JEWELRY,BROOCH,GARNETS,STAR UPON STAR,ALMANDINE,1 1/2 X 1 1/2 IN. | 88.00 |
| JEWELRY,BROOCH,GOLD & PAVED PEARL,WATCH RETURN ON REVERSE, 1 IN. | 200.00 |
| JEWELRY,BROOCH,IVORY CAMEO,SIR WALTER RALEIGH,MOUNTED IN 14K GOLD | 85.00 |
| JEWELRY,BROOCH,IVORY,CARVED,BIRD,3 X 1 IN. | 9.50 |
| JEWELRY,BROOCH,LADY WITH FANCY BONNET,HOLLOWARE TYPE | 10.00 |
| JEWELRY,BROOCH,LEAF,ROSE & MINE DIAMONDS,PEARL,GOLD & SILVER MOUNT. | 250.00 |
| JEWELRY,BROOCH,LOCKET,OVAL PLAQUE,MINE DIAMOND,SEED PEARLS, GOLD,ENGLAND | 125.00 |
| JEWELRY,BROOCH,LOVER'S KNOT,OPAL CENTER,1 IN.,10K | 28.00 |
| JEWELRY,BROOCH,MADONNA AND CHILD,PAINTED ON PORCELAIN,GOLD ROPE EDGE | 22.50 |
| JEWELRY,BROOCH,MARY ANDERSON,ACTRESS,1858,GOLD FRAME, PORCELAIN. | 65.00 |
| JEWELRY,BROOCH,MINIATURE OF ALLEGORICAL FIGURES,GOLD FRAME, PEARLS. | 175.00 |
| JEWELRY,BROOCH,PANSY,CENTER PEARL,CAN BE WORN AS PENDANT, GOLD,1 3/8 IN. | 125.00 |
| JEWELRY,BROOCH,PENDANT,HEART,MINE DIAMONDS,GOLD,PLATINUM, CIRCA 1880 | 1,100.00 |
| JEWELRY,BROOCH,PORCELAIN,FORGET-ME-NOTS,SCHUMANN PORZELLAN, BAVARIA. | 25.00 |
| JEWELRY,BROOCH,PORTRAIT,GIRL DRESSED IN PURPLE OUTFIT, PORCELAIN. | 27.50 |
| JEWELRY,BROOCH,PORTRAIT,THE VALKYRIE,ENAMEL,DIAMONDS,PEARLS, GOLD,LIMOGES | 975.00 |
| JEWELRY,BROOCH,PURPLE CABOCHON AMETHYST HEART,GOLD,7/8 IN. | 225.00 |
| JEWELRY,BROOCH,SHELL CAMEO,LADY'S HEAD,DIAMOND NECKLACE, WHITE GOLD FRAME. | 65.00 |
| JEWELRY,BROOCH,SHELL CAMEO,WOMAN'S HEAD,SCROLL RIM, 1 5/8 IN.LONG. | 65.00 |
| JEWELRY,BROOCH,TEN MINE DIAMONDS,WEIGH 1.20 CARATS,OPENWORK GOLD MOUNT. | 200.00 |
| JEWELRY,BROOCH,TOPAZ QUARTZ,TURQUOISE,HALF PEARLS,ONE PEARL MISSING,GOLD. | 125.00 |

```
JEWELRY,BROOCH,TURQUOISE,HALF PEARLS,MONOGRAM,GOLD,ENGLAND,
   CIRCA 1840........................................................  175.00
JEWELRY,BROOCH,VIOLIN,GOLD,1 1/2 IN.LONG.......................  150.00
JEWELRY,BROOCH,WREATH,GOLD & PAVED PEARL,1 1/4 IN..........   75.00
JEWELRY,BROOCH,WREATH,OWL,MINE DIAMONDS,TWO RUBIES,GOLD,
   ENGLAND........................................................  375.00
JEWELRY,BUTTERFLY,OPENS TO DANCE CARD,PENCIL,MIRROR,SILVER,
   1790-1810......................................................  125.00
JEWELRY,CAMEO,BROWN,WHITE,WOMAN WITH CHERUB HOLDING MIRROR..   28.50
JEWELRY,CHAIN,DIAMOND SHAPE SLIDE,FIVE PEARLS,ONE OPAL,GOLD,
   48 IN..........................................................   25.00
JEWELRY,CHAIN,FOUR AMETHYST LINKS,BRASS FASTENERS,14K GOLD..   50.00
JEWELRY,CHAIN,HEAVY-ROPED,14-KARAT YELLOW GOLD.............   75.00
JEWELRY,CHAIN,PLATINUM,10 ORIENTAL PEARLS SET 2 IN.APART,
   17 IN.LONG.....................................................   55.00
JEWELRY,CHAIN,ROPE,CYLINDER CATCH,13 IN.LONG..............   42.00
JEWELRY,CHAIN,WATCH,CAMEO HEAD ON SLIDE,GOLD-FILLED,36 IN...   30.00
JEWELRY,CHAIN,WATCH,FIVE PEARLS & OPAL IN SLIDE,GOLD-FILLED,
   48 IN..........................................................   20.00
JEWELRY,CHAIN,WATCH,FOUR OPALS IN SLIDE,GOLD-FILLED,48 IN...   25.00
JEWELRY,CHAIN,WATCH,LADY'S,SLIDE CONTAINS PEARL............   27.50
JEWELRY,CHAIN,WATCH,SLIDE,SIX TINY PEARLS,RED STONE,GOLD,
   44 IN..........................................................   10.00
JEWELRY,CHAIN,WATCH,TWISTED OVAL LINKS,ROVING TOGGLE,14K
   GOLD,20 IN.LONG................................................  150.00
JEWELRY,CHARM,OWL HEAD,GOLD....................................   20.00
JEWELRY,CHATELAINE,SILVER,AMETHYST STONES,BELT,NOTE PAD,
   BOTTLE,PILLBOX.................................................  375.00
JEWELRY,CHOKER,AMETHYST BEADS,STRUNG ON CHAIN,GOLD BEADS
   BETWEEN........................................................   10.00
JEWELRY,CHOKER,AMETHYST QUARTZ,CARVED AMETHYST QUARTZ CLASP,
   13 1/2 IN......................................................   45.00
JEWELRY,CHOKER,GREEN JADE,VARIEGATED,14K CLASP,17 1/2 IN....  150.00
JEWELRY,CHOKER,ROSE QUARTZ,CARVED FLORAL MOTIF QUARTZ CLASP,
   13 1/2 IN......................................................   35.00
JEWELRY,CLIP,DRAGONFLY,MINE DIAMONDS,SEVEN RUBIES,GOLD,
   SILVER,1890....................................................1,000.00
JEWELRY,COMB,TEN BLUE-JEWELED SWIRLING APOSTROPHES,FLARED,
   SPANISH........................................................   25.00
JEWELRY,CROSS,BAROQUE PEARLS,PEARL-STUDDED CHAIN,GOLD.......  150.00
JEWELRY,CROSS,BLACK ONYX,GOLD,INNER CROSS OF PEARLS,
   2 5/8 IN.LONG..................................................   50.00
JEWELRY,CROSS,CHIP DIAMOND,10K.................................   14.00
JEWELRY,CROSS,GARNET,ALMANDINE,ELEVEN STONES SET IN GOLD,
   1 1/2 IN.......................................................   35.00
JEWELRY,CROSS,PIN OR PENDANT,23 DIAMONDS,TOTAL WEIGHT
   4 1/4 CARATS...................................................1,500.00
JEWELRY,CROSS,SILVER,ENAMEL,STUDDED WITH TURQUOISE,GARNETS,
   2 1/4 IN.LONG..................................................   65.00
JEWELRY,CROSS,TURQUOIS-STUDDED,1 1/2 IN.LONG...............   50.00
JEWELRY,CUFF LINKS,COIN SILVER,HALF DIMES DATED 1853,1863,
   SOLID POST.....................................................   20.00
JEWELRY,CUFF LINKS,ELK'S TOOTH,GOLD,B.P.O.E.,BABY ELK'S
   TEETH FOR FOB..................................................   13.00
JEWELRY,CUFF LINKS,GREEN JADE,PAIR.............................    6.00
JEWELRY,CUFF LINKS,LION HEAD,HIGH RELIEF,OVAL,STERLING
   SILVER.........................................................   18.00
JEWELRY,CUFF LINKS,MAN'S,ROLLED GOLD PLATE,FOUR MATCHING
   VEST BUTTONS...................................................    7.00
JEWELRY,CUFF LINKS,MOUNTED BRONZE HEADS OF MEDUSA,ART
   NOUVEAU,PAIR...................................................   15.00
JEWELRY,CUFF LINKS,OVAL,ENGRAVED CREST,WINGED CROWN,GOLD,
   PAIR...........................................................   85.00
JEWELRY,CUFF LINKS,OVAL,MONOGRAM,14K GOLD,PAIR..............   22.00
JEWELRY,CUFF LINKS,STUDS,VEST BUTTONS,MOTHER-OF-PEARL,
   DIAMOND,GOLD...................................................  225.00
JEWELRY,CUFF LINKS,THREE-DIMENSIONAL HEADS OF MEDUSA,BRONZE,
   PAIR...........................................................   15.00
JEWELRY,DIADEM,CHASED GOLD ARCH,FACETED CORAL BEADS,CIRCA
   1837...........................................................  210.00
JEWELRY,DROP,CAMEO,10K GOLD MOUNTING.........................   25.00
JEWELRY,EARRINGS,BLACK OPAL DANGLE,14-KARAT CHAIN,BALL TOP,
   PAIR...........................................................  100.00
JEWELRY,EARRINGS,DANGLE TEARDROP,AMBER INCLUSION,14-KARAT
   GOLD,PAIR......................................................   48.00
JEWELRY,EARRINGS,DIAMOND CENTERS,TOTAL WEIGHT OF 80 POINTS,
   GOLD...........................................................  350.00
JEWELRY,EARRINGS,DIAMOND IN ROSE SETTING,FOR PIERCED EARS,
   PAIR...........................................................   40.00
JEWELRY,EARRINGS,DROP,CORAL,PIERCED,PAIR....................   22.50
JEWELRY,EARRINGS,DROP,MOUNTED OPALS,OPENWORK,GOLD,3/4 IN.,
```

```
PAIR.................................................................... 95.00
JEWELRY,EARRINGS,DROP,PRONG-MOUNTED FIRE OPALS,VICTORIAN,
   PIERCED............................................................... 90.00
JEWELRY,EARRINGS,FIERY,TEARDROP,FRENCH BACK,WEIGHT
   4.10 CARATS,PAIR..................................................... 310.00
JEWELRY,EARRINGS,FILIGREE,COBALT STONE,FOR PIERCED EARS,PAIR     18.50
JEWELRY,EARRINGS,FLOWER FORM,GOLD,3/4-IN.DIAMETER,PAIR......      75.00
JEWELRY,EARRINGS,GOLD OPENWORK,OPAL,DROP,PIERCED,
   3/4 IN.LONG,PAIR..................................................... 90.00
JEWELRY,EARRINGS,JADE,GREEN,CARVED,PENDANT,14-KARAT GOLD,
   CHINA,PAIR.......................................................... 285.00
JEWELRY,EARRINGS,JADE HOOP,GREEN,MOTTLED,CHINA,PAIR....           75.00
JEWELRY,EARRINGS,MILLVILLE PAPERWEIGHT BUTTON,GOLD,BLUE,RED,
   PIERCED,PAIR........................................................ 25.00
JEWELRY,EARRINGS,MOTTLED GREEN JADE HOOP DANGLES ON 14-KARAT
   CHAIN,PAIR.......................................................... 65.00
JEWELRY,EARRINGS,OPAL ON WIRE BACK,1 CARAT,FOR PIERCED EARS,
   PAIR................................................................ 35.00
JEWELRY,EARRINGS,OPENWORK GOLD,82-POINT DIAMOND CENTER,PAIR.    350.00
JEWELRY,EARRINGS,PANSY,MINE DIAMONDS,FOUR RED PASTES,GOLD,
   SILVER,PAIR........................................................ 500.00
JEWELRY,EARRINGS,PAPERWEIGHT,WINFIELD RUTTER,PAIR...........      20.00
JEWELRY,EARRINGS,PEARL,7 MM,PIERCED,PAIR.....................     15.00
JEWELRY,EARRINGS,PENDANT,ETRUSCAN STYLE,GOLD,J.TURNER,
   LONDON,PAIR........................................................ 140.00
JEWELRY,EARRINGS,SIX CEYLON MOONSTONES,GOLD-FRAMED,AMETHYST,
   14K,PAIR........................................................... 185.00
JEWELRY,EARRINGS,STERLING SILVER LEAF,AMETHYST STONE,PAIR...       7.50
JEWELRY,EARRINGS,TOURMALINE,ROSE SETTINGS,PIERCED,PAIR......      38.00
JEWELRY,FOB,B.P.O.E.,ELK TEETH,GOLD.........................       8.50
JEWELRY,FOB,WATCH,GUN,FIRES,AUSTRIA,1 3/4 IN................      12.50
JEWELRY,GLASSES,NOSE-PINCHER,GOLD RIM,SPRING CHAIN.........        4.00
JEWELRY,HAIRPIN,14K WHITE GOLD,FILIGREE,FIVE DIAMONDS,
   SAPPHIRES.......................................................... 135.00
JEWELRY,LAVALIERE,AQUAMARINE-TYPE STONE,TEARDROP PEARL,
   CHAIN,10K GOLD..................................................... 35.00
JEWELRY,LAVALIERE,CAMEO,WHITE & YELLOW GOLD FILIGREE CHAIN..      45.00
JEWELRY,LAVALIERE,PEAR-SHAPE BLACK OPAL,SEVEN MINE DIAMONDS,
   GOLD,CHAIN......................................................... 650.00
JEWELRY,LAVALIERE,ROSE DIAMOND,2 1/2 CARATS,CHAIN,EARLY 19TH
   CENTURY............................................................ 250.00
JEWELRY,LOCKET,BLACK JET FRONT,GOLD BASKET,FLORAL,DIAMOND
   CHIPS,PORTUGAL..................................................... 110.00
JEWELRY,LOCKET,FOB,REVOLVING,GRAY ONYX ONE SIDE,RED ONYX
   OTHER,GOLD......................................................... 55.00
JEWELRY,LOCKET,HEART,ROSE DIAMONDS,BLACK ENAMEL,GOLD,ENGLAND    200.00
JEWELRY,LOCKET,JADE,WHITE,CARVED,DRAGONS,BAT,LONG-LIFE
   CHARACTER,3 IN..................................................... 35.00
JEWELRY,LOCKET,PENDANT,ROSE DIAMONDS,OPENWORK GOLD MOUNT,
   CIRCA 1870......................................................... 325.00
JEWELRY,LOCKET,PENDANT,ROSE DIAMONDS,SUNBURST MOTIF,ONYX,
   GOLD,ENGLAND....................................................... 225.00
JEWELRY,LOCKET,RAISED DESIGN,OVAL,ROPE CHAIN,14K GOLD.......      35.00
JEWELRY,LOCKET,TURQUOISE,HALF PEARLS,OVAL,CHAIN,GOLD,
   ENGLAND,1860....................................................... 250.00
JEWELRY,LORGNETTE CHAIN,STERLING SILVER WITH CARNELIAN BEADS     12.00
JEWELRY,NECKLACE,14 FLAT BEADS,HAND-PAINTED ROSES,LIMOGES
   TYPE............................................................... 50.00
JEWELRY,NECKLACE,52 AMBER INCLUSION CHUNK BEADS,VARIOUS
   SIZES,GOLD CLASP................................................... 80.00
JEWELRY,NECKLACE,AMBER BEADS,CARNELIAN AGATE BEADS,PENDANTS.    225.00
JEWELRY,NECKLACE,AMBER BEADS,CARVED TO LOOK LIKE ROSES,
   24 IN.LONG......................................................... 38.00
JEWELRY,NECKLACE,AMBER BEADS,GRADUATED,HANDMADE,KNOTTED,
   36 IN.............................................................. 300.00
JFWELRY,NECKLACE,AMBERINA BEADS.............................      25.00
JEWELRY,NECKLACE,AMETHYST CRYSTAL GRADUATING WITH GOLD BEAD
   ON CHAIN........................................................... 65.00
JEWELRY,NECKLACE,AMETHYST PENDANT,EMERALD CUT,SET IN 10K
   GOLD,1924.......................................................... 30.00
JEWELRY,NECKLACE,AVENTURINE,BAROQUE CULTURE PEARLS,16 IN.,
   EARRINGS........................................................... 75.00
JEWELRY,NECKLACE,BAROQUE PEARLS ALTERNATING WITH GARNET
   BEADS,16 IN........................................................ 35.00
JEWELRY,NECKLACE,CAMEO,STERLING,CHAIN.......................      30.00
JEWELRY,NECKLACE,CARNELAINS,STRUNG ON GOLD WIRE.............      40.00
JEWELRY,NECKLACE,CARNELIAN BEADS,HAND-CUT,POLISHED,CHINA,
   24 IN.LONG.........................................................  7.00
JEWELRY,NECKLACE,CARNELIAN BEADS,RUST-ORANGE,GRADUATED,
   18 IN.LONG......................................................... 45.00
JEWELRY,NECKLACE,CARVED CORAL,20 IN.LONG....................     165.00
```

JEWELRY,NECKLACE,CARVED PEKING GLASS,ROYAL BLUE,DOUBLE STRAND LENGTH...... 48.00
JEWELRY,NECKLACE,CHERRY AMBER BEADS,CARVED,KNOTTED,34 IN.... 90.00
JEWELRY,NECKLACE,CINNEBAR BEADS,CHINESE CLASP............... 15.00
JEWELRY,NECKLACE,CULTURED PEARLS,PEARL-STUDDED CLASP, 15 IN.LONG...... 40.00
JEWELRY,NECKLACE,FACET-CUT AMBER BEADS,GRADUATED,30 IN.LONG. 35.00
JEWELRY,NECKLACE,FACETED AMETHYST BEADS,14K GOLD CLASP...... 38.00
JEWELRY,NECKLACE,FLEXIBLE ROPE,PENDANTS,GOLD............... 325.00
JEWELRY,NECKLACE,FLOWER PENDANT,THREE-PETALED FLOWER EACH SIDE,GARNETS...... 85.00
JEWELRY,NECKLACE,GOLD ROPE,ELEVEN CORAL PENDANTS,CORAL CLASP 140.00
JEWELRY,NECKLACE,GOLD-FILLED MESH WITH 1-IN.BLACK & WHITE CAMEO STONE...... 45.00
JEWELRY,NECKLACE,GOLD,AMETHYSTS & PEARLS,BOW SHAPE.......... 45.00
JEWELRY,NECKLACE,GOLD,GREEN,WHITE ENAMEL ORNAMENTS,SEED PEARLS...... 525.00
JEWELRY,NECKLACE,GOLDEN TIGER EYE,STRING OF BEADS,19 IN.LONG 35.00
JEWELRY,NECKLACE,GREEN JADE BEADS,CARVED JADE CLASP, 16 1/2 IN.LONG...... 125.00
JEWELRY,NECKLACE,GREEN JADE BEADS,PIERCED,JADE CLASP,15 IN.. 175.00
JEWELRY,NECKLACE,GREEN JADE BEADS,2-IN.JADE PENDANT,KNOTTED, 20 IN...... 225.00
JEWELRY,NECKLACE,IVORY BEADS,IVORY CLASP,24 IN.LONG......... 15.00
JEWELRY,NECKLACE,JADE,APPLE GREEN,GRADUATED,15 IN.LONG...... 250.00
JEWELRY,NECKLACE,JADE,120 BEADS,GREEN,14K GOLD FASTENER..... 375.00
JEWELRY,NECKLACE,JET BEADS,ON GOLD CHAIN,GOLD BEADS IN BETWEEN,22 IN...... 85.00
JEWELRY,NECKLACE,LAPIS LAZULI,GRADUATING FLAT,ROUND BEAD BETWEEN,16 IN...... 85.00
JEWELRY,NECKLACE,LAPIS LAZULI,WHITE CORAL,SOME PINK,14K CLASP,17 IN...... 75.00
JEWELRY,NECKLACE,MOTHER-OF-PEARL,GRADUATED,14 IN........... 9.00
JEWELRY,NECKLACE,MULTISTRAND SEED PEARL,GOLD BOX CLASP, 15 IN.LONG...... 300.00
JEWELRY,NECKLACE,RED AMBER BEADS,MATCHED,36 IN.LONG......... 75.00
JEWELRY,NECKLACE,STRING OF ETRUSCAN-STYLE GOLD BEADS, GRADUATING,15 IN...... 225.00
JEWELRY,NECKLACE,STRING OF GOLD BEADS,1/4-IN.DIAMETER, 16 1/2 IN.LONG...... 100.00
JEWELRY,NECKLACE,STRING OF HOPI INDIAN BEADS,400 MATCHED SHELL BEADS...... 200.00
JEWELRY,NECKLACE,TURQUOISE BEADS,GRADUATED,CHINA........... 50.00
JEWELRY,NECKLACE,TURQUOISE NUGGETS,KNOTTED,36 IN........... 75.00
JEWELRY,NECKLACE,VENETIAN GLASS BEADS,CORAL COLOR,16-IN., EARRINGS...... 6.98
JEWELRY,PENDANT,AMBER INCLUSION,14-KARAT CHAIN............ 88.00
JEWELRY,PENDANT,AMBER,SEMICYLINDER SHAPE,CLOTH RIBBON,TASSEL 35.00
JEWELRY,PENDANT,BALL SHAPE,OPALS,EMERALDS,MINE DIAMONDS, GOLD,SILVER...... 375.00
JEWELRY,PENDANT,CARVED CARNELIAN,LEAF & BUD MOTIF,1 7/8 IN.. 22.00
JEWELRY,PENDANT,DARK RED BEADS WITH GOLD STONE HEART....... 20.00
JEWELRY,PENDANT,DIAMOND CHIP & BAROQUE PEARL ON GOLD CHAIN, 1920,15 IN...... 35.00
JEWELRY,PENDANT,FIERY OPAL,15-POINT DIAMOND,14-KARAT GOLD FRAME & CHAIN...... 150.00
JEWELRY,PENDANT,FISH,BAROQUE PEARL,RUBIES,ROSE DIAMOND, EMERALD,GOLD...... 900.00
JEWELRY,PENDANT,FORM OF BIRD,RED AMBER,GOLD LEAVES,1 IN..... 25.00
JEWELRY,PENDANT,GREEN JADE,CARVED,DIAMOND,ENAMEL TRIM....... 200.00
JEWELRY,PENDANT,HEAD OF WOMAN,BLUE ENAMEL,CHAIN,GOLD,SIGNED GUILBERT...... 180.00
JEWELRY,PENDANT,HORSE,BODY HAS 16 DIAMONDS,RUBY EYE,14K CHAIN...... 50.00
JEWELRY,PENDANT,JADE,GREEN,WHITE,FORM OF ANCIENT LOCK, 2 IN.WIDE...... 45.00
JEWELRY,PENDANT,LOCKET,MINE DIAMONDS,FOX HEAD BAR PIN,GOLD, SILVER,1890...... 475.00
JEWELRY,PENDANT,ORIENTAL CARVED CARNELIAN,FLORAL MOTIF,2 IN. 60.00
JEWELRY,PENDANT,SNAKE WRAPPED AROUND PEARL,DIAMOND,GOLD CHAIN...... 125.00
JEWELRY,PENKNIFE,DEEPLY EMBOSSED,FULL FIGURE LADY BOTH SIDES,14K GOLD...... 25.00
JEWELRY,PIN,ARROW,MINE DIAMONDS,RUBY,GOLD MOUNT,CIRCA 1880.. 900.00
JEWELRY,PIN,BAR,DIAMOND-ENCRUSTED BIRDS,TWO PEARLS,GOLD, CIRCA 1890...... 225.00
JEWELRY,PIN,BAR,ENAMELED FLORAL............................ 5.00
JEWELRY,PIN,BAR,ENGRAVED WITH RAISED ORNAMENTS,HOLLOWARE TYPE...... 10.00
JEWELRY,PIN,BAR,FILIGREE,SMALL DIAMOND,14K................. 32.00
JEWELRY,PIN,BAR,FIRE OPAL,GOLD............................. 22.00

```
JEWELRY,PIN,BAR,GARNET........................................      20.00
JEWELRY,PIN,BAR,MINE DIAMONDS,THREE-FACETED SAPPHIRES,GOLD,
   SILVER.....................................................     350.00
JEWELRY,PIN,BAR,THREE DIAMONDS,TOTAL WEIGHT-35 POINTS,GOLD,
   2 1/4 IN...................................................     200.00
JEWELRY,PIN,BAR,TWO GREEN-ENAMELED LILY PADS,PERIDOT CENTER,
   GOLD......................................................      95.00
JEWELRY,PIN,BIRD,ROSE DIAMONDS,GOLD & SILVER MOUNT,ENGLAND..     100.00
JEWELRY,PIN,BOUTONNIERE,BRASS,FILIGREE,ENGLAND,CIRCA 1850...      15.00
JEWELRY,PIN,CAMEO,BLACK GROUND,WOMAN'S PROFILE IN WHITE,
   GOLD,OVAL..................................................     175.00
JEWELRY,PIN,CAMEO,BLACK LAVA,WOMAN'S PROFILE,GRECIAN HAIRDO,
   GOLD,OVAL..................................................      85.00
JEWELRY,PIN,CAMEO,BLACK,WHITE,WOMAN'S PROFILE,GRAPES IN
   HAIR,GOLD..................................................     175.00
JEWELRY,PIN,CAMEO,BROWN,WHITE SHELL,WOMAN,CHILD,OVAL,GOLD...      75.00
JEWELRY,PIN,CAMEO,LADY'S HEAD,CARVED FLOWERS IN HAIR &
   DRESS,GOLD FRAME...........................................      58.00
JEWELRY,PIN,CAMEO,REBECCA AT WELL,GOLD FRAME,2 X 1 1/2 IN...      47.50
JEWELRY,PINK,CAMEO,WOMAN'S HEAD,WHITE ON BLACK GROUND,
   6 PEARLS,2 1/2 IN..........................................     175.00
JEWELRY,PIN,CAMEO,14K.........................................      35.00
JEWELRY,PIN,CORAL,OPENWORK BORDER,OVAL,GOLD,1 3/8 IN........      75.00
JEWELRY,PIN,CRESCENT,PEARL-STUDDED,PLATINUM TIPS,GOLD,
   1 1/2 IN...................................................      40.00
JEWELRY,PIN,CRESCENT,PEARL-STUDDED,PLATINUM TIP,GOLD,
   1 1/4 IN...................................................      40.00
JEWELRY,PIN,CRESCENT,PEARLS,PRONG-MOUNTED SAPPHIRES,PLATINUM
   TIP,I IN...................................................      75.00
JEWELRY,PIN,DIAMONDS,SAPPHIRES,FLORAL SPRAY,PLATINUM & GOLD,
   2 1/4 IN................................................1,250.00
JEWELRY,PIN,DRAGONFLY,OLIVINE EYES,TWO RUBIES,GOLD,
   1 1/4 IN.LONG..............................................     150.00
JEWELRY,PIN,EMBOSSED LOVER'S KNOT,GOLD,DIAMOND IN CENTER,
   1-IN.DIAMETER..............................................     125.00
JEWELRY,PIN,ENAMELED AMERICAN FLAG,DIAMOND AT TOP OF POLE,
   GOLD.......................................................      25.00
JEWELRY,PIN,FLEUR-DE-LIS,THREE PEARLS,GOLD,1 1/4 IN........      45.00
JEWELRY,PIN,FLORAL SPRAY,GARNET-STUDDED,3 1/4 IN...........     150.00
JEWELRY,PIN,FLOWER,CARVED IVORY............................      10.00
JEWELRY,PIN,FOUR-LEAF CLOVER,GOLD,7/8 IN...................      25.00
JEWELRY,PIN,FOUR-LEAF CLOVER,GOLD,1 IN.....................      25.00
JEWELRY,PIN,HORSESHOE,DIAMOND-STUDDED,PLATINUM & GOLD
   MOUNTING...................................................     350.00
JEWELRY,PIN,HORSESHOE,GOLD,PLATINUM STUDS,2 1/8 IN.........      30.00
JEWELRY,PIN,IVORY HAND CLASPED ON GOLD BAR,WRISTLET CARVING,
   GOLD BAND..................................................      20.00
JEWELRY,PIN,LOVER'S KNOT,ALLOVER BLACK ENAMEL,GOLD,
   1-IN.DIAMETER..............................................      45.00
JEWELRY,PIN,MOON & STAR,GARNET.............................      55.00
JEWELRY,PIN,MOSAIC,MULTICOLORED BUTTERFLY,GOLD BORDER,OVAL,
   FLORENTINE.................................................      50.00
JEWELRY,PIN,MOURNING,JET,GOLD,PLAITED HAIR IN PIN,INSCRIBED,
   1838,PAIR..................................................      75.00
JEWELRY,PIN,OPAL,FIVE PEARLS,TWO DIAMONDS,GOLD,1 3/8 IN.....     450.00
JEWELRY,PIN,SHELL CAMEO,RAISED FIGURES OVER CORAL,THREE
   MUSES,GOLD FRAME...........................................      37.50
JEWELRY,PIN,SHIRTWAIST,CRESCENT SHAPE,15 PEARLS SET IN GOLD
   MOUNTING...................................................      25.00
JEWELRY,PIN,SPIDER,TURQUOISE STONE,STERLING SILVER.........      12.50
JEWELRY,PIN,STICK,FLOWER SHAPE,PEARLS,10K GOLD.............      15.00
JEWELRY,PIN,STICK,GOLD,PURPLE & WHITE ENAMEL,DIAMOND CENTER.      38.00
JEWELRY,PIN,SUNBURST,38-POINT DIAMOND IN CENTER,GOLD,
   1-IN.DIAMETER..............................................     300.00
JEWELRY,PIN,SWORD,BLUE ENAMEL,PEARLS,GOLD,3 1/8 IN.........      60.00
JEWELRY,PIN,TWO LIONS,BLUE SAPPHIRES,GOLD..................      55.00
JEWELRY,PIN,VIOLIN,GOLD,1 1/2 IN...........................     150.00
JEWELRY,PIN,WATCH,GOLD,ART NOUVEAU GIRL WITH FLOWING HAIR...      27.50
JEWELRY,PIN,WISHBONE,ENAMELED FOUR-LEAF CLOVER,10K GOLD.....      20.00
JEWELRY,PIN,WREATH,GOLD & PAVED PEARL,1-IN.DIAMETER........      75.00
JEWELRY,PIN,WREATH,GOLD,7/8 IN.............................      25.00
JEWELRY,RING,AQUAMARINE STONE,CROWN SETTING,GOLD...........      29.95
JEWELRY,RING,CABOCHON GREEN JADE CENTER,DIAMONDS,PLATINUM &
   GOLD MOUNT.................................................     350.00
JEWELRY,RING,CAMEO,GIRL,PINK GROUND,ORNATE MOUNTING & SHANK.      25.00
JEWELRY,RING,CHILD'S,CAMEO,GOLD............................      30.00
JEWELRY,RING,CORAL,SEED PEARLS,GOLD-FILLED,SIZE 5..........      15.00
JEWELRY,RING,DIAMOND CLUSTER,WEIGHT 1.50 CARATS,GOLD MOUNT,
   ENGLAND,1850...............................................     250.00
JEWELRY,RING,EGYPTIAN DESIGN,FORM OF SARCOPHAGUS,MUMMY,DOOR,
   GOLD.......................................................     450.00
```

```
JEWELRY,RING,EMBOSSED WOMAN'S HEAD,RUBIES,DIAMONDS IN HAIR,
   GOLD..................................................    175.00
JEWELRY,RING,EMBOSSED,6-MILLIMETER OVAL ANGEL SKIN CORAL,22K    75.00
JEWELRY,RING,ENAMELED JESTER'S HEAD,DIAMOND IN MOUTH,GOLD,
   1/2 IN................................................    175.00
JEWELRY,RING,FIVE EMERALDS & ROSE DIAMONDS SET IN A ROW.....     95.00
JEWELRY,RING,FIVE OVAL TURQUOISE IN A ROW,14K GOLD.........      38.00
JEWELRY,RING,FIVE SMALL DIAMONDS IN A ROW,PLATINUM MOUNTING
   ON GOLD...............................................      38.00
JEWELRY,RING,FORM OF ENGLISH BULLDOG HEAD,RUBY EYES,GOLD....    150.00
JEWELRY,RING,FOUR OVAL GARNETS IN A ROW....................     29.00
JEWELRY,RING,GARNET CLUSTER................................     40.00
JEWELRY,RING,GOLD & ENAMEL MOUNT,19 ROSE DIAMONDS..........    475.00
JEWELRY,RING,GOLD PLATE,CINNEBAR,CHINA.....................      9.50
JEWELRY,RING,GYPSY STYLE,FACETED RUBY CENTER,DIAMOND ON EACH
   SIDE,GOLD............................................1,000.00
JEWELRY,RING,HEART-SHAPE GARNET SURROUNDED BY 30 GARNETS,
   GOLD..................................................     35.00
JEWELRY,RING,JADE,MOUNTED IN SILVER GILT FILIGREE..........     28.00
JEWELRY,RING,LADY'S,AMBER,HELD IN HIGH CROWN OPENWORK
   PRONGS,14K GOLD.......................................    125.00
JEWELRY,RING,LADY'S,BLACK PEARL,TWO BLUE SAPPHIRES,WHITE
   GOLD..................................................     85.00
JEWELRY,RING,LADY'S,FIERY OPAL,THREE DIAMONDS,14K YELLOW
   GOLD..................................................     75.00
JEWELRY,RING,LADY'S,RED CORAL CAMEO,LADY'S HEAD,GOLD.......     25.00
JEWELRY,RING,LOCKET,STRIPED AGATE,GOLD.....................    145.00
JEWELRY,RING,MAN'S,CAMEO,STERLING MOUNT,LEAVES & GRAPE
   CLUSTER ON SIDE.......................................     75.00
JEWELRY,RING,MAN'S,SKULL AND CROSSBONES,STERLING SILVER.....     5.00
JEWELRY,RING,MARQUISE SHAPE DIAMOND,75 POINT,GOLD MOUNT.....    475.00
JEWELRY,RING,MASON'S,ONE SYMBOL,14K GOLD...................     20.00
JEWELRY,RING,MASON'S,BLACK ONYX,10K........................     15.00
JEWELRY,RING,MEDUSA'S FACE,PERIDOT EYES,JEWELS IN HAIR,14K
   GOLD..................................................     75.00
JEWELRY,RING,MOONSTONE,14K.................................     25.00
JEWELRY,RING,MOURNING,AGATE,GOLD,SAYS THOMAS BURNHAM DIED
   JUNE 6,1782...........................................     49.00
JEWELRY,RING,MOURNING,CLASSICAL FIGURE,SAYS REST IN PEACE,
   18TH CENTURY..........................................     85.00
JEWELRY,RING,MOURNING,LAPIS LAZULI,ROSE DIAMOND,MARQUISE
   SHAPE,GOLD............................................    150.00
JEWELRY,RING,MOURNING,MINE DIAMONDS,ENAMEL GROUND....ILLUS..1,200.00
JEWELRY,RING,MOURNING,MINE DIAMONDS,ENAMEL FIELD.....ILLUS..   325.00
JEWELRY,RING,MOURNING,MINE DIAMONDS,ENAMEL FIELD,FLORAL,
   GOLD,SILVER...........................................    375.00
JEWELRY,RING,MOURNING,ROSE DIAMONDS,ENAMEL,1780......ILLUS..   225.00
```

MOURNING RING,
ROSE DIAMONDS,
ENAMEL, 1780

MOURNING RING,
MINE DIAMONDS,
ENAMEL GROUND

MOURNING RING,
MINE DIAMONDS,
ENAMEL FIELD

```
JEWELRY,RING,ONE-CARAT SAPPHIRE,TEN MINE DIAMONDS,GOLD &
   SILVER MOUNT..........................................    275.00
JEWELRY,RING,OPAL,10K......................................     14.00
JEWELRY,RING,OPAL SOLITAIRE,PRONG-MOUNTED,GOLD.............     20.00
JEWELRY,RING,OPAL,ROSE & MINE DIAMONDS,GOLD MOUNT,CIRCA
   1880..................................................    400.00
JEWELRY,RING,OVAL FACET AMETHYST,PRONG MOUNTING,GOLD,
   15/16 IN..............................................    200.00
JEWELRY,RING,PRINCESS,THREE SAPPHIRES IN A ROW,18 ROSE
   DIAMONDS,14K..........................................    125.00
JEWELRY,RING,PRONG-MOUNTED DIAMOND,1/2 CARAT,GOLD.........    275.00
JEWELRY,RING,STAR RUBY,ROSE DIAMONDS,GOLD & SILVER MOUNT,
   1885..................................................    325.00
JEWELRY,RING,STERLING SILVER,1-IN.AGATE STONE.............      6.50
JEWELRY,RING,TIFFANY MOUNTING,GARNET,14K..................     25.00
JEWELRY,RING,TIFFANY MOUNTING,TURQUOISE,14K...............     17.50
```

```
JEWELRY,RING,TIFFANY SETTING,EMERALD COLOR TOURMALINE.......     35.00
JEWELRY,RING,TURQUOISE, PAWN,  INDIAN,STERLING SILVER.......     20.00
JEWELRY,RING,1/4-CARAT DIAMOND,PYRAMID SETTING,18K WHITE
   GOLD..................................................       100.00
JEWELRY,RING,10K GOLD,GENUINE GARNET.......................      17.50
JEWELRY,RING,10K GOLD,1-CARAT SYNTHETIC RUBY...............      16.00
JEWELRY,RING,32ND-DEGREE MASON,FIVE SYMBOLS,VIRTUS JUNXIT
   MORS,14K GOLD.........................................       40.00
JEWELRY,RING,38-POINT DIAMOND,GOLD.........................     200.00
JEWELRY,SNAKE,BEADED,SAYS TURKISH PRISONERS,CYPRESS,1917,
   4 1/2 IN.LONG.........................................       60.00
JEWELRY,STICKPIN,BAROQUE PEARL IN SCROLLS WITH GARLAND
   BELOW,GOLD............................................       40.00
JEWELRY,STICKPIN,BIRD CLAW GRASPING TIGER TOOTH,SILVER CAP
   ON END................................................       10.00
JEWELRY,STICKPIN,BOWKNOT,GOLD..............................       6.50
JEWELRY,STICKPIN,CIRCLE,14K................................       8.00
JEWELRY,STICKPIN,CIRCLE OF TURQUOISE WITH PEARLS...........      22.00
JEWELRY,STICKPIN,CLOSED LOVER'S KNOT,CLAW-MOUNTED PEARL,GOLD     15.00
JEWELRY,STICKPIN,CRESCENT OF WHOLE ROUND PEARLS............      35.00
JEWELRY,STICKPIN,CRESCENT SHAPE,MOTHER-OF-PEARL TOP,
   GOLD-FILLED..........................................        2.50
JEWELRY,STICKPIN,CRESCENT,SIX OPALS,ONE DIAMOND,
   PRONG-MOUNTED........................................       125.00
JEWELRY,STICKPIN,DOG IN COLOR UNDER GLASS..................      10.00
JEWELRY,STICKPIN,EAGLE,MEDAL ATTACHED SAYS REMEMBER THE
   MAINE................................................        7.00
JEWELRY,STICKPIN,FLAT OVAL GOLDSTONE,GOLD..................      15.00
JEWELRY,STICKPIN,FLEUR-DE-LIS WITH 18 PEARLS,GOLD..........      40.00
JEWELRY,STICKPIN,FORGET-ME-NOT WITH CLAW-MOUNTED PEARL,GOLD      10.00
JEWELRY,STICKPIN,FROG,HOLDS RED & GREEN SEMIPRECIOUS STONES,
   BRASS................................................        7.50
JEWELRY,STICKPIN,GARNET,OPALS,ATTACHED BY CHAIN TO ENGRAVED
   HORSESHOE............................................       25.00
JEWELRY,STICKPIN,GOLFER IN KNICKERS,CADDY,PAINTED UNDER
   GLASS................................................       15.00
JEWELRY,STICKPIN,GREEN TRANSLUCENT JADE,IN GOLD BEZEL......      18.00
JEWELRY,STICKPIN,HEAD,CHEST AND FRONT LEGS OF BOSTON BULL,
   IVORY................................................        6.00
JEWELRY,STICKPIN,HORSE & HORSESHOE,GOLD-FILLED.............       2.95
JEWELRY,STICKPIN,HORSESHOE OF WHOLE ROUND PEARLS..........      45.00
JEWELRY,STICKPIN,HORSESHOE SHAPE,DIAMONDS,WEIGHT THREE
   CARATS,GOLD,1890.....................................       550.00
JEWELRY,STICKPIN,LACY,RECTANGULAR,DIAMOND CENTER..........      22.00
JEWELRY,STICKPIN,MASON'S,14K GOLD.........................      10.00
JEWELRY,STICKPIN,MATRIX OPAL,14K GOLD.....................      22.00
JEWELRY,STICKPIN,OPAL.....................................      45.00
JEWELRY,STICKPIN,OVAL CABOCHON BLOODSTONE,GOLD............      20.00
JEWELRY,STICKPIN,OVAL CABOCHON TURQUOISE,GOLD.............      20.00
JEWELRY,STICKPIN,OVAL TOP,AMETHYST STONE,GOLD-FILLED......       2.50
JEWELRY,STICKPIN,OVAL,BLUE STONE,FOUR CLEAR STONES,
   GOLD-FILLED..........................................        2.95
JEWELRY,STICKPIN,ROUND CABOCHON MOONSTONE IN DOUBLE GOLD
   RING.................................................       25.00
JEWELRY,STICKPIN,SCARAB,GOLD..............................      22.00
JEWELRY,STICKPIN,SNAKE ENTWINED AROUND BAROQUE PEARL......      22.00
JEWELRY,STICKPIN,SOLID GOLD TOP,MASONIC SQUARE & COMPASS...       4.75
JEWELRY,STICKPIN,TWO RUBY BERRIES,THREE GREEN ENAMEL HOLLY
   LEAVES,GOLD..........................................       50.00
JEWELRY,STUD,MAN'S DRESS SHIRT,DULL 14K GOLD,SET OF 3......      15.00
JEWELRY,STUD,MAN'S DRESS SHIRT,MOTHER-OF-PEARL,14K GOLD
   CENTER,3............................................        15.00
JEWELRY,TIECLIP,WALLS OF TROY BORDER,CAT'S-EYE IN CENTER,
   OVAL................................................        30.00
JEWELRY,TIEPIN,CAMEO,10K GOLD.............................      18.50
JEWELRY,TIE TACK,CORAL ROSE...............................       9.50
JEWELRY,TIE TACK,GOLD AND ETCHED BLACK ENAMEL.............      12.50
JEWELRY,WATCH,SEE WATCH
JEWELRY,WATCH CHAIN,DOUBLE STRAND,SLIDE,SWIVEL,BAR,CIRCA
   1870,GOLD............................................       125.00
JEWELRY,WATCH CHAIN,ENGRAVED SLIDE HAS THREE GARNETS,
   GOLD-FILLED,48 IN....................................       29.00
JEWELRY,WATCH CHAIN,LADY'S,OPAL SLIDE.....................      48.00
JEWELRY,WATCH CHAIN,MAN'S,LONG & SHORT LINKS,STERLING
   SILVER,14 IN.LONG....................................       35.00
JEWELRY,WATCH CHAIN,MAN'S,ORNATE GOLD KNIFE ATTACHED,
   13 1/2 IN............................................       16.50
JEWELRY,WATCH CHAIN,SILVER,JET CLOISSONE BEADS............      10.00
JEWELRY,WATCH CHAIN,WOVEN HAIR,11 IN.LONG.................       7.50
JEWELRY,WATCH FOB,ADVERTISING,LOCKHART'S JEWELRY,KONOSHA,
   WISCONSIN............................................        4.00
```

```
JEWELRY,WATCH FOB,ALLIS CHALMERS TRACTOR DIVISION............     7.50
JEWELRY,WATCH FOB,BRASS,ST.PATRICK'S DAY,MARCH 17,LEATHER
  STRAP.....................................................     3.75
JEWELRY,WATCH FOB,FACE OF AMERICAN INDIAN,ARROWHEAD SHAPE...     6.50
JEWELRY,WATCH FOB,REPOUSSE DESIGN,MONOGRAM,STERLING SILVER..     5.00
JEWELRY,WATCH FOB,WOOLWORTH BUILDING,NEW YORK...............     5.75
JEWELRY,WATCH HOLDER,INDIAN HEAD,WHITE,HANGING,7 IN.HIGH....    15.00
JEWELRY,WATCH KEY,FORM OF HORSE'S HOOF,GOLD,2 1/4 IN.LONG...    75.00
JEWELRY,WATCH SLIDE WITH CAMEO.............................     20.00
JEWELRY,WEDDING BAND,ENGRAVED FLOWERS WITH DIAMOND &
  SAPPHIRE,GOLD.............................................   125.00
JEWELRY,WEDDING BAND,TURNED KNOT CENTER,GOLD,PLATINUM.......    35.00
JU-I SCEPTER,JADE,GRAY,11 1/4 IN.LONG,CURVED SHAFT &
  BRANCHES..................................................   225.00
JU-I SCEPTER,RUSTIC STEM,BRANCHES OF POLYPOROUS FUNGUS,
  SOAPSTONE.................................................     80.00
JU-I SCEPTER,WHITE GLASS,S-SHAPE SHAFT,SHOU MEDALLION,
  14 1/4 IN.LONG............................................   140.00


          KATE GREENAWAY,WHO WAS A FAMOUS ILLUSTRATOR OF
          CHILDREN'S BOOKS,DREW PICTURES OF CHILDREN IN HIGH-
          WAISTED EMPIRE DRESSES. SHE LIVED FROM 1846 TO 1901.
          HER DESIGNS APPEAR ON CHINA,GLASS,AND OTHER PIECES.
KATE GREENAWAY,BOWL,SUGAR,CHILDREN PLAYING BALL,COVER,
  3 1/2 IN.TALL.............................................    15.00
KATE GREENAWAY,BUTTON,LITTLE GIRL,BRASS,SET OF 4............    10.00
KATE GREENAWAY,COFFEEPOT,CHILDREN PLANTING TREE,
  5 1/2 IN.TALL.............................................    40.00
KATE GREENAWAY,COMPOTE,BOYS FISHING,FARMYARD SCENES,CLEAR,
  FOOTED...................................................     14.00
KATE GREENAWAY,CUP & SAUCER,CHILDREN TEACHING DOG..........     12.50
KATE GREENAWAY,FIGURINE,GIRL,BISQUE,20 IN..................     17.00
KATE GREENAWAY,HOLDER,MATCH,BOY,BISQUE.....................     14.00
KATE GREENAWAY,LAMP BASE,TWO GIRLS READING UNDER TREE,DOG,
  BRISTOL.14 IN.............................................    60.00
KATE GREENAWAY,LAMP,FAIRY,GIRL,PEDESTAL,PARIAN,7 IN.HIGH....    43.00
KATE GREENAWAY,MUG,PINK GROUND,FIGURES.....................      3.50
KATE GREENAWAY,NAPKIN RING,CHILDREN PLAYING,STERLING,SIGNED.    14.00
KATE GREENAWAY,PLATE,BREAD,FIGURES IN CENTER,11 IN.........     25.00
KATE GREENAWAY,PLATE,GIRL,BOY,FENCE,OCEAN,BLACK RIM,9 IN....    20.00
KATE GREENAWAY,PLATE,GIRL,UMBRELLA,CHICKS,OCEAN,BLACK RIM,
  9 IN.....................................................     20.00
KATE GREENAWAY,PLATE,TWO GIRLS,IN VELVET-COVERED WOODEN
  FRAME, 4 IN...............................................    35.00
KATE GREENAWAY,RING,NAPKIN,FIGURAL,CHILD FEEDING DOG........    40.00
KATE GREENAWAY,SALT & PEPPER,IN BASKET.....................     13.50
KATE GREENAWAY,SALT,GIRL WITH MUFF,4 1/2 IN.TALL...........     22.00
KATE GREENAWAY,SALT,PEPPER,FIGURAL,TOP HAT,ROSY CHEEKS,
  FLORAL BASE...............................................    25.00
KATE GREENAWAY,SHAKER,SALT,GIRL.................. 15.00 TO     16.00
KATE GREENAWAY,TEAPOT,CHILDREN ON COVER & POT,5 IN.........     25.00
KATE GREENAWAY,TRAY,BOY WITH HOOP,GIRLS PLAYING,SILVER
  FRAME,16 X 12 IN..........................................    95.00
KAUFFMANN,BOWL,PANELS,CLASSICAL FIGURES,FLORAL,MARK,AUSTRIA.    27.50
KAUFFMANN,BOWL,SCENE,DANCING MAIDEN,CHERUB,COBALT,LAVENDER
  HANDLES...................................................    70.00
KAUFFMANN,BOX,CLASSICAL SCENE,SIGNED,2 3/4-IN.DIAMETER......    23.00
KAUFFMANN,BOX,CLASSICAL SCENE,GOLD TRIM,HINGED COVER,SIGNED,
  2 IN.HIGH.................................................    18.00
KAUFFMANN,BOX,SCENE ON COVER,PORCELAIN,BRASS HINGE & CLASP..    24.50
KAUFFMANN,BOX,WHITE GROUND,FIGURES,HINGED LID,3 IN. X
  3-IN.DIAMETER.............................................    25.00
KAUFFMANN,CLOCK,SIGNED,PORCELAIN...........................     62.50
KAUFFMANN,CUP & SAUCER,GREEK MYTHOLOGICAL SCENES,GOLD TRIM,
  GERMANY...................................................    22.50
KAUFFMANN,CUP & SAUCER,PLATE,CLASSICAL SCENE,GOLD TRIM,CROWN
  MARK,SIGNED...............................................    20.00
KAUFFMANN,CUP & SAUCER,PLATE,GOLD ENAMEL,CLASSICAL FIGURES,
  BEEHIVE MARK..............................................    45.00
KAUFFMANN,DISH,ICE CREAM,SCROLLS,FLORAL,CLASSICAL FIGURES,
  12 SAUCES.................................................    95.00
KAUFFMANN,DISH,PAINTING IN CENTER,GREEN RETICULATED BORDER,
  8 IN.....................................................     20.00
KAUFFMANN,PLATE,BLUE & GOLD GROUND,THREE ROWS OF HOLES IN
  BORDER...................................................     34.50
KAUFFMANN,PLATE,CLASSICAL FIGURES,TWO HANDLES,BEEHIVE &
  AUSTRIA MARKS.............................................    39.50
KAUFFMANN,PLATE,CLASSICAL FIGURES,WOMAN,THREE ATTENDANTS,
  GILT,9 1/2 IN.............................................    25.00
KAUFFMANN,PLATE,FIVE CLASSICAL FIGURES,GREEN & GOLD BORDER,
```

```
    BEEHIVE MARK.................................................    27.50
KAUFFMANN,PLATE,FOUR CLASSICAL FIGURES OF WOMEN,BLUE BORDER,
    SIGNED......................................................    30.00
KAUFFMANN,PLATE,ICE CREAM,HAND-PAINTED CLASSIC MAIDENS,
    CHERUBS,SET OF 6............................................    39.50
KAUFFMANN,PLATE,LADIES,CHERUB,SIGNED,ROYAL VIENNA,7 IN......    10.00
KAUFFMANN,PLATE,MEDALLION,SCENE,BLUE,GOLD,BEEHIVE MARK,
    9 7/8 IN.,PAIR..............................................    73.00
KAUFFMANN,PLATE,PORTRAIT,LADIES & CHERUB ON STOOL,BLUE......    65.00
KAUFFMANN,PLATE,PORTRAIT,THREE LADIES IN CENTER,OPENWORK
    BORDER,AUSTRIA..............................................    35.00
KAUFFMANN,PLATE,SCENES,WOMEN,CHILDREN,GLADES,CZECHOSLOVAKIA,
    10 IN.,PAIR.................................................    85.00
KAUFFMANN,PLATE,SERVING,CLASSICAL DANCING WOMEN,GOLD,10 IN..    10.00
KAUFFMANN,PLATE,SLEEPING WOMAN,BY STREAM,ANGEL HOVERING
    OVER,SIGNED.................................................    42.50
KAUFFMANN,PLATE,THREE LADIES,CHERUB,GARDEN,PIERCED FOR
    HANGING,SIGNED..............................................    39.00
KAUFFMANN,PLATE,THREE MEN,ONE WOMAN,SIGNED,7 IN.............    12.50
KAUFFMANN,PLATE,TURQUOISE,GOLD,CREAM,CLASSICAL SCENE,SIGNED.    17.00
KAUFFMANN,PLATE,TWO LADIES,SEATED,MAN HOLDING WREATH,BLUE,
    GOLD BORDER.................................................    35.00
KAUFFMANN,TEAPOT,CREAMER,SUGAR,TWO CUPS & SAUCERS,SCENES,
    BEEHIVE,AUSTRIA............................................   195.00
KAUFFMANN,VASE,ALLEGORICAL SCENE,HANDLES,BEEHIVE MARK,
    AUSTRIA,5 IN.TALL...........................................    35.00
KAUFFMANN,VASE,CLASSICAL SCENE,RED,GREEN,GOLD,ROYAL VIENNA,
    BEEHIVE,PAIR................................................    75.00
    KAYSERZINN,SEE PEWTER
```

        KAZIUN GLASS HAS BEEN MADE BY CHARLES KAZIUN SINCE
        1942. HIS PAPERWEIGHTS HAVE BEEN GAINING FAME STEADILY.
        MOST OF HIS GLASS AND ALL OF THE PAPERWEIGHTS ARE
        SIGNED WITH A K DESIGNED CANE WORKED INTO THE DESIGN.
        HE MAKES BUTTONS,EARRINGS,PERFUME BOTTLES,AND
        PAPERWEIGHTS.

```
    KAZIUN,SEE ALSO,PAPERWEIGHT
KAZIUN,BOTTLE,PAPERWEIGHT,RED ROSE IN STOPPER,SIGNED,
    4 1/2 IN....................................................   250.00
KAZIUN,BOTTLE,SCENT,STOPPER..................................   235.00
KAZIUN,BUTTON,PAPERWEIGHT,DARK BLUE GROUND,RED FLOWER.......    20.00
KAZIUN,PAPERWEIGHT,GREEN FIELD,ALPINE FLOWER CENTER,PEDESTAL
    BASE.......................................................   145.00
KAZIUN,PAPERWEIGHT,GREEN JASPER GROUND,RED & YELLOW SNAKE...   350.00
KAZIUN,PAPERWEIGHT,RED ROSE,CANES,YELLOW GROUND,PEDESTAL,
    1 3/4 IN...................................................   195.00
KAZIUN,PAPERWEIGHT,YELLOW & RED LILY,BLUE & GOLDSTONE GROUND
    BASE.......................................................   170.00
KAZIUN,PERFUME,BLUE & GOLD SPATTER BASE,PINK FLORAL,GREEN
    STEMS,STOPPER..............................................   275.00
```

        KELVA GLASSWARE WAS MADE BY THE C.F. MONROE COMPANY
        OF MERIDEN,CONNECTICUT,ABOUT 1904. IT IS A PALE PASTEL
        PAINTED GLASS DECORATED WITH FLOWERS,DESIGNS,OR SCENES.

```
KELVA,BOX,BLUE GROUND,APPLE BLOSSOMS,SIGNED,4 1/2 IN........    85.00
KELVA,BOX,BLUE,PINK FLORAL,PINK LINING,SIGNED..............   335.00
KELVA,BOX,JEWEL,GREEN BROCADE,LARGE PINK POPPIES,SILVER
    GRAPE TRIM,COVER...........................................   135.00
KELVA,BOX,JEWEL,SIX-SIDED,GREEN,PINK,FLORAL,SIGNED..........   195.00
KELVA,BOX,MOTTLED BLUE GROUND,PINK DECOR OUTLINED WHITE
    ENAMEL BEADING.............................................   145.00
KELVA,BOX,SEA GREEN MOTTLED GROUND,WILD ROSE DECOR,COVER,
    8 IN.ACROSS................................................   275.00
KELVA,VASE,BLUE GROUND,ROSE DECOR,GOLD SCROLL WORK,BEADED
    TOP,8 IN...................................................   135.00
```

        KEW BLAS IS THE NAME USED BY THE UNION GLASS COMPANY
        OF SOMERVILLE,MASSACHUSETTS. THE NAME REFERS TO AN
        IRIDESCENT GOLDEN GLASS MADE FROM THE 1890S TO 1924.

```
KEW BLAS,TUMBLER,SIGNED,3 1/2 IN.HIGH.......................    65.00
KEW BLAS,VASE,GREEN,GOLD,BLUE IRIDESCENT,8 1/2 IN.HIGH......    60.00
KEW BLAS,VASE,RED IRIDESCENT OVER OPAL,GOLD & BRONZE COLOR
    DECOR,10 IN................................................   195.00
KEW BLAS,VASE,IRIDESCENT GLASS,ROSE,5 IN.HIGH,SIGNED........   150.00
```

        KEWPIES WERE FIRST PICTURED IN THE LADIES HOME JOURNAL
        BY ROSE O'NEILL. THE PIXIE-LIKE FIGURES BECAME AN
        IMMEDIATE SUCCESS,AND KEWPIE DOLLS STARTED APPEARING
        IN 1911. KEWPIE PICTURES AND OTHER ITEMS SOON FOLLOWED.

```
KEWPIE,BOTTLE,PERFUME,SEATED,CROWN TOP,PORCELAIN,2 IN.......      6.50
KEWPIE,BOTTLE,TALCUM,HAND-PAINTED,GILT,CORK IN BOTTOM,ROYAL
   AUSTRIA...............................................      12.00
KEWPIE,CAMEL-TYPE CLOCK,TWO SMALL,SQUARE VASES,SIGNED ROSE
   O'NEILL...............................................      92.50
KEWPIE,CANDY CONTAINER,BY BARREL,1915.............. 35.00 TO      38.00
KEWPIE,CANDY CONTAINER,GEORGE BORGFELDT,3/4 OUNCES..........      18.00
KEWPIE,COASTER,ROSE O'NEILL,SIGNED,RUDOLSTADT...............      24.50
KEWPIE,CREAMER,PINK LUSTER FINISH,KEWPIES PLAYING SOLDIER,
   ROSE O'NEILL..........................................      37.50
KEWPIE,CREAMER,PINK LUSTER TRIM,ROSE O'NEILL,2 3/4 IN.HIGH.      22.50
KEWPIE,CREAMER,TUMBLING KEWPIES,GREEN JASPERWARE,SIGNED ROSE
   O'NEILL...............................................      95.00
KEWPIE,CUP & SAUCER,DEMITASSE,PINK LUSTER TRIM,ROSE O'NEILL.      22.50
KEWPIE,CUP & SAUCER,SIGNED ROSE O'NEILL,WILSON,GERMANY......     125.00
KEWPIE,DISH,FEEDING,CHILD'S,DOING A HANDSTAND,SIGNED ROSE
   O'NEILL...............................................      38.00
KEWPIE,DOLL,BISQUE,ACTION,THE TRAVELER,MARKED ROSE O'NEILL
   ON GRIP...............................................      95.00
KEWPIE,DOLL,BISQUE,BLUE WINGS,PAINTED,SIGNED NIPPON,
   5 IN.HIGH.............................................      30.00
KEWPIE,DOLL,BISQUE,JAPAN,4 IN..............................       3.50
KEWPIE,DOLL,BISQUE,ROSE O'NEILL,PAPER LABELS,4 1/2 IN.......      33.00
KEWPIE,DOLL,BISQUE,SIGNED ROSE O'NEILL,4 1/2 IN.TALL........      42.50
KEWPIE,DOLL,BISQUE,SIGNED ROSE O'NEILL,5 1/4 IN.............      35.00
KEWPIE,DOLL,BISQUE,ROSE O'NEILL,SIGNED,7 1/4 IN.............      65.00
KEWPIE,DOLL,BISQUE,SIGNED,7 IN.............................      45.00
KEWPIE,DOLL,BISQUE,SITTING,THUMB IN MOUTH,4 1/2 IN.........      25.00
KEWPIE,DOLL,BISQUE,TWO STICKERS,5 1/4 IN...................      65.00
KEWPIE,DOLL,BISQUE,4 1/2 IN................................      55.00
KEWPIE,DOLL,BISQUE,6 1/2 IN.HIGH...........................       9.00
KEWPIE,DOLL,BLUE WINGS,COMPOSITION,SIGNED ON CHEST,ROSE
   O'NEILL,12 IN.........................................      35.00
KEWPIE,DOLL,BRIDE & GROOM,HUGGERS,ROSE O'NEILL,2 1/2 IN.....      40.00
KEWPIE,DOLL,CAMEO,MARKED ROSE O'NEILL,11 IN................      15.00
KEWPIE,DOLL,CELLULOID,2 IN.................................       4.00
KEWPIE,DOLL,CELLULOID,4 IN.................................       1.50
KEWPIE,DOLL,CHALK,11 IN....................................       5.50
KEWPIE,DOLL,COMPOSITION,JOINTED AT HIPS & SHOULDERS,10 IN...      25.00
KEWPIE,DOLL,COMPOSITION ON BASE,PAPER LABEL,REPAINTED,
   12 1/2 IN.............................................      22.50
KEWPIE,DOLL,COMPOSITION,ROSE O'NEILL STAMP ON CHEST,11 IN...      30.00
KEWPIE,DOLL,COMPOSITION,STICKER OF RED PAPER HEART ON CHEST,
   GERMANY...............................................      27.50
KEWPIE,DOLL,DRESSED,CELLULOID,MARK,2 1/2 IN................      14.00
KEWPIE,DOLL,DRESSED,SIGNED ROSE O'NEILL,4 1/2 IN...........      27.00
KEWPIE,DOLL,ELBOWS ON KNEES,CHALK.........................      17.50
KEWPIE,DOLL,FROZEN CELLULOID,ROSE O'NEILL,STICKER,2 1/2 IN..       6.50
KEWPIE,DOLL,IN POWDER PUFF WITH SKIRT,CELLULOID............      15.00
KEWPIE,DOLL,PAPIER-MACHE,JOINTED ARMS,ON ROUND BASE,ROSE
   O'NEILL,13 IN.........................................      75.00
KEWPIE,DOLL,RED WOOL SUIT,CAMEO CO.,13 IN..................      20.00
KEWPIE,DOLL,RUBBER,MARKED CAMEO,10 1/2 IN.TALL.............      10.00
KEWPIE,DOLL,SIGNED ROSE O'NEILL,BISQUE,5 IN.TALL...........      45.00
KEWPIE,DOLL,SIGNED ROSE O'NEILL,BISQUE,8 IN................      80.00
KEWPIE,DOLL,SIGNED ROSE O'NEILL,5 1/8 IN...................      41.50
KEWPIE,DOLL,STATIONARY FEET,MOVABLE HANDS,SIGNED O'NEILL,
   4 1/2 IN..............................................      25.00
KEWPIE,DOLL,WEARING DRESS,BISQUE,ROSE O'NEILL,SIGNED,TWO
   PAPER LABELS..........................................      47.00
KEWPIE,HAIR RECEIVER,GREEN,PINK KEWPIES & FLOWERS,HANDLES,
   ROSE O'NEILL..........................................      35.00
KEWPIE,HATPIN HOLDER,BLUE,WHITE,ROSE O'NEILL,JASPERWARE,
   GERMANY...............................................      35.00
KEWPIE,HATPIN HOLDER,GREEN JASPERWARE,PINK KEWPIES,SIGNED
   ROSE O'NEILL..........................................      95.00
KEWPIE,MOLD,FOR CHOCOLATE,HINGED,PEWTER,8 IN...............      12.00
KEWPIE,MOLD,ICE CREAM,TWO PARTS,HINGED,PEWTER..............      25.00
KEWPIE,MUG,DECOR HAS SIX KEWPIES,SIGNED ROSE O'NEILL,
   3 1/4 IN.HIGH.........................................      12.00
KEWPIE,MUG,SHAVING,TRANSFER DESIGN........................      38.00
KEWPIE,PLANTER,PINK,PORCELAIN.............................      15.00
KEWPIE,PLAQUE,PADDLE SHAPE,DECOUPAGE,FELT BACK,ATTENDING
   RABBIT IN BED.........................................      16.00
KEWPIE,PLAQUE,3 MERMAID KEWPIES WITH CHICK & FROG,PADDLE
   SHAPE,5 3/4 IN........................................      16.00
KEWPIE,PLASTER,POINTED HEAD,SITTING,PINK,7 IN.............       5.00
KEWPIE,PLATE,BLUE GROUND,GOLD RIM,SIGNED ROSE O'NEILL,ROYAL
   RUDALSTADT............................................      55.00
KEWPIE,PLATE,SIGNED ROSE O NEILL,GERMANY,ROYAL RUDOLSTADT,
   7 3/4 IN..............................................      16.50
```

```
KEWPIE,PLATE,SIGNED ROSE O'NEILL,6 IN........................      50.00
KEWPIE,PORRINGER,STERLING SILVER.............................      54.00
KEWPIE,POSTCARD,CHRISTMAS STOCKING...........................       6.00
KEWPIE,POSTCARD,CHRISTMAS,BRING YOU JOY......................       6.00
KEWPIE,POSTCARD,CHRISTMAS,MISTLETOE..........................       6.00
KEWPIE,POSTCARD,EASTER THEME,SIGNED ROSE O'NEILL.............       5.00
KEWPIE,POSTCARD,KLEVER KARD EASEL,HAVING A GREAT TIME,ROSE
   O'NEILL,1915..............................................       5.00
KEWPIE,POSTCARD,KLEVER KARD EASEL,I'M A HAPPY XMAS POSTMAN,
   ROSE O'NEILL..............................................       5.00
KEWPIE,POSTCARD,KLEVER KARD EASEL,I'M SOME WARD DOG,ROSE
   O'NEILL,1915..............................................       5.00
KEWPIE,POSTCARD,KLEVER KARD EASEL,INVITED TO A BRIDGE PARTY,
   ROSE O'NEILL..............................................       5.00
KEWPIE,POSTCARD,KLEVER KARD EASEL,TWIXT LOVE AND DUTY,ROSE
   O'NEILL,1915..............................................       5.00
KEWPIE,POSTCARD,SINGING A CHRISTMAS CAROL....................       6.00
KEWPIE,SHOT GLASS,CLEAR,ENAMEL KEWPIE,SIGNED,1 1/2 IN........      27.50
KEWPIE,SITTING WITH BLACK CAT IN LAP,BISQUE,MARKED ROSE O
   NEILL....................................................      125.00
KEWPIE,STICKPIN,CELLULOID....................................       9.00
KEWPIE,TEAPOT,CREAMER,SUGAR,LID,CHILD'S,PORCELAIN,SIGNED
   ROSE O'NEILL..............................................      85.00
KEWPIE,TEAPOT,CREAMER,SUGAR,RUNNING,PLAYING,TAUPE,WHITE,ROSE
   O'NEILL..................................................      149.50
KEWPIE,TOOTHPICK,CLEAR GLASS,3 1/4 IN.TALL...................      14.00
KEWPIE,TOOTHPICK,KEWPIE STANDING BESIDE HOLDER,SIGNED
   GEO.BORGFELDT.............................................      40.00
KEWPIE,TRAY,ICE CREAM,SIGNED ROSE O'NEILL....................      35.00
KEWPIE,TRAY,ROSE O'NEILL.....................................      10.00
KEWPIE,VASE,BLUE,WHITE,ROSE O'NEILL,JASPERWARE,GERMANY,
   6 1/2 IN.TALL............................................      35.00
KEWPIE,VASE,BLUE,WHITE,SQUARE,ROSE O'NEILL,JASPERWARE,
   GERMANY,4 1/2 IN.........................................      40.00


       KIMBALL GLASS COMPANY OF VINELAND,NEW JERSEY,WORKED
       IN THE EARLY 1900S. THE FIRM WAS MANAGED BY COLONEL
       EWAN KIMBALL,WHO HAD WORKED WITH SEVERAL OTHER GLASS
       FIRMS,INCLUDING THE COMPANY OF KIMBALL AND DURAND.
       HIS GLASS WAS MADE THROUGH THE 1930S.
       KIMBALL,SEE ALSO,CLUTHRA
KIMBALL,BOWL,ROSE,CLUTHRA IN WHITE,SIGNED,4 IN.HIGH X
   4 IN.WIDE...............................................      165.00
KIMBALL,VASE,BLUE,WHITE INSIDE,CURVED SCALLOPS,7 IN.HIGH....      60.00
KIMBALL,VASE,CLUTHRA,BLUE,GRAY-BLUE SPIRALS,RANDOM YELLOW
   IRIDESCENT..............................................      155.00
KIMBALL,VASE,CLUTHRA,BLUE,GRAY-BLUE SPIRALS,YELLOW LINING,
   SIGNED,10 IN............................................      150.00
KIMBALL,VASE,CLUTHRA,POWDER BLUE,SIGNED.....................      252.50
KIMBALL,VASE,WHITE SATIN GROUND,ENAMELED FLORAL,DURAND,
   11 IN.,PAIR.............................................      250.00
   KITCHEN,SEE ALSO,STORE,TOOL,WOODEN,IRON
KITCHEN,APPLE PEELER,IRON........................ 5.00 TO      12.00
KITCHEN,BISCUIT CUTTER,HANDLE,SET OF 3......................       5.00
KITCHEN,BOARD,COOKIE,LARGE FISH,12 X 24 IN..................      40.00
KITCHEN,BOWL,BURL,7 1/2-IN.DIAMETER,2 1/2 IN.HIGH...........      25.00
KITCHEN,BOWL,BURL,10 IN.DIAMTER,5 1/4 IN.HIGH,1/2 IN.THICK..      75.00
KITCHEN,BOWL,BUTTER,BIRD'S-EYE INSIDE & OUTSIDE,
   14 1/2-IN.DIAMETER.......................................      20.00
KITCHEN,BOWL,BUTTER,OVAL,MAPLE,17 IN........................      15.00
KITCHEN,BOWL,CHOPPING,WOODEN,21 IN. X 12 IN.................      20.00
KITCHEN,BOWL,COTTAGE CHEESE,DRAIN HOLES IN BOTTOM,INNER
   DRAIN,MAPLE.............................................      25.00
KITCHEN,BOWL,MAPLE,OBLONG,HAND-HEWN,FOOD CHOPPER,11 X
   19 1/2 IN.LONG..........................................      18.00
KITCHEN,BOX,KNIFE,COMPARTMENTS,CENTER CARRYING HANDLE,PINE..       4.95
KITCHEN,BOX,SALT,TWO COMPARTMENTS,COVER,HANDLE,11 1/4 X
   8 IN.HIGH...............................................      40.00
KITCHEN,BREAD WARMER,DATED 1897.............................       5.50
KITCHEN,BUCKET,SUGAR,COVER,BAIL,PINE,8 1/2-IN.DIAMETER,
   9 IN.HIGH...............................................      10.00
KITCHEN,BUCKET,SUGAR,MAPLE..................................      11.00
KITCHEN,BUTTER CHURN,DASHER TYPE,STRAP,WOODEN...............      28.00
KITCHEN,BUTTER CHURN,ROUNDED BODY,TIN,WOODEN PADDLES,IRON
   HANDLE,11 IN............................................      27.50
KITCHEN,BUTTER PADDLE,BROAD BOWL,HOOK HANDLE,HAND-HEWN,MAPLE       6.00
KITCHEN,BUTTER PADDLE,BURL MAPLE............................      15.00
KITCHEN,BUTTER PADDLE,HAND-HEWN,WOODEN......................       3.50
KITCHEN,BUTTER PRINT,CHEESE BOX DOVETAILED,TURNED PLUNGER
   HANDLE,PINE.............................................      20.00
```

```
KITCHEN,BUTTER PRINT,PADDLE SHAPE,WOOD.....................     10.00
KITCHEN,BUTTER STAMP,STAR DESIGN,INITIALS..................     11.50
KITCHEN,CABBAGE CUTTER,TWO BLADES,WOODEN HANDLE,5 IN. X
   5 1/2 IN...............................................      5.00
KITCHEN,CANISTER,WINDMILL PATTERN,SQUARE-HINGED TOP,TIN.....     6.00
KITCHEN,CHERRY STONER,ENTERPRISE...........................      6.00
KITCHEN,CHERRY STONER,1917.................................      7.50
KITCHEN,CHOPPING BOWL,WOODEN,21 X 12 IN....................     20.00
KITCHEN,CHOPPING KNIFE.............................ILLUS..       3.00
KITCHEN,CHURN,TIN,SOLDERED JOINTS,MARKED FRIES,9 1/2 IN.HIGH    18.50
KITCHEN,CLOTHES SPRINKLER,SIDE OPENING,COPPER,NICKEL BAND &
   KNOB...................................................      5.00
KITCHEN,COFFEEPOT,COPPER,BRASS TOP,PEWTER SPOUT & HANDLE,
   CIRCA 1890.............................................     15.00
KITCHEN,COOKIE BOARD,CARVED PEOPLE,26 1/2 X 5 1/2 IN.......     55.00
KITCHEN,COOKIE BOARD,CARVINGS OF MAN,WOMAN,ANIMAL,SHIP,
   TURKEY,SWAN,DOG........................................     52.00
KITCHEN,COOKIE BOARD,CUTOUT FIGURES OF MAN,WOMAN,WOODEN,
   BRASS RING.............................................      8.00
KITCHEN,COOKIE BOARD,PICTURES OF PEOPLE,FLOWERPOT,LION,SHIP,
   DOG,TURKEY.............................................     52.50
```

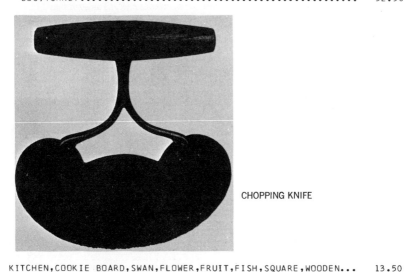

CHOPPING KNIFE

```
KITCHEN,COOKIE BOARD,SWAN,FLOWER,FRUIT,FISH,SQUARE,WOODEN...    13.50
KITCHEN,COOKIE BOARD,TWO FANCY SWORDS,17 X 5 1/2 IN........     49.00
KITCHEN,CORN DRYER,TEN-EAR,IRON............................      2.50
KITCHEN,CORN SHELLER,HAND,WOODEN HANDLE,PATENT DATE 1869....    18.50
KITCHEN,CROCK,BLUEBIRD,GRAY,W.ROBERTS,BINGHAMTON,N.Y.,TWO
   GALLONS................................................     25.00
KITCHEN,CROCK,CANNING,WOODEN BAIL,GLASS TOP,PATENT 1884,
   7 1/2 IN...............................................     15.00
KITCHEN,CRUMBER SET,PAPIER-MACHE,ORIGINAL FLOWERS,BRUSH.....     7.00
KITCHEN,CUTTER,BISCUIT,JENNY WREN ON HANDLE,TIN............      2.75
KITCHEN,DIPPER,OVAL,WOODEN,BURL,5-IN.BOWL,9 1/2 IN.LONG.....    30.00
KITCHEN,EGG BEATER,GLASS JAR,METAL TOP,GEARS,ADVERTISING
   LABEL..................................................     10.00
KITCHEN,EGG BEATER,IRON TOP,WIRE BEATERS,PATENT DATE 1885,
   NORTH BROS.............................................      8.50
KITCHEN,EGG BEATER,1885,IRON...............................      4.50
KITCHEN,EGG POACHER,SIX EGGS,IRON HANDLE,PATENT NOVEMBER 3,
   1885,TIN...............................................      9.50
KITCHEN,EGG WHIP,WIRE,HANDMADE.............................      2.50
KITCHEN,FLOUR DISPENSER,TIN & BRASS,GERMANY,26 IN.TALL,
   12 IN.WIDE.............................................     45.00
KITCHEN,FOOD CHOPPER & SAUSAGE STUFFER,DATED 1882,IRON......    15.00
KITCHEN,FOOD CHOPPER,SIX BLADES,IRON.......................      4.25
KITCHEN,FOOD CHOPPER,WOODEN HANDLE,SINGLE BLADE............      2.50
KITCHEN,FORK,HEARTH-COOKING,TWO TINES,HAND-WROUGHT,HANGS,
   14 IN..................................................     10.00
KITCHEN,FORK,TWO-TINED,WOODEN HANDLE.......................      1.25
KITCHEN,FORK,WOOD,IRON TINES...............................     12.50
KITCHEN,FRUIT JAR TOOL FOR REMOVING JARS FROM CANNER,WOODEN.     8.50
KITCHEN,FUNNEL,CAKE,PENNSYLVANIA DUTCH.....................      9.75
KITCHEN,FUNNEL,GLASS,DATED 1884............................      7.50
KITCHEN,GRATER,NUTMEG,DATED 1896,TIN & WOOD,5 IN.LONG.......     5.00
KITCHEN,GRATER,VEGETABLE,BLUE,CLAMPS ON TABLE,SCHROETER,IRON     6.50
KITCHEN,GRATER,VEGETABLE,CRANK HANDLE,HOPPER TOP,TIN & IRON.    12.50
```

```
KITCHEN,HOLDER,TOWEL,ROLLER,WOODEN.......................    8.50
KITCHEN,HOOK,S,FOR HANGING POTS ON CRANE,IRON,9 1/4 IN.LONG.  6.50
KITCHEN,ICE CREAM FREEZER,PATENT 1890.....................   18.50
KITCHEN,ICE CREAM FREEZER,WOODEN BUCKET, WHITE MOUNTAIN,
    ONE GALLON............................................   14.50
KITCHEN,ICE CREAM FREEZER,WOODEN PAIL,QUART...............   10.00
KITCHEN,ICE SHAVER,UNIVERSAL,IRON.........................    3.25
KITCHEN,IRON,CHARCOAL.....................................    8.50
KITCHEN,IRON,FLAT,CHIMNEY,USES COAL OR WOOD...............   19.95
KITCHEN,IRON,FLUTING,BRASS ROLLERS,CRANK HANDLE,CROWN,DATED
    1875..................................................   15.00
KITCHEN,IRON,FLUTING,CRANK,CLAMP,INSERT TOOL IRONS,ROYAL 80. 30.00
KITCHEN,IRON,FLUTING,GENEVA,TWO-PIECE,DATED 1866..........    9.00
KITCHEN,IRON,FLUTING,PAT.DATE 1870,KNOX..................    24.50
KITCHEN,IRON,FLUTING,ROCKER TYPE,TWO-PIECE,THE STAR.......    9.50
KITCHEN,IRON,FLUTING,SIGNED ON HANDLE GENEVA,ILLINOIS.....   15.00
KITCHEN,IRON,FLUTING,TABLETOP,BRASS ROLLERS,STENCIL,
    PAT.NOV.28,1875.......................................   22.50
KITCHEN,IRON,FLUTING,THE BEST.............................    5.00
KITCHEN,IRON,SLEEVE,DETACHABLE HANDLE,MARKED GRAND UNION TEA
    CO...................................................    3.75
KITCHEN,IRON,SLEEVE,HUB,HANDLE,EMBOSSED WAFFLE DESIGN.......  8.50
KITCHEN,IRON,SLEEVE,MARKED GRAND UNION TEA CO.,DETACHABLE
    HANDLE...............................................    3.75
KITCHEN,IRON,SLEEVE,MARKED THE TAYLOR NO.1,DETACHABLE HANDLE  3.75
KITCHEN,KNIFE BOX,ROUNDED ENDS,HICKORY,8 1/2 X 13 IN.LONG... 12.00
KITCHEN,KRAUT CHOPPER,WOODEN HANDLE......................    3.00
KITCHEN,KRAUT CUTTER,WOODEN........................ 3.00 TO   4.00
KITCHEN,LADLE,BUTTER,BURL,6-IN.DIAMETER PADDLE............   10.00
KITCHEN,LARD PRESS,PEDESTAL LEGS,FIVE SECTIONS,SCREW,GALLON
    SIZE.................................................   13.00
KITCHEN,MANGLE IRON,WOODEN RACK,HAND CRANK...............   39.50
KITCHEN,MEASURE,LIP,NO.8 ON HANDLE,BRASS,TIN-LINED,1/2 PINT.  9.00
KITCHEN,MEASURE,PINT,TIN......................... 1.95 TO    2.00
KITCHEN,MEASURE,QUART,TIN.................................    2.50
KITCHEN,MILK CAN,20 LIQUID QUARTS........................    7.00
KITCHEN,MILL,COTTAGE CHEESE,SIGNED LOUIS P.SMITH,DATED JUNE
    9,1874...............................................   22.50
KITCHEN,MOLD,BUTTER,ACORNS & FLOWERS,ONE POUND...........   15.00
KITCHEN,MOLD,BUTTER,DANDELIONS,ONE POUND.................   15.00
KITCHEN,MOLD,BUTTER,FLORAL,WOOD..........................    9.00
KITCHEN,MOLD,BUTTER,FOUR SECTIONS,ACORNS,FLOWERS,SQUARE,
    WOODEN,ONE POUND.....................................   11.75
KITCHEN,MOLD,BUTTER,LEAVES,SMALL FLOWERS,WOODEN..........    8.50
KITCHEN,MOLD,BUTTER,ROUND,SWAN,ONE POUND.................   20.00
KITCHEN,MOLD,BUTTER,SHAPE OF A HOUSE,WOOD................   30.00
KITCHEN,MOLD,BUTTER,WOOD,COW DESIGN,TAMPER...............   45.00
KITCHEN,MOLD,BUTTER,WOOD,SWAN............................   25.00
KITCHEN,MOLD,CANDLE,BENCH,SIX MOLDS,CIRCA 1750...........  145.00
KITCHEN,MOLD,LADYFINGER,IRON.............................    5.00
KITCHEN,MOLD,MUFFIN,IRON.................................    5.00
KITCHEN,MOLD,TAFFY,SHAPE OF T.ROOSEVELT'S HEAD...........   18.00
KITCHEN,MOUSETRAP,WOOD,CATCHEMALIVE,INSTRUCTIONS ON BOX....   2.50
KITCHEN,MUFFIN PAN,11 HOLES,IRON.........................    5.00
KITCHEN,PADDLE,BUTTER,HANDMADE,MAPLE.....................    5.00
KITCHEN,PADDLE,BUTTER,WOODEN.............................    3.50
KITCHEN,PADDLE,FOR STIRRING MAPLE SYRUP,WOOD.............    1.00
KITCHEN,PAN,ANGEL FOOD CAKE,TIN..........................    9.00
KITCHEN,PAN,CORN BREAD,1/2 EAR CORN SHAPE,IRON,PAT.1920,
    15 IN................................................   10.00
KITCHEN,PAN,HANDMADE,RIVETED HANDLE,COPPER,5 1/4-IN.DIAMETER 29.50
KITCHEN,PAN,HANDMADE,RIVETED HANDLE,COPPER,7 3/4-IN.DIAMETER 29.50
KITCHEN,PAN,HANDMADE,RIVETED HANDLE,COPPER,9 1/4-IN.DIAMETER 35.00
KITCHEN,PAN,HANDMADE,RIVETED HANDLE,COPPER,
    10 1/4-IN.DIAMETER...................................   49.00
KITCHEN,PAN,JELLY,HANDLES,BRASS,9-IN.DIAMETER............   16.50
KITCHEN,PAN,MUFFIN,IRON..................................    4.50
KITCHEN,PAN,MUFFIN,SIX FLUTED HOLES,TIN..................    2.00
KITCHEN,PARER,APPLE,MAKER LOCKEY & HOWLAND,PATENT DATE 1856,
    IRON.................................................    8.50
KITCHEN,PARER,APPLE,MFG.C.E.HUDSON,LEOMINISTER,MASS.,
    PAT.1/14/1882,IRON...................................    8.50
KITCHEN,PASTRY JIGGER,CRIMPING WHEEL,CRUST PIERCER,HAND
    FORGED,BRASS.........................................   10.00
KITCHEN,PASTRY WHEEL,STRAIGHT FLAT HANDLE,18TH CENTURY,
    2-IN.WHEEL...........................................    9.50
KITCHEN,PEACH PEELER,SINCLAIR SCOTT......................    8.00
KITCHEN,PEEL,HAND-WROUGHT,RAM HORN ON END OF HANDLE,IRON,
    36 IN.LONG...........................................   28.50
KITCHEN,PEEL,WOODEN HANDLE,IRON..........................    5.00
KITCHEN,PEELER,APPLE,GEAR-DRIVEN,DATED 1882,IRON.........    6.50
```

```
KITCHEN,PIE CRIMPER,WOODEN WHEEL...........................     4.00
KITCHEN,PIE JAGGING WHEEL,BONE,WOODEN HANDLE...............    12.50
KITCHEN,PIE LIFTER,ADJUSTABLE IRON........................     3.50
KITCHEN,PIE LIFTER,TURNED WOODEN HANDLE,THUMB OPERATES
  BRACKET.................................................    10.00
KITCHEN,POTATO MASHER,CURLY MAPLE,14 IN...................     5.00
KITCHEN,POTATO MASHER,WOODEN.....................  2.50 TO     4.00
KITCHEN,PRESSING BOARD,HANDLE FOR RUBBING WRINKLES OUT OF
  CLOTHING...............................................    17.50
KITCHEN,RACK,UTENSIL,IRON,HAND FORGED.....................    18.00
KITCHEN,RAISIN SEEDER,MARKED THE CROWN,PAT.OCT.26,'88.....     6.50
KITCHEN,ROLLING PIN,AMBER.................................    25.00
KITCHEN,ROLLING PIN,BIRDS-EYE MAPLE,RED HANDLES...........    22.50
KITCHEN,ROLLING PIN,BLUE GLASS HANDLES,BRASS-LINED THREADS,
  SCREW-ON...............................................    25.00
KITCHEN,ROLLING PIN,KNOB ENDS,15 IN.LONG..................     6.95
KITCHEN,ROLLING PIN,SCREW LID,GLASS.......................     4.00
KITCHEN,ROLLING PIN,TIGER MAPLE...........................    14.00
KITCHEN,ROLLING PIN,WHITE,WOODEN HANDLE,CAMBRIDGE GLASS CO..    18.00
KITCHEN,RUG BEATER,WIRE...................................     3.00
KITCHEN,SADIRON,DETACHABLE HANDLE,MARKED CHAGRIN FALLS,OHIO.    2.95
KITCHEN,SADIRON,HOLDER,MARKED COLEBROOK IRON CO.,POTTSTOWN,
  PA.....................................................     7.00
KITCHEN,SADIRON,HOLDER,MARKED FERROSTEEL,CLEVELAND........     5.00
KITCHEN,SADIRON,HOLDER,MARKED THE CLEVELAND FOUNDRY CO.....     5.00
KITCHEN,SADIRON,MARKED OBER 7.............................     2.95
KITCHEN,SADIRON,SWIRLED HANDLE............................     4.50
KITCHEN,SADIRON,WITH ROUNDED HEEL FOR POLISHING...........     5.00
KITCHEN,SALT BOX,PINE,HANGING WALL-TYPE,PAINTED,7 IN. X
  9 IN.HIGH..............................................    18.00
KITCHEN,SAUSAGE STUFFER ............................ILLUS.    12.00
KITCHEN,SCOOP,APPLE BUTTER,LOOP HANDLE,PINE...............    22.50
```

SAUSAGE STUFFER

```
KITCHEN,SCOOP,BUTTER,KNOB HANDLE,WOODEN...................     7.50
KITCHEN,SCOOP,CRANBERRY,HANDMADE,WOODEN TINES & HANDLE,
  13 IN.TALL.............................................    22.50
KITCHEN,SCOOP,FLOUR,TIN...................................     2.00
KITCHEN,SCOOP,SUGAR,TIN...................................     4.50
KITCHEN,SCRUB BOARD,CUT CORRUGATIONS,WOODEN...............    35.00
KITCHEN,SHIRT RUFFLER,KNOX,1870...........................    22.00
KITCHEN,SKIMMER,GRANITEWARE...............................     2.00
KITCHEN,SOUP SKIMMER,TIN..................................     3.00
KITCHEN,SPICE BOX,NINE DRAWERS,PORCELAIN KNOBS,IRON HANDLE
  AT TOP,PINE............................................    37.50
KITCHEN,SQUEEZER,LEMON,HINGED,WOODEN PRESS................     8.00
KITCHEN,SQUEEZER,LEMON,WOODEN,REFINISHED..................     8.00
KITCHEN,SQUEEZER,LEMON,MAPLE..............................     9.50
KITCHEN,SQUEEZER,LEMON,WOOD AND IRON......................     3.00
KITCHEN,SQUEEZER,LEMON,WOODEN.............................    12.00
KITCHEN,SQUEEZER,LEMON,WOODEN PRESSER.....................     5.00
KITCHEN,SQUEEZER,YANKEE LIDON,HINGED,IRON.................     4.00
KITCHEN,STIRRER,CHOCOLATE,THREE LOOSE RINGS ABOVE BASE,
  CARVED,WOODEN..........................................     5.00
KITCHEN,STOVE,ORNATE,GRATES,GEM CITY STOVE MFG.CO.,QUINCY,
  ILL.,1900..............................................    75.00
KITCHEN,STOVE,PORCELAIN,WHITE,BROWN TRIM,CUPIDS CARRYING
  TORCH.................................................    59.50
KITCHEN,SUGAR DEVIL,DATED JULY 27,1876,WOODEN HANDLE,IRON...    32.00
KITCHEN,TOASTER,FIREPLACE,WOODEN HANDLE,IRON..............    32.50
KITCHEN,TOASTER,FIREPLACE,11 IN. X 16 IN..................    17.50
KITCHEN,TRAY,BUTTER,WOODEN,21 1/2 IN. X 11 1/2 IN.........    18.00
```

```
KITCHEN,TRENCHER,BUTTER,HAND-HEWN,MAPLE,5 IN. X 13 IN. X
   21 IN..................................................   30.00
KITCHEN,TROUGH,DOUGH,HAND HEWN FROM A SINGLE LOG............   65.00
KITCHEN,WAFER IRON,PENNSYLVANIA,5-IN.DIAMETER WAFER PLATES,
   26 IN.LONG.............................................   45.00
KITCHEN,WAFFLE IRON,CLUBS,HEARTS,DIAMONDS,SPADES DESIGN.....   10.00
KITCHEN,WAFFLE IRON,FIREPLACE,HAND-WROUGHT HANDLES,IRON,
   35 IN.LONG.............................................   33.50
KITCHEN,WAFFLE MAKER,TWO HANDLES,IRON......................    4.75
KITCHEN,WASHBOARD,BRASS KING...............................    3.75
KITCHEN,WASHBOARD,CHESTNUT,CUTOUT PENN.HEARTS,TREENWARE,
   PENN.DUTCH.............................................  115.00
KITCHEN,WASHBOARD,ROLLER,WOOD..............................   20.00
KITCHEN,WASHBOARD,STIPPLED & CLEAR,PRESSED GLASS,6 IN. X
   8 3/4 IN...............................................   12.00
KITCHEN,WESSON OIL MAKER WITH BEATER,CLEAR WITH EMBOSSED
   RECIPE.................................................    4.50
KITCHEN,WRINGER,CLOTHES,HAND CRANK,CAN BE FASTENED ON TUB,
   METAL..................................................    8.50
KNIFE REST,MOTHER-OF-PEARL,FLOWER-LIKE ENDS,SILVER INSETS IN
   BAR,PAIR...............................................   22.50
KOCH,BOWL,TINTED GROUND,APPLES,10 IN.......................   45.00
KOCH,BOWL,TINTED GROUND,STRAWBERRIES,8 1/2 IN..............   45.00
KOCH,PLATE,APPLE SPRAYS,SIGNED,7 1/2 IN....................   35.00
KOCH,PLATE,APPLE,SIGNED,7 1/2 IN...........................   13.50
KOCH,PLATE,APPLE,8 1/2 IN..................................   16.50
KOCH,PLATE,APPLES,DEEP GREEN TO YELLOW,SIGNED,10 3/4 IN.....   33.00
KOCH,PLATE,APPLES,LEAVES,SCALLOPED EDGE,SIGNED,6 IN.........   25.00
KOCH,PLATE,APPLES,SIGNED,6 IN..............................   27.00
KOCH,PLATE,APPLES,SIGNED,7 1/2 IN..........................   32.00
KOCH,PLATE,APPLES,SIGNED,8 IN..............................   39.50
KOCH,PLATE,CAKE,STRAWBERRY DECOR,FRUIT,FLORAL,OPEN HANDLES,
   SENTA BAVARIA..........................................   75.00
KOCH,PLATE,CHERRIES,8 1/2 IN...............................   14.00
KOCH,PLATE,FRUITS,9 IN.....................................   22.50
KOCH,PLATE,GRAPES,BLACKBERRIES,PURPLE & GREEN,SIGNED,
   8 3/8 IN...............................................   32.00
KOCH,PLATE,GRAPES,GREEN TO YELLOW,GOLD BAND,SCALLOPED,
   8 1/2 IN...............................................   22.00
KOCH,PLATE,GRAPES,PURPLE & GREEN,SIGNED,8 1/2 IN...........   25.00
KOCH,PLATE,GRAPES,PURPLE & GREEN,SIGNED,J.C.LOUISE,BAVARIA,
   8 1/2 IN...............................................   18.00
KOCH,PLATE,GRAPES,SIGNED,7 1/2 IN..........................   28.50
KOCH,PLATE,GRAPES,SIGNED,8 1/2 IN.................. 19.00 TO   27.50
KOCH,PLATE,GRAPES,SIGNED,9 IN..............................   45.00
KOCH,PLATE,GRAPES,THREE SIGNATURE,8 1/2 IN.................   46.00
KOCH,PLATE,GRAPES,UNEVEN EDGE,8 IN.........................   39.50
KOCH,PLATE,VINTAGE GRAPES,SIGNED,8 IN......................   38.00
KOCH,PLATE,VINTAGE GRAPES,SIGNED,9 IN......................   45.00
KOCH,PLATE,VINTAGE,SIGNED IN THREE PLACES,8 1/2 IN.........   45.00


       KPM IS PART OF ONE OF THE MARKS USED BY THE MEISSEN
       FACTORY ABOUT 1723-KONIGLICHE PORZELLAN MANUFAKTUR.
       OTHER LATER FIRMS USING THE LETTERS INCLUDE THE ROYAL
       MANUFACTORY OF BERLIN,GERMANY,THAT WORKED FROM 1832 TO
       1847. A FACTORY IN SCHEIBE,GERMANY,USED THE MARK IN
       1928. THE MARK WAS ALSO USED IN WALDENBURG,GERMANY,
       AND OTHER GERMAN CITIES DURING THE TWENTIETH CENTURY.
KPM,CUP,COLLAR BASE,PANELS,CLASSIC FIGURES,WINGED WARRIOR,
   1840,MARK..............................................   95.00
KPM,FIGURINE,GARDEN HOUSE,TILE ROOF,BOY,GIRL,CAT,BIRD,
   FLOWERS,11 IN.HIGH.....................................  250.00
KPM GERMANY,CREAMER,SUGAR,VIOLETS,GREEN & PINK GROUND,SATIN
   FINISH.................................................   40.00
KPM GERMANY,CUP,SAUCER,DEMITASSE,WHITE GROUND,PINK ROSE
   DECOR,CIRCA 1830.......................................   35.00
KPM GERMANY,CUP,SAUCER,WHITE GROUND,RED FLORAL,CIRCA 1837,
   BLUE MARK..............................................   35.00
KPM GERMANY,DISH,RAISED FLORAL & LEAVES,COVER,OVAL,
   12 1/2 IN. X 10 IN.....................................   35.00
KPM GERMANY,DISH,RAISED FLORAL IN CORNERS,WHITE,OPEN,SQUARE,
   1820...................................................   30.00
KPM GERMANY,DISH,SERVING,FLORAL CENTER,PINK & GOLD EDGE,13 X
   9 IN...................................................   10.00
KPM GERMANY,MUG,SHAVING,FLORAL DECOR,NAME IN GOLD..........   12.50
KPM GERMANY,PLAQUE,SEMINUDE GIRL HOLDING ARROW,LION,
   PORCELAIN,6 X 8 IN.....................................  640.00
KPM GERMANY,PLATE,CAKE,PINK TULIPS,PIERCED HANDLES,9 IN.....    8.50
KPM GERMANY,PLATE,FLORAL,SWAGS,GOLD-ENCRUSTED EDGE,CIRCA
   1830,7.................................................   60.00
```

KPM GERMANY,PLATE,FRUIT CENTER,COLOR BORDER.................    7.50
KPM GERMANY,VASE,WHITE,GREEN,HAND-PAINTED FLORAL,FEATHER
   MARK,6 IN.................................................   21.00
KPM,PAINTING ON PORCELAIN,FRAME,7 1/2 IN. X 10 IN..........  550.00
KPM,PICTURE,PORCELAIN,GIRL,HANDS IN CHAINS,FRAME,12 X 16 IN.  495.00
KPM,PICTURE,PORCELAIN,MAN,WOMAN,CHILDREN,FRAME,15 X 20 IN...1,185.00
KPM,PICTURE,PORCELAIN,SEMINUDE GIRL HOLDING ARROW,LION,6 X
   8 IN..................................................... 640.00
KPM,PICTURE,PORCELAIN,SEMINUDE GIRL,ARM AROUND LION,SIGNED,
   8 X 6 IN.................................................  590.00
KPM,PICTURE,PORCELAIN,SEMINUDE GIRLS,PANELS,KNOELLES,FRAME,
   31 X 24 IN.............................................2,495.00
KPM,TEAPOT,CREAMER,SUGAR,TRAY,TWO CUPS & SAUCERS,FLOWERS,
   BUTTERFLIES.............................................. 160.00


    KUTANI WARE IS A JAPANESE PORCELAIN MADE AFTER THE
    MID-SEVENTEENTH CENTURY. MOST OF THE PIECES FOUND
    TODAY ARE NINETEENTH-CENTURY.
KUTANI,CUP & SAUCER,FLORAL,BIRD,GOLD,SIGNED,SET OF 4........   15.00
KUTANI,CUP,SAUCER,PLATE,HAND-PAINTED,LITHOPHANE GIRL IN
   CENTER,JAPAN.............................................   18.00
KUTANI,CUP,SAUCER,PLATE,LITHOGRAPH,JAPANESE LADY............   20.00
KUTANI,FIGURINE,ROBED WOMAN,BLUE,MARK,6 1/2 IN.............    25.00
KUTANI,JAR,GINGER,BIRDS,HAND-PAINTED,BLUE DOUBLE RING MARK,
   11 IN.,PAIR.............................................   75.00
KUTANI,PLATE,QUAIL AMID WILD GRASSES......................     20.00
KUTANI,PLATTER,SILVER DECOR,MOUNTAIN,TREES.................    12.50
KUTANI,TEA CADDY,SIGNED WITH ORIENTAL CHARACTERS,COVER,
   6 1/2 X 5 1/4 IN........................................   17.50
KUTANI,TEAPOT,SCENIC,CREAMER,SUGAR,FOUR CUPS & SAUCERS,
   GEISHA GIRL DECOR.......................................   35.00
KUTANI,VASE,DOUBLE GOURD,SEAL MARK,3 1/2 IN................    18.00
KUTANI,VASE,ORIENTAL COLORING,GOLD,EWER SHAPE,MARK,PAIR.....   62.50
KUTANI,VASE,SEAL MARK,3 1/2 IN............................     18.00


    LALIQUE GLASS WAS MADE BY RENE LALIQUES FACTORY IN
    PARIS,FRANCE,FROM 1860 TO 1945. THE GLASS WAS MOLDED,
    PRESSED,AND ENGRAVED. MANY OF THE MOST FAMILIAR DESIGNS
    WERE CLEAR OR WITH A BLUISH-TINGED GLASS MOLDED INTO
    BIRDS,ANIMALS,OR FOLIAGE.
LALIQUE,BOTTLE,ALLOVER RAISED FLORAL,OVOID SHAPE,CUT &
   FACETED STOPPER.........................................   50.00
LALIQUE,BOTTLE,PERFUME,DOUBLE FLOWER,STOPPER,SIGNED,
   3 1/2 IN.HIGH...........................................   34.00
LALIQUE,BOTTLE,PERFUME,FROSTED,BLACK DOTS,SPHERICAL,SIGNED..   38.00
LALIQUE,BOTTLE,PERFUME,LOTUS BLOSSOM SHAPE,BEADED STOPPER,
   FROSTED,SIGNED..........................................   35.00
LALIQUE,BOWL,FINGER,PLATE,CLAMSHELL DESIGN,OPALESCENT,SIGNED   65.00
LALIQUE,BOWL,FISH MOTIF,SHELLFISH IN CENTER,SHELL FEET,
   MARKED FRANCE...........................................   60.00
LALIQUE,BOWL,FISH,BUBBLES,OPALESCENT EDGE,SHALLOW,FRANCE,
   14 IN.ROUND.............................................  110.00
LALIQUE,BOWL,FLORAL PANELS,LION'S PAW BASE,13 IN............   65.00
LALIQUE,BOWL,GOLDEN-FROSTED,FLOWER SHAPE,SIX LARGE PETALS,
   9-IN.DIAMETER...........................................   50.00
LALIQUE,BOWL,INTAGLIO CUT SATIN COLUMBINES,CRYSTAL GROUND,
   BLOWN,5 IN..............................................   35.00
LALIQUE,BOWL,PLATTER,SWIRL COMET DECOR,OPALESCENT,BLOCK
   LETTER SIGNATURE........................................   95.00
LALIQUE,BOWL,SEASHELL OPALESCENT,9 1/2 IN.WIDE.............    95.00
LALIQUE,BOWL,SEASHELL,CLEAR TO OPALESCENT,UNDERPLATE,FRANCE,
   SIGNED..................................................   75.00
LALIQUE,BOWL,SEASHELL PATTERN,5 1/4-IN.DIAMETER,UNDERPLATE..   75.00
LALIQUE,BOWL,WHEAT PATTERN,FLAT FORM,SIGNED,10 1/4 IN.......   65.00
LALIQUE,CUP & SAUCER,RAISED OVERLAPPING LEAVES,CUT PATTERN..   32.00
LALIQUE,DECANTER,CLEAR BODY,FROSTED NECK & STOPPER,CIRCLE
   DESIGN,8 IN.............................................   35.00
LALIQUE,DECANTER,EMBOSSED NUDES,FROSTED,FULL FIGURE NUDE
   STOPPER,PAIR............................................  300.00
LALIQUE,DISH,RING,FROSTED SWAN ON SAUCER BASE,SCRIPT
   SIGNATURE...............................................   45.00
LALIQUE,DISH,SAUCE,INTAGLIO CUPIDS,ROSES,SCRIPT SIGNATURE,
   5 X 1 1/4 IN............................................   15.00
LALIQUE,FIGURINE,FROSTED LOVE BIRDS ON SAUCER,BASE,
   3 3/4 IN.DIAMETER.......................................   19.50
LALIQUE,GARNITURE SET,OCTAGONAL BOWL,PAIR CANDLESTICKS,
   FROSTED LEAF............................................   85.00
LALIQUE,HOLDER,PLACE CARD,FROSTED PEARS,GRAPES,OVER RAIL
   FENCE...................................................   35.00

```
LALIQUE,JAR,FLOWER CLUSTERS DRAPING DOWN,SIGNED,6 IN.HIGH...        12.00
LALIQUE,JAR,POWDER,HOBNAIL,MATCHING COLOGNE & PERFUME.......        75.00
LALIQUE,KNIFE REST,CLEAR CENTER,FROSTED SWIRL DESIGN AT
  ENDS,SIGNED.................................................      19.00
LALIQUE,KNIFE REST,CRYSTAL CENTER,FROSTED KNOB ENDS,SIGNED,
  PAIR......................................................       21.50
LALIQUE,KNIFE REST,DUMBBELL,ST.HUBERT.......................        12.50
LALIQUE,KNIFE REST,PANSY BORDER,MARKED LALIQUE,FRANCE.......        12.50
LALIQUE,PAPERWEIGHT,FISH,PERCH,ROUND BASE,MARKED,FRANCE,7 X
  4 IN.HIGH..................................................       45.00
LALIQUE,PERFUME,CLEAR & FROSTED,STOPPER,SIGNED,4 1/2 IN.HIGH        48.00
LALIQUE,PERFUME,FROSTED,FEMALE FIGURES,SIGNED,FRANCE,
  3 IN.TALL.................................................        22.50
LALIQUE,PERFUME,GOLD TOP,LEATHER CASE,SIGNED,PAIR...........        50.00
LALIQUE,PERFUME,KISSING DOVES,SIGNED,4 IN.HIGH..............        30.00
LALIQUE,PIN,NUDE LADY AMONG TREES,BLUE STONES,SILVER GILT,
  SIGNED....................................................        50.00
LALIQUE,PLATE,ANNUAL,1965................................1,200.00
LALIQUE,PLATE,ANNUAL,1966...................275.00 TO     300.00
LALIQUE,PLATE,ANNUAL,1967...................175.00 TO     180.00
LALIQUE,PLATE,ANNUAL,1968...................................       110.00
LALIQUE,PLATE,BERRY & LEAVES DECOR,SCRIPT SIGNED,
  8 3/4-IN.DIAMETER.........................................        21.50
LALIQUE,PLATE,CHERUB CENTER,SCRIPT SIGNATURE...............         30.00
LALIQUE,PLATE,CRYSTAL,ENAMEL CLUSTER OF CHERRIES,MARK,
  8 1/2 IN..................................................        15.00
LALIQUE,PLATE,INTAGLIO CUT,SCALLOPED PATTERN,SATIN,
  10 IN.DIAMETER............................................        45.00
LALIQUE,PLATE,MARTHA WASHINGTON............................         35.00
LALIQUE,PLATE,OPALESCENT ENDS FORM FEET,SHELL PATTERN,
  SIGNED,10 1/2 IN..........................................        67.50
LALIQUE,PLATE,PANSY BORDER,MARKED LALIQUE,FRANCE,6 IN.......        22.50
LALIQUE,PLATE,SERVING,RAISED CUT FEATHER PATTERN,
  11 IN.DIAMETER............................................        48.00
LALIQUE,PLATE,SERVING,RAISED OVERLAPPING LEAVES,CUT PATTERN,
  13 1/2 IN.................................................        60.00
LALIQUE,PLATE,VAN GOGH,VAN DYCK,PAIR.......................         50.00
LALIQUE,PLATTER,INTAGLIO CUT,TREES,CAMPHOR GLASS FINISH ON
  UNDERSIDE.................................................        65.00
LALIQUE,SALT,DOUBLE ROW ARROW POINTS,FROSTED AROUND EDGE,
  SIGNED....................................................        12.25
LALIQUE,STATUETTE,RAM'S HEAD & FISH,4 & 14 IN.LONG,SIGNED...       130.00
LALIQUE,STATUETTE,BIRDS,6,SIGNED,2 1/4 TO 3 1/2 IN.HIGH.....       200.00
LALIQUE,TOOTHPICK,FROSTED CHERUBS & GRAPES,SCRIPT SIGNATURE.        18.00
LALIQUE,TRAY,ONE GREEN,ONE PURPLE,BLACK LETTER MARK,
  5 3/4 IN.,PAIR............................................         8.00
LALIQUE,VASE,BOTTLE SHAPE,FROSTED LEAVES,BLUE GROUND,SIGNED,
  10 IN.TALL................................................        60.00
LALIQUE,VASE,FROSTED GRAPE PATTERN,SIGNED,BULBOUS,10 IN. X
  10 IN.....................................................       175.00
LALIQUE,VASE,FROSTED GROUND,BLUE-GREEN FERNS,PEAR SHAPE,
  SIGNED,6 1/2 IN...........................................        68.00
LALIQUE,VASE,FROSTED,CARVED FRUIT & TREES,10 1/2 IN.TALL....        75.00
LALIQUE,VASE,FROSTED,CARVED ROSES,LEAVES,PANELS,SCALLOPED
  RIM,FOOTED................................................        75.00
LALIQUE,VASE,FROSTED,DANCING NUDES,FOOTED,9 IN.TALL.........        85.00
LALIQUE,VASE,FROSTED,DEER,FOREST,SIGNED IN BLOCK LETTERS,
  6 1/2 IN.TALL.............................................        60.00
LALIQUE,VASE,FROSTED,THISTLE,SIGNED R.LALIQUE,FRANCE,
  8 1/2 IN.TALL.............................................        75.00
LALIQUE,VASE,GRAY,ALLOVER LEAF PATTERN,FLATTENED BALL SHAPE,
  7 IN.HIGH.................................................        85.00
LALIQUE,VASE,HOBNAILS ON LOWER PORTION,UPPER PART IS CLEAR,
  8 IN......................................................        85.00
LALIQUE,VASE,LOTUS BLOSSOM,PROTRUDING PETALS,10 X
  10 IN.ROUND...............................................       150.00
LALIQUE,VASE,OPALESCENT,FERN LEAF DESIGN,SIGNED.8 1/2 X
  8 IN.ROUND................................................        75.00
LALIQUE,VASE,SAPPHIRE BLUE,EAGLE HEAD HANDLES,SIGNED,
  6 7/8 IN.TALL.............................................       195.00
LAMP,ALADDIN,ALACITE,PAIR..................................         42.50
LAMP,ALADDIN,CLEAR,BURNER..................................          8.00
LAMP,ALADDIN,ELECTRIFIED,WITH SHADE HOLDERS,BRASS,PAIR......        37.00
LAMP,ALADDIN,FUEL VESSEL,CLEAR,NU-TYPE MODEL B,PATENT
  PENDING...................................................         8.50
LAMP,ALADDIN,GREEN,HOBNAILS,LOCK ON CHIMNEY,BRASS SHIELD FOR
  TOP.......................................................        24.00
LAMP,ALADDIN,LINCOLN DRAPE,PINK............................         25.00
LAMP,ALCOHOL,COMBINATION CURLING IRON HEATER,EMBOSSED,
  STERLING SILVER...........................................        45.00
LAMP,ALCOHOL,GLASS COVER,3 1/2 IN.HIGH.....................          4.50
```

LAMP,AMBER RIBBED FONT,BRASS CONNECTOR TO DARKER AMBER BASE,
10 IN.TALL..................................................... 27.00
LAMP,AMERICAN OIL,CORNELIUS & CO.OF PHILA.,1849,BRASS,SHADE,
26 IN.HIGH..................................................... 550.00
LAMP,ASTRAL,CLEAR & FROSTED TULIP SHADE,WIRED,PRISMS,26 IN.. 125.00
LAMP,ASTRAL,CLEAR & FROSTED TULIP SHADE,WIRED,PRISMS,18 IN.. 95.00
LAMP,BANQUET,ASTRAL SHADE,RUFFLED,ETCHED,ORNATE BRASS BASE,
WIRED.......................................................... 145.00
LAMP,BANQUET,BRASS BASE,PORCELAIN SHADE,HAND-PAINTED,INDIAN,
34 IN.......................................................... 135.00
LAMP,BANQUET,BRASS FONT,ORNATE IRON,21 IN.HIGH.............. 30.00
LAMP,BANQUET,CHERUBS HOLD BALL SHADE,HAND-PAINTED FLORAL,
BRASS,30 IN.................................................... 89.00
LAMP,BANQUET,CUPIDS SLAYING DRAGONS ON FONT,BRASS,MARBLE
BASE,PINK SHADE................................................ 150.00
LAMP,BANQUET,FROSTED FLEUR-DE-LIS GLOBE,ONYX STEM,
REFINISHED,BRASS,WIRED......................................... 85.00
LAMP,BANQUET,OPALESCENT SWIRL SHADE......................... 125.00
LAMP,BANQUET,ORNATE FONT,TURNED STEMS,BUFFED,BRASS,
19 1/4 IN.HIGH................................................. 52.00
LAMP,BANQUET,PIERCED & ORNATE BRASS,CUPID STEM,BALL SHADE,
PINK ROSES..................................................... 195.00
LAMP,BANQUET,PORCELAIN SHADE,BALL SHAPE,FLORAL,BRASS BASE,
FILIGREE FONT.................................................. 145.00
LAMP,BANQUET,THREE TIERS,ONYX BASE,BALL SHADE,FLEUR-DE-LIS
DECOR,WIRED.................................................... 215.00
LAMP,BASE FLUTED BRASS COLUMN,TURQUOISE GLASS RELIEF FONT... 27.50
LAMP,BASE,FOX,NO SHADE,MADE OF CORAL,15 IN.HIGH............. 500.00
LAMP,BASE,WHALE OIL,SANDWICH GLASS.......................... 36.00
LAMP,BEADED PEACOCK,8 IN. X 9 IN............................ 175.00
LAMP,BEEHIVE PATTERN,PEWTER COLLARS,FLINT GLASS,RIBBED FONT,
6 IN.,PAIR..................................................... 38.00
LAMP,BENT GLASS SHADE,SHADED TAN,ORNATE BRONZE BASE,
21 IN.HIGH..................................................... 85.00
LAMP,BETTY,IRON.......................................ILLUS.. 18.00

IRON BETTY LAMP

LAMP,BETTY,CRUZEE,CIRCA 1780,IRON........................... 29.50
LAMP,BETTY,DOUBLE,OPEN...................................... 22.50
LAMP,BETTY,TWIN WICK,PICK,HANGER,COPPER..................... 65.00
LAMP,BLOWN-OUT FLORAL,PAIRPOINT............................. 300.00
LAMP,BLUE FLORAL SPRAY,GREEN LEAF,BURNER,CHIMNEY,MILK GLASS,
9 1/2 IN....................................................... 22.00
LAMP,BOAT LIGHT,KEROSENE BURNER,BULL'S-EYE LENSES,RING
HANDLE,10 IN.HIGH.............................................. 39.00
LAMP,BOUDOIR,TIFFANY-TYPE LEADED SHADE,ORNATE IRON,20 IN.... 39.00
LAMP,BOY ON BASE,AMBER GLASS SHADE IS ROSE HE SMELLS,
9 1/4 IN.TALL.................................................. 60.00
LAMP,BRACKET,DOUBLE PLACE FOR FONTS......................... 12.00
LAMP,BRACKET,KEROSENE,MERCURY REFLECTOR..................... 19.25
LAMP,BRACKET,MERCURY GLASS REFLECTOR,CHIMNEY,IRON BAND...... 22.00
LAMP,BRACKET,MERCURY REFLECTOR.............................. 16.50
LAMP,BRASS,KEROSENE,ALADDIN,CHIMNEY,SHADE WITH FLOWERS...... 29.50
LAMP,BRASS,POLISHED & LACQUERED,AMBER GLASS SHADE,RAISED
EAGLE.......................................................... 38.50
LAMP,BUGGY,CANDLEHOLDER,GLASS,PATENT,RAYDYOT,10 IN.......... 25.00
LAMP,BULBOUS,BRASS,TWO HANDLES,WHITE PORCELAIN SHADE,ROSES,
WIRED.......................................................... 145.00
LAMP,BULLET-SHAPE BASE,SAYS ADMIRAL DEWEY'S LAMP,BATTLESHIP
MAINE.......................................................... 100.00
LAMP,BURNER,CHIMNEY,HAND-PAINTED COREOPSIS,MILK GLASS,23 X
6 IN.HIGH...................................................... 30.00
LAMP,CAMPHENE,EGG-SHAPE FONT,NICKLED BRASS,5 1/2 IN.HIGH.... 15.00
LAMP,CAMPHENE,PETTICOAT,BRASS,TWO PRONG BURNER,WEIGHTED BASE 63.00
LAMP,CAMPHENE,URN SHAPE,7 1/2 IN.HIGH....................... 95.00
LAMP,CANDELABRUM BASE,TWO SHADES,MOTTLED GREEN,PAPE. LABEL
SAYS MURANO.................................................... 150.00
LAMP,CANDLE,FILIGREE LACY BRASS,LARGE COLORED JEWELS,CHAIN.. 49.50

LAMP,CARAMEL SLAG SHADE,TREE TRUNK TYPE BASE,21 IN.......... 89.50
LAMP,CARRIAGE LIGHT,KEROSENE,SIDE CLAMP SLOT,BAIL HANDLE,
    DIETZ,7 1/2 IN............................................ 12.50
LAMP,CARRIAGE,BEVEL GLASS,12 IN.HIGH,PAIR.................... 45.00
LAMP,CARRIAGE,BEVELED GLASS FRONT,SILVER TRIM,RUBY GLASS
    REAR,OVAL,PAIR........................................... 110.00
LAMP,CARRIAGE,BRASS FRAME,TWO GLASS PANELS WITH CUTOUT
    STARS,10 1/2 IN.......................................... 25.00
LAMP,CARRIAGE,BRASS,IRON MOUNTING BRACKET,DUTCH,
    27 1/2 IN.TALL,PAIR..................................... 75.00
LAMP,CARRIAGE,HEXOGONAL,BEVEL GLASS,BRASS HOOD & EAGLE,CIRCA
    1820,PAIR............................................... 250.00
LAMP,CARRIAGE,OIL,RED REFLECTOR,BLACK,BRASS RIM,H.DUPLEX
    EMBURY MFG.............................................. 16.00
LAMP,CEILING SHADE,PANELS,ORNATE METAL BORDER,YELLOW TO GOLD
    MARBELIZED.............................................. 185.00
LAMP,CHANDELIER,BRASS,OIL LAMPS,ORIGINAL SHADES,SCROLLED
    ARMS,PULL DOWN.......................................... 335.00
LAMP,CHANDELIER,ETCHED PEDESTAL,FIVE CURVED GLASS ARMS,
    PRISMS.................................................. 35.00
LAMP,CHANDELIER,THREE TIERS,225 PRISMS,POLISHED BRASS,HANGS
    DOWN 45 IN.............................................. 750.00
LAMP,CHANDELIER,THREE TIERS,225 PRISMS,HANGS 45 IN.,BRASS,
    30 IN.WIDE.............................................. 750.00
LAMP,CHANDELIER,200 CUT GLASS PRISMS,TEAR DROP,CAMPHOR GLASS
    DOME,WIRED.............................................. 175.00
LAMP,CHEMIST,MINIATURE,BRASS HOLDER,EMBOSSED 1893 PATENT
    DATE,AMBER.............................................. 22.50
LAMP,CHIMNEY,LINCOLN DRAPE & TASSEL,MILK GLASS,PINK......... 25.00
LAMP,CLEAR BLOWN THREADED PEAR SHAPE BOWL,MARBLE BASE,BRASS
    STEM.................................................... 125.00
LAMP,COACH,BRASS,CRYSTAL,17 IN.SQUARE....................... 28.00
LAMP,COACH,BRASS,FRONT & SIDE GLASS,FLEMISH,
    16 1/2 IN.DIAMETER...................................... 28.00
LAMP,COACH,BRASS,27 IN.HIGH,PAIR............................ 55.00
LAMP,COACH,BRASS,6-SIDED,EAGLE ON TOP,FLEMISH,27 IN.HIGH.... 20.00
LAMP,COAL OIL,CLEAR,GREEK KEY.............................. 15.00
LAMP,COLONIAL LADY,WIRED,MARKED OCCUPIED JAPAN,15 IN.TALL,
    PAIR.................................................... 12.00
LAMP,CRANBERRY,MINIATURE.................................... 45.00
LAMP,CRESOLENE VAPO BASE & BURNER.......................... 3.50
LAMP,CRUSIE,IRON........................................... 28.00
LAMP,CRUSIE,TWO PARTS,HANGING,IRON......................... 20.00
LAMP,DENTIST'S,MANY-SIDED,WICK,CAP,DATED 1883,DARK AMBER.... 35.00
LAMP,DESK,DETAIL WORK,CANOPY,BRONZE BASE,WIRED,23 IN........ 17.00
LAMP,DESK,GOOSENECK,COLORED JEWELS IN SHADE,BRONZE,FRANCE,
    WIRED................................................... 45.00
LAMP,DESK,GOOSENECK TYPE,BRASS,ORNATE PRESSED GLASS SHADE... 22.50
LAMP,DESK,SIGNS OF ZODIAC ON SHADE & BASE,BRONZE,TIFFANY.... 250.00
LAMP,DESK,SWIVEL,DOUBLE SHADE,ART GLASS,LILY SHADE,WHITE
    PANELS,LEADED........................................... 140.00
LAMP,ELEPHANT WITH DRUM BASE,METAL,BRONZE FINISH,AMBER SATIN
    SHADE................................................... 25.00
LAMP,EXTENSION,DOUBLE WHALE OIL BURNER,TIN.................. 85.00
LAMP,FACE,KEROSENE,CHIMNEY,17 1/2 IN.TALL.................. 70.00
LAMP,FAIRY,AMBER SWIRL & CUT PATTERN BASE,ACORN SHADE,MARKED
    S.CLARKE................................................ 55.00
LAMP,FAIRY,BEIGE SATIN BASE,WHITE-LINED,SQUARE,WHITE SATIN
    SHADE,DECOR............................................. 125.00
LAMP,FAIRY,BLUE BASE,BULBOUS SHADE,RAISED FLORAL DECOR,CLEAR
    OVERLAY................................................. 80.00
LAMP,FAIRY,BLUE,DIAMOND POINT,CLARKE BASE.................. 22.50
LAMP,FAIRY,BLUE,DIAMOND POINT,CLARKE'S CRICKLITE CLEAR BASE,
    4 IN.HIGH............................................... 45.00
LAMP,FAIRY,BRASS BASE,HANDLED,WHITE TO PINK SHADE,ORANGE
    CORALENE SPRAYS......................................... 75.00
LAMP,FAIRY,CAMPHOR TOP,CLEAR BOTTOM,BLOWN GLASS WICK HOLDER. 38.00
LAMP,FAIRY,CHARTREUSE AND GREEN SATIN GLASS................ 150.00
LAMP,FAIRY,CLEAR BASE,OPAQUE SHADE OF OWL HEAD,RED EYES,
    SIGNED CLARKE........................................... 35.00
LAMP,FAIRY,CLEAR BASE,RED DIAMOND PATTERN ON DOME,CLARKE
    CRICKLITE............................................... 27.00
LAMP,FAIRY,CONE DOME SHADE,CUTOUT HOLES FORM LEAF DESIGN,
    FOOTED,BRASS............................................ 47.00
LAMP,FAIRY,CRANBERRY GLASS SHADE IN HOBNAIL PATTERN,BASE
    MARKED CLARKE........................................... 45.00
LAMP,FAIRY,DOUBLE SCONCE,WHITE CASED SHADE................. 37.50
LAMP,FAIRY,EMBOSSED ROSE & LEAF DESIGN,RED,SATIN GLASS..... 28.50
LAMP,FAIRY,FILIGREE,BEEHIVE SHAPE SHADE,BLUE,AMBER,GREEN,
    JEWELED,BRASS........................................... 55.00
LAMP,FAIRY,GREEN & WHITE,SWIRLS,THORN DECOR AROUND BOTTOM... 35.00

```
LAMP,FAIRY,GREEN MONK HEAD ON FROSTED GROUND,CLARKE BASE....    110.00
LAMP,FAIRY,GREEN SATIN,RIBBED,SIGNED CLARKE BASE,
  3 1/2 IN.TALL.............................................     65.00
LAMP,FAIRY,GREEN SWIRL SHADE,CUP,STEM,PINK FEET,THREE PARTS,
  SATIN GLASS...............................................    200.00
LAMP,FAIRY,HANGING,COBWEB SHADE,VARICOLORED JEWELS,BRASS
  CUP,CHAIN.................................................     73.00
LAMP,FAIRY,LIGHTHOUSE,SATIN,SHADED APRICOT COLOR............     95.00
LAMP,FAIRY,LITHOPHANE,CHILD'S SCENIC SHADE,WHITE PORCELAIN
  BASE,PAIR.................................................    350.00
LAMP,FAIRY,MILK GLASS SHADE,WICK,BURNER,CLEAR BASE,
  U.S.A.PAT.AUG.27,1895.....................................     25.00
LAMP,FAIRY,MOUNTED WITH AMETHYST,RUBY,OPAL,GREEN & AMBER
  JEWELS,BRASS..............................................     95.00
LAMP,FAIRY,OVERLAY BASE,PINK LINING,FLUTED EDGES,
  CANDLEHOLDER,DOME SHADE...................................     55.00
LAMP,FAIRY,PINK QUILTED SATIN GLASS........................     54.00
LAMP,FAIRY,PINK SATIN GLASS SHADE IN DIAMOND PATTERN,BASE
  MARKED CLARKE.............................................     55.00
LAMP,FAIRY,PINK,WHITE SWIRL STRIPES,TWO-PART LINER,RUFFLED
  HOLDER,CLARKE.............................................    245.00
LAMP,FAIRY,RED DIAMOND POINT,SIGNED CLARKE.................     22.50
LAMP,FAIRY,ROSE SATIN TOP,DIAMOND PATTERN,CLEAR CUT BASE,
  SIGNED CLARKE.............................................     80.00
LAMP,FAIRY,YELLOW MOTHER-OF-PEARL,SATIN GLASS..............    135.00
LAMP,FAIRY,YELLOW SATIN GLASS SHADE IN RIBBED PATTERN,BASE
  MARKED CLARKE.............................................     45.00
LAMP,FIGURAL,TALL BUNCH OF SWAMP LILIES,BEADED COVERS,BRASS
  POT,40 IN.................................................     85.00
LAMP,FINGER,LINCOLN DRAPE,BURNER,COBALT....................     42.00
LAMP,FINGER,PANELED WHEAT PATTERN,BRASS COLLAR,HANDLE,
  3 IN.TALL.................................................     10.00
LAMP,FINGER,PEDESTAL FOOT,HEART DESIGN AROUND SIDES,PRESSED
  GLASS,5 IN................................................     12.50
LAMP,FLARING SHADE,FROSTED,ETCHED,BRASS CAN & BURNER,ROYAL
  DOULTON...................................................     39.50
LAMP,FLAT,HEAVY CRIMPED HANDLE,LAVENDER TINT...............      5.00
LAMP,FLOOR,BRASS,PARCHMENT SHADE,CHINESE BRASS TRAY,TEAK
  STAND,4 PIECES............................................     90.00
LAMP,FLOOR,LEADED SHADE,GREEN,AMBER,RED,OPAL,BRONZE BASE,
  6 FEET TALL...............................................    550.00
LAMP,FROSTED CUT GLASS SHADE,SPANISH MAN HOLDS POLE,WOODEN
  BASE,SPELTZER.............................................     45.00
LAMP,GAS,BRASS BASE,GLASS SHADE,FLOWERS,LEAVES,AIR PUMP,
  COLEMAN...................................................     30.00
LAMP,GLASS BASE & SHADE,WHITE,FROSTED,SATIN FINISH,1930....     35.00
LAMP,GLOBE,ORIENTAL SCENES IN GOLD METAL,JAPAN,5 IN.TALL...     25.00
LAMP,GLOW,BURNER,WICK,SAPPHIRE BLUE GLASS CHIMNEY..........     20.00
LAMP,GLOW,EMBOSSED SCROLLS,EMERALD GREEN GLASS,TWO PARTS,
  DATED 1895................................................     38.00
LAMP,GLOW,MILK GLASS TOP,WICK HOLDER,MARKED GLOW NO.0625,
  5 IN.HIGH.................................................     22.50
LAMP,GOLDEN AMBER GLASS,PANELED FONT,RING HANDLE,BURNER....     22.50
LAMP,GONE WITH THE WIND...........................ILLUS..    165.00
LAMP,GONE WITH THE WIND,BALL SHADE,PINK TO CINNAMON,FLORAL,
  BRASS STAND...............................................    140.00
LAMP,GONE WITH THE WIND,BALL SHADE,WHITE GROUND,PINK ROSES,
  WIRED,31 IN...............................................    225.00
LAMP,GONE WITH THE WIND,BRASS STAND,FOOTED,BURNER,TANK,RED
  SHADE,FLORAL..............................................    110.00
LAMP,GONE WITH THE WIND,BROWN BULLDOG ON BASE & SHADE,BRASS
  BASE,25 IN................................................    149.50
LAMP,GONE WITH THE WIND,CASED PINK & WHITE OVERLAY,24 IN...    225.00
LAMP,GONE WITH THE WIND,CUT GLASS,STRAWBERRY DIAMOND,SIGNED
  HINKS,12 IN...............................................    550.00
LAMP,GONE WITH THE WIND,EMBOSSED LION HEAD DECOR,COLONIAL
  SCENES,23 IN..............................................    275.00
LAMP,GONE WITH THE WIND,FROSTED BABY FACES,PRESSED GLASS,
  WIRED,18 IN...............................................     75.00
LAMP,GONE WITH THE WIND,GREEN GROUND,PINK ROSES...........     65.00
LAMP,GONE WITH THE WIND,GREEN TO ROSE COLOR,RED ROSES,WIRED,
  18 IN.HIGH................................................     95.00
LAMP,GONE WITH THE WIND,GREEN-BROWN SPATTER,P & A HORNET,
  8 1/4 IN.HIGH.............................................     95.00
LAMP,GONE WITH THE WIND,GREEN,PINK & BLUE MORNING GLORIES,
  23 IN.HIGH................................................    150.00
LAMP,GONE WITH THE WIND,HANGING,BRISTOL BALL SHADE,ROSES,
  BRASS FRAME...............................................    150.00
LAMP,GONE WITH THE WIND,IRIS DECOR,ROSE COLOR BASE & SHADE,
  WIRED,26 IN...............................................    175.00
LAMP,GONE WITH THE WIND,KEROSENE,DAISY DECOR ON TOP &
```

GONE WITH THE WIND LAMP

```
BOTTOM,PINK.........................................................  45.00
LAMP,GONE WITH THE WIND,LARGE RED ROSES,ELECTRIFIED,
  21 IN.TALL........................................................  72.50
LAMP,GONE WITH THE WIND,LONG FONT,WHITE OPAL GLASS,BRASS,
  FOOTED,CHIMNEY....................................................  85.00
LAMP,GONE WITH THE WIND,MINIATURE,RED SATIN GLASS...........  65.00
LAMP,GONE WITH THE WIND,ORANGE,YELLOW,LAVENDER & PINK
  FLORAL,23 IN.TALL................................................ 125.00
LAMP,GONE WITH THE WIND,ORIENTAL DECOR,DRAGONS,LOTUS
  BLOSSOMS,WIRED................................................... 135.00
LAMP,GONE WITH THE WIND,OVERSHOT INSIDE OF GLASS,ENAMEL
  DECOR,27 IN.HIGH................................................. 350.00
LAMP,GONE WITH THE WIND,PASTEL GROUND,FLORAL,BRASS STAND,
  FLANGE,WIRED..................................................... 110.00
LAMP,GONE WITH THE WIND,PINK,HUNTING SCENE ON FONT & SHADE,
  WIRED............................................................ 200.00
LAMP,GONE WITH THE WIND,PINK,WHITE MEDALLION,GOLD,PANSIES,
  14 1/2 IN.HIGH...................................................  95.00
LAMP,GONE WITH THE WIND,PUFFED PANELS,BEADING,BURNER,
  CHIMNEY,SMALL,PAIR...............................................  65.00
LAMP,GONE WITH THE WIND,RIBBED BASE,MUSHROOM SHAPE,OPAL
  GLASS,GLOBE......................................................  85.00
LAMP,GONE WITH THE WIND,ROSE PATTERN,SATIN GLASS,RED,
  21 IN.HIGH....................................................... 210.00
LAMP,GONE WITH THE WIND,ROSES ON BASE,BALL SHADE............ 150.00
LAMP,GONE WITH THE WIND,SATIN GLASS,RED.................... 250.00
LAMP,GONE WITH THE WIND,SWIRLED PATTERN,CLEAR GLASS,SWIRLS
  ON CHIMNEY.......................................................  27.50
LAMP,GONE WITH THE WIND,URN SHAPE BASE,BRASS EAGLE HANDLES,
  FLORAL SHADE.....................................................  78.00
LAMP,GONE WITH THE WIND,WHITE OPAL,CHIMNEY,ORNATE BRASS
  TRIM,FOOTED......................................................  85.00
LAMP,GONE WITH THE WIND,WHITE TO GREEN SHADING,YELLOW &
  WHITE FLORAL.....................................................  65.00
LAMP,GONE WITH THE WIND,WHITE,FROSTED,RAISED ROSES,24 IN.... 125.00
LAMP,GONE WITH THE WIND,WINTER SCENE,HAND-PAINTED,OVOID
  SHAPE,21 IN.TALL................................................. 175.00
LAMP,GONE WITH THE WIND,YELLOW,GREEN,ROSE GROUND,
  TAM-O'-SHANTER SHADE............................................. 125.00
LAMP,GONE WITH THE WIND,YELLOW,PINK ROSES...................  85.00
LAMP,GOOSENECK,FLEXIBLE,BRASS,BRISTOL GREEN SHADE...........  10.00
LAMP,GREASE,IMPRESSED DECOR ON STEM,TIN.....................  65.00
LAMP,HALL,HANGING,BRASS,CRANBERRY SWIRL SHADE,12 IN.HIGH.... 150.00
LAMP,HAND,BLACKBERRY PATTERN,BULBOUS,FONT,8 IN.HIGH.........   7.50
LAMP,HAND,CLEAR FONT,ORNATE BRASS CONNECTIONS,MARBLE BASE,
  9 IN.HIGH........................................................  32.00
LAMP,HAND,COOLIDGE DRAPE,9 1/4 IN.HIGH......................   9.00
LAMP,HAND,COOLIDGE PATTERN,DRAPE,COBALT,8 IN.HIGH...........  39.50
LAMP,HAND,DOUBLE RINGED BODY,OIL BURNER,HANDLE,CHIMNEY,GREEN  20.00
LAMP,HAND,FINGER HANDLE,CLEAR,DATED 1871....................   7.75
LAMP,HAND,FOOTED,HANDLED,BRASS BURNER,CLEAR OIL FONT,MILK
  GLASS............................................................  47.50
```

```
LAMP,HAND,FROSTED FONT,SQUARE LEAD BASE,CUPIDS,
   10 1/2 IN.HIGH.................................................    10.00
LAMP,HAND,FROSTED,SOUVENIR,1876 CENTENNIAL,BY GILLINDER &
   SONS........................................................    57.50
LAMP,HAND,KNIFE & FORK PATTERN,APPLIED HANDLE,CIRCA 1860,
   BLOWN.......................................................    18.50
LAMP,HAND,LOOP PATTERN,FLINT....................................    14.00
LAMP,HAND,MILK GLASS PEDESTAL BASE,AMETHYST FONT,CHIMNEY,
   7 1/2 IN.HIGH...............................................    50.00
LAMP,HAND,MINIATURE,MOON & STAR PATTERN,CLEAR,BLOWN,MARK....    32.50
LAMP,HAND,PANEL FONT,RING HANDLE,BURNER,GOLDEN AMBER.........    19.50
   LAMP HANDEL,SEE HANDEL
LAMP,HANDLED PEDESTAL,MUSHROOM BURNER,BLUE-GREEN,1865,
   SANDWICH GLASS..............................................    50.00
LAMP,HANGING,14-IN.PORCELAIN SHADE,WINTER FARM SCENE,PRISMS,
   BRASS,WIRED.................................................   165.00
LAMP,HANGING,AZURE BLUE,SATIN GLASS,DIAMOND POINT,BRASS
   FITTINGS....................................................   135.00
LAMP,HANGING,BALL SHAPE,FLOWERS,LEAVES,BRASS TRIM & CHAIN,
   INSIDE BURNER...............................................   145.00
LAMP,HANGING,BRASS FONT HOLDER,GUNDERSON SHADE,PINK TO
   WHITE,PRISMS................................................   135.00
LAMP,HANGING,BRASS FRAME,HAND-PAINTED SHADE,PINK FLORAL,
   PRISMS,14 IN................................................   125.00
LAMP,HANGING,BRASS FRAME,PULL RING,SQUARE SIDES,AMETHYST
   PANELS,14 IN................................................    50.00
LAMP,HANGING,BRASS FRAME,WHITE SHADE,BLUE & YELLOW FLORAL,
   14 IN.WIDE..................................................   125.00
LAMP,HANGING,CLEAR BOTTOM,WHITE OPAL SHADE,CRIMPED,BRASS &
   NICKEL TRIM.................................................    85.00
LAMP,HANGING,CRANBERRY HOBNAIL,COPPER...........................   350.00
LAMP,HANGING,EMBOSSED BRASS FRAME & FONT,HAND-PAINTED SHADE.   145.00
LAMP,HANGING,FRAME,PRISMS,BRASS OIL FONT,CRANBERRY GLASS,
   HOBNAIL.....................................................   375.00
LAMP,HANGING,GREEN TO WHITE BOTTOM,PURPLE GRAPE CLUSTERS,
   GREEN LEAVES................................................   175.00
LAMP,HANGING,HALL,AMBER SHADE,EMBOSSED DESIGN,BRASS CHAINS,
   10-IN.SHADE.................................................    75.00
LAMP,HANGING,HALL,RED SATIN GLOBE,IRIS,CHAINS,
   34 1/2-IN.CIRCUMFERENCE......................................    90.00
LAMP,HANGING,HAMMERED BRASS FONT,DECORATED,PRISMS,BRASS
   FRAME.......................................................    75.00
LAMP,HANGING,HOBNAIL,BURNER,CRANBERRY,56 CRYSTALS,WIRED.....   375.00
LAMP,HANGING,IRON FRAME,BRASS FONT,WHITE SHADE,BURNISHED,
   WIRED.......................................................    65.00
LAMP,HANGING,IRON FRAME,WHITE MILK GLASS SHADE,FROSTED GLASS
   FONT........................................................    65.00
LAMP,HANGING,KEROSENE,REFLECTOR,HANDLE AT BACK,5 1/4 IN.HIGH     9.75
LAMP,HANGING,LANTERN SHAPE,WHITE PANELS,ALLOVER IRON
   GRILLWORK,12 IN.............................................    28.00
LAMP,HANGING,OIL,SWIRL PATTERN,CHIMNEY,BRASS FRAME,AMBER,
   11 IN.TALL..................................................    65.00
LAMP,HANGING,OPALESCENT,HOBNAIL,BRASS REEL CANOPY,PRISMS,NOT
   WIRED.......................................................   195.00
LAMP,HANGING,ORNATE BRASS FRAME,FONT,GREEN TO BROWN SHADE,
   FLORAL,PRISMS...............................................   100.00
LAMP,HANGING,PINK MORNING GLORY DECOR,CENTER BAR,BRASS FONT,
   PRISMS......................................................   125.00
LAMP,HANGING,PINK POTTERY,ENAMEL DECOR..........................    87.00
LAMP,HANGING,PORCELAIN SHADE,FONT,BEIGE ROSES,YELLOW FLORAL,
   BRASS FRAME.................................................   150.00
LAMP,HANGING,PORCELAIN SHADE,ROSES,FONT,BRASS HOLDER,CHAINS,
   WIRED.......................................................   150.00
LAMP,HANGING,PULL-DOWN TYPE,PAINTED FLORAL ON BRISTOL SHADE,
   IRON........................................................    85.00
LAMP,HANGING,RED GLASS SHADE,OPALESCENT HOBS,PRISMS,BRASS
   FONT,HOLDER.................................................   185.00
LAMP,HANGING,ROSE TO PINK SATIN GLASS SHADE,RAISED DECOR,
   CHAIN.......................................................   125.00
LAMP,HANGING,SCENES,LOVERS,MOTHER,CHILD,PASTORAL,LITHOPHANE,
   12 IN.LONG..................................................   225.00
LAMP,HANGING,YELLOW OVERLAY,WHITE LINED SHADE,BRASS HOLDER,
   PRISMS......................................................   200.00
LAMP,HANGING,11 1/2-IN.PORCELAIN SHADE,RAYO NICKEL..........    35.00
LAMP,HEARSE,BEVELED GLASS PANES,BRASS UNDER NICKEL PLATE,
   29 IN.,PAIR.................................................   300.00
LAMP,HEARSE,BEVELED GLASS,COPPER & BRASS,WIRED,PAIR.........   250.00
LAMP,HURRICANE,CANDLE,SPRING DEVICE HOLDS BEADED CHIMNEY,
   TIN,PAIR....................................................    25.00
LAMP,HURRICANE,GRAPES,VINES,PRISMS,CLEAR PEDESTAL,CRANBERRY,
   PAIR........................................................    18.00
```

LAMP,JEWELER,WICK........................................ 4.50
LAMP,KEROSENE,BLACK GLASS BASE,FROSTED STEM,CLEAR FONT,
   RIBBON DECOR,1890...................................... 75.00
LAMP,KEROSENE,BLACK OPAQUE BASE,PRESSED GLASS FONT,BRASS
   COLLAR,9 IN........................................... 30.00
LAMP,KEROSENE,CLEAR,GREEN,APPLIED HANDLE,BURNER INTACT,NO
   CHIMNEY............................................... 18.00
LAMP,KEROSENE,CLEAR,TRADEMARK OIL GUARD LAMP,PAT.DATE 1870,
   PAIR.................................................. 16.50
LAMP,KEROSENE,DOUBLE HANDLE,CLEAR GLASS,DATED 1868......... 22.00
LAMP,KEROSENE,DRAPE CHIMNEY,CLEAR GLASS................... 6.00
LAMP,KEROSENE,HAND-BLOWN,CHIMNEY,OVAL SHAPE,7 IN.HIGH...... 4.50
LAMP,KEROSENE,HAND-MOLDED,FROSTED GLOBE,ETCHED DECOR,BRASS
   FITTINGS,1867......................................... 65.00
LAMP,KEROSENE,LINCOLN DRAPE,PINK-BEIGE,WHITE SHADE,MILK
   GLASS................................................ 40.00
LAMP,KEROSENE,METAL CUPID PEDESTAL,BURNER,CHIMNEY.......... 17.00
LAMP,KEROSENE,NAILHEAD PATTERN,PEWTER UPPER HALF OF LADY
   FORMS STEM............................................ 45.00
LAMP,KITCHEN,CLEAR,FLORAL,OIL FILLER,1876,10 IN............ 25.00
LAMP,LANTERN SHAPE,FROSTED WHITE PANELS,BLACK IRON
   GRILLWORK,HANGING..................................... 42.50
LAMP,LANTERN,BARN,CANDLE HOLDER,VENT PIPES,ORIGINAL GLASS,
   24 IN.HIGH............................................ 95.00
LAMP,LANTERN,NYCS RAILROAD INSPECTOR..................... 19.50
LAMP,LANTERN,POLICE ON RED GLOBE........................ 14.00
LAMP,LANTERN,SKATERS,TIN,MARKED JEWEL,7 IN.HIGH........... 9.95
LAMP,LARD BURNER,HANDLED,PEDESTAL,SAUCER,TIN.............. 20.00
LAMP,LEADED GLASS SHADE,FLORAL,16-IN.DIAMETER,BRONZE BASE... 235.00
LAMP,LEADED,LILAC ROSETTES,MEDALLIONS,AMBER,BLUE,SCROLL
   FRAME,19 IN.TALL...................................... 575.00
LAMP,LINCOLN DRAPE.................................ILLUS.. 39.50

LINCOLN DRAPE LAMP

LAMP,LOG CABIN,AMBER,PATENT 1868......................... 80.00
LAMP,LOG CABIN,CLEAR GLASS.............................. 85.00
LAMP,LUCERNE,ROMAN SPOUT,CHAINS,IMPLEMENTS FOR WICK CARE,
   BRASS,25 IN........................................... 65.00
LAMP,MARBLE BASE,BRASS,RUBY SHADE,ETCHED GRAPES,CUT GLASS
   PRISMS,PAIR........................................... 24.50
LAMP,MARINE,HANDLE,BRASS,PERKINS,18 IN.TALL.............. 75.00
LAMP,MILK GLASS BASE,BERRY DECOR,TWO STEP,CLEAR FONT,11 IN.,
   PAIR.................................................. 55.00
LAMP,MILK GLASS BASE,CLEAR BOWL,BRASS CONNECTION,10 IN...... 35.00
LAMP,MILLEFIORI,BROWN,BLUE,RED,DOME SHADE,10 IN.TALL........ 245.00
LAMP,MILLEFIORI,CIRCA 1890,13 IN.TALL.................... 160.00
LAMP,MILLEFIORI,DOME SHADE,ORANGE,RED,GREEN,BROWN,
   13 1/2 IN.HIGH........................................ 249.50
LAMP,MINATURE,BRASS PEDESTAL,SWIRLED MILK GLASS FONT,
   CHIMNEY,1877,6 IN..................................... 22.50
LAMP,MINATURE,COLORFUL SHADE,SIGNED,PAIRPOINT............. 125.00
LAMP,MINER,BETTY,HOOK HANDLE FOR HANGING,WROUGHT IRON,
   22 IN.HIGH............................................ 32.50
LAMP,MINER,BETTY,IRON,BOWL 5-IN.DIAMETER,23 IN.HIGH,
   INCLUDING HANDLE...................................... 37.50
LAMP,MINER,BRASS,TIN,MARKED GEO.ANTON,MONONGAHELA CITY,
   PENNSYLVANIA.......................................... 10.00

```
LAMP,MINER,CARBIDE...................................................   3.00
LAMP,MINER,CARBIDE,BRASS.............................................   6.00
LAMP,MINER,CHAMBER,CHICKEN ON BOWL,IRON..............................  52.00
LAMP,MINER,MARKED THE BALDWIN LAMP,PAT.1900..........................   7.95
LAMP,MINER,MARKED THE BALDWIN LAMP,PATENT 1900-06,BRASS..............   7.95
LAMP,MINER,SOLID BRASS,TOP SECTION PLATED,ENGLAND....................  28.00
LAMP,MINER,STEEL & BRASS,HOOK HANGER,WOLF,ENGLAND,11 IN..............  36.00
LAMP,MINER,STRAIGHT SPOUT,DATED MARCH 29,1904,G.ANTON & SON,
    MONONGAHELA......................................................  10.00
LAMP,MINIATURE,GREEN,HANDLE,CHIMNEY,MARKED ON SIDE LITTLE
    GEM..............................................................  27.50
LAMP,MINIATURE,HAND PAINTED,MILK GLASS,PAIR..........................  35.00
LAMP,MINIATURE,RED,SATIN GLASS.......................................  95.00
LAMP,MINIATURE,TULIP SHADE,MEDALLION BASE,RED SATIN..................  89.50
LAMP,MINIATURE,VAPO CRESOLENE,MILK GLASS CHIMNEY.....................  12.00
LAMP,MISSION,CARAMEL SLAG IN SHADE,OAK,24 IN.........................  45.00
LAMP,MOLDED GLASS,OIL,35 IN. HIGH.................................... 120.00
LAMP,MOORISH CRACKLE,10 IN.HIGH,PAIR................................. 175.00
LAMP,NIGHT LIGHT,PYRAMID,RIBBED SHADE,BRASS BASE,STRAP
    HANDLE,CLARKE....................................................  20.00
LAMP,NIGHT,ELFIN,BRASS FONT,KEROSENE BURNER,GLASS CHIMNEY,
    MILLER,4 IN......................................................  15.00
LAMP,NIGHT,PAIRPOINT,PINK,YELLOW ROSES,ORCHID ROSES,9 1/2 &
    8 IN.,PAIR....................................................... 225.00
LAMP,NIGHT,REFLECTOR,LITTLE BROWNIE,7 1/2 IN.........................  12.00
LAMP,NUTMEG,BAIL,CHIMNEY,COBALT......................................  16.50
LAMP,NUTMEG,COBALT GLASS,NICKLED BRASS...............................  35.00
LAMP,NUTMEG,GREEN WITH BRASS,GREEN CHIMNEY...........................  25.00
LAMP,OIL,ALLOVER RAISED DESIGN.......................................  15.00
LAMP,OIL,BEEHIVE SHAPE,FLINT,7 IN.HIGH...............................  18.00
LAMP,OIL,BRASS & COPPER,FRANCE.......................................  37.50
LAMP,OIL,CHIMNEY,BRASS,MARBLE BASE,20 IN.TALL........................  20.00
LAMP,OIL,CLEAR,BLACKBERRY............................................  36.50
LAMP,OIL,DOUBLE HANDLE,BURNER,CHIMNEY,SIGNED RIPLEY OIL
    LAMP,1866........................................................  20.00
LAMP,OIL,GREEN FONT,DAISY,BUTTON,CLEAR BLOWN STEM,IRON BASE,
    WIRED,20 IN......................................................  16.00
LAMP,OIL,GREEN FONT,METAL BASE,MATADOR,20-IN.BURNER,FRANCE..........  25.00
LAMP,OIL,HAND-PAINTED MOSS ROSES,BRASS TRIM,IRON BASE,WIRED,
    14 IN............................................................  25.00
LAMP,OIL,METAL,VICTORIAN,CIRCA 1850.................................. 110.00
LAMP,OIL,MINIATURE,LIGHT GREEN,6 IN.HIGH.............................  26.00
LAMP,OIL,PEDESTAL,CLEAR GLASS HANDLE.................................   7.50
LAMP,OIL,RAISED FLOWERS IN BORDER,BURNER,CHIMNEY,AMETHYST
    GLASS............................................................  27.50
LAMP,OIL,RING HANDLE,GUARD,DATED 1870................................   8.50
LAMP,OIL,THREE FACES IN FONT,CAMPHOR FINISH,IRON BASE...............  75.00
LAMP,OIL,VICTORIAN,BRASS & MARBLE,CIRCA 1840........................  60.00
LAMP,PALMETTE,6-LOOP STEM,SCALLOPED BASE,DECOR ON FONT,
    8 1/2 IN.TALL....................................................  22.50
LAMP,PAN,DOUBLE CRUSIE,TWISTED HOOK,SECOND PAN ON RATCHED
    HOOK,SIGNED......................................................  45.00
LAMP,PEACOCK,BEADED,BRONZE & MARBLE,24 IN.HIGH,16 IN.WIDE........... 350.00
LAMP,PEACOCK,BEADED,BRONZE,16 1/2 IN.HIGH........................... 300.00
LAMP,PEANUT,OIL,LARGE................................................  15.00
LAMP,PEG,FROSTED GROUND,ENAMELED FLORAL DECOR.......................  24.50
LAMP,PEW,CRANBERRY THUMBPRINT GLOBE,ROUND COPPER BASE,
    17 1/2 IN.HIGH................................................... 150.00
LAMP,PIANO,FLOOR TYPE,MARBLE TOP,PORCELAIN BALL SHADE,
    FLORAL,BRASS..................................................... 175.00
LAMP,PIANO,HAND-PAINTED GLOBE,BRASS & COPPER,NEWLY WIRED &
    POLISHED......................................................... 100.00
LAMP,POLITICAL RALLY LIGHT,OIL FONT,WIND SHIELD,SWIVELS ON
    HOLDER,TIN.......................................................  16.00
LAMP,PULLMAN,ENAMELED BLACK OVER NICKEL,SHADE HAS BIRDS &
    FLOWERS,WIRED....................................................  35.00
LAMP,PULPIT,CANDLE,SPRING BASE,COPPER & BRASS,11 1/2 IN.HIGH........  45.00
LAMP,PULPIT,CANDLE,SPRING BASE,NICKLED BRASS,12 1/2 IN.HIGH.........  50.00
LAMP,QUEEN VICTORIA HEAD,PRINCE ALBERT HEAD,BLUE,ENGLAND,
    4 1/2 IN.,PAIR...................................................  50.00
LAMP,RAILROAD LANTERN,CHESAPEAKE & OHIO..............................   8.00
LAMP,RAILROAD,CABOOSE,KEROSENE,WALL FIXTURE,DRESSEL,
    ARLINGTON,N.J....................................................  35.00
LAMP,RAILROAD,FOR CABOOSE,KEROSENE,SAYS  DRESSEL,ARLINGTON,
    N.J..............................................................  35.00
LAMP,RAILROAD,SWITCH,BULL'S-EYE,GREEN,AMBER,OIL FONT,
    ARLINGTON DRESSEL................................................  40.00
LAMP,RAYO TYPE,BROWN ISINGLASS SHADE,MARKED YOUNG AMERICA...........  95.00
LAMP,RAYO TYPE,BUFFED,POLISHED,BRASS,WHITE SHADE....................  37.00
LAMP,RAYO TYPE,UMBRELLA SHADE,HAND-PAINTED,WHITE TO BLUE,
    FLORAL,WIRED.....................................................  45.00
```

| | |
|---|---|
| LAMP,RAYO,BURNISHED & ELECTRIFIED........................ | 28.00 |
| LAMP,RAYO,EMBOSSED,BRASS,OPAL SHADE,CHIMNEY,WIRED,20 IN.HIGH | 29.50 |
| LAMP,RAYO,POLISHED,LACQUERED,BRASS,AMBER SHADE,RAISED EAGLE DESIGN,WIRED...................................... | 38.50 |
| LAMP,RAYO,WHITE SHADE.................................. | 27.50 |
| LAMP,REFLECTOR,TIN ON BRASS,MADE BY BRIDGEPORT BRASS COMPANY | 38.00 |
| LAMP,REVERSE PAINTING,ROCKS,TREES,WATER,JEFFERSON CO.,1879, 18 IN........................................... | 85.00 |
| LAMP,ROMAN KEY DESIGN,CLEAR,FROSTED SHADE,PRISMS,BRONZE BASE,ASTRAL........................................ | 85.00 |
| LAMP,ROMAN KEY,BURNER,CHIMNEY.......................... | 22.50 |
| LAMP,ROMAN KEY,BURNER,CHIMNEY,CLEAR.................... | 15.00 |
| LAMP,ROUND BASE,CLAW FEET,GLOBE,MARKED L.C.T.,15 IN.TALL.... | 75.00 |
| LAMP,SATIN GLASS MUSHROOM SHADE,FLORAL,IRON BASE,GILT,WIRED. | 57.50 |
| LAMP,SHADE,CROWN,GRAPES,LEAVES,LEADED,24 1/2-IN.DIAMETER.... | 300.00 |
| LAMP,SHADE,HANGING,FRUIT,LEADED,20-IN.DIAMETER......... | 325.00 |
| LAMP,SHADE,HANGING,TIFFANY TYPE,PETAL SECTIONS,BEADED FRINGE,22 IN......................................... | 250.00 |
| LAMP,SHADE,PANEL,LEADED,TIFFANY-TYPE,CEILING FIXTURE........ | 135.00 |
| LAMP,SHADE,UMBRELLA TYPE,WHITE,RED FLORAL,LEAVES,LEADED GLASS............................................. | 163.00 |
| LAMP,SHADE,VILLAGE SCENE,LANDSCAPE,YELLOW & GREEN,PAIRPOINT, 15 1/2 IN........................................... | 100.00 |
| LAMP,SHELL,CARVED CAMEO SCENE,TWO LADIES FLOATING ON CLOUDS. 5 IN.HIGH........................................... | 45.00 |
| LAMP,SHIP,SANTA MARIA,IRON,11 IN.TALL.................. | 7.00 |
| LAMP,SICKROOM,IRON FRAME,MINIATURE,CRESOLENE.......... | 11.00 |
| LAMP,SIGNAL,OIL BOAT,3 1/2-IN.DIAMETER,8 IN.HIGH........... | 20.00 |
| LAMP,SKATER,BRASS,BAIL,7 IN........................... | 16.50 |
| LAMP,SKATING,BRASS,CLEAR CHIMNEY,CHAIN FOR CARRYING,DATED 4/5/64............................................. | 25.00 |
| LAMP,SPARKING,WHALE OIL BURNER,BRASS COLLAR,RING HANDLE,STAR & T.P............................................. | 40.00 |
| LAMP,SQUARE BASE,SCALLOPED,ROUND FONT,BURNER,WICK,CHIMNEY, GREEN,EMBOSSED...................................... | 18.00 |
| LAMP,STANDARD,TRIPOD BASE,SCROLL DECOR,THREE CANDLE ARMS, WIRED,IRON,PAIR...................................... | 80.00 |
| LAMP,STATUE,MISS LIBERTY,HOLDS TWO THREE-ARMED TORCHES, BRONZE,4 1/2 FEET.................................... | 495.00 |
| LAMP,STUDENT,BRASS,WHITE MELON SHADE,FLOWERS,ELECTRIC,CIRCA 1909............................................... | 95.00 |
| LAMP,STUDENT,DOUBLE,BRONZE BASE,7 IN.PANELED GREEN SHADES, 21 IN.HIGH.......................................... | 150.00 |
| LAMP,STUDENT,REBURNISHED BRASS,DATED APRIL 24,1877,POST & CO.,CINCINNATI...................................... | 185.00 |
| LAMP,STUDENT,SINGLE,ACORN FONT,CHIMNEY,SHADE,GREEN,WIRED.... | 75.00 |
| LAMP,STUDENT,SINGLE,AMBER SHADE,EAGLE DESIGN,BRASS,WIRED.... | 85.00 |
| LAMP,STUDENT,SINGLE,CHIMNEY,BURNISHED,BRASS,WHITE SHADE, 7 IN............................................... | 90.00 |
| LAMP,STUDENT,URN FONT,GREEN OVERLAY SHADE,WIRED,POLISHED, 10 IN.............................................. | 175.00 |
| LAMP,STUDENT,WHITE SHADE,CHIMNEY,BURNISHED,BRASS,7 IN....... | 90.00 |
| LAMP,STUDENT,WHITE SHADE,CHIMNEY,PATENT 1879,BURNISHED, BRASS,7 IN.......................................... | 85.00 |
| LAMP,TABLE,AMBER-CHIPPED GROUND,FOREST SCENE,METAL BASE & FINIAL,CAMEO........................................ | 250.00 |
| LAMP,TABLE,BRASS BASE,GLASS SHADE,GREEN,WHITE LINING,ROUND, 19 IN.HIGH.......................................... | 25.00 |
| LAMP,TABLE,BUST OF SHAKESPEARE,METAL,GLASS FONT,PAT.1868, 20 IN.............................................. | 50.00 |
| LAMP,TABLE,CUT DESIGN ON BASE & SHADE,DAISY,BUTTON,PANELS, 14 IN.............................................. | 29.50 |
| LAMP,TABLE,FROSTED BALL SHADE,CHARIOT SCENE,BRASS BASE,PINK SATIN FONT......................................... | 150.00 |
| LAMP,TABLE,LEADED GLASS SHADE,GEOMETRIC PATTERN,BRONZE BASE, 29 IN.HIGH.......................................... | 175.00 |
| LAMP,TABLE,MINIATURE,CLEAR BOWL,HAND-PAINTED,WICK,CHIMNEY, 7 IN............................................... | 10.00 |
| LAMP,TABLE,OIL,COBALT FONT,OPAQUE STEM,STEP-UP BASE,SANDWICH GLASS.............................................. | 75.00 |
| LAMP,TABLE,OPAQUE CUSTARD,GIRL,TREES,FLOWERS,MARY GREGORY, 10 IN.TALL.......................................... | 185.00 |
| LAMP,TABLE,OPENWORK FLORAL FONT,HANDLES,BRASS,UMBRELLA SHADE | 60.00 |
| LAMP,TABLE,PINK PORCELAIN & BRASS BASE,BRASS CONNECTOR,CUT GLASS FONT......................................... | 65.00 |
| LAMP,TABLE,VICTORIAN,CHIMNEY,GREEN-WHITE GROUND,ROSES,WIRED, 27 1/2 IN.......................................... | 175.00 |
| LAMP,TEMPLE,JAR,WIRE-COVER,DRAGON HANDLES,TEAK BASE,FAMILLE ROSE,35 IN.......................................... | 385.00 |
| LAMP,TIFFANY SEE TIFFANY | |
| LAMP,TIFFANY TYPE,STAINED GLASS,LEADED,BRASS BASE........... | 175.00 |

LAMP,TORCHERE,CARVED,GILT WOOD,POOR CONDITION,5 FEET HIGH,
   PAIR...................................................... 900.00
LAMP,TORCHERE,GILT WOOD & GLASS,ON STAND,ITALIAN,44 IN.HIGH. 90.00
LAMP,TORCHERE,MAHOGANY,9 1/2-IN.DIAMETER,38 IN.HIGH......... 160.00
LAMP,TREE TRUNK BASE,TIFFANY-TYPE SHADE IN CARAMEL SLAG,
   21 IN..................................................... 89.50
LAMP,UMBRELLA TYPE,LEADED,SIX PANELS WITH SCENE............. 100.00
**LAMP,URN,**CARVED RAISED FLORAL,BIRDS,GREEN QUARTZ,WIRED,
   **26** IN. TALL............................................. 165.00
LAMP,WALL,ALADDIN,NICKEL OVER BRASS,NO.9,BRACKET........... 15.00
LAMP,WALL,BONNET,TIN....................................... 35.00
LAMP,WALL,FROSTED,RING-TYPE HOLDER,PRESSED GLASS........... 15.00
LAMP,WHALE OIL,BRASS....................................... 15.00
LAMP,WHALE OIL,CLEAR,FLINT,TWO-PRONGED BURNER,SNUFFER CAPS,
   FONT,13 IN................................................ 75.00
LAMP,WHALE OIL,FONT,FOOTED,7 1/2 IN.HIGH................... 95.00
LAMP,WHALE OIL,HAND-PAINTED DEER,GEESE,HANDMADE,SIGNED,
   GREECE.................................................... 12.50
LAMP,WHALE OIL,HEART & THUMBPRINT,10 IN.................... 55.00
LAMP,WHALE OIL,HEXAGONAL-TAPERED GLOBE,TWIN BURNERS,
   11 1/4 IN.HIGH............................................ 87.50
LAMP,WHALE OIL,PEDESTAL,TIN............................... 95.00
LAMP,WHALE OIL,THREE-MOLD,THUMBPRINT,RIB,PEWTER COLLAR,
   WAFER-JOINED.............................................. 55.00
LAMP,WHALE OIL,TULIP PATTERN.............................. 50.00
LAMP,WHALE OIL,WICK,BURNER,GREEN SHADE,GOLD FLEUR-DE-LIS
   DECOR,19 IN............................................... 95.00
LAMP,WHITE-RIBBED SHADE,INSIDE DECOR,CORALENE OVERLAY,
   ENAMEL,PAIRPOINT.......................................... 225.00
LAMP,WICKER,ORNATE CELLULOID SHADE,BUTTERFLIES,25 IN....... 35.00
LANTERN,AMBER LEADED GLASS,COPPER......................... 18.00
LANTERN,BUGGY,RED BULL'S-EYE REFLECTOR.................... 10.00
LANTERN,CANDLE,BRASS,USED IN TANNERY...................... 42.50
LANTERN,CANDLE,DARKROOM,USED FOR DEVELOPING FILM,TIN...... 2.50
LANTERN,CANDLE,PAUL REVERE TYPE,GEOMETRIC DESIGN,PIERCED,TIN 50.00
LANTERN,CANDLE,PEARL EDGE,CHIMNEY HELD BY WIRE & SPRING TO
   TIN BASE,1894............................................. 10.00
LANTERN,CANDLE,PIERCED,GEOMETRIC DESIGN,PAUL REVERE TYPE,TIN 85.00
LANTERN,CANDLE,PIERCED,HOLDER,HEAT DEFLECTOR,TIN........... 65.00
LANTERN,CANDLE,SWIRL,FAN DESIGN,PIERCED,TIN............... 85.00
LANTERN,CANDLE,TIN & GLASS................................ 10.00
LANTERN,CANDLE,WALNUT,GLASS,TIN, 11 IN................ILLUS.. 72.50
LANTERN,CANDLE,WOOD,HAND-CRAFTED,BAIL HANDLE,TIN HOLDER,
   SQUARE FOOTED............................................. 52.50
LANTERN,CAR INSPECTOR,DIETZ............................... 12.50
LANTERN,CARRIAGE,BEVEL GLASS,5 X 5 IN.,RED FACET REFLECTOR,
   11 IN.TALL................................................ 25.00
LANTERN,CARRIAGE,ROUND & RECTANGULAR LENSES,TIN FLANGE,
   19 IN..................................................... 28.00
LANTERN,DIETZ KING........................................ 35.00
LANTERN,DIETZ POST,GLOBE,25 IN.HIGH...................... 75.00
LANTERN,FARM,DIETZ,MARKED MONARCH U.S.A.,RED GLASS GLOBE,
   13 1/2 IN................................................. 15.00
LANTERN,FOLDING TYPE,CANDLE,MARKED STONEBRIDGE,DATED 1906... 20.00
LANTERN,FOLDING,STONEBRIDGE,PAT.NOVEMBER 20,1906,TIN....... 22.00
LANTERN,GLOBE,BELL SYSTEM,RED............................. 12.50
LANTERN,HAND,TRIANGULAR,WOODEN,BAIL,17 1/2 IN.HIGH......... 55.00

WALNUT CANDLE LANTERN

```
LANTERN,HEADLIGHT,INTERURBAN ARC.............................  70.00
LANTERN,HEAVY METAL,FUEL TANK.........................ILLUS..  12.50
LANTERN,INSPECTOR'S,HOODED,RAILROAD..........................  22.50
LANTERN,KEROSENE,BAIL,CLEAR GLOBE,J.D.BROWN,PAT.1860,TIN,
  15 IN.HIGH...............................................  60.00
LANTERN,MARKER LIGHT,RAILROAD,BULL'S-EYE,RED,BLUE,ERIE,OIL
  FONT,ADLAKE.............................................  40.00
LANTERN,MINER'S,WITH HAILWOOD'S PATENTED SNUFFER,IRON,
  ENGLAND.................................................  25.00
LANTERN,PANORAMA,CENTURY OF PROGRESS,1933,6 X 4 IN.........   7.00
LANTERN,PAUL REVERE,PUNCHED TIN......................ILLUS..  45.00
LANTERN,PIERCED,PAUL REVERE,TIN......................ILLUS..  50.00
LANTERN,POLICE,KEROSENE BURNER,BULL'S-EYE LENS,PAT.APRIL
  1886,TIN................................................  12.50
LANTERN,RAILROAD,ADAMS & WESTLAKE,ADLAKE RELIABLE,1913,
  6 IN.GLOBE.............................................  20.00
LANTERN,RAILROAD,AMBER GLOBE,ADLAKE KERO 1-53 C & O
  STAMPED ON FRAME.......................................  15.00
LANTERN,RAILROAD,ARMSPEAR,LV RR SIGNED ON FRAME & CLEAR
  GLOBE..................................................   8.00
LANTERN,RAILROAD,BELL BOTTOM,BRASS TOP TO SMOKESTACK,LV RR..  20.00
LANTERN,RAILROAD,BELL BOTTOM,CLEAR GLOBE,MARKED DIETZ,B R &
  P ON FRAME.............................................  10.00
LANTERN,RAILROAD,BELL BOTTOM,DIETZ NO.6,NEW YORK CENTURY....  15.00
LANTERN,RAILROAD,BRASS BURNER,FRAME,RED GLOBE,SAYS DEL &
  HUDSON CO.1909.........................................  20.00
LANTERN,RAILROAD,C & NW,BLUE GLASS,HANDLE,12 IN.HIGH,PAIR...  75.00
```

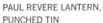

HEAVY METAL LANTERN, FUEL TANK

PAUL REVERE LANTERN,
PUNCHED TIN

PUNCHED TIN PAUL REVERE
LANTERN

LANTERN,RAILROAD,CHICAGO & N.W.,CLEAR SQUAT GLOBE,SIGNED ON
FRAME...................................................... 8.00
LANTERN,RAILROAD,CLEAR GLOBE,BOTH LANTERN & GLOBE MARKED
N.Y.N.H.&H.R.R............................................. 7.75
LANTERN,RAILROAD,CLEAR GLOBE,MARKED LV RR VESTA............ 15.00
LANTERN,RAILROAD,DRESSEL ARLINGTON,N.J.,PURPLE,RED,BLUE,
BEVEL LENS,IRON............................................ 50.00
LANTERN,RAILROAD,GREEN GLOBE,MARKED LV RR ADAMS & WESTLAKE
ADLAKE..................................................... 15.00
LANTERN,RAILROAD,PAT.1910,DIETZ VULCAN,PITTSBURGH SHAWMUT &
NOR........................................................ 25.00
LANTERN,RAILROAD,PENNSYLVANIA,SQUAT GLOBE,RIBBED,RED,SIGNED
ON FRAME................................................... 8.00
LANTERN,RAILROAD,RED,RIBBED,SQUAT GLOBE,PENNSYLVANIA MARKED
ON FRAME................................................... 8.00
LANTERN,RAILROAD,SIGNAL & LANTERN CO.,5 1/4 IN.GLOBE....... 15.00
LANTERN,RAILROAD SWITCH,RED,GREEN GLASS,BURNERS............ 45.00
LANTERN,SHIP,CORNER-TYPE,ONE WITH RED GLASS,OTHER WITH
GREEN,BRASS,PAIR........................................... 49.00
LANTERN,SHIP,KEROSENE,RED & GREEN GLASS,MARKED PORT &
STARBOARD,PAIR............................................. 57.50
LANTERN,SHIP,RIBBED RED GLOBE,KNOB ON TOP,HANDLE,BOTTOM
OPENS FOR OIL.............................................. 30.00
LANTERN,SHIP'S,BRASS....................................... 58.00
LANTERN,SHIP'S,KEROSENE LAMP INSIDE,RUBY GLOBE,BRASS,
19 IN.HIGH................................................. 195.00
LANTERN,SIGNAL,RAILROAD,KEROSENE,SIGNED CORNING PAT.OCT.10,
1905,PAIR.................................................. 100.00
LANTERN,SKATER,ORKA,GLOBE,GERMANY.......................... 7.50
LANTERN,SKATER,TIN......................................... 12.00
LANTERN,SKATING,CHAIN WITH FINGER RING,PATENT 1867,BRASS.... 25.00
LANTERN,SKATING,PANELED GLASS GLOBE SAYS PERKO WONDER
JUNIOR,TIN................................................. 20.00
LANTERN,SWITCHMAN'S,CLEAR GLOBE,FRISCO..................... 9.50
LANTERN,TOLE,CRIMPED BACKPLATE,BRASS WICK HOLDER,CLEAR
CHIMNEY,TIN,PAIR........................................... 38.00
LANTERN,TOP HANDLES,THREE GLASS SIDES,COPPER,WIRED,
16 IN.HIGH,PAIR............................................ 80.00
LANTERN,TORCH,TRAIN,BRASS & IRON,WICK,WICK CAP,KEROSENE,
12 1/2 IN.HIGH............................................. 22.50
LANTERN,WHALE OIL,OCTAGONAL-TAPERED GLASS GLOBE,TIN........ 55.00
LAPIS LAZULI,JAR,POWDER,ATOMIZER PERFUME,LARGE PERFUME,SMALL
PERFUME.................................................... 175.00


LE GRAS IS A NAME THAT APPEARED ON FRENCH CAMEO GLASS
OF THE LATE NINETEENTH AND EARLY TWENTIETH CENTURIES.
LE GRAS,BOWL,AUTUMN LEAVES,ENAMELED,SAUCE SHAPE,CAMEO GLASS,
3 X 8 IN................................................... 145.00
LE GRAS,BOWL,BEIGE,BROWN,GREEN-CASED,SCENIC,SIGNED,
4 1/2 IN.TALL.............................................. 175.00
LE GRAS,BOWL,ENAMELED HOUSE & BARN,TREES,CAMEO GLASS,SIGNED,
OVAL....................................................... 60.00
LE GRAS,BOWL,ROSE,ENAMELED WINTER SCENE,SCALLOPED TOP,8 X
7 1/2 IN. TALL............................................. 80.00
LE GRAS,BOWL,ROSE,BIRDS,TREES,SNOW,FLARED TOP,SIGNED, 4 IN.
X 4 IN.TALL................................................ 80.00
LE GRAS,BOWL,ROSE,ENAMELED,WINTER SCENE,CRIMPED TOP,6 IN.
TALL....................................................... 55.00
LE GRAS,BOWL,ROSE,WINTER SCENE,CRIMPED TOP,SIGNED.......... 65.00
LE GRAS,BOWL,ROSE,YELLOW & RED GROUND,ENAMELED AUTUMN
LEAVES,BLUEBERRIES......................................... 85.00
LE GRAS,LAMP,GREEN,ORANGE,TREES,FOLIAGE,ELECTRIC,SIGNED,
7 1/4 IN. TALL............................................. 145.00
LE GRAS,VASE,ACID CUT BACK SWIRL PANEL OF FAN MOTIF,GREEN
GROUND,9 IN................................................ 175.00
LE GRAS,VASE,BROKEN EGG,AUTUMN CAMEO SCENE,ENAMEL DECOR,
5 1/2 IN................................................... 95.00
LE GRAS,VASE,BROWN & GREEN UNDER WATER PLANTS,SIGNED....... 165.00
LE GRAS,VASE,BROWN,ORANGE LEAVES,ENAMELED,16 IN.HIGH,
5-IN.DIAMETER.............................................. 76.00
LE GRAS,VASE,BUTTERFLIES,FLORAL,ORANGE & YELLOW GROUND,
ENAMELED,6 IN.............................................. 60.00
LE GRAS,VASE,CAMEO,CARVED,ENAMELED,ROAD,WOODS,LAKE,SKY,
CYLINDER SHAPE............................................. 175.00
LE GRAS,VASE,CAMEO,CUT BACK FOLIAGE,MAROON ON FROSTED,
SIGNED,9 IN. HIGH.......................................... 80.00
LE GRAS,VASE,CAMEO,FLORAL,DEEP CUT,BULBOUS,FRANCE,SIGNED,
5 IN.HIGH.................................................. 125.00
LE GRAS,VASE,CAMEO,FOUR-SIDED,TREES,MOUNTAINS,WATER,FOLIAGE,
6 IN....................................................... 69.00

```
LE GRAS,VASE,CAMEO,FOREST SCENE,SIGNED,8 IN.HIGH............     55.00
LE GRAS,VASE,CAMEO,GREEN BERRIES,LEAVES,WHITE,GREEN,PINK
  GROUND,HANDLES.............................................    250.00
LE GRAS,VASE,CAMEO,GREEN,MOTTLED ORANGE,DEEP FLORAL CUT,
  5 IN.HIGH.................................................     125.00
LE GRAS,VASE,CAMEO,GREEN,WHITE,CARVED APPLE BLOSSOMS,SIGNED,
  8 1/2 IN..................................................     185.00
LE GRAS,VASE,CAMEO,GREEN,YELLOW,COBALT DECOR,ACID CUT TO
  CLEAR,13 IN...............................................     300.00
LE GRAS,VASE,CAMEO,MAPLE LEAVES,NUTS,BROWN,GREEN,ORANGE,
  9 IN.TALL.................................................     135.00
LE GRAS,VASE,CAMEO,MAROON CUT BACK FOLIAGE ON FROSTED
  GROUND,FRANCE.............................................      80.00
LE GRAS,VASE,CAMEO,ORANGE,BROWN LEAVES,ENAMELED,SIGNED,
  16 IN.HIGH................................................      68.50
LE GRAS,VASE,CAMEO,PINK,WHITE,DRAPE DECOR,SIGNED,9 IN.TALL..    105.00
LE GRAS,VASE,CAMEO,SCENIC,MAN,SHEEP,PINK,ORANGE,BLUE,GREEN,
  BROWN,5 IN................................................      90.00
LE GRAS,VASE,CAMEO,SCENIC,SHEPHERD,SHEEP,TREES,MOUNTAINS,
  6 1/2 IN..................................................      82.50
LE GRAS,VASE,CAMEO,SHEPHERD & SHEEP ON MOUNTAIN,SIGNED,
  13 IN.TALL................................................     150.00
LE GRAS,VASE,CAMEO,WHITE APPLE BLOSSOMS,GREEN BACKGROUND,
  8 1/2 IN..................................................     185.00
LE GRAS,VASE,CAMEO,WOODED SCENE,GREEN,YELLOW,BLUE,SQUARE
  SHAPE,2 3/4 IN............................................      95.00
LE GRAS,VASE,ENAMELED TREES & WATER SCENE,SWANS,FLORAL,
  MOUNTAINS,SIGNED..........................................      85.00
LE GRAS,VASE,ORANGE GROUND,BROWN MAPLE LEAVES,11 IN.HIGH....    100.00
LE GRAS,VASE,PINK CRACKLE GROUND,RED MAPLE LEAVES,SIGNED,
  9 IN.HIGH.................................................     135.00
LE GRAS,VASE,PINK GROUND,DARK RED FOLIAGE,SIGNED, 7 IN......     75.00
LE GRAS,VASE,RED & YELLOW GROUND,ENAMELED FLORAL,LEAVES,
  SIGNED,13 IN.TALL.........................................      60.00
LE GRAS,VASE,SCENIC,ENAMEL,WATER,TREES,SAILBOATS,GREEN,
  ORANGE,11 IN..............................................      37.50
LE GRAS,VASE,SCENIC,ENAMEL,WATER,TREES,SAILBOATS,BROWN,
  GREEN,10 3/4 IN...........................................      35.00
LE GRAS,VASE,SCENIC,ENAMEL,WATER,TREES,SAILBOATS,BROWN,
  ORANGE,8 3/4 IN...........................................      25.00
LE GRAS,VASE,SCENIC,MAN & GOATS ON MOUNTAIN,SIGNED,
  6 1/2 IN.HIGH.............................................      75.00
LE GRAS,VASE,SNOW SCENE,ORANGE,WHITE,BLACK,SIGNED,11 IN.HIGH     75.00
LE GRAS,VASE,STICK,CAMEO,CAFE AU LAIT MATTE FINISH GROUND,
  HONEYSUCKLE...............................................     150.00
LE GRAS,VASE,STICK,FLORAL,ACID CUT,ENAMEL,SIGNED,16 IN.TALL.    150.00
LE GRAS,VASE,SUMMER TREE SCENE,POINTED EDGE,SIGNED,5 1/2 IN.
  TALL......................................................      93.50
LE GRAS,VASE,WINTER SNOW SCENE,ORANGE GROUND,BARE TREES,
  9 IN.,PAIR................................................     225.00
LE GRAS,VASE,WOODLAND SCENE,ENAMEL,BULBOUS BASE,SIGNED,
  10 1/2 IN.,PAIR...........................................     375.00
LE VERRE FRANCAIS,BOWL,CAMEO,FROSTY GROUND,GREEN,ORANGE,
  SIGNED CHARDER............................................     450.00
LE VERRE FRANCAIS,BOWL,ORANGE,BROWN OVERLAY,YELLOW GROUND,
  OVINGTON BROS.............................................     125.00
LE VERRE FRANCAIS,CHALICE,CAMEO,LAVENDER GROUND,CUT LAVENDER
  FLORAL....................................................     135.00
LE VERRE FRANCAIS,EWER,CAMEO,MOTTLED CREAM SATIN GROUND,
  PURPLE LEAVES.............................................     150.00
LE VERRE FRANCAIS,LAMP,CAMEO,AQUA,FROST,CUT BUBBLES,
  BUTTERFLIES,15 IN.........................................     375.00
LE VERRE FRANCAIS,LAMP,CAMEO,MUSHROOM SHAPE TOP,SIGNED,13 X
  21 IN.HIGH................................................     350.00
LE VERRE FRANCAIS,LAMP,TABLE,CAMEO,GEOMETRIC DECOR,MUSHROOM
  SHADE.....................................................     400.00
LE VERRE FRANCAIS,NIGHT LIGHT,CREAMY,ORANGE,MAROON FRUIT,
  IRON BASE.................................................     125.00
LE VERRE FRANCAIS,PITCHER,CAMEO,BROWN,RED,ORANGE,BULBOUS,
  10 IN.HIGH................................................     275.00
LE VERRE FRANCAIS,VASE,CAMEO,MAROON FLYING GEESE,
  CAT-O-NINE-TAILS,MOTTLE...................................     175.00
LE VERRE FRANCAIS,VASE,CAMEO,MOTTLED ORANGE,BROWN,THREE
  DESIGNS,SIGNED............................................     250.00
LE VERRE FRANCAIS,VASE,CAMEO,TORTOISESHELL COLOR,ORANGE
  COLOR,PEDESTAL............................................     425.00
LE VERRE FRANCAIS,VASE,CAMEO,YELLOW MOTTLED GROUND,SEEDPODS,
  GREEN LEAVES..............................................      95.00
LE VERRE FRANCAIS,VASE,CAMEO,YELLOW,BLUE,ORANGE,BERRY
  FLORAL,8 IN...............................................     110.00
LE VERRE FRANCAIS,VASE,GEOMETRIC-CUT PATTERN,SIGNED,
```

```
    11 IN.TALL........................................    75.00
LE VERRE FRANCAIS,VASE,MOTTLED GROUND,ORANGE,BLACK FLORAL,
    CAMEO,FRANCE......................................   150.00
LE VERRE FRANCAIS,VASE,PEACH GROUND,RED FLORAL,PEDESTAL,
    CAMEO,11 1/2 IN...................................   150.00
LE VERRE FRANCAIS,VASE,WHITE GROUND,BROWN FLORAL,SIGNED,
    7 IN.............................................   125.00
LE VERRE FRANCAIS,VASE,YELLOW GROUND,COBALT & ORANGE FLORAL,
    7 3/4 IN.........................................   110.00
LEATHER,CASE,ARCHITECT TRAVELING,GOLD/TOOLED BLACK,19 IN.
    LONG.............................................   250.00
```

        LEEDS POTTERY WAS MADE AT LEEDS,YORKSHIRE,ENGLAND,
    FROM 1774 TO 1878. MOST LEEDS WARE WAS NOT MARKED.
    EARLY LEEDS PIECES HAD DISTINCTIVE TWISTED HANDLES WITH
    A GREENISH GLAZE ON PART OF THE CREAMY WARE. LATER WARE
    OFTEN HAD BLUE BORDERS ON THE CREAMY POTTERY.

```
LEEDS,CUP PLATE,BLUE EDGE..............................     8.00
LEEDS,MUG,WATCHFUL EYE THROUGH SILENT TONGUE,SECRET HEART...    55.00
LEEDS,PLATE,CREAM COLOR,CABLE MOLDING,PIERCED BORDER,CIRCA
    1810,PAIR........................................    55.00
LEEDS,PLATTER,BLUE EDGE,MARKED IMPRESSED NUMBER............    25.00
LEEDS,PLATTER,GREEN EDGE...............................    26.00
LEEDS,SOUP,GREEN EDGE..................................    26.00
```

        LENOX CHINA WAS MADE IN TRENTON,NEW JERSEY,AFTER 1906.
    THE FIRM ALSO MAKES A PORCELAIN SIMILAR TO BELLEEK.
    LENOX,SEE ALSO,BELLEEK

```
LENOX BOTTLE,WOMAN'S HEAD SHAPE,SAYS HATTIE CARNEGIE
    COSMETICS,SIGNED.................................    55.00
LENOX,COFFEE SERVICE,MING PATTERN,TALL POT,SQUATTY BOWL,
    LARGE CREAMER...................................    45.00
LENOX,JAR,MUSTARD,TALL,GREEN,OVERLAID WITH SILVER,BAIL,LID..    18.00
LENOX,MUG,GOLF SCENE,PAIR..........................100.00 TO   125.00
LENOX,PLATE,AURORA,STERLING SILVER RIM,7 IN...............     9.75
LENOX,PLATE,MING TREE PATTERN,GILT,10 1/2 IN.............     7.00
LENOX,SALT,SWAN,OFF-WHITE,ONE LARGE & FOUR SMALL,SET......    42.00
LENOX,TOBY,WILLIAM PENN,WHITE,BELLEEK....................    75.00
LENOX,TRAY,PIN,GOLD BAND,5-IN.DIAMETER..................    10.00
    LIGHTING DEVICES,SEE CANDLEHOLDER,CANDELSTICK,LAMP,ETC.
```

        LIMOGES PORCELAIN HAS BEEN MADE IN LIMOGES,FRANCE,
    SINCE THE MID-19TH CENTURY. FINE PORCELAINS WERE MADE
    BY MANY FACTORIES INCLUDING HAVILAND,AHRENFELDT,
    GUERIN,POUYAT,ELITE,AND OTHERS.
    LIMOGES,SEE ALSO,HAVILAND

```
LIMOGES,BASKET,CORONET,ROSES,GREEN & GOLD BAROQUE TRIM,GILT
    HANDLE,5 IN......................................    22.50
LIMOGES,BASKET,OVAL,WHITE GROUND,HAND-PAINTED ROSES,GOLD,
    5-IN.DIAMETER....................................    20.00
LIMOGES,BASKET,SUGAR,FLORAL,GREEN TO BROWN GROUND,
    HAND-PAINTED.....................................    14.00
LIMOGES,BASKET,WASTE,GOLD-SCROLLED TOP,ROSES,HAND-PAINTED,
    SIGNED,FOOTED....................................   115.00
LIMOGES,BEDSIDE SET,TRAY,COVERED PITCHER,MUG,MATCH HOLDER,
    WIDE PINK BAND...................................    35.00
LIMOGES,BOUILLON CUPS & SAUCERS,TWO-HANDLED,HAVILAND,FRANCE,
    SET OF 6.........................................    25.00
LIMOGES,BOWL,BERRY,YELLOW ROSES,DEWDROPS,GILT,12 DISHES,
    SIGNED JERAB.....................................   145.00
LIMOGES,BOWL,FLORAL CENTER,DARK BLUE & GOLD BORDER,SIGNED,
    9 1/2 IN.........................................     4.50
LIMOGES,BOWL,FRUIT,HAND-PAINTED VIOLETS,GOLD RIM,
    10-IN.DIAMETER...................................    16.50
LIMOGES,BOWL,HAND-PAINTED FLORAL,SIGNED,8 1/2 IN. X
    2 IN.HIGH........................................    14.00
LIMOGES,BOWL,PINK-LAVENDER FLORAL,SCALLOPED,GOLD,J.POUYAT,
    6 PLATES.........................................    25.00
LIMOGES,BOWL,PINK,YELLOW ROSE SPRAYS,SCALLOP & SHELL RIM,
    EMBOSSING........................................    15.00
LIMOGES,BOWL,PUNCH,GRAPE PATTERN,12 3/4-IN.DIAMETER,SIX
    PUNCH CUPS.......................................   250.00
LIMOGES,BOWL,PUNCH,ROSES,ORNATE GOLD FEET & SCALLOPED TOP,
    SIGNED...........................................    75.00
LIMOGES,BOWL,RED & YELLOW ROSES,SHALLOW,CORONET,SIGNED,
    8 1/2 IN.........................................    18.50
LIMOGES,BOWL,SMALL ROSE SPRAYS,GOLD SCALLOPED EDGE,LOW,
    9 1/2 IN.........................................     9.00
```

LIMOGES,BOWL,WHIPPED CREAM,BACHELOR BUTTONS INSIDE &
  OUTSIDE,FOOTED,GILT........................................ 7.50
LIMOGES,BOWL,WHITE,PINK,YELLOW FLORAL,KNOB ON COVER,SIGNED
  C.AHRENFELDT.............................................. 25.00
LIMOGES,BOX,ALLOVER DECOR,GOLD,PINK,RED,WHITE,ENAMEL,ORMULU
  CLASP.................................................... 225.00
LIMOGES,BOX,ALLOVER PURPLE VIOLETS,ENCRUSTED GOLD,COVER,
  HAND-PAINTED............................................. 45.00
LIMOGES,BOX,ENAMELED SCENES,HOUSE,STREAM,BOY & GIRL ON
  COVER,COPPER............................................. 225.00
LIMOGES,BOX,GREEN BORDER,HAND-PAINTED FLORAL,SIGNED RENO,
  5 1/2 IN.SQUARE.......................................... 22.50
LIMOGES,BOX,HEART-SHAPED,WHITE,BEADED DESIGN ON TOP &
  BOTTOM,FRANCE............................................ 10.00
LIMOGES,BOX,PATCH,BURGUNDY,BLUE & WHITE ENAMEL,OVAL,
  2 1/2 IN.LONG............................................ 25.00
LIMOGES,BOX,PATCH,VIOLET COLOR,FIGURES IN MEDALLION,GOLD
  TRIM,1 X 2 IN............................................ 20.00
LIMOGES,BOX,POWDER,HAND-PAINTED CHERUBS IN CLOUDS,GOLD TRIM. 12.00
LIMOGES,BOX,POWDER,PINK,ENAMELED BLUE FLOWERS,COVER......... 10.00
LIMOGES,BOX,RED ENAMELED FLORAL,PORTRAIT COVER,LADY,
  GENTLEMAN,COPPER......................................... 250.00
LIMOGES,BROOCH,WILD ROSES,VIOLETS,OPENWORK RIM,14K GOLD,
  CHAIN RING............................................... 65.00
LIMOGES,BUTTER PAT,MAN,LADY,RAISED ENAMEL,MOUNTED ON WHITE
  SILK,FRAME,3............................................. 95.00
LIMOGES,CACHEPOT,GREEN GROUND,GILT ELEPHANT HANDLES,PORTRAIT
  MEDALLION................................................ 125.00
LIMOGES,CASSEROLE,BLUE & WHITE FLORAL,PLATTER,AHRENFELDT &
  CO.,1880................................................. 40.00
LIMOGES,CASSEROLE,WHITE,GOLD & GREEN GEOMETRIC PATTERN,
  UNDERPLATE............................................... 30.00
LIMOGES,CELERY,MEDALLION,GOLD RIM,HAND-PAINTED,FRANCE...... 27.00
LIMOGES,CHOCOLATE POT,BLUE,HAND-PAINTED,COVER.............. 40.00
LIMOGES,CHOCOLATE POT,BULBOUS BOTTOM,HAND-PAINTED ROSES,
  RAISED GOLD.............................................. 35.00
LIMOGES,CHOCOLATE POT,GREEN & CREAM WITH GOLD,PINK & WHITE
  CARNATIONS............................................... 26.00
LIMOGES,CHOCOLATE POT,ROSE DECOR,GOLD TRIM,HAND-PAINTED,
  SIGNED & DATED........................................... 35.00
LIMOGES,CHOCOLATE POT,WHITE GROUND,PEACH COLOR DECOR,GILT... 67.50
LIMOGES,CHOCOLATE POT,WHITE,HAND-PAINTED ROSE SPRAYS,ELITE
  FRANCE MARK.............................................. 48.00
LIMOGES,CHOCOLATE POT,WHITE,PINK FLOWERS,GREEN BAND........ 30.00
LIMOGES,COCOA POT,PINK SPRAYS,GOLD......................... 28.00
LIMOGES,COFFEEPOT,PINK,BLUE FLORAL,GOLD,5 CUPS & OVAL-SHAPED
  SAUCERS.................................................. 125.00
LIMOGES,COFFEEPOT,THISTLE PATTERN,FRUIT FINIAL,GOLD TRIM,
  CLEAR.................................................... 18.00
LIMOGES,COMPOTE,PINK FLORAL INSIDE & OUTSIDE,GOLD,SCALLOPED,
  10 IN.HIGH............................................... 65.00
LIMOGES,CREAMER & SUGAR,POPPIES,LEAVES,GOLD,ARTIST-SIGNED
  BARBOE................................................... 39.50
LIMOGES,CREAMER & SUGAR,ROSE GARLAND,BOAT-SHAPED,TRAY,
  HAND-PAINTED............................................. 38.00
LIMOGES,CREAMER & SUGAR,SPRAYS OF VIOLETS,WHITE GROUND,GOLD,
  MARKED................................................... 25.00
LIMOGES,CREAMER & SUGAR,WHITE GROUND,CHERUBS,SCALLOPED BASES
  & TOPS................................................... 27.50
LIMOGES,CUP,BOULLION,SAUCER,WHITE EMBOSSED DESIGN,GOLD,SET
  OF 10.................................................... 75.00
LIMOGES,CUP & SAUCER,ALLOVER DESIGN,VIOLETS,GOLD TRIM ON
  HANDLE & RIMS............................................ 12.00
LIMOGES,CUP & SAUCER,BLUE STRIPE,PINK FLOWERS.............. 3.50
LIMOGES,CUP & SAUCER,BOUILLON,HAND-DECORATED FLORAL........ 14.00
LIMOGES,CUP & SAUCER,CHOCOLATE,PINK SPRAYS,GOLD,3 SETS..... 8.00
LIMOGES,CUP & SAUCER,DEMITASSE,FLORAL,FRANCE,SET OF 6...... 30.00
LIMOGES,CUP & SAUCER,DEMITASSE,FLORAL,MARKED D & C FRANCE,
  SET OF 6................................................. 30.00
LIMOGES,CUP & SAUCER,DEMITASSE,FLOWER SPRAYS............... 3.50
LIMOGES,CUP & SAUCER,EMERALD GREEN,INTERMINGLED GOLD FLORAL,
  GOLD BORDER.............................................. 7.50
LIMOGES,CUP & SAUCER,FLORAL,GOLD,C.H.FIELD,HAVILAND........ 15.00
LIMOGES,CUP & SAUCER,NARBONNE PATTERN,GREEN BAND,GOLD
  FILIGREE................................................. 5.00
LIMOGES,CUP & SAUCER,PEACH,GREEN,BIRDS,HAND PAINTED........ 12.00
LIMOGES,CUP & SAUCER,PINK ROSES........................... 5.00
LIMOGES,DINNER SET,72 PIECES,SERVICE FOR 8,APPLE BLOSSOM,
  T.HAVILAND............................................... 300.00
LIMOGES,DISH,BONE,PINK MORNING GLORIES,BASSETT,AUSTRIA,SET
  OF 4..................................................... 15.00

LIMOGES,DISH,BONE,SCALLOPED EDGE,GOLD,FLORAL,SET OF 6....... 25.00
LIMOGES,DISH,CANDY,FORGET-ME-NOTS,HANDLE,SCALLOPED,
  5 1/4-IN.DIAMETER................................ 6.00
LIMOGES,DISH,CHEESE,FLORAL,GOLD TRIM,COVER,FRANCE,9 IN..... 22.00
LIMOGES,DISH,DUNO,OBLONG,8 IN.............................. 8.00
LIMOGES,DISH,PIN,VIOLETS,COVER,FRANCE,3 1/2-IN.DIAMETER.... 8.50
LIMOGES,DISH,RELISH,BUNCH OF RED RADISHES,GREEN LEAVES,GILT
  TOP.................................................. 8.50
LIMOGES,DISH,SERVING,FLORAL,GOLD,CENTER HANDLE,THREE
  SECTIONS,J.POUYAT................................... 35.00
LIMOGES,DISH,THREE SECTIONS,GREEN,ROSE COLOR,GOLD,SIGNED
  M.MARTIN,1909....................................... 30.00
LIMOGES,DISH,VEGETABLE,CREAM-WHITE,GOLD TRIM,SQUARE HANDLES,
  COVER............................................... 20.00
LIMOGES,DISH,VEGETABLE,THE LOUVRE,T.HAVILAND,COVER......... 22.00
LIMOGES,DOLL,WALKING,20 IN................................ 125.00
LIMOGES,GAME SET,BLUE SCENIC,WATER BACKGROUND,BIRDS,PLATTER,
  6 PLATES........................................... 150.00
LIMOGES,GRAVY BOAT,ATTACHED TRAY,PINK ROSES,GREEN LEAVES,
  GOLD,HAVILAND....................................... 9.50
LIMOGES,GRAVY BOAT,HAND-PAINTED ROSES,ATTACHED SAUCER...... 12.00
LIMOGES,HAIR RECEIVER,BLUE FORGET-ME-NOTS,HAND-PAINTED..... 8.50
LIMOGES,HAIR RECEIVER,CORONET,PINK FLORAL,GREEN & GOLD
  GROUND,BEADING...................................... 6.50
LIMOGES,HAIR RECEIVER,GREEN TO WHITE GROUND,GOLD,RED &
  YELLOW ROSES........................................ 12.00
LIMOGES,HOLDER,HATPIN,FORGET-ME-NOT,4 IN.................. 15.00
LIMOGES,HOLDER,HATPIN,GREEN GROUND,FLORAL DESIGN,
  ARTIST-SIGNED....................................... 14.50
LIMOGES,HOLDER,HATPIN,PINK ROSE FESTOONS,WHITE,GOLD,ATTACHED
  SAUCER.............................................. 20.00
LIMOGES,INKWELL,YELLOW IRIS DECOR......................... 10.00
LIMOGES,JAR,MARMALADE,FLORAL,GOLD,COVER,SERVING PLATE,MARKED
  J.POUYAT............................................ 35.00
LIMOGES,JAR,MARMALADE,LARGE PINK FLOWERS,GOLD,MARKED
  J.P.L.J.,LID,PLATE.................................. 35.00
LIMOGES,JAR,POWDER,RED & PINK ROSES,HAND-PAINTED,
  5-IN.DIAMETER....................................... 8.00
LIMOGES,MUG,INDIAN IN FULL HEADDRESS,ARTIST-SIGNED,6 IN.HIGH 40.00
LIMOGES,MUG,SHAVING,FLORAL,NAME.......................... 20.00
LIMOGES,NAPPIE,PINK FLOWERS,GREEN LEAVES,GOLD EDGE,6 IN.... 17.50
LIMOGES,PAINTING ON PORCELAIN,EMPRESS EUGENIE,FRAME,3 1/2 X
  3 IN................................................ 48.50
LIMOGES,PILLBOX,HAND-PAINTED DECOR INSIDE & OUTSIDE,
  HEART-SHAPE,HINGED.................................. 14.00
LIMOGES,PITCHER,CIDER,RUST COLOR GROUND,APPLES,HAND-PAINTED,
  SQUAT............................................... 55.00
LIMOGES,PITCHER,CUPIDS,GOLD,6 IN......................... 18.00
LIMOGES,PITCHER,FLOWERS,GOLD DRAGON HANDLE,ARTIST-SIGNED,
  1842,14 IN......................................... 150.00
LIMOGES,PITCHER,LEMONADE,LEMONS AROUND BOTTOM,GOLD RIM &
  HANDLE.............................................. 18.50
LIMOGES,PITCHER,MONK DRINKING,HOLDS BASKET OF BOTTLES,
  HAND-PAINTED........................................ 65.00
LIMOGES,PITCHER,PINK & GREEN FLOWERS,HAVILAND,5 IN.TALL.... 7.50
LIMOGES,PITCHER,PURPLE,RED,WHITE GRAPES,TANKARD,
  14 1/2 IN.TALL...................................... 75.00
LIMOGES,PLAQUE,GAME BIRD,BLUE GROUND,ROCOCO BORDER,13 IN.... 85.00
LIMOGES,PLAQUE,GAME,TWO LARGE BIRDS,ROCOCO GOLD BORDER,
  SIGNED MUVILLE...................................... 75.00
LIMOGES,PLAQUE,PORTRAIT,MONK,ROCOCO GOLD SCALLOP,EMBOSSED,
  11 7/8 IN........................................... 27.50
LIMOGES,PLAQUE,ROMAN,CHARIOT,HORSES,BLACK JASPERWARE,BRONZE
  FRAME.............................................. 150.00
LIMOGES,PLATE,ALLOVER STRAWBERRY DESIGN,10 IN............. 10.00
LIMOGES,PLATE,ALLOVER THISTLE DESIGN,10 IN............... 10.00
LIMOGES,PLATE,APPLES,LEAVES,ARTIST-INITIALED,MARKED LIMOGES,
  FRANCE,9 IN......................................... 15.00
LIMOGES,PLATE,ASTERS,HAND-PAINTED,SIGNED,8 1/2 IN......... 16.00
LIMOGES,PLATE,BAND OF PINK ROSES,GREEN LEAVES,GOLD TRIM,
  HAVILAND............................................ 4.00
LIMOGES,PLATE,BEIGE GROUND,FLORAL,HAND-PAINTED,SCALLOPED,
  9 IN.,SET OF 11.................................... 159.50
LIMOGES,PLATE,BIRD,FRANCE,9 1/2 IN....................... 24.50
LIMOGES,PLATE,BIRD,TREES,ARTIST SIGNED L.COUDERT,FRANCE
  CORONET,10 IN....................................... 32.00
LIMOGES,PLATE,CAKE,FLORAL,FRANCE,SET OF 6................ 30.00
LIMOGES,PLATE,CAKE,FLORAL,MARKED D & C FRANCE,SET OF 6..... 30.00
LIMOGES,PLATE,CAKE,VENICE PATTERN,PINK ROSES ON BORDER,
  PATENT 1896........................................ 14.50
LIMOGES,PLATE,CHOP,BLACKBERRIES,WIDE GOLD BORDER,MARK,

12-IN.DIAMETER............................................... 25.00
LIMOGES,PLATE,COUPLE IN 18TH CENTURY ATTIRE,RUFFLED RIM,
WHITE,GOLD,9 IN............................................. 18.00
LIMOGES,PLATE,CREAM GROUND,BLUE FLOWERS,LACY,MARKED,8 IN.,
PAIR........................................................ 15.00
LIMOGES,PLATE,DESSERT,FLORAL SPRAYS,GOLD TRIM,
7 3/8-IN.DIAMETER,SET OF 4.................................. 7.50
LIMOGES,PLATE,DUCK IN WATER,SKY,FLORAL,GOLD,HAND-PAINTED,
9 1/4 IN................................................... 12.50
LIMOGES,PLATE,DUCKS IN FLIGHT ABOVE MARSH,GOLD,HAND-PAINTED,
9 1/4 IN................................................... 12.50
LIMOGES,PLATE,ENAMEL,HAND-PAINTED LILIES OF THE VALLEY,
CORONET,FRANCE............................................. 8.50
LIMOGES,PLATE,FISH,CORONET,HAND-PAINTED,SIGNED PUVIS....... 25.00
LIMOGES,PLATE,FISH,ROCOCO GOLD BORDER,PIERCED FOR HANGING,
10 IN...................................................... 35.00
LIMOGES,PLATE,FLORAL,ROSES,GILT BORDERS AROUND RIM,
10-IN.DIAMETER............................................. 5.00
LIMOGES,PLATE,FORGET-ME-NOTS,YELLOW CENTER,MARKED J.P.L.,
HAND-PAINTED............................................... 4.00
LIMOGES,PLATE,FUCHSIA & PERIWINKLE IRIS,COIN GOLD EDGE,
7 1/2 IN................................................... 10.00
LIMOGES,PLATE,GAME BIRD AT STREAM,GOLD,HAND-PAINTED,
9 1/4 IN................................................... 12.50
LIMOGES,PLATE,GAME BIRD,FLORAL,ROCOCO GOLD SCALLOPS,
9 7/8 IN................................................... 39.00
LIMOGES,PLATE,GAME BIRD,SKY,FLORAL GROUND,GOLD SPECKLE,
9 1/4 IN................................................... 12.50
LIMOGES,PLATE,GAME,CORONET,QUAIL,PIERCED.................... 65.00
LIMOGES,PLATE,GAME,DEER,TREES,LAKE,BEIGE & GRAY ON WHITE,
HAVILAND................................................... 10.00
LIMOGES,PLATE,GAME,DUCKS,TREES,LAKE,BEIGE & GRAY ON WHITE,
HAVILAND................................................... 10.00
LIMOGES,PLATE,GAME,GROUSE,TREES,LAKE,BEIGE & GRAY ON WHITE,
HAVILAND................................................... 10.00
LIMOGES,PLATE,GAME,PHEASANT,SIGNED LA COUDERT,CORONET,10 IN. 52.00
LIMOGES,PLATE,GAME,PHEASANT,SIGNED MAX,CORONET,9 3/4 IN..... 85.00
LIMOGES,PLATE,GAME,PHEASANTS,CORONET,SIGNED L.CONDER,
10 1/4-IN.DIAMETER......................................... 25.00
LIMOGES,PLATE,GAME,STANDING BIRD,BUSHES,CORONET,ARTIST
L.COUDERT.................................................. 49.50
LIMOGES,PLATE,GAME,TWO BIRDS ALOFT,MARSHES,SIGNED DUBOIS,
10 IN...................................................... 40.00
LIMOGES,PLATE,GAME,TWO GEESE FLYING OVER POND,
13 3/4-IN.DIAMETER......................................... 75.00
LIMOGES,PLATE,GAME,TWO QUAILS,ARTIST-SIGNED,SCALLOPED,GOLD,
CORONET.................................................... 43.00
LIMOGES,PLATE,GOLD & BROWN FLORAL,HAND-PAINTED,SIGNED...... 6.75
LIMOGES,PLATE,GOLD BORDER,OLD ENGLISH S,MARKED J.P.L.,SET OF
5.......................................................... 20.00
LIMOGES,PLATE,GOLD CENTER,COBALT BORDER,GOLD TRIM,J.POUYAT,
7 3/4 IN................................................... 26.00
LIMOGES,PLATE,GOLD SCALLOPED,HANGING BIRD,SIGNED,14 IN..... 75.00
LIMOGES,PLATE,GOOSEBERRY DECOR,PINK,GREEN,TAN,WHITE GROUND,
9 IN....................................................... 15.00
LIMOGES,PLATE,GRAPE CLUSTERS,MARKED LA SEYNIL LIMOGES,P & P
FRANCE..................................................... 16.50
LIMOGES,PLATE,GREEN GROUND,YELLOW NASTURTIUMS,HAND-PAINTED,
8 IN.,3.................................................... 12.00
LIMOGES,PLATE,HAND-PAINTED CLASSICAL DESIGN,SIGNED BY
ARTIST,GOLD EDGE........................................... 15.00
LIMOGES,PLATE,HAND-PAINTED,FLORAL,BEIGE GROUND,9 IN.,SET OF
11......................................................... 89.50
LIMOGES,PLATE,HAND-PAINTED,GOLD ROCOCO,SCALLOPED,HOLLY,
11 1/2 IN.................................................. 53.00
LIMOGES,PLATE,IVORY COLOR GROUND,FLORAL,SCALLOPED,
HAND-PAINTED,SET OF 11..................................... 159.50
LIMOGES,PLATE,IVORY GROUND,FLORAL,SCALLOPED,HAND-PAINTED,
9 IN.,SET OF 11............................................ 159.50
LIMOGES,PLATE,LAVENDER BOWS & FLORAL,RIBBED BORDER,
T.HAVILAND,9 IN.,6......................................... 18.00
LIMOGES,PLATE,OYSTER,CONCAVE OYSTER SHELLS,BLUE GROUND,GREEN
RIBBON,10...............................................1,100.00
LIMOGES,PLATE,OYSTER,FLORAL SPRAYS......................... 12.50
LIMOGES,PLATE,OYSTER,FLOWER GARLANDS....................... 8.00
LIMOGES,PLATE,OYSTER,PINK & YELLOW FLOWERS,WEEDS,BUTTERFLY,
FISH,9 IN.................................................. 35.00
LIMOGES,PLATE,OYSTER,PINK ROSES,WHITE DAISIES,SCALLOPED,GOLD
EDGE,8..................................................... 75.00
LIMOGES,PLATE,PHEASANTS,GOLD SPECKLE,HAND-PAINTED,9 1/4 IN.. 12.50
LIMOGES,PLATE,PINK ROSES,BLUE FORGET-ME-NOTS,GILT,7 IN...... 4.50

```
LIMOGES,PLATE,PINK ROSES,DAISIES,BLUE RIBBONS,7 1/2 IN......      2.50
LIMOGES,PLATE,POPPIES,LEAVES,GOLD,ARTIST-SIGNED BARBOE,
  9 1/4 IN.................................................     29.50
LIMOGES,PLATE,PORTRAIT,GIRL PROFILE,FROUFROU NECKLINE,GREEN
  SHADING.................................................     18.00
LIMOGES,PLATE,PORTRAIT,INDIAN,WHITE SWAN CROW IN FULL
  FEATHERED HEADGEAR......................................     50.00
LIMOGES,PLATE,PORTRAIT,MARIE ANTOINETTE,SIGNED.............     34.50
LIMOGES,PLATE,PORTRAIT,MME.DE STAEL,TURQUOISE BORDER,
  ARTIST-SIGNED...........................................     25.00
LIMOGES,PLATE,PORTRAIT,MME.RECAMIER,TURQUOISE BORDER,
  ARTIST-SIGNED...........................................     25.00
LIMOGES,PLATE,PORTRAIT,QUEEN LOUISE,SCALLOPED,ARTIST-SIGNED,
  9 3/8 IN................................................     23.50
LIMOGES,PLATE,PORTRAIT,REINE HORTENSE,TURQUOISE BORDER,GOLD,
  SIGNED..................................................     25.00
LIMOGES,PLATE,RED ROSES,ARTIST-SIGNED,8 IN.................     10.00
LIMOGES,PLATE,ROSE & BLUE FLORAL,GILT,MARKED GDA,7 1/2 IN...     3.50
LIMOGES,PLATE,ROSE & LAVENDER FLORAL DESIGN,THEODORE
  HAVILAND................................................      5.00
LIMOGES,PLATE,ROSE PATTERN,GOLD SCALLOP,6 1/4 IN.,SET OF 4..     6.50
LIMOGES,PLATE,ROSES,LILACS,UNEVEN GOLD EDGE,HAND-PAINTED,
  8 1/2 IN................................................     16.00
LIMOGES,PLATE,SEASCAPE,HAND-PAINTED,ARTIST SIGNED,8 1/2 IN..     18.00
LIMOGES,PLATE,SHEPARDESS,BOY,SHEEP,RESTING BESIDE RIVER,
  9 1/2 IN................................................     18.00
LIMOGES,PLATE,STRAWBERRIES,HAND-PAINTED,DATED,9 IN.........     15.00
LIMOGES,PLATE,WHITE GROUND,ALLOVER BLUE FLORAL,GOLD RIM,TWO
  HANDLES.................................................     15.00
LIMOGES,PLATE,WHITE,GEOMETRIC,GOLD GREEK KEY BORDER,9 IN.,
  SET OF 12...............................................     48.00
LIMOGES,PLATE,WHITE,GOLD BORDER,LARGE OLD ENGLISH S,
  6 1/4 IN.,SET OF 5......................................     20.00
LIMOGES,PLATE,WHITE,PINK & GREEN POPPIES,T.HAVILAND,
  9 1/2 IN.,SET OF 7......................................     36.00
LIMOGES,PLATTER,ICE CREAM,FLORAL SPRAYS,GOLD TRIM HANDLES,
  EMBOSSED RIM............................................     10.00
LIMOGES,PLATTER,ICE CREAM,PINK ROSES,SCALLOPED,HANDLES,
  6 PLATES................................................     35.00
LIMOGES,PLATTER,PINK & BLUE FLOWERS,GREEN LEAVES,15 IN......     12.00
LIMOGES,PLATTER,PINK FLORAL,GREEN LEAVES,10 1/2 X 9 IN......     12.00
LIMOGES,RAMEKIN,GOLD BORDER,HAVILAND.......................      7.50
LIMOGES,SALT DIP,GOLD DECOR,HEXAGONAL......................      3.50
LIMOGES,SALT DISH,MOTHER-OF-PEARL,GOLD BAND,FOOTED,SET OF 4.     16.00
LIMOGES,SHAKER,SALT & PEPPER,DAISIES,PAINTED GOLD TOP,FRANCE      4.00
LIMOGES,SHAVING MUG,HAND-PAINTED PURPLE ASTERS,ARTIST
  SIGNED,1899.............................................     18.50
LIMOGES,SOUP,PINK GARLANDS OF FLOWERS,SET OF 12............     25.00
LIMOGES,SUGAR,BLUE MEDALLIONS,RAISED GOLD,GOLD HANDLES,
  FINIAL,OVAL.............................................      9.00
LIMOGES,SUGAR,HAND-PAINTED ROSES,GREEN GROUND..............      8.50
LIMOGES,TEA CADDY,BLUE,GREEN,HAND-PAINTED..................     16.00
LIMOGES,TEA CADDY,YELLOW,SHADED GREEN FERNS,GOLD SCROLLS,
  OVAL LID................................................     18.00
LIMOGES,TEA SET,PEACH,GOLD SPOUT,HANDLES & FINIALS,
  HAND-PAINTED,3 PIECES...................................     75.00
LIMOGES,TEA SET,TWISTED HANDLES,SMALL ROSES,TEAPOT,SUGAR &
  CREAMER.................................................     25.00
LIMOGES,TEAPOT,CREAMER,SUGAR,U.S.GREAT SEAL,WHITE,GOLD TRIM.     35.00
LIMOGES,TEAPOT,SUGAR,CREAMER,WASTE BOWL,PINK FLOWERS,GOLD
  TRIM....................................................     65.00
LIMOGES,TRAY,DEEP RED & GREEN GROUND,RED CHERRIES,MARK,
  13 IN.ROUND.............................................     35.00
LIMOGES,TRAY,DRESSER,COVERED POWDER JAR....................     15.00
LIMOGES,TRAY,DRESSER,CREAMY YELLOW,SCALLOPED EDGE,
  HAND-PAINTED FIRS.......................................     18.50
LIMOGES,TRAY,DRESSER,IVORY COLOR GROUND,PINK ROSES,BLUE
  FLORAL,GOLD.............................................      9.50
LIMOGES,TRAY,DRESSER,LARGE PINK ROSES,10 1/2 IN............     10.00
LIMOGES,TRAY,DRESSER,PASTEL GREEN,PINK ROSES,INITIAL R IN
  CENTER..................................................     15.00
LIMOGES,TRAY,DRESSER,PINK & GREEN FLORAL GARLAND BORDER,
  HAVILAND................................................     28.00
LIMOGES,TRAY,DRESSER,PINK ROSE SPRAY,11 IN. X 8 1/2 IN......     17.00
LIMOGES,TRAY,DRESSER,RING TREE,POWDER BOX,PIN TRAY,
  CANDLESTICK,FLORAL......................................     45.00
LIMOGES,TRAY,DRESSER,WHITE CENTER,BLUE BORDER,FLORAL,FRANCE,
  11 1/2 IN...............................................      8.00
LIMOGES,TRAY,DRESSER,WHITE ROSES..........................     15.00
LIMOGES,TRAY,PIN,CERISE & LAVENDER GROUND,PURPLE FLORAL,
  PALLET SHAPE............................................     35.00
```

```
LIMOGES,TRAY,PINK APPLE BLOSSOMS,GREEN LEAVES,GOLD EDGE,
    12 1/2 X 17 IN............................................   45.00
LIMOGES,TRAY,PINK,WHITE ROSES,SIGNED SHERRATT,8 X 12 IN.LONG    25.00
LIMOGES,TRAY,VIOLET SPRAYS,KIDNEY SHAPE,HAND-PAINTED,
    12 1/2 X 9 1/4 IN.........................................   18.00
LIMOGES,TUREEN,SOUP,PINK FLORAL ON BORDER,CHARLES FIELD
    HAVILAND..................................................   19.00
LIMOGES,TUREEN,SOUP,PINK ROSES,GREEN LEAVES,THEO.HAVILAND...    28.00
LIMOGES,TUREEN,SOUP,WHITE GROUND,ROSES,BOW FINIAL,GOLD,
    COVER,16 IN...............................................   28.00
LIMOGES,VASE,BUD,BULBOUS,YELLOW,WHITE FLORAL,IVORY GROUND,
    SIGNED BAIL...............................................   18.00
LIMOGES,VASE,FAURE MARTY,ENAMELED,SIGNED,FRANCE,4 IN.TALL...    75.00
LIMOGES,VASE,GIRL AS BUTTERFLY,BATS,GOLD TRIM,ARTIST-SIGNED,
    15 IN.HIGH................................................   50.00
LIMOGES,VASE,WHITE,BLUE TOP BAND,HAND-PAINTED DOGWOOD,SIGNED
    H.WILSON..................................................   25.00


      LINEN INCLUDES ALL TYPES OF TABLE LINENS,AND HOUSEHOLD
      LINENS SUCH AS COVERLETS,QUILTS,FABRICS,ETC.
    LINEN,SEE ALSO,NEEDLEWORK
LINEN,AFGHAN,MULTICOLORED STRIPES,BLACK EDGE,HAND-CROCHETED,
    44 X 78 IN................................................   21.00
LINEN,ALTAR CLOTH,ENDPIECE,EMBROIDERY,POPPY,BLUE,SCENE,
    ITALY,26 IN.LONG..........................................   95.00
LINEN,BANQUET CLOTH,ROSE BORDER,MONOGRAM,108 X 72 IN.,
    12 NAPKINS,IRELAND........................................   38.00
LINEN,BEDSPREAD,FLOWER MEDALLION,GOLD SATIN,CHINA,75 X
    98 IN.,PAIR...............................................   59.50
LINEN,BEDSPREAD,HOMESPUN,BLUE,WHITE,REVERSIBLE,FRINGE,85 X
    72 IN.....................................................   62.50
LINEN,BEDSPREAD,POPCORN PATTERN,CROCHETED,90 X 106 IN.......   35.00
LINEN,BEDSPREAD,WOVEN MICKEY MOUSE CHARACTERS,FULL SIZE.....   30.00
LINEN,BLANKET,HOMESPUN,WHITE,WOOL TRIM.....................   18.00
LINEN,BONNET,WOODEN HOOP,CIRCA 1790........................   17.00
LINEN,CAP,BED,SILK,OPENINGS FOR EARS,1868..................    3.00
LINEN,CAP,EMBROIDERED,LACY ORGANDY,RIBBONS,1865............    3.00
LINEN,CARPET,EIGHTEEN OBLONG PANELS,NEEDLEWORK,171 IN. X
    91 IN.................................................1,850.00


      LINEN OR WOOL COVERLETS WERE MADE DURING THE EIGHTEENTH
      CENTURY. MOST OF THE COVERLETS DATE FROM 1800 TO 1850.
      FOUR TYPES WERE MADE: THE DOUBLE WOVEN, JACQUARD,SUMMER
      AND WINTER,AND OVERSHOT.
LINEN,COVERLET,BLUE & WHITE,BETHANY GENESEE CO.,N.Y.,1838...    85.00
LINEN,COVERLET,DOUBLE BED SIZE,HAND-LOOMED,SIGNED P.LORENZ,
    1840......................................................  110.00
LINEN,COVERLET,FIVE COLORS,WOVEN LINEN & WOOL,ALLOVER
    FLORAL,82 X 82 IN.........................................   75.00
LINEN,COVERLET,HOMESPUN,BLUE & WHITE,DATED 1837............   150.00
LINEN,COVERLET,INDIAN,PINK,YELLOW,WHITE,FULL SIZE,DATED
    1844......................................................  125.00
LINEN,COVERLET,PATCHWORK,LOG CABIN PATTERN,SPLIT CORNERS FOR
    POSTER BED................................................   37.50
LINEN,COVERLET,RED,OTHER SIDE BLUE,DOUBLE-WOVEN,DESIGN,75 X
    76 IN.....................................................   85.00
LINEN,COVERLET,WOVEN IN SOMERSET,OHIO,DATED 1849,BLUE.......   50.00
LINEN,CURTAIN,NET,BATTENBERG LACY TRIM,THREE YARDS LONG,TWO
    PAIRS.....................................................   27.50
LINEN,DINNER CLOTH,ECRU DAMASK,HEMSTITCHED,52 X 70 IN.,
    6 NAPKINS,18 IN...........................................   35.00
LINEN,DOILY,ECRU LINEN,CROCHET LACE BORDER,19 IN.ACROSS.....   25.00
LINEN,DRESS,CHRISTENING,TUCKS,EMBROIDERY,MADE IN 1886.......   18.00
LINEN,DRESSER SCARF,BATTENBERG,5 FEET LONG X 15 IN.WIDE.....   22.00
LINEN,DUSTER,AUTO,FITTED,PRINCESS STYLE,CAPE COLLAR,
    28 BUTTONS,SIZE 18........................................   16.50
LINEN,HANDBAG,CREWEL,FRENCH SCENE ON BOTH SIDES,5 1/2 X
    5 IN......................................................   25.00
LINEN,HANDKERCHIEF,LINEN,HANDMADE,EMBROIDERED,NAME,1835,
    24 IN.SQUARE..............................................    3.98
LINEN,LACE,LIGHT ECRU,4 1/2 IN.WIDE,4 YDS..................   14.00
LINEN,LAP ROBE,DOG IN CENTER,GLASS EYE,BROWN & WHITE PLAID,
    45 X 62 IN................................................   19.00
LINEN,LAP ROBE,RED,YELLOW ROSES,FLORAL CORNERS,BLACK PLUSH..   35.00
LINEN,LAP ROBE,SLEIGH,HORSE HEAD DESIGN,GLASS EYE,WOOLEN,
    49 X 61 IN................................................   45.00
LINEN,MANDARIN SQUARE,NEEDLEWORK,CORAL-BEADED SUN,SILVER
    THREADS,13 IN.............................................   45.00
LINEN,PICTURE,NOBLEMAN,INDIANS,EMBROIDERED,CHENILLE,WOVEN,
```

| | |
|---|---:|
| 18 X 22 IN......................................... | 70.00 |
| LINEN,PILLOW SHAM,RED EMBROIDERY,BIRDS,FOLIAGE,PAIR......... | 13.00 |
| LINEN,PILLOW,HAND-PAINTED MAN,WOMAN,SIGNED GRACE LOPEZ,SILK. | 25.00 |
| LINEN,QUILT,CRAZY,EMBROIDERED,SILK,VELVET,HANDMADE.......... | 30.00 |
| LINEN,QUILT,LOG CABIN PATTERN,MADE FROM PIECES OF WOOL & COTTON,75 IN. | 38.50 |
| LINEN,QUILT,PATCH,HANDMADE,FULL SIZE, FOR POST BED.......... | 69.00 |
| LINEN,QUILT,PATCHWORK,COLOR STRIPS,BLACK YARN TACKING,WOOL, 52 X 72 IN. | 20.00 |
| LINEN,QUILT,PATCHWORK,MADE FROM PAVILION BANNERS,N.Y.WORLD'S FAIR,1939. | 45.00 |
| LINEN,QUILT,PATCHWORK,SILK & VELVET,LOG CABIN DESIGN,SILK BACK,LACE. | 45.00 |
| LINEN,QUILT,PINE TREE DESIGN,RED,WHITE,39 IN. X 39 IN....... | 20.00 |
| LINEN,QUILT,SQUARE BLOCKS OF ROSES,BUDS,LEAVES,HANDMADE,78 X 90 IN. | 59.00 |
| LINEN,QUILT,STARS,YELLOW & RED CALICO BORDER,WHITE-LINED, 80 X 88 IN. | 28.50 |
| LINEN,QUILT,WEDDING RING PATTERN,DOUBLE BED.................. | 70.00 |
| LINEN,ROBE,PRIEST,BLUE SILK,GOLD THREAD BOTTOM,GOLD DRAGONS, BIRDS,CHINA. | 10.00 |
| LINEN,RUG,HOOKED,D.A.R.SEAL DESIGN,36 X 42 IN............... | 20.00 |
| LINEN,RUG,MOUNTAIN GOAT FUR,42 X 50 IN..................... | 25.00 |
| LINEN,RUG,NEEDLEWORK,GROSSE POINT,ENGLAND,86 IN. X 41 IN.... | 275.00 |
| LINEN,RUG,WOOL,INCA ALPACA,INDIAN DESIGNS IN BROWNS,14 X 18 FEET. | 600.00 |
| LINEN,RUNNER,BANQUET TABLE,LACE INSETS,HANDMADE,ITALY,44 IN. X 114 IN. | 25.00 |
| LINEN,SAMPLER,ALPHABET,DOG,HORSE,NAME,AGE 12,1828,FRAME,19 X 26 IN. | 40.00 |
| LINEN,SAMPLER,ALPHABET,GIRL,BOY,GUITAR,FRAME,APRIL 1844, BROOKLYN,N.Y. | 55.00 |
| LINEN,SAMPLER,ALPHABET,NUMERALS,VERSE,FLORAL,SIGNED,1813, FRAME,16 IN. | 55.00 |
| LINEN,SAMPLER,ALPHABET,NUMBERS,DESIGNS,BIRDS-EYE MAPLE FRAME,16 X 10 IN. | 35.00 |
| LINEN,SAMPLER,ALPHABET,NUMBERS,NAMES OF TWO GIRLS,DIED 1836, DATED 1837. | 29.75 |
| LINEN,SAMPLER,CHURCH OF KIRKLEATHAM,BY ELIZABETH CUNDELL, 1834,ENGLAND. | 35.00 |
| LINEN,SAMPLER,CHURCH,DWELLING,FIGURES,CROSS-STITCH,16 1/2 X 16 IN. | 60.00 |
| LINEN,SAMPLER,CORA S. WATKINS,WORKED IN 10TH YEAR OF HER AGE,1869,FRAME. | 14.50 |
| LINEN,SAMPLER,FLORAL,SAYS BRISTOL SCHOOL,ADELINE GREEN,MAPLE FRAME. | 50.00 |
| LINEN,SAMPLER,HOUSE,BIRDS,TREES,SIGNED MARGARET SINCLAIR, OCT.20,1842. | 25.00 |
| LINEN,SAMPLER,HOUSE,VERSE,FRAME WITH CARVED LEAVES AT CORNERS. | 10.00 |
| LINEN,SAMPLER,NEUTRAL GROUND,ALPHABET,NUMBERS,URNS,FLOWERS, FRAME,10 IN. | 32.50 |
| LINEN,SAMPLER,PURPLE ON WHITE,ALPHABET,NUMBERS,DATED 1874, 9 X 19 IN.LONG. | 17.50 |
| LINEN,SCARF,BUREAU,BLUE SILK VELVET,TASSELS,CHENILLE EMBROIDERY,42 IN. | 5.00 |
| LINEN,SHAWL,BLACK SILK,EMBROIDERED,FRINGE,SPAIN,5 FT.SQUARE. | 150.00 |
| LINEN,SHAWL,BLACK,FRINGE,1868,43 IN. X 72 IN............... | 5.98 |
| LINEN,SHAWL,CREAM SILK GROUND,CREAM EMBROIDERY,FRINGE,52 X 54 IN. | 25.00 |
| LINEN,SHAWL,PIANO,WHITE SILK,EMBROIDED RED ROSES,LONG FRINGE | 18.00 |
| LINEN,SHAWL,SILK,EMBROIDERED,WHITE ON WHITE,FLORAL,CHINA, FRINGE,60 IN. | 22.00 |
| LINEN,SHAWL,SILK,RED VELVET BROCADE,ROSES,FRINGE,CHINA,62 X 40 IN. | 12.00 |
| LINEN,SHAWL,SPANISH TYPE,RED GROUND,EMBROIDERED WHITE ROSES, SILK. | 25.00 |
| LINEN,SHAWL,SPANISH,BLACK SILK,FLOWERS,FRINGE................ | 6.50 |
| LINEN,SHAWL,SPANISH,HAND-EMBROIDERED,LONG FRINGE, 54 IN.SQUARE. | 25.00 |
| LINEN,SHEET,CENTER SEAM,HOMESPUN,,90 IN. X 69 IN............ | 20.00 |
| LINEN,SPREAD,FULL SIZE,NEEDLEWORK,BLUE,WHITE,PEACOCK,FLORAL, DATED 1820. | 100.00 |
| LINEN,SPREAD,LINDBERGH,PINK,STATUE OF LIBERTY,EIFFEL TOWER, 100 X 86 IN. | 15.00 |
| LINEN,TABLECLOTH,BATTENBURG,50 IN......................... | 20.00 |
| LINEN,TABLECLOTH,DAMASK,TULIP PATTERN,70 IN. X 72 IN........ | 35.00 |
| LINEN,TABLECLOTH,EMBROIDERED,OAK LEAF PATTERN,GREEN,BROWN, 66 X 52 IN. | 17.50 |
| LINEN,TABLECLOTH,HOMESPUN,CREAM COLOR,CROCHETED EDGE LACE, | |

```
  68 X 64 IN.................................................    15.00
LINEN,TABLECLOTH,LACE,ECRU,90 X 72 IN.......................    10.00
LINEN,TABLECLOTH,OYSTER WHITE,CUT WORK,IRELAND,72 IN. X
  84 IN....................................................    35.00
LINEN,TABLECLOTH,RED,WHITE,FLORAL,FRINGE,LEAF BORDER,54 X
  68 IN....................................................    25.50
LINEN,TABLECLOTH,ROSES,LACE,HAND-CROCHETED,72 IN. X 50 IN...     6.75
LINEN,TABLECLOTH,TAPESTRY,ALLOVER PATTERN,56 IN.SQUARE......    24.50
LINEN,TABLECLOTH,TWO-POINT VENICE LACE,HANDMADE,72 X
  108 IN.,12 NAPKINS.......................................   300.00
LINEN,TABLECLOTH,TWO-POINT VENICE LACE,HANDMADE,
  54 IN.SQUARE,6 NAPKINS...................................   150.00
LINEN,THROW,PAISLEY,RED CENTER,FRINGED,10 1/2 FEET X
  5 1/2 FEET...............................................   200.00
LINEN,WALL HANGING,SILK BAND,CHINESE SCENE,SATIN,BROCADE,RED
  LINED....................................................    19.50
```

        LITHOPHANES ARE PORCELAIN PICTURES MADE BY CASTING CLAY
        IN LAYERS OF VARIOUS THICKNESSES. WHEN A PIECE IS HELD
        TO THE LIGHT,A PICTURE OF LIGHT AND SHADOW IS SEEN
        THROUGH IT. MOST LITHOPHANES DATE FROM THE 1825 TO 1875
        PERIOD. A FEW ARE STILL BEING MADE.

```
LITHOPHANE,CANDLE SHIELD,THREE SCENES,ORNATE WOODEN FRAME,
  FOLDING..................................................    45.00
LITHOPHANE,CANDLE SHIELD,WOMAN SEATED,PIERCED METAL FRAME &
  BASE,12 IN...............................................    70.00
LITHOPHANE,CANDLESTAND,WHITE,PORCELAIN,SCENIC,METAL STAND,
  BLACK,PEDESTAL...........................................    48.00
LITHOPHANE,FARM FAMILY,6 1/8 IN. X 4 5/8 IN.................    30.00
LITHOPHANE,MOTHER,CHILD,PUPPY,6 1/8 IN. X 4 5/8 IN.........     30.00
LITHOPHANE,MOUNTED IN RED & BLUE COLORED GLASS LEADED FRAME,
  5 1/2 IN.................................................    47.00
LITHOPHANE,NIGHT LIGHT,TEA WARMER,FOUR SCENICS,INSET........    65.00
LITHOPHANE,PLAQUE,FOREST SCENE,4 1/4 IN. X 5 IN.............    25.00
LITHOPHANE,PLAQUE,GIRL AND TREE IN MOONLIGHT,4 X 4 1/2 IN...    25.00
LITHOPHANE,PLAQUE,GIRL STANDING IN DOORWAY,2 5/8 IN. X
  3 1/4 IN.................................................    17.00
LITHOPHANE,PLAQUE,LOVERS IN BOAT,4 X 4 1/2 IN...............    25.00
LITHOPHANE,PLAQUE,LOVERS IN BOAT,VILLAGE IN DISTANCE,4 1/8 X
  4 5/8 IN.................................................    27.00
LITHOPHANE,PLAQUE,MOTHER DRESSING CHILD,4 X 4 1/2 IN........    25.00
LITHOPHANE,PLAQUE,TWO WOMEN AT DOORWAY,4 X 4 1/2 IN.........    25.00
LITHOPHANE,SHADE,LEADED,PANELS,CHILDREN SCENES,4-IN. X
  4-IN.DIAMETER............................................    85.00
LITHOPHANE,SHADE,ON WHALE OIL BASE,FIVE PANEL,CHILDREN
  SCENES,WIRED.............................................   175.00
LITHOPHANE,SHADE,PANELS,CHILDREN SCENES,LOG CABIN,10 X
  5 1/4 X 5 1/4 IN.........................................   225.00
LITHOPHANE,TEA WARMER,FOUR GERMAN SCENE INSERTS,BURNER,
  CONVERTED................................................    55.00
LITHOPHANE,TEA WARMER,FOUR PANELS..........................    65.00
```

        EGERMANN OR EGGERMAN GLASS WAS MADE BY FRIEDRICH
        EGERMANN IN BOHEMIA ABOUT 1830. HIS GLASS WAS MADE TO
        RESEMBLE POLISHED STONE AND HAS OFTEN BEEN MISTAKEN
        FOR CARVED POLISHED AGATE. THE GLASS IS CALLED
        LITHYALIN.

```
LITHYALIN,BOWL,EGGERMAN,CIRCA 1835,8 1/4-IN.DIAMETER........   125.00
LITHYALIN,LETTER RACK,EGGERMAN,GREEN,BLUE,TAN SWIRLS,GILT...   165.00
```

        LIVERPOOL,ENGLAND,HAS BEEN THE SITE OF SEVERAL POTTERY
        AND PORCELAIN FACTORIES FROM 1716 TO 1785. SOME
        EARTHENWARE WAS MADE WITH TRANSFER DECORATIONS. SADLER
        AND GREEN MADE PRINT-DECORATED WARES FROM 1756. MANY OF
        THE PIECES WERE MADE FOR THE AMERICAN MARKET AND
        FEATURED PATRIOTIC EMBLEMS SUCH AS EAGLES,FLAGS,AND
        OTHER SPECIAL-INTEREST MOTIFS.

```
LIVERPOOL,CUP & SAUCER,BLACK TRANSFER COWS,SCENERY,
  HANDLELESS...............................................    25.00
LIVERPOOL,CUP & SAUCER,BLACK TRANSFER,OLD CASTLE,CHURCH,
  HANDLELESS...............................................    25.00
LIVERPOOL,CUP & SAUCER,CIRCA 1800..........................    35.00
LIVERPOOL,CUP & SAUCER,PINK LUSTER BAND,TRANSFER,HANDLELESS.    27.50
LIVERPOOL,MUG,ODD FELLOWS,SYMBOL,POTTERY FROG INSIDE,VERSE,
  ROPE HANDLE..............................................    85.00
LIVERPOOL,PLATE,BLUE CHINESE DESIGN,OCTAGONAL,1780,
  8 5/8 IN.,PAIR...........................................    65.00
```

LOETZ GLASS WAS MADE IN AUSTRIA IN THE LATE
NINETEENTH CENTURY. MANY PIECES ARE SIGNED LOETZ,
LOETZ-AUSTRIA,OR AUSTRIA AND A PAIR OF CROSSED ARROWS
IN A CIRCLE. SOME UNSIGNED PIECES ARE CONFUSED WITH
TIFFANY GLASS.

LOETZ,BOWL,FINGER,TRAY,THREE-PETAL,THREADED,CRANBERRY GLASS.          50.00
LOETZ,BOWL,GREEN SHADING TO GOLD,PINCHED-IN SIDES, 4 IN. X
  5 1/2 IN...........................................................   100.00
LOETZ,BOWL,ROSE,GREEN,CRIMPED TOP,5 IN.HIGH,7 IN.ROUND......          125.00
LOETZ,BOWL,ROSE,PURPLE,BRONZE HOLDER,FEMALE FIGURES SUPPORT
  BOWL,AUSTRIA......................................................    55.00
LOETZ,BOWL,ROSE,SCALLOPED,TURNED-IN EDGE,RED-LINED,SMOOTH
  PONTIL,AUSTRIA....................................................    55.00
LOETZ,INKWELL,TRICORN,GREEN IRIDESCENT,PURPLE,WHITE IN BASE,
  BLOWN INSERT......................................................    95.00
LOETZ,LAMP,MUSHROOM SHADE,TURQUOISE IRIDESCENT,BASE,WOMEN'S
  FACES,20 IN.......................................................   175.00
LOETZ,PITCHER,WATER,IRIDESCENT GREEN,PANELED INSIDE,
  SCALLOPED TOP,SIGNED..............................................   225.00
LOETZ,SPRINKLER,ROSE WATER,BLUE-GREEN,IRIDESCENT,GOOSENECK
  SHAPE,11 IN.......................................................    95.00
LOETZ,TUMBLER,JUICE,GOLD IRIDESCENT SPECKLING,3 IN.HIGH.....          40.00
LOETZ,VASE,AMBER,IRIDESCENT,RAINDROP SPECKLES,BLUE & GREEN
  HIGHLIGHTS........................................................    50.00
LOETZ,VASE,BLUE IRIDESCENT,GOLD & PINK THREADS,AMBER FOOT,
  FLOWER-FORM.......................................................    98.00
LOETZ,VASE,BLUE SPECKLING,DEEPLY PINCHED SIDES,PETAL LIP,
  5 1/2 IN.TALL.....................................................    55.00
LOETZ,VASE,BLUE,GREEN,LAVENDER LINING,DIMPLED,AUSTRIA,
  6 1/2 IN.X 6 IN...................................................   110.00
LOETZ,VASE,BLUE,GREEN,PINK,BULBOUS BOTTOM,RIBBED,11 1/2 IN..          95.00
LOETZ,VASE,BLUE,IRIDESCENT,SILVER INLAID FLORAL,LEAF,
  PINCHED-IN BODY...................................................   150.00
LOETZ,VASE,BLUE,IRIDESCENT,SILVER INLAID FLORAL & LEAF
  DECOR,8 1/2 IN....................................................   150.00
LOETZ,VASE,CONNECTED LOOP DECOR,CYLINDRICAL,SILVERY-GOLD,
  14 IN.HIGH........................................................   225.00
LOETZ,VASE,DARK BLUE IRIDESCENT,WHITE FLOWERS,SIGNED,
  8 1/2 IN.,PAIR....................................................   250.00
LOETZ,VASE,DECOR,TWO ORNATE EARS,SIGNED,15 IN.HIGH.........           195.00
LOETZ,VASE,GOLD IRIDESCENCE,ALLOVER DESIGN,SCALLOPED TOP,
  5 1/2 IN.TALL.....................................................    48.00
LOETZ,VASE,GOLD IRIDESCENT SPECKLING,CHALICE SHAPE,SIGNED,
  6 IN.HIGH.........................................................   100.00
LOETZ,VASE,GOLD IRIDESCENT,SILVER COLLAR & FOOT,5 1/2 IN....          75.00
LOETZ,VASE,GREEN,IRIDESCENT SPLOTCHES,GROUND PONTIL,GREEN
  HANDLES,4 IN......................................................    50.00
LOETZ,VASE,GREEN,IRIDESCENT,EMBOSSED EAGLES,BRASS COLLAR,
  6 IN.HIGH.........................................................    95.00
LOETZ,VASE,HONEYCOMB GROUND,PURPLE GRAPES,SIGNED,AUSTRIA,
  NOV.1891..........................................................   185.00
LOETZ,VASE,IRIDESCENT,BULBOUS,AUSTRIA,7 IN.HIGH............           125.00
LOETZ,VASE,PEACOCK BLUE,IRIDIZED,OPTIC-RIBBED TREES,RUFFLED,
  4 1/2 IN..........................................................    48.00
LOETZ,VASE,RED CASE,SILVER-BLUE PULLUP DESIGN,5 1/4 IN......          125.00
LOETZ,VASE,RED-GOLD IRIDESCENT,MUSHROOM BASE,SERPENT
  ENTWINED,8 1/2 IN.................................................    30.00
LOETZ,VASE,ROSE,COPPER,GREEN,TOP LOOKS LIKE TURNED-BACK
  PETALS............................................................    85.00
LOETZ,VASE,SILVERY BLUE & GOLD IRIDESCENT,LOW PEDESTAL BASE,
  7 IN.TALL.........................................................    50.00
LOETZ,VASE,SWIRL PATTERN,IRIDESCENT,TAPERED,5 IN.TALL.......          58.00
LOETZ,VASE,TULIP DECOR,SIGNED,7 IN.HIGH...................           190.00
LOETZ,VASE,TURQUOISE,IRIDESCENT,BULBOUS,STERLING SILVER
  BAND,5 IN.HIGH....................................................   127.00
LOETZ,VASE,9 1/4 IN. HIGH,SIGNED...........................           200.00


LOTUS WARE WAS MADE BY THE KNOWLES,TAYLOR AND KNOWLES
COMPANY OF EAST LIVERPOOL,OHIO,FROM 1890 TO 1900.

LOTUS WARE,BERRY SET,THREE PIECES.........................           270.00
LOTUS WARE,BOWL,HAND-PAINTED ROSES,TWO PIERCED TURQUOISE
  MEDALLIONS........................................................   375.00
LOTUS WARE,BOWL,PINK ROSE SPRAYS,SCALLOPED,MARKED K.T.K.,
  5-IN.DIAMETER.....................................................    90.00
LOTUS WARE,BOWL,ROSE,GREEN FISHSCALES,22K GOLD TOP,1895,MARK         350.00
LOTUS WARE,BOWL,ROSE,SIGNED,DATED.........................           600.00
LOTUS WARE,CREAMER,WHITE,CLASSIC SHAPE,MARKED KTK..........          135.00
LOTUS WARE,PITCHER,CREAM..................................           185.00
LOTUS WARE,VASE,CREMONIAN PATTERN,PINK & BLUE FLORAL,GOLD
  HANDLES,6 IN......................................................   125.00

LOTUS WARE,VASE,DARK GREEN GROUND,APPLIED WHITE VIOLETS,
  LEAVES,8 IN......................................................  600.00
LUNEVILLE,BOWL,ORIENTAL DESIGN,KIMONA FIGURES,FRANCE,
  FAYENCE,1778.....................................................  75.00
LUNEVILLE,VASE,GRAY MOTTLED,16 IN.................................  75.00


      LUSTERWARE WAS MEANT TO RESEMBLE COPPER,SILVER,OR GOLD.
    IT HAS BEEN USED SINCE THE SIXTEENTH CENTURY. MOST OF
    THE LUSTER FOUND TODAY WAS MADE DURING THE NINETEENTH
    CENTURY.
LUSTER,BLUE,PITCHER,MOTTLED FLORAL,MARKED BAVARIA WUNSIEDEL,
  5 1/2 IN........................................................  25.00
LUSTER,COPPER,BOWL,FLORAL ON GREEN BAND,3 1/2 X 5 1/4 IN....  42.00
LUSTER,COPPER,BOWL,PINK LUSTER INSIDE,FOOTED,2 3/4- X
  5-IN.DIAMETER...................................................  35.00
LUSTER,COPPER,CHALICE,BEADED BORDER,ENAMELED FLORAL DECOR,
  4 1/2 IN.HIGH...................................................  48.00
LUSTER,COPPER,COMPOTE,ROYAL BLUE BAND,THREE RAISED GROUPS,
  GIRL,CAT,1820...................................................  45.00
LUSTER,COPPER,CREAMER,3 IN. HIGH.......................ILLUS.  12.50
LUSTER,COPPER,CREAMER,BLUE BAND,3 IN............................  35.00
LUSTER,COPPER,CREAMER,BLUE FLORAL BAND,4 IN.................  15.00
LUSTER,COPPER,GOBLET,PINK & WHITE FLORAL,GREEN LEAVES.....  60.00
LUSTER,COPPER,GOBLET,TWO PURPLE BANDS,FLORAL,4 1/2 IN.HIGH..  65.00
LUSTER,COPPER,MASTER SALT,BROWN BAND DECOR....................  18.00
LUSTER,COPPER,MUG,BLUE BAND,GREYHOUND,COW IN RELIEF,
  3 IN.TALL.......................................................  58.00
LUSTER,COPPER,MUG,BLUE BAND,PINK LUSTER BAND AT TOP,WHITE
  LINING..........................................................  17.50
LUSTER,COPPER,MUG,BLUE,TAN......................................  27.50
LUSTER,COPPER,MUG,CHILD'S,BLUE,3 1/4 IN..............ILLUS.  12.50
LUSTER,COPPER,MUG,CHILD'S,SUNDERLAND BAND............ILLUS..  22.50
LUSTER,COPPER,MUG,ENAMELED BLUE FLORAL,BEADED TRIM.........  30.00
LUSTER,COPPER,MUG,ONE TAN & FOUR BLUE BANDS,BEADED,2 3/4 IN.  25.00
LUSTER,COPPER,MUG,ORANGE BANDS,3 1/2-IN.DIAMETER,
  3 1/2 IN.HIGH...................................................  35.00
LUSTER,COPPER,MUG,SHAVING,FLORAL & LEAF BAND................  35.00
LUSTER,COPPER,MUG,TAN GROUND,PINK STRIPES,BEADED BORDER AT
  BASE............................................................  35.00
LUSTER,COPPER,MUSTACHE CUP & SAUCER,LEFT-HANDED,THREE
  BROTHERS,SHIP...................................................  69.50
LUSTER,COPPER,PITCHER,BEADED BLUE BAND,CHERUBS ON SLEIGH,
  BIRDS,FLORAL....................................................  59.50
LUSTER,COPPER,PITCHER,BLUE BAND WITH PINK ROSES,6 IN.HIGH...  75.00
LUSTER,COPPER,PITCHER,BLUE BAND,BEADED BAND AT TOP,5 IN.TALL  35.00
LUSTER,COPPER,PITCHER,BLUE BAND,5 IN.TALL....................  30.00
LUSTER,COPPER,PITCHER,BLUE,WHITE & YELLOW FLORAL,ORNATE
  HANDLE,7 1/4 IN.................................................  73.50
LUSTER,COPPER,PITCHER,BULBOUS,ANGELS ON SIDES,BLUE SCROLL,
  6 IN............................................................  39.00
LUSTER,COPPER,PITCHER,BULBOUS,BEADED,BLUE BANDS,5 1/4 IN....  35.00
LUSTER,COPPER,PITCHER,BULBOUS,BLUE BAND TRIM,4 IN...........  15.00
LUSTER,COPPER,PITCHER,BULBOUS,BLUE BAND TRIM,3 1/2 IN.......  14.00
LUSTER,COPPER,PITCHER,BULBOUS,BLUE BAND TRIM,4 1/4 IN.......  18.00
LUSTER,COPPER,PITCHER,BULBOUS,BLUE BAND TRIM,5 IN...........  20.00
LUSTER,COPPER,PITCHER,BULBOUS,DANCING FIGURES,BLUE SCROLL,
  8 IN............................................................  38.00
LUSTER,COPPER,PITCHER,BULBOUS,DANCING FIGURES,BLUE SCROLL,
  5 1/2 IN........................................................  30.00
LUSTER,COPPER,PITCHER,BULBOUS,DEATH MASK HANDLE,FLORAL,
  BEADING,6 IN....................................................  59.00
LUSTER,COPPER,PITCHER,BULBOUS,DECORATED BAND AROUND BODY,
  DEER,7 IN.......................................................  37.00
LUSTER,COPPER,PITCHER,BULBOUS,DIAMOND SHAPES FORM BODY,
  FLORAL ED NECK..................................................  45.00
LUSTER,COPPER,PITCHER,BULBOUS,FLOW BLUE WIDE BAND TRIM,5 IN.  22.00
LUSTER,COPPER,PITCHER,BULBOUS,PAINTED ROSES ON SIDES,
  7 1/4 IN........................................................  35.00
LUSTER,COPPER,PITCHER,BULBOUS,TWO BOYS RESTING,BLUE SCROLL,
  7 IN............................................................  45.00
LUSTER,COPPER,PITCHER,BULBOUS,UP-DOWN RIDGES,HAWKS SPOUT,
  6 IN............................................................  45.00
LUSTER,COPPER,PITCHER,BULBOUS,WIDE BLUE NECK BAND,5 1/2 IN..  35.00
LUSTER,COPPER,PITCHER,CANARY BAND,TRANSFER,4 1/4 IN. ILLUS..  37.50
LUSTER,COPPER,PITCHER,ENAMEL ROSES,GREEN LEAVES,6 IN........  29.00
LUSTER,COPPER,PITCHER,ENAMELED FLORAL ON BLUE BOTTOM &
  COPPER TOP,7 IN.................................................  65.00
LUSTER,COPPER,PITCHER,HAND-PAINTED FLORAL DECOR,
  4 1/2 IN.TALL...................................................  28.00
LUSTER,COPPER,PITCHER,IRISH GETTY,REGISTRY MARK IN BASE,

COPPER LUSTER PITCHER    COPPER LUSTER CHILD'S MUG    COPPER LUSTER PITCHER

```
  1843.....................................................    72.00
LUSTER,COPPER,PITCHER,MINIATURE,BLUE BAND,TAN DOTS,1 1/2 IN.   12.00
LUSTER,COPPER,PITCHER,MINIATURE,ORANGE BAND,3 IN.HIGH.......   15.00
LUSTER,COPPER,PITCHER,MINIATURE,SANDED BAND,2 1/2 IN.ILLUS.    12.50
LUSTER,COPPER,PITCHER,PANELED,FLORAL PAINTING IN EACH PANEL
  & COLLAR TOP.............................................    59.50
LUSTER,COPPER,PITCHER,PINK FLOWERS,8 IN.TALL...............    65.00
LUSTER,COPPER,PITCHER,PINK LUSTER FLORAL ON TAN BAND,
  5 IN.HIGH................................................    28.00
LUSTER,COPPER,PITCHER,PINK,BANDS,BLUE BANDS,CIRCA 1820,
  5 3/4 IN.TALL............................................    42.00
LUSTER,COPPER,PITCHER,PURPLE FLORAL BAND,4 1/4 IN.HIGH.....    45.00
LUSTER,COPPER,PITCHER,RAISED FIGURES,GREEN DECOR,8 IN.TALL..   65.00
LUSTER,COPPER,PITCHER,RAISED FLORAL DECOR,3 3/4 IN.HIGH.....   20.00
LUSTER,COPPER,PITCHER,ROYAL BLUE BAND,FLORAL SPRAYS,CIRCA
  1820,4 IN.TALL...........................................    35.00
LUSTER,COPPER,PITCHER,SAND-COLOR BAND,FLORAL,5 IN.HIGH.....    40.00
LUSTER,COPPER,PITCHER,SIX-SIDED,PAINTED FLORAL ON TWO SIDES,
  7 3/4 IN.................................................    45.00
LUSTER,COPPER,PITCHER,SOUVENIR,SIR HENRY HAVELOCK,SIR COLIN
  CAMPBELL.................................................    85.00
LUSTER,COPPER,PITCHER,TAN BAND,3 1/2 IN..............ILLUS..   20.00
LUSTER,COPPER,PITCHER,TAN FLORAL TOP,BEADED BORDER,
  3 1/2 IN.HIGH............................................    18.00
LUSTER,COPPER,PITCHER,TWO WIDE YELLOW BANDS,LUSTER DESIGN,
  4 IN.HIGH................................................    30.00
LUSTER,COPPER,PITCHER,WIDE WHITE BAND,PINK FLORAL,
  5 1/2 IN.HIGH............................................    49.00
LUSTER,COPPER,PITCHER,YELLOW BAND AT TOP,BLUE & GOLD DECOR,
  2 1/2 IN.TALL............................................    18.00
LUSTER,COPPER,PITCHER,YELLOW BAND WITH GOLD DESIGN,3 IN.HIGH   30.00
LUSTER,COPPER,PITCHER,YELLOW BORDER AT TOP,GOLD ENAMEL TRIM,
  5 IN.TALL................................................    35.00
LUSTER,COPPER,PITCHER,YELLOW,WHITE,BLUE FLOWERS,GOOSE
  HANDLE,7 IN.HIGH.........................................    32.00
LUSTER,COPPER,PITCHER,8 IN...............................      75.00
LUSTER,COPPER,SALT,MASTER,BLUE BAND,EMBOSSED PINK ROSES,
  FOOTED..................................................     18.50
LUSTER,COPPER,SALT,MASTER,BROWN BAND DECOR................     18.00
LUSTER,COPPER,SALT,MASTER,FLOWERS AROUND BOWL,2 1/4 IN.HIGH.   15.00
LUSTER,COPPER,SALT,MASTER,GOLD LUSTER DESIGN ON BLUE BAND...   35.00
LUSTER,COPPER,SUGAR BOWL,BLUE AND TAN BANDS,2 3/4- X
  4-IN.DIAMETER...........................................     20.00
LUSTER,COPPER,SUGAR BOWL,BLUE BAND,BEADED,3 1/2- X
  6-IN.DIAMETER...........................................     32.00
LUSTER,COPPER,SUGAR BOWL,BLUE BAND,RAISED FLORAL,CHILDREN,
  FOOTED..................................................     37.00
  LUSTER,COPPER,TEA LEAF,SEE IRONSTONE,TEA LEAF
LUSTER,COPPER,TEAPOT,BLUE BAND,ENGLAND,4 1/2 IN...........     16.50
LUSTER,COPPER,TEAPOT,DARK BLUE BAND,FLORAL DECOR,EAGLE
  HANDLE,5 IN.HIGH........................................     48.00
LUSTER,COPPER,TEAPOT,GOLD LEAF TRAILING DESIGN,DARK BAND,
```

COPPER LUSTER
MINIATURE PITCHER

COPPER LUSTER
CHILD'S MUG

COPPER LUSTER CREAMER

*Courtesy Museum of Fine Arts, Boston. Gift of Mrs. Samuel Cabot*

From *Early American Embroidery Designs*
by MILDRED J. DAVIS

*Courtesy Museum of Fine Arts, Boston.
Gift of Mrs. Kennard Winsor*

*Courtesy Essex Institute, Salem, Massachusetts*

BUFFALO POTTERY

From *The Book of Buffalo Pottery* by VIOLET and SEYMOUR ALTMAN

From *The Encyclopedia of Glass Paperweights* by PAUL HOLLISTER, JR.

GLASS PAPERWEIGHTS

From *Glass Paperweights of the Bergstrom Art Center* by EVELYN CAMPBELL CLOAK

JAPANESE WOOD BLOCK PRINT

Hiroshige: *Landscape at Whirlpool Straits in Awa*
From *A Treasury of Japanese Wood Block Prints* by SADAO KIKUCHI

## BISQUE HEAD DOLLS

From *The Collector's Encyclopedia of Dolls*
by DOROTHY S., ELIZABETH A.,
and EVELYN J. COLEMAN

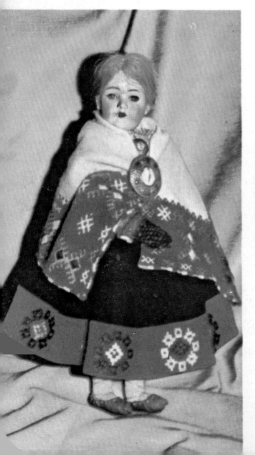

COPPER-RIMMED BUTTONS

From *The Collector's Encyclopedia of Buttons* by SALLY LUSCOMB

ROOKWOOD POTTERY AFTER WORLD WAR II

From *The Book of Rookwood Pottery* by HERBERT PECK

*Courtesy Helen Eisenberg*

TIFFANY VASES AND LAMP

From *Louis C. Tiffany: Rebel in Glass* by ROBERT KOCH

```
    BEADED RIM.................................................    45.00
LUSTER,COPPER,TOOTHPICK,BAND.....................................    25.00
LUSTER,COPPER,TOOTHPICK,BLUE OUTSIDE.............................    20.00
LUSTER,COPPER,TOOTHPICK,BLUE SANDED BAND,2 IN.HIGH..............    19.00
LUSTER,COPPER,URN,CIRCULAR FOOT PAINTED IN GOLD,BANDING OF
    MAIDENS................................................... 130.00
LUSTER,CUP & SAUCER,PINK,RUST FLORAL,SPRIGS,BLUE LEAVES,
    BANDING,1810..............................................    22.00
LUSTER,CUSPIDOR,INDIVIDUAL,PINK..................................     9.50
LUSTER,FAIRYLAND,VASE,PORTLAND VASE MOTIF MARK,BLUE,
    BUTTERFLIES,7 IN.......................................... 300.00
LUSTER,PINK,BOWL,COPPER & FLORAL.................................    22.50
LUSTER,PINK,BOWL,MOTTLED NAVY BLUE & PINK CENTER,SIGNED
    FIELDING DEVON............................................    40.00
LUSTER,PINK,BOWL,SOUP,PINK BUTTERFLIES...........................    12.00
LUSTER,PINK,BOWL,SUGAR,HOUSES,FLORAL,COPPER OVERTONES,
    CZECHOSLOVAKIA............................................    16.50
LUSTER,PINK,CREAMER,BOAT SHAPE,FLOWER MEDALLIONS,CIRCA 1825,
    WIDE SPOUT................................................    40.00
LUSTER,PINK,CREAMER,COPPER & FLORAL..............................    25.00
LUSTER,PINK,CREAMER,COPPER LUSTER FLORAL SPRAYS,3 1/2 IN....    18.50
LUSTER,PINK,CREAMER,FIGURES OF HOPE & FAITH ON SIDES.........    27.50
LUSTER,PINK,CUP & SAUCER,BERRY & LEAF.........................    14.00
LUSTER,PINK,CUP & SAUCER,BUTTERFLY PATTERN,HANDLELESS.......    27.00
LUSTER,PINK,CUP & SAUCER,DEMITASSE,HEART HANDLE.............    13.50
LUSTER,PINK,CUP & SAUCER,DEMITASSE,HOUSE PATTERN...........    20.00
LUSTER,PINK,CUP & SAUCER,DEMITASSE,SOUVENIR,HARTFORD,CONN.,
    GERMANY...................................................     3.00
LUSTER,PINK,CUP & SAUCER,FLORAL DECOR,BAND,SET OF 8.......    125.00
LUSTER,PINK,CUP & SAUCER,HANDLELESS...........................    24.50
LUSTER,PINK,CUP & SAUCER,HOUSE PATTERN,WISHBONE HANDLE......    16.00
LUSTER,PINK,CUP & SAUCER,LEAF & BERRY DESIGN.................    14.00
LUSTER,PINK,CUP & SAUCER,SCHOOLHOUSE,HANDLELESS.............    20.00
LUSTER,PINK,CUP & SAUCER,SWAGS,YELLOW,BLUE,GREEN,PINK,SADDLE
    HANDLE....................................................    22.00
LUSTER,PINK,DISH,BUTTER,COVER....................................    11.00
LUSTER,PINK,JUG,STAG PATTERN,8 IN.TALL...........................    68.00
LUSTER,PINK,MUG,CHILD'S,FORGET-ME-NOT,GOLD TRIM.............     5.00
LUSTER,PINK,MUG,RAISED WHITE FLOWERS,PANELED & SCALLOPED TOP    10.00
LUSTER,PINK,PITCHER,LID,5 IN.HIGH................................    23.00
LUSTER,PINK,PITCHER,PAIR,CIRCA 1850,8 IN. HIGH...................    50.00
LUSTER,PINK,PITCHER,RAISED STAG HUNT DECOR,DEER,TREE,THORN
    HANDLE....................................................    68.00
LUSTER,PINK,PITCHER,STAFFORDSHIRE,CIRCA 1825.................   210.00
LUSTER,PINK,PITCHER,TRANSFER,WITH URN,FLORAL,STAFFORDSHIRE,
    8 & 4 IN.................................................. 125.00
LUSTER,PINK,PLATE,HOUSE PATTERN,EMBOSSED FLORAL RIM........    10.00
LUSTER,PINK,PLATE,RED FLORAL,HAND-PAINTED,CIRCA 1800,
    7-IN.DIAMETER.............................................    15.00
LUSTER,PINK,SLIPPER,SOUVENIR,BELLEVILLE,ILLINOIS............    17.50
LUSTER,PINK,SLIPPER,SOUVENIR,CONCORD,NEW HAMPSHIRE..........    12.00
LUSTER,PINK,TEA CADDY,SUNDERLAND,SAILOR'S FAREWELL VERSE,
    SHIP,OVAL.................................................    35.00
LUSTER,SILVER,COFFEEPOT,TEAPOT,CREAMER,SUGAR,
    PORCELAIN-LINED,MELON RIB................................. 175.00
LUSTER,SILVER,CREAMER & SUGAR,RESIST,FLOWERS & LEAVES
    PATTERN...................................................    12.00
LUSTER,SILVER,MUG,PURPLE LUSTER LINING,CIRCA 1820,
    3 5/8 IN.HIGH.............................................    58.00
LUSTER,SILVER,PITCHER,8 IN.......................................    65.00
LUSTER,SILVER,SYRUP,RESIST,FLOWERS & LEAVES,COVER,UNDERPLATE    13.00
LUSTER,SILVER,TEAPOT,COFFEEPOT,CREAMER,SUGAR................   100.00
LUSTER,SILVER,TEAPOT,CREAMER,SUGAR,DATED 1915,BAVARIA.......    18.50
LUSTER,SILVER,TEAPOT,GADROON BANDING,1825,STAFFORDSHIRE,OVAL
    WOOD BOX..................................................    45.00
LUSTER,SILVER,TOBY,SHAKER,SALT,FULL FIGURE...................    75.00
LUSTER,SLIPPER,PINK,MARKED GERMANY,5 IN.LONG................    12.00
LUSTER,TEAPOT,GOLD FLORAL,LEAVES,ACORN FINIAL,COVER,PINK,
    CIRCA 1819................................................    79.50


        LUSTRES ARE MANTEL DECORATIONS OR PEDESTAL VASES WITH
        MANY HANGING GLASS PRISMS. THE NAME REALLY REFERS TO
        THE PRISMS,AND IT IS PROPER TO REFER TO A SINGLE GLASS
        PRISM AS A LUSTRE. EITHER SPELLING,LUSTER OR LUSTRE,IS
        CORRECT.
LUSTRES,BLUE,WHITE ENAMEL FLORAL,CUT GLASS PRISMS,10 IN.,
    PAIR...................................................... 138.00
LUSTRES,BOHEMIAN GLASS,ONE ROW CRYSTAL PRISMS,CIRCA 1890,
    14 IN.TALL................................................ 135.00
LUSTRES,CAFE AU LAIT,ENAMEL DECOR,6-IN.CUT PRISMS,BRISTOL,
```

```
13 IN....................................................  148.00
LUSTRES,CREAMY WHITE,ROSES,HAND-PAINTED,GOLD EDGE,CUT
   CRYSTALS,PRISMS.........................................   55.00
LUSTRES,ENAMELED DECOR,GOLD,RUBY,SINGLE ROW OF PRISMS.......  160.00
LUSTRES,ENAMELED FLOWERS,CUT GLASS PRISMS,COBALT BLUE.......  150.00
LUSTRES,GREEN,MEDALLION,FLOWERS,PRISMS,11 IN.TALL..........  125.00
LUSTRES,ORANGE ON WHITE,GREEN FLORAL,GIRLS' FACES,PRISMS,
   BRISTOL................................................  175.00
LUSTRES,PINK,ENAMELED BLUE FORGET-ME-NOTS,SPEAR POINT
   PRISMS,14 1/2 IN........................................  145.00
LUSTRES,PINK,HAND-PAINTED FLORAL,GOLD TRIM,PRISMS,BRISTOL,
   13 IN.TALL.............................................  150.00
LUSTRES,WHITE CUT TO CRANBERRY,PRISMS,PAIR.................  225.00
LUSTRES,WHITE,FROSTED,CAMPHOR GLASS,ENGLAND,PAIR...........  175.00
LUSTRES,WHITE,PINK ENAMEL TRIM,CUT GLASS PRISMS,ENGLAND,
   13 IN.TALL,PAIR........................................  175.00
```

LUTZ GLASS WAS MADE IN THE 1870S BY NICHOLAS LUTZ AT
THE BOSTON AND SANDWICH COMPANY. HE MADE A
DELICATE AND INTRICATE THREADED GLASS OF SEVERAL
COLORS. OTHER SIMILAR WARES ARE REFERRED TO AS LUTZ.

```
LUTZ,BOWL,BERRY,THREADED,CRIMPED,RUFFLED,BLUE,SANDWICH,
   UNDERPLATE.............................................   25.00
LUTZ,BOWL,BERRY,THREADED,CRIMPED,RUFFLED,PINK,SANDWICH,
   UNDERPLATE.............................................   25.00
LUTZ,BOWL,BERRY,THREADED,CRIMPED,RUFFLED,GREEN,SANDWICH,
   UNDERPLATE.............................................   25.00
LUTZ,BOWL,BLUE,GOLD,WHITE BANDS,CRIMPED EDGE,7 IN.WIDE,
   2 IN.HIGH.............................................   60.00
LUTZ,BOWL,CLEAR,RUFFLED,BLUE THREADING,MATCHING PLATE.......   45.00
LUTZ,BOWL,FINGER,APRICOT COLOR,UNDERPLATE,SANDWICH.........   65.00
LUTZ,BOWL,FINGER,CANARY YELLOW,THREADED,FLUTED,CRIMPED.....   35.00
LUTZ,BOWL,FINGER,DIAMOND-QUILTED,THREADED,CRANBERRY,5 IN....   47.50
LUTZ,BOWL,FINGER,OPALESCENT,RED THREADING,GROUND PONTIL,
   TRICORN SHAPE..........................................   40.00
LUTZ,BOWL,THREADED WHITE TO PALE LAVENDER,FLUTED TOP,4 IN. X
   5 IN..................................................   79.00
LUTZ,CUP & SAUCER,BLUE,WHITE,YELLOW,FILIGREED PANELS,
   LATTICINO.............................................   45.00
LUTZ,CUP & SAUCER,DEMITASSE,LATTICINO PINK & WHITE STRIPES..   40.00
LUTZ,CUP & SAUCER,DEMITASSE,MULTICOLORED STRIPED ART GLASS..   35.00
LUTZ,CUP & SAUCER,FILIGREE PANELS OF WHITE & YELLOW,GOLD,
   LATTICINO.............................................   45.00
LUTZ,CUP & SAUCER,LATTICINO,FILIGREE PANELS,WHITE,BLUE,GOLD,
   YELLOW................................................   45.00
LUTZ,CUP,SAUCER,FILIGREE PANELS,WHITE,BLUE,GOLD,WHITE,
   YELLOW,LATTICINO.......................................   45.00
LUTZ,CUP,SAUCER,TWISTED YELLOW,GOLD & WHITE BANDS,SCALLOPED
   SAUCER................................................   45.00
LUTZ,DISH,BONBON,SWIRLED CANDY CANE,RED,GOLD...............   75.00
LUTZ,DISH,NUT,THREADED,FOOTED..............................   40.00
LUTZ,EWER,SPIRAL STRIPES,BLUE,WHITE,GOLD,APPLIED PEDESTAL,
   HANDLE,10 IN..........................................  225.00
LUTZ,PLATE,FILIGREE PANELS OF WHITE & WHITE WITH GOLDSTONE,
   LATTICINO.............................................   39.50
LUTZ,PLATE,FILIGREE PANELS OF WHITE,GREEN,OUTLINED IN GOLD,
   LATTICINO.............................................   39.50
LUTZ,PLATE,FILIGREE PANELS,WHITE,GREEN,GOLD,DEEP CENTER,
   LATTICINO.............................................   39.50
LUTZ,PLATE,FILIGREED PANELS,WHITE,GREEN,GOLD,LATTICINO,
   7 1/2 IN..............................................   39.50
LUTZ,PLATE,PALE BLUE,GOLD FLECK THREAD & PINK-GOLD DROPS
   UNDER RIM.............................................   17.50
LUTZ,SYRUP,THREADED,CLEAR,PEWTER RIM,COVER,HANDLE..........   25.00
LUTZ,TOOTHPICK,BLUE,WHITE LATTICINO STRIPING,GOLDSTONE RIM,
   FLINT.................................................   60.00
LUTZ,TUMBLER,GREEN,GOLD,WHITE BANDS,PINCHED SIDES,FLARED LIP   45.00
LUTZ,TUMBLER,PINK & WHITE STRIPED.........................   35.00
LUTZ,TUMBLER,PINK,GOLD,WHITE BANDS,PINCHED SIDES,FLARED LIP.   45.00
LUTZ,VASE,BLUE-GREEN IRIDESCENT,4 IN......................   33.00
LUTZ,VASE,BLUE,WHITE,GOLD WHITE BANDS,APPLIED CLEAR THREAD
   ON NECK...............................................   70.00
LUTZ,VASE,WHITE,FROSTED,EMBOSSED,CRANBERRY THREADS AT TOP &
   BOTTOM,4 IN...........................................   27.50
LUXARDO,SEE BOTTLE,LUXARDO
```

MAASTRICHT,HOLLAND,HAD A LARGE POTTERY CALLED THE
SPHINX,WHICH WAS ESTABLISHED IN 1836 BY PETRUS REGOUT.
THE FIRM MADE TRANSFER PRINTED IRONSTONE DINNER SETS

MARKED WITH THE WORDS MAASTRICHT,OR PETRUS REGOUT.
TWENTIETH-CENTURY WARES WERE ALSO MADE BY THE FIRM.

| | |
|---|---|
| MAASTRICHT,PLATE,BLUE,BUFF,CASTLE SCENE,STAMPED PETRUS REGOUT CO................................................. | 10.00 |
| MAASTRICHT,PLATE,FLOW BLUE,PAIR................................ | 16.00 |
| MAASTRICHT,PLATE,LARGE PINK & WHITE ROSES,TERRA COTTA BORDER,9 1/2 IN........................................ | 10.00 |
| MAASTRICHT,TEA TILE,ORIENTAL SCENE,PETRUS REGOUT CO......... | 12.50 |

MAJOLICA IS ANY POTTERY GLAZED WITH A TIN ENAMEL.
MOST OF THE MAJOLICA FOUND TODAY IS DECORATED WITH
LEAVES,SHELLS,BRANCHES,AND OTHER NATURAL SHAPES AND IN
NATURAL COLORS. IT WAS A POPULAR NINETEENTH-CENTURY
PRODUCT.

| | |
|---|---|
| MAJOLICA,BOOT,LACING,GREEN..................................... | 7.50 |
| MAJOLICA,BOTTLE,FIGURAL,SKELETON IN SHROUD, POISON, 5 3/4 IN.HIGH............................................ | 14.00 |
| MAJOLICA,BOWL,DRAGON HOLDS BASE,GINORI,3 IN.WIDE X 6 IN.LONG X 5 IN.TALL............................................ | 27.50 |
| MAJOLICA,BOWL,FULL LEAF IN BASE,SHALLOW,10-IN.DIAMETER, 2 IN.DEEP............................................... | 20.00 |
| MAJOLICA,BOWL,LEAF SHAPE....................................... | 25.00 |
| MAJOLICA,CAKE STAND,EMBOSSED PURPLE PANSIES,WHITE GROUND, BLUE EDGE.............................................. | 21.50 |
| MAJOLICA,CAKE STAND,LILY PAD TOP,POND LILY CENTER,HERON PEDESTAL............................................... | 35.00 |
| MAJOLICA,CHOCOLATE POT,GOLD,FRUIT DECOR,SIX CUPS & SAUCERS, CREAMER,SUGAR.......................................... | 25.50 |
| MAJOLICA,COMPOTE,SUNFLOWERS,MARKED G.S.H...................... | 50.00 |
| MAJOLICA,CREAMER,GREEN & YELLOW LOVEBIRDS,PINK LINING,4 IN.. | 10.00 |
| MAJOLICA,CREAMER,MAIZE,ORCHID LINED........................... | 10.00 |
| MAJOLICA,CREAMER,SQUATTY,VIOLET INTERIOR,YELLOW DIAMONDS, LEAVES................................................. | 9.00 |
| MAJOLICA,CUP & SAUCER,COBALT,YELLOW,BROWN,GREEN,HANDLELESS.. | 4.50 |
| MAJOLICA,DISH,GREEN & WHITE,HEART SHAPE,8 IN.................. | 10.00 |
| MAJOLICA,DISH,LEAF,ETRUSCAN.................................... | 17.00 |
| MAJOLICA,DISH,LEAF,GREEN ON DARK BLUE,IMPRESSED MINTONS, 13 IN.................................................. | 12.00 |
| MAJOLICA,DISH,ORCHID-SHAPED,GREEN,PINK,YELLOW,LID,5 X 6 IN.LONG.............................................. | 20.00 |
| MAJOLICA,DISH,PICKLE,LEAF,GREEN CENTER,PINK,BROWN TO TAN, 7 1/2 IN............................................... | 11.00 |
| MAJOLICA,DISH,SARDINE,ATTACHED PLATE,THREE SARDINES ON TOP OF LID................................................. | 30.00 |
| MAJOLICA,DISH,SARDINE,BOAT-SHAPED,ATTACHED BASKET,CARP ON LID,9 1/2 IN............................................ | 55.00 |
| MAJOLICA,DISH,SHELL,ETRUSCAN.........................ILLUS.. | 18.50 |
| MAJOLICA,FIGURINE,BOY WITH PIPE,GIRL KNITTING,7 IN.HIGH,PAIR | 95.00 |
| MAJOLICA,JAR,TOBACCO,BOY LEANS AGAINST LID,MULTICOLORED..... | 23.00 |
| MAJOLICA,JAR,TOBACCO,PINK FLORAL,GREEN & BLUE TRIM,PIPE ON LID,5 1/2 IN............................................ | 27.50 |
| MAJOLICA,JARDINIERE,IRIS DESIGN,STAND,26 IN.HIGH............. | 95.00 |
| MAJOLICA,JUG,BLUE GROUND,DOG,CHILD,FOOTED,PEWTER LID, 7 IN.HIGH.............................................. | 17.50 |

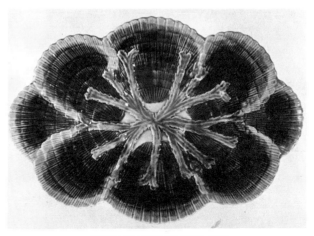

ETRUSCAN MAJOLICA SHELL DISH

MAJOLICA,PAPERWEIGHT,OWL ON TREE,SIGNED MAYER,4 X 2 3/4 IN.. 15.00
MAJOLICA,PITCHER,BLUE,PINK FLORAL,PINK LINING,TREE BARK
HANDLE,7 IN.................................................. 35.00
MAJOLICA,PITCHER,CHILD WITH LARGE DOG,6 1/2 IN.............. 25.00
MAJOLICA,PITCHER,CORN,GREEN LEAVES,PINK LINING,6 1/2 IN.TALL 22.50
MAJOLICA,PITCHER,CORN,YELLOW GRAINS,LEAVES,ROSE,PINK
INTERIOR,8 IN.............................................. 18.00
MAJOLICA,PITCHER,COW,BLUE & BROWN,5 1/2 IN. HIGH........... 12.00
MAJOLICA,PITCHER,CREAM GROUND,BLACKBERRY BRANCHES,PINK
FLORAL,2 3/4 IN............................................ 5.00
MAJOLICA,PITCHER,ETRUSCAN,SHELL & SEAWEED,SIGNED,QUART SIZE. 85.00
MAJOLICA,PITCHER,FERN PATTERN.............................. 40.00
MAJOLICA,PITCHER,FIGURAL,FISH,TAIL FORMS HANDLE,GREEN,PINK,
WHITE..................................................... 68.00
MAJOLICA,PITCHER,FISH,6 1/2 IN............................. 25.00
MAJOLICA,PITCHER,FISH,10 IN.HIGH........................... 25.00
MAJOLICA,PITCHER,FOREST,GREEN,BROWN,5 IN................... 10.00
MAJOLICA,PITCHER,GREEN GROUND,YELLOW POND LILIES,ROPE
HANDLE,6 1/4 IN............................................ 18.00
MAJOLICA,PITCHER,GREEN TO BROWN,FACE FORMS FRONT,EARS & HAIR
ON SIDES.................................................. 35.00
MAJOLICA,PITCHER,GREEN,ROSES,6 IN.HIGH.................... 14.00
MAJOLICA,PITCHER,HAWK AFTER CHICKENS,7 3/4 IN.............. 40.00
MAJOLICA,PITCHER,MILK,GREEN & BEIGE....................... 15.00
MAJOLICA,PITCHER,OWL,9 IN.HIGH............................ 25.00
MAJOLICA,PITCHER,PINK BLOSSOMS,BARK DESIGN,6 1/4 IN.TALL.... 12.00
MAJOLICA,PITCHER,PORTRAIT,WINGED DRAGON HANDLE,BERRIES,
LEAVES,12 1/4 IN.......................................... 65.00
MAJOLICA,PITCHER,PORTRAIT,WOMAN,LEFT-HANDED,3 1/2 IN........ 75.00
MAJOLICA,PITCHER,ROOSTER,11 IN.HIGH....................... 28.00
MAJOLICA,PITCHER,SHELL & SEAWEED,ETRUSCAN,QUART SIZE....... 85.00
MAJOLICA,PITCHER,THE KILL,RABBITS,PHEASANTS,FOX,DOG HANDLE,
10 IN..................................................... 55.00
MAJOLICA,PITCHER,WATER,BROWN TREE BARK SURFACE,PINK ROSE,
LEAVES.................................................... 25.00
MAJOLICA,PLATE,BASKET WEAVE,BLACKBERRY LEAVES,BLOSSOMS,
8 1/4 IN.................................................. 10.00
MAJOLICA,PLATE,BIRD,AQUA,8 1/2 IN......................... 8.00
MAJOLICA,PLATE,BLUE,GREEN FERN BORDER,8 3/4-IN.DIAMETER..... 9.50
MAJOLICA,PLATE,BLUE,WHITE FLOWERS,RED BERRIES,LEAVES,MARKED
GERMANY................................................... 12.50
MAJOLICA,PLATE,COBALT PEACOCK TAIL FEATHERS COVER CENTER,
9 IN...................................................... 9.00
MAJOLICA,PLATE,DUCK IN CENTER,WHITE,BLUE & PINK FORAL,
8 1/4 IN.................................................. 9.00
MAJOLICA,PLATE,FISH DESIGN,WEDGWOOD....................ILLUS.. 15.00
MAJOLICA,PLATE,GREEN & RUST LEAVES,7 IN................... 12.00
MAJOLICA,PLATE,IVORY GROUND,GREEN LEAVES,FERNS,ROSES,8 IN... 9.00
MAJOLICA,PLATE,PORTRAIT IN CENTER,BLUE BORDER,FLORAL ON RIM,
GERMANY................................................... 9.00
MAJOLICA,PLATE,STRAWBERRY PATTERN,GREEN GLAZE,9-IN.DIAMETER. 10.00
MAJOLICA,PLATTER,BROWN,GREEN,TWO HANDLES,11 X 8 IN......... 10.00
MAJOLICA,PLATTER,GREEN,RED,YELLOW,MAPLE LEAF,11 1/2 X
8 1/2 IN.................................................. 17.50
MAJOLICA,PLATTER,LEAF,12 IN. X 8 IN....................... 18.50

WEDGWOOD MAJOLICA PLATE, FISH DESIGN

```
MAJOLICA,PLATTER,RAISED FERN & LEAF DESIGN,MOTTLED
  TORTOISESHELL BOTTOM.................................... 22.50
MAJOLICA,PLATTER,WHITE ASPARAGUS BODY,LEAF BORDER,
  BLUEBERRIES............................................ 29.00
MAJOLICA,SHOE,BROWN,AQUA LINING,MICE,MARKED W & S,9 1/2 X
  6 1/2 IN.TALL.......................................... 48.00
MAJOLICA,SUGAR,CAULIFLOWER COVER,ETRUSCAN................. 25.00
MAJOLICA,SUGAR,GREEN & YELLOW EAR OF CORN,COVER.......... 45.00
MAJOLICA,SYRUP JUG,MINIATURE,HOLDS ONE CUP............... 35.00
MAJOLICA,SYRUP,AQUA & GREEN FOLIAGE,BROWN HANDLE,SQUATTY,
  PEWTER TOP............................................. 18.00
MAJOLICA,SYRUP,GREEN,YELLOW,PINEAPPLE DESIGN,PEWTER HINGED
  LID,FINIAL............................................. 30.00
MAJOLICA,SYRUP,PEWTER TOP,SIGNED BENNETT,1878............ 25.00
MAJOLICA,SYRUP,SUNFLOWER PATTERN,ETRUSCAN,PEWTER TOP..... 35.00
MAJOLICA,SYRUP,SUNFLOWER,PURPLE GROUND,BROWN HANDLE,PEWTER
  TOP,SIGNED............................................. 57.50
MAJOLICA,SYRUP,WILD ROSE................................. 15.00
MAJOLICA,TANKARD,MILK,YELLOW,GRAY ELEPHANT,PINK LINING,
  P.T.BARNUM,JUMBO....................................... 50.00
MAJOLICA,TEA SET,BROWN GROUND,SUNFLOWER,TEAPOT,SUGAR,CREAMER 24.00
MAJOLICA,TEAPOT,SHELL & SEAWEED,SIGNED,ETRUSCAN.......... 60.00
MAJOLICA,TEAPOT,SHELL AND SEAWEED....................... 75.00
MAJOLICA,TOOTHPICK,ENAMEL DECOR,THREE HANDLES........... 12.00
MAJOLICA,TRAY,AQUA GROUND,LAVENDER ENDS,WATER LILY IN CENTER 25.00
MAJOLICA,TRAY,YELLOW,BUFF,GREEN,BROWN,LEAF SHAPE,7 1/2 X
  11 IN..................................................  9.50
MAJOLICA,VASE,BLACKBERRY DECOR.......................... 15.00
MAJOLICA,VASE,BLUE & GREEN FLOWERS,PALE GREEN LINING,OBLONG. 10.00
MAJOLICA,VASE,BLUE DECOR,PANEL WITH SEA URCHIN,TWO HANDLES,
  8 1/2 IN............................................... 17.50
MAJOLICA,VASE,CREAM TO TAN AT BASE,ACORN,GREEN LEAVES,PURPLE
  LINING,PAIR............................................ 14.50
MAJOLICA,VASE,GREEN,BROWN,PINK FLORAL,BOW-SHAPE HANDLES,
  1899,12 IN.HIGH........................................ 38.00
MAJOLICA,VASE,GREEN,WHITE FLORAL,BROWN LEAF IN RELIEF,
  6 1/2 IN............................................... 22.50
MAJOLICA,VASE,SAND,ENAMEL UNDERGLAZE FLORAL DECOR,FOOTED,
  6 1/2 IN.,PAIR......................................... 25.00
MAJOLICA,VASE,WALL,GOLD,BROWN,GREEN,MASKED MAN'S HEAD,
  SARREGUEMINES.......................................... 27.00
MALACHITE & CORAL,BOTTLE,SNUFF,TREE TRUNK,BIRD,LEAFAGE,BIRD
  FORM STOPPER.......................................... 225.00
MALACHITE,BOTTLE,SNUFF,FISH FORM,CORAL STOPPER,WAVE SCROLL
  IVORY STAND........................................... 200.00
MALACHITE,BOTTLE,SNUFF,TOAD FORM,CORAL STALK FORM STOPPER... 175.00
MALACHITE,BOTTLE,SNUFF,TOAD FORM,PEARL STOPPER.......... 110.00
MALACHITE,BOTTLE,SNUFF,WHITE JADE PLAQUES,BEARDED MEN,BLUE
  SODALITE LID.......................................... 150.00
MALACHITE,BOX,CIGARETTE,RUSSIAN SILVER-MOUNTED,CIRCA 1860,
  C.S................................................... 700.00
MALACHITE,CHEST,JEWEL.RUSSIAN,19TH CENTURY,2 3/8 IN. HIGH... 525.00
MALACHITE,FIGURE,BUDDHA,3 1/2 IN. HIGH,WOOD STAND....... 175.00
MALACHITE,GROUP,3 IN. HIGH,BOY WITH FAN,RABBIT,WOOD STAND... 180.00
MALACHITE,GROUP,5 IN. HIGH,WOMAN & BRANCH OF PEACHES....... 275.00
MALACHITE,TRAY,RUSSIAN,19TH CENTURY,11 1/4 IN. LONG........ 325.00
MANTELPIECE,CARRARA MARBLE,VITRUVIAN SCROLLING,REEDED
  GROUND,4 FEET HIGH.................................... 150.00
MANTELPIECE,MARBLE,BLACK,WHITE,D-SHAPE TOP,LOUIS XVI,48 X
  73 1/2 IN.WIDE........................................ 350.00
MANTELPIECE,PINE,CARVED,ENGLISH,C.1740...............ILLUS..1,800.00


        MARBLES OF GLASS WERE MADE DURING THE NINETEENTH
        CENTURY, VENETIAN SWIRL,CLEAR GLASS,AND SULFIDES,
        MARBLES WITH FROSTED WHITE ANIMAL FIGURES IMBEDDED IN
        THE GLASS WERE POPULAR. HANDMADE CLAY MARBLES WERE MADE
        IN MANY PLACES,BUT MOST OF THEM CAME FROM THE POTTERY
        FACTORIES OF OHIO AND PENNSYLVANIA. OCCASIONALLY,REAL
        STONE MARBLES OF ONYX,CARNELIAN,OR JASPER CAN BE FOUND.
MARBLE,AKRO AGATE,LOT OF 100............................  7.00
MARBLE,BENNINGTON TYPE,ASSORTED SIZES,LOT OF 70.........  8.75
MARBLE,CANDY STRIPE,COLOR SWIRL,BENNINGTON,AGATE,25..... 35.00
MARBLE,CANDY STRIPE,6-IN.DIAMETER....................... 22.50
MARBLE,CLAY,BENNINGTON,10...............................  2.00
MARBLE,CLAY,LOT OF 100..................................  1.50
MARBLE,CLAY,SEVERAL COLORS,LOT OF 40....................  4.00
MARBLE,COLOR SWIRL,CANDY STRIPE,BENNINGTON,DESIGNED CLAY,25. 35.00
MARBLE,COLORED STRIPES..................................  8.00
MARBLE,GLASS AGATE,SMALL,15.............................  1.00
MARBLE,GLAZED,CLAY,15................................... 12.00
```

ENGLISH CARVED PINE
MANTEL, C. 1740

```
MARBLE,INDIAN,STONE,20............................................  5.00
MARBLE,LARGE THREADED SWIRL,1 3/4 IN........................  11.00
MARBLE,MULTICOLORED,7 1/2-IN.CIRCUMFERENCE..................  30.00
MARBLE,SMALL SWIRLS,CLEARIES,AKRO AGATES,PORCELAINS,
     BENNINGTON,20................................................  18.00
MARBLE,STRIPED,1 1/4-IN.DIAMETER............................   8.00
MARBLE,STRIPED,2-IN.DIAMETER................................  16.00
MARBLE,STRIPED,3/4-IN.DIAMETER..............................   2.50
MARBLE,STRIPES,GLASS,9......................................  12.50
MARBLE,SULFIDE,BEAR,6 1/2 IN................................  20.00
MARBLE,SULFIDE,CAMEL........................................  20.00
MARBLE,SULFIDE,CAMEL,1 5/8-IN.DIAMETER......................  25.00
MARBLE,SULFIDE,COW,2-IN.DIAMETER............................  20.00
MARBLE,SULFIDE,DOG..........................................  20.00
MARBLE,SULFIDE,DOG,1 3/4-IN.DIAMETER........................  30.00
MARBLE,SULFIDE,ELEPHANT,6 1/2 IN............................  20.00
MARBLE,SULFIDE,FIGURE OF RAM INSIDE,1 1/2-IN.DIAMETER.......  14.00
MARBLE,SULFIDE,FROG,1 1/4-IN.DIAMETER.......................  18.00
MARBLE,SULFIDE,GOAT.........................................  20.00
MARBLE,SULFIDE,GREEN COW....................................  20.00
MARBLE,SULFIDE,HORSE........................................  20.00
MARBLE,SULFIDE,HORSE,1 5/8-IN.DIAMETER......................  25.00
MARBLE,SULFIDE,RABBIT,CRYSTAL,1 1/4-IN.DIAMETER.............  25.00
MARBLE,SULFIDE,RAM,CRYSTAL,1 5/8 IN.........................  30.00
MARBLE,SULFIDE,SITTING DOG,CRYSTAL,2-IN.DIAMETER............  35.00
MARBLE,SULFIDE,SITTING SQUIRREL,CRYSTAL,1 3/4 IN............  30.00
MARBLE,SULFIDE,WALKING BEAR INSIDE,6 1/2-IN.CIRCUMFERENCE...  27.50
MARBLE,SULFIDE,WOLF,CRYSTAL,1 1/2-IN.DIAMETER...............  30.00
MARBLE,SWIRL,1-INCH DIAMETER................................   4.00
MARBLE,SWIRL,2-IN.DIAMETER........................... 13.50 TO  20.00
MARBLE,SWIRL,RED,GREEN,1 1/2-IN.DIAMETER....................  15.00
MARBLE,THREADED SWIRL SHOOTER,1 3/4 IN......................  10.00
MARBLE,THREADED SWIRL,AGATE.................................   2.00
```

```
        MARY GREGORY GLASS IS IDENTIFIED BY A CHARACTERISTIC
        WHITE FIGURE PAINTED ON DARK GLASS. IT WAS MADE FROM
        1870 TO 1910. THE NAME REFERS TO ANY GLASS DECORATED
        WITH A WHITE SILHOUETTE FIGURE AND NOT JUST THE
        SANDWICH GLASS ORIGINALLY PAINTED BY MISS MARY GREGORY.
MARY GREGORY,ALE GLASS,AMBER,BOY,GIRL,TINTED FACE,WHITE
     CLOTHES,BLOWN...........................................  30.00
MARY GREGORY,BOTTLE,BARBER,BOY FIGURE,AMETHYST..............  75.00
MARY GREGORY,BOTTLE,LIQUEUR,AMBER,WHITE ENAMEL GIRL,FOLIAGE,
     STOPPER................................................  50.00
MARY GREGORY,BOWL,FINGER,GREEN,BOY BLOWING BUBBLES,POLISHED
     PONTIL.................................................  39.00
MARY GREGORY,BOWL,ROSE,WHITE ENAMEL GIRL & FOLIAGE,GOLD
     BANDS,CRANBERRY........................................  45.00
MARY GREGORY,BOWL,WHITE EMBOSSED BOY,FLORAL,COBALT GROUND,
     SILVER LID.............................................  69.00
```

```
MARY GREGORY,BOX,GIRL,FLOWER,BIRD,HINGED COVER,COBALT.......     200.00
MARY GREGORY,BOX,HINGED COVER,FOOTED,AMBER,4 X 4 IN.HIGH....      70.00
MARY GREGORY,BOX,HINGED,CRANBERRY,4 IN.WIDE,2 1/2 IN.HIGH...      60.00
MARY GREGORY,BOX,JEWEL,BLACK GLASS,WHITE ENAMEL WOMAN
   FEEDING COCKATOO.......................................     175.00
MARY GREGORY,BOX,JEWEL,BLACK,BOY WAVING HAT,BRASS STANDARD,
   ROUND...............................................      67.50
MARY GREGORY,BOX,PATCH,SAPPHIRE BLUE,GIRL WITH BALL,FOLIAGE,
   2 IN................................................      67.00
MARY GREGORY,BOX,PATCH,WHITE ENAMELED BOY & SHRUBS,HINGED,
   2 1/4 X 1 IN.........................................      45.00
MARY GREGORY,BOX,PATCH,WHITE ENAMELED BOY,SHRUBS,2 1/4 X
   1 IN.HIGH............................................      45.00
MARY GREGORY,BOX,PORTRAIT,LADY,MURRHINA BLUE COLOR,HINGED...      75.00
MARY GREGORY,BOX,PURPLE,BOY,FOLIAGE,GOLD HINGES,CLASP,STAND,
   FEET................................................     115.00
MARY GREGORY,CREAMER,BLUE,BOY,TINTED FEATURES,CLEAR HANDLE,
   SHARP PONTIL.........................................      49.50
MARY GREGORY,CREAMER,GREEN,BOY IN WHITE PICKING FLOWERS,GOLD
   BAND................................................      52.00
MARY GREGORY,CRUET,BLUE,WHITE DECOR,BOY.....................      30.00
MARY GREGORY,CRUET,BLUE,WHITE DECOR,GIRL....................      42.50
MARY GREGORY,CRUET,BULBOUS,OUTDOOR SCENE,GIRL,APPLIED
   HANDLE,STOPPER.......................................      40.00
MARY GREGORY,CRUET,CLEAR,BOY & FOLIAGE,GOLD TRIM,8 IN.......      55.00
MARY GREGORY,CRUET,CRANBERRY GLASS,STOPPER..................      18.00
MARY GREGORY,DECANTER,BOY FIGURE,WHITE FOLIAGE,PANELED,
   SAPPHIRE BLUE........................................      65.00
MARY GREGORY,DECANTER,GIRL PICKING FLOWER,CLEAR,PANELED,
   BLOWN STOPPER........................................      55.00
MARY GREGORY,DECANTER,SMALL GIRL WITH BALLOON,TINTED
   FEATURES,CLEAR.......................................      55.00
MARY GREGORY,DECANTER,WHITE,GOLD ENAMELED FLOWERS,SIGNED....      37.50
MARY GREGORY,GLASS,JUICE,BLUE,WHITE SWANS,YELLOW BILLS,WHITE
   REEDS...............................................      20.00
MARY GREGORY,GOBLET,LITTLE GIRL WITH BOUQUET OF FLOWERS,
   CRANBERRY............................................      20.00
MARY GREGORY,GOBLET,WHITE ENAMEL BOY WITH FLOWERS,CRANBERRY
   GLASS...............................................      25.00
MARY GREGORY,JAR,CANDY,GIRL IN TREES,WHITE ENAMELED,COVER,
   6 IN................................................      35.00
MARY GREGORY,JAR,COOKIE,COBALT GROUND,WHITE ENAMEL,CHERUB,
   LILIES,LID...........................................      69.00
MARY GREGORY,JAR,CRACKER,BOY HOLDING FLOWERS BY FENCE,SILVER
   LID & BAIL...........................................      56.50
MARY GREGORY,JAR,PICKLE,RUBY,GIRL PLAYING IN SAND PILE......      15.00
MARY GREGORY,JUICE GLASS,GREEN,BOY & GIRL,FOLIAGE IN WHITE,
   PANEL,BLOWN..........................................      22.00
MARY GREGORY,LAMP,KEROSENE,ENAMEL FOLIAGE,GIRL,BALLOON,
   BURNER..............................................      60.00
MARY GREGORY,LAMP,WHITE ENAMEL GIRL,FOLIAGE,VASELINE,FLORAL
   SHADE,23 IN..........................................     185.00
MARY GREGORY,LAMP,WHITE PAINTING OF GIRL IN GOWN,
   TORTOISESHELL,23 IN..................................     250.00
MARY GREGORY,MUG,CRANBERRY,HANDLED.........................      75.00
MARY GREGORY,MUG,GREEN,PANELED,BOY & FLORALS,BLOWN..........      28.00
MARY GREGORY,NIGHT LIGHT,CANDLE,TWO-PIECE,CRANBERRY & WHITE,
   7 IN.TALL............................................     125.00
MARY GREGORY,PERFUME,BOY & GIRL,TINTED FACES,BLUE,BRISTOL,
   5 IN.,PAIR...........................................     110.00
MARY GREGORY,PERFUME,BOY,TREES IN WHITE,CRANBERRY GLASS,
   6 1/2 IN.HIGH........................................      18.00
MARY GREGORY,PERFUME,GIRL IN DUST CAP,CUT STOPPER,6 IN......      30.00
MARY GREGORY,PITCHER,BLUE,WHITE,5 IN.TALL...................      80.00
MARY GREGORY,PITCHER,BOY,GIRL,TINTED FACES,CLEAR,9 IN.HIGH,
   3 TUMBLERS...........................................      95.00
MARY GREGORY,PITCHER,BRIDE,TWO ATTENDANTS,TINTED FACES,
   11 1/2 IN.TALL.......................................     150.00
MARY GREGORY,PITCHER,CLEAR,GIRL FIGURES,3 IN.HIGH,PORRIDGE
   BOWL................................................      40.00
MARY GREGORY,PITCHER,ENAMELED BOY FLYING KITE,CRANBERRY,
   2 3/4 IN.HIGH........................................      95.00
MARY GREGORY,PITCHER,GIRL,CLEAR,FOUR TUMBLERS,TWO BOYS,TWO
   GIRLS...............................................     150.00
MARY GREGORY,PITCHER,GREEN,GOLD DEER........................      75.00
MARY GREGORY,PITCHER,INVERTED THUMBPRINT,GIRL IN WHITE,
   AMBER,1889...........................................     160.00
MARY GREGORY,PITCHER,PAINTED FACES & HAIR,CLEAR,5 TUMBLERS..     165.00
MARY GREGORY,PITCHER,TANKARD,AMBER,9 1/4 IN.TALL............      65.00
MARY GREGORY,PITCHER,WATER,CLEAR,RUFFLED TOP,FIVE TUMBLERS..     200.00
MARY GREGORY,PITCHER,WATER,GIRL,PAINTED FACE,HOLDS FAN,
```

CRANBERRY,RIBBED......................................... 135.00
MARY GREGORY,PITCHER,WATER,GIRLS,TINTED FEATURES,BIRDS,
DRAGONFLIES,CLEAR....................................... 90.00
MARY GREGORY,PITCHER,WATER,INVERTED THUMBPRINT,BLUE,WHITE
FIGURE.................................................. 35.00
MARY GREGORY,PITCHER,WATER,THREE SCENES WITH BROWN-HAIRED
GIRL,CLEAR............................................. 75.00
MARY GREGORY,PITCHER,WATER,WHITE ENAMEL,GIRL,FLORAL,
5 MATCHING TUMBLERS.................................... 150.00
MARY GREGORY,PITCHER,WATER,YOUNG GIRLS,DANCING,TREES,SHRUBS,
ENAMEL................................................. 55.00
MARY GREGORY,PITCHER,WHITE,FLUTED,GIRL,SHRUBBERY,9 IN.TALL.. 65.00
MARY GREGORY,STEIN,BLUE PANELS,WHITE ENAMEL BOY,TINTED FACE,
FOLIAGE................................................ 50.00
MARY GREGORY,STEIN,INVERTED THUMBPRINT,BOY ON ONE,GIRL ON
OTHER,PAIR............................................. 175.00
MARY GREGORY,STEIN,INVERTED THUMBPRINT,BOY,AUBURN HAIR,HONEY
AMBER,LID.............................................. 72.50
MARY GREGORY,STEIN,MAN SMOKING PIPE,TINTED FACE,CUT PRISM &
PEWTER TOP............................................. 75.00
MARY GREGORY,STEIN,TINTED FEATURES,HONEY AMBER,8 1/2 IN..... 75.00
MARY GREGORY,SYRUP,GIRL IN WHITE,FIELD,SILVER PLATE TOP..... 18.00
MARY GREGORY,TEA WARMER,AMETHYST,WHITE CHILDREN FIGURES,
SILVER HOLDER.......................................... 65.00
MARY GREGORY,TOOTHPICK,CRANBERRY........................... 12.00
MARY GREGORY,TOOTHPICK,SAPPHIRE BLUE...................... 65.00
MARY GREGORY,TUMBLER,CLEAR,FIGURE OF BOY CLIMBING TREE...... 85.00
MARY GREGORY,TUMBLER,CLEAR,WHITE ENAMELED BOY,GIRL,PAIR..... 56.00
MARY GREGORY,TUMBLER,CRANBERRY,INVERTED THUMBPRINT,ENAMEL
BOY,GIRL,PAIR.......................................... 82.50
MARY GREGORY,TUMBLER,GREEN,ALL-WHITE FIGURE................ 23.00
MARY GREGORY,TUMBLER,GREEN,ENAMELED,BOY,GIRL,OCTAGONAL
SHAPE,PAIR............................................. 78.00
MARY GREGORY,TUMBLER,PAINTED FACE & ARM,ENAMEL,CLEAR,
3 3/4 IN.HIGH.......................................... 20.00
MARY GREGORY,TUMBLER,SOUVENIR,WORLD'S FAIR 1893,BOY,
CRANBERRY.............................................. 35.00
MARY GREGORY,TUMBLER,WORLD'S FAIR,DATED 1893,CRANBERRY GLASS 15.00
MARY GREGORY,VASE,AMBER GROUND,GIRL PICKING TWIGS,WHITE,
FLUTED,6 1/2 IN........................................ 75.00
MARY GREGORY,VASE,BLACK,FLARE TOP,WHITE ENAMEL GIRL,BOY,
8 1/4 IN.,PAIR......................................... 159.00
MARY GREGORY,VASE,BLUE,GIRL HOLDING FLOWERS,RUFFLED,
SANDWICH,8 IN.......................................... 110.00
MARY GREGORY,VASE,BLUE,WHITE ENAMELED GIRL & FLORAL,
5 IN.TALL.............................................. 38.00
MARY GREGORY,VASE,BLUE,WHITE-ENAMELED BOY,GIRL,GOLD,7 IN.,
PAIR................................................... 48.00
MARY GREGORY,VASE,BOY BLOWING TRUMPET,GIRL DANCING,
CRANBERRY,PAIR......................................... 165.00
MARY GREGORY,VASE,BOY WITH HOOP,GREEN,APPLIED RING HANDLE,
6 5/8 IN.TALL.......................................... 50.00
MARY GREGORY,VASE,BOY,APPLIED SHELL DECOR ON SIDES,GOLD,
GREEN GROUND........................................... 125.00
MARY GREGORY,VASE,BOY,GIRL IN WHITE COLOR,COBALT BASE,
FLORAL,6 IN.,PAIR...................................... 75.00
MARY GREGORY,VASE,BOY,GIRL,WHITE FOLIAGE,PANELS,BLOWN,
CRANBERRY,PAIR......................................... 75.00
MARY GREGORY,VASE,BOY,GREEN,5 3/4 IN...................... 30.00
MARY GREGORY,VASE,EMERALD GREEN,WHITE ENAMEL BOY WITH
FLOWERS,7 IN........................................... 55.00
MARY GREGORY,VASE,GIRL HOLDING FAN,BOY WITH PAIL,CRANBERRY,
1880,PAIR.............................................. 165.00
MARY GREGORY,VASE,GREEN GLASS,CRIMP FLARED TOP,ROUGH PONTIL,
8 IN................................................... 25.00
MARY GREGORY,VASE,GREEN PANELS,WHITE ENAMELED GIRL,FOLIAGE,
11 IN.TALL............................................. 45.00
MARY GREGORY,VASE,GREEN,GIRL,BOY,WHITE ENAMEL DECOR,RUFFLED,
11 IN.,PAIR............................................ 50.00
MARY GREGORY,VASE,GREEN,LID,LADY ON STEPS,WATER,SWAN,BIRDS
IN FLIGHT.............................................. 147.50
MARY GREGORY,VASE,INVERTED THUMBPRINT,WHITE BOY FIGURE,
CRANBERRY.............................................. 40.00
MARY GREGORY,VASE,JACK-IN-THE-PULPIT,DARK GREEN,WHITE ENAMEL
GIRL,8 IN.............................................. 50.00
MARY GREGORY,VASE,MELON RIB,APPLIED REEDED HANDLES,
CRANBERRY,13 IN.,PAIR.................................. 175.00
MARY GREGORY,VASE,PAINTED FACE & ARM,CONE SHAPE,FLARED BASE,
7 IN.HIGH.............................................. 35.00
MARY GREGORY,VASE,THUMBPRINT GROUND,CRANBERRY.............. 45.00
MARY GREGORY,VASE,WHITE ENAMEL BOY & FLORALS,AMBER,PANEL,

```
   IRIDESCENT.......................................................   35.00
MARY GREGORY,VASE,WHITE ENAMELED GIRL,FOLIAGE,CRANBERRY,
   7 IN.TALL.....................................................   40.00
MARY GREGORY,VASE,WHITE ENAMELED GIRL,FOLIAGE,CRANBERRY,
   9 IN.TALL.....................................................   45.00
MARY GREGORY,WATER SET,COBALT.....................................  189.00
MARY GREGORY,WINE,STEMMED,WHITE FIGURES,COBALT BLUE..........   15.00
MASONIC,BROOCH,PEARL SEED BORDER,14K..............................   10.00
MASONIC,CUP & SAUCER,EMBLEMS,VERSE,PINK LUSTER,SUNDERLAND...   35.50
MASONIC,DEDICATION STONE,VIRGINIA CITY,1887.................   65.00
MASONIC,JAR,TOBACCO,EMBLEM ON LID,SIGNED,DATED,ROYAL
   BAYREUTH......................................................  125.00
MASONIC,MOLD,ICE CREAM............................................   10.00
MASONIC,MUG,BLUE,MOUNTAIN LODGE NO.281,ALTOONA,PA.,1911.....   17.50
MASONIC,MUG,LULU TEMPLE,1904......................................   22.50
MASONIC,MUG,SHAVING,EMBLEM,NAME IN GOLD......................   30.00
MASONIC,MUG,SHAVING,EMBLEM,NAMES,GOLD & BLUE FLOWERS,WHITE
   PORCELAIN.....................................................   22.00
MASONIC,MUG,SHAVING,SHRINE INSIGNIA,PINK,GOLD...............   18.00
MASONIC,MUSTACHE CUP & SAUCER,SUNDERLAND LUSTER,PINK.......   68.00
MASONIC,PAPERWEIGHT,BLUE BUBBLE BASE,SQUARE,DIVIDERS,MAKER
   J.GENTILE.....................................................   15.00
MASONIC,PAPERWEIGHT,BLUE LODGE,BLUE GROUND,WHITE SYMBOL.....    6.75
MASONIC,PAPERWEIGHT,BLUE,SQUARE,DIVIDER,MAKER CHARLIE
   DAGENHEIM.....................................................   20.00
MASONIC,PAPERWEIGHT,SHRINER,BLUE GROUND,WHITE SYMBOL........    6.75
MASONIC,PITCHER,HERRMANN LODGE NO.125,1911,11 IN.TALL.......   30.00
MASONIC,PLATE,COVENANT LODGE,1909,SYMBOLS,SKY EFFECT,
   9 3/4 IN......................................................   10.00
MASONIC,PLATE,EMBLEM,EDGEWATER LODGE,PINK ROSES,GREEN
   LEAVES,GERMANY................................................   12.50
MASONIC,PLATE,KENSINGTON ROYAL ARCH,PHILADELPHIA,1911,
   8 3/4 IN......................................................    7.50
MASONIC,PLATE,SYRIAN,LOS ANGELES,1906,RAISED SYMBOLS,FLORAL
   DECOR.........................................................   17.00
MASONIC,PLATTER,EMBLEMS,SCALLOPED RIM,FLOW BLUE TYPE,GILT
   DECOR.........................................................   26.00
MASONIC,PLATTER,MASONIC & SHRINER EMBLEMS,SCALLOPED RIM,
   BLUE,GOLD.....................................................   35.00
MASONIC,PRINT,GEORGE WASHINGTON AS RULER OF HIS LODGE,BLACK,
   WHITE,FRAME...................................................  125.00
MASONIC,PRINT,JERUSALEM-JERICHO,PYTHIAN KNIGHTHOOD,
   PETTIBONE,1890,PAIR...........................................   12.50
MASONIC,RING,BLUE LODGE,10K GOLD..................................   17.50
MASONIC,RING,EMBLEM ON RED STONE,STERLING SILVER,MADE IN
   MEXICO........................................................   15.00
MASONIC,SHAVING MUG,NAME IN GOLD..................................   45.00
MASONIC,SHAVING MUG,R.S.BONAR ON BASE,EUGENE BERNINGHAUS,
   OHIO,LIMOGES..................................................   47.50
MASONIC,SPOON,ISLAM TEMPLE,SAN FRANCISCO,ENGRAVED 1902......    5.50
MASONIC,SPOON,KNIGHT IN ARMOR,WILLIAMSPORT,1905,BALDWIN
   11 COMMANDERY.................................................   10.00
MASONIC,SPOON,TEMPLE,BATTLE CREEK.................................    4.00
MASONIC,SWORD,PARADE,MARKED A.F.FOSTER & SONS................   55.00
MASONIC,TANKARD,PORTRAIT,ST.JOHN'S LODGE,PHILADELPHIA,BLUE,
   11 1/4 IN.....................................................   18.00
MASONIC,TRAY,CARD,ALTOONA,PHILADELPHIA,MAY,1899.............   25.00
MASONIC,TUMBLER,WHISKEY,VERTICAL PANELS,EMBLEMS,DICE IN
   HOLLOW BOTTOM.................................................   40.00
MASONIC,WATCH FOB,ONYX TOP,GOLD SYMBOL,GOLD.................   35.00


      MASONIC SHRINE GLASSWARE WAS MADE FROM 1893 TO 1917.
      IT IS OCCASIONALLY CALLED SYRIAN TEMPLE SHRINE
      GLASSWARE. MOST PIECES ARE DATED.
MASONIC,SHRINE,BOTTLE,WINE,SAN FRANCISCO 1902 SYRIA TEMPLE..   37.50
MASONIC,SHRINE,CHAMPAGNE,CRANBERRY,GOLD ROPE VASE,SYRIA,
   ST.PAUL,MINN..................................................   15.00
MASONIC,SHRINE,CHAMPAGNE,ROCHESTER,1911,SYMBOLS,PEDESTAL
   STEM..........................................................   33.00
MASONIC,SHRINE,CHAMPAGNE,ROCHESTER,NEW YORK,1911............   24.50
MASONIC,SHRINE,CHAMPAGNE,SCIMITARS & LEAF BASE,LOUISVILLE,
   1909..........................................................   35.00
MASONIC,SHRINE,CHAMPAGNE,SYRIA TEMPLE,PITTSBURGH,1909,
   2 SCIMITERS...................................................   19.00
MASONIC,SHRINE,CUP,ALMA'S TEMPLE,1914.............................   22.00
MASONIC,SHRINE,CUP,FISH HANDLE,SYRIA TEMPLE,1904...........   30.00
MASONIC,SHRINE,CUP,INDIAN HEAD,SYRIA TEMPLE,1903...........   30.00
MASONIC,SHRINE,CUP,LOVING,PITTSBURGH,PENNSYLVANIA,1910,
   3 3/4 IN......................................................   20.00
MASONIC,SHRINE,CUP,LOVING,3 HANDLES,SOLOMON'S LODGE NO.114,
```

PHILA.,1909........................................................ 35.00
MASONIC,SHRINE,CUP,SWORD HANDLE MARKED SYRIA,INDIAN,
PITTSBURGH,1903.................................................... 21.50
MASONIC,SHRINE,CUP,SYRIA TEMPLE,APPLIED HANDLE,1896......... 42.50
MASONIC,SHRINE,CUP,THREE HANDLES,SYRIA TEMPLE,1905........... 32.50
MASONIC,SHRINE,CUP & SAUCER,SYRIA TEMPLE,1906............... 30.00
MASONIC,SHRINE,CUP & SAUCER,SYRIAN TEMPLE,1906,LOS ANGELES.. 25.00
MASONIC,SHRINE,GOBLET,CLEAR,GOLD BASE,SYRIA,LOUISVILLE,KY.,
1909.............................................................. 15.00
MASONIC,SHRINE,GOBLET,SYMBOLS,GOLD COLOR BUFFALO,1899,
PEDESTAL.......................................................... 35.00
MASONIC,SHRINE,GOBLET,SYRIA,PITTSBURGH,1908,CRANBERRY....... 35.00
MASONIC,SHRINE,GOBLET,SYRIA TEMPLE,1899..................... 30.00
MASONIC,SHRINE,GOBLET,SYRIA TEMPLE,1900..................... 30.00
MASONIC,SHRINE,GOBLET,SYRIA TEMPLE,1902..................... 32.50
MASONIC,SHRINE,GOBLET,SYRIA TEMPLE,1907..................... 30.00
MASONIC,SHRINE,GOBLET,SYRIA TEMPLE,1909..................... 35.00
MASONIC,SHRINE,GOBLET,SYRIA TEMPLE,1910..................... 35.00
MASONIC,SHRINE,GOBLET,SYRIA TEMPLE,1911..................... 35.00
MASONIC,SHRINE,GOBLET,WINE,SYRIA SHRINER,1899,GREEN,GOLD
SYMBOLS,PEDESTAL.................................................. 28.00
MASONIC,SHRINE,MUG,ALCHYMIA TEMPLE,MEMPHIS,EMBLEM,5 IN.TALL. 7.00
MASONIC,SHRINE,MUG,ATLANTIC CITY,1904...................... 25.00
MASONIC,SHRINE,MUG,INDIAN,PITTSBURGH,1903.................. 25.00
MASONIC,SHRINE,MUG,PITTSBURGH,FISH HANDLE,ATLANTIC CITY,
1904.............................................................. 39.50
MASONIC,SHRINE,MUG,SYRIA,INDIAN CHIEF,SARATOGA 1903......... 21.00
MASONIC,SHRINE,MUG,THREE-SCIMITAR HANDLED,NIAGARA FALLS,
1905.............................................................. 35.00
MASONIC,SHRINE,TUMBLER,OKLAHOMA CITY,1953.................. 5.00
MASONIC,SHRINE,TUMBLER,RIBBED,SYRIA TEMPLE,1901............ 35.00
MASONIC,SHRINE,TUMBLER,TEMPLE CHICAGO,SEPIA,OPAQUE,GOLD
TRIM,RAYED BASE................................................... 9.00
MASONIC,SHRINE,WINE,PILLARED STEM,SAN FRANCISCO,1902........ 35.00
MATCH HOLDER,CHEST,LIFT-UP COVER,WALL,STRIKER,IRON,
3 3/4 IN.LONG..................................................... 8.95
MATCH HOLDER,MAN WITH CANE,TREE STUMP HOLDS MATCHES,
6 1/2 IN.TALL..................................................... 15.00
MATCH HOLDER,OAKEN BUCKET,BLUE,METAL BALE.................. 12.50
MATCH HOLDER,SHAPE OF BULLDOG'S HEAD,HAND-PAINTED,PORCELAIN,
AUSTRIA........................................................... 14.00
MATCH HOLDER,WOOD,CARVED,BIRD NEXT TO BARREL............... 8.00
MATCH HOLDER,WOOD,CARVED,FOX NEXT TO TREE TRUNK............ 8.00


MEAKIN IS A NAME USED BY SEVERAL VICTORIAN ENGLISH
POTTERY FIRMS. ALFRED MEAKIN PRODUCED FROM 1875 TO THE
PRESENT TIME. CHARLES MEAKIN WORKED FROM 1883 TO 1889,
HENRY MEAKIN WORKED FROM 1873 TO 1882,AND J. & G.
MEAKIN PRODUCED FROM 1851 TO THE PRESENT TIME.
MEAKIN,BOAT,GRAVY,PINK & BLUE FLOWERS,HANLEY,ENGLAND........ 3.50
MEAKIN,BOWL,PITCHER,WHEAT PATTERN,WHITE IRONSTONE........... 75.00
MEAKIN,DISH,BUTTER,DRAIN,HANDLE,COVER,IRONSTONE,COAT OF ARMS
MARK.............................................................. 10.50
MEAKIN,GRAVY BOAT,GREEN-GOLD,FLOWERS,5 IN.HIGH............. 15.00
MEAKIN,PLATE,BIRD,EMBOSSED BORDER,8 3/4 IN.,PAIR........... 8.50
MECHANICAL BANK,SEE BANK,MECHANICAL


MEERSCHAUM PIPES AND OTHER CARVED PIECES OF MEERSCHAUM
DATE FROM THE NINETEENTH CENTURY TO THE PRESENT TIME.
MEERSCHAUM,HOLDER,CIGAR,DOG,CARVED......................... 10.00
MEERSCHAUM,PIPE BOWL,CARVED MAN,LARGE HAT,SMOKING PIPE,NO
STEM.............................................................. 25.00
MEERSCHAUM,PIPE,AMBER BIT & STEM,CARVING BY J.STEHR,1870,
21 X 10 IN.....................................................1,500.00
MEERSCHAUM,PIPE,BROWN SHELL HANDLE,ETCHED GOLD BAND........ 15.00
MEERSCHAUM,PIPE,CARVED BOXER & SPANIEL,AMBER STEM,CASE,
4 1/2 IN.......................................................... 50.00
MEERSCHAUM,PIPE,CARVED NUDE,CASE,7 1/2 IN.LONG............. 225.00
MEERSCHAUM,PIPE,HORSE,HOUSE,BUSHES,CARVED,SIGNED J.H.,MARKED
1800.............................................................. 65.00
MEERSCHAUM,PIPE,LADY'S,CARVED IVORY BOY RIDING DOG......... 50.00
MEERSCHAUM,PIPE,NUDE LADY ON FLOWER BRANCH,AMBER STEM,SUEDE
CASE.............................................................. 30.00
MEERSCHAUM,PIPE,OBLONG SILVER COVER FOR BOWL,SILVER STEM.... 25.00


MEISSEN IS A TOWN IN GERMANY WHERE PORCELAIN HAS BEEN
MADE SINCE 1710. ANY CHINA MADE IN THAT TOWN CAN BE
CALLED MEISSEN,ALTHOUGH THE FAMOUS MEISSEN FACTORY
MADE THE FINEST PORCELAINS OF THE AREA.

```
MEISSEN,PERFUME,APPLIED FLOWERS,ROSE ON TOP..............      70.00
MEISSEN,PLATE,COBALT,GOLD SCALLOPED BORDER,ALLOVER
  PORTRAITS,MARK,PAIR.....................................     115.00
MEISSEN,PLATE,DARK BLUE,GOLD OAK LEAF,CROSSED SWORD MARK,
  8 1/2 IN..............................................       35.00
MEISSEN,PLATE,GREEN DRAGON CHASING FIERY ORANGE PEARL,GOLD,
  PAIR..................................................       30.00
MEISSEN,PLATE,HAND-PAINTED APPLE & GRAPES,CROSSED SWORDS
  MARK,8 IN.............................................       23.00
MEISSEN,PLATE,PANELS,CLASSIC FIGURES,FLOWERS,CROSSED SWORD
  MARK,8 IN.............................................       27.00
MEISSEN,PLATE,ROBIN ON TWIG,BUTTERFLIES,SCROLLED BORDER,
  MARK,11 1/2 IN........................................      160.00
MEISSEN,PLATE,SAYS PRIV.SCHEIBENSCHUTZEN,CROSSED RIFLES &
  TARGET CENTER.........................................       35.00
MEISSEN,PLATE,WHITE,FLORAL CENTER,BASKET WEAVE BORDER,10 IN.   17.50
MEISSEN,PLATTER,NAMED SCENIC,DOT PERIOD 1763-74,18 IN. LONG.  475.00
MEISSEN,STATUETTE GROUP,DOT PERIOD 1763-74,9 1/2 IN. HIGH...  125.00
MEISSEN,STATUETTE,REINDEER,CIRCA 1750,3 IN. HIGH.....ILLUS..  500.00
MEISSEN,STEIN,CROSSED SWORD MARK,13 IN.HIGH..............     750.00
```

MEISSEN
BOWL

MEISSEN
STATUETTE

MEISSEN ROCOCO
SCENT BOTTLE

MEISSEN
FLAGON

MEISSEN FIGURAL
SCENT BOTTLE

MEISSEN CANDELABRA, C. 1745

MEISSEN,TEA & COFFEE SERVICE,FLORAL,WITH A CONTEMPORARY
  SALT,21 PIECES........................................... 800.00
MEISSEN,TEA BOWL & SAUCER,YELLOW,CIRCA 1735................ 325.00
MEISSEN,TEAPOT,BOUQUETS,BARK HANDLE & SPOUT,LADYBUG,FLORAL,
  ROSEBUD KNOB............................................. 115.00
MEISSEN,TEAPOT,CIRCA 1740-50,3 1/2 IN. HIGH,CROSSED SWORDS
  MARK.................................................... 140.00
MEISSEN,TRAY,BLUE,WHITE,ORIENTAL DECOR,FLOWERING BRANCH,
  INSECTS,FLORAL.......................................... 100.00
MEISSEN,TUREEN,COVERED,BIRDS,CIRCA 1760,CROSSED SWORDS MARK. 200.00
MEISSEN,TUREEN,SOUP,FLORAL,LEMON FINIAL,CROSSED SWORD MARK,
  1760,12 IN.............................................. 725.00
MEISSEN,URN,HAND-PAINTED,AUGUSTUS REX MARK,CIRCA 1790,ONE
  RESTORED,PAIR........................................... 950.00
MEISSEN,VASE,INDIAN PINK PATTERN,GOLD DOTS & EDGE,CROSSED
  SWORD MARK.............................................. 35.00
MENNECY,JAR,SCATTERED BLOSSOMS,HIGH DOME COVER,ROSEBUD
  FINIAL,1760............................................. 130.00
MENNECY,TUREEN,COVERED,CIRCA 1750,5 1/2 IN. LONG........... 325.00


       MERCURY OR SILVERED GLASS WAS FIRST MADE IN THE 1850S.
       IT LOST FAVOR FOR A WHILE BUT BECAME POPULAR AGAIN
       ABOUT 1910. IT LOOKS LIKE A PIECE OF SILVER.
MERCURY GLASS,ATOMIZER,BULBOUS,3 IN.ACROSS BOTTOM,4 IN.HIGH. 18.00
MERCURY GLASS,BOTTLE,CENTER INDENTATION,BULBOUS,SCREW TOP,
  6 1/2 IN.HIGH........................................... 27.50
MERCURY GLASS,BOWL,GILT INTERIOR,4 1/2 IN.................. 65.00
MERCURY GLASS,BOWL,ROSE................................... 4.50
MERCURY GLASS,BOWL,ROSE,GERMANY,3 1/2 IN.................. 8.00
MERCURY GLASS,CANDLEHOLDER,SIGNED CHEZ,PAIR............... 18.00
MERCURY GLASS,CHALICE,WHITE GRAPE & LEAF DECOR,GOLD COLOR
  LINING.................................................. 15.00
MERCURY GLASS,DISH,SWEETMEAT,SECTIONED.................... 7.00
MERCURY GLASS,DOORKNOB,PAIR............................... 12.50
MERCURY GLASS,DOORKNOB,SPINDLE,PAIR....................... 12.50
MERCURY GLASS,GOBLET...................................... 18.00
MERCURY GLASS,GOBLET,6 1/2 IN.HIGH....................... 15.00
MERCURY GLASS,HUMIDOR,GOLD COLOR LINING.................. 50.00
MERCURY GLASS,MUG,SAYS FOR A GOOD BOY,CLEAR HANDLE,FOOTED
  BASE,3 IN.HIGH.......................................... 12.00
MERCURY GLASS,ORNAMENT,CHRISTMAS,BALL,3-IN.DIAMETER....... 6.50
MERCURY GLASS,ORNAMENT,CHRISTMAS,GRAPES,3-IN.DIAMETER..... 6.50
MERCURY GLASS,ORNAMENT,CHRISTMAS,PEAR SHAPE,3-IN.DIAMETER... 6.50
MERCURY GLASS,SALT DIP,THREE GLASS FEET.................. 7.50
MERCURY GLASS,SALT,FOOTED................................. 6.00
MERCURY GLASS,SALT,MASTER,PLAIN,FOOTED,3 1/8 IN.TALL,
  3 5/8-IN.DIAMETER....................................... 10.00
MERCURY GLASS,SALT,THREE LEGS,TINY....................... 7.50
MERCURY GLASS,TIEBACK,FLORAL,4-IN.DIAMETER,2 PAIRS....... 40.00
MERCURY GLASS,TIEBACK,GRAPES,PAIR................ 12.00 TO 15.00
MERCURY GLASS,TIEBACK,4-IN.DIAMETER,PAIR................. 20.00
MERCURY GLASS,VASE,BLUE TOP,FLOWER ON FRONT,7 3/8 IN.HIGH... 8.00
MERCURY GLASS,VASE,ENAMEL FLORAL DECORATION,8 IN......... 9.00
MERCURY GLASS,VASE,FLORAL BAND,14 1/2 IN................. 17.50
MERCURY GLASS,VASE,GOLD COLOR,10 IN.HIGH................. 22.00
MERCURY GLASS,WINE,GOLD-LINED............................ 18.50
METAL,EAGLE FINIAL,PAINTED,19TH CENTURY,AMERICAN......... 300.00


       METTLACH,GERMANY,IS A CITY WHERE THE VILLEROY AND BOCH
       FACTORIES WORKED. STEINS FROM THE FIRM ARE KNOWN AS
       METTLACH STEINS. THEY DATE FROM ABOUT 1842.
METTLACH,ASHTRAY,NO.4-3196-08,CREAM COLOR,GREEN DECOR,CASTLE
  MARK.................................................... 6.00
METTLACH,BEAKER,CASTLE MARK,SIGNED GESCHUTZI............. 30.00
METTLACH,BEAKER,NO.1139,1/4 LITER,MAN PLAYING VIOLIN..... 25.00
METTLACH,BOWL,PUNCH,NO.2633,THREE QUARTS,DRINKING SCENE,
  MUSCIANS,COVER.......................................... 250.00
METTLACH,BOWL,PUNCH,NO.3433,ETCHED GRAPE DECOR,BROWN,TAN,
  PURPLE,COVER............................................ 155.00
METTLACH,COMPOTE,NO.3336,CASTLE MARK,10 IN.TALL,
  9-1/2 IN.DIAMETER....................................... 110.00
METTLACH,CUP & SAUCER,BLUE WEDGWOOD FIGURE MEDALLIONS,ORNATE
  SILVER.................................................. 45.00
METTLACH,CUP & SAUCER,SALT GLAZE FINISH,FRAMED WEDGWOOD
  MEDALLIONS.............................................. 65.00
METTLACH,DECANTER,NO.1335,TAN & BROWN GROUND,FLORAL,HANDLE,
  7 IN.TALL............................................... 65.00
METTLACH,DISH,NO.1748,HANDLES,GLAZED,CASTLE MARK,12 IN. X
  9 1/2 IN................................................ 82.50

```
METTLACH,JAR,BISCUIT,TAN GROUND,RAISED FLORAL,SILVER PLATE
  TOP,HANDLE..............................................    50.00
METTLACH,MATCH HOLDER,NO.136,TREE STUMP,CIGARETTE
  COMPARTMENT,STRIKER.....................................    75.00
METTLACH,MUG,BEER,NO.2360,1/4 LITER,CASTLE MARK............    54.50
METTLACH,MUG,HIRES ROOT BEER,SIGNED.......................    30.00
METTLACH,MUG,NO.1095,TAVERN SCENE,HANDLE,VILLEROY & BOCH...    45.00
METTLACH,MUG,NO.2217,B.P.O.E.,1897,MINNEAPOLIS,MINNESOTA...    50.00
METTLACH,MUG,NO.2217,4/10 LITER,PUG,FIVE GIRLS' FACES,VERSE.   35.00
METTLACH,PITCHER,NO.3257,PAINTED FROGS,SIGNED L O G,
  11 IN.TALL.............................................   145.00
METTLACH,PLANTER,ETCHED DESIGN,CREAM,GRAY,BROWN,BLACK,CASTLE
  MARK,8 IN..............................................    80.00
METTLACH,PLANTER,NO.1462,FOUR SCENES,ETCHED,FOOTED,6 IN. X
  13 IN.HIGH.............................................   250.00
METTLACH,PLAQUE,CAMEO,BLUE,WHITE,WARRIORS,HORSE,CLOUDS,
  18 IN. X 21 IN.......................................1,200.00
METTLACH,PLAQUE,NO.1290,EAGLE,AMERICAN FLAG,E PLURIBUS UNUM,
  13 1/4 IN..............................................   110.00
METTLACH,PLAQUE,NO.1769,MEDIEVAL BATTLE SCENE,ETCHED,MARK,
  14 1/2 IN..............................................   290.00
METTLACH,PLAQUE,NO.2070 & 2071,ETCHED,15-1/4 IN.DIAMETER,
  PAIR...................................................   575.00
METTLACH,PLAQUE,NO.2148 & 2149,ETCHED,16-1/2 IN.DIAMETER...   575.00
METTLACH,PLAQUE,NO.2287,ETCHED,17-IN.DIAMETER.............   350.00
METTLACH,PLAQUE,NO.2623,CASTLE MARK,7 7/8 IN..............   100.00
METTLACH,PLAQUE,NO.2625,CASTLE MARK,7 7/8 IN..............   100.00
METTLACH,PLAQUE,NO.2626,CASTLE MARK,7 7/8 IN,.............   100.00
METTLACH,PLAQUE,NO.5042,NOBLEMAN,RUFFLED COLLAR,SIGNED
  F.HALS,12 IN...........................................    70.00
METTLACH,PLAQUE,NO.7013,BLUE,WHITE,SIGNED STAHL,MARK,
  18-IN.DIAMETER.........................................   375.00
METTLACH,PLAQUE,NO.7053,CAMEO,DANCING MUSES,20-IN.DIAMETER,
  PAIR...................................................   900.00
METTLACH,PLAQUE,NO.7053,THREE DANCING MUSES,CAMEO,
  20-IN.DIAMETER,PAIR....................................   900.00
METTLACH,PLAQUE,NO.7067 & 7068,CAMEO,FRAME,4 IN. X 6 IN.,
  PAIR...................................................   500.00
METTLACH,PLAQUE,NO.7072,CAMEO,FRAME,6 IN. X 8 IN..........   350.00
METTLACH,PLATE,CAKE,FLORAL,MERCURY MARK,VILLEROY & BOCH,
  GERMANY,13 IN..........................................    20.00
METTLACH,PLATE,GEOMETRIC DESIGN,BLUE,WHITE,TAN,FLORAL,
  NO.2960,HANGER.........................................    65.00
METTLACH,PLATE,NO.3321,CASTLE,8 3/4 IN....................    15.00
METTLACH,PLATTER,FISH,COLORED FISH,FLORAL,CORAL,VILLEROY &
  BOCH...................................................    85.00
METTLACH,SHIELD,PUG,BLACK EAGLE & DRESDEN,11 IN. X 13 IN.,
  PAIR...................................................   200.00
METTLACH,STEIN,HIRES ROOT BEER,SIGNED.....................    20.00
METTLACH,STEIN,NO.6,BIBICAL,VILLEROY & BOCH...............   125.00
METTLACH,STEIN,NO.675,1/2 LITER,BEIGE-CARAMEL COLOR,BARREL
  SHAPE..................................................   125.00
METTLACH,STEIN,NO.1028,1/2 LITER..........................    85.00
METTLACH,STEIN,NO.1028,1/2 LITER,RAISED FIGURES,SIGNED....    75.00
METTLACH,STEIN,NO.1095,1/2 LITER..........................   110.00
METTLACH,STEIN,NO.1155,1/2 LITER,MOSAIC...................   135.00
METTLACH,STEIN,NO.1258,1/2 LITER,MOSAIC...................   135.00
METTLACH,STEIN,NO.1266,1/2 LITER,BLUE & WHITE
  FIGURES.......................................  90.00 TO   145.00
METTLACH,STEIN,NO.1288,3/10 LITER,HOPS & LEAVES...........   135.00
METTLACH,STEIN,NO.1370,1/2 LITER..........................   110.00
METTLACH,STEIN,NO.1455,MOSAIC.............................   225.00
METTLACH,STEIN,NO.1467,1/2 LITER,BEIGE,VILLEROY &
  BOCH...................................... 135.00 TO   150.00
METTLACH,STEIN,NO.1471,1/2 LITER,MUSICIANS................   245.00
METTLACH,STEIN,NO.1526,1/2 LITER..........................    65.00
METTLACH,STEIN,NO.1526,1/2 LITER,COMMEMORATION,BLACK,WHITE..  135.00
METTLACH,STEIN,NO.1526,1 LITER,TAN,PEWTER TOP,THUMB REST,
  MERCURY MARK...........................................    95.00
METTLACH,STEIN,NO.1526,3 LITERS,PUG.......................   185.00
METTLACH,STEIN,NO.1526-1076,1/2 LITER,SIGNED SCHLITT,NO LID.   55.00
METTLACH,STEIN,NO.1526/1108,1 LITER,PUG...................   125.00
METTLACH,STEIN,NO.1526/1145,1/2 LITER,PUG.................    65.00
METTLACH,STEIN,NO.1527,1/2 LITER..........................   165.00
METTLACH,STEIN,NO.1533,1 LITER............................   150.00
METTLACH,STEIN,NO.1536,1/2 LITER,CASTLE MARK..............   150.00
METTLACH,STEIN,NO.1566,1/2 LITER,HIGH-WHEEL BIKE,CASTLE MARK  140.00
METTLACH,STEIN,NO.1571,1 1/2 LITERS.......................   225.00
METTLACH,STEIN,NO.1642,1/2 LITER,TAPESTRY.................   165.00
METTLACH,STEIN,NO.1643,1/2 LITER,ETCHED BEER DRINKER WITH
  DOG....................................................   150.00
```

```
METTLACH,STEIN,NO.1648,1 LITER,TAPESTRY...................    150.00
METTLACH,STEIN,NO.1654,1/2 LITER.........................    165.00
METTLACH,STEIN,NO.1662,1/2 LITER,TAPESTRY......... 135.00 TO 145.00
METTLACH,STEIN,NO.1725,1/4 LITER,CAMEO ON TOP,
   SIGNED.................................... 150.00 TO 165.00
METTLACH,STEIN,NO.1735,3 LITERS..........................    225.00
METTLACH,STEIN,NO.1739,THREE LITERS,RELIEF...............    250.00
METTLACH,STEIN,NO.1740,CASTLE MARK.......................     85.00
METTLACH,STEIN,NO.1786,1 LITER,ETCHED....................    350.00
METTLACH,STEIN,NO.1788,3/10 LITER,CREAM,GREEN,BUFF,RAISED
   JEWELS................................................    150.00
METTLACH,STEIN,NO.1803,1/4 LITER,FLEUR-DE-LIS............     95.00
METTLACH,STEIN,NO.1909,1/2 LITER.........................    110.00
METTLACH,STEIN,NO.1915,1/2 LITER....................ILLUS..   120.00
METTLACH,STEIN,NO.1947,1/2 LITER,DRINKER & CAT..........    245.00
METTLACH,STEIN,NO.1972,1/4 LITER,FOUR SEASONS,FOUR GIRLS....  150.00
METTLACH,STEIN,NO.1977,1/2 LITER,CASTLE MARK.............    125.00
METTLACH,STEIN,NO.1997,ETCHED CASTLE MARK,1/2 LITER........  135.00
METTLACH,STEIN,NO.2001..................................    325.00
METTLACH,STEIN,NO.2002..............................ILLUS..   225.00
```

METTLACH STEIN, NO. 1915

METTLACH STEIN, NO. 2002

```
METTLACH,STEIN,NO.2025,1/2 LITER,NUDE CHERUBS..............   235.00
METTLACH,STEIN,NO.2028,1/2 LITER,TAVERN SCENE,
   ARTIST-SIGNED.............................. 235.00 TO 245.00
METTLACH,STEIN,NO.2035,1 LITER,BACCHUS DRUNK..............   285.00
METTLACH,STEIN,NO.2054,1/2 LITER,DATED '92........        235.00
METTLACH,STEIN,NO.2057,1/2 LITER,DANCERS WITH STEINS........  245.00
METTLACH,STEIN,NO.2082,1/2 LITER,WILLIAM TELL,CROSSBOW,KING,
   LORD..................................................   235.00
METTLACH,STEIN,NO.2086,1/4 LITER,BLUE WITH WHITE
   FIGURES................................... 65.00 TO  95.00
METTLACH,STEIN,NO.2091,1/2 LITER,ETCHED...................   195.00
METTLACH,STEIN,NO.2096,3 LITERS,ETCHED...................   175.00
METTLACH,STEIN,NO.2123,1/2 LITER,ENGRAVED,SIGNED SCHLITT....  245.00
METTLACH,STEIN,NO.2171,1/4 LITER....................ILLUS..   90.00
METTLACH,STEIN,NO.2181,1/4 LITER....................ILLUS..  100.00
METTLACH,STEIN,NO.2182,1 1/2 LITERS,BLUE & WHITE WEDGWOOD
   TYPE FIGURES...........................................   125.00
METTLACH,STEIN,NO.2184,3/10 LITER,DANCING GNOMES,BEETS,
   PEWTER TOP............................................   160.00
METTLACH,STEIN,NO.2184,1/2 LITER....................ILLUS..   70.00
METTLACH,STEIN,NO.2204,1/2 LITER,BLACK EAGLE,DATED 1900.....  250.00
METTLACH,STEIN,NO.2217,MINNEAPOLIS,MINNESOTA,B.P.O.E.,1897..   55.00
METTLACH,STEIN,NO.2247,3/10 LITER,CASTLE MARK.............   150.00
METTLACH,STEIN,NO.2580,1/2 LITER.........................   250.00
METTLACH,STEIN,NO.2581,1/2 LITER,ETCHED,SIGNED...........   225.00
METTLACH,STEIN,NO.2628,1/2 LITER,CAMEO...................   200.00
METTLACH,STEIN,NO.2775,1 LITER,PILSENER,PUG,DRILLED FOR LAMP  85.00
METTLACH,STEIN,NO.2833D,1/2 LITER........................   175.00
METTLACH,STEIN,NO.2833D,1/2 LITER,CASTLE MARK............   225.00
METTLACH,STEIN,NO.2903..............................ILLUS..  150.00
METTLACH,STEIN,NO.2937,1/2 LITER,SCENE,CAT,FISH IN WREATHS,
   CASTLEMARK............................................   215.00
METTLACH,STEIN,NO.3024,WHITE CAMEO FIGURES IN RELIEF,INLAY
   COVER,13 IN............................................  165.00
METTLACH,STEIN,NO.3043,1/2 LITER,ETCHED..................   190.00
METTLACH,STEIN,NO.3079,1/2 LITER,PEWTER COVER,
   FLORAL.................................... 95.00 TO 105.00
METTLACH,STEIN,NO.3243,ETCHED...........................   125.00
METTLACH,STEIN,NO.3249,1/2 LITER,TYROLEANS...............   235.00
```

METTLACH STEIN,
NO. 2181

METTLACH STEIN,
NO. 2171

METTLACH STEIN,
NO. 2184

METTLACH STEIN, NO. 2903

```
METTLACH,STEIN,1/4 LITER,PICTURE OF ST.ALICE HOTEL,MARKED,
   DATED 1909...............................................     20.00
METTLACH,STEIN,3/10 LITER,PICTURE OF SOL DUC,HOT SPRINGS,
   CASTLE-MARKED...........................................      20.00
METTLACH,STEIN,1/2 LITER,CAMEO SCENES INSET,TOP............     150.00
METTLACH,STEIN,1 LITER,TWO RAISED DEER ON COVER,10 IN.......     32.00
METTLACH,TILE,LITHOGRAPH,COLOR,DUTCH FARM SCENE,VILLEROY &
   BOCH,PAIR...............................................      25.00
METTLACH,TRAY,NO.1748,LEAF SHAPE,RAISED MEDALLIONS,HANDLES,
   13 1/2 IN...............................................      75.00
METTLACH,TUMBLER,NO.18,1/4 LITER,CHERUBS,DOGS,RABBITS,SCENE,
   SIGNED STAHL............................................      45.00
METTLACH,TUMBLER,NO.2327,COAT OF ARMS ON SIDE,VILLEROY &
   BOCH...................................................       34.00
METTLACH,TUREEN,NO.1562,FLORAL,LEAVES,HANDLES,FINIAL,MERCURY     22.00
METTLACH,VASE,BLUE,BROWN BAND AROUND NECK,CASTLE MARKS,
   9 IN.,PAIR.............................................      110.00
MICKEY MOUSE,DISH SET,TOY,JAPAN,8 PIECES...................      12.00
MICKEY MOUSE,FIGURINE,BISQUE..............................      10.00
MICKEY MOUSE,SPOON,SILVER PLATE...........................       6.50
MICKEY MOUSE,SPOON,WILLIAM ROGERS & COMPANY...............       3.50
MICKEY MOUSE,TOY,PULL,DRUMMER,WOODEN......................       2.50
MICKEY MOUSE,WATCH,WRIST..................................      50.00
MICKEY MOUSE,WATCH,WRIST,INGERSOL.............. 40.00 TO       100.00


      MILK GLASS WAS NAMED FOR ITS MILKY WHITE COLOR. IT WAS
   FIRST MADE IN ENGLAND DURING THE 1700S. THE HEIGHT OF
   ITS POPULARITY IN THE UNITED STATES WAS FROM 1870 TO
   1880. IT IS NOW CORRECT TO REFER TO SOME COLORED GLASS
   AS BLUE MILK GLASS,BLACK MILK GLASS,ETC.
      MILK GLASS,SEE ALSO,COSMOS
MILK GLASS,BANK,LOG CABIN,YELLOW & GOLD PAINT,4 IN.HIGH.....     22.50
MILK GLASS,BASKET,BLACK,REGISTRY MARK......................      15.00
MILK GLASS,BASKET,DOUBLE SALT,BASKET WEAVE,PAT.APP.JULY 21,
   1874...................................................       18.00
MILK GLASS,BASKET,PINCHED TOP,SOWERBY,CRESTED BIRD MARK.....     25.00
MILK GLASS,BELL,APPLIED OPALESCENT HANDLE,11 3/4 IN.TALL,
   7-IN.BASE..............................................       70.00
```

```
MILK GLASS,BOTTLE,BARBER.............................      25.00
MILK GLASS,BOTTLE,BARBER,BULBOUS BASE................      25.00
MILK GLASS,BOTTLE,BARBER,PORCELAIN STOPPER...........      12.50
MILK GLASS,BOTTLE,BAY RUM,PAINTED FLORAL,WHITE,PEWTER
  STOPPER...........................................       20.00
MILK GLASS,BOTTLE,COLOGNE...........................       14.00
MILK GLASS,BOTTLE,COLOGNE,LEAF DESIGN,STOPPER,9 IN.TALL,PAIR  30.00
MILK GLASS,BOTTLE,CORDIAL,ENAMELED LADY,FLORAL,PEWTER
  COLLAR,CAP,1780...................................       60.00
MILK GLASS,BOTTLE,DRESSER,DAISY PATTERN,OVAL,HOLLOW STOPPER,
  9 1/2 IN..........................................       15.00
MILK GLASS,BOTTLE,DRESSER,PAINTED DECOR WITH GOLD TRIM,
  STOPPER,10 IN.....................................       16.50
MILK GLASS,BOTTLE,DRESSER,SLOPED,RAISED DESIGN,PAINTED
  LEAVES,STOPPER....................................       16.00
MILK GLASS,BOTTLE,DRESSER,STOPPER,9 IN.HIGH,PAIR....       20.00
MILK GLASS,BOTTLE,ELEPHANT BASE,MAHARAJAH STOPPER,GREEN,
  FRANCE,PAIR.......................................       60.00
MILK GLASS,BOTTLE,FIGURAL,DICE,GROUND LIP,3 1/4 IN.HIGH....   8.50
MILK GLASS,BOTTLE,SAYS BAY RUM,PANELED SIDES & NECK,GREEN,
  6 1/4 IN.TALL.....................................        6.50
MILK GLASS,BOTTLE,SNUFF,WHITE,ENAMELED..............      825.00
MILK GLASS,BOTTLE,TOILET WATER,BLUE & WHITE FLORAL,BLOWN,
  STOPPER,1 QUART...................................       18.00
MILK GLASS,BOTTLE,TOILET WATER,SWIRL LEAF DECOR,STOPPER.....  18.50
MILK GLASS,BOWL,ACANTHUS LEAF,PAT.APRIL 23,1878,BLUE....     37.50
MILK GLASS,BOWL,BEADED RIB,FLARED TOP,OPAQUE WHITE..........  18.75
MILK GLASS,BOWL,BLACK,SET IN STERLING SILVER BASE,
  10-IN.DIAMETER....................................       25.00
MILK GLASS,BOWL,BLACK,STERLING OVERLAY,POINSETTIA & LEAVES,
  FOOTED,9 IN.......................................       16.00
MILK GLASS,BOWL,BUTTONS & BOWS,FOOTED,PINK,SCALLOPED,11 IN..  12.50
MILK GLASS,BOWL,CENTER,SIX-SIDED,FLANGE,CUT & ETCHED,FOOTED,
  GREEN,13 IN.......................................       38.00
MILK GLASS,BOWL,DAISY PATTERN,PAINTED FLORAL,LEAVES,WHITE,
  8 1/4 IN..........................................       72.50
MILK GLASS,BOWL,DAISY,OPEN EDGE DECOR...............       75.00
MILK GLASS,BOWL,DARK & LIGHT BLUE STREAKS,CHERRY BLOSSOMS,
  OPEN,HANDLES......................................       12.00
MILK GLASS,BOWL,FLARED LACY EDGE,12-IN.DIAMETER.....       35.00
MILK GLASS,BOWL,FLORAL CENTER,LATTICE EDGE,MATCHING PLATE...  75.00
MILK GLASS,BOWL,FRUIT,OPENWORK BORDER,3 LEGS,
  SOWERBY,1876............................ 43.00 TO       45.00
MILK GLASS,BOWL,HAT SHAPE,BERRIES...................        9.00
MILK GLASS,BOWL,KNOBBY EDGE,ATTERBURY...............       45.00
MILK GLASS,BOWL,LACY,SCROLL WITH EYE,BLUE,2 IN.DEEP,
  6 3/4-IN.DIAMETER.................................       32.50
MILK GLASS,BOWL,OPEN LATTICE,9 1/4 IN...............       24.50
MILK GLASS,BOWL,OPENWORK EDGE,LIGHT BLUE,7 IN.......       13.00
MILK GLASS,BOWL,PUNCH,LEAF PATTERN,FOOTED,12 CUPS...       13.50
MILK GLASS,BOWL,ROSE,LEAF DESIGN,PAIR...............       12.00
MILK GLASS,BOWL,ROSE,RAISED POPPY,FROSTED,BLACK,6 IN. X
  11 IN.............................................       12.00
MILK GLASS,BOWL,SCROLL & EYE,BLUE,7 IN..............       20.00
MILK GLASS,BOWL,SUGAR,CHERRY,TWIG FINIAL............       22.50
MILK GLASS,BOWL,SUGAR,COVER,PINK,GRAPE,FOOTED.......        7.50
MILK GLASS,BOWL,SUGAR,FORGET-ME-NOT,COVER...........       15.00
MILK GLASS,BOWL,SUGAR,SAWTOOTH,FLINT,MESH TEETH,COVER,ACORN
  FINIAL............................................       40.00
MILK GLASS,BOWL,SUGAR,TWIN HORN.....................       32.50
MILK GLASS,BOWL,WHITE,CRINKLED LACY EDGE,7 1/2 X
  3 1/2 IN.HIGH.....................................       18.00
MILK GLASS,BOX,GLOVE,FIVE KITTENS ON LID,10 1/2 X 4 X
  2 1/2-IN.DIAMETER.................................       30.00
MILK GLASS,BOX,GLOVE,WHITE,LID & BOTTOM MARKED 17,3 1/2 X
  10 IN.............................................       20.00
MILK GLASS,BOX,PINK,BLUE,YELLOW,ENAMELED DECOR,METAL
  CLOSING,COVER.....................................       22.00
MILK GLASS,BOX,RAISED DESIGN,COLLAR,COVER...........       15.00
MILK GLASS,BOX,TRINKET,OVAL,LID,4 1/2 IN. X 3 IN....       10.00
MILK GLASS,BOX,WHITE,RABBIT LID,4 1/2 IN.LONG.......       35.00
MILK GLASS,BUTTER,JACOB'S COAT,COVER................       25.00
MILK GLASS,BUTTER,PINK BORDER,COSMOS................      110.00
MILK GLASS,BUTTER,RIBBED,HAND-PAINTED VIOLETS,COVER.       22.00
MILK GLASS,BUTTER,SAWTOOTH COVER,FLINT..............       47.50
MILK GLASS,CAKE STAND,FOOTED,PINK,10 IN. X 5 IN.HIGH.      12.50
MILK GLASS,CANOE,HANGING,DAISY & BUTTON,8 1/2 IN.LONG.      35.00
MILK GLASS,CAT,WHITE................................       35.00
MILK GLASS,CHICK & EGGS, EASTER GREETING ...........       13.75
MILK GLASS,CHICK ON SLEIGH..........................       37.00
MILK GLASS,COMPOTE,ATLAS,ATTERBURY,9 IN.-DIAM...... 75.00 TO  95.00
```

```
MILK GLASS,COMPOTE,BASKET WEAVE,OPEN LATTICE,FOOTED,BLUE....     47.50
MILK GLASS,COMPOTE,BASKET WEAVE BASE,LATTICE EDGE...........     30.00
MILK GLASS,COMPOTE,BLUE,FERN & TWIG,STIPPLED GROUND,OPEN,
  6 IN.....................................................     25.00
MILK GLASS,COMPOTE,BLUE,RAISED SCROLL DECOR,OPEN,6 IN.SQUARE    24.50
MILK GLASS,COMPOTE,CHARTREUSE..............................     45.00
MILK GLASS,COMPOTE,FIERY OPALESCENT,LOOPED EDGE,ATTERBURY,
  8-IN.DIAMETER............................................     40.00
MILK GLASS,COMPOTE,FLORAL DECOR IN CENTER,LATTICE AT TOP,
  8 1/2 X 9 IN.............................................     50.00
MILK GLASS,COMPOTE,FLORAL DECOR,LATTICE,8 3/4-IN.DIAMETER,
  7 1/4 IN.HIGH............................................     62.50
MILK GLASS,COMPOTE,JENNY LIND,OPEN,WHITE,7 1/2 IN. HIGH     *
  75.00 TO.................................................     85.00
MILK GLASS,COMPOTE,JENNY LIND,HIGH STANDARD................     55.00
MILK GLASS,COMPOTE,JENNY LIND,OPEN,WHITE,7 1/2 IN.HIGH,
  8 1/2-IN.DIAMETER........................................     75.00
MILK GLASS,COMPOTE,OPEN LATTICE EDGE,BASKET WEAVE INTERIOR &
  STEM,BLUE................................................     45.00
MILK GLASS,COMPOTE,PINK,COVER,SQUARE SHAPE,7 IN.TALL.......     10.00
MILK GLASS,COMPOTE,RIBBED STEM,OPAQUE WHITE................     32.50
MILK GLASS,COMPOTE,SCROLL DECOR,HEXAGONAL..................     50.00
MILK GLASS,COMPOTE,STANDING ROOSTER COVER,WESTMORELAND,
  8 1/2 IN.HIGH............................................     10.00
MILK GLASS,CORNUCOPIA,RAYED BASE,PINK,PAIR.................      9.00
MILK GLASS,CREAMER & SUGAR,CHERRIES ON ONE SIDE,GRAPES ON
  OTHER SIDE...............................................     18.00
MILK GLASS,CREAMER & SUGAR,CORNUCOPIA PATTERN,COVER,BLUE,
  GOLD PAINT...............................................     38.00
MILK GLASS,CREAMER & SUGAR,PANELED WHEAT,WHITE.............     57.50
MILK GLASS,CREAMER,BASKET WEAVE,PATENT JUNE 30,'74.........     14.50
MILK GLASS,CREAMER,DIAMOND BLOCK...........................     25.00
MILK GLASS,CREAMER,DOLPHIN.................................     65.00
MILK GLASS,CREAMER,PANELED WHEAT,RINGED BASE...............     32.00
MILK GLASS,CREAMER,PRINCESS FEATHER,APPLIED HANDLE,FLINT....    45.00
MILK GLASS,CRUET,EMBOSSED FLORAL,PANELS,STOPPER,HANDLE,
  WHITE,5 1/4 IN...........................................     27.50
MILK GLASS,CRUET,GRAPE,LEAF,CABLE,GREEN,PINK & GOLD DECOR...     27.50
MILK GLASS,CRUET,IVY PATTERN...............................     39.00
MILK GLASS,CUP & SAUCER,CANDLEWICK,OPAQUE WHITE............     12.50
MILK GLASS,CUP,EGG,BASKET WEAVE............................      8.50
MILK GLASS,CUP,EGG,BASKET WEAVE,FOOTED,PAT.JUNE 30,1874.....     9.50
MILK GLASS,CUP,EGG,BASKET WEAVE,WHITE,PAT.JUNE 30,1874.....     15.00
MILK GLASS,CUP,EGG,BEADED SWIRL,FOOTED,OPAQUE WHITE........      4.75
MILK GLASS,CUP,EGG,BLACKBERRY,OPAQUE WHITE,FOOTED..........      8.75
MILK GLASS,CUP,EGG,CHICK WITH EGG ON BACK,BLUE.............      6.50
MILK GLASS,CUP,EGG,DOUBLE,BLACKBERRY,OPAQUE WHITE..........     12.50
MILK GLASS,CUP,PUNCH,CHILD'S,WILD ROSE PATTERN.............      5.00
MILK GLASS,CUP,PUNCH,FLEUR-DE-LIS & TASSEL,OPAQUE WHITE.....     8.75
MILK GLASS,CUSPIDOR,GOLD TRIM..............................      9.00
MILK GLASS,DECANTER,ACTRESS PATTERN,STOPPER................     26.50
MILK GLASS,DECANTER,WINE,BLUE,EMBOSSED DECOR...............     18.00
MILK GLASS,DISH,ADMIRAL DEWEY COVER........................     22.00
MILK GLASS,DISH,BATTLESHIP MAINE,COVER............. 30.00 TO    45.00
MILK GLASS,DISH,BLACKBERRY,OVAL,WHITE......................     20.00
MILK GLASS,DISH,BLUE & WHITE CAT ON BLUE RIBBED BASE,COVER..    25.00
MILK GLASS,DISH,BLUE DOG WITH WHITE HEAD,WHITE BASE........     20.00
MILK GLASS,DISH,BLUE,COVER,WHITE HEAD......................     25.00
MILK GLASS,DISH,BLUE,OVAL,SWIMMING DUCK COVER,5 IN.........     22.50
MILK GLASS,DISH,BRITISH LION,COVERED.......................     22.00
MILK GLASS,DISH,BUTTER,ROYAL OAK,COLORED LEAVES............     36.50
MILK GLASS,DISH,CAT COVER,SPLIT RIB BASE...................     50.00
MILK GLASS,DISH,CONE SHAPE,OCTAGONAL RIM,ETCHED BOUQUET,
  LATTICE,BLACK............................................     12.50
MILK GLASS,DISH,COVER IS RINGED HAND WITH DOVE,7 IN. X 4 IN.    52.00
MILK GLASS,DISH,CRIMPED LACY EDGE,ATTERBURY,WHITE..........     32.00
MILK GLASS,DISH,CUPPED HANDS WITH GRAPES...................     12.50
MILK GLASS,DISH,DESSERT,DAISY & TREE OF LIFE,FLAT,OPAQUE
  WHITE,4 1/2 IN...........................................      8.75
MILK GLASS,DISH,DOG COVER,SPLIT RIB BASE...................     50.00
MILK GLASS,DISH,DOG ON BLUE RIBBED BASE,COVER..............     27.50
MILK GLASS,DISH,DOG-ON-CASQUE COVER,WHITE..................     60.00
MILK GLASS,DISH,DOUBLE HANDS,LEAVES & GRAPES AT WRIST,
  7 1/2 IN.LONG............................................     17.50
MILK GLASS,DISH,DOVE COVER,SPLIT RIB BASE..................     50.00
MILK GLASS,DISH,DUCK,GRASS BASE,COLOR VARIATION............     25.00
MILK GLASS,DISH,FISH SHAPE,PATENT MARK,9 1/2 X 6
  IN............................................... 10.50 TO    17.50
MILK GLASS,DISH,FISH,OPEN,PAT.JUNE 4,1862..................     16.50
MILK GLASS,DISH,FOX,RIBBED,RIBBED BASE,WHITE,ATTERBURY,DATED   115.00
MILK GLASS,DISH,FROG LID,SPLIT RIB BASE,WHITE,SIGNED MCKEE..   195.00
```

```
MILK GLASS,DISH,HAND & DOVE,COVER,PATENT-DATED..... 65.00 TO     75.00
MILK GLASS,DISH,HEN COVER,WHITE,BLUE HEAD.................        22.50
MILK GLASS,DISH,KITTEN COVER,WHITE,5 IN..................        18.50
MILK GLASS,DISH,LAMB COVER,SPLIT RIB BASE,OVAL,5 1/2 IN....      37.50
MILK GLASS,DISH,LION COVER,ATTERBURY,PAT.AUG.6,
   1889..................................................  55.00 TO  80.00
MILK GLASS,DISH,LION COVER,INSCRIBED THE BRITISH LION.......     38.00
MILK GLASS,DISH,LION COVER,MARKED K.........................     30.00
MILK GLASS,DISH,LION COVER,SPLIT RIB BASE,WHITE,MCKEE.......    135.00
MILK GLASS,DISH,MULE-EARED RABBIT,COVER.....................     17.50
MILK GLASS,DISH,OPEN SWAN,BLACK,10 IN.......................     25.00
MILK GLASS,DISH,PEKINGESE DOG COVER,WHITE,SANDWICH..........    215.00
MILK GLASS,DISH,PINTAIL DUCK,COVER..........................     25.00
MILK GLASS,DISH,POPE LEO XIII COVER,NAME EMBOSSED ON LID,
   WHITE....................................................     55.00
MILK GLASS,DISH,QUAIL COVER.................................     28.50
MILK GLASS,DISH,RABBIT,MULE-EARED...........................     15.00
MILK GLASS,DISH,RAISED SHELLS AROUND CENTER,DOLPHIN-FOOTED..     37.50
MILK GLASS,DISH,RECLINING RABBIT,COVER......................     10.00
MILK GLASS,DISH,RIBBED,CAT LID,5 X 4 1/2 IN.HIGH............     20.00
MILK GLASS,DISH,ROOSTER COVER,BLUE,SIGNED PORTIEUX,9 IN.HIGH     75.00
MILK GLASS,DISH,ROOSTER COVER,WHITE,FRANCE,SIGNED PORTIEUX..     85.00
MILK GLASS,DISH,SANTA CLAUS ON SLEIGH.......................     45.00
MILK GLASS,DISH,SQUIRREL COVER,SPLIT RIB BASE,MCKEE.........     50.00
MILK GLASS,DISH,SQUIRREL FINIAL ON COVER....................     65.00
MILK GLASS,DISH,STEAMBOAT COVER,WHITE,MARKED WHEELING.......     18.50
MILK GLASS,DISH,STRAWBERRY-SHAPED,RED,GREEN FINIAL,COVER....      4.50
MILK GLASS,DISH,SWAN COVER,OPEN NECK,BLUE...................     42.50
MILK GLASS,DISH,TURKEY,RIBBED BASE..........................     18.00
MILK GLASS,DISH,TURTLE......................................     45.00
MILK GLASS,DISH,UNCLE SAM COVER.............................     22.00
MILK GLASS,DISH,UNCLE SAM ON BATTLESHIP.....................     45.00
MILK GLASS,DISH,WHITE HEN WITH BLUE HEAD....................     16.00
MILK GLASS,DOLPHIN,COVER....................................     65.00
MILK GLASS,DRESSER SET,BLACK,TRAY,BOWL,TWO PERFUMES,SILVER
   DEPOSIT..................................................     22.00
MILK GLASS,DRESSER SET,COVERED POWDER,TRAY,SOAP DISH,BORDER
   DESIGN...................................................     12.00
MILK GLASS,EASTER EGG,CHICK HATCHING FROM EGG,SAYS JUST OUT.      5.00
MILK GLASS,EASTER EGG,HAND-PAINTED,SATIN FINISH,11 1/2 X
   13 IN....................................................     12.00
MILK GLASS,EPERGNE,HOBNAIL,THREE LILIES,FIERY OPALESCENT,
   WHITE....................................................     15.00
MILK GLASS,EWER,GOURD SHAPE,HANDLE,18 IN.TALL...............     32.00
MILK GLASS,EWER,ORANGE & WHITE POPPIES,TWO HANDLES.........      50.00
MILK GLASS,FIGURINE,CAR,OPEN STYLE,MARKED VALLERYSTAHL,5 IN.      7.50
MILK GLASS,FIGURINE,MAN,WOMAN,COLONIAL,PAIR.................     15.00
MILK GLASS,FIGURINE,OWL,LIFE-SIZE...........................     45.00
MILK GLASS,FOX ON BASE,LACY EDGE,RIBBED,ATTERBURY,
   MARK.PAT.AUG.6,1889......................................     70.00
MILK GLASS,GOBLET,BERRY PATTERN,SET OF 12...................    100.00
MILK GLASS,GOBLET,BLACK.....................................      6.00
MILK GLASS,GOBLET,CANDLEWICK,OPAQUE WHITE...................     17.50
MILK GLASS,HAND WITH GRAPES,SATIN FINISH,AMERICAN & ENGLISH
   MARKS....................................................     16.00
MILK GLASS,HAT,OPEN PONTIL ON CROWN,BRIM HAS FOLDED RIM,
   2 7/8 IN. WIDE...........................................     37.50
MILK GLASS,HEN ON BASKET,WHITE,5 IN....... 16.00 TO  25.00
MILK GLASS,HEN,BLUE,ON BASKET-WEAVE NEST,6 IN...... 18.50 TO  25.00
MILK GLASS,HOLDER,MATCH,BUTTERFLY...........................     18.00
MILK GLASS,HOLDER,MATCH,FORGET-ME-NOTS,BEADED,GILT,
   HAND-PAINTED.............................................      9.00
MILK GLASS,HOLDER,SPOON,HORSE HEAD MEDALLION................     24.00
MILK GLASS,JAR,ADVERTISING,MYSIS,LID,LABELS,CONTENTS........      6.00
MILK GLASS,JAR,APPLE,RED & YELLOW,COVER.....................      8.00
MILK GLASS,JAR,BARBER,FOR CREAM,METAL TOP...................      8.50
MILK GLASS,JAR,BLUE,SANILOL.................................      5.50
MILK GLASS,JAR,COOKIE,PINK,COVER,9 IN.HIGH..................     10.00
MILK GLASS,JAR,COOKIE,WHITE,EMBOSSED FLORAL,SCALLOPED FLARE
   BASE,LID.................................................     15.00
MILK GLASS,JAR,DRESSER,GREEN TRIM,LID.......................      7.50
MILK GLASS,JAR,PEDESTAL,BLUE................................     18.00
MILK GLASS,JAR,PINK,GRAPES,COVER............................     15.00
MILK GLASS,JAR,POWDER,DOG DECOR,DOG FINIAL,PINK.............     15.00
MILK GLASS,JAR,POWDER,RED-BROWN,WHITE KELP DECOR,FOOTED.....      3.50
MILK GLASS,JAR,STRAWBERRY,RED,COVER.........................      8.00
MILK GLASS,LAMP BASE,MINIATURE,GROOVED,TWO DOLPHINS,BLUE....     25.00
MILK GLASS,LAMP,BROWN DUTCH SCENES,MATCHING CHIMNEY SHADE,
   7 IN.....................................................     36.00
MILK GLASS,LAMP,EMBOSSED BLOCK & DOT DESIGN,YELLOW PAINTED
   GROUND,7 IN..............................................     35.00
```

MILK GLASS,LAMP,EMBOSSED SCROLL DESIGN,SQUARE BASE,BRISTOL
  SHADE,6 IN.................................................... 22.50
MILK GLASS,LAMP,GLOW,PAINTED YELLOW FLORAL,EMBOSSED DECOR,
  BASE,CHIMNEY.................................................. 55.00
MILK GLASS,LAMP,HANGING,ALLOVER PATTERN,BUFF GROUND,
  REFLECTOR,MINIATURE.......................................... 42.00
MILK GLASS,LAMP,HEXAGONAL LANTERN-TYPE CHIMNEY TO MATCH
  BASE,6 1/2 IN................................................ 20.00
MILK GLASS,LAMP,KEROSENE,BULBOUS,COLORED FLORAL IN RELIEF,
  CHIMNEY...................................................... 45.00
MILK GLASS,LAMP,OIL,FLORAL....................................... 14.00
MILK GLASS,LAMP,ORANGE GROUND,FLORAL,MATCHING CHIMNEY SHADE,
  9 IN......................................................... 54.00
MILK GLASS,LAMP,RIB PATTERN,BALL SHADE,MINIATURE................. 40.00
MILK GLASS,LAMP,WHITE,RAISED FLORAL DESIGN,6 IN.HIGH............. 45.00
MILK GLASS,MATCH SAFE,JOLLY JESTER,HANGING,OPAQUE WHITE......... 25.00
MILK GLASS,MUFFINEER,POPPY PATTERN.............................. 17.50
MILK GLASS,MUG,BEADED MEDALLION PATTERN,2 1/2 IN.HIGH........... 15.00
MILK GLASS,MUG,CHILD'S,WINTER SCENE,TOM & JERRY,MARKED MCKEE     2.50
MILK GLASS,MUG,FLORAL,SAYS REMEMBER ME,3 1/4 IN................. 28.00
MILK GLASS,MUG,THREE LITTLE PIGS,WHITE.......................... 3.00
MILK GLASS,MUG,WHITE............................................ 22.00
MILK GLASS,MUSTARD,LOG CABIN,PAPER LABELS,3 IN. X 3 1/2 IN.
  X 4 IN...................................................... 27.00
MILK GLASS,NAPPIE,SCROLL & EYE,BLUE,6 1/2 IN.................... 18.00
MILK GLASS,ORNAMENT,CHRISTMAS TREE,BLUE,MOTTLED,ENGLAND,
  1 1/4 IN.................................................... 12.00
MILK GLASS,PAPERWEIGHT,FIGURAL,OWL STANDS ON TWO BOOKS,
  WHITE,OPALESCENT............................................ 13.00
MILK GLASS,PIPE,SOUVENIR OF MOHAWK TRAIL........................ 8.00
MILK GLASS,PIPE,SOUVENIR,BLUE,ENAMELED FLOWERS................. 10.00
MILK GLASS,PITCHER,LITTLE BOY,OPAQUE WHITE..................... 125.00
MILK GLASS,PITCHER,MILK,FEATHER................................ 17.50
MILK GLASS,PITCHER,SHELL & SEAWEED,3 1/2 IN.TALL.............. 25.00
MILK GLASS,PITCHER,SYRUP,WHITE,PINK MEDALLION WITH APPLES,
  GRAPES,6 IN................................................. 22.50
MILK GLASS,PITCHER,WATER,TANKARD,BEADED CIRCLE,APPLIED
  HANDLE,WHITE................................................ 47.50
MILK GLASS,PLAQUE,WINDMILLS IN RELIEF,OVAL,9 X 6 IN........... 7.50
MILK GLASS,PLATE,ANCHOR & YACHT................................ 12.50
MILK GLASS,PLATE,APPLE BLOSSOM CENTER,LATTICE EDGE. 25.00 TO    30.00
MILK GLASS,PLATE,APPLE BLOSSOM CENTER,LATTICE EDGE,
  10 1/2 IN................................................... 35.00
MILK GLASS,PLATE,BLACK HEART,SCENIC CENTER,8 IN............... 15.00
MILK GLASS,PLATE,BLACK WICKET,SCENIC,8 IN..................... 8.00
MILK GLASS,PLATE,BLACK,WICKET BORDER,PAINTING OF CAT IN
  CENTER,9 IN................................................. 12.50
MILK GLASS,PLATE,BLACK,5 1/2-IN. DIAMETER..................... 9.50
MILK GLASS,PLATE,BLACK,7 1/2 IN. SQUARE...................... 11.50
MILK GLASS,PLATE,BREAD,ROCK OF AGES,ATTERBURY................ 67.50
MILK GLASS,PLATE,CAKE,PINK APPLE BLOSSOMS,STAND............... 22.00
MILK GLASS,PLATE,COLUMBUS,OPAQUE WHITE....................... 27.50
MILK GLASS,PLATE,CROWN BORDER,WHITE,7 IN..................... 12.00
MILK GLASS,PLATE,CUPID & PSYCHE,7 IN............. 8.00 TO     12.50
MILK GLASS,PLATE,DOG FACE IN RELIEF,6 IN..................... 17.50
MILK GLASS,PLATE,DOUBLE FORGET-ME-NOTS,8 1/4 IN.............. 12.00
MILK GLASS,PLATE,EAGLE,FLAG,FLEUR-DE-LIS,STAR BORDER,DATED
  1903,7 IN................................................... 15.00
MILK GLASS,PLATE,EAGLE,FLAG,STAR BORDER,FLEUR-DE-LIS,DATED
  9/8/03...................................................... 15.00
MILK GLASS,PLATE,EASTER,BROWN DECOR,6 IN..................... 6.00
MILK GLASS,PLATE,EMBOSSED DAHLIA DESIGN,ORNATE EDGE,6 IN.... 12.00
MILK GLASS,PLATE,FERN CENTER,HEART BORDER,OPEN EDGE,8 IN.... 22.00
MILK GLASS,PLATE,FLORAL IN CENTER,LATTICE-EDGED,10 1/4 IN... 16.50
MILK GLASS,PLATE,FOUR PANSIES,GOLD SCROLLS,10 IN............ 18.00
MILK GLASS,PLATE,GEORGE WASHINGTON,STAR BORDER.............. 18.00
MILK GLASS,PLATE,GOTHIC EDGE,BLACK,5 1/4 IN................. 10.00
MILK GLASS,PLATE,GOTHIC,7 IN................................ 6.00
MILK GLASS,PLATE,H BORDER,7 IN.............................. 6.00
MILK GLASS,PLATE,H BORDER,9 IN.............................. 7.50
MILK GLASS,PLATE,HAND-PAINTED ROSES,10 IN................... 7.50
MILK GLASS,PLATE,HEARTS DESIGN,7-1/4 IN.DIAMETER............ 4.75
MILK GLASS,PLATE,LACY,CRANBERRY GLASS DOME,DOTS,TREE TRUNK
  HANDLE,5 IN................................................. 28.00
MILK GLASS,PLATE,LACY,SCROLL WITH EYE,BLUE,8-IN.DIAMETER.... 35.00
MILK GLASS,PLATE,OPENWORK,FLEUR-DE-LIS BORDER,6 1/4 IN...... 10.00
MILK GLASS,PLATE,PEG BORDER,BLUE,5 1/4 IN................... 8.50
MILK GLASS,PLATE,PORTRAIT,COLUMBUS,DATES 1492-1892,OPEN
  BORDER...................................................... 25.00
MILK GLASS,PLATE,RAISED INDIAN HEAD IN CENTER,7 IN.......... 25.00
MILK GLASS,PLATE,S BORDER,OPEN,BLACK,SQUARE................. 8.00

```
MILK GLASS,PLATE,S BORDER,WHITE,7 1/2 IN.SQUARE.............    9.00
MILK GLASS,PLATE,SCROLL & EYE,BLUE,10 IN....................   25.00
MILK GLASS,PLATE,SCROLL,WAFFLE,BLUE & BLACK BORDER,7 IN.....    5.00
MILK GLASS,PLATE,SHELL & CLUB,WHITE........................     6.00
MILK GLASS,PLATE,SHELL BORDER,STAMP DECOR,8 1/2 IN.SQUARE...   15.00
MILK GLASS,PLATE,SMALL PINWHEEL,BLACK,8 IN.................     9.00
MILK GLASS,PLATE,THE CONTRARY MULE........................    16.50
MILK GLASS,PLATE,THREE OWLS...............................    15.00
MILK GLASS,PLATE,THREE OWLS,LATTICE EDGE,GILT,7 1/2 IN......   11.50
MILK GLASS,PLATE,TRIANGLE S,8 IN..........................    15.00
MILK GLASS,PLATE,WHITE PAINTING OF BOY,RAKE,DOG,
  FORGET-ME-NOTS,BLACK....................................    27.50
MILK GLASS,PLATE,WHITE,SHELL & CLUB,5 IN...................     6.00
MILK GLASS,PLATE,WHITE,WICKET,5 IN........................      6.00
MILK GLASS,PLATE,WHITE,WICKET,9 IN........................      8.00
MILK GLASS,PLATE,WICKET BORDER,BLACK,9 1/4-IN.DIAMETER......   10.00
MILK GLASS,PLATE,WICKET EDGE,BLACK,9 IN....................    12.50
MILK GLASS,PLATE,WICKET OPENWORK RIM,8 3/4-IN.DIAMETER......   11.50
MILK GLASS,PLATE,WICKET,WHITE,5 IN........................      6.00
MILK GLASS,PLATE,WICKET,WHITE,9 IN........................      8.00
MILK GLASS,PLATE,WILD ROSE,LATTICE EDGE............ 24.50 TO   40.00
MILK GLASS,PLATTER,CHERRIES,OPEN HANDLES,BLUE.............     12.00
MILK GLASS,PLATTER,RETRIEVER...................... 29.50 TO    65.00
MILK GLASS,RELISH,GRAPE BAND,BOAT SHAPE,8 1/2 IN..........     12.00
MILK GLASS,ROLLING PIN,FORGET-ME-NOT DECOR,12 1/2 IN.LONG...   25.00
MILK GLASS,ROLLING PIN,MAPLE HANDLES......................    14.50
MILK GLASS,ROLLING PIN,WOODEN HANDLES,IMPERIAL MFG.CO.,
  CAMBRIDGE,OHIO..........................................     8.50
MILK GLASS,S BORDER,TRIANGLE SHAPE,WHITE,8 IN.............     12.50
MILK GLASS,SALT & PEPPER SHAKERS,HEN & RABBIT DESIGN,
  EGG-SHAPED.............................................     30.00
MILK GLASS,SALT & PEPPER SHAKERS,SQUATTY MELON-RIBBED,
  FORGET-ME-NOT,PINK.....................................     35.00
MILK GLASS,SALT & PEPPER,MELON RIB,RAISED FORGET-ME-NOTS,
  PINK..................................................      30.00
MILK GLASS,SALT & PEPPER,RIBBED,FOOTED...................      8.50
MILK GLASS,SALT CELLAR,SINGLE HANDLE,BASKET WEAVE,ATTERBURY,
  DATED.................................................      27.50
MILK GLASS,SALT,BASKETWEAVE,PEDESTAL,HANDLED,DATED 1874.....    8.50
MILK GLASS,SALT,BLACKBERRY,FOOTED........................     15.00
MILK GLASS,SALT,DAHLIA,BEADED,BLUE.......................     12.00
MILK GLASS,SALT,EMBOSSED DESIGN AROUND TOP,ROUND,BLUE,
  1 1/2 IN. HIGH........................................       8.50
MILK GLASS,SALT,HEN....................................        8.00
MILK GLASS,SALT,LEAF PALM..............................       12.00
MILK GLASS,SALT,MASTER,BIRCH LEAF......................        7.00
MILK GLASS,SALT,MASTER,BLACKBERRY,FOOTED...............       15.00
MILK GLASS,SALT,MASTER,BLACKBERRY,OPAQUE WHITE,FOOTED.......   12.00
MILK GLASS,SALT,MASTER,CHARTREUSE......................       12.00
MILK GLASS,SALT,MELON RIB,DARK BLUE....................        8.00
MILK GLASS,SALT,OPEN,FEET IN FLEUR-DE-LIS PATTERN,BLUE,
  1 3/4 IN.SQUARE......................................       10.00
MILK GLASS,SALT,OVERLAPPING LEAVES.....................       13.00
MILK GLASS,SALT,PEPPER,CRUET,TRAY,FORGET-ME-NOT PATTERN,BLUE   75.00
MILK GLASS,SALT,PUFFED FLORAL DECOR....................        6.00
MILK GLASS,SALT,ROSE LEAF,FOOTED,OPAQUE WHITE..........        8.75
MILK GLASS,SALT,SCALLOPED,PATENT DATE 1875,OPAQUE WHITE.....    8.75
MILK GLASS,SAUCEBOAT,DOLPHIN COVER.....................       40.00
MILK GLASS,SAUCE,BLACKBERRY,FLAT,OPAQUE WHITE,4 IN.....        6.50
MILK GLASS,SHAKER,ADVERTISING G.E.MONITOR TOP REFRIGERATOR,
  PAIR................................................         7.50
MILK GLASS,SHAKER,FIGURAL,WOMAN'S HEAD,WHITE,3 1/8 IN.,PAIR.   12.00
MILK GLASS,SHAKER,SALT & PEPPER,BLUE...................        8.00
MILK GLASS,SHAKER,SALT & PEPPER,RIBBED,FLOWER SPRAYS........    9.00
MILK GLASS,SHAKER,SALT,BLUE,PANELED SHELL..............        9.50
MILK GLASS,SHAKER,SALT,CORN............................        6.00
MILK GLASS,SHAKER,SALT,EGG SHAPE,THREE RABBITS,RAISED,TIN
  TOP................................................         18.00
MILK GLASS,SHAKER,SALT,FIGURAL,HEN & CHICKS ON ONE,RABBIT ON
  OTHER,WHITE........................................         12.00
MILK GLASS,SHAKER,SALT,HEN & RABBIT....................       15.00
MILK GLASS,SHAKER,SALT,LEAF BASE,ORIGINAL TOP..........        5.00
MILK GLASS,SHAKER,SALT,PAINTED SAILBOATS,PAIR..........        8.50
MILK GLASS,SHAKER,SALT,RIBBED..........................        4.50
MILK GLASS,SHAKER,SALT,SCROLL PATTERN,BLUE.............        8.75
MILK GLASS,SHAKER,SALT,SHELL...........................        8.00
MILK GLASS,SHAKER,SUGAR,BLUE,PUFFY EMBOSSED DIAMOND-LIKE
  DESIGN,TIN LID.......................................       29.50
MILK GLASS,SHAKER,SUGAR,EMBOSSED PASTEL FLORAL,BRASS TOP....   32.50
MILK GLASS,SHAKER,SUGAR,FORGET-ME-NOT PATTERN,GREEN........    34.00
MILK GLASS,SHAKER,SUGAR,RIBBED,ENAMELED................       17.50
```

| | |
|---|---|
| MILK GLASS,SHAKER,SUGAR,ROYAL OAK,COLORED LEAVES............ | 19.50 |
| MILK GLASS,SLIPPER,DAISY & BUTTON,BLUE..................... | 16.50 |
| MILK GLASS,SPOONER,BLACKBERRY............................. | 12.50 |
| MILK GLASS,SPOONER,DOUBLE LOOP............................ | 12.50 |
| MILK GLASS,SPOONER,PINK SHELL FEET,SCROLL,PURPLE VIOLETS, HAND-PAINTED............................................. | 14.50 |
| MILK GLASS,SPOONER,ROMAN CROSS,WHITE,FOOTED............... | 12.50 |
| MILK GLASS,SPOONER,ROSE LEAF,OPAQUE WHITE................. | 9.75 |
| MILK GLASS,SPOONHOLDER,BLACKBERRY,WHITE................... | 12.00 |
| MILK GLASS,SQUEEZER,LEMON,FIERY WHITE..................... | 10.00 |
| MILK GLASS,SQUEEZER,LEMON,GREEN........................... | 4.00 |
| MILK GLASS,SQUEEZER,LEMON,IMPRINTED SUNKIST............... | 4.50 |
| MILK GLASS,SWAN,BLACK,8 1/2 IN.LONG,3 IN.HIGH............. | 12.50 |
| MILK GLASS,SWAN,RAISED WING,WHITE,ATTERBURY............... | 85.00 |
| MILK GLASS,SWAN,SQUARE BLOCK,WHITE,ATTERBURY.............. | 85.00 |
| MILK GLASS,SWAN,WHITE,CLOSED NECK,ON BASKET BASE.......... | 17.50 |
| MILK GLASS,SWAN,WHITE,MARKED PORTIEUX,FRANCE,4 1/2 X 5 1/2 X 6 IN.LONG............................................... | 45.00 |
| MILK GLASS,SWAN,YELLOW BILL,OPEN,8 IN.LONG................ | 8.00 |
| MILK GLASS,SYRUP,EMBOSSED TULIPS,TOP...................... | 10.50 |
| MILK GLASS,SYRUP,FAT SWIRL BODY,TIN LID,5 IN.............. | 22.50 |
| MILK GLASS,SYRUP,FORGET-ME-NOT PATTERN,GREEN.............. | 55.00 |
| MILK GLASS,SYRUP,IRIS MADE IN THE GLASS................... | 25.00 |
| MILK GLASS,THERMOMETER,FLORAL BRASS FRAME,5 IN. X 1 1/4 IN.. | 8.00 |
| MILK GLASS,TOOTHPICK,BLUE,EMBOSSED FLORAL,REGISTRATION MARK. | 16.00 |
| MILK GLASS,TOOTHPICK,BLUE,FLORAL AROUND TOP,ORNATE LEGS..... | 15.00 |
| MILK GLASS,TOOTHPICK,CHICKEN.............................. | 10.00 |
| MILK GLASS,TOOTHPICK,ELEPHANT'S HEAD,CURLED-UP TRUNK...... | 12.00 |
| MILK GLASS,TOOTHPICK,FLORAL,THREE HANDLES................. | 22.50 |
| MILK GLASS,TOOTHPICK,HAT,BRIM,5 IN.WIDE................... | 12.00 |
| MILK GLASS,TOOTHPICK,HAT,THREADED......................... | 6.00 |
| MILK GLASS,TOOTHPICK,HOBNAIL.............................. | 3.00 |
| MILK GLASS,TOOTHPICK,OWL,WINGS SPREAD..................... | 15.00 |
| MILK GLASS,TOOTHPICK,RELIEFS,SQUARE SHAPE,HIGH & LOW TOP, FOOTED................................................... | 9.50 |
| MILK GLASS,TOOTHPICK,RIBBED............................... | 2.50 |
| MILK GLASS,TOOTHPICK,SHELL & SPRIG,PINK................... | 30.00 |
| MILK GLASS,TOOTHPICK,SUNSET PATTERN,BLUE.................. | 20.00 |
| MILK GLASS,TOOTHPICK,UNCLE SAM,RED,WHITE,BLUE,STARS,STRIPES. | 18.00 |
| MILK GLASS,TOOTHPICK,WHITE,SNAKE COILED AROUND BOTTOM HALF.. | 12.50 |
| MILK GLASS,TRAY,DRESSER,IRREGULAR OVAL,BLUE,11 IN......... | 19.50 |
| MILK GLASS,TRAY,DRESSER,POWDER BOX,PIN BOX,PANSIES,SCALLOPED COVERS,GOLD.............................................. | 21.00 |
| MILK GLASS,TRAY,DRESSER,RAISED BORDER DESIGN.............. | 10.00 |
| MILK GLASS,TRAY,EMBOSSED ROSES & POPPY BORDER,LADY'S CAMEO SILHOUETTE............................................... | 15.50 |
| MILK GLASS,TRAY,FISH,WHITE,FOOTED,OVAL,DATED 1872,11 IN. LONG.................................................... | 20.00 |
| MILK GLASS,TRAY,PIN,IRREGULAR MOLDED EDGES,WHITE,6 IN..... | 3.25 |
| MILK GLASS,TRAY,PIN,RAISED DECOR,OPEN HANDLES,OVAL........ | 5.00 |
| MILK GLASS,TRAY,VERSAILLES,OVAL........................... | 12.50 |
| MILK GLASS,TUMBLER,BEADED SWAG,PAIR....................... | 7.00 |
| MILK GLASS,TUMBLER,CANDLEWICK,OPAQUE WHITE................ | 15.00 |
| MILK GLASS,TUMBLER,CUBE PATTERN........................... | 10.00 |
| MILK GLASS,TUMBLER,HOPALONG CASSIDY....................... | 4.00 |
| MILK GLASS,TUMBLER,LOUISIANA PURCHASE EXPOSITION,WHITE...... | 15.00 |
| MILK GLASS,TUMBLER,PINK BORDER,COSMOS..................... | 35.00 |
| MILK GLASS,TUMBLER,SCROLL,OPAQUE WHITE.................... | 10.00 |
| MILK GLASS,TUMBLER,SOUVENIR,LOUISIANA PURCHASE EXPOSITION, WHITE................................................... | 15.00 |
| MILK GLASS,TUMBLER,SOUVENIR,ST.LOUIS WORLD'S FAIR, SCENIC.......................................... 9.00 TO | 45.00 |
| MILK GLASS,TUMBLER,THUMBPRINT,WHITE....................... | 10.00 |
| MILK GLASS,VASE,APPLE BLOSSOMS,OPAQUE WHITE,7 IN.TALL...... | 6.75 |
| MILK GLASS,VASE,BLUE,LILY PATTERN,RUFFLED,6 1/2 IN........ | 12.75 |
| MILK GLASS,VASE,BLUE,RAISED ROSE DECOR,8 IN............... | 22.50 |
| MILK GLASS,VASE,BUTTERFLY,POPPY,BLACK,SIGNED.............. | 15.00 |
| MILK GLASS,VASE,CELERY,STAR PATTERN....................... | 25.00 |
| MILK GLASS,VASE,FLOWER SHAPE,LILIES OF THE VALLEY,7 IN.HIGH. | 8.50 |
| MILK GLASS,VASE,FLUTED,HELD BY HAND,BLOWN,7 3/4 IN........ | 15.00 |
| MILK GLASS,VASE,INDIAN RIDING PONY,WAVING FEATHERED STAFF, BROWN SHADES............................................. | 17.50 |
| MILK GLASS,VASE,INDIAN,BROWN TONES,7 IN................... | 35.00 |
| MILK GLASS,VASE,IRIS,HERRINGBONE,9 IN.HIGH................ | 10.00 |
| MILK GLASS,VASE,LOVEBIRDS,WHITE........................... | 35.00 |
| MILK GLASS,VASE,PAINTED ARAB'S FACE,BROWN................. | 18.00 |
| MILK GLASS,VASE,SPILL,JACK & JILL IN RELIEF,PEACOCK MARK, 3 1/2 IN.HIGH............................................ | 39.00 |
| MILK GLASS,VASE,STERLING SILVER TRIM,BLACK,MARKED REX,NEW ORLEANS,1917............................................ | 15.00 |
| MILK GLASS,VASE,SWAN,BLUE,6 1/2 IN.HIGH,PAIR.............. | 50.00 |

MILK GLASS,VIAL,HORSES' HEADS,WREATH,CHESTNUT SHAPE,2 IN....    8.00

> MILLEFIORI MEANS MANY FLOWERS. IT IS A TYPE OF
> GLASSWORK POPULAR IN PAPERWEIGHTS. MANY SMALL FLOWER-
> LIKE PIECES OF GLASS ARE GROUPED TOGETHER TO FORM A
> DESIGN.

MILLEFIORI,SEE ALSO,PAPERWEIGHT
MILLEFIORI,CREAMER,ALTERNATING CANES & RED FLOWER SPRAYS,
   STRIPED HANDLE....................................................  110.00
MILLEFIORI,CUP & SAUCER,AMBER HANDLE............................   39.00
MILLEFIORI,CUP & SAUCER,CANDY CANE PATTERN,SATIN FINISH.....   40.00
MILLEFIORI,CUP,SAUCER,CLEAR EAR-SHAPED HANDLE...............   50.00
MILLEFIORI,GLOBE,LIGHT,SPHERE,4-1/2 IN.DIAMETER,
   2 1/4-IN.DIAMETER OPENING.......................................   85.00
MILLEFIORI,LAMP,GREEN PREDOMINATING,MUSHROOM SHADE,WIRED,
   18 IN...........................................................  300.00
MILLEFIORI,NEWEL-POST,PAPERWEIGHT,CANES,ROSES,FACETED,WOODEN
   STAND,PAIR......................................................  800.00
MILLEFIORI,SPOONER,FOOTED,6 IN. TALL...........................   28.00
MILLEFIORI,VASE,URN SHAPE......................................  125.00
MINIATURE,BED WARMER,FLORAL & LEAVES DECOR,WOODEN HANDLE,
   9 3/4 IN.LONG...................................................   22.00
MINIATURE,BELL,COW,CURVED OVERHANDLE,BRASS,1 3/8 IN. X
   7/8 IN..........................................................    6.00
MINIATURE,BOWL,BLUE PORCELAIN INSIDE,HANDLES,BRASS RIMMED
   COPPER,CHINA....................................................   12.00
MINIATURE,BUCKET,OLD OAKEN,PRESSED GLASS,WIRE HANDLE,
   2 5/8 IN.HIGH...................................................    6.00
MINIATURE,CANDLESTICK,WICK,BRASS,1 5/8 IN. HIGH,PAIR........    5.00
MINIATURE,CARAFE,STOPPER,BRASS,1 1/2 IN.HIGH,TWO WINE CUPS..    5.00
MINIATURE,COAL HOD,HANDLE,BACK HOLD,BRASS,2 IN. X 3 IN......    6.50
MINIATURE,COUCH,WHITE,RED & BLUE FLORAL,GOLD FRAME,
   PORCELAIN,7 IN.LONG.............................................   35.00
MINIATURE,DESK,GOV.WINTHROP,HANDMADE,CHERRY WOOD,MAPLE
   INLAY,16 IN.HIGH................................................  100.00
MINIATURE,FLAT IRON,ON TRIVET,IRON,3 IN.LONG.................    5.00
MINIATURE,FURNITURE,ARMCHAIR,PAIR,SPANISH CARVED WALNUT,17TH
   CENTURY.........................................................  700.00
MINIATURE,FURNITURE,CABINET,GERMAN ROSEWOOD,19TH CENTURY....   80.00
MINIATURE,FURNITURE,CABINET,LOUIS PHILIPPE INLAID WALNUT &
   MAHOGANY........................................................  125.00
MINIATURE,FURNITURE,COMMODE,ITALIAN FRUITWOOD,19TH CENTURY..  200.00
MINIATURE,FURNITURE,COMMODE,LOUIS XV PROVINCIAL,CARVED OAK..  150.00
MINIATURE,FURNITURE,COMMODE,LOUIS XV PROVINCIAL,18TH CENTURY  550.00
MINIATURE,FURNITURE,COMMODE,NAPOLEON III,PAINTED,19TH
   CENTURY.........................................................   40.00
MINIATURE,FURNITURE,COMMODE,NORTHERN ITALIAN KINGWOOD,18TH
   CENTURY.........................................................  500.00
MINIATURE,FURNITURE,CONSOLE DESSERTE,LOUIS XVI MAHOGANY
   1791............................................................  225.00
MINIATURE,FURNITURE,DESK,ITALIAN WALNUT,CABINET,17TH CENTURY  225.00
MINIATURE,FURNITURE,POUDREUSE,ITALIAN ROSEWOOD & KINGWOOD,
   19TH CENTURY....................................................  125.00
MINIATURE,FURNITURE,SECRETAIRE A ABATTANT,EMPIRE MAHOGANY...   50.00
MINIATURE,FURNITURE,TABLE,CONSOLE,ITALIAN FRUITWOOD,19TH
   CENTURY.........................................................   75.00
MINIATURE,FURNITURE,TABLE,FRENCH INLAID,19TH CENTURY........   70.00
MINIATURE,FURNITURE,TABLE,GAMES,NEAR EASTERN,INLAID
   FRUITWOOD.......................................................   60.00
MINIATURE,FURNITURE,TABLE,WORK,ITALIAN MAHOGANY & FRUITWOOD.  175.00
MINIATURE,GRINDER,PEPPER,DESIGNED TOP KNOB & HANDLE KNOB,
   BRASS,1 1/4 IN..................................................   10.00
MINIATURE,JUG,WATER,BULBOUS,BRASS OVER HANDLE SECURED TO
   2 BALLS,BRASS...................................................   10.00
MINIATURE,KETTLE,HANDLE,COVER,BRASS,1 X 1/2 IN..............   10.00
MINIATURE,KETTLE,OPEN,BULBOUS,BRASS HANDLE,TWO GROOVED
   MIDDLE RIM,COPPER...............................................    8.50
MINIATURE,LAMP,CLEAR THOUSAND-EYE HOBNAIL PANEL BASE,
   CHIMNEY,WICK....................................................    2.50
MINIATURE,PITCHER,WATER,BULBOUS,BRASS CURVED HANDLE,COPPER,
   1 3/4 IN........................................................   10.00
MINIATURE,PITCHER,WATER,HANDMADE,HAND-PAINTED FLOWER,COPPER,
   1 1/8 IN........................................................    5.00
MINIATURE,TEAKETTLE,BRASS,1 IN.HIGH............................    6.00
MINIATURE,TEAKETTLE,COPPER & BRASS,4 IN.HIGH.................   12.00
MINIATURE,TEAKETTLE,COPPER,HELSINKI,1 1/2 IN.HIGH...........   10.00
MINIATURE,TEAKETTLE,COPPER,2 IN. X 1 1/2 IN..................    9.50
MINIATURE,TEAKETTLE,COPPER,2 1/8 IN. X 1 3/4 IN.............   10.00
MINIATURE,TEAKETTLE,COVER,COPPER,2 1/8 IN. X 1 3/4 IN.......   10.00
MINIATURE,TEAPOT,CREAMER,TEAPOT,SIX CUPS,SAUCERS,SILVER
   FILIGREE........................................................   65.00

MINIATURE,TUB,BATH,DAISY & BUTTON,HONEY AMBER,9 IN. LONG X
   4 IN. WIDE...................................................        65.00
MINIATURE,VASE,BULBOUS,TWO HIGH ARCH HANDLES,BRASS,1 3/8 IN.          8.50


     MINTON CHINA HAS BEEN MADE IN ENGLAND FROM 1793 TO THE
        PRESENT TIME.
MINTON,BOWL & PITCHER,BLUE,GARLANDS OF LEAVES,MARKED........        37.00
MINTON,BOWL,BLUE WILLOW,10 IN. X 4 1/2 IN.DEEP.............        25.00
MINTON,BOWL,BOAT SHAPE,FOOTED,BLUE & WHITE,ORANGE FLOWERS,
   GOLD TOP....................................................        18.00
MINTON,BOWL,LAPIS BLUE,TROUGH SHAPE,WILD VINE,11 IN.LONG....        50.00
MINTON,BOWL,SOUP,GAUDY BRICK RED & FLOW BLUE...............        14.50
MINTON,BOX,WHITE,RAISED BLUE ENAMEL GREEK KEY,ROSES,OVAL,
   3 1/2 IN.LONG...............................................        15.00
MINTON,CHOCOLATE POT,WHITE,ETCHED & GOLD-ENCRUSTED BORDER,
   ENGLAND,11 IN...............................................        45.00
MINTON,COMPOTE,PANELS,ENAMELED ROSES,BLUE BORDER,SIGNED,
   8 1/2 IN.ACROSS.............................................        33.50
MINTON,CREAMER,SUGAR,SIX DEMITASSE CUPS,CHINTZ PATTERN......        25.00
MINTON,CUP,SAUCER,DEMITASSE,BLUE DECOR IN PANELS ENCLOSED BY
   GOLD RIMS...................................................        12.00
MINTON,DISH,VEGETABLE,FLORAL DESIGN,TWO HANDLES,COVER.......        15.00
MINTON,FIGURINE,TWO WOMEN RECLINING ON COUCH,PARIAN,CIRCA
   1851,4 1/2 IN...............................................       125.00
MINTON,JARDINIERE,CORNER PILLARS TOPPED WITH NUMPHS,FAWNS,
   MEDALLIONS..................................................       175.00
MINTON,JUG,BLUE & WHITE JASPER,4 1/2 IN.HIGH..............        22.00
MINTON,JUG,BLUE & WHITE,JASPERWARE,4 1/4 IN.HIGH... 17.00 TO        19.00
MINTON,PITCHER,DANCING FIGURES,SAYS POUSSIN'S BACCHANALIAN
   DANCE,PARIAN................................................       125.00
MINTON,PITCHER,SYRUP,GRAPES & GOLD DECOR ON WHITE-LEADED TOP        22.50
MINTON,PLATE,BLUE,GOLD,ECRU,10-IN.DIAMETER,SET OF 12........       250.00
MINTON,PLATE,ENAMELED BIRDS & FLOWERS,9 IN.................        10.00
MINTON,PLATE,HAND-ENAMELED,MULTICOLORED BORDER,DRAPED
   FLORAL,9 IN.,5.............................................        22.00
MINTON,PLATE,HOT,TREE OF LIFE PATTERN,LION-FOOTED,
   6 1/2-IN.DIAMETER..........................................        15.00
MINTON,PLATE,INDIAN TREE PATTERN,9 IN......................         6.00
MINTON,PLATE,OYSTER,SHELL,SEAWEED,GREEN,IRIDESCENT,DATED
   1843,MAJOLICA...............................................        20.00
MINTON,PLATE,ROUGE FLAMBE,9 IN.............................        28.00
MINTON,PLATE,SALAD,COBALT,GOLD BAND EDGE,6 1/2 IN.,SET OF 6.        22.00
MINTON,SOUP,DARK BLUE,RED DESIGN,IMPRESSED MARK,10 IN.......        10.00
MINTON,STEIN,2 LITERS,HIGH RELIEF FIGURES OF DANCERS,PEWTER
   TOP........................................................       100.00
MINTON,TEAPOT,SUGAR,CREAMER,WHITE,GOLD TRIM,RED ROSES,
   SCROLLS,ENGLAND.............................................        75.00
MINTON,TILE,BLACK,WHITE,COWS,GRAZING,DRINKING AT STREAM,
   FRAME......................................................         9.50
MINTON,TILE,BLUE,WHITE,6 IN.SQUARE.........................         5.00
MINTON,TILE,BOSTON STATE HOUSE,DARK BLUE,STOKE ON
   TRENT,1818....................................... 15.00 TO        34.00
MINTON,TILE,CLASSIC SCENE,MAIDEN FEEDING FAWNS,BROWN,WHITE,
   MARKED......................................................        21.00
MINTON,URN,DARK BLUE,YELLOW,GREEN..........................        20.00
MINTON,VASE,BROWN,GREEN,TURQUOISE,IMPRESSED MARK,10 IN.HIGH.        67.50
MINTON,VASE,COBALT & COIN GOLD,5 IN.HIGH...................        35.00
MINTON,VASE,CREAM,GREEN,TURQUOISE,MAJOLICA,MINTON IMPRESSED,
   10 IN.HIGH..................................................        67.50
MINTON,VASE,FARM SCENES,BLUE,5 1/2-IN.DIAMETER CENTER,
   8 IN.HIGH...................................................        28.50
MINTON,VASE,PILGRIM BOTTLE SHAPE,BIRDS,CLEMATIS,BUTTERFLY,
   W.MUSSILL,1867..............................................       135.00
MINTON,VEGETABLE,BLUE,COVER,DELFT,ENGLAND..................        26.00


     MOCHA WARE IS AN ENGLISH-MADE PRODUCT THAT WAS SOLD IN
        AMERICA DURING THE EARLY 1800S. IT IS A HEAVY POTTERY
        WITH PALE COFFEE AND CREAM COLORING. DESIGNS OF BLUE,
        BROWN,GREEN,ORANGE,OR BLACK OR WHITE WERE ADDED TO THE
        POTTERY.
MOCHA,BOWL,TAN,BLUE & WHITE FEATHER BAND,2 1/2 IN.HIGH,
   5 IN.WIDE...................................................        45.00
MOCHA,BOWL,YELLOW,WHITE & BLACK BANDS,5 IN.HIGH X
   11-1/2 IN.DIAMETER..........................................        65.00
MOCHA,CHAMBER POT,CREAMWARE,BLUE,GREEN,BROWN BANDS,LEAF
   HANDLE,COVER................................................        64.00
MOCHA,DISH,MASTER SALT,NARROW GREEN BANDS,WIDE BLUE BAND,
   PEDESTAL FOOT...............................................        18.00
MOCHA,MUG,BLACK SEAWEED,BROWN,BLUE & BLACK STRIPES,

| | |
|---|---:|
| 2 1/2-IN.DIAMETER.......................................... | 32.50 |
| MOCHA,MUG,BORDER BANDED BY BLEEDING BLACK BANDS,SOFT PASTE, | |
| 3 5/8 IN.HIGH............................................ | 38.00 |
| MOCHA,MUG,BUFF GROUND,WHITE BANDS OUTLINED IN BROWN, | |
| 3 3/4 IN.HIGH........................................... | 30.00 |
| MOCHA,MUG,FOUR BLUE BANDS.................................. | 25.00 |
| MOCHA,MUG,RED GROUND,BLACK,BLUE,CREAM MOTTLING, | |
| GREEN-THREADED TOP...................................... | 135.00 |
| MOCHA,MUG,SEAWEED PATTERN,6 IN..................... 27.50 TO | 65.00 |
| MOCHA,MUG,SHAVING,YELLOW GROUND,WHITE BANDS,3 IN.HIGH, | |
| 3 1/2-IN.DIAMETER....................................... | 25.00 |
| MOCHA,MUG,WHITE GROUND,BLUE BANDS,4 IN. X 4 IN............. | 30.00 |
| MOCHA,MUG,WHITE,WIDE BLUE BAND AT TOP,THREE SMALLER BANDS AT | |
| BOTTOM.................................................. | 30.00 |
| MOCHA,MUG,YELLOW,BLACK BANDS,SOFT PASTE.................... | 35.00 |
| MOCHA,PITCHER,FERN,8 1/2 IN.TALL........................... | 100.00 |
| MOCHA,PITCHER,TAN,BLACK & WHITE BANDS,BLUE SEAWEED,4 IN.HIGH | 29.50 |
| MODEL,SHIP,CLIPPER SOVEREIGN OF SEAS,BUILT TO SCALE,1850, | |
| 38 X 26 IN.......................................... 1,000.00 | |
| MODEL,SHIP,FULLY RIGGED,WOODEN,10 IN.LONG.................. | 35.00 |
| MODEL,SHIP,SAILING,GLASS-CASED............................. | 75.00 |
| MODEL,SHIP,SANTA MARIA,WOODEN,22 IN. X 22 IN............... | 40.00 |
| MODEL,SHIP,SCHOONER,LUMBER,FOUR MASTS,RIGGED,1890 PERIOD, | |
| 4 FEET LONG............................................. | 150.00 |
| MODEL,SHIP,SCHOONER,SULTANA,NAMESAKE BUILT IN BOSTON 1767, | |
| 17 IN.LONG.............................................. | 120.00 |
| MODEL,SHIP,19TH CENTURY,CARVED............................. | 80.00 |
| MODEL,STAGECOACH,GLASGOW-EDINBURGH REPLICA,COACHMEN,HORSES, | |
| 53 IN.HIGH.............................................. | 400.00 |
| MOLD,SEE ALSO PEWTER,TIN,ETC. | |
| MOLD,BREAD,TWO-PIECE,TIN................................... | 10.00 |
| MOLD,BULLET,BRASS SPATTERED IRON,5 IN.LONG................. | 9.00 |
| MOLD,BULLET,HOLDS 12,BRASS,9 1/2 IN........................ | 16.00 |
| MOLD,BULLET,IRON.......................................... | 12.00 |
| MOLD,BULLET,SMALL CALIBER,BRASS,4 3/4 IN................... | 10.00 |
| MOLD,BUTTER,ACORN,THREE FLOWERS,SHOE BASE,WOODEN,5 1/4 X | |
| 6 1/8 IN................................................ | 15.00 |
| MOLD,BUTTER,CARVED SWAN ON WATER,PLUNGER TYPE, | |
| 4 1/4 IN.SQUARE......................................... | 20.00 |
| MOLD,BUTTER,CHERRIES & LEAVES,FOUR PIECES,WOODEN........... | 15.00 |
| MOLD,BUTTER,COW IMPRINT,GLASS,WOODEN HANDLE................ | 60.00 |
| MOLD,BUTTER,COW,GLASS..................................... | 55.00 |
| MOLD,BUTTER,DESIGN,WOODEN,ONE POUND........................ | 12.00 |
| MOLD,BUTTER,DOUBLE ACORN,RECTANGULAR,TWO POUNDS............ | 16.50 |
| MOLD,BUTTER,DOVE-TAILED,BRASS HOOKS,SHOE BASE,THREE DESIGNS, | |
| WOODEN.................................................. | 15.00 |
| MOLD,BUTTER,EIGHT-PETAL FLOWER,PENNSYLVANIA DUTCH DECOR, | |
| WOODEN.................................................. | 17.50 |
| MOLD,BUTTER,FLEUR-DE-LIS,GLASS............................. | 28.00 |
| MOLD,BUTTER,FLORAL,1/2 LB.SIZE,WOODEN...................... | 6.50 |
| MOLD,BUTTER,FLOWERS & LEAVES,HANDMADE,ROUND................ | 12.00 |
| MOLD,BUTTER,PINEAPPLE & ACORN DESIGN,WOODEN................ | 9.00 |
| MOLD,BUTTER,PINEAPPLE DESIGN,PLUNGER TYPE,THREE-PIECE, | |
| WOODEN,3 1/4 IN......................................... | 6.95 |
| MOLD,BUTTER,PLUNGER TYPE,WOODEN,1 1/2 IN.DIAMETER.......... | 5.00 |
| MOLD,BUTTER,ROSETTE DESIGN,SQUARE,ONE POUND................ | 6.50 |
| MOLD,BUTTER,SINGLE FLORAL,TALL............................ | 14.50 |
| MOLD,BUTTER,SIX-SIDED,PEWTER BAND,PLUNGER,PINEAPPLE PRINT, | |
| ONE POUND............................................... | 15.00 |
| MOLD,BUTTER,STAR DESIGN,SQUARE............................. | 12.50 |
| MOLD,BUTTER,STAR PATTERN,SQUARE,WOODEN..................... | 9.50 |
| MOLD,BUTTER,STRAWBERRY PATTERN,WOODEN...................... | 17.00 |
| MOLD,BUTTER,SWAN.......................................... | 22.50 |
| MOLD,BUTTER,SWAN,WOODEN................................... | 35.00 |
| MOLD,BUTTER,TWO PINEAPPLE,TWO STRAWBERRY,4................. | 9.00 |
| MOLD,BUTTER,WHEAT PATTERN,WOODEN........................... | 14.50 |
| MOLD,BUTTER,WHEAT SHEAF,ROUND,1/2 POUND.................... | 12.50 |
| MOLD,BUTTER,WITH CORE,GLASS............................... | 35.00 |
| MOLD,BUTTER,WOODEN,ONE POUND............................... | 10.00 |
| MOLD,CAKE,LAMB,IRON....................................... | 18.50 |
| MOLD,CANDLE,SEE,TIN,MOLD,CANDLE | |
| MOLD,CANDY,CHOCOLATE,SECTIONS OF AUTOMOBILES,SHIPS,TRAINS, | |
| DIRIGIBLES.............................................. | 18.50 |
| MOLD,CANDY,SMILING PIG ON EACH SIDE,CLIP,PEWTER........... | 6.00 |
| MOLD,CHEESE,HANDMADE,PEDESTAL BASE,WOODEN,9 IN.DIAMETER, | |
| 8 IN.HIGH............................................... | 11.00 |
| MOLD,CHOCOLATE,RABBIT,DOUBLE,TIN........................... | 8.00 |
| MOLD,CHOCOLATE,TWO SEPARATED SANTA CLAUSES,PEWTER,7 1/2 X | |
| 7 IN.WIDE............................................... | 45.00 |
| MOLD,CIGAR,TWO SECTIONS,TEN CAVITIES,WOODEN................ | 10.00 |
| MOLD,CIGAR,10-CIGAR,WOODEN,13 IN.LONG...................... | 8.50 |

MOLD,CIGAR,20-CIGAR,WOODEN,22 IN.LONG......................  9.50
  MOLD,ICE CREAM,SEE,PEWTER,MOLD
MOLD,JELLY,PATTERNED,TIN,COPPER THISTLE DESIGN,7 IN.LONG.... 12.50
MOLD,MAPLE SUGAR,TWO CARVED HEARTS,WOODEN................... 15.00
MOLD,MELON SHAPE,HANDLE,TWO PIECE,TIN,6 1/2 IN.LONG.........  2.75
MOLD,PUDDING,FLUTED,COVER,TIN,4 1/2 IN.TALL,
  7-3/4 IN.DIAMETER........................................  8.50
MONART,VASE,PINK BOTTOM TO COBALT TOP,PAPER LABEL,13 IN..... 175.00
MONTE JOYE,BOTTLE,MADE FOR GRAND MARNIER LIQUOR,CAMEO GLASS,
  GREEN.................................................... 80.00
MONTE JOYE,VASE,CARVED,ENAMELED RED POPPIES,AMETHYST GROUND,
  CAMEO,20 IN.............................................. 260.00
MOORCROFT,BASKET,METAL HOLDER & HANDLE,SIGNED,5-IN.DIAMETER. 48.00
MOORCROFT,BASKET,SIGNED.................................... 55.00
MOORCROFT,BOWL,BLACK GROUND,COLORFUL FRUIT,ARTIST-SIGNED,
  10 IN................................................... 45.00
MOORCROFT,BOWL,BLUE GROUND,MAUVE,PINK,PANSIES,GREEN LEAVES,
  LOW STANDARD............................................ 75.00
MOORCROFT,BOWL,BLUE,LEMONS,PLUMS,GRAPES,TURNED-IN RIM,
  6-IN.DIAMETER........................................... 25.00
MOORCROFT,BOWL,COBALT,RED & BLUE FRUITS,GREEN LEAVES,
  6-IN.DIAMETER........................................... 16.00
MOORCROFT,BOWL,GREEN,ORCHID COLOR INTERIOR,4-1/2 IN.DIAMETER 25.00
MOORCROFT,BOWL,PEACH DECOR,8 IN........................... 24.00
MOORCROFT,BOX,COBALT GROUND,PURPLE,ORANGE,GREEN FLOWERS,
  COVER................................................... 45.00
MOORCROFT,BOX,ORANGE & MAROON FLOWERS,GREEN GROUND,KNOB
  FINIAL.................................................. 30.00
MOORCROFT,CANDLEHOLDER,BLUE GROUND,ROSE-PEACH COLOR FRUIT,
  8 IN.,PAIR.............................................. 67.50
MOORCROFT,COMPOTE,COBALT GROUND,RED FLORAL,GREEN LEAVES,
  PEWTER STAND............................................ 35.00
MOORCROFT,COMPOTE,GREEN IRIDESCENT,BURSLEM NO.M67-4,
  6 1/2-IN.DIAMETER....................................... 33.00
MOORCROFT,COMPOTE,IRIDESCENT GREEN,PEDESTAL,6 1/2 IN. X
  5 1/2 IN................................................ 29.00
MOORCROFT,JAR,BISCUIT,DEEP BLUE GROUND,ALLOVER RAISED RED
  FRUIT,ENGLAND........................................... 45.00
MOORCROFT,JAR,DARK BLUE GROUND,ROSE-PEACH COLOR FRUIT DECOR,
  COVER,6 IN.............................................. 67.50
MOORCROFT,LAMP,SCENIC,TREES,GREEN,BLUE,RED,YELLOW,BRASS
  BASE,14 IN.TALL......................................... 225.00
MOORCROFT,PITCHER,BLUE GROUND,PURPLE,ORANGE,GREEN FLOWERS,
  8 IN.TALL............................................... 70.00
MOORCROFT,VASE,BLUE,LEMONS,PLUMS,GRAPES,BALUSTER SHAPE,
  10 IN.HIGH.............................................. 55.00
MOORCROFT,VASE,BUD,LIGHT TO DARK GREEN,TREES,8 IN.TALL...... 32.00
MOORCROFT,VASE,BUD,WHITE,RED & AVOCADO GREEN FLORAL DECOR,
  8 IN.HIGH............................................... 55.00
MOORCROFT,VASE,COBALT BLUE GROUND,RED & PURPLE POPPIES,
  6 IN.TALL............................................... 34.00
MOORCROFT,VASE,COBALT GROUND,YELLOW & PURPLE PANSIES,
  BULBOUS,3 1/2 IN........................................ 37.50
MOORCROFT,VASE,DARK BLUE,FRUITS,10 1/2 IN.................. 45.00
MOORCROFT,VASE,DARK BLUE TO LIGHT GREEN GROUND,MULTICOLORED
  FLORAL,5 IN............................................. 32.50
MOORCROFT,VASE,DARK GREEN,LARGE ROSE,BLUE FLORAL,BULBOUS,
  SLENDER NECK............................................ 55.00
MOORCROFT,VASE,DEEP BLUE,GRAPES,LEAVES,PLUMS,PEACHES,LEMONS,
  SIGNED.................................................. 45.00
MOORCROFT,VASE,FLORAL DECOR,MARKED,5 IN.................... 17.50
MOORCROFT,VASE,LIGHT ORANGE IRIDESCENT,CYLINDER,
  10 1/4 IN.HIGH.......................................... 35.00
MOORCROST,VASE,MINIATURE,BLUE,PANSY DECOR,3 IN. HIGH........ 10.00
MOORCROFT,VASE,PURPLE & PINK PANSIES,BLUE GROUND,SILVER
  COLLAR,6 IN.HIGH........................................ 65.00
MOORCROFT,VASE,RED,YELLOW,GREEN LEAVES,BLUE & RED BERRIES,
  FOOTED,6 IN............................................. 23.00
MOORCROFT,VASE,WHITE GROUND,BLUE VIOLETS,SIGNED W.M.,
  1 3/4 IN.HIGH........................................... 40.00
MOORCROFT,VASE,WHITE GROUND,BLUE,GREEN & PINK FLOWERS,
  5 IN.TALL............................................... 45.00
MOORCROFT,VASE,WHITE TO COBALT,YELLOW,PINK,ORANGE FLOWERS,
  BULBOUS,6 IN............................................ 45.00
MOORCROFT,VASE,YELLOW IRIDESCENT,PURPLE GRAPES,TWO HANDLES,
  5 IN.TALL............................................... 75.00


        MOSER GLASS WAS MADE BY KOLOMON MOSER IN THE EARLY
        1900S. THE ART NOUVEAU TYPE GLASSWARE HAD DETAILED
        EXOTIC ENAMEL DESIGNS.

MOSER,BOOKEND,COBALT BLUE,GOLD EDGES,GERMAN WORD FOR SAMPLE,
    PAIR............................................................. 350.00
MOSER,BOWL,VINTAGE DECOR,OBLONG,FOOTED,CRANBERRY,7 IN....... 60.00
MOSER,BOX,ETCHED GOLD DECOR,COVER,ROUND,SIGNED,AMETHYST,BALL
    FEET............................................................. 135.00
MOSER,CANDLESTICK,ALEXANDRITE,CUBE TYPE,ROUND BASE,SIGNED,
    10 IN.,PAIR...................................................... 150.00
MOSER,CANDLESTICK,AMETHYST GLASS,SIGNED,PAIR,MATCHING BOWL.. 95.00
MOSER,CARAFE,WATER,APPLIED AMBER RIGAREE & ROSETTES,GOLD
    LEAVES,FLORAL................................................... 100.00
MOSER,COLOGNE,BAND OF GILT & CAMEO FIGURES,WOMEN,STOPPER,
    CARLSBAD........................................................ 50.00
MOSER,COLOGNE,GREEN TO CLEAR,INTAGLIO FLORAL,OVOID SHAPE,
    CARLSBAD........................................................ 125.00
MOSER,COLOGNE,OLIVE GREEN,JEWELED,ENAMEL,MATCHING STOPPER,
    GILT FEET....................................................... 165.00
MOSER,COMPOTE,GOLD BAND CLASSIC FIGURES ENCIRCLES BOWL,
    AMETHYST,SIGNED................................................. 225.00
MOSER,COMPOTE,GOLD CLASSIC LEAF & CLUSTER DESIGN,AMETHYST,
    CARLSBAD........................................................ 135.00
MOSER,CUP & SAUCER,PALE GREEN,GOLD ENAMELING,RUFFLED EDGES,
    HANDLELESS...................................................... 75.00
MOSER,CUP & SAUCER,PINK & BLUE ENAMELED FLORAL,GOLD,
    PEDESTALED CUP.................................................. 47.50
MOSER,JAR,CRACKER,PANEL,CUT CRYSTAL,AMETHYST,SILVER COVER,
    6 1/2 IN.HIGH.................................................. 85.00
MOSER,JAR,PICKLE,AMETHYST,MAN & LADY DRINKING TEA,GOLD
    GARLANDS,12 IN.................................................. 325.00
MOSER,JAR,TOBACCO,PANELS,FLORAL,LEAVES,RAYED STAR BASE,CUT
    GLASS........................................................... 45.00
MOSER,LEMONADE,AMBER,ENAMEL & GOLD......................... 35.00
MOSER,TOOTHPICK,CLEAR,CRYSTAL,INTAGLIO CUT................. 14.50
MOSER,TUMBLER,ENAMELED FERN LEAVES & BEES.................. 67.50
MOSER,TUMBLER,JUICE,RUBY,GOLD BANDS........................ 12.50
MOSER,TUMBLER,PAPERWEIGHT,4 IN............................. 25.50
MOSER,VASE,ALLOVER GOLD DECOR,BALL-SHAPED,CRANBERRY,
    5 1/4 IN.TALL.................................................. 75.00
MOSER,VASE,AMBER,FISH,PINK & WHITE ENAMELED SEAWEED,
    7 1/2 IN....................................................... 300.00
MOSER,VASE,AMETHYST TO CLEAR,ACID CUT BACK FLORALS,CARLSBAD,
    8 X 3 IN....................................................... 95.00
MOSER,VASE,AMETHYST TO CLEAR,INTAGLIO CUT,SIGNED MOSER
    KARLSBAD,PAIR.................................................. 300.00
MOSER,VASE,AMETHYST,GOLD ENGRAVED MEDALLIONS,SCRIPT-SIGNED.. 195.00
MOSER,VASE,BLUE,7 1/2 IN.HIGH............................... 75.00
MOSER,VASE,BUD,INTAGLIO CUT,CLEAR.......................... 45.00
MOSER,VASE,CARLSBAD,CLEAR TO AMETHYST,FLORAL,SIGNED,ACID CUT 95.00
MOSER,VASE,CLEAR BOTTOM TO YELLOW TOP,DECOR................ 50.00
MOSER,VASE,DEEP PURPLE,SIGNED,AUSTRIA...................... 100.00
MOSER,VASE,ENAMELED WATER SCENE,WAVES,FISH,LILIES,AMBER,
    5 1/2 IN.TALL.................................................. 55.00
MOSER,VASE,GOLD ENGRAVED MEDALLIONS,AMETHYST GROUND,SIGNED,
    4 IN.HIGH...................................................... 195.00
MOSER,WINE,AMBER,GOLD & ENAMELED FLOWERS,SIGNED,5 1/2 IN.... 95.00
MOSER TYPE,VASE,ENAMELED FLORAL,COBALT,9 1/2 IN.TALL....... 65.00
MOSER TYPE,VASE,GREEN TO CLEAR,LARGE FLOWERS,INTAGLIO CUT... 32.50


    MOSS ROSE CHINA WAS MADE BY MANY FIRMS FROM 1808 TO
    1900. IT REFERS TO ANY CHINA DECORATED WITH THE MOSS
    ROSE FLOWER.
MOSS ROSE,BOWL,SUGAR,COVER,SOFT PASTE,SQUARE............... 12.50
MOSS ROSE,BOX,TOOTHBRUSH,HAVILAND.......................... 22.00
MOSS ROSE,COMPOTE,FLORAL CENTER,GOLD & PINK BAND ON EDGE,LOW
    STANDARD....................................................... 10.00
MOSS ROSE,COMPOTE,LOW,WEDGWOOD,1859 REG. MARK,IRONSTONE..... 35.00
MOSS ROSE,CREAMER & SUGAR.................................. 35.00
MOSS ROSE,CREAMER,PINK SCROLLS,STRIPES,5 3/4 IN.TALL....... 12.00
MOSS ROSE,CREAMER,SOFT PASTE,SQUARE........................ 12.50
MOSS ROSE,CUP & SAUCER,GOLD LUSTER BAND,SET OF 6........... 15.00
MOSS ROSE,CUP & SAUCER,HAVILAND............................ 12.50
MOSS ROSE,CUP & SAUCER,IRONSTONE,MEAKIN.................... 12.50
MOSS ROSE,CUP & SAUCER,PINK SCROLLS,STRIPES................ 8.00
MOSS ROSE,DISH,BONE........................................ 4.00
MOSS ROSE,DISH,CAKE,OPEN HANDLES,HAVILAND,9 1/2-IN.DIAMETER. 15.00
MOSS ROSE,DISH,SAUCE,SQUARE,MARKED A.MEAKIN................ 3.00
MOSS ROSE,MUG,SHAVING,MADDOCK.............................. 15.00
MOSS ROSE,PITCHER,IRONSTONE,WALLACE & CHETWOOD,8 IN.TALL.... 25.00
MOSS ROSE,PLATE,BAVARIAN................................... 3.00
MOSS ROSE,PLATE,CAKE,CLOSED EAR HANDLES,WHITE,10 IN........ 6.50
MOSS ROSE,PLATE,CAKE,OPEN HANDLE,9 3/4-IN.DIAMETER......... 10.00

```
MOSS ROSE,PLATE,CAKE,WEDGWOOD.................................    12.50
MOSS ROSE,PLATE,CAKE,10 IN....................................     9.50
MOSS ROSE,PLATE,FOUR SPRAYS ON WHITE IRONSTONE,
  7 1/4-IN.DIAMETER...........................................     7.00
MOSS ROSE,PLATE,IRONSTONE,MEAKIN,8 3/4 IN.....................     9.50
MOSS ROSE,PLATTER, GIVE US THIS DAY,  OVAL,GILT,IRONSTONE,
  OPEN HANDLES................................................    12.00
MOSS ROSE,PLATTER,C.FIELD HAVILAND,12 IN. X 18 IN.............    18.50
MOSS ROSE,RING TREE,HAND-PAINTED..............................     8.00
MOSS ROSE,SAUCER,JOHNSON BROTHERS,ENGLAND,WINDSORWARE.........     1.00
MOSS ROSE,SUGAR,MAROON LINE ACCENTS,COVER,7 1/4 IN.HIGH.......    18.00
MOSS ROSE,TEAPOT..............................................    35.00
MOSS ROSE,TEAPOT,PINK SCROLLS,STRIPES,LONG SPOUT,9 IN.TALL,
  6-IN.DIAMETER...............................................    22.00
MOSS ROSE,TEAPOT,SIX CUPS & SAUCERS...........................    60.00
```

        MOTHER-OF-PEARL OR PEARL SATIN GLASS WAS FIRST MADE IN
        THE 1850S IN ENGLAND AND IN MASSACHUSETTS. IT WAS A
        SPECIAL TYPE OF MOLD-BLOWN SATIN GLASS WITH AIR BUBBLES
        IN THE GLASS,GIVING IT A PEARLIZED COLOR.

```
MOTHER-OF-PEARL,BASKET,RASPBERRY TO WHITE,DIAMOND QUILTED,
  6 X 7 IN.HIGH...............................................   245.00
MOTHER-OF-PEARL,BOWL,BLUE,DIAMOND-QUILTED,ROSE LINING,
  CRIMPED,FLORAL..............................................   550.00
MOTHER-OF-PEARL,BOWL,DIAMOND-QUILTED,BLUE,ROSE INTERIOR,
  FLORAL DECOR................................................   600.00
MOTHER-OF-PEARL,BOWL,RASPBERRY TO WHITE,DRAPE,FOOTED,8 X
  3 IN.HIGH...................................................   375.00
MOTHER-OF-PEARL,BOWL,ROSE,BRASS FLOWER HOLDER TOP............    25.00
MOTHER-OF-PEARL,BOWL,ROSE,CRIMPED TOP,LIGHT PINK BASE,WHITE
  LINING.....................................................    70.00
MOTHER-OF-PEARL,BOWL,ROSE,DIAMOND-QUILTED,PINK TO WHITE,17 X
  4 IN.HIGH...................................................   150.00
MOTHER-OF-PEARL,BOWL,ROSE,ROSE-PINK,HERRINGBONE,WHITE
  LINING,SCALLOPED............................................   146.00
MOTHER-OF-PEARL,BOX,AZURE BLUE,DIAMOND-QUILTED,WHITE LINING,
  SELF COVER..................................................   115.00
MOTHER-OF-PEARL,CASTOR,PICKLE,FISH SCALE,FORGET-ME-NOTS,
  BLUE,TONGS..................................................   425.00
MOTHER-OF-PEARL,CREAMER,QUILTED,YELLOW.......................   145.00
MOTHER-OF-PEARL,CRUET,HERRINGBONE,CAMPHOR HANDLE,PEDESTAL
  BASE.......................................................   250.00
MOTHER-OF-PEARL,EWER,BUTTERSCOTCH TO PINK,CAMPHOR HANDLE,
  SATIN GLASS.................................................   165.00
MOTHER-OF-PEARL,EWER,DIAMOND QUILT,GRADUATED PINK,7 1/2 IN.   130.00
MOTHER-OF-PEARL,EWER,RAINBOW,CAMPHOR HANDLES,8 IN....ILLUS..     4.75
MOTHER-OF-PEARL,EWER,SALMON PINK,HERRINGBONE,MELON RIB,
  CAMPHOR HANDLE..............................................   125.00
MOTHER-OF-PEARL,JAR,COOKIE,PINK TO ROSE,ENAMELED PANSIES,
  SILVER TOP..................................................   185.00
```

RAINBOW MOTHER-OF-PEARL EWER,
CAMPHOR HANDLES

```
MOTHER-OF-PEARL,KNIFE,FORK,CARVED,CIRCA 1840,SIX OF EACH....      75.00
MOTHER-OF-PEARL,KNIFE,PEN,ROTARY INTERNATIONAL SEAL.........       4.50
MOTHER-OF-PEARL,LAMP,FAIRY,PINK,PRESSED GLASS BASE MARKED
  CLARKE....................................................      85.00
MOTHER-OF-PEARL,LAMP,FAIRY,QUILTED,PINK,CLARKE BASE.........      80.00
MOTHER-OF-PEARL,LAMP,FAIRY,ROSE COLOR,PRESSED GLASS BASE
  MARKED CLARKE.............................................      90.00
MOTHER-OF-PEARL,MUG,DIAMOND-QUILTED,BLUE,GOLD TWIG DECOR,
  BEADING,5 IN..............................................     450.00
MOTHER-OF-PEARL,MUG,PINK TO ROSE,ENAMEL FLORAL,APPLIED
  CAMPHOR HANDLE............................................     125.00
MOTHER-OF-PEARL,NAPPIE,STEVENS & WILLIAMS,ORANGE INSIDE,
  WHITE OUTSIDE.............................................     150.00
MOTHER-OF-PEARL,PEN,FEATHER SHAPE..........................       4.00
MOTHER-OF-PEARL,PERFUME,TURQUOISE,ACORNS,FLORAL,STERLING
  SILVER TOP................................................     350.00
MOTHER-OF-PEARL,PITCHER,DIAMOND-QUILTED RAINBOW,THORN
  HANDLE,6 1/2 IN...........................................     850.00
MOTHER-OF-PEARL,PITCHER,DIAMOND-QUILTED,RED,REEDED CAMPHOR
  HANDLE....................................................     128.00
MOTHER-OF-PEARL,PITCHER,MILK,BLUE,APPLIED FROSTED EDGE &
  REEDED HANDLE.............................................     175.00
MOTHER-OF-PEARL,SHADE,MOIRE PATTERN,PAIR...................     135.00
MOTHER-OF-PEARL,SHADE,UMBRELLA SHAPE,DIAMOND PATTERN,10 IN..      75.00
MOTHER-OF-PEARL,SHADE,WHITE LEADING,JEWELS,9-IN.DIAMETER....     225.00
MOTHER-OF-PEARL,SHAKER,SALT,DEEP MAROON,DIAMOND-QUILTED,
  PEWTER TOP................................................      65.00
MOTHER-OF-PEARL,TUMBLER,DIAMOND-QUILTED,DEEP YELLOW TO WHITE      65.00
MOTHER-OF-PEARL,TUMBLER,DIAMOND-QUILTED,BLUE...............     115.00
MOTHER-OF-PEARL,TUMBLER,DIAMOND-QUILTED,APRICOT COLOR.......     115.00
MOTHER-OF-PEARL,TUMBLER,FUCHSIA TO WHITE,HAND-PAINTED,
  ENAMEL,FLORAL.............................................      80.00
MOTHER-OF-PEARL,TUMBLER,HERRINGBONE PATTERN,BLUE...........      75.00
MOTHER-OF-PEARL,TUMBLER,HERRINGBONE SATIN,YELLOW SHADING TO
  WHITE.....................................................      55.00
MOTHER-OF-PEARL,TUMBLER,HONEYCOMB PATTERN,PINK.............      85.00
MOTHER-OF-PEARL,TUMBLER,WHITE,DIAMOND-QUILTED,GOLD DECOR....     165.00
MOTHER-OF-PEARL,TUMBLER,YELLOW TO WHITE....................      40.00
MOTHER-OF-PEARL,VASE,APRICOT TO GOLD,QUILTED,WHITE-LINED,
  8 IN.TALL.................................................      75.00
MOTHER-OF-PEARL,VASE,BLUE,BULBOUS,LONG NECK,QUILTED,
  10 IN.TALL................................................      65.00
MOTHER-OF-PEARL,VASE,BLUE,PEDESTAL BASE,VERRE MOIRE MOTIF,
  9 3/4 IN..................................................     135.00
MOTHER-OF-PEARL,VASE,BLUE TO WHITE,RIVULET PATTERN,
  QUATREFOIL TOP,5 IN.......................................     160.00
MOTHER-OF-PEARL,VASE,CELERY,BLUE,HERRINGBONE,RIBBED MOLD,
  SCALLOPED TOP.............................................      95.00
MOTHER-OF-PEARL,VASE,CORALENE DECOR,RAINBOW COLORS,
  6 1/2 IN.TALL.............................................     850.00
MOTHER-OF-PEARL,VASE,CRIMP TOP,RAINDROP SATIN SHADES TO
  BUTTERSCOTCH..............................................      45.00
MOTHER-OF-PEARL,VASE,DIAMOND-QUILTED,RAINBOW,8 1/2 IN.HIGH..     875.00
MOTHER-OF-PEARL,VASE,DIAMOND-QUILTED,ROSE COLOR,
  6 1/2 IN.HIGH,PAIR........................................     320.00
MOTHER-OF-PEARL,VASE,DIAMOND-QUILTED,ROSE TO PINK,CAMPHOR
  EDGE,9 IN.................................................     125.00
MOTHER-OF-PEARL,VASE,DIAMOND-QUILTED,SHADED BLUE TO WHITE,
  FLUTED,5 IN...............................................     130.00
MOTHER-OF-PEARL,VASE,GOLD COLOR,WIDE DIAMONDS,SCALLOPED,
  SATIN GLASS...............................................      98.50
MOTHER-OF-PEARL,VASE,HERRINGBONE PATTERN,PEACH TO APRICOT,
  PEDESTAL,9 IN.............................................     145.00
MOTHER-OF-PEARL,VASE,HERRINGBONE,DEEP CORAL TO WHITE.......     147.00
MOTHER-OF-PEARL,VASE,HERRINGBONE,DEEP ROSE TO PINK,PLEATED
  TOP.......................................................     115.00
MOTHER-OF-PEARL,VASE,HERRINGBONE,SALMON TO PINK,CASED,CLEAR
  HANDLE,4 IN...............................................     120.00
MOTHER-OF-PEARL,VASE,HOBNAIL,YELLOW,5 1/2 IN.TALL..........     650.00
MOTHER-OF-PEARL,VASE,JUG SHAPE.............................      45.00
MOTHER-OF-PEARL,VASE,LIGHT BLUE TO WHITE,GROUND PONTIL,
  5 1/4 IN.HIGH.............................................      95.00
MOTHER-OF-PEARL,VASE,MELON SECTIONS,PINK TO APRICOT,CAMPHOR
  HANDLES,PAIR..............................................     190.00
MOTHER-OF-PEARL,VASE,PEACOCK EYE PATTERN,COIN GOLD DECOR,
  BLACK,6 3/4 IN......................................... 1,250.00
MOTHER-OF-PEARL,VASE,RAINDROP PATTERN,BLUE OVERLAY,WHITE
  INTERIOR,8 IN.............................................      65.00
MOTHER-OF-PEARL,VASE,RAINDROP PATTERN,GOLD COLOR,SHORT FOOT
  BASE......................................................      85.00
MOTHER-OF-PEARL,VASE,RASPBERRY RED TO ROSE PINK,RAINDROP
```

| | |
|---|---:|
| PATTERN,PAIR........................................... | 185.00 |
| MOTHER-OF-PEARL,VASE,ROSE BOWL SHAPE,LIGHT TO DARK YELLOW, CAMPHOR FEET............................................ | 65.00 |
| MOTHER-OF-PEARL,VASE,RUFFLED TOP,DEEP ROSE TO PINK,QUILTED, 6 IN................................................... | 80.00 |
| MOTHER-OF-PEARL,VASE,STICK,BULBOUS,TAPERED NECK,BLUE, 10 1/2 IN.TALL......................................... | 65.00 |
| MOTHER-OF-PEARL,VASE,STICK,DIAMOND PATTERN,BUTTERSCOTCH, WHITE LINING........................................... | 75.00 |
| MOTHER-OF-PEARL,VASE,STICK,ORANGE,DIAMOND-QUILTED, 8 1/2 IN.TALL.......................................... | 85.00 |
| MOTHER-OF-PEARL,VASE,STICK,RAINDROP,GREEN,7 1/2 IN..... | 110.00 |
| MOTHER-OF-PEARL,VASE,SWIRL DESIGN,GREEN THREADING AROUND NECK,PAIR.............................................. | 175.00 |
| MOVIE,SEE ALSO PHOTOGRAPHY | |
| MOVIE,CARTOON,400-FOOT REEL,16 MM,TWO REELS.............. | 10.00 |
| MOVIE,FILM,BARNEY GOOGLE,16 MM,DATED 1919............... | 8.00 |
| MOVIE,PROJECTOR AND CAMERA,8 MM,UNIVEX................. | 12.50 |
| MOVIE,PROJECTOR,HAND-OPERATED CRANK,DATED 1920,KEYSTONE MOVIE GRAPH,FILM........................................ | 18.00 |
| MOVIE,PROJECTOR,PATHE,BUILT-IN GENERATOR,SIX REELS OF FILM 1900 ERA,CASE........................................... | 300.00 |
| MOVIE,PROJECTOR,SOUND,R.C.A.,16 MM.................... | 625.00 |
| MOVIE,PROJECTOR,16 MM,FILM............................ | 125.00 |
| MOVIE,SOUND MACHINE,SCOPITONE,16 MM,COIN-OPERATED,WITH 36 MOVIES............................................... | 795.00 |

MOUNT WASHINGTON GLASS WAS MADE AT THE MOUNT WASHINGTON
GLASS CO. LOCATED IN NEW BEDFORD,MASSACHUSETTS. MANY
TYPES OF ART GLASS WERE MADE THERE FROM 1850 TO THE
1890S.

| | |
|---|---:|
| MT.WASHINGTON GLASS,SEE ALSO BURMESE | |
| MT.WASHINGTON,BOWL,DRAPE,CHARTREUSE,BLUISH-WHITE LINING, CAMPHOR FEET........................................... | 75.00 |
| MT.WASHINGTON,BOWL,HOBSTAR,ALLOVER CUT,1880,8 IN........... | 38.50 |
| MT.WASHINGTON,BOWL,ROSE,STRIPES,ENAMELED WHITE & ORANGE FLORAL,GILT............................................. | 52.50 |
| MT.WASHINGTON,BOWL,ROSE,WESTMINSTER PATTERN,2 1/2 IN.HIGH... | 55.00 |
| MT.WASHINGTON,BOWL,SUGAR,BULBOUS,FLARED & CRIMPED RIM,GROUND PONTIL,WHITE........................................... | 35.00 |
| MT.WASHINGTON,BOX,LUSTERLESS WHITE,ALLOVER FLORAL,BRASS COLLARS,FOOTED......................................... | 65.00 |
| MT.WASHINGTON,BRIDE'S BASKET,PINK TO YELLOW,DIAMOND-QUILTED, SQUARE................................................. | 250.00 |
| MT.WASHINGTON,CREAMER,OPALESCENT,PANSY DECOR,SILVER TOP & HANDLE................................................. | 37.50 |
| MT.WASHINGTON,CUP,SAUCER,PANSY DECOR OUTLINED IN GOLD, BEADING,CRYSTAL........................................ | 120.00 |
| MT.WASHINGTON,DISH,SWEETMEAT,DIAMOND QUILTED,CREAM TO PINK, SILVER HOLDER.......................................... | 265.00 |
| MT.WASHINGTON,DISH,SWEETMEAT,DIAMOND QUILTED,RUFFLED,SILVER HOLDER................................................. | 265.00 |
| MT.WASHINGTON,FLOWER FROG,PANSIES,WHITE SATIN GLASS,MUSHROOM SHAPE................................................. | 75.00 |
| MT.WASHINGTON,INKWELL,WHITE GROUND,YELLOW PANSIES,SATIN GLASS,SQUARE........................................... | 155.00 |
| MT.WASHINGTON,JAR,COOKIE,OPAL GROUND,PINK FLOWERS,GREEN LEAVES................................................. | 75.00 |
| MT.WASHINGTON,JAR,PICKLE,RIBBED,APPLE BLOSSOMS,DRAGONFLIES, SILVER LID............................................. | 90.00 |
| MT.WASHINGTON,MUSTARD POT,OPAQUE WHITE,ENAMEL FLORAL,SILVER HANDLE,LID............................................. | 75.00 |
| MT.WASHINGTON,MUSTARD,BLUE,LARGE PINK WILDFLOWER,LID........ | 39.50 |
| MT.WASHINGTON,MUSTARD,LUSTERLESS WHITE,RIBBED,SILVER TOP... | 39.50 |
| MT.WASHINGTON,MUSTARD,WHITE,OPAQUE,RIBBED,PINK FLOWERS,BLUE BEADING............................................... | 45.00 |
| MT.WASHINGTON,PITCHER,ENGRAVED FERNS,LEAVES,BELLFLOWERS, CRANBERRY,1880......................................... | 65.00 |
| MT.WASHINGTON,PITCHER,SPATTER,ORANGE,WHITE,PINK,ENAMELED BIRD,TREE............................................... | 65.00 |
| MT.WASHINGTON,PLANTER,ALLOVER SCROLLS,RIBBING,PINK TO WHITE, FERN DECOR............................................. | 90.00 |
| MT.WASHINGTON,PLATE,COMMEMORATES PILGRIM LANDING,DATED DEC.21,1620............................................. | 50.00 |
| MT.WASHINGTON,SALT & PEPPER,FLORAL,LEAF,OPALWARE, SILVER-PLATED HOLDER................................... | 60.00 |
| MT.WASHINGTON,SALT & PEPPER,LAY-DOWN EGG SHAPE,PINK,BLUE, ENAMELED FLORAL........................................ | 55.00 |
| MT.WASHINGTON,SALT & PEPPER,PINK FLOWERS,TOPS.............. | 40.00 |
| MT.WASHINGTON,SALT SHAKER,STRAIGHT-SIDED CYLINDRICAL SHAPE, | |

```
FLORAL,4 IN......................................................  12.00
MT.WASHINGTON,SALT,BEADED,DECOR,OPEN.............................  22.00
MT.WASHINGTON,SALT,INDIVIDUAL,MELON SHAPE,FLORAL,BLUE DOTS
  ON RIM.........................................................  29.00
MT.WASHINGTON,SALT,MASTER,MELON SHAPE,FLORAL,BLUE DOTS ON
  RIM............................................................  69.00
MT.WASHINGTON,SALT,MELON RIB,BEADED,VIVID DECOR,OPEN............  24.00
MT.WASHINGTON,SHAKER,RIBBED..................................... 600.00
MT.WASHINGTON,SHAKER,SALT,COLUMBIAN EXPOSITION 1893,EGG,
  LIE-DOWN TYPE..................................................  39.50
MT.WASHINGTON,SHAKER,SALT,FLORAL DECOR,PEPPER,BERRY DECOR...  70.00
MT.WASHINGTON,SHAKER,SALT,MELON SHAPE,SATIN,PEACH COLOR,
  DAISIES........................................................  17.50
MT.WASHINGTON,SHAKER,SALT,PEACH COLOR,ENAMEL PINK & BLUE
  FLOWERS........................................................  35.00
MT.WASHINGTON,SHAKER,SALT & PEPPER,BLUE,IVORY,LEAVES........  65.00
MT.WASHINGTON,SHAKER,SALT,PEPPER,BURMESE,BARREL SHAPE,SILVER
  PLATE TOPS..................................................... 126.50
MT.WASHINGTON,SHAKER,SALT,SATIN GLASS,EGG SHAPE,PAIR........  40.00
MT.WASHINGTON,SHAKER,SALT,SATIN GLASS,ENAMEL FLORAL,BARREL
  SHAPE,PAIR.....................................................  45.00
MT.WASHINGTON,SHAKER,SALT,STRAIGHT-SIDED CYLINDRICAL SHAPE,
  FLORAL,4 IN....................................................  12.00
MT.WASHINGTON,SHAKER,SALT,WHITE,COLUMBIA EXPOSITION,1893....  30.00
MT.WASHINGTON,SHAKER,SUGAR,ALBERTINE,EGG SHAPE,YELLOW,OAK
  LEAVES,ACORNS.................................................. 135.00
MT.WASHINGTON,SHAKER,SUGAR,BEIGE,MELON RIBS,METAL TOP.......  35.00
MT.WASHINGTON,SHAKER,SUGAR,BLUE GROUND,RED FUCHSIAS,SILVER
  TOP,6 1/2 IN...................................................  42.50
MT.WASHINGTON,SHAKER,SUGAR,CORAL SHADING TO CREAM,ENAMELED
  BLUE DOTS...................................................... 165.00
MT.WASHINGTON,SHAKER,SUGAR,EGG SHAPE,ENAMELED ORANGE FLORAL,
  PEWTER COVER................................................... 125.00
MT.WASHINGTON,SHAKER,SUGAR,MELON RIB,PASTEL FLOWERS,SATIN,
  SCREW TOP......................................................  39.00
MT.WASHINGTON,SHAKER,SUGAR,MELON RIB,ROSE DECOR.............  65.00
MT.WASHINGTON,SHAKER,SUGAR,PINK & BLUE DECOR,EGG SHAPE,PAIR. 125.00
MT.WASHINGTON,SUGAR,LUSTERLESS,WHITE,GROUND PONTIL,BULBOUS,
  CRIMPED RIM....................................................  35.00
MT.WASHINGTON,SYRUP,OPAL,LIGHT BLUE GROUND,LILIES,LEAVES,
  YELLOW,RED.....................................................  37.50
MT.WASHINGTON,TOOTHPICK,AUTUMN-COLORED LEAVES..............  37.50
MT.WASHINGTON,TOOTHPICK,MELON-SHAPED BOTTOM,VIOLETS,BLUE
  BEADED TOP.....................................................  47.50
MT.WASHINGTON,TOOTHPICK,OPAQUE WHITE,MELON RIB,VIOLETS,
  BLUE-BEADED TOP................................................  42.50
MT.WASHINGTON,TOOTHPICK,VIOLET DECOR,WHITE GROUND,MELON
  SHAPE..........................................................  39.50
MT.WASHINGTON,VASE,BEIGE-YELLOW TO WHITE,WILD ROSES,GRAY
  LEAVES,7 IN....................................................  70.00
MT.WASHINGTON,VASE,BLUE,HONEYCOMB PATTERN,CAMPHOR EDGE,
  5 1/2 IN.,PAIR................................................. 110.00
MT.WASHINGTON,VASE,CAMEO,INTAGLIO CUT,CASED,ROSE COLOR ON
  WHITE.......................................................... 345.00
MT.WASHINGTON,VASE,GREEN,ENAMELED BLOSSOMS,WHITE CASING,
  11 IN.,PAIR.................................................... 185.00
MT.WASHINGTON,VASE,VERONA,GREEN,GOLD,LILIES,RIBS,FLARED TOP,
  10 IN.HIGH.....................................................  95.00
MUELLER FRERES,LAMP,MUSHROOM SHAPE,MOTTLED BLUE,GRAY,WHITE,
  LUNEVILLE...................................................... 140.00
MUELLER FRERES,SHADE,MOTTLED ORANGE & DARK BLUE,SIGNED......  12.50
MUELLER FRERES,VASE,BLUE TO CRANBERRY,MARKED,LUNEVILLE,
  6 1/2 IN.......................................................  65.00
MUELLER FRERES,VASE,CAMEO,FLORAL PONTIL,PURPLE,PINK,AQUA,
  IVORY,9 IN..................................................... 185.00
MUELLER FRERES,VASE,CAMEO,ORANGE GROUND,BLACK SCENIC,TREES,
  WATER,6 IN..................................................... 160.00
MUELLER FRERES,VASE,CAMEO,SIGNED,FRANCE,14 1/2 IN. HIGH..... 145.00
MUELLER FRERES,VASE,MOTTLED PINK,GREEN,PURPLE,WHITE,SIGNED,
  7 IN...........................................................  50.00
MUELLER FRERES,VASE,ORANGE,BLUE,SIGNED,11 1/2 IN... 85.00 TO 110.00
MUELLER FRERES,VASE,PURPLE ON GRAY GROUND,SIGNED,5 1/2 X
  3 1/2 IN. HIGH................................................. 105.00
MUFFINEER,BEADED,THREE CURVED FEET,STERLING SILVER,5 IN.TALL  12.00
MUFFINEER,CRANBERRY GLASS.......................................  35.00
MUFFINEER,FLORAL,GREEN,GOLD,SQUATTY,4 1/2 IN.HIGH,
  4-IN.DIAMETER..................................................  10.50
MUFFINEER,GREEN AT TOP TO CLEAR,VERTICAL PANELS,ZIGZAG CUT
  NEAR BASE......................................................  27.50
MUFFINEER,OPALESCENT,LID........................................  22.50
MUFFINEER,OPAQUE,RED............................................  15.00
```

```
MUFFINEER,PORCELAIN,SILVER TOP,ENGLAND.....................    9.50
MUFFINEER,SILVER,8 IN.HIGH................................   85.00
MUFFINEER,SPANISH LACE,RASPBERRY SATIN....................   56.00
MURANO,SALT,SNAIL SHAPE,IRIDESCENT,AQUA...................   30.00
MUSIC BOX,CELESTE FLUTE WITH ORGAN,THREE BELLS,NO.CO13,BIRD
  STRIKERS...............................................  550.00
MUSIC,ACCORDION PLAYER,PAUL LOSCHE,BASS & SNARE DRUMS,
  CYMBAL,TRIANGLE.......................................2,450.00
MUSIC,ACCORDION,MILANO...................................   85.00
MUSIC,AEOLEON ORCHESTRELL,ELECTRIFIED,12 ROLLS...........  500.00
MUSIC,ALBUM,MOVEMENT MOUNTED ON BACK,AVERAGE CONDITION...   79.00
MUSIC,ALBUM,SACRED SPIRITUAL MUSIC.......................    8.00
MUSIC,ALBUM,SWISS MOVEMENT ON BACK,FAMILY PHOTOGRAPHS IN
  ALBUM.................................................   99.00
MUSIC,BIRDCAGE,LOUIS XVI STYLE,PAIR BLUEBIRDS,GILT BRONZE,
  19 IN.HIGH..........................................1,650.00
MUSIC,BOOK,A SONG BOOK,AMHERST,1798......................   50.00
MUSIC,BOOK,A SONG BOOK,NEW YORK,1761.....................   75.00
MUSIC,BOOK,A TRIBUTE TO THE SWINISH MULTITUDE,NEW YORK,1795.  75.00
MUSIC,BOOK,AMERICAN ACADEMY OF COMPLIMENTS,WILMINGTON,1797..  25.00
MUSIC,BOOK,AMERICAN COCK ROBIN,NEW YORK,1774.............   50.00
MUSIC,BOOK,BLACKBIRD SONG BOOK,PHILADELPHIA,1769.........   50.00
MUSIC,BOOK,DIDBIN'S MUSEUM,PHILADELPHIA,1797.............   20.00
MUSIC,BOOK,FEAST OF MERRIMENT,PHILADELPHIA,1795..........   25.00
MUSIC,BOOK,FREEMASONS POCKET COMPANION,PORTSMOUTH,N.H.,1798.  25.00
MUSIC,BOOK,GENTLEMEN & LADIES COMPLETE SONGSTER,WORCESTER,
  1795..................................................   20.00
MUSIC,BOOK,JEMMY CARSON'S COLLECTION OF BALLADS,
  PHILADELPHIA,1762.....................................   75.00
MUSIC,BOOK,JOVIAL SONGSTER,BALTIMORE,1798................   20.00
MUSIC,BOOK,LITTLE ROBIN RED BREAST,WORCESTER,1786-87.....   25.00
MUSIC,BOOK,LOYAL AND HUMOROUS SONGS,NEW YORK,1779........   50.00
MUSIC,BOOK,MASONIC SONGS,WATERFORD,NEW YORK,1797.........   35.00
MUSIC,BOOK,MEDLEY OR NEW PHILADELPHIA SONGSTER,PHILADELPHIA,
  1795..................................................   25.00
MUSIC,BOOK,MERMAID OR NAUTICAL SONGSTER,NEW YORK,1793....   40.00
MUSIC,BOOK,MERMAID OR NAUTICAL SONGSTER,NEW YORK,1798....   25.00
MUSIC,BOOK,MISS ASHMORE'S CHOICE COLLECTION OF SONGS,BOSTON,
  1771..................................................   50.00
MUSIC,BOOK,MONSTROUS GOOD SONGS FOR 1792,BOSTON,1792.....   50.00
MUSIC,BOOK,MOTHER GOOSE'S MELODY,WORCESTER,MASSACHUSETTS,
  1785..................................................   50.00
MUSIC,BOOK,MOTHER GOOSE'S MELODY,WORCESTER,MASSACHUSETTS,
  1794..................................................   35.00
MUSIC,BOOK,MOTHER GOOSE'S MELODY,WORCESTER,MASSACHUSETTS,
  1799..................................................   25.00
MUSIC,BOOK,NAUTICAL SONGSTER OR SEAMAN'S COMPANION,
  BALTIMORE,1798........................................   25.00
MUSIC,BOOK,NEWEST FASHION,BOSTON,1798....................   25.00
MUSIC,BOOK,PADDY'S RESOURCE,NEW YORK,1798................   25.00
MUSIC,BOOK,PADDY'S RESOURCE,PHILADELPHIA,1796............   25.00
MUSIC,BOOK,PATRIOTIC SONGSTER FOR JULY 4TH,1798,BALTIMORE,
  1798..................................................   75.00
MUSIC,BOOK,PATRIOTIC MEDLEY,NEW YORK,1800................   25.00
MUSIC,BOOK,PHILADELPHIA JEST BOOK,PHILADELPHIA,1790......   50.00
MUSIC,BOOK,PHILADELPHIA POCKET COMPANION,PHILADELPHIA,1794..  40.00
MUSIC,BOOK,PHILADELPHIA SONGSTER,PHILADELPHIA,1789.......   50.00
MUSIC,BOOK,SONGS FOR THE AMUSEMENT OF CHILDREN,MIDDLETOWN,
  1790..................................................   50.00
MUSIC,BOOK,SONGS,COMIC,SATYRICAL & SENTIMENTAL,PHILADELPHIA,
  1777..................................................   75.00
MUSIC,BOOK,SONGS,COMIC,SATYRICAL & SENTIMENTAL,PHILADELPHIA,
  1778..................................................   50.00
MUSIC,BOOK,SONGS,NAVAL & MILITARY,NEW YORK,1779..........   75.00
MUSIC,BOOK,THE AMERICAN COCK ROBIN,NEW YORK,1764.........   50.00
MUSIC,BOOK,THE AMERICAN LADIES POCKET BOOK,PHILADELPHIA,
  1798..................................................   25.00
MUSIC,BOOK,THE AMERICAN MOCK-BIRD,NEW YORK,1760..........   50.00
MUSIC,BOOK,THE AMERICAN MUSICAL MISCELLANY,NORTHAMPTON,1798.  25.00
MUSIC,BOOK,THE AMERICAN SONGSTER,BALTIMORE,1799..........   20.00
MUSIC,BOOK,THE AMERICAN SONGSTER,BOSTON,1795.............   25.00
MUSIC,BOOK,THE AMERICAN SONGSTER,NEW YORK,1788...........   30.00
MUSIC,BOOK,THE AMERICAN SONGSTER,PORTSMITH,1790..........   25.00
MUSIC,BOOK,THE AMOROUS SONGSTER,NEW YORK,1800............   20.00
MUSIC,BOOK,THE APOLLO,PHILADELPHIA,1789..................   25.00
MUSIC,BOOK,THE APOLLO,PHILADELPHIA,1791..................   20.00
MUSIC,BOOK,THE BALTIMORE SONGSTER,BALTIMORE,1798.........   35.00
MUSIC,BOOK,THE CHARMER,PHILADELPHIA,1790.................   25.00
MUSIC,BOOK,THE CHARMS OF MELODY,PHILADELPHIA,1788........   40.00
MUSIC,BOOK,THE COLUMBIA SONGSTER,NEW YORK,1797...........   35.00
MUSIC,BOOK,THE COLUMBIAN SONGSTER,NEW YORK,1795..........   50.00
```

```
MUSIC,BOOK,THE COMPANION,PROVIDENCE,1799.....................   20.00
MUSIC,BOOK,THE DEMOCRATIC SONGSTER,BALTIMORE,1794............   25.00
MUSIC,BOOK,THE ECHO OR COLUMBIA SONGSTER,BROOKFIELD,1800....   25.00
MUSIC,BOOK,THE ECHO OR FEDERAL SONGSTER,BROOKFIELD,1798.....   25.00
MUSIC,BOOK,THE FESTIVAL OF MIRTH,NEW YORK,1800..............   15.00
MUSIC,BOOK,THE FREEMASONS MONITOR,ALBANY,1797...............   25.00
MUSIC,BOOK,THE FREEMASONS POCKET BOOK,NEW YORK,1782.........   35.00
MUSIC,BOOK,THE HUMMING BIRD,BOSTON,1798.....................   15.00
MUSIC,BOOK,THE JOVIAL SONGSTER,BOSTON,1800..................   15.00
MUSIC,BOOK,THE MOCKING BIRD,PHILADELPHIA,1793...............   50.00
MUSIC,BOOK,THE NIGHTINGALE OF LIBERTY OR DELIGHTS OF
  HARMONY,N.Y.,1797........................................   35.00
MUSIC,BOOK,THE NIGHTINGALE OR CHARMS OF MELODY,BALTIMORE,
  1798.....................................................   50.00
MUSIC,BOOK,THE NIGHTINGALE OR SONGSTER'S COMPANION,
  PHILADELPHIA,1791........................................   50.00
MUSIC,BOOK,THE PLEASING SONGSTER,PHILADELPHIA,1795..........   50.00
MUSIC,BOOK,THE REPUBLICAN HARMONIST,PHILADELPHIA,1800.......   50.00
MUSIC,BOOK,THE SAILOR'S MEDLEY,PHILADELPHIA,1800............   25.00
MUSIC,BOOK,THE SCOTS MUSICAL MUSEUM,PHILADELPHIA,1797.......   35.00
MUSIC,BOOK,THE SELECT SONGSTER,NEW HAVEN,1796..............   35.00
MUSIC,BOOK,THE SKYLARK,WORCESTER,1795.......................   25.00
MUSIC,BOOK,THE SKYLARK,WORCESTER,1797.......................   20.00
MUSIC,BOOK,THE SOCIAL HARMONY,NEW YORK,1795.................   35.00
MUSIC,BOOK,THE SONGSTER'S ASSISTANT,SUFFIELD,1800...........   25.00
MUSIC,BOOK,THE SONGSTER'S MAGAZINE,PHILADELPHIA,1795........   50.00
MUSIC,BOOK,THE STORM OR THE AMERICAN SYREN,WILLIAMSBURG,
  1773.....................................................   75.00
MUSIC,BOOK,THE SYREN OR VOCAL ENCHANTRESS,WILMINGTON,1797...   35.00
MUSIC,BOOK,THE SYREN,PHILADELPHIA,1800......................   25.00
MUSIC,BOOK,THE THEATRICAL SONGSTER,BOSTON,1797..............   35.00
MUSIC,BOOK,THE VOCAL CHARMER,PHILADELPHIA,1793..............   25.00
MUSIC,BOOK,THE VOCAL COMPANION,PHILADELPHIA,1796............   25.00
MUSIC,BOOK,THE VOCAL ENCHANTRESS,PHILADELPHIA,1791..........   50.00
MUSIC,BOOK,THE VOCAL INSTRUCTOR,MASSACHUSETTS,1797..........   50.00
MUSIC,BOOK,THE VOCAL REMEMBRANCER,PHILADELPHIA,1793.........   50.00
MUSIC,BOOK,THE WARBLING SONGSTER,OR CURE FOR DULLNESS,
  PHILADELPHIA,1795........................................   50.00
MUSIC,BOOK,THE WHIM OF THE DAY,BOSTON,1798..................   25.00
MUSIC,BOOK,THE YOUNG MASONS MONITOR, NEW YORK,1789..........   35.00
MUSIC,BOOK,TOM THUMB SONG BOOK,BOSTON,1795..................   50.00
MUSIC,BOOK,TOMMY THUMB'S SONG BOOK,WORCESTER,1788...........   50.00
MUSIC,BOOK,WINTER EVENINGS AMUSEMENT,BOSTON,1795............   25.00
MUSIC,BOOK,WOOD LARK SONG BOOK,PHILADELPHIA,1769............   50.00
MUSIC,BOX,8 TUNES,15 1/4 IN.,2-PART COMB,MATCHING TABLE.....  795.00
MUSIC,BOX,ATLAS ORGANETTE,16 KEY,REED ORGAN,METAL DISC,
  UNREBUILT,7 IN...........................................   99.00
MUSIC,BOX,AUTOMATIC DISC CHANGE,PARLOR MODEL,STYLE 35,
  REGINA,12 DISCS.........................................2,750.00
MUSIC,BOX,AUTOPHONE,ORGAN,PAPER STRIP,MAKER H.B.HORTON,1880,
  13 IN.HIGH...............................................  249.00
MUSIC,BOX,BELL,MULTICOLORED TUNE CARD,TUNE INDICATOR,
  6-IN.CYLINDER,1890.......................................  449.00
MUSIC,BOX,BELL,STEEL COMB,BIRD STRIKER,GENEVA,1880,PAILLARD.  749.00
MUSIC,BOX,BIRDCAGE,BIRD MOVES AND SINGS....................  125.00
MUSIC,BOX,BREMOND,INLAID WOOD CANOPY,STORAGE DRAWERS,
  BREMOND,54 IN.HIGH.....................................5,995.00
MUSIC,BOX,CAPITOL CUFF,NO.DO26-TYPE A,SIX CUFFS............  800.00
MUSIC,BOX,CARVED MAHOGANY,CHERUB SCENE,20 1/2-IN.DISC,
  CABINET,CRITERION......................................1,295.00
MUSIC,BOX,CELESTE FLUTE,NO.CO13,ORGAN,THREE BELLS,BIRD
  STRIKERS................................................  550.00
MUSIC,BOX,CHRISTMAS TREE HOLDER,ROTATES,TWO TUNES,
  14-IN.DIAMETER..........................................  125.00
MUSIC,BOX,COIN-OPERATED,,ROTATES 12 RECORDS,REGINA,
  12 RECORDS.............................................2,500.00
MUSIC,BOX,CONCERTINA MERNOD FRERES,15 IN.-CYLINDERS..ILLUS..  750.00
MUSIC,BOX,CONCERTINA,TWELVE TUNES,15 IN.CYLINDER,MERMOD
  FRERES..................................................  749.00
MUSIC,BOX,CRITERION,TABLE MODEL,DOUBLE COMB,CHERUB SCENE ON
  LID.....................................................  295.00
MUSIC,BOX,CUFF,TYPE A CAPITOL NO.DO26,SIX CUFFS............  800.00
MUSIC,BOX,CYLINDER,8 TUNES,OUTSIDE CRANK,SWISS,5 1/2 IN.....  275.00
MUSIC,BOX,CYLINDER,8 TUNES,GEOMETRIC INLAY ON LID,13 IN.....  450.00
MUSIC,BOX,CYLINDER,BELL,RESTORED IN LONDON.................  497.00
MUSIC,BOX,CYLINDER,BELLS,INLAY BOX,10 TUNES,24 X 13 X 11....  550.00
MUSIC,BOX,CYLINDER,CHROME-PLATED WORKS & CYLINDER,EIGHT
  TUNES...................................................  185.00
MUSIC,BOX,CYLINDER,DANCING DOLLS...........................  585.00
MUSIC,BOX,CYLINDER,DAWKINS,PIANOFORTE STYLE COMBS,NINE
  BELLS,24 IN.HIGH.........................................  795.00
```

CONCERTINA MERNOD FRERES
MUSIC BOX

```
MUSIC,BOX,CYLINDER,DAWKINS,RESTORED,8 TUNES.................   497.00
MUSIC,BOX,CYLINDER,DAWKINS,RESTORED,SIX TUNES................   275.00
MUSIC,BOX,CYLINDER,EIGHT AIR,NICOLE FRERES...................   455.00
MUSIC,BOX,CYLINDER,FIVE BELLS,TWELVE TUNES...................   375.00
MUSIC,BOX,CYLINDER,FOUR TUNES,INLAID TOP.....................   175.00
MUSIC,BOX,CYLINDER,HIDDEN DRUM & BELLS,SWITZERLAND,1880......   395.00
MUSIC,BOX,CYLINDER,IN WRITING DESK,CLOCK,STORAGE DRAWER,
  CIRCA 1900.................................................   495.00
MUSIC,BOX,CYLINDER,INTERCHANGEABLE,36 TUNES,REFINISHED CASE,
  FRANCE..................................................1,335.00
MUSIC,BOX,CYLINDER,MANDOLIN ATTACHMENT,ON TABLE WITH DRAWER
  FOR STORAGE...............................................   895.00
MUSIC,BOX,CYLINDER,MATCHING TABLE,INLAID LYRE & GARLAND
  MOTIF ON LID..............................................   795.00
MUSIC,BOX,CYLINDER,MATCHING TABLE,INTERCHANGEABLE,
  HARP-PICCOLO STYLE......................................1,495.00
MUSIC,BOX,CYLINDER,NICOLE FRERES,8 TUNES,RESTORED IN LONDON.   455.00
MUSIC,BOX,CYLINDER,NICOLE,SIX TUNES,RESTORED IN LONDON......   375.00
MUSIC,BOX,CYLINDER,NINE BELLS,RESTORED......................   497.00
MUSIC,BOX,CYLINDER,SWISS,TUNE CARD..........................   425.00
MUSIC,BOX,CYLINDER,SWISS,20 TUNE,TUNE CARD..................   425.00
MUSIC,BOX,CYLINDER,TEN TUNES,OUTSIDE WIND...................   165.00
MUSIC,BOX,CYLINDER,THREE BELLS,BUTTERFLY HAMMERS............   337.00
MUSIC,BOX,CYLINDER,THREE BELLS,PLAYS 16 TUNES,CIRCA 1890,
  18 IN.HIGH................................................   289.00
MUSIC,BOX,DANCING DOLLS,9-IN.CYLINDER,LANGDORFF & FILS,
  GENEVA....................................................   995.00
MUSIC,BOX,DOUBLE COMB,OAK CASKET CASE,CRITERION,NINE
  15-1/2 IN.DISCS...........................................   395.00
MUSIC,BOX,DOUBLE COMB,WALNUT CASE,SYMPONIUM,THREE
  12-IN.DISCS...............................................   310.00
MUSIC,BOX,EDISON AMBEROLA,CYLINDER..........................    90.00
MUSIC,BOX,FORM OF A SWISS CHALET,BOTTLE COMPARTMENT,
  B.A.BREMOND,GENEVA........................................   595.00
MUSIC,BOX,FORTUNA,TABLE MODEL,DOUBLE COMB,USES 11-IN.DISC,
  SCENIC LID................................................   395.00
MUSIC,BOX,FOUR TUNE,CYLINDER,OUTSIDE WIND...................   150.00
MUSIC,BOX,GRAND PIANO SHAPE,RED ENAMEL,LIFT LID OVER KEYS,
  SWISS.....................................................   125.00
MUSIC,BOX,JUKE,PLAYS 78 RPM RECORDS,COIN-OPERATED,MAPLE.....   350.00
MUSIC,BOX,KALLIOPE,SIX COMBS,TWELVE BELLS,20 1/2-IN.DISC,
  39 IN.HIGH..............................................1,495.00
MUSIC,BOX,KALLIOPE,WOODEN CASE,PLAYS 13 1/4-IN.METAL DISCS,
  10 DISCS..................................................   300.00
MUSIC,BOX,LOCHMANN,WINDING ROD,21 5/8-IN.DISC,GOLD LEAF
  DECOR,42 IN...............................................   895.00
MUSIC,BOX,MAHOGANY,CHERUB SCENE,11 3/4-IN.DISC,CRITERION,
  6 DISCS...................................................   295.00
MUSIC,BOX,MANDOLIN TONE,PAN MOTIF PIPES,TWELVE TUNES,MERMOD
  FRERES....................................................   595.00
MUSIC,BOX,MANDOLINE,NO.C012,CYLINDER,POLISHED,11 IN.........   225.00
MUSIC,BOX,MANDOLINE,NO.C014,CYLINDER,POLISHED,WALNUT,8 IN...   185.00
```

MUSIC,BOX,MCTAMMANY VICTORIA ORGANETTE,14-NOTE RANGE,PAPER
    STRIP,BLACK............................................ 119.00
MUSIC,BOX,MECHANICAL ORGUINETTE ORGAN,PAPER STRIPS,1880..... 119.00
MUSIC,BOX,MECHANISM ELECTRO-PLATED,SWISS,BY D.ALLARD & CO.,
    11 IN.HIGH.........................................1,050.00
MUSIC,BOX,MERMOD FRERES,CYLINDER,SIX-TUNE PROGRAM CARD ON
    LID................................................. 450.00
MUSIC,BOX,MERMOD FRERES,INTERCHANGEABLE,TWO CYLINDERS....... 500.00
MUSIC,BOX,MERMOD FRERES,MANDOLIN,TWELVE-TUNE,INDICATOR,
    18 IN.HIGH.......................................... 595.00
MUSIC,BOX,NEEDLE,HIS MASTER'S VOICE,DOG,HORN,FILLED WITH
    NEEDLES............................................. 15.00
MUSIC,BOX,NICKELODEON,SEEBURG,STYLE K,PIANO,MANDOLIN,
    XYLOPHONE,62 IN....................................2,495.00
MUSIC,BOX,NICOLE FRERES,KEY WIND,PLAYS EIGHT TUNES,
    13-IN.CYLINDER...................................... 495.00
MUSIC,BOX,NINE CYLINDERS,THREE CYLINDER CASES,11-IN.
    CYLINDERS,PAILLARD.................................1,495.00
MUSIC,BOX,OLYMPIC,11 3/4-IN.DISC,CRANK,F.G.OTTO & SONS,
    JERSEY CITY,N.J..................................... 149.00
MUSIC,BOX,ON TABLE,EIGHT-TUNE CYLINDER,HAND-LETTERED TUNE
    CARD,SWISS.........................................1,495.00
MUSIC,BOX,ORCHESTRA,AUTOMATIC FIGURES MOVE WHEN MUSIC PLAYS,
    CIRCA 1880........................................1,995.00
MUSIC,BOX,ORCHESTRA,DRUM,BELLS,AUTOMATIC TUNE INDICATOR..... 449.00
MUSIC,BOX,ORCHESTRA,THREE ANIMATED MANDARIN FIGURES PLAY SIX
    BELLS............................................... 995.00
MUSIC,BOX,ORCHESTRAL,STORAGE BIN,COIN OPERATED,REGINA,
    6 FT.6 IN.HIGH....................................1,995.00
MUSIC,BOX,ORCHESTRAL,STORAGE BIN,COIN OPERATED,REGINA,
    7 FT.4 IN.HIGH....................................1,995.00
MUSIC,BOX,ORGAN,SERAPHONE,PAPER ROLL,GOLD TRANSFER DECOR,
    12 IN.HIGH.......................................... 129.00
MUSIC,BOX,ORPHENION,TABLE MODEL,PATTERNED WALNUT CASE,
    24 IN.HIGH.......................................... 495.00
MUSIC,BOX,PAILLARD,BELLS,COMB,CYLINDER,33 IN.HIGH LID OPEN,
    27 IN.WIDE........................................1,295.00
MUSIC,BOX,PAILLARD,CYLINDER,FIVE ENGRAVED BRASS BELLS,TUNE
    CARD..............................................1,295.00
MUSIC,BOX,PAILLARD,CYLINDER,SIX BELLS,BEE & BIRD STRIKERS,
    1880............................................... 749.00
MUSIC,BOX,PAILLARD,INTERCHANGEABLE,NINE CYLINDERS,THREE
    CYLINDER CASES....................................1,495.00
MUSIC,BOX,POLYPHON,BOTTOM DRAWER,COIN-OPERATED,WALNUT CASE,
    4 FT.6 IN.......................................... 795.00
MUSIC,BOX,POLYPHON,DOUBLE COMB,COIN-OPERATED,WALNUT CASE,
    40 IN.TALL......................................... 749.00
MUSIC,BOX,POLYPHON,DOUBLE COMB,MATCHING WALNUT BASE FOR
    STORAGE,7 FT......................................1,595.00
MUSIC,BOX,POLYPHON,DUPLEX MUSICAL COMB,COIN-OPERATED,WALNUT
    CASE,3 FT.......................................... 695.00
MUSIC,BOX,POLYPHON,GRANDFATHER CLOCK,CAN BE SET TO PLAY ON
    THE HOUR..........................................1,995.00
MUSIC,BOX,POLYPHON,MATCHING BASE CABINET,24 1/2-IN.DISC,
    92 IN.HIGH........................................2,595.00
MUSIC,BOX,POLYPHON,TABLE MODEL,LEVER WINDS THE INSTRUMENT,
    SCENIC ON LID...................................... 195.00
MUSIC,BOX,POLYPHON,UPRIGHT,BOTTOM CABINET,GINGERBREAD,
    76 IN.HIGH........................................1,995.00
MUSIC,BOX,POLYPHON,UPRIGHT,COIN-OPERATED,PLAYS
    19 5/8-IN.DISCS,3 FT.HIGH.......................... 695.00
MUSIC,BOX,POLYPHON,UPRIGHT,DOUBLE COMB,COIN-OPERATED,
    23 IN.HIGH......................................... 395.00
MUSIC,BOX,POLYPHON,UPRIGHT,DOUBLE COMB,COIN-OPERATED,WALNUT,
    92 IN.HIGH........................................2,295.00
MUSIC,BOX,POLYPHON,UPRIGHT,DOUBLE COMB,WALNUT CASE,
    34 IN.HIGH......................................... 595.00
MUSIC,BOX,POLYPHON,UPRIGHT,MATCHING BASE CABINET,STORAGE,
    WALNUT,89 IN......................................2,295.00
MUSIC,BOX,POLYPHON,UPRIGHT,ON BASE,STORAGE BIN,91 IN.HIGH,
    SIX DISCS.........................................1,495.00
MUSIC,BOX,POLYPHON,UPRIGHT,PLAYS 19 5/8 IN.DISCS,38 IN.HIGH. 669.00
MUSIC,BOX,POLYPHON,WITH BASE,WALNUT,24 1/2 IN.DISCS,6 FT.
    5 IN.HIGH.........................................1,995.00
MUSIC,BOX,POLYPHON,15 8-INCH RECORDS....................... 200.00
MUSIC,BOX,POLYPHONE,PHOTO UNDER LID,TEN 9 1/2-IN.DISCS...... 180.00
MUSIC,BOX,REED ORGAN,12-IN.METAL DISC,EBONY CASE,ATLAS
    ORGANETTE.......................................... 249.00
MUSIC,BOX,REGINA,AUTOMATIC,NO.33,TWELVE 39-IN.DIAMETER METAL
    DISCS.............................................2,600.00
MUSIC,BOX,REGINA,CABINET,18 X 21 X 11 IN., ELEVEN

16-IN.DISCS.......................................... 485.00
MUSIC,BOX,REGINA,CONCERTO ORCHESTRION,BELLS,CYMBALS,DRUMS,
8 FT. 2 IN......................................3,995.00
MUSIC,BOX,REGINA,DISC-CHANGING,20 3/4 IN.DISC,69 IN.HIGH,
12 DISCS.......................................2,995.00
MUSIC,BOX,REGINA,DISC,COMB,MATCHING CABINET,STORAGE,
MAHOGANY,15 1/2 IN.............................1,295.00
MUSIC,BOX,REGINA,MAHOGANY,EIGHTEEN 15 1/2-IN.DISCS.......... 450.00
MUSIC,BOX,REGINA,MAHOGANY,10 DISCS,9 3/4 X 21 1/2 IN....... 575.00
MUSIC,BOX,REGINA,MANDOLIN ORCHESTRA,THREE ROLLS OF POPULAR
NUMBERS........................................2,495.00
MUSIC,BOX,REGINA,NO. 35,DISC-CHANGING,BANJO ATTACHMENT,
12 DISCS.......................................2,495.00
MUSIC,BOX,REGINA,ORCHESTRAL CORONA NO.34,AUTOMATIC DISC
CHANGER........................................2,795.00
MUSIC,BOX,REGINA,ORCHESTRAL,BOTTOM HAS STORAGE BIN,6 FT.
6 IN.HIGH......................................1,995.00
MUSIC,BOX,REGINA STYLE 11,SINGLE COMB,MAHOGANY CASE,CIRCA
1890........................................... 525.00
MUSIC,BOX,REGINA,STYLE 25,UPRIGHT,ORNATE MAHOGANY CASE,
DOUBLE COMB....................................1,595.00
MUSIC,BOX,REGINA,STYLE 34,AUTOMATIC CHANGER,COIN-OPERATED,
OAK CASE.......................................2,295.00
MUSIC,BOX,REGINA,STYLE 34,COMMERCIAL MODEL,ELECTRIFIED......1,295.00
MUSIC,BOX,REGINA,STYLE 34,PIANO ORCHESTRION,STORAGE RACK,
5 FT. 5 IN.....................................2,495.00
MUSIC,BOX,REGINA,STYLE 36,COIN-OPERATED,CHANGER,NEEDS
MAINSPRING WORK................................1,995.00
MUSIC,BOX,REGINA,UPRIGHT MODEL NO.36,AUTOMATIC CHANGER,
12 DISCS.......................................1,900.00
MUSIC,BOX,REGINA,UPRIGHT,DUPLEX STEEL COMBS,ORNATE MAHOGANY
CASE,72 IN.....................................1,995.00
MUSIC,BOX,ROLLER ORGAN,ON FEET,MCTAMMANY ORGANETTE,14 1/2 X
6 IN.TALL...................................... 125.00
MUSIC,BOX,SERAPHONE,ORGAN,PAPER ROLL,20 NOTES,12 IN.HIGH.... 129.00
MUSIC,BOX,SINGING BIRD,ENGRAVED CASE,ENAMEL,LAKE SCENE,
SILVER GILT.................................... 325.00
MUSIC,BOX,SIX TUNES,OUTLINED ON CARD ON LID,MERMOD FRERES,
ST.CROIX....................................... 450.00
MUSIC,BOX,STELLA,PLAYS 17-IN.DISCS,CONSOLE CABINET,30 TUNE
SHEETS......................................... 650.00
MUSIC,BOX,STELLA,15-IN.DISC................................ 350.00
MUSIC,BOX,STELLA,30 DISC................................... 325.00
MUSIC,BOX,SWISS BELL,DANCING DOLLS,MAKER LANGDORFF,GENEVA,
INLAID CASE.................................... 995.00
MUSIC,BOX,SWISS,CHALET,EIGHT TUNES,BOTTLE STORAGE
COMPARTMENT,BREMOND............................ 595.00
MUSIC,BOX,SWISS,COMB,FOUR BELLS,DANCING DOLLS,MAKER
LANGDORFF & FILS............................... 995.00
MUSIC,BOX,SWISS,CYLINDER,BELLS,PLAYS EIGHT TUNES,,CIRCA
1900,18 IN.HIGH................................ 399.00
MUSIC,BOX,SWISS,CYLINDER,EIGHT TUNES,LYRE MOTIF ON LID,
BURLED WOOD TABLE.............................. 795.00
MUSIC,BOX,SWISS,CYLINDER,GEOMETRIC INLAY ON LID,
RECONDITIONED.................................. 450.00
MUSIC,BOX,SWISS,CYLINDER,INTERCHANGEABLE,ON TABLE WITH
STORAGE DRAWER.................................1,295.00
MUSIC,BOX,SWISS,CYLINDER,PLAYS TEN TUNES,FLORAL MOTIF ON
LID,13 IN.HIGH................................. 299.00
MUSIC,BOX,SWISS,CYLINDER,THREE BELLS,BLACK FINISH,PLAYS
EIGHT TUNES.................................... 249.00
MUSIC,BOX,SWISS,CYLINDER,THREE METAL BELLS,BUTTERFLY
STRIKERS,NEEDS WORK............................ 299.00
MUSIC,BOX,SWISS,CYLINDER,ZITHER ATTACHMENT,PLAYS 11 TUNES,
15 IN.HIGH..................................... 450.00
MUSIC,BOX,SYMPHONION,CIGARETTE VENDING MACHINE,GLASS PANEL,
24 IN.HIGH..................................... 595.00
MUSIC,BOX,SYMPHONION,FOR TABLE OR WALL,19 1/8-IN.DISC,
WALNUT,33 IN.HIGH.............................. 995.00
MUSIC,BOX,SYMPHONION,MATCHING CABINET,192 PLAYING TEETH ON
COMB,8 FT......................................2,795.00
MUSIC,BOX,SYMPHONION,SIX COMBS,USES THREE DISCS
SIMULTANEOUSLY,6 FT.HIGH.......................2,495.00
MUSIC,BOX,SYMPHONION,TABLE MODEL,TWO COMBS,INSTRUCTION SHEET
ON LID......................................... 349.00
MUSIC,BOX,SYMPHONION,TWO SOUND CHAMBERS,GINGERBREAD CASE,
4 FT.HIGH...................................... 995.00
MUSIC,BOX,TABLE MODEL,COMB,THREE BELLS,TUNE CARD,INDICATOR,
18 IN.HIGH..................................... 449.00
MUSIC,BOX,TABLE MODEL,REGINA,27 IN.,40 DISCS.............. 850.00
MUSIC,BOX,THREE INTERCHANGEABLE CYLINDERS,MATCHING TABLE,

SWITZERLAND..............................................1,295.00
MUSIC,BOX,TWELVE TUNES,ZITHER ATTACHMENT,SWITZERLAND,1880...   450.00
MUSIC,BOX,TWO OPPOSED MUSIC COMBS,11 5/8-IN.DISC,SYMPHONION,
6 DISCS.................................................   349.00
MUSIC,BOX,UPRIGHT,BASE,24 1/2-IN.DISC,POLYPHON,
6 FT.5 IN.HIGH.........................................2,495.00
MUSIC,BOX,UPRIGHT,DISC,KALLIOPE,BELLS,HOLDER CABINET BASE,
7 FEET TALL............................................1,975.00
MUSIC,BOX,UPRIGHT,STORAGE,COIN SLOT,27 IN.DISC,REGINA,
6 FT.10 IN.HIGH........................................2,295.00
MUSIC,BOX,UPRIGHT,WALNUT,24 1/2-IN.DISC,COIN SLOT,POLYPHON,
92 IN.HIGH.............................................2,295.00
MUSIC,BOX,UPRIGHT,25 1/4-IN.DISC,VISIBLE APPARATUS,
SYMPHONION,6 FT.HIGH...................................1,995.00
MUSIC,BOX,VICTORIA,CYLINDER,BELLS,CLOCK ON TOP,MAKER
B.H.ABRAHAMS...........................................   449.00
MUSIC,BOX,VICTORIA,CYLINDER,UPRIGHT,BELLS,TEN-TUNE
REPERTOIRE,1900........................................   449.00
MUSIC,BOX,WALNUT CABINET,25 1/4-IN.DISC,SYMPHONION,
8 FT.TALL,6 DISCS......................................2,795.00
MUSIC,BOX,WITH ORGAN,INTERCHANGEABLE CYLINDER TYPE,
SWITZERLAND,1880.......................................2,495.00
MUSIC,BOX,ZITHER ATTACHMENT,TUNE SELECTOR,SIX TUNES,BURL
WALNUT CASE............................................   650.00
MUSIC,BOX,10-TUNE CYLINDER.............................   135.00
MUSIC,BOX,12-TUNE CYLINDER,FIVE BELLS.................   375.00
MUSIC,BOX,17-IN.CYLINDER,BELLS,DRUM,CASTANETS.........   635.00
MUSIC,CALLIOPE,53 WHISTLE,NATIONAL,MANUAL OR AUTOMATIC ROLL,
RESTORED...............................................5,750.00
MUSIC,CALLIOPE,COSET,MANUAL,REBUILT,BRASS POLISHED.........1,995.00
MUSIC,CALLIOPE,COSET,MANUAL,45 BRASS PIPES,RESTORED........2,095.00
MUSIC,CALLIOPE,DISC PLAYER,SINGLE COMB,TABLE MODEL,14 DISCS,
9 1/2 IN...............................................   327.00
MUSIC,CALLIOPE,TABLE MODEL,DISC,SINGLE COMB,FOURTEEN
9 1/2-IN.DISCS.........................................   327.00
MUSIC,CASKET,MECHANICAL,ORGUINETTE CO.,CIRCA 1877,ONE
ROLL-FOUR SONGS........................................   150.00
MUSIC,CLARIONA,REED PIPE,PAPER ROLL,14 NOTES,USES 8-IN.-WIDE
PAPER..................................................    79.00
MUSIC,CLOCK,BRACKET,FUSEE MECHANISM,PLAYS SIX AIRS,BELLS,
R.PARSONS..............................................1,000.00
MUSIC,CLOCK,BRACKET,MUSICAL BELLS,CHIMES..............   700.00
MUSIC,CLOCK,BRACKET,RED LACQUER,GEORGE III,EARDLEY NORTON,
LONDON,18 IN...........................................   650.00
MUSIC,CLOCK,CYLINDER MOVEMENT,FIGURINE,SEATED GODDESS,
PORCELAIN FACE.........................................   495.00
MUSIC,CLOCK,FLUTE-PLAYING,ANIMATED FIGURES,UNRESTORED,
93 IN.HIGH.............................................1,495.00
MUSIC,CLOCK,GRANDFATHER,ANIMATED,AUTOMATON FIGURES,SWISS
LAKE SCENE.............................................1,495.00
MUSIC,CLOCK,MATTE GOLD FINISH,FORM OF SEATED GODDESS,
PORCELAIN FACE.........................................   595.00
MUSIC,CLOCK,ORGAN,AUTOMATIC FIGURES,MAKER A.MUKLE,1850,
93 IN.HIGH.............................................2,995.00
MUSIC,CLOCK,ORMOLU,MATTE GOLD FINISH,PULL CORD WINDS TUNE
MOVEMENT...............................................   495.00
MUSIC,COB,FOR CONCERT ROLLER ORGAN....................     5.00
MUSIC,CONCERTINA,MINIATURE ACCORDIAN SHAPE,ROSEWOOD,
MOTHER-OF-PEARL KEYS...................................    28.50
MUSIC,CONCERTINA,PLAYER,TANZBAR,PAPER ROLL,ACCORDION
BELLOWS,CASE...........................................   295.00
MUSIC,CONCERTINA,ROLL-OPERATED,CARRYING CASE,TANZBAR........   395.00
MUSIC,CYLINDERS,FOR EDISON PHONOGRAPH,SIX..............    15.00
MUSIC,DIORAMA,SIX HORSES SPIN AS MOVEMENT PLAYS,
18 IN.SQUARE,8 IN.HIGH.................................   295.00
MUSIC,DISC CHANGER,REGINA,PARLOR MODEL,15 1/2-IN.DISC,NEEDS
GEAR WORK..............................................1,795.00
MUSIC,DISC ORGAN PLAYER,ARITISON,SIX DISCS............   185.00
MUSIC,DISC PLAYER,AUTOMAT,THIRTY-FOUR 17-IN.DISCS,BELLS,
WALL,GLASS DOOR........................................   985.00
MUSIC,DISC PLAYER,AUTOMAT,WALL MODEL,ETCHED GLASS DOOR,
BELLS,34 DISCS.........................................   985.00
MUSIC,DISC PLAYER,POLYPHONE,PHOTO UNDER LID,10 DISCS........   180.00
MUSIC,DISC PLAYER,POLYPHONE,TABLE MODEL,DOUBLE COMB,
REFINISHED.............................................   690.00
MUSIC,DISC PLAYER,POLYPHONE,WALL,COIN,TEN DISCS....595.00 TO   650.00
MUSIC,DISC PLAYER,SYMPHONIOM,COIN-OPERATED,DOUBLE COMB,WALL,
10 DISCS...............................................   650.00
MUSIC,DISC PLAYER,TABLE MODEL,POLYPHONE,DOUBLE COMB,PLAYS
15 1/2-IN.DISC.........................................   690.00
MUSIC,DISC PLAYER,WALL TYPE,POLYPHONE,RESTORED,TEN

```
    19 5/8-IN.DISCS.....................................    700.00
MUSIC,DISC,SYMPHONIOM,TABLE MODEL,REFINISHED,12 DISCS,
    9 1/2 IN...........................................    303.00
MUSIC,DOLL,PHONOGRAPH,MAE STARR,FIVE CYLINDERS.............    115.00
MUSIC,DOUBLE MILLS,PIANO & TWO VIOLINS,VIOLANO-VIRTUOSO,
    5 FT.9 IN.HIGH...................................3,395.00
MUSIC,DRUM,BASS,PARADE TYPE,SLINGERLAND................     50.00
MUSIC,DRUM,CIVIL WAR,RED HOOPS,PAINTED EAGLE,SAYS MAINE
    FIRST CAVALRY......................................    200.00
MUSIC,DULCIMER,BUILT-IN CASE,HAMMERS...................    200.00
MUSIC,GERMAN BEER HALL ORCHESTRATION,AIDA,DRUMS,CYMBALS,
    XYLOPHONE,9 FT...................................2,215.00
MUSIC,GERMAN BEER HALL ORCHESTRATION,FRANKFURT,TWO 10-TUNE
    BARRELS,1860.....................................1,710.00
MUSIC,GERMAN ELDORADO BEER HALL ORCHESTRATION,THREE BARRELS,
    COIN...............................................    990.00
MUSIC,GRAMOPHONE,OVAL TOP OAK CASE,HANDLE,HORN,COLUMBIA,
    8 RECORDS..........................................     85.00
MUSIC,GRANDEZZA,WEBER,PIANO,XYLOPHONE,40 ROLLS.........1,570.00
MUSIC,GUITAR ZITHER,CASE...............................     50.00
MUSIC,HARMONICA,MARINE BAND,1896,N.HOHNER..............     10.00
MUSIC,HARP,AUTOMATIC,WURLITZER,STYLE A,SIX-TUNE ROLL,
    UNRESTORED.......................................2,495.00
MUSIC,HARPSICHORD,PIANO KEYBOARD,CIRCA 1765............1,400.00
MUSIC,HORN FOR EDISON PHONOGRAPH,MORNING GLORY,RED,ROSES
    INSIDE,SCALLOPS....................................     35.00
MUSIC,HORN,GRAPHONE....................................     95.00
MUSIC,HORN,MORNING GLORY,BRASS.........................     45.00
MUSIC,HORN,MORNING GLORY,EDISON,ORIGINAL DECOR.........     35.00
MUSIC,HORN,MORNING GLORY,ON BASE,MAGNOVOX..............     25.00
MUSIC,HURDY-GURDY,CART,AUTOMATIC SELECTOR,TWO ROLLS MUSIC,
    SIX TUNES EACH.....................................    600.00
MUSIC,HURDY-GURDY,TWELVE SONGS,TWO CYLINDERS,ON CART....1,000.00
MUSIC,JENNY JUNE,BY STEPHEN FOSTER,PUBLISHER FIRTH,SONS &
    CO.,1863...........................................      5.00
MUSIC,JUKE BOX,A M I,COIN-OPERATED.....................    100.00
MUSIC,JUKE BOX,COIN-OPERATED,MAPLE,78 RPM RECORDS......    350.00
MUSIC,JUKE BOX,ROCKOLA,COIN-OPERATED...................    100.00
MUSIC,JUKE BOX,WURLITZER,COIN-OPERATED.................    100.00
MUSIC,LIMONAIRE,49 KEYS................................    500.00
MUSIC,LOWRY ORGANO.....................................    250.00
MUSIC,MACHINE,SINGLE VIOLIN,MILLS,COIN-OPERATED,SERIAL
    NO.1831..........................................1,950.00
MUSIC,MANDOLA,GERMAN...................................     75.00
MUSIC,MANDOLIN HARP,KEY,PICK,MALLET,PATENT 1894,WOODEN..     22.50
MUSIC,MANDOLIN,GIBSON,FLAT TYPE........................     40.00
MUSIC,MANDOLIN,GOURD TYPE..............................     40.00
MUSIC,MANDOLIN,MARTIN..................................     35.00
MUSIC,MELODEON,FOLDING LYRE BASE,WALNUT CASE,37 X 20 IN..    110.00
MUSIC,MELODEON,GEHRHARD NEEDHAM,ROSEWOOD CASE..........    265.00
MUSIC,MELODEON,PEARL INLAY,HAND-PAINTED ABOVE KEYBOARD,
    ROSEWOOD,53 IN...................................1,150.00
MUSIC,MILLS VIOLANO,COMPLETELY RESTORED,INSIDE AND OUTSIDE..2,000.00
MUSIC,MUSIC ROLL PUNCH,MAKES STANDARD .069 HOLE FOR EDITING
    OR REPAIR..........................................      8.45
MUSIC,NICKELODEON,10-TUNE PIANO MANDOLIN,DIME SLOT,ART GLASS1,800.00
MUSIC,NICKELODEON,BELGIUM CAFE,COIN-OPERATED,OAK CABINET....    950.00
MUSIC,NICKELODEON,BELGIUM CAFE,10-TUNE CYLINDER,ORNATE
    MIRRORS,CASEWORK...................................    950.00
MUSIC,NICKELODEON,BELGIUM CAFE,10-TUNE CYLINDER........    795.00
MUSIC,NICKELODEON,CAFE,10-TUNE BARREL,FRANCE...........    850.00
MUSIC,NICKELODEON,CAFE,10-TUNE CYLINDER,ORNATE MIRRORS,
    CASEWORK,BELGIUM...................................    950.00
MUSIC,NICKELODEON,CAFE,MIRRORS,CASEWORK,BELGIUM....795.00 TO    950.00
MUSIC,NICKELODEON,EMPRESS,PIANO,MANDOLIN,BELLS,NEEDS WORK,
    56 IN.HIGH.......................................1,995.00
MUSIC,NICKELODEON,LINK/MARCOLA,CABINET STYLE,ART GLASS
    PANELS,UNRESTORED................................3,495.00
MUSIC,NICKELODEON,LINK,STYLE C,ART GLASS FRONT,15-TUNE ROLL,
    FLUTE PIPES......................................3,495.00
MUSIC,NICKELODEON,MANDOLIN ATTACHMENT,OAK,CREMONA,RESTORED,
    3 ROLLS..........................................1,400.00
MUSIC,NICKELODEON,NATIONAL,SELECTOR,DOG RACE,FERRIS WHEEL
    CHANGER..........................................1,600.00
MUSIC,NICKELEODEON,PEERLESS,44 NOTES,ORNATE BEVELED GLASS,
    NEEDS WORK.........................................    895.00
MUSIC,NICKELODEON,PIANO ETCHED MIRRORS,COIN-OPERATED,
    10 TUNE,ITALY......................................    850.00
MUSIC,NICKELODEON,PIANO WITH ROLL CHANGER,NUMBER WHEEL,SLOT,
    NATIONAL.........................................1,495.00
MUSIC,NICKELODEON,PIANO WITH XYLOPHONE,WEBER GRANDEZZA,
```

```
 12 ROLLS.............................................1,895.00
MUSIC,NICKELODEON,PIANO,ETCHED MIRRORS,COIN-OPERATED,
 10 TUNES,FRANCE...................................... 850.00
MUSIC,NICKELODEON,PIANO,MANDOLIN,XYLOPHONE,SEEBURG STYLE E..2,495.00
MUSIC,NICKELODEON,PIANO,NATIONAL,COIN SLOT,ROLL CHANGER,OAK
 CASE................................................1,495.00
MUSIC,NICKELODEON,PIANO,WEBER GRANDEZZA,XYLOPHONE,
 12 MULTITUNE ROLLS.................................1,895.00
MUSIC,NICKELODEON,PIERRE EICH,VIOLIN,PIANO,MANDOLIN,24 ROLLS1,995.00
MUSIC,NICKELODEON,REGINA SUBLIMA....................1,200.00
MUSIC,NICKELODEON,SEEBURG JR.,COIN-OPERATED..........1,495.00
MUSIC,NICKELODEON,SEEBURG K T,UNRESTORED.............2,350.00
MUSIC,NICKELODEON,SEEBURG K T,WITH PIPES,RECONDITIONED......2,750.00
MUSIC,NICKELODEON,SEEBURG,STYLE C,ART GLASS FRONT,OAK CASE,
 57 IN.HIGH.........................................2,495.00
MUSIC,NICKELODEON,SEEBURG,STYLE K,EAGLE ART GLASS,MANDOLIN,
 XYLOPHONE..........................................1,895.00
MUSIC,NICKELODEON,SEEBURG,STYLE L,PIANO,MANDOLIN,UNRESTORED. 995.00
MUSIC,NICKELODEON,WEBER GRANDEZZA,XYLOPHONE,MANDOLIN,OAK
 CASE,74 IN.HIGH....................................1,895.00
MUSIC,NICKELODEON,WESTERN ELECTRIC..................1,450.00
MUSIC,NICKELODEAN,UPRIGHT,REBUILT,REFINISHED,CREMONA.......1,250.00
MUSIC,ORCHESTRAL,REGINA,CORONA,COIN-OPERATED,QUARTERED OAK
 CASE,66 IN.........................................2,995.00
MUSIC,ORCHESTRATION,AIDA,TWO 10-TUNE BARRELS,DRUMS,CYMBALS,
 9 FEET TALL........................................2,215.00
MUSIC,ORCHESTRATION,ELDORADO,THREE BARRELS,XYLOPHONE,COIN,
 GERMANY............................................. 990.00
MUSIC,ORCHESTRATION,PIANO,PIPES,WEBER BRABO,18 ROLLS........1,760.00
MUSIC,ORCHESTRATION,TWO 10-TUNE BARRELS,DRUMS,BELLS,
 FRANKFURT,GERMANY..................................1,710.00
MUSIC,ORCHESTRATION,VIOLIN,XYLOPHONE,PIPES,PIANO,PHILIPPS,
 80 ROLLS...........................................2,495.00
MUSIC,ORCHESTRATION,WEBER BRABO,PIANO PLAYING WITH PIPES,
 18 ROLLS...........................................1,760.00
MUSIC,ORCHESTRION ORGAN,DECAP,BELGIUM,PIPES,ROLLS,TRACKER
 BAR,114 IN.........................................3,900.00
MUSIC,ORCHESTRION,BARREL PIANO,COIN-OPERATED,ITALY.......... 650.00
MUSIC,ORCHESTRION,COINOLA MIDGET,WITH VIOLIN & FLUTE PIPES,
 63 IN.HIGH.........................................2,295.00
MUSIC,ORCHESTRION,DECAP,COIN-OPERATED,MANDOLIN,VIOLIN,
 UNRESTORED.......................................... 995.00
MUSIC,ORCHESTRION,HUPFELD HELIOS,UPRIGHT PIANO,MANDOLIN,
 CELLO,VIOLIN.......................................3,495.00
MUSIC,ORCHESTRION,INTERIOR COMPONENTS VISIBLE,LOSCHE PIANO,
 RESTORED...........................................5,995.00
MUSIC,ORCHESTRION,KUHL & KLATH,NO.34,COIN-OPERATED,
 XYLOPHONE,UNRESTORED................................ 995.00
MUSIC,ORCHESTRION,KUHL & KLATH,PIANO,XYLOPHONE,UNRESTORED... 895.00
MUSIC,ORCHESTRION,NELSON WIGGEN,STYLE 6,CLEAR GLASS FRONT,
 69 IN.HIGH.........................................6,995.00
MUSIC,ORCHESTRION,NELSON WIGGEN,STYLE 8,PIANO,MANDOLIN,
 XYLOPHONE,BELLS....................................3,295.00
MUSIC,ORCHESTRION,ORGAN,DECAP,FLUTES,PICCOLOS,BASS PIPES,
 CYMBAL.............................................3,900.00
MUSIC,ORCHESTRION,PHILLIPS PIANELLA,PIANO,XYLOPHONE,
 UNRESTORED.......................................... 995.00
MUSIC,ORCHESTRION,PHILLIPS,MANDOLIN,XYLOPHONE,UNRESTORED.... 995.00
MUSIC,ORCHESTRION,PIANO,MANDOLIN,XYLOPHONE,KUHL & KLATH,
 GERMANY............................................. 895.00
MUSIC,ORCHESTRION,POPPER,TRAP WORK,CYMBAL,DRUMS,UNRESTORED..1,750.00
MUSIC,ORCHESTRION,SEEBURG,STYLE KT,XYLOPHONE,CASTANETS,
 TRIANGLE,3 ROLLS...................................2,495.00
MUSIC,ORCHESTRION,SEEBURG,STYLE TK CABINET..........ILLUS.2,495.00
MUSIC,ORCHESTRION,WEBER BRABO,WITH ACCORDION,VIOLIN PIPES,
 OAK CASE...........................................3,495.00
MUSIC,ORCHESTRION,WEBER OTERO,PIANO,MANDOLIN,VIOLIN PIPES,
 XYLOPHONE,DRUM.....................................4,995.00
MUSIC,ORCHESTRION,WEBER STYRIA,PIANO,MANDOLIN,VIOLIN,DRUMS,
 11 FEET TALL.......................................5,495.00
MUSIC,ORCHESTRION,WEBER UNIKA,PIANO,XYLOPHONE,UNRESTORED.... 995.00
MUSIC,ORCHESTRION,WURLITZER,ORNATE ART GLASS FRONT,STYLE BX,
 OAK CASE...........................................4,995.00
MUSIC,ORGAN,92 KEYS,MORTIER,DECAP FRONT,RESTORED............8,800.00
MUSIC,ORGAN,153 BANDS,DOUBLE TRACKER,WURLITZER.............5,500.00
MUSIC,ORGAN,BAND,ARIZAN/WURLITZER,STYLE C-1 MILITARY BAND,
 NEEDS WORK.........................................3,495.00
MUSIC,ORGAN,BAND,BRUDER,FAIRGROUND,46 KEYLESS SYSTEM,NEEDS
 WORK...............................................3,495.00
MUSIC,ORGAN,BAND,FAIRGROUND,BRUDER,TROMBONE,DRUM,TRIANGLE,
 75 IN.HIGH.........................................3,995.00
```

SEEBURG ORCHESTRIAN, STYLE TK CABINET

MUSIC,ORGAN,BAND,MOUNTED ON TRAILER.........................3,750.00
MUSIC,ORGAN,BAND,ORNAMENTAL FRONT,GAVIOLI MECHANISM,30 FT.X
  17 FT.HIGH.................................................8,000.00
MUSIC,ORGAN,CAROUSEL,BRUDER,10-TUNE CYLINDER,FRONT NEEDS
  REPAINTING................................................2,050.00
MUSIC,ORGAN,CASPARINI,52 KEYS,PIPES,BOOKS,7 FEET TALL.......3,600.00
MUSIC,ORGAN,CHURCH,FALSE PIPES,SIDE CRANK,MAKER DORALION,
  10 FEET HIGH...............................................  300.00
MUSIC,ORGAN,COIN-OPERATED,JAZZ FLUTES,BASS,VIOLIN,VIOLA,
  DRUMS,BURSENS.............................................4,995.00
MUSIC,ORGAN,CONCERT PLAYER,GLASS FRONT,18 X 12..............  250.00
MUSIC,ORGAN,CONCERT,ROLLER,12 COBS..........................  200.00
MUSIC,ORGAN,DANCE,BURSENS,77 KEYS,CONTINUOUS OPERATION,8 FT.
  7 IN.HIGH.................................................4,995.00
MUSIC,ORGAN,DANCE,DECAP UNIVOX,COMBINES PIPES WITH
  ELECTRONICS,BOOKS.........................................2,600.00
MUSIC,ORGAN,DANCE,MORTIER,101 KEYS,BOOKS,PIPES.............3,995.00
MUSIC,ORGAN,DANCE,MORTIER,84 KEYS,REFINISHED OAK FRONT,
  RESTORED..................................................4,750.00
MUSIC,ORGAN,ENGLISH BARREL,TEN TUNES PER BARREL,STORAGE,
  UNRESTORED................................................  995.00
MUSIC,ORGAN,ENGLISH CHURCH BARREL,PLAYS TEN TUNES,UNRESTORED  595.00
MUSIC,ORGAN,FAIR,LIMONAIRE,BRASS PIPES,DRUMS,20 TUNES,
  RESTORED,REPAINTED........................................2,475.00
MUSIC,ORGAN,FAIR,TABLETOP,ORNATE,BOOK-OPERATED..............  895.00
MUSIC,ORGAN,FAIR,WELLERHAUSE,55 KEYS,750 FEET BOOK MUSIC,
  CARVED,PAINTING...........................................5,750.00
MUSIC,ORGAN,FAIR,52 KEYS,CASPARINI,BOOKS,PIPES,7 FEET TALL..3,600.00
MUSIC,ORGAN,FAIR,57 KEYS,GAVIOLI,ORNATE OPEN FRONT,BOOK
  MUSIC SELECTION...........................................3,250.00
MUSIC,ORGAN,FAIRGROUND,LIMONAIRE,FLUTE,VIOLIN,BASS,NEEDS
  RESTORING.................................................2,995.00
MUSIC,ORGAN,GAVIOLI,57 KEYS,ORNATE OPEN FRONT,BOOK MUSIC....3,250.00
MUSIC,ORGAN,GRINDER,CART,BAGICALUPO,TWO BARRELS,WITH THREE
  EXTRA TUNES...............................................1,500.00
MUSIC,ORGAN,HAND CRANK,CASE,ORGUINETTE,PLAYS,SHOULD BE
  REBUILT,4 ROLLS...........................................   90.00
MUSIC,ORGAN,HAND,SYMPHONIA,WILCOX-WHITE,REBUILT.............  250.00
MUSIC,ORGAN,HURDY-GURDY,CRANK HANDLE,TWO CYLINDERS,CARRYING
  CASE......................................................  995.00
MUSIC,ORGAN,LIMONAIRE,BRASS PIPES,DRUMS,RESTORED,REPAINTED..2,475.00
MUSIC,ORGAN,LIMONAIRE,FIFTY-KEY SIZE,GOLD LETTERING,MUSIC
  BOOKS.....................................................3,900.00
MUSIC,ORGAN,MILITARY BAND,HERSHELL SPILLMAN,13 BRASS PIPES,
  REBUILT...................................................3,000.00
MUSIC,ORGAN,MORTIER,81 KEYS,CARVED,PAINTED,ORNATE,RESTORED,
  11 FEET HIGH..............................................7,000.00
MUSIC,ORGAN,MORTIER,92 KEYS,DECAP FRONT,RESTORED & REPAINTED
  IN EUROPE.................................................8,800.00
MUSIC,ORGAN,PLAYER,AEOLIAN,707 PIPES,13 RANKS,RESTORED,
  200 ROLLS.................................................8,000.00
MUSIC,ORGAN,PLAYER,HAMMOND,SIDE SPEAKER CHEST,70 ROLLS......2,500.00
MUSIC,ORGAN,PLAYER,TWENTY-TWO STOPS,9 3/8-IN.PAPER ROLLS,
  WILCOX-WHITE..............................................  495.00

```
MUSIC,ORGAN,PUMP,KIMBALL,WALNUT.............................   250.00
MUSIC,ORGAN,PUMP,PORTABLE,FOLDS,ROSEWOOD CASE,30 IN.LONG,
   30 IN.HIGH.................................................   165.00
MUSIC,ORGAN,ROLLER,LARGE CASE,CHAUTAUGA,11 ROLLS.............   200.00
MUSIC,ORGAN,ROLLER,WOODEN COB,20 METAL REEDS,PAPER LABEL,
   13 IN.HIGH.................................................   179.00
MUSIC,ORGAN,ROLLER,WOODEN COB,20 REEDS,REBUILT,12 IN.HIGH...   149.00
MUSIC,ORGAN,SAX,ACCORDIAN,DRUMS,PIPES,84 KEYS,MORTIER.......3,000.00
MUSIC,ORGAN,SPINET,MASON & HAMLIN,1870......................   600.00
MUSIC,ORGAN,TABLETOP,ORNATE,BOOK-OPERATED...................   895.00
MUSIC,ORGAN,WELLERHAUSE,53 KEYS,ORNATE FRONT,130 YARDS BOOK
   MUSIC....................................................3,550.00
MUSIC,ORGAN,WELLERHAUSE,55 KEYS,CARVINGS,PAINTINGS,REBUILT..5,750.00
MUSIC,ORGANETTE,PAPER STRIP,14-NOTE SCALE,REBUILT...........   139.00
MUSIC,ORGUINETTE,PAPER ROLL,14 REEDS,CRANK,MECHANICAL
   ORGUINETTE CO.............................................   119.00
MUSIC,PERFORATOR,ROBOTYPE,UP TO 9 1/2 IN.PAPER..............   200.00


   THE PHONOGRAPH,INVENTED BY THOMAS EDISON IN THE
   1880S,HAS BEEN MADE BY MANY FIRMS.
MUSIC,PHONOGRAPH,AUTOMATIC,MULTIPHONE,HOLDS 24 CYLINDERS,
   1910....................................................1,995.00
MUSIC,PHONOGRAPH,COLUMBIA,KEYWIND...........................    45.00
MUSIC,PHONOGRAPH,COMBINATION MACHINE,MODEL K,EDISON,
   25 RECORDS................................................   250.00
MUSIC,PHONOGRAPH,CONSOLE MODEL,EDISON,1904..................   150.00
MUSIC,PHONOGRAPH,CONSOLE,CYLINDER,EDISON,BUILT-IN HORN,
   36 IN.HIGH.................................................    85.00
MUSIC,PHONOGRAPH,CYLINDER,COLUMBIA..........................    90.00
MUSIC,PHONOGRAPH,CYLINDER,CONSOLE STYLE,RECORDS.............   125.00
MUSIC,PHONOGRAPH,CYLINDER,EDISON,HORN.......................   135.00
MUSIC,PHONOGRAPH,CYLINDER,EDISON,METAL HORN,BRASS RIM.......   125.00
MUSIC,PHONOGRAPH,CYLINDER,EDISON,MORNING GLORY HORN,
   18 RECORDS................................................    95.00
MUSIC,PHONOGRAPH,CYLINDER,HORN,EDISON,RECORDS...............   145.00
MUSIC,PHONOGRAPH,DOLL,MAE STARR,SIX CYLINDERS,30 IN.........   110.00
MUSIC,PHONOGRAPH,EDISON AMBEROLA............................    17.00
MUSIC,PHONOGRAPH,EDISON AMBEROLA,CYLINDER,MODEL 30..........    75.00
MUSIC,PHONOGRAPH,EDISON GEM,HORN............................   125.00
MUSIC,PHONOGRAPH,EDISON,1904,CONSOLE........................   150.00
MUSIC,PHONOGRAPH,EDISON,CYLINDER,MORNING-GLORY HORN,
   20 RECORDS................................................   135.00
MUSIC,PHONOGRAPH,EDISON,HORN,8 RECORDS......................   125.00
MUSIC,PHONOGRAPH,EDISON,INSIDE HORN,AMBEROLA,30 CYLINDER
   RECORDS...................................................   150.00
MUSIC,PHONOGRAPH,EDISON,STAND,BRASS HORN,25 CYLINDER RECORDS   115.00
MUSIC,PHONOGRAPH,ELECTRIC CYLINDER,OUTSIDE HORN,OAK CABINET,
   ALVA......................................................   850.00
MUSIC,PHONOGRAPH,FLOWER HORN,EDISON,12 RECORDS..............    89.00
MUSIC,PHONOGRAPH,HORN,EIGHT CYLINDERS,EDISON................   125.00
MUSIC,PHONOGRAPH,MODERNOLA,ROUND,FLOOR,LEADED GLASS GRAPE
   SHADE,1911................................................   375.00
MUSIC,PHONOGRAPH,PORTABLE,LOOKS LIKE BOX-TYPE CAMERA,WINDUP,
   4 X 6 IN..................................................    75.00
MUSIC,PHONOGRAPH,PORTABLE,VICTROLA NO.2,VICTOR TALKING
   MACHINE CO.,1906..........................................    35.00
MUSIC,PHONOGRAPH,SMALL HORN,EDISON STANDARD.................   100.00
MUSIC,PHONOGRAPH,TABLE,CYLINDER,EDISON,OAK CASE,BUILT-IN
   HORN......................................................    65.00
MUSIC,PHONOGRAPH,VICTOR MODEL E,HORN,REPRODUCER CONTAINER...   145.00
MUSIC,PHONOGRAPH,VICTOR MODEL VV-IV,OAK CASE,1904,12 X
   14 IN.....................................................    18.00
MUSIC,PHONOGRAPH,VICTOR,TABLE MODEL,INSIDE HORN,1915........    20.00
MUSIC,PHONOGRAPH,VICTROLA,CABINET,ELECTRIFIED...............    25.00
MUSIC,PHONOGRAPH,30 MODEL,FIVE CYLINDERS,EDISON.............    95.00
MUSIC,PIANINO,10 ROLLS,WURLITZER..........................1,250.00
MUSIC,PIANO & CART,STREET,10 TUNES ON BARREL................   362.00
MUSIC,PIANO ROLL,WILLIAM TELL,FOLLIES OF 1913,MARCHES,15....    10.00
MUSIC,PIANO ROLL,20......................................        36.00
MUSIC,PIANO WITH XYLOPHONE,WEBER GRANDEZZA,40 ROLLS........1,570.00
MUSIC,PIANO,BARREL,COIN-OPERATED,ENGLAND....................   400.00
MUSIC,PIANO,BARREL,COIN-OPERATED,XYLOPHONE..................   495.00
MUSIC,PIANO,CONCERT GRAND,ROSEWOOD,STEINWAY,78 IN.LONG.....1,000.00
MUSIC,PIANO,CONSOLE,ELECTRIC ORGAN COMBINATION,HANSON.......   650.00
MUSIC,PIANO,DIENSTS MEZON,BURLED WALNUT,CARVINGS............   725.00
MUSIC,PIANO,EMPIRE STYLE,UPRIGHT,MAHOGANY,HENRI HERZ,PARIS,
   47 IN.HIGH..............................................1,200.00
MUSIC,PIANO,GRAND,ANDREAS CHRISTENSEN,DENMARK,RESTORED,NOT A
   SELF PLAYER.............................................1,350.00
MUSIC,PIANO,GRAND,HAND-CARVED CASE,CABRIOLE LEGS,WEBER,1884,
```

```
REBUILT...................................................3,500.00
MUSIC,PIANO,GRAND,PLAYER,AMPICO,CHICKERING STYLE B..........2,495.00
MUSIC,PIANO,GRAND,PLAYER,FRANKLIN AMPICO,MAHOGANY,CABINET,
  110 ROLLS...............................................1,000.00
MUSIC,PIANO,GRAND,PLAYER,MODEL A,J.C.FISCHER,REBUILT,BENCH,
  25 ROLLS................................................1,995.00
MUSIC,PIANO,GRAND,REPRODUCING,BLUNTHNER WELTE,FIFTY 98 HOLE
  ROLLS..................................................1,950.00
MUSIC,PIANO,GRAND,SQUARE,ROSEWOOD,WEBER,RESTORED & RESTRUNG,
  1865....................................................  400.00
MUSIC,PIANO,GRAND,SQUARE,STEINWAY,NO.3237,CIRCA 1863,STOOL..2,300.00
MUSIC,PIANO,ITALIAN STREET,10-TUNE BARREL,UNRESTORED........  650.00
MUSIC,PIANO,KEYBOARD ORCHESTRION,VISIBLE BELLS,HUPFELD
  HELIOS.................................................3,495.00
MUSIC,PIANO,KUHL & KLATZ,50 ROLLS..........................  995.00
MUSIC,PIANO,KUHL & KLATZ,COIN-OPERATED,ELECTRIC 88 NOTE,TEN
  4 TUNE ROLLS...........................................  560.00
MUSIC,PIANO,KUHL & KLATZ,30 ROLLS..........................  875.00
MUSIC,PIANO,MECHANICAL,REGINA,ORCHESTRA,MANDOLIN,STYLE 304,
  1919...................................................2,495.00
MUSIC,PIANO,ORCHESTRATION,PHILIPPS,DRUMS,XYLOPHONE,CARVED &
  MIRROR FRONT...........................................2,890.00
MUSIC,PIANO,PAINTING ON BACK,44 IN.TALL,BENCH,CIRCA 1918....  495.00
MUSIC,PIANO,PLAYER WITH XYLOPHONE,MANDOLIN ATTACHMENT,WEBER
  GRANDEZZA..............................................1,895.00
MUSIC,PIANO,PLAYER,BABY GRAND,AMPICO,WILLIAM KNABE..........1,250.00
MUSIC,PIANO,PLAYER,BRASTED,ELECTRIC,88 NOTES,75 ROLLS.......  565.00
MUSIC,PIANO,PLAYER,CHICKERING,STYLE B,AMPICO,GRAND,12 ROLLS.2,495.00
MUSIC,PIANO,PLAYER,DIENSTS MEZON,CARVINGS,BURLED WALNUT.....  725.00
MUSIC,PIANO,PLAYER,ELECTRIC................................  300.00
MUSIC,PIANO,PLAYER,ELECTRIC OR FOOT PEDAL,BENCH,W.W.KIMBAL,
  40 ROLLS...............................................  395.00
MUSIC,PIANO,PLAYER,FOOT OPERATED...........................  200.00
MUSIC,PIANO,PLAYER,GERVAERT,BRUSSELS,ELECTRIC,COIN-OPERATED,
  100 ROLLS..............................................  540.00
MUSIC,PIANO,PLAYER,GRAND,AMPICO,5 FT.6 IN.,100 ROLLS.......3,500.00
MUSIC,PIANO,PLAYER,HOBART M.CABLE,RECONDITIONED,WITH
  400 ROLLS..............................................  650.00
MUSIC,PIANO,PLAYER,KOHLER CAMPBELL.........................  450.00
MUSIC,PIANO,PLAYER,LUCIEN ORR,50 ROLLS,BRASS CANDLEHOLDERS..  795.00
MUSIC,PIANO,PLAYER,MARSHALL & WENDELL,AMPICO ACTION,
  RESTORED,25 ROLLS......................................  650.00
MUSIC,PIANO,PLAYER,ORGAN REEDS,PUSH-UP,WILCOX & WHITE
  VORSETZER,50 ROLLS.....................................  410.00
MUSIC,PIANO,PLAYER,PHILIPPS-FEURICH,35 ROLLS...............  560.00
MUSIC,PIANO,PLAYER,UPRIGHT,JACOB BROS.,MANDOLIN ATTACHMENT,
  RESTORED...............................................  700.00
MUSIC,PIANO,REPRODUCING,HUPFELD PHONOLA,TAKES 73-NOTE ROLLS,
  50 ROLLS...............................................  575.00
MUSIC,PIANO,REPRODUCING,UPRIGHT,HUPFIELD,RESTORED,50 ROLLS..  770.00
MUSIC,PIANO,ROLL CHANGING,COIN SLOTS,TUNE SELECTOR,NATIONAL.1,495.00
MUSIC,PIANO,STEINWAY,GRAND,XO PLAYER,DUO-ART,NEW TUBING,
  10 ROLLS...............................................3,800.00
MUSIC,PIANO,STREET,CART,10 TUNES ON BARREL.................  362.00
MUSIC,PIANO,STREET,SPANISH,CART WITH DONKEY & MAN,TWO ROLLS.  850.00
MUSIC,PIANO,UPRIGHT,PLAYER,ROLLS,MARSHALL & WENDELL.........1,050.00
MUSIC,PIANOLA,PUSH-UP PLAYER FOR PIANO,75 ROLLS............  225.00
MUSIC,PLAYER,DISC,POLYPHONE,WALL TYPE,10 DISCS,RESTORED,
  19 5/8 IN..............................................  700.00
MUSIC,PLAYER,DISC,UPRIGHT,KOMET,STORAGE IN BASE,DOUBLE COMB,
  BELLS,9 FEET...........................................1,825.00
MUSIC,PLAYER,HUPFELD,PUSH-UP,25 ROLLS......................  310.00
MUSIC,PLAYER,PUSH-UP,AEOLIAN VOERSETZER,RESTORED,50 MUSIC
  ROLLS..................................................  200.00
MUSIC,PLAYER,UPRIGHT,DISC,KOMET,STORAGE CABINET BASE,
  REFINISHED,9 FT........................................1,825.00
MUSIC,POLYPHON,6-IN.DISCS..................................  165.00
MUSIC,PRAXINOSCOPE,PICTURES MOUNTED ON CAROUSEL MOVE & MUSIC
  PLAYS..................................................1,295.00
MUSIC,PUSH UP-PLAYER & ORGAN REEDS,WILCOX & WHITE VORSETZER,
  50 ROLLS...............................................  410.00
MUSIC,R C A VICTROLA DOG...................................   25.00
MUSIC,RADIO SPEAKER,OUTSIDE................................   15.00
MUSIC,RADIO,CHAIRSIDE,REFINISHED,1930 MODEL,ZENITH.........  195.00
MUSIC,RADIO,CRYSTAL SET,EARPHONES,IN WOODEN BOX............   12.00
MUSIC,RADIO,CRYSTAL,DE FOREST REFLEX D-10,EARPHONES,ANTENNA,
  PATENT 1908............................................  150.00
MUSIC,RADIO,CRYSTAL,PHILMORE...............................    4.00
MUSIC,RADIOLA,TABLE MODEL,WOODEN CABINET,SPEAKER,R C A......   50.00
MUSIC,RECORD,CYLINDER......................................    1.00
MUSIC,RECORD,CYLINDER,EDISON...............................    2.00
```

MUSIC,RECORD,ONE-SIDED........................................ 1.25
MUSIC,REGINA NO.11,DUPLEX.............................ILLUS.. 400.00
MUSIC,REGINAPHONE,STYLE 240,STOP & START LEVER,NEEDS HORN
    WORK..................................................... 995.00
MUSIC,REPRODUCER,EDISON,MODEL C,MODEL H,BOTH.................. 25.00
MUSIC,REPRODUCER,UPRIGHT,APOLLO,200 RED-X ROLLS,50 REGULARS,
    ROLL CABINET............................................. 650.00
MUSIC,ROLL,PAPER,ROLMONICA,3 1/4 IN.LONG,8................... 10.00
MUSIC,ROLMONICA CHROMATIC PLAYER,BAKELITE,FOUR ROLLS........ 10.00
MUSIC,SEASCAPE,MEDITERRANEAN,SHIP ROCKS AS TUNE PLAYS,GLASS
    DOME..................................................... 595.00
MUSIC,SEEBURG REPRODUCO,REBUILT,CONVERTED TO A ROLLS,
    REFINISHED..........................................1,750.00
MUSIC,SHEET,A DIALOGUE OF PEACE,PUBLISHER BRADFORD,

REGINA MUSIC BOX

    PHILADELPHIA............................................. 50.00
MUSIC,SHEET,A DIRGE OR SEPULCHRAL SERVICE,PUBLISHER
    O.HOLDEN,BOSTON.......................................... 50.00
MUSIC,SHEET,ABSENCE MAKE THE HEART GROW FONDER,1900......... 1.00
MUSIC,SHEET,ACQUISITION OF LOUISIANA,WILLIG,PHILADELPHIA,
    PRIOR 1826............................................... 15.00
MUSIC,SHEET,ACTIONS SPEAK LOUDER THAN WORDS,1891............ 1.00
MUSIC,SHEET,ADAMS & LIBERTY,WORDS & MUSIC,PRIOR 1800........ 15.00
MUSIC,SHEET,ADAMS MARCH,MUSIC,BOSTON,PUBLISHER VON HAGEN,
    PRIOR 1800............................................... 10.00
MUSIC,SHEET,AFTER THE BALL,WITHOUT AN ILLUSTRATION ON COVER,
    1892..................................................... 2.00
MUSIC,SHEET,AL FRESCO,WITH AN ILLUSTRATED COVER,1904........ 2.00
MUSIC,SHEET,ALICE BLUE GOWN,1919........................... 1.00
MUSIC,SHEET,ALKNOMOOK,WORDS & MUSIC,PUBLISHER GILFERT,NEW
    YORK..................................................... 15.00
MUSIC,SHEET,ALL ON ACCOUNT OF ELIZA,1910................... 2.00
MUSIC,SHEET,ALOHA,1909..................................... 2.00
MUSIC,SHEET,AMERICA & BRITTANIA PEACE,PUBLISHER WILLIG,
    PHILADELPHIA............................................. 50.00
MUSIC,SHEET,AMERICAN CAPTIVES EMANCIPATION,WILLIG,PHILA.,
    PRIOR 1826............................................... 15.00
MUSIC,SHEET,AMERICAN STAMP POLKA,PUBLISHER WM.A.POND & CO.,
    N.Y.,1864................................................ 50.00
MUSIC,SHEET,AMERICAN,COMMERCE & FREEDOM,PUBLISHER,B.CARR,
    PHILADELPHIA............................................. 25.00
MUSIC,SHEET,AN ODE FOR THE WASHINGTON BENEVOLENT SOCIETY,
    HILL,PRIOR 1826.......................................... 25.00
MUSIC,SHEET,ARISE,ARISE,COLUMBIA,WILLIG,PHILADELPHIA,PRIOR
    1826..................................................... 20.00
MUSIC,SHEET,AROUSE,AROUSE,COLUMBIA'S SONS AROUSE,GRAUPNER,
    PRIOR 1826............................................... 15.00
MUSIC,SHEET,BANJO SONG,WORDS & MUSIC,GEIB,NEW YORK,PRIOR
    1826..................................................... 20.00
MUSIC,SHEET,BATTLE OF LAKE CHAMPLAIN & PLATTSBURG,NASH,PRIOR
    1826..................................................... 50.00
MUSIC,SHEET,BATTLE OF THE WABASH,PUBLISHER BLAKE,PHILA.,
    PRIOR 1826............................................... 25.00
MUSIC,SHEET,BEAUTIFUL DREAMER,COVER READS THE LAST SONG
    WRITTEN,1864............................................. 10.00
MUSIC,SHEET,BECAUSE,1895................................... 1.00

```
MUSIC,SHEET,BIRD IN A GILDED CAGE,1904.....................    2.00
MUSIC,SHEET,BIRTHDAY OF WASHINGTON,PUBLISHER BACON & HART,
   PRIOR 1826.............................................   25.00
MUSIC,SHEET,BRING MY BROTHER BACK TO ME,PUBLISHER
   S.T.GORDON,1863........................................    3.00
MUSIC,SHEET,BROTHER SOLDIERS ALL HAIL,PUBLISHER B.CARR,
   PHILADELPHIA...........................................   50.00
MUSIC,SHEET,CAISSONS GO ROLLING ALONG,1918................    1.00
MUSIC,SHEET,CAMPTOWN RACES,PUBLISHED BY F.T.BENTEEN,1850...    5.00
MUSIC,SHEET,CAPT.TRUXTON OR HUZZA FOR THE CONSTITUTION,
   PUBLISHER HEWITT.......................................   25.00
MUSIC,SHEET,CHORUS SUNG BEFORE GENERAL WASHINGTON,PUBLISHER
   H.RICE................................................  100.00
MUSIC,SHEET,COLUMBIA & LIBERTY,ANY PUBLISHER,PRIOR 1800....   50.00
MUSIC,SHEET,COLUMBIA LAND OF LIBERTY,PUBLISHER GRAUPNER,
   PRIOR 1826.............................................   15.00
MUSIC,SHEET,COMRADES FILL NO GLASS FOR ME,PUBLISHER MILLER &
   BEACHAM................................................    3.00
MUSIC,SHEET,DEAD MARCH & MONODY,PUBLISHER B.CARR,
   PHILADELPHIA...........................................   50.00
MUSIC,SHEET,FIGHTING FOR THE FLAG DAY & NIGHT,BY STEPHEN
   COLLINS FOSTER.........................................   15.00
MUSIC,SHEET,FOR THE DEAR OLD FLAG I DIE,PUBLISHER H.WATERS,
   N.Y.,1863..............................................    5.00
MUSIC,SHEET,FRANKIE & JOHNNY,1896.........................    2.00
MUSIC,SHEET,FREEDOM TRIUMPHANT,WORDS & MUSIC,ANY PUBLISHER..   50.00
MUSIC,SHEET,FUNERAL ELEGY,PUBLISHER THOMAS & ANDREWS,BOSTON.   50.00
MUSIC,SHEET,GIVE THE STRANGER HAPPY CHEER,PUBLISHER
   F.D.BENTEEN,1851.......................................    5.00
MUSIC,SHEET,GIVE THIS TO MOTHER,BY STEPHEN C.FOSTER,
   WUNDERMANN,N.Y.........................................    3.00
MUSIC,SHEET,GOOD BYE MY LADY LOVE,1904....................    1.00
MUSIC,SHEET,GREAT BABY SHOW,BY STEPHEN COLLINS FOSTER......   25.00
MUSIC,SHEET,HAIL LIBERTY,PUBLISHER B.CARR,PHILADELPHIA,PRIOR
   1800...................................................   50.00
MUSIC,SHEET,HAIL PATRIOTS ALL,PUBLISHER GILFERT,NEW YORK,
   PRIOR 1800.............................................   50.00
MUSIC,SHEET,HAIL,HAIL THE GANG'S ALL HERE,1917............    2.00
MUSIC,SHEET,HAPPY DAYS ARE HERE AGAIN,1929................    1.00
MUSIC,SHEET,HAPPY HOURS AT HOME,BY STEPHEN FOSTER,DALY,N.Y.,
   1862...................................................    5.00
MUSIC,SHEET,HEAVEN WILL PROTECT THE WORKING GIRL,1909.......    2.00
MUSIC,SHEET,HONEST OLD ABE,PUBLISHER BLODGETT & BRADFORD,
   BUFFALO................................................   10.00
MUSIC,SHEET,HOT TIME IN THE OLD TOWN TONIGHT,1896..........    2.00
MUSIC,SHEET,I AIN'T GOT NOBODY,1916.......................    1.00
MUSIC,SHEET,I'LL BE A SOLDIER,STEPHEN FOSTER,DALY,N.Y.,1861.    5.00
MUSIC,SHEET,I'LL BE HOME TOMORROW,BY STEPHEN FOSTER,FIRTH,
   POND & CO..............................................    5.00
MUSIC,SHEET,I'LL TAKE YOU HOME AGAIN,KATHLEEN,1876..........    2.00
MUSIC,SHEET,I'M JUST WILD ABOUT HARRY,1921................    1.00
MUSIC,SHEET,I'VE BEEN WORKING ON THE RAILROAD,1894..........    2.00
MUSIC,SHEET,ILLUSTRATION,ANY PUBLISHER,PRIOR 1800.............   25.00
MUSIC,SHEET,INDEPENDENT & FREE,PUBLISHER B.CARR,
   PHILADELPHIA,PRIOR 1800................................   50.00
MUSIC,SHEET,LAST ROUND-UP,1933............................    1.00
MUSIC,SHEET,LET ME CALL YOU SWEETHEART,1910...............    1.00
MUSIC,SHEET,LIBERTY'S THRONE,PUBLISHER J.& M.PAFF,NEW YORK,
   PRIOR 1800.............................................   50.00
MUSIC,SHEET,LITTLE BROWN JUG,1880.........................    2.00
MUSIC,SHEET,MANSION OF PEACE,PUBLISHER WILLIG,PHILADELPHIA,
   PRIOR 1800.............................................   50.00
MUSIC,SHEET,MASSA GEORGE WASHINGTON & GENERAL LAFAYETTE,
   RILEY,N.Y..............................................  100.00
MUSIC,SHEET,MOTHER PIN A ROSE ON ME,1905..................    1.00
MUSIC,SHEET,MY PONY BOY,1909..............................    1.00
MUSIC,SHEET,NEGRO PHILOSOPHY,PUBLISHER HEWITT,NEW YORK,PRIOR
   1800...................................................   25.00
MUSIC,SHEET,NEW PATRIOTIC SONG,PUBLISHER HEWITT,NEW YORK,
   PRIOR 1800.............................................   50.00
MUSIC,SHEET,OH YOU BEAUTIFUL DOLL,1911....................    1.00
MUSIC,SHEET,OH,DEM GOLDEN SLIPPERS,1879...................    2.00
MUSIC,SHEET,OH,JOHNNY,OH JOHNNY OH,1917...................    1.00
MUSIC,SHEET,OH,SUSANNA,FOSTER'S NAME NOT SHOWN,PUBLISHER,
   C.HOLT,JR.,1848........................................   50.00
MUSIC,SHEET,OLD BLACK JOE,PRICE ON COVER IS 2 1/2,FIRTH,POND
   & CO.,1860.............................................   10.00
MUSIC,SHEET,OLD FOLKS AT HOME,FOSTER'S NAME NOT ON TITLE
   PAGE,1853..............................................   15.00
MUSIC,SHEET,OUR COUNTRY IS OUR SHIP,PUBLISHER GILFERT,N.Y.,
   PRIOR 1800.............................................   50.00
```

MUSIC,SHEET,PRESIDENT'S MARCH,ILLUSTRATION,ANY PUBLISHER,
  PRIOR 1800...................................................  25.00
MUSIC,SHEET,PUT ON YOUR OLD GREY BONNETT,1909...............   2.00
MUSIC,SHEET,PUT YOUR ARMS AROUND ME HONEY,1910..............   1.00
MUSIC,SHEET,RAMBLING WRECK FROM GEORGIA TECH,1919...........   1.00
MUSIC,SHEET,RISE COLUMBIA,PUBLISHER VON HAGEN,BOSTON,PRIOR
  1800.......................................................  25.00
MUSIC,SHEET,RULE NEW ENGLAND,PUBLISHER GILFERT,NEW YORK,
  PRIOR 1800.................................................  50.00
MUSIC,SHEET,SEMPER FIDELIS,1893.............................   2.00
MUSIC,SHEET,SEVEN SONGS FOR THE HARPSICHORD,PUBLISHER
  AITKEN,PRIOR 1800.......................................... 100.00
MUSIC,SHEET,SHAKER HYMNS,TWO SHEETS,5 1/2 IN. X 9 IN........   6.50
MUSIC,SHEET,SIDEWALKS OF NEW YORK,1894......................   1.00
MUSIC,SHEET,STAR-SPANGLED BANNER,PUBLISHED BY CARR'S MUSIC
  STORE,1814..............................................1,500.00
MUSIC,SHEET,STRIKE UP THE BAND HERE COMES A SAILOR,1900.....   2.00
MUSIC,SHEET,SWEET ADELINE,1903..............................   1.00
MUSIC,SHEET,SWEET ROSY O'GRADY,1896.........................   1.00
MUSIC,SHEET,SWEETHEART OF SIGMA CHI,1912....................   1.00
MUSIC,SHEET,SYLVIA,1914.....................................   1.00
MUSIC,SHEET,THE AMERICAN SOLDIER,PUBLISHER WILLIG,
  PHILADELPHIA..............................................  25.00
MUSIC,SHEET,THE AMERICAN TAR,PUBLISHER R.TAYLOR,PHILADELPHIA  50.00
MUSIC,SHEET,THE BAND PLAYED ON,1896.........................   2.00
MUSIC,SHEET,THE BATTLE OF TRENTON,PUBLISHER HEWITT,NEW YORK. 100.00
MUSIC,SHEET,THE CONSTITUTION OR LIBERTY FOREVER,PUBLISHER
  B.CARR.,PHILA.............................................  50.00
MUSIC,SHEET,THE DESPONDING NEGRO,PUBLISHER B.CARR,
  PHILADELPHIA..............................................  25.00
MUSIC,SHEET,THE FEDERAL OVERTURE,PUBLISHER B.CARR,
  PHILADELPHIA..............................................  50.00
MUSIC,SHEET,THE GREEN MOUNTAIN FARMER,PUBLISHER HEWITT,NEW
  YORK......................................................  25.00
MUSIC,SHEET,THE LIBERTY SONG,PUBLISHED BY MEIN & FLEEMING,
  BOSTON,1768.............................................2,000.00
MUSIC,SHEET,THE MIDSHIPMAN,PUBLISHER VON HAGEN,BOSTON,PRIOR
  1800.......................................................  25.00
MUSIC,SHEET,TO ARMS COLUMBIA,PUBLISHER B.CARR,PHILADELPHIA,
  PRIOR 1800.................................................  50.00
MUSIC,SHEET,TRUXTON'S VICTORY,PUBLISHER THOMAS & ANDREWS,
  PRIOR 1800.................................................  50.00
MUSIC,SHEET,WASHINGTON & INDEPENDENCE,PUBLISHER GILFERT,
  PRIOR 1800................................................. 100.00
MUSIC,SHEET,WASHINGTON GUARDS,PUBLISHER WILLIG,PHILADELPHIA,
  PRIOR 1800................................................. 100.00
MUSIC,SHEET,WILLARD'S ONE-STEP MADE JOHNSON HESITATE........   7.50
MUSIC,SHEET,YANKEE DOODLE,WORDS & MUSIC,ANY EDITION PRIOR
  1800.......................................................  25.00
MUSIC,SOLOPHONE,ART GLASS,BEVELED MIRRORS,102 PIPES,VIOLIN,
  SAXOPHONE...............................................3,750.00
MUSIC,STAND,CHERUB WITH VIOLIN,BIRDCAGE,DOLPHIN,BRONZE
  FINISH,ROCOCO.............................................  47.50
MUSIC,STAND,HAND-CARVED BEARS,TWO HAVE MUSICAL MOVEMENTS,ONE
  ON PEDESTAL............................................... 495.00
MUSIC,STAND,SCROLL MOTIF,URN FINIAL,TRIANGULAR BASE,BUN
  FEET,MAHOGANY............................................. 275.00
MUSIC,SYMPHONION,TABLE MODEL,TWELVE 9 1/2-IN.DISCS.......... 303.00
MUSIC,SYMPHONION,UPRIGHT,19 1/8-IN.DISCS.................... 575.00
MUSIC,TABLE,CYLINDER,TUNE CARD,12 TUNES,BLACK ENAMEL,DOUBLE
  MAINSPRING................................................ 700.00
MUSIC,TALKING MACHINE,OUTSIDE HORN,STANDARD.................  75.00
MUSIC,THE VOCAL MAGAZINE,PHILADELPHIA,1783..................  50.00
MUSIC,THEATRE ORCHESTRA,CREMONA,STYLE M3,PHOTOPLAYER,5 X
  14 FEET HIGH............................................7,995.00
MUSIC,UKELIN,32 STRINGS,BOW,BOX.............................  25.00
MUSIC,VICTROLA,FLOOR MODEL,EDISON,PLAYS DISC-TYPE RECORDS...  30.00
MUSIC,VICTROLA,OUTSIDE HORN,1908............................ 100.00
MUSIC,VICTROLA,TABLE MODEL..................................  35.00
MUSIC,VIOLANO-VIRTUOSO,DOUBLE MILLS,TWO VIOLINS,REBUILT,
  69 IN.HIGH..............................................3,395.00
MUSIC,VIOLANO-VIRTUOSO,QUARTERED OAK CASE,PARTIALLY
  RESTORED,63 IN.HIGH.....................................1,695.00
MUSIC,VIOLANO-VIRTUOSO,TWO VIOLINS,5-TUNE ROLL,69 IN.HIGH...3,495.00
MUSIC,VIOLIN ORCHESTRATION,PHILIPPS,XYLOPHONE,PIPES,PIANO,
  80 ROLLS................................................2,495.00
MUSIC,VIOLIN PIANO,MIRRORS,ESCUTCHEONS,PIERRE EICH,24 ROLLS.1,995.00
MUSIC,VIOLIN PLAYER,QUARTERED OAK CASE,MILLS
  VIOLANO-VIRTUOSO,64 IN.HIGH.............................1,995.00
MUSIC,VIOLIN,COPY OF STRADIVARIUS,NEW STRINGS,1865,FRANCE...  70.00
MUSIC,VIOLIN,SINGLE,MILLS,COIN-OPERATED,SERIAL NO.1831......1,950.00

```
MUSIC,ZITHER,DATED 1890.....................................   22.00
MUSIC,ZITHER,HAWAIIAN TREMOLA,INSTRUCTIONS,CASE............   50.00
MUSIC,ZITHER,PAT.MAY 20,1894,ORIGINAL DECOR................   65.00
```

```
        MUSTACHE CUPS WERE POPULAR FROM 1850 TO 1900.
        A LEDGE OF CHINA OR SILVER HELD THE HAIR OUT OF THE
        LIQUID IN THE CUP.
MUSTACHE CUP,BLUE DAISIES..................................   12.00
MUSTACHE CUP,BLUE,FLORAL,SQUARE SHAPE......................   18.00
MUSTACHE CUP,BLUE,PINK,GOLD,ROSES,PORTRAIT OF LADY,PORCELAIN  12.00
MUSTACHE CUP,BROWN MATTE GLAZE,LEFT-HANDED,CIRCA 1890......   25.00
MUSTACHE CUP,DUCK DECOR,SILVER WASH EDGE,LEFT-HANDED,CIRCA
  1890.....................................................   30.00
MUSTACHE CUP,HEALTH & HAPPINESS WRITTEN IN GOLD ON CUP,
  SAUCER...................................................   17.50
MUSTACHE CUP,LAVENDER FLOWER,GOLD..........................   21.00
MUSTACHE CUP,LEFT-HANDED,GAY 90S,SAUCER....................   50.00
MUSTACHE CUP,LEFT-HANDED,MAUVE,WHITE FLORAL,GILT,BAVARIAN... 275.00
MUSTACHE CUP,LEFT-HANDED,PORCELAIN.........................    6.00
MUSTACHE CUP,LEFT-HANDED,THREE BROTHERS SHIP,VERSE,COPPER
  LUSTER,SAUCER............................................   41.50
MUSTACHE CUP,LOVE THE GIVER.......................ILLUS..     22.00
MUSTACHE CUP,MEDALLION,FARM,BARN,RURAL SCENE,FLORAL,GOLD
  BANDS....................................................   12.50
MUSTACHE CUP,PINK LUSTER,APPLIED GOLD TRIM.................   25.00
MUSTACHE CUP,RED FLOWER,THINK OF ME IN GOLD,MATCHING MUG...   15.00
MUSTACHE CUP,RED ROSES,GOLD TRIM,SAUCER....................   25.00
MUSTACHE CUP,ROSES,GOLD SPATTER,WHITE,GERMANY..............   12.50
MUSTACHE CUP,SAUCER,LAVENDER,PURPLE BEADED LEAF CLUSTER,
  GILT,GERMANY.............................................   27.50
MUSTACHE CUP,SHIP ON OCEAN,VERSE,PINK,SUNDERLAND...........   39.50
MUSTACHE CUP,TRANSFER DESIGN,ROSES,IRIS DECOR,GERMANY......   15.00
MUSTACHE CUP,WHITE,BLUE & PINK FLORALS,GOLD,SAUCER.........   28.50
MUSTACHE CUP,WHITE,GOLD,INSCRIBED GEORGE HINCHLIFFE BORN
  SEPTR 4TH 1878...........................................   18.00
MUSTACHE CUP & SAUCER,ALLOVER VIOLETS,GOLD,SQUARE CUP,MARKED
  BRANDENBURG..............................................   30.00
MUSTACHE CUP & SAUCER,APPLIED PEARS,LEAVES,GOLD RIM,BRIDE &
  GROOM SET................................................   50.00
MUSTACHE CUP & SAUCER,BLUE,WHITE,SCROLLED SHELLS,GERMANY...   35.00
MUSTACHE CUP & SAUCER,BRIGHT PINK,FLORAL DECOR.............   50.00
MUSTACHE CUP & SAUCER,CIRCA 1800,NORWAY....................   27.50
MUSTACHE CUP & SAUCER,CIRCA 1840..................ILLUS..     32.50
```

MUSTACHE CUP,
LOVE THE GIVER

MUSTACHE CUP AND
SAUCER, C. 1840

```
MUSTACHE CUP & SAUCER,COBALT & WHITE GROUND,PINK & WHITE
  MUMS.....................................................   25.00
MUSTACHE CUP & SAUCER,COBALT MEDALLION,GOLD RAISED LETTERS
  SAY PRESENT..............................................   25.00
MUSTACHE CUP & SAUCER,COCK WEATHERVANE,HAND-PAINTED,PLAIN
  SAUCER...................................................   18.00
MUSTACHE CUP & SAUCER,DARK RED,YELLOW,SQUARE SHAPE,GOLD,X
  MARK.....................................................   17.50
MUSTACHE CUP & SAUCER,EMBOSSED WITH NETTING,BLUE,WHITE,
  LILIES,LEAVES............................................   30.00
MUSTACHE CUP & SAUCER,EMBOSSED,SCALLOPED,GOLD TRIM,A PRESENT
  FROM JERSEY..............................................   30.00
MUSTACHE CUP & SAUCER,ENGRAVED FLORAL PATTERN,SILVER PLATE..  40.00
MUSTACHE CUP & SAUCER,FLORAL SPRAY,GERMAN INSCRIPTION,
  GERMANY..................................................   25.00
MUSTACHE CUP & SAUCER,FLORAL,BLUE BANDS....................   25.00
MUSTACHE CUP & SAUCER,FUCHSIA FLORAL,GREEN LEAVES,GOLD TRIM.  16.50
MUSTACHE CUP & SAUCER,GOLD VINES,PURPLE & BLUE FLORAL,
  LEAVES,PORCELAIN.........................................   35.00
MUSTACHE CUP & SAUCER,LAVENDER,BLUE,WHITE FLORAL,MARKED MADE
  IN GERMANY...............................................   25.00
MUSTACHE CUP & SAUCER,MOSS ROSE DECOR,PORCELAIN............   15.00
```

MUSTACHE CUP & SAUCER,ORIENTAL DECOR,PORTRAITS IN
  MEDALLIONS,RUST,GOLD............................................ 37.00
MUSTACHE CUP & SAUCER,PALE BLUE GROUND,EMBOSSED GOLD FLORAL,
  BANDS,FOOTED.................................................... 45.00
MUSTACHE CUP & SAUCER,PASTEL SHADED PINK FLOWERS,GOLD HANDLE      20.00
MUSTACHE CUP & SAUCER,PINK LUSTER,SAYS GIFT FROM BRIGHTON IN
  GOLD........................................................... 45.00
MUSTACHE CUP & SAUCER,PORTRAIT OF WOMAN IN RED GOWN,GOLD
  TRIM........................................................... 27.50
MUSTACHE CUP & SAUCER,QUADRUPLE SILVER PLATE,MARKED
  ROCKFORD,RESILVERED............................................ 38.00
MUSTACHE CUP & SAUCER,QUILTED,BLUE,ORANGE,BITTERSWEET VINE,
  DESIGN INSIDE.................................................. 25.00
MUSTACHE CUP & SAUCER,RAISED FLORAL DECOR,GOLD, REMEMBER ME,
  GERMANY........................................................ 18.00
MUSTACHE CUP & SAUCER,RAISED GOLD & FLORAL DESIGN............ 37.50
MUSTACHE CUP & SAUCER,RIBBED,TURQUOISE & GOLD STRIPES,
  FLORAL,GOLD.................................................... 33.50
MUSTACHE CUP & SAUCER,ROYAL BLUE ONION TYPE FLORAL DECOR.... 12.00
MUSTACHE CUP & SAUCER,SCENE,ALL DAY COFFEE BREAK,MARKED
  LISBON,16 OZ................................................... 45.00
MUSTACHE CUP & SAUCER,SILVER BEADING,ENGRAVED FLORAL DECOR,
  SILVER......................................................... 27.00
MUSTACHE CUP & SAUCER,SWIRL RIB,FLORAL,GOLD.................. 17.50
MUSTACHE CUP & SAUCER,THREE BROTHERS SHIP,COPPER LUSTER..... 35.00
MUSTACHE CUP & SAUCER,WHITE GROUND,GREEN FLORAL,ENGLANTINE,
  GERMANY........................................................ 35.00
MUSTACHE CUP & SAUCER,WHITE,CUPID ON CUP HANDLE............. 27.00
MUSTACHE CUP & SAUCER,WHITE,FLORAL,GOLD TRIM,WELMAR,GERMANY. 20.00
MUSTACHE CUP & SAUCER,WHITE,GOLD,A PRESENT FROM ACCRINGTON.. 15.00
MUSTACHE CUP & SAUCER,WHITE,PANELS,GOLD RIM,FLAT LIP........ 28.50


    NAILSEA GLASS WAS MADE IN THE BRISTOL DISTRICT IN
  ENGLAND FROM 1788 TO 1873. MANY PIECES WERE MADE WITH
  LOOPINGS OF COLORED GLASS AS DECORATIONS.
NAILSEA,BOTTLE,GREEN,WHITE LOOPINGS,PEROXIDE IN GOLD,
  STOPPER,5 1/2 IN............................................... 42.50
NAILSEA,BOTTLE,SAPPHIRE BLUE,WHITE LOOPINGS,BLOWN,STOPPER,
  12 IN.TALL.................................................... 52.00
NAILSEA,BOWL,ROSE,THREADED,BERRY PONTIL,TRICORNERED,BLUE,
  FOOTED........................................................ 145.00
NAILSEA,CARAFE,PLATE,MINATURE,19TH CENTURY.................. 97.00
NAILSEA,CASTOR SET,FOUR BOTTLES,CRUET,SALT,PEPPER,MUSTARD,
  YELLOW,BLUE................................................... 75.00
NAILSEA,CRUET,BLUE,WHITE SWIRLS,CUT STOPPER,FOOTED. 65.00 TO  75.00
NAILSEA,CRUET,DARK RED,WHITE LOOPINGS,ROUND BALL STOPPER.... 15.00
NAILSEA,CUP & SAUCER,BLUE SWIRL............................. 55.00
NAILSEA,EPERGNE,LILY,GREEN APPLIED RIM,SCALLOPS,BRASS
  CONNECTIONS................................................... 58.00
NAILSEA,LAMP,FAIRY,BLUE,SATIN GLASS,CLEAR BASE,CLARKE,
  4 1/2 IN.TALL................................................. 110.00
NAILSEA,LAMP,FAIRY,SAPPHIRE BLUE SATIN,CRIMPED-EDGE BASE,
  MARKED CLARKE................................................. 210.00
NAILSEA,PERFUME,HEART SHAPE,MULTICOLORED,MERCURY GLASS
  STOPPER....................................................... 28.00
NAILSEA,PERFUME,PINK & WHITE LOOPINGS,BLOWN STOPPER,
  8 IN.HIGH..................................................... 60.00
NAILSEA,ROLLING PIN,CLEAR GREEN GLASS,RUBY & WHITE LOOPINGS,
  14 IN......................................................... 65.00
NAILSEA,SHADE,GAS,WHITE LOOPINGS,FLUTED TOP,4-IN.FITTER..... 13.00
NAILSEA,VASE,BLUE SATIN..................................... 50.00


    NAKARA IS A TRADE NAME FOR A WHITE GLASSWARE MADE
  AROUND 1900 THAT WAS DECORATED IN PASTEL COLORS. IT
  WAS MADE BY THE C.F. MONROE COMPANY OF MERIDEN,
  CONNECTICUT.
NAKARA,BOX,HINGED,7 1/2 IN.SQUARE.......................... 190.00
NAKARA,BOX,JEWEL,BLUE GROUND,PINK FLOWERS,OPEN,SIGNED C.F.M.  85.00
NAKARA,BOX,JEWEL,BLUE,MOLDED COVER,PANSY,LINING,SIGNED...... 125.00
NAKARA,BOX,JEWEL,PINK TO AVOCADO,SATIN,PINK POPPIES,FOLIAGE,
  BRASS TRIM.................................................... 125.00
NAKARA,BOX,JEWELRY,OLIVE GROUND,WHITE DOTS,APPLE BLOSSOMS,
  OPEN.......................................................... 60.00
NAKARA,BOX,OPEN,GREEN GROUND,PINK ROSES,WHITE BEADING,
  COLLAR,HANDLES................................................ 115.00
NAKARA,BOX,PINK TO YELLOW,CHERUBS,WHITE BEADED FRAME ON LID,
  3 3/4 IN...................................................... 110.00
NAKARA,BOX,RING,GREEN TO WHITE,PINK ROSES,BRASS COLLARS,
  C.F.MONROE.................................................... 70.00

NAKARA,BOX,RING,SAGE GREEN,PINK WILD ROSES,SILK LINING...... 85.00
NAKARA,BOX,ROSE TO PINK,EMBOSSED BRASS BANDS,HINGED TOP,
   LINING,SIGNED.............................................. 135.00
NAKARA,BOX,ROSES,ROSEBUDS,MOSS GREEN GROUND,SIGNED,
   3 1/2 IN.TALL............................................. 125.00
NAKARA,LAMP,GREEN GROUND,ORCHID,SIGNED,26 IN. X 9 IN.HIGH... 125.00
NAKARA,NAPKIN RING,OCTAGON PANELS,ENAMEL DOTTING,SCROLLS,
   CIRCLES,BLUE.............................................. 48.00
NAKARA,TRAY,JEWELRY,GREEN,WHITE DOT SWIRLS,APPLE BLOSSOMS,
   5-IN.DIAMETER............................................. 65.00
NAKARA,VASE,BLUE SHADING TO PINK,WHITE BEADED SCROLLS,
   POINSETTIA,9 IN........................................... 165.00


     NANKING CHINA IS A BLUE AND WHITE PORCELAIN MADE IN
     CHINA FOR EXPORT DURING THE EIGHTEENTH CENTURY.
NANKING,TEAPOT,BLUE,WHITE,TWISTED HANDLE,LID................ 175.00


     NAPKIN RINGS WERE POPULAR FROM 1869 TO ABOUT 1900.
NAPKIN RING,ANGEL,OPENWORK BASE,FLORAL EDGE,SAYS MAMMA,
   SILVER PLATE.............................................. 38.00
NAPKIN RING,BOY STANDING.........................ILLUS.. 25.00
NAPKIN RING,BRASS, SOUVENIR DE FRANCE,  CROWN,COAT OF ARMS.. 3.50
NAPKIN RING,BRASS,RAISED MEDALLION,CROWN IN CENTER, GOTT MIT
UNS ....................................................... 4.00

NAPKIN RING

NAPKIN RING,CHILD'S,ENGRAVED SCENE,NAME,STERLING SILVER..... 10.00
NAPKIN RING,EMBOSSED CHICKENS,CHICKS,NICKEL PLATE,ENGLAND... 22.00
NAPKIN RING,ETCHED LEAVES ON BALL FEET,FANS,BIRDS,FLORAL,
   MERIDEN & CO.............................................. 38.00
NAPKIN RING,FIGURAL,AMERICAN EAGLE ON EACH SIDE,SILVER PLATE 22.00
NAPKIN RING,FIGURAL,DOG,PAWS ON RING,ORNATE ROCOCO BORDER,
   SILVER PLATE.............................................. 33.00
NAPKIN RING,FIGURAL,KANGAROO & OSTRICH..................... 35.00
NAPKIN RING,FLORAL DECOR,HAND-PAINTED,GILT BRANCHES,
   PORCELAIN................................................. 13.50
NAPKIN RING,IVORY,INITIAL.................................. 5.00
NAPKIN RING,PANELED MOTHER-OF-PEARL,SILVER BANDS AT TOP &
   BOTTOM,2 IN............................................... 15.00
NAPKIN RING,PEWTER,EMBOSSED FLOWERS,SCALLOPED EDGE,DATED
   CHRISTMAS 1892........................................... 8.00
NAPKIN RING,PORCELAIN,FIGURAL,MICKEY MOUSE,1 3/4 IN........ 12.00
NAPKIN RING,PORCELAIN,HAND-PAINTED,MARKED AUSTRIA,DATED
   1912..................................................... 22.00
NAPKIN RING,PORCELAIN,HAND-PAINTED ROSES,GOLD.............. 15.00
NAPKIN RING,PORCELAIN,RED ROSES,GREEN LEAVES,WIDE GOLD RIM,
   HAND-PAINTED............................................. 17.00
NAPKIN RING,RUSSIAN SILVER,BEADED RIMS,NIELLO.............. 20.00
NAPKIN RING,SILVER PLATE,BARREL ON TWIGS.................. 13.00
NAPKIN RING,SILVER PLATE,BARREL SETS ON GRAPE LEAVES........ 18.50
NAPKIN RING,SILVER PLATE,CHERUB ON LEAF BASE,1 1/2 IN....... 29.50
NAPKIN RING,SILVER PLATE,CHICK,RESILVERED.................. 25.00

NAPKIN RING,SILVER PLATE,CUPID WITH SHEAF OF ARROWS......... 32.00
NAPKIN RING,SILVER PLATE,DOG,DOGHOUSE,MERIDEN COMPANY....... 34.50
NAPKIN RING,SILVER PLATE,EAGLES ON BOTH SIDES,HOLD RING,
   ROGERS & BROS............................................. 22.00
NAPKIN RING,SILVER PLATE,ENGRAVED WITH RAISED FLOWERS,ON
   8-IN.TRAY................................................ 26.00
NAPKIN RING,SILVER PLATE,ENGRAVED,DOVES ON SIDES........... 15.00
NAPKIN RING,SILVER PLATE,ENGRAVED,ROUND STANDARD,ROGERS &
   BROTHERS................................................ 18.00
NAPKIN RING,SILVER PLATE,FAN DECOR,TURNED-UP SAUCER,BUDS,
   DOUBLE HANDLE........................................... 32.00
NAPKIN RING,SILVER PLATE,FIGURAL,BABY BIRD.................. 20.00
NAPKIN RING,SILVER PLATE,FIGURAL,CHERUB.................... 20.00
NAPKIN RING,SILVER PLATE,FIGURAL,EAGLE,WINGS UP,EACH END.... 35.00
NAPKIN RING,SILVER PLATE,FIGURAL,EGYPTIAN HEADS............. 15.00
NAPKIN RING,SILVER PLATE,FIGURAL,FLOWER URN................ 28.00
NAPKIN RING,SILVER PLATE,FIGURAL,GROUP OF FLOWERS.......... 26.00
NAPKIN RING,SILVER PLATE,FIGURAL,LILY PAD,WATER LILY BUD,
   RESILVERED............................................. 35.00
NAPKIN RING,SILVER PLATE,FIGURAL,LILY PAD & BUD,SAYS  BURT . 20.00
NAPKIN RING,SILVER PLATE,FIGURAL,LITTLE BOY DOING JIG....... 26.00
NAPKIN RING,SILVER PLATE,FIGURAL,TRIANGULAR WITH ENTWINED
   WISHBONES.............................................. 20.00
NAPKIN RING,SILVER PLATE,FIGURAL,TWO PEARS,LEAVES.......... 15.00
NAPKIN RING,SILVER PLATE,FIGURAL,TWO TURTLES ON LEAF FRONDS,
   RESILVERED............................................. 22.00
NAPKIN RING,SILVER PLATE,FIGURAL,WISHBONE,CHICK,ETCHED
   FLOWERS,DERBY.......................................... 20.00
NAPKIN RING,SILVER PLATE,FLYING CHERUB ON SIDE............. 32.00
NAPKIN RING,SILVER PLATE,HELD BY TWO FOXES ON A PLATFORM.... 19.50
NAPKIN RING,SILVER PLATE,OWL ON BRANCH..................... 18.00
NAPKIN RING,SILVER PLATE,RAM HEAD ON TOP,FOUR BALL FEET..... 19.00
NAPKIN RING,SILVER PLATE,RELIEF,BEES,WINGS SPREAD,RESILVERED 35.00
NAPKIN RING,SILVER PLATE,RESTING ON LADDER-BACK CHAIR,
   EMBOSSED............................................... 38.00
NAPKIN RING,STERLING SILVER,BEADED EDGE,SAYS RUTH LUFKIN.... 3.50
NAPKIN RING,STERLING SILVER,BIRD,FLORAL,KITTIE FROM MOTHER,
   1882................................................... 4.75
NAPKIN RING,STERLING SILVER,BUTTERFLY ON TOP,FOOTED........ 18.50
NAPKIN RING,STERLING SILVER,CHASED WITH FLORALS & SCROLLS... 13.00
NAPKIN RING,STERLING SILVER,EGG CUP,SPOON,MONOGRAM,LINED
   CASE................................................... 19.00
NAPKIN RING,STERLING SILVER,EIGHT-SIDED................... 3.75
NAPKIN RING,STERLING SILVER,ENGRAVED H.T.HEALY............. 2.95
NAPKIN RING,STERLING SILVER,FOUR-LEAF CLOVER BANDS,NAME
   ENGRAVED............................................... 15.00
NAPKIN RING,STERLING SILVER,GRAPES IN RELIEF............... 6.00
NAPKIN RING,STERLING SILVER,INITIALED W.R.,HAND-HAMMERED.... 3.75
NAPKIN RING,STERLING SILVER,IRREGULAR EDGE,RAISED FLORAL
   DECOR,INITIAL.......................................... 5.00
NAPKIN RING,STERLING SILVER,PLAIN WITH BEADED EDGE,INITIALED 4.50
NAPKIN RING,STERLING SILVER,ROLLED RIMS,HEAVY DECOR,
   INSCRIBED NAME,1894.................................... 14.00
NAPKIN RING,STERLING SILVER,RUFFLE EDGE LEAF,BEETLE,INITIALS 30.00
NAPKIN RING,STERLING SILVER,WHIPPET...................... 35.00
NAPKIN RING,TWISTED PORCELAIN,APPLIED FLOWER.............. 10.00


       NASH GLASS WAS MADE IN CORONA,NEW YORK,BY ARTHUR NASH
       AND HIS SONS AFTER 1919. HE HAD WORKED AT THE WEBB
       FACTORY IN ENGLAND AND FOR THE TIFFANY GLASSWORKS IN
       THE UNITED STATES.
NASH,BOWL,CHINTZ,AQUA STRIPES,GREEN MOTTLING BETWEEN,
   7 1/2 IN.DIAMETER...................................... 85.00
NASH,BOWL,CYPRIOTE BUBBLE,BLUE,BROWN CHINTZ,SIGNED,
   7 1/2 IN.DIAMETER...................................... 275.00
NASH,BOWL,ROSE,GREEN,SHADES OF GOLD & PURPLE,14 IN.WIDE,
   6 IN.HIGH.............................................. 275.00
NASH,DECANTER,PAIR,16 1/4 IN. HIGH,SIGNED................. 225.00
NASH,DISH,GOLD,STRETCHED EDGE,IRIDESCENT,SIGNED........... 150.00
NASH,VASE,GREEN GLASS,11 1/2 IN. HIGH.................... 130.00
NASH,VASE,OPTIC LEAF DESIGN,PEACOCK BLUE,SIGNED,7 IN.HIGH... 280.00
NASH,VASE,OPTIC LEAF SHAPE DESIGN ON LOWER PART,GOLD
   IRIDESCENT,5 IN........................................ 140.00
   NEEDLEWORK,SEE,LINEN,RUG


       NETSUKE ARE SMALL IVORY,WOOD,METAL,OR PORCELAIN
       PIECES USED AS THE BUTTON ON THE END OF A CORD HOLDING
       A JAPANESE MONEY POUCH. THE EARLIEST DATE FROM THE
       SIXTEENTH CENTURY.

NETSUKE,AMERICAN COUPLE,SEVENTEENTH CENTURY COSTUME,GYOKUHO,
    IVORY............................................... 120.00
NETSUKE,BOY,ROBED,HOLDS LARGE GOURD ON SHOULDER,IVORY,WORN.. 40.00
NETSUKE,DOG,ON AWABI SHELL,STRING,LACQUER,WOODEN........... 100.00
NETSUKE,DOG,SEATED,KNOTTED COLLAR,LACQUER,NAGOYA SCHOOL,
    WOODEN............................................... 60.00
NETSUKE,DUTCHMAN,ELONGATED BODY,STAINED,IVORY........ILLUS. 500.00
NETSUKE,FIGURE OF A DOG,PLAYING WITH SANDAL,UNSTAINED,IVORY. 100.00
NETSUKE,FIGURE OF BOY ON RECUMBENT OX,MASANAO OF YARADA,
    WOODEN............................................... 250.00
NETSUKE,FIGURE OF GROOM WASHING HORSE,SOSUI OF TOKYO,WOODEN. 375.00
NETSUKE,FIGURE OF KINKO ON HIS CARP,18TH CENTURY,IVORY...... 225.00
NETSUKE,FIGURE OF MAN,BAGGY TROUSERS,ROBE,ROUND HAT,CARVED,
    IVORY................................................ 60.00
NETSUKE,FIGURE OF MONKEY ON A TORTOISE,TOMOKAZU OF GIFU,
    WOODEN............................................... 475.00
NETSUKE,FIGURINE,MONKEY,SOAPSTONE,1 1/4 IN................. 5.00
NETSUKE,FIGURINE,THREE MEN PLAYING INSTRUMENTS,1 1/4 X
    1 1/4 IN.HIGH........................................ 27.00
NETSUKE,FOX WOMAN,BELTED ROBE,COWL,PAW HOLDS STAFF,LACQUER,
    WOODEN............................................... 275.00
NETSUKE,HAKO,SEVEN GODS,SIGNED TEIMIN,BOXWOOD............. 180.00
NETSUKE,HATCHING EGG,SIGNED.............................. 17.50
NETSUKE,HORSE,GRAZING,SCROLL-ENGRAVED SADDLE CLOTH,LACQUER,
    WOODEN............................................... 120.00
NETSUKE,HU KUNG,HOLDS LEAVES,BOWL,IVORY..............ILLUS.. 350.00
NETSUKE,LOTUS POD,MOVABLE SEEDS,STALK BENT TO FORM THE
    KIMOTOSHI,WOODEN..................................... 100.00
NETSUKE,MAN BEATING DRUM,IVORY,SIGNED..................... 28.00
NETSUKE,MAN HOLDS TURTLE,CARVED IVORY,2 1/8 IN.,1 IN.WIDE... 25.00
NETSUKE,MAN ON FUGU FISH,INSCRIBED TOYOMASA,IVORY........... 175.00
NETSUKE,MICE ON PILE OF MILLET,SIGNED OKATORI.........ILLUS.. 200.00
NETSUKE,MODEL OF WASP IN A PEAR,SIGNED,NAGOYA SCHOOL,WOODEN. 550.00
NETSUKE,MONKEY,HAIRWORK,HOLDS GOURD,LEANS ON FUGU FISH,
    BOXWOOD.............................................. 70.00
NETSUKE,MONKEY,PATTERNED COAT,HOLDS BRANCH,DETAILS WORN,
    TOSHINAO,IVORY....................................... 45.00
NETSUKE,MONKEY,SIGNED RANTEI,IVORY...................ILLUS.. 350.00
NETSUKE,NODDER,GOOD,EVIL,SIGNED,2 1/2 IN.HIGH,PAIR........ 65.00
NETSUKE,NOTEI,HOLDS UCHIVA,KOHOSAI OF OSAKA,IVORY....ILLUS.. 70.00
NETSUKE,ONI,LEGS FORM THE HIMOTOSHI,MASAKAZU OF GIFU,WOODEN. 400.00
NETSUKE,SHISHI,HAIRWORK HAS BEEN STAINED,IVORY............. 140.00
NETSUKE,SHISHI,SNARLING MOUTH,18TH CENTURY,IVORY........... 150.00
NETSUKE,SHISHI,YOUNG CUBS,DETAILS WORN,IVORY.........ILLUS.. 160.00
NETSUKE,SITTING MAN HOLDS RABBIT,HOLES FOR BELT,CARVED
    IVORY,1 IN.WIDE...................................... 25.00
NETSUKE,SUMO WRESTLERS,SIGNED KOKUSAI,IVORY..........ILLUS.. 500.00
NETSUKE,SWAN,HEAD TURNED BACK,HOLDS FISH IN MOUTH,CARVED
    IVORY................................................ 32.00
NETSUKE,TIGER,SNARLING,HAIRWORK IS WORN,SIGNED TOMOCHIKA,
    IVORY................................................ 225.00
NETSUKE,TWO MEN,TUGGING AT PIECE OF CORAL,SIGNED TOMOCHIKA,
    IVORY................................................ 125.00
NETSUKE,WALNUT,PIERCED HOLE FOR THE HIMOTOSHI,CARVED WAVE
    GROUND............................................... 80.00
NETSUKE,WOLF,MASSIVE FORM,RECLINES,DETAILS ARE WORN,CARVED,
    WOODEN............................................... 80.00
NETSUKE,WOMAN WASHING,SIGNED SHUGYOKU,IVORY.............. 225.00


    NEWCOMB POTTERY WAS FOUNDED BY ELLSWORTH AND WILLIAM
WOODWARD AT SOPHIE NEWCOMB MEMORIAL COLLEGE,NEW
ORLEANS,LOUISIANA,IN 1896.THE WORK CONTINUED THRU THE
1940'S. PIECES OF THIS ART POTTERY ARE MARKED WITH THE
LETTER N INSIDE THE LETTER C.
NEWCOMB POTTERY,PLATE,FIGS,LEAVES,BLUE GROUND,ARTIST-SIGNED,
    8 1/4 IN............................................. 40.00
NEWCOMB POTTERY,VASE,COLLEGE,ARTIST AFS,4 1/2 IN.TALL,
    6-IN.DIAMETER........................................ 55.00
NEWCOMB POTTERY,VASE,COLLEGE,PINE NEEDLES,PINECONES,BLUE
    GROUND,6 IN.......................................... 87.50
NEWCOMB POTTERY,VASE,PALE BLUE,MATTE FINISH,MARKED,
    8 1/4 IN.HIGH........................................ 55.00
NEWHALL,CREAMER,MULTICOLORED,CIRCA 1830.................. 40.00
NEWHALL,MUG,LAVENDER,ORIENTAL SCENE,2 IN.TALL.......... 25.00
NEWHALL,TEAPOT STAND,ORIENTAL DECOR,OBLONG SHAPE,MARKED 421,
    CIRCA 1790........................................... 70.00
NEWHALL,TEAPOT,CREAMER,SUGAR,ORIENTAL DECOR,PAIR CREAMERS,
    COW.................................................. 150.00
NEWHALL,TEAPOT,ORIENTAL FIGURES,SWAN FINIAL.............. 145.00
NIELLO,MATCH CASE,BLACK GROUND,SILVER DECOR OF GRAPES,

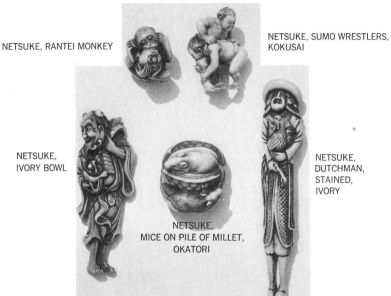

NETSUKE, RANTEI MONKEY

NETSUKE, SUMO WRESTLERS, KOKUSAI

NETSUKE, IVORY BOWL

NETSUKE, DUTCHMAN, STAINED, IVORY

NETSUKE, MICE ON PILE OF MILLET, OKATORI

NETSUKE, SHISHTI, YOUNG CUBS, IVORY

NETSUKE, HOTEI HOLDS UCHIVA, IVORY

```
LEAVES,1 X 2 IN....................................................   40.00
NILOAK,VASE,BEACH SCENE,CLAM DIGGERS,BOATS,ARTIST J.PETRA...   67.50


     NIPPON MARKED PORCELAIN WAS MADE IN JAPAN AFTER 1891.
NIPPON,BASKET,PINK FLOWERS,GREEN BORDER,GOLD TRIM,HANDLE,2 X
   4 IN.LONG.........................................................    5.00
NIPPON,BONBON,BUTTERFLIES,FLORAL,FOUR SECTIONS..............   10.00
NIPPON,BOWL,BERRY,APPLE BLOSSOMS,GOLD TRIM,SIX SAUCE DISHES.   18.00
NIPPON,BOWL,BERRY,BLUEBIRD,GRAPES,AUTUMN LEAVES,
   HAND-PAINTED,6 1/4 IN..............................................    5.00
NIPPON,BOWL,BERRY,RISING SUN,HAND-PAINTED,PINK,BLUE,GOLD,
   6 SAUCES..........................................................   17.50
NIPPON,BOWL,BERRY,WHITE GROUND,ISLAND,BOATS,BIRDS,BLACK,
   GOLD,6 DISHES.....................................................   25.00
NIPPON,BOWL,BIRD OF PARADISE,CHRYSANTHEMUM,LIGHT GREEN &
   BLACK BORDER......................................................   42.50
NIPPON,BOWL,COBALT BLUE SCALLOPED EDGE,LARGE PINK & RED
   ROSES INSIDE......................................................   15.00
NIPPON,BOWL,CREAM-BROWN,PINK ROSES,LEAVES,GOLD,HAND-PAINTED,
   7 1/2 IN..........................................................   10.00
NIPPON,BOWL,ENCRUSTED WITH GOLD DECOR,HANDLE,
   7 1/2-IN.DIAMETER.................................................   10.00
NIPPON,BOWL,GOLD & RED EDGE AND FEET,WATER SCENE INSIDE,
   GOLD,6 IN.........................................................    7.50
NIPPON,BOWL,GREEN GROUND,PINK & YELLOW FLORAL,GOLD BORDER,
   SCALLOPED.........................................................   20.00
NIPPON,BOWL,HAND-PAINTED,BLUE,YELLOW,GOLD,10 IN.............   12.00
```

NIPPON,BOWL,LARGE PURPLE & BLUE FLOWERS,GOLD TRIM,
    HAND-PAINTED,7 IN........................................... 12.50
NIPPON,BOWL,MAYONNAISE,GREEN,TAN FLORAL,GOLD,HAND-PAINTED,
    FOOTED,PLATE............................................... 8.00
NIPPON,BOWL,MAYONNAISE,RISING SUN,ROSES,SHADED YELLOW
    GROUND,GOLD,LADLE.......................................... 8.00
NIPPON,BOWL,NUT,PINK & BLUE FLOWERS,FOUR INDIVIDUAL FOOTED
    BOWLS...................................................... 25.00
NIPPON,BOWL,NUT,TAN RIM,FLORAL,OVAL,HAND-PAINTED,7 1/2 IN. X
    4 1/2 IN................................................... 5.00
NIPPON,BOWL,ORIENTAL LADIES,SCENERY INSIDE,BLUE BORDER,
    SIGNED..................................................... 11.00
NIPPON,BOWL,PINK & RED ROSES,FOOTED,5 1/4 IN............... 5.50
NIPPON,BOWL,PINK FLOWERS,YELLOW STAMEN,TWO BIRDS ON BOUGH IN
    CENTER..................................................... 10.00
NIPPON,BOWL,PINK,RED,YELLOW ROSES,GOLD TRIM,MARKED,
    11 IN.WIDE,3 IN.DEEP....................................... 25.00
NIPPON,BOWL,RIVER,TREE,HOUSE,GOLD HANDLES,HAND-PAINTED,
    9 1/2 IN................................................... 15.00
NIPPON,BOWL,ROSE,CORALENE BEADING,GREEN,PINK FLORAL,GOLD,
    FOOTED,5 IN................................................ 55.00
NIPPON,BOWL,WINDMILL SCENE INSIDE,BEADED EDGE & FEET,
    HAND-PAINTED,7 IN.......................................... 12.00
NIPPON,BOX,POWDER,CLOVERS,GOLD,HAND-PAINTED............... 5.00
NIPPON,BOX,POWDER,WHITE,GOLD & RED STRIPES,BASKET WITH
    FLOWERS ON LID............................................. 49.50
NIPPON,BOX,ROSE,GREEN,GOLD BEADING,THREE SMALL FEET........ 17.50
NIPPON,BOX,YELLOW & PINK ROSES,HEAVY GOLD BEADING,LID,
    2 1/2-IN.DIAMETER.......................................... 10.00
NIPPON,BUTTER PAT,FLOWERS,GILT,HANDLE,MARKED,SET OF 4....... 15.00
NIPPON,BUTTER TUB,ROSES,GOLD BEADING,DRAIN,HAND-PAINTED,
    HANDLES,MARKED............................................. 12.50
NIPPON,CAKE,M WREATH,BLUE,GRAY,EMBOSSED FIERY DRAGONS,
    6 INDIVIDUALS.............................................. 35.00
NIPPON,CANDLEHOLDER,POINSETTIAS & FIR DECOR................ 6.50
NIPPON,CANDLESTICK,WHITE,BAND & VIOLETS ON TOP & BOTTOM,
    HAND-PAINTED............................................... 3.50
NIPPON,CELERY,CREAMY WHITE,HANDLES,GILT,HAND-PAINTED,12 IN.
    X 5 IN..................................................... 10.00
NIPPON,CHOCOLATE PITCHER,SINGLE ROSE ALLOVER PATTERN,6 CUPS
    & SAUCERS................................................. 37.50
NIPPON,CHOCOLATE POT,ALLOVER PURPLE VIOLETS,GREEN LEAVES,
    GOLD,8 1/2 IN.............................................. 16.50
NIPPON,CHOCOLATE POT,CREAM BORDER,GOLD,ROSES,HAND-PAINTED... 16.00
NIPPON,CHOCOLATE POT,FLORAL,PINK,GREEN,YELLOW,GOLD,GREEN
    MARK....................................................... 25.00
NIPPON,CHOCOLATE POT,FOUR CUPS & SAUCERS,CREAMY GROUND,BLUE
    WATER,SWANS................................................ 25.00
NIPPON,CHOCOLATE POT,GEISHA GIRL SCENES,FLORAL,COBALT TRIM,
    GOLD....................................................... 15.00
NIPPON,CHOCOLATE POT,MULTICOLORED GROUND,PINK & YELLOW
    ROSES,GOLD................................................. 16.00
NIPPON,CHOCOLATE POT,ORANGE,TREES,WATER,HAND-PAINTED,5 CUPS,
    6 SAUCERS.................................................. 18.50
NIPPON,CHOCOLATE POT,ORIENTAL SCENE,WHITE,BLUE,RAISED
    BEADING,4 CUPS............................................. 22.00
NIPPON,CHOCOLATE POT,PINK,WHITE SWIRLED BLOSSOMS,GOLD STEMS,
    COVER...................................................... 27.00
NIPPON,CHOCOLATE POT,ROSES,GOLD,HAND-PAINTED,SIX CUPS &
    SAUCERS.................................................... 22.00
NIPPON,CHOCOLATE POT,ROYAL BLUE WITH HEAVY GOLD CRUSTING.... 15.00
NIPPON,CHOCOLATE POT,WHITE,BANDS OF MULTICOLORED FLOWERS,
    4 CUPS,SAUCERS............................................. 27.50
NIPPON,CHOCOLATE SET,POT,4 CUPS & SAUCERS,WHITE GROUND,ROSE
    & LEAF DECOR.............................................. 23.50
NIPPON,COASTER,PINK FLORAL,BEADING,HAND-PAINTED,GILT,4 IN.,
    PAIR....................................................... 7.00
NIPPON,COCOA POT,FLORAL,DEEP GOLD CRUSTING,HAND-PAINTED..... 15.00
NIPPON,COMPOTE,YELLOW-ORANGE POND LILIES,GOLD RIM,
    HAND-PAINTED,5 IN.HIGH..................................... 18.00
NIPPON,CREAMER & SUGAR,GOLD,GREEN,PINK,YELLOW DECOR,MELON
    RIB,FOOTED................................................. 12.50
NIPPON,CREAMER & SUGAR,TAN GROUND,PINK ROSES,HAND-PAINTED,
    SUN MARK................................................... 7.50
NIPPON,CREAMER & SUGAR,TREES,WATER,MATTE,HAND-PAINTED,COVER. 8.00
NIPPON,CREAMER & SUGAR,WHITE,WIDE YELLOW BORDER TOP EDGE.... 4.00
NIPPON,CREAMER,WATER SCENE,HAND-PAINTED,COVER.............. 8.50
NIPPON,CUP & SAUCER,CHILD'S,CIRCUS ANIMALS,PEOPLE,SET OF 5.. 10.00
NIPPON,CUP & SAUCER,CHOCOLATE,PINK ROSES,YELLOW,GOLD TRIM... 5.00
NIPPON,CUP & SAUCER,CHOCOLATE,VIOLET FLORAL,GOLD,GREEN,DARK
    RED........................................................ 5.00

NIPPON,CUP & SAUCER,DEMITASSE,WHITE GROUND,FLORAL,GILT,
　MARKED................................................. 2.50
NIPPON,CUP & SAUCER,MT.FUJIYAMA SCENE,LAKE,TREES,
　HAND-PAINTED,SET OF 6.................................. 11.75
NIPPON,CUP & SAUCER,PINK & YELLOW FLOWERS,GOLD............ 4.00
NIPPON,CUP & SAUCER,PORTRAIT OF LADY...................... 3.50
NIPPON,CUP,BOUILLON,TWO HANDLES,HAND-PAINTED,SAUCER....... 4.00
NIPPON,CUP,EGG,WHITE,WIDE YELLOW BORDER TOP EDGE,PAIR..... 5.00
NIPPON,CUP,SAUCER,DEMITASSE,ORIENTAL SCENE,PAGODA,BRIDGE,
　LADIES,SET OF 6....................................... 14.95
NIPPON,DECANTER,WINDMILL SCENE,BEADING,HANDLE,STOPPER,WICKER
　HOLDER................................................ 32.50
NIPPON,DISH,BLUE FLOWER MOTIF,GOLD,HAND-PAINTED,7 1/2 IN... 10.00
NIPPON,DISH,BOAT SHAPE,HAND-PAINTED WINDMILL SCENE,7 1/2 IN. 5.00
NIPPON,DISH,CANDY,BLACK,GOLD,PINK ROSES,HAND-PAINTED...... 6.00
NIPPON,DISH,CANDY,CREAM GROUND,TAN FLORAL,GREEN LEAVES,GOLD,
　HAND-PAINTED.......................................... 7.00
NIPPON,DISH,CANDY,DAINTY FLORAL,FOOTED................... 4.00
NIPPON,DISH,CANDY,GRAY-WHITE GROUND,YELLOW FLORAL,GOLD,OVAL,
　HANDLES............................................... 6.00
NIPPON,DISH,CANDY,LIGHT GREEN GROUND,PINK APPLE BLOSSOMS,
　GILT,CRIMPED.......................................... 8.50
NIPPON,DISH,CANDY,PEACH COLOR ROSES,GOLD,TWO OPEN HANDLES,
　OVAL,7 1/4 IN......................................... 6.50
NIPPON,DISH,CANDY,PINK FORAL,HAND-PAINTED,6 IN........... 6.00
NIPPON,DISH,CANDY,RISING SUN,ROSES,RAISED GREEN DECOR,HANDLE 5.00
NIPPON,DISH,CANDY,ROSE FLORAL,COBALT,GOLD RIM,TWO HANDLES,
　HAND-PAINTED.......................................... 6.50
NIPPON,DISH,CANDY,SHADED YELLOW GROUND,ROSES,GOLD TRIM,OVAL,
　HANDLES............................................... 6.00
NIPPON,DISH,CELERY,FLOWERS,HAND-PAINTED,GOLD TRIM......... 8.00
NIPPON,DISH,CELERY,YELLOW BORDER & FLORAL,GOLD,SIX MATCHING
　SALTS................................................. 16.50
NIPPON,DISH,CHEESE,FLORAL,GILT,HAND-PAINTED,COVER,7 1/2 IN. 16.00
NIPPON,DISH,CRACKER & CHEESE,FLORAL,HAND-PAINTED.......... 10.00
NIPPON,DISH,CUCUMBER,FLORAL,GOLD,PERFORATED FOR DRAINAGE,
　HAND-PAINTED.......................................... 12.00
NIPPON,DISH,FLORAL & GOLD DECOR,7 1/2 IN................. 7.50
NIPPON,DISH,NUT,FLORAL TRIM,HAND-PAINTED,FOOTED.......... 3.00
NIPPON,DISH,NUT,FLORAL,GOLD TRIM,HAND-PAINTED,6 INDIVIDUAL
　DISHES................................................ 12.50
NIPPON,DISH,RELISH,OBLONG,HAND-PAINTED,1 IN.GOLD BORDER
　TRIM,8 IN.LONG........................................ 6.50
NIPPON,DISH,RELISH,PINK,BLUE,GOLD-FLOWERED BORDER,11 1/2 X
　5 1/2 IN.............................................. 18.50
NIPPON,DISH,SAUCE,HAND-PAINTED,GOLD BANDS,4 IN.SQUARE,SET OF
　4..................................................... 10.00
NIPPON,DISH,SCENE,SWANS,POND,LILY PADS,GOLD TRIM,
　HAND-PAINTED,8 1/2 IN................................. 8.75
NIPPON,DISH,TOAST,GOLD DECOR,YELLOW PANELS,COVER,
　7 1/2-IN.DIAMETER..................................... 11.00
NIPPON,DISH,WHITE,BLUE & BROWN FLORAL,GOLD TRIM,7 IN...... 6.00
NIPPON,DOLL,PENNY,PAPIER-MACHE BODY,STRUNG ARMS,LEGS,MOVABLE
　HEAD.................................................. 10.00
NIPPON,HAIR RECEIVER,HAND-PAINTED........................ 7.50
NIPPON,HAIR RECEIVER,ORNATE,GOLD,TALL-FOOTED,MATCHING BOX
　WITH COVER............................................ 14.50
NIPPON,HAIR RECEIVER,PINK ROSES,WHITE GROUND,COBALT & GOLD
　TRIM.................................................. 8.00
NIPPON,HAIR RECEIVER,VIOLETS,COBALT TRIM,HAND-PAINTED,MARKED 12.50
NIPPON,HAIR RECEIVER,WHITE,BLUE,BIRDS ON COVER........... 6.50
NIPPON,HOLDER,HATPIN,CAMEO LAKE SCENE,BOAT,ENAMEL,PURPLE,
　ORANGE,GREEN.......................................... 20.00
NIPPON,HOLDER,HATPIN,ENAMELED DESIGN..................... 6.50
NIPPON,HOLDER,HATPIN,GOLD,RED BERRIES,GREEN LEAVES,5 IN.HIGH 12.50
NIPPON,HOLDER,HATPIN,ORCHID & GREEN FLORAL,GOLD TRIM,
　HAND-PAINTED.......................................... 7.50
NIPPON,HOLDER,HATPIN,WHITE WITH ORANGE POPPY,GOLD TRIM.... 10.00
NIPPON,JAR,BISCUIT,LAVENDER,GREEN,GOLD DOTS,THREE HANDLES,
　FOOTED,SIGNED......................................... 15.00
NIPPON,JAR,CRACKER,FLORAL,GOLD.......................... 16.00
NIPPON,JAR,CRACKER,GREEN & PINK PATTERN,GOLD............. 8.50
NIPPON,JAR,JAM,PINK ROSES,GOLD,HAND-PAINTED,MATCHING SAUCER. 20.00
NIPPON,JAR,JAM,UNDERPLATE,BLUE FLORAL,GOLD............... 6.00
NIPPON,JAR,JELLY,RISING SUN,BLUE FORGET-ME-NOTS,GILT,
　HAND-PAINTED.......................................... 12.00
NIPPON,JAR,MUSTARD,ATTACHED SAUCER,COVER,HAND-PAINTED.... 4.00
NIPPON,JAR,POWDER,PINK & GREEN ENAMEL BEADING,GOLD BEADING,
　COVER,FOOTED.......................................... 22.00
NIPPON,JAR,POWDER,PINK,WHITE,RAISED GOLD DECOR,HAND-PAINTED,
　MAPLE LEAF............................................ 12.50

NIPPON,JAR,TOBACCO,BROWN TONES,ENGLISH BULLDOG ON ONE PANEL,
   HAND-PAINTED........................................... 18.00
NIPPON,JAR,TOBACCO,HAND-PAINTED GOLFING SCENE............... 12.00
NIPPON,KNIFE REST,FOOTED,PINK FLOWERS & GOLD............... 7.50
NIPPON,LEMONADE SET,HAND-PAINTED FLOWERS,SIGNED,PITCHER,FIVE
   CUPS.................................................. 25.00
NIPPON,LEMONADE SET,LARGE PINK ROSES,HAND-PAINTED,GOLD,
   PITCHER,SIX CUPS..................................... 60.00
NIPPON,MAYONNAISE SET,LADLE,AZALEA,HAND-PAINTED............ 10.00
NIPPON,MAYONNAISE SET,SHADED BROWNS,SCENIC,HAND-PAINTED,
   THREE PIECES......................................... 6.50
NIPPON,MAYONNAISE SET,WHITE,FLORAL,GOLD TRIM,HAND-PAINTED,
   THREE PIECE.......................................... 8.00
NIPPON,MAYONNAISE,LADLE,PLATE,GREEN,ROSES,GOLD GARLANDS,SUN
   MARK................................................. 8.50
NIPPON,MUG,SHAVING,HAND PAINTED PICTURE OF LION'S HEAD...... 15.00
NIPPON,MUSTARD POT & LID,PURPLE ASTERS,GOLD,ARTIST-SIGNED,
   2 X 2 1/2 IN......................................... 8.50
NIPPON,NUT SET,BOWL,6 MATCHING SMALL BOWLS,3 LEGS,FLOWERS... 30.00
NIPPON,NUT SET,FLORAL,GOLD TRIM,SEVEN PIECES.............. 7.00
NIPPON,PITCHER,CREAM,BLUE GROUND,ROSES,GOLD TRACING,
   WHEELOCK,TOKYO,JAPAN................................. 37.50
NIPPON,PITCHER,FLOWER BORDER,GILT,6 IN.HIGH............... 7.50
NIPPON,PITCHER,RED,PINK ROSES,CREAMY GROUND,STIPPLED GOLD,
   COBALT TOP........................................... 29.50
NIPPON,PLATE,BLUE,WHITE,FRUIT BLOSSOMS,HAND-PAINTED,8 IN.... 4.00
NIPPON,PLATE,BOUQUET OF DAISIES & BACHELOR BUTTONS,
   ARTIST-SIGNED........................................ 10.50
NIPPON,PLATE,CAKE,EIGHT FLOWER MEDALLIONS,ROSES,TULIPS,GOLD,
   10 IN................................................ 8.00
NIPPON,PLATE,CAKE,FLORAL,GOLD,HAND-PAINTED,HANDLES,9 1/2 IN. 9.50
NIPPON,PLATE,CAKE,ORANGE FLORAL,MEDALLION,GOLD,HANDLES,SIX
   SMALL PLATES......................................... 15.00
NIPPON,PLATE,CAKE,YELLOW ENAMEL,PINK ROSES,HANDLE,SIX
   SMALLER PLATES....................................... 25.00
NIPPON,PLATE,GOLD MEDALLION IN CENTER,ROSE GARLANDS,DAISIES,
   HAND-PAINTED......................................... 7.00
NIPPON,PLATE,GRAY & GREEN,TAN POPPIES,HAND-PAINTED,7 1/2 IN. 4.50
NIPPON,PLATE,HAND-PAINTED FARM & WATER SCENE,10 IN.......... 12.50
NIPPON,PLATE,PINK & ROSE FLOWERS,GOLD,9 3/4-IN.DIAMETER..... 8.00
NIPPON,PLATE,PINK & YELLOW ROSES,GOLD RIM,HAND-PAINTED,
   8 IN.,PAIR........................................... 12.00
NIPPON,PLATE,TOAST,BLUE,GOLD,PINK FLORAL,HAND-PAINTED,COVER. 10.00
NIPPON,PLATE,WHITE WITH GOLD FLORAL,10 IN.................. 10.00
NIPPON,PLATE,WHITE,BLUEBIRDS & FLORAL ON BORDER,9 1/2 IN.... 3.50
NIPPON,PLATTER,PINK ROSES,GOLD,OVAL,HANDLED,14 IN.LONG...... 12.50
NIPPON,PLATTER,WILD GAME BIRDS,MEDALLIONS,HAND-PAINTED,SIX
   PLATES,FORK.......................................... 160.00
NIPPON,RING TREE,GOLD BAND,VIOLETS........................ 12.50
NIPPON,SALAD SET,TRAY,MUSTARD,SPOON,OIL,VINEGAR BOTTLES,
   2 SHAKERS,MARKED..................................... 12.50
NIPPON,SALT,GOLD JEWELED BORDER,WHITE SWAN,WILLOWS,BLUE
   GROUND,OVAL.......................................... 9.50
NIPPON,SALT,INDIVIDUAL,HAND-PAINTED,FOOTED................. 3.00
NIPPON,SALT,INDIVIDUAL,WHITE,GOLD BAND,TWO GOLD HANDLES,SET
   OF 4................................................. 12.00
NIPPON,SALT & PEPPER,WHITE,WIDE YELLOW BORDER TOP EDGE...... 3.00
NIPPON,SALT CELLAR,DELAWARE WATER GAP VIEW,PAIR........... 4.75
NIPPON,SALT DIP,BORDER OF ROSES,GOLD & BLUE MARGIN,
   HAND-PAINTED,OVAL.................................... 3.00
NIPPON,SALT DIP,HAND-PAINTED,FOOTED....................... 2.25
NIPPON,SHERBET,GRAPES,GOLD TRIM........................... 6.00
NIPPON,SHERBET,PINK,RED ROSES,GOLD,STEMMED................ 6.50
NIPPON,SUGAR,SCENIC,COVER,GREEN MARK...................... 5.00
NIPPON,SUGAR & CREAMER,COVER,PASTEL FLOWERS............... 5.00
NIPPON,SYRUP,COVER,PLATE,HAND-PAINTED..................... 10.50
NIPPON,SYRUP,M WREATH,HAND-PAINTED COUNTRY SCENE,COVER,TRAY. 10.00
NIPPON,TEA SET,TALL POT,CREAMER & SUGAR,6 CUPS & SAUCERS,
   GOLD DECOR........................................... 45.00
NIPPON,TEA STRAINER,ROMAN KEY DESIGN,GOLD,GREEN BORDER,WHITE
   GROUND............................................... 12.00
NIPPON,TEAPOT,CREAMER,SUGAR,BLUE,WATER LILIES,SWANS......... 25.00
NIPPON,TEAPOT,CREAMER,SUGAR,WHITE GROUND,PINK ROSES ON
   BORDER,GILT,MARK..................................... 12.75
NIPPON,TEAPOT,FLORAL,FIGURES,SCENES,SUGAR,CREAMER,4 CUPS &
   SAUCERS.............................................. 40.00
NIPPON,TEAPOT,INDIVIDUAL,HAND-PAINTED..................... 3.00
NIPPON,TEAPOT,LAVENDER VIOLETS,GOLD,HAND-PAINTED,6 CUPS &
   SAUCERS.............................................. 32.50
NIPPON,TEAPOT,LAVENDER,BLACK,GREEN,GOLD,BLUE IRIS,CREAMER &
   SUGAR................................................ 29.50

```
NIPPON,TEAPOT,PINK FLORAL,BEADING,GOLD TRIM,HAND-PAINTED,
   CREAMER,SUGAR....................................................   40.00
NIPPON,TEAPOT,SUGAR,CREAMER,6 CUPS,6 SAUCERS,SCENE,
   MOUNTAINS,TREES.................................................   45.00
NIPPON,TEAPOT,WHITE GROUND,ROSE SWAGS,CREAMER,SUGAR,4 CUPS &
   SAUCERS........................................................   16.00
NIPPON,TILE,TEA,BLUE FORGET-ME-NOTS,GILT,HAND-PAINTED.......    6.50
NIPPON,TOOTHPICK,PALE BLUE,BAND OF HAND-PAINTED FLOWERS
   AROUND TOP,MARK................................................    7.50
NIPPON,TOOTHPICK,PINK ROSES,GREEN LEAVES,THREE HANDLES,
   HAND-PAINTED...................................................    3.75
NIPPON,TRAY,CELERY,FLORAL BORDER,RAISED GOLD RIM............    7.50
NIPPON,TRAY,DRESSER,HAND-PAINTED FLOWERS,GOLD,WHITE GROUND..   12.50
NIPPON,TRAY,DRESSER,HAND-PAINTED,8 IN. X 6 IN..............    3.50
NIPPON,TRAY,DRESSER,HAND-PAINTED FLOWERS,GOLD,WHITE GROUND..   12.50
NIPPON,TRAY,DRESSER,ORIENTAL ROOSTER,HAND-PAINTED..........    5.00
NIPPON,TRAY,DRESSER,WHITE,HAND-PAINTED BORDER..............    6.00
NIPPON,TRAY,HAIR RECEIVER,POWDER JAR,SMALL COMPOTE,
   HAND-PAINTED...................................................   20.00
NIPPON,TRAY,HATPIN HOLDER,HAIR RECEIVER,POWDER BOX,PINK
   FIRS,GOLD TRIM.................................................   30.00
NIPPON,TRAY,PINK ROSES,10 IN.ROUND.........................    6.50
NIPPON,TRAY,SANDWICH,SMALL PINK & YELLOW FLOWERS,10 IN......   10.00
NIPPON,TRAY,TEA,BLUE FLOWERS,GREEN VINES,8 1/2 X 5 IN.,PAIR.    3.00
NIPPON,TUMBLER,SCENIC,HAND-PAINTED.........................    4.50
NIPPON,URN,COBALT,GREEN,WHITE,PINK,RED,COVER,11 IN.TALL,
   8 IN.WIDE......................................................   75.00
NIPPON,VASE,AUTUMN SCENE,GOLD TRIM,HAND-PAINTED,10 IN.HIGH..   35.00
NIPPON,VASE,BLACK SHIP DECOR,BROWN GROUND,9 IN.............   20.00
NIPPON,VASE,BLACK,GOLD,ROSES,PEDESTAL BASE,SIDE HANDLES,
   HAND-PAINTED...................................................   11.50
NIPPON,VASE,BLACKBIRDS IN FLIGHT,GOLD HANDLES AT TOP,9 IN.,
   PAIR...........................................................   37.50
NIPPON,VASE,BLUE-GREEN,GOLD RIM,GOLD HANDLES,HAND-PAINTED,
   10 IN..........................................................   15.00
NIPPON,VASE,BROWN GROUND,YELLOW ROSES,GOLD,HANDLES,
   8 1/2 IN.,PAIR.................................................   35.00
NIPPON,VASE,BROWN LEAF TRIM,10 IN..........................   35.00
NIPPON,VASE,GREEN FOLIAGE,RED ROSES,CREAM BASE,HANDLES,
   10 IN.HIGH,PAIR................................................  100.00
NIPPON,VASE,GREEN GROUND,BLUE COLUMBINE,GOLD TRIM,GOLD
   HANDLES,11 IN..................................................   35.00
NIPPON,VASE,GREEN,BEIGE,FOUR HANDLES,SQUARE OPENING.........   18.00
NIPPON,VASE,MOUNTAIN,LAKE SCENE,GOLD,BEADING,HAND-PAINTED,
   4 X 4 1/2 IN...................................................   12.50
NIPPON,VASE,OAK LEAF,SQUATTY,PAIR..........................   25.00
NIPPON,VASE,ORIENTAL SCENE,LARGE FLORAL,HAND-PAINTED,
   16 IN.TALL.....................................................   20.00
NIPPON,VASE,PANELS,MOUNTAINS,WATER,HAND-PAINTED,HANDLES,M IN
   WREATH.........................................................    8.50
NIPPON,VASE,SAILING SHIPS,BRONZE,GOLD,FOOTED,HAND-PAINTED,
   10 IN.TALL.....................................................   24.50
NIPPON,VASE,SCENIC DECOR,TWO GOLD HANDLES,6 IN.WIDE,
   8 IN.TALL......................................................   17.00
NIPPON,VASE,SKY,STREAM,FOREST,HAND-PAINTED,SIDE HANDLES,
   10 IN..........................................................   15.00
```

NODDERS OR NODDING FIGURES OR PAGODS ARE PORCELAIN
FIGURES WITH HEADS AND HANDS THAT ARE ATTACHED TO
WIRES. ANY SLIGHT MOVEMENT CAUSES THE PARTS TO MOVE UP
AND DOWN. EXAMPLES WERE MADE IN MANY COUNTRIES DURING
THE EIGHTEENTH AND NINETEENTH CENTURIES.

```
NODDER,BISQUE,CHINESE MAN,ROBE,DROOPY MUSTACHE,WOMAN,ROBE,
   3 IN.,PAIR.....................................................   42.00
NODDER,BISQUE,MAN,MUSTACHE,TURBAN,SEATED CROSS-LEGGED,
   SCIMITAR.......................................................   30.00
NODDER,CANDLESTICK,BISQUE,SEESAW,CHILDREN SWAYING,TREE TRUNK
   BASE...........................................................   55.00
NODDER,CHILD,BISQUE.............................................ILLUS.   32.50
NODDER,EGYPTIAN QUEEN,ON KNEES IN PRAYING POSITION,GOLD &
   BROWN,BISQUE...................................................   30.00
NODDER,GIRL HOLDING PUPPY UNDER CAPE,GREEN CLOTHES,BROWN
   TRIM,BISQUE....................................................   25.00
NODDER,GRANDMA IN CHAIR,WOOD,PAPIER-MACHE,5 IN.HIGH.........   10.00
NODDER,MONK IN BROWN HABIT,HOLDS STEIN IN ONE HAND,LEAVES IN
   OTHER,BISQUE...................................................   35.00
NODDER,STAFFORDSHIRE,MAN,WOMAN,PAIR........................  150.00
```

NORITAKE MARKED PORCELAIN WAS MADE IN JAPAN AFTER 1904
BY NIPPON TOKI KAISHA.

NODDER, CHILD, BiSQUE

| | |
|---|---|
| NORITAKE,BOWL,BIRDS,FRUIT,HAND-PAINTED,M MARK,9 1/2 IN...... | 10.00 |
| NORITAKE,BOWL,FERNAND PATTERN,OVAL,9 1/4 IN................ | 10.50 |
| NORITAKE,BOWL,GOLD,BLUE,YELLOW PATTERN,PROTRUDING CORNERS,<br>   HANDLE,8 IN............................................. | 8.00 |
| NORITAKE,BOWL,VEGETABLE,YELLOW & GOLD AUTUMN SCENE,<br>   HAND-PAINTED,11 IN...................................... | 14.00 |
| NORITAKE,BOWL,YELLOW GROUND,ALLOVER LANDSCAPE,10 IN........ | 8.00 |
| NORITAKE,BOWL,YELLOW GROUND,YELLOW,WHITE CHECKS,SCALLOPED<br>   BORDER,FLORAL............................................. | 7.00 |
| NORITAKE,BOX,TRINKET,BLACK GROUND,COLORFUL LADIES PLAYING<br>   INSTRUMENTS.............................................. | 18.00 |
| NORITAKE,BUTTER CHIP,SCENIC,TWO HANDLES,GOLD TRIM,<br>   HAND-PAINTED,SET OF 6.................................... | 9.00 |
| NORITAKE,BUTTER PAT,BIRDS,FLOWERS,SET OF 4................. | 5.00 |
| NORITAKE,BUTTER TUB,AZALEA................................ | 18.00 |
| NORITAKE,CAKE SET,HAND-PAINTED FLORAL CENTERS,RED MARK,SEVEN<br>   PIECES.................................................. | 10.00 |
| NORITAKE,CAKE SET,ROSE DECOR,7 PIECES..................... | 17.00 |
| NORITAKE,CANDLESTICK,WHITE,LIGHT BLUE FLORAL,PAIR.......... | 8.50 |
| NORITAKE,CHOCOLATE POT,PINK,FIVE CUPS & SAUCERS.... 19.00 TO | 22.00 |
| NORITAKE,CREAMER & SUGAR,AZALEA........................... | 15.00 |
| NORITAKE,CREAMER & SUGAR,BLUE FLORAL,ROSES,GOLD,<br>   HAND-PAINTED,MARKED..................................... | 8.50 |
| NORITAKE,CREAMER & SUGAR,WHITE GROUND,BLUE FLOWER,BROWN<br>   BORDER,GOLD,MARK........................................ | 16.50 |
| NORITAKE,CREAMER & SUGAR,4 CUPS & SAUCERS,M.CORTEZ......... | 12.50 |
| NORITAKE,CUP & SAUCER,BOUILLON,THE SEDAN,SET OF 7.......... | 7.00 |
| NORITAKE,CUP & SAUCER,DEMITASSE,SEDALIA,SET OF EIGHT....... | 40.00 |
| NORITAKE,CUP & SAUCER,MUSTACHE,SHADED BLUE LAKE SCENE,TREE,<br>   SWAN.................................................... | 25.00 |
| NORITAKE,CUP,EGG,BAND OF FLOWERS.......................... | 3.25 |
| NORITAKE,CUP,EGG,FLORAL DECOR............................. | 4.00 |
| NORITAKE,CUP,SAUCER,RAISED BUNCHES OF PINK CARNATIONS,GOLD,<br>   HAND-PAINTED............................................ | 9.00 |
| NORITAKE,DINNER SET,AZALEA PATTERN,SERVICE FOR SIX,<br>   100 PIECES.............................................. | 150.00 |
| NORITAKE,DISH,BLUE,GOLD FLOWERS,HAND-PAINTED,MARKED,<br>   6-1/2 IN.DIAMETER....................................... | 15.00 |
| NORITAKE,DISH,BUTTER,HAND-PAINTED FLOWERS,SEPARATE LINER,<br>   COVER................................................... | 8.50 |
| NORITAKE,DISH,BUTTER,SCALLOPED TOP,HAND-PAINTED........... | 15.00 |
| NORITAKE,DISH,CANDY,WATER LILY DESIGN,<br>   HAND-PAINTED,6.................................... 7.00 TO | 7.50 |
| NORITAKE,DISH,CELERY,AZALEA............................... | 16.00 |
| NORITAKE,DISH,DEEP,FLOWERS IN BOTTOM,HAND-PAINTED.......... | 4.00 |
| NORITAKE,DISH,RELISH,AZALEA,7 IN.......................... | 14.00 |
| NORITAKE,DISH,RELISH,DIVIDED,8 1/2 IN..................... | 11.50 |
| NORITAKE,DISH,SALAD,AZALEA,7 3/4 IN....................... | 3.50 |
| NORITAKE,DISH,SAUCE,AZALEA................................ | 2.75 |
| NORITAKE,GRAVY BOAT,UNDER PLATE,IVORY BORDER,RAISED GOLD,<br>   HAND-PAINTED............................................ | 11.50 |
| NORITAKE,HAIR RECEIVER,FLORAL,GOLD,IVORY COLOR BORDER,<br>   HAND-PAINTED............................................ | 5.00 |
| NORITAKE,JAR,POWDER,YELLOW & GREEN,WHITE POPPIES.......... | 10.00 |
| NORITAKE,MAYONNAISE SET,AZALEA,THREE PIECES............... | 18.00 |
| NORITAKE,PICKLE,FLORAL,HAND-PAINTED,OVAL.................. | 6.00 |
| NORITAKE,PITCHER,AZALEA PATTERN,PINK,YELLOW,HAND-PAINTED,<br>   3 IN.HIGH............................................... | 6.75 |
| NORITAKE,PLATE,AZALEA PATTERN,GREEN MARK,7 1/2 IN......... | 2.50 |
| NORITAKE,PLATE,BLUE,WHITE,PHOENIX BIRD,SET OF FOUR........ | 15.00 |
| NORITAKE,PLATE,CAKE,AZALEA................................ | 9.50 |
| NORITAKE,PLATE,CAKE,LAKE & SUNSET SCENE,HANDLES,SIX SMALL<br>   PLATES................................................. | 15.00 |
| NORITAKE,PLATE,CAKE,LAKE,TREES,SWAN,HAND-PAINTED,OPEN<br>   HANDLES................................................. | 11.00 |
| NORITAKE,PLATE,CREAM & TAN,PINK ROSES,6 1/2 IN............ | 3.00 |

NORITAKE,PLATE,DINNER,THE SEDAN,SET OF 6..................... 6.00
NORITAKE,PLATE,FLORAL SPRAY,AQUA LUSTER TRIM,GOLD CENTER
  HANDLE....................................................... 5.50
NORITAKE,PLATE,HAND-PAINTED SCENE,HANDLES,9 1/4 IN.......... 5.00
NORITAKE,PLATE,LEMON,TAN BAND,LEMONS IN CENTER,HANDLE....... 3.00
NORITAKE,PLATE,SOUP,DRESALDA,FLORAL,GOLD,8 1/8 IN.,SET OF 6. 22.00
NORITAKE,PLATE,TEA,BLUE,WHITE,PHOENIX BIRD,SET OF FOUR...... 10.00
NORITAKE,RAMMEKIN,WHITE,BLUE & YELLOW FLORAL BORDER,
  UNDERPLATE.................................................. 4.50
NORITAKE,SALT DIP,ACORN,HAND-PAINTED,FLUTED EDGE,FOOTED..... 2.50
NORITAKE,SHAKER,SUGAR,GREEN BANDS,FLORAL,GOLD TOP,6 IN.HIGH. 7.00
NORITAKE,SPOONER,BLACK,GOLD TRIM,OBLONG,TWO HANDLES......... 8.00
NORITAKE,SUGAR,OPEN,PEARLIZED IRIDESCENT,FLOWERS,HANDLES,
  PAIR....................................................... 5.00
NORITAKE,SYRUP,AZALEA,TRAY.................................. 8.50
NORITAKE,TUB,BUTTER,AZALEA,INSERT.......................... 8.50
NORITAKE,TUREEN,VEGETABLE,GOLD HANDLES,HAND-PAINTED FLOWERS,
  COVER,10 IN................................................ 8.50
NORITAKE,VASE,WHITE CENTER,FLORAL,HANDLES,BLACK............. 12.50
NORITAKE,VASE,YELLOW GROUND,SALMON & PINK ROSES,GOLD
  HANDLES,PAIR............................................... 45.00


        NORTHWOOD GLASS COMPANY WORKED IN MARTINS FERRY,OHIO,
        FROM 1888. THEY MARKED SOME PIECES WITH THE LETTER N IN
        A CIRCLE. MANY PIECES OF CARNIVAL GLASS WERE MADE BY
        THIS COMPANY.
NORTHWOOD,SEE ALSO,CARNIVAL GLASS
NORTHWOOD,BANANA BOAT,RED GRAPES,GOLD CABLE & LEAVES,FOOTED. 35.00
NORTHWOOD,BERRY SET,THUMBPRINT,RED GRAPES,GOLD CABLE &
  LEAVES,7 PIECES............................................ 50.00
NORTHWOOD,BOWL,BEADED CIRCLE,RUFFLED,CLEAR & OPALESCENT,
  FOOTED..................................................... 8.00
NORTHWOOD,BOWL,BERRY,BLOCK PATTERN,CLEAR,N MARK,5
  SAUCES.................................... 23.00 TO         25.00
NORTHWOOD,BOWL,GREEN-GOLD,GREEN TREE BARK FEET,SIGNED N..... 35.00
NORTHWOOD,BOWL,GREEN,DAHLIA,RUFFLED EDGE,FOOTED............. 22.00
NORTHWOOD,BOWL,OPALESCENT,BUTTON PANELS,BLUE................ 14.50
NORTHWOOD,BOWL,ROSE SHOW,8 1/2 IN........................... 25.00
NORTHWOOD,BOWL,ROSE,DAISY & PLUME...................ILLUS.. 17.50

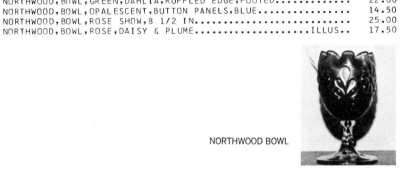

NORTHWOOD BOWL

NORTHWOOD,BOWL,ROSE,GREEN,OPAL TRIM ON TOP,LEAF & BEADS,
  FOOTED..................................................... 15.00
NORTHWOOD,BOWL,WHITE,BROWN LEAVES,RED FLOWERS,9 IN.......... 17.00
NORTHWOOD,BUTTER,BASKET WEAVE,GOLD LEAVES,RED CHERRIES,
  COVER,CLEAR................................................ 37.50
NORTHWOOD,CANDLESTICK,GRAPE PATTERN,MARK,5 1/2 IN........... 15.00
NORTHWOOD,CELERY HOLDER,MARK,5 1/4 IN....................... 10.00
NORTHWOOD,CREAMER & SUGAR,CLEAR,PEACH PATTERN,GOLD,COVER.... 35.00
NORTHWOOD,CREAMER & SUGAR,PEACH PATTERN,GOLD TRIM,MARK...... 32.50
NORTHWOOD,CREAMER,ALASKA,CLEAR & OPALESCENT................. 16.00
NORTHWOOD,CREAMER,CHERRY,CLEAR,RED FRUIT,GOLD CABLE,N MARK.. 20.00
NORTHWOOD,CREAMER,GOLD ROSE,MARK........................... 22.00
NORTHWOOD,CREAMER,SPOONER,COVERED SUGAR,STRAWBERRIES,RED,
  GOLD BAND,MARK............................................. 75.00
NORTHWOOD,CREAMER,SUGAR,SPOONER,DRAPE PATTERN,TURQUOISE,GOLD
  TRIM....................................................... 95.00
NORTHWOOD,DISH,CLEAR OPALESCENT,MILKY RIBS,RUFFLED,ARGONAUT,
  SIGNED..................................................... 27.50
NORTHWOOD,DISH,SAUCE,GREEN-GOLD,MEMPHIS,MARK,SET OF 4....... 22.00
NORTHWOOD,DISH,SAUCE,PANELED CHERRY........................ 5.50
NORTHWOOD,LAMP BASE,BLUE-WHITE GOOFUS FINISH,PEACOCK FANTAIL 45.00
NORTHWOOD,PITCHER,BLUE SWIRL,RUFFLED TOP,BULBOUS,FIVE
  TUMBLERS,MARK.............................................. 65.00
NORTHWOOD,PITCHER,CHERRIES,CLEAR,N MARK,6 TUMBLERS.......... 125.00
NORTHWOOD,PITCHER,CHERRIES,DAISIES,HAND-PAINTED,COBALT,
  6 TUMBLERS................................................. 125.00
NORTHWOOD,PITCHER,CLEAR,RED CHERRIES,GILT,MARK,ONE TUMBLER.. 50.00

NORTHWOOD,PITCHER,GREEN,GOLD,BUCKLE & STAR,FIVE TUMBLERS,
 MARKED N.................................................. 55.00
NORTHWOOD,PITCHER,PANEL,PURPLE GRAPES,GOLD TRIM,CLEAR,SIX
 TUMBLERS................................................. 195.00
NORTHWOOD,PITCHER,TANKARD,RED GRAPES,GOLD CABLE & LEAVES.... 90.00
NORTHWOOD,PUNCH SET,MEMPHIS,CLEAR,9 3/4-X
 11 1/2-IN.DIAMETER,6 CUPS................................ 125.00
NORTHWOOD,SAUCE,GREEN & GOLD,MARK,SET OF 4.................. 19.00
NORTHWOOD,SAUCE,PANELED CHERRY............................. 5.00
NORTHWOOD,SPOONER,BASKET WEAVE,GOLD LEAVES,RED CHERRIES,
 CLEAR.................................................... 17.00
NORTHWOOD,SPOONER,CLEAR,PANELED,THUMBPRINT,RED CHERRIES,GOLD
 TRIM,MARK................................................ 20.00
NORTHWOOD,SPOONER,GOLD ROSE................................ 18.00
NORTHWOOD,SUGAR,BASKET WEAVE,GOLD LEAVES,RED CHERRIES,COVER,
 CLEAR.................................................... 25.00
NORTHWOOD,SUGAR,GOLD ROSE,COVER,MARK....................... 25.00
NORTHWOOD,TUMBLER,BASKET WEAVE,GOLD LEAVES,RED CHERRIES,
 CLEAR.................................................... 12.00
NORTHWOOD,TUMBLER,DRAPE PATTERN,TURQUOISE,OPALESCENT,SET OF
 6........................................................ 84.00
NORTHWOOD,TUMBLER,DRAPE,BLUE OPALESCENT,GOLD TRIM........... 14.00
NORTHWOOD,TUMBLER,FROSTED GLASS,ENAMELED FLOWERS,SIGNED N... 15.00
NORTHWOOD,TUMBLER,GREEN,GOLD,ORIENTAL POPPY................ 9.50
NORTHWOOD,TUMBLER,ORIENTAL POPPY,GREEN,GOLD TRIM........... 8.00
NORTHWOOD,TUMBLER,RED STRAWBERRIES,GOLD TRIM............... 7.50
NORTHWOOD,TUMBLER,WATER LILY,CATTAILS,BLUE OPALESCENT,SET OF
 5........................................................ 55.00
NORTHWOOD,VASE,FROSTY WHITE................................ 35.00
NORTHWOOD,VASE,GREEN BOTTOM TO DEEP AMBER,SIGNED,10 IN...... 18.00
NORTHWOOD,VASE,GREEN TO IRIDESCENT ORANGE,RUFFLED TOP,
 SIGNED,19 IN............................................. 11.00
NORTHWOOD,VASE,OPALESCENT,BLUE,SIGNED...................... 40.00
NORTHWOOD,VASE,PEACOCK FANTAIL,BLUE,WHITE,GOOFUS FINISH..... 35.00
NORTHWOOD,VASE,WHITE,BLUE,SATIN,SIX TWISTED CAMPHOR FEET,
 7 IN.HIGH............................................... 450.00
NORTHWOOD,WATER SET,DRAPERY PATTERN,BLUE,MARK,7 PIECES...... 90.00
NUART,GLOBE,GAS,MARIGOLD IRIDESCENT,SIGNED................. 10.00
NUART,SHADE,GOLD,IRIDESCENT,SCALLOPED BOTTOM,SIGNED,
 5 1/4 IN.HIGH............................................ 18.00
NUART,SHADE,GOLD,IRIDESCENT,SCALLOPED BOTTOM,5 1/2 IN.HIGH,
 PAIR..................................................... 35.00
NYMPHENBURG,DOVE,FANNED-OUT TAIL,GOLD COLOR BASE,5 X
 5 IN.HIGH,PAIR........................................... 75.00

OLD IVORY,BERRY SET,NO.16.................................. 75.00
OLD IVORY,BERRY SET,NO.16,SEVEN PIECES..................... 68.50
OLD IVORY,BERRY SET,NO.84.................................. 75.00
OLD IVORY,BOWL,BERRY,NO.15................................. 30.00
OLD IVORY,BOWL,BERRY,NO.84................................. 33.00
OLD IVORY,BOWL,NO.15,SILESIA,6 1/2 IN...................... 13.00
OLD IVORY,BOWL,NO.15,SILESIA,10 1/4 IN..................... 22.50
OLD IVORY,BOWL,NO.73....................................... 34.50
OLD IVORY,BOWL,PATTERN NO.15,10 IN......................... 35.00
OLD IVORY,BOWL,SALAD,NO.84,9 1/2-IN.DIAMETER............... 28.00
OLD IVORY,BOWL,SUGAR,PINK & WHITE DOGWOOD,VIOLETS,COVER,
 SILESIA.................................................. 25.00
OLD IVORY,BOWL,VEGETABLE,9 3/4 IN.......................... 23.00
OLD IVORY,BOWL,VEGETABLE,NO.32,9 1/2 IN.................... 23.00
OLD IVORY,CELERY,NO.28..................................... 24.50
OLD IVORY,CELERY,VII,SILESIA,12 X 5 1/2 IN................. 21.50
OLD IVORY,CHOCOLATE POT,NO.36,PEACH COLOR ROSES............ 85.00
OLD IVORY,CREAMER & SUGAR,NO.82.............. 60.00 TO 65.00
OLD IVORY,CREAMER & SUGAR,NO.84............................ 38.00
OLD IVORY,CREAMER,NO.1,SUGAR,NO.0,LILIES OF THE VALLEY,GILT,
 GREEN FERNS.............................................. 45.00
OLD IVORY,CREAMER,NO.11.................................... 16.50
OLD IVORY,CREAMER,NO.16.................................... 25.00
OLD IVORY,CREAMER,PINK FLORAL,GILT,4 1/2 IN.HIGH........... 16.00
OLD IVORY,CREAMER,PINK FLORAL,GOLD,HAND-PAINTED,CROWN MARK,
 GERMANY.................................................. 16.00
OLD IVORY,CREAMER,PINK ROSES,CROWN 7/869 MARK,4 1/2 IN.HIGH. 16.00
OLD IVORY,CUP & SAUCER,NO.105,ORANGE POPPIES,GREEN LEAVES... 16.50
OLD IVORY,CUP & SAUCER,NO.16............................... 35.00
OLD IVORY,CUP & SAUCER,SET OF 5............................ 20.00
OLD IVORY,DISH,CANDY,RING HANDLE,NO.XV,6 1/2 IN............ 25.00
OLD IVORY,DISH,PINK ROSES,RUFFLE EDGE,8-IN.DIAMETER........ 20.00
OLD IVORY,DISH,RELISH,NO.16............................... 17.50
OLD IVORY,DISH,RELISH,NO.84,6 1/2 IN...................... 12.00
OLD IVORY,DISH,SAUCE,NO.200,SILESIA,5 IN.................. 11.50
OLD IVORY,DISH,SAUCE,PATTERN NO.200,5 IN.................. 12.00

| | |
|---|---|
| OLD IVORY,DISH,SAUCE,PATTERN NO.84,5 IN. | 13.00 |
| OLD IVORY,HAIR RECEIVER,LAVENDER WILD ROSE DECOR,MARKED, GERMANY,NO.5 | 18.00 |
| OLD IVORY,HAIR RECEIVER,PINK THISTLES,GREEN LEAVES,GERMANY | 12.00 |
| OLD IVORY,MAYONNAISE SET,PATTERN NO.75 | 30.00 |
| OLD IVORY,NAPPIE,PATTERN,NO.16,SILESIA | 22.50 |
| OLD IVORY,PICKLE,OVAL,6 1/2 IN. | 12.00 |
| OLD IVORY,PLATE,BREAD & BUTTER,NO.IV. | 9.00 |
| OLD IVORY,PLATE,BREAD & BUTTER,NO.16. | 9.00 |
| OLD IVORY,PLATE,CAKE. | 34.00 |
| OLD IVORY,PLATE,CAKE,NO.IV,10 IN. | 20.00 |
| OLD IVORY,PLATE,CAKE,NO.XV,6 1/4-IN.DIAMETER. | 8.00 |
| OLD IVORY,PLATE,CAKE,NO.15,10 IN. | 30.00 |
| OLD IVORY,PLATE,CAKE,NO.16,OPEN HANDLES,10 IN. | 30.00 |
| OLD IVORY,PLATE,CAKE,NO.33,PAIR. | 22.00 |
| OLD IVORY,PLATE,CAKE,NO.84,10 IN. | 32.50 |
| OLD IVORY,PLATE,CAKE,NO.200,10-IN.DIAMETER. | 32.50 |
| OLD IVORY,PLATE,CAKE,OPEN HANDLE,NO.84,SILESIA. | 25.00 |
| OLD IVORY,PLATE,CAKE,PATTERN NO.84,10 IN. | 36.00 |
| OLD IVORY,PLATE,CAKE,10-IN.DIAMETER,15 IN.HIGH. | 32.00 |
| OLD IVORY,PLATE,NO.XI,8 1/2-IN.DIAMETER. | 20.00 |
| OLD IVORY,PLATE,NO.8,8 1/4 IN.,SET OF 3. | 16.50 |
| OLD IVORY,PLATE,NO.15,6 IN. | |
| OLD IVORY,PLATE,NO.15,6 1/4 IN. | 13.50 |
| OLD IVORY,PLATE,NO.16,6 IN. | 14.00 |
| OLD IVORY,PLATE,NO.16,6 1/4 IN.,SET OF 8. | 8.00 |
| OLD IVORY,PLATE,NO.16,6 1/2 IN. | 13.50 |
| OLD IVORY,PLATE,NO.22,HOLLY BERRIES,6 1/4 IN. | 8.00 |
| OLD IVORY,PLATE,NO.34,HANDLE,10 IN. | 25.50 |
| OLD IVORY,PLATE,NO.75,6 IN. | 13.50 |
| OLD IVORY,PLATE,NO.76,6 1/4 IN. | 13.50 |
| OLD IVORY,PLATE,NO.82,10-IN.DIAMETER. | 60.00 |
| OLD IVORY,PLATE,NO.200,SILESIA,6 IN. | 11.00 |
| OLD IVORY,PLATE,NO.200,6 IN. | 12.00 |
| OLD IVORY,PLATE,NO.200,7 1/2 IN. | 13.00 |
| OLD IVORY,PLATE,NO.200,7 1/2 IN.,SET OF 6. | 78.00 |
| OLD IVORY,PLATE,NO.200,8 1/2 IN. | 14.00 |
| OLD IVORY,PLATE,PEACH COLOR & WHITE FLORAL,GOLD RIM,SILESIA, 8 3/4 IN. | 15.00 |
| OLD IVORY,RELISH NO.XV. | 16.50 |
| OLD IVORY,RELISH,OVAL,HANDLE. | 14.00 |
| OLD IVORY,SALT & PEPPER,PATTERN NO.84. | 25.00 |
| OLD IVORY,SALT,NO.84,PAIR. | 34.00 |
| OLD IVORY,SAUCE,CROWN 200 MARK. | 7.50 |
| OLD IVORY,SAUCE,NO.XXXII. | 10.00 |
| OLD IVORY,SAUCE,5 IN.,SET OF 4. | 6.00 |
| OLD IVORY,SHAKER,SALT,PAIR. | 12.00 |
| OLD IVORY,TOOTHPICK,NO.84,2 IN. | 22.00 |
| OLD IVORY,TRAY,RELISH,PATTERN NO.16,11 1/2 IN. | 32.00 |
| OLD IVORY,TRAY,ROLL,PATTERN NO.84. | 37.00 |
| ONION,BOWL,MEISSEN,CROSSED SWORDS,11 IN. OBLONG,2 IN. DEEP, COVER. | 60.00 |
| ONION,BOWL,MEISSEN,CROSSED SWORDS,OVAL,FOOTED,FLARED HANDLES | 80.00 |
| ONION,BOWL,SUGAR,ROSEBUD & LEAF FINIAL ON COVER,MEISSEN. | 22.00 |
| ONION,COFFEEPOT,MEISSEN,ROSE FINIAL. | 55.00 |
| ONION,CUP,EGG. | 5.00 |
| ONION,CUP & SAUCER,BLUE,WHITE,MEISSEN,CROSSED SWORDS MARK. | 15.00 |
| ONION,CUP & SAUCER,DEMITASSE,MEISSEN. | 12.75 |
| ONION,DISH,BLUE ON WHITE,CROSSED SWORDS MARK,MEISSEN,9 IN. | 64.00 |
| ONION,DISH,BLUE,WHITE,MEISSEN,CROSSED SWORDS MARK ON FRONT & BACK,9 IN. | 64.00 |
| ONION,DISH,CHEESE & CRACKER,FLOWER FINIAL,MEISSEN. | 37.00 |
| ONION,JAR,SPICE,BARREL SHAPE,COVER,GERMANY. | 5.50 |
| ONION,KNIFE,FRUIT,BLUE,MARKED UCHATIUSBRONCE GERMANY,SET OF 6. | 25.00 |
| ONION,PITCHER,6 IN. | 10.00 |
| ONION,PLATE,9 IN. ILLUS. | 12.50 |
| ONION,PLATE,BLUE,WHITE,MARKED DRESDEN,GERMANY. | 5.00 |
| ONION,PLATE,BLUE,WHITE,SCALLOPED,JOHNSON BROTHERS,ENGLAND, 9 IN. | 15.00 |
| ONION,PLATE,CAKE,BLUE,WHITE,MARKED DRESDEN. | 5.00 |
| ONION,PLATE,MEISSEN,8 IN.,SET OF 6. | 50.00 |
| ONION,PLATE,SOUP,BLUE,WHITE,MARKED DRESDEN. | 5.00 |
| ONION,PLATE,SOUP,MEISSEN,SCALLOPED,CROSSED SWORD MARK, 9 1/2 IN. | 22.00 |
| ONION,PLATTER,BLUE,WHITE,MARKED DRESDEN,GERMANY. | 10.00 |
| ONION,PLATTER,MEISSEN,10 IN. X 19 1/2 IN. | 50.00 |
| ONION,PLATTER,MEISSEN,CROSSED SWORDS,16 IN. | 50.00 |
| ONION,TEAPOT,BLUE & RED,GERMANY. | 35.00 |
| ONION,TEAPOT,BULBOUS,ROSEBUD & LEAF FINIAL,MEISSEN. | 45.00 |
| ONION,TUMBLER,BLUE,HOF-MASCHENDORF,BAVARIA,CIRCA 1878,SET OF | |

ONION PLATE

```
5.............................................................    15.00
ONION,TUREEN,BLUE,2 1/2-QT.SIZE...............................    35.00
ONION,TUREEN,BLUE,9 1/2 IN.WIDE X 8 IN.TALL...................    32.00
ONION,TUREEN,MEISSEN,BLUE,COVER,CROSSED SWORD MARK,13 IN.
  LONG........................................................   150.00
```

OPALESCENT GLASS IS TRANSLUCENT GLASS THAT HAS THE
BLUISH-WHITE TONES OF THE OPAL GEMSTONE. IT IS OFTEN
FOUND IN PRESSED GLASSWARES MADE IN VICTORIAN TIMES.
SOME DEALERS USE THE TERMS OPALINE AND OPALESCENT FOR
ANY OF THE BLUISH-WHITE TRANSLUCENT WARES.

```
OPALESCENT,BASKET,MINIATURE,PINK..............................    35.00
OPALESCENT,BOTTLE,SCENT,PEWTER SCREW TOP......................    30.00
OPALESCENT,BOWL,ALLOVER HORSEMAN DECOR,BAROLAC,SIGNED,3 X
  5 IN........................................................    39.00
OPALESCENT,BOWL,BLUE,SIGNED MCK...............................    50.00
OPALESCENT,BOWL,CLEAR & OPAQUE WHITE STRIPES,SQUATTY,6 3/4 X
  2 1/2 IN....................................................    25.00
OPALESCENT,BOWL,ROSE,GREEN,EMBOSSED,BEADED PATTERN,RUFFLED..     18.00
OPALESCENT,BOWL,ROSE,PEACH COLOR,WHITE LINING,FLUTED EDGE...     25.00
OPALESCENT,BOWL,ROSE,PINK STRIPE,CRYSTAL PULLED-UP PETALS,
  FOOTED......................................................    42.00
OPALESCENT,BOWL,SALAD,LIGHT GREEN,MAROON THREADING,SILVER
  RIM,HANDLES.................................................    48.00
OPALESCENT,CANDLESNUFFER,CLEAR STRIPE,ENAMEL FLORAL,DUNCE
  HAT SHAPE...................................................    30.00
OPALESCENT,CANDLESNUFFER,ENAMEL DECOR,STRIPES................     18.00
OPALESCENT,CREAMER,ALASKA,LION LEG,BLUE......................     50.00
OPALESCENT,CREAMER,WHITE,BEADED SHELL PATTERN................     10.00
OPALESCENT,CRUET,COIN SPOT,7 IN..............................     55.50
OPALESCENT,DISH,APPLE GREEN,LACY EDGE,FOOTED.................     13.50
OPALESCENT,DISH,BUTTER,TOKYO,GREEN,COVER.....................     37.50
OPALESCENT,EPERGNE,LIME GREEN,THREE LILIES,BASKETS ON TWO
  CRYSTAL ARMS................................................   185.00
OPALESCENT,FIGURINE,ST.THERESA,SIGNED ETLING,FRANCE,
  8 1/4 IN.HIGH...............................................    15.00
OPALESCENT,PITCHER,WATER,BEADED SWAG,PINK FLOWERS,WHITE,FOUR
  TUMBLERS....................................................   100.00
OPALESCENT,PITCHER,WATER,COIN SPOT,BLUE,REED HANDLE..........     75.00
OPALESCENT,PITCHER,WATER,PALM BEACH,BLUE.....................     65.00
OPALESCENT,PLATE,TOKYO PATTERN,GREEN.........................     14.50
OPALESCENT,SALT & PEPPER,BIRD................................     19.00
OPALESCENT,SHAKER,SUGAR,THUMBPRINT,GREEN,BULBOUS.............     22.00
OPALESCENT,SHAKER,SUGAR,VARIANT OF SPANISH LACE.............      16.50
OPALESCENT,SPOONER,ALASKA,BLUE...............................     45.00
OPALESCENT,SPOONER,BLUE,IRIS,MEANDER.........................     27.50
OPALESCENT,SPOONER,CLEAR,IRIS,MEANDER........................     17.50
OPALESCENT,SYRUP,COIN SPOT...................................     21.00
OPALESCENT,SYRUP,SWIRL PATTERN,RESILVERED TOP,6 IN.TALL.....      37.50
OPALESCENT,TOOTHPICK,IRIDESCENT,FOOTED.......................     15.00
OPALESCENT,TOOTHPICK,RIBBED..................................     15.00
OPALESCENT,TUMBLER,BLUE,INVERTED FAN & FEATHER..............      35.00
OPALESCENT,TUMBLER,COIN SPOT.................................     15.00
OPALESCENT,TUMBLER,SHRINE,MINNEAPOLIS,1917,THREE MEN & MULE,
  OPAQUE......................................................    28.00
OPALESCENT,VASE,ALLOVER HIGH RELIEF FLORAL,SIGNED JOBLINGS
  OPALIQUE....................................................    65.00
OPALESCENT,VASE,CORN,CRINKLED HUSK HANDLES,8 IN.TALL........      40.00
OPALESCENT,VASE,FLAT OVAL SHAPE,FEMALE NUDES WITH FLOWING
  HAIR,ETLING.................................................    78.00
```

OPALINE GLASS OR OPAL GLASS WAS MADE IN WHITE, APPLE GREEN, AND OTHER COLORS. THE GLASS HAD A MATTE SURFACE AND A LACK OF TRANSPARENCY. IT WAS OFTEN GILDED OR PAINTED. IT WAS A POPULAR MID-NINETEENTH-CENTURY EUROPEAN GLASSWARE.

| | |
|---|---:|
| OPALINE, BOTTLE, BARBER, SIGNED E.W. INC ...................... | 12.00 |
| OPALINE, BOTTLE, SCENT, GOLD COLOR LEAVES, APPLIED TURQUOISE SNAKE ON NECK ..................................... | 30.00 |
| OPALINE, BOWL, PUNCH, UNDERPLATE, LADLE, GOLD & BLUE ENAMEL DECOR, BALL FINIAL ................................... | 95.00 |
| OPALINE, BOWL, RAISED DESIGN, BIRDS, SIGNED EZAN, FRANCE, 10 IN ... | 23.00 |
| OPALINE, BOWL, SATIN FINISH, CHERRY PATTERN, SIGNED, FRANCE, 10 IN ..................................... | 10.50 |
| OPALINE, BOX, BLUE, PINK & WHITE FLOWERS ON TOP, HINGED ........ | 38.00 |
| OPALINE, BOX, GREEN JEWEL-LIKE DECOR, BRASS ORMOLU ON RIM & LID, GERMANY ..................................... | 42.00 |
| OPALINE, BOX, PATCH, PINK, CHERUBS, 2 1/2-IN. DIAMETER ........... | 25.00 |
| OPALINE, BUTTER, ROSES, BEADED, COVER ..................... | 32.00 |
| OPALINE, HOLDER, MATCH, PIPE SHAPE, SOUVENIR ................. | 5.00 |
| OPALINE, INKWELL, SANDER, BLUE, SILVER DEPOSIT, GOLD STRIPING, FLUTED, PAIR ..................................... | 75.00 |
| OPALINE, LAMP, MINIATURE, APPLE GREEN, 2 3/4 INCHES TO BURNER ... | 18.00 |
| OPALINE, OIL & VINEGAR, PEDESTAL BASE, GOLD TRIM, FRANCE ........ | 85.00 |
| OPALINE, PAPERWEIGHT, PINECONE PATTERN ..................... | 12.50 |
| OPALINE, PERFUME, OPAQUE WHITE, GOLD ENAMELING, CIRCA 1850, ENGLAND ..................................... | 75.00 |
| OPALINE, SUGAR, ROSES, COVER ............................ | 25.00 |
| OPALINE, TUMBLER, RAISED PATTERN ......................... | 18.00 |
| OPALINE, VASE, APPLIED CLEAR LEAF SPRAY, GROUND LIP, 4 3/4 IN ... | 12.50 |
| OPALINE, VASE, BLUE, COIN DOT OVERLAY, 10 1/2 IN. HIGH ......... | 65.00 |
| OPALINE, VASE, BULBOUS, FRENCH ROSE, 4 IN. HIGH ............... | 47.50 |
| OPALINE, VASE, CREAMY GROUND, ENAMELED FLORAL, LEAVES, GOLD RIM, FRANCE, 8 IN ..................................... | 22.00 |
| OPALINE, VASE, FIERY, ORIENTAL CLASSIC SHAPE, 9 IN. TALL ........ | 80.00 |
| OPALINE, VASE, FROSTED WHITE, GOLD, BLUE, APPLIED PORCELAIN OF LADY, 15 IN ..................................... | 65.00 |
| OPALINE, VASE, GIRL WITH RAKE, BOY WITH STICK, TREE, 4 1/2 IN., PAIR ..................................... | 24.00 |
| OPALINE, VASE, GRAY, ENAMEL FLORAL, BUTTERFLIES, CLASSIC SHAPE, FRANCE, 16 IN ..................................... | 60.00 |
| OPALINE, VASE, GREEN, CLASSIC LINES, 3 1/2 IN ................. | 35.00 |
| OPALINE, VASE, PINK, FIERY, RUFFLED TOP, BULBOUS BOTTOM, 8 IN. HIGH | 25.00 |
| OPALINE, VASE, SATIN GROUND, SAWTOOTH EDGE, HAND-PAINTED FLORAL, 10 1/2 IN ..................................... | 40.00 |
| OPALINE, WINE, U-SHAPE BOWL, 2 3/8-IN. DIAMETER, SET OF 4 ........ | 22.50 |
| OPERA GLASSES, MOTHER-OF-PEARL BODY & HANDLE, MARKED BADERE PARIS ..................................... | 25.00 |
| OPERA GLASSES, MOTHER-OF-PEARL, BRASS, HANDLE ............... | 23.00 |
| OPERA GLASSES, MOTHER-OF-PEARL, BRASS, MARKED PARIS ........... | 25.00 |
| OPERA GLASSES, MOTHER-OF-PEARL, CARMEN, FIGARO, ENAMEL, FRANCE ... | 165.00 |
| OPERA GLASSES, MOTHER-OF-PEARL, DEMAIRE FILS PARIS ........... | 15.00 |
| OPERA GLASSES, MOTHER-OF-PEARL, LEATHER CASE, SATIN LINED, LE MAURE, FRANCE ..................................... | 25.00 |
| OPERA GLASSES, MOTHER-OF-PEARL, LEFILS, PARIS ............... | 18.50 |
| OPERA GLASSES, MOTHER-OF-PEARL, LEMAIRE, FRANCE ............. | 22.00 |
| OPERA GLASSES, MOTHER-OF-PEARL, MARKED LECLERC PARIS .......... | 17.00 |
| OPERA GLASSES, MOTHER-OF-PEARL, MARKED LEMAIRE FABI, PARIS, LEATHER CASE ..................................... | 22.00 |
| OPERA GLASSES, MOTHER-OF-PEARL, PINK, LE MAIRE, FRANCE ......... | 15.00 |
| OREFORS, PERFUME, ANIMALS, FISH, INCISED, CRYSTAL, STOPPER, SET OF 4 ..................................... | 50.00 |
| OREFORS, VASE, ELVIN OLSTROM, 7 IN. HIGH, SIGNED .............. | 575.00 |
| OREFORS, VASE, SWIRLED STRIPES IN BRICK RED, PAPERWEIGHT, SIGNED, 10 IN. HIGH ..................................... | 48.00 |
| ORGAN, SEE MUSIC, ORGAN | |
| ORPHAN ANNIE, MUG, BETTLEWARE ........................... | 7.50 |

OWENS POTTERY WAS MADE IN ZANESVILLE, OHIO, FROM 1891 TO 1928. ART POTTERY, HENRI DEUX WARE, FEROZA WARES, AND OTHERS WERE ALSO MADE THERE.

| | |
|---|---:|
| OWENS, HOLDER, LETTER, FLORAL DECOR ON FRONT, 4 1/2 X 3 1/2 IN. HIGH ..................................... | 24.00 |
| OWENS, HOLDER, MATCH, UTOPIA ............................ | 21.00 |
| OWENS, PITCHER, BROWN, ORANGE & YELLOW FLOWER, LEAVES, FOOTED, 5 1/2 IN ..................................... | 68.00 |
| OWENS, PITCHER, BULBOUS, BROWN, ORANGE & YELLOW FLORAL, LEAVES, UTOPIAN ..................................... | 57.50 |
| OWENS, PITCHER, ORANGE TULIPS, GREEN LEAVES, GREEN GROUND, TANKARD, 10 IN ..................................... | 43.00 |
| OWENS, PITCHER, TANKARD, BERRIES & LEAVES, MARKED, ARTIST | |

INITIALED,12 IN............................................. 54.50
OWENS,PITCHER,TANKARD,OPALESCENT LINE,GOLD-COATED,GREEN,
CHERRIES...................................................... 65.00
OWENS,PITCHER,UTOPIAN,FLORAL,BULBOUS,6 IN.................. 55.00
OWENS,PITCHER,UTOPIAN,YELLOW DAFFODILS,LEAVES,7 1/4 X
3 1/4 IN.HIGH............................................. 45.00
OWENS,URN,UTOPIAN,MATTE GLAZE,CLOVER DECOR,ARTIST-SIGNED,
3 1/2 IN.HIGH............................................. 35.00
OWENS,VASE,BROWN,GLAZED,JUG TYPE,SWIRLED BODY,YELLOW FLORAL,
UTOPIAN................................................... 28.50
OWENS,VASE,LOTUS LINE,GREEN SHAMROCKS,PASTEL GREEN TO PINK
GROUND,4 IN.............................................. 95.00
OWENS,VASE,PANSY DECOR,10 IN.HIGH......................... 38.00
OWENS,VASE,UTOPIA,RUST-ORANGE PANSIES,5 3/4 IN.HIGH....... 30.00
OWENS,VASE,UTOPIAN,BROWN,ORANGE MUMS,LEAVES,SIGNED,5 IN.HIGH 35.00
OWENS,VASE,UTOPIAN,LEAF DECOR,NARROW NECK,4 IN............. 25.00
OWENS,VASE,UTOPIAN,PANSY DECOR,6 IN....................... 28.00
OWENS,VASE,UTOPIAN,THREE-SIDED,SIGNED,4 IN................ 33.00

PAINTING,SEE,PICTURE,PRINT

PAIRPOINT CORPORATION WAS A SILVER AND GLASS FIRM
FOUNDED IN NEW BEDFORD,MASSACHUSETTS,IN 1880.
PAIRPOINT,BOTTLE,BARBER,CHASED,SILVER PLATE,SIGNED.......... 125.00
PAIRPOINT,BOX,URN WITH FLAME PATTERN,HINGED SILVER LID,CUT
GLASS..................................................... 65.00
PAIRPOINT,CANDLESTICK,COPPER WHEEL CUTTING,SILVER LEAVES ON
BASE,PAIR................................................. 135.00
PAIRPOINT,CANDLESTICK,SILVER OWL & TREE LIMB,SIGNED,
9 IN.TALL,PAIR............................................ 50.00
PAIRPOINT,CANDLESTICK,YELLOW,INDENTED DIAMONDS,GILDED METAL,
11 IN.,PAIR............................................... 47.50
PAIRPOINT,CASTOR,PICKLE,ETCHED LEAF & FLORAL INSERT,FOOTED,
SILVER,TONGS.............................................. 45.00
PAIRPOINT,COMPOTE,OLD COLONY PATTERN,BUBBLE IN STANDARD,
SILVER BASE,PAIR.......................................... 250.00
PAIRPOINT,DECANTER,BULBOUS,ORANGE,RIBBED INSIDE,STOPPER,
5 IN.HIGH................................................. 22.00
PAIRPOINT,DISH,CANDY,THREE FRUITS,MARK,6 1/4 IN........... 9.00
PAIRPOINT,LAMP,BEIGE & GOLD DECOR,MAHOGANY BASE,SIGNED,
19 IN.TALL................................................ 125.00
PAIRPOINT,LAMP,BLOWN RED FLOWERS,SIGNED BASE.............. 285.00
PAIRPOINT,LAMP,FROSTED SHADE,RAINBOW IRIDESCENT,BRASS-PLATED
BASE,25 IN................................................ 195.00
PAIRPOINT,LAMP,PETAL CLOSED TOP,ROSES,LEAVES,BUTTERFLIES,
BRASS BASE................................................ 350.00
PAIRPOINT,LAMP,RADIO,GLOBE IS OF FRUITS................... 45.00
PAIRPOINT,LAMP,ROSES,BIRDS,SIGNED,SHADE 14-IN.DIAMETER.... 225.00
PAIRPOINT,PERFUME,AIRTRAPS,PAPERWEIGHT,FLOWER FINIAL ON
STOPPER,PAIR.............................................. 135.00
PAIRPOINT,PLATE,WHITE,LUSTERLESS,SWEET PEAS,BUTTERFLY,10 IN. 37.50
PAIRPOINT,SHADE,BECKWITH,TREES,ALLOVER LAVENDER EFFECT,
21 IN.HIGH................................................ 350.00
PAIRPOINT,SHADE,DUTCH WINDMILLS,ARTIST-SIGNED,ONE LIGHT,
9 IN.HIGH,PAIR............................................ 350.00
PAIRPOINT,THERMOMETER,DESK,FIGURE OF BASEBALL PLAYER...... 45.00
PAIRPOINT,TRAY,DESK,OPENWORK GALLERY,ALCOHOL BURNER,
COMPARTMENT............................................... 14.00
PAIRPOINT,TRAY,WATER SCENE IN CENTER,RESILVERED,15 IN. X
11 1/2 IN................................................. 45.00
PAIRPOINT,VASE,BASE TAPERS,OVERLAY,COBALT,6 1/2 IN.OPENING,
6 IN.TALL................................................. 28.50
PAIRPOINT,VASE,CAMELLIA,DEEP PINK,WAFFLE MARK ON BOTTOM,
10 1/2 IN.HIGH............................................ 250.00
PAIRPOINT,VASE,COPPER WHEEL ENGRAVED IN WATERFORD PATTERN,
AMBER RIM................................................. 48.00
PAIRPOINT,VASE,GOLD DECOR SET WITH COLORED STONES,14 IN.,
PAIR...................................................... 150.00
PANTIN,VASE,GOLD IRIDESCENT,SIGNED,2-IN.TOP OPENING,
5 1/4 IN.HIGH............................................. 95.00
PAPERWEIGHT,1837 ON CENTER CANE,MILLEFIORI,PEDESTAL,
3 1/4-IN.DIAMETER......................................... 100.00
PAPERWEIGHT,1885 UNCIRCULATED SILVER DOLLAR IN MAGNIFYING
GLASS..................................................... 10.00
PAPERWEIGHT,1885,FLORAL DESIGN,DATED...................... 15.00
PAPERWEIGHT,1890,ELK'S HEAD,3 1/2-IN.DIAMETER,2 1/4 IN.HIGH. 31.00
PAPERWEIGHT,ABRAHAM LINCOLN,BLACK & WHITE PORTRAIT,COLORED
CANES..................................................... 15.00
PAPERWEIGHT,ABRAHAM LINCOLN,BLACK & WHITE PORTRAIT,GLASS
CANES,BLUE,RED............................................ 15.00
PAPERWEIGHT,ADVERTISEMENT,BELL TELEPHONE,BLUE............. 15.00

```
PAPERWEIGHT,ADVERTISING EL RECO CIGARS,FIGURE OF MAN,IRON...      4.50
PAPERWEIGHT,ADVERTISING,ARCHER BARKER CHAIR,PAT.1882,
   PICTURES CHAIR.................................................   10.00
PAPERWEIGHT,ADVERTISING,FAT LITTLE MAN,BRONZE-PLATED IRON,
   3 1/2 IN.......................................................   10.00
PAPERWEIGHT,ADVERTISING,JEWELRY STORE,FULL CALENDAR 1892,
   CERAMIC........................................................   27.00
PAPERWEIGHT,ADVERTISING,KEYSTONE POTTERY,TRENTON,
   2 1/2 IN.LONG..................................................   15.00
PAPERWEIGHT,ADVERTISING,WHITE CLOVER BUTTER,4 IN. X
   2 1/2 IN.......................................................    4.75
PAPERWEIGHT,AMERICAN,GREEN,5-CENT COIN IN CENTER,13 STARS,
   3 IN...........................................................  295.00
PAPERWEIGHT,AMERICAN,MULTICOLORED MARBLE DECOR,
   3 9/16-IN.DIAMETER.............................................   70.00
PAPERWEIGHT,AMERICAN EAGLE,FLAG,THE AMERICAN FIRE,
   PHILADELPHIA,1810..............................................   30.00
   PAPERWEIGHT,BACCARAT SEE BACCARAT,PAPERWEIGHT
PAPERWEIGHT,B.P.O.E.,SULFIDE ELK'S HEAD OVER PINK & YELLOW
   FLORAL.........................................................   35.00
PAPERWEIGHT,BALL,STANDING FROSTED LILY,RED,BLUE,WHITE LACY
   EDGE PETALS....................................................   49.50
PAPERWEIGHT,BARKER,ORANGE FLOWER,GREEN STEM,SIGNED..........      85.00
PAPERWEIGHT,BARKER,POINSETTIA,GREEN GROUND,BASE,SIGNED,
   2-IN.DIAMETER..................................................   85.00
PAPERWEIGHT,BASILICA OF ST.ANNE DE BEAUPRE,4 X 2 1/2 IN.....       2.95
PAPERWEIGHT,BELL SHAPE,ELECTRIC BLUE,SOLID GLASS............      12.00
PAPERWEIGHT,BELL SHAPE,MARKED MOUNTAIN STATES TELEPHONE,BLUE
   GLASS..........................................................   12.50
PAPERWEIGHT,BELL TELEPHONE,MISSOURI & KANSAS,BLUE GLASS.....      32.00
PAPERWEIGHT,BELL TELEPHONE,NEW YORK,BLUE........... 15.00 TO      25.00
PAPERWEIGHT,BIRDS ON BRANCH,MADE IN CHINA..................       4.00
PAPERWEIGHT,BLOWN GLASS SWAN IN POND,GREEN WEEDS,
   3 1/16-IN.DIAMETER..........................................5,000.00
PAPERWEIGHT,BLUE,WHITE FLORAL,GOLDSTONE CENTER,SAYS
   SARA-JOHN 1892-1911...........................................   45.00
PAPERWEIGHT,BLUE SPATTER GROUND,GOLDSTONE..................       3.50
PAPERWEIGHT,BLUE TO BLACK,HOURGLASS SHAPE,SAND,5 1/2 IN.....       8.50
PAPERWEIGHT,BOHEMIAN,MILLEFIORI,2 5/16-IN.DIAMETER.........      60.00
PAPERWEIGHT,BRASS EAGLE ON PEDESTAL,MARBLE BASE............       5.50
PAPERWEIGHT,BUBBLE CENTER,RIPPLE-LIKE UMBRELLA ROCK GARDEN..      20.00
PAPERWEIGHT,BUBBLES INSIDE OF FRUIT........................      10.00
PAPERWEIGHT,BUST OF LINCOLN,SIGNED ED ST.CLAIR,SULFIDE.....      60.00
PAPERWEIGHT,CANES,BLUE,ORANGE,YELLOW,WHITE,RED,BOTTOM CURVED
   INWARD,PAIR....................................................   55.00
PAPERWEIGHT,CANES,FLORETTE,STAR CUT BASE,OPAQUE RED OVERLAY,
   2 15/16 IN.....................................................  350.00
PAPERWEIGHT,CHRISTMAS CANDY ENDS,BRIGHT-COLORED.............      12.00
PAPERWEIGHT,CLEAR BACKGROUND,CANE FLOWERS,CIRCA 1848,ENGLAND     150.00
PAPERWEIGHT,CLEAR GLASS OVER RUBY GLASS,PUMPKIN SHAPE.......       8.00
PAPERWEIGHT,CLICHY,BLUE & WHITE SWIRL,3 IN...........ILLUS..     600.00
PAPERWEIGHT,CLICHY,BLUE GROUND,FLORETTES,CANES,
   2 7/8-IN.DIAMETER..............................................  500.00
PAPERWEIGHT,CLICHY,BOUQUET OF FLOWERS,3-IN.DIAMETER.........5,000.00
PAPERWEIGHT,CLICHY,BOUQUET OF VIOLETS,2 3/4-IN.DIAMETER.....2,000.00
PAPERWEIGHT,CLICHY,CANES,FLORAL,GREEN LEAVES,RED,BLUE,
   1 1/2-IN.DIAMETER..............................................  275.00
PAPERWEIGHT,CLICHY,CHEQUER,CRIMSON FLORETTE,FLORETTES,
   3-IN.DIAMETER..................................................  325.00
PAPERWEIGHT,CLICHY,CONCENTRIC MILLEFIORI,GREEN,WHITE,
   2 3/4-IN.DIAMETER..............................................  500.00
PAPERWEIGHT,CLICHY,DAISY,BLUE,YELLOW STAMENS,FLORETTE
   CENTER,2 13/16 IN...........................................1,100.00
PAPERWEIGHT,CLICHY,DAISY TYPE FLOWER,PINK,
   GREEN-WHITE-CRIMSON CENTER..................................1,600.00
PAPERWEIGHT,CLICHY,FLOWER,TEN MAUVE PETALS,WHITE TIPS,
   2 15/16 IN..................................................2,300.00
PAPERWEIGHT,CLICHY,GREEN MOSS GROUND,WHITE STARHEADS,
   FLORETTES,2 3/4 IN..........................................2,100.00
PAPERWEIGHT,CLICHY,MILLEFIORI,CANES,ROSES,FLORETTES,FACETED,
   2 5/8 IN.......................................................  170.00
PAPERWEIGHT,CLICHY,MILLEFIORI,GREEN & PINK ROSE,FLORETTES,
   2 1/8 IN.......................................................  225.00
PAPERWEIGHT,CLICHY,MILLEFIORI,PINK,WHITE,BLUE,GREEN
   FLORETTES,2 5/8 IN.............................................  150.00
PAPERWEIGHT,CLICHY,MILLEFIORI,TURQUOISE DOUBLE OVERLAY,
   3 3/16 IN...................................................2,500.00
PAPERWEIGHT,CLICHY,MILLEFIORI,UPSET MUSLIN GROUND,
   2 7/8-IN.DIAMETER..............................................  125.00
PAPERWEIGHT,CLICHY,PINK GROUND,3 1/8-IN.DIAMETER.....ILLUS..     700.00
PAPERWEIGHT,CLICHY,PINK ROSE,CANES,2 1/4 IN................     390.00
```

PAPERWEIGHT,CLICHY,RED FLOWER,MERCURY LEAVES,YELLOW,WHITE,
GREEN PETALS.................................................... 250.00
PAPERWEIGHT,CLICHY,RED GROUND,GREEN & WHITE ROSES,
2 7/16-IN.DIAMETER............................................. 800.00
PAPERWEIGHT,CLICHY,SWEET PEA,PINK,WHITE,MAUVE,LEAVES,
2 3/4-IN.DIAMETER...........................................1,700.00
PAPERWEIGHT,CLICHY,TURQUOISE GROUND,3 3/16 IN........ILLUS.. 650.00
PAPERWEIGHT,CLICHY,VERRE,OPALINE,FLOWER,LEAVES,3 3/4 X
2 5/8 IN....................................................... 950.00
PAPERWEIGHT,CLICHY,WHITE,PINK,GREEN,2 7/16 IN........ILLUS..1,100.00
PAPERWEIGHT,CLICHY,WHITE,TURQUOISE,RED,3 1/16 IN.....ILLUS.. 450.00
PAPERWEIGHT,CLICHY,WHITE ROSES AROUND CENTRAL PINK FLORET,
2 1/2 IN....................................................... 285.00
PAPERWEIGHT,COLORED SPECKLING,WHITE CROSS IN CENTER......... 25.00
PAPERWEIGHT,CROWN,BLUE WREATH,PINK CENTER,2 1/2-IN.DIAMETER. 12.00
PAPERWEIGHT,CROWN,COLORED RIBBONS,WHITE LATTICE,
3-IN.DIAMETER................................................. 15.00
PAPERWEIGHT,CUT GLASS EAGLE,INSIDE ADVERTISING............. 50.00
PAPERWEIGHT,D'ALBRET,FRANKLIN D. ROOSEVELT,OVERLAY.......... 160.00
PAPERWEIGHT,D'ALBRET,GENERAL DOUGLAS MACARTHUR............. 62.00
PAPERWEIGHT,D'ALBRET,KING OF SWEDEN........................ 55.00
PAPERWEIGHT,D'ALBRET,LEONARDO DA VINCI..................... 62.00
PAPERWEIGHT,D'ALBRET,MARK TWAIN,SULFIDE.................... 62.00
PAPERWEIGHT,DOME SHAPE,COLORED SPATTERINGS,FLOWERS,CRYSTAL
BUBBLES,GREEN................................................. 55.00
PAPERWEIGHT,DOME SHAPE,CAPITOL,WASHINGTON,D.C.,
3 IN.-DIAMETER................................................ 2.95
PAPERWEIGHT,DOME SHAPE,FIVE-PETALED FLOWERS,SPATTERINGS,LACY
GROUND........................................................ 55.00
PAPERWEIGHT,DOME TOP,FROM A FRIEND......................... 10.00
PAPERWEIGHT,DOME,BLUE FLECKS,SESQUICENTENNIAL,MCMINNVILLE,
TENN.......................................................... 27.50
PAPERWEIGHT,DOME,INTAGLIO CUT ON BOTTOM,ADVERTISING........ 10.00
PAPERWEIGHT,DOOR STOP,CLEAR,TWO FLOWERS,LEAVES,MURANO,2 X
7 X 7 IN...................................................... 32.00
PAPERWEIGHT,DRAGONFLY,YELLOW FLOWER,CANE SETUPS,ST.LOUIS,
CIRCA 1951.................................................... 285.00
PAPERWEIGHT,ENGLAND,1848,BLUE,RED ROD,SIX WHITE FLOWERS,
2 1/4 IN...................................................... 225.00
PAPERWEIGHT,FIGURINE,RAM,CARVED,ON BRASS BASE,MARKED CHINA,
2 IN.HIGH..................................................... 8.00
PAPERWEIGHT,FLORAL DESIGN,DATED 1899 ON THE INSIDE......... 15.00
PAPERWEIGHT,FLORAL DESIGN,HAND-BLOWN,2 1/4-IN.DIAMETER...... 3.50
PAPERWEIGHT,FLORAL,BUBBLES,PONTIL BOTTOM................... 26.50

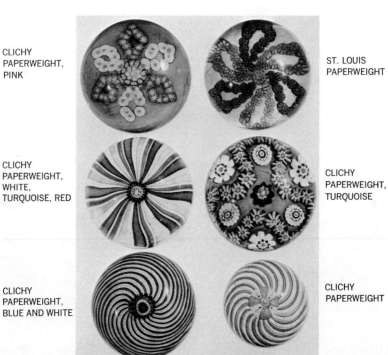

CLICHY
PAPERWEIGHT,
PINK

ST. LOUIS
PAPERWEIGHT

CLICHY
PAPERWEIGHT,
WHITE,
TURQUOISE, RED

CLICHY
PAPERWEIGHT,
TURQUOISE

CLICHY
PAPERWEIGHT,
BLUE AND WHITE

CLICHY
PAPERWEIGHT

```
PAPERWEIGHT,FLORAL,BUTTERFLY,DOMED,CRYSTAL...................    12.50
PAPERWEIGHT,FLORAL,SIGNED ST.CLAIR...............  8.00 TO       10.50
PAPERWEIGHT,FORM OF FROG ON LILY PAD,EMERALD GREEN,19TH
  CENTURY....................................................    18.50
PAPERWEIGHT,GEORGE WASHINGTON,WHITE MAT,RED,WHITE,BLUE
  SPATTER,1959...............................................    20.00
PAPERWEIGHT,GLASS,GREEN,COIN ON CLOUD OF.RED,WHITE,BLUE
  GLASS,AMERICAN.............................................   195.00
PAPERWEIGHT,GLASS BALL,METAL STAND,FILLED WITH CHEMICAL,
  ST.JOSEPH LEAD.............................................     6.00
PAPERWEIGHT,GLASS COVERED WITH LEAD FILIGREE,PATENT JUNE 23,
  1892,3 IN..................................................    25.00
PAPERWEIGHT,GLASS HORSESHOE,DOMED MAGINIFYING CENTER,
  PAT.OCT.3,1899.............................................    12.50
PAPERWEIGHT,GLASS,STAR HOTEL,STAR ISLAND,MAINE,4 IN. X
  2 1/2 IN...................................................     2.95
PAPERWEIGHT,HACKER,SNAKE,2-IN.DIAMETER......................    75.00
PAPERWEIGHT,HACKER,SNAKE,BLACK,YELLOW,YELLOW GROUND,
  2 1/8-IN.DIAMETER..........................................   100.00
PAPERWEIGHT,HACKER,SNAKE,BROWN,YELLOW,PEBBLE GROUND,
  2 1/4-IN.DIAMETER..........................................    70.00
PAPERWEIGHT,HACKER,PINK DAISY,BLUE PEBBLE GROUND,
  2 3/16-IN.DIAMETER.........................................    70.00
PAPERWEIGHT,HAND,BRASS,4 3/4 IN.LONG,2 3/4 IN.WIDE..........     1.50
PAPERWEIGHT,HAROLD J. HACKER,BUNCH OF PURPLE GRAPES ON GREEN
  LEAVES....................................................    350.00
PAPERWEIGHT,HAROLD J. HACKER,COBRA..........................   425.00
PAPERWEIGHT,HAROLD J. HACKER,OCTOPUS........................   425.00
PAPERWEIGHT,HOUND DOG,BRASS,5 IN. X 2 1/2 IN. X
  3 1/2 IN.TALL..............................................    15.00
PAPERWEIGHT,INDIAN CHIEF IN CENTER,MARBLE-LIKE GROUND.......     4.00
PAPERWEIGHT,INLAID MOTHER-OF-PEARL PINK ROSE,STONE LEAVES,
  ALABASTER..................................................    15.00
PAPERWEIGHT,IRIDESCENT,FOUR-BALL,2 5/8 IN. HIGH.............    27.50
PAPERWEIGHT,IRON,PUPPY WITH FLY ON HIS HIP,1 1/2 IN.HIGH....     8.00
PAPERWEIGHT,ISLINGTON,MILLEFIORI,CLOSELY PACKED,CARTHORSE
  SILHOUETTE.................................................   550.00
PAPERWEIGHT,JOE BARKER......................................    85.00
PAPERWEIGHT,KAZIUN,ROSE,BLUE BACKGROUND, 1 1/2-IN.DIAMETER..   275.00
PAPERWEIGHT,LILY,ST.CLAIR...................................    12.00
PAPERWEIGHT,LION,AMBER......................................    15.00
PAPERWEIGHT,LION,BRONZE,ENGLAND,3 X 6 IN.LONG,2 1/2 LBS.....    28.50
PAPERWEIGHT,LYNDON B.JOHNSON,SIGNED J.G.....................    20.00
PAPERWEIGHT,MAGNUM SIZE,3 FLOWERS,4-IN. DIAMETER,3 1/2 LBS..    18.00
PAPERWEIGHT,MARTHA WASHINGTON,WHITE MAT,RED,WHITE,BLUE
  SPATTER,1959...............................................    20.00
PAPERWEIGHT,MC KINLEY,ROUND,3 IN............................     4.00
PAPERWEIGHT,MILLEFIORI,3-IN.DIAMETER........................     6.00
PAPERWEIGHT,MILLEFIORI,CANES,FLORETTES,WHITE LATTICINIO
  GROUND,2 3/8 IN............................................   125.00
PAPERWEIGHT,MILLEFIORI,CLICHY,CANES,WHITE STAVES,
  2 11/16-IN.DIAMETER........................................   200.00
PAPERWEIGHT,MILLEFIORI,CLICHY,PINK CANES,FOUR FLORETTES,
  3 1/8 IN...................................................   100.00
PAPERWEIGHT,MILLEFIORI,LADIES...............................    15.00
PAPERWEIGHT,MILLEFIORI,MT.VERNON,VIRGINIA,LABEL,
  2 1/2-IN.DIAMETER..........................................    50.00
PAPERWEIGHT,MILLVILLE,PINK ROSE,GREEN LEAVES,PEDESTAL,
  3 7/16-IN.DIAMETER.........................................   950.00
PAPERWEIGHT,MILLVILLE,SAILING SHIP,PEDESTAL,
  3 1/2-IN.DIAMETER..........................................   800.00
PAPERWEIGHT,MINIATURE,MILLEFIORI,BLUE FLORETTE,CANES,1 3/M
  IN.DIAMETER................................................   100.00
PAPERWEIGHT,MONADNOCK LAKE & MOUNTAIN,DUBLIN,N.H.,
  2 3/4-IN.DIAMETER..........................................     2.95
PAPERWEIGHT,MOSES IN THE BULRUSHES,FROSTED.................     30.00
PAPERWEIGHT,MULTICOLORED CANES ON LACE & RIBBON GROUND,DOG,
  BEE,BOHEMIA................................................   350.00
PAPERWEIGHT,MULTICOLORED CANES,CAMPHOR & CLEAR BALL CENTER,
  3 IN.HIGH..................................................    15.00
PAPERWEIGHT,MULTIFACETED,MULTICOLORED FLORAL IN CENTER,I
  1/2 IN....................................................     20.00
PAPERWEIGHT,MURANO,COBALT BUBBLE BASE,YELLOW,BLUE,GREEN
  LILIES,3 IN...............................................     15.00
PAPERWEIGHT,MURANO,FISH AQUARIUM,MULTICOLORED FISH SWIMMING
  AMID SEAWEED...............................................    15.00
PAPERWEIGHT,MURANO,FISH SWIMMING AMONG SEAWEED,5 X 4 X
  1 1/2 IN..................................................     15.00
PAPERWEIGHT,MURANO,MUSHROOM,MINIATURE,MILLEFIORI,1 1/2 X
  1 1/2 IN..................................................     13.00
PAPERWEIGHT,MURANO,RED ROSE AGAINST GREEN LEAVES,FOOTED,
```

```
      6 IN.TALL............................................    63.00
PAPERWEIGHT,MURANO,SIX CONCAVE CUT WINDOWS,MILLEFIORI,
      3 1/2 X 2 IN.........................................    31.00
PAPERWEIGHT,MURANO,SIX-FACETED,BLUE & WHITE MILLEFIORI,3 X
      2 1/2 IN.............................................    21.00
PAPERWEIGHT,NAME BILL PRINTED INSIDE,SIGNED D.,3-IN.DIAMETER    14.00
PAPERWEIGHT,NEW ENGLAND,APPLE,YELLOW,RED,2 3/4-IN.DIAMETER..   160.00
PAPERWEIGHT,NEW ENGLAND,BLUE CLEMATIS,FACETED,
      2 7/16-IN.DIAMETER...................................   250.00
PAPERWEIGHT,NEW ENGLAND,CANES,WHITE LATTICINIO GROUND,
      FACETED,2 5/8 IN.....................................   275.00
PAPERWEIGHT,NEW ENGLAND,CENTRAL FLORETTE,RED,BLUE,WHITE,
      YELLOW RIBBON........................................   350.00
PAPERWEIGHT,NEW ENGLAND,DOUBLE CLEMATIS,PINK PETALS,
      2 7/8-IN.DIAMETER....................................   170.00
PAPERWEIGHT,NEW ENGLAND,FIVE PEARS,FIVE CHERRIES,LEAVES,
      LATTICINIO...........................................   275.00
PAPERWEIGHT,NEW ENGLAND,FIVE PEARS,FOUR CHERRIES,LATTICINIO
      BASKET...............................................   450.00
PAPERWEIGHT,NEW ENGLAND,FLAT BOUQUET,LATTICINIO,FACETED,
      2 3/8 IN.............................................   160.00
PAPERWEIGHT,NEW ENGLAND,FLAT BOUQUET,PINK GROUND,LATTICINIO
      THREADS..............................................   160.00
PAPERWEIGHT,NEW ENGLAND,FLAT BOUQUET,UPSET MUSLIN GROUND,
      2 7/8 IN.............................................   200.00
PAPERWEIGHT,NEW ENGLAND,MINIATURE,MILLEFIORI,
      1 15/16-IN.DIAMETER..................................    40.00
PAPERWEIGHT,NEW ENGLAND,PINK & WHITE CANES ABOVE LATTICINIO
      BASKET...............................................   140.00
PAPERWEIGHT,OCTAGONAL SHAPE,FACETED CUTTINGS,INITIALED
      MEDALLION,STEMS......................................    55.00
PAPERWEIGHT,OVAL,GLASS,ADVERTISING FIELD WOODWORKING
      MACHINES,BOSTON......................................     2.95
PAPERWEIGHT,PEAR,SLAB,ONYX,3 1/2 X 2 1/2 IN...............    15.00
PAPERWEIGHT,PENGUIN IN THE SNOW...........................     4.00
PAPERWEIGHT,PERPETUAL CALENDAR,ADVERTISING HALEY'S INKS,
      GLASS,1894...........................................     2.95
PAPERWEIGHT,PERTHSIRE,MINIATURE,HAND-BLOWN FLOWERS,GROUP OF
      SIX..................................................    30.00
PAPERWEIGHT,PETRIFIED WALNUT,2 X 4 IN.....................     6.00
PAPERWEIGHT,PICTURE OF WOMAN,SEWING MACHINE,NEW HOME SEWING
      MACHINES.............................................     3.95
PAPERWEIGHT,PINCHBECK,BIBLICAL SCENE,JOSEPH,ROBED MEN,CAMEL,
      SILVERED.............................................   350.00
PAPERWEIGHT,PINCHBECK,DUKE OF WELLINGTON,3 1/16-IN.DIAMETER.   240.00
PAPERWEIGHT,PINCHBECK,SOLDIERS SEATED AT CAMPFIRE,SPIT,PIG,
      3 1/4 IN.............................................   300.00
PAPERWEIGHT,PINK CLEMATIS,LARGE BUBBLE IN CENTER,1 AT TIP OF
      EACH PETAL...........................................    55.00
PAPERWEIGHT,PLYMOUTH ROCK,IMPRESSED INSCRIPTION IN BASE.....    17.50
PAPERWEIGHT,PORTRAIT,ABRAHAM LINCOLN,BLACK & WHITE,COLORED
      CANES................................................    15.00
PAPERWEIGHT,PORTRAIT,JOHN KENNEDY,CLEAR GROUND,WHITE SULFIDE    30.00
PAPERWEIGHT,PRESIDENT MCKINLEY,TEMPLE OF MUSIC,1901.........     7.50
PAPERWEIGHT,PYRO-PHOTO OF GRANT AND HIS TOMB,2 1/2 X 4 IN...     2.50
PAPERWEIGHT,PYRO-PHOTO OF WHITE HOUSE,2 1/2 X 4 IN.........     2.50
PAPERWEIGHT,RECTANGULAR,FLAT,MC KINLEY PORTRAIT...........     8.00
PAPERWEIGHT,RECTANGULAR,PAUL'S BRIDGE,HYDE PARK,MASS.,4 X
      2 1/2 IN.............................................     2.95
PAPERWEIGHT,RECTANGULAR,STATE HOUSE,BOSTON,MASS.,GLASS,4 X
      2 1/2 IN.............................................     2.95
PAPERWEIGHT,ROCK GARDEN,SAYS WASHINGTON,D.C.,3 IN. X 2 IN...    25.00
PAPERWEIGHT,ROOKWOOD,1928,GREEN FISH......................    10.00
PAPERWEIGHT,ROSE FLOWER INSIDE,GLASS......................    18.00
PAPERWEIGHT,SANDWICH,BLUE CLEMATIS,WHITE & PINK CANE,
      2 11/16-IN.DIAMETER..................................   160.00
PAPERWEIGHT,SANDWICH,BLUE DOUBLE CLEMATIS,2 5/8-IN.DIAMETER.    80.00
PAPERWEIGHT,SANDWICH,CRUCIFORM,BLUE CROSS,RED & BLUE PEBBLE
      GROUND...............................................    80.00
PAPERWEIGHT,SANDWICH,CRUCIFORM,GREEN CROSS,PEBBLE GROUND,
      2 7/8 IN.............................................   250.00
PAPERWEIGHT,SANDWICH,DOUBLE CLEMATIS,FACETED,3-IN.DIAMETER..   300.00
PAPERWEIGHT,SANDWICH,FIVE LEAVES,STALK,GREEN,YELLOW,ORANGE,
      MAUVE................................................   140.00
PAPERWEIGHT,SANDWICH,FOUR PEARS,FOUR CHERRIES,LATTICINIO,
      2 13/16 IN...........................................   325.00
PAPERWEIGHT,SANDWICH,FOUR PEARS,FOUR CHERRIES,LATTICINIO,
      3-IN.DIAMETER........................................   225.00
PAPERWEIGHT,SANDWICH,PINK DOUBLE CLEMATIS,PEBBLE GROUND,
      2 13/16 IN...........................................    80.00
PAPERWEIGHT,SIGNED JACK ZIMMERNA,MULTICOLORED.............    50.00
```

```
PAPERWEIGHT,SILVER COLOR SPANIEL DOG,BLACK GROUND,DOME SHAPE          13.00
PAPERWEIGHT,SNAKE,MOTTLED JASPER GROUND,2 3/4-IN.DIAMETER...          325.00
PAPERWEIGHT,SNOWSTORM,GLAZED BENNINGTON POTTERY BASE.......           35.00
PAPERWEIGHT,SOUVENIR,YELLOWSTONE PARK,WATER,SNOW,BROWN BEAR,
  4 IN.HIGH...............................................            7.00
PAPERWEIGHT,ST.CLAIR,FLORAL,SIGNED........................           10.50
PAPERWEIGHT,ST.CLAIR,PEAR SHAPE,IRIDESCENT,LARGE TEARDROP
  BUBBLES.................................................           40.00
PAPERWEIGHT,ST.LOUIS,1848,PINK SPIRAL,MUSHROOM,
  3 1/8-IN.DIAMETER.....................................2,500.00
PAPERWEIGHT,ST.LOUIS,BONBON ANGLAIS,DANCING GIRL SILHOUETTE,
  CANES..................................................          140.00
PAPERWEIGHT,ST.LOUIS,CANES,FLORETTE,PEBBLE GROUND,
  2 5/8-IN.DIAMETER......................................          150.00
PAPERWEIGHT,ST.LOUIS,CARPET GROUND,BLUE,WHITE,PINK CANE,
  3 3/8 IN.............................................2,800.00
PAPERWEIGHT,ST.LOUIS,CENTRAL FLORETTE,GREEN JASPER GROUND,
  2 5/8 IN...............................................           90.00
PAPERWEIGHT,ST.LOUIS,DAHLIA,LATTICINIO,FACETED,
  2 1/2-IN.DIAMETER......................................          250.00
PAPERWEIGHT,ST.LOUIS,DAHLIA,MAUVE,2 7/8-IN.DIAMETER........1,000.00
PAPERWEIGHT,ST.LOUIS,DAHLIA,PINK,LEAVES,STAR CUT BASE,
  2 13/16 IN............................................1,500.00
PAPERWEIGHT,ST.LOUIS,DAHLIA,PINK PETALS,2 1/2-IN.DIAMETER...1,400.00
PAPERWEIGHT,ST.LOUIS,DEEP PINK DAHLIA,STAR CUT BASE,
  3 1/16-IN.DIAMETER....................................1,000.00
PAPERWEIGHT,ST.LOUIS,FLAT,BOUQUET,2 7/8-IN.DIAMETER........          550.00
PAPERWEIGHT,ST.LOUIS,FLAT BOUQUET,CLEMATIS,BLUE GROUND,
  3-IN.DIAMETER.........................................1,100.00
PAPERWEIGHT,ST.LOUIS,FLAT BOUQUET,POMPON,PANSY,CANES,
  2 11/16-IN.DIAMETER...................................1,200.00
PAPERWEIGHT,ST.LOUIS,FLORAL GARLAND,RED & WHITE JASPER
  GROUND,2 5/8 IN........................................          900.00
PAPERWEIGHT,ST.LOUIS,FLORETTE,TWISTED GAUZE STRANDS,RIBBONS,
  3 1/8 IN...............................................          650.00
PAPERWEIGHT,ST.LOUIS,FLORETTES,AMBER FLASH BASE,2 1/2 IN....          225.00
PAPERWEIGHT,ST.LOUIS,FLORETTES,CANES,AMBER FLASH GROUND,
  2 1/4 IN...............................................          175.00
PAPERWEIGHT,ST.LOUIS,FLORETTES,PINK & WHITE JASPER GROUND,
  2 1/2 IN...............................................          180.00
PAPERWEIGHT,ST.LOUIS,FLORETTES,RED JASPER GROUND,
  3 3/16-IN.DIAMETER.....................................          225.00
PAPERWEIGHT,ST.LOUIS,FOUR RED CHERRIES,BROWN STALKS,LEAVES,
  2 5/8 IN...............................................          450.00
PAPERWEIGHT,ST.LOUIS,FUCHSIA,TWO BUDS,OPEN FLOWER,LEAVES,
  2 7/8 IN.............................................2,000.00
PAPERWEIGHT,ST.LOUIS,GREEN & BLUE CANES,WHITE & PINK
  FLORETTES,4 IN.........................................          550.00
PAPERWEIGHT,ST.LOUIS,GREEN CARPET GROUND,BLUE,PINK,WHITE,
  2 7/16 IN.............................................2,250.00
PAPERWEIGHT,ST.LOUIS,LILAC COLOR POMPON,LATTICINIO,
  2 1/4-IN.DIAMETER......................................          900.00
PAPERWEIGHT,ST.LOUIS,MILLEFIORI,CANES,FLORETTES,
  3 1/2-IN.DIAMETER......................................          750.00
PAPERWEIGHT,ST.LOUIS,MILLEFIORI,CANES,MUSLIN,FACETED,
  2 1/2-IN.DIAMETER......................................           60.00
PAPERWEIGHT,ST.LOUIS,MILLEFIORI,PINK,BLUE,YELLOW,1 1/2 IN...          115.00
PAPERWEIGHT,ST.LOUIS,MINIATURE,GREEN JASPER GROUND,FLORETTE,
  1 7/8 IN...............................................          130.00
PAPERWEIGHT,ST.LOUIS,MINIATURE,MILLEFIORI,2-IN.DIAMETER.....          130.00
PAPERWEIGHT,ST.LOUIS,OPAQUE WHITE,PINK OVERLAY,MOLDED
  SALAMANDER ON TOP.....................................1,500.00
PAPERWEIGHT,ST.LOUIS,PANSY,MAUVE,YELLOW,STAR CUT BASE,
  3 1/4-IN.DIAMETER......................................          250.00
PAPERWEIGHT,ST.LOUIS,PEAR,THREE CHERRIES,LEAVES,LATTICINIO,
  2 7/16 IN.............................................1,000.00
PAPERWEIGHT,ST.LOUIS,PEARS,CHERRIES,LEAVES,LATTICINIO
  BASKET,2 3/8 IN........................................          700.00
PAPERWEIGHT,ST.LOUIS,PELARGONIUM,RED FLOWER,WHITE LATTICINIO
  GROUND................................................1,150.00
PAPERWEIGHT,ST.LOUIS,PINK DAHLIA,CANE,DIAMOND CUT BASE,
  2 1/2-IN.DIAMETER....................................1,150.00
PAPERWEIGHT,ST.LOUIS,PIPPIN,PEARS,CHERRIES,LATTICINIO
  BASKET,3 3/16 IN.......................................          800.00
PAPERWEIGHT,ST.LOUIS,POMPON,LATTICINIO GROUND,
  2 13/16-IN.DIAMETER...................................1,200.00
PAPERWEIGHT,ST.LOUIS,POMPON,PINK TRANSLUCENT GROUND,
  LATTICINIO............................................1,300.00
PAPERWEIGHT,ST.LOUIS,RED CHERRIES,STRIPED PIPPIN,PEAR,
  LEAVES,2 1/2 IN........................................          700.00
PAPERWEIGHT,ST.LOUIS,SCRAMBLED CANES,STRIPS,CAMEL
```

SILHOUETTE,2 11/16 IN............................................. 80.00
PAPERWEIGHT,ST.LOUIS,SIX TURNIPS,LEAVES,LATTICINIO BASKET,
  2 9/16 IN....................................................... 750.00
PAPERWEIGHT,ST.LOUIS,STRAWBERRY,FLOWER,2 9/16-IN.DIAMETER... 900.00
PAPERWEIGHT,ST.LOUIS,TWO CHERRIES,DIAMOND CUT GROUND,
  3 1/16-IN.DIAMETER............................................1,150.00
PAPERWEIGHT,ST.LOUIS,TWO PEARS,APPLE,FOUR CHERRIES,
  LATTICINIO,2 5/8 IN............................................. 600.00
PAPERWEIGHT,ST.LOUIS,UPRIGHT BOUQUET,FACETED,
  2 13/16-IN.DIAMETER...........................................1,500.00
PAPERWEIGHT,ST.LOUIS,UPRIGHT BOUQUET,SERRATED GREEN LEAVES,
  2 13/16 IN....................................................1,800.00
PAPERWEIGHT,ST.LOUIS,UPRIGHT BOUQUET,WHITE LATTICINIO
  RIBBONS,3 1/4 IN................................................ 950.00
PAPERWEIGHT,ST.LOUIS,WHITE FLORETTE,GAUZE,COLOR RIBBONS,
  2 9/16 IN.....................................................1,100.00
PAPERWEIGHT,ST.LOUIS,YELLOW GROUND,3 1/16 IN........ILLUS..3,250.00
PAPERWEIGHT,ST.LOUIS,YELLOW PEAR,RED CHERRIES,LATTICINIO,
  3 1/8 IN......................................................1,500.00
PAPERWEIGHT,STAR SHAPE,A MERRY CHRISTMAS..................... 10.00
PAPERWEIGHT,STRAWBERRY PLANT,SANDWICH,2 1/4-IN.DIAMETER..... 375.00
PAPERWEIGHT,SWIRLS,BUBBLES,YELLOW,GREEN,SIGNED GENTILE...... 12.00
PAPERWEIGHT,SWIRLS,ST.ANDREW CROSSES,GLASS,BLACK BOTTOM,
  3-IN.DIAMETER................................................. 18.00
PAPERWEIGHT,SULFIDE,DEATH MASK OF NAPOLEON I,ON CUSHION,
  3 1/8 IN...................................................... 650.00
PAPERWEIGHT,SULFIDE,GENERAL KOSSUTH,INSCRIPTION,
  2 10/16-IN.DIAMETER........................................... 90.00
PAPERWEIGHT,SULFIDE,GEORGE WASHINGTON,GREEN GLASS,
  2 5/8-IN.DIAMETER............................................. 225.00
PAPERWEIGHT,SULFIDE,POPE PIUS X,CRYSTALLO-CERAMIE,
  2 5/8-IN.DIAMETER............................................. 90.00
PAPERWEIGHT,SULFIDE,PORTRAIT,MAN,CRAVAT,FRILLED SHIRT,
  3 1/8-IN.DIAMETER............................................. 60.00
PAPERWEIGHT,SULFIDE,SADI CARNOT,OPAQUE ORANGE GROUND,
  3 5/16-IN.DIAMETER............................................ 140.00
PAPERWEIGHT,THREE RED CHERRIES,FOUR LEAVES,2 1/2-IN.DIAMETER 450.00
PAPERWEIGHT,TURTLE IN CENTER,CRYSTAL,3 1/2 IN.ACROSS........ 60.00
PAPERWEIGHT,TURTLE,GREEN GLASS,6 IN......................... 25.00
PAPERWEIGHT,UNION GLASS CO.,SOMMERVILLE, MASS.,PINK,WHITE
  SPATTER,FLOWER................................................ 18.00
PAPERWEIGHT,WALTER ZENTSH IN WHITE LETTERS IN DOUBLE CIRCLE,
  1900,LILIES.................................................... 20.00
PAPERWEIGHT,WHITE LACE GROUND,HOLLOW RIBBONS,CONE,ST.LOUIS
  CROWN WEIGHT.................................................. 350.00
PAPERWEIGHT,WHITE LATTICINIO GROUND,COLORED FLORAL,NEW
  ENGLAND GLASS CO.............................................. 250.00
PAPERWEIGHT,WHITE LATTICINIO GROUND,CANE FLORAL,NEW ENGLAND
  GLASS CO...................................................... 175.00
PAPERWEIGHT,WHITEFRIAR,1848,MILLEFIORI,3 1/8-IN.DIAMETER.... 110.00
PAPERWEIGHT,WHITEFRIAR,CHEQUER,FLORETTES,PINK GAUZE TUBING,
  LATTICINIO.................................................... 110.00
PAPERWEIGHT,WHITEFRIAR,GREEN CANES,OVERALL FACETS,
  3-IN.DIAMETER................................................. 100.00
PAPERWEIGHT,WHITTEMORE,NO.3,FLAT,PLAIN,GRAPES............... 85.00
PAPERWEIGHT,WHITTEMORE,NO.3,POINSETTIA,FLAT................. 85.00
PAPERWEIGHT,WHITTEMORE,NO.3,TILTED YELLOW ROSE.............. 95.00
PAPERWEIGHT,WHITTEMORE,POINSETTIA,WHITE GROUND,FLAT......... 90.00
PAPERWEIGHT,WHITTEMORE,WHITE FLOWERS,GREEN STEM,MOTTLED ROSE
  GROUND,FLAT................................................... 70.00
PAPERWEIGHT,WHITTEMORE,YELLOW FLOWER,BUD,MOTTLED ROSE
  GROUND,FLAT................................................... 70.00
PAPERWEIGHT,WHITTEMORE,YELLOW ROSE,PEDESTAL,UPRIGHT HEIGHT
  2 3/4 IN...................................................... 110.00
PAPERWEIGHT,WILD ROSE ONE SIDE,GREEN LEAVES WITH FROGS OTHER
  SIDE,CHINA.................................................... 65.00
PAPERWEIGHT,WILL ROGERS,YELLOW............................. 125.00
PAPERWEIGHT,WITTEMERE,YELLOW LIZARD,BROWN STRIPES,PINK
  GROUND,2 IN................................................... 125.00
PAPERWEIGHT,YSART,BLUE SWIMMING FISH,PEBBLED GROUND,SHELLS,
  OPAQUE BASE................................................... 250.00
PAPERWEIGHT,YSART,BUTTERFLY,ORANGE IRIDESCENT BODY,CANES,
  3-IN.DIAMETER................................................. 325.00
PAPERWEIGHT,YSART,CUT GLASS,RED POINSETTIA CANES,RED & BLACK
  BED........................................................... 195.00
PAPERWEIGHT,YSART,MILLEFIORI,LATTICINIO,CANES,3-IN.DIAMETER. 100.00
PAPERWEIGHT,YSART,MULTICOLOR FLOWER BOUQUET,MILLEFIORI CANES 425.00

PAPIER-MACHE IS A DECORATIVE FORM MADE FROM PAPER
MIXED WITH GLUE,CHALK,AND OTHER INGREDIENTS,THEN

MOLDED AND BAKED, IT BECOMES VERY HARD AND CAN BE
DECORATED. BOXES, TRAYS, AND FURNITURE WERE MADE OF
PAPIER-MACHE. SOME OF THE EARLY-NINETEENTH-CENTURY
PIECES WERE DECORATED WITH MOTHER-OF-PEARL.

| | |
|---|---:|
| PAPIER-MACHE, SEE ALSO, FURNITURE | |
| PAPIER-MACHE, BOX, MOTHER-OF-PEARL INLAY, STAR CENTER, BLACK, HINGE, 4 IN.LONG | 20.00 |
| PAPIER-MACHE, BOX, PATCH, MOTHER-OF-PEARL INLAY, 3 1/2 IN | 10.00 |
| PAPIER-MACHE, BOX, RING, BLACK, HAND-PAINTED DECOR | 2.00 |
| PAPIER-MACHE, BOX, SNUFF, BLACK, TWO CHILDREN FEEDING GOAT & COW ON COVER | 8.00 |
| PAPIER-MACHE, BOX, SNUFF, BOW FRONT, PEWTER INLAY ON LID, MEDALLION, BLACK | 10.00 |
| PAPIER-MACHE, BOX, SNUFF, BROWN, LADY'S SLIPPER, SLIDING COVER | 9.00 |
| PAPIER-MACHE, BOX, SNUFF, PEWTER INLAY, LIMA BEAN SHAPE | 7.50 |
| PAPIER-MACHE, BOX, SNUFF, PEWTER INLAY ON RIM & CENTER OF LID | 10.00 |
| PAPIER-MACHE, BOX, SNUFF, SCROLLED SILVER INLAY, 3 1/2 X 2 X 1 IN | 25.00 |
| PAPIER-MACHE, BOX, SNUFF, SHOE SHAPE, HINGED LID | 18.50 |
| PAPIER-MACHE, DESK, LAP, MOTHER-OF-PEARL INLAY FLORAL DECOR, SLANT TOP COVER | 29.75 |
| PAPIER-MACHE, EASTER EGG, RED, CHICKEN AND RABBIT DESIGN | 5.00 |
| PAPIER-MACHE, FIGURINE, HEAD OF FRANKLIN D.ROOSEVELT, ENCASED IN WOODEN BOX | 350.00 |
| PAPIER-MACHE, FIGURINE, OWL, GLASS EYES, 16 IN | 9.00 |
| PAPIER-MACHE, STAND, INK, BIRDS, FLORAL, TWO CUT GLASS BOTTLES, UCCHI, LONDON | 160.00 |
| PAPIER-MACHE, STATIONERY RACK, CHINESE GILT DECOR, 7 IN.WIDE | 40.00 |
| PAPIER-MACHE, TRAY, BIRD, HAND-PAINTED FLORAL, INLAID MOTHER-OF-PEARL FLORAL | 175.00 |
| PAPIER-MACHE, TRAY, BIRDS, FLORAL, JENNERS & BETTRIDGE, SET OF FOUR, GRADUATED | 500.00 |
| PAPIER-MACHE, TRAY, CARD, GOLD ORIENTAL DESIGN, 6 1/2-IN.DIAMETER | 8.00 |
| PAPIER-MACHE, TRAY, CARD, HAND-PAINTED PEACOCK SCENE, BRONZE HANDLE, SIGNED | 18.00 |
| PAPIER-MACHE, TRAY, CARTOUCHE SHAPE, HUNTING SCENE, LACQUER, ON STAND | 150.00 |
| PAPIER-MACHE, TRAY, DOG, PAINTED, 8-IN.DIAMETER | 32.00 |
| PAPIER-MACHE, TRAY, HAND-PAINTED, CAPITOL, WASHINGTON, D.C., 14 IN. X 11 IN | 3.00 |
| PAPIER-MACHE, TRAY, LACQUERED, BLACK GROUND, BUTTERFLIES, BIRDS, FLORAL, 31 IN | 160.00 |
| PAPIER-MACHE, TRAY, MOTHER-OF-PEARL BLOSSOMS INLAY, GOLD WIRE VINE BORDER | 28.00 |
| PAPIER-MACHE, TRAY, ON STAND, FORMS FOLDING TABLE, FOLIAGE, BUTTERFLIES | 325.00 |
| PAPIER-MACHE, TRAY, PAINTING OF DOG, 8-IN.DIAMETER | 32.00 |
| PAPIER-MACHE, TRAY, SCALLOPED SHELL SHAPE, GOLD STARS & TRIM, HANDLED | 12.00 |
| PAPIER-MACHE, TRAY, WINE, RECESSES FOR DECANTERS, MOTHER-OF-PEARL INLAY | 80.00 |

PARIAN IS A FINE-GRAINED, HARD PASTE PORCELAIN NAMED FOR
THE MARBLE IT RESEMBLES. IT WAS FIRST MADE IN ENGLAND IN
1846 AND GAINED IN FAVOR IN THE UNITED STATES ABOUT
1860. FIGURES, TEA SETS, VASES, AND OTHER ITEMS WERE MADE
OF PARIAN AT MANY ENGLISH AND UNITED STATES FACTORIES.

| | |
|---|---:|
| PARIAN, BOX, EMBOSSED FLOWERS, WHITE, COVER, 3 1/4-IN. DIAMETER | 20.00 |
| PARIAN, BOX, TRINKET, WHITE, BLUE, DEAD GAME BIRDS ON TOP | 25.00 |
| PARIAN, BUST OF COLUMBUS, 8 IN | 19.50 |
| PARIAN, BUST OF SHAKESPEARE, MOUNTED ON BLACK VELVET, FRAME, 9 1/4 X 11 IN | 48.00 |
| PARIAN, BUST OF SHAKESPEARE, 8 IN | 19.50 |
| PARIAN, BUST, DICKENS, 11 IN.HIGH | 65.00 |
| PARIAN, BUST, GARFIELD, 8 1/4 IN | 35.00 |
| PARIAN, BUST, MIRANDA, SIGNED W.O.MARSHALL, COPELAND, 11 IN.HIGH | 125.00 |
| PARIAN, CANDLEHOLDER, CUPID, MOLDED GRAPES, APPLIED TINTED LEAVES, 6 IN | 25.00 |
| PARIAN, CREAMER, MINIATURE, SHEAF OF WHEAT, TOUCHES OF BLUE | 5.00 |
| PARIAN, DISH, SWEETMEAT, LILY PAD PATTERN, COVER, PLATE, SAM L.ALCOCK & CO | 65.00 |
| PARIAN, DOLL, PIERCED EARS, TURN HEAD, BREAST PLATE, WIG, DRESSED, 23 IN.HIGH | 215.00 |
| PARIAN, EWER, ALLOVER RELIEF DESIGN, RING HANDLE, 1850, COPELAND, 8 IN.HIGH | 65.00 |
| PARIAN, FIGURINE, BUST OF CLYTE, 8 IN.WIDE, 11 IN.HIGH | 30.00 |
| PARIAN, FIGURINE, BUST OF COMTE D'ORSAY, COPELAND, DATED 1859, 11 IN.HIGH | 50.00 |
| PARIAN, FIGURINE, BUST OF DANTE, 5 IN.TALL | 12.00 |

PARIAN,FIGURINE,BUST OF DICKENS,16 IN.HIGH,9 IN.ACROSS......      65.00
PARIAN,FIGURINE,BUST OF LADY,FLOWERS IN HAIR,BUTTERFLY ON
  SHOULDER,8 IN..........................................      18.50
PARIAN,FIGURINE,BUST OF ROBERT BURNS,5 1/4 IN.TALL..........      15.00
PARIAN,FIGURINE,BUST OF VENUS,SIGNED R.C.19,8 IN............      26.00
PARIAN,FIGURINE,BUST OF VENUS,SIGNED RC19,8 IN.............      28.00
PARIAN,FIGURINE,BUST OF WOMAN,DRAPED DRESS,BENNINGTON TYPE,
  7 1/2 IN..............................................      25.00
PARIAN,FIGURINE,BUST OF WOMAN,MORNING GLORIES IN HAIR,
  BUTTERFLY..............................................      20.00
PARIAN,FIGURINE,CROMWELL,BUST,8 X 5 IN.....................      22.50
PARIAN,FIGURINE,CUPID,PEDESTAL,8 1/2 IN.HIGH,PAIR..........      18.00
PARIAN,FIGURINE,DOG GUARDING A BASKET OF FRUIT.............      35.00
PARIAN,FIGURINE,GIRL HOLDS SHEATH OF WHEAT,GIRL HOLDS
  PITCHER,PAIR...........................................      60.00
PARIAN,FIGURINE,HEN,TWO CHICKS ON NEST,YELLOW BASKET,
  6 1/2 IN.LONG..........................................      48.00
PARIAN,FIGURINE,LION,THREE-STEP BASE,FOOT ON BALL,7 1/2 X
  6 IN.HIGH.............................................      27.50
PARIAN,FIGURINE,LITTLE RED RIDING HOOD,WOLF,7 1/2 IN.TALL...      18.50
PARIAN,FIGURINE,MARGUERITE,SIGNED S.TERRY,DATED 1868,
  21 IN.TALL............................................     135.00
PARIAN,FIGURINE,THE AMAZON,IMPRESSED MINTON & JOHN BELL,
  FEB.1868,WHITE.........................................     135.00
PARIAN,PITCHER,CREAM COLOR TOP,COBALT BLUE,FOX HUNT SCENE,
  3 1/2 IN.TALL..........................................      18.50
PARIAN,PITCHER,LAVENDER,WHITE RAISED BABES IN THE WOODS.....      65.00
PARIAN,PITCHER,LAVENDER,WHITE,GRAPES,LEAVES,BACCHUS MASK
  SPOUT,ALCOCK...........................................      52.50
PARIAN,PITCHER,LEAF DESIGN,PEWTER TOP,ENGLAND,MARKED JUNE
  19,1857,7 IN..........................................      45.00
PARIAN,PITCHER,RAISED COLOR VIOLET FIGURES,SAMUEL ALCOCK....     150.00
PARIAN,PITCHER,WHITE,HUNTING SCENE,TREE TRUNK HANDLE,1880,
  7 1/2 IN.TALL..........................................      42.00
PARIAN,PITCHER,WHITE,RELIEF TULIP DESIGN,9 IN.TALL..........      37.50
PARIAN,PLAQUE,GREEK FIGURES,MAN,WOMAN,BIRD,BABY,RABBIT,
  11-IN.DIAMETER.........................................     125.00
PARIAN,SHAKER,FIGURAL,OWL,4 IN............................      20.00
PARIAN,TRAY,BREAD,SAYS GET THY BREAD WITH JOY AND
  THANKFULNESS...........................................      18.50
PARIAN,VASE,BLUE & WHITE,BENNINGTON TYPE,5 IN. TALL.......      22.00
PARIAN,VASE,BLUE & WHITE,8 IN. HIGH,PAIR..................      35.00
PARIAN,VASE,BLUE & WHITE,BENNINGTON TYPE,11 IN.TALL......      95.00
PARIAN,VASE,CORN,6 1/2 IN.................................      25.00
PARIAN,VASE,GRAPE DECOR,BLUE SPOTTING,7 IN................      30.00
PARIAN,VASE,HAND HOLDS SHELL VASE WITH GOLD & WHITE BEADS,
  6 1/4 IN..............................................      14.00
PARIAN,VASE,HAND,LACY CUFF ON WRIST,FLOWER-SHAPED VASE,FERN
  DECOR,6 IN............................................      18.00
PARIAN,VASE,WHITE,ROSE BOUQUET,BENNINGTON TYPE,8 IN........      25.00
PARIS,BASKET,FRUIT,PAIR,CIRCA 1810.......................     220.00
PARIS,CLOCK,19TH CENTURY,13 1/2 IN. HIGH..................     100.00
PARIS,COMPOTE,CIRCULAR RETICULATE BOWL,FLARING FOOT,WHITE,
  GOLD,PAIR.............................................     130.00
PARIS,COMPOTE,FLARING HEXAGONAL BOWL,PIERCED TRELLIS SIDES,
  PAIR.................................................     190.00
PARIS,PLATE,DESSERT,19TH CENTURY,38 PIECES................     400.00
PARIS,PLATE,TRANSFER PRINTED IN SEPIA,CAVETTO,WOMAN,CLOUDS,
  PAIR.................................................      60.00
PARIS,SAUCEBOAT,PAIR,EMPIRE,SHELL-SHAPED.................     100.00
PARIS,SUGAR BOWL,COVERED,CIRCA 1810......................      30.00
PARIS,VASE,WHITE,GOLD,SPRAYS OF HUGE BLOSSOMS,RAM HEAD
  HANDLE,PAIR..........................................      70.00
PATE DE VERRE,BOWL,CIRCLES,STRIPES,YELLOW INSIDE,A.WALTER
  NANCY,10 IN..........................................     410.00
PATE DE VERRE,BOWL,GRAY GROUND,GREEN & CRANBERRY BLOTCHES,
  DECORCHMONT..........................................     375.00
PATE DE VERRE,BOWL,GRAY,TRANSLUCENT,AMETHYST POPPIES,BY
  G.ARGY ROUSSEAU......................................     385.00
PATE DE VERRE,BOX,TERRA COTTA MASK OF MAN,AUTUMN LEAVES,
  G.ARGY ROUSSEAU......................................     750.00
PATE DE VERRE,BOX,WILD STRAWBERRY BLOSSOMS,PORTRAIT LID,
  A.WALTER,NANCY.......................................     350.00
PATE DE VERRE,DISH,DRAGONFLY,SIGNED WALTER,NANCY.........     360.00
PATE DE VERRE,OWL & MOUSE ON DISH,SIGNED DAUM NANCY,7 IN. X
  7 IN.HIGH...........................................     585.00
PATE DE VERRE,PAPERWEIGHT,LAVENDER,ROUND,FLAT,3 1/2 IN. X
  1 1/4 IN...........................................      10.00
PATE DE VERRE,PENDANT,PURPLE FLOWER CLUSTER,GRAY GROUND,
  SIGNED G.A.R.......................................      65.00
PATE DE VERRE,PLAQUE,WOMAN STANDING IN FOUNTAIN,SIGNED A.H.,

FRAME,13 IN............................................... 225.00
PATE DE VERRE,TRAY,MOTTLED GREEN,MOLDED RED CHERRIES,GREEN
LEAVES,SIGNED............................................. 285.00
PATE DE VERRE,VASE,YELLOW FLY,BLUE,YELLOW,SIGNED WALTERS,
2 1/4 IN................................................. 175.00


PATE SUR PATE MEANS PASTE ON PASTE. THE DESIGN WAS
MADE BY PAINTING LAYERS OF SLIP (WHICH SEE) ON THE
PIECE UNTIL A RELIEF DECORATION WAS FORMED. THE METHOD
WAS DEVELOPED AT THE SEVRES FACTORY IN FRANCE ABOUT
1850. IT BECAME EVEN MORE FAMOUS AT THE ENGLISH MINTON
FACTORY ABOUT 1870.

PATE SUR PATE,BOWL,CENTER CAMEO,LADY,SERAPH,GREEN GROUND,
ROAL,GERMANY............................................. 60.00
PATE SUR PATE,DISH,CANDY,HANDLE,PEDESTAL,SIGNED BIRKS,8 X
5 IN.HIGH................................................ 425.00
PATE SUR PATE,PICTURE,WOMAN,CHERUB,BLACK,BLUE,WHITE,VELVET
MAT,FRAME................................................ 210.00
PATE SUR PATE,PLAQUE,DRAPED MUSE,BLUE GROUND,SIGNED,4 1/2 X
7 IN.,PAIR............................................... 140.00
PATE SUR PATE,PLAQUE,NEPTUNE,BLUE GROUND,FRAME,MINTON,7 IN.
X 9 IN................................................... 125.00
PATE SUR PATE,PLATE,BLUE & WHITE MEDALLIONS,GOLD SWAGS,
SIGNED BIRK,6............................................ 110.00
PATE SUR PATE,PLATE,BLUE,GOLD,WHITE CLASSICAL FIGURES,
NEIDERVILLE,9 IN......................................... 24.50
PATE SUR PATE,VASE,BLUE & WHITE,ARTIST TOVY,MARK LIMOGES,
8 1/2 IN.,PAIR........................................... 150.00
PATE SUR PATE,VASE,BLUE,LAVENDER PLAQUE,WHITE FIGURINE,
9 1/2 IN................................................. 90.00
PATE SUR PATE,VASE,LAVENDER GROUND,BLUE & WHITE FIGURES,
9 IN..................................................... 85.00
PATE SUR PATE,VASE,LIGHT GREEN GROUND,WHITE FLORAL,SIGNED,
8 1/2 IN.HIGH............................................ 89.00
PATE SUR PATE,VASE,PEARLIZED BACKGROUND,WHITE OVER BLACK
FIGURE,HANDLES........................................... 35.00
PATE SUR PATE,VASE,WHITE & BLUE MEDALLION,GREEN FLORAL,
SIGNED BIRK,7 IN......................................... 250.00


PEACHBLOW GLASS ORIGINATED ABOUT 1883 AT HOBBS,
BROCKUNIER AND COMPANY OF WHEELING,WEST VIRGINIA. IT
IS A GLASS THAT SHADES FROM YELLOW TO PEACH. IT WAS
LINED IN WHITE. NEW ENGLAND PEACHBLOW IS A ONE-LAYER
GLASS WITH A LINING SHADING FROM RED TO WHITE. MOUNT
WASHINGTON PEACHBLOW SHADES FROM PINK TO BLUE.
REPRODUCTIONS OF PEACHBLOW HAVE BEEN MADE,BUT THEY
ARE OF A POOR QUALITY AND CAN BE DETECTED.

PEACHBLOW,SEE ALSO,GUNDERSON,PEACHBLOW
PEACHBLOW,BOWL,ASHES OF ROSES,RUFFLE,SANDWICH.............. 100.00
PEACHBLOW,BOWL,FINGER,GLOSSY,RUFFLED TOP,5 1/4 X
2 1/2-IN.DIAMETER........................................ 300.00
PEACHBLOW,BOWL,FOOTED,NEW MARTINSVILLE,WEST VIRGINIA,11 IN.. 140.00
PEACHBLOW,BOWL,ROSE,MATTE FINISH,NEW ENGLAND,4 IN.TALL,
4-IN.DIAMETER............................................ 195.00
PEACHBLOW,BOWL,ROSE,PINK,SANDWICH GLASS,4 1/2 IN............ 55.00
PEACHBLOW,BOWL,ROSE,SANDWICH GLASS......................... 62.00
PEACHBLOW,BOWL,ROSE,SOUVENIR,WORLD'S FAIR 1893,CRIMPED,ACID,
NEW ENGLAND.............................................. 85.00
PEACHBLOW,BOWL,RUFFLED,SANDWICH,2 1/2 IN.HIGH,
6 1/4-IN.DIAMETER........................................ 150.00
PEACHBLOW,BOWL,SHALLOW,LOW FEET,MARTINSVILLE............... 25.00
PEACHBLOW,BOWL,SUGAR,WILD ROSE,NEW ENGLAND................. 195.00
PEACHBLOW,BRIDE'S BASKET,DEEP ROSE TO LAVENDER TO PINK,
SILVER HOLDER............................................ 300.00
PEACHBLOW,CASTOR,PICKLE,VIOLETS,FLORAL,BALL SHAPE,SILVER
HOLDER,FORK.............................................. 125.00
PEACHBLOW,CREAMER,NEW ENGLAND,3 IN.TALL.................... 360.00
PEACHBLOW,CREAMER,RIBBED,NEW ENGLAND,3 IN.................. 230.00
PEACHBLOW,CREAMER,VERTICAL RIBBING,NEW ENGLAND GLASS CO.,
3 IN.TALL................................................ 345.00
PEACHBLOW,CREAMER,WHEELING,RED SHADING HALFWAY DOWN,AMBER
HANDLE................................................... 448.00
PEACHBLOW,CREAMER,WHEELING,4 1/2 IN....................... 625.00
PEACHBLOW,CREAMER,WHEELING,4 1/4 IN.HIGH.................. 530.00
PEACHBLOW,CRUET,MAHOGANY TO FUCHSIA TO YELLOW,AMBER HANDLE,
WHEELING................................................. 650.00
PEACHBLOW,DARNER,NEW ENGLAND.............................. 60.00
PEACHBLOW,DISH,NEW MARTINSVILLE,RUFFLED,4 1/2 IN.SQUARE,
2 IN.HIGH................................................ 135.00

```
PEACHBLOW,FINGERBOWL SET,WEBB,COIN GOLD DECORATION..........    750.00
PEACHBLOW,PEAR,CURVED STEM,GLOSSY,NEW ENGLAND,5 IN.HIGH.....    120.00
PEACHBLOW,PITCHER,AMBER RIBBED HANDLE,RUFFLED CLOVER SHAPE
   TOP,6 IN.TALL............................................     69.50
PEACHBLOW,PITCHER,INVERTED THUMBPRINT,STRAWBERRY TO PEACH
   COLOR,URN...............................................     195.00
PEACHBLOW,PITCHER,WHEELING,MATTE,CREAMY LINING,CAMPHOR
   HANDLE,3 3/4 IN.........................................     385.00
PEACHBLOW,RUMMER,WHEELING,ACID CUT.........................     215.00
PEACHBLOW,SPOONER,GLOSSY,RUFFLED TOP,NEW ENGLAND...........     350.00
PEACHBLOW,SUGAR,WILD ROSE,ACID FINISH,RIBBED,APPLIED HANDLES    250.00
PEACHBLOW,SYRUP,WHEELING.........................  565.00 TO    595.00
PEACHBLOW,TOOTHPICK,NEW ENGLAND,DEEP PINK TO
   WHITE,SQUARE..............................  250.00 TO       275.00
PEACHBLOW,TOOTHPICK,SQUARE MOUTH,NEW ENGLAND...............     175.00
PEACHBLOW,TOOTHPICK,TRICORNERED,PINK,GLOSSY,NEW ENGLAND
   GLASS CO................................................     265.00
PEACHBLOW,TUMBLER,DEEP RASPBERRY COLOR HALFWAY DOWN,GLOSSY..    275.00
PEACHBLOW,TUMBLER,DEEP RASPBERRY COLOR HALFWAY DOWN,ACID....    250.00
PEACHBLOW,TUMBLER,FUCHSIA,WHEELING,GLOSSY..................     195.00
PEACHBLOW,TUMBLER,NEW ENGLAND,ACID.........................     325.00
PEACHBLOW,TUMBLER,RASPBERRY COLOR TWO-THIRDS OF THE WAY DOWN    250.00
PEACHBLOW,TUMBLER,WHEELING.......................  225.00 TO   330.00
PEACHBLOW,TUMBLER,WHEELING,ACID FINISH.....................     248.00
PEACHBLOW,TUMBLER,WILD ROSE,GLOSSY DEEP ROSE TO WHITE.......    275.00
PEACHBLOW,VASE,COLON,10 IN. TALL...........................       2.50
PEACHBLOW,VASE,DUSKY PINK TO PINKISH WHITE,BIRD,BUTTERFLY,
   TREE,SANDWICH............................................    185.00
PEACHBLOW,VASE,LILY,WILD ROSE,ACID FINISH,NEW ENGLAND,
   9 3/4 IN.................................................    300.00
PEACHBLOW,VASE,MORGAN,WHEELING,GLOSSY,GRIFFIN HEAD OFF STAND    550.00
PEACHBLOW,VASE,SANDWICH GLASS,TRIFOIL TOP,PINK HOMOGENOUS...     45.00
PEACHBLOW,VASE,SANDWICH GLASS,YELLOW AT BOTTOM,ENAMELED
   DECOR,7 1/2 IN...........................................     75.00
PEACHBLOW,VASE,STICK,GLOSSY APPLIED RIGAREE COLLAR,WHEELING,
   8 1/2 IN.................................................    700.00
PEACHBLOW,VASE,STICK,MAHOGANY SHADING TO AMBER,GLOSSY,
   8 1/4 IN.TALL............................................    500.00
PEACHBLOW,VASE,TEARDROP,MAHOGANY TO FUCHSIA TO LEMON-YELLOW,
   WHEELING.................................................    575.00
PEACHBLOW,VASE,TRUMPET,CRIMPED TOP,GLOSSY,NEW ENGLAND,11 IN.    300.00
PEACHBLOW,VASE,WHEELING,4 IN.ACROSS SHOULDER,4 1/4 IN.TALL..    490.00
PEKING ENAMEL,BOWL,PAINTED ENAMEL EUROPEAN FIGURES.........     350.00
PEKING ENAMEL,CUP,WINE,EUROPEAN FIGURES....................     175.00
PEKING ENAMEL,VASE,GILDED METAL,EUROPEAN FIGURES...........     225.00
PEKING ENAMEL,WINEPOT,FIGURES.......................ILLUS..     450.00


     PEKING GLASS IS A CHINESE CAMEO GLASS OF THE EIGHTEENTH
     AND NINETEENTH CENTURIES.
PEKING GLASS,BEAKER,BRONZE-FORM,PAINTED ENAMEL FIGURES......    475.00
PEKING GLASS,BOTTLE,SNUFF,AMBER COLOR,QUARTZ STOPPER........     38.00
PEKING GLASS,BOTTLE,SNUFF,BLACK & WHITE....................     400.00
PEKING GLASS,BOTTLE,SNUFF,BLUE GEOMETRIC PATTERN OVER WHITE,
   JADE STOPPER.............................................     35.00
PEKING GLASS,BOTTLE,SNUFF,BROWN,18TH CENTURY,2 1/2 IN.......    160.00
```

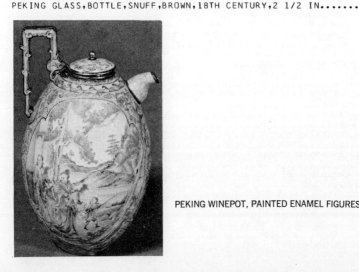

PEKING WINEPOT, PAINTED ENAMEL FIGURES

```
PEKING GLASS,BOTTLE,SNUFF,CORAL RED & WHITE..................    225.00
PEKING GLASS,BOTTLE,SNUFF,FIVE COLORS.......................    125.00
PEKING GLASS,BOTTLE,SNUFF,SIMULATING TAN AGATE,CARVED MASKS,
  STOPPER..................................................     45.00
PEKING GLASS,BOTTLE,SNUFF,TREE,STAG,BIRD,BAT,CAMEO,JADE
  STOPPER & COLLAR.........................................     90.00
PEKING GLASS,BOTTLE,SNUFF,VARIEGATED AGATE,CARNELIAN STOPPER    40.00
PEKING GLASS,BOTTLE,SNUFF,WHITE,JADE STOPPER...............     40.00
PEKING GLASS,BOTTLE,SNUFF,YELLOW SATIN-LINED BOX,SET OF SIX.   250.00
PEKING GLASS,BOTTLE,SNUFF,YELLOW,IMPERIAL..................    550.00
PEKING GLASS,BOWL,BLUE,BLOWN,4 1/2-IN.DIAMETER.............     25.00
PEKING GLASS,BOWL,RUBY,4 1/4 IN.HIGH,10 1/2 IN.ACROSS,TEAK
  STAND...................................................    145.00
PEKING GLASS,BOWL,SAPPHIRE BLUE,CHINESE MARKINGS AT BOTTOM,
  8 3/4 X 4 IN............................................     85.00
PEKING GLASS,BOX,GREEN,ENAMEL,LID DECOR IN CARNELIAN &
  MOTHER-OF-PEARL.........................................     97.50
PEKING GLASS,FLOWER,YELLOW,WHITE CENTER,RED DOTS,PETALS,
  METAL SHANK.............................................     10.00
PEKING GLASS,PLATE,JADE GREEN,8 1/2-IN.DIAMETER,PAIR.......     37.50
PEKING GLASS,STATUETTE,MOTHER PIG & FAMILY,MINIATURE.......      3.95
PEKING GLASS,TUMBLER,GRAY-GREEN...........................     55.00
PEKING GLASS,VASE,ALLOVER FLORAL CARVING,CELADON GREEN,
  TRUMPET SHAPE...........................................     55.00
PEKING GLASS,VASE,CAMEO,YELLOW,RAISED FLORAL,WOODEN BASE,
  4 1/4 IN.,PAIR..........................................     70.00
PEKING GLASS,VASE,LIGHT GREEN,2 IN........................     17.50
PEKING GLASS,VASE,WHITE GROUND,CARVED RED FLORAL,
  8 1/2 IN.HIGH,PAIR......................................    475.00
PEKING GLASS,VASE,YELLOW,BIRD,FLOWERING BRANCH,CARVED,TEAK
  BASE,12 IN..............................................    450.00


        PELOTON GLASS IS EUROPEAN GLASS WITH SMALL THREADS OF
        COLORED GLASS ROLLED ONTO THE SURFACE OF CLEAR OR
        COLORED GLASS. IT IS SOMETIMES CALLED SPAGHETTI OR
        SHREDDED COCONUT GLASS.
PELOTON GLASS,BOWL,ROSE,MINIATURE,MULTICOLOR..............    215.00
PELOTON GLASS,JAR,COOKIE,CAMPHOR GROUND,SILVER COVER,SATIN..    48.00
PELOTON GLASS,PITCHER,CLEAR OVERSHOT,PASTEL SPAGHETTI,CLEAR
  HANDLE..................................................     98.00
PELATON GLASS,SYRUP,CAMPHOR BASE,CRANBERRY LOOPINGS,PEWTER
  TOP & HANDLES...........................................    150.00
PELOTON GLASS,VASE,GREEN GROUND,BLUE THREADS,PURPLE-GOLD
  IRIDESCENT..............................................     50.00
PELOTON GLASS,VASE,GREEN,TWO HANDLES,STEUBEN..............     70.00
PELOTON GLASS,VASE,OPAQUE,RED,BLUE,YELLOW STRANDS,FLUTED,
  5 IN....................................................    150.00
PELOTON GLASS,VASE,VASELINE-GREEN STRIADS OVER CRYSTAL,
  RUFFLED,4 1/2 IN........................................     28.00
PETIT JACOB,URN,GOLD & WHITE,HANGING GRAPES,COVER,SIGNED,
  8 IN.HIGH...............................................    150.00
PEWABIC,VASE,IRIDESCENT BLUE,CLASSIC SHAPE,8 IN.HIGH X
  5-IN.DIAMETER...........................................     32.00


        PEWTER IS A METAL ALLOY OF TIN AND LEAD. SOME OF THE
        PEWTER MADE AFTER ABOUT 1840 HAS A SLIGHTLY DIFFERENT
        COMPOSITION AND IS CALLED BRITANNIA METAL.
PEWTER,ASHTRAY,HOUND DOG FORMS THE HANDLE,3 IN............      6.00
PEWTER,ASHTRAY,LEAF SHAPE,SMALL PIECE OF JADE INSET,
  7 IN.LONG...............................................     29.00
PEWTER,BASKET-TRAY,HEART SHAPE,ORCHID IN CENTER OF BOWL,
  KAYSERZINN 4287.........................................     59.00
PEWTER,BASKET,OLD COLONIAL,7-IN.DIAMETER..................      5.00
PEWTER,BOWL,BAPTISMAL,5 3/4-DIAMETER................ILLUS..     20.00
PEWTER,BOWL,FOOTED,MARKED OLD ENGLISH GENUINE PEWTER,
  4-IN.DIAMETER...........................................      4.50
PEWTER,BOWL,FOOTED,RAY SILVER COMPANY,10 IN...............     12.00
PEWTER,BOWL,FOOTED,REED & BARTON,6 IN.ACROSS,4 1/2 IN.HIGH..    24.00
PEWTER,BOWL,FRUIT,LOW PEDESTAL,CONTINENTAL MARK,
  10-IN.DIAMETER..........................................     15.00
PEWTER,BOWL,FRUIT,SIDE HANDLES,PEDESTAL,MAYFLOWER,
  9 IN.ACROSS.............................................     22.00
PEWTER,BOWL,HIGH-FOOTED BASE,MARKED POOLE,CIRCA 1900,
  6-IN.DIAMETER...........................................      7.50
PEWTER,BOWL,LEAF DESIGN ON COVER WITH JADE FOR FRUIT,
  10-IN.DIAMETER..........................................    150.00
PEWTER,BOWL,MARKED L.H.VAUGHAN,TAUNTON,MASS.,
  7 5/8-IN.DIAMETER.......................................      9.75
PEWTER,BOWL,ON PEDESTAL,MARKED FEDERAL SOLID,3 X
```

PEWTER BAPTISMAL BOWL

```
    7 1/2-IN.DIAMETER....................................    12.50
PEWTER,BOWL,PEDESTAL,FEDERAL,3 IN.HIGH,7 1/2-IN.DIAMETER....   12.50
PEWTER,BOWL,ROUND PEDESTAL BASE,MARKED L.H.VAUGHAN,TAUNTON,
  MASS................................................        9.95
PEWTER,BOWL,TURNED-UP HANDLE EACH SIDE,SHALLOW,MADE FOR
  R.H.MACY,9 IN.......................................        10.00
PEWTER,BOX,SNUFF,ENGRAVED NATHANIEL BREWER,HALIFAX,ORNATE
  BORDER,3 IN.........................................        40.00
PEWTER,BOX,SNUFF,FLORAL,OBLONG,1 1/2 IN. X 3 IN.............   25.00
PEWTER,BOX,SNUFF,WATCH SHAPE...............................    35.00
PEWTER,CANDELABRA,HOLDS THREE CANDLES,9 1/2 IN.,PAIR.......    50.00
PEWTER,CANDELABRA,THREE CANDLE,MARKED PEWTER BY POOLE,
  TAUNTON,MASS........................................        55.00
PEWTER,CANDLEHOLDER,SCOOP DISH,HOLDER,SNUFFER,DIXON,
  6-IN.DIAMETER.......................................        40.00
PEWTER,CANDLESTICK,AMERICAN,12 IN.HIGH.....................    70.00
PEWTER,CANDLESTICK,AMERICAN,9 1/2 IN.HIGH,PAIR.............   125.00
PEWTER,CANDLESTICK,FLARED TOP,ROUND BASE,MARKED CRESCENT,
  4 IN.HIGH,PAIR......................................         6.75
PEWTER,CANDLESTICK,MERIDEN CO.,6 1/4 IN.HIGH...............    10.00
PEWTER,CANDLESTICK,PUSH-UP,BEADING AROUND BASE & CUP,
  9 1/2 IN.TALL,PAIR..................................       125.00
PEWTER,CANDLESTICK,SAUCER WITH HANDLE......................    27.00
PEWTER,CANDLESTICK,THREE-BRANCH,LOW........................     8.00
PEWTER,CASTOR,PEPPER,CIRCA 1830............................     8.00
PEWTER,CHALICE,1803,8 IN.HIGH..............................    90.00
PEWTER,CHARGER,CONTINENTAL MARKS,16-IN.DIAMETER............    95.00
PEWTER,CHARGER,ETON COLLEGE CREST ON RIM,CIRCA 1740,ENGLAND,
  16 1/2 IN...........................................       145.00
PEWTER,CHARGER,J.DUNCOMBE,1706,18-IN.DIAMETER..............   150.00
PEWTER,CHARGER,LONDON,16 5/8 IN.............. 185.00 TO      195.00
PEWTER,CHARGER,RAISED CENTER,TOUCH MARK,THOMAS LANYON,1830,
  20 IN...............................................       290.00
PEWTER,CHARGER,RAISED MORNING GLORIES IN CENTER,MARKED
  KAYSERZINN..........................................        95.00
PEWTER,CHARGER,ROSE & CROWN,15-IN.DIAMETER.................   100.00
PEWTER,CHARGER,WIDE RIM,PATINA,JOHN SEDGWICK,1750,
  16 1/2-IN.DIAMETER..................................       135.00
PEWTER,CHARGER,22 1/2-IN.DIAMETER..........................   295.00
PEWTER,COFFEEPOT,ACORN FINIAL,R.DUNHAM.....................    68.00
PEWTER,COFFEEPOT,AMERICAN,CIRCA 1840,8 1/2 IN.TALL.........    47.50
PEWTER,COFFEEPOT,CREAMER,SUGAR,MARKED SOLID PEWTER ON BOTTOM   25.00
PEWTER,COFFEEPOT,E.SMITH,10 1/2 IN. HIGH............ILLUS..   125.00
PEWTER,COFFEEPOT,JAMES DIXON & SON,13 1/2 IN.........ILLUS..    95.00
PEWTER,COFFEEPOT,MARKED PATENT JUNE 5,1862,LID,9 IN.........   32.50
PEWTER,COFFEEPOT,SIGNED F.PORTER...........................   175.00
PEWTER,COFFEEPOT,SIGNED H.B.WARD...........................    95.00
PEWTER,COFFEEPOT,SIGNED LEONARD,REED & BARTON,AMERICAN......    75.00
PEWTER,COFFEEPOT,SIGNED R.DUNHAM,11 IN.HIGH................    85.00
PEWTER,COFFEEPOT,TANKARD,FRUIT FINIAL,DUNHAM,8 3/4 IN.......   120.00
PEWTER,COFFEEPOT,WOODEN HANDLE,JAMES DIXON & SONS,11 1/4 IN.    90.00
PEWTER,COFFEEPOT,9 IN......................................    70.00
PEWTER,COMPOTE,MARKED PEWTER,5 IN.HIGH,6-IN.DIAMETER.......     6.95
PEWTER,COMPOTE,MARKED WINTHROP,NO.2222,8 IN.WIDE,
  3 3/4 IN.TALL.......................................        32.00
PEWTER,COMPOTE,7 1/2 IN.HIGH X 6 1/2-IN.DIAMETER...........    10.00
PEWTER,CREAMER & SUGAR,MARKED GENUINE PEWTER...............    17.50
PEWTER,CREAMER,FOOTED,4 1/2 IN.HIGH........................     5.00
PEWTER,CREAMER,PAUL REVERE MINATURE,MARKED REED & BARTON,
```

PEWTER COFFEEPOT,
E. SMITH

PEWTER COFFEEPOT, JAMES DIXON

PEWTER TEAPOT,
ROSWELL GLEASON

```
    2 1/2 IN.HIGH.................................................    4.75
PEWTER,CREAMER,SHELDON & FELTMAN,5 IN..........................   75.00
PEWTER,CREAMER,SUGAR,TRAY,COACH PULLED BY TWO HORSES,MARKED,
    W.S.N........................................................   15.00
PEWTER,DISH,BEES GATHERING HONEY,FLOWER SHAPE,MARKED
    KAYSERZINN,6 IN..............................................    8.75
PEWTER,DISH,BUTTER,INTERNATIONAL,8 1/2 IN.LONG.................    7.00
PEWTER,DISH,BUTTER,THE COLONIAL,COVER..........................   20.00
PEWTER,DISH,LEAF SHAPE,STEM FORMS HANDLE,MARKED NEKRASSOF,
    17 1/2 IN.LONG...............................................   14.75
PEWTER,DISH,LEAF-SHAPED,FOOTED,7 1/2 IN.LONG...................    4.75
PEWTER,FLAGON,16 IN.HIGH,8-IN.DIAMETER.........................  125.00
PEWTER,FLASK,OVAL,1860,LEATHER COVERING........................   22.00
PEWTER,FOOT WARMER,OVAL,AMERICAN,14 X 8 1/2 IN.................   42.50
PEWTER,FRAME,CASTOR,SIGNED PUTNAM,9 IN.HIGH....................  125.00
PEWTER,FRAME,15 IN. X 10 1/8 IN................................   15.00
PEWTER,GOBLET,FOOTED,JAMES YATES,ENGLAND.......................   12.50
PEWTER,GOBLET,INSCRIBED MARY ANN...............................   35.00
PEWTER,GRAVY BOAT..............................................   14.75
PEWTER,GRAVY BOAT ON LEAF SHAPE UNDER PLATE,CRICKET ON
    HANDLE,KAYSERZINN............................................   34.00
PEWTER,GRAVY BOAT,MADE FOR R.H.MACY............................    8.00
PEWTER,HEARING AID HORN,FLARE MIDDLE MADE OF HORN,11 IN.....   30.00
PEWTER,HOLDER,FLOWER,BASE,APRON,PIERCED LINER,
    9 1/2-IN.DIAMETER............................................   18.50
PEWTER,HOLDER,MATCH,GLASS LINER,WOODEN BASE,CIRCA 1840.......   12.00
PEWTER,INKSTAND,KAYSERZINN.....................................   70.00
PEWTER,INKSTAND,TWO PEN DRAWERS,INKWELL,FOUR PEN HOLES,1800,
    3 X 5 IN.....................................................   69.00
PEWTER,INKWELL,CAPSTON,FONT,SIX HOLES,8-IN.DIAMETER.........   50.00
PEWTER,INKWELL,DOME TOP,4-IN.DIAMETER..........................   45.00
PEWTER,INKWELL,HINGED LID,SIX QUILL HOLES,4 7/8-IN.DIAMETER.   45.00
PEWTER,INKWELL,POTTERY INSERT,ENGLAND,1830,7-IN.DISC BASE...   48.00
PEWTER,INKWELL,ROUND,DUTCH.....................................   32.50
PEWTER,INKWELL,ROUND,FLARES TOWARD BASE,HOLE FOR QUILL PEN,
    2 1/4 IN.TALL................................................   35.00
PEWTER,JUG,LID WITH THUMB REST,ATKIN BROS.,8 IN..............   48.50
PEWTER,LADLE,FIDDLEBACK HANDLE,MARKED SAVAGE,15 IN.LONG.....   85.00
PEWTER,LADLE,ONE-CUP BOWL,HALF HANDLE IS TURNED WOOD,18TH
    CENTURY,16 IN................................................   39.00
PEWTER,LADLE,SOUP,ROUND FLARING BOWL...........................   25.00
PEWTER,LAMP,DOUBLE SOCKET,ROCKFORD,18 IN.TALL..................   22.00
PEWTER,LAMP,SAUCER BASE,HANDLE,3 1/2 IN........................   80.00
PEWTER,LAMP,STUDENT,WHITE HALF SHADE...........................   98.00
PEWTER,LAMP,WHALE OIL,16 IN....................................  149.00
PEWTER,LAMP,WHALE OIL,1844...........................ILLUS..  125.00
PEWTER,LAMP,WHALE,GIMBAL,SCOOP BASE,AMERICAN,4 1/2 IN.......  125.00
PEWTER,LAMP,WHALE,SCOOP BASE,SIGNED R.GLEASON,5 1/2 IN.....  150.00
PEWTER,MEASURE,CIRCA 1840......................................   12.00
PEWTER,MEASURE,POLISHED,ENGLAND,1/4 GILL TO 1 QUART,SET OF
    SIX..........................................................  225.00
PEWTER,MEASURE,SIX MEASURES,1 QT. TO 1/4 GILL,ENGLAND,1820..  195.00
PEWTER,MEASURE,STRAIGHT-SIDED,FROM LITER TO CENTILITER,
    FRANCE.......................................................  125.00
PEWTER,MOLD,CANDY,ELEPHANT.....................................    8.00
PEWTER,MOLD,CANDY,HORSE & RIDER,THREE CAVITIES.............    5.00
PEWTER,MOLD,CANDY,SQUIRREL,THREE CAVITIES.....................    5.00
PEWTER,MOLD,CANDY,TURKEY,HANDLE,7 IN.TALL.....................   30.00
PEWTER,MOLD,CHOCOLATE,LIBERTY BELL SHAPE,DOUBLE.............   12.00
```

PEWTER LAMP, WHALE OIL

```
PEWTER,MOLD,CHOCOLATE,TWO SEPARATED SANTA CLAUSES,
  7 1/2 IN.TALL.............................................    45.00
PEWTER,MOLD,CIGAR........................................       12.00
PEWTER,MOLD,CONFECTIONARY,EAGLE & SHIELD.....................   25.00
PEWTER,MOLD,ICE CREAM,AMERICAN EAGLE,N.R.A...................   42.50
PEWTER,MOLD,ICE CREAM,BRIDE,GROOM,PAIR......................    25.00
PEWTER,MOLD,ICE CREAM,BUNCH OF GRAPES.......................    12.00
PEWTER,MOLD,ICE CREAM,FLORAL................................    12.50
PEWTER,MOLD,ICE CREAM,HATCHET SHAPE,GEORGE WASHINGTON'S
  PROFILE ON LID............................................    10.00
PEWTER,MOLD,ICE CREAM,LONG FLOWER BLOOM,5 IN................    12.00
PEWTER,MOLD,ICE CREAM,PINEAPPLE SHAPE,TWO PIECES,HINGED,
  2 3/4 IN.HIGH.............................................     7.75
PEWTER,MOLD,ICE CREAM,SANTA CLAUS.................. 14.00 TO    17.50
PEWTER,MOLD,ICE CREAM,STANDING INDIAN CHIEF,PATENT 1896.....    20.00
PEWTER,MOLD,ICE CREAM,UNCLE SAM.............................    17.00
PEWTER,MOLD,ICE CREAM,WEDDING BELL SHAPE....................    12.50
PEWTER,MOLD,PUMPKIN SHAPE,HANDLE,HINGES,JOES BROS.DOWN ST.,
  PICCADILLY................................................    60.00
PEWTER,MOLD,SPOON,B.B.COOK,ST.JOHNSBURY,VERMONT,
  7 3/4 IN.LONG.............................................   400.00
PEWTER,MOLD,SPOON,8 IN.LONG.................................   250.00
PEWTER,MUG,ALE,GLASS BOTTOM,SIGNED REED & BARTON............     8.50
PEWTER,MUG,BLEEDING HEART DESIGN,KAYSERZINN NO.4301,SET OF
  5.........................................................    85.00
PEWTER,MUG,COPPER SHIELD, HARVARD DECENNIAL 1903 ...........    10.00
PEWTER,MUG,DRAGON ENGRAVING,SIGNED,GLASS BOTTOM.............    10.00
PEWTER,MUG,KNIGHT OF TEMPLARS,34TH TRIENNIAL CONCLAVE,
  PHILA.,SEPT.,1919.........................................    12.00
PEWTER,MUG,MARKED J.DIXON & SONS............................    65.00
PEWTER,MUG,NO.186,ETCHED HAROLD HEDGE CORYELL,HARVARD,1905,
  COPPER SHIELD.............................................    30.00
PEWTER,MUG,TANKARD SHAPE,EARLY 19TH CENTURY,MAKER TOUCH
  INSIDE,ENGLAND............................................    60.00
PEWTER,MUG,TWO ROWS OF BANDING,FLARED BOTTOM,JAMES YATES,
  QUART,6 IN.HIGH...........................................    45.00
PEWTER,MUSTARD POT,PEWTER SPOON.............................    28.00
PEWTER,MUSTARD,BLUE LINER,BONE SPOON,PIERCED BOTTOM,HINGED
  LID.......................................................    28.00
PEWTER,NAPKIN RING,CLOVER DESIGN............................     3.00
PEWTER,PITCHER,WATER,MARKED REED & BARTON,NO.5500/9,
  8 IN.TALL.................................................    30.00
PEWTER,PITCHER,WATER,ROCKFORD...............................    10.00
PEWTER,PITCHER,WINE,MARKED FEDERAL SOLID PEWTER,9 IN........    16.50
PEWTER,PLATE,CIRCA 1756,WALTER THOMAS MARK,ENGLAND,9 IN.....    35.00
PEWTER,PLATE,EMBOSSED BORDER,MARKED KAYSERZINN,
  .9 1/2-IN.DIAMETER........................................    22.50
PEWTER,PLATE,HOT WATER,TWO OXBOW HANDLES,CIRCA 1800,YATES &
  BIRCH.....................................................    55.00
PEWTER,PLATE,LONDON,8 IN....................................    65.00
PEWTER,PLATE,MARKED RICHARD YATES,ENGLAND,9 1/2 IN..........    30.00
PEWTER,PLATE,PIECRUST EDGE,ENGLISH TOUCH MARKS,9-IN.DIAMETER    40.00
PEWTER,PLATE,RELIEF PORTRAIT,LADY,FLOWING HAIR,OCTAGONAL,
  8 1/2 IN..................................................    25.00
PEWTER,PLATE,RICHARD YATES,ENGLAND,9 1/2 IN.................    55.00
PEWTER,PLATE,8 1/2 IN.,SET OF 4.............................   150.00
PEWTER,PLATTER,OVAL,MARKED C.A.WOODWARD,TAUNTON,MASS.,
  12 IN.LONG................................................     7.75
```

PEWTER,PORRINGER,CROWN HANDLE,AMERICAN,4 1/2-IN.DIAMETER.... 175.00
PEWTER,PORRINGER,SOLID HANDLE,18TH CENTURY,CROWNED X ON
  BOTTOM,5 1/4 IN................................................. 65.00
PEWTER,SALT & PEPPER,Q.S.CO.,NO.167H......................... 6.00
PEWTER,SALT & PEPPER,SIDE HANDLES,MARKED GENUINE PEWTER BY
  QUAKER........................................................... 4.75
PEWTER,SALT & PEPPER,SIDE HANDLES,MARKED V.LOLLO PEWTER,
  2 1/2 IN.HIGH.................................................... 3.95
PEWTER,SALT DIP,VIKING SHIP,SPOON............................ 4.75
PEWTER,SALVER,ROGERS,1881,14 IN.ROUND........................ 18.50
PEWTER,SHAKER,COCKTAIL,ENGRAVED DECOR,HUIKEE-SWATOW......... 20.00
PEWTER,SHAKER,SALT & PEPPER,HANDLED,MARKED FEDERAL PEWTER,
  4 3/8 IN.TALL................................................... 10.00
PEWTER,SHAKER,SALT & PEPPER,ONE HANDLE ON EACH,FEDERAL...... 12.00
PEWTER,SHAKER,SALT,PEDESTAL FOOT,18TH CENTURY,5 1/2 IN.TALL. 30.00
PEWTER,SPOON,SERVING......................................... 4.75
PEWTER,STEIN,HINGED LID,MARKED CS ON TOP.................... 68.50
PEWTER,STEIN,HUNTING SCENES,COAT OF ARMS,FLORAL,DOME TOP,
  18TH CENTURY.................................................... 110.00
PEWTER,STEIN,NO.382,COMMONWEALTH COUNTRY CLUB,MAY 4,1907,
  8 1/2 IN.TALL................................................... 20.00
PEWTER,SYRUP,OPEN TOP,KAYSERZINN MARK NO.4220,12-IN.DIAMETER 75.00
PEWTER,SYRUP,TRAY,MARKED DOWD RODGERS CO.................... 25.00
PEWTER,TANKARD,ENGRAVED H.G.C. SECOND PRIZE,1901,HINGED LID,
  WOOD & SON..................................................... 25.00
PEWTER,TANKARD,GLASS BOTTOM,BOSTON ATHLETIC ASSOC.,1887,
  BILLIARDS ..................................................... 20.00
PEWTER,TEAPOT,1850,AMERICAN,8 1/2 IN.HIGH................... 35.00
PEWTER,TEAPOT,ACORN FINIAL ON LID,SIGNED STURGIS NO.181,
  CIRCA 1860.................................................... 33.00
PEWTER,TEAPOT,BLOSSOM & LEAF FINIAL,PEAR SHAPE,8 IN.TALL.... 55.00
PEWTER,TEAPOT,COFFEEPOT,COVERED SUGAR,SIGNED J.D.LOCKE,NEW
  YORK.......................................................... 375.00
PEWTER,TEAPOT,ENGRAVED,ROUND,FOOTED,MARKED DAF,WM.TAYLOR.... 45.00
PEWTER,TEAPOT,F.PORTER,WESTBROOK,MAINE,7 1/2 IN.HIGH........ 125.00
PEWTER,TEAPOT,FLOWER KNOB,CIRCA 1810,5 3/4 IN.TALL.......... 40.00
PEWTER,TEAPOT,LEAF DESIGN ON COVER WITH JADE FOR FRUIT...... 75.00
PEWTER,TEAPOT,MARKED PATENT JUNE 5,1862,LID,9 IN........... 32.50
PEWTER,TEAPOT,MELON RIB,MELON FINIAL ON LEAF,SIGNED JAMES
  DIXON & SON................................................... 49.00
PEWTER,TEAPOT,MELON RIBBED,FINIAL,JAMES DIXON & SON,7 X
  10 IN......................................................... 58.00
PEWTER,TEAPOT,ROSWELL GLEASON,10 IN...................ILLUS.. 145.00
PEWTER,TEASPOON,HEART-SHAPED HANDLE,SET OF FOUR............. 20.00
PEWTER,TEASPOON,PLAIN HANDLE WITH HEART JOINING AT BOWL,SET
  OF FOUR....................................................... 20.00
PEWTER,TEASPOON,SET OF SIX.................................. 30.00
PEWTER,TOOTHPICK,SETTING BIRD,CRADLED ON A WISHBONE......... 30.00
PEWTER,TRAY,CARD............................................ 4.75
PEWTER,TRAY,EMBOSSED POPPY,MARKED KAYSERZINN,9 1/2 IN.LONG,
  7 1/2 IN.WIDE................................................. 20.00
PEWTER,TRAY,EMBOSSED,SIGNED KAYSERZINN,18 IN. X 11 1/2 IN... 75.00
PEWTER,TRAY,HOT-WATER COMPARTMENT,WOODEN FEET & HANDLES,
  DIXON & SONS.................................................. 90.00
PEWTER,TRAY,HUNTING SCENE,DIANA,MAIDEN,WOLFHOUNDS,STAG,16 X
  9 IN......................................................... 65.00
PEWTER,TRAY,MARKED IN SHIELD W.I.COWLISHAW,BOSTON,15 IN.LONG 125.00
PEWTER,TRAY,NYMPHS PLAY IN WATER,CATTAILS,WATER LILIES,
  10 1/2 X 6 IN................................................. 35.00
PEWTER,VASE,QUIRKY DESIGN,LIBERTY & CO.,7 1/2 IN............ 45.00


        PHOENIX GLASS COMPANY WAS FOUNDED IN 1880 IN
    PENNSYLVANIA. THE FIRM MADE COMMERCIAL PRODUCTS SUCH
    AS LAMP SHADES,BOTTLES,GLASSWARE. COLLECTORS TODAY ARE
    INTERESTED IN THE SCULPTURED GLASSWARE MADE BY THE
    COMPANY IN THE 1930'S UNTIL THE MID-1950'S.
PHOENIX,BOWL,DIVING GIRL,SATIN FINISH,PINK,GREEN,OBLONG..... 135.00
PHOENIX,BOWL,PALE GREEN,LOVEBIRDS,VINES,14 IN. WIDE......... 85.00
PHOENIX,BOX,TRINKET,BIRD,FLOWERS,GREEN,COVER................ 16.50
PHOENIX,JAR,GINGER,BIRDS,COVER,MARK,9 1/2 IN.TALL........... 55.00
PHOENIX,LAMP BASE,WHITE,BLUE RAISED FLOWER DESIGN........... 50.00
PHOENIX,LAMP,BLUEBERRIES,BROWN LEAVES,GREEN VINES,OPAL ART
  GLASS......................................................... 40.00
PHOENIX,PLATE,GREEN CHERRIES................................ 10.00
PHOENIX,TEAPOT,GOLD & WINE COLOR LUSTER,CZECHOSLOVAKIA,
  7 IN.HIGH..................................................... 15.00
PHOENIX,TUMBLER,FROSTY PINK HUMMINGBIRD & MORNING GLORIES IN
  RELIEF........................................................ 10.00
PHOENIX,VASE,BEIGE GROUND,WHITE GEESE IN FLIGHT............. 48.00
PHOENIX,VASE,BLUE GROUND,WHITE BELL SHAPE FLORAL,7 IN.TALL.. 35.00

```
PHOENIX,VASE,BLUE,FLORAL IN RELIEF,TAPERED,SATIN,14 N.TALL..   100.00
PHOENIX,VASE,BLUE,FREESIA FAN,PAPER LABEL..................    75.00
PHOENIX,VASE,BLUEBIRD......................................    65.00
PHOENIX,VASE,BRILLIANTE,BULBOUS,PINECONE DECOR,LAVENDER,
   6 1/2 IN.HIGH..........................................     20.00
PHOENIX,VASE,CAMEO TYPE,PINK GROUND,FLOWERS & LEAVES,
   9 3/4 IN.TALL..........................................     42.00
PHOENIX,VASE,CARAMEL GROUND,WHITE MORNING GLORIES,PAPER
   LABEL,7 IN.HIGH........................................     47.50
PHOENIX,VASE,DRAGONFLY,WHITE AND GREEN....................     30.00
PHOENIX,VASE,GRAY GROUND,PEARLIZED WHITE NUDE DANCING GIRL,
   12 IN.HIGH.............................................     75.00
PHOENIX,VASE,GREEN GROUND,PALM LEAVES,7 IN.HIGH...........     28.00
PHOENIX,VASE,OWLS.........................................     35.00
PHOENIX,VASE,OWLS IN RELIEF,FROSTY WHITE,6 IN.............     10.00
PHOENIX,VASE,PALE PINK GROUND,WHITE FLORAL,LEAVES,
   9 3/4 IN.TALL..........................................     45.00
PHOENIX,VASE,PALE YELLOW,BROWN PINECONES,GREEN NEEDLES,
   7 IN.HIGH..............................................     47.50
PHOENIX,VASE,PINK GROUND,SCULPTURED TRUMPET VINE,7 IN.TALL..   35.00
PHOENIX,VASE,PINK GROUND,WHITE LEAVES & VINES,LABEL.......     65.00
PHOENIX,VASE,PINK GROUND,WHITE WILD GEESE IN RELIEF,
   11 1/2 IN.HIGH.........................................     58.00
PHOENIX,VASE,PINK MAUVE GROUND,WHITE BELLFLOWERS,7 IN.TALL..   38.50
PHOENIX,VASE,RAISED CARNATIONS,7 IN.TALL,6 IN.ACROSS......     12.00
PHOENIX,VASE,SCULPTURED GLASS,WHITE,CRYSTAL OVERLAY,BIRDS ON
   SIDES.................................................      65.00
PHOENIX,VASE,SCULPTURED WHITE FLORAL,BLUE GROUND,
   7 1/2 IN.TALL.........................................      25.00
PHOENIX,VASE,TAN GROUND,WHITE & BROWN GEESE,9 1/4 IN.HIGH...   55.00
PHOENIX,VASE,WHITE GROUND,BLUE LEAVES,GRASSHOPPERS,
   7 1/2 IN.TALL.........................................      72.50
PHOENIX,VASE,WHITE GROUND,BLUE,GREEN,BROWN FLORAL,7 IN.TALL.   32.00
PHOENIX,VASE,WHITE GROUND,BROWN GRASSHOPPERS,GREEN GRASS
   BLADES,7 IN...........................................      55.00
PHOENIX,VASE,WHITE GROUND,ORANGE BIRDS,BLUE LEAVES,8 IN.....   32.50
PHOENIX,VASE,WHITE GROUND,PEACH COLOR FLORAL,SATIN,
   11 IN.HIGH............................................      48.00
PHOENIX,VASE,WHITE GROUND,PEACH FLORAL,GREEN LEAVES,
   12 1/2 IN.HIGH........................................      60.00
PHOENIX,VASE,YELLOW GROUND,DANCING GIRL,BUFF & IVORY......     65.00
   PHONOGRAPH,SEE MUSIC,PHONOGRAPH
   PHOTOGRAPHY,SEE ALSO MOVIE
PHOTOGRAPHY,CAMERA,CINE KODAK,MODEL B,16 MM,CASE..........     30.00
PHOTOGRAPHY,CAMERA,FILMO,NO.12531,16 MM,LEATHER CASE,
   VELVET-LINED..........................................      45.00
PHOTOGRAPHY,CAMERA,FOLDING,KODAK,1915,CASE,USES FILM
   NO.A-122..............................................      25.00
PHOTOGRAPHY,CAMERA,KEYSTONE,MODEL A2404,ADJUSTABLE LENS,
   16 MM.................................................      25.00
PHOTOGRAPHY,CAMERA,RECTIFIER,NO.4,FOR PORTRAIT,BRASS......     20.00
PHOTOGRAPHY,CAMERA,SOUND,THREE LENSES IN TURRET,8 MM......    125.00
PHOTOGRAPHY,DAGUERREOTYPE CASE,GOLD LEAF FRAME,VELVET-LINED.    6.00
PHOTOGRAPHY,DAGUERREOTYPE CASE,GUTTA PERCHA,OVAL,RAISED
   FRUIT & FLOWERS.......................................       6.50
PHOTOGRAPHY,DAGUERREOTYPE CASE,HARD RUBBER,EMBOSSED,
   GOLD-FRAMED TINTYPE...................................       5.00
PHOTOGRAPHY,DAGUERREOTYPE CASE,HINGED COVER,2 1/2 IN. X
   3 IN..................................................       7.50
PHOTOGRAPHY,DAGUERREOTYPE CASE,MOTHER-OF-PEARL FLOWER INSIDE   30.00
PHOTOGRAPHY,DAGUERREOTYPE CASE,WOMAN ON HORSE,SOLDIER
   INSIDE,3 X 5 IN.......................................      25.00
PHOTOGRAPHY,DAGUERROTYPE,VELVET CASE,1 3/4 IN. X 2 1/4 IN...    7.50
PHOTOGRAPHY,MAGIC LANTERN,CHIMNEY,OIL LAMP,REFLECTOR,
   20 NARROW SLIDES......................................      40.00
PHOTOGRAPHY,MAGIC LANTERN,EIGHT SLIDES...................      20.00
PHOTOGRAPHY,MAGIC LANTERN,KEROSENE BURNER,REFLECTOR,LENS,
   TIN,11 SLIDES.........................................      25.00
PHOTOGRAPHY,MAGIC LANTERN,KEROSENE LAMP,WOODEN BASE,TIN,
   8 SLIDES..............................................      28.50
PHOTOGRAPHY,MAGIC LANTERN,THREE SLIDES...................      15.00
PHOTOGRAPHY,MAGIC LANTERN SLIDE,CIRCUS SUBJECTS,COLORED,
   GROUP OF 27...........................................      45.00
PHOTOGRAPHY,MAGIC LANTERN SLIDE,TIN FRAME,ROUND OPENING,LOT
   OF 5..................................................      15.00
PHOTOGRAPHY,PHOTOGRAPH,TROLLEY AT WORCESTER,1910,FRAME,
   25 IN. X 30 IN........................................      20.00
PHOTOGRAPHY,PHOTOGRAPH QUEEN VICTORIA,EASEL FRAME,ROYAL
   CREST.................................................      15.00
PHOTOGRAPHY,PHOTOGRAPH,TWENTIETH CENTURY LIMITED,21 IN. X
   11 IN.................................................      20.00
```

```
PHOTOGRAPHY,PHOTOGRAVURE OF COLUMBIAN EXPOSITION,1893,BY
   J.W.JACKSON,80..............................................    20.00
PHOTOGRAPHY,POSTCARD PROJECTOR,TWO HOLDERS,TUNGSTEN LAMPS,
   CIRCA 1915..................................................    22.50
PIANO,SEE MUSIC,PIANO
PICKARD CREAMER,GOLD COLOR,3-IN.DIAMETER,3 IN.TALL...........     12.00
PICKARD,BOWL,FLOWERS & LEAVES,SCALLOPED BORDER,GOLD,SIGNED
   KRICEHR.....................................................    22.50
PICKARD,BOWL,GOLD COLOR,FOOTED,1 IN.HIGH,3-IN.DIAMETER.......      8.00
PICKARD,BOWL,SILVER & GOLD DESIGN,CREAM GROUND,9 IN.SQUARE..     20.00
PICKARD,BOWL,STRAWBERRY,LEAVES,GOLD,FLUTED TOP,THREE
   HANDLES,8 IN.TALL...........................................    40.00
PICKARD,BOX,PALE YELLOW GROUND,VIOLETS,GOLD,ROUND,COVER,
   4 IN.HIGH...................................................    18.00
PICKARD,CANDLESTICK,ALLOVER ETCHED GOLD,3 1/2 IN.HIGH,PAIR..     28.00
PICKARD,CANDLESTICK,SHADED CREAM GROUND,IRIS,GOLD,9 IN.HIGH.     23.00
PICKARD,CREAMER & SUGAR,ALLOVER GOLD,RAISED FLOWER DESIGN,
   MARKED......................................................    25.00
PICKARD,CREAMER & SUGAR,GOLD COLOR,AQUA TRIM,COVER..........     16.50
PICKARD,DISH,CANDY,FLORAL,GOLD BORDER & TRIM,TWO HANDLES,
   7-IN.DIAMETER...............................................    15.00
PICKARD,DISH,OPEN HANDLES,7 3/4 IN..........................     15.00
PICKARD,HOLDER,HATPIN,VIOLETS,GOLD,SIGNED,4 3/4 IN..........     22.50
PICKARD,JAR,CANDY,COVER,SIGNED,8 IN.HIGH....................     20.00
PICKARD,PITCHER,CIDER,GOLD COLOR,BLUE TRIM,HEXAGONAL........     40.00
PICKARD,PITCHER,PURPLE GRAPES,BROWN,MAROON GROUND,ARTIST
   SEIDEL,LIMOGES..............................................    72.50
PICKARD,PLATE,CAKE,ETCHED GOLD CENTER,WATER LILY BORDER,
   SIGNED JAMES................................................    25.00
PICKARD,PLATE,DELICATE FLORAL,GOLD LEAF MARK,SIGNED MURK,
   7 IN........................................................     8.50
PICKARD,PLATE,FLORAL,GOLD,MARK,7 1/2 IN.....................      8.50
PICKARD,PLATE,FRUIT,BLOSSOMS,LEAVES,GOLD,ARTIST-SIGNED,
   8 1/2 IN....................................................    18.00
PICKARD,PLATE,GOLD COLOR,BLUE & PINK DECOR,8 1/2 IN.........     10.00
PICKARD,PLATE,PASTEL GROUND,VIOLETS,GREEN LEAVES,GOLD EDGE,
   8 IN........................................................    14.00
PICKARD,RELISH,PINK & BLUE FLORAL,GILT,OPEN HANDLES,MARK....     12.00
PICKARD,SALT & PEPPER,ALL GOLD,4 IN.TALL....................     12.00
PICKARD,SHAKER,SALT & PEPPER,GOLD ETCHED....................      8.50
PICKARD,TEAPOT,ALLOVER GOLD COLOR,3 IN.TALL,8 IN.WIDE.......     39.00
PICKARD,TEAPOT,DUTCH SCENES,UNGLAZED WHITE..................     25.00
PICKARD,VASE,FLORAL,GOLD,SIGNED,12 IN.......................     42.50
PICKARD,VASE,WHITE GROUND,DUTCH SCENES,BOATS,GIRL,TULIPS,
   ARTIST RAWLINS..............................................    27.50
PICTURE,AMERICAN EAGLE & SHIELD,CARVED & POLYCHROMED,CHINESE    600.00
PICTURE,AQUATINT,BOTANICAL,WINGED PASSION FLOWER,FRAME,26 X
   22 IN.......................................................    45.00
PICTURE,AQUATINT,SHOOTING,PHEASANT,DUCK,WOOD COCK,SNIPE,
   1791,F.P.COOK,4.............................................   750.00
PICTURE,BROADSIDE,PATIENCE IN A PUNT,BY HENRY BLUNBURRY,
   FRAME.......................................................    35.00
PICTURE,CAMEO,APOLLO,CHARIOT,MUSES,ANGEL,MOSAIC FRAME,
   3 3/4 X 3 1/2 IN............................................   285.00
PICTURE,CAMPAIGN WALKING CANE OF PRESIDENT JAMES K.POLK.....    150.00
PICTURE,CASTLES PAINTED ON REVERSE OF CONVEX GLASS,OVAL,PAIR     35.00
PICTURE,CHENILLE EMBROIDERY,19TH CENTURY,16 IN. X 18 IN.....    200.00
PICTURE,CORK CARVING OF CHINESE TEMPLES,SILK-COVERED FRAME,
   GROUP OF 4..................................................    40.00
PICTURE,DAVID & GOLIATH,STEEL ENGRAVING,SIGNED J.COVENS ET
   C.MORTIER...................................................    35.00
PICTURE,ENGRAVED,HEBREW MARRIAGE CEREMONY,PRINTED 1722,9 X
   15 IN.......................................................    15.00
PICTURE,ENGRAVED,HEBREW REDEMPTION OF FIRSTBORN,PRINTED,
   1722,9 X 15 IN..............................................    15.00
PICTURE,ENGRAVING,U.S.PRESIDENTS,10.........................      7.50
PICTURE,ENGRAVING,BLACK & WHITE,BARTOLOZZI STIPPLES,1785....      4.00
PICTURE,ENGRAVING,COLORED,REDUCTION OF HAVANA,1762,FRAME....    285.00
PICTURE,ENGRAVING,EQUESTRIAN & ARMOUR,HAND COLORED,1828.....      5.00
PICTURE,ENGRAVING,HANCOCK HOUSE,BOSTON,FRAME,14 IN. X 12 IN.     30.00
PICTURE,ENGRAVING,JOHN HANCOCK,BY LONGACRE FROM PAINTING BY
   COPLEY,1808.................................................    30.00
PICTURE,ENGRAVING,MOSCOW,BY R.BOWYER,COLOR,MARKED PALL MALL,
   1814,FRAME..................................................    60.00
PICTURE,ENGRAVING,PAUL REVERE,BOSTON MASSACRE........ILLUS..8,000.00
PICTURE,ENGRAVING,U.S.MILITARY BATTLES,15...................     12.00
PICTURE,ENGRAVING,U.S.MILITARY MEN,32.......................     22.00
PICTURE,ENGRAVING,U.S.PROMINENT PEOPLE,17...................     12.50
PICTURE,ENGRAVING,WHITMAN & JAPAN PAPER,ENGLISH,1890,ORNATE
   BORDER......................................................     2.50
PICTURE,ETCHING,CAFE SCENE,GATHERING OF ARTISTS,JEAN
```

PAUL REVERE, BOSTON
MASSACRE, ENGRAVING

| | |
|---|---:|
| FRANCOIS RAFFAELLI............................................ | 300.00 |
| PICTURE,ETCHING,COLOR,WALTZ DREAM,L.ICART,20 IN. X 24 IN.... | 40.00 |
| PICTURE,ETCHING,DONNER LAKE BY GEORGE MATHIS,WAGON TRAIN, LAKE,CLIFFS..................................................... | 10.00 |
| PICTURE,ETCHING,ST.THOMAS CHURCH,NEW YORK,BY MAX POLLOCK, FRAME....................................................... | 20.00 |
| PICTURE,ETCHING,WALL ST.,N.Y.C.,SIGNED LOUIS ZACTOR,FRAME, 17 X 21 IN.................................................. | 25.00 |
| PICTURE,ETCHING,WHITE-TAILED DEER,BY BENSON MOORE,FRAME, 5 IN. X 4 IN.................................................. | 75.00 |
| PICTURE,ETCHING,WINTER ON THE POTOMAC,SIGNED BENSON MOORE... | 35.00 |
| PICTURE,FOUR SEASONS,WOOD-CARVED,17TH CENTURY,WOMEN IN DETAIL,16 IN.................................................. | 500.00 |
| PICTURE,GEORGE III SILK EMBRODIDERY MAP OF BRITISH ISLES.... | 30.00 |
| PICTURE,GRISAILLE PAINTING OF HARPERS FERRY,19TH CENTURY.... | 180.00 |
| PICTURE,HARDSTONE PANEL,CARVED,FLORAL,FRUIT,CHINESE,16 1/2 X 50 1/2 IN.................................................. | 700.00 |
| PICTURE,IVORY,LADY,BRASS & TAPESTRY FRAME,SIGNED HALLAIS.... | 90.00 |
| PICTURE,LITHOGRAPH,ANGELS,CHILD,CRIB,BY MAURICE DENIS,FRAME, 12 X 9 IN.................................................... | 95.00 |
| PICTURE,LITHOGRAPH,BAILLEE,MORNING PRAYER,COLOR,FRAME....... | 14.00 |
| PICTURE,LITHOGRAPH,FROM PAINTING BY J.O.LEWIS,CHIPPEWA CHIEF,18 IN.,PAIR.............................................. | 200.00 |
| PICTURE,LITHOGRAPH,FROM WRIGHT'S BOOK,PUBLISHED 1873,8 1/2 X 11 IN....................................................... | 5.00 |
| PICTURE,LITHOGRAPH,LITTLE BOY FAST ASLEEP,WIDE AWAKE,FRAME, PAIR........................................................ | 95.00 |
| PICTURE,LITHOGRAPH,MRS.LINCOLN,OVAL FRAME................... | 20.00 |
| PICTURE,LITHOGRAPH,NEGRO CHILDREN,WATERMELON,FRAME, HABELBERG,1890,PAIR......................................... | 125.00 |
| PICTURE,LITHOGRAPH,PORTRAIT OF LOUIS VALTAT,STONE-SIGNED, RENOIR,FRAME................................................ | 565.00 |
| PICTURE,LITHOGRAPH,QUEEN LOUISE,GUSTAV RICHTER,BERLIN,1879, FRAME....................................................... | 45.00 |
| PICTURE,LITHOGRAPH,WORLD'S FAIR,1876,PHILADELPHIA,FRAME..... | 35.00 |
| PICTURE,LITHOPHANE,FOX HUNT,COLOR,5 1/2 X 5 IN.............. | 30.00 |
| PICTURE,LITHOPHANE,MAN & WOMAN IN BOAT,4 1/2 X 5 IN......... | 25.00 |
| PICTURE,LITHOPHANE,OLD GENTLEMAN & GIRL,3 IN. X 3 3/4 IN.... | 20.00 |
| PICTURE,LITHOPHANE,READING LESSON,OLD WOMAN,CHILD,4 1/2 X 5 IN...................................................... | 25.00 |
| PICTURE,LITHOPHANE,SCENES,WISSAHIEKON NEAR LOG CABIN,5 X 5 IN.HIGH.................................................. | 25.00 |
| PICTURE,LITHOPHANE,SCENES,CHILDREN,PEOPLE,SIGNED PPM.HANGING CHAINS,PAIR................................................. | 70.00 |
| PICTURE,LITHOPHANE,SCENIC,PEOPLE,GLASS FRAME,6 1/2 X 7 1/2 IN.,CHAIN.............................................. | 55.00 |
| PICTURE,LITHOPHANE,WINTER SCENE,BOY,GIRL,TWO BOYS ON BRICK | |

```
WALL,PAIR...............................................        55.00
PICTURE,MAP,NEW YORK STATE,1901,LINEN BACK,42 IN. X 46 IN...      8.50
PICTURE,MAP,WESTERN HEMISPHERE,DATED 1824,FRAME,16 IN. X
  17 IN..................................................        65.00
PICTURE,MATANZAS,AMERICAN SHIP,BY WILLIAM H. YORKE,1881.....  4,400.00
PICTURE,MEZZOTINT,PRINTED IN COLOR,CHILDREN PLAYING,GILT
  FRAME,SET OF 3.........................................       245.00
PICTURE,MICHIGAN IN THE WAR,ROBERTSON,1861.................      10.00
PICTURE,MINIATURE,ENAMEL,LADY,HENRY SPICER,CIRCA 1800,OVAL,
  3 1/2 IN...............................................       200.00
PICTURE,MINIATURE,IVORY,COURT LADY,PLUMES IN HAIRDO,SIGNED
  HERLEY.................................................        75.00
PICTURE,MINIATURE,IVORY,DUCHESS OF DEVONSHIRE,HAND-PAINTED,
  FRAME..................................................        69.50
PICTURE,MINIATURE,IVORY,GENTLEMAN,AMERICAN,1815......ILLUS.      70.00
PICTURE,MINIATURE,IVORY,GIRL,CIRCA 1815,3 3/8 IN......ILLUS..   100.00
PICTURE,MINIATURE,IVORY,GIRL,ERMINE CAPE,SIGNED STADLER,
  FRAME..................................................        45.00
PICTURE,MINIATURE,IVORY,GIRL,METAL FRAME,FRANCE............      41.00
PICTURE,MINIATURE,IVORY,GIRL,WHITE DRESS,SIGNED HEINRICH
  GUNZL PRINT............................................        40.00
PICTURE,MINIATURE,IVORY,LADY,MANNER OF LEWIS VASLET,CIRCA
  1790,2 3/8 IN..........................................        30.00
PICTURE,MINIATURE,IVORY,LADY,PEARLS,PINK DRESS,SIGNED DAVIS,
  FRAME..................................................       125.00
PICTURE,MINIATURE,IVORY,MAN,B.V.D.GOLTZ,1807,WITH MINIATURE
  OF MAN,2...............................................        30.00
PICTURE,MINIATURE,IVORY,MAN,BLACK COAT,VEST,CRAVAT,AMERICAN,
  1830...................................................        80.00
PICTURE,MINIATURE,IVORY,MAN,BY JAMES PEALE,2 IN......ILLUS..    525.00
PICTURE,MINIATURE,IVORY,MAN,MANNER OF BENJAMIN TROTT,CIRCA
  1820,OVAL..............................................        70.00
PICTURE,MINIATURE,IVORY,MAN,PHILIP JEAN,1795.........ILLUS..    150.00
PICTURE,MINIATURE,IVORY,MAN,THOMAS SULLY,1840,OVAL,3 3/4 IN.    140.00
PICTURE,MINIATURE,IVORY,MARIE ANTOINETTE,SILVER FRAME,SIGNED
  LUCAS..................................................        60.00
PICTURE,MINIATURE,IVORY,MARY STUART,HAND-PAINTED,BRASS FRAME     71.50
PICTURE,MINIATURE,IVORY,OFFICER,CONTINENTAL SCHOOL,DATED
  1830,2 1/2 IN..........................................        40.00
PICTURE,MINIATURE,IVORY,RUSSIAN OFFICER,DE CHAMISSO..ILLUS..    100.00
PICTURE,MINIATURE,IVORY,TATYANA VLADIMIROVNA AS CHILD,
  RUSSIA,1845............................................        70.00
PICTURE,MINIATURE,IVORY,TWO CHILDREN,JOHN W. DODGE...ILLUS..    225.00
```

IVORY MINIATURE, MAN, PHILIP JEAN

IVORY MINIATURE, RUSSIAN OFFICER, DE CHAMISSO

IVORY MINIATURE, MAN, BY JAMES PEALE

IVORY MINIATURE, AMERICAN GENTLEMAN

IVORY MINIATURE, TWO CHILDREN, JOHN W. DODGE

IVORY MINIATURE, GIRL, C. 1815

```
PICTURE,MINIATURE,IVORY,UNFINISHED SKETCH,WOMAN,OVAL,
  2 1/2 IN.........................................................    50.00
PICTURE,MINIATURE,LADY,EMPIRE DRESS,FRANCE,1815,4 1/8 IN....   100.00
PICTURE,MINIATURE,LADY,LADY,RED-BROWN DRESS,M.B.RUSSELL,
  1843,3 3/4 IN...................................................    40.00
PICTURE,MINIATURE,OVAL,LADY,WHITE DRESS,BLUE BOW,CIRCA 1770,
  2 5/8 IN.......................................................    80.00
PICTURE,MONTANA LEGISLATURE,1911.................................     3.00
PICTURE,MOSAIC,DUTCH BOY & GIRL,BLUE,TILE,FRAME.................     8.00
PICTURE,MOSAIC,PRESBYTERIAN CHURCH,BROWN,TILE,FRAME............     8.00
PICTURE,NEEDLEPOINT,FOUR SEASONS,FRAMES,9 1/2 X 11 1/2 IN.,
  GROUP OF 4.....................................................    45.00
PICTURE,NEEDLEPOINT,PAIR,ENGLISH,18TH CENTURY,OVAL HEIGHT
  17 IN..........................................................   170.00
PICTURE,NEEDLEPOINT,PORTRAIT OF GEORGE WASHINGTON,19TH
  CENTURY........................................................   200.00
PICTURE,NEEDLEWORK,MEMORIAL TO ELLEN JACKSON,1836,FRAME,
  25 IN.SQUARE...................................................    85.00
PICTURE,NEEDLEWORK,SILK,OVAL FORM,REGENCY,14 X 11 1/2 IN.,
  PAIR...........................................................   200.00
PICTURE,NEEDLEWORK,SILK,OVAL,REGENCY,LADY,DOG,TREE,FRAME,
  16 IN.,PAIR....................................................   230.00
PICTURE,NEEDLEWORK,VICTORIAN,19TH CENTURY,AMERICAN............    50.00
PICTURE,NOCCALULA FALLS,GADSDEN,ALA.,OIL,FRAME,32 IN.WIDE,
  6 FT.TALL......................................................   250.00
PICTURE,OIL,BLUE GROUND,PINK & YELLOW ROSES,SIGNED J.WILSON,
  1901...........................................................    30.00
PICTURE,OIL,CHARACTER STUDY,MAN,BOOK,CHRISTIAN W.DIETRICH,
  MUSEUM STAMP...................................................   950.00
PICTURE,OIL,CZAR ALEXANDER I,FRAME,19TH CENTURY,26 1/2 X
  21 IN..........................................................   275.00
PICTURE,OIL,FAMILY IN LIVING ROOM,BY C.DETTI,FRAME,30 X
  48 IN.......................................................1,200.00
PICTURE,OIL,GRAPES,ORANGES,PLUMS,SIGNED N.M.CHICK,FRAME.....    45.00
PICTURE,OIL,HARBOR SCENE,FISHING CRAFT,BY W.KENT,FRAME,
  18 IN..........................................................    55.00
PICTURE,OIL,HOLLAND SCENE BY D.WELL,22 X 30 IN.............   225.00
PICTURE,OIL,NUDE NEAR POND,BY A.P.LUCAS,FRAME,30 IN. X
  36 IN..........................................................   750.00
PICTURE,OIL,PANSIES,BLUE SHADING,GOLD RELIEF FRAME,14 IN. X
  11 IN..........................................................    65.00
PICTURE,OIL,STILL LIFE BY J.G.SAVILE............................   350.00
PICTURE,OIL,TWO-MASTED SCHOONER,SIGNED I.P.1835,FRAME,27 IN.
  X 34 IN........................................................   575.00
PICTURE,OIL,WOMAN,VIOLA,TABLE,FRUIT BASKET,DATED 1818,21 IN.   285.00
PICTURE,OIL ON BRISTOL BOARD,MAN,CANOE,MOUNTAINS,FRAME,12 X
  14 IN..........................................................    38.00
PICTURE,OIL ON CANVAS, NEAR TROY,N.Y.,   BRADLEY BUCKLIN,14 X
  21 IN..........................................................   400.00
PICTURE,OIL ON CANVAS,FIVE HUNGRY PUPPIES,1885,BENSON,15 X
  22 IN..........................................................    95.00
PICTURE,OIL ON CANVAS,HEAD & SHOULDERS OF DOG,ARTIST
  W.J.HAYS,1860,FRAME............................................    75.00
PICTURE,OIL ON CANVAS,SCOTTISH LOCH SCENE,EDWIN BULLER,CIRCA
  1874,PAIR......................................................    79.50
PICTURE,OIL ON CANVAS,THE HUNT,SIGNED GAY,7 IN. X 9 IN.,SET
  OF 3........................................................1,000.00
PICTURE,PAINTING,BATTLESHIP IN HARBOR,STATUE OF LIBERTY,
  ALFRED E.BISHOP................................................   850.00
PICTURE,PAINTING,BIRD,SIGNED JENKINS,6 IN. X 15 IN.,SET OF
  2..............................................................   400.00
PICTURE,PAINTING,CATS PLAYING WITH SPILLED MILK,BRUNEL
  NEVILLE,FRAME..................................................   350.00
PICTURE,PAINTING,CHINESE LADY,SERVANTS,CHINESE EXPORT,24 X
  30 IN.,PAIR.................................................3,950.00
PICTURE,PAINTING,CHINESE RICE PAPER,GENTLEMAN,LADY,ROBED,
  FRAME,PAIR.....................................................    28.00
PICTURE,PAINTING,GENERAL ALLENBY AT GATE OF JERUSALEM,BY
  PERCY E.MORAN..................................................   800.00
PICTURE,PAINTING,INDIAN,BY ROBERT ERDMAN,1915,FRAME,GROUP OF
  3..............................................................   650.00
PICTURE,PAINTING,LADY,SERVANTS,FRAME,1850,CHINA,24 X 30 IN..
  PAIR........................................................3,950.00
PICTURE,PAINTING,LAKE GEORGE,SIGNED PERKINS,14 IN. X 20 IN..    12.00
PICTURE,PAINTING,NOBLE LADY,SERVANTS BINDING FEET,CHINESE
  EXPORT,PAIR.................................................4,950.00
PICTURE,PAINTING,NOBLE LADY,SERVANTS,1850,GILT FRAME,CHINESE
  EXPORT,PAIR.................................................4,950.00
PICTURE,PAINTING,OLD MAN READING PAPER,ARTIST P.LOIM,FRAME,
  23 X 18 IN.....................................................   150.00
PICTURE,PAINTING,PRIMITIVE,NEW YORK,OLD WORLD BUILDINGS,
```

```
  FRAME,39 IN..........................................        90.00
PICTURE,PAINTING,SCOTTISH LOCH SCENE,EDWIN BULLER,1874,PAIR.    79.50
PICTURE,PAINTING,SHIP ON OCEAN,OIL,SIGNED K.KOSTER,16 X
  24 IN...............................................         35.00
PICTURE,PAINTING,SHIPS PASSING IN THE PANAMA CANAL,ALFRED
  E.BISHOP............................................        850.00
PICTURE,PAINTING,SIGNING OF VERSAILLES TREATY,BY PERCY
  EDWARD MORAN......................................1,200.00
PICTURE,PAINTING,SIX HORSES PULLING MEN IN SLEIGH,H.LEWIS,
  FRAME..............................................        650.00
PICTURE,PAINTING,STILL LIFE,YELLOW ROSES,BY CARL H.FISCHER,
  ENGLAND,FRAME......................................        175.00
PICTURE,PAINTING,TWO CATS,GOLDFISH BOWL,J.DOLPH,FRAME,10 X
  20 IN...............................................        450.00
PICTURE,PAINTING,VENETIAN SCENE,ARTIST O.H.BOGERT,FRAME,40 X
  28 IN...............................................        400.00
PICTURE,PAINTING ON BOARD,HORSE IN FIELD,HAY WAGON,FIGURES,
  DATED 1880.........................................          9.00
PICTURE,PAINTING ON GLASS,MAIDENS,PATTERNED ROBES,HOLD
  SYMBOLS,32 IN......................................        130.00
PICTURE,PAINTING ON GLASS,THREE STAR GODS WATCH HSI WANG MU,
  FRAME,CHINA........................................        200.00
PICTURE,PAINTING ON GLASS,WOMAN,BLUE BROCADE ROBES,HOLDS
  JU-I SCEPTRE.......................................        225.00
PICTURE,PAINTING ON IVORY,COURT LADY,SIGNED,RHINESTONE
  FRAME,3 1/2 IN.....................................         60.00
PICTURE,PAINTING ON IVORY,MME.RECAMIER,SIGNED RODIER,FRAME..   185.00
PICTURE,PAINTING ON IVORY,NAPOLEON,HAND-PAINTED,FRAME,
  2 1/2 X 1 1/2 IN...................................         24.50
PICTURE,PAINTING ON IVORY,PORTRAIT,LADY,SIGNED L.HELD,FRAME,
  3 X 2 IN...........................................         45.00
PICTURE,PAINTING ON IVORY,QUEEN,SIGNED DUDAN,BRASS FRAME,
  1 7/8 IN...........................................         69.00
PICTURE,PAINTING ON IVORY,TWO CHILDREN,SIGNED,FRAME,4 1/4 X
  3 1/4 IN...........................................        125.00
PICTURE,PAINTING ON PARCHMENT,SELF-PORTRAIT OF J.B.TETAR VAN
  ELVEN,1825.........................................        250.00
PICTURE,PAINTING ON PORCELAIN,GIRL SELLING PINECONES,FRAME,
  4 X 6 IN...........................................        155.00
PICTURE,PAINTING ON PORCELAIN,GIRL,SIGNED WAGNER,OVAL,FRAME,
  5 X 7 IN...........................................        350.00
PICTURE,PAINTING ON PORCELAIN,LADY,SIGNED,GOLD LEAF FRAME,
  5 X 7 IN...........................................        385.00
PICTURE,PAINTING ON PORCELAIN,MADONNA & CHILD,FRAME,7 1/2 X
  11 IN..............................................        175.00
PICTURE,PAINTING ON PORCELAIN,MAN,ROMAN COSTUME,BUST,
  BISCUIT,8 IN.HIGH..................................         40.00
PICTURE,PAINTING ON PORCELAIN,MINIATURE,LADIES,FRAME,
  3 IN.DIAMETER,3....................................        200.00
PICTURE,PAINTING ON PORCELAIN,PORTRAIT,GIRL,WAGNER,FRAME,
  5 IN. X 7 IN.......................................        325.00
PICTURE,PAINTING ON PORCELAIN,PROFILE,GIRL,SIGNED BECKER,
  FRAME,5 X 7 IN.....................................        350.00
PICTURE,PAINTING ON PORCELAIN,SEMINUDE GIRL,FRAME,5 X 7 IN..   400.00
PICTURE,PAINTING ON PORCELAIN,SIGNED CLEMENS,FRAME,8 1/2 X
  11 1/2 IN..........................................        550.00
PICTURE,PAINTING ON PORCELAIN,SIGNED G.LE COUTY,FRAME,11 X
  24 IN...............................................        450.00
PICTURE,PAINTING ON PORCELAIN,VELVET MAT,FRAME,4 1/2 X
  6 1/4 IN...........................................        250.00
PICTURE,PAINTING ON SILK,HELEN,WALLACE,C.H.MAY,1810,20 X
  24 1/2 IN..........................................        250.00
PICTURE,PAINTING ON TILE,GIRL,BUTTERFLIES,BY H.CATELIN,
  FRAME,17 X 22 IN...................................        400.00
PICTURE,PAINTING ON VELVET,19TH CENTURY.....................    40.00
PICTURE,PAINTING ON WOOD,PROFILE OF LADY,OFF-SHOULDER DRESS,
  LONG HAIR..........................................         18.00
PICTURE,PAINTING ON WOOD,WOMAN WRITING LETTER,SIGNED
  E.PORTIELJE,FRAME..................................        125.00
PICTURE,PAINTING ON WOOD PANEL,CHILD HOLDS TOY HORSE,EDUARD
  FRERE,1885.........................................        500.00
PICTURE,PENCIL ETCHING,MALLARDS IN FLIGHT,BY R.H.PALENSKE,
  13 X 16 IN.........................................         30.00
PICTURE,PHOTOGRAVURE,LONDON,1825,WIDE MARGINS,8 IN. X 6 IN..     1.50
PICTURE,PLAQUE MOUNTED ON CARVED STAND,FIGURE OF IVORY &
  SOAPSTONE,CHINA....................................        115.00
PICTURE,PLAQUE,LACQUER,JADE TABLE,VASE,PEKIN FLOWERS,TEAK
  STAND,28 IN........................................        975.00
PICTURE,PORCELAIN,FOREST SCENE,HUNTRESS PURSUED BY SOLDIERS,
  7 X 10 IN..........................................        325.00
PICTURE,PORCELAIN,GARDEN SCENE,HAND-PAINTED,FRAME,7 3/4 X
```

8 1/2 IN.,PAIR.............................................................. 300.00
PICTURE,PORCELAIN,GIRL,BLACK HAIR,PINK SHAWL,BLUE SKIRT,
  WOODEN FRAME.............................................................. 16.00
PICTURE,PORCELAIN,GIRL,DRESS,HAT,WAGNER,3 1/2 X 2 1/2 IN....... 115.00
PICTURE,PORCELAIN,GIRL HOLDING JUG,SIGNED WAGNER,4 X 6 IN... 335.00
PICTURE,PORCELAIN,GIRL HOLDS FLOWERS & JUG,SIGNED WAGNER,
  FRAME,4 X 6 IN............................................................ 285.00
PICTURE,PORCELAIN,GIRL,LAUREL WREATH ON HEAD,SIGNED WAGNER,
  FRAME,3 IN................................................................ 115.00
PICTURE,PORCELAIN,GIRL,LONG BROWN HAIR,WAGNER,FRAME,3 1/2 X
  2 1/2 IN.................................................................. 98.00
PICTURE,PORCELAIN,GIRL LEANING ON WATER FOUNTAIN,FRAME,5 X
  7 1/2 IN.................................................................. 365.00
PICTURE,PORCELAIN,GIRL,VELVET MAT,SHADOW BOX FRAME,GERMANY,
  16 IN..................................................................... 250.00
PICTURE,PORCELAIN,HAND-PAINTED,GIRL,FILIGREE BRASS FRAME,4 X
  4 3/4 IN.................................................................. 40.00
PICTURE,PORCELAIN,KING,FULL DRESS,ENAMEL TRIM,WAGNER,3 1/2 X
  2 1/2 IN.................................................................. 125.00
PICTURE,PORCELAIN,POPE LEO,HAND-PAINTED,ORMOLU FRAME,7 IN... 65.00
PICTURE,PORCELAIN,PORTRAIT,GIRL HOLDING FLOWERS,FRAME,
  SONTAY,6 X 4 IN........................................................... 225.00
PICTURE,PORCELAIN,PORTRAIT,GIRL,HOLDS FLOWERS,BY SONTAY,
  FRAME,5 X 6 IN............................................................ 200.00
PICTURE,PORCELAIN,PORTRAIT,GIRL,SIGNED WAGNER,OVAL,3 X 4 IN. 125.00
PICTURE,PORCELAIN,PORTRAIT,QUEEN,CROWN,LONG VEIL,NECKLACE,
  ENAMEL,WAGNER............................................................. 135.00
PICTURE,PORCELAIN,QUEEN LOUISE,WAGNER,3 1/2 X 2 1/2 IN....... 125.00
PICTURE,PORCELAIN,RAPHAEL'S MADONNA OF THE CHAIR,
  HAND-PAINTED,FRAME,1850................................................... 55.00
PICTURE,PORCELAIN,RUTH,R.DOTTRICH,K.P.M.BLANK,FRAME,14 X
  13 IN..................................................................... 450.00
PICTURE,PORCELAIN,SEMINUDE GIRL,BLOND HAIR,FRAME,SIGNED,6 X
  8 IN...................................................................... 195.00
PICTURE,PORCELAIN,SEMINUDE GIRL HOLDING A THREAD,SIGNED
  SONTAY.................................................................... 175.00
PICTURE,PORCELAIN,SEMINUDE GIRL ON MOUNTAIN,BY WAGNER,FRAME,
  5 X 7 IN.................................................................. 395.00
PICTURE,PORCELAIN,SEMINUDE,LONG BLOND HAIR,UNSIGNED,3 1/2 X
  4 1/2 IN.................................................................. 165.00
PICTURE,PORCELAIN,SEMINUDE OF MADALINE,FRAME,4 1/2 X
  3 1/2 IN.................................................................. 150.00
PICTURE,PORCELAIN,SEMINUDE,SIGNED WAGNER,5 X 7 IN........... 395.00
PICTURE,PORCELAIN,THREE OVALS IN FRAME,QUEEN,HER MOTHER,
  PRINCE,BY WAGNER.......................................................... 300.00
PICTURE,PORCELAIN,TITLED THE MARRIAGE,BY ANNIE SHAW,NO
  GLAZE,9 X 16 IN........................................................... 275.00
PICTURE,PORCELAIN,TROUBADOR,SIGNED M.TORTOSA,SEVILLA,20 X
  24 IN..................................................................... 450.00
PICTURE,PORCELAIN,WOMAN,OVAL FRAME,SIGNED WAGNER,4 IN. X
  5 IN...................................................................... 275.00
PICTURE,PORTRAIT OF A YACHT,OIL ON CANVAS,BY CHARLES
  S.RALEIGH,1876.........................................................2,050.00
PICTURE,PORTRAIT OF MARGARET FISHER,F.R.SPENCER,1856,GILT
  FRAME..................................................................... 975.00
PICTURE,PORTRAIT ON IVORY,MME.POMPADOUR,BLUE GOWN,BRASS
  FRAME,3 1/4 IN............................................................ 75.00
PICTURE,PORTRAIT ON PORCELAIN,CLARA SCHUMANN,BY MARTSEN,
  1843...................................................................... 85.00
PICTURE,PORTRAIT,LADY,ENAMEL,SIGNED,BRONZE FRAME,FRANCE,
  6 1/4 IN.SQUARE........................................................... 175.00
PICTURE,PORTRAIT,LIFE SIZE,LADY IN YELLOW BUSTLE GOWN,ARTIST
  S.J.EDDY.................................................................. 185.00
PICTURE,PORTRAIT,MARGARET MEYER,WIFE OF HUNLOKE PALMER,FRAME 800.00
PICTURE,PORTRAIT,YOUNG WOMAN,SIGNED SAMUEL FULLER,CIRCA
  1795...................................................................... 750.00
PICTURE,POSTER,MOVIE,WRITTEN IN CHINESE,ANCIENT DRESS ON
  MOVIE STARS,50............................................................ 25.00
PICTURE,POSTER,SILENT SCREEN STAR,FRAMED WITH GLASS......... 15.00
  PICTURE,PRINT SEE PRINT
PICTURE,PROFILE OF A.LINCOLN IN BEESWAX,MOUNTED ON RED
  VELVET,FRAME,1866......................................................... 90.00
PICTURE,PUNCHED PAPER SAMPLER,THE OLD ARM CHAIR, CHAIR IN
  CENTER,FRAME.............................................................. 22.00
PICTURE,SILHOUETTE,CAPT.TWITCHELL,WIFE,SETTLERS OF BETHEL,
  ME.,FRAME................................................................. 85.00
PICTURE,SILHOUETTE,CAPTAIN ENOCH PREBLE'S WIFE,SIGNED BACHE
  PATENT,1800............................................................... 100.00
PICTURE,SILHOUETTE,CHALK,PROFILE,RUFFLED CAP,CURVED GLASS,
  BRASS FRAME............................................................... 40.00
PICTURE,SILHOUETTE,COLONIAL MAN,LADY,5 IN. X 6 IN.,PAIR..... 5.00

PICTURE,SILHOUETTE,MAN,OVERCOAT,TOP HAT,UMBRELLA,FRAME,
EDOUART,12 IN...................................................... 125.00
PICTURE,SILK EMBROIDERY,BLUE GROUND,PEACOCK,ORIENTAL,23 IN.
X 17 IN........................................................... 25.00
PICTURE,SILK PAINTING,BIRD IN PINE TREE,13 X 16 IN.......... 6.50
PICTURE,STEEPLECHASE SCENE,1837,FRAME,PAIR................. 75.00
PICTURE,TAPESTRY,DUTCH FAMILY SCENE,FARMYARD,WINDMILLS,
BOATS,57 X 19 IN.................................................. 28.50
PICTURE,THE AMERICAN BASTILE,MARSHALL...................... 15.00
PICTURE,THREE SWALLOWS ON DOGWOOD LIMB,WHITE BLOSSOMS,ON
VELVET,FRAME...................................................... 40.00
PICTURE,TIMOTHY B.CURTIS,SARGT.IN CO.A.,3RD ME.VOLS.,CIVIL
WAR,FRAME......................................................... 5.00
PICTURE,TINSEL,COMPOTE OF FRUIT IN WALNUT FRAME,GOLD LINER,
15 X 3 IN......................................................... 18.00
PICTURE,TINSEL,PANSIES,2 IN. X 3 IN........................ 7.50
PICTURE,TRUE FRUITS,J.HUNGERFORD SMITH CO.,ROCHESTER,N.Y.,
TIN,FRAME......................................................... 45.00
PICTURE,WATERCOLOR,BIRD,ARTIST BENSON B. MOORE,OVAL FRAME,
6 X 4 IN.......................................................... 95.00
PICTURE,WATERCOLOR,BLACK,WHITE,ARTIST LUCY GREEN,DATED 1912,
22 X 15 IN........................................................ 50.00
PICTURE,WATERCOLOR,CAPT.EDWARD PELLEW,ROYAL NAVY,ARTIST
T.HEAPHY,1802..................................................... 295.00
PICTURE,WATERCOLOR,CLIPPER SHIP THERMOPYLA,1868,FRAME,18 IN.
X 23 IN........................................................... 250.00
PICTURE,WATERCOLOR,ENMORE CASTLE,1780,FRAME,31 1/2 X 23 IN.,
PAIR.............................................................. 495.00
PICTURE,WATERCOLOR,GIRL SURROUNDED BY YELLOW FLOWERS,ICART,
16 X 20 IN........................................................ 50.00
PICTURE,WATERCOLOR,GIRL,FLOWING HAIR,ORANGE GOWN,SIGNED
HARRY WOOLLEY..................................................... 40.00
PICTURE,WATERCOLOR,GOLFER,GIRL,1900,SIGNED,FRAME,13 1/4 X
9 1/4 IN.......................................................... 10.00
PICTURE,WATERCOLOR,INDIAN ENCAMPMENT BESIDE STREAM,SIGNED
HOERTH,FRAME...................................................... 85.00
PICTURE,WATERCOLOR,LITTLE BLONDE GIRL,SIGNED JOHN A.PARKER,
FRAME............................................................. 285.00
PICTURE,WATERCOLOR,MANCHURIA,SIGNED,SILK BROCADE-COVERED
PORTFOLIO,14...................................................... 60.00
PICTURE,WATERCOLOR,NEW ENGLAND SEASCAPE,SIGNED LOUIS
K.HARLOW.......................................................... 25.00
PICTURE,WATERCOLOR,PORT OF MARSEILLES,VESSELS,SCHOONERS,16 X
21 IN............................................................. 135.00
PICTURE,WATERCOLOR,SCENE,BORDER,CHINA,11 X 10 IN........... 3.00
PICTURE,WATERCOLOR,SHIP,THREE MASTS,BARKENTINE,ARTIST
A.LUZZO,GENOA,1892................................................ 225.00
PICTURE,WOODROW WILSON,STARS,STRIPES,COPYRIGHT 1919,FRAME,
12 X 16 IN........................................................ 12.50
PICTURE,WOOL EMBROIDERY SHIP,CIRCA 1810........... 100.00 TO 150.00
PICTURE,WOOL EMBROIDERY,BIBLICAL EPISODE,MAT,CIRCA 1815,17 X
19 IN............................................................. 100.00
PICTURE,WOVEN SILK,JOAN OF ARC,AS SHEPHERDESS,CROOK IN HAND,
SHEEP............................................................. 35.00
PICTURE,WOVEN SILK,JOAN OF ARC,AS SOLDIER,SWORD,SHIELD,FLAG,
ARMOR............................................................. 35.00
PICTURE,WOVEN SILK,TAVERN SCENE,SIGNED POHLSON,FRANCE,FRAME,
11 X 10 IN........................................................ 60.00
PICTURE FRAME,SEE FURNITURE,FRAME


PIGEON BLOOD GLASS IS ANY GLASSWARE WITH A DEEP RED
COLOR. IT IS A VERY AMBIGUOUS TERM.
PIGEON BLOOD,SEE ALSO,RUBY,CRANBERRY
PIGEON BLOOD,VASE,BRANCHES,LEAVES,WHITE FLOWERS,JAPANESE
CLOISONNE......................................................... 32.50
PIGEON BLOOD,VASE,BULBOUS,SLENDER NECK,ENAMEL TRIM,10 IN.
TALL.............................................................. 22.50
PINK SLAG,SEE SLAG
PIPE,BONE,CARVED,HAND-PAINTED PORCELAIN BOWL,SAYS GRUSS AUS
WIEN,24 IN........................................................ 139.50
PIPE,BRIAR,ELEPHANT'S HEAD,HORSE'S HEAD,IVORY EYES,
HAND-CARVED,PAIR.................................................. 42.50
PIPE,BRIAR,INLAID CIRCLES OF MOTHER-OF-PEARL,14 1/2 IN.LONG
STEM.............................................................. 19.50
PIPE,BRIAR,SILVER FITTINGS & LID,WOODEN STEM,FLEXIBLE,28 IN. 35.00
PIPE,BRIAR,STUYVESANT,CURVED STEM,7 1/2 IN................. 12.50
PIPE,BURGOMEISTER,PORCELAIN BOWL,CLASSIC SCENE,GERMANY,
30 IN.LONG........................................................ 23.00
PIPE,CHURCHILL IN TOP HAT,HAND-CARVED,ITALY................ 15.00
PIPE,CLAY,MARKED RAOB............................................. 4.00

PIPE,MANHATTAN,STRAIGHT,BENT,GOLD BAND,CASE,PAIR............  100.00
PIPE,MEERSCHAUM,SAILOR,WOMAN'S HEAD,WEARS HELMET & MONOCLE,
  EAGLE CLAW,3............................................  150.00
PIPE,ONE SILVER,ONE BRASS,BAMBOO TAPER,CARVED,COLORED DECOR,
  BOX,CHINA..............................................   35.00
PIPE,OPIUM,BRASS & BAMBOO,CHINA............................   15.00
PIPE,PINK LUSTER BOWL,GOLD MEDALLION,ZUR ERINNERUNG,FLORAL,
  WOODEN STEM.............................................   28.00
PIPE,PORCELAIN BOWL,HAND-PAINTED,CARVED BONE,CHAIN, GRUSS
  AUS WIEN ..............................................  139.50
PIPE,PORCELAIN BOWL,WOODEN STEM,HINGED LID,SCENE,HUNTERS,
  RABBITS,39 IN..........................................   20.00
PIPE,PSYCHE'S ARM TIPS JAR FOR CUPID TO DRINK,CARVED,
  LIVERPOOL CASE.........................................   58.50
PIPE,WATER,ORNATE,BRASS,TURKISH,58 IN.TALL.................   85.00
PIPE,WATER,TURKISH,HAND-CARVED BOWL,DEER,PINT-SIZE WATER JAR  20.00
PLASTER,BUST,LINCOLN,SIGNED J.M.BAILLY,1865,10 IN...........   18.00
PLASTER,FIGURINE,BIRD,RED,YELLOW,ORANGE,GREEN,PAIR.........   50.00
PLASTER,PLAQUE,INDIAN CHIEF,SQUAW,COLORFUL,PAIR............   42.50
  PLATE,SEE UNDER SPECIAL TYPES SUCH AS ABC,CALENDAR,
  CHRISTMAS


     PLATED AMBERINA WAS MADE BY THE NEW ENGLAND GLASS WORKS
     AFTER 1886.IT ALWAYS HAS A CREAM-COLORED OR CHARTREUSE
     LINING AND A RIBBED REDDISH EXTERIOR.
PLATED AMBERINA,FINGERBOWL................................1,700.00
PLATED AMBERINA,PITCHER,WATER.............................  950.00
PLATED AMBERINA,TUMBLER...................................  900.00
  PLATED SILVER,SEE SILVER PLATE


     PLIQUE A JOUR IS AN ENAMELING PROCESS. THE ENAMEL WAS
     LAID BETWEEN THIN RAISED METAL LINES AND HEATED. THE
     FINISHED PIECE HAS TRANSPARENT ENAMEL HELD BETWEEN
     THE THIN METAL WIRES.
PLIQUE A JOUR,BOWL,HANDLE,3-IN.DIAMETER...................1,000.00
PLIQUE A JOUR,CUP & SAUCER,RUSSIAN GILDED SILVER,1891,ENAMEL1,800.00
PLIQUE A JOUR,GLASS HOLDER,SIGNED SATYHOV,RUSSIA..........1,400.00
PLIQUE A JOUR,SPOON,CADDY,RUSSIAN,CIRCA 1880..............  375.00
PLIQUE A JOUR,SPOON,NOT SIGNED............................   90.00
PLIQUE A JOUR,TEASPOON,RUSSIAN GILDED SILVER,ENAMEL,1890....  300.00
POLITICAL CAMPAIGN,BANDANNA,CENTER HEAD OF THEODORE
  ROOSEVELT,1912.........................................   35.00
POLITICAL CAMPAIGN,BANDANNA,GARFIELD & MAC ARTHUR,DATED
  1880,COTTON............................................   48.00
POLITICAL CAMPAIGN,BANDANNA,PORTRAITS OF GARFIELD & ARTHUR,
  1880,RED...............................................   18.00
POLITICAL CAMPAIGN,BANDANNA,ROOSEVELT-FAIRBANKS,1904,FLAG,
  EAGLE,PORTRAIT.........................................   75.00
POLITICAL CAMPAIGN,BANDANNA,WE WANT WILLKIE...............   16.50
POLITICAL CAMPAIGN,BANK,TAFT & SHERMAN,HAT,STARS,STRIPES,
  MILK GLASS.............................................   37.50
POLITICAL CAMPAIGN,BANNER,FRANKLIN D.ROOSEVELT...........   10.00
POLITICAL CAMPAIGN,BUTTON,AL SMITH.......................    4.00
POLITICAL CAMPAIGN,BUTTON,AL SMITH PICTURE................    8.50
POLITICAL CAMPAIGN,BUTTON,BRYAN..........................    4.00
POLITICAL CAMPAIGN,BUTTON,COOLIDGE.......................    4.00
POLITICAL CAMPAIGN,BUTTON,EVERY BUDDY FOR WILLKIE.......    2.00
POLITICAL CAMPAIGN,BUTTON,F.D.ROOSEVELT,PICTURE,DONKEY ON
  CORD...................................................    2.50
POLITICAL CAMPAIGN,BUTTON,GOLDWATER,ELEPHANT WEARING
  GLASSES,GOLD COLOR.....................................    5.00
POLITICAL CAMPAIGN,BUTTON,GROVER CLEVELAND...............    2.00
POLITICAL CAMPAIGN,BUTTON,HAYES,STARS & STRIPES..........    6.00
POLITICAL CAMPAIGN,BUTTON,HAYES,1 IN.....................    .6.00
POLITICAL CAMPAIGN,BUTTON,HAYES,1 1/2 IN.................    8.00
POLITICAL CAMPAIGN,BUTTON,HERBERT HOOVER PICTURE,CHAIN & BAR
  ATTACHED...............................................    8.50
POLITICAL CAMPAIGN,BUTTON,HOOVER.........................    4.00
POLITICAL CAMPAIGN,BUTTON,HOOVER & CURTISS,PICTURE.......    1.50
POLITICAL CAMPAIGN,BUTTON,HUGHES.........................    4.00
POLITICAL CAMPAIGN,BUTTON,I WANT ROOSEVELT AGAIN.........    1.75
POLITICAL CAMPAIGN,BUTTON,KEEP COOL WITH COOLIDGE........    1.25
POLITICAL CAMPAIGN,BUTTON,LANDON & KNOX,ELEPHANT,SUNFLOWER..   1.50
POLITICAL CAMPAIGN,BUTTON,LANDON & KNOX,FELT SUNFLOWER......   3.75
POLITICAL CAMPAIGN,BUTTON,LANDON & KNOX, PICTURE.........    1.50
POLITICAL CAMPAIGN,BUTTON,LANDON-KNOX,1936,SUNFLOWER.....    7.50
POLITICAL CAMPAIGN,BUTTON,NAME,COOLIDGE & DAWES..........    1.50
POLITICAL CAMPAIGN,BUTTON,NAME,HOOVER,7/8-IN. DIAMETER......   1.50
POLITICAL CAMPAIGN,BUTTON,NAME,LANDON....................    1.25

POLITICAL CAMPAIGN,BUTTON,NAME,LANDON-KNOX.................. 1.75
POLITICAL CAMPAIGN,BUTTON,NAME,NIXON-LODGE.................. 1.25
POLITICAL CAMPAIGN,BUTTON,NAME,STEVENSON................... 1.25
POLITICAL CAMPAIGN,BUTTON,PARKER........................... 4.00
POLITICAL CAMPAIGN,BUTTON,PORTRAIT,LAFOLLETTE-WHEELER,
  BRONZE,1 IN.............................................. 14.00
POLITICAL CAMPAIGN,BUTTON,PORTRAIT,ROOSEVELT-GARNER,BRONZE,
  1 IN.................................................... 14.00
POLITICAL CAMPAIGN,BUTTON,REPEAL PROHIBITION............... `1.25
POLITICAL CAMPAIGN,BUTTON,ROOSEVELT,A SQUARE DEAL ALL
  AROUND,1912............................................. 6.00
POLITICAL CAMPAIGN,BUTTON,ROOSEVELT-WALLACE,EAR OF CORN
  PICTURE................................................. 2.00
POLITICAL CAMPAIGN,BUTTON,SAYS I LIKE IKE.................. 1.25
POLITICAL CAMPAIGN,BUTTON,SAYS NO THIRD TERM............... 2.00
POLITICAL CAMPAIGN,BUTTON,SAYS VOTE NO ON WOMAN SUFFRAGE.... 3.00
POLITICAL CAMPAIGN,BUTTON,SPEED RECOVERY,RE-ELECT HOOVER,
  LARGE................................................... 4.00
POLITICAL CAMPAIGN,BUTTON,SUNFLOWER,LANDON & KNOX.......... 1.00
POLITICAL CAMPAIGN,BUTTON,TAFT............................. 6.00
POLITICAL CAMPAIGN,BUTTON,TAFT,BROWN & WHITE............... 5.00
POLITICAL CAMPAIGN,BUTTON,THEODORE ROOSEVELT,BRASS.......... 5.00
POLITICAL CAMPAIGN,BUTTON,WALLACE FOR PRESIDENT,NO PICTURE,
  6....................................................... 1.00
POLITICAL CAMPAIGN,BUTTON,WALLACE,PICTURE,4................ 1.00
POLITICAL CAMPAIGN,BUTTON,WENDELL WILLKIE PORTRAIT,1940,
  1 1/2 IN................................................ 3.75
POLITICAL CAMPAIGN,BUTTON,WILLKIE & MC NARY,RED,WHITE,BLUE.. 2.00
POLITICAL CAMPAIGN,BUTTON,WILLKIE FOR PRESIDENT............ 1.25
POLITICAL CAMPAIGN,BUTTON,WILSON........................... 4.00
POLITICAL CAMPAIGN,BUTTON,WILSON,1 1/2 IN.................. 6.00
POLITICAL CAMPAIGN,BUTTON,WIN WITH WILSON,FULL COLOR PICTURE 15.00
POLITICAL CAMPAIGN,BUTTON,WINGS FOR AMERICA WILLKIE........ 2.00
POLITICAL CAMPAIGN,BUTTON,WOODROW WILSON,PICTURE,
  1 1/4 IN.-DIAMETER...................................... 8.50
POLITICAL CAMPAIGN,MUG,HARDING,2 IN.TALL................... 14.00
POLITICAL CAMPAIGN,NOISEMAKER,THEODORE ROOSEVELT,ZIGZAG SNAP 22.50
POLITICAL CAMPAIGN,PICTURE,WIN WITH WILLKIE................ 3.00
POLITICAL CAMPAIGN,PLATE,RAISED BUST OF BRYAN IN CENTER,
  FLAGS,EAGLE............................................. 16.50
POLITICAL CAMPAIGN,PLATE,TAFT-SHERMAN,1908,GOP STANDARD
  BEARERS,TIN............................................. 17.00
POLITICAL CAMPAIGN,PLATE,WILLIAM H.TAFT,SMILE DARN YOU SMILE 14.00
POLITICAL CAMPAIGN,POSTER,FRANKLIN ROOSEVELT.............. 11.00
POLITICAL CAMPAIGN,POSTER,IKE............................. 10.00
POLITICAL CAMPAIGN,POSTER,LINCOLN-HAMLIN,1864,REPRINT,
  9 1/2 IN................................................ 7.50
POLITICAL CAMPAIGN,STICKPIN,U.S.GRANT,STARS AROUND PORTRAIT,
  BRASS.................................................. 40.00
POLITICAL CAMPAIGN,WATCH FOB,TAFT & SHERMAN,BRYAN & KERN,
  1908,PAIR.............................................. 20.00
POLITICAL CAMPAIGN,WATCH FOB,THEODORE ROOSEVELT,PICTURE,
  G.O.P,................................................. 17.50


        POMONA GLASS IS CLEAR WITH A SOFT AMBER BORDER
        DECORATED WITH PALE BLUE OR ROSE-COLORED FLOWERS AND
        LEAVES. THE COLORS ARE VERY,VERY PALE. THE BACKGROUND
        OF THE GLASS IS COVERED WITH A NETWORK OF FINE LINES.
        IT WAS MADE FROM 1885 TO 1888 BY THE NEW ENGLAND GLASS
        COMPANY.
POMONA,BOWL,FINGER,RUFFLED AMBER RIM....................... 58.00
POMONA,BOWL,FINGER,RUFFLED EDGE........................... 110.00
POMONA,BOWL,FINGER,RUFFLED EDGE,FIRST GRIND............... 95.00
POMONA,BOWL,ROSE,AMBER BASE & SCALLOPED TOP,FOUR APPLIED
  FEET.................................................... 110.00
POMONA,BOX,ALLOVER FLORAL & FRUIT DECOR ON BASE,PARROTS,
  BRANCH ON COVER......................................... 45.00
POMONA,CELERY,THUMBPRINT,AMBER CRIMPED TOP................ 95.00
POMONA,CREAMER,AMBER HANDLE,RIM,FEET...................... 85.00
POMONA,CUP,PUNCH,AMBER,BLUE CORNFLOWERS................... 87.00
POMONA,CUP,PUNCH,CORNFLOWER PATTERN,AMBER & BLUE STAIN..... 85.00
POMONA,CUP,PUNCH,DIAMOND-QUILTED PATTERN,FIRST GRIND....... 70.00
POMONA,CUP,PUNCH,DIAMOND-QUILTED,AMBER LEAF PATTERN &
  HANDLE,FIRST GRIND...................................... 42.00
POMONA,MUG,HAND-PAINTED FLORAL,APPLIED HANDLE,AMBER FLASHING
  EDGE.................................................... 4.50
POMONA,PITCHER,BLUE,FLORAL DECOR,6 1/2 IN.HIGH............. 420.00
POMONA,PITCHER,CORNFLOWER DECOR,AMBER STAIN............... 325.00
POMONA,PITCHER,ENCIRCLEMENT OF BLUE FLOWERS,6 1/2
  IN..................................................... 420.00 TO 656.00

POMONA,PITCHER,FLASHED AMBER TOP,ETCHED LOWER PORTION,
    BULBOUS........................................................ 300.00
POMONA,PITCHER,FROSTED BAND,EMBOSSED FLOWER BUDS,LEAVES,SIX
    TUMBLERS....................................................... 225.00
POMONA,PITCHER,MILK,BLUE FLOWERS,6 1/2 IN.TALL................. 367.00
POMONA,PITCHER,RUFFLED TOP,APPLIED HANDLE,CORNFLOWERS,MARK,
    10 IN......................................................... 125.00
POMONA,PITCHER,SECOND GRIND,7 1/4 IN.......................... 185.00
POMONA,PITCHER,TANKARD,12 IN.,FOUR TUMBLERS,HANDLED,
    5 1/4 IN...................................................... 500.00
POMONA,PITCHER,WATER,AMBER TOP & HANDLE,BULBOUS,
    7 1/2 IN.HIGH.................................................. 75.00
POMONA,PITCHER,WATER,AMBER TOP,ENAMELED FLOWERS,THUMBPRINT,
    ACID FINISH................................................... 115.00
POMONA,SHAKER,SUGAR,FROSTED BAND WITH EMBOSSED FLORAL,
    BULBOUS....................................................... 36.00
POMONA,SPOONER,PANSY & BUTTERFLY.............................. 80.00
POMONA,TOOTHPICK,AMBER STAINED RIM,BABY DIAMOND QUILTED
    INTERIOR...................................................... 95.00
POMONA,TOOTHPICK,ENAMELED FLOWERS............................. 57.00
POMONA,TOOTHPICK,TRICORNERED................................. 89.00
POMONA,TUMBLER,BLUE CORNFLOWERS............................... 65.00
POMONA,TUMBLER,CORNFLOWER DECOR,AMBER STAIN................... 75.00
POMONA,TUMBLER,CORNFLOWER PATTERN,DIAMOND-QUILTED............ 77.50
POMONA,TUMBLER,CORNFLOWERS.................................... 70.00
POMONA,TUMBLER,DIAMOND-QUILTED,CORNFLOWER DECOR.............. 75.00
POMONA,TUMBLER,DIAMOND-QUILTED,CORNFLOWERS,AMBER,BLUE........ 77.50
POMONA,TUMBLER,ENAMEL FLOWER DESIGN........................... 60.00
    PORCELAIN, SEE ALSO,BOW,COPELAND,NIPPON,RS PRUSSIA,ETC.
    BONE,DISH,BOX,TOOTHPICK,ETC.
PORCELAIN,ASHTRAY,MICKEY MOUSE,PLUTO,COPYRIGHT WALT E.DISNEY  30.00
PORCELAIN,BASKET,MOTHER-OF-PEARL FINISH,CARAMEL,WHITE,
    CZECHOSLOVAKIA................................................. 7.50
PORCELAIN,BERRY SET,PINK FLOWERS,SERVING BOWL,6 INDIVIDUAL
    BOWLS,GERMANY................................................. 32.50
PORCELAIN,BERRY SET,VIOLET DECOR,SIGNED D FRENA,7 PIECES.... 65.00
PORCELAIN,BONBONNIERE,PUG,CIRCA 1760......................1,300.00
PORCELAIN,BONBONNIERE,TERRIER,CIRCA 1760,PROBABLY
    FURSTENBERG...............................................2,800.00
PORCELAIN,BOOKEND,BROWN GROUND,EMBOSSED INDIAN CHIEF,
    5 3/4 IN.,PAIR................................................ 12.00
PORCELAIN,BOOTIE,FLORAL DECOR,GERMANY......................... 12.00
PORCELAIN,BOOTIE,PINK BOW,3 IN................................ 6.00
PORCELAIN,BOTTLE,SNUFF,DECORATED & MOLDED,19TH CENTURY...... 350.00
PORCELAIN,BOTTLE,SNUFF,ENAMELED,TAO KUANG.................... 120.00
PORCELAIN,BOTTLE,SNUFF,FAMILLE ROSE.......................... 100.00
PORCELAIN,BOTTLE,SNUFF,WHITE-GLAZED,LEAF FORM................ 50.00
PORCELAIN,BOWL & DISH,MIRAB PANELS,FLORAL SPRAYS,COBALT,
    GOLD,CIRCA 1810............................................... 90.00
PORCELAIN,BOWL,BERRY,CHERRIES,GOLD,SIGNED FRENCH STUDIOS,
    6 SAUCES...................................................... 50.00
PORCELAIN,BOWL,BLUE,PINK MUMS,WHITE DAISIES.................. 62.00
PORCELAIN,BOWL,CENTERPIECE,OPENWORK,FRUIT,HAND-PAINTED,
    FOOTED,FRANCE................................................. 225.00
PORCELAIN,BOWL,CHILD'S,CHICKS,RABBITS,MATCHING CUP.......... 12.50
PORCELAIN,BOWL,FIGURAL DECORATION,CIRCA 1785................. 125.00
PORCELAIN,BOWL,FRUIT,BIRDS,FLOWERS,LAVENDER,GOLD,WHITE,
    HAND-PAINTED.................................................. 15.00
PORCELAIN,BOWL,FRUIT,WHITE,TURQUOISE,SCENES,WINGED CHERUBS,
    4 SMALL BOWLS................................................. 35.00
PORCELAIN,BOWL,ITALIAN,CHINOISERIE DECOR,COVER,COZZI,1765... 200.00
PORCELAIN,BOWL,OPEN,OVAL,ORIENTAL PATTERN,SYRACUSE,
    9 3/4 IN.LONG................................................. 2.00
PORCELAIN,BOWL,PINK,PEACH FLORAL,GREEN FOLIAGE,GOLD SPATTER
    RIM,10 IN..................................................... 9.00
PORCELAIN,BOWL,RAISED SCROLL,GOLD TRACERY,MULTICOLORED
    FLORAL,SCALLOPED............................................. 25.00
PORCELAIN,BOWL,RICE,CHINA,6 IN................................ 9.75
PORCELAIN,BOWL,RICE,GREEN,HENNA,PANELED,COVER,CHINA,SET OF
    10............................................................ 39.50
PORCELAIN,BOWL,RICE,WHITE INTERIOR,APRICOT COLOR OUTSIDE,
    BIRDS,CHINA................................................... 6.50
PORCELAIN,BOWL,ROSE,CREAMY GROUND,RED & YELLOW MUMS,SIGNED D
    & C,FRANCE................................................... 35.00
PORCELAIN,BOWL,ROSE,PINK & WHITE ROSES,LEAVES,GOLD TRIM,
    FOOTED....................................................... 25.00
PORCELAIN,BOWL,ROSES,LEAVES,GOLD BORDER,CIRCA 1890,
    9 3/4 IN.WIDE................................................ 20.00
PORCELAIN,BOWL,SERVING,WHITE GROUND,CARNATION SPRIGS,BLUE
    EDGE......................................................... 8.50
PORCELAIN,BOWL,SIGNED GARDINER,TEAK STAND,RUSSIA,

```
    8-IN.DIAMETER.......................................    125.00
PORCELAIN,BOWL,SUGAR,WHITE,HANDLES,GOLD TRIM,TWIG FINIAL,5 X
    7 IN.HIGH..........................................     16.50
PORCELAIN,BOWL,WHITE FLORAL,SPRIGS OF PINK,YELLOW,LAVENDER,
    GOLD...............................................    125.00
PORCELAIN,BOWL,WHITE,HEADS WITH BEARDS FORM HANDLES,GREEN,
    TAN................................................     25.00
PORCELAIN,BOX,BEIGE GROUND,DAISY SPRAYS ON COVER,GOLD,
    VIENNA,AUSTRIA.....................................     14.50
PORCELAIN,BOX,EGG-SHAPED,PORTRAIT SCENE ON TOP,SIGNED
    ANGELICA KAUFFMANN.................................     24.00
PORCELAIN,BOX,GOLD & MULTICOLORED ENAMELING,CREST ON LID,
    HINGED,FRANCE......................................     55.00
PORCELAIN,BOX,HAND-PAINTED FLORAL,GILT,COVER,TRAY,1850,
    FRANCE.............................................     45.00
PORCELAIN,BOX,JEWEL,OVAL,MINIATURE PORTRAIT ON LID,ALLOVER
    BRASS WORK.........................................     22.00
PORCELAIN,BOX,JEWEL,PORTRAIT ON LID,ALLOVER ORNATE BRASS
    WORK,OVAL..........................................      8.50
PORCELAIN,BOX,PAIR,BERLIN,SUGAR,4 1/4 IN. LONG........    150.00
PORCELAIN,BOX,PATCH,FULL FIGURE OF NUDE WOMAN,OVAL,2 IN.....   42.00
PORCELAIN,BOX,PATCH,PORTRAIT,HAND-PAINTED,BLUE,CREAMY,
    MOTTLED,1 3/4 IN...................................     18.00
PORCELAIN,BOX,PINK,ENAMEL,BIRD,FLORAL,BUTTERFLY,BRASS
    FITTINGS,3 1/2 IN..................................     37.50
PORCELAIN,BOX,PINK,FLORAL,GOLD TRIM,MARKED
    ORLIK-HAND-PAINTED,4 X 3 IN........................      7.00
PORCELAIN,BOX,PLAYING CARD,KING OF HEARTS ON COVER,FOUR
    SUITS ON SIDES.....................................     10.00
PORCELAIN,BOX,POWDER,FLORAL,COVER.....................      3.00
PORCELAIN,BOX,POWDER,HAIR RECEIVER LID FITS BASE OF POWDER,
    HAND-PAINTED.......................................     12.50
PORCELAIN,BOX,SNUFF,BLUE & WHITE,19TH CENTURY.........     90.00
PORCELAIN,BOX,TRINKET,DIAMOND SHAPE,VIOLET DECOR,4 IN......    5.00
PORCELAIN,BOX,TRINKET,MAROON,FLORAL PANEL ON LID,GOLD TRIM,
    FRANCE.............................................     22.00
PORCELAIN,BOX,TRINKET,MOTHER-OF-PEARL,FLORAL DECOR ON TOP,
    BRASS HINGE........................................     15.00
PORCELAIN,BOX,YELLOW GROUND,ROSE SPRAY ON COVER,MARK,
    ELBOGEN,PAIR.......................................     25.00
PORCELAIN,BULB POT,BLUE,WHITE,FIVE HOLES FOR BULBS,
    LOTUS-FORM CUP,CHINA...............................     65.00
PORCELAIN,CACHEPOT,WHITE,FLORAL,FOOTED,WORCESTER,2 1/2 X
    2 1/4 IN.HIGH......................................     30.00
PORCELAIN,CAKE STAND,HAND-PAINTED FRUIT CENTER,MEDALLIONS,
    GOLD,3 PLATES......................................     45.00
PORCELAIN,CANDLEHOLDER,FLORAL,SWIRL,SCALLOPED BOTTOM,FLUTED
    TOP RIM............................................      7.50
PORCELAIN,CANDLESTICK,CHAMBER,RED ROSES,GREEN SHADING.......    5.00
PORCELAIN,CANDLESTICK,FLORAL,4 1/2 IN.TALL............      3.50
PORCELAIN,CANDLESTICK,PURPLE ASTERS,PAIR.............       5.00
PORCELAIN,CASE,CALLING CARD,BLACK LACQUER,HINGED TOP,VELVET
    LINING.............................................     24.00
PORCELAIN,CELERY SET,LONG DISH,SIX SMALL SALTS,WHITE,GOLD
    BAND...............................................     12.50
PORCELAIN,CHAMBER SET,FLORAL SPRAYS,7 PIECES..........    150.00
PORCELAIN,CHAMBER SET,PINK STRAPWORK ON TURQUOISE,5 PIECES..   50.00
PORCELAIN,CHAMBER SET,SPRIGS OF PINK ROSES...........     150.00
PORCELAIN,CHAMBERSTICK,EMBOSSED,FLANGE TOP OF CANDLE SOCKET,
    FLORAL.............................................     12.50
PORCELAIN,CHEESE BOARD,BLUE FLORAL GARLANDS,GILT,5 3/4 IN. X
    9 3/4 IN...........................................     14.50
PORCELAIN,CHOCOLATE POT,HAND-PAINTED,FIELD FLOWERS,ENAMEL,
    EMBOSSING..........................................     23.50
PORCELAIN,COMPOTE,WHITE,GOLD & GREEN BORDER,FLORAL CENTER,
    8 1/2 IN.WIDE......................................     22.50
PORCELAIN,CONDIMENT SET,WHITE,FLORAL,BOWS ON LIDS,FRANCE,SIX
    PIECE..............................................    120.00
PORCELAIN,CREAMER & SUGAR,RAISED PASTEL PETALS FORM FLOWER,
    GOLD-WASHED........................................     25.00
PORCELAIN,CREAMER,DUCK SHAPE,CZECHOSLOVAKIA,4 3/4 IN.HIGH...    4.75
PORCELAIN,CREAMER,FIGURAL,CROW,BLACK,GERMANY.........      12.50
PORCELAIN,CREAMER,FIGURAL,DUCK,CZECHOSLOVAKIA,4 3/4 IN.HIGH.    4.75
PORCELAIN,CREAMER,FIGURAL,PIG,STANDING,SMILING,DRESSED,
    MARKED GES GESCH...................................     10.00
PORCELAIN,CREAMER,FIGURAL,WILD BOAR,MARKED GES GESCH.......    14.00
PORCELAIN,CREAMER,GRAPES,BUTTERFLIES,MARKED LOSO WARE,
    BURSLEM,ENGLAND....................................      9.75
PORCELAIN,CREAMER,ROOSTER SHAPE,GERMANY...............      6.00
PORCELAIN,CREAMER,STANDING COW,WEARING DRESS,TAIL HANDLE,
    COVER..............................................     17.50
```

```
PORCELAIN,CREAMER,WHITE GROUND,PINK FLORAL DECOR,LID........    6.00
PORCELAIN,CREAMER,45-STAR FLAG,SAYS OLD GLORY,CARLSBAD
  CHINA,AUSTRIA.................................................    4.75
PORCELAIN,CRUET,PEDESTAL FOOT,HAND-PAINTED,BLUE DRAPE,
  FLOWERS,GERMANY..............................................   45.00
PORCELAIN,CUP,CHRISTMAS,SANTA,TOYS,SAYS MERRY CHRISTMAS.....   12.00
PORCELAIN,CUP,EGG,FLORAL DECOR,FRANCE,MATCHING SAUCER.......   10.00
PORCELAIN,CUP,EGG,ROSES,GOLD DECOR,SET OF 3................   15.00
PORCELAIN,CUP,EGG,VIOLETS,FRANCE...........................    7.50
PORCELAIN,CUP,MUSTACHE,PINK ROSES..........................    5.00
PORCELAIN,CUP,WINE,CELADON GROUND,FLORAL,VINES,1 1/4 IN.HIGH   16.50
PORCELAIN,CUP & SAUCER,BERLIN,WHITE,CIRCA 1750,WEGELY
  FACTORY.....................................................  120.00
PORCELAIN,CUP & SAUCER,CAKE PLATE,CHILD'S,CLOWNS,DOGS,
  PERFORMERS,GERMANY...........................................    8.00
PORCELAIN,CUP & SAUCER,COLORED PICTURE OF PENARTH BEACH.....    8.50
PORCELAIN,CUP & SAUCER,CUTOUT BEAR HANDLE,KORNILOW BROS.,
  RUSSIA,1900.................................................   30.00
PORCELAIN,CUP & SAUCER,EMBOSSED INDIAN HEAD,GOLD TOMAHAWK,
  SPEAR.......................................................   14.50
PORCELAIN,CUP & SAUCER,FIGURES OF FAITH,HOPE,CHARITY,PINK
  LUSTER BANDS................................................   25.00
PORCELAIN,CUP & SAUCER,FRENCH EMPIRE,JEWELED,FOOTED.........  135.00
PORCELAIN,CUP & SAUCER,ORIENTAL PATTERN,CROWN & VICTORIA,
  CZECHOSLOVAKIA..............................................    5.00
PORCELAIN,CUP & SAUCER,PORTRAIT,KING EDWARD VII,QUEEN
  ALEXANDRIA..................................................    6.00
PORCELAIN,CUP & SAUCER,ROSES,HAND-PAINTED,MARKED GERMANY....    6.95
PORCELAIN,CUP & SAUCER,SETTER DOG,POINTING,LANDSCAPE,GERMANY   11.00
PORCELAIN,CUP & SAUCER,WEDDING BAND PATTERN,WHITE,GOLD BAND,
  SET OF 8....................................................   60.00
PORCELAIN,CUP & SAUCER,WHITE,BLUE FLORAL FORMS WORD DAD,
  LEFTON CHINA................................................    9.00
PORCELAIN,CUP & SAUCER,WHITE,HAND PAINTED,BLUE,GOLD,
  ROSETTES,DEMITASSE..........................................   18.50
PORCELAIN,CUSPIDOR,LADY'S,WHITE,MULTICOLOR FLORAL DECOR,
  GERMANY.....................................................   22.50
PORCELAIN,CUSPIDOR,RED & PINK ROSES,3 3/4 IN.HIGH,
  6 1/2-IN.DIAMETER...........................................   12.50
PORCELAIN,CUSPIDOR,WHITE GROUND,PINK ROSES,GREEN LEAVES,8 X
  5 IN.TALL...................................................   25.00
PORCELAIN,CUSPIDOR,WHITE GROUND,RED ROSES,GERMANY...........   22.50
PORCELAIN,DECANTER,BLUE,SILVER DEPOSIT TRIM................   65.00
PORCELAIN,DISH,BONE,PINK BLOSSOMS,GREEN LEAVES,SCALLOPED,
  GOLD EDGE,3.................................................    6.50
PORCELAIN,DISH,BONE,PINK DAISIES,MADDOCK...................    3.50
PORCELAIN,DISH,BONE,PINK FLORAL,LEAVES,SCALLOPED,JOHNSON
  BROS.,12....................................................   38.00
PORCELAIN,DISH,BUTTER,TOP IS FULL-LENGTH FIGURE OF A DUTCH
  MAID........................................................   50.00
PORCELAIN,DISH,CELERY,WHITE,PINK ROSES,GREEN LEAVES,GOLD
  TRIM,GERMANY................................................    9.50
PORCELAIN,DISH,CHEESE,BERRIES,GRAPES,PLUMS,ROUND,COVER......   12.50
PORCELAIN,DISH,CHEESE,FLORAL,BLACK & TAN TRIM,WEDGE SHAPE...   15.00
PORCELAIN,DISH,CHEESE,RIBBED,SHADED PINK & YELLOW ROSES,
  HANDLE,9 IN.................................................   22.00
PORCELAIN,DISH,CHEESE,ROSE CLUSTERS,GOLD,BONN,GERMANY,7 X
  8 5/8 IN....................................................   22.00
PORCELAIN,DISH,CHEESE,SLANT TOP,FRUIT BLOSSOMS.............   19.50
PORCELAIN,DISH,CHEESE,YELLOW FLOWERS,WEDGE SHAPE...........   12.50
PORCELAIN,DISH,CHINESE CHARACTERS,EARTH,SUN,DRAGONS,MING
  DYNASTY,1573................................................   24.95
PORCELAIN,DISH,HONEY,PINK,BLUE FLORAL,GREEN FOLIAGE,WHITE
  INSIDE,FINIAL...............................................   10.00
PORCELAIN,DISH,LEAF SHAPE,HAND-PAINTED ROSES,MARKED WEIMAR,
  GERMANY,7 IN................................................    3.75
PORCELAIN,DISH,LOBSTER CENTER HANDLE,TWO SECTIONS,ROSES,
  13 1/2 X 14 IN..............................................   34.00
PORCELAIN,DISH,OVAL,WHITE GROUND,MULTICOLORED FLORAL,CHINA,
  4 1/2 IN.LONG...............................................    4.50
PORCELAIN,DISH,PIN,WHITE,GREEN & YELLOW FLORAL,MARKED,
  GERMANY.....................................................    8.00
PORCELAIN,DISH,RELISH,WHITE GROUND,ORCHID ROSES,MARKED
  C.T.GERMANY.................................................    8.00
PORCELAIN,DISH,SALAD,DIVIDED,ACORN DECOR,GOLD,CENTER HANDLE,
  OVAL........................................................   23.50
PORCELAIN,DISH,SALT,PINK ROSES INSIDE & OUTSIDE,GOLD RIM,
  OPEN,AUSTRIA,6..............................................   15.00
PORCELAIN,DISH,SAUCE,BLUE,ORIENTAL SCENE,5 1/2 IN..........    2.50
PORCELAIN,DISH,SOAP,BLUE FORGET-ME-NOTS,OVAL..............    8.50
PORCELAIN,DISH,SOAP,FLORAL,COVER...........................    4.50
```

```
PORCELAIN,DISH,SPOON HOLDER,GREEN,LAVENDER,YELLOW,LEAVES,
  FLOWERS.................................................    65.00
PORCELAIN,DISH,VEGETABLE,PINK FLORAL,TWO HANDLES,COVER,
  VADERY,1875.............................................    12.00
PORCELAIN,DOORKNOB,HAND-PAINTED PINK ROSES,BLUE DAISIES,
  GOLD,PAIR...............................................    10.00
PORCELAIN,EGG,DECORATED,BEEHIVE MARK,3 IN.LONG.............    17.00
PORCELAIN,EGG,EASTER,GREEN & PURPLE ENAMELING,SAYS EASTER,
  7 1/2 IN................................................     8.50
PORCELAIN,EGG,EASTER,ON SLED,PULLED BY BOY,LILY OF THE
  VALLEY,GERMANY..........................................    35.00
PORCELAIN,EGG,EASTER,VIOLETS..............................     4.50
PORCELAIN,EGG,EASTER,WHITE & GREEN ENAMELING,SAYS EASTER,
  10 1/2 IN...............................................    10.50
PORCELAIN,EGG,FLORAL WITH CYRILLIC INSCRIPTION CHRIST IS
  RISEN,RUSSIA............................................   175.00
PORCELAIN,FERNER,WHITE,VIOLETS,GREEN,GOLD,3 IN.DEEP,
  9-IN.DIAMETER...........................................    22.50
PORCELAIN,FIGURINE,BOY,CRUMPLED HAT,TORN PANTS,GIRL,SCARF,
  SHAWL,PAIR..............................................    19.00
PORCELAIN,FIGURINE,CHINESE LADY,DECORATED ROBE,SIGNED,CHINA,
  9 IN.,PAIR..............................................    48.00
PORCELAIN,FIGURINE,DUTCH MAID,HOLDS BASKET OF FISH,8 IN.TALL   25.00
PORCELAIN,FIGURINE,EMPEROR,EMPRESS,CHINA,14 IN.,PAIR......    80.00
PORCELAIN,FIGURINE,GEORGE WASHINGTON,MARKED,6 IN.HIGH.....    45.00
PORCELAIN,FIGURINE,GEORGE,MARTHA WASHINGTON,BUST,GERMANY,
  5 1/2 IN.,PAIR..........................................    18.50
PORCELAIN,FIGURINE,ITALIAN,CENTAUR,RUFFIANS,ROCKWORK BASE,
  WHITE,ESTE..............................................   350.00
PORCELAIN,FIGURINE,ITALIAN,YOUTHS,TREE,LE NOVE,ROCOCO,
  ANTONIBON FACTORY.......................................   100.00
PORCELAIN,FIGURINE,JURO JIN,JAPANESE GOD OF LONGEVITY,ROBE,
  HOLDS SCROLL............................................    45.00
PORCELAIN,FIGURINE,LADY HOLDS LETTER,MAN HOLDS MANDOLIN,
  FRANCE,PAIR.............................................    75.00
PORCELAIN,FIGURINE,LORELEI SITTING ON AN OPEN SHELL,SWAN,
  ROSES,4 1/2 IN..........................................     7.50
PORCELAIN,FIGURINE,QUEEN ISABELLA,KING FERDINAND,BY
  J.A.HANNONG,PAIR......................................2,200.00
PORCELAIN,FIGURINE,TWO DALMATIAN DOGS,HAND-PAINTED,GERMANY,
  10 1/4 IN...............................................    47.50
PORCELAIN,FIGURINE,TWO DOGS,SIGNED S.H.CLARK,FRANCE,IN
  SHADOW BOX FRAME........................................   275.00
PORCELAIN,FIGURINE,WOMAN,BY GARDINER,RUSSIA,8 1/2 IN.HIGH...  250.00
PORCELAIN,FIGURINE,WOMAN,FLOWING DRESS,LARGE HAT,HOLDS
  PARASOL.................................................    75.00
PORCELAIN,FOO DOG,PAIR....................................    95.00
PORCELAIN,FOOD WARMER,ENAMELED,PHOENIX & DRAGON,BRONZE
  HANDLES,3 PIECES........................................    65.00
PORCELAIN,FRAME,BUTTONS,DOUBLE CRISSCROSS,2 1/2 IN. X 4 IN..   15.00
PORCELAIN,FRAME,SCROLL SHAPE,HAND-PAINTED,LEONARD,AUSTRIA,
  5 X 4 IN................................................    27.50
PORCELAIN,GARDEN SEAT,BLUE & WHITE,CHINESE,19TH CENTURY.....  450.00
PORCELAIN,GARDEN SEAT,CHINESE,BLUE & WHITE,19TH CENTURY,
  19 1/4 IN. HIGH.........................................   500.00
PORCELAIN,GRAVY BOAT,SHELL SHAPE,PINK ROSE WREATHS,GOLD
  OUTLINE,AUSTRIA.........................................     9.00
PORCELAIN,HAIR RECEIVER,HAND-PAINTED,THREE COIN GOLD FEET...    6.00
PORCELAIN,HAIR RECEIVER,PINK & YELLOW ROSES,BLUE TRIM,CREAM
  GROUND..................................................     7.00
PORCELAIN,HAIR RECEIVER,RED & PURPLE FLOWERS..............     6.00
PORCELAIN,HAIR RECEIVER,VIOLETS AT TOP & BOTTOM,HEXAGONAL,
  SIGNED PEPLER...........................................     7.50
PORCELAIN,HAIR RECEIVER,WHITE PUFFED,GREEN LEAF VINES,GOLD
  FLOWERS.................................................    47.50
PORCELAIN,HAIR RECEIVER,WHITE,BLUE & PINK FORGET-ME-NOTS,
  SIGNED ROLFE............................................     8.50
PORCELAIN,HAIR RECEIVER,WHITE,FLORAL,SCROLLS,LEONARD,VIENNA,
  AUSTRIA.................................................     7.50
PORCELAIN,HATPIN HOLDER,ROSE DECOR,4 1/2 IN...............    10.00
PORCELAIN,HATPIN HOLDER,ROSE GARLANDS,LEAVES,MARK
  RE.NO.495408,4 3/8 IN...................................    10.00
PORCELAIN,HATPIN,HAND-PAINTED.............................     4.50
PORCELAIN,HOLDER,LETTER,YELLOW FLOWER SPRAYS,THREE SCALLOPED
  TIERS...................................................    45.00
PORCELAIN,HOLDER,MATCH,SHAPE OF OPERA GLASSES,FLORAL DECOR..    8.00
PORCELAIN,HOLDER,MENU,EASEL BACK,BIRDS & FLORAL,3 1/2 IN. X
  4 3/4 IN................................................     9.50
PORCELAIN,HOLDER,TOOTHBRUSH,SALMON-COLOR ROSES,GREEN GROUND,
  GERMAN MARK.............................................     6.50
PORCELAIN,INKSTAND,MELON SHAPE,SCROLLWORK BASE,WELL,SAND
```

```
POT,PARIS,1840.........................................    90.00
PORCELAIN,INKSTAND,OVERALL APPLIED FLORAL,CUPID,TWO WELLS,
   GERMANY...............................................    85.00
PORCELAIN,INVALID FEEDER,WHITE,PINK ROSES...............    10.50
PORCELAIN,JAR,BISCUIT,BLUE,WHITE,BOATS,PEOPLE,SILVER PLATE
   COVER,BURSLEM.........................................    30.00
PORCELAIN,JAR,BISCUIT,FLORAL,GREEN BORDER,SCALLOPED BASE,
   MARKED ENGLAND........................................    30.00
PORCELAIN,JAR,CRACKER,ALHAMBRA,RED,GREEN,TAN,MATCHING PLATE,
   MARK..................................................    39.50
PORCELAIN,JAR,CRACKER,DESERT SCENE,VICTORIA CHINA,
   CZECHOSLOVAKIA........................................    20.00
PORCELAIN,JAR,CRACKER,FLORAL,SCALLOPED COVER,BEADING,GOLD
   SPATTER...............................................    10.00
PORCELAIN,JAR,CRACKER,VIOLETS,GOLD & COBALT BORDERS,FOOTED..    28.50
PORCELAIN,JAR,DRESSER,WHITE,PINK & GRAY FLORAL,BRASS HINGE,
   3 IN.TALL.............................................    22.50
PORCELAIN,JAR,JAM,FLORAL,SILVER COVER & BAIL,ENGLAND,
   5 IN.TALL.............................................    22.00
PORCELAIN,JAR,JAM,ROSES,COVER,HOLE ON BOTTOM TO PUSH JAR
   OUT,HANDLE............................................    20.00
PORCELAIN,JAR,MUSTARD,HAND-PAINTED PINK DAISIES,GREEN
   FOLIAGE...............................................     4.50
PORCELAIN,JAR,ROSE,COBALT BLUE SCENIC,MOUNTAINS,HOUSES,BOAT,
   COVER,10 IN...........................................    21.50
PORCELAIN,JAR,TOBACCO,FACE OF DOG,6 IN.HIGH.............    50.00
PORCELAIN,JUG,MORNING GLORIES,TWIG HANDLE,CIRCA 1850,MARKED
   T.J.MAYER.............................................    55.00
PORCELAIN,KNIFE REST,HAND-PAINTED,FRANCE................    22.00
PORCELAIN,KNIFE REST,HOLLY BERRIES,GOLD TRIM,ARTIST
   INITIALED.............................................    45.00
PORCELAIN,MATCHBOX,GOLD FLOWERS,COVER...................     6.00
PORCELAIN,MUG,ALLOVER GREEN & GOLD DECOR................     5.00
PORCELAIN,MUG,BEIGE GROUND,BROWN BIRDS & LEAVES.........     6.00
PORCELAIN,MUG,BUST OF INDIAN,MULTICOLORED,BROWN GROUND,
   4 3/4 IN.HIGH.........................................    12.00
PORCELAIN,MUG,CHILD'S,APPLE BLOSSOMS,GIRLS..............     6.00
PORCELAIN,MUG,CHILD'S,HANDLE,GOLD LETTERS SAY  A PRESENT,
   2 1/4 IN.HIGH.........................................     6.50
PORCELAIN,MUG,CHILD'S,BEARS PLAYING FOOTBALL............     9.00
PORCELAIN,MUG,CHILD'S,BEARS,ENGLAND.....................     3.00
PORCELAIN,MUG,CHILD'S,SCENE,FOUR CHILDREN & SNOWMAN.....    15.00
PORCELAIN,MUG,FAMILLE ROSE,CIRCA 1780...................   110.00
PORCELAIN,MUG,FOOTBALL SHAPE,HAND-PAINTED,UNIV.OF PENNA.,
   SEAL,SIGNED...........................................    20.00
PORCELAIN,MUG,GREEN,YELLOW,HAND-PAINTED BLACKBERRIES,
   4 1/2 IN..............................................     7.50
PORCELAIN,MUG,PORTRAIT,FALSTAFF,HAND-PAINTED,GOLD LIZARD
   HANDLE,ONE PINT.......................................    82.50
PORCELAIN,MUG,SCUTTLE,PINK FLOWERS......................    18.50
PORCELAIN,MUSTARD,PARROTS,SPOON MAKES A TAIL,COVER,SALT,
   PEPPER,GERMANY........................................    15.00
PORCELAIN,MUSTARD,PUMP-TYPE,BOY STRADDLES PUMP,ATTACHED
   DOUBLE SALT DIPS......................................    17.50
PORCELAIN,MUSTARD,SEASHELL SHAPE,MOTTLED LUSTER,SPOON....    15.00
PORCELAIN,NAPKIN RING,SEE NAPKIN RING
PORCELAIN,OWL,SIGNED H.RUOFF,8 IN.HIGH..................   175.00
PORCELAIN,PERFUME,BARREL SHAPE,FLORAL DECOR,1 7/8 IN.LONG...     5.00
PORCELAIN,PIPE,BRASS BOWL COVER,PAINTED FARM SCENE ON FRONT,
   WOOD STEM.............................................    15.00
PORCELAIN,PITCHER & WASHBOWL,WHITE,16-IN.BOWL,
   12 1/2-IN.PITCHER.....................................    28.00
PORCELAIN,PITCHER,BLUE ROSES,GRINDLEY,ENGLAND...........     4.00
PORCELAIN,PITCHER,BOWL,PINK,WHITE BLOSSOMS,LEAVES,GILT,
   ORNATE HANDLE.........................................    35.00
PORCELAIN,PITCHER,FLORAL PATTERN IN BLUES & REDS,STOKE ON
   TRENT,ENGLAND.........................................    12.50
PORCELAIN,PITCHER,LAVENDER SCENES,OCTAGON-SHAPED SEAL,MARKED
   DELAWARE..............................................    50.00
PORCELAIN,PITCHER,TANKARD,RAISED ENAMEL DECOR,INTERIOR HAS
   SCENE,CHINA...........................................    55.00
PORCELAIN,PITCHER,TANKARD,SCROLLS,VINES,HAND-PAINTED DRAPED
   BUST..................................................   195.00
PORCELAIN,PITCHER,WRIGHT & GRIEGS,OLD RODERICK DHU,HIGHLAND
   WHISKEY...............................................     8.00
PORCELAIN,PLAQUE,GIRL HOLDING A JUG,SIGNED WAGNER,4 IN. X
   6 IN..................................................   335.00
PORCELAIN,PLAQUE,SEMINUDE,SIGNED WAGNER,5 IN. X 7 IN........   395.00
PORCELAIN,PLAQUE,VICTORIAN LADY,8 IN. X 10 IN.,PAIR.....    85.00
PORCELAIN,PLATE,ACORNS,FALL FOLIAGE,HAND-PAINTED,AUSTRIA,
   8 1/4 IN..............................................     7.50
```

```
PORCELAIN,PLATE,BASKET-WEAVE,HALF UNFOLDED FAN,TASSEL,
  VARICOLORED,12........................................  150.00
PORCELAIN,PLATE,BLUE BAND,PINK ROSES,PASTORAL SCENE,
  9 3/4 IN..............................................   22.50
PORCELAIN,PLATE,BLUEBIRD DECOR,CARROLLTON,9 IN..............    4.50
PORCELAIN,PLATE,BLUEBIRD DECOR,CARROLLTON,7 IN..............    4.00
PORCELAIN,PLATE,BLUE,WHITE,ORCHIDS,HAND-PAINTED,8 IN........    4.50
PORCELAIN,PLATE,CAKE,BIRD,LEAFY BRANCH,ROSE,YELLOW,MARKED
  C.T.,AUSTRIA..........................................   27.50
PORCELAIN,PLATE,CAKE,OPEN HANDLES,PINK & WHITE LILIES,
  P.D.VESSRA,GERMANY....................................   12.50
PORCELAIN,PLATE,CHILD'S,BABY BUNTING NURSERY RHYME,1906.....    9.50
PORCELAIN,PLATE,CHILD'S,NURSERY SCENE IN CENTER,DOG & CAT ON
  BORDER................................................   12.50
PORCELAIN,PLATE,CHOP,GREEN,ROSES,SIGNED L.P.SHIELDS,1902,
  13 1/2 IN.............................................   50.00
PORCELAIN,PLATE,COLONIAL SCENE,SIGNED WATTEAU,FLORAL DORE
  FOOTED HOLDER.........................................   28.00
PORCELAIN,PLATE,CONGREGATIONAL CHURCH,LINCOLN,MAINE.........    4.00
PORCELAIN,PLATE,CREAM & BLACK,WHITE POPPIES,6 1/4 IN........    3.50
PORCELAIN,PLATE,CREAM & BLUE,BROWNISH-TAN POPPIES,
  HAND-PAINTED,AUSTRIA..................................    4.00
PORCELAIN,PLATE,CREAM & BLUE,TAN POPPIES,HAND-PAINTED,
  AUSTRIA,7 IN..........................................    4.00
PORCELAIN,PLATE,CREAM & BLUE,TWO LARGE ORCHIDS,HAND-PAINTED,
  8 1/2 IN..............................................    5.00
PORCELAIN,PLATE,CREAM & GRAY,PURPLE GRAPE CLUSTERS,SIGNED,
  DATED 1914............................................    4.00
PORCELAIN,PLATE,CREAM & GREEN GROUND,FRUIT BLOSSOMS,SIGNED,
  7 IN..................................................    4.50
PORCELAIN,PLATE,CREAM GROUND,GOLD,DAISIES,6 1/2 IN.,SET OF
  6.....................................................   14.50
PORCELAIN,PLATE,DESSERT,ABSTRACT PATTERN,KORNILOW BROS.,
  RUSSIA,SET OF 7.......................................   45.00
PORCELAIN,PLATE,DINNER,BLUE BORDER,PINK ROSETTES,WHIELDON
  WARE,ENGLAND..........................................    4.50
PORCELAIN,PLATE,DINNER,RUSSIAN,MOLDED DECORATION,19TH
  CENTURY...............................................  250.00
PORCELAIN,PLATE,ENAMEL FLORAL,BEE,BLUE BORDER,GOLD,
  BROWNFIELD,PAIR.......................................   85.00
PORCELAIN,PLATE,FIVE CLUSTERS OF VIOLETS & PANSIES,9 IN.....    4.50
PORCELAIN,PLATE,FLORAL,PORTRAIT SCENES AROUND RIM,VIENNA,
  AUSTRIA...............................................   10.00
PORCELAIN,PLATE,FRUIT BLOSSOMS,GREEN LEAVES,HAND-PAINTED,
  SIGNED,6 IN...........................................    3.00
PORCELAIN,PLATE,FRUITS,HAND-PAINTED,MARKED CT ALTWASSER,SET
  OF 12.................................................   50.00
PORCELAIN,PLATE,GREEN TRIM,PINK ROSES,9 IN.................    3.50
PORCELAIN,PLATE,HAND-PAINTED CHERUBS EATING GRAPES,SCROLL
  BORDER................................................   20.00
PORCELAIN,PLATE,HAND-PAINTED ON OLD TRANSFER OF ROYAL
  STREET,NEW ORLEANS....................................   10.00
PORCELAIN,PLATE,LAVENDER ON WHITE,ITALY PATTERN BY MEAKIN,
  9 3/4 IN..............................................    8.50
PORCELAIN,PLATE,MOTHER,CHILD,DOLL,ENGRAVED BY ADAMS BUCK,
  1815,3 IN.............................................   40.00
PORCELAIN,PLATE,NAPKIN,WHITE,WILDFLOWER SPRAY,BEADED CENTER,
  FRINGE................................................   15.00
PORCELAIN,PLATE,ORIENTAL PATTERN,SYRACUSE,8 3/4 IN..........    1.50
PORCELAIN,PLATE,OYSTER,CIRCLE OF GREEN LEAVES,EMBOSSED
  SALMON SCROLLS........................................    8.50
PORCELAIN,PLATE,OYSTER,GOLD-SCALLOPED EDGE,MARKED WITH
  SHIELD & WEIMAR.......................................   15.00
PORCELAIN,PLATE,OYSTER,SHELL DESIGN,UNION PORCELAIN WORKS,
  GREENPOINT,N.Y........................................   28.00
PORCELAIN,PLATE,PAIR MOUNTED IN PEWTER,JOINED WITH JADE
  HANDLE,TUNG CHIH......................................  125.00
PORCELAIN,PLATE,PAIR,FAMILLE ROSE,CIRCA 1745...............  275.00
PORCELAIN,PLATE,PINK & CREAM GROUND,LARGE PLUMS,GREEN
  LEAVES,8 1/2 IN.......................................   14.50
PORCELAIN,PLATE,PINK & RED ROSES,HAND-PAINTED,SIGNED BEYER
  ON FRONT..............................................   17.50
PORCELAIN,PLATE,PINK & TAN ORCHIDS,9 IN....................    3.00
PORCELAIN,PLATE,REDDISH PINK LUSTER,RABBIT IN CENTER,FRANCE,
  7 IN..................................................   12.50
PORCELAIN,PLATE,SCALLOPED RIM,ORCHIDS,6 1/2 IN.............    3.00
PORCELAIN,PLATE,SERVING,IMPERIAL EAGLE IN CROSS-STITCH
  DESIGN,RUSSIA.........................................   75.00
PORCELAIN,PLATE,SILVER LUSTER,PALE PINK ROSES,SIGNED,
  6 1/2 IN..............................................    3.50
PORCELAIN,PLATE,SILVER LUSTER,VIOLETS,HAND-PAINTED,6 1/2 IN.    3.75
```

```
PORCELAIN,PLATE,SOUVENIR,BRISCOE SCHOOL,BEVERLY,MASS.,
  7 3/4 IN.......................................................   3.75
PORCELAIN,PLATE,SOUVENIR,GRAY GABLES,BUZZARDS BAY,MASS.,
  6 1/4 IN.......................................................   2.95
PORCELAIN,PLATE,TAN GROUND,TWO BIRDS ON TREE LIMB,FRUIT
  BLOSSOMS,10 IN.................................................  19.50
PORCELAIN,PLATE,TAN RIM,GOLD TRIM,FLORAL WREATH,BASKET OF
  ROSES,8 IN.....................................................   4.00
PORCELAIN,PLATE,VIENNA,FLORAL,SCALLOPED EDGE,MOLDED OZIER
  BORDER,6...................................................... 175.00
PORCELAIN,PLATE,WHITE,BLUE BORDER,FLORAL,JAPAN,CHIKARAMACHI.       3.00
PORCELAIN,PLATE,WILLIAM MCKINLEY,1897-1901,8 3/4-IN.DIAMETER     120.00
PORCELAIN,PLATE,YELLOW-GREEN,AUTUMN LEAVES,VINES,BERRIES,
  HANDLES,10 IN..................................................  14.50
PORCELAIN,PLATE,12,BERLIN,DESSERT.............................. 300.00
PORCELAIN,PLATE,2,FAMILLE ROSE,CIRCA 1770......................  80.00
PORCELAIN,PLATTER,BLUEBIRD DECOR,CARROLLTON,11 IN.............    8.00
PORCELAIN,PLATTER,PINK FLORAL,MARX & GUTHERZ MARK,CARLSBAD,
  13 1/2 IN.....................................................  15.00
PORCELAIN,POT,CHAMBER,ALLOVER GREEN & GOLD DECOR.............  10.00
PORCELAIN,POT,CHOCOLATE,MELON RIB,PINK ROSES,GOLD SCALLOP
  BASE,8 3/4 IN.................................................  18.00
PORCELAIN,RELISH,PINK,HAND-PAINTED FLORAL,GOLD TRIM.........  10.00
PORCELAIN,ROOSTER,SIGNED SAMSON,27 IN.HIGH................... 900.00
PORCELAIN,RUSSIAN,CUP & SAUCER,CIRCA 1810,GARDNER,MARKED G.. 125.00
PORCELAIN,RUSSIAN,CUP & SAUCER,NICHOLAS I,1825-55,IMPERIAL.. 110.00
PORCELAIN,RUSSIAN,EWER,POPOFF,CIRCA 1830,7 3/4 IN. HIGH..... 100.00
PORCELAIN,RUSSIAN,FIGURE OF MAN,CIRCA 1830.................. 400.00
PORCELAIN,RUSSIAN,FIGURE,COACHMAN,GARDNER,19TH CENTURY...... 475.00
PORCELAIN,RUSSIAN,FIGURE,GEORGIAN WOMAN,CIRCA 1830,POPOFF... 300.00
PORCELAIN,RUSSIAN,GROUP,BISQUE,CIRCA 1890,GARDNER,7 IN. TALL 450.00
PORCELAIN,RUSSIAN,GROUP,BISQUE,GARDNER,CIRCA 1890............ 550.00
PORCELAIN,RUSSIAN,PLATE,CIRCA 1820,9 1/4-IN. DIAMETER.......  70.00
PORCELAIN,RUSSIAN,STATUETTE,JEWISH MAN,GARDNER,1810-20,
  7 1/4 IN. HIGH............................................... 450.00
PORCELAIN,RUSSIAN,TAZZA,GARDNER,CIRCA 1890.................. 100.00
PORCELAIN,RUSSIAN,TEA SERVICE,KORNILOV,19TH CENTURY........ 350.00
PORCELAIN,RUSSIAN,TRAY,BREAD,CIRCA 1870,GARDNER,17 IN. LONG. 175.00
PORCELAIN,SAKE SERVER,BIRD CHIRPS WHEN POURING,RUST,GOLD,
  6 TINY CUPS..................................................  20.00
PORCELAIN,SALT & PEPPER,SHAPE OF PIG,CORK BOTTOM,PAIR.......  13.00
PORCELAIN,SALT,HAND-DECORATED,ARTIST INITIALS,GOLD TRIM,
  GERMANY,SET OF 6.............................................   7.50
PORCELAIN,SALT,TAN,ACORNS,FOOTED,2 1/2 IN.WIDE,
  1 1/4 IN.HIGH,SET OF 6.......................................  15.00
PORCELAIN,SHAKER,SALT,PEPPER,SUGAR,GOLD NETTING,BLUE FLORAL.  20.00
PORCELAIN,SHAKER,SUGAR,WHITE,ROSE DECOR,GOLD TOP,CORK
  BOTTOM,GERMANY...............................................  15.00
PORCELAIN,SHAKER,TALCUM,VIENNA,AUSTRIA......................   6.00
PORCELAIN,SHOE,ANGEL RECEIVES A LETTER FROM BIRD,
  HAND-PAINTED,5 IN.LONG.......................................  25.00
PORCELAIN,SHOE,BABY'S,COVERED WITH SNOW,BLUE,PINK FLORAL....  18.00
PORCELAIN,SHOE,DUTCH,BLUE,PAINTED FLOWERS ON TOE,6 IN.LONG..   5.00
PORCELAIN,SHOE,DUTCH,FLORAL,MARKED GERMANY..................   5.00
PORCELAIN,SHOE,GOLD RUFFLE TOP,LACES.......................   8.00
PORCELAIN,SHOE,GREEN,WHITE TOE,RED TIES,MAUVE TOP,3 1/2 X
  5 IN.LONG....................................................   8.00
PORCELAIN,SHOE,HIGH-BUTTON,GOLD IRIDESCENT,PANEL,WHITE
  FLORAL DECOR.................................................   6.50
PORCELAIN,SHOE,PINK,APPLIED ROSES & LEAVES,6 IN.............   6.00
PORCELAIN,SHOE,RED ROSES,SCROLLS,WHITE GROUND,COBALT,GOLD,
  1879,4 IN....................................................  32.00
PORCELAIN,SHOE,WHITE TOE,RED TIES,MAUVE TOP,5 IN.LONG,
  3 1/2 IN.HIGH................................................   8.00
PORCELAIN,SHOE,WHITE,GREEN & GOLD TRIM,FLOWERS ON TOE,
  GERMANY......................................................  12.00
PORCELAIN,SLIPPER,EMBOSSED,DECOR...........................   8.00
PORCELAIN,SLIPPER,PINK FRONT,WHITE AT BACK,MEDALLION,ROSE,
  SCROLLS......................................................  14.00
PORCELAIN,SLIPPER,WHITE,GOLD HEEL,FORGET-ME-NOT ON TOE......   6.50
PORCELAIN,SLIPPER,WHITE,PORTRAIT ON TOE,LADY DRESSED IN
  PINK,GOLD TRIM...............................................   6.50
PORCELAIN,SPITTOON,LADY'S,WHITE............................  15.00
PORCELAIN,SPOON,RICE,WHITE,CHINESE,SET OF THREE............  15.00
PORCELAIN,SPOONER,PINK-LAVENDER CARNATIONS,TWO HANDLES,
  GERMANY......................................................  18.00
PORCELAIN,SQUEEZER,LEMON,WHITE,HANDLE,SIGNED ARCADE........  17.50
PORCELAIN,STAND,MENU,BORDER LIKE CROWN DERBY,WHITE CENTER,
  ENGLAND......................................................  15.00
PORCELAIN,STATUETTE,RUSSIAN,BOLOGNESE TERRIER,1840...ILLUS..1,650.00
PORCELAIN,STRAINER,TEA,ROSES...............................   8.50
```

RUSSIAN BOLOGNESE TERRIER PORCELAIN STATUETTE, 1840

```
PORCELAIN,SUGAR & CREAMER,PINK,RED ROSES,HAND-PAINTED,
  VICTORIAN,GERMANY.................................................   15.00
PORCELAIN,SUGAR SCOOP,ENAMELED,FOOTED,CIRCULAR HANDLE,CHINA.   12.75
PORCELAIN,SYRUP,BROWN LUSTER GROUND,FLORAL,LID..............    8.50
PORCELAIN,SYRUP,CREAMER,SUGAR,ROYAL ROCHESTER,FRAUNFELTER...   20.00
PORCELAIN,SYRUP,FLOWERS,PEWTER LID.........................   15.00
PORCELAIN,SYRUP,SILVER LUSTER..............................   35.00
PORCELAIN,TEA CADDY,BLUE & WHITE...........................   22.00
PORCELAIN,TEA STRAINER,BLUE FLORAL,HAND-PAINTED,
  ARTIST-SIGNED,UNDERPLATE.................................   12.00
PORCELAIN,TEA STRAINER,CHECKERED BEIGE-TONE,HAND-PAINTED
  ROSES...................................................    9.50
PORCELAIN,TEA STRAINER,JONQUIL YELLOW,SMALL WHITE BLOCKS,
  ROSEBUDS................................................   11.00
PORCELAIN,TEA STRAINER,PINK,GOLD TRIM......................   12.50
PORCELAIN,TEA STRAINER,WHITE,BLACK BEADED TRIM,ORANGE
  FLORAL,HOLDER...........................................   15.00
PORCELAIN,TEA STRAINER,WHITE,BLUE TRIM,HAND-PAINTED PEONIES.   17.50
PORCELAIN,TEA STRAINER,WHITE,GOLD,VIOLETS,MATCHING HOLDER...   17.50
PORCELAIN,TEAPOT,CREAMER,SUGAR,SIX CUPS & SAUCERS,TRAY,FRUIT
  DECOR...................................................   85.00
PORCELAIN,TEAPOT,FLOWER DESIGN,LID,TRIVET,SIGNED P.KENT.....   18.00
PORCELAIN,TEAPOT,FOUR-CUP SIZE,H.C.GOSS,FALCON MARK ON POT &
  LID.....................................................   50.00
PORCELAIN,TEAPOT,GIRL & BOY PICTURE,6 1/2 IN...............    6.50
PORCELAIN,TEAPOT,GOLD,BROWN,BLUE DECOR.....................   17.00
PORCELAIN,TEAPOT,GREEN BAND,SILVER TRIM,BANQUET............    7.50
PORCELAIN,TEAPOT,LIGHT BLUE,GOLD TRIM......................    3.00
PORCELAIN,TEAPOT,PINK LUSTER,PICTURE OF ENTRANCE TO HARBOR,
  ST.JOHN.................................................    3.00
PORCELAIN,TEAPOT,PINK ROSES,GOLD TRIM,REST,ENGLAND.........   20.00
PORCELAIN,TEAPOT HOLDER,HAND-PAINTED,DATED 1925............    8.50
PORCELAIN,TILE,TEA,WHITE & LAVENDER LILAC SPRAYS,SWIRLED
  EDGE....................................................   16.00
PORCELAIN,TILE,WHITE,RAISED DRAGON IN ORANGE,RED,GOLD,CHINA,
  10 IN.WIDE..............................................  165.00
PORCELAIN,TOAST RACK,WHITE.................................   15.00
PORCELAIN,TOAST RACK,WHITE,FOUR DIVIDERS,8 IN.LONG.........   12.00
PORCELAIN,TOOTHBRUSH HOLDER,ALLOVER GREEN & GOLD DECOR......    6.00
PORCELAIN,TOOTHBRUSH HOLDER,FLORAL.........................    2.50
PORCELAIN,TOOTHPICK,MAN,REVOLUTIONARY PERIOD COSTUME........   15.00
PORCELAIN,TOOTHPICK,PURPLE GROUND,PINK FLORAL,GOLD TRIM.....    7.50
PORCELAIN,TOOTHPICK,WOMAN,REVOLUTIONARY PERIOD COSTUME,WIG..   15.00
PORCELAIN,TRAY,CELERY,COUPLE IN GARDEN,YELLOW DAISY RIM,
  GERMANY.................................................   26.50
PORCELAIN,TRAY,CELERY,LIGHT TO DARK BLUE GROUND,YELLOW
  ROSES,GERMANY...........................................   12.50
PORCELAIN,TRAY,DRESSER,IRIS,COBALT TRIM,21 IN. X 6 IN.......   24.00
PORCELAIN,TRAY,DRESSER,RING TREE,CANDLESTICKS,BOXES,
  TURQUOISE FLORAL........................................   27.50
PORCELAIN,TRAY,PERFUME,GREEN,PURPLE GRAPES,LAVENDER TRIM,
  GOLD EDGE...............................................   30.00
PORCELAIN,TRAY,PIN,BLUE & WHITE,SCENIC,GOLD BORDER,4 1/2 IN.
```

```
   X 3 IN.....................................................    4.00
PORCELAIN,TRAY,PIN,GREEN LINING,CHINA.........................    4.00
PORCELAIN,TRAY,PIN,PORTRAIT OF MAN,ROYAL COSTUME,SIGNED
   LEFEBURE..................................................    4.50
PORCELAIN,TRAY,RING,FLORAL....................................    2.50
PORCELAIN,TRAY,YELLOW & PINK ROSES,HAND-PAINTED,12 X
   12 1/2 IN.................................................   45.00
PORCELAIN,TREE,RING,LEFT HAND,GOLD,COBALT,FLORAL,
   HAND-PAINTED,ONE PIECE....................................   22.00
PORCELAIN,TUMBLER,WHITE GROUND,PINK ROSES,BLUE SHADING AT
   TOP,GERMANY...............................................   10.50
PORCELAIN,TUREEN & STAND,COVERED,CIRCA 1780,FOO DOG FINIAL &
   STAND....................................................  150.00
PORCELAIN,TUREEN,CHILD'S,CIRCUS FIGURES,CLOWN,PINK PIG,
   GERMANY,OVAL..............................................    8.00
PORCELAIN,URN,MAROON,GOLD GRIM,BLUE FLORAL,BRASS BASE,
   FRANCE,11 IN.,PAIR........................................   35.00
PORCELAIN,URN,VIEUX,INVERTED CAMPANA SHAPE,MASK HANDLES,
   13 1/2 IN.,PAIR...........................................  250.00
PORCELAIN,VASE,BUD,WHITE CAMEO LADY,FLOWER BOUQUETS,
   GREEN-CASED,GERMANY.......................................   24.00
PORCELAIN,VASE,CONE-SHAPED,FIGURE,EIGHTEENTH-CENTURY
   COSTUME,20 IN.,PAIR.......................................  400.00
PORCELAIN,VASE,CONE-SHAPED,FLORAL,GILT,PARIS,CIRCA 1840,
   20 IN.HIGH,PAIR...........................................  125.00
PORCELAIN,VASE,DARK GREEN GROUND,RASPBERRIES,BLOSSOMS,
   LEAVES,PAIR...............................................   55.00
PORCELAIN,VASE,DRAGON & PHOENIX,PINK PEONIES,LONG NECK,
   11 1/2 IN.................................................  200.00
PORCELAIN,VASE,EGGSHELL,WHITE,MULTICOLORED FLORAL,TEAK
   STAND,CHINA,PAIR..........................................   60.00
PORCELAIN,VASE,ETCHED BIRDS & LEAVES,GUNMETAL & SILVER,
   SIGNED LORENA.............................................    7.50
PORCELAIN,VASE,GREEN GROUND,GOOD LUCK SYMBOLS,BATS,CHINA,
   7 1/2 IN.,PAIR............................................  195.00
PORCELAIN,VASE,HAND-PAINTED FLORAL,CROSSED SWORDS UNDER
   GLAZE,5 IN................................................   18.00
PORCELAIN,VASE,MELON SHAPE,WHITE GROUND,RUST COLOR FLORAL,
   LEONARD,6 IN..............................................   12.50
PORCELAIN,VASE,QUAIL,CHERRY BRANCHES,PEACOCK,CHINA,
   11 1/2 IN.,PAIR...........................................  145.50
PORCELAIN,VASE,RECTANGULAR,HAND-PAINTED,COUNTRY SCENE,
   CZECHOSLOVAKIA............................................   14.00
PORCELAIN,VASE,RED,SILVER-COLORED DRAGON,SIGNED,7 IN.......   20.00
PORCELAIN,VASE,SCENE,DUCK HUNT,SWAN NECK HANDLES,PARIS,1825,
   13 IN.,PAIR...............................................  175.00
PORCELAIN,VASE,WHITE GROUND,GREEN,RED FLORAL,SQUARE SHAPE,
   11 IN.,PAIR...............................................   75.00
PORCELAIN,WALL SAFE,MINIATURE,WHITE,FLORAL DECOR...........    8.00
PORTOBELLO,CUP,SAUCER,DARK BROWN,YELLOW TRANSFER,ORIENTAL
   FIGURES,1810..............................................   65.00
PORTRAIT CUP & SAUCER,FAT MAN,STICKPIN, I AM NOT GREEDY,I
   LIKE A LOT ...............................................   15.00
PORTRAIT,BOWL,GIRL,WIDE HAT,VEIL,MAROON BORDER,YELLOW ROSES,
   10 IN.....................................................    6.00
PORTRAIT,CHOCOLATE POT,QUEEN LOUISE,ERMINE ROBE,MARKED CT
   GERMANY...................................................   45.00
PORTRAIT,DISH,SAUCE,HEAD,SHOULDERS,GIRL,SIGNED NICOLLETT,
   CROWN,PAIR................................................   35.00
PORTRAIT,DISH,SQUARE,PURPLE DECOR,GOLD RIM,WOMAN,
   C.T.ALTWASSER,SILESIA.....................................   17.50
PORTRAIT,HOLDER,HATPIN,YELLOW GROUND,PORCELAIN.............   25.00
PORTRAIT,PLATE,ABRAHAM LINCOLN,WIFE,10 IN..................    9.00
PORTRAIT,PLATE,BABY,SWAGS,FRUIT,FLOWERS,BLUE RIM,
   ARTIST-SIGNED,DERBY.......................................   62.50
PORTRAIT,PLATE,BLOND HEAD,TURQUOISE,GOLD SCROLL,SIGNED
   CONSTANCE.................................................   35.00
PORTRAIT,PLATE,BLOND WOMAN,COPYRIGHT 1907,MEEK CO.,
   ADVERTISING,TIN...........................................   11.50
PORTRAIT,PLATE,BOY HOLDS FLOWERS BEHIND BACK,GIRL LOOKS SHY,
   YELLOW TRIM...............................................   12.50
PORTRAIT,PLATE,CLASSICAL FIGURES,LANDSCAPE BACKGROUND,
   C.T.GERMANY...............................................   47.50
PORTRAIT,PLATE,GARFIELD,BORDER OF THIRTEEN STARS,FLAGS,
   SHIELD,6 IN...............................................   20.00
PORTRAIT,PLATE,GEORGE & MARTHA WASHINGTON,MT.VERNON,PIERCED,
   GERMANY...................................................   10.00
PORTRAIT,PLATE,GIRL,BROWN CURLS,WHITE DRESS,ELBOW ON TABLE,
   GERMANY ..................................................    8.00
PORTRAIT,PLATE,GIRL,DARK HAIR,SHADES OF BLUE,GOLD,SIGNED
   GERMANY...................................................   21.00
```

PORTRAIT,PLATE,GIRL,GOLD DRESS,SIGNED P.ASTONI,THREE CROWN
  MARK.................................................... 45.00
PORTRAIT,PLATE,GIRL'S HEAD,HAND-PAINTED,SIGNED EMIL,1881,
  5 1/4 IN................................................ 14.00
PORTRAIT,PLATE,HEAD OF APOLLO,BEADED CAMEO CENTER,CROWN
  MARK,VORBIJOU........................................... 18.00
PORTRAIT,PLATE,HENRI IV,COBALT BORDER,SEVRES,9 1/2 IN....... 125.00
PORTRAIT,PLATE,HIS MAJESTY,JOHNSON BROS.,10 1/2 IN.......... 4.50
PORTRAIT,PLATE,LADIES,CUPID,LATTICE RIM,WHITE,8 IN.,PAIR.... 32.50
PORTRAIT,PLATE,LADY,HEAD & SHOULDERS,LARGE HAT WITH ROSES,
  SCALLOPED.............................................. 15.00
PORTRAIT,PLATE,LADY,HEAD & SHOULDERS,PINK EMBOSSED,RAISED
  GOLD,9 3/4 IN.......................................... 34.00
PORTRAIT,PLATE,LADY,HEAD & SHOULDERS,ROYAL BLUE,GOLD,
  TRACERY,9 1/2 IN....................................... 14.00
PORTRAIT,PLATE,LADY,SHOULDERS & HEAD,SWIRLED & PEARLIZED
  RIM,AUSTRIA............................................ 10.00
PORTRAIT,PLATE,LADY,TIN,9 IN............................... 40.00
PORTRAIT,PLATE,LADY DESCENDING STAIRS IN GARDEN,SCALLOPED,
  BEADED BORDER.......................................... 10.00
PORTRAIT,PLATE,LOUIS XV,COBALT BORDER,SEVRES,9 1/2 IN....... 125.00
PORTRAIT,PLATE,LOUIS XV,RIVIERA,CARLSBAD,GREEN,TAN,GOLD,
  SIGNED,9 IN............................................ 40.00
PORTRAIT,PLATE,LOUIS XVI,GREEN,WHITE,ROSE GARLANDS,MARKED
  C.T.GERMANY............................................ 35.00
PORTRAIT,PLATE,LUCILLE,HAND-PAINTED BY HARRISON FESNER,1903,
  9 1/2 IN............................................... 25.00
PORTRAIT,PLATE,MAN HOLDS DOVE,WOMAN HOLDS BASKET OF FLOWERS,
  GARDEN,8 IN............................................ 12.50
PORTRAIT,PLATE,MAN OFFERING LADY APPLE,SWIRL EDGE,PINK
  BEADING................................................ 12.50
PORTRAIT,PLATE,MARIE ANTOINETTE,COBALT BORDER,SEVRES,
  9 1/2 IN............................................... 125.00
PORTRAIT,PLATE,MARIE DE MEDICIS,COBALT BORDER,SEVRES,
  9 1/2 IN............................................... 125.00
PORTRAIT,PLATE,MARTHA WASHINGTON,WHITE GROUND,ROSE BORDER,
  GERMANY,8 IN........................................... 14.50
PORTRAIT,PLATE,NAPOLEON,GOLD & GREEN TRIM,CARLSBAD,AUSTRIA,
  6 IN................................................... 30.00
PORTRAIT,PLATE,ONE BLACK,ONE WHITE ANGEL,GOLD SCALLOPED RIM,
  8 IN................................................... 32.50
PORTRAIT,PLATE,PEASANT GIRL HOLDING STEINS,BROWN BORDER,
  9 1/2 IN............................................... 18.00
PORTRAIT,PLATE,PEASANT GIRL STRUMMING GUITAR,BROWN BORDER,
  9 1/2 IN............................................... 18.00
PORTRAIT,PLATE,PRESIDENT & MRS.EISENHOWER,8 IN.SQUARE....... 10.00
PORTRAIT,PLATE,QUEEN ELIZABETH II,10 1/2 IN................ 10.00
PORTRAIT,PLATE,QUEEN LOUISE,FULL LENGTH,SCALLOPED EDGE,
  10 1/4 IN.............................................. 6.00
PORTRAIT,PLATE,QUEEN LOUISE,GOLD TRACERY OVER MOSS,ZS MARK,
  8 3/8 IN............................................... 19.00
PORTRAIT,PLATE,THREE LADIES,BROWNISH HUES,SIGNED
  A.KAUFFMANN,GERMANY.................................... 24.50
PORTRAIT,PLATE,THREE LADIES,SPADE,SIGNED SAPPHIRE,KARLSBAD,
  AUSTRIA................................................ 28.00
PORTRAIT,PLATE,TIN,HAND-PAINTED PORTRAIT OF GIRL,FRAME,
  16 IN.SQUARE,PAIR...................................... 45.00
PORTRAIT,PLATE,WOMAN DRAPED IN SHEER GARMENT,MARKED
  CARLSBAD,AUSTRIA....................................... 19.00
PORTRAIT,PLATE,WOMAN,DARK HAIR,1905,VIENNA,TIN............. 16.00
PORTRAIT,SHOE,HAND-PAINTED MEDALLION,ANGEL,FLYING BIRD,
  PORCELAIN.............................................. 21.50
PORTRAIT,VASE,BLUE OVERLAY,HAS BIRD ON LIMB WITH INSET
  PICTURE,6 1/2 IN....................................... 24.00
PORTRAIT,VASE,BULBOUS,LIGHT BROWN DECOR,TWO HANDLES,AUSTRIA,
  5 IN................................................... 5.00
PORTRAIT,VASE,BUST OF WOMAN,BROWN SHADES,AUSTRIA............ 7.00
PORTRAIT,VASE,CAVALIER,COBALT BLUE,GOLD,RING HANDLES,
  BEEHIVE,1900,10 IN..................................... 45.00
PORTRAIT,VASE,ENAMELED,VITRIFIED,SIGNED RICHARDSON,4 IN.HIGH 115.00
PORTRAIT,VASE,JENNY LIND,GOLD-BEADED MEDALLION EDGE,
  7 IN.HIGH.............................................. 45.00
PORTRAIT,VASE,MARIE ANTOINETTE,FRAMED IN BEADED BANDS,
  PORCELAIN,FRANCE....................................... 55.00
PORTRAIT,VASE,PORCELAIN MEDALLIONS,GIRL,FLORAL,GREEN BASE,
  13 IN.TALL............................................. 135.00
POSTCARD ALBUM,32 EASTER CARDS............................ 3.00
POSTCARD ALBUM,100 CHRISTMAS CARDS........................ 10.00
POSTCARD ALBUM,1900-1930,165 CARDS........................ 15.00
POSTCARD ALBUM,1900-1930,300 CARDS........................ 27.50
POSTCARD ALBUM,CIRCA 1908-10,128 CARDS.................... 10.00

```
POSTCARD ALBUM,CIRCA 1910,190 CARDS.........................      12.00
POSTCARD ALBUM,EARLY 1900S,130 CARDS........................       9.50
POSTCARD ALBUM,STEAMBOATS,SHIPS,290.........................      35.00
POSTCARD ALBUM,VIEWS,227 CARDS..............................      10.50
POSTCARD ALBUM,WALL STREET,N.Y.,LEAP YEAR,SANTA'S TROLLEYS,
    248 VIEWS..............................................        8.00
POSTCARD,ABE LINCOLN,POSTMARKED FEB.12,1909.................       2.00
POSTCARD,ABRAHAM LINCOLN,EMBOSSED,1909 CENTENNIAL,UNUSED,4..       1.00
POSTCARD,AMERICAN JOURNAL EXAMINER,1906,3,LEANDER & LULU...        1.00
POSTCARD,AVIATION,CIRCA 1909,12.............................      32.00
POSTCARD,BATHING BEAUTY................................ILLUS..    15.00
POSTCARD,BUSTER BROWN,3.....................................       1.00
POSTCARD,CATS,ALBUM,80......................................      20.00
POSTCARD,CHRISTMAS,CHILDREN,GROUP OF 10.....................       1.50
POSTCARD,CIRCA 1900,1000....................................      25.00
POSTCARD,CONEY ISLAND,TINSEL,2..............................       1.50
POSTCARD,EASTER,PRE-1914,SET OF 5...........................       1.25
POSTCARD,EASTER,SET OF 10...................................       1.50
POSTCARD,EASTER,SOME DATING BACK TO 1909,50.................       5.00
POSTCARD,ERIE CANAL,MOHAWK VALLEY,SCHENECTADY,ALBUM,25......      15.00
POSTCARD,FIGURES DONE IN STAMPS,HAND-WATERCOLORED,CHINA,10..      25.00
POSTCARD,FIRE ENGINE,HORSE-DRAWN............................       1.50
POSTCARD,FRANCE,ALBUM,275 CARDS.............................      75.00
POSTCARD,GIBSON GIRL........................................        .10
POSTCARD,GREETING,SCENIC,CIRCA 1900,ALBUM,298...............      16.00
POSTCARD,HAND-DRAWN,HAND-TINTED,SIGNED,DATE BACK TO 1908,60.      10.00
POSTCARD,HAPPY HOOLIGAN,4...................................       1.00
POSTCARD,INDIANS,ALBUM,70...................................      17.50
POSTCARD,KATZENJAMMER KIDS,5................................       1.00
POSTCARD,LEATHER,LACED WITH BROWN RIBBON FOR HANGING,16.....       8.00
POSTCARD,LOWER N.Y. FROM AIRSTRIP,LASHS BITTERS,1911........       2.00
POSTCARD,NEW YORK,ALBUM,500.................................      10.00
POSTCARD,NEW YORK VIEWS,ALBUM,200...........................      10.00
POSTCARD,PICTORIAL,1900-1920,12.............................       1.00
POSTCARD,POLO GROUNDS,HOME OF N.Y.GIANTS,MC GRAW INSERT,
    1917...................................................        2.00
POSTCARD,PRE-1915,50........................................       3.00
POSTCARD,PRESIDENT WILSON & CABINET,PHOTOGRAPH..............       3.50
POSTCARD,PRESIDENTS,AUTOGRAPHED,1789-1883,EAGLE,EMBLEM,
    21 CARDS...............................................        3.25
POSTCARD,PRESIDENTS,PICTURES IN OVALS WITH FLAGS & EAGLES,
    GROUP OF 25............................................       30.00
POSTCARD,PRIOR 1915,SOME CLAPSADDLE,TUCKS,GELATIN,600......       35.00
POSTCARD,RAILROAD STATION,4.................................       2.00
POSTCARD,REX BITTERS........................................       3.00
POSTCARD,SAN FRANCISCO EARTHQUAKE & FIRE,1906,GROUP OF 7....       6.50
POSTCARD,SANTA,CLAPSADDLE,BRUNDAGE,WINCH,BIEN,WALL,TUCK,
    ALBUM,1907,197.........................................       45.00
POSTCARD,SANTA CLAUS,TWO....................................       1.00
```

BATHING BEAUTY POSTCARD

```
POSTCARD,SCENES,COMICS,1900,112 CARDS,LEATHER ALBUM........   8.50
POSTCARD,SHIP,SIDE-WHEELER,3...........................   1.50
POSTCARD,SHIPS,BRIDGES,AUTOS,100......................   9.00
POSTCARD,SHIPS,SAILBOATS,ALBUM,100....................  18.50
POSTCARD,ST.PATRICK,SET OF 10.........................   1.50
POSTCARD,ST.PATRICK'S DAY,5...........................   2.00
POSTCARD,STATE OF VIRGINIA,SCENIC,186.................  30.00
POSTCARD,STREET SCENES WITH OLD CARS & STREETCARS,ALBUM,100. 20.00
POSTCARD,THANKSGIVING,CIRCA 1900,10...................   2.00
POSTCARD,VALENTINE,SET OF 10..........................   1.50
POSTCARD,VIEWS,GREETINGS,3000......................... 100.00
POSTCARD,160 CARDS,1900-1930,ALBUM....................  ·8.50
POSTCARD,1906 SAN FRANCISCO EARTHQUAKE VIEW,GROUP OF 8......   3.75
    POTTERY,SEE ALSO,BUFFALO POTTERY,STAFFORDSHIRE,WEDGWOOD,
      ETC.............................................
POTTERY,BASKET,FLOWERS,BLUE,YELLOW,RED,CREAMY BASE,ITALY....  25.00
POTTERY,BEER MUG,SCHLITZ..............................   9.00
POTTERY,BOWL,KOREAN,TWO FIGURES OF OLD MEN APPLIED ON SIDE.. 150.00
POTTERY,BOX,SALT,HANGING,BLUE,WOODEN LID..............  12.00
POTTERY,CHURN,PIG EARS,BROWN & TAN,SMALL BLUE 3 IN HEART ON
      FRONT...........................................  17.50
POTTERY,COFFEEPOT,BEEHIVE MARK,SIGNED HESSIAN POTTERY
      WACHTERBACH,9 IN.................................  35.00
POTTERY,CUSPIDOR,TAN TREE BARK EFFECT,LEAVES,BROWN GLAZE
      INTERIOR.........................................   8.50
POTTERY,DECANTER,WINE,OVERALL CRIMSON FLORAL,HAND-PAINTED,
      FOOTED,HUNGARY...................................   9.00
POTTERY,FIGURINE,BUDDHA,MING,POLYCHROME FRONT,BLUE,YELLOW,
      BLACK,8 IN....................................... 180.00
POTTERY,FIGURINE,OWL,SETO WARE,1830,9 1/2 IN.TALL...........  38.00
POTTERY,GARDEN SEAT,PAIR,CHINESE,BLUE-GLAZED,RETICULATED,
      20 IN.HIGH....................................... 200.00
POTTERY,FIGURINE,RAM,CURLED HORNS,ROCKWORK MOUND,CIRCA 1800,
      5 IN.HIGH........................................ 200.00
POTTERY,JARDINIERE,RAISED SWIRLS,TOP SCALLOPS,FLORAL,BROWN,
      ZANESVILLE.......................................  32.00
POTTERY,MOLD,PUDDING,TURK'S HEAD,HAND-MOLDED REDWARE,3 X
      7 IN.............................................  14.00
POTTERY,MOLD,WHITE,PINEAPPLE DESIGN INSIDE,OVAL,8 1/2 IN. X
      5 1/4 IN.........................................  18.00
POTTERY,MUG,PICTURE OF HORSE ON SIDE,WHITE,GLAZED,COUNT
      FLEET...........................................   4.50
POTTERY,MUG,SAYS WOMAN LOVES BUT ONCE,THAT IS,THE SAME MAN..   5.00
POTTERY,MUSTARD POT,HUNTING SCENE,BLUE,CIRCA 1856...........  15.00
POTTERY,PITCHER,BUTTERMILK,BLUE,PINK,GREEN FLORAL,WHITE TO
      PINK GROUND......................................  10.00
POTTERY,PITCHER,MOTTLED BLUE,RAISED PATTERN ON NECK,NEW
      HAMPSHIRE,6 IN...................................  30.00
POTTERY,PITCHER,NEW ENGLAND BATTER,TAN,GREEN BANDS,
      MEDALLION,COWS...................................   7.50
POTTERY,PITCHER,WHITE WITH COLORED EMBOSSED FLORAL DECOR,
      STAR,7 1/4 IN....................................  10.00
POTTERY,PLAQUE,BROWN GLAZE,THREE RAISED RABBITS,CARROTS,
      FOLEY,13 1/2 IN..................................  35.00
POTTERY,POT,BOSTON BEAN,DORCHESTER,1954...............  10.00
POTTERY,PUMPKIN,PUMPKIN FLOWERS,SIGNED K.T.KOREY,
      13-IN.DIAMETER...................................  14.00
POTTERY,TEA SET,PITCHER SHAPED LIKE ALADDIN'S LAMP,SUGAR,
      CREAMER,PINK.....................................  21.00
POTTERY,VASE,DAISIES,PUSSY WILLOWS,FOLIAGE,BLUE,.
      HAND-PAINTED,15 IN.,PAIR......................... 125.00
POTTERY,VASE,GREEN TULIP DECOR,HAMPSHIRE,SIGNED.............  25.00
POTTERY,VASE,IRIDESCENT,BLUE,GREEN,GOLD OVER PURPLE,9 IN....  34.00
POTTERY,VASE,IRIDESCENT,GOLD,GREEN,BLUE LACY VINE EFFECT,
      C.MESSIER........................................  75.00
POTTERY,VASE,LEOPARD SKIN GLAZE,FOOTED,1901,MARTIN BROTHERS,
      5 IN.............................................  55.00
POTTERY,VASE,PEACOCK BLUE,GREEN,LAVENDER SWIRLS,CYLINDRICAL
      SHAPE............................................  80.00
POTTERY,WALL PLAQUE,SCULPTURED WOMAN IN GRECIAN ROBE,SIGNED
      P.IPSEN..........................................  55.00
POTTERY,WATER COOLER,BLUE INCISED BANDS,LEAVES,9 1/2 X
      12 1/2 IN.HIGH...................................  37.50
    POWDER HORN,SEE WEAPON,POWDER HORN
```

PRATT WARE MEANS TWO DIFFERENT THINGS. IT WAS AN EARLY
STAFFORDSHIRE POTTERY,CREAM-COLORED WITH COLORED
DECORATIONS,MADE BY FELIX PRATT DURING THE LATE
EIGHTEENTH CENTURY. THERE WAS ALSO PRATT WARE MADE
WITH TRANSFER DESIGNS DURING THE MID-NINETEENTH CENTURY.
PRATT,BOWL,MALACHITE BORDER,GOLD LINING,TRANSFER PRINT,

```
W.F.WITHERINGTON................................................  192.00
PRATT,CANDLEHOLDER,GREEK CHARIOT SCENE,FENTON,PAIR...........   45.00
PRATT,COMPOTE,PASTORAL SCENE,4 IN.HIGH,8 3/4 IN.DIAMETER....   95.00
PRATT,FIGURINE,AUTUMN,ALLEGORICAL,HOLDS SHEAF OF WHEAT,NEALE
  & PALMER.....................................................  40.00
PRATT,FIGURINE,POODLE DOG,1 1/2 IN. X 2 IN. X 3 IN.,PAIR....   80.00
PRATT,JAR,POMADE,SAYS PEACE,SIGNED BY AUSTIN................   32.50
PRATT,LID, PEACE,  PASTORAL SCENE,PEOPLE,LAMPS,SIGNED J.
  AUSTIN......................................................  36.00
PRATT,LID, THE LATE PRINCE CONSORT .........................   36.00
PRATT,LID, WHO'LL BUY MY LAVENDER ..........................   27.50
PRATT,LID,CHARING CROSS,ALBERT MEMORIAL,BLACK FRAME,PAIR....   75.00
PRATT,PLATE,A LETTER FROM THE DIGGINGS,BLUE BORDER,SIGNED
  J.AUSTIN....................................................  25.00
PRATT,PLATE,BLACK GROUND,CLASSIC GREEK DESIGN,10 IN.........   25.00
PRATT,PLATE,BLUE BOY,ACORN BORDER,8-1/2 IN.DIAMETER.........   32.00
PRATT,PLATE,BOYS PEEPING THROUGH DOORWAY INTO SCHOOLROOM,
  1834,9 1/2 IN...............................................  40.00
PRATT,PLATE,CAKE,CASTLE SCENE,PEDESTAL......................   40.00
PRATT,PLATE,CLASSIC GREEK DESIGN ON SOLID BLACK GROUND,
  10 IN.......................................................  25.00
PRATT,PLATE,DEEP FUCHSIA,GOLD BAND CLASSIC GREEK RUINS IN
  MEDALLION...................................................   9.00
PRATT,PLATE,PASTORAL SCENE,YELLOW BORDER,SIGNED J.A.,
  7-1/2 IN.DIAMETER...........................................  25.00
PRATT,PLATE,ROYAL BLUE BORDER,DECOR,10 IN...................   24.00
PRATT,PLATE,THE BEST CARD,FENTON............................   35.00
PRATT,PLATE,THE HOP QUEEN,9 1/4 IN..........................   65.00
PRATT,PLATE,THE TRUANT,9 1/4 IN.............................   65.00
PRATT,URN,HUNT SCENE,DATED AUGUST 19,1856,FENTON,4 IN.HIGH..   25.00
PRATT,VASE,RED,BLACK HUNTING SCENES,CIRCA 1856.............   20.00
PRESSED GLASS,SEE ALSO,COSMOS,CROESUS,MONKEY,ETC.
PRESSED GLASS,BANANA BOAT,DELAWARE,EMERALD GREEN,
  SILVER-HANDLED HOLDER.......................................  59.00
PRESSED GLASS,BANANA BOAT,GREEN FLOWER & VINE...............   25.00
PRESSED GLASS,BANANA STAND,LOW FOOT.........................   45.00
PRESSED GLASS,BANANA STAND,PANELED THISTLE..................   38.50
PRESSED GLASS,BASKET,BASKET WEAVE ON OUTSIDE,HANDLE,7 IN....    8.00
PRESSED GLASS,BASKET,COLONIAL PATTERN,ETCHED RIBBON &
  FLORAL,HANDLE...............................................  16.50
PRESSED GLASS,BASKET,PANELED THISTLE........................   30.00
PRESSED GLASS,BASKET,12 PANELS,ROPE HANDLE,SCALLOPED,STAR B,
  CLEAR.......................................................   8.50
PRESSED GLASS,BELL,NOTCH-CUT HANDLE,ADVERTISING RUBEL
  FURNITURE CO................................................  20.00
PRESSED GLASS,BELL,SMOKE,WIRE,SCREW EYE,8 IN................   16.50
PRESSED GLASS,BERRY SET,COLORADO,GREEN,7 PIECES.............  165.00
PRESSED GLASS,BOAT,DAISY & BUTTON,CLEAR,9 IN................   12.00
PRESSED GLASS,BOBECHE,ROMAN KEY.............................    1.50
PRESSED GLASS,BOTTLE,BALL BASE,COMES APART TO USE BASE AS
  BOWL,9 IN...................................................  19.00
PRESSED GLASS,BOTTLE,BAR,HORN OF PLENTY,FLINT...............   55.00
PRESSED GLASS,BOTTLE,BAR,MASSACHUSETTS PATTERN..............   12.50
PRESSED GLASS,BOTTLE,CASTOR,MUSTARD,KING'S CROWN PATTERN....    5.00
PRESSED GLASS,BOTTLE,PERFUME,CORDOVA PATTERN,POINTED
  STOPPER,7 IN.TALL...........................................   9.50
PRESSED GLASS,BOTTLE,SCENT,DAISY & BUTTON,METAL CAP.........   10.00
PRESSED GLASS,BOTTLE,WATER,CUBE WITH FAN....................   12.00
PRESSED GLASS,BOTTLE,WATER,PINEAPPLE & FAN..................   24.00
PRESSED GLASS,BOTTLE,WINE,MODEL PEERLESS K3,FINDLAY,OHIO,
  8 1/4 IN....................................................  15.00
PRESSED GLASS,BOWL,BANANA,DELAWARE,CRANBERRY,GOLD...........   45.00
PRESSED GLASS,BOWL,BERRY,ALASKA,GREEN,FLUTED & RUFFLED,
  FOOTED,8 1/2 IN.............................................  39.50
PRESSED GLASS,BOWL,BERRY,BIRD & STRAWBERRY..................   20.00
PRESSED GLASS,BOWL,BERRY,DELAWARE,BOAT SHAPE,CRANBERRY,GOLD.   39.50
PRESSED GLASS,BOWL,BERRY,DELAWARE,GREEN.....................   37.50
PRESSED GLASS,BOWL,BERRY,DEW & RAINDROP,6 SAUCES............   35.00
PRESSED GLASS,BOWL,BERRY,DIAMOND & BUTTON,SIX MATCHING
  SAUCES......................................................  18.50
PRESSED GLASS,BOWL,BERRY,HEXAGONAL,CUT LOG FEET,7 IN.ACROSS.   75.00
PRESSED GLASS,BOWL,BERRY,PANELED THISTLE,FLARING,
  9 1/2-IN.DIAMETER...........................................  16.00
PRESSED GLASS,BOWL,BERRY,PANELED THISTLE,SIDES TURNED UP....   16.00
PRESSED GLASS,BOWL,BERRY,RED-FLASHED,OREGON,8-IN.DIAMETER...   17.50
PRESSED GLASS,BOWL,BROKEN COLUMN,6 1/2 IN...................   12.00
PRESSED GLASS,BOWL,BUTTON ARCHES,FLASHED RED,CLEAR BAND.....   35.00
PRESSED GLASS,BOWL,CENTERPIECE,PANELED THISTLE..............   22.50
PRESSED GLASS,BOWL,CHERRY,STIPPLED,8 1/2-IN.DIAMETER........    9.50
PRESSED GLASS,BOWL,COLORADO,GREEN,GILT,FOOTED,5-IN.DIAMETER.   12.00
PRESSED GLASS,BOWL,COLORADO,GREEN,SCALLOPED,FOOTED,
```

```
    8 1/2-IN.DIAMETER.............................................   28.00
PRESSED GLASS,BOWL,COLORADO,RUFFLED,FOOTED,SIX MATCHING
    SAUCES....................................................  145.00
PRESSED GLASS,BOWL,CONSOLE,ENGRAVED FLORAL,GREEN BASE,
    HAWKES,CANDLESTICK........................................   55.00
PRESSED GLASS,BOWL,CUPID & VENUS,LOW,FOOTED...............   18.00
PRESSED GLASS,BOWL,CUT LOG,SCALLOPED TOP,8 IN. X 2 3/4 IN...   13.00
PRESSED GLASS,BOWL,DELAWARE,GREEN.....................ILLUS..   30.00
PRESSED GLASS,BOWL,DELAWARE,GREEN,GOLD,OVAL........ 22.00 TO   35.00
PRESSED GLASS,BOWL,DELAWARE,GREEN,OVAL,SCALLOPED,GILT,
    12 IN.LONG................................................   30.00
```

DELAWARE PRESSED GLASS BOWL, GREEN

```
PRESSED GLASS,BOWL,FINGER,APPLE GREEN,FLINT..................    8.00
PRESSED GLASS,BOWL,FINGER,FROSTED ARTICHOKE,FLINT,MATCHING
    PLATE.....................................................   15.00
PRESSED GLASS,BOWL,FLUTED,CLEAR,MARKED KRY-STAL,RAYED BASE,
    9-IN.DIAMETER.............................................    9.50
PRESSED GLASS,BOWL,FROSTED CUPIDS ON EACH SIDE,ST.LOUIS
    DEPOSE,FLINT..............................................   95.00
PRESSED GLASS,BOWL,FRUIT,DELAWARE,BOAT SHAPE,ROSE COLOR,GILT   25.00
PRESSED GLASS,BOWL,FRUIT,INVERTED STRAWBERRY,FLARED,DEEP....   25.00
PRESSED GLASS,BOWL,FRUIT,PANELED THISTLE,FOOTED..............   13.50
PRESSED GLASS,BOWL,FRUIT,RED BERRIES,GOLD TRIM,6 SAUCES.....   32.00
PRESSED GLASS,BOWL,JEWELED MOON & STAR,10-IN.DIAMETER.......   10.00
PRESSED GLASS,BOWL,LEAF FORM,IRREGULAR SHAPE,10 1/2 X 7 IN..   10.00
PRESSED GLASS,BOWL,LOUISIANA BERRY,SIX SAUCES...............   30.00
PRESSED GLASS,BOWL,MANHATTAN,8 1/2 IN.......................    9.00
PRESSED GLASS,BOWL,OBLONG,EMERALD GREEN,FIVE OBLONG SAUCES..   72.50
PRESSED GLASS,BOWL,PANELED THISTLE,6 1/2 IN.................    7.00
PRESSED GLASS,BOWL,PRISM & SAWTOOTH,LOW PEDESTAL,
    9 1/4-IN.DIAMETER.........................................   40.00
PRESSED GLASS,BOWL,PUNCH,ALLOVER PATTERN,SEPARATE STAND.....   95.00
PRESSED GLASS,BOWL,PUNCH,CHILD'S,FOOTED,3 1/2 X 5 IN.HIGH,
    4 PUNCH CUPS..............................................   32.00
PRESSED GLASS,BOWL,PUNCH,CHILD'S,FOUR CUPS,HANDLED,LADLE....   39.50
PRESSED GLASS,BOWL,PUNCH,MINIATURE,CUT PATTERN,FOOTED,GOLD
    TRIM,5 IN.................................................    6.50
PRESSED GLASS,BOWL,PUNCH,SEPARATE PEDESTAL,LADLE,6 CUPS.....   35.00
PRESSED GLASS,BOWL,RELISH,OVAL,PANELED THISTLE..............   10.00
PRESSED GLASS,BOWL,ROSE,FINE-CUT & HOBNAIL VARIANT,5 IN.HIGH    8.75
PRESSED GLASS,BOWL,ROSE,PANELED THISTLE,6 1/2-IN.DIAMETER...   22.00
PRESSED GLASS,BOWL,ROSE,PINEAPPLE & FAN,4 1/2 IN.HIGH.......   10.50
PRESSED GLASS,BOWL,ROSE,SCALLOPED TOP......................   12.50
PRESSED GLASS,BOWL,ROSE,THUMBPRINT,OVAL....................   12.50
PRESSED GLASS,BOWL,STIPPLED STAR,FLUTED,GILLINDER OF
    PITTSBURGH,1870...........................................   10.00
PRESSED GLASS,BOWL,SUGAR,BULL'S-EYE,SCALLOPED,FLINT,GREEN...   25.00
PRESSED GLASS,BOWL,SUGAR,CATHEDRAL,COVER....................   17.50
PRESSED GLASS,BOWL,SUGAR,COVER,FEATHER,INDIANA SWIRL.........   20.00
PRESSED GLASS,BOWL,SUGAR,DAISY,MEDALLION,COVER..............   11.50
PRESSED GLASS,BOWL,SUGAR,DEER,FROSTED DOG,COVER.............   39.00
PRESSED GLASS,BOWL,SUGAR,FLEUR-DE-LIS,DRAPE,COVER...........   12.50
PRESSED GLASS,BOWL,SUGAR,FOR SUGAR LUMPS,SQUARE,SILVER
    HOLDER....................................................   30.50
PRESSED GLASS,BOWL,SUGAR,FOUR PETAL,PAGODA LID,FLINT........   42.50
PRESSED GLASS,BOWL,SUGAR,HORN OF PLENTY,COVER,FLINT.........   42.50
PRESSED GLASS,BOWL,SUGAR,LINCOLN DRAPE,OPEN................   20.00
PRESSED GLASS,BOWL,SUGAR,MICHIGAN,GOLD.....................   16.50
PRESSED GLASS,BOWL,SUGAR,SCROLL WITH FLOWERS,COVER.........   14.50
PRESSED GLASS,BOWL,SUGAR,SUNK TEARDROP,COVER...............   10.00
PRESSED GLASS,BOWL,SUGAR,VIKING,COVER......................   18.50
PRESSED GLASS,BOWL,SUGAR,WHEAT AND BARLEY,COVER............   15.00
PRESSED GLASS,BOWL,VEGETABLE,BEADED DEWDROP,2 X 6 X
    8 1/2 IN.LONG.............................................   12.00
PRESSED GLASS,BOX,POWDER,RIBBED PATTERN,MATCHING TOP........    4.50
PRESSED GLASS,BUTTER CHIP,LACY,3 IN........................   10.00
PRESSED GLASS,BUTTER,BELLFLOWER,PLAIN EDGE,COVER,FLINT......   55.00
PRESSED GLASS,BUTTER,BUTTON ARCHES,GOLD BAND...............   35.00
```

```
PRESSED GLASS,BUTTER,CANE & MEDALLION......................    28.50
PRESSED GLASS,BUTTER,COLORADO,GREEN,GOLD,COVER..............    65.00
PRESSED GLASS,BUTTER,DAKOTA,COVER...........................    19.50
PRESSED GLASS,BUTTER,DAKOTA,ETCHED..........................    25.00
PRESSED GLASS,BUTTER,DRAPERY VARIANT,COVER..................    16.75
PRESSED GLASS,BUTTER,FROSTED FLOWER BAND,LOVEBIRD FINIAL ON
   COVER...................................................    49.50
PRESSED GLASS,BUTTER,HORN OF PLENTY,COVER...................    50.00
PRESSED GLASS,BUTTER,LACY TYPE,FLORAL PATTERN,BLUE,COVER....    14.50
PRESSED GLASS,BUTTER,PANELED HOBNAIL,COVER..................    16.75
PRESSED GLASS,BUTTER,RIBBON,COVER...........................    21.50
PRESSED GLASS,BUTTER,SCALLOPED LINES,COVER..................    16.75
PRESSED GLASS,BUTTER,SEDAN,COVER............................    16.75
PRESSED GLASS,BUTTER,SPIRAL IVY,COVER.......................    16.75
PRESSED GLASS,BUTTER,STIPPLED BAR,COVER.....................    16.75
PRESSED GLASS,BUTTER,WAFFLE PATTERN,COVER...................    20.00
PRESSED GLASS,BUTTER,44 PATTERN,COVER.......................    12.00
PRESSED GLASS,BUTTON HOOK,CLEAR,SWIRLED CANE,10 1/2 IN......    15.00
PRESSED GLASS,CAKE STAND,ACTRESS,FROSTED STEM &
   BASE,10.............................................. 49.50 TO  65.00
PRESSED GLASS,CAKE STAND,ACTRESS,6 1/2 IN.HIGH,
   10-IN.DIAMETER........................................    50.00
PRESSED GLASS,CAKE STAND,BIRD & STRAWBERRY..................    20.00
PRESSED GLASS,CAKE STAND,BIRD & STRAWBERRY,9-IN.DIAMETER....    22.50
PRESSED GLASS,CAKE STAND,BLEEDING HEART,9 1/2-IN.DIAMETER,
   6 IN.HIGH.............................................    18.00
PRESSED GLASS,CAKE STAND,BLEEDING HEART,8 IN................    22.00
PRESSED GLASS,CAKE STAND,BROKEN COLUMN,9 3/4-IN.DIAMETER,
   7 1/4 IN.HIGH..........................................    35.00
PRESSED GLASS,CAKE STAND,BUCKLE WITH STAR..................    12.00
PRESSED GLASS,CAKE STAND,CABLE MEDALLION...................    10.00
PRESSED GLASS,CAKE STAND,CHAIN PATTERN,9 IN................     9.00
PRESSED GLASS,CAKE STAND,CROSSBAR,FINECUT,6 1/4 IN.HIGH,
   9-IN.DIAMETER..........................................    15.00
PRESSED GLASS,CAKE STAND,CRYSTAL WEDDING...................    20.00
PRESSED GLASS,CAKE STAND,DAISIES & PANELS,9 IN.............     8.00
PRESSED GLASS,CAKE STAND,DAKOTA,ETCHED....................    25.00
PRESSED GLASS,CAKE STAND,DAKOTA,9 1/2 IN...................    14.00
PRESSED GLASS,CAKE STAND,DIAMOND MEDALLION,SCALLOPED EDGE...    12.00
PRESSED GLASS,CAKE STAND,DIAMOND MEDALLION,PLAIN EDGE......    10.00
PRESSED GLASS,CAKE STAND,FEATHER DUSTER...................     8.50
PRESSED GLASS,CAKE STAND,FESTOON,10 IN....................    14.00
PRESSED GLASS,CAKE STAND,FLATTENED SAWTOOTH,9 IN.SQUARE....    10.00
PRESSED GLASS,CAKE STAND,FROSTED HAND.....................    22.50
PRESSED GLASS,CAKE STAND,FROSTED HAND,CLEAR TABLE,9 IN. X
   7 1/2 IN.HIGH..........................................    30.00
PRESSED GLASS,CAKE STAND,GOOD LUCK,HORSESHOE,10 X
   7 1/2 IN.HIGH..........................................    25.00
PRESSED GLASS,CAKE STAND,JACOB'S LADDER....................    22.00
PRESSED GLASS,CAKE STAND,MEDALLION,APPLE GREEN.............    35.00
PRESSED GLASS,CAKE STAND,PANELED DAISY....................    14.00
PRESSED GLASS,CAKE STAND,PRISCILLA,10 IN.HIGH.............    18.00
PRESSED GLASS,CAKE STAND,QUARTERED BLOCKS,11 IN...........     9.75
PRESSED GLASS,CAKE STAND,ROSE IN SNOW....................    25.00
PRESSED GLASS,CAKE STAND,ROSE SPRIG,9 IN.SQUARE...........    14.50
PRESSED GLASS,CAKE STAND,ROSETTE & PALM..................    20.00
PRESSED GLASS,CAKE STAND,SAWTOOTH PATTERN,10 IN.SQUARE,
   7 IN.HIGH..............................................    25.00
PRESSED GLASS,CAKE STAND,SHELL & TASSEL...................    16.50
PRESSED GLASS,CAKE STAND,SWIRL,8 1/2 IN...................     7.50
PRESSED GLASS,CAKE STAND,THREE FACE,10 3/8-IN.DIAMETER.....    85.00
PRESSED GLASS,CAKE STAND,THREE FRUITS.....................     8.00
PRESSED GLASS,CAKE STAND,TURNED-UP EDGE OF LOOPS,
   10 1/2-IN.DIAMETER.....................................    15.00
PRESSED GLASS,CAKE STAND,U.S.COIN GLASS,1892
   DOLLARS,10....................................300.00 TO   375.00
PRESSED GLASS,CAKE STAND,VICTORIA,12 1/2-IN.DIAMETER.......    85.00
PRESSED GLASS,CAKE STAND,WISCONSIN........................    16.75
PRESSED GLASS,CANDLEHOLDER,COLONIAL PATTERN,IMPERIAL JEWELS,
   BLUE,PAIR..............................................    27.50
PRESSED GLASS,CANDLESTICK,DIAMOND POINT,8 IN.HIGH,PAIR......    25.00
PRESSED GLASS,CANDLESTICK,SWIRLED BASE,ZIPPER ON RISER,PAIR.    22.00
PRESSED GLASS,CANDLESTICK,TWISTED STEM,BLUE,7 IN.TALL,PAIR..    12.50
PRESSED GLASS,CELERY,1000-EYE............................    19.50
PRESSED GLASS,CELERY,BARBERRY............................    15.50
PRESSED GLASS,CELERY,BEADED GRAPE........................    18.50
PRESSED GLASS,CELERY,BEADED HORSES' HEADS,STEM,FOOTED,
   7 3/4 IN.HIGH..........................................    16.50
PRESSED GLASS,CELERY,BLACKBERRY..........................    22.00
PRESSED GLASS,CELERY,BLOCKED ARCHES......................     8.50
PRESSED GLASS,CELERY,BRYCE...............................    15.00
```

```
PRESSED GLASS,CELERY,CENTENNIAL,1776-1876...................    19.00
PRESSED GLASS,CELERY,COLUMNED THUMBPRINTS...................     8.00
PRESSED GLASS,CELERY,CUPID & VENUS.............. 19.50 TO       19.75
PRESSED GLASS,CELERY,CURTAIN...............................    16.50
PRESSED GLASS,CELERY,CZARINA...............................     8.50
PRESSED GLASS,CELERY,DAISY & BUTTON,AMBERETTE..............    35.00
PRESSED GLASS,CELERY,DAISY & BUTTON,THUMBPRINT,CLEAR.......    12.50
PRESSED GLASS,CELERY,DAISY & BUTTON WITH V ORNAMENT........    22.50
PRESSED GLASS,CELERY,DAISY & BUTTON,X BAR..................    19.50
PRESSED GLASS,CELERY,DAISY & BUTTON WITH THUMBPRINT COLUMNS.   16.50
PRESSED GLASS,CELERY,DAISY WITH CLEAR STRIPE...............     8.50
PRESSED GLASS,CELERY,DIAMOND POINT,FLINT...................    35.00
PRESSED GLASS,CELERY,ETCHED POST,SQUARE PANES..............    19.50
PRESSED GLASS,CELERY,ETCHED SWAN,FOOTED,10 IN..............    24.50
PRESSED GLASS,CELERY,FERN BURST...........................      8.50
PRESSED GLASS,CELERY,FLEUR-DE-LIS DRAPE....................    13.50
PRESSED GLASS,CELERY,FLORIDA PALM..........................    10.50
PRESSED GLASS,CELERY,FROSTED ROMAN KEY,FLINT...............    47.50
PRESSED GLASS,CELERY,FROSTED ROMAN KEY,SIGNED,DATED,11 IN...   57.50
PRESSED GLASS,CELERY,GRASSHOPPER...........................    16.00
PRESSED GLASS,CELERY,HERON.................................    22.50
PRESSED GLASS,CELERY,HOBNAIL,RUFFLED TOP EDGE,THUMBPRINT
  BASE.....................................................    13.50
PRESSED GLASS,CELERY,HONEYCOMB..................... 9.50 TO    10.50
PRESSED GLASS,CELERY,HORN OF PLENTY........................    68.00
PRESSED GLASS,CELERY,HORN OF PLENTY,FLINT..................    62.50
PRESSED GLASS,CELERY,HORSEHEAD MEDALLION...................    25.00
PRESSED GLASS,CELERY,HUBER.................................    22.50
PRESSED GLASS,CELERY,JACOB'S LADDER........................    18.50
PRESSED GLASS,CELERY,JERSEY SWIRL..........................    16.50
PRESSED GLASS,CELERY,LATTICE...............................    14.00
PRESSED GLASS,CELERY,LOOP..................................    10.50
PRESSED GLASS,CELERY,LOOP & DART...........................    15.00
PRESSED GLASS,CELERY,OAK LEAF BAND.........................    21.50
PRESSED GLASS,CELERY,PANSIES,FORGET-ME-NOTS................    15.00
PRESSED GLASS,CELERY,PINWHEEL & FLORAL,TWO HANDLES.........    10.50
PRESSED GLASS,CELERY,PLEAT & PANEL.........................    15.00
PRESSED GLASS,CELERY,PRISM PATTERN.........................    18.00
PRESSED GLASS,CELERY,RIBBED PALM PATTERN,FLINT.............    45.00
PRESSED GLASS,CELERY,ROSE SPRIG............................    15.00
PRESSED GLASS,CELERY,ROSETTE & PALM........................    11.50
PRESSED GLASS,CELERY,SANDWICH IVY,FLINT....................    52.50
PRESSED GLASS,CELERY,SANDWICH WAFFLE,FLINT.................     35.00
PRESSED GLASS,CELERY,SKILTON...............................     9.00
PRESSED GLASS,CELERY,SOUVENIR,WASHINGTON CENTENNIAL........    19.00
PRESSED GLASS,CELERY,STAR & PILLAR.........................    15.00
PRESSED GLASS,CELERY,STIPPLED DAISY PATTERN................    10.00
PRESSED GLASS,CELERY,STIPPLED FLOWER BAND,FLINT............    17.50
PRESSED GLASS,CELERY,STIPPLED FORGET-ME-NOT PATTERN.......     17.50
PRESSED GLASS,CELERY,STIPPLED STAR.........................    17.50
PRESSED GLASS,CELERY,SWIRL,TWO HANDLES,FOOTED..............    22.50
PRESSED GLASS,CELERY,TALL,CLEAR,DAISY & BUTTON,THUMBPRINT...   12.50
PRESSED GLASS,CELERY,THREADING.............................    15.00
PRESSED GLASS,CELERY,TORPEDO...............................    22.50
PRESSED GLASS,CELERY,TWO HANDLES,PANELED THISTLE...........    18.00
PRESSED GLASS,CELERY,VIKING........................ 18.50 TO   19.50
PRESSED GLASS,CELERY,WAFFLE,FLINT.................. 28.00 TO   37.50
PRESSED GLASS,CHAMPAGNE,DAHLIA.............................    16.50
PRESSED GLASS,CHAMPAGNE,LILY OF THE VALLEY................     27.50
PRESSED GLASS,CHAMPAGNE,NEW ENGLAND PINEAPPLE..............    50.00
PRESSED GLASS,CHAMPAGNE,ROMAN KEY,FROSTED,FLINT............    34.00
PRESSED GLASS,CHRISTMAS LIGHT,DIAMOND-QUILTED,BLUE-GREEN....   10.00
PRESSED GLASS,CLARET,WAFFLE & THUMBPRINT,6.................   185.00
PRESSED GLASS,COMPOTE,ACTRESS,CLEAR,COVER,8 IN.............    82.50
PRESSED GLASS,COMPOTE,ACTRESS,FROSTED BASE,COVER,
  11 1/2 IN.HIGH...........................................    67.00
PRESSED GLASS,COMPOTE,ALLOVER BLOCK & DIAMOND DESIGN,FLINT,
  6-IN.DIAMETER............................................    21.00
PRESSED GLASS,COMPOTE,AMBER,WILDFLOWER,COVER,HIGH STANDARD..   25.00
PRESSED GLASS,COMPOTE,ATLAS,OPEN,7 3/4-IN.DIAMETER,
  6 3/4 IN.HIGH............................................     8.00
PRESSED GLASS,COMPOTE,BABY FACE,FROSTED,COVER,HIGH STANDARD,
  12 1/2 IN................................................   145.00
PRESSED GLASS,COMPOTE,BABY FACE,11 IN.HIGH,4 1/2-IN.OPENING.   35.00
PRESSED GLASS,COMPOTE,BABY THUMBPRINT,BLOCK STEM,9 IN.TALL..   22.50
PRESSED GLASS,COMPOTE,BARBERRY,COVERED,8 1/2 IN......ILLUS..   20.00
PRESSED GLASS,COMPOTE,BARLEY,OPEN,8-IN.DIAMETER,
  6 1/2 IN.HIGH............................................     9.00
PRESSED GLASS,COMPOTE,BUCKLE WITH STAR,OPEN,8 3/4 IN........   16.50
PRESSED GLASS,COMPOTE,BULL'S-EYE,COVER,10 IN...............    32.50
PRESSED GLASS,COMPOTE,BULL'S-EYE,DIAMOND POINT,LOW STANDARD,
```

PRESSED GLASS BARBERRY COMPOTE

```
  6 IN.................................................... 15.00
PRESSED GLASS,COMPOTE,BULL'S-EYE,DIAMOND POINT,OPEN,6 3/4 X
  8 IN.HIGH.............................................. 24.00
PRESSED GLASS,COMPOTE,BULL'S-EYE,FLINT,COVER.............. 50.00
PRESSED GLASS,COMPOTE,BULL'S-EYE,OPEN,8-IN.DIAMETER,
  8 IN.HIGH.............................................. 15.00
PRESSED GLASS,COMPOTE,BULL'S-EYE & DAISY,COVER............ 23.00
PRESSED GLASS,COMPOTE,CANADIAN,COVER,HIGH STANDARD,11 IN... 65.00
PRESSED GLASS,COMPOTE,CLEAR,FROSTED LION,LID,
  5 1/2-IN.DIAMETER...................................... 25.00
PRESSED GLASS,COMPOTE,CLEAR,OPEN,8 IN..................... 12.00
PRESSED GLASS,COMPOTE,COLORADO,CLEAR,OPEN,7 IN............ 18.50
PRESSED GLASS,COMPOTE,CONICAL TOP,SHORT PEDESTAL,
  9 1/2 IN.HIGH......................................... 25.00
PRESSED GLASS,COMPOTE,COVERED,CLASSIC................ILLUS.. 38.00
PRESSED GLASS,COMPOTE,DIAMOND THUMBPRINT,10-IN.DIAMETER..... 65.00
PRESSED GLASS,COMPOTE,CROW'S-FOOT..........................  9.75
PRESSED GLASS,COMPOTE,CRYSTAL WEDDING,COVER,7 IN............ 28.00
PRESSED GLASS,COMPOTE,CURTAIN.............................. 15.00
PRESSED GLASS,COMPOTE,DAISY & BUTTON,CROSSBAR,COVER........ 20.00
PRESSED GLASS,COMPOTE,DAISY & BUTTON,THUMBPRINT,LOW STAND,
  COVER,6 3/4 IN......................................., 62.50
PRESSED GLASS,COMPOTE,DAISY & DIAMOND,OPEN,8 1/4 IN.SQUARE..  9.00
PRESSED GLASS,COMPOTE,DAKOTA,ETCHED,OPEN,6-IN.DIAMETER..... 20.00
PRESSED GLASS,COMPOTE,DEER & DOG,COVER,9 IN................ 55.00
PRESSED GLASS,COMPOTE,DIAMOND POINT,OPEN.................. 15.00
PRESSED GLASS,COMPOTE,FLINT,6 IN.X 8 IN................... 20.00
PRESSED GLASS,COMPOTE,FLORAL,DRAPES,CASTLE,SAILBOAT,COVER,
  9 IN.................................................. 50.00
PRESSED GLASS,COMPOTE,FROSTED HAND IS STEM,TWO-WAY LATTICE
  PATTERN............................................... 21.00
PRESSED GLASS,COMPOTE,FROSTED LION,LION HEAD FINIAL ON COVER 69.50
PRESSED GLASS,COMPOTE,FROSTED LION,LION HEAD,6 IN......... 65.00
PRESSED GLASS,COMPOTE,FROSTED LION,LOW STANDARD,COVER...... 40.00
PRESSED GLASS,COMPOTE,FRUIT,PANEL,BLUE,DAISY & BUTTON,FLOWER
  SHAPE................................................. 59.50
PRESSED GLASS,COMPOTE,FRUIT,PANELS,CANES,ETCHED BERRIES,
  8 IN.TALL............................................. 19.50
PRESSED GLASS,COMPOTE,FRUIT,THUMBPRINT,FLINT,8 1/2 X
```

CLASSIC PRESSED GLASS COMPOTE

```
    7 1/2 IN.TALL.......................................     21.00
PRESSED GLASS,COMPOTE,GOOD LUCK,HORSESHOE,OPEN,9 X
    9 1/4-IN.DIAMETER..................................     30.00
PRESSED GLASS,COMPOTE,GOTHIC,FLINT,OPEN,8 IN..........     30.00
PRESSED GLASS,COMPOTE,GREEN,PANEL & DAISIES,PEDESTAL..     10.00
PRESSED GLASS,COMPOTE,HAMILTON........................     29.00
PRESSED GLASS,COMPOTE,HONEYCOMB,OPEN,ATTACHED BASE,FLINT,
    9 IN.TALL.........................................     23.00
PRESSED GLASS,COMPOTE,HONEYCOMB,RECLINING LION FINIAL,CABLE
    RIM,12 IN.........................................     75.00
PRESSED GLASS,COMPOTE,HORN OF PLENTY,FLINT,SCALLOPED TOP,
    5 3/4 IN.HIGH.....................................     44.50
PRESSED GLASS,COMPOTE,HORN OF PLENTY,LOOP STEM,7-IN.DIAMETER  45.00
PRESSED GLASS,COMPOTE,JACOB'S LADDER,LOW STANDARD......     15.00
PRESSED GLASS,COMPOTE,JACOB'S LADDER,OPEN,7 1/2 IN.....     12.50
PRESSED GLASS,COMPOTE,JACOB'S LADDER,OPEN,8 IN.........     13.50
PRESSED GLASS,COMPOTE,JACOB'S LADDER,OPEN,8 5/8 IN. X
    8 1/4 IN.TALL.....................................     22.50
PRESSED GLASS,COMPOTE,JELLY,1000-EYE,THREE-KNOB TYPE,BLUE,
    5 IN.TALL.........................................     22.50
PRESSED GLASS,COMPOTE,JELLY,ATLAS,OPEN.................     12.50
PRESSED GLASS,COMPOTE,JELLY,BEADED DEWDROP,FOOTED,5 1/4 X
    3 1/4 IN.HIGH.....................................      9.00
PRESSED GLASS,COMPOTE,JELLY,FISHSCALE,OPEN.............     10.00
PRESSED GLASS,COMPOTE,JELLY,FISHSCALE,OPEN,4 1/2 IN. X
    4 3/4 IN..........................................     12.50
PRESSED GLASS,COMPOTE,JELLY,PANELED THISTLE,5 IN.TALL,
    5-IN.DIAMETER.....................................     16.00
PRESSED GLASS,COMPOTE,JELLY,POGO STICK,OPEN............      9.00
PRESSED GLASS,COMPOTE,JELLY,TREE OF LIFE BOWL,CLEAR HAND,
    5 1/2 X 6 IN......................................     27.50
PRESSED GLASS,COMPOTE,JELLY,X-RAY,GREEN,GILT...........     19.00
PRESSED GLASS,COMPOTE,JENNY LIND,CIRCA 1880...........    150.00
PRESSED GLASS,COMPOTE,LEAF & BERRY ETCHING,DAKOTA,9 X
    9 IN.TALL.........................................     25.00
PRESSED GLASS,COMPOTE,LINCOLN DRAPE,FLINT,OPEN,7 IN....     35.00
PRESSED GLASS,COMPOTE,LION,COVER,HIGH STANDARD,11 IN...     85.00
PRESSED GLASS,COMPOTE,LION HEAD,8 IN...................     75.00
PRESSED GLASS,COMPOTE,LOOP,8 IN. X 4 IN................     24.00
PRESSED GLASS,COMPOTE,LOOP & DART,PORTLAND WITH ROUND
    ORNAMENTS,LID.....................................     37.50
PRESSED GLASS,COMPOTE,LOZENGES,COVER,8 IN. X 8 IN......     12.00
PRESSED GLASS,COMPOTE,MARIGOLD,HEARTS & FLOWERS,6 X
    5 3/4 IN.HIGH.....................................     12.50
PRESSED GLASS,COMPOTE,MINERVA,LOW,8 IN.................     37.50
PRESSED GLASS,COMPOTE,OREGON,OPEN.....................     10.00
PRESSED GLASS,COMPOTE,PANELED DEWDROP,COVER,7 IN. X
    10 IN.HIGH........................................     24.00
PRESSED GLASS,COMPOTE,PANELED THISTLE.................      9.50
PRESSED GLASS,COMPOTE,PANELED THISTLE,7 1/2 IN.HIGH....     22.00
PRESSED GLASS,COMPOTE,PANELED THISTLE,PEDESTAL,5 1/4 X
    8 IN.HIGH.........................................     22.50
PRESSED GLASS,COMPOTE,PETAL & LOOP,OPEN,11-IN.DIAMETER.     75.00
PRESSED GLASS,COMPOTE,PLUME,OPEN,7 3/4-IN.DIAMETER,
    7 3/4 IN.HIGH.....................................     15.00
PRESSED GLASS,COMPOTE,RIBBED ACORN,OPEN...............     32.00
PRESSED GLASS,COMPOTE,RIBBED GRAPE,FLINT..............     30.00
PRESSED GLASS,COMPOTE,RIBBED IVY,FLINT,8-IN.DIAMETER...     32.00
PRESSED GLASS,COMPOTE,RIBBED IVY,SCALLOPED,FLINT,8 IN..     35.00
PRESSED GLASS,COMPOTE,RIBBED PALM,LOW STANDARD,FLINT...     35.00
PRESSED GLASS,COMPOTE,ROSETTE MEDALLION,COVER,6 1/2 IN. X
    10 IN.............................................     15.00
PRESSED GLASS,COMPOTE,ROSETTE WITH PINWHEELS,COVER,8 IN.    12.50
PRESSED GLASS,COMPOTE,SAWTOOTH & LOOPS,FLINT..........     37.50
PRESSED GLASS,COMPOTE,SENECA LOOP,FLINT,OPEN,9 1/4 IN..     17.50
PRESSED GLASS,COMPOTE,SHELL & TASSEL,5 1/2 IN. DIAM. ILLUS..  25.00
PRESSED GLASS,COMPOTE,SHELL & TASSEL,8-IN.DIAMETER,
    7 1/2 IN.TALL.....................................     16.50
PRESSED GLASS,COMPOTE,SHELL & TASSEL,8 IN.HIGH,
    8 1/2-IN.DIAMETER.................................     22.50
PRESSED GLASS,COMPOTE,SHELL & TASSLE,COVER,6 IN.SQUARE,
    7 IN.HIGH.........................................     27.00
PRESSED GLASS,COMPOTE,SHELL BOWL,DOLPHIN STEM,BAKEWELL
    PEARS,6 DISHES....................................    145.00
PRESSED GLASS,COMPOTE,SMOCKING PATTERN,FLINT,8 IN.TALL,
    8-IN.DIAMETER.....................................     39.00
PRESSED GLASS,COMPOTE,SPIREA BAND,BLUE,OPEN...........     24.00
PRESSED GLASS,COMPOTE,STAR IN BULL'S-EYE,FAN,10 IN....     12.50
PRESSED GLASS,COMPOTE,STAR OF DAVID,COVER,7 1/2 IN.....      7.50
PRESSED GLASS,COMPOTE,TEXAS,OPEN,8 1/4 IN.............     23.50
```

PRESSED GLASS SHELL AND TASSEL COMPOTE

```
PRESSED GLASS,COMPOTE,THUMBPRINT,COVER,6 1/2 IN. X 7 IN.HIGH    16.00
PRESSED GLASS,COMPOTE,THUMBPRINT,COVER,FLINT,
   29-IN.CIRCUMFERENCE.........................................  25.00
PRESSED GLASS,COMPOTE,THUMBPRINT,WAFER JOINT,UNEVEN RIM,10 X
   9 IN.HIGH.................................................. 110.00
PRESSED GLASS,COMPOTE,TREE OF LIFE BOWL,FROSTED HAND,OPEN,
   10 X 10 IN.................................................  45.00
PRESSED GLASS,COMPOTE,TREE OF LIFE,PITTSBURGH,FROSTED HAND &
   STEM,1884..................................................  36.00
PRESSED GLASS,COMPOTE,WASHINGTON CENTENNIAL,OPEN,8 3/4 IN...    18.50
PRESSED GLASS,COMPOTE,WESTWARD HO,7 3/4 IN...........ILLUS..    90.00
PRESSED GLASS,COMPOTE,WESTWARD HO,8 IN..............100.00 TO  145.00
PRESSED GLASS,COMPOTE,WESTWARD HO,COVER,8-IN.DIAMETER.......   110.00
PRESSED GLASS,COMPOTE,WESTWARD HO,COVER,HIGH STANDARD,11 IN.    95.00
PRESSED GLASS,COMPOTE,WESTWARD HO,LOW STANDARD,COVER,
   7 1/2 IN.HIGH..............................................  87.50
PRESSED GLASS,COMPOTE,WESTWARD HO,OVAL,COVER,6 3/4 X
   4 1/4 IN...................................................  82.50
```

PRESSED GLASS COMPOTE, WESTWARD HO

```
PRESSED GLASS,COMPOTE,WISCONSIN,OPEN,8 IN...................    17.50
PRESSED GLASS,COMPOTE,ZENITH BLOCK,RUFFLED TOP,
   9 1/2-IN.DIAMETER..........................................  15.00
PRESSED GLASS,CORDIAL,ARGUS.................................    14.00
PRESSED GLASS,CORDIAL,HEART,THUMBPRINT,3 IN.HIGH............    10.00
PRESSED GLASS,CORDIAL,HORN OF PLENTY.......................     45.00
PRESSED GLASS,CREAMER & SUGAR,CLEAR,MARKED KRYSTOL.........      8.50
PRESSED GLASS,CREAMER & SUGAR,DAISY & BUTTON,AMBERETTE.....     89.50
PRESSED GLASS,CREAMER & SUGAR,DAISY & BUTTON,ETCHED FLORAL,
   FOOTED....................................................   15.00
PRESSED GLASS,CREAMER & SUGAR,INTAGLIO CUT BUTTERFLIES &
   LEAVES....................................................   12.00
PRESSED GLASS,CREAMER & SUGAR,MOON & STAR,COVER............     38.00
PRESSED GLASS,CREAMER & SUGAR,PINEAPPLE,FLINT,NEW ENGLAND...   135.00
PRESSED GLASS,CREAMER & SUGAR,RIBBED,COVER,NEW YORK,FLINT...    70.00
PRESSED GLASS,CREAMER & SUGAR,SCROLL,FLORAL................     25.00
PRESSED GLASS,CREAMER & SUGAR,VIRGINIA,CLEAR,GILT EDGES.....    15.00
PRESSED GLASS,CREAMER,ACTRESS..................... 25.00 TO     62.00
PRESSED GLASS,CREAMER,ALABAMA PATTERN......................     10.00
PRESSED GLASS,CREAMER,AUSTRIAN.............................      9.50
PRESSED GLASS,CREAMER,BABY THUMBPRINT,DAKOTA,ETCHED,PEDESTAL    12.00
PRESSED GLASS,CREAMER,BALL & SWIRL................ 10.00 TO     13.00
```

```
PRESSED GLASS,CREAMER,BARLEY.................................      11.00
PRESSED GLASS,CREAMER,BIRD & STRAWBERRY......................      16.00
PRESSED GLASS,CREAMER,BUTTON ARCHES,FLASHED RED,CLEAR BAND..      35.00
PRESSED GLASS,CREAMER,CANADIAN...............................      17.50
PRESSED GLASS,CREAMER,CANE & MEDALLION.......................      15.00
PRESSED GLASS,CREAMER,CANE INSERT............................       6.50
PRESSED GLASS,CREAMER,COLORADO,GREEN,FOOTED..................      16.00
PRESSED GLASS,CREAMER,COLORADO,GREEN,MINNIE & JEWELL,1909,
  3 1/2 IN...................................................      15.00
PRESSED GLASS,CREAMER,CORD & TASSEL..........................      12.50
PRESSED GLASS,CREAMER,CORN,EMERALD,GOLD......................      18.00
PRESSED GLASS,CREAMER,CUPID & PSYCHE.............. 15.00 TO       20.00
PRESSED GLASS,CREAMER,CUPID & VENUS..........................      17.00
PRESSED GLASS,CREAMER,DEER & DOG,APPLIED HANDLE..............      32.50
PRESSED GLASS,CREAMER,DELAWARE,GREEN,GILT....................      28.50
PRESSED GLASS,CREAMER,DOUBLE DOUGHNUT........................      12.00
PRESSED GLASS,CREAMER,EDGERTON...............................       7.00
PRESSED GLASS,CREAMER,EGYPTIAN................... 15.00 TO       22.00
PRESSED GLASS,CREAMER,EMBOSSED DEER,LIGHT GREEN,PITTSBURGH..      32.00
PRESSED GLASS,CREAMER,ETCHED AMAZON..........................      18.50
PRESSED GLASS,CREAMER,FESTOON.................... 10.00 TO       15.00
PRESSED GLASS,CREAMER,FLORIDA PALM...........................       9.50
PRESSED GLASS,CREAMER,FROSTED CIRCLE.........................      21.50
PRESSED GLASS,CREAMER,GARFIELD DRAPE.........................      16.50
PRESSED GLASS,CREAMER,HIDALGO,CLEAR..........................      18.50
PRESSED GLASS,CREAMER,HUMMINGBIRD,CLEAR......................      27.50
PRESSED GLASS,CREAMER,HUMMINGBIRD,LIGHT BLUE.................      35.00
PRESSED GLASS,CREAMER,JACOB'S LADDER,STANDARD................      15.00
PRESSED GLASS,CREAMER,JEWEL BAND.............................       9.00
PRESSED GLASS,CREAMER,LIBERTY................................       5.00
PRESSED GLASS,CREAMER,LILY OF THE VALLEY,APPLIED HANDLE.....      27.50
PRESSED GLASS,CREAMER,OVAL STAR..............................       8.50
PRESSED GLASS,CREAMER,PANELED DEWDROP........................      10.00
PRESSED GLASS,CREAMER,PANELED THISTLE........................      12.00
PRESSED GLASS,CREAMER,POINTED HOBNAIL,STAR BAND..............      10.00
PRESSED GLASS,CREAMER,POINTED JEWEL..........................       8.50
PRESSED GLASS,CREAMER,PORTLAND'S JEWEL.......................       9.75
PRESSED GLASS,CREAMER,RIBBED FORGET-ME-NOTS..................       9.50
PRESSED GLASS,CREAMER,RIBBED PALM,FLINT......................      47.50
PRESSED GLASS,CREAMER,ROBIN HOOD,GREEN.......................      16.50
PRESSED GLASS,CREAMER,SCALLOPED TOP,THUMBPRINT BASE,HOBNAIL.       8.00
PRESSED GLASS,CREAMER,SCROLL WITH FLOWERS....................       9.00
PRESSED GLASS,CREAMER,SHERATON...............................      11.00
PRESSED GLASS,CREAMER,STIPPLED MEDALLION.....................      12.50
PRESSED GLASS,CREAMER,SUGAR,BROKEN COLUMN,COVER.............      45.00
PRESSED GLASS,CREAMER,SUGAR,BUTTER,DELAWARE,GREEN,GILT,
  COVERS....................................................      95.00
PRESSED GLASS,CREAMER,SUGAR,BUTTER,SCROLL,CANE BAND,FANS,
  STAINED RUBY..............................................      95.00
PRESSED GLASS,CREAMER,SUGAR,SPOONER,BUTTER,COVERS,DELAWARE,
  CRANBERRY.................................................     175.00
PRESSED GLASS,CREAMER,SUGAR,SPOONER,BUTTER,STIPPLED HEART,
  HOTEL SIZE................................................      82.50
PRESSED GLASS,CREAMER,SUGAR,SPOONER,COVERED BUTTER,VIKING...      60.00
PRESSED GLASS,CREAMER,SUNBURST,MEDALLION.....................      10.00
PRESSED GLASS,CREAMER,SUNFLOWER..............................      20.00
PRESSED GLASS,CREAMER,SWAG,GREEN.............................      12.00
PRESSED GLASS,CREAMER,SWAN,TREE..............................      22.50
PRESSED GLASS,CREAMER,TEARDROP,BLUE..........................      22.50
PRESSED GLASS,CREAMER,WATER LILY & CATTAIL...................       6.50
PRESSED GLASS,CREAMER,WESTWARD HO............... 50.00 TO       55.00
PRESSED GLASS,CREAMER,WILD FLOWER............................      12.50
PRESSED GLASS,CREAMER,WORLD'S FAIR,1893,HOMOGENOUS,BLUE,
  RIBBED,LIBBEY.............................................     185.00
PRESSED GLASS,CREAMER,ZIPPER.................................       9.00
  PRESSED GLASS,CRUET,SEE ALSO,CRUET
PRESSED GLASS,CRUET,BEADED SWIRL.............................      13.00
PRESSED GLASS,CRUET,BLUE,DAISY & BUTTON......................      22.50
PRESSED GLASS,CRUET,BROKEN COLUMN,MATCHING STOPPER..........      35.00
PRESSED GLASS,CRUET,BULL'S-EYE,FLINT.........................      20.00
PRESSED GLASS,CRUET,CUT LOG,STOPPER..........................      16.50
PRESSED GLASS,CRUET,HEART WITH THUMBPRINT....................      22.50
PRESSED GLASS,CRUET,HOBSTAR..................................       7.50
PRESSED GLASS,CRUET,INVERTED THUMBPRINT,HOLLOW BLOWN
  STOPPER,GREEN-BLUE........................................      47.00
PRESSED GLASS,CRUET,PANELED THISTLE,STOPPER..................      18.50
PRESSED GLASS,CRUET,PEACOCK FEATHER,STOPPER..................      12.00
PRESSED GLASS,CRUET,TENNIS NET DESIGN ON BODY,TENNIS RACQUET
  HANDLES...................................................      25.00
PRESSED GLASS,CRUET,TULIP PATTERN,BUBBLE STOPPER,8 1/2 IN...      45.00
PRESSED GLASS,CRUET,VINEGAR,CHILD'S,MATCHING PEPPER SHAKER,
```

```
     SALT DIP,TRAY.................................................   25.00
PRESSED GLASS,CRUET,VINEGAR,ZIPPER,PAIR..........................   15.00
PRESSED GLASS,CRUET,WINE,CLEAR,SHARP PONTIL,MULTIFACETED
     STOPPER,HANDLE..............................................   39.50
PRESSED GLASS,CUP & SAUCER,LION,SAUCER HAS 3 1/4-IN.DIAMETER     15.00
PRESSED GLASS,CUP,EGG,ASHBURTON,FLINT............................   15.00
PRESSED GLASS,CUP,EGG,CABLE,FLINT................................   25.00
PRESSED GLASS,CUP,EGG,DIAMOND POINT..............................   12.50
PRESSED GLASS,CUP,EGG,FROSTED LION...............................   45.00
PRESSED GLASS,CUP,EGG,HORN OF PLENTY.............................   18.00
PRESSED GLASS,CUP,EGG,NEW ENGLAND PINEAPPLE,FLINT............   16.50
PRESSED GLASS,CUP,EGG,RIBBED PALM................................   15.00
PRESSED GLASS,CUP,EGG,SQUARE FLUTE,FLINT.........................    8.50
PRESSED GLASS,CUP,PUNCH,AZTEC....................................    3.00
PRESSED GLASS,CUP,PUNCH,CHILD'S..................................    5.00
PRESSED GLASS,CUP,PUNCH,DIAMOND,STRAWBERRY,HOBSTAR,
     2 3/4 IN.HIGH...............................................    3.50
PRESSED GLASS,DECANTER,BAR LIP,RIBBED,FLINT,NO STOPPER......   35.00
PRESSED GLASS,DINNER SERVICE,TEASEL PATTERN,110 PIECES......1,800.00
PRESSED GLASS,DISH,BANANA,PANELED THISTLE,OVAL,SIDES
     TURNED-UP...................................................   25.00
PRESSED GLASS,DISH,BERRY,PLUME,RED-FLASHED BORDER,SET OF 6..   35.00
PRESSED GLASS,DISH,BIRD COVER,BLUE,SPLIT RIB BASE,
     5 1/2 IN.LONG...............................................   17.50
PRESSED GLASS,DISH,BUTTER,BIRD & STRAWBERRY,COVER...........   27.00
PRESSED GLASS,DISH,BUTTER,COLORADO,GREEN,GILT...............   85.00
PRESSED GLASS,DISH,BUTTER,COLORADO,GREEN,GILT,FOOTED........   95.00
PRESSED GLASS,DISH,BUTTER,DAISY & BUTTON,COVER..............   25.00
PRESSED GLASS,DISH,BUTTER,DAKOTA,COVER...........................   14.00
PRESSED GLASS,DISH,BUTTER,DIAGONAL BAND,COVER..................   12.00
PRESSED GLASS,DISH,BUTTER,FLAT KNOB,HORN OF PLENTY,COVER,
     FLINT.......................................................   37.50
PRESSED GLASS,DISH,BUTTER,FROG,BLUE,HIGBEE......................   36.00
PRESSED GLASS,DISH,BUTTER,ROSETTE,COVER..........................   15.00
PRESSED GLASS,DISH,BUTTER,SHRINE.................................   24.00
PRESSED GLASS,DISH,BUTTER,SWAN,COVER.............................   27.00
PRESSED GLASS,DISH,BUTTER,WILLOW OAK,COVER......................   14.00
PRESSED GLASS,DISH,CANDY,BABY GRAND PIANO SHAPE,LIFT-OFF
     TOP,4 3/4 IN................................................   22.00
PRESSED GLASS,DISH,CANDY,FAN SHAPE,DAISY BUTTON,COBALT BLUE.   12.00
PRESSED GLASS,DISH,CANDY,MOON & STAR VARIANT,CRANBERRY
     CENTER,COVER................................................   20.00
PRESSED GLASS,DISH,CANDY,RUFFLED,GREEN,GOLD,COLORADO,
     7 1/2-IN.DIAMETER...........................................   15.00
PRESSED GLASS,DISH,CANE,COSMOS DOME LID,FOOTED...............   10.00
PRESSED GLASS,DISH,CELERY,FOLDED,STARS & STRIPES PATTERN,
     11 IN......................................................   12.00
PRESSED GLASS,DISH,CHEESE,ACTRESS...............................  125.00
PRESSED GLASS,DISH,CHEESE,SAWTOOTH..............................   22.50
PRESSED GLASS,DISH,CHICKEN,COVER,AMBER,7 IN....................   35.00
PRESSED GLASS,DISH,DAISY & BUTTON,CLEAR CENTER,BLUE EDGE,
     SQUARE......................................................   22.50
PRESSED GLASS,DISH,DAISY & BUTTON,FAN SHAPE,CLEAR............    3.50
PRESSED GLASS,DISH,HONEY,PANELED THISTLE,ROUND,TWO HANDLES,
     COVER.......................................................   35.00
PRESSED GLASS,DISH,PICKLE,BEADED LOOP,ROUND ENDS,9 1/2 X
     5 IN.......................................................    4.50
PRESSED GLASS,DISH,PICKLE,CHAIN & STAR..........................    7.50
PRESSED GLASS,DISH,PICKLE,DEWDROP & STAR........................    8.50
PRESSED GLASS,DISH,PICKLE,GOOD LUCK.............................    6.50
PRESSED GLASS,DISH,PICKLE,GOOD LUCK,OVAL........................   12.00
PRESSED GLASS,DISH,PICKLE,STAR ROSETTE..........................   10.00
PRESSED GLASS,DISH,PICKLE,ZIPPER,TWO HANDLES,RICHARD &
     HARTLEY,1880...............................................    8.00
PRESSED GLASS,DISH,RABBIT COVER,CLEAR,RED PAINTED EYES......    8.00
PRESSED GLASS,DISH,RELISH,LOOP & FAN............................    6.50
PRESSED GLASS,DISH,RELISH,ROSE IN SNOW..........................    6.00
PRESSED GLASS,DISH,SALT,DIAMOND-QUILTED,TULIP SHAPE,STIEGEL
     TYPE,FLINT..................................................   55.00
PRESSED GLASS,DISH,SAUCE,ACTRESS,FOOTED.........................    8.50
PRESSED GLASS,DISH,SAUCE,CANE INSERT............................    4.00
PRESSED GLASS,DISH,SAUCE,CHERRY.................................    4.00
PRESSED GLASS,DISH,SAUCE,CUPID & VENUS,FOOTED...................    5.00
PRESSED GLASS,DISH,SAUCE,CUPID'S HUNT,FOOTED....................    8.50
PRESSED GLASS,DISH,SAUCE,EGYPTIAN,FOOTED........................    8.50
PRESSED GLASS,DISH,SAUCE,FEATHER,FLAT,..........................    4.00
PRESSED GLASS,DISH,SAUCE,GARFIELD DRAPE.........................    6.00
PRESSED GLASS,DISH,SAUCE,LEAF MEDALLION,PURPLE,GOLD.........   12.00
PRESSED GLASS,DISH,SAUCE,PEACOCK FEATHER,4 1/2-IN.DIAMETER,
     SET OF 4...................................................   16.00
PRESSED GLASS,DISH,SAUCE,ROSE IN SNOW...........................    4.00
```

```
PRESSED GLASS,DISH,SAUCE,SHELL & TASSEL,FOOTED..............     6.00
PRESSED GLASS,DISH,SAUCE,STRAWBERRY.......................     7.00
PRESSED GLASS,DISH,SAUCE,WESTWARD HO,FROSTED,4 IN..........    20.00
PRESSED GLASS,DISH,TURKEY COVER,CLEAR,7 IN.HIGH..............    65.00
PRESSED GLASS,DISH,TWIG FEET,COVER,8 IN.WIDE...............   110.00
PRESSED GLASS,DOUGHNUT STAND,BEADED BAND..................    10.00
PRESSED GLASS,EGG CUP,ARGUS...............................    13.50
PRESSED GLASS,EGG CUP,ASHBURTON...........................    12.00
PRESSED GLASS,EGG CUP,BELLFLOWER,FLARED TOP...............    18.50
PRESSED GLASS,EGG CUP,BUCKLE,FLINT........................    14.00
PRESSED GLASS,EGG CUP,FROSTED LION........................    45.00
PRESSED GLASS,EGG CUP,HONEYCOMB,FLINT,SET OF 4............    25.00
PRESSED GLASS,EGG CUP,PINEAPPLE,FLINT.....................    16.00
PRESSED GLASS,FIGURINE,BUDDHA,BUTTERSCOTCH GLASS,SIGNED
  GILLINDER...............................................    45.00
PRESSED GLASS,FLOWER HOLDER,CAR WALL,CLEAR................     4.50
PRESSED GLASS,FLYTRAP,TABLE,BEEHIVE-SHAPED,FOOTED,DATED
  OCT.28,1890,7 IN........................................    35.00
PRESSED GLASS,FUNNEL,MOLDED,CLEAR,RIBS,FLINT,7 5/8 IN.HIGH..    28.00
PRESSED GLASS,GLASS,WINE,MARIGOLD,CLEAR STEM..............     7.00
PRESSED GLASS,GOBLET,1000-EYE............... 12.75 TO     16.50
PRESSED GLASS,GOBLET,1000-EYE,SET OF 8....................   120.00
PRESSED GLASS,GOBLET,ACORN................................    15.00
PRESSED GLASS,GOBLET,APPLE GREEN WILD FLOWER..............    20.00
PRESSED GLASS,GOBLET,ASHBURTON,FLINT......................    18.00
PRESSED GLASS,GOBLET,BANDED FLUTE,FLINT...................    11.00
PRESSED GLASS,GOBLET,BANDED PRISM.........................     3.00
PRESSED GLASS,GOBLET,BARBERRY.............................    14.00
PRESSED GLASS,GOBLET,BARREL,FLINT,ASHBURTON...............    18.50
PRESSED GLASS,GOBLET,BEADED GRAPE MEDALLION......... 9.50 TO    12.50
PRESSED GLASS,GOBLET,BEADED LOOP..........................     8.00
PRESSED GLASS,GOBLET,BEADED OVALS.........................     6.00
PRESSED GLASS,GOBLET,BEER TASTERS,LION BREWERY,EXPORT,
  CINCINNATI,OHIO.........................................    13.50
PRESSED GLASS,GOBLET,BELCHER LOOP,FLINT...................    14.50
PRESSED GLASS,GOBLET,BELLFLOWER.....................ILLUS..    18.00
```

PRESSED GLASS BELLFLOWER GOBLET

```
PRESSED GLASS,GOBLET,BELLFLOWER,FINE RIB,FLINT..... 14.00 TO    17.00
PRESSED GLASS,GOBLET,BELLFLOWER,FINE RIB,FLINT,6 1/4 IN.HIGH    12.50
PRESSED GLASS,GOBLET,BLACKBERRY...........................    15.00
PRESSED GLASS,GOBLET,BLEEDING HEART,KNOB STEM.............    15.00
PRESSED GLASS,GOBLET,BUCKLE...............................     7.00
PRESSED GLASS,GOBLET,BULL'S-EYE,FLEUR-DE-LIS..............    22.50
PRESSED GLASS,GOBLET,BULL'S-EYE & CUBE,FLINT..............    40.00
PRESSED GLASS,GOBLET,BULL'S-EYE & DAISY,SET OF 6..........    45.00
PRESSED GLASS,GOBLET,BULL'S-EYE & DAISY............. 8.00 TO    18.00
PRESSED GLASS,GOBLET,CABLE,FLINT..........................    32.50
PRESSED GLASS,GOBLET,CANE.................................     7.50
PRESSED GLASS,GOBLET,CARDINAL BIRD........................    12.50
PRESSED GLASS,GOBLET,CHAIN AND STAR BAND..................     8.00
PRESSED GLASS,GOBLET,CHAIN WITH STAR............... 9.00 TO    10.00
PRESSED GLASS,GOBLET,CLEAR,APPLIED STEM,ENGRAVED GEOMETRIC
  FIGURES................................................    38.00
PRESSED GLASS,GOBLET,COLONIAL,KNOB STEM,FLINT.............    32.50
PRESSED GLASS,GOBLET,COMET,FLINT..........................    40.00
PRESSED GLASS,GOBLET,CORCORAN.............................    10.50
PRESSED GLASS,GOBLET,CORD & TASSEL........................     9.50
PRESSED GLASS,GOBLET,CURTAIN TIEBACK......................    10.00
PRESSED GLASS,GOBLET,CUT & BLOCK..........................     8.50
PRESSED GLASS,GOBLET,DAISIES IN OVAL PANEL................     6.50
PRESSED GLASS,GOBLET,DAISIES,3 PANELED....................     7.50
PRESSED GLASS,GOBLET,DAISY & BUTTON,NARCISSUS....... 8.50 TO    11.50
PRESSED GLASS,GOBLET,DAISY & BUTTON,PANELS,SET OF 3.........    25.00
PRESSED GLASS,GOBLET,DAISY & BUTTON,PANELED THUMBPRINT......     8.50
PRESSED GLASS,GOBLET,DAKOTA...............................     9.50
```

```
PRESSED GLASS,GOBLET,DAKOTA,ETCHED.................. 10.00 TO    16.50
PRESSED GLASS,GOBLET,DEIRDRE.........................           5.00
PRESSED GLASS,GOBLET,DIMES,UNITED STATES COIN GLASS.........   235.00
PRESSED GLASS,GOBLET,EGG IN SAND.............................   12.50
PRESSED GLASS,GOBLET,EGYPTIAN................................   18.75
PRESSED GLASS,GOBLET,EMERALD GREEN,HERRINGBONE...........       27.50
PRESSED GLASS,GOBLET,ETCHED LILY OF THE VALLEY,KNOB STEM....    25.00
PRESSED GLASS,GOBLET,EUREKA,FLINT............................    9.50
PRESSED GLASS,GOBLET,EXCELSIOR,FLINT.........................   15.00
PRESSED GLASS,GOBLET,FANS,BABY'S BREATH BAND.............       18.00
PRESSED GLASS,GOBLET,FEDORA LOOP,POLISHED PONTIL,FLINT......    35.00
PRESSED GLASS,GOBLET,FERRIS WHEEL PATTERN....................   12.50
PRESSED GLASS,GOBLET,FINE RIB WITH BAND......................   10.00
PRESSED GLASS,GOBLET,FINE RIB,CUT OVALS,FLINT,1850,5 1/2 IN.    95.00
PRESSED GLASS,GOBLET,FLUTE,BESSEMER,FLINT....................   17.50
PRESSED GLASS,GOBLET,FLUTE,NEW ENGLAND,FLINT.................   17.50
PRESSED GLASS,GOBLET,G.A.R.ARMY OF REPUBLIC VETERANS,
   SEPT.27,1887.............................................   35.00
PRESSED GLASS,GOBLET,GARDEN FERN.............................    6.00
PRESSED GLASS,GOBLET,GOOD LUCK,PRAYER RUG,KNOB STEM.........    17.50
PRESSED GLASS,GOBLET,GOTHIC,FLINT............................   28.00
PRESSED GLASS,GOBLET,GRADUATED DIAMOND.......................    6.00
PRESSED GLASS,GOBLET,GRAPE...................................   12.50
PRESSED GLASS,GOBLET,GRAPE & FESTOON.........................   14.00
PRESSED GLASS,GOBLET,GRAPE MEDALLION.........................   12.50
PRESSED GLASS,GOBLET,HAIRPIN WITH THUMBPRINT,FLINT..........    26.50
PRESSED GLASS,GOBLET,HAMILTON,FLINT..........................   17.00
PRESSED GLASS,GOBLET,HAMILTON,LEAF...........................   18.00
PRESSED GLASS,GOBLET,HEART WITH THUMBPRINT...................   14.50
PRESSED GLASS,GOBLET,HERRINGBONE & IVY,SET OF 6.............    24.00
PRESSED GLASS,GOBLET,HORN OF PLENTY PATTERN,FLINT...........    37.50
PRESSED GLASS,GOBLET,HORSESHOE,GOOD LUCK,KNOB STEM.........     18.00
PRESSED GLASS,GOBLET,IONIA......................... 4.50 TO     7.50
PRESSED GLASS,GOBLET,JEWEL AND DEWDROP.......................   17.50
PRESSED GLASS,GOBLET,JEWEL BAND..............................    8.00
PRESSED GLASS,GOBLET,JEWELED HEART...........................   20.00
PRESSED GLASS,GOBLET,KING'S CROWN,GREEN-FLASHED.............    14.50
PRESSED GLASS,GOBLET,LAREDO HONEYCOMB,FLINT..................   10.00
PRESSED GLASS,GOBLET,LATTICE.................................    6.50
PRESSED GLASS,GOBLET,LEAF & BERRY ETCHING,NAME STEWART,
   DAKOTA.................................................... 10.00
PRESSED GLASS,GOBLET,LIBERTY BELL................... 18.50 TO   21.00
PRESSED GLASS,GOBLET,LILY OF THE VALLEY......................   24.50
PRESSED GLASS,GOBLET,LINCOLN DRAPE...........................   33.00
PRESSED GLASS,GOBLET,LOOP WITH DEWDROP.......................   10.50
PRESSED GLASS,GOBLET,MAGNET & GRAPE,CLEAR LEAF.............      7.50
PRESSED GLASS,GOBLET,MASTER ARGUS PATTERN,FLINT.... 30.00 TO    37.50
PRESSED GLASS,GOBLET,MITRED THUMBPRINT.......................    7.00
PRESSED GLASS,GOBLET,NEW ENGLAND PINEAPPLE...................   22.50
PRESSED GLASS,GOBLET,NEW ENGLAND PINEAPPLE,FLINT.............   35.00
PRESSED GLASS,GOBLET,ODD FELLOW..............................   20.00
PRESSED GLASS,GOBLET,OPEN ROSE & CABBAGE ROSE........ILLUS..    10.00
PRESSED GLASS,GOBLET,PALM,RIBBED,FLINT.......................   14.50
PRESSED GLASS,GOBLET,PANELED ACORN BAND......................   10.00
PRESSED GLASS,GOBLET,PANELED CANE............................   10.00
PRESSED GLASS,GOBLET,PANELED FLOWERS.........................   22.50
PRESSED GLASS,GOBLET,PANELED NIGHTSHADE......................   10.50
PRESSED GLASS,GOBLET,PANELED POTTED FLOWER...................   10.00
PRESSED GLASS,GOBLET,PANELED STEM,BARREL,HUBER,FLINT........    12.00
PRESSED GLASS,GOBLET,PANELED SUNFLOWER.......................   12.00
PRESSED GLASS,GOBLET,PANELED THISTLE.........................   12.00
PRESSED GLASS,GOBLET,PARROT & FAN............................   15.00
PRESSED GLASS,GOBLET,PHILADELPHIA CENTENNIAL.................   29.00
PRESSED GLASS,GOBLET,PINEAPPLE,FLINT,NEW ENGLAND.............   32.50
PRESSED GLASS,GOBLET,PLEAT & PANEL...........................    8.00
```

PRESSED GLASS OPEN ROSE AND CABBAGE ROSE GOBLET

PRESSED GLASS,GOBLET,PLEAT BAND,FLINT...................... 18.00
PRESSED GLASS,GOBLET,POWDER & SHOT,FLINT.................... 22.50
PRESSED GLASS,GOBLET,PRISM & CRESCENT,FLINT................ 37.50
PRESSED GLASS,GOBLET,PRISM & FLUTE,FLINT................... 17.50
PRESSED GLASS,GOBLET,PRISMS & HEXAGONS..................... 6.75
PRESSED GLASS,GOBLET,RIBBED IVY,FLINT.............. 17.50 TO 18.00
PRESSED GLASS,GOBLET,RIBBED LOOP,FLINT..................... 30.00
PRESSED GLASS,GOBLET,RIBBED PALM.......................... 14.00
PRESSED GLASS,GOBLET,RIBBED PALM LEAF,FLINT................ 18.00
PRESSED GLASS,GOBLET,ROMAN ROSETTE........................ 18.00
PRESSED GLASS,GOBLET,ROSE OF SHARON....................... 14.00
PRESSED GLASS,GOBLET,SAWTOOTH,BULB STEM,FLINT.............. 28.00
PRESSED GLASS,GOBLET,SCARAB PATTERN,FLINT................. 60.00
PRESSED GLASS,GOBLET,SNAKESKIN & DOT...................... 5.00
PRESSED GLASS,GOBLET,SPRIG................................ 13.50
PRESSED GLASS,GOBLET,STRAWBERRY........................... 10.50
PRESSED GLASS,GOBLET,SUGAR PEAR.......................... 21.50
PRESSED GLASS,GOBLET,TACKLE BLOCK,FLINT................... 26.00
PRESSED GLASS,GOBLET,TEXAS BULL'S-EYE..................... 11.00
PRESSED GLASS,GOBLET,THREE FACE........................... 39.50
PRESSED GLASS,GOBLET,THREE PANEL,CLEAR.................... 4.50
PRESSED GLASS,GOBLET,THUMBPRINT,BARREL SHAPE,CLEAR......... 14.00
PRESSED GLASS,GOBLET,VALENCIA WAFFLE...................... 14.50
PRESSED GLASS,GOBLET,WAFFLE & THUMBPRINT,KNOB STEM,FLINT.... 27.50
PRESSED GLASS,GOBLET,WAFFLE,KNOB STEM,FLINT............... 14.50
PRESSED GLASS,GOBLET,WATER,DEER & DOE,LILY OF THE VALLEY.... 29.00
PRESSED GLASS,GOBLET,WEDDING RING......................... 17.50
PRESSED GLASS,GOBLET,WHISKEY TESTER,RINGED & FRAMED OVALS,
  2 1/2 IN................................................ 25.00
PRESSED GLASS,GOBLET,YUMA LOOP............................ 6.00
PRESSED GLASS,HAIR RECEIVER,POWDER DISH,HEART DESIGN,WHITE
  METAL TOPS.............................................. 10.00
PRESSED GLASS,HAT,FEDORA,CLEAR............................ 6.50
PRESSED GLASS,HOLDER,STRING,BEEHIVE STYLE,THUMBPRINT BASE... 12.00
PRESSED GLASS,HONEY SET,DEWDROP,OVAL,SIX SAUCE DISHES....... 50.00
PRESSED GLASS,ICE BUCKET,FANS,CROSSBAR,TAB HANDLES,
  6-IN.DIAMETER........................................... 8.50
PRESSED GLASS,JAR,COOKIE,PINEAPPLE & FAN,9 IN.TALL.......... 35.00
PRESSED GLASS,JAR,JAM,SAWTOOTH,COVER...................... 10.00
PRESSED GLASS,JAR,MARMALADE,HERON,COVER................... 12.50
PRESSED GLASS,JAR,POWDER,BASKET WEAVE,GOLD DOGS,GOLD RABBIT
  ON LID.................................................. 12.00
PRESSED GLASS,JELLY,CLEAR CIRCLE,FOOTED................... 7.50
PRESSED GLASS,KNIFE REST,DIAMOND,FAN ENDS,3 IN.,PAIR....... 5.00
PRESSED GLASS,KNIFE REST,DIAMOND,CURVED HIGH ENDS,3 1/8 IN.. 3.00
PRESSED GLASS,KNIFE REST,DIAMOND,FAN ENDS,3 1/4 IN.......... 2.50
PRESSED GLASS,KNIFE REST,HIGH CURVED ENDS,PINWHEEL ON
  BOTTOM,3 3/4 IN......................................... 3.50
PRESSED GLASS,LAMP,FINGER,DIAMOND BAND,YELLOW,THREE MOLD,
  BRASS FITTINGS.......................................... 35.00
PRESSED GLASS,LAMP,FINGER,HANDLE,PEDESTAL FOOT,MARKED OIL
  GUARD,1870.............................................. 10.00
PRESSED GLASS,LAMP,HAND,BURNER,CHIMNEY,HANDLE,STEM,DATED
  1870,13 IN.HIGH......................................... 12.00
PRESSED GLASS,LAMP,HARP,FLINT,9 IN........................ 55.00
PRESSED GLASS,LAMP,HEART & THUMBPRINT,GREEN,FLINT,PEDESTAL.. 35.00
PRESSED GLASS,LAMP,KEROSENE,STEM,METAL BASE............... 12.00
PRESSED GLASS,LAMP,MARRIAGE,TWIN FONT,BLOWN IN MOLD,RIPLEY &
  CO.,1870............................................... 550.00
PRESSED GLASS,MOLD,BUTTER,FLEUR-DE-LIS,1 POUND............. 25.00
PRESSED GLASS,MUG,BEER,SANDWICH LOOP,FLINT,APPLIED STRAP
  HANDLE,4 IN............................................. 12.50
PRESSED GLASS,MUG,BIRD & HARP,CLEAR,3 1/8 IN.HIGH........... 16.00
PRESSED GLASS,MUG,BUTTON,ARCHES,RUBY TOP,ALDEN,1900........ 8.00
PRESSED GLASS,MUG,BUTTON,ARCHES,RUBY TOP,HOT SPRINGS,ARK.,
  1904.................................................... 8.00
PRESSED GLASS,MUG,CHILD'S,1000 EYE,CLEAR.................. 6.50
PRESSED GLASS,MUG,CHILD'S,POINTED HOBNAIL,3 IN.HIGH......... 10.00
PRESSED GLASS,MUG,CUPID AND VENUS,3 1/2 IN................. 7.00
PRESSED GLASS,MUG,CUT LOG................................. 6.50
PRESSED GLASS,MUG,GOOSEBERRY.............................. 17.50
PRESSED GLASS,MUG,POINTED HOBNAIL......................... 6.50
PRESSED GLASS,MUG,ROMAN ROSETTE........................... 7.00
PRESSED GLASS,MUSTARD POT,BARREL SHAPE,OVAL GROUND FACETS,
  FLINT................................................... 6.50
PRESSED GLASS,NAPPIE,COLORADO,CLEAR,TRICORNERED HANDLE...... 7.50
PRESSED GLASS,PAPERWEIGHT,BUDDHA FIGURE,MOSS GREEN,
  SIGNATURE,GILLANDER..................................... 25.00
PRESSED GLASS,PERFUME,FLINT,STOPPER,IN ORNATE METAL HOLDER,
  FOOTED.................................................. 22.50
PRESSED GLASS,PERFUME,THUMBPRINT,GREEN,PEDESTAL BASE,SIGNED

```
       H,5 IN.................................................    12.00
PRESSED GLASS,PICKLE JAR,CLEAR,SILVER PLATE FRAME,TONGS.....    25.00
PRESSED GLASS,PITCHER,1000-EYE,BLUE RIM & BASE,WHITE CENTER.    55.00
PRESSED GLASS,PITCHER,BALL & SWIRL,TANKARD.................    32.00
PRESSED GLASS,PITCHER,BEAD & CHAIN,6 IN.HIGH...............    11.00
PRESSED GLASS,PITCHER,CLEAR,FIG & CHERRY..................    20.00
PRESSED GLASS,PITCHER,DELAWARE,ROSE,GILT,9 IN.............    45.00
PRESSED GLASS,PITCHER,FEATHER DUSTER PATTERN,GREEN,8 IN....    22.50
PRESSED GLASS,PITCHER,FROSTED & CLEAR,ROYAL IVY,APPLIED
    HANDLE.................................................    27.50
PRESSED GLASS,PITCHER,LEAF & DART.........................    11.00
PRESSED GLASS,PITCHER,LEAF MEDALLION,PURPLE,GOLD,FIVE
    TUMBLERS..............................................   165.00
PRESSED GLASS,PITCHER,MAGNET & GRAPE,CLEAR................    13.50
PRESSED GLASS,PITCHER,MAGNOLIA,CLEAR......................    25.00
PRESSED GLASS,PITCHER,MILK,1000-EYE WITH RUBY BAND RIM......    42.50
PRESSED GLASS,PITCHER,MILK,BASKET WEAVE...................    15.00
PRESSED GLASS,PITCHER,MILK,BEADED LOOP....................    15.00
PRESSED GLASS,PITCHER,MILK,BEVEL DIAMOND,STAR VARIANT.......    11.50
PRESSED GLASS,PITCHER,MILK,CHECKERBOARD...................    16.50
PRESSED GLASS,PITCHER,MILK,CUPID & VENUS..................    20.00
PRESSED GLASS,PITCHER,MILK,CUT LOG.......................    12.50
PRESSED GLASS,PITCHER,MILK,DAHLIA........................    19.50
PRESSED GLASS,PITCHER,MILK,DAISY & BUTTON,OVAL MEDALLION,
    8 IN..................................................    12.00
PRESSED GLASS,PITCHER,MILK,DAISY & BUTTON,X BAR...........    23.50
PRESSED GLASS,PITCHER,MILK,ETCHED BUTTON BAND.............    27.50
PRESSED GLASS,PITCHER,MILK,FEATHER & BLOCK................    12.50
PRESSED GLASS,PITCHER,MILK,FISHSCALE.....................    16.50
PRESSED GLASS,PITCHER,MILK,GARFIELD DRAPE................    25.00
PRESSED GLASS,PITCHER,MILK,HERRINGBONE,EMERALD GREEN........    27.50
PRESSED GLASS,PITCHER,MILK,LILY OF THE VALLEY.............    57.50
PRESSED GLASS,PITCHER,MILK,MARYLAND......................    13.50
PRESSED GLASS,PITCHER,MILK,PANEL HERRINGBONE.............    14.50
PRESSED GLASS,PITCHER,MILK,ROSE SPRIG....................    22.50
PRESSED GLASS,PITCHER,MILK,ROSETTE.......................    18.50
PRESSED GLASS,PITCHER,MILK,SAWTOOTH,APPLIED & CRIMPED
    HANDLE,8 IN.HIGH......................................    38.50
PRESSED GLASS,PITCHER,MILK,SHERATON......................    13.50
PRESSED GLASS,PITCHER,MILK,TANKARD,TORPEDO...............    29.50
PRESSED GLASS,PITCHER,ROSE SPRIG,9 1/2 IN.TALL...........    16.00
PRESSED GLASS,PITCHER,SYRUP,LINCOLN DRAPE,APPLIED HANDLE,
    METAL TOP.............................................    35.00
PRESSED GLASS,PITCHER,TANKARD,FLOWER & BAND DECOR,BUBBLE,
    11 1/2 IN.............................................    18.00
PRESSED GLASS,PITCHER,WATER,1000-EYE,BLUE,KNOB BASE,
    10 1/2 IN.HIGH........................................    72.50
PRESSED GLASS,PITCHER,WATER,BASKET WEAVE,CLEAR,8 1/2 IN.....    15.00
PRESSED GLASS,PITCHER,WATER,BEADED LOOP,COMPOTE,SUGAR BASE,
    8 GOBLETS.............................................   135.00
PRESSED GLASS,PITCHER,WATER,BLOCK & FAN..................    12.00
PRESSED GLASS,PITCHER,WATER,BUTTON ARCHES,GOLD BAND.......    20.00
PRESSED GLASS,PITCHER,WATER,CABBAGE ROSE.................    62.50
PRESSED GLASS,PITCHER,WATER,CANE.........................    15.00
PRESSED GLASS,PITCHER,WATER,CANE,CLEAR...................    18.00
PRESSED GLASS,PITCHER,WATER,COLORADO,GILT,GREEN..........   110.00
PRESSED GLASS,PITCHER,WATER,COTTAGE......................    17.50
PRESSED GLASS,PITCHER,WATER,CRAQUELLE,GROUND PONTIL,APPLIED
    REED HANDLE...........................................    35.00
PRESSED GLASS,PITCHER,WATER,DAKOTA,ETCHED,TANKARD........    32.50
PRESSED GLASS,PITCHER,WATER,DELAWARE.....................    60.00
PRESSED GLASS,PITCHER,WATER,DELAWARE,GREEN...............    45.00
PRESSED GLASS,PITCHER,WATER,DELAWARE,GREEN,FLARE SKIRT BASE,
    GOLD..................................................    78.00
PRESSED GLASS,PITCHER,WATER,DELAWARE,GREEN,GILT..........    65.00
PRESSED GLASS,PITCHER,WATER,DELAWARE,GREEN WITH GOLD........    55.00
PRESSED GLASS,PITCHER,WATER,DEWEY,48 STARS...............    37.50
PRESSED GLASS,PITCHER,WATER,DIAMOND POINT,CRIMPED,GROUND
    PONTIL,FLINT..........................................   100.00
PRESSED GLASS,PITCHER,WATER,ETCHED DAKOTA,FERN,BERRY,
    TANKARD,HANDLE........................................    30.00
PRESSED GLASS,PITCHER,WATER,FEATHER......................    16.50
PRESSED GLASS,PITCHER,WATER,FEATHER,8 IN.................    18.00
PRESSED GLASS,PITCHER,WATER,FESTOON......................    22.50
PRESSED GLASS,PITCHER,WATER,FISHSCALE....................    12.50
PRESSED GLASS,PITCHER,WATER,FOOTED,DAISY & BUTTON,PANEL,
    AMBER.................................................    10.00
PRESSED GLASS,PITCHER,WATER,GRAPE & VINE,CANADIAN,CIRCA
    1890..................................................    22.50
PRESSED GLASS,PITCHER,WATER,HOBNAIL......................    14.50
PRESSED GLASS,PITCHER,WATER,HORN OF PLENTY,FLINT,
```

```
    8 1/2 IN.HIGH..........................................   225.00
PRESSED GLASS,PITCHER,WATER,JEWEL WITH DEWDROP.............    22.50
PRESSED GLASS,PITCHER,WATER,LOTUS & INSECT..................   35.00
PRESSED GLASS,PITCHER,WATER,MEPHISTOPHELES,1000-EYE,DEVIL,
    BLOWN..............................................       75.00
PRESSED GLASS,PITCHER,WATER,OSTERLUND,CIRCA 1876...........    15.00
PRESSED GLASS,PITCHER,WATER,PANELED FORGET-ME-NOT..........    21.00
PRESSED GLASS,PITCHER,WATER,PANELED STRAWBERRY.............    75.00
PRESSED GLASS,PITCHER,WATER,RIBBED PALM....................   85.00
PRESSED GLASS,PITCHER,WATER,RIBBED PALM,FLINT,9 IN.........    85.00
PRESSED GLASS,PITCHER,WATER,SHELL & JEWEL..................   12.50
PRESSED GLASS,PITCHER,WATER,SHELL & JEWEL,8 IN.............    15.00
PRESSED GLASS,PITCHER,WATER,SHELL & JEWEL,8 TUMBLERS.......    85.00
PRESSED GLASS,PITCHER,WATER,STORK,CLEAR....................   39.50
PRESSED GLASS,PITCHER,WATER,TANKARD,PILLOWS & CIRCLES,
    13 1/4 IN..........................................       19.50
PRESSED GLASS,PITCHER,WATER,VENETIAN PATTERN,CLEAR,SQUARE
    SHAPE..............................................       20.00
PRESSED GLASS,PITCHER,WATER,VIKING.........................   22.00
PRESSED GLASS,PITCHER,WATER,WESTWARD HO,9 1/2 IN.HIGH......    85.00
PRESSED GLASS,PITCHER,WATER,WHEAT & BARLEY.................   25.00
PRESSED GLASS,PITCHER,WILD FLOWER,CLEAR,8 1/2 IN...........    14.50
PRESSED GLASS,PLATE,1000-EYE,CLEAR,FOLDED CORNERS,
    10 IN.SQUARE.......................................       17.50
PRESSED GLASS,PLATE,ANTHEMION,10 IN........................   10.00
PRESSED GLASS,PLATE,BREAD,GEN.ULYSSES GRANT,PATRIOT,PANEL
    BORDER.............................................       18.00
PRESSED GLASS,PLATE,BREAD,ATLANTIC CABLE,BLUE..............    18.50
PRESSED GLASS,PLATE,BREAD,CLASSIC WARRIOR..................   80.00
PRESSED GLASS,PLATE,BREAD,DAISY & BUTTON,BLUE,OVAL,9 X
    14 IN..............................................       27.50
PRESSED GLASS,PLATE,BREAD,DEER & PINE,13 X 7 1/2 IN........    22.50
PRESSED GLASS,PLATE,BREAD,GARFIELD DRAPE,WE MOURN..........    30.00
PRESSED GLASS,PLATE,BREAD,GARFIELD,MEMORIAL................   22.50
PRESSED GLASS,PLATE,BREAD,GOOD LUCK,HORSESHOE HANDLES,
    13 IN.LONG.........................................       20.00
PRESSED GLASS,PLATE,BREAD,LIBERTY BELL,SIGNERS.............    35.00
PRESSED GLASS,PLATE,BREAD,LORD'S SUPPER,GILT FIGURES,CIRCA
    1891...............................................       16.50
PRESSED GLASS,PLATE,BREAD,LORD'S SUPPER..........ILLUS..     12.50
```

LORD'S SUPPER PRESSED
GLASS BREAD PLATE

```
PRESSED GLASS,PLATE,BREAD,ROCK OF AGES,MILK GLASS INSERT....   35.00
PRESSED GLASS,PLATE,BREAD,SHEAF OF WHEAT CENTER, GIVE US
    THIS DAY ..........................................       18.50
PRESSED GLASS,PLATE,BREAD,WASTE NOT--WANT NOT..............    16.50
PRESSED GLASS,PLATE,BREAD,WHEAT............................   14.00
PRESSED GLASS,PLATE,BROKEN COLUMN,7-IN.DIAMETER............    20.00
PRESSED GLASS,PLATE,CAKE,BIRD & STRAWBERRY.................   18.00
PRESSED GLASS,PLATE,CAKE,DAHLIA,9-IN.DIAMETER..............    17.50
PRESSED GLASS,PLATE,CAKE,FROSTED MAPLE LEAF,11-IN.DIAMETER..   20.00
PRESSED GLASS,PLATE,CAKE,HAND,FROSTED,9-IN.DIAMETER,
    7 1/2 IN.HIGH......................................       45.00
PRESSED GLASS,PLATE,CAKE,ROSETTE,PINWHEELS,STANDARD........     9.00
PRESSED GLASS,PLATE,CAKE,THREE FACE,9-IN.DIAMETER,7 IN.HIGH.   75.00
PRESSED GLASS,PLATE,CURRIER & IVES,HOME TO THANKSGIVING,
    10 1/2 IN..........................................       25.00
PRESSED GLASS,PLATE,CURRIER & IVES,HOMESTEAD IN WINTER,
    8 1/2 IN.SQUARE....................................       12.50
PRESSED GLASS,PLATE,CURRIER & IVES,TRAIN,PINK ROSE BORDER,
    10 1/2 IN..........................................       30.00
PRESSED GLASS,PLATE,DAISY & BUTTON,CLEAR,SQUARE...........    10.00
```

```
PRESSED GLASS,PLATE,DRAPED STAR.........................   15.00
PRESSED GLASS,PLATE,EGYPTIAN,CAMEL,TENT,PALM TREES,HANDLES,
  10 IN...................................................   22.50
PRESSED GLASS,PLATE,FISHSCALE,ROUNDED CORNERS,9 IN.SQUARE...   15.00
PRESSED GLASS,PLATE,IOWA CITY,ELAINE,BORDER...............   50.00
PRESSED GLASS,PLATE,MANHATTAN,6 IN........................    7.00
PRESSED GLASS,PLATE,ROSE IN SNOW,6 IN.....................   11.00
PRESSED GLASS,PLATE,ROSETTE & PALMS,10-IN.DIAMETER........   15.00
PRESSED GLASS,PLATE,ROSETTE,CLEAR,CLOSED HANDLE,
  9-IN.DIAMETER...........................................    7.50
PRESSED GLASS,PLATE,TEA,HORN OF PLENTY,FLINT,6 1/4 IN.......   28.00
PRESSED GLASS,PLATTER,BREAD,CUPID'S HUNT..................   28.50
PRESSED GLASS,PLATTER,BREAD,EGYPTIAN,GIVE US THIS DAY,13 X
  8 1/2 IN.................................................   16.50
PRESSED GLASS,PLATTER,BREAD,GARFIELD IN MEMORIAL,FROSTED
  BUST CENTER.............................................   30.00
PRESSED GLASS,PLATTER,BREAD,GOOD LUCK,HORSE SHOE HANDLES....   25.00
PRESSED GLASS,PLATTER,BREAD,LIBERTY BELL,OVAL,CLEAR.......   28.50
PRESSED GLASS,PLATTER,CAKE,STIPPLED DAHLIA PATTERN,CLOSED
  HANDLES,9 IN............................................   15.00
PRESSED GLASS,PLATTER,IOWA CITY,BEEHIVE, BE INDUSTRIOUS,
  BORDER.................................................   40.00
PRESSED GLASS,POLAR BEAR,CLEAR & FROSTED.................  125.00
PRESSED GLASS,POWDER HORN,DAISY & BUTTON,10 IN............   18.00
PRESSED GLASS,POWDER HORN,DAISY & BUTTON,14 IN............   25.00
PRESSED GLASS,POWDER HORN,HANDLE,7 1/2 IN.................    4.50
PRESSED GLASS,PUNCH BOWL SET,BOWL,PLATE,LADLE,BOHEMIAN,AMBER   65.00
PRESSED GLASS,RELISH,ACTRESS,CLEAR,7 IN. X 4 1/2 IN.......   25.00
PRESSED GLASS,RELISH,BEADED LOOP,9 IN.....................    8.00
PRESSED GLASS,RELISH,CHAIN WITH STAR.....................    6.50
PRESSED GLASS,RELISH,DAISY PATTERN,PANELS,OVAL,7 1/4 X
  5 1/4 IN................................................    8.00
PRESSED GLASS,RELISH,JACOB'S LADDER,CLEAR................    5.00
PRESSED GLASS,RELISH,OVAL,PANELED THISTLE,4 1/2 X 8 IN.....   10.00
PRESSED GLASS,RELISH,SOUVENIR,REVOLUTIONARY WAR CENTENNIAL,
  1776-1876...............................................   25.00
PRESSED GLASS,SALT,FOOTED,OCTAGON TOP,GROOVES,OVERALL
  FACETS,FLINT............................................    8.00
PRESSED GLASS,SALT,LILY PAD,GREEN........................  300.00
PRESSED GLASS,SALT,MASTER,ARCHED LEAF,FLINT..............    9.00
PRESSED GLASS,SALT,MASTER,BELLFLOWER,FINE RIB,SCALLOPED TOP,
  PEDESTAL................................................   22.50
PRESSED GLASS,SALT,MASTER,BELLFLOWER,SINGLE VINE,OPEN.......   15.00
PRESSED GLASS,SALT,MASTER,BLEEDING HEART.................   18.50
PRESSED GLASS,SALT,MASTER,BLUE,WAFFLE BOTTOM,BULGING CENTER
  PANEL..................................................   32.00
PRESSED GLASS,SALT,MASTER,SAWTOOTH,JAGGED-EDGE TOP,SHORT
  PEDESTAL,CLEAR.........................................   10.00
PRESSED GLASS,SALT,MASTER,SAWTOOTH CIRCLE,FLINT..........    8.75
PRESSED GLASS,SALT,MASTER,THUMBPRINT,PEDESTAL BASE,FLINT....    5.00
PRESSED GLASS,SALT,PANELED THISTLE,FLORAL OVAL,FOOTED.......    3.50
PRESSED GLASS,SALT,POINTED HOBNAIL,PEWTER TOP,PAIR.........   10.00
PRESSED GLASS,SALT & PEPPER,BLUE,THUMBPRINT,ENAMELED LILY OF
  THE VALLEY.............................................   22.50
PRESSED GLASS,SALT & PEPPER,BUTTON ARCHES,GOLD BAND........   15.00
PRESSED GLASS,SALT & PEPPER,IRIS & MEANDER,GREEN,GOLD TRIM..   25.00
PRESSED GLASS,SALT DIP,LARGE T-PRINT.....................    1.50
PRESSED GLASS,SALT DIP,OPEN,ROUND,FANCY PANEL,FINE-CUT
  PATTERN,SET OF 10.......................................    9.50
PRESSED GLASS,SALT DIP,PANELED THISTLE,THREE-FOOTED,
  2 1/2-IN.DIAMETER.......................................    5.50
PRESSED GLASS,SAUCE,BARBERRY,WITH OVAL BERRIES,2-FOOTED,
  4-IN.DIAMETER...........................................    6.00
PRESSED GLASS,SAUCE,BEADED MIRROR,FLAT,FLINT,4 IN.........    5.50
PRESSED GLASS,SAUCE,BIRDS AT FOUNTAIN,FLAT,5 IN..........    6.00
PRESSED GLASS,SAUCE,BLACKBERRY BAND,4 IN.................    4.50
PRESSED GLASS,SAUCE,BULL'S-EYE IN DAISY,AMETHYST EYES,GOLD
  TRIM...................................................    3.00
PRESSED GLASS,SAUCE,CHANDELIER,FLAT,3 1/4 IN.............    4.50
PRESSED GLASS,SAUCE,COLORADO,GILT,ROUND,FOOTED...........   15.00
PRESSED GLASS,SAUCE,CORD DRAPERY,4 1/4 IN................    4.50
PRESSED GLASS,SAUCE,CUBE WITH FAN........................    5.00
PRESSED GLASS,SAUCE,CUPID & VENUS,FOOTED............. 5.00 TO    7.00
PRESSED GLASS,SAUCE,DAISY & BUTTON BAND,BEADED PANEL.......    3.00
PRESSED GLASS,SAUCE,DAISY & BUTTON,THUMBPRINT,PALE BLUE,
  SQUARE.................................................    6.50
PRESSED GLASS,SAUCE,DELAWARE,GREEN.......................   15.00
PRESSED GLASS,SAUCE,DELAWARE,PINK,GILT,FOUR-PETAL FLOWER,
  OVAL..................................................   32.00
PRESSED GLASS,SAUCE,DIAMOND POINT,SCALLOPED,FOOTED.........    5.00
PRESSED GLASS,SAUCE,DICKINSON,FLINT,4 IN.................    6.50
```

PRESSED GLASS,SAUCE,FANS WITH CROSSBAR...................... 3.50
PRESSED GLASS,SAUCE,FISHSCALE,FLAT,4 IN.................... 4.00
PRESSED GLASS,SAUCE,FLORIDA,FLAT,CLEAR,4 1/4 IN........... 5.00
PRESSED GLASS,SAUCE,GALLOWAY,FLAT,4 1/4 IN................ 3.50
PRESSED GLASS,SAUCE,GOOD LUCK,HORSESHOE IN BASE,FLAT........ 7.00
PRESSED GLASS,SAUCE,HUCKLE,FLAT,4 IN....................... 3.25
PRESSED GLASS,SAUCE,INVERTED FERN,FLINT,4 IN............... 6.00
PRESSED GLASS,SAUCE,JACOB'S LADDER,FLAT,4 1/2-IN.DIAMETER,4. 18.00
PRESSED GLASS,SAUCE,LATTICE,FLAT,4 IN...................... 83.75
PRESSED GLASS,SAUCE,LOTUS,FLAT,PORRIGER HANDLE,5 1/2 IN..... 5.50
PRESSED GLASS,SAUCE,MALTESE CROSS,AMBER DIAGONAL STRIPE,
    FLAT,3 1/2 IN.......................................... 5.50
PRESSED GLASS,SAUCE,OPALESCENT HOBNAIL IN SQUARE,VESTA,FLAT,
    4 1/2 IN.............................................. 8.75
PRESSED GLASS,SAUCE,OPEN ROSE,FLAT,4 IN.................... 4.25
PRESSED GLASS,SAUCE,OVAL LENS & STAR,FLAT................. 3.75
PRESSED GLASS,SAUCE,PANELED THISTLE,4 1/2-IN.DIAMETER...... 8.00
PRESSED GLASS,SAUCE,PLUME,FLAT,SQUARE,4 3/4 IN............. 4.50
PRESSED GLASS,SAUCE,PRINCESS FEATHER,FLINT,4 IN........... 6.50
PRESSED GLASS,SAUCE,RETICULATED CORD,FLAT,4 3/8 IN......... 4.00
PRESSED GLASS,SAUCE,RIBBON,FLAT,4 IN...................... 4.25
PRESSED GLASS,SAUCE,ROSE SPRIG,PORRINGER HANDLE,FLAT,4 IN... 6.50
PRESSED GLASS,SAUCE,SEDAN,FLAT,4 1/4 IN.................... 3.75
PRESSED GLASS,SAUCE,STIPPLED CHAIN,FLAT,FLINT,4 1/2 IN...... 4.25
PRESSED GLASS,SAUCE,STIPPLED CHAIN,FLINT.................... 4.25
PRESSED GLASS,SAUCE,SUNBURST.............................. 3.50
PRESSED GLASS,SAUCE,TAPE MEASURE.......................... 4.00
PRESSED GLASS,SAUCE,TORPEDO,FLAT,3 1/2 IN................. 6.00
PRESSED GLASS,SAUCE,VIKING................................ 6.00
PRESSED GLASS,SHADE,GAS TYPE,OPALESCENT,RUFFLED TOP,
    5-IN.BOTTOM........................................... 9.00
PRESSED GLASS,SHADE,PETAL,GREEN OUTER,PINK INNER,WIRED,BRASS
    CHAIN................................................. 225.00
PRESSED GLASS,SHAKER,SALT,BANDED PORTLAND.................. 7.00
PRESSED GLASS,SHAKER,SALT,COLORADO,GREEN.................. 8.00
PRESSED GLASS,SHAKER,SALT,WHITE TO CLEAR,RIB,METAL TOP,
    TIFFIN, OHIO.......................................... 10.00
PRESSED GLASS,SHOE,DAISY & BUTTON,APPLE GREEN.............. 12.00
PRESSED GLASS,SHOE,ON SKATE,RED STAINING ON TOP PART,
    4 IN.HIGH............................................. 18.50
PRESSED GLASS,SLIPPER,FRENCH STYLE,CENTENNIAL,SIGNED,
    GILLINDER............................................. 18.00
PRESSED GLASS,SLIPPER,FROSTED,MARKED GILLINDER & SON,6 IN... 14.00
PRESSED GLASS,SLIPPER,SOUVENIR,CENTENNIAL 1876,CLEAR,SIGNED
    GILLINDER............................................. 20.00
PRESSED GLASS,SLIPPER,SOUVENIR,CENTENNIAL 1876,FROSTED,
    SIGNED GILLINDER...................................... 22.50
PRESSED GLASS,SPILL,BELLFLOWER,FLINT...................... 16.50
PRESSED GLASS,SPILL,DIAMOND,FLINT......................... 12.50
PRESSED GLASS,SPILL,HAMILTON,FLINT........................ 12.50
PRESSED GLASS,SPILL,HORN OF PLENTY,FLINT.................. 20.00
PRESSED GLASS,SPILL,THUMBPRINT............................ 17.00
PRESSED GLASS,SPOON HOLDER,HAMILTON,PEDESTAL FOOT,FLINT..... 10.00
PRESSED GLASS,SPOONER,AEGIS............................... 6.75
PRESSED GLASS,SPOONER,ARCHED LEAF,FLINT.................. 22.50
PRESSED GLASS,SPOONER,BASKET WEAVE,CLEAR................. 8.50
PRESSED GLASS,SPOONER,BEADED ACORN WITH LEAF BAND,FLINT..... 13.50
PRESSED GLASS,SPOONER,BEADED GRAPE MEDALLION.............. 8.50
PRESSED GLASS,SPOONER,BELLFLOWER,FLINT.................... 14.00
PRESSED GLASS,SPOONER,BEVEL DIAMOND,STAR................. 7.50
PRESSED GLASS,SPOONER,BROKEN COLUMN....................... 11.00
PRESSED GLASS,SPOONER,BRYCE............................... 7.00
PRESSED GLASS,SPOONER,BUCKLE WITH STAR................... 10.00
PRESSED GLASS,SPOONER,BUDDED IVY PATTERN................. 10.00
PRESSED GLASS,SPOONER,BUTTON & PANEL...................... 7.50
PRESSED GLASS,SPOONER,BUTTON ARCHES,FLASHED RED,CLEAR BAND.. 20.00
PRESSED GLASS,SPOONER,BUTTON ARCHES,GOLD BAND............. 18.00
PRESSED GLASS,SPOONER,BUTTON ARCHES,RED-FLASHED TOP........ 16.00
PRESSED GLASS,SPOONER,COLORADO,GREEN..................... 45.00
PRESSED GLASS,SPOONER,CORDIAL............................ 14.00
PRESSED GLASS,SPOONER,CUPID AND VENUS.................... 11.50
PRESSED GLASS,SPOONER,DIAGONAL BAND,CLEAR............... 7.50
PRESSED GLASS,SPOONER,DIAMOND ROSETTES,FLINT............. 14.00
PRESSED GLASS,SPOONER,DOUBLE SPEAR....................... 7.00
PRESSED GLASS,SPOONER,ESTHER,GREEN....................... 45.00
PRESSED GLASS,SPOONER,ETCHED SEASHELL.................... 12.50
PRESSED GLASS,SPOONER,FEATHER............................ 10.00
PRESSED GLASS,SPOONER,GARFIELD DRAPE..................... 13.00
PRESSED GLASS,SPOONER,GIANT PRISM,FLINT.................. 10.00
PRESSED GLASS,SPOONER,GRAND.............................. 7.00
PRESSED GLASS,SPOONER,GRAND,SCALLOPED EDGE.............. 8.50

```
PRESSED GLASS,SPOONER,GRAPE FESTOON,STIPPLED LEAF...........         7.00
PRESSED GLASS,SPOONER,HAMILTON,FLINT................ 13.00 TO       15.00
PRESSED GLASS,SPOONER,HONEYCOMB,FLINT......................        12.50
PRESSED GLASS,SPOONER,HORN OF PLENTY.......................        15.00
PRESSED GLASS,SPOONER,LENS & STAR..........................         9.50
PRESSED GLASS,SPOONER,LINCOLN DRAPE,FLINT..................        22.00
PRESSED GLASS,SPOONER,LION.................................        18.00
PRESSED GLASS,SPOONER,MARSH FERN,FOOTED....................         9.00
PRESSED GLASS,SPOONER,ORIENTAL.............................        15.00
PRESSED GLASS,SPOONER,OVAL THUMBPRINT......................        14.00
PRESSED GLASS,SPOONER,PANEL ACORN BAND.....................         8.00
PRESSED GLASS,SPOONER,PINEAPPLE,RIBBED,FLINT...............        15.00
PRESSED GLASS,SPOONER,PLUME & BLOCK........................        11.00
PRESSED GLASS,SPOONER,PRISM ARC............................         7.00
PRESSED GLASS,SPOONER,RIBBON...............................        14.50
PRESSED GLASS,SPOONER,RIBBON CANDY,BRYCE...................         7.00
PRESSED GLASS,SPOONER,ROMEO................................         7.00
PRESSED GLASS,SPOONER,SHELL & JEWEL........................         9.50
PRESSED GLASS,SPOONER,STIPPLED IVY.........................         7.50
PRESSED GLASS,SPOONER,STIPPLED PANEL & BAND................         7.50
PRESSED GLASS,SPOONER,SUNKEN TEARDROP......................         5.00
PRESSED GLASS,SPOONER,TAPE MEASURE.........................         9.00
PRESSED GLASS,SPOONER,THUMBPRINT,STEM......................         8.00
PRESSED GLASS,SPOONER,TIC-TAC-TOE..........................         6.00
PRESSED GLASS,SPOONER,TORPEDO..............................         8.00
PRESSED GLASS,SPOONER,TRIPLE BAR,CABLE.....................         8.50
PRESSED GLASS,SPOONER,TULIP & SAWTOOTH,FLINT...............        14.50
PRESSED GLASS,SPOONER,TWO HANDLES,6 1/4 IN.................        10.00
PRESSED GLASS,SPOONER,UNITED STATES COIN...................        95.00
PRESSED GLASS,SPOONER,WESTWARD HO..........................        50.00
PRESSED GLASS,SPOONER,WHEAT & BARLEY.......................         8.00
PRESSED GLASS,SPOONER,WILDFLOWER,BLUE......................        14.75
PRESSED GLASS,STEIN,3/10 LITER,BUCKLE PATTERN,PEWTER LID,
   GLASS INSERT............................................        17.50
PRESSED GLASS,STEIN,1/2 LITER,SHIELD ON FRONT,PEWTER LID,
   CLEAR INSERT............................................        17.50
PRESSED GLASS,SUGAR & CREAMER,FROSTED,COIN.................        25.00
PRESSED GLASS,SUGAR & SPOONER,LOG CABIN....................        45.00
PRESSED GLASS,SUGAR,ALMOND,THUMBPRINT,OPEN,SCALLOPED RIM,
   PEDESTAL,FLINT..........................................        22.50
PRESSED GLASS,SUGAR,ANTHEMION,COVER........................        16.50
PRESSED GLASS,SUGAR,ASHBURTON,COVER........................        50.00
PRESSED GLASS,SUGAR,BEADED GRAPE MEDALLION,COVER...........        16.00
PRESSED GLASS,SUGAR,BELLFLOWER,DOUBLE VINE,COVER...........        54.00
PRESSED GLASS,SUGAR,BELLFLOWER,OPEN........................        20.00
PRESSED GLASS,SUGAR,BELLFLOWER,SINGLE VINE,COVER...........        52.50
PRESSED GLASS,SUGAR,BIRD & STRAWBERRY,COVER................        22.00
PRESSED GLASS,SUGAR,BLUE OPALESCENT EDGE,OPEN,LION'S LEG....       17.50
PRESSED GLASS,SUGAR,BUTTON ARCHES,FLASHED RED,CLEAR BAND,
   COVER...................................................        40.00
PRESSED GLASS,SUGAR,BUTTON ARCHES,GOLD BAND................        35.00
PRESSED GLASS,SUGAR,COVERED,STARFLOWER.............ILLUS..         18.00
PRESSED GLASS,SUGAR,DAISY & BUTTON,THREE-CORNERED,OPEN,CLEAR       12.00
PRESSED GLASS,SUGAR,DEER & PINE,CLEAR......................        16.50
```

PRESSED GLASS STARFLOWER SUGAR BOWL, COVERED

```
PRESSED GLASS,SUGAR,DIAMOND POINT,COVER......................    32.50
PRESSED GLASS,SUGAR,FANDANGO,OPEN.............................     6.00
PRESSED GLASS,SUGAR,HOBNAIL,BLUE,COVER........................    25.00
PRESSED GLASS,SUGAR,HONEYCOMB,OPEN,FLINT......................    12.00
PRESSED GLASS,SUGAR,INVERTED PALM,FLINT,OPEN..................    15.00
PRESSED GLASS,SUGAR,LOG CABIN,COVER...........................    75.00
PRESSED GLASS,SUGAR,PANELED THISTLE,COVER.....................    25.00
PRESSED GLASS,SUGAR,RIBBED PALM,FLINT.........................    20.00
PRESSED GLASS,SUGAR,RIBBED PALM,OPEN..........................    30.00
PRESSED GLASS,SUGAR,RIBBON,COVER..............................    29.00
PRESSED GLASS,SUGAR,THUMBPRINT,EMERALD GREEN,OPEN.............     7.50
PRESSED GLASS,SYRUP,ATLANTA,LION HEAD,CLEAR...................    36.00
PRESSED GLASS,SYRUP,CURRIER & IVES............................    25.00
PRESSED GLASS,SYRUP,DIAMOND & SUNBURST,PEWTER TOP & SHELL
  LIFTER......................................................    17.00
PRESSED GLASS,SYRUP,FAMOUS,GREEN,PEWTER TOP...................    28.50
PRESSED GLASS,SYRUP,LINCOLN DRAPE.............................    38.00
PRESSED GLASS,SYRUP,LION,PEWTER TOP,DATED JULY 16,'72........   150.00
PRESSED GLASS,SYRUP,PANELED,PEWTER TOP,DATED 1872.............    16.50
PRESSED GLASS,SYRUP,SPIRAL THREAD DESIGN,PANELS,BLOWN,RUSSIA     25.00
PRESSED GLASS,TOOTHPICK,BLUE,COLORADO,FOOTED..................    22.50
PRESSED GLASS,TOOTHPICK,BUTTON ARCHES,GOLD BAND..............     7.50
PRESSED GLASS,TOOTHPICK,BUTTON,ARCHES,RUBY TOP,STATE FAIR,
  1920........................................................     9.50
PRESSED GLASS,TOOTHPICK,COAL SCUTTLE,DAISY & BUTTON,BLUE....    27.50
PRESSED GLASS,TOOTHPICK,COLORADO,BLUE,GILT FEET & RIM........    15.00
PRESSED GLASS,TOOTHPICK,COLORADO,MARIE LOWRIE,GREEN..........    22.50
PRESSED GLASS,TOOTHPICK,DELAWARE,GREEN,GILT..................    30.00
PRESSED GLASS,TOOTHPICK,EMPRESS,DOUBLE ARCH,GREEN............    37.50
PRESSED GLASS,TOOTHPICK,ESTHER,GREEN..........................    40.00
PRESSED GLASS,TOOTHPICK,FORTH FOUR PATTERN,2 HANDLES.........     6.00
PRESSED GLASS,TOOTHPICK,GOLD RIM,THREE HANDLES...............     8.00
PRESSED GLASS,TOOTHPICK,KLONDIKE,FROSTED......................   145.00
PRESSED GLASS,TOOTHPICK,PRISCILLA.............................     9.50
PRESSED GLASS,TOOTHPICK,TEXAS.................................     9.50
PRESSED GLASS,TOOTHPICK,URN SHAPE,CLEAR.......................     4.00
PRESSED GLASS,TRAY,WATER,1000-EYE,CLEAR.......................    20.00
PRESSED GLASS,TRAY,BREAD,BASKET-WEAVE,GIVE US THIS DAY,BLUE.    35.00
PRESSED GLASS,TRAY,BREAD,BREAD IS THE STAFF OF LIFE.........    18.00
PRESSED GLASS,TRAY,BREAD,DEER,PINE TREE,8 X 13 IN...........    22.00
PRESSED GLASS,TRAY,BREAD,EGYPTIAN,CLEOPATRA,INSCRIBED WITH
  MOTTO.......................................................    16.00
PRESSED GLASS,TRAY,BREAD,GOOD LUCK,HORSESHOE,GIVE US THIS
  DAY,CLEAR...................................................    20.00
PRESSED GLASS,TRAY,BREAD,HISTORICAL,GRAND ARMY OF THE
  REPUBLIC,CLEAR..............................................    30.00
PRESSED GLASS,TRAY,BREAD,NELLIE BLY,RAISED PICTURE..........    25.00
PRESSED GLASS,TRAY,BREAD,STAR,TWISTED ROPE RIM,HANDLES,GIVE
  US THIS DAY.................................................    16.00
PRESSED GLASS,TRAY,BREAD,UNITED STATES COIN GLASS,10 X 7 IN.   250.00
PRESSED GLASS,TRAY,CELERY,GREEN BEADED GRAPE,CALIFORNIA,
  10 3/4 IN...................................................    22.50
PRESSED GLASS,TRAY,CURRIER & IVES,BALKY MULE,9 1/2 IN.......    24.50
PRESSED GLASS,TRAY,CURRIER & IVES,MULE AT RAILROAD CROSSING,
  10 IN.ROUND.................................................    35.00
PRESSED GLASS,TRAY,CURRIER & IVES,RAILROAD SERIES,
  12 IN.ROUND.................................................    25.00
PRESSED GLASS,TRAY,DRAPERY,4 X 7 IN...........................     3.00
PRESSED GLASS,TRAY,DRESSER,HEART & THUMBPRINT,GOLD..........    10.00
PRESSED GLASS,TRAY,FAN,YELLOW,BAMBOO ORIENTAL DESIGN,6 IN...    15.00
PRESSED GLASS,TRAY,PIN,CABBAGE ROSE,HANDLES,10 1/2 X
  7 1/4 IN....................................................     8.50
PRESSED GLASS,TRAY,PIN,DELAWARE,GREEN,GOLD ON RIM,6 1/4 X
  3 1/4 IN....................................................    18.00
PRESSED GLASS,TRAY,WATER,BASKET WEAVE,CLEAR...................    15.00
PRESSED GLASS,TRAY,WATER,CURRIER & IVES,COTTAGE MOUNTAIN
  SCENE,AMBER.................................................    28.00
PRESSED GLASS,TRAY,WATER,FESTOON,10-IN.DIAMETER..............    15.00
PRESSED GLASS,TRAY,WATER,KYACK,10-IN.DIAMETER................    12.50
PRESSED GLASS,TRAY,WATER,PRIMROSE.............................    15.00
PRESSED GLASS,TUMBLER,1000-EYE,RAYED BASE,CLEAR,FLINT.......    15.00
PRESSED GLASS,TUMBLER,BEADED CIRCLE...........................    15.00
PRESSED GLASS,TUMBLER,BELLFLOWER,RAYED TO TOP................    37.50
PRESSED GLASS,TUMBLER,BELTED WORCESTER,POLISHED PONTIL,
  FOOTED......................................................    18.00
PRESSED GLASS,TUMBLER,BLUE,DAISY & BUTTON.....................    10.00
PRESSED GLASS,TUMBLER,BULL'S-EYE,FAN..........................    10.00
PRESSED GLASS,TUMBLER,COLORADO,GREEN,GOLD.....................    14.00
PRESSED GLASS,TUMBLER,DELAWARE,CLEAR..........................     8.50
PRESSED GLASS,TUMBLER,DELAWARE,CRANBERRY,GOLD................    18.00
PRESSED GLASS,TUMBLER,DELAWARE,GREEN..........................    15.00
```

```
PRESSED GLASS,TUMBLER,DELAWARE,GREEN WITH GOLD..............   15.00
PRESSED GLASS,TUMBLER,EUREKA,FOOTED.......................    8.00
PRESSED GLASS,TUMBLER,FLUTE,FLINT.........................    9.00
PRESSED GLASS,TUMBLER,HOBNAIL.............................    6.00
PRESSED GLASS,TUMBLER,HORN OF PLENTY......................   45.00
PRESSED GLASS,TUMBLER,HORN OF PLENTY,FLINT................   45.00
PRESSED GLASS,TUMBLER,IRIS,HERRINGBONE,FOOTED,6 1/2 IN.,SET
  OF 6.....................................................   18.00
PRESSED GLASS,TUMBLER,LAUREL WREATH,5 IN.TALL.............    5.00
PRESSED GLASS,TUMBLER,LEAF & DART,FOOTED..................   10.00
PRESSED GLASS,TUMBLER,PAVONIA,NO ETCHING..................    5.00
PRESSED GLASS,TUMBLER,ROYAL IVY,CLEAR TO FROSTED..........   12.50
PRESSED GLASS,TUMBLER,SHELL & JEWEL.......................    5.00
PRESSED GLASS,TUMBLER,SOUVENIR,ST.LOUIS EXPOSITION,1904,
  BUILDINGS................................................   16.00
PRESSED GLASS,TUMBLER,STIPPLED DAISY......................   10.00
PRESSED GLASS,TUMBLER,TOKYO...............................   10.00
PRESSED GLASS,TUMBLER,TONG................................   12.50
PRESSED GLASS,VASE,CAR,WOODPECKER,GREEN...................   12.00
PRESSED GLASS,VASE,CELERY,BASE BAND OF FROSTED CROUCHING
  LIONS,CLEAR TOP..........................................   28.00
PRESSED GLASS,VASE,CELERY,FINE CUT & FAN,GREEN ONION VASE,
  6 X 3 IN.................................................   18.50
PRESSED GLASS,VASE,CELERY,MASCOTTE,CLEAR,8 IN.HIGH........   29.50
PRESSED GLASS,VASE,CELERY,PINEAPPLE & FAN.................   17.50
PRESSED GLASS,VASE,CELERY,RIBBED OPAL.....................   25.00
PRESSED GLASS,VASE,CELERY,U.S.COIN GLASS,FROSTED QUARTERS...  160.00
PRESSED GLASS,VASE,CORNUCOPIA,HANGS,12 IN.LONG............   16.50
PRESSED GLASS,VASE,HOBNAIL,FLARED TOP,OPEN PONTIL,CIRCULAR
  FOOT,7 IN................................................   35.00
PRESSED GLASS,VASE,IMPERIAL JEWEL,PEARL,IRIDESCENT,GERMAN
  CROSS MARK...............................................   47.50
PRESSED GLASS,VASE,PANELED THISTLE,V SHAPE,RUFFLED RIM,
  8 1/2 IN.TALL............................................   18.00
PRESSED GLASS,VASE,PANELED THISTLE,9 1/2 IN.TALL..........   18.50
PRESSED GLASS,VASE,PLAIN & PRISM PANELS,6 1/2 IN..........    5.00
PRESSED GLASS,VASE,SNAIL,11 1/2 IN.HIGH...................   12.00
PRESSED GLASS,VASE,THISTLE,VARIANT,9 IN...................   14.50
PRESSED GLASS,VASE,TULIP,STERLING OVERLAY,5 IN.TALL.......   21.00
PRESSED GLASS,VASE,ZIPPER RIB,FOOTED,10 1/4 IN.TALL.......    8.00
PRESSED GLASS,VASE,ZIPPER RIB,FOOTED,7 1/4 IN.TALL........    5.00
PRESSED GLASS,VINEGAR,CUT NECK,DIAMOND POINT STOPPER,FLINT..  22.50
PRESSED GLASS,WASHBOARD,THE MIDGET WASHER.................    8.00
PRESSED GLASS,WATER SET,RISING SUN,SIX PIECE..............   67.50
PRESSED GLASS,WHISKEY TASTER,SMOCKING,2 1/2 IN.HIGH.......   22.50
PRESSED GLASS,WHISKEY TASTER,PANELS,FLINT.................   15.00
PRESSED GLASS,WINE,BARLEY.................................   12.50
PRESSED GLASS,WINE,BLEEDING HEART.........................   12.50
PRESSED GLASS,WINE,BUCKLE,FLINT...........................   10.00
PRESSED GLASS,WINE,BULL'S-EYE.............................    8.50
PRESSED GLASS,WINE,CHAIN..................................    8.50
PRESSED GLASS,WINE,CUT LOG................................    9.00
PRESSED GLASS,WINE,DIAGONAL BAND & FAN....................    7.00
PRESSED GLASS,WINE,DIAMOND HORSESHOE......................    8.50
PRESSED GLASS,WINE,FLUTE,GROUND PONTIL....................    6.00
PRESSED GLASS,WINE,SENECA LOOP,FLINT......................   15.00
PRESSED GLASS,WINE,SEXTON FLUTE,KNOB STEM,FLINT...........   18.00
PRESSED GLASS,WINE,SPEARHEAD..............................    8.50
PRESSED GLASS,WINE,STEM,HOBSTAR,SET OF SIX................   26.50
PRESSED GLASS,WINE,UMBILICATED SAWTOOTH,GROUND PONTIL.....   18.00
PRESSED GLASS,WINE,UMBILICATED SAWTOOTH,FLINT.............   16.00
PRESSED GLASS,WINE,WAFFLE,THUMBPRINT,GROUND PONTIL........   22.50
PRESSED GLASS,WINE,WAY COLONIAL...........................   22.50
  PRINT,SEE ALSO,CURRIER AND IVES,PICTURE
PRINT,ACTRESS,NORMA TALMADGE,FRAME,23 IN. X 29 IN.........   22.00
PRINT,ALBERT EMILE ARTIGUE,LADY WITH CAMELLIAS,11 1/4 X
  12 1/4 IN................................................   60.00
PRINT,ALPHONSE MARIA MUCHA,CREPUSCULE,1899,14 3/4 X 28 IN...  200.00
PRINT,ALPHONSE MARIA MUCHA,JOB,20 1/4 X 15 1/4 IN.........  325.00
PRINT,ALPHONSE MARIA MUCHA,LA PLUME.....................1,600.00
PRINT,ALPHONSE MARIA MUCHA,MONACO--MONTE CARLO......ILLUS.  325.00
PRINT,ALPHONSE MARIA MUCHA,PARIS 1900................ILLUS..  250.00
PRINT,ALPHONSE MARIA MUCHA,SARAH BERNHARDT,24 1/4 X 16 IN...  325.00
PRINT,ALPHONSE MARIA MUCHA,ZDENKA CERNY,30 3/8 X 41 IN......  200.00
PRINT,AMERICAN,NEW YORK HERALD,MARCH 1896,21 X 14 IN......   30.00
PRINT,ANDREW JOHNSON,FRAME,21 1/2 IN. X 7 IN..............    5.00
PRINT,AUDUBON,BAFFELHEAD DUCKS,AMERICAN WOODCOCK,FRAME,PAIR.  16.50
PRINT,BAILLIE,1845,T.W.DORR,GOVERNOR OF RHODE ISLAND 1842.  150.00
PRINT,BIRD,BLACK ENAMEL ON WOOD,FLOWERED FRAMES,OVAL,PAIR...  15.00
PRINT,BIRD,COLOR,ENGRAVED BY T.JASPER,1873,12 IN. X 15 IN...  10.00
PRINT,BLUE BOY,OLIVE-COLOR FRAME,15 IN X 20 IN............   10.00
```

PRINT, MONACO MONTE CARLO, MUCHA        PRINT, PARIS 1900, MUCHA

PRINT,BREAKING COVER,FULL CRY,MOLDED OAK FRAMES,23 X
29 1/4 IN.,PAIR..................................................... 120.00
PRINT,BUFFORD,LAST MOMENTS OF PRES.LINCOLN,1865,BLACK &
WHITE............................................................... 45.00
PRINT,CHROMO,CHILDREN,SHEEP,PASTURE,ORIGINAL BY B.F.REINHART 10.00
PRINT,CIVIL WAR BATTLES,BY KURZ & ALLISON,18 X 24 IN.,GROUP
OF 7................................................................ 500.00
PRINT,COLUMBIA EXPOSITION,1892,COLOR,GROUP OF 13............. 4.98
PRINT,COMING TO THE CALL,REMINGTON,1908W11 IN. X 16 IN...... 27.00
PRINT,COWBOY DREAM,11 IN. X 16 IN............................... 25.00
PRINT,DR.SYNTAX,BOUND TO TREE,ROBBED OF PROPERTY,1819,6 X
10 IN.,PAIR........................................................ 45.00
PRINT,DUDLEY HARDY,NAVY SMOKING TOBACCO,21 1/4 X 11 1/2 IN.. 40.00
PRINT,EDMOND AMAM-JEAN,PORTRAIT DE MLLE.MORENO,13 1/2 X
14 3/4 IN.......................................................... 225.00
PRINT,ELLIOT,CASSIN'S AUKLETS,ALEUTIAN SEABIRDS.............. 75.00
PRINT,ENGRAVING,SEPIA COLOR,CLASSICAL,BY BARTOLOZZI.......... 7.50
PRINT,FAIR AMERICANS,FRAME,HARRISON FISHER.................... 6.00
PRINT,FORES,SET OF 6,COLORED COACHING,RECOLLECTION
MEZZOTINTS......................................................... 600.00
PRINT,FRANKTUR,1839,HAND-COLORED,JOHN RITTER,READING,PA.,
FRAME.............................................................. 65.00
PRINT,FRANKTUR,1840,HAND-COLORED,A.& W.BLUMER,ALLENTOWN,PA.,
FRAME.............................................................. 65.00
PRINT,FRENCH,IMPRIMERIE CAMIS,LES PLUS GRANDES MACHINES DU
MONDE.............................................................. 70.00
PRINT,FROM FOAL TO FINISH,HORSE,JOSEPH PETRO,SERIES OF 6.... 150.00
PRINT,FRUIT,HAND-COLORED,1869,7 IN. X 6 IN.................... 1.50
PRINT,GEORGE CATLIN,DYING BUFFALO,1844,NORTH AMERICAN INDIAN
PORTFOLIO.......................................................... 150.00
PRINT,GEORGE REES,1880,EDWARD HANLAN OF TORONTO.............. 325.00
PRINT,GEORGES MEUNIER,LOIE FULLER,FOLIES BERGERES,44 3/4 X
32 1/4 IN.......................................................... 375.00
PRINT,GODEY,FROM GODEY MAGAZINE,3.............................. 5.00
PRINT,GODEY,LADIES,CHILDREN,FROM R.H.MACY & CO.,FRAME,13 X
9 1/2 IN........................................................... 10.00
PRINT,GODEY,THREE LADIES,TWO CHILDREN,FRAME,13 X 9 1/2 IN... 10.00
PRINT,HAASIS & LUBRECHT,1871,PARADE OF THE IRISH EXILES..... 150.00
PRINT,HASKELL & ALLEN,SCENE ON DELAWARE RIVER,FOLIO,COLOR... 48.00
PRINT,HIROSHIGE,AGEMATSU ON KISOKAIDO,TRAVELERS,COOLIE,
BRIDGE,SIGNED...................................................... 40.00
PRINT,HIROSHIGE,AKASAKA,KIRIBATA,VILLAGE,TREE-COVERED SLOPE,
RIVER,SIGNED....................................................... 70.00
PRINT,HIROSHIGE,AKIBA TEMPLE GARDEN,UKEJI,LAKE,TREES,MAN
SKETCHING.......................................................... 110.00
PRINT,HIROSHIGE,ASAKUSA,KINRYUSAN,SNOW SCENE AT ASAKUSA
TEMPLE,SIGNED...................................................... 50.00
PRINT,HIROSHIGE,ASHIDA ON KISOKAIDO,TRAVELERS,MOUNTAIN
LANDSCAPE,SIGNED................................................... 40.00
PRINT,HIROSHIGE,BIKUNI BRIDGE IN SNOW,VILLAGE,PEOPLE,SIGNED. 45.00

```
PRINT,HIROSHIGE,DAYBREAK AT THE YOSHIWARA GATES,SIGNED......      80.00
PRINT,HIROSHIGE,IZUMI FROM PROVINCES SERIES,TREES,FIGURES,
   TORII,SIGNED...................................................      70.00
PRINT,HIROSHIGE,KIBA,FUKAGAWA,SNOW SCENE ON THE RIVER,SIGNED      50.00
PRINT,HIROSHIGE,KOMAGATA TEMPLE,AZUMABASHI,CUCKOO FLYING,
   STORMY SKY...................................................      90.00
PRINT,HIROSHIGE,KYOBASHI,TAKEGASHI,RIVER,BRIDGES,PEOPLE,
   SIGNED......................................................     170.00
PRINT,HIROSHIGE,MAPLE OF MAMA,RIVER,FIELDS,MOUNTAINS,TREES,
   SIGNED......................................................     110.00
PRINT,HIROSHIGE,MASAKI,VILLAGE OF SEKIYA,WOODS OF SUIJIN,
   SIGNED......................................................      60.00
PRINT,HIROSHIGE,MATSUIDA ON KISOKAIDO,TRAVELERS,PACK HORSE,
   SIGNED......................................................      40.00
PRINT,HIROSHIGE,MEGURA,TAIKO-BASHI,BRIDGE,PEOPLE,MEGURO
   TEMPLE,SIGNED...............................................     110.00
PRINT,HIROSHIGE,MOTOYAMA FROM KISOKAIDO SERIES,FALLEN PINE,
   TWO WOODSMEN................................................      50.00
PRINT,HIROSHIGE,ODAI FROM KISOKAIDO SERIES,PILGRIMS,STREAM,
   MOUNTAIN....................................................      30.00
PRINT,HIROSHIGE,OMMAYAGASHI,SUMIDA RIVER,WOMEN,FERRY,HOUSES,
   SIGNED......................................................     140.00
PRINT,HIROSHIGE,OPEN TEAHOUSE,TRAVELERS RESTING..............      60.00
PRINT,HIROSHIGE,PLUM GARDEN,KAMEIDO,SIGNED..................     180.00
PRINT,HIROSHIGE,SANNO SHRINE AT NAGATA-NO-BABA,RED SEAL OF
   KIKAKUDO....................................................      30.00
PRINT,HIROSHIGE,SHOHEI-BASHI,KANDA RIVER,RAIN BEATING DOWN
   ON RIVER....................................................     150.00
PRINT,HIROSHIGE,SHUBINOMATSU,ASAKUSA RIVER,SIGNED...........     100.00
PRINT,HIROSHIGE,TAKASAKI FROM KISOKAIDO SERIES,BEGGARS,
   WAYFARERS,VILLAGE...........................................      50.00
PRINT,HIROSHIGE,YOSHIWARA ON TOKAIDO,MT.FUJI,MAN,HORSE......      70.00
PRINT,HIROSHIGE,YOSHIWARA,NIHON-ZUTSUMI,PEOPLE PROMENADING
   ON CAUSEWAY.................................................     110.00
PRINT,HIROSHIGE,YUI FROM THE UPRIGHT TOKAIDO SERIES,SEA,
   CLIFFS,TRAVELERS............................................      35.00
PRINT,HOKKEI,SQUARE SURIMONO,GIRL,ORNATE DRESS,SILVER CHERRY
   BLOSSOM.....................................................      40.00
PRINT,HOKUSAI STYLE,BADGER,INK & COLORS ON SILK,SIGNED
   HOKUSAI MANJI...............................................      10.00
PRINT,HOKUSAI,DRUM BRIDGE KAMAIDO POND,FRAMED,GLAZED........     150.00
PRINT,HOKUSAI,OBAN YOKO-E,COOPER CAULKING CASK.......ILLUS..     600.00
PRINT,HOKUSAI,OBAN YOKO-E,HOLLOW OF DEEP WAVE........ILLUS..1,650.00
PRINT,HOKUSAI,SHICHI-RI BEACH,SIGNED ZEN HOKUSAI I-ITSU
   HITSU.......................................................     125.00
PRINT,JOSEPH SATTLER,PAN,1895-6,13 X 10 IN..................     375.00
PRINT,KELLOGG,BATTLE OF ANTIETAM,FRAME......................      23.00
PRINT,KELLOGG,JOHN QUINCY ADAMS,1844,12 1/4 X 16 3/4 IN.....      25.00
PRINT,KELLOGG,SILHOUETTE OF JOHN CALHOUN,BY W.R.BROWN,FRAME.      35.00
PRINT,KUNISADA,SPRING,JAPAN,9 X 14 IN.......................      10.00
PRINT,KURZ & ALLISON,MISSOURI STATE GUARD VS.U.S.ARMY,1893..      75.00
```

PRINT, COOPER CAULKING, HOKUSAI

PRINT, HOLLOW OF DEEP WAVE, HOKUSAI

PRINT,LEBLOND,MAY DAY,FOLIO,COLOR........................ 28.00
PRINT,LES MODES,PARISIENNES,AT HOME,BY ILLMAN BROS.,1885,
  FRAME.................................................. 9.00
PRINT,LES MODES PARISIENNES,PASTELS,FROM LADY'S FRIEND,FRAME 8.00
PRINT,LEWIS,MEDIZINFLASCHENDORF,NEAR ST.PAUL............. 75.00
PRINT,LINCOLN FAMILY,OVAL,WALNUT FRAME,MOORE & ANNIN,11 X
  9 IN.................................................. 18.00
PRINT,LINDBERGH,SPIRIT OF ST.LOUIS,SIGNED HARPER,22 X
  17 1/2 IN............................................. 10.00
PRINT,LOIE FULLER AUX FOLLIES BERGERES,25 1/4 X 21 1/2 IN... 60.00
PRINT,LOUIS J.RHEAD,LUNBORG'S PERFUMES,17 X 11 1/4 IN....... 250.00
PRINT,MANUEL ORAZI,THEATRE DE LOIE FULLER,EXPOSITION
  UNIVERSELLE........................................... 950.00
PRINT,MARC-AUGUSTE BASTARD,BIERES DE LA MEUSE,29 3/4 X
  20 IN................................................. 90.00
PRINT,MORI SOSEN,MONKEY,SEATED,MOON,SIGNED & SEALED,INK ON
  PAPER,JAPAN........................................... 45.00
PRINT,NAPOLEON,BUST PORTRAIT,COLOR,FRAME,BOILLY,PINXIT
  LEVACHEZ,SCULPT....................................... 50.00
PRINT,NAPOLEON & FAMILY,DRESSED FOR CORONATION,25 X 15 IN... 45.00
PRINT,NEWFOUNDLAND DOG,MAT,14 1/2 X 15 IN............... 10.00
PRINT,NUTTING,ALL SUNSHINE,FRAME....................... 15.00
PRINT,NUTTING,COMING OUT OF ROSA,FRAME 19 X 16 IN....... 14.00
PRINT,NUTTING,FLOMERY PATH,FRAME....................... 8.00
PRINT,NUTTING,GRACE,FRAME.............................. 12.00
PRINT,NUTTING,HONEYMOON DRIVE.......................... 5.00
PRINT,NUTTING,INTERIOR,A BIT OF SEWING,FRAME,15 IN. X 13 IN. 25.00
PRINT,NUTTING,INTERIOR,DAINTY CHINA,FRAME,11 IN. X 18 IN.... 25.00
PRINT,NUTTING,NEIGHBORLY COTTAGES,FRAME................ 10.00
PRINT,NUTTING,OLD TYME FRIENDS,FRAME,14 IN. X 17 IN..... 12.00
PRINT,NUTTING,OUTDOOR SCENE,SIGNED,FRAME............... 6.50
PRINT,NUTTING,SCENIC,GRACE,FRAME,11 IN. X 16 IN........ 10.00
PRINT,NUTTING,SCENIC,NETHERCOTE,FRAME,18 IN. X 22 IN.... 16.00
PRINT,NUTTING,SCENIC,SLACK WATER,FRAME,18 IN. X 14 IN...... 12.00
PRINT,NUTTING,THE SALLYING OF SALLY,FRAME.............. 10.00
PRINT,PAL,RUDGE,54 3/4 X 39 3/4 IN..................... 200.00
PRINT,PETERSON,FROM PETERSON MAGAZINE,3................ 5.00
PRINT,PIERRE MASSEAU,EXACTITUDE-ETAT,38 X 23 1/4 IN.,1932... 90.00
PRINT,PRESIDENTS OF THE U.S.FROM 1789-1850,WATERCOLOR,FRAME. 18.00
PRINT,PRIVAT LIDEMONT,BISCUITS & CHOCOLAT DELACRE,1896,18 X
  26 1/2 IN............................................. 60.00
PRINT,PROVIDENCE FROM PROSPECT TERRACE,1877,HAND-COLORED.... 75.00
PRINT,REMINGTON,HIS FIRST LESSON,1908,11 IN. X 16 IN....... 27.00
PRINT,REMINGTON,INDIAN SCENE,BLACK & WHITE,17IN. X 26IN.,
  FRAMED................................................ 120.00
PRINT,REMINGTON,THE CAPTIVE,BLACK & WHITE,FRAMED,15IN. X
  26 1/2 IN............................................. 150.00
PRINT,REMINGTON,THE EMIGRANTS,WAGON TRAIN UNDER ATTACK...... 30.00
PRINT,REMINGTON,THE FIGHT FOR THE WATER HOLE,1908,11 X
  16 IN................................................. 27.00
PRINT,SQUAW TRAVOIS,CHAS.M.RUSSELL,FRAME,13 X 16 IN........ 27.00
PRINT,SURPRISE ATTACK,CHAS.M.RUSSELL,SIGNED,FRAME,13 X
  16 IN................................................. 9.00
PRINT,SWEET PEAS,GREEN VASE,P.SCHWEINISKI,FRAME,
  9 1/4 IN.SQUARE....................................... 9.00
PRINT,T.ROOSEVELT,PERSONAL AUTOGRAPH,FRAME,18 X 24 IN....... 35.00
PRINT,THE PEOPLE OF DICKENS,BY CHARLES D.GIBSON,1896,12 X
  16 IN................................................. 7.50
PRINT,THE SCOUT,DATED 1909,SIGNED C.M.RUSSEL,FRAME,24 X
  36 IN................................................. 150.00
PRINT,THEODORE ROOSEVELT,DATED 1904,FRAME,7 IN. X 9 IN...... 6.00
PRINT,TOYOKUNI,UTAGAWA I,OBAN,SHOKI,ONI,CARMINE,GREEN,
  YELLOW,SIGNED......................................... 130.00
PRINT,TREASURE PRINCESS,EGGLESTON,CALENDAR,1931,22 X 48 IN. 3.00
PRINT,TWO LADIES,TWO GENTS,MODES DE PARIS,1847,FRAME,PAIR... 15.00
PRINT,UNION PACIFIC RAILROAD,TO THE GOLD FIELDS OF THE BLACK
  HILLS................................................. 285.00
PRINT,UTAMARO,UNHAPPY ONE,SIGNED.................ILLUS..1,050.00
PRINT,WATERCOLOR,RISCHA COOLIE,7 IN. X 9 1/2 IN......... 15.00
PRINT,WHIRLING LOGS,SYMBOLIZES GREAT SPIRIT AND FORMS OF
  PLANT LIFE............................................ 550.00
PRINT,WILL BRADLEY,HARPERS BAZAR,THANKSGIVING 1895,14 X
  9 1/4 IN.............................................. 60.00
PURPLE SLAG,SEE SLAG

QUARTZ,BOTTLE,SNUFF,FLAT FLASK,ROUND SHOULDERS,BLOSSOMS,
  LEAFAGE,CARVED........................................ 60.00
QUARTZ,FIGURINE,ELEPHANT,GREEN,8 IN.HIGH,7 IN.FRONT TO BACK. 125.00
QUARTZ,FIGURINE,ORIENTAL LADY,CARVED,ROSE,TEAKWOOD BASE,
  10 IN................................................. 125.00
QUARTZ,GREEN,INCENSE BURNER,COVERED TRIPOD,6 1/2 IN. HIGH... 350.00

JAPANESE PRINT, UTAMARO, UNHAPPY ONE

```
QUARTZ,ROSE,FIGURE,PUTAI,3 3/4 IN. HIGH,GOD OF HAPPINESS,
  WOOD STAND.............................................    60.00
QUARTZ,ROSE,FIGURINE,ELEPHANT,TRUNK UP,CARVED,4 1/2 X
  4 IN.TALL.............................................    110.00
QUARTZ,ROSE,FIGURINE,KUAN YIN,HOLDS LOTUS BLOSSOM,STAND,WITH
  ASHTRAY...............................................    50.00
QUARTZ,ROSE,GROUP,5 1/2 IN. HIGH,WOMAN,PEONY BRANCH,WOOD
  STAND.................................................    125.00
QUARTZ,ROSE,VASE,POMEGRANATE,12 1/4 IN. HIGH.............1,300.00
QUARTZ,VASE,GRAY WITH SOME GREEN,CARVED FLOWERS,BIRDS,TEAK
  STAND,7 IN............................................    39.50
QUARTZ,VASE,ROSE,DRAGON,BIRD,ROCKWORK,FRUIT,LEAFAGE,STAND,
  8 IN.HIGH.............................................    225.00


      QUEZAL GLASS WAS MADE FROM 1901 TO 1920 BY MARTIN BACH,
      SR. HE MADE IRIDESCENT GLASS OF THE SAME TYPE AS
      TIFFANY.
QUEZAL,BOTTLE,PERFUME,MELBA,GOLD,STOPPER,SIGNED Q,8 IN.TALL.  175.00
QUEZAL,BOTTLE,SCENT,IRIDESCENT GLASS,7 IN. LONG.............  100.00
QUEZAL,BOWL-VASE,IRIDESCENT GOLD COLOR,TURQUOISE LINING,
  RIBBED,2 1/8 IN.......................................    165.00
QUEZAL,BOWL,FINGER,GOLD IRIDESCENT,RIBBED,SIGNED,2 IN.HIGH,
  4-IN.DIAMETER.........................................    75.00
QUEZAL,BOWL,ROSE,GOLD,PURPLE & RED IRIDESCENT,FOOTED,SIGNED.  177.00
QUEZAL,BOWL,ROSE,GREENISH BRONZE IRIDESCENT,SCALLOPED
  COLLAR,TEARDROPS......................................    225.00
QUEZAL,DISH,NUT,BLUE,ROSE,LAVENDER HIGHLIGHTS,RIBBED,
  2 1/2-IN.DIAMETER.....................................    75.00
QUEZAL,LAMP BASE,ORANGE IRIDESCENT,PEACOCK DESIGN,SIGNED,
  13 IN.HIGH............................................    195.00
QUEZAL,LAMP SHADE,GOLD IRIDESCENT,RIBBED,SIGNED,5 1/2 X
  4 3/4 IN.HIGH.........................................    21.00
QUEZAL,LAMP,GOLD IRIDESCENT SHADE,TRIFOLIATE STEM,BRASS,
  14 1/2 IN.TALL........................................    70.00
QUEZAL,LAMP,HANGING,BYZANTINE SHADE,WHITE,FEATHER MOTIF,
  FIXTURES,SIGNED.......................................    345.00
QUEZAL,LAMP,HANGING,BYZANTINE SHAPE,FEATHER MOTIF,SIGNED....  285.00
QUEZAL,NIGHT LIGHT,GOLD IRIDESCENT SHADE,EMBOSSED BRASS
  BASE,9 3/4 IN.........................................    125.00
QUEZAL,NUT CUP,GOLD WITH BLUE IRIDESCENT,SIGNED............  125.00
QUEZAL,PARFAIT,FLORIFORM,GREEN PEACOCK FEATHERING ON WHITE,
  GOLD INTERIOR.........................................    275.00
QUEZAL,PLATE,IRIDESCENT COLORING,SIGNED,6 1/4-IN.DIAMETER...  65.00
QUEZAL,SALT DIP,RIBBED,GOLD IRIDESCENT,SIGNED,1 1/4 X
  2 1/2 IN..............................................    65.00
QUEZAL,SALT,MASTER,RIBBED,GOLD IRIDESCENT,SIGNED...........  80.00
QUEZAL,SHADE FOR HURRICANE LAMP,GOLD,WHITE FEATHER,SIGNED...  95.00
QUEZAL,SHADE,ALLOVER APPLIED AMBER VINES,LEAVES,GOLD LINING,
  PAIR..................................................    65.00
QUEZAL,SHADE,BLUE,SILVER,ALLOVER DESIGN,RIBBED,GOLD-LINED,
  7 IN.HIGH.............................................    75.00
```

| | |
|---|---:|
| QUEZAL,SHADE,CALCITE,FEATHERED,RUFFLED EDGE,5 1/2 IN. X 4 IN. | 55.00 |
| QUEZAL,SHADE,FEATHER & ZIPPER,SQUAT SHAPE,GOLD,CREAMY, 2 1/4-IN.OPENING. | 24.50 |
| QUEZAL,SHADE,FEATHER PATTERN,SIGNED,5 1/2 IN.TALL,PAIR. | 75.00 |
| QUEZAL,SHADE,GAS,BLUE LEAVES,SIGNED,5 IN. | 29.00 |
| QUEZAL,SHADE,GAS,BULBOUS BOTTOM TO 5 IN.FLARED TOP,THREADED GOLD,GREEN. | 45.00 |
| QUEZAL,SHADE,GAS,CHINESE MOTIF,GOLD CALCITE INTERIOR,SIGNED, PAIR. | 125.00 |
| QUEZAL,SHADE,GAS,RIBBED,GOLD IRIDESCENT,BELL SHAPE,SIGNED, 4 3/4 IN.HIGH. | 28.00 |
| QUEZAL,SHADE,GAS,WHITE,GOLD & GREEN FEATHER,GOLD CALCITE INTERIOR,6. | 180.00 |
| QUEZAL,SHADE,GAS,WHITE SATIN,CALCITE GOLD LINING,SIGNED. | 28.00 |
| QUEZAL,SHADE,GOLD,SQUARE SHAPE BASE,SIGNED. | 40.00 |
| QUEZAL,SHADE,GOLD AURENE,CALCITE,SIGNED. | 28.00 |
| QUEZAL,SHADE,GOLD IRIDESCENT,BELL SHAPE,4 1/2 IN.HIGH, 2 1/4-IN.BASE. | 23.00 |
| QUEZAL,SHADE,GOLD IRIDESCENT,FEATHER,CREAMY GROUND, 5 1/4 IN.TALL. | 25.00 |
| QUEZAL,SHADE,GOLD IRIDESCENT,SIGNED,5 IN.HIGH. | 40.00 |
| QUEZAL,SHADE,GOLD IRIDESCENT,SIGNED,5 1/4 IN.TALL. | 25.00 |
| QUEZAL,SHADE,GOLDEN IRIDESCENT,CROSS-HATCHED THREADS, BELL-SHAPE,5. | 225.00 |
| QUEZAL,SHADE,GREEN,WHITE,GOLD FEATHER DESIGN,3 1/4 IN.HIGH. | 55.00 |
| QUEZAL,SHADE,HALL,GOLD,IRIDESCENT,LOBE SHAPE,RIBBED,SIGNED, 3 1/8 IN. | 47.50 |
| QUEZAL,SHADE,IRIDESCENT GOLD,SIGNED,6 X 3 3/4 IN.TALL,PAIR. | 65.00 |
| QUEZAL,SHADE,IRIDESCENT PEARLY LUSTER,PANELED,GOLD INSIDE, BELL-SHAPED. | 32.50 |
| QUEZAL,SHADE,LILY,RIBBED,GOLD IRIDESCENT. | 65.00 |
| QUEZAL,SHADE,MUSTARD-GREEN OUTSIDE,BLUE-GREEN FEATHER DESIGN INSIDE. | 20.00 |
| QUEZAL,SHADE,OPALESCENT WHITE,6 1/4 IN. | 35.00 |
| QUEZAL,SHADE,OPALESCENT WHITE,GREEN,GOLD FEATHER,6 1/2 IN. | 30.00 |
| QUEZAL,SHADE,PEARL IRIDESCENT,GOLD LINING,RIBBED, 2 1/4-IN.OPENING. | 16.00 |
| QUEZAL,SHADE,RIBBED,COLORED DECOR,SIGNED,5 IN.HIGH. | 27.50 |
| QUEZAL,SHADE,RIBBED OPTIC,WHITE OPALESCENT,GOLD LINING, 5 IN.,SET OF 5. | 150.00 |
| QUEZAL,SHADE,RIBBED,SIGNED,6 IN.DEEP,4 1/2-IN.DIAMETER. | 38.00 |
| QUEZAL,SHADE,ROWS OF GOLD IRIDESCENT ZIPPERS,CREAMY,GOLD INTERIOR,SIGNED. | 35.00 |
| QUEZAL,SHADE,THREADED GOLD MOTHER-OF-PEARL,GREEN SPOTS OUT, GOLD INSIDE. | 25.00 |
| QUEZAL,SHADE,WHITE & GOLD,5 1/2 IN.,SET OF 4. | 100.00 |
| QUEZAL,SHADE,WHITE,LEAF DECOR,SPIDER WEB THREADING,GOLD COLOR INSIDE. | 33.00 |
| QUEZAL,SHADE,WHITE,RIBBED,BELL SHAPE,5 IN.HIGH. | 30.00 |
| QUEZAL,TAZZA,GREEN,PINK,GOLD,PURPLE,GOLD IRIDESCENT LINING, 6 IN.HIGH. | 345.00 |
| QUEZAL,VASE,ALLOVER GREEN PULLED DESIGN,STRETCHED GOLD TOP, 11 IN. | 750.00 |
| QUEZAL,VASE,BULBOUS,FEATHER PATTERN,WHITE,GREEN,GOLD,9 IN. | 400.00 |
| QUEZAL,VASE,FLOWER FORM,KING TUT TYPE DOME BASE,SILVER & GOLD DECOR. | 600.00 |
| QUEZAL,VASE,GOLD INTERIOR,WHITE CALCITE EXTERIOR,5 IN.HIGH, SIGNED. | 145.00 |
| QUEZAL,VASE,JACK-IN-THE-PULPIT,BUTTERCUP YELLOW,SIGNED, 9 1/2 IN.HIGH. | 255.00 |
| QUEZAL,VASE,JACK-IN-THE-PULPIT,GOLDEN ORANGE IRIDESCENT, SIGNED,6 IN. | 195.00 |
| QUEZAL,VASE,LILY,SIGNED,4 3/4 IN. | 145.00 |
| QUEZAL,VASE,SATIN GROUND,IRIDESCENT,OPAQUE SILVER-BLUE SWIRLS,7 IN.TALL. | 95.00 |
| QUEZAL,VASE,TRUMPET,FEATHERS,7 IN.HIGH. | 150.00 |
| QUEZAL,VASE,TRUMPET,GOLD WITH PURPLE HIGHLIGHTS. | 145.00 |
| QUILT,SEE LINEN | |

QUIMPER POTTERY WAS MADE IN FINISTERE,FRANCE,AFTER 1900. MOST OF THE PIECES FOUND TODAY WERE MADE DURING THE TWENTIETH CENTURY. A QUIMPER FACTORY HAS WORKED IN FRANCE SINCE THE EIGHTEENTH CENTURY.

| | |
|---|---:|
| QUIMPER,ASHTRAY,BRETON FIGURE IN CENTER,5 1/4-IN.DIAMETER. | 5.00 |
| QUIMPER,BOWL WITH SAUCER,SIGNED HENRIOT QUIMPER,FRANCE,6 IN. | 4.00 |
| QUIMPER,BOWL,PORRIDGE,PEASANT WOMAN,SCENE INSIDE,FLORAL OUTSIDE,SIGNED. | 26.00 |
| QUIMPER,BOWL,PORRIDGE,TWO HANDLES,WHITE. | 8.50 |
| QUIMPER,BUTTER PAT,MAN,WOMAN,TREE DECOR,SIGNED,SET OF 6. | 18.00 |

```
QUIMPER,COFFEEPOT,MELON RIB,SPATTER,SQUARE TOP,BLUE HANDLE,
   10 IN.....................................................   17.00
QUIMPER,HOLDER,FLOWER,BIRD,FLORAL,PILLAR CORNERS,
   6 7/8 IN.TALL.............................................   15.00
QUIMPER,HOLDER,SALT & PEPPER,SEATED FRENCH PEASANT FORMS
   HANDLE,FRANCE.............................................   22.00
QUIMPER,KNIFE REST,WOMAN,FLOWERS..............................   15.00
QUIMPER,KNIFE,FRUIT,KNIFE REST,BRIGHT COLORS,FIGURES,SIGNED.    7.50
QUIMPER,PITCHER,MILK,SIGNED,COVERED SUGAR BOWL...............   18.00
QUIMPER,PITCHER,STOUT WOMAN SHAPE,BLUE PINAFORE,WHITE HOOD..   20.00
QUIMPER,PITCHER,WATER,HENRIOT,8 IN.TALL,4 1/2-IN.OPENING....   22.50
QUIMPER,PLATE,MAN,WOMAN,'93,9 1/2-IN.DIAMETER,PAIR..........   20.00
QUIMPER,PLATE,PEASANT DECOR,YELLOW,BLUE,GREEN,ORANGE........    9.00
QUIMPER,PLATE,PORTRAIT,MAN,WOMAN,SIGNED,9 3/4-IN.DIAMETER,
   PAIR.....................................................   35.00
QUIMPER,PLATE,TULIP,PEASANT WOMAN,MARKED HENRI QUIMPER
   FRANCE,8 IN..............................................    8.50
QUIMPER,PORRINGER,PEASANT,TWO HANDLES,MARKED................    6.50
QUIMPER,PORRINGER,YELLOW GROUND,PEASANT FIGURE,SIGNED,FRANCE   10.00
QUIMPER,SALT,DOUBLE DUTCH SHOE,PEASANTS.....................   18.00
QUIMPER,SALT,DOUBLE,CENTER HANDLE...........................   12.00
QUIMPER,TEAPOT,TWO-CUP,YELLOW GROUND,PEASANT................   25.00
QUIMPER,TRAY,WHITE GROUND,MAN,WOMAN IN BLUE,ORANGE,
   3 SECTIONS,SIGNED........................................   30.00


RAILROAD,TRAY,BREAD,HERALD OF THE ROAD,ATLANTIC COASTLINE,
   SILVER PLATE.............................................   15.00
RAILROAD,TRAY,SERVING,OVAL,PULLMAN CO.,SILVER PLATE,9 IN....   10.00
REDWARE,BOWL,MILK,MOTTLED BROWN,GLAZED FINISH,TAPERED SIDES,
   9 IN.....................................................   16.00
REDWARE,CROCK,PENNSYLVANIA,5 3/4 IN. X 5 IN.HIGH............    7.50
REDWARE,JAR,SNUFF,GLOSSY BLACK GLAZE,8 1/4 IN.TALL,
   5 1/2-IN.DIAMETER........................................   12.50
REDWARE,JUG,GALLON..........................................   16.00
REDWARE,JUG,LEAD-GLAZED,7 1/2 IN.HIGH.......................   25.00
REDWARE,JUG,TWO GALLONS.....................................    5.00
REDWARE,LAMP,FAT,THREE SPOUTS,FRANCE........................   55.00
REDWARE,MOLD,PUDDING,SWIRL RIB,SPECKLED EXTERIOR,
   8-IN.DIAMETER............................................   18.00
REDWARE,MOLD,TURK'S HEAD....................................    9.00
REDWARE,PAN,MILK,12 1/2 IN. X 2 1/2 IN......................   38.00
REDWARE,PLATE,PIE,NEW ENGLAND,8 3/4-IN.DIAMETER,
   1 1/2 IN.HIGH............................................    3.50
REDWARE,POT,APPLE BUTTER....................................   10.00
REDWARE,POT,BARREL SHAPE,RUSTY BROWN GLAZE INSIDE & OUTSIDE,
   5 1/2 IN.................................................   12.50
REDWARE,POT,ROLLED RIM,SPECKLED INTERIOR,4 IN.TALL,
   4 1/4-IN.DIAMETER........................................   10.00
REDWARE,POT,UNGLAZED,BROWN GLAZED INTERIOR,HANDLE...........   15.00
RETABLO,JESUS WITH CROWN OF THORNS,10 IN. X 7 IN...........   20.00
RETABLO,PORTRAIT,MONK,18TH CENTURY,COPPER,16 3/4 IN. X
   12 1/2 IN................................................  240.00
RETABLO,SAGRADA FAMILIA,19TH CENTURY,TIN,11 1/2 IN. X 10 IN.   25.00
RETABLO,ST.JOSEPH WITH CHRIST CHILD,11 3/4 IN. X 10 IN......   30.00
RHINOCEROS HORN COUPE,4 1/4 IN. HIGH.......................  190.00


         RIDGWAY POTTERY HAS BEEN MADE IN THE STAFFORDSHIRE
         DISTRICT IN ENGLAND SINCE 1808 BY A SERIES OF COMPANIES
         WITH THE NAME RIDGWAY. THE TRANSFER DESIGN DINNER SETS
         ARE THE MOST WIDELY KNOWN PRODUCT. THEY ARE STILL BEING
         MADE.
RIDGWAY,COMPOTE,BLUE,FRILLED EDGES,WHITE GROUND,GOLD,FOOTED,
   OPAQUE...................................................  115.00
RIDGWAY,CREAMER & SUGAR,BLUE WILLOW,ORIENTAL,MARK...........    8.00
RIDGWAY,CREAMER,BLUE WILLOW.................................    9.00
RIDGWAY,CUP & SAUCER,BLUE,SCENIC,SCALLOPED RIM,HANDLELESS,
   ALADDIN,1846.............................................   15.00
RIDGWAY,DISH,CEREAL,BLUE WILLOW PATTERN,5 1/2-IN.DIAMETER,
   SET OF 7.................................................   22.00
RIDGWAY,DISH,CRESCENT MOON,WHITE ROSES,GREEN SPRAYS,GOLD,
   PAIR.....................................................    7.00
RIDGWAY,DISH,SAUCE,BLUE WILLOW,FLAT,4 1/4 IN.,SET OF 4.....   10.00
RIDGWAY,DISH,UNEVEN CURVED RIM,FLOW BLUE,ENGLAND,9 IN.SQUARE   18.50
RIDGWAY,EGG CUP,DOUBLE,OSBOURNE PATTERN,FLOW BLUE...........   10.00
RIDGWAY,MUG,BOAT SCENE,4 IN................................   12.50
RIDGWAY,MUG,CARAMEL,SILVER LUSTER,SCENES,SIGNED CD & W......   22.00
RIDGWAY,MUG,COACHING DAYS,SILVER LUSTER HANDLE & RIM........   19.50
RIDGWAY,MUG,COACHING DAYS,YELLOW,SILVER TRIM,4 1/4 IN.......   15.00
RIDGWAY,MUG,COACHING SCENE.................................   18.00
RIDGWAY,MUG,COACHING WAYS & DAYS,RACING THE MAIL,WINTER'S
```

| | |
|---|---:|
| DAY AMUSEMENT | 18.50 |
| RIDGWAY,MUG,WINTER DAY'S AMUSEMENT,RACING THE MAIL | 18.50 |
| RIDGWAY,PITCHER,RAISED PATTERN,BULRUSHES,GRAY,STONEWARE, 6 1/2 IN | 54.00 |
| RIDGWAY,PITCHER,RELIEF SCENES FROM POEM TAM O'SHANTER,1835, STONEWARE | 40.00 |
| RIDGWAY,PITCHER,SCENES FROM ROBERT BURNS POEM, TAM-O'-SHANTER,STONEWARE | 44.00 |
| RIDGWAY,PITCHER,SCENES FROM TAM-O-SHANTER,OLIVE GREEN,SALT GLAZE | 45.00 |
| RIDGWAY,PITCHER,WATER,FLARES OUT TOWARD BASE,BAMBOO FORM HANDLE,7 IN | 15.00 |
| RIDGWAY,PLATE,BLUE WILLOW,ORIENTAL,MARK,10 IN | 8.00 |
| RIDGWAY,PLATE,BLUE WILLOW,5 3/4-IN.DIAMETER | 4.00 |
| RIDGWAY,PLATE,BROWN,COACHING WAYS & DAYS,WAITING FOR THE STAGECOACH | 15.00 |
| RIDGWAY,PLATE,CAKE,BROWN | 10.00 |
| RIDGWAY,PLATE,CITY HALL,N.Y.,DARK BLUE,10 IN | 85.00 |
| RIDGWAY,PLATE,COACHING DAYS | 8.50 |
| RIDGWAY,PLATE,COACHING DAYS & WAYS,CARAMEL,SILVER LUSTER, 10 IN | 19.00 |
| RIDGWAY,PLATE,COACHING DAYS & WAYS,HENRY VII SCENE,CARAMEL, SILVER | 15.00 |
| RIDGWAY,PLATE,COACHING DAYS & WAYS,ST.MARY'S BUTTS AT READING,1887 | 22.50 |
| RIDGWAY,PLATE,DELAWARE,BLUE,DATED MARCH 17,1847,IRONSTONE, 9 1/2 IN | 15.00 |
| RIDGWAY,PLATE,ORIENTAL PATTERN,BLUE,WHITE,SCALLOPED, 9 1/2 IN.,SET OF 6 | 38.00 |
| RIDGWAY,PLATE,WOODLAND PATTERN,6 IN | 3.00 |
| RIDGWAY,PLATTER,ARLINGTON PATTERN,BROWN ON WHITE,15 3/4 X 11 3/4 IN | 12.50 |
| RIDGWAY,PLATTER,BLUE WILLOW,STAFFORDSHIRE,13 3/4 IN. X 10 1/2 IN | 15.00 |
| RIDGWAY,PLATTER,CAPITOL,WASHINGTON,WELL,TREE,20 1/2 IN. X 15 1/2 IN | 375.00 |
| RIDGWAY,PLATTER,WILLOWWARE,DEEP BLUE,MARKED,ENGLAND,17 1/4 X 14 1/4 IN | 15.00 |
| RIDGWAY,POT LID,COACHING DAYS & WAYS,THE VILLAGE CAGE AT LINGFIELD | 10.00 |
| RIDGWAY,POT,CHAMBER,COACHING DAYS & WAYS,THREE SCENES, CARAMEL,SILVER | 45.00 |
| RIDGWAY,POT,PEPPER,BLUE,STAFFORDSHIRE | 22.50 |
| RIDGWAY,SERVICE,DESSERT,CIRCA 1850,16 PIECES | 150.00 |
| RIDGWAY,SYRUP,SHAKESPEARE,SILVER SWIVEL LID,SCENES OVER CARAMEL & LUSTER | 19.00 |
| RIDGWAY,TUMBLER,SEASIDE,BROWN GLAZE | 9.00 |
| RIDGWAY,VASE,GARNITURE OF THREE,COVERED,19TH CENTURY, 4 PIECES | 350.00 |
| RIDGWAY,VASE,SUSPENSION BRIDGE SCENE,TAPERED,ROYAL VISTA WARE,7 1/2 IN | 19.50 |
| ROCK CRYSTAL,BOTTLE,SNUFF,CARVED IN RELIEF,BRANCHES,BIRD | 50.00 |
| ROCK CRYSTAL,FIGURINE,KUAN YIN,HOLDS SCROLL,WOODEN STAND | 100.00 |

ROCKINGHAM IN THE UNITED STATES IS A BROWN GLAZED
POTTERY WITH A TORTOISESHELL-LIKE GLAZE. IT WAS MADE
FROM 1840 TO 1900 BY MANY AMERICAN POTTERIES. THE
MOTTLE BROWN ROCKINGHAM WARES WERE FIRST MADE IN
ENGLAND AT THE ROCKINGHAM FACTORY. OTHER WARES WERE
ALSO MADE BY THE ENGLISH FIRM.

| | |
|---|---:|
| ROCKINGHAM,COFFEEPOT,10 IN.HIGH | 32.50 |
| ROCKINGHAM,CREAMER,COW,BLACK,GOLD LUSTER,4 3/4 IN. X 6 1/4 IN | 25.00 |
| ROCKINGHAM,CUSPIDOR,LADY'S,RAISED FLOWER DECOR | 25.00 |
| ROCKINGHAM,FLASK,RING,RAISED ACORNS,LEAVES,BERRIES,BROWN GLAZE | 45.00 |
| ROCKINGHAM,JAR,TOBACCO,HEAD OF MONK,CAP IS COVER,ENGLAND, 5 3/4 IN.TALL | 24.00 |
| ROCKINGHAM,PITCHER,HERON,CATTAILS,1850,ENGLAND | 87.50 |
| ROCKINGHAM,PITCHER,RAISED TULIPS,LEAVES,BULBOUS,WIDE LIP, 10 IN.HIGH | 45.00 |
| ROCKINGHAM,PLATE,PIE,LIGHT BROWN,9 3/8-IN.DIAMETER | 20.00 |
| ROCKINGHAM,TEAPOT,WHITE,ORANGE & GOLD TRIM,7 IN.HIGH | 62.50 |
| ROCKINGHAM,TOBY,THE SNUFF TAKER,ENGLAND | 65.00 |
| ROCKINGHAM,WINDOW STOP,LION HEAD | 39.00 |
| ROCKINGHAM TYPE,BED PAN | 15.00 |
| ROCKINGHAM TYPE,CUSPIDOR,PETAL DECOR | 15.00 |
| ROCKINGHAM TYPE,FLASK,RING,RAISED ACORNS,LEAVES,BERRIES, BROWN GLAZE | 45.00 |
| ROCKINGHAM TYPE,PITCHER,HUNTING SCENE | 35.00 |

ROCKINGHAM TYPE,SUGAR JAR,COVERED......................... 45.00
ROCKINGHAM TYPE,TEAPOT,CREAMER,SUGAR,WASTE BOWL,WHITE,GOLD
TRIM...................................................... 45.00

JOHN ROGERS STATUES WERE MADE FROM 1859 TO 1892. THE
ORIGINALS WERE BRONZE BUT THE THOUSANDS OF COPIES MADE
BY THE ROGERS FACTORY WERE OF PAINTED PLASTER. EIGHTY
DIFFERENT FIGURES WERE MADE.
ROGERS,STATUE,GOING FOR THE COWS.....................ILLUS.. 215.00

ROOKWOOD POTTERY WAS MADE IN CINCINNATI,OHIO,AFTER
1800. ALL OF THIS ART POTTERY IS MARKED,MOST WITH THE
FAMOUS FLAME MARK. THE R IS REVERSED AND PLACED BACK TO
BACK WITH THE LETTER P. FLAMES SURROUND THE LETTERS.
ROOKWOOD,ASHTRAY,BLACK BAT,WINGS FORM MATCH HOLDER,STRIKER,
1921...................................................... 60.00
ROOKWOOD,ASHTRAY,BLUE,CROW,ARTIST C.M.,NO.1139,YEAR 1922.... 40.00
ROOKWOOD,ASHTRAY,COMEDY-TRAGEDY MASK,BLUE,MATTE,DATED 1930.. 45.00

STATUE, GOING FOR THE COWS, ROGERS

ROOKWOOD,ASHTRAY,LARGE MOSS GREEN ROOK,GLOSSY FINISH,DATED
1949...................................................... 17.50
ROOKWOOD,ASHTRAY,ONE SIDE TURNED IN,RECLINING NUDE FOR
HANDLE,XLVI............................................... 10.00
ROOKWOOD,BASKET,PINK & GREEN MATTE GLAZE,1911,5 1/2 IN. X
6-IN.DIAMETER............................................. 23.00
ROOKWOOD,BOOKEND,GIRL SEATED ON BENCH,PINK TO GREEN-GRAY
MATTE,PAIR................................................ 38.00
ROOKWOOD,BOOKEND,PURPLE,YELLOW BOOK,PINK,GREEN FLORAL,BLACK
ROOK,PAIR................................................. 115.00
ROOKWOOD,BOOKEND,SCENE,SHIPS ON SEA,ARTIST WM.MC DONALD,
DATED 1926,PAIR........................................... 48.00
ROOKWOOD,BOOKEND,SHAPE OF POND LILY & BUDS,DULL FINISH,PAIR. 38.00
ROOKWOOD,BOWL,FLOWER,FROG,THREE HANDLES,BLUE MATTE,1920,
9-IN.DIAMETER............................................. 22.50
ROOKWOOD,BOWL,GREEN LEAVES,BROWN PINECONES,YELLOW GROUND,
XXIX,5 IN................................................. 75.00
ROOKWOOD,BOWL,GREEN,TAN,WHITE & FUCHSIA FLORAL,COSMOS
LEAVES,1886,10 IN......................................... 128.00
ROOKWOOD,BOWL,MARGARET MCDONALD,1927,MAGENTA
MORNING-GLORIES,PINK GROUND............................... 77.50
ROOKWOOD,BOWL,MOTTLED BROWN,RAISED TULIPS,1915,1 3/4 X
3 3/4-IN.DIAMETER......................................... 8.50
ROOKWOOD,BOWL,PINK SHADING,BEADING,1926,4 IN............... 19.50
ROOKWOOD,BOWL,ROSE,BLUE,YELLOW FLOWERS,MATTE GLAZE,H.E.W.,
1901,3 IN.TALL............................................ 65.00
ROOKWOOD,BOWL,ROSE,DEEP ROSE COLOR,XIX.................... 15.00
ROOKWOOD,BOWL,ROSE,TURQUOISE,RED & GREEN FLORAL BORDER,MATTE
GLAZE,1916................................................ 37.50

| | |
|---|---:|
| ROOKWOOD,BOX,PALE YELLOW,FLORAL MOTIF ON LID,COVER,DATED 1946 | 14.00 |
| ROOKWOOD,BOX,POWDER,FIVE PANELS,FINIAL ON COVER,HONEY AMBER, YEAR XXIII | 22.00 |
| ROOKWOOD,BOX,STAMP,FLORAL,SIGNED L.T.,1895,COVER | 80.00 |
| ROOKWOOD,CANDLEHOLDER,PINK,MARKED 1921,6 IN.HIGH,PAIR | 18.00 |
| ROOKWOOD,CANDLESTICK,BROWN,DATED XI,7 IN.HIGH | 45.00 |
| ROOKWOOD,CANDLESTICK,LOW,GREEN,SIGNED & DATED 1926,PAIR | 15.00 |
| ROOKWOOD,CANDLESTICK,PALE BLUE,1920,6 1/2 X 4 1/4 IN.ACROSS BASE,PAIR | 25.00 |
| ROOKWOOD,CANDLESTICK,ROSE COLOR & GREEN,1930,LOW,PAIR | 17.50 |
| ROOKWOOD,CANDLESTICK,SAUCER TYPE,HANDLE ATTACHED TO TOP & BASE,BLUE | 22.50 |
| ROOKWOOD,CANDLESTICK,YELLOW,BROWN,1921,4 IN.BASE, 1 1/2 IN.HIGH | 12.00 |
| ROOKWOOD,CHAMBER STICK,LIGHT BLUE MATTE,LILY PAD SHAPE, TWISTED HANDLE | 15.00 |
| ROOKWOOD,CHAMBER STICK,ROSE FECHHEIMER,1899,BROWN,BERRIES & LEAVES,3 IN. | 135.00 |
| ROOKWOOD,CREAMER & SUGAR,K.SHIRAYAMADANI,1893,FOOTED | 350.00 |
| ROOKWOOD,CREAMER & SUGAR,SHIRAYAMADANI,FOOTED,FORM NO.616, 1893 | 350.00 |
| ROOKWOOD,CREAMER,GREEN GROUND,VIOLETS,LEAVES,E.W.BRAIN,1898, 3 1/2 IN. | 125.00 |
| ROOKWOOD,CREAMER,VAN BRIGGLE,BROWN & OLIVE GLAZE,HOLLY LEAF DESIGN,1902 | 140.00 |
| ROOKWOOD,EWER,BROWN GLAZE,ORANGE NASTURTIUMS,SIGNED ELIZABETH BRAIN,1900 | 125.00 |
| ROOKWOOD,EWER,BROWN TONE,CHERRIES,HIGH GLAZE,LAURA LINDEMAN, 1900 | 195.00 |
| ROOKWOOD,EWER,LARGE CHERRIES,LEAVES,L.E.LINDSMAN,1900 | 165.00 |
| ROOKWOOD,EWER,ORANGE,BROWN,GREEN,GOOSEBERRIES,HOWARD ALTMAN, 1901 | 135.00 |
| ROOKWOOD,EWER,RUST COLOR FLORAL,ADELIZA D.SEHON,1898, 6 1/2 IN.HIGH | 149.00 |
| ROOKWOOD,EWER,UNDERGLAZE DECOR,YELLOW BLOSSOMS,HANDLES, SIGNED LNL,1896 | 115.00 |
| ROOKWOOD,FIGURINE,ELEPHANT,BLUE MATTE,BASE,1920, 5 1/2 IN.HIGH | 37.50 |
| ROOKWOOD,FIGURINE,RABBIT,FREE-STANDING,WHITE MATTE GLAZE, 1910,3 1/4 IN. | 37.50 |
| ROOKWOOD,FIGURINE,REBA,SMALL RABBIT | 7.50 |
| ROOKWOOD,FIGURINE,ST.FRANCIS,TAN,FLAME MARK & CZ, 11 1/2 IN.TALL | 25.00 |
| ROOKWOOD,FLOWER CONTAINER,GREEN SWANS IN RELIEF,1920, NO.2097 | 10.00 |
| ROOKWOOD,FONT,FIGURE OF ST.FRANCIS FORMS THE BACK,CLOTILDA ZANETTA,PAIR | 38.00 |
| ROOKWOOD,HOLY WATER FONT,3/4-IN.FIGURE OF ST.FRANCIS ABOVE, MARK CZ,9 IN. | 16.00 |
| ROOKWOOD,HUMIDOR,SIX-SIDED,COVERED MATCH BOX,TRAY,GREEN MATTE | 55.00 |
| ROOKWOOD,JAR,POTPOURRI,WHITE,EMBOSSED CLIPPER SHIPS,SEA GULLS,1944,PAIR | 75.00 |
| ROOKWOOD,JUG,LAURA A.FRY,FLOWER BLOSSOMS,DATED OCT.13,1883, 4 1/2 IN.TALL | 275.00 |
| ROOKWOOD,JUG,LAVENDER,PINK,FLYING BIRDS,CLOUDS,TREES, ARTIST-SIGNED,9 IN. | 45.00 |
| ROOKWOOD,JUG,LENORE ASBURY,STEMMED CHERRIES,LEAVES,BROWN GLAZE,1898 | 165.00 |
| ROOKWOOD,JUG,ORANGE-BROWN GROUND,YELLOW BERRIES,AMELIA SPRAGUE,1893 | 150.00 |
| ROOKWOOD,MUG,DEEP MOSS TO BROWN TO CINNAMON,RAISED P & STRIPES,1898 | 45.00 |
| ROOKWOOD,MUG,SIGNED ARTIST'S INITIALS ARV,6 IN.TALL, 3-IN.DIAMETER | 62.50 |
| ROOKWOOD,PITCHER,CLASSIC SHAPE,GREEK DESIGN,DATED 1882, 5 3/4 IN. | 275.00 |
| ROOKWOOD,PITCHER,CROCUS DECOR,ARTIST LEONA VAN BRIGGLE,1901, 5 1/2 IN. | 115.00 |
| ROOKWOOD,PITCHER,GREEN,OCHRE,UNDERGLAZE PAINTING,FLORAL,OLGA G.REED,1893 | 125.00 |
| ROOKWOOD,PLAQUE,LENORE ASBURY,1916,MOUNTAIN SCENE,LAKE,9 X 5 IN. | 375.00 |
| ROOKWOOD,PLATE,APPLE BLOSSOMS,SWIRL PATTERN,DATED 1887, 7-IN.DIAMETER | 95.00 |
| ROOKWOOD,STEIN,FLYING EAGLE,TAN GROUND,BEER BARREL, G.WIEDEMANN BREWING | 110.00 |
| ROOKWOOD,TEAPOT,BLUE,BUTTERFLY WING FINIAL,DATED XIX,CREAMER & SUGAR | 90.00 |
| ROOKWOOD,TEAPOT,CREAMER,SUGAR,WHITE,BLUE,VIKING SHIP DESIGN. | 75.00 |

ROOKWOOD,URN,GREEN,TWO HANDLES,DATED 1934................... 23.50
ROOKWOOD,VASE,16 FLAMES,3 1/2 IN.TALL....................... 21.00
ROOKWOOD,VASE,AMETHYST,RAISED DESIGN NEAR MOUTH,MATTE
 FINISH,1930................................................. 22.00
ROOKWOOD,VASE,ANNA MARIE VALENTIEN,POPPIES,BROWN GLAZE,1898,
 9 IN.HIGH.................................................. 160.00
ROOKWOOD,VASE,ARTIST ELIZABETH N.LINCOLN,1924,4 3/4 IN.TALL. 32.50
ROOKWOOD,VASE,AUTUMN LEAVES,HANDLES,BONSALL,1903,7 IN....... 90.00
ROOKWOOD,VASE,BASE FLARES THEN TAPERS TO NECK,6 IN.TALL..... 30.00
ROOKWOOD,VASE,BEIGE TO LEMON,GEOMETRIC BORDER,SIGNED,
 5 3/4 IN.................................................. 27.50
ROOKWOOD,VASE,BEIGE,MATTE,FOOTED,1926,3 1/2 IN.............. 12.50
ROOKWOOD,VASE,BLUE & BROWN MOTTLING,EMBOSSED CROW BAND ON
 BOTTOM,7 IN............................................... 18.00
ROOKWOOD,VASE,BLUE GLAZE,BLUEBIRDS,BLOSSOMING BRANCHES,DATED
 1917...................................................... 95.00
ROOKWOOD,VASE,BLUE GROUND,WHITE CROCUS,WILHELMINE REHM,1904,
 5 1/4 IN.................................................. 115.00
ROOKWOOD,VASE,BLUE TO GREEN,RED BERRIES,GREEN LEAVES,SALLIE
 E.COYNE,1927.............................................. 38.00
ROOKWOOD,VASE,BLUE VELLUM,ORANGE,PINK,BLUE BERRIES,L.ASBURY,
 1919...................................................... 55.00
ROOKWOOD,VASE,BLUE VELLUM,14 FLAMES,7 IN.TALL............... 19.00
ROOKWOOD,VASE,BLUE-GREEN,THREE HANDLES,1921,5 3/4 IN.HIGH... 35.00
ROOKWOOD,VASE,BLUE-GREEN GROUND,PINK WILD ROSES,1902,
 C.STEINLE................................................ 225.00
ROOKWOOD,VASE,BLUE-GREEN MOTTLED GROUND,WHITE GEOMETRIC,XXV
 2895...................................................... 47.50
ROOKWOOD,VASE,BLUE,LEAVES & RED BERRIES ON BORDER,LENORE
 ASBURY,ARTIST............................................. 35.00
ROOKWOOD,VASE,BLUE,PURPLE,FLOWER FIELD,MATTE,WILLIAM
 HENTSCHEL,1913............................................ 50.00
ROOKWOOD,VASE,BLUE,XXXVII,6 IN.............................. 12.00
ROOKWOOD,VASE,BROWN BLENDS,LNL INITIAL,1921,7 IN. TALL...... 8.50
ROOKWOOD,VASE,BROWN GLAZE,CHERRIES,FRANCIS VREELAND,1900,
 7 1/2 IN.HIGH............................................. 165.00
ROOKWOOD,VASE,BROWN GROUND,BLOSSOMS,LENORE ASBURY,1903,
 8 IN.TALL................................................. 135.00
ROOKWOOD,VASE,BROWN TO CARAMEL,TULIPS UP SIDE,INITIALS K.H.,
 1898...................................................... 135.00
ROOKWOOD,VASE,BROWN VELLUM,STRIPES,FLORAL,KATHERINE VAN
 HORNE,1916................................................ 69.00
ROOKWOOD,VASE,BROWN-GREEN,BLUE VIOLETS,ARTIST MARIE
 RAUCHFUSS,1897............................................ 135.00
ROOKWOOD,VASE,BROWN,AUTUMN LEAVES,SIGNED CLARA C.LINDEMAN,
 1900,7 IN.TALL............................................ 175.00
ROOKWOOD,VASE,BROWN,ORANGE TULIPS,LEAVES,TWO HANDLES,
 K.HICKMAN,1898............................................ 110.00
ROOKWOOD,VASE,BROWN,ORANGE,GREEN,NARCISSUS,ELIZA C.LAWRENCE,
 1900...................................................... 130.00
ROOKWOOD,VASE,BROWN,RAISED DECOR,1915,5 IN.................. 22.50
ROOKWOOD,VASE,CACTUS PLANTS,FLORAL,GREEN GLAZE,14 FLAMES,
 NO.687 AND O.............................................. 42.00
ROOKWOOD,VASE,CARAMEL COLOR,LEAVES,L.N.L.,1901,6 1/2 IN..... 125.00
ROOKWOOD,VASE,CARAMEL TO BROWN,YELLOW TULIP,SIGNED,1898..... 115.00
ROOKWOOD,VASE,CHARTREUSE,1945.............................. 9.00
ROOKWOOD,VASE,CORN-COLORED,1927,5 1/4 IN.HIGH,
 3 1/2 IN.ACROSS........................................... 15.00
ROOKWOOD,VASE,COYNE,VELLUM,SCENIC,TREES,LAKE,1920,
 7 1/2 IN.HIGH............................................. 175.00
ROOKWOOD,VASE,DARK BLUE,PINK & BLUE FLORAL,ARTIST LOUISE
 ABEL,8 1/2 IN............................................. 65.00
ROOKWOOD,VASE,DARK BLUE,SWAGS OF BLUE & GREEN DECOR,VELLUM,
 1914...................................................... 47.50
ROOKWOOD,VASE,DEEP BLUE,MATTE GLAZE,DATED 1935,4 IN......... 15.00
ROOKWOOD,VASE,DEEP ROSE & GREEN MATTE,EMBOSSED DESIGN,8 IN.. 24.00
ROOKWOOD,VASE,ELIZABETH N.LINCOLN,1919,RED,ALLOVER FLORAL,
 VELLUM,10 IN.............................................. 65.00
ROOKWOOD,VASE,EMBOSSED ABSTRACT LEAF PATTERN,BLUE TO
 TURQUOISE,9 IN............................................ 22.50
ROOKWOOD,VASE,EMBOSSED WITH DRAGON,FLIES,BLUE,GREEN MATTE
 FINISH.................................................... 12.50
ROOKWOOD,VASE,FIVE-SIDED,PINK,MARKED 1928,4 IN.............. 16.00
ROOKWOOD,VASE,GRAPE VINES & CLUSTERS,PURPLE TO BLUE GROUND,
 L.N.LINCOLN............................................... 145.00
ROOKWOOD,VASE,GREEN & PINK,CONE SHAPE,FLORAL,VELLUM,SIGNED
 XIII...................................................... 60.00
ROOKWOOD,VASE,GREEN DECOR,1910,8 IN.HIGH X 6 1/2-IN.DIAMETER 32.00
ROOKWOOD,VASE,GREEN GROUND,PRANCING DEER,BULBOUS,1932,
 4 3/4 IN.HIGH............................................. 24.50
ROOKWOOD,VASE,GREEN TO BURNT ORANGE,PINK DOGWOOD,

M.H.MCDONALD,1927.......................................    65.00
ROOKWOOD,VASE,GREEN,BLUE,PINK FLORAL,SIGNED S.E.C.,1912,
   VELLUM,6 1/2 IN..........................................    45.00
ROOKWOOD,VASE,GREEN,CALLA LILY SHAPE,DATED 1959,5 IN.TALL...    10.00
ROOKWOOD,VASE,GREEN,GREEK KEY-TYPE BORDER,TURNED-IN TOP,
   VELLUM,IX..............................................    20.00
ROOKWOOD,VASE,GREEN,INCISED FLORAL,PEAR SHAPE,MARY NOURSE,
   1904,10 IN.............................................    95.00
ROOKWOOD,VASE,HENNA FLOWERS,GREEN LEAVES,BOTTLE SHAPE,
   JEANNETTE SWING.........................................    85.00
ROOKWOOD,VASE,HOLLY LEAVES,BERRIES,OLIVE GREEN GROUND,SIGNED
   LVB,1903...............................................    97.00
ROOKWOOD,VASE,INCISED DESIGNS OF PEACOCK FEATHERS,SIGNED
   W.E.H.,8 IN.............................................    28.00
ROOKWOOD,VASE,JOSEPHINE ZETTEL,GRAY GROUND,ALLOVER CLOVER
   DECOR,1902.............................................   145.00
ROOKWOOD,VASE,LAVENDER,MARKED XXX,5 1/2 IN.TALL............    12.00
ROOKWOOD,VASE,LENORE ASBURY,BROWN TO GREEN TO ORANGE,
   LONG-STEMMED ROSES......................................   165.00
ROOKWOOD,VASE,LENORE ASBURY,SCENIC,VELLUM,BLUES,
   11 1/2 IN.TALL.........................................   265.00
ROOKWOOD,VASE,LEONA VAN BRIGGLE,BROWN TO ORANGE GROUND,
   DAISIES,1900...........................................   145.00
ROOKWOOD,VASE,LIGHT BLUE,TWO HANDLES,1940,4 1/2 IN.HIGH....    21.50
ROOKWOOD,VASE,MATTE GREEN,INCISED BORDER DESIGN,
   W.E.HENTSCHEL,1911......................................    35.00
ROOKWOOD,VASE,MATTE,BLUE,OCHER LEAF DECOR,DATED 1926,
   10 1/2 IN.HIGH.........................................    75.00
ROOKWOOD,VASE,METALLIC LUSTER GLAZE,FLORAL,1884,11 IN......    88.00
ROOKWOOD,VASE,MOLDED LILIES AT BASE,GREEN-GRAY MATTE,TRUMPET
   SHAPE,1915.............................................    18.00
ROOKWOOD,VASE,MOSS GREEN,FLORAL MOTIF ON EACH SIDE,DATED
   1952,4 IN.............................................    15.00
ROOKWOOD,VASE,MOTTLED GREEN GROUND,ROOKS,GEOMETRIC BAND,
   1912,6 1/2 IN..........................................    55.00
ROOKWOOD,VASE,MOTTLED SHADES,BLUE,BROWN,SIGNED REVERSE R&P,
   1887,10 IN.............................................    40.00
ROOKWOOD,VASE,MOTTLED YELLOW,GREEN,LEAFY DECOR,HANDLES,
   ARTIST E.BARRETT........................................    65.00
ROOKWOOD,VASE,MUSTARD GOLD,TAPERED,THREE HANDLES,DATED 1928,
   5 IN.................................................     9.50
ROOKWOOD,VASE,MUSTARD TO BROWN,YELLOW FLORAL,ARTIST EDITH
   R.FELTEN,1904..........................................   125.00
ROOKWOOD,VASE,OCHER TO BLUE-GREEN,BRANCHES,RED BERRIES,
   SIGNED L.N.L...........................................    60.00
ROOKWOOD,VASE,OLIVE GREEN,GLOSSY,RAISED MEXICAN FIGURES,
   DATED 1928.............................................    10.00
ROOKWOOD,VASE,OMBROSO,MATTE,BROWN,INCISED VINE,1922,
   3 3/4 IN.HIGH..........................................    48.00
ROOKWOOD,VASE,OMBROSO,SPLATTER,BROWN,GRAY,MATTE,GLOBE SHAPE,
   SIGNED LNL.............................................    42.00
ROOKWOOD,VASE,ORA KING,MAGENTA FLORAL,GREEN LEAFAGE,BLUE TO
   RUST GROUND............................................    45.00
ROOKWOOD,VASE,ORANGE POPPIES & BUDS,ARTIST LORINDA EPPLY,
   1905,5 3/4 IN..........................................    90.00
ROOKWOOD,VASE,PEAR SHAPE,PINK..............................    12.00
ROOKWOOD,VASE,PINK & GREEN MARBLE-LIKE DESIGN,MATTE FINISH,
   DATED 1920.............................................    18.00
ROOKWOOD,VASE,PINK & GREEN TOP,BIRDS IN PANELS,MATTE FINISH,
   7 1/2 IN...............................................    18.00
ROOKWOOD,VASE,PINK,BLUE,GREEN,POPPIES,KATARO SHIRAYAMADANI,
   7 1/2 IN...............................................   115.00
ROOKWOOD,VASE,PINK,GREEN,RIBBED,1932......................    24.00
ROOKWOOD,VASE,PINK,ROOKS & TREES,1929.....................    22.00
ROOKWOOD,VASE,RED-BROWN,RAISED DAISIES & LEAVES,14 FLAMES
   XXVI,6 IN..............................................    27.50
ROOKWOOD,VASE,ROBIN'S-EGG BLUE,BLACK SWIRL,ZIGZAG INDIAN
   DECOR,E.BARRETT........................................    55.00
ROOKWOOD,VASE,ROSE COLOR,URN SHAPE,MATTE FINISH,6 1/2 IN...    15.00
ROOKWOOD,VASE,ROUND COLUMNS,DRAPED MAIDENS,TAN,1930,9 IN...    30.00
ROOKWOOD,VASE,RUST TO RED,GREEN TREE DESIGN,1905,NO.907 &
   E.MARK................................................    22.50
ROOKWOOD,VASE,SCENIC,AUTUMN LANDSCAPE,BLUE & GRAY GROUND,
   EDWARD DIERS...........................................   225.00
ROOKWOOD,VASE,SCENIC,COUNTRYSIDE,LENORE ASBURY,1914,VELLUM,
   9 IN.HIGH..............................................   235.00
ROOKWOOD,VASE,SHADED BLUE,SEA HORSE DECOR,XXI,3 1/4 IN. X
   9 IN..................................................    18.50
ROOKWOOD,VASE,SHADED GREEN & BROWN,CROW DECOR,XII,3 IN. X
   5 IN..................................................    25.00
ROOKWOOD,VASE,SIGNED,W.E.HENTSCHEL,DATED 1914,6 IN.TALL....    35.00

| | |
|---|---|
| ROOKWOOD,VASE,TAN MATTE FINISH,BORDER OF WHITE SWANS, SQUATTY,1921............................................ | 15.00 |
| ROOKWOOD,VASE,THREE PANEL,EMBOSSED LEAF DESIGN,MOTTLED BLUE TO GREEN................................................ | 15.00 |
| ROOKWOOD,VASE,TURQUOISE,FLYING BIRDS,WHEAT,GLOSSY FINISH, SQUATTY,1944............................................ | 16.50 |
| ROOKWOOD,VASE,URN SHAPE,EMBOSSED DESIGN ON SIDES,DULL GLAZE. | 15.00 |
| ROOKWOOD,VASE,VELLUM,AQUA TO PINK GROUND,WILDFLOWERS, C.STEINLE,1911.......................................... | 90.00 |
| ROOKWOOD,VASE,VELLUM,FLORAL,GREEN INTERIOR,ARTIST-SIGNED, 1927,6 1/2 IN.............................................. | 89.00 |
| ROOKWOOD,VASE,VELLUM,PURPLE IRIS,GREEN GROUND,ARTIST LNL, 1921,10 IN.HIGH........................................... | 95.00 |
| ROOKWOOD,VASE,VELLUM,WHITE TO BLUE,DAISIES,MARGARET MC DONALD,7 IN.............................................. | 85.00 |
| ROOKWOOD,VASE,WHITE TO BLUE GROUND,BLUE IVES,BERRIES,SARA SAX 1899............................................... | 165.00 |
| ROOKWOOD,VASE,WIDE BLUE PETALS AROUND VASE,1919,3 IN.TALL, 4 IN.WIDE.............................................. | 12.50 |
| ROOKWOOD,VASE,YELLOW FLOWER DECOR,1895,3 IN.HIGH X 4 1/2-IN.DIAMETER....................................... | 125.00 |

ROSALINE GLASS IS A ROSE-COLORED JADE GLASS THAT WAS MADE BY THE STEUBEN GLASS WORKS IN CORNING,NEW YORK.

| | |
|---|---|
| ROSALINE,CUP & SAUCER,ALABASTER HANDLE.................. | 195.00 |
| ROSALINE,GOBLET,WATER,CIRCULAR ALABASTER BASE.............. | 135.00 |
| ROSALINE,PERFUME,BALLOON SIDES,STEEPLE TOP,SOME ALABASTER, 4 1/2 IN.TALL........................................... | 175.00 |
| ROSALINE,TAZZA,BALUSTER STEM,SIGNED STEVENS & WILLIAMS, 8 IN.ACROSS............................................. | 290.00 |

ROSE MEDALLION CHINA WAS MADE IN CHINA DURING THE NINETEENTH AND TWENTIETH CENTURIES. IT IS A DISTINCTIVE DESIGN PICTURING PEOPLE,FLOWERS,BIRDS,AND BUTTERFLIES. THEY ARE COLORED IN GREENS,PINKS,AND OTHER COLORS.

| | |
|---|---|
| ROSE MEDALLION,BOULLION CUP & SAUCER,COVER................. | 35.00 |
| ROSE MEDALLION,BOULLION,PEOPLE,BIRDS,PLUMS,ROSES,COVER...... | 17.50 |
| ROSE MEDALLION,BOWL,ALLOVER DECOR OF PEOPLE,ROSES,BIRDS, BUTTERFLIES............................................. | 65.00 |
| ROSE MEDALLION,BOWL,ENAMELED,PEOPLE,ROSES,BIRDS,BUTTERFLIES, CANTON................................................. | 25.00 |
| ROSE MEDALLION,BOWL,FRUIT,ROSE PANELS,COSTUME FIGURES,ROSE CENTER,10 IN............................................. | 62.50 |
| ROSE MEDALLION,BOWL,PUNCH,CABBAGE LEAF,13 1/2 IN............ | 295.00 |
| ROSE MEDALLION,BOWL,PUNCH,CANTON,14 1/2-IN.DIAMETER, 6 1/2 IN.DEEP........................................... | 350.00 |
| ROSE MEDALLION,BOWL,RICE,PANELS,6-IN.DIAMETER.............. | 24.00 |
| ROSE MEDALLION,BOWL,SCALLOPED,INSIDE & OUTSIDE DECOR, 8 1/2-IN.DIAMETER....................................... | 75.00 |
| ROSE MEDALLION,BOWL,SCENES,PEOPLE,BIRDS,FLORAL,BUTTERFLIES, 14 IN................................................. | 110.00 |
| ROSE MEDALLION,BOWL,SUGAR,GOLD KNOB LID,FOUR PANELS, 4 1/2 IN.HIGH........................................... | 40.00 |
| ROSE MEDALLION,BOWL,SUGAR,2 PANELS WITH PEOPLE,2 PANELS WITH ROSES................................................. | 25.00 |
| ROSE MEDALLION,BOWL,VERMILLION EDGE OUTLINED IN GOLD,NIPPON, 10 IN................................................. | 21.50 |
| ROSE MEDALLION,BOWL,11 IN. X 10 IN...................... | 75.00 |
| ROSE MEDALLION,BOWL,2 PANELS WITH PEOPLE,2 PANELS WITH ROSES,5 3/8 IN........................................... | 7.50 |
| ROSE MEDALLION,BOX,COVER,1 3/4-IN.DIAMETER,2 1/8 IN.TALL.... | 35.00 |
| ROSE MEDALLION,BOX,COVER,2 3/8-IN.DIAMETER,2 7/8 IN.TALL.... | 45.00 |
| ROSE MEDALLION,BOX,COVER,3 1/8-IN.DIAMETER,3 1/2 IN.TALL.... | 55.00 |
| ROSE MEDALLION,BOX,GILT PEACH & LEAVES FINIAL ON COVER,TRAY. | 72.50 |
| ROSE MEDALLION,CANNISTER,SIGNED,SET OF THREE,GRADUATED, 3 IN.,4 IN.,5 IN........................................ | 175.00 |
| ROSE MEDALLION,CHARGER,ENAMELED,PEOPLE,ROSES,BIRDS,CANTON, 16 IN................................................. | 125.00 |
| ROSE MEDALLION,CHARGER,18 1/4-IN.DIAMETER................. | 175.00 |
| ROSE MEDALLION,COMPOTE,ENAMELED,PEOPLE,ROSES,BIRDS, MEDALLION,CANTON....................................... | 40.00 |
| ROSE MEDALLION,CREAMER................................ | 35.00 |
| ROSE MEDALLION,CREAMER & SUGAR,COVER.................... | 90.00 |
| ROSE MEDALLION,CREAMER,FOOTED,3 1/4 IN.HIGH,3 1/8 IN.WIDE... | 26.00 |
| ROSE MEDALLION,CREAMER,HELMET,3 1/2 X 3 1/4 IN............. | 40.00 |
| ROSE MEDALLION,CREAMER,1 PANEL WITH PEOPLE,1 PANEL WITH ROSES................................................. | 25.00 |
| ROSE MEDALLION,CUP & SAUCER................... 12.50 TO | 15.00 |
| ROSE MEDALLION,CUP & SAUCER,BOUILLON,ENAMELED,PEOPLE,ROSES, | |

| | |
|---|---|
| BIRDS,CANTON.................................................. | 15.00 |
| ROSE MEDALLION,CUP & SAUCER,BUTTERFLIES,BIRDS,ROSES,FIGURES. | 20.00 |
| ROSE MEDALLION,CUP & SAUCER,DEMITASSE............... 18.00 TO | 22.00 |
| ROSE MEDALLION,CUP & SAUCER,DEMITASSE,ENAMELED,PEOPLE,ROSES, | |
| BIRDS,CANTON.................................................. | 10.00 |
| ROSE MEDALLION,CUP & SAUCER,DEMITASSE,HANDLE................. | 18.00 |
| ROSE MEDALLION,CUP & SAUCER,ENAMELED,PEOPLE,ROSES,BIRDS, | |
| MEDALLION,CANTON............................................. | 15.00 |
| ROSE MEDALLION,CUP & SAUCER,HEXAGONAL........................ | 25.00 |
| ROSE MEDALLION,CUP & SAUCER,MARKED CHINA..................... | 30.00 |
| ROSE MEDALLION,CUP & SAUCER,PANELED.......................... | 25.00 |
| ROSE MEDALLION,CUP & SAUCER,ROSES,BUTTERFLIES,CHINESE | |
| SYMBOLS,BIRDS................................................ | 15.00 |
| ROSE MEDALLION,CUP & SAUCER,THORN HANDLE..................... | 30.00 |
| ROSE MEDALLION,CUP & SAUCER,WISHBONE HANDLE.................. | 25.00 |
| ROSE MEDALLION,CUP,BOUILLON,COVER,SAUCER,MARKED CHINA....... | 27.50 |
| ROSE MEDALLION,CUP,DEMITASSE,1 PANEL WITH PEOPLE,1 PANEL | |
| WITH ROSES................................................... | 9.00 |
| ROSE MEDALLION,DISH,CANDY,IRREGULAR SHAPE,CLOSED HANDLE ON | |
| ONE SIDE..................................................... | 12.50 |
| ROSE MEDALLION,DISH,COVER,GOLD ACORN FINIAL,SIGNATURE,8 IN. | |
| X 10 IN...................................................... | 110.00 |
| ROSE MEDALLION,DISH,COVER,10 IN. X 8 IN...................... | 87.50 |
| ROSE MEDALLION,DISH,LEAF-SHAPED,8 1/4 IN..................... | 27.50 |
| ROSE MEDALLION,DISH,OVAL,9 7/8 X 7 7/8 X 1 1/2 | |
| IN.TALL.............................................. 35.00 TO | 85.00 |
| ROSE MEDALLION,DISH,SERVING,DECOR INSIDE & OUTSIDE,GILT, | |
| COVER........................................................ | 75.00 |
| ROSE MEDALLION,DISH,VEGETABLE,COVER,CANTON................... | 125.00 |
| ROSE MEDALLION,DISH,VEGETABLE,OPEN,HANDLED,7 1/2 X 5 3/4 IN. | 42.50 |
| ROSE MEDALLION,DISH,VEGETABLE,PANELS OF ROSES,SCENES, | |
| PEDESTAL BASE,COVER.......................................... | 31.50 |
| ROSE MEDALLION,DISH,VEGETABLE,9 IN.SQUARE.................... | 85.00 |
| ROSE MEDALLION,JAR,BRUSH,5 1/4-IN.HIGH,4 IN.DIAMETER......... | 85.00 |
| ROSE MEDALLION,JAR,POWDER,COVER,4-IN.DIAMETER,2 1/2 IN.HIGH. | 75.00 |
| ROSE MEDALLION,JAR,ROSE,WOODEN STAND,CIRCA 1820, | |
| 5 1/4 IN.TALL................................................ | 75.00 |
| ROSE MEDALLION,JARDINIERE,PAIR,STANDS,19TH CENTURY,8 3/4 IN. | |
| HIGH......................................................... | 425.00 |
| ROSE MEDALLION,LINER FOR MEAT DISH,OVAL SHAPE,12 X 14 IN.... | 110.00 |
| ROSE MEDALLION,MUG,CHINESE SCENE,ROSE FLORAL BAND,GOLD, | |
| HANDLE....................................................... | 59.00 |
| ROSE MEDALLION,MUG,LOWESTOFT-TYPE HANDLE,4 IN.HIGH, | |
| 3 1/2-IN.DIAMETER............................................ | 85.00 |
| ROSE MEDALLION,PITCHER,SCALLOPED RIM,5 1/2 IN................ | 85.00 |
| ROSE MEDALLION,PLAQUE,SCENICS,MEN,PARROT,URN,FLORAL,WOMEN, | |
| COURTYARD.................................................... | 65.00 |
| ROSE MEDALLION,PLAQUE,WARRIORS,HORSES,BANNERS,TEAK FRAME, | |
| 10 IN.HIGH................................................... | 80.00 |
| ROSE MEDALLION,PLATE,2 PANELS WITH PEOPLE,2 PANELS WITH | |
| ROSES,6 IN................................................... | 10.00 |
| ROSE MEDALLION,PLATE,2 PANELS WITH PEOPLE,2 PANELS WITH | |
| ROSES,8 1/2 IN............................................... | 15.00 |
| ROSE MEDALLION,PLATE,7 IN.................................... | 10.00 |
| ROSE MEDALLION,PLATE,7 1/2 IN................................ | 10.00 |
| ROSE MEDALLION,PLATE,8 IN........................... 10.00 TO | 18.00 |
| ROSE MEDALLION,PLATE,9 3/4-IN.DIAMETER....................... | 35.00 |
| ROSE MEDALLION,PLATE,10 IN................................... | 32.50 |
| ROSE MEDALLION,PLATE,12,FAMILLE ROSE,DINNER,19TH CENTURY, | |
| 9 3/4 IN..................................................... | 525.00 |
| ROSE MEDALLION,PLATE,ALLOVER ROSE DECOR,7 1/2-IN.DIAMETER... | 10.00 |
| ROSE MEDALLION,PLATE,BREAD,ENAMELED,PEOPLE,ROSES,BIRDS, | |
| MEDALLION,CANTON............................................. | 8.00 |
| ROSE MEDALLION,PLATE,CHOP,ROSES,BUTTERFLIES,BIRDS,CHINESE | |
| SYMBOLS...................................................... | 75.00 |
| ROSE MEDALLION,PLATE,CONCAVE,9 IN.SQUARE..................... | 59.50 |
| ROSE MEDALLION,PLATE,CUT CORNERS,MARKED MADE IN CHINA, | |
| 7 1/4 IN.SQUARE.............................................. | 15.00 |
| ROSE MEDALLION,PLATE,DEEP,21,FAMILLE ROSE,19TH CENTURY, | |
| 10-IN. DIAM.................................................. | 650.00 |
| ROSE MEDALLION,PLATE,DESSERT,ENAMELED,PEOPLE,ROSES, | |
| MEDALLIONS,CANTON............................................ | 12.00 |
| ROSE MEDALLION,PLATE,DESSERT,12,FAMILLE ROSE,19TH | |
| CENTURY.9-IN. DIAM........................................... | 325.00 |
| ROSE MEDALLION,PLATE,DESSERT,24,FAMILLE ROSE,19TH CENTURY... | 475.00 |
| ROSE MEDALLION,PLATE,DESSERT,24,FAMILLE ROSE, | |
| 8 1/2-IN.DIAMETER............................................ | 575.00 |
| ROSE MEDALLION,PLATE,DINNER,ENAMELED,PEOPLE,ROSES,BIRDS, | |
| PANELS,CANTON................................................ | 25.00 |
| ROSE MEDALLION,PLATE,DINNER,12,FAMILLE ROSE,19TH CENTURY.... | 700.00 |
| ROSE MEDALLION,PLATE,FAMILLE ROSE,19TH CENTURY,SET OF 24.... | 600.00 |

```
ROSE MEDALLION,PLATE,FLORAL,BIRDS,7 3/8 IN...................        13.00
ROSE MEDALLION,PLATE,LATTICE EDGE,8 1/2 IN...................        42.50
ROSE MEDALLION,PLATE,LUNCHEON,ENAMELED,PEOPLE,ROSES,BIRDS,
  CANTON...................................................          13.00
ROSE MEDALLION,PLATE,MARKED MADE IN CHINA,8 1/2 IN..........         12.00
ROSE MEDALLION,PLATE,MUTED COLORS,9 IN......................         22.50
ROSE MEDALLION,PLATE,ROSES,BUTTERFLIES,BIRDS,CHINESE
  SYMBOLS,6 IN.............................................          10.00
ROSE MEDALLION,PLATE,ROSES,BUTTERFLIES,BIRDS,CHINESE
  SYMBOLS,8 1/2 IN.........................................          12.50
ROSE MEDALLION,PLATE,ROSES,BUTTERFLIES,BIRDS,CHINESE
  SYMBOLS,9 1/2 IN.........................................          15.00
ROSE MEDALLION,PLATE,SERVING,ROUND,12-IN.DIAMETER...........         29.50
ROSE MEDALLION,PLATE,SOUP,MARKED,7 1/4 IN., SET OF 6........         85.00
ROSE MEDALLION,PLATE,SOUP,ROSES,BUTTERFLIES,BIRDS,CHINESE
  SYMBOLS.................................................           15.00
ROSE MEDALLION,PLATTER,ENAMELED,PEOPLE,FLORAL,CANTON,
  11 1/2 X 13 1/2 IN.......................................          60.00
ROSE MEDALLION,PLATTER,ENAMELED,PEOPLE,FLORAL,CANTON,
  13 1/2 X 18 IN...........................................         100.00
ROSE MEDALLION,PLATTER,ENAMELED,19TH CENTURY,16-IN. DIAM....        150.00
ROSE MEDALLION,PLATTER,GRAVY WELL,FOOTED,11 1/2 X 15 IN.....         80.00
ROSE MEDALLION,PLATTER,OVAL,12 1/2 X 8 3/4 IN...............         25.00
ROSE MEDALLION,PLATTER,OVAL,13 X 9 3/4 IN...................         64.50
ROSE MEDALLION,PLATTER,OVAL,15 IN.LONG......................        125.00
ROSE MEDALLION,PLATTER,OVAL,7 IN. X 9 IN....................         59.50
ROSE MEDALLION,PLATTER,PANELS,PEOPLE,FLOWERS,BIRDS,16 X
  13 1/2 IN...............................................           75.00
ROSE MEDALLION,PLATTER,13 IN. X 10 IN.......................         75.00
ROSE MEDALLION,PLATTER,13 1/2 IN. X 10 1/2 IN...............         75.00
ROSE MEDALLION,PLATTER,14 3/4 IN. X 11 3/4 IN...............         95.00
ROSE MEDALLION,POT,BRUSH,6 IN.HIGH..........................        110.00
ROSE MEDALLION,POT,BULB,PAIR,FAMILLE ROSE,19TH CENTURY......        800.00
ROSE MEDALLION,PUNCH BOWL,19TH CENTURY,23 1/4-IN. DIAM......      1,500.00
ROSE MEDALLION,PUNCH BOWL,19TH CENTURY,20 1/2-IN. DIAM......        800.00
ROSE MEDALLION,SEAT,GARDEN,PAIR,19TH CENTURY,18 1/2 IN. HIGH      3,000.00
ROSE MEDALLION,SHAKER,SALT & PEPPER,ROSES,BUTTERFLIES,BIRDS.         25.00
ROSE MEDALLION,SHAVING MUG...................................        50.00
ROSE MEDALLION,SPOON,RICE,ENAMELED,PEOPLE,ROSES,BIRDS,
  BUTTERFLIES,CANTON......................................            4.00
ROSE MEDALLION,SPOON,SOUP,SET OF 3..........................          9.00
ROSE MEDALLION,SWEETMEAT SET,TRAYLIKE DISHES IN LACQUERED
  BOX,5 PIECES............................................           95.00
ROSE MEDALLION,TEA SET,IN LINED WICKER CADDY,TWO TEACUPS....         85.00
ROSE MEDALLION,TEAPOT........................................        75.00
ROSE MEDALLION,TEAPOT,BERRY FINIAL,6 IN.HIGH................         100.00
ROSE MEDALLION,TEAPOT,CADDY.................................          70.00
ROSE MEDALLION,TEAPOT,CIRCA 1850,5 1/2 IN.HIGH..............         55.00
ROSE MEDALLION,TEAPOT,CREAMER,COVERED SUGAR,ENAMELED,PEOPLE,
  BIRDS,CANTON............................................           90.00
ROSE MEDALLION,TEAPOT,MARKED CHINA..........................         48.50
ROSE MEDALLION,TEAPOT,MINIATURE,3 1/2 IN.HIGH,5 3/4 IN.LONG.         31.00
ROSE MEDALLION,TEAPOT,MINIATURE,3 1/8 IN.HIGH...............         36.50
ROSE MEDALLION,TEAPOT,PANELS OF PEOPLE,ROSES,BIRDS,DOUBLE
  STRAW HANDLE............................................           45.00
ROSE MEDALLION,TEAPOT,ROSES,BUTTERFLIES,CHINESE SYMBOLS,
  CREAMER & SUGAR.........................................           95.00
ROSE MEDALLION,TEAPOT,TWISTED HANDLE,LID....................         95.00
ROSE MEDALLION,TEAPOT,5 1/2 IN.............................          40.00
ROSE MEDALLION,TRAY,PEONIES,PEOPLE,BUTTERFLIES,BIRDS,
  10 3/4 IN...............................................           77.50
ROSE MEDALLION,TRAY,TRIANGULAR SHAPE,ROUNDED CORNERS........        150.00
ROSE MEDALLION,TUREEN,BLACK BUTTERFLY,ROSE,COVER,
  11 1/2 IN.LONG,CANTON...................................          245.00
ROSE MEDALLION,TUREEN,2,COVERED,STANDS,CIRCA 1810....ILLUS..      2,500.00
ROSE MEDALLION,URN,16 IN.HIGH,9 1/2-IN.DIAMETER.............        200.00
ROSE MEDALLION,URN,BULBOUS,13 IN.HIGH,6 1/2 IN.ACROSS TOP...        150.00
ROSE MEDALLION,VASE,ALLOVER DECOR OF ROSES,SCENES, PEOPLE,
  HOME SCENE..............................................           65.00
ROSE MEDALLION,VASE,BUD,CANTON,1 3/8-IN.DIAMETER X
  8 1/4 IN.HIGH...........................................           35.00
ROSE MEDALLION,VASE,BUD,PANELS,FIGURES,ROSES,BIRDS,
  BUTTERFLY,8 IN.TALL.....................................           37.50
ROSE MEDALLION,VASE,FAMILLE ROSE,19TH CENTURY,34 IN.HIGH,
  STAND..................................................           600.00
ROSE MEDALLION,VASE,FOO DOG HANDLES,10 IN...................        150.00
ROSE MEDALLION,VASE,FOUR PANELS AT BASE & NECK,PAIR.........        115.00
ROSE MEDALLION,VASE,GOLD FOO DOG HANDLES,12 IN.HIGH.........        100.00
ROSE MEDALLION,VASE,PAIR,FAMILLE ROSE,TEMPLE,19TH CENTURY...      1,050.00
ROSE MEDALLION,VASE,PAIR,19TH CENTURY,24 IN. HIGH..........         600.00
ROSE MEDALLION,VASE,PANELS,PEOPLE,ROSES,GOLD TRIM,
```

ROSE MEDALLION TUREEN, C. 1810

```
     5 1/2 IN.TALL.............................................    30.00
ROSE MEDALLION,VASE,RAISED LION & LIZARD DESIGN UNDER FLARE,
     8 1/2 IN................................................    95.00
ROSE MEDALLION,VASE,ROUND TOP,SCALLOPED,4 IN. X 10 IN.HIGH..     55.00
ROSE MEDALLION,VASE,STICK NECK,FIGURES OF PEPLE,ROSES,
     BUTTERFLIES............................................    42.00
ROSE MEDALLION,VASE,10 IN.HIGH,PAIR.........................    195.00
ROSE MEDALLION,VASE,19TH CENTURY,12 3/4 IN. HIGH...........    225.00
ROSE MEDALLION,VASE,2-HANDLED,19TH CENTURY,24 3/4 IN. HIGH..    350.00
ROSE MEDALLION,VASE,9 3/4 IN., PAIR.........................    160.00
ROSE MEDALLION,VEGETABLE,9 IN. SQUARE X 1 5/8 IN.TALL.......     85.00
ROSE MEDALLION,WASHSTAND SET,CHINESE ENAMELED,CIRCA 1850....    525.00
     ROSE O'NEILL,SEE KEWPIE


     ROSE TAPESTRY PORCELAIN WAS MADE BY THE ROYAL BAYREUTH
     FACTORY OF GERMANY DURING THE LATE NINETEENTH CENTURY.
     THE SURFACE OF THE WARE FEELS LIKE CLOTH.
ROSE TAPESTRY,BASKET,CASTLE SCENE,MAJOLICA ROPE HANDLE,
     SIGNED EIFEL............................................    45.00
ROSE TAPESTRY,BASKET,DECOR INSIDE & OUTSIDE,BLUE MARK,
     4 1/2 IN,HIGH...........................................    90.00
ROSE TAPESTRY,BASKET,ROSE SPRAY INSIDE,GOLD,HANDLE,FOOTED,
     ROYAL BAYREUTH..........................................    100.00
ROSE TAPESTRY,BOX,FOOTED,ROYAL BAYREUTH,4 1/4-IN.DIAMETER...     95.00
ROSE TAPESTRY,BOX,JEWEL,OYSTER SHAPE,COVER,ROYAL BAYREUTH,
     GREEN MARK..............................................    85.00
ROSE TAPESTRY,BOX,OVAL,ROYAL BAYREUTH,4 1/4-IN.DIAMETER,PAIR    150.00
ROSE TAPESTRY,BOX,POWDER,COVER,BLACK MARK,ROYAL BAYREUTH....     65.00
ROSE TAPESTRY,BOX,POWDER,COVER,ROYAL BAYREUTH...............     33.00
ROSE TAPESTRY,BOX,POWDER,THREE COLOR ROSES,ROYAL BAYREUTH...     68.00
ROSE TAPESTRY,BOX,ROSES,GREEN ROYAL BAYREUTH BAVARIA,17-IN.
     DIAMETER................................................    89.00
ROSE TAPESTRY,BOX,ROYAL BAYREUTH,3-IN.DIAMETER..............     85.00
ROSE TAPESTRY,CREAMER,CORSET SHAPE,ROYAL BAYREUTH,
     3 3/4 IN.TALL...........................................    120.00
ROSE TAPESTRY,CREAMER,PINCHED SPOUT,3 1/2 IN................     85.00
ROSE TAPESTRY,CREAMER,ROSES IN THREE COLORS,MARK,ROYAL
     BAYREUTH................................................    70.00
ROSE TAPESTRY,CREAMER,ROYAL BAYREUTH,BLUE MARK,3
     1/2..........................................  45.00 TO    98.00
ROSE TAPESTRY,CREAMER,SCENIC,CASTLE,ROYAL BAYREUTH,BLUE MARK    65.00
ROSE TAPESTRY,HAIR RECEIVER,COVER,BLACK MARK,ROYAL BAYREUTH.    65.00
ROSE TAPESTRY,HAIR RECEIVER,COVER,SIGNED....................    115.00
ROSE TAPESTRY,HAIR RECEIVER,COVERED POWDER JAR,FOOTED.......    150.00
ROSE TAPESTRY,HAIR RECEIVER,FIGURE OF MAN & WOMAN,SIGNED,
     ROYAL BAYREUTH..........................................    25.00
ROSE TAPESTRY,HAIR RECEIVER,ROSES IN THREE COLORS,BLUE MARK.    90.00
ROSE TAPESTRY,HAIR RECEIVER,ROYAL BAYREUTH,SIGNED,GOLD FEET.    90.00
ROSE TAPESTRY,HOLDER,HATPIN,CREAM & PINK ROSES,SCROLLS,ROYAL
     BAYREUTH................................................    68.60
```

ROSE TAPESTRY,HOLDER,HATPIN,LACY BASE,SIGNED ROYAL BAYREUTH.        95.00
ROSE TAPESTRY,HOLDER,HATPIN,LADY,GENTLEMAN,ROYAL BAYREUTH,
  BLUE MARK..................................................      68.00
ROSE TAPESTRY,HOLDER,HATPIN,THREE-COLOR ROSES,ROYAL BAYREUTH        95.00
ROSE TAPESTRY,HOLDER,HATPIN,THREE COLORS,ROYAL BAYREUTH,BLUE
  MARK......................................................       85.00
ROSE TAPESTRY,HOLDER,MATCH,HANGING,ROYAL BAYREUTH...........        32.00
ROSE TAPESTRY,JAR,COOKIE,HAND-PAINTED SCENE,WATER,BRIDGE,
  SILVER COVER...............................................       59.00
ROSE TAPESTRY,JAR,POWDER,THREE COLORS......................         75.00
ROSE TAPESTRY,NAPPIE,CLOVERLEAF SHAPE,BLUE MARK,ROYAL
  BAYREUTH...................................................       75.00
ROSE TAPESTRY,NAPPIE,PORTRAIT,ROYAL BAYREUTH,BLUE MARK......        90.00
ROSE TAPESTRY,PITCHER,CORSET SHAPE,BLUE MARK,ROYAL BAYREUTH,
  4 1/2 IN...................................................      125.00
ROSE TAPESTRY,PITCHER,MILK,CORSET SHAPE,ROYAL BAYREUTH,
  4 5/8 IN.TALL..............................................      135.00
ROSE TAPESTRY,PITCHER,MILK,TAN-BROWN GROUND,CASTLE,LAKE,
  ROYAL BAYREUTH.............................................       85.00
ROSE TAPESTRY,PITCHER,ROYAL BAYREUTH,4 IN..................         65.00
ROSE TAPESTRY,PITCHER,SCENIC & GOATS,ROYAL BAYREUTH,BLUE
  MARK......................................................       95.00
ROSE TAPESTRY,PITCHER,THREE-COLOR ROSES,MARK,ROYAL. 78.00 TO       82.00
ROSE TAPESTRY,PITCHER,THREE-COLOR ROSES,PINCHED,ROYAL
  BAYREUTH,BLUE MARK.........................................       85.00
ROSE TAPESTRY,PITCHER,WATER,ROYAL BAYREUTH.................        185.00
ROSE TAPESTRY,PLATE,CAKE,THREE-COLOR ROSES,RECESSED EDGE,
  ROYAL BAYREUTH.............................................       45.00
ROSE TAPESTRY,PLATE,ORNAMENTED RIM,SIGNED,6 IN.............        137.00
ROSE TAPESTRY,PLATE,RAISED ORNAMENTATION,SEVENTEEN ROSES,
  SIGNED,6 IN................................................      135.00
ROSE TAPESTRY,PLATE,SCENIC,ARAB,HORSES,PIERCED,BLUE MARK,
  ROYAL BAYREUTH.............................................      175.00
ROSE TAPESTRY,POT,FLOWER,TWO-PART,HANDLES,ROYAL BAYREUTH....       145.00
ROSE TAPESTRY,RELISH,7 1/2 IN..............................        115.00
ROSE TAPESTRY,SLIPPER,LADY'S,ROYAL BAYREUTH,BLUE MARK.......        95.00
ROSE TAPESTRY,SWEETMEAT,ROYAL BONN,SILVER RIM,HANDLE & COVER        29.50
ROSE TAPESTRY,TEAPOT,CREAMER,OPEN SUGAR,BEADED SCROLL,
  DOULTON...................................................       98.00
ROSE TAPESTRY,TRAY,COVERED POWDER,HAIR RECEIVER,PIN BOX,
  HATPIN HOLDER..............................................      425.00
ROSE TAPESTRY,TRAY,OBLONG,ROYAL BAYREUTH,11 1/4 IN. X 8 IN..       195.00
ROSE TAPESTRY,TRAY,OPEN HANDLE,DEEP,ROYAL BAYREUTH,9 IN.....       100.00
ROSE TAPESTRY,TRAY,OPEN HANDLES,ROYAL BAYREUTH,BLUE MARK,
  8 1/2 X 4 IN...............................................       95.00
ROSE TAPESTRY,TRAY,SWIRLED EDGES,ROYAL BAYREUTH,BLUE MARK,
  10 IN.LONG.................................................      135.00
ROSE TAPESTRY,TRAY,THREE-COLOR ROSES,HANDLES,ROYAL BAYREUTH,
  8 X 4 IN...................................................       90.00
ROSE TAPESTRY,VASE,GOLD HANDLES,MARKED IMPERIAL CROWN CHINA
  AUSTRIA....................................................       65.00
ROSE TAPESTRY,VASE,JUG SHAPE,BLUE MARK,ROYAL BAYREUTH,5 IN..        87.50
ROSE TAPESTRY,VASE,JUG SHAPE,PORTRAIT SCENE,GOLD HANDLES,
  ROYAL BAYREUTH.............................................       65.00
ROSE TAPESTRY,VASE,PERSIAN PATTERN,ARTIST-SIGNED,ROYAL BONN,
  13 IN.TALL.................................................       55.00
ROSE TAPESTRY,VASE,PORTRAIT SCENE,JUG SHAPE,GOLD HANDLES,
  ROYAL BAYREUTH.............................................       65.00


      ROSENTHAL PORCELAIN WAS ESTABLISHED IN SELS,BAVARIA,IN
      1880. THE GERMAN FACTORY STILL CONTINUES TO MAKE FINE-
      QUALITY TABLEWARE AND FIGURINES.
ROSENTHAL,BOWL,BERRY,PINK ROSE SPRAYS,GOLD RIM,SCALLOPED,
  FOOTED,6 PLATES............................................       22.00
ROSENTHAL,BOWL,FLORAL,BASKET-WEAVE EDGE,BAVARIA,7 IN.,
  12 DESSERT PLATES..........................................      120.00
ROSENTHAL,BOX,PORTRAIT,LADY,ORNATE GOLD BORDER ON COVER &
  BASE,5 IN..................................................       25.00
ROSENTHAL,CAKE SET,DONATELLO,WHITE GROUND,PALE BLUE
  CHERRIES,7 PIECES..........................................       85.00
ROSENTHAL,CHOCOLATE POT,LID,BEIGE GROUND,PINECONES,GOLD,
  6 CUPS & SAUCERS...........................................       55.00
ROSENTHAL,COMPOTE,WHITE GROUND,BUNCHES OF VIOLETS,HANDLES,
  GOLD......................................................       22.00
ROSENTHAL,COMPOTE,WHITE GROUND,VIOLETS,LEAVES,RAM HEAD
  HANDLES ...................................................       22.50
ROSENTHAL,COMPOTE,WHITE,BUNCHES OF VIOLETS,HANDLES,GOLD TRIM        35.00
ROSENTHAL,CREAMER & SUGAR,SHADED PURPLE ORCHIDS,GOLD BAND...         8.00
ROSENTHAL,CUP & SAUCER,DEMITASSE,CHIPPENDALE PATTERN, SET OF
  6.........................................................       35.00

ROSENTHAL,DISH,GREEN,ROSES,TWO GOLD HANDLES,6 3/4 IN........  15.00
ROSENTHAL,FISH SET,RAINBOW TROUT,SEAWEED,15-IN.PLATTER,
  6 PLATES,10 IN...........................................  60.00
ROSENTHAL,JAR,CRACKER,VERSAILLES PATTERN,GREEN RIBBON,PINK
  FLORAL,FERNS.............................................  18.50
ROSENTHAL,PLAQUE,BROWN SEPIA,BAVARIAN RED CROSS HELPER,
  SIGNED,1915.............................................  39.00
ROSENTHAL,PLATE,BLUE GROUND,LARGE ROSE,HAND-PAINTED........  13.00
ROSENTHAL,PLATE,BLUE,WHITE ROSES,GREEN FOLIAGE,BLUE & GOLD
  BORDER..................................................   7.50
ROSENTHAL,PLATE,CAKE,THREE WHITE ROSES,GREEN GROUND,
  SCALLOPED,BAVARIA.......................................  11.00
ROSENTHAL,PLATE,COOKIE,CREAM GROUND,PRIMROSES,GILT,OPEN
  HANDLE, 10 IN...........................................  12.00
ROSENTHAL,PLATE,FLOWER DECOR,RELIEF GOLD,BEADED RIM,8 IN....   4.50
ROSENTHAL,PLATE,GAME,GREEN,BLUE,BIRD,HAND-PAINTED,
  ARTIST-SIGNED...........................................  35.00
ROSENTHAL,PLATE,GREEN BORDER,TULIPS,HAND-PAINTED,1907,10 IN.   7.50
ROSENTHAL,PLATE,HOLLY,BERRIES,ARTIST-SIGNED,SCALLOPED EDGE,
  GOLD....................................................   5.75
ROSENTHAL,PLATE,ROSE CLUSTERS,CREAM CENTER,HAND-PAINTED,
  8 1/2 IN................................................   5.00
ROSENTHAL,PLATE,SCENE,DUCK IN MARSH,DUCK FLYING,SIGNED,9 IN.  22.00
ROSENTHAL,PLATE,U.S.SEAL IN CENTER,GEORGE & MARTHA
  WASHINGTON BORDER.......................................  18.00
ROSENTHAL,PLATE,WHITE GRAPES,GREEN & PINK IVY,BLUE GROUND,
  SIGNED..................................................  25.00
ROSENTHAL,PLATE,WHITE,COBALT BORDER,GOLD,10 3/4 IN.,SET OF
  SEVEN...................................................  45.00
ROSENTHAL,PLATTER,FISH,CIRCA 1900,SIX PLATES..............  40.00
ROSENTHAL,PLATTER,WHITE,FLORAL,GOLD BORDER,BAVARIA,
  13-IN.DIAMETER..........................................  25.00
ROSENTHAL,SUGAR,IVORY,PALE ROSES,SIGNED,HAND-PAINTED,COVER..  12.50
ROSENTHAL,TAZZA,NASTURTIUMS,MONBIJOU,HAND-PAINTED,
  9-IN.DIAMETER...........................................  22.50
ROSENTHAL,TEA SET,TEAPOT,CREAMER & SUGAR,RED & YELLOW ROSES,
  HAND-PAINTED............................................  35.00


     ROSEVILLE POTTERY COMPANY WAS ESTABLISHED IN 1891 IN
     ZANESVILLE,OHIO. MANY TYPES OF POTTERY WERE MADE,
     INCLUDING FLOWER VASES.
ROSEVILLE,ASHTRAY,HANDLES,6-IN.BASE DIAMETER,2 1/4 IN.TALL..   8.50
ROSEVILLE,BASKET,BROWN,GREEN,TWIG HANDLE,FROG,MARKED,8 IN...   7.00
ROSEVILLE,BASKET,CACTUS PATTERN,BLUE,HANDLE OVER TOP,10 IN..  14.50
ROSEVILLE,BASKET,FUCHSIA,ATTACHED FROG INSIDE BOTTOM,HANDLE,
  BROWN...................................................  15.00
ROSEVILLE,BASKET,GREEN,PINK,WIDE FLARE OVAL TOP,HANDLE,
  12 1/4 IN.TALL..........................................  17.50
ROSEVILLE,BASKET,HANGING,DONATELLO........................  35.00
ROSEVILLE,BASKET,PINE CONE DECOR,TWIG HANDLE,BROWN,GREEN,
  10 1/2 IN.HIGH..........................................  12.50
ROSEVILLE,BASKET,ROSE TO BROWN,FOXGLOVES IN RELIEF,12 IN....  25.00
ROSEVILLE,BOOKEND,BLUE WITH PINK APPLE BLOSSOMS,PAIR......   7.50
ROSEVILLE,BOOKEND,GREEN AND ROSE,PAIR.....................  14.50
ROSEVILLE,BOOKEND,GREEN,OPEN BOOKS,ROSE FLOWERS,PAIR......  19.50
ROSEVILLE,BOOKEND,GREEN,WHITE FLOWERS,PAIR................  20.00
ROSEVILLE,BOOKEND,MAGNOLIA,PAIR...........................  20.00
ROSEVILLE,BOWL,BLUE GROUND,WHITE LILY DESIGN,11 IN.........  35.00
ROSEVILLE,BOWL,BLUE,FUCHSIA PATTERN,3 1/2 IN.HIGH,
  4-IN.DIAMETER...........................................   6.50
ROSEVILLE,BOWL,BLUE,WHITE IRIS,12 1/2 IN. X 6 1/2 IN.......   8.00
ROSEVILLE,BOWL,BROWN & ORANGE HOLLY DECOR.................   6.50
ROSEVILLE,BOWL,CENTER,ROSE GROUND,PINK HOLLYHOCKS,PAIR
  CANDLESTICKS............................................  20.00
ROSEVILLE,BOWL,CENTERPIECE,BOAT SHAPE,PINK,BROWN,HANDLES,7 X
  14 IN...................................................  12.00
ROSEVILLE,BOWL,DONATELLO,CREAM COLOR,BEIGE,GREEN,9 IN......  18.00
ROSEVILLE,BOWL,DONATELLO,MARK.............................  25.00
ROSEVILLE,BOWL,FLORENTINE,ROUND,SHALLOW,6-IN.DIAMETER......  15.00
ROSEVILLE,BOWL,GREEN,WATER LILIES,LOW,U.S.A.,
  10 1/2-IN.DIAMETER......................................  15.00
ROSEVILLE,BOWL,PINK,BLUE,10-IN.DIAMETER,PAIR CANDLESTICKS,
  3 1/4 IN.,MARK..........................................  22.50
ROSEVILLE,BOWL,ROSE COLOR,SNOWBERRY PATTERN,3 1/2 IN. X
  3 IN.HIGH...............................................   6.00
ROSEVILLE,BOWL,SNOWBERRY LINE,TWIG HANDLES,ORANGE,U.S.A.....  20.00
ROSEVILLE,BOWL,YELLOW,ORCHID LILIES,THREE CANDLE HOLDERS ON
  PLATFORM................................................  25.00
ROSEVILLE,CANDLEHOLDER,BLUE,PINK FLORAL,OPEN HANDLE,
  2 1/2 IN.TALL,PAIR......................................  14.00

```
ROSEVILLE,CANDLEHOLDER,PINK,GREEN SPRIG,TWIG HANDLE,PAIR....    10.00
ROSEVILLE,CANDLEHOLDER,TWO HOLDERS JOINED BY PLAQUE,CHERUBS,
  DONATELLO................................................    17.50
ROSEVILLE,CANDLEHOLDER,WHITE FLOWER..........................     6.00
ROSEVILLE,CANDLESTICK,BLUE,WHITE,GREEN FLORAL DECOR,
  4 IN.TALL,PAIR...........................................    12.00
ROSEVILLE,CANDLESTICK,CHERUBS,DONATELLO,SIGNED,8 1/2 IN.
  HIGH,PAIR................................................    27.50
ROSEVILLE,COMPOTE,OPEN,IMPRESSED DONATELLO R.P.CO.,
  9 1/2 IN.TALL...........................................    22.50
ROSEVILLE,CORNUCOPIA,GREEN,FLOWER,U.S.A.....................    15.00
ROSEVILLE,CREAMER & SUGAR,BROWN GROUND,FLORAL DECOR.........    12.00
ROSEVILLE,EWER,GREEN,POINSETTIA,10 IN.HIGH..................    25.00
ROSEVILLE,JAR,COOKIE,GREEN,WHITE MAGNOLIAS,TWO HANDLES,
  COVER,10 1/2 IN.........................................    19.00
ROSEVILLE,JAR,COOKIE,RUST & GREEN,REGAL LILY,10 1/2 IN.HIGH.    25.00
ROSEVILLE,JARDINIERE,GOLD TO RUST,PINECONES,PINE BOUGH,TWIG
  HANDLES.................................................    20.00
ROSEVILLE,JARDINIERE,GREEN,BROWN,TREE BARK FINISH,RAISED
  LEAF DESIGN.............................................    20.00
ROSEVILLE,JARDINIERE,MINIATURE,GREEN,ALLOVER EMBOSSING......    15.00
ROSEVILLE,LAMP,DONATELLO,BRASS BASE,10 IN...................    25.00
ROSEVILLE,LAMP,FREESIA ON BLUE,ELECTRIC,14 IN...............    30.00
ROSEVILLE,PITCHER,GREEN,CLEMATIS,TANKARD,6 IN.TALL,
  6-IN.DIAMETER...........................................    12.00
ROSEVILLE,PLANTER,GREEN,TAN,FLORAL,TWO HANDLES,3 X 3 1/2 IN.     9.00
ROSEVILLE,TEAPOT,CREAMER,SUGAR,CLEMATIS.....................    25.00
ROSEVILLE,TEAPOT,FLORAL,BLUE,LID............................    15.00
ROSEVILLE,TEAPOT,SNOWBERRY DECOR,GREEN,COVER,MARK...........    13.50
ROSEVILLE,TRAY,LILY OF THE VALLEY,8 IN. X 15 IN.............     8.00
ROSEVILLE,URN,BROWN,GREEN,TWO HANDLES,MARKED,8 IN...........     7.00
ROSEVILLE,VASE,APPLE BLOSSOM,ROSE COLOR,TWIG HANDLES,
  PEDESTAL BASE,9 IN......................................    19.50
ROSEVILLE,VASE,AZTEC,8 IN...................................    14.00
ROSEVILLE,VASE,BEIGE,EMBOSSED IRIS & LEAVES,BLUE GROUND,
  FOOTED,HANDLES..........................................    12.50
ROSEVILLE,VASE,BLEEDING HEARTS,GREEN LEAVES,TWO HANDLES,
  10 IN...................................................    10.50
ROSEVILLE,VASE,BLUE GROUND,MULTICOLORED FLORAL SPRAYS,
  SIGNED,7 3/4 IN.........................................    10.50
ROSEVILLE,VASE,BLUE,FUCHSIA PATTERN,URN SHAPE,6 1/2 X
  8 1/2 IN.TALL..........................................    12.00
ROSEVILLE,VASE,BLUE,YELLOW FLORAL,HANDLES,8 1/2 IN.TALL.....    12.00
ROSEVILLE,VASE,BROWN GROUND,YELLOW FLORAL,HANDLES,NO.390,
  7 1/2 IN................................................     9.75
ROSEVILLE,VASE,BROWN TO BEIGE TO BLUE,7 1/2 IN..............     7.50
ROSEVILLE,VASE,BROWN,FREESIA PATTERN,7 IN.TALL,PAIR.........    15.00
ROSEVILLE,VASE,BUD,BEIGE GROUND,PANELS,WHEAT,TWO HANDLES,
  PEDESTAL................................................     9.00
ROSEVILLE,VASE,BUD,PINK TO ROSE,TWISTED HANDLES ON BASE,
  FOOTED..................................................    12.50
ROSEVILLE,VASE,BUD,PINK TO ROSE,TWO TWISTED HANDLES ON BASE.    12.50
ROSEVILLE,VASE,CORNUCOPIA,BLUE GROUND,HOLLY DESIGN..........    11.00
ROSEVILLE,VASE,DEEP PINK,FLORAL,SQUATTY,TWO HANDLES,
  4 1/2 IN.TALL..........................................     7.00
ROSEVILLE,VASE,DONATELLO.............................ILLUS..    16.00
```

ROSEVILLE VASE, DONADELLO

```
ROSEVILLE,VASE,DONATELLO,CHERUBS & TREES,7 IN.TALL..........    20.00
ROSEVILLE,VASE,DONATELLO,RV MARK,9 IN....................      12.50
ROSEVILLE,VASE,EGYPTIAN STYLE,ROUGH TEXTURE GROUND,ENAMEL
   INSERTS,10 IN..........................................      15.00
ROSEVILLE,VASE,FLORAL,HANDLES,RV STICKER,4 IN. X 6 1/2 IN.,
   PAIP................................................        16.00
ROSEVILLE,VASE,FLORENTINE,FLUTED HALFWAY,FLORAL TOP,PINK,
   GREEN,HANDLES.........................................      25.00
ROSEVILLE,VASE,FOXGLOVE,BLUE,6 IN.......................       10.50
ROSEVILLE,VASE,GREEN CORNUCOPIA,6 IN.,PAIR..............       11.00
ROSEVILLE,VASE,GREEN,FLORAL,U.S.A.......................        8.00
ROSEVILLE,VASE,GREEN,GLOSSY FINISH,MARKED,7 1/2-X
   6-IN.DIAMETER,PAIR....................................      15.00
ROSEVILLE,VASE,GREEN,8 IN...............................        9.00
ROSEVILLE,VASE,LIGHT BLUE,YELLOW FLOWER CLUSTERS,FAN-SHAPED
   TOP,MARK..............................................      27.50
ROSEVILLE,VASE,MING TREE,BROWN LIMBS,PINK LEAVES,GREEN
   GROUND,HANDLES........................................      23.00
ROSEVILLE,VASE,MOTTLED SHADES OF TAN,YELLOW,GREEN,HANDLES,
   6 1/4 IN.............................................       10.00
ROSEVILLE,VASE,OLD COLONY,BLUE ON WHITE,HAND-DECORATED,
   R.R.P.CO.............................................       10.00
ROSEVILLE,VASE,PEDESTAL BASE,WOODS NYMPH ON SIDES,GREEN,FAN
   SHAPE,6 IN...........................................       10.00
ROSEVILLE,VASE,PINE CONE & FROND DECOR,BLUE,CORNUCOPIA
   SHAPE,RED LINING.....................................       18.50
ROSEVILLE,VASE,PINECONE,DARK BLUE,TWIG HANDLES,NO.121-7.....     8.50
ROSEVILLE,VASE,PINK & YELLOW FLORAL,GREEN GROUND,TWO
   HANDLES,NO.105-7.....................................        9.00
ROSEVILLE,VASE,PINK,IRIS DECOR,TWO EARS,MARKED,3 IN.HIGH....     7.50
ROSEVILLE,VASE,ROSE COLOR,WHITE ROSE DECOR,TWO HANDLES,
   6 IN.TALL...........................................         9.00
ROSEVILLE,VASE,SHADED TAN,TWIG & CONE HANDLES,MARKED,
   8 1/2 IN............................................        11.50
ROSEVILLE,VASE,SHERBET CUP SHAPE,GREEN,BROWN TRIM,GLOSSY,
   7 1/2 IN.HIGH.......................................        10.50
ROSEVILLE,VASE,STEP-UP,ROSE COLOR,TWIG HANDLES,APPLE
   BLOSSOMS,7 1/2 IN...................................         7.50
ROSEVILLE,VASE,TAN,CORNUCOPIA ON STAND,POMEGRANATE-LINED,
   PINE CONE DECOR.....................................        18.00
ROSEVILLE,VASE,TRUMPET,GREEN,YELLOW,ORANGE,FLORAL,
   6 1/2 IN.TALL.......................................         7.50
ROSEVILLE,VASE,WALL,BLUE,WHITE FLOWERS,7 1/2 IN.WIDE........     8.50
ROSEVILLE,VASE,WALL,GREEN FLUTED,SWAGS,FLOWERS,ROMA,9 IN....    19.50
ROSEVILLE,VASE,WHITE,MING TREE.........................        12.00
ROSEVILLE,WALL POCKET,CREAM WITH FLOWER SWAG...........         6.00
ROSEWOOD,BOX,JEWELRY,PEARLED KEY ESCUTCHEON,SECRET CACHE....    22.50
ROSEWOOD,TEA CADDY,PEARL ESCUTCHEON...................         85.00
ROYAL AUSTRIA,BLUE FORGET-ME-NOTS,BLUE EDGE,HAND-PAINTED,
   SIGNED,GILT........................................          4.75
ROYAL AUSTRIA,BOTTLE,PERFUME,GREEN,DAISIES,GOLD STOPPER,
   ARTIST SIGNED......................................         10.00
ROYAL AUSTRIA,BOTTLE,PERFUME,PINK & WHITE,ROSES,GOLD
   STOPPER,SIGNED.....................................         10.00
ROYAL AUSTRIA,CREAMER,SUGAR,TRAY,IVORY & GOLD.........        40.00
ROYAL AUSTRIA,HOLDER,HATPIN,GOLD RIM AND MONOGRAM,ON 6-X
   3-IN.TRAY..........................................        10.00
ROYAL AUSTRIA,JAR,POWDER,ROSES,VIOLETS,GOLD BANDS,
   ARTIST-SIGNED......................................        10.00
ROYAL AUSTRIA,JAR,SYRUP,FEATHERY GOLD GROUND,TINY ROSES,O.&
   C.CO..............................................          8.50
ROYAL AUSTRIA,JAR,TOBACCO,PIPE REST,COLORFUL LONG-BEAKED
   BIRD DECOR........................................          7.50
ROYAL AUSTRIA,NAPKIN RING,HALF-MOON SHAPE,HAND-PAINTED
   FLORAL,PORCELAIN..................................         12.50
ROYAL AUSTRIA,PLATE,BIRD,GOOSE IN FLIGHT,GOLD RIM,8 IN......     6.00
ROYAL AUSTRIA,PLATE,CAKE,VIOLETS,OPEN HANDLES,HAND-PAINTED,
   SIGNED............................................         12.00
ROYAL AUSTRIA,PLATE,LEAF DESIGN,GOLD,ARTIST-SIGNED,6 IN.....     6.00
ROYAL AUSTRIA,PLATE,NASTURTIUMS,GOLD BORDER,HAND-PAINTED,
   7 1/2 IN.,SIX.....................................         18.00
ROYAL AUSTRIA,PLATE,ORCHIDS,GOLD,ARTIST-SIGNED,6 IN.........     6.00
ROYAL AUSTRIA,PLATE,PINK & WHITE MOSS ROSES,GREEN BORDER,
   MEDALLIONS........................................         18.00
ROYAL AUSTRIA,PLATE,ROSES,FLOWERS,GOLD,SIGNED,8 3/4 IN......     7.50
ROYAL AUSTRIA,PLATE,VIOLETS,HAND-PAINTED,SIGNED TONNS,9 IN..    20.00
ROYAL AUSTRIA,PLATE,WILD BOAR,HAND-PAINTED,ARTIST SIGNED,
   1914,8 3/4 IN.....................................         12.50
ROYAL AUSTRIA,SALT,RUFFLE TOP,IVORY & GOLD DESIGN,SIGNED....    10.00
ROYAL AUSTRIA,SHAKER,POWDER,CUPID,HAND-PAINTED,1920.........    10.00
ROYAL AUSTRIA,SHAKER,SUGAR,PINK ROSES,GOLD TOP,HAND-PAINTED.    15.50
```

ROYAL AUSTRIA,TEAPOT,WHITE GROUND,MAUVE PINK FLORAL,GOLD
TRIM................................................... 10.50
ROYAL AUSTRIA,TRAY,PIN,ROSES,GOLD,HAND-PAINTED,SIGNED,8 IN.. 9.50
ROYAL AUSTRIA,TUREEN,VEGETABLE,WHITE GROUND,LAVENDER FLORAL,
DOMED LID............................................. 20.00


ROYAL BAYREUTH PORCELAIN WAS MADE IN GERMANY DURING
THE LATE NINETEENTH AND TWENTIETH CENTURIES. MANY TYPES
OF WARES WERE MADE.
ROYAL BAYREUTH,SEE ALSO,ROSE TAPESTRY,SUNBONNET BABIES
ROYAL BAYREUTH,ASHTRAY,ASTER TAPESTRY,PURPLE,WHITE,GREEN
ASTERS,DAISIES........................................ 67.50
ROYAL BAYREUTH,ASHTRAY,FIGHTING COCKS,BLACK MARK............ 23.50
ROYAL BAYREUTH,ASHTRAY,FIGURAL,DEVIL,ARMS OVER TOP,LEGS
AROUND BASE........................................... 27.00
ROYAL BAYREUTH,ASHTRAY,YELLOW GROUND,PENGUINS,4 3/4 IN.LONG. 29.00
ROYAL BAYREUTH,BASKET,GREEN,PINK ROSES,ENTWINED STEM HANDLE,
5 IN.HIGH............................................. 18.50
ROYAL BAYREUTH,BELL,SCENIC,PHEASANT........................ 28.00
ROYAL BAYREUTH,BERRY SET,BUNCH OF GREEN GRAPES,GREEN LEAF,
BOWL,6 SAUCES......................................... 125.00
ROYAL BAYREUTH,BOWL,BERRY,YELLOW & RED ROSES,MARKED......... 65.00
ROYAL BAYREUTH,BOWL,LANDSCAPE,COWS,FOOTED,FLUTED EDGE,
4 3/4-IN.DIAMETER..................................... 32.00
ROYAL BAYREUTH,BOWL,LOBSTER,MOTHER-OF-PEARL FINISH,WHITE,
PINK-PURPLE........................................... 75.00
ROYAL BAYREUTH,BOWL,LOBSTER,OBLONG,BLUE MARK,7 IN.......... 60.00
ROYAL BAYREUTH,BOWL,OPEN,TOMATO,RED,GREEN BASE,BLUE MARK.... 27.50
ROYAL BAYREUTH,BOWL,ROSE,ROSES,WHITE TO PINK SHADING,
LACEWORK RIM,FOOTED................................... 30.00
ROYAL BAYREUTH,BOWL,SALAD,THREE LOBSTERS,GREEN LEAF,8 X
4 IN................................................. 22.00
ROYAL BAYREUTH,BOWL,SUGAR,PANSY,COVER,3 X 3 IN............ 35.00
ROYAL BAYREUTH,BOX,GREEN,LITT.E BO-PEEP,COVER,5 1/2 IN. X
3 1/2 IN............................................. 30.00
ROYAL BAYREUTH,BOX,SHELL SHAPE,LITTLE BO-PEEP,COVER......... 30.00
ROYAL BAYREUTH,CANDLEHOLDER,RED DEVIL,7 IN.TALL............ 125.00
ROYAL BAYREUTH,CANDLESTICK,DEVIL & CARDS................... 45.00
ROYAL BAYREUTH,CANDLESTICK,ELK HEAD,NINE POINTED ANTLERS,
HANDLE,7 IN........................................... 45.00
ROYAL BAYREUTH,CANDLESTICK,GOAT SCENE,BLUE MARK,5 IN.HIGH,
PAIR................................................. 65.00
ROYAL BAYREUTH,CANDLESTICK,PASTORAL SCENE WITH SHEEP....... 16.00
ROYAL BAYREUTH,CANDLESTICK,SCENE,GOATS,BLUE MARK,4 IN.TALL,
PAIR................................................. 45.00
ROYAL BAYREUTH,CANDLESTICK,WHITE,SMALL FLOWER DECOR,BLUE
MARK,4 1/4 IN......................................... 13.50
ROYAL BAYREUTH,CHOCOLATE POT,IVORY,LILAC-TINGED ROSES,5 CUPS
& SAUCERS............................................. 155.00
ROYAL BAYREUTH,CHOCOLATE POT,PINK ROSES.................... 47.50
ROYAL BAYREUTH,CONCH SHELL,MOTHER-OF-PEARL................. 22.00
ROYAL BAYREUTH,CREAMER & SUGAR,APPLE....................... 85.00
ROYAL BAYREUTH,CREAMER & SUGAR,FISHERMAN PATTERN........... 42.00
ROYAL BAYREUTH,CREAMER & SUGAR,FISHING & HUNTING SCENE,BLUE
MARK................................................. 45.00
ROYAL BAYREUTH,CREAMER & SUGAR,RED TOMATO,COVER........... 35.00
ROYAL BAYREUTH,CREAMER,ALLIGATOR.......................... 26.50
ROYAL BAYREUTH,CREAMER,APPLE SHAPE,SOUVENIR,BLUE MARK...... 16.00
ROYAL BAYREUTH,CREAMER,BLACK ANGUS HEAD,RED HORNS,BLUE MARK. 38.00
ROYAL BAYREUTH,CREAMER,BLACK BULL,BLUE MARK................ 32.25
ROYAL BAYREUTH,CREAMER,BLACK CROW,BLUE MARK................ 32.50
ROYAL BAYREUTH,CREAMER,BLACK CROW,OLD BLUE MARK............ 40.00
ROYAL BAYREUTH,CREAMER,BLACK STEER,BLUE MARK............... 30.00
ROYAL BAYREUTH,CREAMER,BUTTERFLY,BLUE MARK................. 35.00
ROYAL BAYREUTH,CREAMER,CARDS,RED DEVIL HANDLE,BLUE MARK..... 45.00
ROYAL BAYREUTH,CREAMER,CAVALIER PORTRAIT,LEFT-HANDED,BLUE
MARK................................................. 30.00
ROYAL BAYREUTH,CREAMER,CEREAL,GREEN,FOX HUNT SCENE IN TOP
BAND,6 1/2 IN......................................... 29.50
ROYAL BAYREUTH,CREAMER,CLOWN,BLUE MARK..................... 25.00
ROYAL BAYREUTH,CREAMER,CLOWN SPOUT........................ 32.00
ROYAL BAYREUTH,CREAMER,CONCH SHELL PATTERN,IRIDESCENT,SAYS
SAVIN ROCK........................................... 20.00
ROYAL BAYREUTH,CREAMER,CONCH SHELL,BLUE MARK.............. 19.00
ROYAL BAYREUTH,CREAMER,CONCH SHELL,IRIDESCENCE,BLUE,GREEN,
ROSE,TAN............................................. 38.00
ROYAL BAYREUTH,CREAMER,CONCH SHELL,SHINY LUSTER............ 22.50
ROYAL BAYREUTH,CREAMER,DEVIL,BLACK MARK.................... 29.00
ROYAL BAYREUTH,CREAMER,DEVIL,CARD,MARKED,4 IN............. 35.00
ROYAL BAYREUTH,CREAMER,DUCK,BLUE MARK,4 IN................. 45.00

```
ROYAL BAYREUTH,CREAMER,ELK HEAD..........................     18.00
ROYAL BAYREUTH,CREAMER,EAGLE,BLUE MARK....................     32.00
ROYAL BAYREUTH,CREAMER,ELK,BLUE MARK......................     25.00
ROYAL BAYREUTH,CREAMER,ELK,POURS FROM MOUTH,ANTLERS ENCIRCLE
   TOP....................................................     35.00
ROYAL BAYREUTH,CREAMER,FIGURAL,ALLIGATOR,BROWN,BLUE MARK,
   SIGNED.................................................     25.00
ROYAL BAYREUTH,CREAMER,FIGURAL,BULL,BLACK,RED HORNS,BLUE
   MARK..................................................      40.00
ROYAL BAYREUTH,CREAMER,FIGURAL,BUTTERFLY..................     65.00
ROYAL BAYREUTH,CREAMER,FIGURAL,CONCH SHELL,PEARLIZED......     42.50
ROYAL BAYREUTH,CREAMER,FIGURAL,DUCK,BLUE MARK.............     41.00
ROYAL BAYREUTH,CREAMER,FIGURAL,FROG,UNSIGNED..............     15.00
ROYAL BAYREUTH,CREAMER,FIGURAL,LEMON,LEAF TRIM & HANDLE...     34.50
ROYAL BAYREUTH,CREAMER,FIGURAL,MOOSE HEAD,GRAY,CARAMEL,
   SIGNED,BLUE MARK.......................................     27.00
ROYAL BAYREUTH,CREAMER,FIGURAL,POPPY,RED,MARK.............     41.00
ROYAL BAYREUTH,CREAMER,FISH HEAD,BLUE MARK................     35.50
ROYAL BAYREUTH,CREAMER,FISH,SOUVENIR......................     12.00
ROYAL BAYREUTH,CREAMER,FROG,BLUE MARK.....................     25.50
ROYAL BAYREUTH,CREAMER,FROG FIGURAL.......................     58.00
ROYAL BAYREUTH,CREAMER,GERANIUM...........................     25.00
ROYAL BAYREUTH,CREAMER,GOATS,BLUE MARK....................     26.00
ROYAL BAYREUTH,CREAMER,GOATS,MOUNTAIN SCENIC..............     15.00
ROYAL BAYREUTH,CREAMER,GOLD ROSES,BLUE MARK...............     21.50
ROYAL BAYREUTH,CREAMER,GREEN,FOX HUNT SCENE IN TOP BAND,BLUE
   MARK...................................................     22.50
ROYAL BAYREUTH,CREAMER,HOBSTAR,BLUE MARK..................     30.00
ROYAL BAYREUTH,CREAMER,HUNTING SCENE,BLUE MARK............     26.50
ROYAL BAYREUTH,CREAMER,LOBSTER,BLUE MARK..................     25.00
ROYAL BAYREUTH,CREAMER,MOOSE HEAD,ANTLERS CIRCLE TOP,BLUE
   MARK...................................................     30.00
ROYAL BAYREUTH,CREAMER,MOOSE HEAD,BLUE MARK....... 22.50 TO    23.50
ROYAL BAYREUTH,CREAMER,OAK LEAF...........................     25.00
ROYAL BAYREUTH,CREAMER,OLD MAN OF THE MOUNTAIN,GREEN,BLUE,
   GRAY,ORANGE............................................     22.00
ROYAL BAYREUTH,CREAMER,ORANGE.............................     35.00
ROYAL BAYREUTH,CREAMER,ORANGE,FLORAL & LEAVES AT TOP &
   HANDLE,BLUE MARK.......................................     19.50
ROYAL BAYREUTH,CREAMER,PARROT,LIME GREEN,BLUE MARK,4 IN...     55.00
ROYAL BAYREUTH,CREAMER,PLAYING CARD,DEVIL HANDLE,
   3 1/2 IN.TALL..........................................     32.00
ROYAL BAYREUTH,CREAMER,POPPY,BLUE MARK............ 22.50 TO    30.50
ROYAL BAYREUTH,CREAMER,PORTRAIT OF GIRL,PURPLE DRESS,WHITE
   SHAWL COLLAR...........................................     22.00
ROYAL BAYREUTH,CREAMER,RED LOBSTER,BLUE MARK..............     25.50
ROYAL BAYREUTH,CREAMER,RED LOBSTER,GREEN LEAF,BLUE MARK...     29.25
ROYAL BAYREUTH,CREAMER,RED,POPPY SHAPE,BLUE MARK... 24.00 TO  29.50
ROYAL BAYREUTH,CREAMER,SCENIC,FISHERMEN ON BOAT,STORMY SEA,
   BLUE MARK..............................................     36.00
ROYAL BAYREUTH,CREAMER,SEAL,BLUE MARK,4 IN................     55.00
ROYAL BAYREUTH,CREAMER,SHIP SCENE,BLUE MARK...............     27.50
ROYAL BAYREUTH,CREAMER,SOUVENIR BASS POINT................     16.00
ROYAL BAYREUTH,CREAMER,STRAWBERRY SHAPE,BLUE MARK.........     32.50
ROYAL BAYREUTH,CREAMER,STRAWBERRY SHAPE,COVER,4 1/4 IN....     16.00
ROYAL BAYREUTH,CREAMER,SUGAR,DUTCH GIRLS,HOUSE,SKY,CLOUDS.     32.50
ROYAL BAYREUTH,CREAMER,SUGAR,FIGURAL,GRAPES,BLUE-PURPLE,
   LEAVES,MARK............................................     56.50
ROYAL BAYREUTH,CREAMER,SUGAR,FIGURAL,PURPLE GRAPE,GREEN TO
   YELLOW LEAF............................................     67.00
ROYAL BAYREUTH,CREAMER,SUGAR,SALT,PEPPER,BLUE,WOMAN,BLUE
   MARK...................................................     65.00
ROYAL BAYREUTH,CREAMER,TWO MUSKETEERS IN WINE CELLAR,ARTIST
   DIXON,MARK.............................................     28.00
ROYAL BAYREUTH,CREAMER,YELLOW ROSES.......................     17.00
ROYAL BAYREUTH,CREAMER,YELLOW ROSES,BLUE MARK.............     16.00
ROYAL BAYREUTH,CUP & SAUCER,DEMITASSE,BROWN GROUND,
   MUSICIANS,BLUE MARK....................................     35.00
ROYAL BAYREUTH,CUP & SAUCER,DEMITASSE,RED POPPY...........     48.00
ROYAL BAYREUTH,CUP & SAUCER,FIGURAL,PINK CABBAGE ROSE,BLUE
   MARK...................................................    110.00
ROYAL BAYREUTH,CUP,SAUCER,COIN GOLD BAND AROUND TOP,PINK &
   BLUE FLORAL............................................      4.50
ROYAL BAYREUTH,CUP,TOMATO,LEAF SAUCER.....................      9.50
ROYAL BAYREUTH,CUP,WEDDING,CORINTHIAN,BLUE MARK...........     35.00
ROYAL BAYREUTH,DISH,CELERY,GREEN GROUND,WHITE & PINK ROSES,
   OPEN ENDS..............................................     55.00
ROYAL BAYREUTH,DISH,CHILD'S,CHILDREN SLIDING ON SNOW,
   HAND-PAINTED...........................................     47.50
ROYAL BAYREUTH,DISH,DEVIL & CARD,SIGNED...................     22.50
ROYAL BAYREUTH,DISH,DRESSER,THREE CORNERS,PINK FLORAL,
```

FOOTED,SIGNED.......................................... 10.00
ROYAL BAYREUTH,DISH,FEEDING,SAND BABIES,BLUE MARK,
7 1/2-IN.DIAMETER...................................... 45.00
ROYAL BAYREUTH,DISH,GREEN LEAVES,PINK RADISH HANDLE,
8 IN.LONG............................................. 19.00
ROYAL BAYREUTH,DISH,LOBSTER CLAW,OPEN,BLACK MARK........ 15.00
ROYAL BAYREUTH,DISH,NUT,GOLD-RETICULATED INSERTS,PINK ROSES,
GOLD EDGE............................................. 22.50
ROYAL BAYREUTH,DISH,RELISH,IVORY,HAND-PAINTED FLOWERS,
SIGNED,HANDLES........................................ 22.50
ROYAL BAYREUTH,DISH,SAUCE,GREEN,RED TOMATOES,5 1/2 IN...... 14.00
ROYAL BAYREUTH,DISH,SAUCE,HAND-PAINTED ROSES,HER MAJESTY,
YELLOW,GREEN.......................................... 4.50
ROYAL BAYREUTH,EWER,CORINTHIAN PATTERN,GREEK KEY,MAROON
GROUND,8 IN........................................... 39.50
ROYAL BAYREUTH,FERNERY,MEN IN BOAT FISHING............. 40.00
ROYAL BAYREUTH,HAIR RECEIVER,HUNTERS ON HORSEBACK,DOGS,GILT
FEET,MARK............................................. 35.00
ROYAL BAYREUTH,HAIR RECEIVER,HUNTERS,DOGS.............. 19.00
ROYAL BAYREUTH,HAIR RECEIVER,LITTLE GIRL HOLDING DOG ON
ROPE,FOOTED........................................... 45.00
ROYAL BAYREUTH,HAIR RECEIVER,PICTURES OF JACK & JILL,BLUE
MARK................................................. 22.50
ROYAL BAYREUTH,HAIR RECEIVER,PINK ROSES,PEARLIZED FINISH,
HIGH-FOOTED........................................... 28.50
ROYAL BAYREUTH,HAIR RECEIVER,SAND BABIES ON BEACH,FOOTED,
2 3/4 IN.HIGH......................................... 35.00
ROYAL BAYREUTH,HAIR RECEIVER,SHADED PINK & GREEN ROSES,BLUE
MARK................................................. 20.00
ROYAL BAYREUTH,HOLDER,HATPIN,THE MUSICIANS,SAUCER...... 35.00
ROYAL BAYREUTH,HUMIDOR,TOMATO.......................... 35.00
ROYAL BAYREUTH,INKWELL,MOOSE,COVER..................... 38.00
ROYAL BAYREUTH,JAR,COOKIE,SCENIC,ANIMALS,HANDLES,MARK...... 75.00
ROYAL BAYREUTH,JAR,POWDER,GIRL,THREE GEESE,COVER,BLUE MARK,
3 1/2 IN............................................. 30.00
ROYAL BAYREUTH,JARDENIERE,MINIATURE,ROSE DECOR,TWO PIECES,
4 IN.HIGH............................................. 38.00
ROYAL BAYREUTH,MATCH HOLDER,CLOWN,BLUE MARK............ 22.00
ROYAL BAYREUTH,MATCH HOLDER,DEVIL & CARD............... 45.00
ROYAL BAYREUTH,MATCH HOLDER,ELK........................ 30.00
ROYAL BAYREUTH,MATCH HOLDER,RED POPPY.................. 39.00
ROYAL BAYREUTH,MUG,BEER,GREEN,TAVERN SCENE............. 42.50
ROYAL BAYREUTH,MUG,BEER,JESTER DESIGN,ARTIST SIGNED,4 X
4 1/2 IN.HIGH......................................... 35.00
ROYAL BAYREUTH,MUG,DEVIL,BLACK MARK,4 1/2 IN........... 25.00
ROYAL BAYREUTH,MUG,SHAVING,WHITE,GOLD TRIM,DATED SEPT.20,
1870,BLUE MARK........................................ 10.00
ROYAL BAYREUTH,MUG,YE OLD BELLE,DRINKING CAVALIERS,GREEN
GROUND,MARK........................................... 24.50
ROYAL BAYREUTH,MUSTARD,TOMATO,GREEN LEAF HANDLE,FEET,TOP,
FINIAL TRIM........................................... 19.00
ROYAL BAYREUTH,MUSTARD,TOMATO,TWO PIECE................ 15.00
ROYAL BAYREUTH,NAPPIE,GREEN GROUND,YELLOW FLORAL,BLUE MARK,
7-IN.DIAMETER......................................... 14.00
ROYAL BAYREUTH,PITCHER,ALLOVER SCENICS,BULLS,HOUSES,BLUE
MARK,4 IN.HIGH........................................ 28.00
ROYAL BAYREUTH,PITCHER,CLOWN,3 1/2 IN.HIGH............. 52.50
ROYAL BAYREUTH,PITCHER,CORINTHIAN,BLACK,WHITE SEATED
FIGURES,5 IN.......................................... 28.00
ROYAL BAYREUTH,PITCHER,CORINTHIAN,ORANGE COLOR,GREEN LINING,
5 1/2 IN............................................. 48.50
ROYAL BAYREUTH,PITCHER,CREAM,GREEN,CRAB FORMS HANDLE,LEAF
PLATE................................................ 30.00
ROYAL BAYREUTH,PITCHER,CREAM,STRAWBERRY-SHAPED,3 3/4 IN.HIGH 32.50
ROYAL BAYREUTH,PITCHER,FIGURAL,BLACK CROW,OPEN ORANGE BEAK,
5 IN.HIGH............................................. 37.50
ROYAL BAYREUTH,PITCHER,GIRL & BOY IN SNOW SCENE,GOLD HANDLE,
4 3/4 IN............................................. 50.00
ROYAL BAYREUTH,PITCHER,HONEY,ROSES, MAY BEE WAS NEVER A GUDE
HONEY BEE ............................................ 25.00
ROYAL BAYREUTH,PITCHER,HUNT SCENE,GREEN,GOLD HANDLE,BLUE
MARK,5 IN............................................. 25.00
ROYAL BAYREUTH,PITCHER,LOBSTER,BLUE MARK,4 IN.HIGH..... 22.50
ROYAL BAYREUTH,PITCHER,LOBSTER,SIGNED,7 IN.TALL........ 58.00
ROYAL BAYREUTH,PITCHER,MELON SHAPE,GREEN STRIPES,VINE
HANDLE,PINK SPOUT..................................... 60.00
ROYAL BAYREUTH,PITCHER,MILK,FIGURAL,LEMON,LEAF TRIM & HANDLE 40.00
ROYAL BAYREUTH,PITCHER,MILK,MUSICIANS,MANDOLIN & VIOLA...... 48.00
ROYAL BAYREUTH,PITCHER,MILK,ROSE TAPESTRY,GREEN MARK....... 97.50
ROYAL BAYREUTH,PITCHER,MILK,SHAPE OF LEMON,BLUE MARK,
6 IN.HIGH............................................. 75.00

```
ROYAL BAYREUTH,PITCHER,MOOSE,MARK.......................   23.50
ROYAL BAYREUTH,PITCHER,NUDE PORTRAIT,BLUE MARK..........   55.00
ROYAL BAYREUTH,PITCHER,POPPY,4 3/4 IN.HIGH..............   35.00
ROYAL BAYREUTH,PITCHER,PORTRAIT,CORSET SHAPE,PINCHED SPOUT,
  7 IN.HIGH.............................................   38.00
ROYAL BAYREUTH,PITCHER,SCENE,FISHERMEN IN BOAT,BLUE MARK,
  5 1/2 IN..............................................   32.50
ROYAL BAYREUTH,PITCHER,SCENE,HORSEBACK RIDERS,DOGS,5 1/2 IN.   25.00
ROYAL BAYREUTH,PITCHER,SHEEP GRAZING,GOLD HANDLE,6 IN...   50.00
ROYAL BAYREUTH,PITCHER,STRAWBERRY SHAPE,VINE HANDLE,LEAF
  SPOUT.................................................   26.00
ROYAL BAYREUTH,PITCHER,TANKARD,SCENE,POLAR BEARS,SNOW,BLUE
  MARK..................................................   50.00
ROYAL BAYREUTH,PITCHER,WATER,FIGURAL,LEMON,LEAF TRIM &
  HANDLE................................................   68.00
ROYAL BAYREUTH,PITCHER,YELLOW APPLE.....................   42.00
ROYAL BAYREUTH,PLATE,BASKET OF FLOWERS,OAK LEAF & ROSE
  BORDER,SET OF 8.......................................   95.00
ROYAL BAYREUTH,PLATE,CAKE,MAN,SCYTHE,CHICKENS,ORANGE-BEIGE,
  GREEN,GOLD............................................   45.00
ROYAL BAYREUTH,PLATE,CORINTHIAN,BLACK,9-IN.DIAMETER.....   38.00
ROYAL BAYREUTH,PLATE,DEVIL AND CARDS.................ILLUS..   55.00
```

ROYAL BAYREUTH PLATE, DEVIL AND CARDS

```
ROYAL BAYREUTH,PLATE,DUTCH CHILDREN,COSTUMED,WINDMILLS,LAKE,
  BLUE MARK.............................................   36.00
ROYAL BAYREUTH,PLATE,DUTCH GIRL,BLUE MARK,7 1/4 IN......   20.00
ROYAL BAYREUTH,PLATE,FISHING SCENE,BLUE MARK,7 IN.......   30.00
ROYAL BAYREUTH,PLATE,GAME,PHEASANTS,SATIN FINISH,SWIRL EDGE,
  10 IN.................................................   78.00
ROYAL BAYREUTH,PLATE,GIRLS IN COLORFUL DRESS,BASKETS OF
  FISH,10 1/2 IN........................................   30.00
ROYAL BAYREUTH,PLATE,HORSEMAN,MAN & WOMAN RIDING,THREE HOUND
  DOGS,PAIR.............................................   85.00
ROYAL BAYREUTH,PLATE,HUNTER,DOG,MOUNTAIN SCENERY,10 1/2 IN..   45.00
ROYAL BAYREUTH,PLATE,HUNTING SCENE,BLUE MARK,7 IN.......   30.00
ROYAL BAYREUTH,PLATE,LEAF BACKGROUND,TOMATO CENTER,
  7 1/2 IN.,PAIR........................................   32.50
ROYAL BAYREUTH,PLATE,LEAF,HANDLE,5 1/2 IN...............   15.00
ROYAL BAYREUTH,PLATE,LEAF,4 3/4-IN.DIAMETER.............    8.50
ROYAL BAYREUTH,PLATE,LITTLE BOY BLUE,1794 BLUE MARK,
  7 1/2-IN.DIAMETER.....................................   52.50
ROYAL BAYREUTH,PLATE,NUT,APRICOT ROSES,PASTELS,LEAVES,GOLD
  RIM,BLUE MARK.........................................    6.00
ROYAL BAYREUTH,PLATE,PHEASANT ON PRAIRIE,GOLD LEAVES,
  1794 BLUE MARK........................................   85.00
ROYAL BAYREUTH,PLATE,SCENIC,TAPESTRY,ARAB & HORSES,PIERCED,
  9 IN..................................................  175.00
ROYAL BAYREUTH,PLATE,SNOW BABIES,WINTER SCENE OF CHILDREN
  SLEDDING,MARK.........................................   22.50
ROYAL BAYREUTH,PLATE,TOMATO WITH LEAF,COVER............   18.00
ROYAL BAYREUTH,PLATE,TOMATO,GREEN CENTER,7 IN..........   15.00
ROYAL BAYREUTH,PLATE,UNDERGLAZE FLORAL DECOR,PICTURE &
  MILLAR MARK...........................................   10.00
ROYAL BAYREUTH,POT,MUSTARD,TOMATO,COVER,BLUE MARK......   17.50
ROYAL BAYREUTH,POT,SYRUP,APPLE.........................   65.00
ROYAL BAYREUTH,SALAD,LEAF WITH TOMATO,5 1/2 IN.........   12.00
ROYAL BAYREUTH,SALT,OPEN,FIGURAL,LOBSTER CLAW..........    7.50
```

ROYAL BAYREUTH,SALT,RAMS ON MOUNTAINTOP,GREEN,BROWN,GILT,
  PEDESTAL,MARK...................................................  16.50
ROYAL BAYREUTH,SHOE,MAN'S OXFORD,SHADES OF BROWN,TAN LACES,
  5 1/4 IN.LONG..................................................  42.00
ROYAL BAYREUTH,STRING HOLDER,HEN'S HEAD.....................  55.00
ROYAL BAYREUTH,SUGAR & CREAMER,TOMATO,MARKED................  30.00
ROYAL BAYREUTH,SUGAR & CREAMER,YELLOW ROSES,SIGNED HER
  MAJESTY........................................................  25.00
ROYAL BAYREUTH,SUGAR,LOBSTER COVER,GREEN LETTUCE LEAF TRAY,
  BLUE MARK......................................................  22.50
ROYAL BAYREUTH,TEA SET,TOMATO,TEAPOT,CREAMER,SUGAR,FOUR CUPS
  & SAUCERS...................................................... 100.00
ROYAL BAYREUTH,TEAPOT,CREAMER,SUGAR,TOMATO..................  75.00
ROYAL BAYREUTH,TEAPOT,PASTEL LAVENDER,YELLOW,PANSIES,BLUE
  MARK...........................................................  72.00
ROYAL BAYREUTH,TEAPOT,STRAWBERRY,BLUE MARK..................  35.00
ROYAL BAYREUTH,TILE,CHILDREN ON SLED SLIDING DOWN HILL,
  6 1/4 IN.......................................................  24.00
ROYAL BAYREUTH,TOMATO,COVER,BLUE MARK.......................  11.00
ROYAL BAYREUTH,TOMATO,COVER,LETTUCE SAUCER..................  15.00
ROYAL BAYREUTH,TOMATO,COVERED,ON A RING-HANDLED PLATE.......  25.00
ROYAL BAYREUTH,TOOTHPICK,CHILDREN PLAYING RING AROUND ROSY,
  FOOTED.........................................................  22.00
ROYAL BAYREUTH,TOOTHPICK,LONGHORN CATTLE SCENE,FARM,TWO
  HANDLES........................................................  33.00
ROYAL BAYREUTH,TOOTHPICK,MUSICIANS,BLUE MARK................  20.00
ROYAL BAYREUTH,TRAY,DEVIL SHAPE,PLAYING CARD MATCH HOLDER...  55.00
ROYAL BAYREUTH,TRAY,PIN,SAND BABIES,CHILDREN RUNNING ON
  BEACH..........................................................  45.00
ROYAL BAYREUTH,TRAY,PIN,TWO CARDS & DEVIL'S HEAD,BLUE MARK..  20.00
ROYAL BAYREUTH,TRAY,ROSE TAPESTRY,SIGNED,10 IN.LONG X
  7 IN.WIDE...................................................... 110.00
ROYAL BAYREUTH,VASE,BLUE,PEASANT LADY,CLOUDS,BLUE MARK,
  5 IN.HIGH......................................................  14.00
ROYAL BAYREUTH,VASE,BROWN TO MAUVE TO PINK,YELLOW & PINK
  ROSES,GILT.....................................................  35.00
ROYAL BAYREUTH,VASE,CAVALIERS,SIGNED DIXON,3 1/2 IN.HIGH....  35.00
ROYAL BAYREUTH,VASE,FARMER WITH SCYTHE,CHICKENS,
  2 3/4 IN.HIGH..................................................  35.00
ROYAL BAYREUTH,VASE,GIRL WITH PUPPY ON LEASH,BLUE MARK,4 IN.  22.50
ROYAL BAYREUTH,VASE,GREEN GROUND,SCENE,HORSES,RIDERS,DOGS,
  MARK,4 IN......................................................  32.50
ROYAL BAYREUTH,VASE,GREEN,HUNTING SCENE,BLACK MARK..........  22.00
ROYAL BAYREUTH,VASE,MULTICOLORED IRIDESCENT,BLUE MARK,
  4 1/4 IN.......................................................  15.00
ROYAL BAYREUTH,VASE,PORTRAIT,PSYCHE,GREEN,GOLD,BLUE MARK,
  7 1/2 IN.......................................................  45.00
ROYAL BAYREUTH,VASE,PORTRAIT,TWO CLASSIC WOMEN,THREE
  HANDLES,3 IN.HIGH..............................................  28.50
ROYAL BAYREUTH,VASE,PORTRAIT,TWO LADIES IN LARGE HATS,
  MINIATURE,MARK.................................................  35.00
ROYAL BAYREUTH,VASE,PORTRAIT,TWO LADIES,BLUE MARK,6 IN.HIGH.  45.00
ROYAL BAYREUTH,VASE,PORTRAITS OF TWO WOMEN,YELLOW,BROWN
  GROUND,HANDLES.................................................  28.50
ROYAL BAYREUTH,VASE,PURPLE & GREEN GRAPES,BLUE MARK,
  5 IN.TALL......................................................  27.50
ROYAL BAYREUTH,VASE,QUAIL,BLUE MARK,4 1/2 IN................  22.50
ROYAL BAYREUTH,VASE,ROSES,RED,PINK,GREEN,3 1/4 IN.TALL......  35.00
ROYAL BAYREUTH,VASE,SAILBOAT,THREE-BAND JEWELING,4 1/2 IN...  35.00
ROYAL BAYREUTH,VASE,THREE DUTCH CHILDREN UNDER UMBRELLA,
  4 1/2 IN.......................................................  22.00
ROYAL BAYREUTH,VASE,WATER SCENE,DEER SCENE,ROSE TAPESTRY,
  4 1/2 IN.,PAIR................................................. 150.00
ROYAL BERLIN,PLATE,CAKE,GILDED OPEN LATTICE EDGE,ENAMEL
  BOUQUETS,SIGNED................................................   7.50
ROYAL BONN,BOWL,BROWN GLAZE,TULIPS,10 IN....................   5.00
ROYAL BONN,BOWL,PUNCH,FLOWER & GOLD DECOR,SIGNED,
  13 1/2-IN.DIAMETER............................................. 125.00
ROYAL BONN,BOWL,PUNCH,FLOWER DECOR,6 IN.HIGH,
  13 1/2-IN.DIAMETER............................................. 125.00
ROYAL BONN,BOWL,WILD ROSE & HEART DECOR,SIGNED,8 IN.WIDE,
  2 1/2 IN.DEEP..................................................  10.00
ROYAL BONN,BOWL,WILD ROSE,BLUE ON WHITE,RAISED DESIGN,7 IN.
  X 4 IN.........................................................  12.00
ROYAL BONN,BOWL,WILD ROSE,WHITE GROUND,BLUE,7 X 3 1/2 IN....  14.00
ROYAL BONN,CLOCK,GREEN & YELLOW GROUND,PINK ROSES,STRIKES,
  11 1/2 IN.HIGH................................................. 100.00
ROYAL BONN,CLOCK,GREEN SCROLLS,PINK,YELLOW FLORAL,BRASS
  FACE,10 IN.TALL................................................  65.00
ROYAL BONN,CLOCK,SHELF,ANSONIA WORKS,LAVENDER PINK,GREEN,
  YELLOW,13 IN................................................... 125.00

ROYAL BONN,COLOGNE,TAPESTRY-LIKE SURFACE,LEAVES,FLOWERS,GOLD
  HANDLES..................................................... 25.00
ROYAL BONN,DISH,BONE,APPLE BLOSSOM PATTERN,BLUE,SET OF 4.... 10.00
ROYAL BONN,DISH,CHEESE,GREEN,COVER WITH HANDLE,CASTLE MARK.. 18.00
ROYAL BONN,DISH,FLORAL SPRAYS,OPENWORK BORDER,HANDLES,OVAL.. 35.00
ROYAL BONN,DISH,SAUCE,WILD ROSE............................. 4.00
ROYAL BONN,EWER,MOSS DECOR,MATTE BEIGE GROUND,9 IN.......... 35.00
ROYAL BONN,JAR,COOKIE,HOPS PATTERN,WHITE GROUND,BLUE FLORAL,
  BLUE MARK.................................................. 22.50
ROYAL BONN,JAR,CRACKER,SCROLL,GOLD TRIM,FLORAL PATTERN,
  SILVER TOP................................................. 32.50
ROYAL BONN,PLATE,CAKE,PINK BAROQUE EDGE,ROSES,GILT,PEDESTAL,
  MARK...................................................... 18.00
ROYAL BONN,PLATE,GREEN GROUND,LARGE PINK FLOWERS,
  8-IN.DIAMETER............................................. 7.50
ROYAL BONN,URN,WHITE ROSES,MULTICOLORED LEAVES,
  13 3/4 IN.HIGH............................................ 35.00
ROYAL BONN,VASE,BLUE GROUND,FLORAL,GOLD TRIM,HANDLES,MARKED,
  12 1/2 IN................................................ 39.00
ROYAL BONN,VASE,DARK GREEN,IRIS DECOR,SIGNED & NUMBERED,
  10 IN.TALL............................................... 51.00
ROYAL BONN,VASE,DELFT,BLUE,WHITE,WINDMILL,7 1/4 X 4 IN...... 35.00
ROYAL BONN,VASE,FLORAL,12 1/2 IN.HIGH X 5-IN.DIAMETER...... 14.50
ROYAL BONN,VASE,FOREST SCENE,MOUNTAINS,FLORAL,HAND-PAINTED,
  10 IN.HIGH............................................... 35.00
ROYAL BONN,VASE,GREEN GROUND,MULTICOLORED FLORAL,GOLD,
  11 IN.HIGH,PAIR.......................................... 75.00
ROYAL BONN,VASE,GREEN GROUND,YELLOW & PINK ROSES,PAIR....... 100.00
ROYAL BONN,VASE,GREEN,IRIS,10 IN.......................... 20.00
ROYAL BONN,VASE,GREEN,PAINTED FLORAL,TWO HANDLES,12 IN.TALL. 75.00
ROYAL BONN,VASE,MULTICOLORED,GREEN,RED-BROWN,BLUE,CREAM
  PREDOMINATING............................................ 22.00
ROYAL BONN,VASE,PORTRAIT,PINK BANDS,GOLD TRIM,DATED 1855,
  HAND-PAINTED............................................. 110.00


    ROYAL COPENHAGEN PORCELAIN AND POTTERY HAS BEEN MADE IN
    DENMARK SINCE 1772. IT IS STILL BEING MADE. ONE OF
    THEIR MOST FAMOUS WARES IS THE CHRISTMAS PLATE SERIES
  ROYAL COPENHAGEN,SEE ALSO,CHRISTMAS PLATE
ROYAL COPENHAGEN,BOTTLE,WINE,ROSENBORG CASTLE............... 18.00
ROYAL COPENHAGEN,BOWL,SCULPTURED FIGURE OF MERMAID IN
  CENTER,6 IN.............................................. 45.00
ROYAL COPENHAGEN,COFFEEPOT,BLUE & WHITE.................... 32.50
ROYAL COPENHAGEN,CUP & SAUCER,BLUE,WHITE,BASKET WEAVE,
  1923 MARK,SET OF 8....................................... 32.00
ROYAL COPENHAGEN,FIGURINE,BEAR,11 IN.LONG,7 IN.HIGH........ 82.00
ROYAL COPENHAGEN,FIGURINE,GUINEA HEN,MARK,6 IN.HIGH........ 45.00
ROYAL COPENHAGEN,MUG,1968,LARGE........................... 24.00
ROYAL COPENHAGEN,MUG,1968,SMALL........................... 15.00
ROYAL COPENHAGEN,PLAQUE,MYTHOLOGICAL FIGURES,
  13 1/4-IN.DIAMETER,PAIR.................................. 275.00
ROYAL COPENHAGEN,PLAQUE,PORTRAIT,FRANKLIN ROOSEVELT,BLUE,
  WHITE,3 1/2 IN........................................... 2.00
ROYAL COPENHAGEN,PLATE,BROWN IRIS PATTERN................. 7.00
ROYAL COPENHAGEN,PLATE,HANGING,SCENES,SQUARE,3 X 3 IN.,SET
  OF 3.................................................... 25.00
ROYAL COPENHAGEN,PLATE,PORTRAIT,MERMAID AT WINTERTIME,
  COBALT,PAIR............................................. 25.00
ROYAL COPENHAGEN,PLATE,VIRGIN ISLANDS..................... 15.00
ROYAL COPENHAGEN,ROOSTER,CIRCA 1925,5 1/2 IN.,PAIR......... 125.00
ROYAL COPENHAGEN,TOBY,JOHN PEEL.......................... 11.00
ROYAL COPENHAGEN,VASE,BLUE BIRD & IRIS,4 3/4 IN........... 35.00
ROYAL COPENHAGEN,VASE,BULBOUS,LONG NECK,HAND-PAINTED
  SCROLLS,11 1/2 IN....................................... 75.00
ROYAL COPENHAGEN,VASE,FLORAL,WAVY LINE DESIGN AT BASE,
  ARTIST-SIGNED........................................... 12.00
ROYAL COPENHAGEN,VASE,PORTRAIT,GIRL WITH BIRDS,CHERUBS,BLUE,
  PAIR.................................................... 110.00
ROYAL COPENHAGEN,VASE,10 1/4 IN. HIGH.................... 50.00


    ROYAL CROWN DERBY COMPANY,LTD. WAS ESTABLISHED IN
    ENGLAND IN 1876.
  ROYAL CROWN DERBY,SEE CROWN DERBY
ROYAL CROWN DERBY,COFFEEPOT,GOLD,BLUE,RED TRIM,BROWN
  TRANSFER FLORAL......................................... 68.00
ROYAL CROWN DERBY,CREAMER,ORIENTAL-TYPE FLOWERS,CROWN MARK.. 12.00
ROYAL CROWN DERBY,CUP & SAUCER,BLUE & WHITE,ORIENTAL DECOR.. 15.00
ROYAL CROWN DERBY,EWER,TURQUOISE GROUND,RAISED GOLD FLORAL
  DECOR,9 IN.............................................. 85.00

```
ROYAL CROWN DERBY,PLATE,DARK BLUE,WHITE & RUST PANELS,
   FLOWERS,9 IN.....................................................   14.00
ROYAL CROWN DERBY,PLATE,FIGURES,FLOWERS,BLUE,WHITE,6 1/4 IN.     10.00
ROYAL CROWN DERBY,TOOTHPICK,WHITE GROUND,FLOWERS.............    10.00
ROYAL CROWN DERBY,TOOTHPICK,WHITE GROUND,FLORAL,GOLD COLOR
   RIM..........................................................   15.00
ROYAL CROWN DERBY,TRAY,WHITE,DARK BLUE FIRS & SWAG DESIGN,
   HANDLES,17 IN................................................   85.00
ROYAL CROWN DERBY,VASE,IVORY COLOR GROUND,RED,GREEN,GILT
   DECOR,10 IN.................................................   100.00
ROYAL CROWN DERBY,VASE,RED,GOLD,6 IN.HIGH...................     90.00
```

ROYAL DOULTON WAS THE NAME USED ON POTTERY MADE AFTER
1902. THE DOULTON FACTORY WAS FOUNDED IN 1815. THEIR
WARES ARE STILL BEING MADE.
ROYAL DOULTON,SEE ALSO,DOULTON

```
ROYAL DOULTON,BEAKER,GREEN TRANSFER,SOLDIER,WORLD WAR I,
   1919........................................................   24.00
ROYAL DOULTON,BOTTLE,DEWARS SCOTCH,COACHMAN,SAYS BEWARE OF
   THE VIDDERS.................................................   65.00
ROYAL DOULTON,BOTTLE,FIGURAL,NEGRO,BLACK CLOAK,HAT,HOLDS
   YELLOW GOBLET...............................................   22.00
ROYAL DOULTON,BOTTLE,WHISKEY,TARTAN-CLAD FIGURE OF ROB ROY,
   BROWN GLAZE.................................................   65.00
ROYAL DOULTON,BOWL & PITCHER,COBALT,GOLD DECOR.............   125.00
ROYAL DOULTON,BOWL,BROWN TONES,SCENE,COACH,SILVER RIM,
   8 IN.DIAMETER...............................................   35.00
ROYAL DOULTON,BOWL,CEREAL,CHILDS,BUNNYKINS,RABBIT FAMILY ON
   FRONT.......................................................   12.50
ROYAL DOULTON,BOWL,FLORAL,ALLOVER DECOR INSIDE,BLACK
   HANDLES,16 IN...............................................   80.00
ROYAL DOULTON,BOWL,PUNCH,BRIER ROSE PATTERN,BASE,10 QT......   150.00
ROYAL DOULTON,BOWL,ROBIN HOOD & LITTLE JOHN.................    9.50
ROYAL DOULTON,BOWL,ROBIN HOOD,FRIEND OF THE POOR............    9.50
ROYAL DOULTON,BOWL,YELLOW,CATHEDRAL WINDOWS,ALTAR,CARDINAL
   IN RED ROBE.................................................   24.50
ROYAL DOULTON,CANDLESTICK,BLUE,BROWN DECORATED BASE & TOP,
   6 1/2 IN....................................................   20.00
ROYAL DOULTON,CANDLESTICK,BODIAN CASTLE DESIGN,CROWN & LION
   MARK........................................................   17.00
ROYAL DOULTON,CANDLESTICK,MOTTLED,BEIGE,BROWN,MARKED,
   9 1/2 IN.HIGH,PAIR..........................................   82.50
ROYAL DOULTON,CHILD'S SET,BOWL,PLATE,EGG CUP,BUNNYKINS......   18.00
ROYAL DOULTON,CREAMER,COUNTESS,NO.523784,3 1/2 IN.HIGH......    6.50
ROYAL DOULTON,CUP & SAUCER,DEMITASSE,LEEDS SPRAYS,SET OF 6..   27.50
ROYAL DOULTON,CUP & SAUCER,PEKIN PATTERN,REG. NO.50423,
   OCTAGONAL...................................................    6.50
ROYAL DOULTON,CUP & SAUCER,STAGECOACH SCENE,YELLOW GROUND,
   BLACK EDGE..................................................   15.00
ROYAL DOULTON,CUSPIDOR,STREET SWEEPER,NIGHT WATCHMAN........   35.00
ROYAL DOULTON,FIGURINE,BALLOON MAN.........................   30.00
ROYAL DOULTON,FIGURINE,CAROLYN.............................   30.00
ROYAL DOULTON,FIGURINE,EASTER DAY..........................   35.00
ROYAL DOULTON,FIGURINE,ENGLISH BULLDOG,SITTING,UNION JACK
   ACROSS BACK.................................................   18.00
ROYAL DOULTON,FIGURINE,LADY,WEARING DEVIL COSTUME,BLACK,
   GREEN,8 IN.HIGH.............................................   75.00
ROYAL DOULTON,FIGURINE,MAUREEN,7 1/2 IN....................   30.00
ROYAL DOULTON,FIGURINE,SILKS AND RIBBONS...................   25.00
ROYAL DOULTON,FIGURINE,TOP O' THE HILL,7 1/2 IN............   30.00
ROYAL DOULTON,FIGURINE,WILLIAMSBURG WIGMAKER...............   42.00
ROYAL DOULTON,JAR,BISCUIT,PINK CLOVER BLOSSOMS,SILVER TOP...   35.00
ROYAL DOULTON,JAR,CRACKER,BLUE,GRAY,SILVER LID,HANDLE,CIRCA
   1879........................................................   50.00
ROYAL DOULTON,JAR,TOBACCO,DUTCH CHILDREN WATCH SUNSET,SIGNED
   NOKE........................................................   65.00
ROYAL DOULTON,JAR,TOBACCO,TAPESTRY,GOLD....................   30.00
ROYAL DOULTON,JUG,BLUE,WIDE BAND OF EMBOSSED GRAPES,BROWN
   HANDLE......................................................   13.50
ROYAL DOULTON,JUG,COBALT,TAN,HEAVEN HELPS THOSE,STOPPER,
   IMPRESSED MARK..............................................   22.50
ROYAL DOULTON,JUG,WHISKEY,TAN GROUND,BLUE FLORAL,SIGNED ESNG   45.00
ROYAL DOULTON,LAMP,TABLE,AUTUMN LEAVES,INCISED,ALLOVER
   DECOR,25 IN.TALL............................................   75.00
ROYAL DOULTON,MUG,ARRIET,2 1/2 IN..........................   15.50
ROYAL DOULTON,MUG,COBALT,MEDALLION SAYS ERIC WALTER 30TH MAY
   1903........................................................   20.00
ROYAL DOULTON,MUG,GRANNY,3 1/2 IN.HIGH.....................   18.50
ROYAL DOULTON,MUG,LORD NELSON,ENGLAND EXPECTS EVERY MAN WILL
   DO HIS DUTY.................................................   49.00
```

ROYAL DOULTON,MUG,PIED PIPER........................... 12.00
ROYAL DOULTON,MUG,REPEAT FIGURES OF PIPE SMOKER,HOUNDS,
  BROWN,TAN,SIGNED..................................... 17.00
ROYAL DOULTON,MUG,SAIREY GAMP,2 1/2 IN................. 15.50
ROYAL DOULTON,MUG,YE OLDE CHESHIRE CHEESE 1667,LONDON STREET
  SCENE............................................... 20.00
ROYAL DOULTON,PITCHER,BEER,PORTRAIT OF MAN GIVING TOAST,
  BACKSIDE MOTTO...................................... 25.00
ROYAL DOULTON,PITCHER,BROWN GROUND,BLUE HEART-SHAPED LEAVES,
  1875................................................ 55.00
ROYAL DOULTON,PITCHER,BULBOUS,PANELED,MOTTO,AMBER,
  9 3/4 IN.TALL....................................... 45.00
ROYAL DOULTON,PITCHER,DICKENSWARE,SCENE,FAGIN,FIREPLACE,
  CUPBOARD,TABLE...................................... 38.00
ROYAL DOULTON,PITCHER,EGYPTIAN,SPHINX HEAD SPOUT,CIRCA 1890,
  STONEWARE........................................... 35.00
ROYAL DOULTON,PITCHER,GRECIAN LADIES IN BAND AT TOP,6 IN.... 20.00
ROYAL DOULTON,PITCHER,HE THAT BUYS LAND,CIRCA 1880,
  STONEWARE,5 IN...................................... 22.50
ROYAL DOULTON,PITCHER,MADRAS,BLUE,WHITE,MARK,8 IN.HIGH...... 27.00
ROYAL DOULTON,PITCHER,MAN PLAYING PIPES OF PAN,SCENIC
  BACKGROUND,5 IN..................................... 28.00
ROYAL DOULTON,PITCHER,MEN PLAYING GOLF,9 IN............ 27.50
ROYAL DOULTON,PITCHER,MILK,ENGLISH COUNTRYSIDE DECOR,
  COTTAGES,5 1/2 IN................................... 20.00
ROYAL DOULTON,PITCHER,MILK,GRAY,BLUE,CRACKLE DESIGN,POLAR
  BEAR BAND........................................... 17.50
ROYAL DOULTON,PITCHER,MILK,ISAAC WALTON,OVERALL PICTURES &
  SAYINGS............................................. 15.00
ROYAL DOULTON,PITCHER,MILK,ISAAC WALTON,PICTURES,SAYINGS,
  PINT SIZE........................................... 25.00
ROYAL DOULTON,PITCHER,MONKS........................... 39.00
ROYAL DOULTON,PITCHER,MONKS,CARDINAL,SAYS THE JACKDAW OF
  RHEIMS,1902......................................... 65.00
ROYAL DOULTON,PITCHER,OLIVER TWIST.................... 16.00
ROYAL DOULTON,PITCHER,TAN,LEAF & FLORAL,LID,7 1/2 IN........ 22.00
ROYAL DOULTON,PITCHER,THATCHED COTTAGE DECOR,4 1/2 IN.HIGH.. 11.50
ROYAL DOULTON,PITCHER,WEDLOCK JOYS,ENGLAND,10 IN. HIGH...... 22.50
ROYAL DOULTON,PITCHER,YE SQUIRE YE PASSENGER,7 IN.HIGH...... 35.00
ROYAL DOULTON,PLAQUE,HANGING,EDWARD VII,QUEEN ALEXANDRA,
  1902,PAIR........................................... 65.00
ROYAL DOULTON,PLATE,ADMIRAL NELSON IN FULL COLOR,FLEET AT
  SPITHEAD............................................ 22.00
ROYAL DOULTON,PLATE,ARUNDEL CASTLE,10 1/2-IN.DIAMETER....... 25.00
ROYAL DOULTON,PLATE,BABY'S,BLACK,WHITE,THREE BLIND MICE..... 12.50
ROYAL DOULTON,PLATE,BATTLE OF HASTINGS................ 20.00
ROYAL DOULTON,PLATE,CASTLE SCENE,LAMBS IN MEADOW,GREEN,
  BROWN,10 1/2 IN..................................... 25.00
ROYAL DOULTON,PLATE,CENTER PORTRAIT,DICKENS,STORY CHARACTERS
  AROUND EDGE......................................... 24.50
ROYAL DOULTON,PLATE,COACH SCENE,8 IN.................. 16.00
ROYAL DOULTON,PLATE,COUNTESS,6-IN.DIAMETER............ 5.00
ROYAL DOULTON,PLATE,DEEP BLUE,WHITE HOUSE,WASHINGTON,D.C.,
  10 IN............................................... 12.50
ROYAL DOULTON,PLATE,DINNER,OLD LEEDS SPRAY,9 1/2 IN.,SET OF
  10.................................................. 39.50
ROYAL DOULTON,PLATE,DON QUIXOTE,SANCHO,WINDMILL,PASTURE
  SCENE............................................... 17.00
ROYAL DOULTON,PLATE,HAND-PAINTED,SILVER RIM,SIGNED SHREVE
  CO.................................................. 15.00
ROYAL DOULTON,PLATE,HORSE & CARRIAGE SCENE............ 12.00
ROYAL DOULTON,PLATE,HORSELESS CARRIAGE,'ITCH YER ON GUVENOR. 29.50
ROYAL DOULTON,PLATE,HORSELESS CARRIAGE,ROOM FOR ONE.. 29.50
ROYAL DOULTON,PLATE,JOYS SHARED WITH OTHERS ARE MORE THAN
  ENJOYED............................................. 12.50
ROYAL DOULTON,PLATE,NANKIN PATTERN,GOLD,10 1/2 IN.,SET OF 8. 65.00
ROYAL DOULTON,PLATE,NURSERY RHYME,LITTLE TOM TUCKER,8 IN.... 12.00
ROYAL DOULTON,PLATE,NURSERY RHYME,OLD WOMAN IN THE SHOE,
  6 1/4 IN............................................ 14.00
ROYAL DOULTON,PLATE,OLD LEEDS SPRAY,9 1/2-IN.DIAMETER....... 5.50
ROYAL DOULTON,PLATE,POOR JO,DICKENSWARE,10 1/2-IN.DIAMETER.. 25.00
ROYAL DOULTON,PLATE,PORTRAIT,LADY SIPS TEA,TEACUP BORDER,
  7 1/2 IN............................................ 23.50
ROYAL DOULTON,PLATE,PORTRAIT,ROBERT BURNS,BORDER PORTRAITS,
  BLUE,10 IN.......................................... 24.00
ROYAL DOULTON,PLATE,PORTRAIT,ROMEO.................... 12.50
ROYAL DOULTON,PLATE,RED FLOWERS IN CENTER,GREEN BORDER,
  10 IN............................................... 5.00
ROYAL DOULTON,PLATE,ROBERT BURNS, HERE'S A HEALTH,  THISTLE,
  12 IN............................................... 20.00
ROYAL DOULTON,PLATE,SAILING VESSELS................... 20.00

ROYAL DOULTON,PLATE,SCENIC,CASTLE,WATER,10 1/2 IN........... 18.00
ROYAL DOULTON,PLATE,SOUVENIR,BLUE,GEO.H.BOWMAN CO.,
   CLEVELAND,10 IN.................................... 10.00
ROYAL DOULTON,PLATE,STORYBOOK,ALICE IN WONDERLAND,7 IN...... 18.50
ROYAL DOULTON,PLATE,STREET SCENE,LAMPLIGHTER ON COBBLESTONE
   STREET............................................... 20.00
ROYAL DOULTON,PLATE,THE DOCTOR,10 1/2 IN................... 25.00
ROYAL DOULTON,PLATE,THE FAT BOY,SCENE WITH MAN,
   LONDON-TO-YORK COACH STOP............................ 22.50
ROYAL DOULTON,PLATE,THE HUNTING MAN,10 1/2 IN.............. 25.00
ROYAL DOULTON,PLATE,THE PARSON,10 1/2 IN................... 25.00
ROYAL DOULTON,PLATE,THE PARSON,TRICORNER HAT,SPECTACLES,WIG,
   RIM DECOR............................................ 17.00
ROYAL DOULTON,PLATE,THE SQUIRE,10 1/2 IN................... 25.00
ROYAL DOULTON,PLATE,WHITE,SCALLOPED,GOLD-ENCRUSTED,
   8 3/4 IN.,TWELVE..................................... 360.00
ROYAL DOULTON,POODLE,5 1/4 IN............................. 10.00
ROYAL DOULTON,SALT,OPEN,PEPPER,JAM POT,COVER,BROWN GROUND,
   BLUE LEAVES.......................................... 20.00
ROYAL DOULTON,SOUP,BEVERLY PATTERN,ROSE BORDER,SCALLOPED,
   GILT,SET OF 6........................................ 18.00
ROYAL DOULTON,TEAPOT,SCENE,KITCHEN,MAN,VERSES,BASKET WEAVE
   BORDER............................................... 35.00
ROYAL DOULTON,TOBY MUG,SIGNED,5 1/2 X 5 1/2 IN............. 30.00
ROYAL DOULTON,TOBY,AULD MAC,BEARDED MAN WITH GRIN.......... 38.00
ROYAL DOULTON,TOBY,DICK TURPIN,HAT,MUSTACHE,WIG............ 38.00
ROYAL DOULTON,TOBY,JESTER,TOUCHSTONE...................... 38.00
ROYAL DOULTON,TOBY,JOHN BARLEYCORN,OLD LAD,2 1/2 IN.HIGH.... 10.00
ROYAL DOULTON,TOBY,JOHN PEEL,3 1/2 IN..................... 18.50
ROYAL DOULTON,TOBY,LORD NELSON........................... 14.00
ROYAL DOULTON,TOBY,PIED PIPER............................ 28.00
ROYAL DOULTON,TOBY,ROBIN HOOD............................ 25.00
ROYAL DOULTON,TOBY,SAIREY GAMP,6 IN.TALL.................. 30.00
ROYAL DOULTON,TOBY,WINSTON CHURCHILL,WITH CIGAR............ 22.50
ROYAL DOULTON,TOOTHPICK,BROWN,TAN,RAISED DECOR,THREE HANDLES 17.50
ROYAL DOULTON,TOOTHPICK,HUNTING SCENE IN HIGH RELIEF,SILVER
   RIM,ROUND............................................ 27.00
ROYAL DOULTON,TOOTHPICK,RELIEF FIGURES,HUNTING SCENE,TAN,
   BROWN,HANDLES........................................ 15.00
ROYAL DOULTON,TUMBLER,SAYS VICTORY 1919,GREEN TRANSFER...... 24.00
ROYAL DOULTON,TUMBLER,THE ALLIES 1919,4 IN................ 10.00
ROYAL DOULTON,VASE,BLUE,BROWN,INCISED DECOR,RAISED BEADING,
   1902,PAIR............................................ 55.00
ROYAL DOULTON,VASE,CARAFE SHAPE,GLAZED MOTTLING,TAPESTRY
   BAND,7 IN............................................ 15.00
ROYAL DOULTON,VASE,COBALT,DESIGNS IN RELIEF,GILT,
   ARTIST-SIGNED,PAIR................................... 75.00
ROYAL DOULTON,VASE,DESERT SCENE,ARABIAN HEADS FORM HANDLES,
   8 3/4 IN............................................. 48.50
ROYAL DOULTON,VASE,IVANHOE FIGURE,FOREST SCENIC BACKGROUND,
   7 1/2 IN.TALL........................................ 25.00
ROYAL DOULTON,VASE,MOTTLED BLUE & PINK,BUTTERFLY DECOR,
   6 IN.TALL............................................ 20.00
ROYAL DOULTON,VASE,VARIEGATED BLUE & GRAY GROUND,BIRDS,
   BRANCH,SIGNED........................................ 85.00
ROYAL DUX,BOWL,TRIANGLE,PINK,GIRL,LONG HAIR,GREEN,ORCHID
   FLOWERS,HANDLES...................................... 75.00
ROYAL DUX,FIGURINE,AFGHAN HOUND,LYING POSITION,GOLD MATTE,
   6 1/2 X 14 IN........................................ 35.00
ROYAL DUX,FIGURINE,BOY IN PINK & GREEN NAPOLEONIC COSTUME,
   7 1/2 IN............................................. 90.00
ROYAL DUX,FIGURINE,BOY,GIRL,PEASANT,CARRYING JUGS,16 IN.,
   PAIR................................................. 200.00
ROYAL DUX,FIGURINE,BOY,GIRL,WATER CARRIERS,ROSE-COLOR ROBE,
   PAIR................................................. 120.00
ROYAL DUX,FIGURINE,CAMEL,RIDER,SERVANT,FEED BAG,
   17 1/2 IN.HIGH....................................... 325.00
ROYAL DUX,FIGURINE,CAT,SIAMESE,GRAY,15 IN.TALL............. 35.00
ROYAL DUX,FIGURINE,CLASSIC WOMAN,IVORY,GREEN,GOLD,
   12 1/4 IN.HIGH,PAIR.................................. 225.00
ROYAL DUX,FIGURINE,DOE,BROWN,WHITE,HIGH GLOSS,MARK,8 X
   11 IN................................................ 40.00
ROYAL DUX,FIGURINE,DOG,IRISH SETTER,POINTER,RUNNING,
   7 1/2 IN.TALL,PAIR................................... 125.00
ROYAL DUX,FIGURINE,ENGLISH SETTER,BIRD IN MOUTH,WHITE
   SPECKLED BROWN....................................... 75.00
ROYAL DUX,FIGURINE,GIRL HOLDING WATER JARS,BOY WITH FISH
   BASKET,PAIR.......................................... 160.00
ROYAL DUX,FIGURINE,GIRL ON SHELL,PRE-1891 MARK,18 IN.TALL... 395.00
ROYAL DUX,FIGURINE,GIRL,RUFFLED DRESS,CARRYING FLOWERS,GOLD
   BASE,8 IN............................................ 52.00

```
ROYAL DUX,FIGURINE,HOUNDS,BROWN,WHITE,TRIANGLE MARK,7 1/2 X
   9 1/2 IN.......................................................   35.00
ROYAL DUX,FIGURINE,LADY HOLDS WATER JUGS,AUSTRIA,
   18 1/8 IN.HIGH,PAIR..........................................   100.00
ROYAL DUX,FIGURINE,LADY,BOWL-SHAPED LILY PADS,LAVENDER IRIS,
   11 IN.LONG...................................................   185.00
ROYAL DUX,FIGURINE,LIONESS,STALKING,OVAL BASE,MARK,7 IN.HIGH   150.00
ROYAL DUX,FIGURINE,MAN CARRYING WATER JUGS,BOHEMIA,PINK
   TRIANGLE MARK................................................    59.00
ROYAL DUX,FIGURINE,PARROT,WHITE BASE,GLAZED,17 IN.LONG,
   8 1/2 IN.TALL...............................................    60.00
ROYAL DUX,FIGURINE,PEASANT GIRL,BOY,PINK,GREEN,TRIANGLE
   MARK,11 IN.,PAIR.............................................    75.00
ROYAL DUX,FIGURINE,REARING STALLION,MATTE WHITE,COBALT BASE,
   16 IN.TALL...................................................    50.00
ROYAL DUX,PLANTER,FIGURE OF BOY ON EDGE PLAYING FLUTE,
   BOHEMIAN,7 IN.HIGH...........................................    65.00
ROYAL DUX,PLANTER,FIGURE OF BOY SITS ON EDGE,PLAYS FLUTE,
   3 1/2 IN....................................................    67.50
ROYAL DUX,PLANTER,GIRL & LION AT ONE END,RED MARK,15 X
   9 1/2 IN....................................................   235.00
ROYAL DUX,VASE,19 1/2 IN...........................ILLUS.    75.00
ROYAL DUX,VASE,APPLIED FLOWERS,MARKED.........................    20.00
ROYAL DUX,VASE,BEIGE GROUND,FLORAL,LEAVES,TWISTED HANDLES,
   12 1/2 IN.TALL..............................................    48.00
```

ROYAL DUX VASE

```
ROYAL DUX,VASE,BEIGE GROUND,GOLD & OLIVE GRAPES IN RELIEF,
   HANDLES,16 IN...............................................    90.00
ROYAL DUX,VASE,CUPID IN RELIEF,4 IN...........................    16.00
ROYAL DUX,VASE,FLORAL DECOR,BOHEMIA,8 IN......................    52.00
ROYAL DUX,VASE,IVORY GROUND,GREEN,PINK,GOLD DECOR,
   11 1/2 IN.,PAIR.............................................   140.00
ROYAL DUX,VASE,IVORY GROUND,PINK FLORAL,GOLD TRACERY,V MARK,
   PAIR........................................................   140.00
```

```
     ROYAL FLEMISH GLASS WAS MADE DURING THE LATE 1880S IN
   NEW BEDFORD,MASSACHUSETTS,BY THE MOUNT WASHINGTON
   GLASS WORKS. IT IS A COLORED SATIN GLASS DECORATED IN
   DARK COLORS WITH GOLD DESIGNS.
ROYAL FLEMISH,COOKIE JAR,SILVER PLATED COVER.........ILLUS..   935.00
ROYAL FLEMISH,JAR,ROSE,GREEN,OCHER,MULBERRY,MEDALLIONS,
   STEEPLE TOP...............................................1,650.00
ROYAL FLEMISH,VASE,COIN MEDALLIONS,PANELED,HANDLES,8 IN.HIGH1,395.00
ROYAL FLEMISH,VASE,ORCHIDS....................................   900.00
ROYAL LANCASTRIAN,BOWL,SILVER LUSTER,ORANGE,YELLOW MOTTLE,
   GLADYS RODGERS..............................................    38.00
ROYAL MUNICH,CHOCOLATE POT,SIX CUPS,SAUCERS,YELLOW & WHITE
   ROSES,GOLD..................................................   125.00
```

ROYAL FLEMISH COOKIE JAR

ROYAL MUNICH,PLAQUE,FRUIT CENTER,GOLD SCROLL EDGE,
 HAND-PAINTED...................................................... 42.50
ROYAL MUNICH,PLATE,GAME,PHEASANT CENTER,MEDALLION BORDER,
 BIRDS,CERISE...................................................... 25.00
ROYAL MUNICH,PLATE,THE CLEANERS PLATE,DARK GREEN BORDER,
 GOLD,10 IN........................................................ 35.00
ROYAL RUDOLSTADT,BOWL,FLOWERS,TIGER LILY,FOOTED,
 5 1/2 IN.ACROSS................................................... 16.00
ROYAL RUDOLSTADT,BOWL,IVORY SATIN FINISH,LARGE ROSES........ 25.00
ROYAL RUDOLSTADT,BOWL,SCENE,SKIER,PLATE,WINTER SCENE,HORSE,
 SLEIGH............................................................ 50.00
ROYAL RUDOLSTADT,BOWL,SHELL SHAPE,WHITE,VIOLETS............. 24.00
ROYAL RUDOLSTADT,BOX,POWDER,WHITE,VIOLETS,COVER............. 12.00
ROYAL RUDOLSTADT,CREAMER,PINK & YELLOW ROSES,GREEN LEAVES,
 COVER,J.KAHN...................................................... 25.00
ROYAL RUDOLSTADT,CUP & SAUCER,MAROON GROUND,PORTRAIT,LADY,
 1 3/4 IN.HIGH..................................................... 14.00
ROYAL RUDOLSTADT,CUP,CUSTARD,HAT SHAPE,PLATE,BLUE,PINK
 MORNING GLORIES................................................... 10.00
ROYAL RUDOLSTADT,DISH,BUTTER,PURPLE,BURNT ORANGE,GREEN
 FLORAL,GILT,COVER................................................. 23.50
ROYAL RUDOLSTADT,DISH,CHEESE & CRACKER,BRIDAL ROSES,
 FORGET-ME-NOTS.................................................... 18.00
ROYAL RUDOLSTADT,DISH,NUT,FOOTED,PRUSSIA.................... 7.50
ROYAL RUDOLSTADT,DISH,PICKLE,BLUE EDGE,PINK ROSES,SIGNED,
 8 IN.LONG......................................................... 14.00
ROYAL RUDOLSTADT,DISH,RELISH,ROSES,GOLD,BLACK DECOR,HANDLES,
 MARKED............................................................ 12.00
ROYAL RUDOLSTADT,DISH,SHELL SHAPE,PINK,BLUE GROUND,YELLOW,
 WHITE ROSES....................................................... 35.00
ROYAL RUDOLSTADT,HOLDER,HATPIN,BLUEBIRD DECOR............... 15.00
ROYAL RUDOLSTADT,HOLDER,HATPIN,LAVENDER BAND,ROSES,PRUSSIA.. 12.00
ROYAL RUDOLSTADT,HOLDER,HATPIN,PALE YELLOW GROUND,SHADED
 ROSES,MARK........................................................ 18.00
ROYAL RUDOLSTADT,MAYONNAISE,UNDERPLATE,LADLE,LAVENDER,GOLD
 FLORAL,MARK....................................................... 22.50
ROYAL RUDOLSTADT,NAPPIE,LEAF SHAPE......................... 14.00
ROYAL RUDOLSTADT,NAPPIE,PINK & YELLOW ROSES,GOLD TRIM,OPEN
 HANDLE............................................................ 12.50
ROYAL RUDOLSTADT,PITCHER,SYRUP,HAND-PAINTED FLOWERS,SIGNED
 STEIN............................................................. 7.50
ROYAL RUDOLSTADT,PLATE,BLOSSOMS,PEACHES,GOLD BAND,8 1/2 IN.. 25.00
ROYAL RUDOLSTADT,PLATE,CAKE,HAND-PAINTED PURPLE VIOLETS,
 14 IN............................................................. 32.50
ROYAL RUDOLSTADT,PLATE,CAKE,LARGE PINK ROSES,GOLD,GREEN,BLUE
 GROUND,MARK....................................................... 18.00
ROYAL RUDOLSTADT,PLATE,CAKE,VIOLETS,GOLD,ARTIST-SIGNED,MARK. 32.50
ROYAL RUDOLSTADT,PLATE,CHILD'S,RABBITS,MARKED PRUSSIA,
 5 1/4-IN.DIAMETER................................................. 6.00
ROYAL RUDOLSTADT,PLATE,GREEN GROUND,WHITE ROSES,8 IN.,PAIR.. 15.00
ROYAL RUDOLSTADT,PLATE,ORANGE & GREEN NASTURTIUMS,SIGNED
 H.LARGNER......................................................... 15.00
ROYAL RUDOLSTADT,PLATE,PINK & WHITE FLOWERS,5 1/2 IN.,SET OF
 6................................................................. 12.00
ROYAL RUDOLSTADT,PLATE,PINK & YELLOW ROSES,FLORAL,GILT
 BORDER,8 1/2 IN................................................... 15.00

```
ROYAL RUDOLSTADT,PLATE,PINK FLOWERS,ARTIST-SIGNED,PRUSSIA,
  6 IN.,SET OF 4.......................................        15.00
ROYAL RUDOLSTADT,PLATE,ROSE DECOR,GOLD EDGE,8 IN...........        12.00
ROYAL RUDOLSTADT,PLATE,WHITE GROUND,FRUITS,GREEN,YELLOW,
  PINK,PURPLE..........................................        15.00
ROYAL RUDOLSTADT,TRAY,PERFUME,WHITE,VIOLETS,8 X 11 IN......        18.00
ROYAL RUDOLSTADT,VASE,MULTICOLOR FLORAL,GOLD CLAW FEET &
  HANDLES,6 IN.........................................        25.00
ROYAL VIENNA,BOWL,MELON SECTIONS,SCENE,VENUS,CHERUB,
  KAUFFMANN,7 3/4 IN...................................       150.00
ROYAL VIENNA,BOX,JEWELRY,BLUE GROUND,PASTEL DECOR,FOOTED,
  BEEHIVE MARK.........................................        28.50
ROYAL VIENNA,COMPOTE,RED,COBALT,GOLD,BEEHIVE MARK..........        32.50
ROYAL VIENNA,DISH,CANDY,DIAMOND-SHAPED MEDALLIONS,COVER,
  5 1/2 IN.HIGH........................................       115.00
ROYAL VIENNA,DISH,CANDY,RED & GOLD FLORAL,TRACERY,
  TRICORNERED,MARK.....................................        24.50
ROYAL VIENNA,EWER,CREAMY GROUND,VIOLET SPRAYS,PINK FLORAL,
  HANDLES,10 IN........................................        39.50
ROYAL VIENNA,JAR,CRANBERRY,PANELS,LADY,DANCING CUPIDS,
  BEEHIVE MARK,COVER...................................        95.00
ROYAL VIENNA,PLATE,BLUE BORDER,GOLD TRIM,1820 MARK,
  ARTIST-SIGNED,12...................................1,455.00
ROYAL VIENNA,PLATE,BROWN GROUND,ROSE,GOLD,SCALLOPED,PALETTE
  MARK.................................................        12.00
ROYAL VIENNA,PLATE,COUNTESS GOWER,CHILD,PALACE ROOM,SIGNED
  KAHN,MARK............................................       185.00
ROYAL VIENNA,PLATE,GAME,QUAIL,FLORAL,GOLD BAND,CROWN &
  BEEHIVE MARK.........................................        65.00
ROYAL VIENNA,PLATE,GARDEN SCENE WITH PEOPLE,BLUE BEEHIVE....       135.00
ROYAL VIENNA,PLATE,GIRL IN GARDEN,FLOWERS,SIGNED WAGNER.....       175.00
ROYAL VIENNA,PLATE,HAND-PAINTED FIGURES,BLUE & GOLD BORDER,
  PAIR.................................................        17.50
ROYAL VIENNA,PLATE,HEGDOR IN PARIS,SIGNED.................       170.00
ROYAL VIENNA,PLATE,LADIES,HANGING,BEEHIVE MARK,
  8 1/2-IN.DIAMETER....................................        32.50
ROYAL VIENNA,PLATE,LIEBESTRAUM,BLUE & GLLD BORDER,SIGNED....       100.00
ROYAL VIENNA,PLATE,PINK & RED ROSES,GOLD TRIM,12 IN........        45.00
ROYAL VIENNA,PLATE,PINK & WHITE MUMS,GOLD CENTER & BORDER,
  ARTIST-SIGNED........................................        18.00
ROYAL VIENNA,PLATE,PORTRAIT,AMOROSA,BURGUNDY,GOLD TRACERY,
  10 1/2 IN............................................        57.00
ROYAL VIENNA,PLATE,PORTRAIT,ARIADNE,GREEN LEAVES IN HAIR,
  SIGNED WAGNER........................................       165.00
ROYAL VIENNA,PLATE,PORTRAIT,BLONDE LADY,DEEP RUBY COLOR
  BORDER,GOLD,MARK.....................................        45.00
ROYAL VIENNA,PLATE,PORTRAIT,BLUE & GOLD BORDER,ARTIST
  BAERSCHNEIDER........................................       110.00
ROYAL VIENNA,PLATE,PORTRAIT,BROWN-HAIRED WOMAN,GOLD BORDER,
  BEEHIVE..............................................        85.00
ROYAL VIENNA,PLATE,PORTRAIT,FLORAL BORDER.................       175.00
ROYAL VIENNA,PLATE,PORTRAIT,GIRL,LONG HAIR,SIGNED WAGNER,
  BLUE BEEHIVE.........................................       125.00
ROYAL VIENNA,PLATE,PORTRAIT,GIRL,SIGNED WAGNER,RED BEEHIVE
  OVERGLAZE............................................       125.00
ROYAL VIENNA,PLATE,PORTRAIT,GOLD BORDER,SIGNED WAGNER,RED
  BEEHIVE..............................................       150.00
ROYAL VIENNA,PLATE,PORTRAIT,GOLD TRACERY,BURGUNDY GROUND,
  9 3/8 IN.............................................        55.00
ROYAL VIENNA,PLATE,PORTRAIT,GRACIOSA,HEAD,SHOULDERS,GOLD
  TRACERY,8 IN.........................................        35.00
ROYAL VIENNA,PLATE,PORTRAIT,HAPSBURG PRINCESS,CREAM GROUND,
  GILT BORDER..........................................        65.00
ROYAL VIENNA,PLATE,PORTRAIT,LADY,RUBY COLOR BORDER,GOLD,
  BEEHIVE MARK.........................................        45.00
ROYAL VIENNA,PLATE,PORTRAIT,SIGNED WAGNER.................       110.00
ROYAL VIENNA,PLATE,PORTRAIT,WOMAN,GOLD BORDER,BEEHIVE MARK,
  LEHNSUCHT............................................        65.00
ROYAL VIENNA,PLATE,PROFILE OF WOMAN,SIGNED WAGNER..........       150.00
ROYAL VIENNA,PLATE,PSYCHE UND AMOR,SCENE,SIGNED WAGNER,
  BEEHIVE MARK.........................................       155.00
ROYAL VIENNA,PLATE,PSYCHE,SIGNED WAGNER,GOLD CRUST BORDER...       165.00
ROYAL VIENNA,PLATE,SIGNED FRITCHIE,9 1/2-IN.DIAMETER.......       125.00
ROYAL VIEANN,PLATE,TELEMACHUS,SIGNED.....................       170.00
ROYAL VIENNA,PLATE,THE GLEANERS,GREEN BAND,GOLD TRACERY,
  BEEHIVE MARK.........................................        28.50
ROYAL VIENNA,PLATE,WHITE & BLACK MEDALLIONS,SIGNED RIENER,
  1749 MARK,12......................................1,800.00
ROYAL VIENNA,PLATE,WOMAN,THREE CUPIDS,BLUE BEEHIVE,
  9 1/2 IN.DIAMETER....................................       150.00
ROYAL VIENNA,SALT DIP,BEADED GOLD EDGE,ORNATE FEET,BEEHIVE..         7.50
```

ROYAL VIENNA,TEAPOT,WHITE,PLUM-COLORED DECOR,HAND-PAINTED,
  BEEHIVE MARK.............................................     75.00
ROYAL VIENNA,TRAY,PORTRAIT,LADY,CREAMY GROUND,GOLD BANDS,
  SCALLOPED...............................................     58.50
ROYAL VIENNA,URN,PORTRAIT,QUEEN LOUISE,CERISE,ORMULU FINIAL,
  14 IN.,PAIR.............................................    195.00
ROYAL VIENNA,VASE,CLASSIC MEDALLION CENTER,BLUE,RED,BEEHIVE
  MARK,PAIR...............................................    145.00
ROYAL VIENNA,VASE,GOLD DECOR,COBALT,8 1/4 IN.HIGH..........     60.00
ROYAL VIENNA,VASE,LORELEI,CUPID MEDALLIONS,SCENES,SCALLOPED,
  DOME STOPPER............................................    185.00
ROYAL VIENNA,VASE,MEDALLION CENTER,BLUE,RED,BEEHIVE MARK,
  12 IN.,PAIR.............................................    138.00
ROYAL VIENNA,VASE,MEDALLIONS,MOTHER,CHILD,MAN HOLDS WREATH,
  19 IN.,PAIR.............................................    200.00
ROYAL VIENNA,VASE,MOSES IN BASKET,MOTHER,CHILDREN ON LIONS,
  SIGNED WAGNER...........................................    150.00
ROYAL VIENNA,VASE,PALACE,JEWELS,PORTRAIT,SCENES,SIGNED
  WAGNER,LID,27 IN.......................................1,200.00
ROYAL VIENNA,VASE,PINK GROUND,PAINTED FIGURE IN CENTER,
  11 1/2 IN.HIGH.........................................    250.00


        ROYAL WORCESTER PORCELAIN AND POTTERY WAS MADE IN
        ENGLAND FROM 1862 TO THE PRESENT TIME. THE FACTORY
        WAS FOUNDED IN 1751 BUT A DIFFERENT NAME WAS USED.
      ROYAL WORCESTER,SEE ALSO WORCESTER
ROYAL WORCESTER,BASKET,BEIGE & GOLD COLOR,GREEN MARK,
  10 1/2 X 5 3/4 IN.......................................     75.00
ROYAL WORCESTER,BOTTLE,PILGRIM,RETICULATED,YELLOW GOLD,
  WHITE,FOOTED............................................    175.00
ROYAL WORCESTER,BOWL,BLACKBERRIES,RED LEAVES,GREEN PANELS,
  FLORAL,3 IN.............................................     30.00
ROYAL WORCESTER,BOWL,GOLD-OUTLINED LEAVES,RETICULATED,GOLD
  ENAMEL..................................................     75.00
ROYAL WORCESTER,BOWL,SALAD,BLUE GROUND,BEIGE ACANTHUS
  LEAVES,SILVER RIM.......................................     85.00
ROYAL WORCESTER,BOWL,SALAD,SILVER RIM,FORK & SPOON WITH
  SILVER BOWLS............................................    185.00
ROYAL WORCESTER,BOWL,SUGAR,HAND-PAINTED FLORAL SPRAYS,GOLD,
  COVER...................................................     55.00
ROYAL WORCESTER,BOX,PIN,ROSE DECOR,COVER,OBLONG,
  3 1/2 IN.LONG...........................................     35.00
ROYAL WORCESTER,CANDLEHOLDER,GILT MOUSE ON WOODEN BASE,
  2 3/4 X 6 IN.LONG.......................................    100.00
ROYAL WORCESTER,CANDLESNUFFER,CHINESE MAN,FAN IN HAND,HAT,
  PIGTAIL.................................................     45.00
ROYAL WORCESTER,CANDLESNUFFER,FIGURINE,MONK HOLDING BOOK,
  WHITE GROUND............................................     35.00
ROYAL WORCESTER,CANDLESNUFFER,WHITE MONKEY HOLDING GILDED
  FLOWER..................................................     35.00
ROYAL WORCESTER,CANDLESNUFFER,OLD GENT,NIGHTCAP,BATHROBE,HAS
  TOOTHACHE...............................................     50.00
ROYAL WORCESTER,CIGARETTE SERVER,PINK ROSES,BLUE,YELLOW
  FLORAL,OVAL.............................................      8.00
ROYAL WORCESTER,COFFEEPOT,BEIGE GROUND,FLOWER CLUSTERS,MASK
  OF WOMAN................................................    135.00
ROYAL WORCESTER,COMPOTE,RETICULATED,PEDESTAL,JEWELED,
  6-IN.DIAMETER...........................................    250.00
ROYAL WORCESTER,CREAMER & SUGAR,FLORAL DECOR INSIDE &
  OUTSIDE,1892............................................     60.00
ROYAL WORCESTER,CREAMER,SUGAR,CREAMY GROUND,LEAVES,SILVER
  PLATE HOLDER............................................     45.00
ROYAL WORCESTER,CREAMER,WHITE,PAIR........................     75.00
ROYAL WORCESTER,CREAMER,YELLOW,PEACH COLOR,REG.NO.234574,
  1898....................................................     25.00
ROYAL WORCESTER,CUP & SAUCER,DEMITASSE,FLORAL,CREAM COLOR
  GROUND,MARK.............................................     17.50
ROYAL WORCESTER,CUP & SAUCER,DEMITASSE,PASTORAL SCENE,
  ARTIST-SIGNED...........................................     35.00
ROYAL WORCESTER,CUP & SAUCER,HAND-PAINTED FLORAL,GOLD
  SCALLOPED EDGE..........................................     32.50
ROYAL WORCESTER,CUP & SAUCER,LATTICINO BORDER,PINK ROSE
  MEDALLION INSERT........................................     10.00
ROYAL WORCESTER,CUP & SAUCER,WIDE LATTICINO BORDER.........     10.00
ROYAL WORCESTER,CUP,SAUCER,DESSERT PLATE,ROSE MEDALLIONS,
  GOLD LATTICING..........................................     10.00
ROYAL WORCESTER,DEMITASSE SET,FLORAL,BUTTERFLIES,SERVES SIX,
  50 PIECES...............................................    395.00
ROYAL WORCESTER,DISH,ENGLISH SCENE,PAIR...................      8.00
ROYAL WORCESTER,DISH,LEAF SHAPE,CREAM TO PEACH,BLUE FLORAL,

```
    10 1/2 IN........................................  55.00
ROYAL WORCESTER,DISH,PEANUT,SHELL SHAPE,MARKED ENGLAND,
    3 1/2 X 3 1/2 IN................................  10.00
ROYAL WORCESTER,EWER,RETICULATED,FLORAL NECK,GOLD RIB,
    11 IN.TALL.....................................  165.00
ROYAL WORCESTER,FIGURINE,INDIAN CHIEF,MODELED BY
    E.M.GERTNER,7 IN.HIGH..........................  17.50
ROYAL WORCESTER,FIGURINE,LADY,DRAPED DRESS,HOLDS BIRD,CREAM,
    GOLD...........................................  85.00
ROYAL WORCESTER,FIGURINE,MAN DRINKS FROM GOURD,WOMAN,HADLEY,
    17 IN.,PAIR....................................  375.00
ROYAL WORCESTER,FIGURINE,MONK,WHITE ROBE,ROSY CHEEKS,GRAY
    BEARD..........................................  95.00
ROYAL WORCESTER,FIGURINE,TURK,TURBAN,GOWN,SASH,SLIPPERS,
    MUSTACHE,1889..................................  110.00
ROYAL WORCESTER,JAR,BISCUIT,POLYCHROME FLORAL,PANELS,GOLD,
    COVER..........................................  95.00
ROYAL WORCESTER,JAR,BISCUIT,SHADED CREAM,POLYCHROME FLORAL
    CENTER.........................................  100.00
ROYAL WORCESTER,NAUTILUS SHELL ON SEAWEED STEM,SHELLS AT
    BASE,MARK......................................  95.00
ROYAL WORCESTER,PITCHER,BASKET WEAVE,APPLIED GREEN & GOLD
    LIZARD,GILT....................................  75.00
ROYAL WORCESTER,PITCHER,BEIGE GROUND,FLORAL SPRAYS,GOLD
    HANDLE,BULBOUS.................................  87.50
ROYAL WORCESTER,PITCHER,BISCUIT GROUND,FLORAL DECOR,TWISTED
    HANDLE,7 IN....................................  48.00
ROYAL WORCESTER,PITCHER,BLUE,WHITE,GOLD DAISIES,CIRCA 1893,
    7 IN.HIGH......................................  125.00
ROYAL WORCESTEP,PITCHER,BULBOUS,MULTICOLORED FLORAL,REEDED
    HANDLE.........................................  55.00
ROYAL WORCESTER,PITCHER,CREAM COLOR GROUND,PURPLE & PINK
    SWEET PEAS.....................................  72.50
ROYAL WORCESTER,PITCHER,CREAM GROUND,FLORAL,1890 MARK,
    5 IN.TALL......................................  55.00
ROYAL WORCESTER,PITCHER,CREAMY GROUND,ENAMELED FLORAL,
    GOLD-RIBBED HANDLE.............................  35.00
ROYAL WORCESTER,PITCHER,CREAMY GROUND,GOLD-TRIMMED FLORAL,
    5 1/2 IN.HIGH..................................  22.00
ROYAL WORCESTER,PITCHER,EWER,HAND-PAINTED DAISIES,BOLD
    RELIEF FLORAL..................................  85.00
ROYAL WORCESTER,PITCHER,FLORAL DECOR,BRANCH HANDLE,6 IN....  48.00
ROYAL WORCESTER,PITCHER,FLORAL DECOR,GOLD,TWISTED GOLD
    HANDLE,6 IN....................................  65.00
ROYAL WORCESTER,PITCHER,GOLD-COLOR ROSES,VINTAGE DECOR NECK,
    DR.WALL........................................  155.00
ROYAL WORCESTER,PITCHER,GREEN & GOLD LIZARD,BASKET WEAVE,
    GOLD ROPE,6 IN.................................  75.00
ROYAL WORCESTER,PITCHER,MINIATURE,BEIGE,PINK & BLUE FLORAL,
    1 3/4 IN.......................................  35.00
ROYAL WORCESTER,PITCHER,WHITE GROUND,BLUE FLORAL,MASK SPOUT,
    DR.WALL........................................  185.00
ROYAL WORCESTER,PLAQUE,QUEEN VICTORIA,CARVED,WHITE PARIAN,
    TERRA COTTA....................................  47.50
ROYAL WORCESTER,PLATE,CHILD'S,THRUSH,PAINTED,4 1/2 IN.......  18.00
ROYAL WORCESTER,PLATE,COMMEMORATION,JUBILEE YEAR,VICTORIA,
    DATED 1887.....................................  17.50
ROYAL WORCESTER,PLATE,DESSERT,PINK,GREEN,PURPLE MARK,
    10-IN.DIAMETER,12..............................  125.00
ROYAL WORCESTER,PLATE,LIGHT BLUE BORDER,GOLD BAND,8 IN.,SET
    OF 6...........................................  23.00
ROYAL WORCESTER,PLATE,PORTRAIT,DR.WALL,PEAR DECOR,DATE MARK
    1936...........................................  15.00
ROYAL WORCESTER,PLATE,WILD ROSES,1900,9 IN.................  17.50
ROYAL WORCESTER,POTPOURRI,FLORAL,GOLD,INNER & OUTER LIDS,
    1904,FINIAL....................................  185.00
ROYAL WORCESTER,POTPOURRI,FLORAL,HAND-PAINTED,PIERCED TOP,
    INNER LID......................................  65.00
ROYAL WORCESTER,RABBIT,WHITE,PINK EARS,RED EYES,2 IN.LONG,
    1 1/2 IN.HIGH..................................  50.00
ROYAL WORCESTER,SALT & PEPPER,WHITE ACORNS,2 1/4 IN.HIGH,
    GREEN MARK.....................................  20.00
ROYAL WORCESTER,SYRUP,FLOWER SPRAYS,GOLD HANDLE,SQUATTY,
    3 3/4 IN.HIGH..................................  28.00
ROYAL WORCESTER,TEAPOT,CREAMER,SUGAR,FOUR CUPS,SAUCERS,
    FLORAL,GOLD....................................  95.00
ROYAL WORCESTER,TEAPOT,FOUR CUPS,CREAM GROUND,HAND-PAINTED
    FLORAL,MARKED..................................  38.00
ROYAL WORCESTER,TRAY,SWEETMEAT,UNDERGLAZED FLORAL,
    HAND-PAINTED LEAVES............................  125.00
ROYAL WORCESTER,VASE,ALLOVER DEGOR,GREEN FORGET-ME-NOTS,GOLD
```

```
    LEAVES...................................................  65.00
ROYAL WORCESTER,VASE,BIRD DECOR,RETICULATED,14 IN.HIGH...... 185.00
ROYAL WORCESTER,VASE,BUD,DECOR,6 1/2 IN....................  24.00
ROYAL WORCESTER,VASE,COMPLETELY RETICULATED & JEWELED,
    7 IN.HIGH............................................... 225.00
ROYAL WORCESTER,VASE,CREAM TO PEACH,CARVED CAMEO,1888,
    13 1/2 IN.,PAIR........................................ 900.00
ROYAL WORCESTER,VASE,CREAM-GOLD COLOR,VINES,BRANCHES,
    5 1/4 IN.HIGH.......................................... 125.00
ROYAL WORCESTER,VASE,CREAMY,GILT,LATTICEWORK,PINK BAND,
    3 1/2 IN.TALL..........................................  35.00
ROYAL WORCESTER,VASE,EWER TYPE,DRAGON HANDLE,IVORY & GOLD
    COLOR,4 IN.............................................  40.00
ROYAL WORCESTER,VASE,FLORAL DECOR,GOLD APPLIED HANDLES,
    11 IN.HIGH.............................................  70.00
ROYAL WORCESTER,VASE,FLORAL,GOLD,RED MARK,REG.2073,3 1/2 X
    3 1/2 IN.TALL..........................................  32.50
ROYAL WORCESTER,VASE,GOLD GOOSE DECOR,6 1/2 IN.............  20.00
ROYAL WORCESTER,VASE,GOLD RIB,HANDLES,ALLOVER FLORAL DECOR,
    MARK,11 IN.............................................  95.00
ROYAL WORCESTER,VASE,GREEN TO ORANGE TOP,TREES,TEMPLES,
    12 IN.HIGH............................................. 118.00
ROYAL WORCESTER,VASE,HERRINGBONE,ROSES,CYCLAMEN,CIRCA 1888,
    12 1/2 IN.............................................. 155.00
ROYAL WORCESTER,VASE,IVORY FINISH,COIN GOLD DECOR,MAYFLY
    INSECTS,1887........................................... 185.00
ROYAL WORCESTER,VASE,IVORY GROUND,ALLOVER GOLD FLORAL,
    LEAVES,EWER SHAPE......................................  48.50
ROYAL WORCESTER,VASE,PINK FLOWERS & FOLIAGE,PURPLE MARK,
    6 IN.TALL..............................................  38.00
ROYAL WORCESTER,VASE,RETICULATED AND JEWELED,7 IN.HIGH..... 235.00
ROYAL WORCESTER,VASE,RETICULATED,ENAMELED,BIRDS IN FLIGHT,
    FLORAL,14 IN........................................... 195.00
ROYAL WORCESTER,VASE,SILVER DOLLAR SHAPE,RETICULATED,FLAT,
    5 1/2 IN.HIGH.......................................... 175.00
ROYAL WORCESTER,VASE,STICK,BIRD DECOR,6 1/2 IN.............  32.00


        R.S.GERMANY PORCELAIN WAS MADE AT THE FACTORY OF
        RHEINHOLD SCHLEGELMILCH AFTER 1869 IN TILLOWITZ,
        GERMANY.IT WAS SOLD BOTH DECORATED AND UNDECORATED.
        RS GERMANY,SEE ALSO RS PRUSSIA
RS GERMANY,ASHTRAY,POPPIES.................................   9.50
RS GERMANY,BASKET,COLORFUL ROSES,HANDLE....................  23.50
RS GERMANY,BASKET,WHITE TO BLUE,FLORAL,RUFFLED,DOUBLE SCROLL
    HANDLE.................................................  12.00
RS GERMANY,BERRY SET,BOWL,FOUR SAUCES,WHITE FLORAL,GREEN,
    GOLD MARK..............................................  38.50
RS GERMANY,BOAT,MAYONNAISE,VIOLETS.........................   9.00
RS GERMANY,BOTTLE,TALCUM,BLUE DECOR,GOLD TOP,CORK BOTTOM,
    PORCELAIN,5 IN.........................................   8.00
RS GERMANY,BOWL,BERRY,AQUA,TURQUOISE,WHITE,IRIS,FLAME BUDS,
    GILT,SET OF 6..........................................  33.00
RS GERMANY,BOWL,BERRY,PEARLY GRAY-APRICOT PASTEL GROUND,
    PANSIES................................................   5.50
RS GERMANY,BOWL,BROWN & GREEN GROUND,MAGNOLIA FLOWERS,
    9 1/4 IN...............................................  27.00
RS GERMANY,BOWL,CLEMATIS DECOR,HEAVILY EMBOSSED,
    9 1/4-IN.DIAMETER......................................  25.00
RS GERMANY,BOWL,EGGSHELL TO GREEN,WHITE TULIPS & LILIES,
    9 1/2 IN...............................................  13.00
RS GERMANY,BOWL,FLORAL,FLOWER FORMS & ABSTRACT FIGURE WORK
    ON BORDER..............................................  48.00
RS GERMANY,BOWL,FLOWER CENTER,BORDER,SHALLOW,7 1/2 IN.......  10.00
RS GERMANY,BOWL,GREEN GROUND,WHITE,YELLOW CARNATIONS,
    BULBOUS,22 1/2 IN......................................  17.00
RS GERMANY,BOWL,GREEN,GOLD FLORAL,TILLOWITZ,9 IN...........  22.00
RS GERMANY,BOWL,GREEN,GOLD,PINK & WHITE POPPIES,10 IN......  22.00
RS GERMANY,BOWL,HAND-PAINTED CARNATIONS,GREEN GROUND,BULBOUS 20.00
RS GERMANY,BOWL,IRIS & ROSE DECOR,EMBOSSED FLORAL ON RIM,
    PANELS.................................................  12.00
RS GERMANY,BOWL,ORANGE TO BROWN AT RIM,ORANGE BAND AT FOOT,
    FLORAL.................................................  22.50
RS GERMANY,BOWL,ORCHID DECOR,BEADED TRIM,5 1/8-IN.DIAMETER..   4.00
RS GERMANY,BOWL,PINK,ORANGE FLORAL,GOLD,REINGOLD
    SCHLEGELMILCH,SIGNED...................................  15.00
RS GERMANY,BOWL,ROSE,PINK ROSES INSIDE & OUTSIDE,SCALLOPED,
    GREEN MARK.............................................  18.00
RS GERMANY,BOWL,SCENIC,TWO FIGURES,MAROON,GOLD,HAND-PAINTED,
    HANDLES................................................  90.00
RS GERMANY,BOWL,SHADED BROWN GROUND,PINK ROSES,
```

```
     9 1/4-IN.DIAMETER......................................     20.00
RS GERMANY,BOWL,SHADED BROWN GROUND,PINK POPPY..............     20.00
RS GERMANY,BOWL,SUGAR,ROSES.................................     12.00
RS GERMANY,BOWL,SUGAR,SHADED GREEN,PINK ROSES,MARKED........     10.00
RS GERMANY,BOWL,TAN GROUND,PINK PEONIES & SNOWBALLS,
     9 1/4-IN.DIAMETER......................................     20.00
RS GERMANY,BOWL,TAN GROUND,ROSES,FLORAL,9 1/4-IN.DIAMETER...     20.00
RS GERMANY,BOWL,TURQUOISE,GILT,PINK & WHITE ROSES,SCALLOPED,
     10 IN..................................................     15.00
RS GERMANY,BOWL,WHITE WILD ROSES,PINE BRANCHES ON BORDER,
     MATCHING PLATE.........................................     30.00
RS GERMANY,BOX,COVER,PORTRAIT,LADY,BLUE & GOLD BORDER,MARK,
     DATED 1913.............................................     35.00
RS GERMANY,BOX,DRESSER,BLUE & WHITE,COVER,ROUND.............     12.00
RS GERMANY,BOX,LUSTER,GOLD TRIM AROUND LID,2 1/2 IN.SQUARE..     10.00
RS GERMANY,CANDLESTICK,INVERTED-CONE SHAPE,FLARED TOP,GREEN,
     LILY,5 IN..............................................     12.00
RS GERMANY,CELERY,PINK ROSES,GOLD,OPEN HANDLES..............     15.00
RS GERMANY,CHOCOLATE POT,CREAM GROUND,PINK IRIS,GOLD,THREE
     CUPS,SAUCERS...........................................     35.00
RS GERMANY,CHOCOLATE POT,SIX CUPS,SAUCERS,CAKE PLATE,BEIGE,
     POPPIES,MARK...........................................    210.00
RS GERMANY,CHOCOLATE POT,TURQUOISE,SATIN FINISH,OVOID,DECOR.     59.00
RS GERMANY,CHOCOLATE POT,WHITE GROUND,BROWN AT TOP,ROSES,
     SCALLOPED..............................................     30.00
RS GERMANY,CREAMER & SUGAR,CREAM & GREEN GROUND,PASTEL
     ROSES,CARNATIONS.......................................     19.50
RS GERMANY,CREAMER & SUGAR,GREEN,CREAM GROUND,PINK & WHITE
     AZALEAS,GILT...........................................     25.00
RS GERMANY,CREAMER & SUGAR,LARGE PINK ROSES,MARKED.........     20.00
RS GERMANY,CREAMER,BROWN,FLORAL.............................      7.50
RS GERMANY,CREAMER,CREAM COLOR,GOLD TOP & HANDLE,LAVENDER &
     GREEN FLORAL...........................................      9.50
RS GERMANY,CREAMER,DAFFODILS................................     10.00
RS GERMANY,CREAMER,DUTCH SCENE,BLUE.........................      8.50
RS GERMANY,CREAMER,FLORAL DECOR.............................      8.00
RS GERMANY,CREAMER,GREEN,APPLE BLOSSOMS,GILT,SIGNED JORDAN
     POND...................................................     20.00
RS GERMANY,CREAMER,PEONY DECOR..............................      8.50
RS GERMANY,CREAMER,ROSE DECOR...............................     25.00
RS GERMANY,CREAMER,ROSES,LEFT-HANDED,4 3/4 IN...............     16.50
RS GERMANY,CREAMER,SQUATTY,LUSTER,LAVENDER-BLUE TRIM,GOLD...      6.50
RS GERMANY,CREAMER,SUGAR,GREEN & TAN GROUND,WHITE FLORAL....     13.50
RS GERMANY,CREAMER,SUGAR,HAND-PAINTED ROSE DECOR,YELLOW,
     BLUE,FOOTED,GOLD.......................................     40.00
RS GERMANY,CREAMER,VIOLETS..................................      7.00
RS GERMANY,CUP & SAUCER,CHOCOLATE,ROSE DECOR................      5.00
RS GERMANY,CUP & SAUCER,ROSE DECOR..........................     21.50
RS GERMANY,CUP & SAUCER,ROSE DECOR,MARK.....................     11.00
RS GERMANY,CUP,NUT,TEA ROSES,IVORY COLOR GROUND,RUFFLED,
     HAND-PAINTED,5.........................................     10.00
RS GERMANY,CUP,SAUCER,CHOCOLATE,WHITE GROUND,BROWN TRIM,
     ROSES,GILT.............................................      7.50
RS GERMANY,DISH,CANDY,ASTERS,GOLD COLOR FEET................      8.50
RS GERMANY,DISH,CANDY,CREAM GROUND,PINK ROSES,HANDLE,FOUR
     FEET...................................................     15.00
RS GERMANY,DISH,CANDY,PASTEL FLORAL SPRAY,GILT,HANDLES,
     HAND-PAINTED...........................................      9.00
RS GERMANY,DISH,CANDY,RED,BLUE,GOLD DECOR,HAND-PAINTED,
     HANDLES,6 1/2 IN.......................................     12.50
RS GERMANY,DISH,CHEESE & CRACKER,GREEN,WHITE FLORAL,BLUE
     MARK...................................................     15.00
RS GERMANY,DISH,DESSERT,TAN,BROWN,RED ROSES,SET OF 4........     18.00
RS GERMANY,DISH,DRESSER,FLOWER DECOR,GOLD EDGE ON COVER,
     DIAMOND SHAPE..........................................     15.00
RS GERMANY,DISH,LARGE PINK ROSES,HANDLED,MARK,7 1/2 IN......     10.00
RS GERMANY,DISH,PICKLE,FLOWERS..............................     18.00
RS GERMANY,DISH,PICKLE,ROSE DECOR,OPEN HANDLES..............     10.00
RS GERMANY,DISH,POWDER,GREEN,BROWN,APRICOT-COLOR POPPY,
     COVER,RED MARK.........................................     18.00
RS GERMANY,DISH,ROSE & DAISY DECOR,PIERCED HANDLES,
     7 1/2 IN.WIDE..........................................     13.50
RS GERMANY,DISH,SERVING,TWO TIERS,UPPER DISH ON PEDESTAL,
     DECOR..................................................     29.00
RS GERMANY,DISH,YELLOW IRIDESCENCE,HAND-PAINTED FLORAL,GOLD
     HANDLES................................................      9.75
RS GERMANY,HAIR RECEIVER,BLUE,YELLOW GROUND,ORANGE BLOSSOM
     DECOR..................................................     17.50
RS GERMANY,HAIR RECEIVER,GREEN,BROWN,APRICOT-COLOR POPPY,RED
     MARK,WREATH............................................     18.00
RS GERMANY,HAIR RECEIVER,ORANGE & WHITE FLOWERS,
```

```
  4 1/2-IN.DIAMETER,PAIR...........................        25.00
RS GERMANY,HAIR RECEIVER,PINK ROSES...............        13.75
RS GERMANY,HAIR RECEIVER,POWDER BOX,OVAL,COVER,CUSTARD
  GLASS,ROSE DECOR.................................        36.50
RS GERMANY,HAIR RECEIVER,SHADED GREEN,TAN GROUND,YELLOW ROSE
  DECOR...........................................        15.00
RS GERMANY,HAIR RECEIVER,TAN GROUND,YELLOW ROSE DECOR......        17.50
RS GERMANY,HOLDER,HATPIN,FLORAL SPRAYS,GOLD TRIM..        15.00
RS GERMANY,HOLDER,HATPIN,IVORY-COLOR GROUND,ROSES,GOLD TRIM,
  4 1/2 IN........................................        18.00
RS GERMANY,HOLDER,HATPIN,MELON RIB,ROSES..................        18.00
RS GERMANY,HOLDER,HATPIN,OLIVE GREEN GROUND,PINK & WHITE
  ROSES...........................................        17.50
RS GERMANY,HOLDER,HATPIN,PINK & WHITE ROSES....... 15.00 TO        17.00
RS GERMANY,HOLDER,HATPIN,PINK ROSES IN BASKET,GREEN RIBBON,
  HAND-PAINTED....................................        12.00
RS GERMANY,HOLDER,HATPIN,RED POPPIES..............        15.00
RS GERMANY,HOLDER,HATPIN,ROSES....................        15.00
RS GERMANY,HOLDER,HATPIN,WHITE GROUND,GREEN,HONEY,GREEN
  POPPIES,MARK....................................        16.00
RS GERMANY,HOLDER,HATPIN,YELLOW FLORAL,HAND-PAINTED,GOLD....        26.00
RS GERMANY,INKWELL,HAND-PAINTED,COVER,MARKED..............        12.50
RS GERMANY,JAR,COOKIE,GREEN,CREAM GROUND,PINK & WHITE
  AZALEAS,GREEN MARK..............................        27.50
RS GERMANY,JAR,CUSTARD,ROSE DECOR,MARKED,COVER............        17.00
RS GERMANY,JAR,MUSTARD,GREEN GROUND,PINK ROSES,GREEN LEAVES.        14.50
RS GERMANY,MUSTARD,PINK,WHITE,YELLOW ROSES................        12.50
RS GERMANY,NAPPIE,BLUE,FLORAL,HANDLED.....................        10.00
RS GERMANY,NAPPIE,ROSE DECOR,HANDLED......................        10.00
RS GERMANY,NUT SET,HAND-PAINTED,FOOTED,7 PIECES...........        29.00
RS GERMANY,PITCHER,MILK,SWIRL SIDES,GREEN,WHITE,GOLD FLORAL,
  BLUE MARK.......................................        28.00
RS GERMANY,PLATE,ALLOVER LARGE PINK ROSES,GOLD EDGE,MARK,
  8 1/2 IN........................................        12.00
RS GERMANY,PLATE,BLACK GROUND,WHITE LILY,GOLD RIM,GREEN MARK        18.50
RS GERMANY,PLATE,BLUE GROUND,FLORAL,LEAVES,GOLD,RUFFLED,
  MATCHING BOWL...................................        13.50
RS GERMANY,PLATE,BROWN TO WHITE GROUND,LAVENDER & WHITE IRIS
  SPRAYS,6........................................        35.00
RS GERMANY,PLATE,CAKE,BEIGE GROUND,PINK ROSES,LEAVES,OPEN
  HANDLES,MARK....................................        13.00
RS GERMANY,PLATE,CAKE,GREEN,WHITE BLOSSOMS,OPEN END........        12.50
RS GERMANY,PLATE,CAKE,HAND-PAINTED,GOLD RIM,TWO OPEN
  HANDLES,9 1/2 IN................................        15.00
RS GERMANY,PLATE,CAKE,ROSES,GOLD,HANDLE,FOUR 6-IN.PLATES....        27.50
RS GERMANY,PLATE,CAKE,ROSES,HANDLES,10 IN.,SIX SMALL PLATES,
  6 IN............................................        32.00
RS GERMANY,PLATE,CAKE,TAN GROUND,THREE LARGE WHITE TULIPS,
  HANDLES.........................................        12.00
RS GERMANY,PLATE,CAKE,TWO LILIES,TAN GROUND,HAND-PAINTED,
  SELF HANDLES....................................        12.50
RS GERMANY,PLATE,CAKE,WHITE & PINK POPPIES,GREEN GROUND,GOLD
  EDGE............................................         8.50
RS GERMANY,PLATE,CUPID & LARGE FLORAL,8 1/2 IN............        35.00
RS GERMANY,PLATE,DESSERT,GREEN,LAVENDER HYDRANGEAS,6 IN.,SET
  OF 3............................................        13.50
RS GERMANY,PLATE,DESSERT,PINK LILY,GREEN GROUND,GREEN MARK..         3.50
RS GERMANY,PLATE,EIGHT PANELS FORM EIGHT DEEP RIM SCALLOPS,
  ROSES...........................................         7.50
RS GERMANY,PLATE,FLORAL,6 1/2-IN.DIAMETER.................         6.00
RS GERMANY,PLATE,FLORAL,GILT,MARK,7 1/2 IN................        10.00
RS GERMANY,PLATE,GREEN GROUND,WHITE FLORAL,GOLD,SCALLOPED,
  HANDLES,LUSTER..................................        22.50
RS GERMANY,PLATE,GREEN PEONY DECOR,HEAVY HAND-PAINTED GOLD
  LEAVES,3........................................        15.00
RS GERMANY,PLATE,GREEN SHADING,DARK TO LIGHT PINK,ROSES,
  GREEN WREATH....................................        12.00
RS GERMANY,PLATE,GREEN,GOLD EDGE,6 1/2 IN.................         4.00
RS GERMANY,PLATE,GREEN,YELLOW,WHITE FLOWERS,SCALLOPED,RED
  MARK,11 IN......................................        38.50
RS GERMANY,PLATE,IVORY & ROSE GROUND,GOLD STRIPE,PASTEL
  FLORAL,MARKED...................................        12.00
RS GERMANY,PLATE,MUTED GREEN GROUND,THREE LARGE WHITE
  ASTERS,GILT.....................................        12.50
RS GERMANY,PLATE,ORCHID DECOR,BEADED TRIM,6 1/2 IN........         6.00
RS GERMANY,PLATE,PASTEL PINK,GREEN,YELLOW,WHITE,FLORAL,OPEN
  HANDLES.........................................        11.50
RS GERMANY,PLATE,PASTEL,RAISED GOLD,THISTLES,IVY,FLOWERS,
  SIGNED..........................................         7.50
RS GERMANY,PLATE,PEACH-COLOR ROSES,PASTEL BLUE GROUND,GILT
  HANDLES.........................................        19.50
```

```
RS GERMANY,PLATE,PEARS,PURPLE PLUMS,LAVENDER BORDER,7 IN....    5.00
RS GERMANY,PLATE,PEONY DECOR,6 1/4 IN......................    5.00
RS GERMANY,PLATE,PINK & GREEN GROUND,DAFFODIL DECOR,
   6 1/2 IN................................................    6.00
RS GERMANY,PLATE,PINK & WHITE FLORAL,GOLD,HANDLE,8 IN.......   10.00
RS GERMANY,PLATE,PINK & WHITE PEONIES,6 IN.................    3.00
RS GERMANY,PLATE,PINK & WHITE POPPIES,SCALLOPED,BEADED,
   6 1/2 IN................................................    5.00
RS GERMANY,PLATE,PINK TULIPS,MARK,6 1/2 IN.................    4.00
RS GERMANY,PLATE,PORTRAIT CENTER,GOLD EDGE,7 3/8 IN.........   12.00
RS GERMANY,PLATE,ROSES,GREEN MARK..........................   15.00
RS GERMANY,PLATE,ROSES,GREEN MARK,7 IN.....................   14.00
RS GERMANY,PLATE,SCENIC,CUPIDS,GOLD DESIGNS,BLUE & GOLD RIM,
   8 1/2 IN................................................   55.00
RS GERMANY,PLATE,SHADED BROWN GROUND,LARGE PINK PEONIES,
   8 3/8 IN................................................   10.00
RS GERMANY,PLATE,SPRAYS OF PINK SHADED LILACS,GOLD DESIGN
   BORDER..................................................   15.00
RS GERMANY,PLATE,THREE ROSES,OPEN HANDLES,6 1/2 IN.........   10.00
RS GERMANY,PLATE,TWO PINK CARNATIONS,HAND-PAINTED,PAIR.....    6.00
RS GERMANY,RELISH,BLUE,MAUVE ROSES,GILT,LOOP HANDLES,BOAT
   SHAPE...................................................   19.00
RS GERMANY,RELISH,GREEN GROUND,FLORAL,ROUND,HAND-PAINTED....   15.50
RS GERMANY,RELISH,GREEN GROUND,PINK FLOWERS................    9.50
RS GERMANY,RELISH,LIFE-SIZE PINK FLOWERS,CENTER HANDLE,8 X
   4 IN....................................................   10.00
RS GERMANY,RELISH,LILY DECOR,FOOTED,MARK...................   13.00
RS GERMANY,RELISH,MOSSY APRICOTS,GOLD,YELLOW,ROSES,LEAVES,
   3 HANDLES...............................................   13.00
RS GERMANY,RELISH,PINK FLORAL,DIVIDED,HANDLED,6 1/2 IN......   10.00
RS GERMANY,RELISH,ROSES,OPEN HANDLES,8 1/2 IN.............   12.50
RS GERMANY,RELISH,WHITE FLOWERS,GREEN LEAVES,GOLD,HANDLES,
   10 1/2 IN.LONG..........................................   16.50
RS GERMANY,RELISH,WHITE SNOWBALL & LAVENDER FLORAL,
   OPEN-HANDLED............................................    9.75
RS GERMANY,SALT & PEPPER,ROSE DECOR........................   12.50
RS GERMANY,SALT DIP,ROSE DECOR,FOOTED,MARK.................    5.75
RS GERMANY,SAUCE,BEIGE GROUND,PINK ROSES,GREEN MARK.........    3.50
RS GERMANY,SAUCE,GREEN,GRAY,WHITE FLORAL,GREEN MARK,SET OF
   6.......................................................   24.00
RS GERMANY,SAUCE,LAVENDER FLORAL,GOLD DECOR,GOLD EDGE,5 IN..    6.00
RS GERMANY,SAUCE,SHADED GROUND,PINK & WHITE ROSES,
   GOLD-BEADED EDGE,6......................................   15.00
RS GERMANY,SAUCEBOAT,PLATE,WHITE GROUND,GILT EDGE...........   12.00
RS GERMANY,SHAKER,TALCUM,YELLOW............................    9.00
RS GERMANY,SUGAR,SHADED YELLOW GROUND,WHITE ROSES,COVER.....    6.50
RS GERMANY,TEAPOT,CREAMER,SUGAR,FLORAL,GOLD TRIM,MARKED,
   3 CAKE PLATES...........................................   25.00
RS GERMANY,TEAPOT,PASTEL,FLORAL,GOLD,SATIN FINISH..........   27.50
RS GERMANY,TEAPOT,SALMON COLOR POPPIES,GOLD TRIM,PLATE,GREEN
   MARK....................................................   24.00
RS GERMANY,TOOTHPICK,FLORAL,THREE HANDLES..................   16.00
RS GERMANY,TOOTHPICK,ORCHID FLORAL,TWO HANDLES.............    8.50
RS GERMANY,TOOTHPICK,WHITE,GILT MONOGRAM & HANDLES,MARKED...   15.00
RS GERMANY,TRAY,CELERY,SALMON PINK & WHITE LILIES,GOLD TRIM,
   OPEN HANDLES............................................   18.00
RS GERMANY,TRAY,DRESSER,GREEN & WHITE TULIPS,LILIES OF THE
   VALLEY..................................................   15.00
RS GERMANY,TRAY,DRESSER,TULIPS & LILIES OF VALLEY..........   17.00
RS GERMANY,TRAY,EMBOSSED FLORAL AROUND EDGES,FLOWER CENTER,
   MARK....................................................   29.50
RS GERMANY,TRAY,PIN,ORANGE POPPY DECOR,MARKED,
   3 3/4 IN.DIAMETER.......................................    6.00
RS GERMANY,VASE,BUD,PICKARD,ALLOVER GOLD FLORAL DECOR,
   HANDLES,5 1/4 IN........................................   10.00
RS GERMANY,VASE,GREEN GROUND,PINK TULIPS,GOLD BAND TOP,
   7 3/4 IN.HIGH...........................................   15.00
RS GERMANY,VASE,GREEN,PINK ROSES,6 IN......................   10.00
RS GERMANY,VASE,IRIS,4 1/2 IN..............................   10.00
RS GERMANY,VASE,RUST,BEIGE,APRICOT ROSES,SLENDER,TAPERING,
   6 1/2 IN.TALL...........................................   13.50
RS GERMANY,VASE,WHITE TO PALE GREEN-MUSTARD,WHITE MAGNOLIAS,
   HANDLES.................................................   12.50
RS GERMANY,VASE,YELLOW & PINK IRIS,HAND-PAINTED,
   4 1/2 IN.HIGH...........................................   12.00
```

        RS PRUSSIA PORCELAIN WAS MADE AT THE FACTORY OF
        RHEINHOLD SCHLEGELMILCH AFTER 1869 IN TILLOWITZ,
        GERMANY.  THE PORCELAIN WAS SOLD DECORATED OR
        UNDECORATED.
        RS PRUSSIA,SEE ALSO RS GERMANY

RS PRUSSIA,BASKET,FLORAL INSIDE & OUTSIDE,BLUE TO WHITE
BOTTOM,FOOTED.................................................. 95.00
RS PRUSSIA,BASKET,PINK & RED ROSES,BLUE TO WHITE BOTTOM,
FOOTED,HANDLE.................................................. 95.00
RS PRUSSIA,BERRY SET,BASKETS OF ROSES,BLUE RIBBONS,BOWS,
5 PIECES...................................................... 128.00
RS PRUSSIA,BERRY SET,BIRDS IN FLIGHT,RED MARK,7 PIECES........ 155.00
RS PRUSSIA,BERRY SET,FLORAL,SCALLOPED,SEVEN PIECE............. 110.00
RS PRUSSIA,BOWL & CRACKER JAR,RED,YELLOW,WHITE................ 265.00
RS PRUSSIA,BOWL,BERRY,FLORAL,GREEN,BROWN,GOLD SERRATED TOP,
6 SAUCES...................................................... 150.00
RS PRUSSIA,BOWL,BERRY,GREEN SHADING TO BLUE & WHITE,ROSES,
SATIN,RED MARK................................................ 100.00
RS PRUSSIA,BOWL,BERRY,GREEN TO WHITE,SCALLOPED RIM,WHITE
FLORAL,4 SAUCES............................................... 120.00
RS PRUSSIA,BOWL,BERRY,GREEN,LILY-OF-THE-VALLEY DECOR,SIX
SMALL BOWLS................................................... 150.00
RS PRUSSIA,BOWL,BERRY,GREEN,TAN,LILY-OF-THE-VALLEY,6 SMALL
BOWLS......................................................... 150.00
RS PRUSSIA,BOWL,BERRY,LILY-OF-THE-VALLEY DECOR,10 3/4 IN.,
6 SMALL BOWLS................................................. 160.00
RS PRUSSIA,BOWL,BERRY,PANELED,HOLLY BERRIES,BLOSSOMS,GREEN
MARK,4 SAUCES................................................. 50.00
RS PRUSSIA,BOWL,BERRY,RED GROUND,FLORAL,SIX MATCHING DISHES,
MARK.......................................................... 98.00
RS PRUSSIA,BOWL,BERRY,RED,FLORAL,RED MARK,6 MATCHING DISHES. 98.00
RS PRUSSIA,BOWL,BERRY,ROSES,LEAVES,5 3/4 IN.DIAMETER,SET OF
4............................................................. 40.00
RS PRUSSIA,BOWL,BERRY,WREATH,STAR,GREEN,WHITE SNOWDROPS,
10 IN......................................................... 32.00
RS PRUSSIA,BOWL,BERRY,YELLOW DAFFODILS,SCALLOPED,GILT,FIVE
SAUCES........................................................ 89.50
RS PRUSSIA,BOWL,BERRY,YELLOW FLORAL,GREEN GROUND,GOLD,FIVE
SAUCES........................................................ 89.50
RS PRUSSIA,BOWL,BLUE-GREEN TO PEARLY GROUND,SHADED PANELS,
BOUQUETS...................................................... 75.00
RS PRUSSIA,BOWL,BLUE,GOLD BORDER,FLORAL SIDES & CENTER,
10-IN.DIAMETER................................................ 65.00
RS PRUSSIA,BOWL,BOUQUET OF ROSES INSIDE,DAISIES,ASTERS,WILD
ROSES,GILT.................................................... 85.00
RS PRUSSIA,BOWL,BOY EATING MELON,TWO BOYS PLAYING WITH DICE,
11 IN......................................................... 350.00
RS PRUSSIA,BOWL,CABBAGE LEAF SHAPE,RED,PURPLE IRIDESCENT
OUTSIDE,FLORAL................................................ 125.00
RS PRUSSIA,BOWL,EMBOSSED GREEN BORDER LUSTER,INSIDE FLORAL,
11 IN......................................................... 46.50
RS PRUSSIA,BOWL,FIVE LARGE PINK ROSES INSIDE,GREEN LEAF
FORMS AN EDGE................................................. 55.00
RS PRUSSIA,BOWL,FLORAL,SATIN FINISH,SCALLOPED,BEADED EDGE,
5 DISHES...................................................... 110.00
RS PRUSSIA,BOWL,FLOWERED EDGE,RUFFLED,MEDALLIONS BETWEEN,RED
MARK,11 IN.................................................... 95.00
RS PRUSSIA,BOWL,FRUIT,GRAPES,EMBOSSED,GOLD EDGE,SIGNED KOHL,
10 IN......................................................... 24.00
RS PRUSSIA,BOWL,GOLD LEAF,HAND-PAINTED ROSES,PANSIES,ASTERS,
8 IN.......................................................... 12.00
RS PRUSSIA,BOWL,GOLD TRACERY MEDALLIONS,BELLFLOWER CHAINS,
RIDGED........................................................ 69.00
RS PRUSSIA,BOWL,GRAY,YELLOW & PINK ROSES,SCALLOPED EDGE,RED
& GREEN MARK.................................................. 48.00
RS PRUSSIA,BOWL,IRIS,ROSES,EMBOSSED,RED MARK,10 1/2 IN....... 58.00
RS PRUSSIA,BOWL,LARGE ROSES,WHITE DAISIES,GOLD SCALLOPS,
10 1/2 IN..................................................... 58.00
RS PRUSSIA,BOWL,LILIES,FOOTED,RED MARK,6 1/2 IN.............. 28.00
RS PRUSSIA,BOWL,LILY DESIGN,FOOTED,RED MARK,
8 1/2-IN.DIAMETER............................................. 35.00
RS PRUSSIA,BOWL,MELON BOY,WHITE,GOLD-OUTLINED FLOWERS,
LEAVES,10 1/2 IN.............................................. 75.00
RS PRUSSIA,BOWL,NUT,GREEN GROUND,WHITE FLORAL,GOLD,PINCHED
SCALLOPS...................................................... 25.00
RS PRUSSIA,BOWL,NUT,PINK ROSES,SCALLOPED EDGE,GILT,FOOTED,
RED MARK...................................................... 20.00
RS PRUSSIA,BOWL,PASTEL & DARK FLORAL,SHELL BORDER,SCALLOPED,
9 IN.......................................................... 65.00
RS PRUSSIA,BOWL,PINK & ORCHID FLORAL,SCALLOPED,GOLD,
10 1/2-IN.DIAMETER............................................ 57.50
RS PRUSSIA,BOWL,PINK & WHITE ROSES,PEARLIZED FINISH,RED MARK 75.00
RS PRUSSIA,BOWL,PINK ROSES IN SUSPENDED BASKET,RED MARK,
10 1/2 IN..................................................... 65.00
RS PRUSSIA,BOWL,PINK ROSES,GRAPES,BLUE-GREEN BORDER,
7 1/4-IN.DIAMETER............................................. 47.00

RS PRUSSIA,BOWL,PINK ROSES,PURPLE FLORAL,GOLD-BEADED EDGE,
   11-IN.DIAMETER....................................................... 59.00
RS PRUSSIA,BOWL,PINK ROSES,SMALL WHITE FLOWERS,RED MARK,
   11-IN.DIAMETER....................................................... 65.00
RS PRUSSIA,BOWL,PINK-GRAY,GOLD BORDER,PINK ROSEBUDS,10 IN... 45.00
RS PRUSSIA,BOWL,PINK,YELLOW POPPY CENTER,EMBOSSED BLUE EDGE,
   SCALLOPED............................................................ 59.00
RS PRUSSIA,BOWL,PURPLE & WHITE GROUND,WHITE FLORAL,
   SCALLOPED,10 IN...................................................... 52.00
RS PRUSSIA,BOWL,PURPLE VIOLETS,RED MARK,11 IN................ 45.00
RS PRUSSIA,BOWL,RAISED BUTTERFLIES,ROSES,SCALLOPED BORDER,
   5 1/2 IN............................................................. 12.50
RS PRUSSIA,BOWL,RED & YELLOW ROSES,GREEN GROUND,GOLD,
   10 1/2 IN............................................................ 22.50
RS PRUSSIA,BOWL,RED,PINK ROSES & DAISIES,11 IN.............. 55.00
RS PRUSSIA,BOWL,ROSE,SCENIC,RED MARK,3 IN.HIGH.............. 110.00
RS PRUSSIA,BOWL,ROSES,DAISIES,SCALLOPED,RED MARK,
   5 1/2-IN.DIAMETER................................................... 11.00
RS PRUSSIA,BOWL,ROSES,GOLD,GREEN SCALLOPED BORDER,10 1/2 IN. 60.00
RS PRUSSIA,BOWL,ROSES,SCALLOPED MEDALLIONS ON EDGES & SIDES,
   10 1/2 IN............................................................ 80.00
RS PRUSSIA,BOWL,RUFFLED EDGES,ROSES,RED MARK................ 45.00
RS PRUSSIA,BOWL,SALAD,PINK POPPY CENTER,SATINIZED,
   10 1/2-IN.DIAMETER.................................................. 59.50
RS PRUSSIA,BOWL,SCENIC,MILL,KNEELING WOMAN,RAISED BAROQUE
   EDGE,YELLOW.......................................................... 85.00
RS PRUSSIA,BOWL,SHALLOW,FLORAL,OPEN HANDLES,GREEN,ROSE,
   YELLOW,RED MARK...................................................... 60.00
RS PRUSSIA,BOWL,SMALL,BLUE,FLORAL,BULBOUS SIDES,10 SCALLOPED
   FEET................................................................. 25.00
RS PRUSSIA,BOWL,SPRING PORTRAIT,RED MARK,5 1/2-IN.DIAMETER.. 125.00
RS PRUSSIA,BOWL,STARFISH DESIGN,BLUE,WHITE ENAMEL FLORAL,
   GOLD TRACERY......................................................... 49.00
RS PRUSSIA,BOWL,SUGAR,GREEN,PINK FLOWERS,COVER,RED MARK..... 32.50
RS PRUSSIA,BOWL,SUGAR,LIME GREEN,ROSES,RUFFLED,GILT,COVER,
   RED MARK............................................................. 50.00
RS PRUSSIA,BOWL,SUGAR,ROSE CLUSTER,RUFFLED EDGE & COVER,BLUE
   BASE................................................................. 50.00
RS PRUSSIA,BOWL,SUGAR,WHITE,BAND OF SMALL FLOWERS,GILT,
   FOOTED............................................................... 50.00
RS PRUSSIA,BOWL,TWO BOYS EATING MELON,DOG,RAISED FLORAL RIM,
   12 IN................................................................ 200.00
RS PRUSSIA,BOWL,TWO BOYS EATING MELON,DOG,RED MARK,11 IN.... 350.00
RS PRUSSIA,BOWL,WATER LILIES,PEARL LUSTER ROSES,GOLD,BEADED,
   SCALLOPED............................................................ 95.00
RS PRUSSIA,BOWL,WHITE & GREEN,APPLE BLOSSOMS,LEAF SHAPE,RED
   MARK................................................................. 52.00
RS PRUSSIA,BOWL,WHITE & PINK ROSES,GOLD-OUTLINED,BEADED
   BORDER,RED MARK...................................................... 75.00
RS PRUSSIA,BOWL,WHITE,FLORAL,FLEUR-DE-LIS,PEARLS,RED MARK,
   10 7/8 IN............................................................ 42.00
RS PRUSSIA,BOWL,WHITE FLORAL,GOLD STEMS,RUFFLED,6 1/8 IN.X
   1 3/4 IN.DEEP....................................................... 28.00
RS PRUSSIA,BOWL,WHITE FLORAL,GRAY-GREEN INTERIOR,SCALLOPED,
   10 1/2 IN............................................................ 45.00
RS PRUSSIA,BOWL,WHITE GROUND,GOLD TRACERY,4 1/2 IN.......... 13.00
RS PRUSSIA,BOWL,WHITE GROUND,PINK ROSES,RED MARK........... 30.00
RS PRUSSIA,BOWL,WHITE GROUND,PINK,GREEN,FLORAL,GOLD,10 IN... 22.50
RS PRUSSIA,BOWL,WHITE GROUND,ROSES,10 IN.................... 60.00
RS PRUSSIA,BOWL,WHITE ROSES,GOLD BAND TRIM,9 IN............. 42.50
RS PRUSSIA,BOWL,YELLOW & MAUVE BACKGROUND,FLORAL,RED MARK,
   5 1/2 IN.,4.......................................................... 57.50
RS PRUSSIA,BOWL,YELLOW ROSES,PANSIES,MAGNOLIA,BLUE TO WHITE
   GROUND............................................................... 60.00
RS PRUSSIA,BOX,TRINKET,COVERED EGG,HAND-PAINTED YELLOW
   ROSES,GREEN MARK..................................................... 27.50
RS PRUSSIA,BUTTER PAT,DOGWOOD PATTERN,EMBOSSED,RED MARK..... 17.00
RS PRUSSIA,BUTTER PAT,FLOWER PROFUSION,SCALLOPED,SATIN
   FINISH,SET OF 6...................................................... 98.00
RS PRUSSIA,BUTTER PAT,RED............................................ 4.00
RS PRUSSIA,CAKE PLATE.....................................ILLUS.. 55.00
RS PRUSSIA,CELERY,BLUE GROUND,SILVERY-WHITE LEAVES,VIOLETS,
   PURPLE FLORAL........................................................ 42.50
RS PRUSSIA,CELERY,FORGET-ME-NOT SPRAY,LEAVES,RIBBON,SIGNED
   ULFDE,HANDLES........................................................ 25.50
RS PRUSSIA,CELERY,FOUR SWANS,EMBOSSED,LOOP ENDS,9 1/2 IN.... 39.50
RS PRUSSIA,CELERY,LILY-OF-THE-VALLEY DECOR,SCALLOPED,GOLD,
   SATIN FINISH......................................................... 45.00
RS PRUSSIA,CELERY,WATER LILY DECOR,HANDLE,RED MARK,12 X
   6 IN................................................................. 40.00
RS PRUSSIA,CELERY,YELLOW DAISY & GREEN LEAF CHAIN,GOLD BANDS 38.50

R. S. PRUSSIAN CAKE PLATE

RS PRUSSIA,CELERY,YELLOW-CARAMEL,MOSSY LAVENDER,OFF-WHITE
PANSY,FLORAL.................................................... 53.00
RS PRUSSIA,CHOCOLATE POT,FLORAL,LAVENDER,TWO HANDLES,FOOTED,
RED MARK........................................................ 65.00
RS PRUSSIA,CHOCOLATE POT,FOUR CUPS & SAUCERS,GREEN GROUND,
WHITE LILIES.................................................... 175.00
RS PRUSSIA,CHOCOLATE POT,GREEN & WHITE PANELS,FLORAL,RED
MARK,10 1/2 IN.................................................. 90.00
RS PRUSSIA,CHOCOLATE POT,MULTICOLOR FLORAL,DOUBLE HANDLE,
SCALLOPS,MARK................................................... 77.50
RS PRUSSIA,CHOCOLATE POT,PINK FLORAL,GILT,SIX CUPS &
SAUCERS,RED MARK................................................ 215.00
RS PRUSSIA,CHOCOLATE POT,POPPIES,CHRYSANTHEMUMS,LILIES,
FLOWER FINIAL................................................... 78.50
RS PRUSSIA,CHOCOLATE POT,PORTRAIT OF TWO TURKEYS,SATIN
FINISH,RED MARK................................................. 150.00
RS PRUSSIA,CHOCOLATE POT,ROSE DECOR,SATIN FINISH,RED MARK... 85.00
RS PRUSSIA,CHOCOLATE POT,ROSES,LEAVES,GILT DECOR,THREE CUPS
& SAUCERS....................................................... 45.00
RS PRUSSIA,CHOCOLATE POT,SWANS,SATIN,RED MARK,6 CUPS,
5 SAUCERS....................................................... 295.00
RS PRUSSIA,CHOCOLATE POT,WATER LILIES,POND,GREEN,BLUE,GOLD
TRIM,RED MARK................................................... 125.00
RS PRUSSIA,CHOCOLATE POT,WHITE & YELLOW LILIES,GREEN & WHITE
GROUND,MARK..................................................... 125.00
RS PRUSSIA,CHOCOLATE POT,WHITE,LILIES,RED MARK,6 CUPS &
SAUCERS......................................................... 275.00
RS PRUSSIA,CHOCOLATE POT,WHITE,LILIES,SIX CUPS & SAUCERS,RED
MARK............................................................ 275.00
RS PRUSSIA,CHOCOLATE POT,YELLOW & PURPLE WISTERIA FLOWERS,
FOOTED.......................................................... 60.00
RS PRUSSIA,CHOCOLATE POT,YELLOW ROSES,GREEN,WHITE PANEL
GROUND,GOLD..................................................... 85.00
RS PRUSSIA,CHOCOLATE SET,WHITE & IVORY GROUND,GREEN FERN,
SERVICE FOR 6................................................... 125.00
RS PRUSSIA,COFFEE SET,DEMITASSE,FLORAL,JEWELS,EACH PIECE
FOOTED,7 PIECES................................................. 228.00
RS PRUSSIA,COFFEEPOT,FLOWER FORMS,GOLD TRACERY,PROFUSE
PASTEL FLORAL................................................... 32.00
RS PRUSSIA,COMPOTE,GREEN,ROSES,GILT,HAND-PAINTED,PEDESTAL,
RED MARK........................................................ 65.00
RS PRUSSIA,CRACKER JAR,GREEN,PINK APPLE BLOSSOMS,RED MARK,
5 1/2 IN.HIGH................................................... 85.00
RS PRUSSIA,CRACKER JAR,GREEN,WHITE WILD FLORAL,RED MARK,
5 1/2 IN.HIGH................................................... 85.00
RS PRUSSIA,CREAMER & SUGAR,BLENDED COLORED VIOLETS,GOLD LID
& HANDLES....................................................... 25.00
RS PRUSSIA,CREAMER & SUGAR,COVER,BULBOUS SECTIONS,FLOWERS,
FOLIAGE......................................................... 55.00
RS PRUSSIA,CREAMER & SUGAR,CREAM GROUND,DELICATE ROSES,GOLD,
RED MARK........................................................ 90.00
RS PRUSSIA,CREAMER & SUGAR,FLORAL DECOR........................ 70.00
RS PRUSSIA,CREAMER & SUGAR,GREEN GROUND;WHITE LILIES,GILT,
RED MARK........................................................ 59.50

RS PRUSSIA,CREAMER & SUGAR,HOLLY BERRIES,BLOSSOMS,IVORY
GROUND,GOLD.................................................. 40.00
RS PRUSSIA,CREAMER & SUGAR,MELON SHAPE,PINK ROSES,LEAVES,
PEARLY FINISH............................................... 85.00
RS PRUSSIA,CREAMER & SUGAR,PINK & YELLOW FLOWERS,
HAND-PAINTED............................................... 25.00
RS PRUSSIA,CREAMER & SUGAR,WHITE GROUND,PINK ROSES,GOLD
MEDALLIONS................................................. 67.50
RS PRUSSIA,CREAMER & SUGAR,YELLOW DAISIES,GREEN LEAF CHAIN,
RED MARK................................................... 80.00
RS PRUSSIA,CREAMER & SUGAR,YELLOW DAISY & GREEN LEAF CHAIN,
GOLD BANDS................................................. 70.00
RS PRUSSIA,CREAMER & SUGAR,YELLOW IRIS PATTERN,MARKED
NO.404..................................................... 25.00
RS PRUSSIA,CREAMER & SUGAR,YELLOW ROSES..................... 75.00
RS PRUSSIA,CREAMER,CALLA LILY DECOR,RED MARK............... 40.00
RS PRUSSIA,CREAMER,CREAM & BLUE,ROSES,PEDESTAL BASE,RED MARK 42.00
RS PRUSSIA,CREAMER,GREEN,FLORAL,LID........................ 20.00
RS PRUSSIA,CREAMER,PANELED,GREEN & WHITE GROUND,WHITE &
PURPLE LILACS.............................................. 7.00
RS PRUSSIA,CREAMER,PINK FLORAL DESIGN,PINK BASE TO WHITE TOP 21.00
RS PRUSSIA,CREAMER,RED ROSES,GOLD LEAF..................... 10.50
RS PRUSSIA,CREAMER,SUGAR,CRACKER JAR,LAVENDER LILAC PATTERN,
RED MARK................................................... 175.00
RS PRUSSIA,CREAMER,SUGAR,RED GROUND,WHITE & RED
CHRYSANTHEMUMS,FOOTED...................................... 67.00
RS PRUSSIA,CREAMER,SUGAR,RED,WHITE,YELLOW,CHRYSANTHEMUM,
FOOTED,RED MARK............................................ 67.00
RS PRUSSIA,CREAMER,SUGAR,SWAN MOTIF,GREEN,BLUE,MOONGLOW
GROUND,RED MARK............................................ 95.00
RS PRUSSIA,CREAMER,SUGAR,YELLOW DAISY & GREEN LEAF CHAIN
DECOR,RED MARK............................................. 75.00
RS PRUSSIA,CUP & SAUCER,BASKET OF FLOWERS,GOLD TRIM,FOOTED,
SET OF 6................................................... 395.00
RS PRUSSIA,CUP & SAUCER,CHOCOLATE,FLORAL DECOR,RED MARK..... 25.00
RS PRUSSIA,CUP & SAUCER,CHOCOLATE,HEXAGON SHAPE,BEIGE TO
GREEN,GOLD TRIM............................................ 5.00
RS PRUSSIA,CUP & SAUCER,CHOCOLATE,PINK ROSES,BROWN GROUND,
GOLD BORDER................................................ 27.50
RS PRUSSIA,CUP & SAUCER,DEMITASSE,GOLD DESIGN,GOLD HANDLE,
FOOTED..................................................... 32.50
RS PRUSSIA,CUP & SAUCER,DEMITASSE,RAISED FLORAL & LEAF
DESIGN,GILT................................................ 30.00
RS PRUSSIA,CUP & SAUCER,DEMITASSE,SATIN,PINK ROSES,SWIRLS,
GOLD,RED MARK.............................................. 25.00
RS PRUSSIA,CUP & SAUCER,DEMITASSE,TURQUOISE GROUND,PINK
FLORAL,RED MARK............................................ 35.00
RS PRUSSIA,CUP & SAUCER,FLOWER GARLANDS,BLUE ON WHITE,
PEDESTAL CUP............................................... 38.50
RS PRUSSIA,CUP & SAUCER,GREEN,PINK & WHITE ROSES,FLARED,
SCALLOPED TOP.............................................. 29.50
RS PRUSSIA,CUP & SAUCER,HAND-PAINTED PINK ROSES,GREEN
GROUND,RED RIM............................................. 35.00
RS PRUSSIA,CUP & SAUCER,PINK & BLUE FLORAL,DEMITASSE,RED
MARK....................................................... 20.00
RS PRUSSIA,CUP & SAUCER,PINK & WHITE ROSES,PANELED,SATIN
FINISH..................................................... 35.00
RS PRUSSIA,CUP & SAUCER,PINK ROSES,EMBOSSED LEAF DESIGN,
GOLD,RED MARK.............................................. 22.00
RS PRUSSIA,CUP & SAUCER,SCENIC,HOUSES,WINDMILL,RED MARK..... 85.00
RS PRUSSIA,CUP & SAUCER,SWAN,RED MARK...................... 48.00
RS PRUSSIA,CUP & SAUCER,WHITE TO GREEN GROUND,YELLOW & WHITE
ROSES...................................................... 42.00
RS PRUSSIA,CUP & SAUCER,WHITE TO GREEN GROUND,ROSE FLORAL
DECOR,RED MARK............................................. 22.00
RS PRUSSIA,CUP,COFFEE,GREEN,WHITE FLOWERS,FOOTED,RED MARK... 20.00
RS PRUSSIA,CUP,SAUCER,CREAMY,PINK,GOLD,FLORAL,FLUTED EDGE,
FOOTED,MARK................................................ 47.00
RS PRUSSIA,CUP,SAUCER,DEMITASSE,WHITE SHADING TO GREEN,PINK
ROSES,GILT................................................. 20.00
RS PRUSSIA,CUP,SAUCER,PLATE,CREAM GROUND,PINK CARNATION,
ORCHID,BLUE,GOLD........................................... 125.00
RS PRUSSIA,CUSPIDOR,PEARL LUSTER,PINK ROSES,LEAVES,OCTAGONAL
SHAPE,MARK................................................. 75.00
RS PRUSSIA,DISH,BERRY,RIBBED TO CENTER FLOWER,GOLD TRIM,
RUFFLED,SET OF 5........................................... 55.00
RS PRUSSIA,DISH,CANDY,FLOWER DECOR,HAND-PAINTED............ 4.50
RS PRUSSIA,DISH,CANDY,LAVENDER PANSIES,GOLD CIRCLES,BOAT
SHAPE,FOOTED............................................... 40.00
RS PRUSSIA,DISH,CANDY,PINK GROUND,RED & YELLOW ROSES,
RUFFLED,GILT............................................... 40.00

RS PRUSSIA,DISH,CANDY,PORTRAIT,WOMAN,HEAD & SHOULDERS,
FLORAL,PEDESTAL.................................................. 24.50
RS PRUSSIA,DISH,CELERY,BLUE GROUND,ORIENTAL POPPIES,DAISIES,
HANDLES......................................................... 55.00
RS PRUSSIA,DISH,CHEESE,5 WHITE MICE,OUTLINE IN BLACK,GOLD
TRIM & HANDLE................................................... 35.00
RS PRUSSIA,DISH,FRUIT,TULIPS,RED MARK............................ 55.00
RS PRUSSIA,DISH,LILACS,RED MARK,5-IN.DIAMETER.................... 15.00
RS PRUSSIA,DISH,NUT,LILIES INSIDE,GREEN BORDER,FOOTED,RED
MARK............................................................ 48.00
RS PRUSSIA,DISH,PICKLE,GREEN,WHITE WILD ROSES,RED MARK,8 X
3 1/2 IN........................................................ 35.00
RS PRUSSIA,DISH,PICKLE,PEARLIZED,RED ROSES,OPEN HANDLES,RED
MARK,9 IN....................................................... 24.50
RS PRUSSIA,DISH,PIN,GREEN GROUND,PINK PEONIES,FLORAL
SCALLOPED BORDER................................................ 23.00
RS PRUSSIA,DISH,POWDER,PINK ROSES,FOLIAGE,TAN GROUND,
SCALLOPED LID................................................... 60.00
RS PRUSSIA,DISH,RELISH,GREEN & WHITE FLORAL SPRAYS,GOLD
TRIM,RED MARK................................................... 38.00
RS PRUSSIA,DISH,TINY PINK ROSES INSIDE & OUT,GOLD TRIM
CROWSFOOT,MARK.................................................. 20.00
RS PRUSSIA,DISH,TRINKET,SHADED BLUE GROUND,CLUSTER OF
FLOWERS,COVER................................................... 25.00
RS PRUSSIA,DRESSER SET,TRAY,TWO COVERED DISHES,PINK FLORAL,
GREEN,GOLD...................................................... 18.50
RS PRUSSIA,FERNER,PINK ROSES,FOLIAGE,14 SCALLOPED FEET,8 X
4 IN.HIGH....................................................... 95.00
RS PRUSSIA,HAIR RECEIVER,BLUE GROUND,ORANGE BLOSSOM DECOR,
GERMANY......................................................... 15.00
RS PRUSSIA,HAIR RECEIVER,CASTLE SCENE,PEARLIZED,RED MARK.... 65.00
RS PRUSSIA,HAIR RECEIVER,GREEN LUSTER,FLORAL,FOOTED,RED MARK 65.00
RS PRUSSIA,HAIR RECEIVER,GREEN,WHITE FLORAL,GOLD DECOR,
SHAMROCK SHAPE.................................................. 35.00
RS PRUSSIA,HAIR RECEIVER,MATCHING COVERED POWDER BOX,RED
STAR,MARKED..................................................... 45.00
RS PRUSSIA,HAIR RECEIVER,PINK FLOWERS,RED MARK.............. 30.00
RS PRUSSIA,HAIR RECEIVER,PINK ROSES,LILACS,OVAL TOP,BULBOUS
PANELS,FEET..................................................... 35.00
RS PRUSSIA,HAIR RECEIVER,POPPIES,GOLD,FOUR-LEAF CLOVER SHAPE
TOP,FOOTED...................................................... 35.00
RS PRUSSIA,HAIR RECEIVER,RAISED FLOWER TOP................. 48.00
RS PRUSSIA,HAIR RECEIVER,SHADED TAN GROUND,GREEN LEAVES,
FOOTED,RED MARK................................................. 40.00
RS PRUSSIA,HAIR RECEIVER,WHITE FLORAL,FOOTED,RED MARK....... 40.00
RS PRUSSIA,HAIR RECEIVER,WHITE GROUND,BLUE & GOLD DESIGN.... 20.00
RS PRUSSIA,HAIR RECEIVER,WHITE,RAISED GOLD FLORAL,LEAF
GARLANDS,RED MARK............................................... 40.00
RS PRUSSIA,HOLDER,HATPIN,ATTACHED PIN TRAY,PINK ROSES,RED
MARK............................................................ 75.00
RS PRUSSIA,HOLDER,HATPIN,PASTEL SHADING,WHITE FLORAL
CLUSTERS,RED MARK............................................... 38.00
RS PRUSSIA,ICE CREAM SET,7 PIECES.............................. 110.00
RS PRUSSIA,JAR,COOKIE,PEARLIZED,FLORAL,GOLD TRIM,TWO
HANDLES,5 1/4 IN................................................ 85.00
RS PRUSSIA,JAR,COOKIE,ROSE DECOR,SATIN FINISH,RED MARK...... 90.00
RS PRUSSIA,JAR,COOKIE,WHITE GROUND,FLORAL,SATIN FINISH,RED
MARK............................................................ 75.00
RS PRUSSIA,JAR,CRACKER,BEADING,FLORAL,PINK LUSTER,TWO
HANDLES,RED MARK................................................ 80.00
RS PRUSSIA,JAR,CRACKER,GREEN & WHITE,WHITE FLOWERS,RAISED
GOLD SPRAYS..................................................... 68.00
RS PRUSSIA,JAR,CRACKER,ORCHID,CREAMY,GOLD GROUND,PINK ROSE
DECOR,FOOTED.................................................... 135.00
RS PRUSSIA,JAR,CRACKER,PANELS OF PINK & WHITE ASTERS,GOLD,
COVER,FINIAL.................................................... 75.00
RS PRUSSIA,JAR,CRACKER,SOFT PASTEL SHADINGS,PROFUSION OF
FRUIT BLOSSOMS.................................................. 85.00
RS PRUSSIA,JAR,CRACKER,SQUATTY,GRAY GROUND,PINK ROSES,TWO
HANDLES......................................................... 87.50
RS PRUSSIA,JAR,JAM,PINK ROSES & GREEN LEAF CHAIN,GILT,PLATE,
COVER........................................................... 70.00
RS PRUSSIA,MANICURE SET,TRAY,BUFFER HOLDER,TWO JARS,
R.SCHLEGELMILCH................................................. 75.00
RS PRUSSIA,MUFFINEER,WHITE,PINK ROSES ON PEARLIZED BASE,
4 1/2 IN........................................................ 45.00
RS PRUSSIA,MUG,SHAVING,BASKET OF ROSES DECOR.............. 60.00
RS PRUSSIA,MUG,SHAVING,FLORAL,PINK,GREEN,RED,BEVEL MIRROR
INSET........................................................... 60.00
RS PRUSSIA,MUG,SHAVING,ROSES,BLUE GROUND,WHITE FLORAL,
DIVIDER,RED MARK................................................ 82.50

RS PRUSSIA,MUG,SHAVING,WHITE PANELS EDGED IN GOLD,ROSES,RED
 MARK.................................................... 175.00
RS PRUSSIA,MUSTARD POT,GREEN,FLORAL,HANDLED,RED MARK........ 39.00
RS PRUSSIA,MUSTARD POT,LILY IN SHADES OF WHITE & GREEN...... 9.00
RS PRUSSIA,MUSTARD POT,LILY-OF-THE-VALLEY DECOR,SATIN
 FINISH,RED MARK........................................ 37.00
RS PRUSSIA,PITCHER,GREEN,PINK PEONIES,SILHOUETTED FLORAL,
 12 1/2 IN.HIGH......................................... 150.00
RS PRUSSIA,PITCHER,MILK,GARDEN SCENE,MARBLE BALUSTRADE,SWANS
 ON POOL............................................... 145.00
RS PRUSSIA,PITCHER,PINK,GREEN,RED MARK,10 IN.........ILLUS.. 45.00
RS PRUSSIA,PITCHER,SYRUP,FLORALS,GREEN & GOLD SHADES,COVER.. 39.00
RS PRUSSIA,PITCHER,TANKARD,FLORAL,LEAF HANDLE.............. 95.00
RS PRUSSIA,PITCHER,WATER,GREEN GROUND,PINK & YELLOW ROSES,
 SCALLOPS.............................................. 165.00
RS PRUSSIA,PLATE,APRICOT,TAN,GREEN,YELLOW,FLORAL,SCROLLED
 BORDER,MARK........................................... 61.00
RS PRUSSIA,PLATE,BLUE & ROSE GROUND,PINK & WHITE PEONIES,
 10 PANELS,7 IN........................................ 23.00
RS PRUSSIA,PLATE,BLUE,CREAM,LAVENDER,GOLD FLOWER CHAIN ON
 RIM,RED MARK.......................................... 55.00
RS PRUSSIA,PLATE,BLUE,YELLOW,CERISE,CHARTREUSE FLORAL,
 ROCOCO,SCALLOPED...................................... 45.00
RS PRUSSIA,PLATE,CAKE,BOYS EATING MELON,PLAYING WITH DICE,
 RED MARK,6 IN......................................... 160.00
RS PRUSSIA,PLATE,CAKE,GREEN GROUND,PINK & YELLOW CARNATIONS,
 HANDLES............................................... 72.00

R. S. PRUSSIA PITCHER

RS PRUSSIA,PLATE,CAKE,LEAF SHAPE,STEM HANDLE,PINK ROSES,
 GREEN MARK............................................ 25.00
RS PRUSSIA,PLATE,CAKE,OPEN-HANDLED....................... 45.00
RS PRUSSIA,PLATE,CAKE,OPEN-HANDLED,PINK & LAVENDER POPPIES,
 FLORAL................................................ 65.00
RS PRUSSIA,PLATE,CAKE,PANELS,SCROLLS,ORANGE BLOSSOMS,GOLD,
 12-IN.DIAMETER........................................ 55.00
RS PRUSSIA,PLATE,CAKE,PIERCED HANDLE,ROSE CENTER,EMBOSSED
 EDGE.................................................. 22.50
RS PRUSSIA,PLATE,CAKE,PINK & WHITE FLOWERS,OPEN HANDLES,RED
 MARK.................................................. 52.50
RS PRUSSIA,PLATE,CAKE,PINK ROSES,DOUBLE-HANDLED,SCALLOPED,
 10 IN................................................. 45.00
RS PRUSSIA,PLATE,CAKE,ROSES,DAISIES,BLUE CORNFLOWERS,OPEN
 HANDLES,MARK.......................................... 75.00
RS PRUSSIA,PLATE,CAKE,TURQUOISE GROUND,PINK FLORAL,
 SCALLOPED,OPEN HANDLE................................. 59.50
RS PRUSSIA,PLATE,CAKE,TWO BOYS EATING MELON,RED MARK,6 IN... 160.00
RS PRUSSIA,PLATE,CASTLE SCENE,8 1/2 IN................... 55.00
RS PRUSSIA,PLATE,DESSERT,HAND-PAINTED,SET OF FIVE........... 30.00
RS PRUSSIA,PLATE,DOUBLE ROSES & BUDS,SALMON COLOR,WHITE
 DAISIES,HANDLES....................................... 68.00
RS PRUSSIA,PLATE,FLEUR-DE-LIS,APRICOT-YELLOW GROUND,FLORAL,
 LEAVES................................................ 53.00
RS PRUSSIA,PLATE,FLEUR-DE-LIS,FLOWER CLUSTERS,OBLONG,
 SCALLOPED,9 1/2 IN.................................... 65.00

RS PRUSSIA,PLATE,FLORAL,SATIN FINISH,SCÁLLOPED,10 IN........ 40.00
RS PRUSSIA,PLATE,GREEN & WHITE GROUND,FLOWER WREATHS,GOLD
SPRAYS,7 IN.................................................. 25.00
RS PRUSSIA,PLATE,GREEN LUSTER,WHITE FLORAL,GILT,SCALLOPED,
RED MARK,6 IN.............................................. 15.00
RS PRUSSIA,PLATE,HAND-PAINTED FLOWERS & LEAVES,RED MARK,
6 IN....................................................... 16.50
RS PRUSSIA,PLATE,HYDRANGEAS,RAISED ENAMEL,COIN GOLD,
8 1/2 IN.................................................... 11.00
RS PRUSSIA,PLATE,LARGE PASTEL ROSES,GOLD,HAND-PAINTED,
8 1/4 IN.................................................... 27.50
RS PRUSSIA,PLATE,LILIES OF THE VALLEY,SHAGGY LEAF POPPIES,
SATIN FINISH............................................... 58.00
RS PRUSSIA,PLATE,MAUVE-LILAC,GOLD BORDER,CENTER DECOR,SATIN,
11 IN...................................................... 95.00
RS PRUSSIA,PLATE,MELON BOYS,RED MARK,9 1/2 IN.............. 164.00
RS PRUSSIA,PLATE,ORANGE,MAUVE DANGLING FLORAL,RAISED GOLD,
11 1/4 IN.................................................. 65.00
RS PRUSSIA,PLATE,PASTEL,FLOWERS,SCALLOPED,RED MARK,6 IN.... 10.00
RS PRUSSIA,PLATE,PINK & WHITE FLOWERS,GREEN GROUND,RED MARK,
6 IN....................................................... 12.00
RS PRUSSIA,PLATE,PINK FLORAL,BLUE,GREEN LEAVES,SCALLOPS,GOLD
BEADS...................................................... 70.00
RS PRUSSIA,PLATE,PINK FLOWERS,GOLD,OPEN HANDLES,11 IN...... 65.00
RS PRUSSIA,PLATE,PINK ROSE DECOR,SCALLOPED,BEADED BORDER,
8 IN....................................................... 27.50
RS PRUSSIA,PLATE,PINK THISTLE,FOUR CUTOUT AREAS AROUND
SCALLOPED RIM.............................................. 10.00
RS PRUSSIA,PLATE,PORTRAIT,GIRL,DARK HAIR,DOTS,FLORAL RIM,
ROSE,GOLD,GREEN............................................ 150.00
RS PRUSSIA,PLATE,PORTRAIT,THREE CHERUBS,RED MARK........... 92.50
RS PRUSSIA,PLATE,PURPLE & WHITE GROUND,WHITE VASE,RED ROSE
DECOR,HANDLE............................................... 62.50
RS PRUSSIA,PLATE,RELISH,DUTCH SCENE,GIRL,HOUSE,WATER WHEEL,
HANDLES.................................................... 165.00
RS PRUSSIA,PLATE,ROSE DECOR,RAISED BORDER,SATIN FINISH,RED
MARK....................................................... 22.00
RS PRUSSIA,PLATE,ROSES,GOLD TRIM,RED MARK,7 1/2 IN......... 16.00
RS PRUSSIA,PLATE,ROSES,GOLD,8 3/4 IN....................... 35.00
RS PRUSSIA,PLATE,ROSES,GREEN TRIM,7 3/8 IN................. 30.00
RS PRUSSIA,PLATE,ROSES,RED MARK,7 1/2 IN................... 30.00
RS PRUSSIA,PLATE,SCENE,THREE SWANS,TREES,FLOWERS,TWO
HANDLES,RED MARK........................................... 95.00
RS PRUSSIA,PLATE,SWANS..................................... 200.00
RS PRUSSIA,PLATE,TURQUOISE SHADING,PINK POPPIES,WHITE
LILIES,RED MARK............................................ 58.00
RS PRUSSIA,PLATE,TWO BOYS EATING MELON,DOG,GOLD,8 1/2 IN.... 265.00
RS PRUSSIA,PLATE,WHITE & PINK PEONIES,SCALLOPED INTO
10 POINTS,7 IN............................................. 25.00
RS PRUSSIA,PLATE,WHITE DAFFODILS,GREEN LUSTER,GOLD,OPEN
HANDLE,9 1/2 IN............................................ 8.50
RS PRUSSIA,PLATE,WHITE,BEADED GOLD SCALLOP,GOLD FLORAL,RED
MARK....................................................... 30.00
RS PRUSSIA,PLATE,WHITE,LILIES,GOLD LEAF GARLANDS,SCALLOPED,
7 IN....................................................... 25.00
RS PRUSSIA,PLATE,WINTER SCENE,GOLD TRIM,RED MARK,8 1/2 IN... 300.00
RS PRUSSIA,PLATTER,FLORAL,ROSES,TWO HANDLES,RED MARK,
11 1/2 IN.................................................. 75.00
RS PRUSSIA,PLATTER,ROSES,FLORAL,HANDLES,RED MARK,11 1/2 IN.. 75.00
RS PRUSSIA,PLATTER,WINTER SCENE,FLORAL DESIGN,TWO HANDLES,
11 IN...................................................... 395.00
RS PRUSSIA,POT,CHOCOLATE,WHITE,BLUE,PINK ROSES,1811,5 CUPS &
SAUCERS.................................................... 35.00
RS PRUSSIA,POT,MUSTARD,PINK,GREEN,GOLD,ROSES,COVER,RED MARK. 38.00
RS PRUSSIA,RELISH,GREEN GROUND,WHITE FLORAL,GOLD STEMS,RED
MARK....................................................... 30.00
RS PRUSSIA,RELISH,ORANGE & YELLOW ROSES,GOLD TRIM,SATIN,TWO
HANDLES.................................................... 45.00
RS PRUSSIA,RELISH,SATIN,ORANGE & YELLOW ROSES,GOLD TRIM,
HANDLES,12 IN.............................................. 45.00
RS PRUSSIA,RELISH,VIOLET COLOR,WHITE FLORAL,SCALLOPED,OPEN
HANDLES,MARK............................................... 32.00
RS PRUSSIA,SALT & PEPPER,SWIRLED GREEN DESIGN,RED ROSES,
ARTIST-SIGNED.............................................. 50.00
RS PRUSSIA,SALT & PEPPER,WHITE,PANELS,PINK WILD ROSES ON
GREEN OVAL................................................. 16.00
RS PRUSSIA,SAUCE,BLUE GROUND,SWANS,WATER LILIES............ 7.00
RS PRUSSIA,SAUCE,BLUE RIBBONS,BOWS,SET OF 3................ 128.00
RS PRUSSIA,SAUCE,PINK,MOLDED IRIS ON EDGE,RED MARK,SET OF 6. 59.00
RS PRUSSIA,SAUCE,SHAG LEAF WHITE FLOWERS,PASTEL LUSTER,SET
OF 6....................................................... 88.00

```
RS PRUSSIA,SHAKER,SALT,PASTEL APRICOT,ROSES................     6.50
RS PRUSSIA,SHAKER,SUGAR,BOUQUET OF PINK & WHITE DAISIES,
   GOLD,SATIN..............................................    60.00
RS PRUSSIA,SHAKER,SUGAR,PINK ROSES,WHITE DAISIES,GOLD
   SCROLLWORK..............................................    65.00
RS PRUSSIA,SHAKER,SUGAR,SATIN FINISH,PINK & WHITE DAISY
   BOUQUET,SCROLLS.........................................    60.00
RS PRUSSIA,SHOE,WHITE,GREEN-AQUA,PINK TEA ROSES,FLORAL,RED
   MARK....................................................    57.00
RS PRUSSIA,SPOONER,WHITE GROUND,GREEN LEAVES,GOLD BERRIES,
   HANDLES,MARK............................................    48.00
RS PRUSSIA,SUGAR,GREEN GROUND,PINK ROSES,EIGHT SMALL FEET,
   COVER,RED MARK..........................................    24.00
RS PRUSSIA,SUGAR,PANELS,PINK,YELLOW ROSES,GOLD,SCALLOPED,RED
   MARK....................................................    27.00
RS PRUSSIA,SUGAR,PINK FLORAL,RUFFLED TOP,MELON SHAPE,RED
   MARK....................................................    45.00
RS PRUSSIA,SUGAR,RAISED FLORAL,GOLD,EIGHT LEGS,RAISED STAR
   MARK....................................................    35.00
RS PRUSSIA,SUGAR,ROSE DECOR,EIGHT GREEN FEET,RED MARK.......    19.00
RS PRUSSIA,SUGAR,ROSE TO YELLOW TO GREEN,FLOWER GROUPING,
   FOOTED,COVER............................................    36.00
RS PRUSSIA,SUGAR,WHITE,FLORAL,FLEUR-DE-LIS,PEARLS,FOOTED,RED
   MARK....................................................    27.50
RS PRUSSIA,SUGAR,WHITE,PINK ROSES,FOOTED,RED MARK..........     35.00
RS PRUSSIA,SYRUP,GREEN GROUND,PINK ROSES,SCALLOPED BASE,
   BEADED RIM,MARK.........................................    32.50
RS PRUSSIA,SYRUP,LILY DECOR,RED MARK.......................     75.00
RS PRUSSIA,SYRUP,PINK ROSES,GILT,BUCKLE TYPE FINIAL,
   SCALLOPED BASE,TOP......................................    60.00
RS PRUSSIA,TEA SET,TRAY,GRAPE PATTERN,7 PIECES.............     49.50
RS PRUSSIA,TEACUP,GREEN,PINK & WHITE WILD ROSES,RED MARK....    27.50
RS PRUSSIA,TEAPOT,BASKET OF FLOWERS DESIGN,SIX CUPS &
   SAUCERS,RED MARK........................................   395.00
RS PRUSSIA,TEAPOT,BASKET OF ROSES,FOOTED,RED MARK,5 IN.TALL.    50.00
RS PRUSSIA,TEAPOT,CALLA LILY DECOR,RED MARK................     75.00
RS PRUSSIA,TEAPOT,COVERED SUGAR,CREAMER,GREEN,ROSES,FOOTED,
   RED MARK................................................   145.00
RS PRUSSIA,TEAPOT,CREAMER,OPEN SUGAR,PORTRAIT.............     275.00
RS PRUSSIA,TEAPOT,CREAMER,SUGAR,EIGHT CUPS & SAUCERS,MELON
   RIB,FLORAL..............................................   750.00
RS PRUSSIA,TEAPOT,CREAMER,SUGAR,LAVENDER,PEONY DECOR,
   SCALLOPED RIMS,GILT.....................................   185.00
RS PRUSSIA,TEAPOT,CREAMER,SUGAR,PINK FLOWERS,GOLD TRIM,
   FOOTED,RED MARK.........................................   130.00
RS PRUSSIA,TEAPOT,PINK DAISY DECOR,GREEN GROUND,GOLD,
   HAND-DECORATED..........................................    37.00
RS PRUSSIA,TEAPOT,PINK FLOWERS,GOLD TRIM,FOOTED,RED MARK,
   CREAMER & SUGAR.........................................   130.00
RS PRUSSIA,TEAPOT,SUGAR,CREAMER,PASTEL ROSES,TEAPOT
   6 IN.HIGH...............................................   148.00
RS PRUSSIA,TEAPOT,THREE SWANS,FIR TREES,7 1/2 X
   4 1/2 IN.HIGH...........................................    80.00
RS PRUSSIA,TEAPOT,WHITE,FLORAL,FLEUR-DE-LIS,PEARLS,FINIAL,
   RED MARK................................................    57.00
RS PRUSSIA,TEAPOT,WHITE,GREEN,ROSE SPRAYS,GOLD TRIM,RED
   MARK,7 IN.HIGH..........................................    46.00
RS PRUSSIA,TOOTHPICK,FLORAL,TWO HANDLES,RED MARK..........     65.00
RS PRUSSIA,TOOTHPICK,PINK ROSES,GREEN TOP,RAISED BASE,
   SCALLOPED FEET..........................................    45.00
RS PRUSSIA,TOOTHPICK,YELLOW ROSES,SCALLOPED BASE & TOP,GILT,
   HANDLES.................................................    47.50
RS PRUSSIA,TRAY,BREAD,PEACH,ORCHID,PINK FLORAL,TURQUOISE
   GROUND,RED MARK.........................................    55.00
RS PRUSSIA,TRAY,CELERY,FLOWER BOUQUETS,ROSES,DAISIES,
   HANDLES,RED MARK........................................    27.50
RS PRUSSIA,TRAY,CELERY,FOUR SWANS,SCENIC,EMBOSSED,GILT
   FLORAL RIM,MARK.........................................    67.50
RS PRUSSIA,TRAY,CELERY,PINK,PEACH ROSES,TAN,GOLD BORDER,CUT
   HANDLES.................................................    59.00
RS PRUSSIA,TRAY,CELERY,ROSES,EMBOSSED,HANDLES,RED MARK,
   9 1/2 IN................................................    18.00
RS PRUSSIA,TRAY,CELERY,ROSES,GOLD,OPENWORK,SATIN,13 1/2 IN..    45.00
RS PRUSSIA,TRAY,CELERY,TRICOLORED ROSES,EMBOSSED,HANDLES,RED
   MARK,12 IN..............................................    34.00
RS PRUSSIA,TRAY,DRESSER,FLORAL CENTER,GREEN & GOLD BORDER,
   HANDLES.................................................    75.00
RS PRUSSIA,TRAY,DRESSER,LIGHT GREEN RIM,ROSE SPRAYS,ANGELS,
   RED MARK................................................    50.00
RS PRUSSIA,TRAY,DRESSER,ORNATE,OPEN HANDLES,RED MARK,12 IN.
   X 8 IN..................................................    69.50
```

RS PRUSSIA,TRAY,DRESSER,PINK FLOWER CENTER,LILY CORNERS,GILT
  HANDLES....................................................... 59.00
RS PRUSSIA,TRAY,DRESSER,PINK,PEACH COLOR,ROSES,DAISIES,
  SCALLOPED,HANDLES............................................. 39.00
RS PRUSSIA,TRAY,DRESSER,ROSE DECOR,COBALT,RED MARK & CHURCH
  STEEPLE....................................................... 50.00
RS PRUSSIA,TRAY,DRESSER,WHITE LILIES,TAUPE BASE,EDGE CUT
  HANDLES....................................................... 37.00
RS PRUSSIA,TRAY,FLORAL SPRAY IN CENTER,EMBOSSED IRIS IN
  CORNERS,RED STAR.............................................. 75.00
RS PRUSSIA,TRAY,PASTEL ROSES,GOLD RIM,OPEN HANDLES,OVAL,
  11 IN......................................................... 65.00
RS PRUSSIA,TRAY,PIN,HEART SHAPE,MELON RIBBED,ROSES,GREEN &
  GOLD GROUND................................................... 18.00
RS PRUSSIA,TRAY,RELISH,BOAT SCENE,RED MARK,11 IN.LONG......... 125.00
RS PRUSSIA,TRAY,RELISH,PORTRAIT,AUTUMN,RED MARK,9 IN.LONG... 165.00
RS PRUSSIA,TRAY,SERVING,WHITE & GREEN FLOWERS,GOLD BORDER,
  RED MARK...................................................... 42.50
RS PRUSSIA,TRAY,SNOWBALLS,RED MARK,11 1/4 X 8 1/4 IN......... 50.00
RS PRUSSIA,TRAY,WHITE DOGWOOD DECOR,RED MARK,9 X 12 3/8 IN.. 50.00
RS PRUSSIA,TRAY,WINTER SCENE,ROOKS,FROZEN LAKE,PINES,HOUSE,
  RED MARK...................................................... 95.00
RS PRUSSIA,TRAY,YELLOW ROSES,RED STAR MARKED,12 IN.LONG,
  9 IN.WIDE..................................................... 45.00
RS PRUSSIA,VASE,BOYS EATING MELON,DOG,MEDALLION,GOLD,RED
  MARK,8 IN.HIGH................................................ 395.00
RS PRUSSIA,VASE,BOYS EATING MELON,SIGNED MELONENESSER
  V.MURILLO,RED MARK............................................ 175.00
RS PRUSSIA,VASE,DARK GREEN TO YELLOW,POMPON & ROSE DECOR,
  GOLD HANDLES.................................................. 165.00
RS PRUSSIA,VASE,GOLD,WHITE,BLUE,SWANS,TREES,WATER,HANDLES,
  RED MARK...................................................... 125.00
RS PRUSSIA,VASE,THATCHED COTTAGE SCENE,COTTAGE & OLD MILL
  SCENE,RED MARK................................................ 115.00


     RUBENA VERDE IS A VICTORIAN GLASS WARE THAT WAS FLASHED
       WITH RED ON THE OUTSIDE.
RUBENA VERDE,BOTTLE,COLOGNE,RED SHADING,CLEAR FACET STOPPER,
  4 1/2 IN...................................................... 35.00
RUBENA VERDE,BOWL,ALLOVER WANDERING VINE PATTERN,APPLIED
  SHELL FEET.................................................... 45.00
RUBENA VERDE,BOWL,FINGER,OPALESCENT,5-IN.DIAMETER............ 28.00
RUBENA VERDE,BOWL,FINGER,PANELED,CLEAR TO CRANBERRY,FLORAL,
  ENAMEL,GILT................................................... 50.00
RUBENA VERDE,BOWL,FRUIT,HOBNAIL.............................. 110.00
RUBENA VERDE,BOWL,HOBNAIL,7 1/2 IN.SQUARE.................... 175.00
RUBENA VERDE,BOWL,ROSE,SWIRL,CRIMPED TOP,4 1/2 IN........... 45.00
RUBENA VERDE,BOX,PANELS,COVER,3 IN.WIDE,2 1/2 IN.HIGH....... 35.00
RUBENA VERDE,CASTOR,PICKLE,CORALENE DECOR,OWLS,SILVER FRAME,
  TONGS......................................................... 135.00
RUBENA VERDE,CELERY,6 1/4 IN................................. 75.00
RUBENA VERDE,CRUET,DAISY,FERN,OPALESCENT,FACETED STOPPER,
  CLEAR HANDLE.................................................. 48.00
RUBENA VERDE,CUP,PUNCH,DIAMOND-QUILTED...................... 16.50
RUBENA VERDE,DECANTER,CUT,CRANBERRY,9 IN.TALL............... 50.00
RUBENA VERDE,DISH,RUFFLED EDGE,FOOTED,2 1/2 IN.HIGH......... 35.00
RUBENA VERDE,DISH,RUFFLED,SILVER STAND,5 IN................. 45.00
RUBENA VERDE,DISH,SAUCE,FROSTED,IN METAL FRAME.............. 65.00
RUBENA VERDE,DOME,INVERTED THUMBPRINT....................... 35.00
RUBENA VERDE,EPERGNE,CLEAR TO OPALESCENT,TWO PIECES,
  12 IN.HIGH.................................................... 110.00
RUBENA VERDE,PERFUME,SWIRL FINECUT & PLAIN PANELS........... 24.00
RUBENA VERDE,PERFUME,SWIRL,MATCHING STOPPER,6 1/2 IN.TALL... 32.50
RUBENA VERDE,PITCHER,BULBOUS,CLEAR TO CRANBERRY,ETCHED,FIVE
  TUMBLERS...................................................... 175.00
RUBENA VERDE,PITCHER,DIAMOND-QUILTED,REEDED HANDLE,SQUARE
  MOUTH,6 IN.HIGH............................................... 87.50
RUBENA VERDE,PITCHER,INVERTED THUMBPRINT,5 IN,TALL.......... 45.00
RUBENA VERDE,PITCHER,INVERTED THUMBPRINT,16-IN.DIAMETER,
  5 1/2 IN.TALL................................................. 92.00
RUBENA VERDE,PITCHER,THUMBPRINT,BULBOUS,SQUARE TOP,5 1/2 IN. 85.00
RUBENA VERDE,PITCHER,WATER,BULBOUS,THUMBPRINT,CLEAR REEDED
  HANDLE........................................................ 75.00
RUBENA VERDE,PITCHER,WATER,HOBNAIL,OPALESCENT,BULBOUS,SQUARE
  TOP,7 IN...................................................... 175.00
RUBENA VERDE,PITCHER,WATER,ROYAL IVY........................ 85.00
RUBENA VERDE,PITCHER,WATER,ROYAL IVY,FROSTED................ 100.00
RUBENA VERDE,SALT & PEPPER,ENAMEL FLORAL DECOR,CRYSTAL...... 68.00
RUBENA VERDE,SHAKER,SUGAR,SWIRL,THREADED PATTERN........... 27.50
RUBENA VERDE,SYRUP,OPALESCENT,COIN SPOT,PEARL SHAPE,METAL

```
   LID,7 1/4 IN..............................................   68.00
RUBENA VERDE,TOOTHPICK,THREADED,1 3/4 IN.HIGH X
   2 1/4-IN.DIAMETER........................................   18.00
RUBENA VERDE,TUMBLER,QUILTED................................   12.00
RUBENA VERDE,TUMBLER,ROYAL OAK..............................   27.50
RUBENA VERDE,TUMBLER,THUMBPRINT.............................   25.00
RUBENA VERDE,VASE,CELERY,ENAMELED,SCALLOPED,BIRD,FLORAL,
   SILVER HOLDER...........................................  110.00
RUBENA VERDE,VASE,DOUBLE TREE TRUNK,THORNS,7 IN.HIGH........   35.00
RUBENA VERDE,VASE,GREEN TO CRANBERRY,APPLIED GREEN RIGAREE,
   9 1/2 IN.HIGH...........................................   45.00
RUBENA VERDE,VASE,GREEN TO CRANBERRY,COIN GOLD FLORAL,
   PANELED,13 1/2 IN.......................................   85.00
RUBENA VERDE,VASE,HOBNAIL,RED SHADING TO GREEN,SCALLOPED
   TOP,7 1/2 IN............................................   28.50
RUBENA VERDE,VASE,IRIS BOUQUET,ENAMEL,10 1/2 IN.HIGH........   62.00
RUBENA VERDE,VASE,SWIRLS,PLEATED TOP,BULBOUS BASE,4 IN......   32.50
RUBENA VERDE,VASE,WHITE ENAMEL DAISIES,GOLD LEAVES,SWIRLED
   PANELS,PAIR.............................................   45.00


   RUBY GLASS IS A DARK RED COLOR. IT WAS A VICTORIAN AND
   TWENTIETH-CENTURY WARE. UNFORTUNATELY THE NAME MEANS
   MANY DIFFERENT TYPES OF RED GLASS.
   RUBY GLASS,SEE ALSO,CRANBERRY,PIGEON BLOOD
RUBY GLASS,BELL,TABLE,DEER & CASTLE,DATED 1904,6 IN.........   25.00
RUBY GLASS,BOTTLE,COLOGNE,TWISTED,THREADED STOPPER..........   75.00
RUBY GLASS,BOTTLE,SCENT,PEWTER SCREW TOP....................   35.00
RUBY GLASS,BOWL,BERRY,SAXON PATTERN,10 SMALLER BOWLS........   15.00
RUBY GLASS,BOWL,ROSE,ROUGH PONTIL,BUBBLES,8-IN.DIAMETER,
   6 1/2 IN.HIGH...........................................   35.00
RUBY GLASS,BOWL,ROSE,3 1/2 IN.HIGH..........................    3.50
RUBY GLASS,CELERY,DAKOTA....................................   28.50
RUBY GLASS,CHALICE,CHECKERBOARD DESIGN ALTERNATING WITH
   CLEAR,FLORAL............................................   75.00
RUBY GLASS,COMPOTE,CLEAR GLASS OVERLAY,SIGNED JEAN BECK,
   MUNICH,4 1/2 IN.........................................   22.00
RUBY GLASS,COMPOTE,THUMBPRINT,7 1/2 IN.HIGH.................   30.00
RUBY GLASS,CORDIAL,THUMBPRINT...............................   20.00
RUBY GLASS,CREAMER,SOUVENIR LAKEMONT PARK...................    9.50
RUBY GLASS,CREAMER,SUGAR,BUTTER,SPOONER,COVERS,GOLD INTAGLIO
   CARNATIONS..............................................   69.50
RUBY GLASS,CUP,PUNCH,THUMBPRINT,HANDLED.....................   14.00
RUBY GLASS,DECANTER,FACET CUT,CLEAR STOPPER.................   16.50
RUBY GLASS,DECANTER,ROSE DECOR,FOUR GLASSES,BOHEMIA.........   50.00
RUBY GLASS,DESSERT,THUMBPRINT,FOOTED........................    2.50
RUBY GLASS,GOBLET,BLOCK.....................................   18.00
RUBY GLASS,GOBLET,DIAMOND DESIGN,SET OF 12..................   42.00
RUBY GLASS,GOBLET,THUMBPRINT................................    2.50
RUBY GLASS,GOBLET,TRUMPET SHAPE,SET OF 8....................   20.00
RUBY GLASS,ICE BUCKET,BAIL..................................   10.00
RUBY GLASS,JAR,CANDY,COIN SPOT DESIGN,OVAL BALL SHAPE,COVER.   25.50
RUBY GLASS,JAR,CANDY,THREE KNOBS FORM BASE,SHORT STEM,CROWN
   FINIAL.................................................   16.00
RUBY GLASS,JAR,COOKIE,PANEL,THUMBPRINT,COVER,8 3/4 IN.TALL..   35.50
RUBY GLASS,LAMP,BLOWN GLASS BURNER,SIGNED GLOW LAMP,INC.....   20.00
RUBY GLASS,MUG,BUTTON ARCHES,HANDLE.........................   10.00
RUBY GLASS,MUG,PEDESTAL FOOT,APPLIED HANDLE,STAINED GLASS,
   4 1/2 IN.TALL...........................................   15.00
RUBY GLASS,MUG,SOUVENIR,ST.LOUIS,1904,SAYS FLORENCE.........   10.00
RUBY GLASS,MUG,SOUVENIR,STATE FAIR,1914,BUTTON ARCHES,
   INVERTED HEART..........................................    7.50
RUBY GLASS,MUG,WORLD'S FAIR,1904,SAYS GEORGE................    7.50
RUBY GLASS,PITCHER,MILK,THUMBPRINT..........................   28.50
RUBY GLASS,PITCHER,SAYS MOTHER,1906,ATLANTIC CITY,FLASHED,
   4 IN....................................................   15.00
RUBY GLASS,PITCHER,SAYS SISTER,1897,ATLANTIC CITY,FLASHED,
   4 IN....................................................   15.00
RUBY GLASS,PITCHER,SOUVENIR,SAYS MOTHER FROM ATLANTIC CITY,
   1899,8 IN...............................................   26.50
RUBY GLASS,PITCHER,WATER,BAND AROUND CENTER,TWO-PIECE MOLD,
   BLOWN...................................................   30.00
RUBY GLASS,PITCHER,WATER,ENGRAVED STAG DECOR,SIX TUMBLERS,
   BOHEMIAN................................................  175.00
RUBY GLASS,PITCHER,WATER,PAIRPOINT..........................   35.00
RUBY GLASS,PITCHER,WATER,TWO TUMBLERS.......................   29.95
RUBY GLASS,SAUCE,THUMBPRINT,BOAT SHAPE......................   13.00
RUBY GLASS,SHAKER,SALT & PEPPER,THUMBPRINT,PEWTER TOPS......   35.00
RUBY GLASS,SHERBET,DIAMOND DESIGN,SET OF 12.................   30.00
RUBY GLASS,SPOONER,GOLD CHERUBS,5 1/4 IN. X 3 1/4 IN........   25.00
RUBY GLASS,SPOONER,SAWTOOTH RIM.............................   22.50
```

RUBY GLASS,SPOONER,TRIPLE TRIANGLE.......................... 13.50
RUBY GLASS,SUGAR,SILVER TOP & FRAME........................ 42.00
RUBY GLASS,SWAN,CLEAR HEAD & NECK,8 IN.LONG................ 6.50
RUBY GLASS,TOOTHPICK,THUMBPRINT.................... 9.00 TO 12.50
RUBY GLASS,TOOTHPICK,THUMBPRINT,FLASHED TOP................ 10.00
RUBY GLASS,TRAY,TWO DECANTERS,EIGHT CORDIALS,ENAMEL DECOR... 195.00
RUBY GLASS,TUMBLER,BAND AROUND CENTER,BLOWN,4 3/4 IN.TALL... 7.00
RUBY GLASS,TUMBLER,CLEAR BASE BAND,MOTHER,1902 ETCHED....... 5.75
RUBY GLASS,TUMBLER,SOUVENIR,JOLIET,ILLINOIS,BUTTON ARCHES... 10.00
RUBY GLASS,TUMBLER,THUMBPRINT.............................. 20.00
RUBY GLASS,TUMBLER,TRIPLE TRIANGLE......................... 12.00
RUBY GLASS,TUMBLER,TWO GOLD BANDS NEAR TOP,4 3/4 IN.HIGH.... 7.00
RUBY GLASS,VASE,AMBER BOTTOM,19 IN.TALL.................... 55.00
RUBY GLASS,VASE,AVENTURINE,SWIRLS,GOLD-DUSTED,SILVER
  PAIRPOINT HOLDER........................................ 40.00
RUBY GLASS,VASE,FLUTED,GILT,DISC STEM...................... 100.00
RUBY GLASS,VASE,MULTICOLOR FLORAL SPRAYS,BUTTERFLY,GOLD,URN
  SHAPE,14 IN............................................. 38.00
RUBY GLASS,WINE,ETCHED,DATED 1892,CLEAR.................... 18.00


        RUDOLSTADT PORCELAIN WAS MADE IN THURINGIA,GERMANY,
        FROM 1854 TO THE TWENTIETH CENTURY.
RUDOLSTADT,BOWL,WHITE TO BLUE,GOLD ON RIM,CLUSTERS OF BLUE
  FLOWERS................................................. 18.00
RUDOLSTADT,BOX,BURGUNDY GROUND,GOLD,PANELS & FLORAL ON LID,
  HINGED,1854............................................. 55.00
RUDOLSTADT,CHOCOLATE POT,YELLOW & WHITE,PASTEL FLOWERS...... 30.00
RUDOLSTADT,CUP & SAUCER,HAPPY FATS......................... 20.00
RUDOLSTADT,DISH,INSETS,HAND-PAINTED CENTERS,PINK LUSTER,
  OYSTER SHAPE............................................ 20.00
RUDOLSTADT,MUG,HAPPY FATS.................................. 25.00
RUDOLSTADT,PLATE,ENAMELED PINK POPPIES,PRUSSIA,8 1/4 IN..... 12.50
RUDOLSTADT,PLATE,WHITE,GOLD,LEAF DECOR,GERMANY,6 1/2 IN..... 9.50
RUDOLSTADT,VASE,FLORAL,GOLD DECOR,SATIN FINISH,GREEN,
  12 1/2 IN............................................... 25.00
RUDOLSTADT,VASE,IVORY COLOR ELEPHANT SEATED AT HORIZONTAL
  HOLLOW LOG.............................................. 15.00
RUSSIAN ENAMEL,BASKET,HANDLE,5-IN.DIAMETER...............1,250.00
RUSSIAN ENAMEL,BOWL,KORSCH,SIGNED KLEBNIKOV,6-IN.DIAMETER...3,000.00
RUSSIAN ENAMEL,GLASS HOLDER............................... 600.00
RUSSIAN ENAMEL,SALT,MASTER,FOOTED,MARKED 84,DATED 1888,
  WORKMASTER N.C.......................................... 95.00
RUSSIAN ENAMEL,SPOON,DEMITASSE,CHAMPLEVE HANDLE,PINK ENAMEL,
  SET OF 8................................................ 500.00
RUSSIAN ENAMEL,SPOON,DEMITASSE,SET OF 5.................... 250.00
RUSSIAN ENAMEL,SPOON,MARKED 84,DATED 1891,WORKMASTER
  INITIALS A.A.,5 IN...................................... 55.00
RUSSIAN ENAMEL,SPOON,SIGNED KUMBERT........................ 50.00
RUSSIAN ENAMEL,TOOTHPICK,HANDLES,MARKED................... 187.00
RUSSIAN,ENAMEL,TEAPOT,CREAMER,COVERED SUGAR,SIGNED CK 84....3,000.00

SABINO,FIGURINE,MADONNA,PRAYING,GOLD COLOR,SIGNED,3 1/8 IN.. 22.50


        SALOPIAN WARE WAS MADE BY THE CAUGHLEY FACTORY OF
        ENGLAND DURING THE EIGHTEENTH CENTURY. THE EARLY PIECES
        WERE DECORATED IN BLUE AND WHITE WITH SOME COLORED
        DECORATIONS. MANY OF THE PIECES CALLED SALOPIAN ARE
        ELABORATE,COLORED-TRANSFER DESIGN,DECORATED TABLEWARES
        MADE DURING THE LATE NINETEENTH CENTURY.
SALOPIAN,BOWL,BLUE & WHITE,11 IN.LONG...................... 85.00
SALOPIAN,CUP & SAUCER,BLUE,WHITE,DEER PATTERN,HANDLELESS.... 85.00
SALOPIAN,SAUCER,TWO BIRDS, COTTAGE,4 7/8-IN.DIAMETER........ 55.00
  SALT AND PEPPER,SEE PRESSED GLASS,PORCELAIN,ETC.


        SALT GLAZE IS A HARD,SHINY GLAZE THAT WAS DEVELOPED FOR
        POTTERY DURING THE EIGHTEENTH CENTURY. IT IS STILL
        BEING MADE.
SALT GLAZE,BASE,DESIGNS IN BLUE,8 IN.TALL,PAIR............. 45.00
SALT GLAZE,MOLD,PUDDING,BROWN,THISTLE CENTER,6 1/2 IN....... 15.00
SALT GLAZE,MUG,COBALT BANDS,APPLIED HANDLE,BARREL SHAPE,
  STONEWARE............................................... 18.00
SALT GLAZE,MUG,WHITE GROUND,BLUE DECOR,TWO HANDLES,
  4 1/2 IN.HIGH........................................... 20.00
SALT GLAZE,PITCHER,APOSTLES,6 IN........................... 45.00
SALT GLAZE,PITCHER,BEIGE,DANCING COUPLE,DATED 1852,7 IN..... 25.00
SALT GLAZE,PITCHER,BLUE,BABIES IN THE WOODS,TRIMMED IN
  LUSTER,7 IN.TALL........................................ 75.00
SALT GLAZE,PITCHER,CREAM,RAISED FIGURES IN COPPER LUSTER,

SCALLOPED TOP................................................ 48.50
SALT GLAZE,PITCHER,GAME,CREAM COLOR GROUND,10 IN.HIGH....... 45.00
SALT GLAZE,PITCHER,MADONNA SCULPTURE,SIGNED MEIGH,DATED
  1846,10 IN.HIGH........................................... 75.00
SALT GLAZE,PITCHER,SAGE GREEN,MARKED DUDSON,CIRCA 1850,5 X
  9 IN.HIGH................................................. 35.00
SALT GLAZE,PITCHER,SAYS PUBLISHED JULY 1,1842,JONES &
  WALLEY,COBRIDGE........................................... 67.50
SALT GLAZE,PITCHER,SCROLLS,GRAPES,BACCHUS HEADS,CIRCA 1845,
  CANE-COLORED.............................................. 55.00
SALT GLAZE,PITCHER,WHITE,GOLD FLOWER,LEAVES,4 1/2 IN.TALL... 32.50
SALT GLAZE,PLATTER,GREEN,BAMBOO SIDES,GIVE US THIS DAY,WHEAT
  HANDLES................................................... 16.50
SALT GLAZE,SYRUP,LEAF PATTERN,REGISTRY BEECH & HANCOCK,
  TUNSTALL,7 IN............................................. 37.50
SALT GLAZE,TEAPOT,BLUE ON GRAY.............................. 36.50
SALT GLAZE,TOOTHPICK,WHITE.................................. 9.50


SAMPLERS WERE MADE IN THE UNITED STATES DURING THE
EARLY 1700S. THE BEST EXAMPLES WERE MADE FROM 1790 TO
1840. LONG NARROW SAMPLERS ARE USUALLY OLDER THAN THE
SQUARE ONES. EARLY SAMPLERS JUST HAD STITCHING OR
ALPHABETS. THE LATER EXAMPLES HAD NUMERALS,BORDERS,AND
PICTORIAL DECORATIONS. THOSE WITH MOTTOS ARE MID-
VICTORIAN.
SAMPLER,CROSS-STITCH,DATED 1848,AMERICAN,FRAMED............. 40.00


SANDWICH GLASS IS ANY ONE OF THE MYRIAD TYPES OF
GLASS MADE BY THE BOSTON AND SANDWICH GLASS WORKS IN
SANDWICH,MASSACHUSETTS,BETWEEN 1825 AND 1888. IT IS
OFTEN VERY DIFFICULT TO BE SURE WHETHER A PIECE WAS
REALLY MADE AT THE SANDWICH FACTORY BECAUSE SO MANY
TYPES WERE MADE THERE AND SIMILAR PIECES WERE MADE AT
OTHER GLASS FACTORIES.
SANDWICH GLASS,SEE ALSO,PRESSED GLASS,ETC.
SANDWICH GLASS,BOTTLE,COLOGNE,OVERSHOT,SQUARE,6 3/4 IN.TALL.   35.00
SANDWICH GLASS,BOTTLE,DIAMOND PATTERN,CLEAR,QUART...........  150.00
SANDWICH GLASS,BOTTLE,SCENT,ENAMEL,PINK,WHITE,GOLD FLORAL,
  SILVER STOPPER............................................ 75.00
SANDWICH GLASS,BOTTLE,SMELLING,IRON PONTIL,BLUE SHADING..... 50.00
SANDWICH GLASS,BOWL,BALTIMORE,PEAR,PINK,STIPPLED............ 65.00
SANDWICH GLASS,BOWL,HEART PATTERN,FLINT,8 IN................ 24.50
SANDWICH GLASS,BOWL,OAK LEAF PATTERN,LACY,6 1/2-IN.DIAMETER. 38.00
SANDWICH GLASS,BOWL,PUNCH,RAYED HAIRPIN PATTERN,TWO PIECES,
  10 CUPS.................................................. 65.00
SANDWICH GLASS,BOX,DRESSER,CLEAR,3 1/2 X 2 1/2 IN.WIDE...... 12.00
SANDWICH GLASS,BOX,THREADED,DECOR ON HINGED LID,
  6-IN.DIAMETER............................................. 40.00
SANDWICH GLASS,CANDLESTICK,FLARING SIX-SIDED,1835,7 IN.,PAIR 65.00
SANDWICH GLASS,CANDLESTICK,PETAL & LOOP,MATCHING BOBECHES,
  PAIR..................................................... 75.00
SANDWICH GLASS,CANDLESTICK,PETAL & LOOP,CANARY,PAIR......... 90.00
SANDWICH GLASS,CANDLESTICK,PETAL & LOOP,FLINT,7 IN.HIGH,PAIR 100.00
SANDWICH GLASS,CANE,OPALESCENT,THREADED..................... 45.00
SANDWICH GLASS,CELERY,TULIP,FLINT,10 IN.HIGH................ 32.50
SANDWICH GLASS,COMPOTE,DIAMOND PATTERN,CLEAR................ 95.00
SANDWICH GLASS,COMPOTE,DOLPHIN STANDARD,VASELINE,6 1/2 IN. X
  5 IN.HIGH................................................ 75.00
SANDWICH GLASS,CREAMER,EMBOSSED DEER,ROUGH PONTIL,LIGHT
  GREEN.................................................... 32.00
SANDWICH GLASS,CUP PLATE,BENJAMIN FRANKLIN,CLEAR........... 45.00
SANDWICH GLASS,CUP PLATE,EAGLE,1831,CLEAR.................. 35.00
SANDWICH GLASS,CUP PLATE,HEARTS........................... 16.00
SANDWICH GLASS,CUP,EGG,MORNING GLORY...................... 180.00
SANDWICH GLASS,CUP,PUNCH,POMONA........................... 65.00
SANDWICH GLASS,DISH,BONBON,PINK OVERSHOT,5 1/2-IN.DIAMETER.. 24.00
SANDWICH GLASS,DISH,BONBON,PINK THREADS,PINCHED SIDES,CLEAR
  HANDLES.................................................. 32.00
SANDWICH GLASS,DISH,HONEY,PEACOCK EYE PATTERN,FLINT........ 16.00
SANDWICH GLASS,DISH,TURKEY COVER,CLEAR.................... 75.00
SANDWICH GLASS,EPERGNE,BLOWN FOR 50TH ANNIVERSARY OF GLASS
  WORKER................................................... 135.00
SANDWICH GLASS,GOBLET,MINIATURE,GROOVES AROUND BODY,OVERALL
  FACETS................................................... 14.00
SANDWICH GLASS,JAR,POMADE,BLACK AMETHYST.................. 57.00
SANDWICH GLASS,JUG,MINIATURE,FIERY OPAL,APPLIED HANDLE,2 IN.
  HIGH..................................................... 30.00
SANDWICH GLASS,LAMP,CLEAR FONT,MILK GLASS BASE,DATED 1871... 45.00
SANDWICH GLASS,LAMP,KEROSENE,CLEAR FONT,RIBBED STEM,

| | |
|---|---|
| 9 1/2 IN.HIGH.................................... | 35.00 |
| SANDWICH GLASS,LAMP,OIL,THUMBPRINT,DIAMOND,OPAQUE WHITE BASE | 75.00 |
| SANDWICH GLASS,LAMP,WAFFLE PATTERN,FLINT................... | 35.00 |
| SANDWICH GLASS,LAMP,WHALE OIL,CONE-SHAPED FONT,RIB BASE, | |
| BLOWN,12 1/2 IN.................................. | 85.00 |
| SANDWICH GLASS,LAMP,WHALE OIL,STAR PATTERN,HEXAGON BASE, | |
| FLINT,11 IN.HIGH................................ | 75.00 |
| SANDWICH GLASS,MUG,CAT AND DOG.......................... | 14.00 |
| SANDWICH GLASS,MUG,MONKEY,CLEAR......................... | 35.00 |
| SANDWICH GLASS,NEWEL POST,ROBIN BLUE..................... | 85.00 |
| SANDWICH GLASS,PAPERWEIGHT,POINSETTIA ON LATTICINO, | |
| 2 1/2-IN.DIAMETER................................. | 180.00 |
| SANDWICH GLASS,PAPERWEIGHT,RED POINSETTIA,WHITE LATTICINO | |
| GROUND,3 IN..................................... | 300.00 |
| SANDWICH GLASS,PERFUME,HOBNAIL,BLOWN,GILT DECOR,STOPPER, | |
| FLINT.......................................... | 45.00 |
| SANDWICH GLASS,PITCHER,CRANBERRY COLOR,APPLIED RIBBED SHELL | |
| HANDLE,BLOWN.................................... | 55.00 |
| SANDWICH GLASS,PITCHER,MILK,TANKARD,ENGRAVED WREATH,INITIAL | |
| F,CLEAR........................................ | 15.00 |
| SANDWICH GLASS,PITCHER,OVERSHOT,BLADDER,NATURALISTIC HANDLE. | 165.00 |
| SANDWICH GLASS,PITCHER,OVERSHOT TANKER,FROSTED TO CRANBERRY. | 92.50 |
| SANDWICH GLASS,PITCHER,TANKARD,CRANBERRY,CLEAR REED HANDLE, | |
| OVERSHOT....................................... | 97.50 |
| SANDWICH GLASS,PITCHER,WATER,PEACHBLOW,HOBNAIL,REEDED HANDLE | 550.00 |
| SANDWICH GLASS,PLATE,CAKE,GREEN,CABLE,RIBBED BALL FEET, | |
| FLINT,11 1/2 IN.................................. | 65.00 |
| SANDWICH GLASS,PLATE,CAKE,HOLLY,PEDESTAL................. | 42.00 |
| SANDWICH GLASS,PLATE,CUP,BENJAMIN FRANKLIN,CLEAR.......... | 45.00 |
| SANDWICH GLASS,PLATE,CUP,EAGLE,1831..................... | 35.00 |
| SANDWICH GLASS,PLATE,PEACOCK EYE,THISTLE,LACY,8-IN.DIAMETER. | 75.00 |
| SANDWICH GLASS,PLATE,PEACOCK FEATHER,THISTLE,SCROLL CENTER, | |
| LACY,8 IN...................................... | 40.00 |
| SANDWICH GLASS,PLATE,RAYED PEACOCK EYE,LACY,DEEP CENTER, | |
| 8 1/2 IN....................................... | 57.50 |
| SANDWICH GLASS,PLATE,TODDY,PRINCE OF WALES DESIGN,FEATHERS, | |
| CROWN,THISTLE................................... | 25.00 |
| SANDWICH GLASS,POT,GLUE,GREEN,GOLD DECOR,METAL TOP......... | 45.00 |
| SANDWICH GLASS,SALT,DOUBLE,CLEAR........................ | 65.00 |
| SANDWICH GLASS,SALT,LACY............................... | 80.00 |
| SANDWICH GLASS,SALT,MASTER,PANELED THUMBPRINT,HEXAGONAL, | |
| FLINT.......................................... | 18.00 |
| SANDWICH GLASS,SALT,MASTER,PETAL,FOOTED,PAIR............. | 25.00 |
| SANDWICH GLASS,SALT,MASTER,RIBBED PATTERN,BULBOUS......... | 5.00 |
| SANDWICH GLASS,SALT,TREE TRUNK.......................... | 12.00 |
| SANDWICH GLASS,SALT,WAFFLE BASE,SCALLOPED TOP,GROOVES,FACETS | 12.00 |
| SANDWICH GLASS,SAUCE,HEART PATTERN,FLINT,4 IN............. | 5.75 |
| SANDWICH GLASS,SAUCE,HEART,FLAT,3 1/2 IN................. | 6.50 |
| SANDWICH GLASS,SAUCE,OVERSHOT,CRANBERRY,SET OF 6.......... | 100.00 |
| SANDWICH GLASS,SAUCE,PEACOCK EYE........................ | 18.00 |
| SANDWICH GLASS,SAUCE,RAYED PEACOCK EYE,LACY,4 3/4 IN....... | 16.50 |
| SANDWICH GLASS,SAUCER,LACY............................. | 18.50 |
| SANDWICH GLASS,SMOKE BELL,FLUTED CRANBERRY RIM,RING FOR | |
| HANGING........................................ | 12.50 |
| SANDWICH GLASS,SPILL HOLDER,CLEAR,PATTERN................ | 18.00 |
| SANDWICH GLASS,SPILL HOLDER,HARP PATTERN,FLINT,CIRCA 1850... | 25.00 |
| SANDWICH GLASS,SPILL HOLDER,PEACOCK BLUE................. | 315.00 |
| SANDWICH GLASS,SPOONER,LOOP,FIERY OPALESCENT,FLINT.......... | 27.50 |
| SANDWICH GLASS,TIEBACK,BRASS FRAME,PAINTED WHITE WITH BLACK | |
| TRIM,PAIR...................................... | 17.00 |
| SANDWICH GLASS,TIEBACK,DARK RED,SCREWS,PAIR.............. | 25.00 |
| SANDWICH GLASS,TIEBACK,FIERY OPALESCENT,BEADED LOOP,PETAL | |
| DECOR,PAIR..................................... | 22.00 |
| SANDWICH GLASS,TIEBACK,LACY,AMBER,PAIR................... | 20.00 |
| SANDWICH GLASS,TIEBACK,LACY,FIERY OPALESCENT,PEWTER SHANK, | |
| PAIR........................................... | 22.00 |
| SANDWICH GLASS,TIEBACK,OPALESCENT,PETAL & SHELL,PAIR........ | 25.00 |
| SANDWICH GLASS,TIEBACK,OPALESCENT,PEWTER SCREW, | |
| 3-IN.DIAMETER,PAIR............................... | 18.50 |
| SANDWICH GLASS,TIEBACK,OPALESCENT,PEWTER STEM, | |
| 2 3/8-IN.DIAMETER,PAIR............................ | 18.00 |
| SANDWICH GLASS,TIEBACK,OPALESCENT,PEWTER STEM, | |
| 4 1/2-IN.DIAMETER,PAIR............................ | 30.00 |
| SANDWICH GLASS,TIEBACK,OPALESCENT,PEWTER POST,4 1/2 IN.,PAIR | 25.00 |
| SANDWICH GLASS,TIEBACK,OPALESCENT,2 1/2-IN.DIAMETER,PAIR.... | 8.00 |
| SANDWICH GLASS,TRAY,ICE CREAM,BLUE,STAR BASE............. | 15.00 |
| SANDWICH GLASS,TUMBLER,CAFE-AU-LAIT,BROWN,BLUE ENAMEL | |
| FLORAL,ACID CUT................................. | 90.00 |
| SANDWICH GLASS,TUMBLER,FIERY OPALESCENT.................. | 145.00 |
| SANDWICH GLASS,TUMBLER,SAPPHIRE BLUE,OVERSHOT............. | 28.00 |
| SANDWICH GLASS,TUREEN,CLEAR,SALT,COVER................... | 110.00 |

SANDWICH GLASS,VASE,EMERALD GREEN,OVERLAY FLOWER SPRAY,CLEAR
  HANDLES............................................... 75.00
SANDWICH GLASS,VASE,OPALESCENT PEACH COLOR,VASELINE RUFFLE,
  15 IN................................................. 175.00
SANDWICH GLASS,VASE,PEACHBLOW,PINK TO LILAC TO BLUE-WHITE,
  ROUGH PONTIL.......................................... 200.00
SANDWICH GLASS,VASE,RIBBED,SPANGLED,WHITE & RED,
  6 1/4 IN.HIGH......................................... 37.00
SANDWICH GLASS,VASE,RUFFLED TOP,ROSE-PEACH,HAND-PAINTED
  FLORAL,6 IN........................................... 110.00
SANDWICH GLASS,VASE,SPANGLED,WHITE,RED,BLUE,BROWN,BLOWN,
  4 IN.HIGH............................................. 135.00
SANDWICH GLASS,VASE,TULIP,CLEAR,FLINT......................... 25.00
SANDWICH GLASS,WHISKEY TASTER,CLEAR........................... 14.00
SANDWICH GLASS,WINE,STAR...................................... 35.00
SANDWICH GLASS,PITCHER,OVERSHOT,BLADDER,NATURALISTIC HANDLE. 165.00


      SARREGUEMINES POTTERY WAS FIRST MADE IN LORRAINE,
      FRANCE,ABOUT 1770. MOST OF THE PIECES FOUND TODAY
      DATE FROM THE LATE NINETEENTH CENTURY.
SARREGUEMINES,BOWL,SOUP,CHINESE MOTIF,8 1/2-IN.DIAMETER,PAIR 12.00
SARREGUEMINES,BOX,PACKET OF LETTERS SHAPE,BLUE BOW,PASTEL
  SPRIGS,COVER ......................................... 45.00
SARREGUEMINES,PITCHER,ROSES,LEAVES IN RELIEF,GREEN,ROSE
  COLOR,8 IN............................................ 20.00
SARREGUEMINES,PLATE,COLORFUL CENTER SCENE,ARTIST-SIGNED,
  FRANCE,8 IN........................................... 7.00
SARREGUEMINES,PLATE,FARMER,PEASANT WOMAN,WINGED CHERUB,
  ARTIST-SIGNED......................................... 9.00
SARREGUEMINES,PLATE,GRAPES,LEAVES,NOTCHED BORDER,HANGING,SET
  OF 4.................................................. 48.00
SARREGUEMINES,PLATE,SCENIC,ARTIST-SIGNED,9 1/2 IN........... 7.50
SARREGUEMINES,PLATE,SONGS OF ROLAND,FAIENCE,7 1/2 IN.,PAIR.. 23.00
SARREGUEMINES,TOBY,MAN'S HEAD SHAPE,BRIGHT COLORS,MARKED.... 40.00
SARREGUEMINES,TOBY,NO.3181,6 1/2 IN.......................... 32.00
SARREGUIMINES,PITCHER,SILVERY BLUE LUSTER,7 IN.............. 16.00


      SATIN GLASS IS A LATE NINETEENTH-CENTURY ART GLASS. IT
      HAS A DULL FINISH THAT IS CAUSED BY A HYDROFLUORIC
      ACID VAPOR TREATMENT. SATIN GLASS WAS MADE IN MANY
      COLORS AND WAS SOMETIMES DECORATED WITH APPLIED
      DECORATIONS.
SATIN GLASS,BASKET,HOBNAIL,PINK,WHITE,CAMPHOR HANDLE,
  WISHBONE FEET......................................... 650.00
SATIN GLASS,BASKET,SWIRL RIBBED,AMBER,PEACH,WHITE,FLUTED
  RIM,5 X 6 IN.......................................... 75.00
SATIN GLASS,BOTTLE,COLOGNE,BLUE,ENAMEL DECOR,STOPPER,
  7 1/2 IN.............................................. 18.00
SATIN GLASS,BOTTLE,COLOGNE,WHITE GROUND,ENAMELED YELLOW
  PANSIES,STOPPER....................................... 30.00
SATIN GLASS,BOTTLE,DRESSER,WHITE,HAND-PAINTED DAISIES,
  8 3/4 IN.TALL......................................... 22.00
SATIN GLASS,BOWL,BLACK,RAISED POPPIES & LEAVES,5 X 7 IN..... 16.50
SATIN GLASS,BOWL,BLACK,ROLLED-BACK EDGE,PEDESTAL,TWO PIECES,
  4 1/2 IN.............................................. 19.00
SATIN GLASS,BOWL,BRIDE'S,WHITE,PASTEL FLORAL ON RIM,
  10 1/4-IN.DIAMETER.................................... 45.00
SATIN GLASS,BOWL,CENTERPIECE,BLACK,TIFFIN LABEL,
  11-IN.DIAMETER TOP.................................... 42.50
SATIN GLASS,BOWL,CENTERPIECE,EXPANDED BASE,BLACK,4 X
  11-IN.TOP DIAMETER.................................... 42.50
SATIN GLASS,BOWL,PUNCH,WHITE,UNDERPLATE,COVER,ENAMEL,GOLD,
  BLUE,RED.............................................. 110.00
SATIN GLASS,BOWL,ROSE,BLACK GROUND,POPPY PATTERN,
  5 1/2 IN.TALL......................................... 20.00
SATIN GLASS,BOWL,ROSE,BLUE................................... 35.00
SATIN GLASS,BOWL,ROSE,BLUE SHADES,3 1/4 IN.HIGH............. 30.00
SATIN GLASS,BOWL,ROSE,BLUE TO WHITE......................... 32.00
SATIN GLASS,BOWL,ROSE,BLUE,CRIMPED TOP...................... 42.50
SATIN GLASS,BOWL,ROSE,BLUE,CRIMPED TOP,4 IN................. 50.00
SATIN GLASS,BOWL,ROSE,BLUE,SIGNED OREOR..................... 45.00
SATIN GLASS,BOWL,ROSE,BLUE,WHITE LINING,CRIMPED TOP........ 35.00
SATIN GLASS,BOWL,ROSE,CASED,PINK SHADED..................... 125.00
SATIN GLASS,BOWL,ROSE,DARK BLUE,PONTIL,4 IN.ACROSS,
  4 1/4 IN.HIGH......................................... 20.00
SATIN GLASS,BOWL,ROSE,DARK TO LIGHT YELLOW,13 IN.ROUND...... 34.00
SATIN GLASS,BOWL,ROSE,GREEN & WHITE,CRIMPED EDGE,
  4-IN.DIAMETER......................................... 35.00
SATIN GLASS,BOWL,ROSE,LIGHT BLUE TO AQUA,DIAMOND-QUILTED,

WHITE LINING.............................................. 59.00
SATIN GLASS,BOWL,ROSE,LIGHT TO DARK YELLOW,CRIMPED TOP,
4 IN.HIGH............................................... 37.50
SATIN GLASS,BOWL,ROSE,LIME COLOR........................... 38.50
SATIN GLASS,BOWL,ROSE,PALE GREEN,ENAMEL DECOR,4 1/2 IN...... 75.00
SATIN GLASS,BOWL,ROSE,PINK & BLUE SPATTER,FLARED TOP,
3 1/2 IN.HIGH........................................... 15.00
SATIN GLASS,BOWL,ROSE,PINK SHADES,HERRINGBONE,4 1/2 IN.HIGH. 95.00
SATIN GLASS,BOWL,ROSE,PINK TO DEEP ROSE,FLORAL BAND,CRIMPED,
CASED................................................... 66.00
SATIN GLASS,BOWL,ROSE,PINK,PLEATED TOP,5 IN.-DIAMETER,
5 IN.TALL............................................... 49.00
SATIN GLASS,BOWL,ROSE,PINK,3 1/2 IN.HIGH,4 1/2-IN.DIAMETER.. 49.00
SATIN GLASS,BOWL,ROSE,RIBBED,STRIPED,ALTERNATING WHITE
LUSTER & MATTE.......................................... 65.00
SATIN GLASS,BOWL,ROSE,SHADED PINK......................... 35.00
SATIN GLASS,BOWL,ROSE,TURQUOISE,UNLINED,3 3/4 IN.HIGH...... 45.00
SATIN GLASS,BOWL,ROSE,TWO-TONED BLUE,FLUTED ON TOP,BLOWN.... 28.50
SATIN GLASS,BOWL,ROSE,WHITE TO BLUE,3 1/2 IN.HIGH.......... 25.00
SATIN GLASS,BOWL,ROSE,WHITE TO BLUE,4 IN.HIGH............. 40.00
SATIN GLASS,BOWL,ROSE,WHITE TO DEEP ROSE,3 1/4 IN.HIGH...... 25.00
SATIN GLASS,BOWL,ROSE,YELLOW TO WHITE,CRIMPED TOP.......... 38.00
SATIN GLASS,BOWL,ROSE,YELLOW-GREEN,CRIMPED TOP............ 35.00
SATIN GLASS,BOWL,ROSE,YELLOW,ENAMEL IN BLUE,WHITE & GOLD
COLOR,3 1/2 IN.......................................... 110.00
SATIN GLASS,BOWL,ROSE,YELLOW,WHITE LINING,3 IN.HIGH........ 50.00
SATIN GLASS,BOWL,ROSE,YELLOW,4-IN.DIAMETER................ 40.00
SATIN GLASS,BOWL,SHELL SHAPE,WHITE CASING,GOLD SCROLLWORK,
GERMANY................................................. 45.00
SATIN GLASS,BOWL,WIDE RIM,JADE GREEN,9-IN.DIAMETER......... 7.00
SATIN GLASS,BOX,CREAMY GROUND,DRAPE DECOR,BEADED WHEEL
DESIGN ON COVER......................................... 65.00
SATIN GLASS,BOX,PALE PINK,ENAMEL FLORAL DECOR ON TOP,
3 1/2 IN.SQUARE......................................... 26.00
SATIN GLASS,CANDLEHOLDER,BLACK,PAPER LABEL,8 1/2 IN.TALL,
PAIR.................................................... 24.00
SATIN GLASS,CASTOR,PICKLE,PINK,WHITE-LINED,SILVER HOLDER,
HANDLE,COVER............................................ 65.00
SATIN GLASS,COMPOTE,BLUE INSIDE,WHITE OUTER CASING,MARKED
EPNS,5 1/2 IN........................................... 67.00
SATIN GLASS,COMPOTE,CREAM TO BITTERSWEET,FLUTED,SILVER PLATE
PEDESTAL................................................ 82.50
SATIN GLASS,COMPOTE,QUILTED,PINK,FOOTED................... 63.00
SATIN GLASS,COMPOTE,WHITE,BLUE RUFFLE EDGE................ 145.00
SATIN GLASS,CRUET,QUILTED,PINK............................ 24.00
SATIN GLASS,DISH,BLACK,SHELL SHAPE,DOLPHIN PEDESTAL BASE,
7 IN.TALL............................................... 14.00
SATIN GLASS,DISH,BLUE ENAMEL FLOWERS,PINK................. 55.00
SATIN GLASS,EASTER EGG,WHITE,BLUE FLORAL,TONGS,HELD HUYLER'S
CHOCOLATES.............................................. 6.00
SATIN GLASS,EGG,WHITE,HAND-PAINTED BLUE FORGET-ME-NOTS,
BLOWN,7 IN.LONG......................................... 12.50
SATIN GLASS,EGG,WHITE,YELLOW PANSY,GREEN LEAVES,EASTER,
HAND-PAINTED............................................ 15.00
SATIN GLASS,EPERGNE,BLUE,SILVER HOLDER,REGISTRY NUMBER,
16 IN.TALL.............................................. 30.00
SATIN GLASS,EPERGNE,FOUR TRUMPETS,BLUE TO AMBER,ROSES,METAL
FRAME................................................... 55.00
SATIN GLASS,EWER,PALE PINK TO BURNT ORANGE,ENAMEL FLORAL,
CASED,9 IN.............................................. 105.00
SATIN GLASS,EWER,PALE TO DEEP BLUE,CASED,ENAMEL DECOR,
7 1/2 IN................................................ 45.00
SATIN GLASS,EWER,PALE TO DEEP BLUE,ENAMEL DECOR,APPLIED
HANDLE,8 IN............................................. 41.00
SATIN GLASS,EWER,PINK TO WHITE,BLUE FLORAL,JEWELED IN GILT,
11 IN.HIGH.............................................. 105.00
SATIN GLASS,JAR,COOKIE,BLUE,DIAMOND & HEART PATTERN,SILVER
LID & HANDLE............................................ 85.00
SATIN GLASS,JAR,COOKIE,DIAMOND-QUILTED,PINK,MATCHING LID.... 100.00
SATIN GLASS,JAR,CRACKER,BLUE & PINK FLOWERS,SILVER TOP &
BAIL.................................................... 25.00
SATIN GLASS,JAR,CRACKER,BLUE,HAND-PAINTED PINK FLORAL,MARKED
A.J.HALL................................................ 62.00
SATIN GLASS,JAR,CRACKER,PINK,ENAMELED FLORAL,RAISED SHELL,
SILVER.................................................. 165.00
SATIN GLASS,JAR,CRACKER,PINK,QUILTED,SILVER PLATE TOP,COVER,
BAIL.................................................... 85.00
SATIN GLASS,JAR,CRACKER,PINK,QUILTED,WHITE LINING,GOLD RIM &
BAIL.................................................... 135.00
SATIN GLASS,JAR,CRACKER,QUILTED,PINK,SILVER PLATE TOP,BAIL.. 125.00
SATIN GLASS,JAR,CRACKER,RELIEF RHEXIAS,BLUE,PINK,CASED,WHITE

GROUND................................................ 125.00
SATIN GLASS,JAR,CRACKER,SWIRL,BLUE,RESILVERED............... 95.00
SATIN GLASS,JAR,CRACKER,WHITE,CASED,BLUE & PINK FLOWERS,
    SILVER COVER...................................... 98.00
SATIN GLASS,JAR,DRESSER,RIBBED,GOLD TRIM,FOOTED,BLACK...... 14.50
SATIN GLASS,JAR,JAM,YELLOW,MELON STRIPE,GOLD LEAF FLORAL,
    SILVER TOP....................................... 175.00
SATIN GLASS,JAR,POWDER,FLORETTE PATTERN,PINK,SILVER COVER... 28.50
SATIN GLASS,JAR,TOBACCO,PINK,SILVER TOP.................... 125.00
SATIN GLASS,LAMP,FAIRY,RASPBERRY COLOR.................... 50.00
SATIN GLASS,LAMP,FAIRY,WHITE,POLKA DOT LINING,CLARKE SAUCER
    BASE............................................. 55.00
SATIN GLASS,LAMP,FAIRY,YELLOW,RIBBED,CLARKE BASE............ 35.00
SATIN GLASS,LAMP,HALL,PINK TO ROSE COLOR.................. 125.00
SATIN GLASS,LAMP,HAND,YELLOW,RAISED ACANTHUS LEAVES,CAMPHOR
    HANDLE........................................... 50.00
SATIN GLASS,LAMP,KEROSENE,DRAPE PATTERN.................. 15.00
SATIN GLASS,LAMP,MINIATURE,GREEN,DRAPE PATTERN,BOBECHE...... 47.50
SATIN GLASS,LAMP,PEG,RIBBED,PINK,CHIMNEY................. 195.00
SATIN GLASS,MUG,DIAMOND-QUILTED,PINK.................... 40.00
SATIN GLASS,PARFAIT SET,WHITE,GOLD TRIM,DECANTER,6 GLASSES.. 37.50
SATIN GLASS,PERFUME,DIMPLED,PINK TO APRICOT,ENAMEL,FLORAL,
    BRASS LID....................................... 125.00
SATIN GLASS,PERFUME,LAVENDER,CASED,LINED,STERLING SILVER
    STOPPER,5 IN..................................... 60.00
SATIN GLASS,PITCHER,BLUE,CLEAR,APPLIED HANDLE,TANKARD,FIVE
    TUMBLERS........................................ 185.00
SATIN GLASS,PITCHER,GUTTATE PATTERN,BULBOUS,PINK,CAMPHOR
    HANDLE,4 IN...................................... 58.00
SATIN GLASS,PITCHER,PUFF-QUILTED,PINK.................... 140.00
SATIN GLASS,PITCHER,QUILTED PATTERN,CLEAR HANDLE,NARROW
    NECK,4 1/4 IN.................................... 35.00
SATIN GLASS,PITCHER,ROSE SHADING TO PINK,CAMPHOR REED
    HANDLE,5 1/2 IN.................................. 95.00
SATIN GLASS,PITCHER,WATER,TAN.......................... 39.00
SATIN GLASS,PITCHER,WATER,TAN,WHITE LINING............... 35.00
SATIN GLASS,PITCHER,WATER,WHITE,LEAF & INSECT DECOR........ 275.00
SATIN GLASS,SALT & PEPPER,PILLOW........................ 45.00
SATIN GLASS,SALT & PEPPER,RAISED SPRAY,PAINTED VIOLETS..... 18.00
SATIN GLASS,SHADE,PEACH COLOR,WHITE LINING,18 IN. X 10 IN... 35.00
SATIN GLASS,SHAKER,SALT,BLUE,WHITE,FLORAL,PEWTER LEAF COVER,
    FOOTED.......................................... 29.00
SATIN GLASS,SHAKER,SUGAR,BLUE,HERRINGBONE DESIGN,HOURGLASS
    SHAPE,7 IN...................................... 100.00
SATIN GLASS,SHAKER,SUGAR,MELON RIB,SHADED BLUE SHOULDER,
    GREEN CLOVER..................................... 65.00
SATIN GLASS,SHAKER,SUGAR,MELON RIB,WHITE TO BLUE,PINK ROSES. 45.00
SATIN GLASS,SHAKER,SUGAR,WHITE,GREEN & PEACH COLOR SPRAYS,
    PEWTER TOP....................................... 42.00
SATIN GLASS,STRIPED IN WHITE,PINK,GRAY,FLUTED RIM,6 1/2 IN.. 78.00
SATIN GLASS,SWAN,OPEN,TURNED HEAD,9 1/2 IN.LONG,
    5 1/2 IN.TALL................................... 30.00
SATIN GLASS,SYRUP,PINK,CURTAIN,DATED TOP................. 125.00
SATIN GLASS,TOOTHPICK,WHITE,ENAMELED DECOR,MELON RIB....... 15.00
SATIN GLASS,TRAY,DRESSER,WHITE,8 1/2 IN. X 11 IN........... 10.00
SATIN GLASS,TUMBLER,DIAMOND-QUILTED,ROBIN BLUE TO PEARLY
    WHITE........................................... 85.00
SATIN GLASS,VASE,BASKET WEAVE,RED TO PINK,CREAM LINING,
    ENGLAND,5 3/4 IN................................. 195.00
SATIN GLASS,VASE,BIRDS,HAND-PAINTED,BLUE,14 IN.HIGH,PAIR.... 160.00
SATIN GLASS,VASE,BLACK GROUND,POPPIES,8 1/2 IN............ 20.00
SATIN GLASS,VASE,BLACK,POPPIES......................... 15.00
SATIN GLASS,VASE,BLUE TO WHITE,BULBOUS,RING ON NECK,
    9 1/2 IN........................................ 120.00
SATIN GLASS,VASE,BLUE-WHITE,BUTTERFLY DECOR,MELON BASE,
    12 IN.HIGH...................................... 125.00
SATIN GLASS,VASE,BLUE,ENAMEL FLORAL,WHITE LINING,CAMPHOR
    FEET,9 IN....................................... 85.00
SATIN GLASS,VASE,BLUE,ENAMELED SEA HORSE MEDALLION,SIGNED
    ROBJ,PARIS...................................... 20.00
SATIN GLASS,VASE,BLUE,QUILTED,ENAMEL FLORAL,5 IN. X
    5 1/4 IN........................................ 225.00
SATIN GLASS,VASE,BLUE,RUFFLED TURNED-OVER TOP,11 IN.,PAIR... 125.00
SATIN GLASS,VASE,BLUE,WHITE CASING,RIBBED,CAMPHOR EDGE
    RUFFLES......................................... 45.00
SATIN GLASS,VASE,BULBOUS,STICK NECK,DIAMOND-QUILTED,PINK,
    11 IN.,PAIR..................................... 175.00
SATIN GLASS,VASE,DARK ROSE SHADING TO WHITE,AMBER RIM AROUND
    TOP............................................. 65.00
SATIN GLASS,VASE,DIAMOND-QUILTED,DELPHINIUM BLUE,COVER,BERRY
    FINIAL.......................................... 190.00

SATIN GLASS,VASE,ETCHED GILT DECOR,GREEN,6 IN.HIGH,PAIR..... 39.00
SATIN GLASS,VASE,EWER,GREEN,BLUE FORGET-ME-NOTS,GOLD,
  PEDESTAL,9 1/2 IN.......................................... 65.00
SATIN GLASS,VASE,FLORAL DECOR,BULBOUS,7 IN.................. 14.00
SATIN GLASS,VASE,GREEN,ETCHED GILT DECOR,6 IN.HIGH,PAIR..... 39.00
SATIN GLASS,VASE,HAND-PAINTED,MARINE,WHITE,3 IN.HIGH........ 15.00
SATIN GLASS,VASE,HONEY TO OFF-WHITE,14 IN.HIGH,6 1/2 IN.WIDE 125.00
SATIN GLASS,VASE,ICE BLUE,QUILTED DESIGN,RUFFLED EDGE,
  4 1/2 IN.TALL............................................. 27.00
SATIN GLASS,VASE,ICE GREEN,MELON RIB,FORGET-ME-NOTS,WHITE
  CASING,PAIR............................................... 60.00
SATIN GLASS,VASE,IRIS PATTERN,BLACK........................ 6.00
SATIN GLASS,VASE,LIGHT BLUE TO DARK BLUE,ENAMELED WHITE &
  YELLOW FLORAL............................................. 85.00
SATIN GLASS,VASE,LIGHT BLUE,PIECRUST FLUTE EDGE,CLEAR TRIM,
  BLOWN.................................................... 40.00
SATIN GLASS,VASE,MOCHA-COLORED,3 1/2 IN..................... 14.00
SATIN GLASS,VASE,PALE GREEN,ENAMEL TREES,CLOUDS,
  HAND-PAINTED,6 1/2 IN..................................... 22.00
SATIN GLASS,VASE,PEACHBLOW COLORING,MELON RIB,WHITE CASING,
  RUFFLED,8 IN............................................. 85.00
SATIN GLASS,VASE,PINK & YELLOW STRIPES,GOURD SHAPE,8 1/2 IN. 50.00
SATIN GLASS,VASE,PINK TO PEACH,FLORAL,HAND-PAINTED,WHITE
  INSIDE,8 IN.............................................. 45.00
SATIN GLASS,VASE,PINK TO ROSE,FLORAL,LEAVES,GOLD-ENCRUSTED,
  6 1/2 IN................................................. 95.00
SATIN GLASS,VASE,PINK,HAND-PAINTED YELLOW & BLUE DECOR,
  FLUTED,RUFFLED........................................... 55.00
SATIN GLASS,VASE,QUILTED,PINK,8 1/2 IN.HIGH................ 175.00
SATIN GLASS,VASE,RAISED FLORAL PATTERN,BLACK,8 X 5 IN....... 22.50
SATIN GLASS,VASE,RASPBERRY TO WHITE,WHITE ENAMELING,
  LACE-DE-BOHEME,STICK..................................... 195.00
SATIN GLASS,VASE,WHITE GROUND,PAINTED FLOWER,BUTTERFLY,
  3 1/2 IN................................................. 22.50
SATIN GLASS,VASE,WHITE TO RUST,GOLD CHERRIES DECOR,CASED.... 55.00
SATIN GLASS,VASE,WHITE,FLUTED RIM,PEDESTAL BOTTOM,6 1/2 IN.. 85.00
SATIN GLASS,VASE,WHITE,HAND-PAINTED FLORAL,GOLD TRIM,
  10 IN.TALL............................................... 42.00
SATIN GLASS,VASE,WHITE,ORNAMENTED PINE BRANCHES,
  2 1/2 IN.HIGH,PAIR....................................... 22.50
SATIN GLASS,VASE,WHITE,SIGNED ECHT DOLHAIN WIRTHS,
  2 1/2 IN.HIGH,PAIR....................................... 37.50
SATIN GLASS,VASE,YELLOW-GREEN TO WHITE,SCENE OF NIAGARA
  FALLS,5 IN.HIGH.......................................... 60.00
SATIN GLASS,VASE,ETCHED GILT DECOR,GREEN,6 IN.HIGH,PAIR..... 39.00


      SATSUMA IS A JAPANESE POTTERY WITH A DISTINCTIVE CREAMY
      BEIGE CRACKLED GLAZE. MOST OF THE PIECES WERE DECORATED
      WITH BLUE,RED,GREEN,ORANGE,OR GOLD. ALMOST ALL THE
      SATSUMA FOUND TODAY WAS MADE AFTER 1860. JAPANESE
      FACES ARE OFTEN A PART OF THE DECORATIVE SCHEME.
SATSUMA,BASKET,DECOR,GOLD,7 IN.HIGH,3-1/2 IN.DIAMETER....... 30.00
SATSUMA,BOTTLE,SAKE,YELLOW,PAIR............................ 110.00
SATSUMA,BOWL,DECOR,HOLY MAN,SIGNED,5 IN.................... 35.00
SATSUMA,BOWL,HOLY MAN,SIGNED,5 IN.......................... 35.00
SATSUMA,COFFEEPOT,KIMONO-CLAD FIGURES IN LANDSCAPE,WISTERIA,
  4 IN.HIGH................................................ 24.00
SATSUMA,CUP & SAUCER,DEMITASSE,BAMBOO & BIRD PATTERN........ 22.00
SATSUMA,CUP & SAUCER,DEMITASSE,BEIGE GROUND,FLORAL DECOR.... 10.00
SATSUMA,CUP & SAUCER,DEMITASSE,BLACK GROUND,GOLD COLOR
  LANDSCAPE,MARK........................................... 25.00
SATSUMA,CUP & SAUCER,DEMITASSE,BLACK GROUND,GOLD COLOR
  BAMBOO DECOR............................................. 15.00
SATSUMA,CUP & SAUCER,DEMITASSE,BLACK GROUND,GOLD BAMBOO
  DESIGN,SIGNED............................................ 15.00
SATSUMA,CUP & SAUCER,DEMITASSE,GOLD & PURPLE FLORAL,SEAL
  MARK.................................................... 25.00
SATSUMA,CUP & SAUCER,DEMITASSE,GOLD LANDSCAPE ON BLACK
  GROUND,MARK............................................. 25.00
SATSUMA,CUP & SAUCER,DEMITASSE,LILAC COLOR WISTERIA VINES... 45.00
SATSUMA,CUP & SAUCER,THOUSAND FACES,DRAGON HANDLE,RED EMPIRE
  MARK.................................................... 50.00
SATSUMA,CUP & SAUCER,WARRIORS,GOLD......................... 8.50
SATSUMA,CUP,BOUILLON,PLATE,FLORAL LINING,CORAL HANDLES,
  BOWKNOTS................................................ 22.50
SATSUMA,CUP,SAUCER,GILT FACES ON MEN,WOMEN,BLACK & WHITE
  ENAMEL DRAGONS.......................................... 22.00
SATSUMA,DISH,ALLOVER MEN & WOMEN PATTERN,SHELL SHAPE,FLORAL
  BORDER.................................................. 225.00
SATSUMA,DISH,BLUE,GOLD & PINK FLORAL,FAN SHAPE,SIGNED,

| | |
|---|---:|
| 4 1/2 IN............................................ | 15.00 |
| SATSUMA,DISH,GOLD & PINK FLOWERS,FAN SHAPE,SIGNED,4 1/2 IN.. | 15.00 |
| SATSUMA,DISH,LANDSCAPE,CRANES,SIGNED,4 IN................... | 15.00 |
| SATSUMA,DISH,MEN,WOMEN,FLORAL BORDER,GOLD,SHELLS,BARNACLES, | |
| SHELL SHAPE......................................... | 225.00 |
| SATSUMA,DISH,OVERALL PATTERN,BIRDS,FLOWERS,COVER,ACORN KNOB, | |
| 8 IN............................................... | 65.00 |
| SATSUMA,DISH,STAMP & CLIP,BUTTERFLY,BIRD,FLORAL,BONE-DISH | |
| SHAPE,MARK......................................... | 16.50 |
| SATSUMA,HATPIN,2 1/2 IN.HEAD,14 IN.LONG..................... | 22.00 |
| SATSUMA,HATPIN,HEAD IS SIZE OF MARBLE....................... | 35.00 |
| SATSUMA,INCENSE BURNER,FORM OF AN ELEPHANT,RETICULATED | |
| COVER,6 IN.HIGH.................................... | 150.00 |
| SATSUMA,JAR,COOKIE,6 IN.HIGH,5-IN.DIAMETER.................. | 30.00 |
| SATSUMA,JAR,FOO DOG FINIAL,6 1/2 IN.TALL.................... | 20.00 |
| SATSUMA,JAR,GINGER,MINIATURE,PIERCED OPENWORK LID,FOOTED, | |
| 3 IN.HIGH.......................................... | 165.00 |
| SATSUMA,JAR,POTPOURRI,MARKED,8 1/2 IN.HIGH.................. | 65.00 |
| SATSUMA,JARDINIERE,MULTICOLORED FIGURES,SCROLLS,SCENES,GOLD, | |
| 7 IN.TALL.......................................... | 35.00 |
| SATSUMA,LANTERN,KASUGA,BROCADE PANELS,FIGURAL SCENES, | |
| 11 IN.HIGH,PAIR.................................... | 225.00 |
| SATSUMA,PITCHER,DRAGON SPOUT,FIGURES,CIRCA 1830,11 IN....... | 350.00 |
| SATSUMA,PITCHER,DRAGON SPOUT,FIGURES,CIRCA 1830,12 IN....... | 350.00 |
| SATSUMA,PLATE,DANCING MAIDENS,COBALT,GILT,SIGNED,RED SEAL, | |
| 12 IN.............................................. | 65.00 |
| SATSUMA,PLATE,GRAY DRAGON,OCCUPIED JAPAN,7 1/2 IN........... | 5.00 |
| SATSUMA,PLATE,RED,GOLD DECOR,DEEP,12-IN.DIAMETER............ | 40.00 |
| SATSUMA,PLATE,THOUSAND FACES,BLACK EMPIRE MARK, | |
| 7-1/2 IN.DIAMETER.................................. | 150.00 |
| SATSUMA,ROOSTER,7 IN.LONG X 8 IN.HIGH,PAIR.................. | 750.00 |
| SATSUMA,SAUCER,1000 FACES................................... | 4.95 |
| SATSUMA,SHAKER,BULBOUS SHAPE,GOLD,PAIR...................... | 15.00 |
| SATSUMA,SUGAR,BAMBOO & BIRD PATTERN,COVER................... | 18.00 |
| SATSUMA,TEAPOT,CHILD'S,SIGNED............................... | 18.00 |
| SATSUMA,TEAPOT,CREAMER,SUGAR,SIX CUPS & SAUCERS,FLORAL | |
| DECOR,MARKED....................................... | 110.00 |
| SATSUMA,TEAPOT,CREAMER,SUGAR,SIX CUPS & SAUCERS,MANY FACES, | |
| ALLOVER GOLD....................................... | 450.00 |
| SATSUMA,TEAPOT,CREAMY GROUND,FLORAL,GOLD,CRACKLE GLAZE, | |
| 4 CUPS & SAUCERS................................... | 60.00 |
| SATSUMA,TEAPOT,MINIATURE,DECOR,GOLD,SIGNED,1-1/4 IN.DIAMETER. | 55.00 |
| SATSUMA,TEAPOT,ORIENTAL FIGURES,5 1/4 IN.................... | 75.00 |
| SATSUMA,TEAPOT,PEACOCK,RUST COLOR FLORAL,GOLD TRIM,MARKED... | 69.50 |
| SATSUMA,TEAPOT,TAN,WHITE DOTS,GREEN FOLIAGE,4 1/4 IN.HIGH... | 12.00 |
| SATSUMA,TEAPOT,THOUSAND FACES,DRAGON HANDLE & SPOUT,GOLD, | |
| 13 1/2 IN.......................................... | 275.00 |
| SATSUMA,URN,FLUTED OPENING,BULBOUS BODY,FOOTED,3 1/2 IN.HIGH | 10.00 |
| SATSUMA,VASE,18 IN..................................ILLUS.. | 110.00 |
| SATSUMA,VASE,CHARACTERS DRESSED IN COURT COSTUME,10 IN.HIGH, | |
| PAIR............................................... | 190.00 |
| SATSUMA,VASE,CIRCA 1880,12 IN.,PAIR......................... | 175.00 |
| SATSUMA,VASE,COBALT,YELLOW,PINK CHRYSANTHEMUMS,BIRD HANDLES, | |
| 18 IN.TALL......................................... | 85.00 |

SATSUMA VASE

SATSUMA,VASE,DARK BLUE GROUND,PANELS,MEN,BOY,COURT COSTUMES,
  1876............................................................ 47.50
SATSUMA,VASE,FRONT PANEL WARRIOR,BACK PANEL IRIS,
  12 1/2 IN.HIGH.................................................. 45.00
SATSUMA,VASE,GOLD-COLOR GROUND,GREEN & YELLOW FLORAL,FLARED
  TOP,9 IN....................................................... 40.00
SATSUMA,VASE,GRASSHOPPERS,BUTTERFLIES,BEES,ELEPHANT HEAD
  HANDLES,PAIR................................................... 45.00
SATSUMA,VASE,GREEN FOLIAGE,RED & GOLD DECOR,MARKED,
  9 3/4 IN.,PAIR................................................. 110.00
SATSUMA,VASE,MULTICOLORED ENAMEL,10 IN.HIGH..................... 18.00
SATSUMA,VASE,OVOID,ENAMEL,GILT,EMPERORS,PALACE ENCLOSURE,
  24 IN.,PAIR.................................................... 200.00
SATSUMA,VASE,SCENES,FOO DOG HANDLES & FINIAL,BULBOUS,FOOTED,
  COVER.......................................................... 59.50
SATSUMA,VASE,TEMPLE PROCESSION,TAPERED,3 X 7 1/4 IN. TALL... 33.50
SATSUMA,VASE,TEMPLE,FIGURES IN FESTIVE KIMONOS,TWO HANDLES,
  SEAL MARK...................................................... 100.00
SATSUMA,VASE,THE LADIES & THE WARRIORS,BLACK MARK,6 IN...... 70.00
SATSUMA,VASE,THOUSAND FACE PATTERN,6 1/2 IN.TALL,PAIR....... 59.00
SAXE,PLATE,HAND-PAINTED FLORAL,GOLD LATTICE BORDER,CROWN
  MARK,11 1/2 IN................................................. 38.00
SCALE,APOTHECARY,BALANCE,BURNISHED BRASS PANS,IRON BASE,SAYS
  10 KILOG....................................................... 65.00
SCALE,APOTHECARY,BRASS......................................... 20.00
SCALE,APOTHECARY,BRASS PANS,FIVE WEIGHTS,CIRCA 1820......... 22.50
SCALE,APOTHECARY,BRASS,MARBLE,WALNUT........................... 45.00
SCALE,APOTHECARY,ONE ROUND PAN,ONE PEAR-SHAPE PAN,BRASS,
  28 IN.TALL..................................................... 115.00
SCALE,BALANCE,IRON,HAND-WROUGHT HOOKS ON EACH END,20 IN.LONG 16.50
SCALE,BALANCE,RED PAINT,GOLD STENCIL,BRASS PAN,WEIGHTS,
  ENTERPRISE,IRON................................................ 27.50
SCALE,BALANCE,STORE TYPE,BRASS SCOOP PAN,WEIGHTS,14 1/2 IN.. 15.00
SCALE,BALANCE,WEIGHTS.......................................... 28.50
SCALE,CANDY,BRASS PANS......................................... 12.50
SCALE,CHEMIST,WOODEN & GLASS CASE,VOLAND & SON,1912,17 X
  15 X 8 IN.DEEP................................................. 55.00
SCALE,COUNTER,DEEP TIN BASKET,14 IN. X 20 IN................... 23.50
SCALE,DRUGSTORE,BROWN MARBLE TOP,WALNUT........................ 25.00
SCALE,DRUGSTORE,MARBLE TOP,OAK................................. 30.00
SCALE,EGG-WEIGHING,ACME........................................ 4.00
SCALE,FISH,BRASS FACE,OBLONG TIN PAN,CHAINS,FRARY,10 IN. X
  4 1/2 IN...................................................... 22.50
SCALE,GOLD DUST,WEIGHTS,BRASS,IN WOODEN BOX.................... 25.00
SCALE,GOLD WEIGHING,BRASS ARMS,PANS,HANDMADE PINE BASE,
  PA.DUTCH,SIGNED................................................ 85.00
SCALE,GOLD,HAND,BRASS BEAM,BRASS PANS,5 IN..................... 8.50
SCALE,GOLD,MAHOGANY-FRAMED CASE,JEWELED PIVOTS,PANS,WEIGHTS,
  H.TROEMNER..................................................... 75.00
SCALE,GOLD,SCOOP TRAY,NICKEL PLATE WEIGHTS,BLACK,IRON FRAME. 42.00
SCALE,GOLD,15 WEIGHTS,BRASS,CASE............................... 52.00
SCALE,GROCER,VEGETABLE TRAY,HANGING,CLOCK FACE................. 18.00
SCALE,HANGING,DOUBLE PAN,13 WEIGHTS,SOME MARKED DRACHM...... 15.00
SCALE,ICE,POLISHED BRASS FACE,27 IN.OVERALL................... 19.50
SCALE,JEWELER,BRASS PANS,MARBLE TOP,DRAWER.................... 37.50
SCALE,JUSTICE,UNGLAZED FIGURE ON GOLD BORDER BASE,BRASS
  SCALES........................................................ 20.00
SCALE,LABORATORY BALANCE,GLASS ON 4 SIDES,BRASS INSIDE,
  18 IN.HIGH.................................................... 65.00
SCALE,NICKLE-PLATED BRASS SCOOP,STENCILING,ONE WEIGHT,IRON.. 24.50
SCALE,PAN,BRASS............................................... 40.00
SCALE,PLATFORM,IRON,10 IN. X 13 IN............................ 7.50
SCALE,POCKET,FOR GOLD WEIGHING,EAGLE,SAYS MADE EXPRESSLY FOR
  CALIFORNIA.................................................... 65.00
SCALE,POSTAL,BRASS ON WOODEN BASE,FIVE WEIGHTS,ENGLAND...... 35.00
SCALE,POSTAL,BRASS,SLATE BASE................................. 18.00
SCALE,POSTAL,BRASS,WOOD BASE,SEVEN BRASS WEIGHTS............. 35.00
SCALE,POSTAL,IRON BASE,BRASS TRAY,BAR & WEIGHT,WEIS.......... 17.50
SCALE,POSTAL,WALNUT BASE,WEIGHTS,RATES IN SHILLINGS,PENCE,
  POUNDS,ENGLAND................................................ 75.00
SCALE,SPRING,MARKED AMERICAN HOUSEKEEPERS SCALE,DATED 1877,
  IRON,BRASS.................................................... 18.00
SCALE,SQUARE SHELF ON CHAINS,BLACK,HOOK TO HANG,36 IN.LONG.. 36.50
SCALE,STORE,WHITE MARBLE TO WEIGH GOODS,BRASS PAINT FINISH,
  15 X 18 IN.................................................... 23.00
SCALE,WEIGHS UP TO 150 POUNDS,C.TORSCHNER,N.Y.,BRASS,
  20 IN.LONG.................................................... 25.00


      SCHNEIDER GLASS IS AN ART NOUVEAU GLASS MADE IN FRANCE.
SCHNEIDER,BOWL-VASE,INFUSED COLORS LIKE PAPERWEIGHT

```
TECHNIQUE,SIGNED....................................... 185.00
SCHNEIDER,BOWL-VASE,COLORS INFUSED IN GLASS,SIGNED,
   6 1/2 IN.HIGH...................................... 145.00
SCHNEIDER,BOWL-VASE,LIKE PAPERWEIGHT,EMBEDDED COLORS,SIGNED,
   7 IN.HIGH......................................... 187.50
SCHNEIDER,BOWL,ROSE,MOTTLED WHITE TO CINAMMON,CHAIN,BLACK
   AMETHYST...........................................  75.00
SCHNEIDER,BOWL,SMOKY TOPAZ,ACID CUT,SIGNED,14 IN. X 3 IN....  58.00
SCHNEIDER,COMPOTE,MOTTLED BLUE,IRON BASE,SIGNED,
   14-IN.DIAMETER.................................... 110.00
SCHNEIDER,COMPOTE,ORANGE & BLUE GLASS,9 1/4 IN. HIGH,SIGNED. 125.00
SCHNEIDER,COMPOTE,YELLOW BASE,CENTER,AMETHYST POST,ORANGE
   BOWL,BLUE EDGE.................................... 265.00
SCHNEIDER,LAMP,WALL,RED TO WHITE SHADE,SIGNED,5 IN.WIDE.....  35.00
SCHNEIDER,PITCHER,MILK,PINK & ROSE TO RUSTY-PINK & BROWN,
   RIGAREE HANDLE.................................... 250.00
SCHNEIDER,PITCHER,MILK,PINK,ROSE MOTTLINGS,RIGAREE HANDLE... 250.00
SCHNEIDER,PITCHER,MILK,ROSE TO PINK TO BROWN MOTTLING,
   RIGAREE HANDLE.................................... 275.00
SCHNEIDER,PLATE,YELLOW CENTER,BLUE MOTTLE,BLUE RIM,SIGNED,
   8 1/4 IN.......................................... 100.00
SCHNEIDER,TAZZA,BURNT ORANGE,BUBBLES,AMETHYST STEM & FOOT,
   7-IN.DIAMETER.....................................  85.00
SCHNEIDER,VASE,BLACK BLOTCHES,SIGNED,OVINGTONS,FRANCE....... 120.00
SCHNEIDER,VASE,BLUE & RED MOTTLE,BLUE HANDLES,SIGNED,
   10 IN.TALL........................................  70.00
SCHNEIDER,VASE,GRAY & BROWN SHADES,FLORAL ON NECK,TRIANGULAR
   SHAPE............................................. 125.00
SCHNEIDER,VASE,GREEN,BROWN,OPEN FLORAL NECK,TRIANGULAR
   SHAPE,7 1/2 IN.................................... 100.00
SCHNEIDER,VASE,PINK ACID CUT BACK,GEOMETRIC DESIGN,BLACK
   BASE,8 IN.HIGH....................................  90.00
SCHNEIDER,VASE,RED SWIRLS,BLUE SPLASHES,PURPLE MOTTLE,
   12 1/2 IN.TALL....................................  80.00
SCHNEIDER,VASE,SHADES OF MAGENTA,SIGNED,22 IN.HIGH.......... 300.00
SCHNEIDER,VASE,URN SHAPE,RED,DARK BLUE MOTTLINGS,SIGNED,
   10 IN.TALL........................................  85.00
SCHNEIDER,VASE,YELLOW GROUND,WHITE MOTTLING,LACY ENAMEL,
   CORSET SHAPE......................................  32.50


     SCRIMSHAW IS BONE OR IVORY OR WHALE'S TEETH CARVED BY
     SAILORS AND OTHERS FOR ENTERTAINMENT DURING THE SAILING
     SHIP DAYS. SOME SCRIMSHAW WAS CARVED AS EARLY AS 1800.
SCRIMSHAW,AMERICAN EAGLE,SHIELD,PORTRAITS,SHIP,WALRUS TUSK,
   PAIR............................................... 550.00
SCRIMSHAW,BALEEN CORSET BUSK,SUN,WHALING SCENE,WHALE,HEART
   WITH LOVE .........................................  30.00
SCRIMSHAW,BOATS,SEAL,DEER HUNT,ALASKAN TUSK,1898.....ILLUS.. 450.00
SCRIMSHAW,CANE,WHALEBONE,37 IN.............................  20.00
SCRIMSHAW,CARPENTER SQUARE,WHALEBONE,BLACK ROSEWOOD HANDLE,
   CIRCA 1840........................................  59.50
SCRIMSHAW,CHALICE,CARVED DECOR,WHALE TOOTH,3 1/2 IN.HIGH....  57.50
SCRIMSHAW,CHAMBERED NAUTILUS SHELL......................... 550.00
SCRIMSHAW,CLOTHESPIN,LOT OF 20............................. 125.00
SCRIMSHAW,CORSET STAY,HOUSES,COUNTRYSIDE,CAT ON KEG,WHALE
   BALEEN,1860.......................................  34.50
SCRIMSHAW,CRIBBAGE BOARD,FISH,INSECT,WOLF,STAG,SAYS ROSA,
   TUSK.............................................. 225.00
SCRIMSHAW,CRIBBAGE BOARD,12 IN.LONG CARVED WALRUS TUSK,
   SEAWEED,KAYAK.....................................  69.00
SCRIMSHAW,DIPPER,WATER,COCONUT SHELL,ROSEWOOD HANDLE,
   WHALEBONE AT ENDS.................................  59.50
SCRIMSHAW,ETCHED,BUST OF MAN,WHALE'S TOOTH,3 IN............  35.00
SCRIMSHAW,FULL-MASTED SHP,SMALL BOAT,WHALERS,WHALE'S TOOTH,
   3 7/8 IN..........................................  55.00
SCRIMSHAW,GAME BOX,CARVED BONE,CRIBBAGE BOARD DESIGN....... 200.00
SCRIMSHAW,GODEY GIRL ON FRONT,HEART,FLOWERS,DOVES ON BACK,
   WHALE TOOTH.......................................  60.00
SCRIMSHAW,JAGGING WHEEL,THREE-TINED FORK & HANDLE,SERPENT
   FORM............................................. 275.00
SCRIMSHAW,LAMP,TABLE,BUTT OF SPERM WHALE JAW,WHALEBONE,SPERM
   TEETH............................................ 950.00
SCRIMSHAW,MAORI INDIAN CHIEF,EUROPEAN WOMAN,WHALE TOOTH,
   1850,6 IN.,PAIR.................................. 195.00
SCRIMSHAW,MISS LIBERTY HOLDING AMERICAN FLAG,SPERM WHALE
   TOOTH............................................ 220.00
SCRIMSHAW,MOTHER,CHILD,HOUND,ROSE SPRAY,TOOTH........ILLUS.. 375.00
SCRIMSHAW,N.A.T.& T.CABLE VIEW,HARBOR SCENE,ALASKA...ILLUS.. 275.00
SCRIMSHAW,NAPKIN RING,ELONGATED STRIPED CAT...............  15.00
SCRIMSHAW,NAPKIN RING,ESKIMO,WALRUS TUSK,PICTURE OF WALRUS
```

```
ON ICE FLOE.....................................................   20.00
SCRIMSHAW,NAPKIN RING,SCALLOPED,GOLD PAINT TRIM,WHALE'S
   TOOTH,1 7/8 IN..............................................   12.00
SCRIMSHAW,NAPOLEON ON HORSEBACK & JOSEPHINE,TOOTH...........  120.00
SCRIMSHAW,NAVAL BATTLE SCENES,SQUARE-RIGGED SAILING SHIPS,
   WHALE TOOTH.................................................  250.00
SCRIMSHAW,PORTRAIT OF HENRY VIII GIVING JEWELRY TO MISTRESS
   PARR.......................................................  120.00
SCRIMSHAW,PORTRAIT OF WHALE SHIP,SPERM WHALE TOOTH..........  225.00
SCRIMSHAW,POWDER HORN,EAGLE,BIRDS,TREES,HORSE,SAILING
   VESSELS,DATE 1777..........................................   65.00
SCRIMSHAW,POWDER HORN,SOLDIERS,FORTRESS,ATTACK ON QUEBEC,
   1775,CANADIAN..............................................  750.00
SCRIMSHAW,POWDER HORN,VIGNETTES,BUILDINGS,PROFILE,
   INSCRIPTION,1775...........................................  750.00
SCRIMSHAW,ROLLING PIN,LIGNUM VITAE.........................   65.00
SCRIMSHAW,ROLLING PIN,WOODEN CENTER,WHALE BONE ENDS,RING
   TURNINGS,KNOBS.............................................   69.50
SCRIMSHAW,RULER,EQUIDISTANT 1/4 IN.APART INCISE LINE
   CARVINGS,WHALEBONE.........................................   37.50
SCRIMSHAW,SAILING SHIP ON WHALE'S TOOTH....................   22.00
SCRIMSHAW,SAILING VESSELS,MAN-OF-WAR,BRITISH FLAG,COCONUT
   SHELL,1840.................................................   54.50
SCRIMSHAW,SEA CHEST,DOVETAILING,HINGED & MOLDED LID,
   WHALEBONE.................................................3,600.00
SCRIMSHAW,SEA GULLS,WHALE IVORY,8 X 3 IN...................  225.00
SCRIMSHAW,SEAL HUNTING SCENE,ALASKAN HARBOR,BOATS,ALASKAN,
   WALRUS TUSK................................................  625.00
SCRIMSHAW,SHIP AT FULL SAIL,WATER,SKY,WHALE'S TOOTH,
   3 1/4 IN...................................................   40.00
SCRIMSHAW,SILVER MOUNT WITH WHALE SHIP,SAYS  PEACE TO OUR
   NATION,  TOOTH.............................................  250.00
SCRIMSHAW,TWO ENGRAVED TEETH,PORTRAIT OF.............ILLUS..  300.00
SCRIMSHAW,UMBRELLA,TERMINATES TO HAND HOLDING SCROLL.......  100.00
SCRIMSHAW,VIEW OF SAG HARBOR,N.Y.,SHIPS,BUILDINGS,FIREHOUSE,
   WHALE TOOTH.................................................  300.00
SCRIMSHAW,VIGNETTES,AMERICAN EAGLE,THREE-MASTED WARSHIP,
   SAILOR,GIRL................................................  275.00
SCRIMSHAW,WHALE TOOTH,NAVAL SCENE,CONFEDERATE & UNION FLAGS,
   INSCRIPTION................................................   85.00
SCRIMSHAW,WHALE TOOTH,VIEW OF SAG HARBOR,N.Y.,STAR BORDER,
   13 1/2 IN.LONG.............................................  300.00
SCRIMSHAW,YARDSTICK,SQUARE REAR EDGE,ROUND BEVEL FRONT EDGE,
   WHALEBONE..................................................   57.50
SCRIMSHAW,YARDSTICK,THREE SECTIONS,ONE PIECE,WHALEBONE,
   36 IN......................................................   44.50
SCRODDLEWARE,TEAPOT,BROWN & TAN,FLINT GLAZE.................  195.00
SCUTTLE MUG,SEE SHAVING MUG
SEWING MACHINE,ELIAS HOWE...................................   60.00
SEXTANT,MAHOGANY CASE,J.E.HAND & SONS CO.,PHILADELPHIA......  200.00
```

SCRIMSHAW, ALASKAN DEER HUNT, BOATS

SCRIMSHAW, MOTHER, CHILD,
HOUND, ROSE SPRAY

SCRIMSHAW, ALASKAN HARBOR SCENE

SCRIMSHAW, PORTRAIT OF WASHINGTON

SEVRES PORCELAIN HAS BEEN MADE IN SEVRES, FRANCE, SINCE 1769. MANY COPIES OF THE FAMOUS WARE HAVE BEEN MADE. THE NAME ORIGINALLY REFERRED TO THE WORKS OF THE ROYAL FACTORY. THE NAME NOW INCLUDES ANY OF THE WARES MADE IN THE TOWN OF SEVRES, FRANCE.

SEVRES, BOWL, CARD, YELLOW, ORMULU HANDLES & FEET, 11-1/8 IN. DIAMETER............................................. 600.00
SEVRES, BOWL, IVY, FROSTED SWIRL, CLEAR PEDESTAL, MARK, 7 1/2 IN. HIGH............................................. 22.00
SEVRES, BOWL, SUGAR, ROSES, POPPIES, LARKSPUR, 1764, 4 1/2 IN. HIGH. 460.00
SEVRES, BOX, PATCH, FLORAL, 1 1/2 IN. X 2 IN................... 20.00
SEVRES, CABARET, APPLE GREEN, 1772............................2,500.00
SEVRES, CLOCK, TWO URNS......................................1,000.00
SEVRES, COFFEE CAN & SAUCER, BLUE & GOLD, 18TH CENTURY......... 350.00
SEVRES, COFFEE CAN & SAUCER, CIRCA 1777, AMERICAN DECORATION... 650.00
SEVRES, COFFEE SERVICE, MEDALLIONS, FLOWER-FILLED BASKETS, 35 PIECES.................................................... 525.00
SEVRES, CREAMER & SUGAR, YELLOW & RED ROSES, GOLD TRIM, MARK, BAVARIA, SIGNED............................................ 22.50
SEVRES, CUP & SAUCER, JEWELED DECORATION, 19TH CENTURY......... 250.00
SEVRES, CUP, SAUCER, CANARY YELLOW GROUND, GOLD DESIGN, DATED 1845, MARK................................................. 60.00
SEVRES, ECUELLE, SCENIC, DOME COVER, SHAPED STAND, 1765, 10 1/4 IN. LONG............................................. 375.00
SEVRES, FIGURINE, ALLEGORICAL, PYGMALION, GALATEA, INSCRIPTION, 14 1/2 IN. HIGH............................................ 325.00
SEVRES, FIGURINE, BACCHUS PORTE PAR LES BACCHANTES.....ILLUS.. 250.00
SEVRES, FIGURINE, BUST, HENRY III, LOUIS XIII, PEDESTAL, SIGNED, 5 1/2 IN., PAIR.......................................... 200.00
SEVRES, FIGURINE, SOLDIER IN FULL DRESS UNIFORM, GUN, SWORD, 9 1/2 IN. TALL............................................ 65.00
SEVRES, FIGURINE, SOLDIER IN FULL DRESS UNIFORM, DRUMMER, 9 1/2 IN. TALL............................................ 65.00
SEVRES, FIGURINE, TROIS GRACES PORTANT L'AMOUR, 10 IN...ILLUS.. 225.00
SEVRES, FRUIT COOLER, ROSES, PANSIES, BLUE, GOLD, LINER, 1780, 8 IN. HIGH, PAIR.......................................... 750.00
SEVRES, JUG, PAIR, GROS BLEU, DATED 1754......................1,350.00
SEVRES, LAMP, PAIR, BLUE & GOLS PORCELAIN & ORMOLU, 30 IN. HIGH. 950.00
SEVRES, PITCHER, BUTTERMILK, PINK ROSES, GOLD TRIM, MARKED....... 7.00
SEVRES, PITCHER, LARGE RED ROSES, GOLD TRIM, TANKARD, MARK....... 15.00
SEVRES, PLAQUE, DEPICTING ROYALTY, MARKED S65, FRAME, 4-1/2 IN. DIAMETER, PAIR..................................... 60.00
SEVRES, PLATE, BLUE, GOLD TRIM & DECOR, SCALLOPED EDGE, 7 IN..... 27.50
SEVRES, PLATE, CHERUBS, WREATH, CROWN, SAYS CHATEAU DES TUILERIES, DATED 1846......................................... 48.00
SEVRES, PLATE, DINNER, WHITE, GOLD BAND, GOLD N, FOR NAPOLEON III, 1868, 12................................................... 350.00
SEVRES, PLATE, FRUIT, APPLES WITH BLOSSOMS, HAND-PAINTED, BAVARIA, 12 1/2 IN.......................................... 45.00
SEVRES, PLATE, LAVENDER GROUND, SNOWBERRIES, HAND-PAINTED,

SEVRES FIGURINE, BACCHUS PORTE PAR LES BACCHANTES

SEVRES FIGURINE, TROIS GRACES PORTANT L'AMOUR

SIGNED,7 1/2 IN.................................... 18.50
SEVRES,PLATE,NAPOLEON SCENIC,ARTIST-SIGNED,MARK,
12-IN.DIAMETER.................................... 90.00
SEVRES,PLATE,OYSTER,CENTER WELL,PLACES FOR SIX OYSTERS,
FLORAL,GILT...................................... 19.50
SEVRES,PLATE,PORTRAIT,ARTIST LAURENT,STAMP READS CHATEAU DES
TUILERIES........................................ 145.00
SEVRES,PLATE,PORTRAIT,GEORGE WASHINGTON,HAND-PAINTED,
BAVARIA,9 IN..................................... 20.00
SEVRES,PLATE,PORTRAIT,GEORGE WASHINGTON,GREEN,GOLD BORDER,
BAVARIA,10 IN.................................... 10.00
SEVRES,PLATE,PORTRAIT,GOLD FLORAL BORDER,PANSY BACKGROUND,
THOMAS,BAVARIA................................... 28.00
SEVRES,PLATE,ROSES,ARTIST-SIGNED GRUND,8 1/2 IN.......... 30.00
SEVRES,PLATE,ROSES,TURQUOISE BORDER,CIRCA 1780,
9 1/2-IN.DIAMETER................................ 95.00
SEVRES,PLATE,SHADED GREEN,WHITE BUNNIES AROUND EDGE,
7 3/4 IN.,SET OF 8............................... 42.50
SEVRES,PLATE,SOUP,WHITE,GOLD LP,CROWN,BAND,FOR LOUIS
PHILLIPE,1848,4.................................. 125.00
SEVRES,PLATE,TAN GROUND,FIVE WHITE MICE,BAVARIA,6 3/4 IN.... 4.50
SEVRES,PLATE,YELLOW ROSES,SIGNED PHILLIPS,PIERCED,8 1/2 IN.. 18.00
SEVRES,PLATTER,PORTRAIT,GOLD BAROQUE EDGE OVER PINK,
5 DESSERT PLATES................................. 250.00
SEVRES,STATUETTE,SET OF 4,BISQUE,DANCERS,12 TO 13 1/2 IN.
HIGH............................................. 250.00
SEVRES,TEA SERVICE,4-PIECE,DATED 1769.................. 425.00
SEVRES,TRAY,BLUE & ROSE COLOR MOTIF,11 1/4 IN. LONG........ 750.00
SEVRES,URN,HEROIC SCENE,HAND-PAINTED,SOFT PASTE,MARKED D,
COVER...........................................1,250.00
SEVRES,URN,MULTICOLORED ENAMELED TOP,BASE,LID,
12 1/4 IN.HIGH,PAIR.............................. 350.00
SEVRES,VASE,COBALT & GOLD,SCENE,SIGNED LUCOT,COVER,
16 IN.HIGH,PAIR.................................. 750.00
SEVRES,VASE,LANDSCAPE,MYTHOLOGICAL SCENE,LID,52
IN.,PAIR............................... 1400.00 4,500.00
SEVRES,VASE,PEOPLE,GARDEN,CASTLE,LID,SIGNED VAUTRIN,1755,
5 1/4 IN.,PAIR................................... 375.00
SEVRES,VASE,PORTRAITS,RED,PARIS,17 1/2 IN.TALL,PAIR......... 350.00
SEVRES,VASE,SCENE,COBALT,GOLD,SIGNED LUCOT,15 IN.HIGH,PAIR.. 650.00
SEVRES,VASE,TURQUOISE,WHITE,FLORAL,ORMOLU BANDS,1771,
6 1/2 IN.HIGH.................................... 85.00
SEWER TILE,LION,OHIO,10 IN. X 28 1/2 IN.,PAIR........ILLUS. 750.00
SEWER TILE,POODLE,CREAM COLOR,OHIO,9 1/2 IN................ 32.50
SEWER TILE,POODLE,SEATED,REDDISH,10 1/2 IN................. 25.00
SEWING MACHINE,FOR LEATHER HARNESS,HAND-OPERATED,WILCOX &
GIBBS,1871....................................... 18.00
SEWING MACHINE,HAND MODEL,1926,SINGER..................... 11.00
SEWING MACHINE,PEDAL,SINGER............................... 15.00

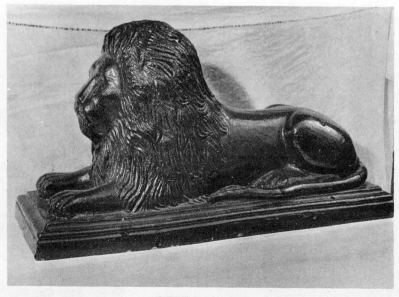

SEWER TILE, LION, OHIO

SHAVING MUGS WERE POPULAR FROM 1860 TO 1900. MANY TYPES
WERE MADE INCLUDING OCCUPATIONAL MUGS FEATURING
PICTURES OF THE MAN'S JOB. THERE WERE SCUTTLE MUGS,
SILVER-PLATED MUGS,GLASS-LINED MUGS,AND OTHERS.
SHAVING MUG,SEE ALSO,SHAVING MUG,SCUTTLE TYPE,SILVER
PLATE,SHAVING

| | |
|---|---|
| SHAVING MUG,ADVERTISING,LEFT-HANDED,GERMANY................. | 37.50 |
| SHAVING MUG,ATTACHED BEVEL MIRROR,BRUSH RACK,SILVER PLATE... | 24.00 |
| SHAVING MUG,B.P.O.E.,ELK HOLDING CLOCK IN ANTLERS, HAND-PAINTED,NAME...................................... | 20.00 |
| SHAVING MUG,BAND OF FLOWERS & LEAVES,COPPER LUSTER.......... | 35.00 |
| SHAVING MUG,BLUE & GOLD FLOWERS,PORCELAIN................... | 7.50 |
| SHAVING MUG,BLUE & WHITE FLOWERS,SOAP DRAIN,PORCELAIN....... | 10.50 |
| SHAVING MUG,BLUE FLORAL,GOLD,RAISED WHITE SWIRL,REST........ | 10.00 |
| SHAVING MUG,BLUE FLORAL,SOAP REST,ATTACHED MIRROR.......... | 20.00 |
| SHAVING MUG,BLUE,BUTTERFLY,FLOWERS,DATED JULY 16,1867....... | 30.00 |
| SHAVING MUG,BLUISH CAST,MILK GLASS......................... | 12.50 |
| SHAVING MUG,BRIDGE,BOATS,SKYLINE,BUILDINGS,DIVIDED.......... | 40.00 |
| SHAVING MUG,BROWN WILD ROSE,CARTWRIGHT BROS................. | 2.50 |
| SHAVING MUG,BROWN,RAISED MOOSE HEAD ON PINK BRANCH.......... | 15.00 |
| SHAVING MUG,BRUSH REST,VAN BERGH CO.,CIRCA 1892,SILVER...... | 12.50 |
| SHAVING MUG,CHARACTER,CHINESE HEAD......................... | 45.00 |
| SHAVING MUG,CHARACTER,NEGRO HEAD........................... | 65.00 |
| SHAVING MUG,COBALT BLUE & GOLD,SAYS PRESENT................ | 14.00 |
| SHAVING MUG,COPPER LUSTER,BANDS,FLORAL,LEAVES,GREEN,YELLOW, RED.................................................... | 35.00 |
| SHAVING MUG,CREAM COLOR,RAISED RED & WHITE DECOR,GOLD RIM... | 10.00 |
| SHAVING MUG,CREAM GROUND,GREEN & GOLD HORN OF PLENTY,MARKED PATENT 1882............................................ | 12.50 |
| SHAVING MUG,CREAM TO LAVENDER,GOLD FLORAL,ORNATE HANDLE, PORCELAIN.............................................. | 17.50 |
| SHAVING MUG,DARK BLUE IVY VINES,HAND-PAINTED,PORCELAIN...... | 12.50 |
| SHAVING MUG,DIVIDED,BRIDGE,BOATS,SKYLINE,BUILDINGS.......... | 40.00 |
| SHAVING MUG,DRY GOODS MERCHANT,OCCUPATIONAL................. | 69.00 |
| SHAVING MUG,EAGLE DECOR,3 1/2 IN......................... | 15.00 |
| SHAVING MUG,EAGLE ON ONE SIDE,VIOLETS ON OTHER,BRANDENBURG, BRUSH,SOAP............................................. | 17.50 |
| SHAVING MUG,EMBOSSED CHERUBS,FLORAL,LEAF HANDLE,INSERT, SILVER,ADELPHI......................................... | 30.00 |
| SHAVING MUG,EMBOSSED CHERUBS,FLORAL,SOAP & BRUSH INSERTS, SILVER................................................. | 30.00 |
| SHAVING MUG,EMBOSSED DECOR,SHELF,PORCELAIN................. | 14.50 |
| SHAVING MUG,EMBOSSED DEER & FOLIAGE,SHADED SEPIA TO GREEN COLOR.................................................. | 25.00 |
| SHAVING MUG,EMBOSSED FLOWERS,PATENT 1900,SILVER PLATE....... | 14.00 |
| SHAVING MUG,EMBOSSED HANDLE,REMOVABLE SOAP DISH,SILVER PLATE | 27.50 |
| SHAVING MUG,FLARED BASE,GOLD TRIM,F.C.HODGES IN BLACK SCRIPT | 8.00 |
| SHAVING MUG,FLORAL DECOR,FRANK DENISE IN GOLD,PORCELAIN..... | 15.00 |
| SHAVING MUG,FLORAL DECOR,PORCELAIN......................... | 16.50 |
| SHAVING MUG,FLORAL PATTERN................................. | 5.00 |
| SHAVING MUG,FLORAL,GOLD,LUSTER,SOAP TRAY................... | 9.75 |
| SHAVING MUG,FLOW BLUE,MADE IN PORTUGAL..................... | 12.50 |
| SHAVING MUG,FLOWERS & VINES............................... | 18.00 |
| SHAVING MUG,FLYING WILD DUCKS,FOX,WINTER SCENE,POTTERY...... | 27.50 |
| SHAVING MUG,FOUR RUNNING COWS,NAME WILLIAM SMILEY IN GOLD... | 27.50 |
| SHAVING MUG,FRATERNAL,ITALIAN-AMERICAN SOCIETY.............. | 40.00 |
| SHAVING MUG,FRATERNAL,K OF C............................... | 30.00 |
| SHAVING MUG,FRATERNAL,ODD FELLOWS.......................... | 27.50 |
| SHAVING MUG,FRATERNAL,ODD FELLOWS INSIGNIA,FLORAL,GOLD SCROLLS,BORDERS........................................ | 55.00 |
| SHAVING MUG,GARLANDS,ROSES,GOLD,3 3/4 IN.TALL.............. | 22.50 |
| SHAVING MUG,GIRL FIGURE FORMS HANDLE,PORCELAIN............. | 17.50 |
| SHAVING MUG,GOLD LEAF SPRAY,GOLD RIM,PORCELAIN............. | 12.00 |
| SHAVING MUG,GOLD OUTSIDE,RAISED RED,BLUE,GREEN DECOR........ | 18.00 |
| SHAVING MUG,GREEN FROG,SMOKES PIPE,ON TOADSTOOL, STAFFORDSHIRE.......................................... | 15.00 |
| SHAVING MUG,GREEN,GOLD,STEAM-DRIVEN FIRE ENGINE DECAL,NAME.. | 15.00 |
| SHAVING MUG,GREEN,WHITE,ORCHID & GREEN GRAPES,GILT, PORCELAIN,GERMANY...................................... | 8.50 |
| SHAVING MUG,INDIAN CHIEF,ART NOUVEAU,UNGER BROS.MARK, STERLING SILVER........................................ | 95.00 |
| SHAVING MUG,INDIAN HEAD,PAINTED,WHITE GROUND............... | 15.00 |
| SHAVING MUG,LADIES,PINK,GOLD EMBOSSED PATTERN.............. | 12.00 |
| SHAVING MUG,LADY'S,PEACH,WHITE FLORAL,SHELF................ | 7.00 |
| SHAVING MUG,LADY'S,PORCELAIN............................... | 15.00 |
| SHAVING MUG,LADY'S,FLORAL DECOR,SHELF,PORCELAIN............ | 7.50 |
| SHAVING MUG,LAVENDER,VIOLET DECOR.......................... | 8.00 |
| SHAVING MUG,LEFT-HANDED,WHITE.............................. | 18.00 |
| SHAVING MUG,LEFT-HANDED,WITH MIRROR,SOAP RACK.............. | 37.00 |
| SHAVING MUG,LILACS,BLACK BRUSH............................. | 18.50 |
| SHAVING MUG,LITTLE GIRL WITH UMBRELLA...................... | 10.00 |

```
SHAVING MUG,LUSTER & FLORAL DECOR............................  15.00
SHAVING MUG,MAN DRIVING A TEAM & WAGON................ILLUS..  75.00
SHAVING MUG,MAN'S NAME IN GOLD......................ILLUS..     7.50
SHAVING MUG,MARKED A.WALROUS,ADVERTISING,THE CLIMAX BARBER
  CHAIR......................................................  18.00
SHAVING MUG,MAROON,WHITE GROUND,GOLD,ROSES,HIGGINS & SEITER,
  AUSTRIA...................................................  11.75
SHAVING MUG,MINIATURE,COAT OF ARMS OF HOVE,PORCELAIN........   4.50
SHAVING MUG,MINIATURE,CREST,2 1/4 IN.HIGH..................    5.00
SHAVING MUG,MOCHA,YELLOW GROUND,WHITE BANDS,3 1/2 X
  3 IN.HIGH.................................................  25.00
SHAVING MUG,MOSS ROSE PATTERN,IRONSTONE.....................  15.00
SHAVING MUG,NAME OF GOVERNOR MCCRAY OF INDIANA,POLITICAL
  CAMPAIGN BUTTON...........................................  65.00
SHAVING MUG,NEGRO ON YELLOW HALF MOON PLAYING BANJO,CLOUDS..  65.00
SHAVING MUG,OCCUPATIONAL,BARBERSHOP.........................  75.00
SHAVING MUG,OCCUPATIONAL,BASEBALL PLAYER,CROSSED BATS,BALL.. 125.00
SHAVING MUG,OCCUPATIONAL,BICYCLE,SIGNED RUTHERFORD..........  80.00
SHAVING MUG,OCCUPATIONAL,BLACKSMITH...................ILLUS..  60.00
SHAVING MUG,OCCUPATIONAL,BOILERMAKER,NAME IN GOLD..........   65.00
SHAVING MUG,OCCUPATIONAL,BRICKLAYER'S TOOLS,NAME,GOLD.......  60.00
SHAVING MUG,OCCUPATIONAL,BUTCHER,STEER'S HEAD,TOOLS.........  80.00
SHAVING MUG,OCCUPATIONAL,BUTCHER,SYMBOLS....................  55.00
SHAVING MUG,OCCUPATIONAL,CARPENTER..........................  65.00
SHAVING MUG,OCCUPATIONAL,ENGINE,NAME IN GOLD................  57.50
SHAVING MUG,OCCUPATIONAL,ENGINE & COAL CAR...........ILLUS..  65.00
SHAVING MUG,OCCUPATIONAL,FLORAL,DRAPERIES,NAME,SIGNED
  MELCHIOR BROS............................................   45.00
SHAVING MUG,OCCUPATIONAL,HORSE BREEDER,NAME IN GOLD.........  65.00
SHAVING MUG,OCCUPATIONAL,HORSE,J.H.INGALLS..................  40.00
SHAVING MUG,OCCUPATIONAL,LIVERY STABLE......................  80.00
SHAVING MUG,OCCUPATIONAL,LOCOMOTIVE & TENDER................  75.00
SHAVING MUG,OCCUPATIONAL,MACHINE LATHE......................  65.00
SHAVING MUG,OCCUPATIONAL,MASON..............................  65.00
SHAVING MUG,OCCUPATIONAL,PLASTERER TOOLS,NAME...............  50.00
```

| SHAVING MUG, ENGINE AND COAL CAR | SHAVING MUG, MAN'S NAME | SHAVING MUG, DRAPES AND FLOWERS | SHAVING MUG, BLACKSMITH | SHAVING MUG, TEAM AND WAGON |
|---|---|---|---|---|

```
SHAVING MUG,OCCUPATIONAL,RAILROAD,SAYS ALEXANDER MITCHELL,
  BLACK & WHITE............................................  70.00
SHAVING MUG,OCCUPATIONAL,TELEGRAPH..........................  55.00
SHAVING MUG,OCCUPATIONAL,TELEGRAPH KEY & HAND,NAME,SUPPLY
  HOUSE STAMP..............................................   56.00
SHAVING MUG,OCCUPATIONAL,TELEGRAPH OPERATOR,NAME THOMAS
  K.PIPPIN IN GOLD.........................................  75.00
SHAVING MUG,OCCUPATIONAL,TELEGRAPHER'S KEY,NAME.............  49.00
SHAVING MUG,OCCUPATIONAL,THE COOPER.........................  55.00
SHAVING MUG,OCCUPATIONAL,THREE HORSES' HEADS,ORANGE GROUND,
  NAME....................................................   65.00
SHAVING MUG,OCCUPATIONAL,TINSMITH...........................  65.00
SHAVING MUG,OCCUPATIONAL,TRANSFER PHOTO,STEAM ENGINE,BLACK,
  WHITE...................................................   70.00
SHAVING MUG,OLD-FASHIONED GIRL,BRUSH,CELLULOID CASE.........  35.00
SHAVING MUG,ORNATE,BRUSH HOLDER,MARKED BRANDENBURG..........  10.00
SHAVING MUG,PANELED DESIGN,CLEAR GLASS......................   2.95
SHAVING MUG,PANELS,SCENES,SOAP REST,BRUSH,PATENT 1888.......  14.00
SHAVING MUG,PICTURES RED INDIAN MOTORCYCLE,MARKED ARCHIE
  O.ANDERSON..............................................   47.50
SHAVING MUG,PINK & RED ROSES,GOLD,PORCELAIN.................   7.50
SHAVING MUG,PINK & WHITE BARBER POLE STRIPES,TRANSFER OF
  SINGING QUARTET.........................................   32.00
SHAVING MUG,PINK & WHITE ROSES,SOAP SHELF,3 1/2 IN.HIGH.....  12.00
SHAVING MUG,PINK LUSTER & WHITE,GOLD ROSE...................  18.00
SHAVING MUG,PINK LUSTER,EMBOSSED LEAVES,BEE,SOAP
  COMPARTMENT,LEFT-HANDED..................................  28.50
SHAVING MUG,PINK ROSE GARLANDS,SCALLOPED,BARREL SHAPE,
  PORCELAIN...............................................   12.50
SHAVING MUG,PINK,RED,GOLD,WITH REST.........................  12.00
SHAVING MUG,PORTRAIT OF WILD BILL CODY,MARKED BRANDENBURG,
  GERMANY.................................................   15.00
```

| | |
|---|---|
| SHAVING MUG,PORTRAIT,BEARDED MAN SMOKING A PIPE............ | 17.00 |
| SHAVING MUG,PORTRAIT,BEARDED MAN,BLUE,ROSES,GOLD TRIM, GERMANY............................................ | 12.50 |
| SHAVING MUG,PORTRAIT,PRESIDENT HARRISON,ATTACHED SOAP CUP, MILK GLASS.......................................... | 38.00 |
| SHAVING MUG,PORTRAIT,TWO GIRLS,BLUE ATTIRE,FLOPPY HATS, BOUQUETS........................................... | 17.00 |
| SHAVING MUG,PORTRAIT,WOMAN,FLOWING HAIR,PINK,BISQUE,GOLD TRIM,MARK.......................................... | 75.00 |
| SHAVING MUG,PURPLE & GOLD TRIM,PAT.1870 MARK.............. | 15.00 |
| SHAVING MUG,PURPLE DRAPES & FLOWERS,NAME...........ILLUS.. | 10.00 |
| SHAVING MUG,PURPLE VIOLETS,SAYS IN GOLD FOR A NEW SHAVER.... | 7.00 |
| SHAVING MUG,PURPLE,PINK,YELLOW FLOWERS,BRUSH REST,PORCELAIN. | 15.00 |
| SHAVING MUG,RAISED DESIGN,LAVENDER FLORAL,GREEN LEAVES, 3 1/4-IN.DIAMETER..................................... | 16.00 |
| SHAVING MUG,RED & YELLOW ROSES,GOLD,PORCELAIN,3 1/2 IN.HIGH. | 6.75 |
| SHAVING MUG,REMOVABLE SOAP DISH,BRUSH REST,EMBOSSED FLORAL, SILVER PLATE........................................ | 19.50 |
| SHAVING MUG,ROBIN DECOR ON SIDE,OPAQUE PINK-LAVENDER GLASS, HANDLE............................................. | 27.50 |
| SHAVING MUG,ROSE SPRAYS,GOLD RIM,SOAP REST,PORCELAIN........ | 11.50 |
| SHAVING MUG,ROSES & LEAVES,MARKED SEVRES STYLE,MADELINE, BAVARIA............................................ | 10.00 |
| SHAVING MUG,ROSES,GILT,SAYS W.H.CLEVELAND................ | 15.00 |
| SHAVING MUG,ROSES,HAND-PAINTED,MARKED C.T.ALTWASSER,SILESIA. | 16.00 |
| SHAVING MUG,ROUND MIRROR ON SIDE,PORCELAIN................ | 18.00 |
| SHAVING MUG,SALMON SHADES,BLUE & YELLOW POPPIES,GOLD TRIM & HANDLE............................................. | 18.50 |
| SHAVING MUG,SCENE,WATER,SWANS,HAND-PAINTED............... | 18.00 |
| SHAVING MUG,SCUTTLE,CREAM GROUND,PINK & WHITE ROSES,MARKED STAFFORDSHIRE....................................... | 18.50 |
| SHAVING MUG,SCUTTLE,ELK HEAD ON FRONT,PLACE FOR BRUSH....... | 25.00 |
| SHAVING MUG,SCUTTLE,ELK PORTRAIT,GREENERY,BROWN GROUND,PLACE FOR BRUSH.......................................... | 25.00 |
| SHAVING MUG,SCUTTLE,FLORAL & GOLD DECOR,EMBOSSED FLOWERS.... | 20.00 |
| SHAVING MUG,SCUTTLE,FLOWER MART SCENE,SQUARE,BRUSH HOLDER ABOVE HANDLE........................................ | 15.00 |
| SHAVING MUG,SCUTTLE,MARINER COMPASS,SAILOR POEM,TRANSFER, PURPLE LUSTER....................................... | 37.50 |
| SHAVING MUG,SCUTTLE,MARKED UNION SHAVING MUG,PAT.SEPT.20, 1870,IRONSTONE...................................... | 16.00 |
| SHAVING MUG,SCUTTLE,MARKED UNION,PATENT SEPT.20,1870, IRONSTONE.......................................... | 12.00 |
| SHAVING MUG,SCUTTLE,ORANGE FLORAL,GREEN LEAVES,WHITE GROUND, 3 3/4 IN........................................... | 25.00 |
| SHAVING MUG,SCUTTLE,PINK LUSTER,WHITE RAISED LILY-OF-THE-VALLEY DECOR............................. | 18.50 |
| SHAVING MUG,SCUTTLE,PINK ROSES......................... | 19.00 |
| SHAVING MUG,SCUTTLE,PORTRAIT.......................... | 12.00 |
| SHAVING MUG,SCUTTLE,ROSE PATTERN,GERMANY................. | 17.50 |
| SHAVING MUG,SCUTTLE,WHITE PORCELAIN,ROSE DECOR............. | 13.50 |
| SHAVING MUG,SEPARATE INSERT FOR BRUSH,SILVER PLATE......... | 22.50 |
| SHAVING MUG,SHADED GREEN TO BLUE,HUNTING DOG PROFILE........ | 22.00 |
| SHAVING MUG,SHADED ROSES,GREEN FOLIAGE,HAND-PAINTED,GERMANY. | 12.50 |
| SHAVING MUG,SHADED ROSES,MOTHER-OF-PEARL TOP,PLACE FOR SOAP, PORCELAIN.......................................... | 14.00 |
| SHAVING MUG,SHAPE OF CHINESE COOLIE HEAD,QUEUE IS HANDLE.... | 24.00 |
| SHAVING MUG,SHELL SCUTTLE,HAND-PAINTED FLORAL,PORCELAIN..... | 15.00 |
| SHAVING MUG,SIDE PARTITION FOR BRUSH,HANDLE,TIN........... | 9.50 |
| SHAVING MUG,SILVER PLATE,SOAP TRAY,BRUSH HOLDER,ENGRAVED DECOR............................................. | 14.00 |
| SHAVING MUG,SILVER,SITS ON A MOUNTAIN GOAT HORN,HINGED COVER | 59.00 |
| SHAVING MUG,SOUVENIR,ST. LOUIS WORLD'S FAIR,1904........... | 12.50 |
| SHAVING MUG,SPORTSMAN,MAN FISHING BY STREAM,NAME,SUPPLY HOUSE STAMP........................................ | 42.00 |
| SHAVING MUG,SPORTSMAN,MAN HUNTING IN WOODS WITH DOGS,NAME... | 42.00 |
| SHAVING MUG,TAN BAND,PINK FLORAL,EXCELSIOR 1886............. | 11.50 |
| SHAVING MUG,TAYLOR WITH ASSISTANTS,SIGNED ROSETTI, HAND-PAINTED CROWN.................................. | 35.00 |
| SHAVING MUG,THREE BROTHERS SHIP,VERSE,PINK LUSTER,SUNDERLAND | 29.50 |
| SHAVING MUG,THREE RIFLES & BAYONETS IN NATURAL COLORS,GOLD SABERS,NAME......................................... | 57.50 |
| SHAVING MUG,TIN,MILK GLASS INSERT...................... | 6.00 |
| SHAVING MUG,TIN,4 IN.HIGH............................. | 14.75 |
| SHAVING MUG,VINES OF PURPLE FLOWERS,GREEN LEAVES,IRONSTONE.. | 15.00 |
| SHAVING MUG,WHITE GROUND,GOLD FILIGREE,REST,2 1/2 IN.HIGH... | 12.00 |
| SHAVING MUG,WHITE SOAP REST,GOLD TRIM................... | 12.50 |
| SHAVING MUG,WHITE,BLUE FLOWERS,UNION,PAT.SEPT.20,1870....... | 17.00 |
| SHAVING MUG,WHITE,DOUBLE HANDLES,MILK GLASS............... | 10.00 |
| SHAVING MUG,WHITE,GOLD ACCENTS,F.S.SANFORD IN GOLD LETTERS.. | 16.00 |
| SHAVING MUG,WHITE,GOLD BAND AT TOP & BOTTOM,NAME IN GOLD.... | 23.00 |

SHAVING MUG,WHITE,GOLD DECOR,NAME IN GOLD,MADE BY HAVILAND &
CO.......................................................... 12.75
SHAVING MUG,WHITE,GOLD LEAVES,NAME............................ 23.00
SHAVING MUG,WHITE,MARKED EXCELSIOR PAT.1870................... 9.95
SHAVING MUG,WHITE,MOLDED SWIRL BODY,FLORAL DECOR............. 10.00
SHAVING MUG,WHITE,PINK BAND,RUST FLORAL,LEAVES,GOLD,SOAP
SHELF,POTTERY................................................ 9.00
SHAVING MUG,WHITE,PORCELAIN,BRUSH REST,MARKED EXCELSIOR,
PATENT 1870................................................. 9.95
SHAVING MUG,WHITE,ROSE DESIGN,GERMANY......................... 8.50
SHAVING MUG,YELLOW GROUND,WHITE & BLACK BANDS................ 20.00
SHAVING MUG,YELLOW GROUND,YELLOW,WHITE,BLACK BANDS,
3 1/2 IN.HIGH.............................................. 20.00
SHEFFIELD, SEE SILVER PLATE, SHEFFIELD
SHIP,MODEL OF 3-MASTED,30 IN. LONG......................... 275.00
SHIP,MODEL,CANADIENNE,TWO-MASTED,RED,18 IN. X 20 IN......... 45.00
SHIP,MODEL,FRIGATE,SOME PARTS OF ABALONE,BONE,17 1/4 IN.LONG 700.00
SHIP,MODEL,NELSON'S FLAGSHIP,BONE,15 IN.LONG.............1,100.00
SHIP,MODEL,SANTA MARIA,WOODEN,CANVAS SAILS,22 IN.HIGH X
22 IN.LONG................................................. 67.50
SHIP,MODEL,SCHOONER,IN QUART BOTTLE........................ 55.00
SHIP,MODEL,U.S.FRIGATE BOSTON,BONE,22 IN.LONG............4,000.00
SHIP,WHEEL................................................ 175.00


SHIRLEY TEMPLE DISHES,BLUE GLASSWARE,AND ANY OTHER
SOUVENIR-TYPE OBJECTS WITH HER NAME AND PICTURE ARE
NOW COLLECTED.
SHIRLEY TEMPLE,BOOK,SONG................................... 10.00
SHIRLEY TEMPLE,BOWL........................................ 4.00
SHIRLEY TEMPLE,BOWL & PITCHER.............................. 7.50
SHIRLEY TEMPLE,BOWL,CEREAL,PORTRAIT,COBALT BLUE............ 6.50
SHIRLEY TEMPLE,BOWL,MUG,PITCHER........................... 13.50
SHIRLEY TEMPLE,CREAMER........................... 2.50 TO 4.50
SHIRLEY TEMPLE,CREAMER & CEREAL........................... 10.00
SHIRLEY TEMPLE,CREAMER,BLUE................................ 4.00
SHIRLEY TEMPLE,CREAMER,COBALT BLUE......................... 6.00
SHIRLEY TEMPLE,CREAMER,PORTRAIT,COBALT BLUE................ 6.50
SHIRLEY TEMPLE,DOLL,COMPOSITION,DRESSED,18 IN............. 75.00
SHIRLEY TEMPLE,DOLL,PIN ON DRESS,22 IN.................... 60.00
SHIRLEY TEMPLE,DOLL,SIGNED,18 IN.......................... 25.00
SHIRLEY TEMPLE,MUG......................................... 6.00
SHIRLEY TEMPLE,MUG,PORTRAIT,COBALT BLUE.................... 6.50
SHIRLEY TEMPLE,PICTURE,SIGNED HELLO EVERYBODY SHIRLEY
TEMPLE,FRAME.............................................. 12.00
SHIRLEY TEMPLE,PICTURE,SIGNED SHIRLEY TEMPLE,EASEL FRAME,7 X
7 IN...................................................... 7.50
SHIRLEY TEMPLE,PITCHER........................... 4.00 TO 8.00
SHIRLEY TEMPLE,PITCHER,COBALT BLUE............... 4.50 TO 7.50
SHIRLEY TEMPLE,TUMBLER,HANDLE............................. 3.50
SILESIA,BOWL,BERRY,IRIS,9 IN.,4 SAUCES................... 35.00
SILESIA,BOWL,GOLD ON SCALLOPED RIM,EMBOSSED LEAVES,FLOWERS,
LOW PEDESTAL............................................. 54.00
SILESIA,BOWL,PALE LILACS,DEEP............................ 20.00
SILESIA,BOWL,PINK & WHITE MUMS,BEADED CREAM SCALLOPED
BORDER,9 IN............................................. 30.00
SILESIA,BOWL,PINK & WHITE MUMS,BLUE SCALLOPED RIM,MARK,
9-IN.DIAMETER........................................... 25.00
SILESIA,BOWL,POPPIES,WHITE FLOWERS,GOLD BEADING,
9 3/4-IN.DIAMETER....................................... 20.00
SILESIA,BOWL,SALAD,CLAM SHELLS,SEASHELLS,SNAILS,GREEN,MAUVE,
6 PLATES................................................ 32.50
SILESIA,CHOCOLATE POT,WHITE,GRAPE DECOR,4 CUPS........... 33.00
SILESIA,CREAMER & SUGAR,IVORY,CREAMER MEASURES 4 1/2 IN.. 48.00
SILESIA,CREAMER & SUGAR,WILD ROSE DECOR,HAND-PAINTED,
R.S.TILLOWITZ........................................... 25.00
SILESIA,CREAMER,VIOLETS.................................. 8.00
SILESIA,DISH,CANDY,GREEN,GOLD,WHITE FLORAL,HAND-PAINTED,
TILLOWITZ............................................... 7.00
SILESIA,DISH,CREAM & GREEN SHADED GROUND,PINK ROSES,VIOLETS,
TILLOWITZ............................................... 14.50
SILESIA,DISH,GREEN EDGE TO WHITE-GREEN CENTER,DAISIES,
HAND-PAINTED,6 IN....................................... 6.00
SILESIA,DISH,RELIEF SWIRLS,LILAC SPRAYS,SHELL SHAPE,HANDLES,
7 1/4 IN................................................ 17.50
SILESIA,DISH,RELISH,GREEN GROUND,FLORAL,TILLOWITZ,
10 1/2 IN.LONG.......................................... 15.00
SILESIA,DISH,RELISH,MOTHER-OF-PEARL FINISH,FLORAL,OVAL.... 10.00
SILESIA,DISH,RELISH,WHITE GROUND,FLORAL OUTLINED WITH WHITE
ENAMEL,GOLD............................................. 10.00
SILESIA,HAIR RECEIVER,PINK & YELLOW ROSES,BEADING ON EDGE... 8.00

```
SILESIA,HOLDER,HATPIN,PINK & WHITE ROSES,SCALLOPED BASE.....   15.00
SILESIA,JAR,POWDER,FORGET-ME-NOT DECOR,COVER,SIGNED.........    8.00
SILESIA,PITCHER,TAN TO WHITE,PINK ROSES,GOLD TRIM,6 IN......   12.50
SILESIA,PLATE,APPLES,BERRIES,HAND-PAINTED UNDER GLAZE,
   C.T.ALTWASSER.............................................    8.00
SILESIA,PLATE,APPLES,BERRIES,PAINTED UNDER GLAZE,
   C.T.ALTWASSER,7 1/2 IN....................................    8.50
SILESIA,PLATE,CAKE,FLORAL,GOLD DECOR,HAND-PAINTED...........   14.00
SILESIA,PLATE,GREEN,LAVENDER IRIS,GREEN VINES,7 IN..........    6.00
SILESIA,PLATE,OLD IVORY,XXXIII,6 IN.........................    9.50
SILESIA,PLATE,PEACHES,BERRIES,PAINTED UNDER GLAZE,
   C.T.ALTWASSER.............................................    8.50
SILESIA,PLATE,PEACHES,BLUEBERRIES,HAND-PAINTED UNDER GLAZE,
   C.T.ALTWASSER.............................................    8.00
SILESIA,PLATE,PEARS,BERRIES,PAINTED UNDER GLAZE,
   C.T.ALTWASSER,7 1/2 IN....................................    8.50
SILESIA,PLATE,PEARS,GRAPES,HAND-PAINTED UNDER GLAZE,
   C.T.ALTWASSER.............................................    8.00
SILESIA,PLATE,PEONIES,HAND-PAINTED,R.S.TILLOWITZ,5 1/2 IN...    3.50
SILESIA,PLATE,PIE,DARK GRAY SHADING,ROSES,MARKED,6 IN.......    4.50
SILESIA,PLATE,PINK FLOWERS,BOWKNOTS,7 1/2 IN.,SET OF 6......   15.00
SILESIA,PLATE,ROSES,CARNATIONS,HANDLES,9 1/2 IN.............    9.00
SILESIA,PLATE,STRAWBERRIES,BLOSSOMS,HAND-PAINTED,7 5/8 IN...    9.50
SILESIA,PLATE,YELLOW & GREEN LUSTER,HANDLES,10 IN...........   10.00
SILESIA,PLATE,YELLOW,BROWN,WHITE & PINK ROSES,GOLD RIM,
   2 HANDLES,9 IN............................................   18.00
SILESIA,RELISH,WHITE GROUND,GOLD TRACERY,PINK & YELLOW
   FLORAL,TILLOWITZ..........................................   13.00
SILESIA,VASE,RED & PINK ROSES,HAND-PAINTED,10 IN.HIGH,
   4-IN.DIAMETER.............................................   36.00
SILHOUETTE,SEE PICTURE,SILHOUETTE
SILVER,AMERICAN,BASKET,CAKE,CIRCA 1830,MARQUAND & CO........  700.00
SILVER,AMERICAN,BASKET,CAKE,EDWARD ROCKWELL,CIRCA 1810......2,000.00
SILVER,AMERICAN,BASKET,SWEETMEAT,CIRCA 1850,BALL,BLACK & CO.  250.00
SILVER,AMERICAN,BASKET,SWEETMEAT,WILLIAM GALE & SON,CIRCA
   1860....................................................    70.00
SILVER,AMERICAN,BOWL & COVER,BALL,BLACK & CO.,CIRCA 1868....  140.00
SILVER,AMERICAN,BOWL,DANIEL VAN VOORHIS,CIRCA 1790..........  725.00
SILVER,AMERICAN,BOX,SNUFF,WILLIAM HOMES,CIRCA 1800..........  250.00
SILVER,AMERICAN,CAN,ELIAS PELLETREAU,CIRCA 1770.............3,500.00
SILVER,AMERICAN,CAN,JOHN BURT,CIRCA 1740....................3,500.00
SILVER,AMERICAN,CAN,LEWIS & SMITH,CIRCA 1805................  500.00
SILVER,AMERICAN,CENTERPIECE,DUHME & CO.,1870................  275.00
SILVER,AMERICAN,COFFEEPOT,ANDREW E.WARNER,CIRCA 1860........  300.00
SILVER,AMERICAN,COFFEEPOT,CIRCA 1780.................ILLUS..3,750.00
SILVER,AMERICAN,COFFEEPOT,JAMES MUSGRAVE,CIRCA 1795.........6,000.00
SILVER,AMERICAN,COFFEEPOT,19TH CENTURY......................  150.00
SILVER,AMERICAN,CAN,ELEAZER BAKER,CIRCA 1780...............1,250.00
SILVER,AMERICAN,CANDELABRA,3 LIGHT,PAIR,THEODORE B.STARR,
   CIRCA 1885...............................................  250.00
```

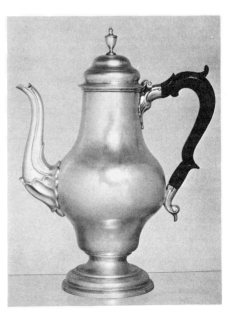

AMERICAN SILVER COFFEEPOT, C. 1780

```
SILVER,AMERICAN,CREAMER & COVERED SUGAR BOWL,CIRCA 1810.....    350.00
SILVER,AMERICAN,CREAMER,DAVID HALL,CIRCA 1790..............    900.00
SILVER,AMERICAN,CREAMER,GEORGE W.RIGGS,CIRCA 1805...........    400.00
SILVER,AMERICAN,CREAMER,JOHN CRAWFORD,CIRCA 1825...........    170.00
SILVER,AMERICAN,CUP,CIRCA 1870,TIFFANY & CO................    140.00
SILVER,AMERICAN,CUP,EGG,WILLIAM KIMBERLY,CIRCA 1790..ILLUS..    500.00
SILVER,AMERICAN,CUP,FLETCHER & GARDINER,CIRCA 1825,8 IN.
  HIGH................................................1,000.00
SILVER,AMERICAN,CUP,JULEP,3,A & G WELLES,CIRCA 1810.........1,000.00
SILVER,AMERICAN,CUP,PAIR,JOSEPH RICHARDSON,CIRCA 1790.......1,800.00
SILVER,AMERICAN,CUP,THREE-HANDLED,MARTELE,CIRCA 1900.......    275.00
SILVER,AMERICAN,DISH,FISH,MAZARIN,CIRCA 1880,TIFFANY & CO...    425.00
SILVER,AMERICAN,DISH,PAIR,VEGETABLE,CIRCA 1840,BALL,TOMPKINS
  & BLACK.............................................    500.00
SILVER,AMERICAN,DREDGER,JOHN WENDOVER,CIRCA 1725.....ILLUS..1,500.00
SILVER,AMERICAN,FLATWARE,17 PIECES,E.COOK,CIRCA 1820........     50.00
SILVER,AMERICAN,LADLE,TODDY,WILLIAM BREED,CIRCA 1750.......    400.00
SILVER,AMERICAN,MUG,CIRCA 1840,BALL,TOMPKINS & BLACK.......    150.00
SILVER,AMERICAN,MUG,COVERED,CIRCA 1820,BALDWIN & JONES......    275.00
SILVER,AMERICAN,MUG,E.STEBBINS & CO.,CIRCA 1840............    130.00
SILVER,AMERICAN,MUG,J.BAILEY & CO.,CIRCA 1850.............    275.00
SILVER,AMERICAN,MUG,JONATHAN OTIS,CIRCA 1750..............    800.00
SILVER,AMERICAN,NIP,SUGAR,PAIR,CIRCA 1760............ILLUS..1,700.00
SILVER,AMERICAN,PITCHER,STEPHEN RICHARDS,CIRCA
  182514 1/2 IN. HIGH................................    750.00
SILVER,AMERICAN,PITCHER,WATER,TWO GOBLETS...........ILLUS..1,000.00
SILVER,AMERICAN,PITCHER,WATER,CIRCA 1830,FREDERICK MARQUAND.1,110.00
SILVER,AMERICAN,PITCHER,WATER,CIRCA 1840,BALL,TOMPKINS &
  BLACK..............................................    250.00
SILVER,AMERICAN,PITCHER,WATER,PAIR,CIRCA 1815,FARNAM & WARD.1,000.00
SILVER,AMERICAN,PITCHER,WATER,PAIR,CIRCA 1840,BALL,TOMPKINS
```

AMERICAN SILVER
DREDGER, C. 1725

AMERICAN SILVER EGG CUP,
C. 1790

AMERICAN SILVER
SUGAR NIP,
C. 1760

AMERICAN
SILVER TEASPOON,
PAUL REVERE,
C. 1780

```
  & BLACK.............................................    950.00
SILVER,AMERICAN,PITCHER,WATER,TWO GOBLETS............ILLUS..1,000.00
SILVER,AMERICAN,PLATE,PAIR,CIRCA 1820,FLETCHER & GARDINER...1,300.00
SILVER,AMERICAN,PORRINGER,ELIAS PELLETREAU,CIRCA 1750.......2,500.00
SILVER,AMERICAN,PORRINGER,GEORGE CARLETON,CIRCA 1810........    375.00
SILVER,AMERICAN,PORRINGER,JOHN BURT,CIRCA 1740.............2,100.00
SILVER,AMERICAN,SALT CELLAR,EPHRAIM BRASHER,CIRCA 1770......    300.00
SILVER,AMERICAN,SALT CELLAR,PAIR,ROBERT & WILLIAM WILSON,
  CIRCA 1830.........................................    225.00
SILVER,AMERICAN,SALT CELLAR,SET OF 6,CIRCA 1850,BALL,BLACK &
  CO................................................    200.00
SILVER,AMERICAN,SALVER,BENNETT & CALDWELL,CIRCA 1845........    225.00
SILVER,AMERICAN,SALVER,PHILIP SYNG,CIRCA 1760...............2,250.00
SILVER,AMERICAN,SALVER,WILLIAM L.ADAMS,CIRCA 1830.........    225.00
SILVER,AMERICAN,SAUCEBOAT,PAIR,WOOD & HUGHES,CIRCA 1870.....    300.00
SILVER,AMERICAN,SNUFFERS & TRAY,SHEPHERD & BOYD,CIRCA 1810..1,200.00
SILVER,AMERICAN,SPOON,BASTING,CIRCA 1760,THOMAS CLARK......    400.00
SILVER,AMERICAN,SPOON,OVAL TIP,1795,JOEL SAYRE,N.Y.,5 IN.,
```

SILVER WATER PITCHER AND TWO GOBLETS

```
   SET OF 6................................................  150.00
SILVER,AMERICAN,SPOON,SUGAR,ORNATE DECOR,GORHAM............   10.00
SILVER,AMERICAN,SUGAR BOWL,COVERED,TIFFANY & CO.,CIRCA 1864.  130.00
SILVER,AMERICAN,SUGAR BOWL,COVERED,W.GALE & SON,CIRCA 1860..  150.00
SILVER,AMERICAN,TANKARD,LEWIS FUETER,CIRCA 1770............5,000.00
SILVER,AMERICAN,TANKARD,SAMUEL VERNON,CIRCA 1730.........10,000.00
SILVER,AMERICAN,TEA & COFFEE SET,4 PIECES,TIFFANY & CO.,
   CIRCA 1875.............................................1,100.00
SILVER,AMERICAN,TEA & COFFEE SET,5 PIECES,W.G.FORBES,CIRCA
   1796..................................................3,750.00
SILVER,AMERICAN,TEA CADDY,ROUND,REPOUSSE FLOWER DESIGN,
   S.KIRK & SON...........................................   55.00
SILVER,AMERICAN,TEA SET,3 PIECES,CIRCA 1810.........ILLUS..1,200.00
```

AMERICAN SILVER TEA SET

```
SILVER,AMERICAN,TEA SET,3 PIECES,GALE WOOD & HUGHS,CIRCA
   1835..................................................  550.00
SILVER,AMERICAN,TEA SET,3 PIECES,NICHOLAS J.BOGART,CIRCA
   1825..................................................  425.00
SILVER,AMERICAN,TEA SET,4 PIECES,BALL,TOMPKINS & BLACK,CIRCA
   1840..................................................  700.00
SILVER,AMERICAN,TEA SET,4 PIECES,JOHN TARGEE,CIRCA 1830....,  700.00
SILVER,AMERICAN,TEA TRAY,OVAL,2-HANDLED,CIRCA 1840,BALL,
   TOMPKINS & BLACK......................................1,300.00
SILVER,AMERICAN,TEA URN,CIRCA 1840,BALL,TOMPKINS & BLACK....  800.00
SILVER,AMERICAN,TEAPOT,BENJAMIN BURT,CIRCA 1770............5,750.00
SILVER,AMERICAN,TEAPOT,CIRCA 1740.........................1,200.00
SILVER,AMERICAN,TEAPOT,GARRET SCHANCK,CIRCA 1795..........2,200.00
SILVER,AMERICAN,TEAPOT,SIGNED MONTEITH..............ILLUS..1,350.00
SILVER,AMERICAN,TEAPOT,SUGAR BOWL & WASTE BOWL,CIRCA 1830,
   GARRET EOFF...........................................  500.00
SILVER,AMERICAN,TEAPOT & COFFEEPOT,J.W.TUCKER & CO.,CIRCA
   1900..................................................  400.00
SILVER,AMERICAN,TEASPOON,PAUL REVERE,CIRCA 1780......ILLUS..2,000.00
SILVER,AMERICAN,TRAY,2-HANDLED,TIFFANY & CO.,CIRCA 1900.....  800.00
SILVER,AMERICAN,TUREEN,SAUCE,PAIR,COVERED,JOSEPH LORING,
   CIRCA 1810............................................1,400.00
```

SILVER TEAPOT, SIGNED
MONTEITH

SILVER,AMERICAN,WAITER,PETER L.KRIDER,CIRCA 1860............ 150.00
SILVER,AUSTRIAN,BOX,SNUFF,OBLONG,ENGINE-TURNED & INITIALED,
3 1/4 IN.LONG............................................. 65.00
SILVER,AUSTRIAN,EWER,1813................................... 210.00
SILVER,CANADIAN,LADLE,VEGETABLE,SET,FIDDLEBACK,1840,J S & S,
ONTARIO.................................................. 65.00
SILVER,CHINESE,SEDAN CHAIR DRAWN BY TWO COOLIES,MINIATURE,
4 1/2 IN.LONG............................................ 55.00
SILVER,CHINESE,SWAN,MINIATURE,2 IN.LONG.................... 20.00

        COIN SILVER WAS MADE IN AMERICA BEFORE 1860. COIN
        SILVER WAS MADE FROM MELTED CURRENCY AND USUALLY HAS A
        SILVER CONTENT OF ABOUT 800 OR 900 PARTS SILVER.
        STERLING SILVER IS 925 PARTS SILVER WITH 75 PARTS
        COPPER. MOST COIN SILVER SPOONS ARE THIN,HANDMADE
        PIECES.
    SILVER,COIN,SEE,SILVER,AMERICAN
SILVER,COIN,COFFEEPOT,FLUTED,CIRCA 1840,PHILADELPHIA,
8 1/2 IN.................................................. 450.00
SILVER,COIN,DISH,BUTTER,EMBOSSED COUNTRY SCENE,DRAIN,BAILEY
& CO.,1840............................................... 250.00
SILVER,COIN,FISH SLICE,ENGRAVED BLADE,CUTOUT FISH,1845,
BAILEY & CO.............................................. 55.00
SILVER,COIN,FORK,CHILD'S,INITIALS H.T.F.,GRAY & LIBBY,
BOSTON,1850.............................................. 4.95
SILVER,COIN,FORK,KING PATTERN,CIRCA 1840,CURRY & PRESTON,
PHILA.,12................................................ 450.00
SILVER,COIN,KETTLE,SWINGING,SQUARE BASE,FOOTED,BAILEY & CO.,
1850.....................................................1,250.00
SILVER,COIN,KNIFE,BUTTER,BY J.E.CALDWELL & CO.,PHILADELPHIA,
CIRCA 1848............................................... 9.95
SILVER,COIN,KNIFE,BUTTER,INITIAL,GORDON & CO.,BOSTON,
PAT.1850................................................. 9.95
SILVER,COIN,KNIFE,BUTTER,SERVING,ENGRAVING ON FRONT,INITIAL,
CHAMBERLAIN.............................................. 9.95
SILVER,COIN,KNIFE,CAKE,THREAD EDGE PATTERN,1830,R. &
W.WILSON,PHILA........................................... 85.00
SILVER,COIN,KNIFE,CAST PLUME & ARROWHEAD HANDLE,PATENT 1861. 10.00
SILVER,COIN,KNIFE,FRUIT,POCKET,RAISED GRAPES,LEAVES,BY M & A 4.95
SILVER,COIN,KNIFE,POCKET,FOLDING,MARKED................... 7.00
SILVER,COIN,KNIFE,POCKET,FRUIT,WITH NUT PICK,ENGRAVED HANDLE
& BLADE................................................. 5.95
SILVER,COIN,KNIFE,SERVING,BUTTER,J.E.CALDWELL & CO.,
PHILADELPHIA,1848....................................... 9.95
SILVER,COIN,LADLE,GRAVY,JOSEPH RAYNES,LOWELL,MASS.,CIRCA
1835,7 1/2 IN........................................... 19.75
SILVER,COIN,LADLE,GRAVY,MARKED RUTLAND,VT.,CIRCA 1840,
6 1/2 IN.LONG........................................... 12.75
SILVER,COIN,LADLE,MUSTARD,THREADED,INSCRIBED JULIA.......... 7.50
SILVER,COIN,LADLE,PUNCH,INITIALS,CIRCA 1850,BY C.A.W.CROSBY,

```
BOSTON.........................................................   69.75
SILVER,COIN,LADLE,SOUP,SALISBURY & CO.,CIRCA 1830...........   75.00
SILVER,COIN,MUG,ENGRAVED NAME,CIRCA 1850..................   24.75
SILVER,COIN,MUG,ENGRAVING,BY C.BARD & SON,PHILADELPHIA,1850.  140.00
SILVER,COIN,PITCHER,TRAY,PRESENTED TO JAMES SEATH,1859,
  JACCARD & CO....................................................1,250.00
SILVER,COIN,SALT,MARKED LEONARD & WILSON,PHILADELPHIA,1847,
  PAIR.........................................................   75.00
SILVER,COIN,SALT,MASTER,GILT-LINED,REPOUSSE DECOR,GORHAM,
  1840,PAIR....................................................   60.00
SILVER,COIN,SALT,OPEN,REPOUSSE,1845,S.KIRK & SON,
  1 1/8 IN.HIGH,PAIR...........................................   75.00
SILVER,COIN,SALT,OPEN,SCALLOPED,FOOTED,CIRCA 1870,
  1 3/4 IN.HIGH,PAIR...........................................   65.00
SILVER,COIN,SERVER,A.PITTS,REVERSE SIDE,T.D.WILBUR...........   12.00
SILVER,COIN,SERVER,CAKE,A.SANBORN,LOWELL,MASS.,CIRCA 1850,
  10 1/4 IN.LONG...............................................   29.75
SILVER,COIN,SHOVEL,MASTER SALT,INITIAL,BY WILLIAM PRATT &
  BROTHER,1830.................................................    5.95
SILVER,COIN,SHOVEL,MASTER SALT,INITIAL,MAKER A.SANBORN,
  LOWELL,MASS.,1850............................................    5.95
SILVER,COIN,SHOVEL,SALT,MASTER,WILLIAM PRATT & BROS.,CIRCA
  1830.........................................................    5.95
SILVER,COIN,SPOON,BERRY,RAISED FRUIT IN BOWL,J.MCKAY,
  EDINBURGH,1810...............................................   35.00
SILVER,COIN,SPOON,DESSERT,FIDDLE-SHAPE HANDLE,MAKER B.&
  M.SWAN,BOSTON................................................    7.50
SILVER,COIN,SPOON,DESSERT,J.B.GINOCHIO,N.Y.,CIRCA 1837,PAIR.   12.50
SILVER,COIN,SPOON,DESSERT,MAKER OWENS & DUBOSQ,PHILA.,1840..    7.00
SILVER,COIN,SPOON,DESSERT,MONOGRAM,H.L.WEBSTER,PROVIDENCE,
  R.I.,1842....................................................    7.00
SILVER,COIN,SPOON,DESSERT,MONOGRAM,MAKER L.LADOMUS,
  PHILADELPHIA,1830............................................    8.50
SILVER,COIN,SPOON,ICE CREAM,GILT BOWL,ENGRAVED PATTERN,
  MONOGRAM,12..................................................   90.00
SILVER,COIN,SPOON,MASTER SALT,BEADED HANDLE,1850,PAIR.......    8.00
SILVER,COIN,SPOON,MASTER SALT,BY N.HARDING,BOSTON,CIRCA
  1830.........................................................    4.95
SILVER,COIN,SPOON,MASTER SALT,BY SETH E.BROWN,CONCORD,N.H.,
  CIRCA 1820...................................................    4.95
SILVER,COIN,SPOON,MASTER SALT,COFFIN HANDLE,INITIALS N.R.,
  1790.........................................................    5.95
SILVER,COIN,SPOON,MASTER SALT,DATED 1835....................    9.00
SILVER,COIN,SPOON,MASTER SALT,FIDDLE-STYLED PATTERN,
  J.KIRKHAM,1840..............................................    6.50
SILVER,COIN,SPOON,MASTER SALT,GEORGE APPLETON,SALEM,MASS.,
  1850.........................................................    5.95
SILVER,COIN,SPOON,MASTER SALT,INITIAL,FARRINGTON &
  HUNNEWELL,BOSTON,1835........................................    5.95
SILVER,COIN,SPOON,MASTER SALT,INITIAL,PATENT 1855...........    5.95
SILVER,COIN,SPOON,MASTER SALT,SHELL BOWL,INITIALS,CIRCA
  1821,T.CHANDLER..............................................    5.95
SILVER,COIN,SPOON,MUSTARD,ENGRAVED CONKEY,EZRA B.BOOTH,
  ROCHESTER,1835...............................................    6.95
SILVER,COIN,SPOON,MUSTARD,FIDDLEBACK........................   10.00
SILVER,COIN,SPOON,MUSTARD,INITIAL B.,PALMER & BACHELDERS,
  BOSTON,1830..................................................    6.95
SILVER,COIN,SPOON,MUSTARD,INITIAL,BY NEWELL HARDING,BOSTON,
  CIRCA 1820...................................................    6.95
SILVER,COIN,SPOON,MUSTARD,INITIALS,BIGELOW BROS.& KENNARD,
  BOSTON,1845..................................................    6.95
SILVER,COIN,SPOON,MUSTARD,LINCOLN & REED,BOSTON,CIRCA 1835..    6.95
SILVER,COIN,SPOON,MUSTARD,LONG HANDLE,SHELL BOWL,CLARK,
  SAWYER & CO.,1840............................................    6.95
SILVER,COIN,SPOON,MUSTARD,LONG HANDLE,W.M.VIRGIN,CIRCA 1830.    6.95
SILVER,COIN,SPOON,MUSTARD,SHELL BOWL,STRAW & TEWKSBURY,CIRCA
  1830.........................................................    6.95
SILVER,COIN,SPOON,SALT,MASTER,STRAW & TEWKSBURY,CIRCA 1830..    5.95
SILVER,COIN,SPOON,SALT,OVAL BOWL,J.HOLDEN CO................    5.50
SILVER,COIN,SPOON,SALT,ROUND BOWL,FIDDLEBACK HANDLE.........    5.00
SILVER,COIN,SPOON,SERVING,BERRY,R.C.ACTON,CIRCA 1850,
  9 IN.LONG....................................................   19.75
SILVER,COIN,SPOON,SERVING,FIDDLEBACK,MARKED HOWE,N.Y........   12.00
SILVER,COIN,SPOON,SERVING,MARKED WILLARD & HAWLEY,1869......   10.00
SILVER,COIN,SPOON,STUFFING,ELONGATED FIDDLEBACK,WM.SEAL,
  PHILA.,PAIR..................................................  300.00
SILVER,COIN,SPOON,SHEAF OF WHEAT ON HANDLE,J.STODDER,N.Y.C.
  1826-1829....................................................   13.50
SILVER,COIN,SUGAR SHELL,CIRCA 1850,BY A.& W.WOOD,NEW YORK..    9.95
SILVER,COIN,SUGAR SHELL,ENGRAVED,INITIAL,SMITH &
  CHAMBERLAIN,SALEM,MASS.......................................    9.95
```

SILVER,COIN,SUGAR SHELL,FIDDLEBACK,1840,WM.BRADY,POTTSVILLE,
PA.,7 IN.................................................. 45.00
SILVER,COIN,SUGAR SHELL,INITIALS M.A.C.,G.BROWN,BARNESVILLE,
OHIO,1830................................................. 9.95
SILVER,COIN,SUGAR SHELL,MONOGRAM,BY BAILEY & CO.,
PHILADELPHIA,1848......................................... 9.95
SILVER,COIN,SUGAR SHELL,MONOGRAM,MAKER,T.IRELAND,CIRCA 1840. 9.95
SILVER,COIN,SUGAR SHELL,OLIVE PATTERN,BIGELOW BROS.&
KENNARD,BOSTON,1845....................................... 9.95
SILVER,COIN,SUGAR SHELL,STONE & BALL,NEW YORK,CIRCA 1850.... 12.00
SILVER,COIN,SUGAR SHELL,T.IRELAND,CIRCA 1840............... 9.95
SILVER,COIN,SUGAR SHELL,WILLIAM W. WHITE & SON,NEW YORK,
CIRCA 1840................................................ 9.95
SILVER,COIN,TABLESPOON,BY FARRINGTON & HUNNEWELL,BOSTON,
1835...................................................... 7.95
SILVER,COIN,TABLESPOON,BY H.HOLTON,CIRCA 1850,MARKED PURE
COIN...................................................... 7.75
SILVER,COIN,TABLESPOON,INITIAL C.,C.A.W.CROSBY,BOSTON,1850.. 5.95
SILVER,COIN,TABLESPOON,INITIAL,BY L.KIMBALL & SON,BOSTON,
CIRCA 1850................................................ 7.75
SILVER,COIN,TABLESPOON,INITIAL,NEWELL HARDING,BOSTON,1820... 5.95
SILVER,COIN,TABLESPOON,J.BAILEY,UTICA,N.Y.,CIRCA 1850...... 7.95
SILVER,COIN,TABLESPOON,MONOGRAM,JEFFREY BRACKETT,BOSTON,
CIRCA 1830,PAIR........................................... 18.00
SILVER,COIN,TABLESPOON,MONOGRAM,MAKER H.HARDING,BOSTON,CIRCA
1835...................................................... 8.50
SILVER,COIN,TABLESPOON,NAME ENGRAVED,CIRCA 1825,BY
T.C.PHINNEY............................................... 7.75
SILVER,COIN,TABLESPOON,SCROLLED & CRESTED MEDALLION HANDLE,
S.H.JOHNSON............................................... 9.50
SILVER,COIN,TABLESPOON,TIPPED END,O.D.SEYMOUR,HARTFORD,
CONN.,CIRCA 1840.......................................... 9.00
SILVER,COIN,TABLESPOON,TIPPED HANDLE,MONOGRAM,1850,MAKER
O.D.SEYMOUR............................................... 9.50
SILVER,COIN,TABLESPOON,TURN-DOWN HANDLE,MAKER H. HARRIS,
ALBANY,N.Y.,1820.......................................... 9.00
SILVER,COIN,TABLESPOON,TWO-PART CONSTRUCTION,19TH CENTURY,
J.LADOMAS................................................. 9.50
SILVER,COIN,TEA CADDY,BOSTON MAKER........................ 145.00
SILVER,COIN,TEA CADDY,SHAPE OF SEDAN COACH,CROWN ON TOP OF
LID....................................................... 65.00
SILVER,COIN,TEASPOON,A.L.BURBANK,WORCESTER,MASS.,CIRCA 1840,
SET OF 6.................................................. 26.75
SILVER,COIN,TEASPOON,A.STOWELL & CO.,BOSTON............... 3.95
SILVER,COIN,TEASPOON,BY FARRINGTON & HUNNEWELL,BOSTON,1835.. 3.95
SILVER,COIN,TEASPOON,BY SHEPHERD & BOYD,1810.............. 8.00
SILVER,COIN,TEASPOON,CIRCA 1820,BY NEWELL HARDING,BOSTON,SET
OF 6...................................................... 26.75
SILVER,COIN,TEASPOON,CIRCA 1830,BY R.H.BAILEY,WOODSTOCK,
VERMONT................................................... 3.95
SILVER,COIN,TEASPOON,EAGLE TOUCHMARK,CARTER & CABERY,CIRCA
1850...................................................... 3.95
SILVER,COIN,TEASPOON,ENGRAVED E.BEMIS,DAVIS,WATSON & CO.,
BOSTON,1820,12............................................ 49.75
SILVER,COIN,TEASPOON,ENGRAVED MONOGRAM,TIPPED END,PRATT &
REATH,SET OF 6............................................ 30.00
SILVER,COIN,TEASPOON,ENGRAVED S.J.LIFE,BUTLER & MC CARTHY,
PHILA.,1850............................................... 3.95
SILVER,COIN,TEASPOON,ENGRAVED,INITIAL,BY GEORGE APPLETON,
SALEM,MASS................................................ 3.95
SILVER,COIN,TEASPOON,FIDDLE-SHAPE HANDLE,MAKER PALMER &
BATCHELDER,10............................................. 50.00
SILVER,COIN,TEASPOON,FIDDLEBACK,CIRCA 1835,G.RUSSELL,
PHILADELPHIA,12........................................... 120.00
SILVER,COIN,TEASPOON,FIDDLEBACK,MONOGRAMMED M.P.,SET OF SIX. 25.00
SILVER,COIN,TEASPOON,FIDDLEBACK,SHELL MOTIF,R & W WILSON,
PHILA.,1830............................................... 15.00
SILVER,COIN,TEASPOON,INITIAL,NEWELL HARDING,BOSTON,1820,SET
OF 6...................................................... 26.75
SILVER,COIN,TEASPOON,INITIAL,SET OF 7..................... 24.50
SILVER,COIN,TEASPOON,INITIALS,BY KNOWLES & LADD,PROVIDENCE,
R.I.,1850,7............................................... 28.75
SILVER,COIN,TEASPOON,INITIALS,E.SMITH,ALBANY,N.Y.,CIRCA
1837,SET OF 6............................................. 26.75
SILVER,COIN,TEASPOON,INITIALS,FARRINGTON & HUNNEWELL,BOSTON,
CIRCA 1850................................................ 3.75
SILVER,COIN,TEASPOON,INITIALS,MAKER E.LESCURE,PHILA.,EAGLE
MARK...................................................... 4.50
SILVER,COIN,TEASPOON,INITIALS,W.D.FENNO & SON,WORCESTER,
MASS,SET OF 12............................................ 49.75
SILVER,COIN,TEASPOON,KNOWELS & LADD,PROVIDENCE,R.I.,CIRCA

```
    1850,SET OF 7.........................................      27.75
SILVER,COIN,TEASPOON,MAKER W.BAILY IN RECTANGLE,PHILA.,1820,
    SET OF 5..........................................        25.00
SILVER,COIN,TEASPOON,MONOGRAM,B.C.HOPPER,SET OF 4..........      20.00
SILVER,COIN,TEASPOON,MONOGRAM,M.C.RICH,CIRCA 1835,SET OF 5..     25.00
SILVER,COIN,TEASPOON,MONOGRAM,MAKER P.MILLER,PROVIDENCE,
    R.I.,1800,PAIR....................................        15.00
SILVER,COIN,TEASPOON,MONOGRAM,VOUTE & MURPHEY..............       5.00
SILVER,COIN,TEASPOON,PINCH WAIST,HARDING,BOSTON,MASS.,1840,
    SET OF 5..........................................        28.00
SILVER,COIN,TEASPOON,T.S.ABBOTT........................          4.75
SILVER,COIN,TEASPOON,TWO-PART BACK CONSTRUCTION,MAKER JOHN
    TANGUY,1800.......................................         9.50
SILVER,COIN,TEASPOON,TWO-PART CONSTRUCTION,W.BAILY,
    PHILADELPHIA,1820,5...............................        25.00
SILVER,COIN,TEASPOON,WILLIAM MOULTON...................          9.00
SILVER,COIN,TONGS,DESSERT,SHELL ENDS,PHILADELPHIA,1790,G.W.&
    H.,7 IN...........................................        45.00
SILVER,COIN,TONGS,SPOON END,S.BROWN,6 1/2 IN...........         35.00
SILVER,COIN,VASE,BUD,ENGRAVED DECOR,RAM HEAD HANDLES,GORHAM,
    1870,7 IN.........................................        75.00
SILVER,COIN,WATCH,HUNTING CASE.........................         25.00
SILVER,CONTINENTAL,BOX,VIOLIN,GILTED,ORNATE,EMBOSSED SCENES,
    12 1/2 IN.........................................       450.00
SILVER,DANISH,SPOON,COFFEE,POINTED TIP HANDLES,CIRCA 1888,
    SET OF 6..........................................        60.00
SILVER DEPOSIT,BOWL,DOLPHIN FEET,10 1/2-IN.DIAMETER,
    4 IN.DEEP.........................................        12.00
SILVER DEPOSIT,BOWL,SUGAR,BIRD & FLOWER DESIGN,TWO HANDLES..      8.50
SILVER DEPOSIT,VASE,BUD................................         13.00
SILVER,DUTCH,AUTO,MINIATURE,CIRCA 1900,2 IN.LONG.........       65.00
SILVER,DUTCH,BICYCLE,CIRCA 1900,5 IN.LONG...............       110.00
SILVER,DUTCH,BOX,BISCUIT,1793.........................        400.00
SILVER,DUTCH,BOX,TOBACCO,BERGEN OP ZOOM,CIRCA 1810...ILLUS..    200.00
```

DUTCH SILVER TOBACCO BOX

```
SILVER,DUTCH,BOX,TOBACCO,ENGRAVED SCENE,FISHERMEN,MARKED
    B.G.,GOUDA,1804...................................       100.00
SILVER,DUTCH,CLOCK,MINIATURE,GRANDFATHER,CIRCA 1900.........    150.00
SILVER,DUTCH,ETUI,18TH CENTURY.........................         70.00
SILVER,DUTCH,FIGURINE,COACH,DRIVER,TWO PRANCING HORSES,
    5 1/2 IN.LONG.....................................        50.00
SILVER,DUTCH,STRAINER,TEA,EMBOSSED FIGURES ON BORDER,
    SCALLOPED.........................................        25.00
SILVER,DUTCH,TEA CADDY,HEAVY REPOUSSE..................         18.50
SILVER,DUTCH,TEAPOT,1844...............................        240.00
SILVER,ENGLISH,BASKET,CAKE,GEORGE III,WILLIAM PLUMMER,1774..    750.00
SILVER,ENGLISH,BASKET,CAKE,PIERCED SIDES,FOLIATE DESIGN,
    BEADING,13 IN.....................................       150.00
SILVER,ENGLISH,BASKET,SWEETMEAT,GEORGE III,1773.............    200.00
SILVER,ENGLISH,BEAKER,LONDON,1795,PETER & ANN BATEMAN.......    495.00
SILVER,ENGLISH,BISCUIT KNIFE,IVORY HANDLE..............         10.00
SILVER,ENGLISH,BOWL,BLEEDING,SHIELD,MARKED T.S.H.E.,LONDON,
    1693..............................................       400.00
SILVER,ENGLISH,BOWL,CANDY,MARKED N S & CO.,5 1/2 IN.ACROSS..     13.50
SILVER,ENGLISH,BUGLE,GEORGE III,WILLIAM TANT,1811...........    850.00
SILVER,ENGLISH,BUTTER KNIFE,ASYMMETRICAL BLADE,ROCOCO
    HANDLE,C.ELEY,1828................................        14.00
SILVER,ENGLISH,BUTTER KNIFE,FIDDLE END,ASYMMETRICAL BLADE,
    HL,LONDON,1864....................................         8.00
SILVER,ENGLISH,CADDY SCOOP,SAMUEL PEMBERTON,BIRMINGHAM,1806,
    2 1/2 IN..........................................        50.00
SILVER,ENGLISH,CADDY SPOON,SHELL BOWL,WM.ELEY & WM.FEARN,
    LONDON,1806.......................................        65.00
```

SILVER,ENGLISH,CAKE BASKET,GADROON RIM,REEDED HANDLE,PAUL
 STORR,1815..............................................1,600.00
SILVER,ENGLISH,CAKE BASKET,GEORGE II,BY PETER ARCHAMBO,
 LONDON,1738.............................................3,500.00
SILVER,ENGLISH,CANDLESTICK,4,GEORGE III,1818,CRADDOCK & REID4,250.00
SILVER,ENGLISH,CANDLESTICK,4,GEORGE III,TABLE,JOHN HORSLEY,
 1761...................................................1,800.00
SILVER,ENGLISH,CANDLESTICK,BAROQUE,DETACHABLE BOBECHE,
 12 IN.,PAIR.............................................. 68.00
SILVER,ENGLISH,CANDLESTICK,CRESTED CIRCULAR BASES,BELL-SHAPE
 SCONCE,PAIR............................................. 150.00
SILVER,ENGLISH,CANDLESTICK,GEORGE II,JOHN CAFE,LONDON,1750,
 SET OF 4...............................................4,500.00
SILVER,ENGLISH,CANDLESTICK,ROCOCO,ARMS OF ENGLISH LORD,
 10 1/2 IN............................................... 950.00
SILVER,ENGLISH,CANDLESTICK,WILLIAM CAFE,1757,12 IN.HIGH,SET
 OF FOUR................................................2,500.00
SILVER,ENGLISH,CASTER,GEORGE II,THOMAS GILPIN,1743.......... 120.00
SILVER,ENGLISH,CHOCOLATE POT,GEORGE III,1763...............3,000.00
SILVER,ENGLISH,CHOCOLATE POT,QUEEN ANNE,HUMPHREY PAYNE,
 LONDON,1710............................................7,500.00
SILVER,ENGLISH,CHRISTENING MUG,MONOGRAM,DATED 1786,2 1/4 X
 3 IN.HIGH............................................... 200.00
SILVER,ENGLISH,CHRISTENING SET,SPOON & FORK,INITIALS,GEORGE
 ADAMS,1854.............................................. 30.00
SILVER,ENGLISH,COFFEEPOT,GEORGE II,EDWARD VINCENT,1736......1,300.00
SILVER,ENGLISH,COFFEEPOT,MAKER MARK W.C.,LONDON,1775,
 12 IN.HIGH.............................................1,500.00
SILVER,ENGLISH,COOLER,WINE,PAIR,WILLIAM IV,1833,E.E.J. &
 W.BARNARD.............................................2,000.00
SILVER,ENGLISH,COOLER,WINE,STANDS,2,11 1/4 IN.HIGH.........5,250.00
SILVER,ENGLISH,CREAM BOAT,1876............................. 150.00
SILVER,ENGLISH,CREAMER,BEADED LIP,LOOP HANDLE,PEDESTAL,
 H.BATEMAN,1784.......................................... 225.00
SILVER,ENGLISH,CREAMER,CREST,MOTTO,REEDED LIP,GILT INTERIOR,
 1801.................................................... 130.00
SILVER,ENGLISH,CREAMER,GEORGE III,1776..................... 110.00
SILVER,ENGLISH,CREAMER,GEORGE III,1768..................... 125.00
SILVER,ENGLISH,CREAMER,REPOUSSE,CHASED,SWAGS OF FLOWERS,
 W.BOND,1756............................................. 50.00
SILVER,ENGLISH,CRUET STAND,HOLDS EIGHT BOTTLES,PETER,ANN,
 WM.BATEMAN,1802......................................... 300.00
SILVER,ENGLISH,CRUET,SIX BOTTLES,PAUL STORR STAND,LONDON,
 C.1810.................................................1,500.00
SILVER,ENGLISH,CRUET,TWO CUT GLASS BOTTLES,THREE SILVER
 CASTORS,1767............................................ 800.00
SILVER,ENGLISH,CUP,CHALICE,SCALLOPED REPOUSSE APRON ON
 BOTTOM,COVER............................................ 100.00
SILVER,ENGLISH,CUP,COVER,COAT OF ARMS,1760,13 1/2 IN.HIGH... 324.00
SILVER,ENGLISH,CUP,DOME BASE,OPENWORK BRACKET STEM,MINERVA
 FINIAL ON LID........................................... 100.00
SILVER,ENGLISH,CUP,EGG,TRUMPET FOOT,HESTER BATEMAN,1787,
 2 1/2 IN.HIGH........................................... 275.00
SILVER,ENGLISH,DESSERT FORK,GEORGE ANGELL,LONDON,1858,
 7 IN.LONG,SET OF 3...................................... 25.00
SILVER,ENGLISH,DESSERT SPOON,FIDDLE END,JOHN STONE EXETER,
 1858,SET OF 6........................................... 60.00
SILVER,ENGLISH,DISH,ENTREE,PAIR,SILVER PLATE WARMER,
 SHEFFIELD.............................................1,850.00
SILVER,ENGLISH,DISH,MEAT,CARTER,SMITH & SHARPE,1779,OVAL,
 18 1/2 IN.LONG.......................................... 450.00
SILVER,ENGLISH,DISH,MEAT,PAIR,GEORGE IV,1823,BENJAMIN SMITH.1,050.00
SILVER,ENGLISH,DISH,NUT,GADROON BORDER,LONDON,1802,R.&
 S.HENNELL,PAIR.......................................... 650.00
SILVER,ENGLISH,DRESSING SET,SILVER-GILT MOUNTS,1869,ASPREY &
 CO...................................................1,100.00
SILVER,ENGLISH,EPERGNE,GEORGE III,1805.............ILLUS.3,000.00
SILVER,ENGLISH,EWER,PAUL STORR,1827................ILLUS.3,500.00
SILVER,ENGLISH,FIGURINE,LION,WALKING POSITION,1900,
 16 1/4 IN.LONG.......................................... 350.00
SILVER,ENGLISH,FISH SERVICE,1883........................... 275.00
SILVER,ENGLISH,FISH SET,MOTHER-OF-PEARL HANDLES,SIX KNIVES &
 FORKS.................................................. 120.00
SILVER,ENGLISH,FISH SLICE,ASYMMETRICAL BLADE,FIDDLE END,
 LONDON,1845............................................. 48.00
SILVER,ENGLISH,FLOWER,SET OF 6,1851,MESSRS.HANCOCK.........1,350.00
SILVER,ENGLISH,FUNNEL,WINE,BY FRS.HOWDEN,EDINBURGH,CIRCA
 1815,4 1/2 IN........................................... 95.00
SILVER,ENGLISH,GINGER JAR,RAISED ROSES,5 1/2 IN............. 40.00
SILVER,ENGLISH,INKSTAND,GEORGE III,1769,EDWARD VINCENT......2,100.00
SILVER,ENGLISH,INKSTAND,GEORGE III,EMES & BARNARD,1818...... 600.00

GEORGE III SILVER EPERGNE

ENGLISH SILVER EWER, PAUL STORR, 1827

ENGLISH SILVER INKSTAND, JOHN CROUCH, 1806

| | |
|---|---|
| 8 3/4 IN............................................. | 75.00 |
| SILVER,ENGLISH,MARROW SCOOP,LONDON,1772,THOMAS CHAWNER...... | 98.00 |
| SILVER,ENGLISH,MARROW SCOOP,SAMUEL BLACKBORROW,LONDON,CIRCA 1730,9 IN............................................. | 95.00 |
| SILVER,ENGLISH,MARROW SCOOP,1789,MARY & ELIZABETH SUMNER, 9 IN................................................ | 95.00 |
| SILVER,ENGLISH,MARROW SCOOP,18TH CENTURY.................... | 95.00 |
| SILVER,ENGLISH,MATCH SAFE,OVERALL CHASING,HAS CIRCLET FOR CHAIN............................................... | 12.00 |
| SILVER,ENGLISH,MUG,BALUSTER SHAPE,MOLDED FOOT,THOMAS MASON, LONDON,1745......................................... | 275.00 |
| SILVER,ENGLISH,MUG,CHILD'S,HOOPED,GILT-LINED,LONDON,1806, JOHN EMES.......................................... | 215.00 |
| SILVER,ENGLISH,MUG,PAIR,1846............................. | 230.00 |
| SILVER,ENGLISH,MUSTARD POT,GEORGE III,DRUM,LONDON 1790...... | 100.00 |
| SILVER,ENGLISH,MUSTARD POT,OPENWORK,BLUE GLASS LINER,NO SPOON.............................................. | 12.00 |
| SILVER,ENGLISH,MUSTARD POT,PIERCED FOLIAGE,COBALT LINER, G.UNITE,1860......................................... | 75.00 |
| SILVER,ENGLISH,OVAL TIP,HESTER BATEMAN,LONDON,1787,5 IN.,SET OF 3................................................ | 105.00 |
| SILVER,ENGLISH,PLATE,DINNER,8,GEORGE III,1799-1809.......... | 1,600.00 |
| SILVER,ENGLISH,PLATE,DINNER,GEORGE III,LONDON,1785/DUBLIN 1802,12............................................. | 4,500.00 |
| SILVER,ENGLISH,PLATE,SOUP,14,VICTORIAN,1894................ | 800.00 |
| SILVER,ENGLISH,PLATE,SOUP,GEORGE III,WILLIAM SUMNER,1814.... | 160.00 |
| SILVER,ENGLISH,PLATTER,GADROON BORDER,SHELL MOTIF,1820, 17 3/4 IN.LONG....................................... | 200.00 |
| SILVER,ENGLISH,PLATTER,GADROON BORDER,SHELL MOTIF,1820, 20 IN.LONG.......................................... | 250.00 |
| SILVER,ENGLISH,POT COVER & STAND,HONEY,GEORGE III,1800...... | 500.00 |
| SILVER,ENGLISH,SALT CELLAR,2 PAIRS,GEORGE III,LONDON 1768 & 1775............................................... | 90.00 |
| SILVER,ENGLISH,SALT CELLAR,GEORGE III,2,1804............... | 100.00 |
| SILVER,ENGLISH,SALT CELLAR,OCTAGONAL BOAT SHAPE,PEDESTAL, I.R.,1793,PAIR...................................... | 90.00 |
| SILVER,ENGLISH,SALT CELLAR,PAIR,FIGURE,1850...........ILLUS.. | 1,300.00 |
| SILVER,ENGLISH,SALT CELLAR,PAIR,FIGURE,1850...........ILLUS.. | 750.00 |
| SILVER,ENGLISH,SALT CELLAR,4,1841........................ | 200.00 |
| SILVER,ENGLISH,SALT CELLER,PAIR,1850,FIGURE..........ILLUS.. | 800.00 |
| SILVER,ENGLISH,SALT SPOON,FIDDLE END,GEORGE ADAMS,LONDON, 1851,PAIR.......................................... | 12.00 |
| SILVER,ENGLISH,SALT SPOON,FIDDLE END,JAMES BEEBE,LONDON, 1836,PAIR.......................................... | 12.00 |
| SILVER,ENGLISH,SALT SPOON,FIDDLE END,MONOGRAM,W.R.SMILY, LONDON,1847,PAIR.................................... | 12.00 |
| SILVER,ENGLISH,SALT SPOON,FIDDLE END,MONOGRAM,JAMES BEEBE, LONDON,1824........................................ | 6.00 |
| SILVER,ENGLISH,SALVER,CIRCA 1830,14 1/2 IN. DIAMETER........ | 450.00 |
| SILVER,ENGLISH,SALVER,GEORGE III,1788,CROUCH & HANNAM....... | 600.00 |
| SILVER,ENGLISH,SALVER,GEORGE III,R.REW OR RUGG,1778......... | 1,400.00 |
| SILVER,ENGLISH,SALVER,GEORGE III,ROBERT SALMON 1792........ | 450.00 |
| SILVER,ENGLISH,SALVER,GEORGE IV,1829,W.K.REID.............. | 2,000.00 |
| SILVER,ENGLISH,SAUCEBOAT,GADROON EDGE,C SCROLL HANDLE, FOOTED,1897........................................ | 45.00 |
| SILVER,ENGLISH,SAUCE LADLE,LIPPED BOWL,GEORGE NANGLE,DUBLIN, 1812,PAIR.......................................... | 75.00 |
| SILVER,ENGLISH,SAUCE LADLE,MARKED SA,LONDON,1811,7 IN.LONG.. | 28.00 |

ENGLISH SILVER SALTCELLARS, 1850

```
SILVER,ENGLISH,SCOOP,CHEESE,GREEN IVORY HANDLE,PETER & ANN
   BATEMAN,1798.........................................   190.00
SILVER,ENGLISH,SCOOP,CHEESE,GREEN IVORY HANDLE,SAMUEL
   PEMBERTON,1811........................................    20.00
SILVER,ENGLISH,SERVER,FOUR RAMS' HEADS,ROLL-UNDER COVER,
   SHEFFIELD.............................................    95.00
SILVER,ENGLISH,SIFTER LADLE,FIDDLE END,INITIAL,MARK JF,
   EXETER,1857...........................................    18.00
SILVER,ENGLISH,SIFTER LADLE,MOTHER-OF-PEARL HANDLE,GEORGE
   UNITE,1867............................................    18.00
SILVER,ENGLISH,SOUP LADLE,FIDDLE END,MARKED WE,LONDON,1830,
   8 1/2 IN..............................................    75.00
SILVER,ENGLISH,SPOON,ARM RISING FROM CROWN & HOLDING DAGGER,
   1804..................................................    25.00
SILVER,ENGLISH,SPOON,BERRY,ROSES,BERRIES,HALLMARKED 1780,
   BATEMAN,PAIR..........................................   225.00
SILVER,ENGLISH,SPOON,CADDY,JOCKEY CAP,KING'S HEAD,LION
   PASSANT,1790..........................................   140.00
SILVER,ENGLISH,SPOON,GRAVY,ENGRAVED TERMINALS,THOMAS
   WALLACE,1793,PAIR.....................................    70.00
SILVER,ENGLISH,SPOON,MARROW..............................    75.00
SILVER,ENGLISH,SPOON,MASTER SALT,RAISED SHELL ON HANDLE,
   NEWCASTLE,1849........................................     8.00
SILVER,ENGLISH,SPOON,MUSTARD,CIRCA 1814..................    15.00
SILVER,ENGLISH,SPOON,OVAL TIP,PETER,WILLIAM BATEMAN,1808,
   5 IN.,SET OF 6........................................   120.00
SILVER,ENGLISH,SPOON,SALT,CIRCA 1789.....................    20.00
SILVER,ENGLISH,SPOON,SALT,CRESTED,LONDON,1829,WILLIAM
   CHAWNER,SET OF 4......................................    36.00
SILVER,ENGLISH,SPOON,SERVING,CIRCA 1787..................    50.00
SILVER,ENGLISH,SPOON,SERVING,HESTER BATEMAN,CIRCA 1784...   105.00
SILVER,ENGLISH,SPOON,SERVING,RATTAIL,CIRCA 1722..........   105.00
SILVER,ENGLISH,SPOON,STUFFING,CRESTED,CIRCA 1789-90,
   R.CROSSLEY,LONDON.....................................    75.00
SILVER,ENGLISH,SPOON,STUFFING,LONDON,CIRCA 1816..........    75.00
SILVER,ENGLISH,STAND,DECANTER,GEORGE III,1779,THOMAS HEMING.   200.00
SILVER,ENGLISH,STRAINER,LEMON,CONCENTRIC PATTERN,S.HERBERT &
   CO.,1754..............................................   100.00
SILVER,ENGLISH,STRAINER,LEMON,GEORGE II,1730,JAMES WILKES...   275.00
SILVER,ENGLISH,SUGAR BASKET,BLUE GLASS LINING,1782,BURRAGE
   DAVENPORT.............................................   850.00
SILVER,ENGLISH,SUGAR BOWL,GEORGE II,1758,SHAW & PRIEST...   650.00
SILVER,ENGLISH,SUGAR CRUSHER,FORM OF HARLEQUIN HOLDING
   SNAKES,1862...........................................   125.00
SILVER,ENGLISH,SUGAR TONGS,BEADED EDGE,THOMAS CHAWNER,
   LONDON,1771...........................................    25.00
SILVER,ENGLISH,SUGAR TONGS,KING'S PATTERN,SPOON ENDS,MARY
   CHAWNER,1835..........................................    25.00
SILVER,ENGLISH,SUGAR TONGS,MONOGRAM,MARK WN,LONDON,1817..    12.00
SILVER,ENGLISH,SUGAR TONGS,QUEEN'S PATTERN,SPOON ENDS,
   LONDON,1855...........................................    14.00
```

```
SILVER,ENGLISH,SUGAR TONGS,SPOON ENDS,LONDON,1808...........    12.00
SILVER,ENGLISH,SUGAR TONGS,SPOON ENDS,MARK GT,LONDON,1816...    12.00
SILVER,ENGLISH,TABLESPOON,OVAL TIP,CRESTED,HESTER BATEMAN,
  1785,SET OF 3.............................................   225.00
SILVER,ENGLISH,TABLESPOON,OVAL TIP,PETER,ANN,WILLIAM
  BATEMAN,1802.............................................     35.00
SILVER,ENGLISH,TABLESPOON,TWO-PART CONSTRUCTION,DOROTHY
  LANGLANDS,PAIR...........................................     38.00
SILVER,ENGLISH,TANKARD,S SCROLL HANDLE,FLAT COVER,DOME FOOT,
  JOHN BUCK...............................................1,200.00
SILVER,ENGLISH,TEA & COFFEE SET,4 PIECES,R.HENNELL,
  1852-1859..............................................1,100.00
SILVER,ENGLISH,TEA SET,3 PIECES,WILLIAM IV,LONDON 1833......   400.00
SILVER,ENGLISH,TEAKETTLE,BALL-SHAPED,FOOTED STAND,ACORN
  FINIAL..................................................    450.00
SILVER,ENGLISH,TEAKETTLE,LAMP STAND,WALTER TWEEDIE...ILLUS..1,000.00
SILVER,ENGLISH,TEAPOT,COFFEEPOT,CREAMER,SUGAR BOWL,M.HALL &
  CO.,1873...............................................1,400.00
SILVER,ENGLISH,TEAPOT,COFFEEPOT,CREAMER,SUGAR,WASTE BOWL,
  BARNARD,1867...........................................1,000.00
SILVER,ENGLISH,TEAPOT,COFFEEPOT,SUGAR BOWL,CREAMER,
  W.BATEMAN,1814.........................................1,500.00
SILVER,ENGLISH,TEAPOT,CREST,INITIALS,WILLIAM PLUMMER,LONDON,
  1784..................................................    300.00
SILVER,ENGLISH,TEAPOT,QUEEN ANNE,FOOTED,BLACK WOODEN HANDLE.   350.00
SILVER,ENGLISH,TEAPOT,STAND,CREAMER,SUGAR,WILLIAM ABDY,
  R.HENNELL..............................................    550.00
SILVER,ENGLISH,TEAPOT,SUGAR,CREAMER,WILLIAM BATEMAN,DATE
  1816..................................................    850.00
SILVER,ENGLISH,TEASPOON,FIDDLE END,INITIAL,MARK WB,LONDON,
  1831,SET OF 3..........................................     12.00
SILVER,ENGLISH,TEASPOON,FIDDLE END,INITIAL,MARK WH,EXETER,
  1825,SET OF 3..........................................     12.00
SILVER,ENGLISH,TEASPOON,FIDDLE END,R.HENNELL,LONDON,1832,SET
  OF 3...................................................     12.00
SILVER,ENGLISH,TEASPOON,PETER,ANNE & WILLIAM BATEMAN,LONDON,
  1801,6.................................................     95.00
SILVER,ENGLISH,TEASPOON,ROUND END,INITIAL,CHRIS &
  T.W.BARKER,LONDON,1802.................................      5.00
SILVER,ENGLISH,TEASPOON,ROUND END,INITIAL,MARK HS,LONDON,
  1798,PAIR..............................................     10.00
SILVER,ENGLISH,TOAST RACK,EIGHT SECTIONS...................    20.00
SILVER,ENGLISH,TONGS,SUGAR,PETER & WILLIAM BATEMAN.........   135.00
SILVER,ENGLISH,TONGS,5 1/2 IN.............................     15.00
SILVER,ENGLISH,TRAY,ON COPPER,1860,TWO HANDLES,26 IN.LONG...   115.00
SILVER,ENGLISH,TRAY,REEDED RIM & HANDLES,OVAL,MARKED,1799,
  20 IN.LONG.............................................    850.00
SILVER,ENGLISH,TUREEN,SAUCE,BOAT SHAPE,URN FINIAL ON LID,
  1898,PAIR..............................................    125.00
SILVER,ENGLISH,TUREEN,SAUCE,COVER,WILLIAM SIMMONS,1808,
  8 IN.LONG..............................................    675.00
SILVER,ENGLISH,TUREEN,SOUP,BEADING,LEAVES,ARMORIALS,DRAPERY,
  KANDLER,1770..........................................1,900.00
SILVER,ENGLISH,TUREEN,SOUP,FLORAL,SHELLWORK,WATERHOUSE,
  HODSON & CO...........................................2,000.00
SILVER,ENGLISH,VINAIGRETTE,PIERCED INNER LID,JOSEPH
  WILLMORE,1818.........................................     90.00
SILVER,ENGLISH,WAITER,ENGRAVED ARMORIALS,SHELL,FOLIATE
  CARTOUCHE,7 IN.........................................    220.00
SILVER,ENGLISH,WAITER,GEORGE III,1809,PETER & WILLIAM
  BATEMAN...............................................    400.00
```

ENGLISH SILVER TEA KETTLE, LAMPSTAND, WALTER TWEEDIE

```
SILVER,ENGLISH,WAITER,THREE CLAW & BALL SUPPORTS,1783,
  7-IN.DIAMETER.........................................    125.00
SILVER,ENGLISH,WAITER,1882................................    170.00
SILVER,ENGLISH,WINE FUNNEL,STRAINER,BY PETER & ANN BATEMAN,
  LONDON,1793..........................................     300.00
SILVER,ENGLISH,WINE LABEL,OLD ENGLISH B,GEORGE UNITE,
  BIRMINGHAM,1868......................................      25.00
SILVER,FRENCH,BOX,CIGARETTE,BLACK & WHITE ENAMEL DECOR,
  PANELS,PORTRAIT......................................      85.00
SILVER,FRENCH,CANDELABRA,PAIR,LOUIS XV,FRANCOIS JOUBERT,
  1767...............................................  4,500.00
SILVER,FRENCH,CANDLESTICK,LOUIS XV,ANTOINE BAILLY,PARIS,
  1754,TWO PAIRS......................................  3,500.00
SILVER,FRENCH,COFFEEPOT,LOUIS XV,PARIS 1762...............    425.00
SILVER,FRENCH,COFFEEPOT,LOUIS XVI,PARIS 1779,DENIS FRANKSON.   600.00
SILVER,FRENCH,DISH,CONSERVE,SLOTTED RIM,COVER,ANTOINE
  HIENCE,1815.........................................     100.00
SILVER,FRENCH,DISH,EMPIRE,CIRCA 1810.....................     60.00
SILVER,FRENCH,DISH,MEAT,PAIR,19TH CENTURY................    500.00
SILVER,FRENCH,FORK,DESSERT,FIDDLE,THREAD PATTERN,CREST,SET
  OF 12..............................................      50.00
SILVER,FRENCH,PEDOMETER,WHITE ENAMEL DIAL,ROMAN NUMERALS....    35.00
SILVER,FRENCH,SALT CELLAR,2,TRENCHER,LOUIS XV,1759..........    350.00
SILVER,FRENCH,SALT CELLAR,PIERCED DECOR,REEDED BORDER,
  C.P.V.,SET OF 4.....................................     225.00
SILVER,FRENCH,SNUFFBOX,MARIE ANTOINETTE D'AUTRICHE REINE DE
  FRANCE,1774.........................................     100.00
SILVER,FRENCH,STATUETTE,PAIRS,CIRCA 1830.................    200.00
SILVER,FRENCH,TEA CADDY,BOMBE SHAPE,RUSTIC SCENE IN
  REPOUSSE,FRUIT......................................      60.00
SILVER,FRENCH,TEA TRAY,2-HANDLED,19TH CENTURY............    950.00
SILVER,FRENCH,TUREEN,SOUP,LOUIS XVI,BY FRANCOIS LEDAGRE,
  PARIS,1787.........................................  3,750.00
SILVER,FRENCH,WINE TASTER,KIDNEY SHAPE THUMBPIECE,ENGRAVED
  RENAUT 1821........................................      60.00
SILVER,GERMAN,BEAKER,CIRCA 1680....................ILLUS..    800.00
SILVER,GERMAN,BEAKER,DOUBLE,PARCEL-TILT,TWO CUPS,EMBOSSED,
  PROFILE BUST.......................................      90.00
SILVER,GERMAN,BEAKER,ENGRAVED INSCRIPTION,LONG LIVE THE
  BATCHELORS,WESEL...................................     170.00
SILVER,GERMAN,BEAKER,THREAD BAND DECOR,MARKED M.M.,AUGSBURG,
  1700..............................................     190.00
SILVER,GERMAN,CANDLE SCISSORS,ORNATE.....................     22.00
SILVER,GERMAN,CANDLESTICK,PAIR,CIRCA 1770..........ILLUS.1,200.00
SILVER,GERMAN,CANDLESTICK,TABLE,1824.....................    100.00
SILVER,GERMAN,CHALICE,DOME HEXAFOIL BASE,SHELLS,PANELS,
  MARKED,8 1/2 IN....................................     200.00
SILVER,GERMAN,DISH,ALLOVER PIERCED,CHERUBS,BIRDS,ROSES,OVAL,
  800 MARK..........................................      38.00
SILVER,GERMAN,DISH,SIDEBOARD,BY JOHANN RUTGERS,COLOGNE,CIRCA
  1720.............................................  4,000.00
SILVER,GERMAN,DISH,SWEETMEAT,PARCEL-GILT,CIRCA 1680.........    90.00
SILVER,GERMAN,EWER,CIRCA 1860............................    160.00
SILVER,GERMAN,PURSE,MESH.................................      7.00
SILVER,GERMAN,PURSE,MESH,MARKED.........................       8.00
SILVER,GERMAN,SPOON,DEMITASSE,ENAMEL SCENIC,MARKED
  SPITINGSEE,PAIR....................................      12.00
SILVER,GERMAN,SPOON,6,PARCEL-GILT,CIRCA 1600.........  3,250.00
SILVER,GERMAN,TEA STRAINER,WOMAN & CHILD ON HANDLE..........     5.00
```

GERMAN
SILVER
BEAKER,
C. 1680

GERMAN SILVER
CANDLESTICKS,
C. 1770

```
SILVER,GERMAN,TEAPOT,COFFEEPOT,CREAMER,SUGAR,TRAY,ROCOCO,
   FOLIATE,1900.............................................   500.00
SILVER,GERMAN,TUREEN & COVER,SOUP,CIRCA 1900................   275.00
SILVER,HUNGARIAN,CHALICE,LATE 15TH CENTURY.................. 3,500.00
SILVER,IRISH,BOWL,EVERTED SCALLOP RIM,DUBLIN,CIRCA 1770,
   5 1/4 IN..................................................   100.00
SILVER,IRISH,CASTER,GEORGE II,CIRCA 1750....................   175.00
SILVER,IRISH,CUP,GEORGE III,CIRCA 1770......................   350.00
SILVER,IRISH,SALT,MASTER,ENGRAVED,ON LEGS...................    80.00
SILVER,ITALIAN,BELL,TABLE,19TH CENTURY......................   140.00
SILVER,JAPANESE,BEEHIVE LANTERN ON POLE,MINIATURE,3 1/4 IN..    45.00
SILVER,JAPANESE,SHRINE,MINIATURE,2 IN.......................    45.00
SILVER,NORWEGIAN,BEAKER,FOLIAGE,JOHAN PETER OLSEN RUST,
   TRONDHJEMS,1730..........................................   140.00
SILVER,NORWEGIAN,SPOON,COFFEE,TWISTED HANDLE,SET OF 6.......    15.00
SILVER,NORWEGIAN,TABLESPOON,DATED 1814,SET OF 6.............    35.00
SILVER PLATE,BASKET,DOUBLE LOOP,APPLIED FLORAL,FOOTED,
   ROGERS,SMITH,1883........................................    85.00
SILVER PLATE,BASKET,FLOWER,PIERCED FLORAL,GEOMETRIC,
   GLASS-LINED,WILCOX.......................................    25.00
SILVER PLATE,BASKET,LUMP SUGAR,PIERCED,AMERICAN.............    12.00
SILVER PLATE,BASKET,ORNATE EDGE,EMBOSSED,BAIL HANDLE,
   PAIRPOINT CO.............................................    15.00
SILVER PLATE,BASKET,SUGAR,PIERCED GEOMETRIC PATTERN,COBALT
   INSERT...................................................    15.00
SILVER PLATE,BOWL,PUNCH,CREST,SHEFFIELD,MATTHEW BOULTON,
   11 1/2 IN................................................   350.00
SILVER PLATE,BOWL,PUNCH,INITIALED,1847 ROGERS BROS.,14 X
   9 1/2 IN.TALL............................................   100.00
SILVER PLATE,BOWL,SUGAR,RAILROAD,BURLINGTON ROUTE,HANDLES,
   LID......................................................    25.00
SILVER PLATE,BOWL,SUGAR,ROCOCO,FOUR CLAW FEET,COVER.........     9.00
SILVER PLATE,BOWL,SUGAR,UNION PACIFIC RAILROAD,COVER........    25.00
SILVER PLATE,BOX,COLLAR BUTTON,QUADRUPLE,RED SATIN LINING,
   PAIRPOINT................................................    10.00
SILVER PLATE,BOX,COLLAR,COLLAR SHAPE,COLLAR BUTTON HANDLE,
   1894,PAIRPOINT...........................................    18.50
SILVER PLATE,BOX,JEWELRY,EMBOSSED FLORAL DECOR,FOOTED,
   LINING,RESILVERED........................................    20.00
SILVER PLATE,BOX,MATCH,PIG SHAPE,HEAD OPENS,SCRATCHER ON
   BELLY....................................................    19.00
SILVER PLATE,CAKE BASKET,BEADED BORDERS,GOTHIC ARCHES,
   SHEFFIELD,1780...........................................    90.00
SILVER PLATE,CAKE STAND,HIGH PEDESTAL BASE,HANDLE,MERIDEN,
   CONN.....................................................     9.00
SILVER PLATE,CANDELABRUM,FIVE LIGHTS,GADROON,SHELL,
   SHEFFIELD,31 IN.,PAIR....................................   525.00
SILVER PLATE,CANDLESNUFFER,SCISSOR BOX TYPE,ORNATE
   EMBOSSING,FOOTED.........................................    16.00
SILVER PLATE,CANDLESNUFFER,SCISSOR TYPE,FLOWER RELIEFS,HIGH
   FEET.....................................................    55.00
SILVER PLATE,CANDLESNUFFER,SCISSORS,TRIMMER,HIGH RELIEF
   PROFUSION,FOOTED.........................................    55.00
SILVER PLATE,CANDLESTICK,HAMMERED DESIGN,DERBY CO.,10 IN.,
   PAIR.....................................................    10.00
SILVER PLATE,CANDLESTICK,VICTORIAN,CLAW FEET,MARKED HARTFORD
   SILVER CO................................................    10.00
SILVER PLATE,CASTOR,SEE CASTOR
SILVER PLATE,CASTOR,PICKLE,DOUBLE,EMBOSSED BIRDS,FLORAL,
   CRYSTAL INSERTS..........................................    51.00
SILVER PLATE,CHALICE,LEAF,ROSE,PARKER GUARDS,OCT.18,1854,
   7 IN.HIGH................................................    48.00
SILVER PLATE,CHEESE SCOOP,9 1/2 IN.LONG.....................    20.00
SILVER PLATE,COFFEE URN,CREAMER,SUGAR,IVORY HANDLES,REED &
   BARTON 1876.............................................   350.00
SILVER PLATE,COFFEE URN,VASE SHAPE,IVORY SPIGOT,URN FINIAL,
   SHEFFIELD................................................   120.00
SILVER PLATE,COFFEEPOT,GREEK KEY DESIGN ON BAND,PEDESTAL
   FOOT,10 IN.TALL..........................................    28.00
SILVER PLATE,COFFEEPOT,MARKED QUEEN MARY CUNARD STEAMSHIP
   LINES....................................................    12.00
SILVER PLATE,COFFEEPOT,PEACOCKS,TREES IN RELIEF,QUAD PLATE,
   FOOTED,13 IN.............................................    17.50
SILVER PLATE,COFFEEPOT,SPOONER,CREAMER,SUGAR,LION HEAD LEGS,
   PRESENTATION.............................................    85.00
SILVER PLATE,COFFEEPOT,WARRIOR HEAD MEDALLIONS ON SIDES,
   FOOTED,8 IN.HIGH.........................................    45.00
SILVER PLATE,CORN HOLDER,ATTACHED STAND,PAT.1896,SET OF 4...     3.95
SILVER PLATE,CORN HOLDERS,PATENT 1896,ATTACHED STAND,SET OF
   4........................................................     3.95
SILVER PLATE,CREAMER & SUGAR,ENGRAVED VINTAGE GRAPE DECOR,
```

PAIRPOINT.................................................... 40.00
SILVER PLATE,CREAMER & SUGAR,MARKED BENEDICT,1916,EPNS-B.
  M.M.,...................................................... 15.00
SILVER PLATE,CREAMER & SUGAR,ORNATE,QUADRUPLE............... 15.00
SILVER PLATE,CREAMER & SUGAR,SPOONER,DOMED BUTTER DISH,
  FLORAL DESIGN............................................. 48.00
SILVER PLATE,CREAMER,SUGAR,ENGRAVED,MARK BENEDICT,B.B.,
  ENGLAND,1804............................................. 10.00
SILVER PLATE,CREAMER,UNION PACIFIC RAILROAD,HINGED LID...... 22.50
SILVER PLATE,CRUMBER & TRAY,ORNATE,REPLATED................ 42.50
SILVER PLATE,CUP & SAUCER,MARKED MERIDEN,CONN.............. 5.00
SILVER PLATE,CUP & SAUCER,MERIDEN CO....................... 15.00
SILVER PLATE,CUP,BABY'S,THREE BUNNIES,ONE EATING CARROT,SAYS
  BABY...................................................... 3.50
SILVER PLATE,CUP,LOVING,NANTUCKET ATHLETIC CLUB,1909,WOMEN'S
  DOUBLE.................................................... 8.50
SILVER PLATE,DECANTER WAGON,MOLDED RIMS,FLORAL,BONE ROLLERS,
  SHEFFIELD................................................. 90.00
SILVER PLATE,DISH,BONBON,FLORAL PATTERN,DERBY SILVER CO..... 7.50
SILVER PLATE,DISH,BUTTER,COVER,GLASS INSERT,F.B.ROGERS,
  5-IN.DIAMETER............................................. 8.50
SILVER PLATE,DISH,BUTTER,ETCHED FLORAL,HANDLES,KNIFE REST.... 18.00
SILVER PLATE,DISH,BUTTER,INSERT,ACORN FINIAL,CIRCA 1880.... 19.00
SILVER PLATE,DISH,BUTTER,KNIFE REST INSERT,HANDLES,COVER,
  HARTFORD CO............................................... 14.00
SILVER PLATE,DISH,ENTREE,BEADED DECOR,DETACHABLE HANDLE,10 X
  12 IN..................................................... 55.00
SILVER PLATE,DISH,ENTREE,COVER,GADROON,FOLIATE BORDER,
  SHEFFIELD,PAIR............................................ 125.00
SILVER PLATE,DISH,ENTREE,COVER,HEATER BASE,SHEFFIELD,
  15 1/4 IN.LONG............................................ 120.00
SILVER PLATE,DISH,JUMPING FISH & FLY IN RELIEF,FLUTED,
  PAIRPOINT,6 IN............................................ 6.00
SILVER PLATE,DISH,MEAT,COVER,HEATER BASE,LAMP STAND FOR
  ENTREE DISH,1830.......................................... 60.00
SILVER PLATE,DISH,MEAT,GADROON RIM,PAIR CANDLESTICKS,
  SHEFFIELD................................................. 100.00
SILVER PLATE,DISH,SHELL,DOLPHIN-FOOTED,BRITISH COIN IN
  HANDLE,9 IN............................................... 7.50
SILVER PLATE,DISH,VEGETABLE,SCROLLED,OVAL,FLUTED,12 IN...... 7.50
SILVER PLATE,DRESSER SET,MIRROR,COMB,BRUSH,CHERUBS,BIRD,
  ROSES,ORNATE.............................................. 25.00
SILVER PLATE,EGG HOLDER,THREE EGGS,ONE SHAKER,NOTCH FOR
  SPOONS,FOOTED............................................. 16.00
SILVER PLATE,FISH SET,KNIVES,FORKS,IVORY HANDLES,
  VELVET-LINED CASE,6....................................... 50.00
SILVER PLATE,HOLDER,TWINE.................................. 12.00
SILVER PLATE,HUMIDOR,TURTLES WITH RIDERS FOR HANDLES,
  RESILVERED................................................ 150.00
SILVER PLATE,INKWELL,DEER,TREE BRANCH,ACORNS,RAM HORN FEET,
  OVAL...................................................... 20.00
SILVER PLATE,INKWELL,TWO CRYSTAL INSERTS,HINGED COVERS...... 50.00
SILVER PLATE,JUG,SYRUP,ETCHED SPRAY FLOWERS,WREATH,7 IN.TALL 18.00
SILVER PLATE,KNIFE REST,BIRD ON EACH END,3 IN.............. 10.00
SILVER PLATE,KNIFE REST,CAROUSEL HORSE AT EACH END......... 32.00
SILVER PLATE,KNIFE REST,CHILD WITH A FOWL IN HIS LAP AT
  ENDS,PAIR................................................. 22.00
SILVER PLATE,KNIFE REST,DOGS ON ENDS...................... 6.50
SILVER PLATE,KNIFE REST,GOAT AT EACH END................... 4.95
SILVER PLATE,KNIFE REST,JACKSTRAW ENDS,PAIR................ 3.95
SILVER PLATE,KNIFE REST,PHEASANT ON EACH END............... 12.00
SILVER PLATE,KNIFE REST,SQUIRREL ENDS,RESILVERED,
  3 3/4 IN.LONG............................................. 38.00
SILVER PLATE,LADLE,PUNCH,SIGNED PAIRPOINT,CUT GLASS HANDLE,
  HOBSTARS.................................................. 85.00
SILVER PLATE,MATCH HOLDER,POCKET,STRIKER,ORNATELY ENGRAVED.. 10.00
SILVER PLATE,MATCH SAFE,BOOK FORM,ENGRAVED,OPENS BACK,FRONT,
  RING ON TOP............................................... 13.00
SILVER PLATE,MATCH SAFE,CLASSICAL FIGURES ON SIDES......... 8.00
SILVER PLATE,MATCH SAFE,DIAGONAL STRIPES................... 10.00
SILVER PLATE,MATCH SAFE,MOOSE ONE SIDE,HUNTER WITH DOG ON
  OTHER SIDE................................................ 17.00
SILVER PLATE,MIRROR & HAIRBRUSH,CHERUBS PLAYING MUSICAL
  INSTRUMENTS............................................... 25.00
SILVER PLATE,MIRROR PLATEAU,BACCHANALIAN MASKS,SCROLLS,
  FLORAL,SHEFFIELD.......................................... 100.00
SILVER PLATE,MIRROR,SHAVING,BRUSH HOLDER,MILK GLASS INSERT.. 12.00
SILVER PLATE,MUG,CHILD'S,SIGNED PAIRPOINT.................. 4.50
SILVER PLATE,MUG,CHILD'S,CAT EYEING BIRD,FLORAL ETCHING,
  2 3/4 IN.HIGH............................................. 8.00
SILVER PLATE,MUG,SHAVING,PAIRPOINT,MELON RIB,SOAP & BRUSH

```
INSERTS........................................................  17.50
SILVER PLATE,MUG,SHAVING,SOAP INSERT,BRUSH REST ON HANDLE,
  FOOTED.......................................................  23.00
SILVER PLATE,MUG,SHAVING,TWO SECTIONS,RAISED FLORAL,
  QUADRUPLE PLATE..............................................   9.50
SILVER PLATE,MUG,SHAVING,WITH BRUSH,MARKED VICTOR...........    8.00
  SILVER PLATE,NAPKIN HOLDER,SEE NAPKIN HOLDER
SILVER PLATE,PERFUME,STOPPER,2 3/8 X 1 1/4 X 1/4 IN........     4.00
SILVER PLATE,PITCHER,ICE WATER,ON HOLDER,RESILVERED.......   150.00
SILVER PLATE,PITCHER,QUADRUPLE,LOW-FOOTED,ENGRAVED FLORAL,
  MONOGRAM.....................................................  37.50
SILVER PLATE,PITCHER,TILTING ON STAND...............ILLUS..    85.00
SILVER PLATE,PITCHER,WATER,FLORAL ENGRAVING,APPLIED ROSEBUDS
  ON HANDLE....................................................  28.00
SILVER PLATE,PLATE,FRUIT,RAISED FRUIT DECOR,GORHAM,
  12-IN.DIAMETER...............................................  15.00
SILVER PLATE,PLATTER,CHASED WORK ON SURFACE,ROPED EDGE,
  ROGERS BROS..................................................  40.00
SILVER PLATE,PLATTER,FISH,FOOTED,BENEDICT,10 IN. X 19 IN....    27.00
SILVER PLATE,SALT & PEPPER,IN FORM OF STANDING PIGS........     7.50
SILVER PLATE,SALT DIP,ANIMAL HANDLES,2 3/4 IN.ACROSS.......     4.50
SILVER PLATE,SALVER,ENGRAVED CREST,MOTTO,FOUR SUPPORTS,
  SHEFFIELD....................................................  80.00
SILVER PLATE,SALVER,ENTREE DISH,VEGETABLE DISH,MEAT DISH,
  LIDS,SHEFFIELD...............................................  30.00
SILVER PLATE,SAMOVAR,GADROON TRIM,IVORY HANDLES & BASE,NO
  CHIMNEY,RUSSIA............................................... 110.00
SILVER PLATE,SHAKER,PEPPER,SHAPE OF OWL,GLASS EYES,3 IN.HIGH    2.75
SILVER PLATE,SHAKER,SALT,PEPPER,NAPKIN RING,ON CART PULLED
  BY ANGEL..................................................... 125.00
```

SILVER PLATE PITCHER ON STAND

```
SILVER PLATE,SHAVING CUP,SOAP INSERT,BRUSH HOLDER,EMBOSSED
  FLORAL.......................................................  18.50
SILVER PLATE,SHAVING MUG,TUFTS,BOSTON......................     12.00
SILVER PLATE,SHAVING STAND,MIRROR,CUP,BRUSH HOLDER,MERIDEN
  CO...........................................................  35.00
SILVER PLATE,SHEFFIELD,CANDLESTICK,GADROON BORDERS,CIRCA
  1800......................................................... 105.00
SILVER PLATE,SHEFFIELD,CANDLESTICK,TABLE,PAIR,CIRCA 1820....   200.00
SILVER PLATE,SHEFFIELD,COMPOTE,PEDESTAL,VINTAGE EDGE,SECOND
  PIERCED EDGE.................................................  25.00
SILVER PLATE,SHEFFIELD,DISH & COVER,MEAT,CIRCA 1820......... 100.00
SILVER PLATE,SHEFFIELD,DISH RING,CIRCA 1780................   350.00
SILVER PLATE,SHEFFIELD,INKSTAND,CIRCA 1810................   200.00
SILVER PLATE,SHEFFIELD,SALVER,POINTED OVAL,FOOTED,CRESTED,
  1816,H.FREETH................................................ 250.00
SILVER PLATE,SHEFFIELD,SNUFFER & TRAY,CIRCA 1825............ 100.00
SILVER PLATE,SHEFFIELD,SUGAR,BLUE GLASS LINING,COVER,CIRCA
  1790......................................................... 145.00
SILVER PLATE,SHEFFIELD,TANKARD,WOODEN BOTTOM,CIRCA 1784,
  N.SMITH & CO................................................. 275.00
SILVER PLATE,SHEFFIELD,TEA TRAY,CIRCA 1780,28 1/2 IN. LONG.. 425.00
SILVER PLATE,SHEFFIELD,TEA TRAY,CIRCA 1790................   275.00
SILVER PLATE,SHEFFIELD,WAX BOX AND SNUFFER,CIRCA 1790....... 140.00
SILVER PLATE,SHEFFIELD,WINE TASTER,RAISED LEAF DESIGN,SNAKE
  HANDLE.......................................................  35.00
SILVER PLATE,SPOON,BERRY,FLORAL HANDLE,FLOWER IN GOLD-PLATED
  BOWL.........................................................  18.00
SILVER PLATE,SPOON,ENAMELED GOLD SCENE,DACHL-INNSBRUCK,
  5 1/4 IN.....................................................  25.00
```

SILVER PLATE,SPOON,ENAMELED SCENE OF BOZEN SCHLOSS,
RUNKELSTEIN,5 1/4 IN........................................ 17.50
SILVER PLATE,SPOON,ENAMELED SCENE,DACHL-INNSBRUCK,
SPADE-SHAPED BOWL........................................... 25.00
SILVER PLATE,SPOON,LIGGETT'S DOSE MEASURING MEDICINE,CURVED
HANDLE...................................................... 2.75
SILVER PLATE,SPOON,SOUVENIR,SEE SOUVENIR SPOON
SILVER PLATE,SPOON WARMER,SHAPED LIKE THE CHAMBERED NAUTILUS  40.00
SILVER PLATE,SPOON HOLDER...........................ILLUS.. 25.00
SILVER PLATE,SPOON HOLDER,COVERED SUGAR,12-SPOON,BIRD IN
FLIGHT FINIAL.............................................. 37.50
SILVER PLATE,STRAINER,TEA,ADVERTISING,TETLEY,HANDLE,CUP LIP,
EMBOSSING.................................................. 2.00
SILVER PLATE,SUGAR & SPOONER,RAISED ROSE PATTERN,MARKED
DERBY SILVER............................................... 12.00
SILVER PLATE,SUGAR BOWL SPOON HOLDER,PEDESTAL,BIRD FINIAL ON
LID........................................................ 43.00
SILVER PLATE,SYRUP,ETCHED FLOWERS,BULBOUS,LID,ONEIDA,
RESILVERED................................................. 12.00
SILVER PLATE,TABLE PLATEAU,THREE SECTIONS,FOLIATE LEGS,
53 IN.LONG................................................. 250.00
SILVER PLATE,TANKARD,WATER,TAPESTRY DESIGN,W.B.MANUFACTURING
CO......................................................... 22.50
SILVER PLATE,TEAKETTLE ON CRADLE,ALCOHOL BURNER,13 IN. HIGH. 85.00
SILVER PLATE,TEA STRAINER,BRASS SIEVE,COBALT LINER,FOOTED,
GERMANY.................................................... 12.00
SILVER PLATE,TEA TRAY,31 IN. LONG.......................... 150.00
SILVER PLATE,TEA URN,SHELL & SCROLL RIM,PEDESTAL BASE,
SHEFFIELD,1825............................................. 160.00
SILVER PLATE,TEAPOT,CREAMER,SUGAR,CIRCULAR FORM,GADROON

SILVER PLATE SPOONHOLDER

BORDER,SHEFFIELD........................................... 60.00
SILVER PLATE,TEAPOT,CREAMER,SUGAR,COVER,SPOON HOLDER,BIRD
DECOR,MERIDIAN............................................. 75.00
SILVER PLATE,TEAPOT,CREAMER,SUGAR,SIX CUPS,SAUCERS,SPOONS,
CHILD'S,1880............................................... 150.00
SILVER PLATE,TEAPOT,ENGRAVED DESIGN,SQUATTY,QUADRUPLE,
HARTFORD,TEN-CUP........................................... 27.00
SILVER PLATE,TEAPOT,FISH SPOUT,JAMES W.TUFTS,7 1/2 IN.TALL.. 32.50
SILVER PLATE,TEAPOT,MERIDEN,3 1/2 IN....................... 12.50
SILVER PLATE,TEASPOON,ACTRESS,ONEIDA....................... 3.50
SILVER PLATE,TEASPOON,GEORGE WASHINGTON,JOHN Q.ADAMS,PAIR... 10.00
SILVER PLATE,TOAST RACK,SWAN SHAPE,7 3/4 IN.ACROSS,5 IN.HIGH 20.00
SILVER PLATE,TONGS,FOR PICKLE CASTOR,6 3/4 IN.............. 3.75
SILVER PLATE,TOOTHPICK,BIRD & WISHBONE..................... 12.50
SILVER PLATE,TOOTHPICK,BIRD IS PERCHED ON BACK PART,WINGS
SPREAD..................................................... 22.00
SILVER PLATE,TOOTHPICK,BIRDS,WINGS UP,ON POINT AT SIDE,
RESILVERED................................................. 16.50
SILVER PLATE,TOOTHPICK,CHERUB ON SIDE,HAND SUPPORTS HOLDER,
RESILVERED................................................. 16.50
SILVER PLATE,TOOTHPICK,CHICK ON WISHBONE................... 10.00
SILVER PLATE,TOOTHPICK,CHICK SITTING BESIDE EGG,SAYS BEST
WISHES..................................................... 7.50
SILVER PLATE,TOOTHPICK,ENGRAVED TAKE YOUR PICK,STEVENS
SILVER CO.................................................. 8.50
SILVER PLATE,TOOTHPICK,FIGURAL,BIRD,BRANCH,EMBOSSED FLORAL,
MIDDLETON CO............................................... 16.00
SILVER PLATE,TOOTHPICK,FULL FIGURE DRESSED LADY,ROGERS
BROTHERS,NO.2302........................................... 27.50

```
SILVER PLATE,TOOTHPICK,GOLD-WASHED..........................      8.00
SILVER PLATE,TOOTHPICK,MOUSE AT SIDE........................     24.00
SILVER PLATE,TOOTHPICK,PEDESTAL,SHEFFIELD...................      6.50
SILVER PLATE,TOOTHPICK,RELIEF CHERUB,RESILVERED.............     16.50
SILVER PLATE,TOOTHPICK,URN SHAPE,ETCHED SCROLLS,LEAVES,
  ACORNS....................................................     10.00
SILVER PLATE,TOOTHPICK,VICTORIAN LADY AT SIDE,DERBY SILVER
  COMPANY...................................................     19.50
SILVER PLATE,TRAVELING LIGHT,FOUR-FOOTED,HANDLED,ATTACHED
  SNUFFER...................................................     14.00
SILVER PLATE,TRAY,BREAD,ORNATE DECOR,PASTRY SERVER,SIGNED
  PAIRPOINT.................................................      8.00
SILVER PLATE,TRAY,PULLMAN CO.,RAILROAD,OVAL,10 IN...........     12.00
SILVER PLATE,TRAY,TEA,GADROON RIM,FOLIAGE & FLORAL HANDLES,
  SHEFFIELD.................................................    140.00
SILVER PLATE,TUMBLER,RIBBED AT BOTTOM,CENTER BAND,FLARED
  BANDING AT TOP............................................      7.00
SILVER PLATE,WATCH STAND,CHERUBS,CURVED GLASS DOOR,HALL,
  ELTON CO.,8 IN............................................     54.00
SILVER PLATE,WINE COOLER,CAMPANA SHAPE,GADROON BORDER,
  SHEFFIELD,1815............................................    160.00
SILVER PLATE,WINE COOLER,REEDED BANDS,LION MASK,RING
  HANDLES,SHEFFIELD.........................................     80.00
SILVER,POLISH,SPOON,SOUP....................................     12.00
SILVER,PORTUGUESE,LADLE,STRAINER,PIERCED HOLES IN BOWL,
  LISBON HALLMARK...........................................     25.00
SILVER,RUSSIAN,BASKET,CAKE,CIRCA 1900,10 IN. LONG,FOOTED
  BASE.....................................................     200.00
SILVER,RUSSIAN,BASKET,SUGAR,ENGRAVED,FLORAL,BALL FEET,
  84 MARK..................................................      52.00
SILVER,RUSSIAN,BEAKER,MOSCOW 1766,3 IN. HIGH,BIRDS,
  C-SCROLLS,FLOWERS........................................     225.00
SILVER,RUSSIAN,BEAKER,MOSCOW 1791,3 IN. HIGH,BIRDS & FLOWERS    220.00
SILVER,RUSSIAN,BEAKER,PARCEL-GILT,CIRCA 1760................     225.00
SILVER,RUSSIAN,BEAKER,PARCEL-GILT,UNKNOWN MASTER............  1,000.00
SILVER,RUSSIAN,BEAKER,REPOUSSE,CHASED WITH DRAPERY WREATH,
  FOLIATE,1793.............................................     200.00
SILVER,RUSSIAN,BELL,TABLE,1851,CARL TEGELSTEN...............    400.00
SILVER,RUSSIAN,CANDELABRUM,THREE LIGHTS,HALLMARKED & DATED
  1892,17 IN...............................................     300.00
SILVER,RUSSIAN,CANDLESTICK,DATED 1858,11 1/2 IN.HIGH,PAIR...    160.00
SILVER,RUSSIAN,CASE,CIGARETTE,WOMAN,SAPPHIRE NECKLACE,
  EMERALD CLASP............................................     155.00
SILVER,RUSSIAN,CASE,NIELLO TRIM,HAND-MADE...................     45.00
SILVER,RUSSIAN,COFFEEPOT,CIRCA 1900,IVAN CHLEBNIKOV,MOSCOW,
  9 IN. HIGH...............................................     190.00
SILVER,RUSSIAN,COFFEEPOT,CIRCA 1900,8 1/2 IN. HIGH,ART
  NOUVEAU..................................................     200.00
SILVER,RUSSIAN,COFFEEPOT,NIELLO,MOSCOW,1870,5 1/2 IN. HIGH..    175.00
SILVER,RUSSIAN,CREAMER,REPOUSSE BORDER,OPENWORK HANDLE,MARK
  84,1834..................................................     175.00
SILVER,RUSSIAN,CUP,KOVSH,ENGRAVED GEOMETRIC DESIGNS,1890,
  13 1/2 IN.LONG...........................................     725.00
SILVER,RUSSIAN,CUP,VODKA,ENGRAVED FLORAL,FOOTED,DATED 1893,
  3 3/4 IN.HIGH............................................      32.50
SILVER,RUSSIAN,CUP,WINE,CEREMONIAL,ENGRAVED,PEDESTAL,
  4 IN.TALL................................................      32.00
SILVER,RUSSIAN,DISH,CANDY,DANITCHEVSKY-VILNO 1866,3 PIECES..    180.00
SILVER,RUSSIAN,HOLDER,TEA GLASS,OXIDIZED,CIRCA 1900,
  VLADIMIROV...............................................     170.00
SILVER,RUSSIAN,JAR,POWDER,G.P.GRATCHEV,CIRCA 1900,3 3/4 IN.
  HIGH.....................................................     125.00
SILVER,RUSSIAN,KNIFE,6,FISH,PAVEL OVCHINNIKOV,MOSCOW,1896,
  MONOGRAM AM..............................................      80.00
SILVER,RUSSIAN,KOVSH,GILT,MOSCOW 1866,5 1/2 IN. LONG........    200.00
SILVER,RUSSIAN,LADLE,MONOGRAM,MARKED 84.....................     60.00
SILVER,RUSSIAN,LADLE,MOSCOW,CIRCA 1770,11 IN. LONG..........    190.00
SILVER,RUSSIAN,MUG,CAMPANA SHAPE,ENGRAVED,FOLIATE,SCENE,
  COVER,1860...............................................     100.00
SILVER,RUSSIAN,MUG,1885....................................     190.00
SILVER,RUSSIAN,NAPKIN RING,BLACK ENAMEL OF BASILICA,ALLOVER
  CHASING,MARK.............................................      65.00
SILVER,RUSSIAN,NAPKIN RING,ETCHED FLOWER & FOLIAGE,ROLLED
  RIM......................................................      23.00
SILVER,RUSSIAN,PAPERWEIGHT,F.I.,CIRCA 1880,11 IN. LONG......    200.00
SILVER,RUSSIAN,SALT,OPEN,BEADED DESIGN,FOOTED,2-IN.DIAMETER,
  PAIR.....................................................      55.00
SILVER,RUSSIAN,SALT,PANELED,FOOTED,GOLD-LINED,OVAL,OPEN,18TH
  CENTURY..................................................      55.00
SILVER,RUSSIAN,SERVING SET,SPOON,LEMON FORK,TONGS,STRAINER,
  BLACK ENAMEL.............................................     200.00
```

```
SILVER,RUSSIAN,SHOT CUP,ENGRAVED HOUSE ON FRONT,MARKED 84,
  ST.PETERSBURG....................................................    16.00
SILVER,RUSSIAN,SPOON,DESSERT,FIDDLEBACK,DATED 1875..........    20.00
SILVER,RUSSIAN,SPOON,SERVING,AA OVER 1868,84 MARK..........    20.00
SILVER,RUSSIAN,TABLESPOON,FIDDLE AND SHELL PATTERN,DATED
  1847,PAIR......................................................    50.00
SILVER,RUSSIAN,TABLESPOON,FIDDLEBACK PATTERN,DATED 1872.....    20.00
SILVER,RUSSIAN,TABLESPOON,FIDDLEBACK WITH SHELL,DATED 1847,
  PAIR...........................................................    50.00
SILVER,RUSSIAN,TANKARD,PARCEL-GILT,ENAMEL,GERMAN GOTTLIEB
  UNGER 1798....................................................2,500.00
SILVER,RUSSIAN,TEA STRAINER,SCROLLWORK ON RIM,MARKED 84,
  DATED 1843.....................................................    40.00
SILVER,RUSSIAN,TEASPOON,10,GILDED & NIELLO,S.S.,MOSCOW 1844.   120.00
SILVER,RUSSIAN,TRAY,BREAD,ST.PETERSBURG,1867,12 3/4-IN.
  DIAMETER.......................................................   225.00
SILVER,RUSSIAN,VASE,IVAN CHLEBNIKOV,MOSCOW,1874,8 3/4 IN.
  HIGH...........................................................   140.00
SILVER,RUSSIAN,VODKA CUP....................................    20.00
SILVER,SCOTTISH,FORK,FIDDLE PATTERN,CREST,MOTTO,ALEXANDER
  EDMONSTON,6....................................................   110.00
SILVER,SCOTTISH,SALT CELLAR,GEORGE III,FRANCIS HOWDEN,CIRCA
  1800...........................................................   150.00
SILVER,SCOTTISH,TEAKETTLE,LAMP STAND,KERR & DEMPSTER,HUGH
  GORDON,1747.................................................1,200.00
SILVER,SCOTTISH,TEAPOT,SUGAR BOWL & CREAMER,GEORGE III,1800.   600.00
  SILVER,SHEFFIELD,SEE SILVER PLATE,SHEFFIELD


       STERLING SILVER IS MADE WITH 925 PARTS OF SILVER OUT OF
       1,000 PARTS OF METAL. THE WORD STERLING IS A QUALITY
       GUARANTEE USED IN THE UNITED STATES AFTER ABOUT 1860.
SILVER,STERLING,ASHTRAY,HOLLY LEAF,RED BERRIES,6 IN.LONG....     6.00
SILVER,STERLING,ATOMIZER,PERFUME,COMPLETE WITH BULB.........    10.00
SILVER,STERLING,BAG,EMBOSSED FRAME,WOMEN'S HEADS,5 1/4 IN...    35.00
SILVER,STERLING,BASKET,HELMET SHAPE,PIERCED HANDLE &
  BORDERS,FOOTED.................................................    35.00
SILVER,STERLING,BASKET,MOVABLE HANDLE,FLORAL DECORATION,
  20 IN.TALL.....................................................   165.00
SILVER,STERLING,BASKET,NUT DISH,PIERCED,HANDLE,TOWLE........    20.00
SILVER,STERLING,BASKET,OPENWORK,DECOR AROUND TOP,20 IN.TALL.   135.00
SILVER,STERLING,BASKET,OPENWORK,FLORAL DECOR,MOVABLE HANDLE,
  MARKED 800.....................................................    85.00
SILVER,STERLING,BASKET,SUGAR,ENGRAVED DESIGN,MONOGRAM.......    37.50
SILVER,STERLING,BASKET,SWEETMEAT,17TH CENTURY...............   365.00
SILVER,STERLING,BELT,NINE PLAQUES,MYTHOLOGICAL FACE,WOMEN,
  25 IN..........................................................   175.00
SILVER,STERLING,BODKIN,ALLOVER FLORAL DECOR,MEDALLION FOR
  MONOGRAM,PAIR..................................................    12.50
SILVER,STERLING,BONBON,SCALLOPED RIM,FLARING PANELED SIDES,
  GORHAM.........................................................    15.00
SILVER,STERLING,BOOKMARK,TWO CHERUBS........................    10.00
SILVER,STERLING,BOOKMARK....................................     2.50
SILVER,STERLING,BOWL,BOAT-SHAPED,TWO SCULPTURED SWANS FORM
  ENDS,GORHAM....................................................   500.00
SILVER,STERLING,BOWL,CHILD'S,ENGRAVED SCENES FROM FAIRY
  TALES,7 IN.....................................................    50.00
SILVER,STERLING,BOWL,FRUIT,SCALLOPED SIDES,FLORAL CLUSTERS,
  OVAL...........................................................    58.00
SILVER,STERLING,BOWL,PIERCED WREATH,HOLLY MOTIF,REED &
  BARTON,9 1/4 IN................................................    40.00
SILVER,STERLING,BOWL,PIERCED,WOMAN'S HEAD,LEAVES,BLOSSOMS,
  10 IN..........................................................    95.00
SILVER,STERLING,BOWL,PUNCH,EMBOSSED FLORAL,DOUBLE-LIPPED
  LADLE.......................................................1,250.00
SILVER,STERLING,BOWL,SHELL,LOBSTER,ENGRAVED,MARKED 925 OVER
  1000,7 IN......................................................    20.00
SILVER,STERLING,BOWL,SUGAR,GOLD-WASHED,FLUTED,BEADED EDGE,
  SINGLE FLORAL..................................................     5.00
SILVER,STERLING,BOX,CIGAR,PAINTED HUNTING SCENE ON LID,
  HINGED.........................................................    38.00
SILVER,STERLING,BOX,CIGARETTE,BAMBOO & BIRD MOTIF,
  TEAK-LINED,SEPT.1899...........................................     9.00
SILVER,STERLING,BOX,CIGARETTES,TWO GILT COMPARTMENTS,
  MONOGRAM.......................................................    75.00
SILVER,STERLING,BOX,ENGRAVED DESIGN,FLOWERS,SCROLLS,
  800 MARK,HINGED LID............................................    18.00
SILVER,STERLING,BOX,JEWEL,BEADED BORDER,PIERCED SIDES,VELVET
  LINING.........................................................    32.00
SILVER,STERLING,BOX,MATCH,HINGED COVER,HIGH RELIEF
  MYTHOLOGICAL FIGURES...........................................     8.50
```

```
SILVER,STERLING,BOX,ORNATE,CHASED HINGED BOX,4 IN. X 3 IN...      25.00
SILVER,STERLING,BOX,PATCH,ENAMEL,BLUE,ROSEBUDS.............      18.00
SILVER,STERLING,BOX,PATCH,ENGRAVED........................      10.00
SILVER,STERLING,BOX,PILL,EMBOSSED BASKET OF FLOWERS,
  GOLD-WASHED INSIDE.....................................      20.00
SILVER,STERLING,BOX,PILL,FLORAL REPOUSSE,GOLD WASH INSIDE...      10.00
SILVER,STERLING,BOX,PILL,RAISED DELLA ROBBIA CHILD IN
  SWADDLING CLOTHES......................................      15.00
SILVER,STERLING,BOX,SNUFF,ENAMEL DECOR,CHILDREN,GARDEN,OVAL,
  FRANCE.................................................     225.00
SILVER,STERLING,BOX,SNUFF,REPOUSSE WINDMILL SCENE ON HINGED
  COVER,OVAL.............................................      15.00
SILVER,STERLING,BOX,SOAP,EGG-SHAPED,HINGED,ENGRAVED F.......      10.00
SILVER,STERLING,BOX,SOAP,EMBOSSED ROSES,LEAVES,GORHAM.......      22.50
SILVER,STERLING,BRIDE'S BASKET,20 IN.TALL,PAIR CANDLESTICKS,
  10 IN.TALL.............................................     275.00
SILVER,STERLING,BRUSH,PIG,BLACK BRISTLES,2 3/4 X 1 3/4 IN...       6.50
SILVER,STERLING,BUTTER PAT,FLOWERED EDGE,MAKER HOWARD
  COMPANY,SET OF 6.......................................      24.00
SILVER,STERLING,BUTTER PAT,MAKER WALLCE,2 3/4-IN.DIAMETER,
  SET OF FOUR............................................      12.50
SILVER,STERLING,BUTTONHOOK................................      12.00
SILVER,STERLING,BUTTONHOOK,INITIALS.......................       2.95
SILVER,STERLING,CAKE KNIFE,WEDDING BELLS ON BLADE,1872,
  10 IN.LONG.............................................      45.00
SILVER,STERLING,CAKE SERVER,PIERCED,FLORAL HANDLE..........      25.00
SILVER,STERLING,CALLING CARD CASE,WITH CHAIN..............      22.00
SILVER,STERLING,CANDELABRA,FIVE LIGHTS,ENGLAND,
  14 1/4 IN.HIGH,PAIR....................................     375.00
SILVER,STERLING,CANDELABRA,GEOMETRIC DESIGN,200 PRISMS,
  WIRED,PAIR.............................................   2,800.00
SILVER,STERLING,CANDELABRUM,TWISTED ROPE DESIGN,
  THREE-CANDLE,11 IN.,PAIR...............................     200.00
SILVER,STERLING,CANDLEHOLDER,LOW,PAIR.....................       8.00
SILVER,STERLING,CANDLESTICK,COAT OF ARMS,ROCOCO,GEORGIAN,
  1813,LONDON............................................     950.00
SILVER,STERLING,CANDLESTICK,FLUTED,BAILEY,BANKS,BIDDLE,
  10 IN.,PAIR............................................     125.00
SILVER,STERLING,CANDLESTICK,ROCOCO,COAT OF ARMS,LONDON,1813,
  10 1/2 IN..............................................     950.00
SILVER,STERLING,CANDLESTICK,WHITING DIVISION OF GORHAM,
  6 IN.HIGH,PAIR.........................................      45.00
SILVER,STERLING,CANDLESTICK,10 IN.HIGH,SET OF 4...........     165.00
SILVER,STERLING,CARD CASE,LADY'S,ALLOVER DECOR,1860,BY
  ABRAHAM TUPPY..........................................      25.00
SILVER,STERLING,CARD CASE,MONOGRAM,3 1/4 X 2 1/2 IN........       7.50
SILVER,STERLING,CASE,EYEGLASS,EMBOSSED SCROLL & LEAVES,
  MONOGRAM...............................................      12.50
SILVER,STERLING,CASTOR,PICKLE,DOUBLE,CRYSTAL PATTERN
  INSERTS,FINIAL LIDS....................................      73.00
SILVER,STERLING,CIGAR CUTTER,LADY WITH FLOWING HAIR........      10.00
SILVER,STERLING,CIGAR CUTTER,PATENT MAY,1910..............       3.50
SILVER,STERLING,CIGARETTE CASE............................      35.00
SILVER,STERLING,CIGARETTE CASE,EMBOSSED FOLIAGE DECOR,
  GORHAM,1895............................................      22.00
SILVER,STERLING,CIGARETTE CASE,MONOGRAM,4 1/2 X 3 IN.......      10.00
SILVER,STERLING,CIGARETTE HOLDER,TELESCOPED,CARRYING RING,
  1-IN.CASE..............................................       6.50
SILVER,STERLING,CLOTHES BRUSH,HAIR BRUSH,MIRROR,ORNATE
  FLORAL................................................      30.00
SILVER,STERLING,COFFEE SERVICE,ROPE TRIM,GORHAM,5 PIECES....     785.00
SILVER,STERLING,COFFEEPOT,EMBOSSED CHERUBS,WOODEN HANDLE,
  LION FINIAL............................................     150.00
SILVER,STERLING,COFFEEPOT,ONE-CUP,CREAMER FITS ON TOP,BUTTER
  POT IS LID.............................................      22.00
SILVER,STERLING,COFFEEPOT,PLYMOUTH PATTERN,MONOGRAM,WOODEN
  HANDLE,GORHAM..........................................     110.00
SILVER,STERLING,COFFEEPOT,PLYMOUTH,SUGAR BASKET,CREAMER,
  GORHAM.................................................     210.00
SILVER,STERLING,COMPOTE,ALLOVER RAISED STRAWBERRIES,KIRK &
  SONS..................................................     950.00
SILVER,STERLING,COMPOTE,MONOGRAM,GORHAM,4 3/4 IN. X
  5 3/4-IN.DIAMETER......................................      10.00
SILVER,STERLING,COMPOTE,OPENWORK BASE,WALLS OF TROY DESIGN,
  BOAT SHAPE.............................................     250.00
SILVER,STERLING,COMPOTE,ROYAL OAK PATTERN,FIVE FEET,GORHAM,
  1902..................................................     150.00
SILVER,STERLING,COMPOTE,VINTAGE/GRAPE PATTERN,MONOGRAM,OPEN,
  PAIR..................................................     750.00
SILVER,STERLING,CORKSCREW,CIGAR SHAPE,TOP UNSCREWS,CORKSCREW
  PULLS OUT.............................................      10.00
```

```
SILVER,STERLING,CORKSCREW,MONOGRAM,TUSK HANDLE..............    22.50
SILVER,STERLING,CORKSCREW,STAG HANDLE,LATE 19TH CENTURY.....    35.00
SILVER,STERLING,CORN HOLDER,SHAPED LIKE EAR OF CORN IN HUSK,
  SET OF 6.................................................    22.00
SILVER,STERLING,CREAM JUG,HELMET,LONDON,1791,MAKER W.J.,
  6 IN....................................................   195.00
SILVER,STERLING,CREAMER & SUGAR,ALLOVER FLORAL,COVER,DATED
  DEC.10,1874.............................................   350.00
SILVER,STERLING,CROSS,PAVED WITH SCOTTISH TOPAZES,ENGLAND,
  7 1/2 IN................................................   300.00
SILVER,STERLING,CUP & SAUCER,DEMITASSE,GOLD AURENE & CALCITE
  LINER...................................................   165.00
SILVER,STERLING,CUP,CHILD'S,2 1/2 IN.TALL,MARKED...........     2.50
SILVER,STERLING,CUP,THREE HANDLES,CREST,HOWARD & CO.,N.Y.,
  1900....................................................   150.00
SILVER,STERLING,CUP,WINE,MARRIAGE,ENAMEL,JEWELED,CIRCA 1800.   200.00
SILVER,STERLING,DESSERT HOLDERS,CUT CRYSTAL CUP,SET OF 8....    60.00
SILVER,STERLING,DISH,BOAT SHAPE,OPENWORK EDGE,FOOTED,GORHAM,
  5 IN.LONG...............................................    35.00
SILVER,STERLING,DISH,BONBON,ROPE TRIM,5-IN.DIAMETER........     8.00
SILVER,STERLING,DISH,CLAMSHELL SHAPE,MARKED WALLACE,
  3 1/2 IN.LONG...........................................     5.50
SILVER,STERLING,DISH,ENTREE,COVER,FLORAL,TIFFANY & CO.,1900,
  10 IN...................................................   450.00
SILVER,STERLING,DISH,ENTREE,COVER,FLORAL,FOLIAGE,A.JACOBY &
  CO.,1900................................................   400.00
SILVER,STERLING,DISH,NUT,FOOTED,PIERCED BORDER,2 1/2 X
  1 IN.,SET OF 8..........................................    32.00
SILVER,STERLING,DISH,NUT,LACY SCALLOP EDGE,EMBOSSED WILD
  ROSE,OVAL,6.............................................    27.50
SILVER,STERLING,DISH,ROYAL DANISH,INTERNATIONAL,8 IN.LONG,
  4 1/2 IN.WIDE...........................................    25.00
SILVER,STERLING,DRESSER SET,ENAMELED,CARVED GREEN JADE
  CENTER,9 PIECES.........................................   400.00
SILVER,STERLING,EVENING BAG,FILIGREE,CHAIN................    25.00
SILVER,STERLING,FIGURINE,NAPOLEON WHEN GENERAL,1 1/2 IN.HIGH    6.50
SILVER,STERLING,FLASK,CAP,NO.427,5/8 PINT.................    25.00
SILVER,STERLING,FLASK,INDIAN,FEATHERED HEADDRESS,MATCH SAFE,
  UNGER,SET...............................................   160.00
SILVER,STERLING,FLASK,LIQUOR,ALLOVER-EMBOSSED,SCALLOPED,
  MONOGRAM,6 IN...........................................    55.00
SILVER,STERLING,FORK,B.R. & B.CO.,1865,9 1/2 IN...........    35.00
SILVER,STERLING,FORK,LEMON,CLOISONNE LEMON & LEAF INSET ON
  HANDLE..................................................    12.50
SILVER,STERLING,FORK,LEMON,THREE-TINED....................     4.75
SILVER,STERLING,FORK,OYSTER,DATED 1895,SET OF 8...........    24.00
SILVER,STERLING,FORK,OYSTER,EMBOSSED FISHERMAN ON HANDLE,
  GORHAM,12...............................................    72.00
SILVER,STERLING,FORK,OYSTER,ORNATE,INITIAL,DATED 1900,SET OF
  6.......................................................    18.00
SILVER,STERLING,FORK,STEEL PRONGS,FOUR,FOUR FIDDLE PATTERN
  TEASPOONS...............................................    85.00
SILVER,STERLING,GOBLET,FANCY SCROLLWORK...................     8.50
SILVER,STERLING,GOBLET,WATER,WALLS OF TROY BORDER,GORHAM,SET
  OF 6....................................................   240.00
SILVER,STERLING,GRAPE SHEARS,ORNATE HANDLE................    15.00
SILVER,STERLING,GRAVY BOAT & TRAY,BEADED BORDER,MONOGRAM,
  OVAL....................................................   125.00
SILVER,STERLING,HAIRPIN,HEAVY CHASED......................     3.00
SILVER,STERLING,HANDBAG,ENGRAVED,CHAIN,3 1/2 X 2 1/2 IN....    10.00
SILVER,STERLING,HANDBAG,MESH..............................    85.00
SILVER,STERLING,HOLDER,PLACE CARD,OPENWORK,CUPIDS,FLOWERS,
  TREE,TWELVE.............................................   180.00
SILVER,STERLING,ICE BUCKET,PIERCED BAND AROUND TOP,FEET,
  GLASS INSERT............................................    37.50
SILVER,STERLING,INKWELL,SCROLL,LEAF SHAPE TRAY,CRYSTAL
  INSERT..................................................    32.50
SILVER,STERLING,KNIFE,BUTTER,ORNATE HANDLE,INITIAL B,STOWELL
  & CO....................................................     4.50
SILVER,STERLING,KNIFE,BUTTER,SUGAR SPOON,MARKED MICHIE......    25.00
SILVER,STERLING,KNIFE,FISH,FORK,12 EACH,TEN SILVER PLATE
  KNIVES,FORKS............................................   140.00
SILVER,STERLING,KNIFE,FORK,FRUIT,BEADING,MARCUS UNTER DEN
  LINDEN,TWELVE...........................................    75.00
SILVER,STERLING,KNIFE,FRUIT,POCKET,GORHAM.................     4.75
SILVER,STERLING,KNIFE,PIE,ENGRAVED,MARKED N.HARDING,CIRCA
  1795....................................................    15.00
SILVER,STERLING,LADLE,DICKENSON,14 IN.....................    65.00
SILVER,STERLING,LADLE,PUNCH,MARKED HENRY TISDALE,NEWPORT,
```

```
    12 IN.LONG.............................................    65.00
SILVER,STERLING,LADLE,SAUCE,EMBOSSED HANDLE,GOLD-WASHED BOWL      7.50
SILVER,STERLING,LADLE,SHELL BOWL,FLORAL,CURVED HANDLE,10 IN.
    LONG.................................................     35.00
SILVER,STERLING,LADLE,SOUP,CURVED HANDLE,SCROLL & LEAF
    DECOR,W & H MARK.....................................     60.00
SILVER,STERLING,LADLE,SOUP,LOUIS XV PATTERN.................     18.50
SILVER,STERLING,LADLE,TODDY,TEAKWOOD HANDLE.................     55.00
SILVER,STERLING,MATCHBOX COVER,ETCHED SAILING SHIP ON TOP...      4.50
SILVER,STERLING,MATCH CASE,EMBOSSED,MARKED PAT.1/12/04,
    MONOGRAM.............................................     17.00
SILVER,STERLING,MATCH SAFE,HIGHLY EMBOSSED..................     13.00
SILVER,STERLING,MATCH SAFE,POCKET,ORNATE....................      5.75
SILVER,STERLING,MATCH SAFE,POCKET,STRIKER BOTTOM,ROSES,GOLD
    WASH LINING..........................................     15.00
SILVER,STERLING,MATCH SAFE,REPOUSSE,ANIMAL HEAD,CENTER OVAL,
    GORHAM...............................................     12.00
SILVER,STERLING,MAYONNAISE,5-IN.DIAMETER,3 1/2 IN.HIGH,LADLE     17.50
SILVER,STERLING,MINT SERVER,PIERCED,SCALLOPED,GOLD-WASHED,
    PAT.1895.............................................      7.50
SILVER,STERLING,MIRROR,COMB,BRUSH...........................     45.00
SILVER,STERLING,MIRROR,HAND,BEADED,INITIALED................     15.00
SILVER,STERLING,MIRROR,HAND,ENGRAVED MEDALLION IN CENTER,
    14 IN.LONG...........................................     17.00
SILVER,STERLING,MIRROR,HAND,REPOUSSE ROSES,BAROQUE SHAPE,
    10 IN.LONG...........................................     27.00
SILVER,STERLING,MIRROR,RAISED FLOWERS,CHERUBS,GORHAM,8 1/2 X
    7 1/4 IN.............................................     22.00
SILVER,STERLING,MONEY CLIP,MONOGRAM.........................      3.50
SILVER,STERLING,MUG,BABY'S,DATED 1871,REED & BARTON.........     12.50
SILVER,STERLING,MUG,BABY'S,GORHAM...........................     15.00
SILVER,STERLING,MUG,CHASED DECOR,GADROON BANDS,1877,GORHAM,
    1/2 PINT.............................................     40.00
SILVER,STERLING,MUG,CHILD'S,ETCHED ESKIMO,INDIAN,ETC.,
    STEVENSON VERSE......................................     20.00
SILVER,STERLING,MUG,SCROLLED LEAF BORDER,MONOGRAM,1870,
    GORHAM,1/2 PINT......................................     57.50
SILVER,STERLING,MUSTACHE CURLING IRON.......................      8.50
SILVER,STERLING,MUSTARD POT,CRANBERRY LINER,MONOGRAM........     20.00
SILVER,STERLING,MUSTARD POT,OPENWORK,SCROLLED HANDLE,COBALT
    GLASS LINER..........................................     15.00
SILVER,STERLING,MUSTARD,OPENWORK,CLEAR GLASS INSERT.........      8.50
SILVER,STERLING,MUSTARD,SPOON,COVER,SIGNED THEODORE STARR,
    2 3/4 IN.HIGH........................................     75.00
  SILVER,STERLING,NAPKIN RING,SEE NAPKIN RING
SILVER,STERLING,NEEDLE CASE,EMBOSSED SCROLLS & LEAVES.......      9.00
SILVER,STERLING,NIGHT-LIGHT,ALCOHOL,CURLING IRON HEATER,
    EMBOSSED.............................................     46.00
SILVER,STERLING,PENCIL,OWL,END OF TAIL PULLS OUT............     15.00
SILVER,STERLING,PERFUME,FLASK SHAPE,HAND-CHASING,SAYS
    JENNIE,3 1/2 IN......................................     10.00
SILVER,STERLING,PICTURE FRAME,EASEL BACK,4 X 5 3/4 IN.,EDGE
    3/8 IN.WIDE..........................................      5.00
SILVER,STERLING,PINCE-NEZ HOLDER,SMOKE SKIN.................     12.50
SILVER,STERLING,PITCHER,DOUBLE C HANDLE WITH SPUR,GORHAM,
    8 3/8 IN.TALL........................................     65.00
SILVER,STERLING,PITCHER,PORCELAIN-LINED,TILTS,GOBLET,REED &
    BARTON...............................................    325.00
SILVER,STERLING,PITCHER,REPOUSSE WITH MARK 1102,S.KIRK &
    SON,1845.............................................    600.00
SILVER,STERLING,PITCHER,WATER,BEADING ON SHOULDER,FLOWERS ON
    HANDLE...............................................     75.00
SILVER,STERLING,PITCHER,WATER,EMBOSSED FLORAL,SAYS PRIZE
    CONTEST 1902.........................................    225.00
SILVER,STERLING,PITCHER,WATER,ORNATE EMBOSSING,FLORAL
    MOTIFS,GORHAM........................................    300.00
SILVER,STERLING,PITCHER,WATER,REPOUSSE,MONOGRAM,A.JACOBI &
    CO...................................................    450.00
SILVER,STERLING,PITCHER,WATER,TIFFANY CO.,7 1/2 IN.HIGH.....    425.00
SILVER,STERLING,PLAQUE,WALL,BIRTH OF VENUS,AFTER BOTTICELLI,
    UNFRAMED.............................................    325.00
SILVER,STERLING,PLATE,BREAD & BUTTER,PAIR...................      7.50
SILVER,STERLING,PLATE,BREAD & BUTTER,RAISED CHASED BORDER,
    GORHAM,12............................................    135.00
SILVER,STERLING,PLATE,MONOGRAM,TOTAL WEIGHT 1 1/2 POUNDS,SET
    OF 6.................................................     85.00
SILVER,STERLING,PORRINGER,MISS MUFFET SCENE.................     15.00
SILVER,STERLING,PORRINGER,ROUND HANDLE......................     16.50
SILVER,STERLING,PURSE,MESH,ENGRAVED FRAME,GREEN STONE CLASP,
    STRAP,7 IN...........................................     22.00
SILVER,STERLING,RAMEKIN,EMBOSSED FLORAL,PORCELAIN INSERT,
```

GORHAM,SET OF 6.......................................... 150.00
SILVER,STERLING,RAMEKIN,EMBOSSED SCENE,FIGURES,BALTIMORE
    SILVER CO.,12.......................................... 300.00
SILVER,STERLING,RAMEKIN,PIERCED,HANDLE,WHITE PORCELAIN
    LINER,SET OF 10........................................ 120.00
SILVER,STERLING,SALT,INDIVIDUAL,OPEN,LILY PAD BASE,12....... 84.00
SILVER,STERLING,SALT,MASTER,COBALT BLUE GLASS LINER,
    2 1/2 IN.............................................. 14.00
SILVER,STERLING,SALT,MASTER,COBALT LINER..................... 23.00
SILVER,STERLING,SALT,ONE SHAPE OF BUTTER TUB,ONE SHAPE OF
    BATHTUB,PAIR.......................................... 16.50
SILVER,STERLING,SALT,OPEN,OVAL,ON MULTIFACETED BASE,GEORG
    JENSEN................................................ 15.00
SILVER,STERLING,SALT,PEPPER,ALLOVER ENGRAVED ROSES,SIGNED
    S.KIRK & SON.......................................... 100.00
SILVER,STERLING,SALT,PEPPER,GLASS-LINED,3 1/4 IN.HIGH....... 8.00
SILVER,STERLING,SALT,SHELL,FOOTED,2 1/2 X 3 IN.............. 5.00
SILVER,STERLING,SALT & PEPPER,COLONIAL DESIGN,URN SHAPE,
    BELL-SHAPE TOP........................................ 10.00
SILVER,STERLING,SALT & PEPPER,FORM OF BIRDS,CONTINENTAL,
    1 1/2 IN.HIGH......................................... 38.50
SILVER,STERLING,SALT & PEPPER,FORM OF ORIENTAL FISHERMAN,
    FISH UNDER ARM........................................ 35.00
SILVER,STERLING,SALT & PEPPER,FORM OF PHEASANT,CONTINENTAL,
    8 1/4 IN.LONG......................................... 100.00
SILVER,STERLING,SALT & PEPPER,PIERCED,AMETHYST GLASS LINERS. 30.00
SILVER,STERLING,SALT DIP,ENGRAVED,FOOTED,OPEN,SPOON......... 8.00
SILVER,STERLING,SALT DIP,FOOTED............................. 10.00
SILVER,STERLING,SALT DIP,NO.1065,OCTAGONAL BOAT SHAPE,
    MONOGRAM,GORHAM,6..................................... 25.00
SILVER,STERLING,SALT DIP,PLEATED WITH STARLIKE PETALS,SET OF
    SIX.................................................. 15.00
SILVER,STERLING,SALT DISH,GOLD INSIDE,STERLING SALT SPOON,
    CASE,SET OF 6......................................... 47.50
SILVER,STERLING,SAUCEBOAT,FLUTED,RIBBED,SHELL FEET,
    MONTGOMERY BROS....................................... 48.00
SILVER,STERLING,SCISSORS,FLORAL HANDLE...................... 6.00
SILVER,STERLING,SEAL,INVERTED CONE SHAPE BLUE AGATE TOP, H ,
    3 IN.LONG............................................ 17.00
SILVER,STERLING,SEAL,REPOUSSE FLORAL & SCROLL DECOR ON
    HANDLE END, T........................................ 10.00
SILVER,STERLING,SERVER,CAKE,ACORN PATTERN,JENSEN,10 3/8 IN.. 45.00
SILVER,STERLING,SEWING BIRD,ORNATE,CUSHION,PATENT 1853...... 22.50
SILVER,STERLING,SHEARS,GRAPE,ORNATE GRAPE CLUSTER HANDLE.... 15.00
SILVER,STERLING,SHERBET,CUTOUT DESIGN,ETCHED GLASS REMOVABLE
    INSERT,PAIR.......................................... 25.00
SILVER,STERLING,SHERBET,GOBLET,MONOGRAM,WHITING DIV.OF
    GORHAM,9 OF EACH...................................... 325.00
SILVER,STERLING,SHERBET,MEDALLIONS OF SERPENT & GODS,
    925 STERLING,SIX...................................... 350.00
SILVER,STERLING,SHOEHORN,EMBOSSED ROSES & FOLIAGE,GORHAM,
    1900................................................. 15.00
SILVER,STERLING,SHOEHORN,FINE DECORATION,MONOGRAM,
    8 3/4 IN.LONG........................................ 7.50
SILVER,STERLING,SHOEHORN,ORNATE SCRIPT MONOGRAM,6 IN........ 12.50
SILVER,STERLING,SHOEHORN,RAISED FLORAL DESIGN,INITIAL H..... 7.50
SILVER,STERLING,SHOEHORN,WOMAN WITH FLOWING HAIR ON HANDLE.. 10.00
SILVER,STERLING,SOAPBOX,SCROLL,ACANTHUS LEAF,MONOGRAM,HINGED
    LID................................................. 15.00
SILVER,STERLING,SPOON,BABY'S,RING HANDLE,ENGRAVED NAME IN
    BOWL,1884............................................ 3.95
SILVER,STERLING,SPOON,BOUILLON,FLORAL ON HANDLE END,SET OF
    6.................................................... 25.00
SILVER,STERLING,SPOON,COFFEE,SUNFLOWER PATTERN,MARKED 950,
    SET OF SIX........................................... 25.00
SILVER,STERLING,SPOON,DEMITASSE,FLOWERED BACK & FRONT,
    GOLD-WASHED,6........................................ 25.00
SILVER,STERLING,SPOON,DEMITASSE,GEORGE WASHINGTON,GOLD WASH
    BOWL................................................. 7.00
SILVER,STERLING,SPOON,DEMITASSE,GOLD WASH BOWL,PASTEL ENAMEL
    DECOR,7.............................................. 85.00
SILVER,STERLING,SPOON,DEMITASSE,GOLD-DIPPED SHELL,SET OF 6.. 18.00
SILVER,STERLING,SPOON,DEMITASSE,HANDLES ARE REPOUSSE
    FLORALS,SET OF 12.................................... 35.00
SILVER,STERLING,SPOON,DEMITASSE,INITIAL,SET OF 6............ 18.00
SILVER,STERLING,SPOON,DEMITASSE,LANCASTER ROSE,MONOGRAM,SET
    OF 6................................................. 20.00
SILVER,STERLING,SPOON,DEMITASSE,SET OF 6,TONGS,LEATHER CASE. 25.50
SILVER,STERLING,SPOON,DEMITASSE,TWO ASTERS ON HANDLE,SET OF
    6.................................................... 18.00
SILVER,STERLING,SPOON,DEMITASSE,TWO ROSES & LEAVES ON

HANDLES,SET OF 6........................................... 18.00
SILVER,STERLING,SPOON,FULL FIGURE OF INDIAN FORMS HANDLE,
4 1/4 IN.LONG............................................. 10.00
SILVER,STERLING,SPOON,ICE CREAM SODA SIPPER,LEAF-SHAPED,
BOWL,SET OF 8............................................. 15.00
SILVER,STERLING,SPOON,MASTER SALT,FIDDLEBACK,WILL EROS,
LONDON,1841,PAIR.......................................... 12.50
SILVER,STERLING,SPOON,NUT,BARONIAL,MONOGRAMMED,DATED 1900,
GORHAM.................................................... 12.50
SILVER,STERLING,SPOON,NUT,MARY CHILTON,MONOGRAM,TOWLE....... 7.50
SILVER,STERLING,SPOON,SALT,ALLOVER EMBOSSED FLORAL PATTERN,
SET OF 6.................................................. 21.00
SILVER,STERLING,SPOON,SALT,FIDDLEBACK,WM.N.VENNING,NEW
BRUNSWICK,PAIR............................................ 85.00
SILVER,STERLING,SPOON,SALT,OPENWORK HANDLE,BELLFLOWERS,
LEAVES,SET OF 4........................................... 25.00
SILVER,STERLING,SPOON,SERVING,GOLD-WASHED BOWL,ROSES FORM
HANDLE.................................................... 85.00
SILVER,STERLING,SPOON,SERVING,HAND CHASED DESIGN,J.L.HICKS.. 9.50
SILVER,STERLING,SPOON,SERVING,MONOGRAM,BUTTERCUP PATTERN,
GORHAM.................................................... 16.50
SILVER,STERLING,SPOON,SOUVENIR,SEE SOUVENIR SPOON
SILVER,STERLING,SPOON,TEA BALL,ACORN PATTERN,JENSEN........ 25.00
SILVER,STERLING,SPOON,TRAVELING,DOUBLE,OPENWORK CENTER...... 15.00
SILVER,STERLING,SPOON,ZODIAC,SEPTEMBER,GORHAM,PAT.MARCH 20,
1894,FORK................................................ 21.00
SILVER,STERLING,STRAIGHT PEN,EMBOSSED,ORNATE............... 12.00
SILVER,STERLING,STRAINER,TEA,BEADING,BLACK WOODEN HANDLE.... 8.00
SILVER,STERLING,SUGAR CUBE CONTAINER,OPENWORK SIDES,FOOTED,
HANDLE,6 IN.............................................. 15.00
SILVER,STERLING,SUGAR SHELL,GOLD-WASHED,1860,7 IN.......... 30.00
SILVER,STERLING,SUGAR SHELL,MONOGRAM,PAT.8-28-1900,SIMON &
CO....................................................... 8.00
SILVER,STERLING,TABLESPOON,POINTED HANDLE,C.P. ON BACK,
VENICE,1840,PAIR......................................... 18.00
SILVER,STERLING,TAZZA,PAIR,SIX BREAD & BUTTER PLATES,
TIFFANY,1900............................................. 250.00
SILVER,STERLING,TEA & COFFEE SERVICE,PLYMOUTH PATTERN,
GORHAM,5 PIECES.......................................... 650.00
SILVER,STERLING,TEA BALL................................... 6.00
SILVER,STERLING,TEA BALL,CHAIN,RING....................... 6.00
SILVER,STERLING,TEA BALL,HINGED,CHAIN,RING................ 10.00
SILVER,STERLING,TEA CADDY,MEN,WOMAN,BABY,LION & KEY MARK.... 165.00
SILVER,STERLING,TEA EGG,CHAIN,RING........................ 8.00
SILVER,STERLING,TEA SERVICE,FLORAL,CAMBODIAN HUNTERS,
ANIMALS,3 PIECES......................................... 350.00
SILVER,STERLING,TEA STRAINER,HANDLE....................... 9.00
SILVER,STERLING,TEAKETTLE,LAMPSTAND,S.KIRK & SON,BALTIMORE,
13 IN.HIGH............................................... 375.00
SILVER,STERLING,TEAPOT,COFFEEPOT,CREAMER,SUGAR,WASTE,GORHAM. 650.00
SILVER,STERLING,TEAPOT,COFFEEPOT,CREAMER,SUGAR,SLOP BOWL,
PLYMOUTH,GORHAM.......................................... 850.00
SILVER,STERLING,TEAPOT,FLUTED SIDES,BLACK WOODEN HANDLE,
GORHAM,7 IN.HIGH......................................... 75.00
SILVER,STERLING,TEASPOON,CENTURY PATTERN,MAKER DOMINICK &
HAFF,SET OF 12........................................... 55.00
SILVER,STERLING,TEASPOON,ENAMELED BOWL,MORRO CASTLE,EMBOSSED
HANDLE................................................... 30.00
SILVER,STERLING,TEASPOON,ENAMELED,BLUE,WHITE,CIRCLE SHAPE
HANDLE................................................... 15.00
SILVER,STERLING,TEASPOON,MONOGRAMMED W.P.G.,SET OF SIX..... 18.00
SILVER,STERLING,TEASPOON,ORNATE,FLORAL,INITIAL,MARKED 800,
SET OF 12................................................ 60.00
SILVER,STERLING,TEASPOON,POPPY PATTERN,GORHAM............. 24.00
SILVER,STERLING,TEASPOON,ST.CLOUD,MONOGRAM,GORHAM......... 6.50
SILVER,STERLING,TEASPOON,ZODIAC,APRIL-TAURUS,DATED 1909,
GORHAM................................................... 12.00
SILVER,STERLING,TEASPOON,ZODIAC,OCTOBER SCORPION,PAT.1894,
GORHAM................................................... 15.00
SILVER,STERLING,THIMBLE.................................... 4.50
SILVER,STERLING,THIMBLE HOLDER,EMBOSSED FLOWER MEDALLION,
HINGED COVER............................................. 25.00
SILVER,STERLING,THIMBLE SHOT CUP,ENGRAVED JUST A THIMBLEFUL. 10.00
SILVER,STERLING,THIMBLE,CHERUBS,GARLAND OF FLOWERS,SIZE 8... 8.50
SILVER,STERLING,THIMBLE,EMBOSSED CHERUBS HOLDING GARLANDS... 15.00
SILVER,STERLING,THIMBLE,ENGRAVED.......................... 8.00
SILVER,STERLING,THIMBLE,ENGRAVED GOLD BAND,SIZE 9......... 6.50
SILVER,STERLING,THIMBLE,FLEUR-DE-LIS,SIZE 8............... 6.00
SILVER,STERLING,THIMBLE,TAILORED BAND,SIZE 8............. 4.00
SILVER,STERLING,THREAD WINDER,BOW TIE SHAPE,EMBOSSED BEADS &
SCROLLS.................................................. 8.00

SILVER,STERLING,TOAST RACK,FOUR SECTIONS,ALCOHOL BURNER,
ENGLAND........................................................ 90.00
SILVER,STERLING,TONGS,GOODWIN & DODD,HARTFORD,CONN.,CIRCA
1812........................................................... 35.00
SILVER,STERLING,TONGS,SUGAR,BY DURGIN,CONCORD,N.H............ 12.50
SILVER,STERLING,TONGS,SUGAR,ENAMELED,GOLD OVERLAY,NORWAY,
4 IN.LONG...................................................... 15.00
SILVER,STERLING,TONGS,SUGAR,FAIRFAX PATTERN,CLAW ENDS,MAKER
DURGIN......................................................... 9.50
SILVER,STERLING,TONGS,SUGAR,ORNATE EMBOSSED FLORAL HANDLES,
CLAWS.......................................................... 10.00
SILVER,STERLING,TONGS,SUGAR,PIERCED HANDLE.................... 8.00
SILVER,STERLING,TONGS,SUGAR,VIOLET PATTERN,INITIAL,WALLACE.. 10.00
SILVER,STERLING,TOOTHPICK,REPOUSSE,REMOVABLE CAP,RING FOR
CHAIN.......................................................... 10.00
SILVER,STERLING,TOOTHPICK,URN SHAPE,THREE HANDLES,FLOWERS IN
RELIEF......................................................... 15.00
SILVER,STERLING,TRAY,BREAD,FLORAL MOTIF,HAND-WROUGHT,PIERCED
HANDLES........................................................ 225.00
SILVER,STERLING,TRAY,CALLING CARD,LEAF SHAPE,CLIPS FOR
HANGING,PAIR................................................... 37.50
SILVER,STERLING,TRAY,CALLING CARD,LEAF SHAPE,ORIENTAL....... 37.50
SILVER,STERLING,TRAY,CALLING CARD,LEAF SHAPE,ORIENTAL,
HANGING CLIP................................................... 37.50
SILVER,STERLING,TRAY,CALLING CARD,LEAF-SHAPED,HANGING CLIP,
PAIR........................................................... 37.50
SILVER,STERLING,TRAY,CARD...................................... 3.50
SILVER,STERLING,TRAY,CARD,HAMMERED,6 1/2-IN.DIAMETER........ 18.00
SILVER,STERLING,TRAY,CHERUBS,ROSES,VINES ON BORDER,
9 1/2 IN.LONG.................................................. 25.00
SILVER,STERLING,TRAY,FILIGREE,1-INCH TRIM,SHEFFIELD......... 185.00
SILVER,STERLING,TRAY,PIN,EMBOSSED MAIDEN,FLOWING HAIR,WATER
LILIES......................................................... 28.50
SILVER,STERLING,TRAY,REPOUSSE BORDER,DAFFODILS,GORHAM,
14-IN.DIAMETER................................................. 175.00
SILVER,STERLING,VASE,FLARES TO 3 1/4-IN.OPENING,
6 1/2 IN.HIGH.................................................. 8.25
SILVER,STERLING,VASE,PRESENTATION,ANTLERS PINNED IN ACORN
SOCKETS,1903................................................... 475.00
SILVER,STERLING,VASE,URNS,GARLANDS,CORNUCOPIAS,J.E.CALDWELL
CO.,10 IN...................................................... 40.00
SILVER,STERLING,VASE,WEIGHTED BASE,12 1/2 IN.HIGH........... 30.00
SILVER,STERLING,WALKING STICK,ENGRAVED DCB,1903,.925....... 16.50
SILVER,STERLING,WHISTLE,BY JOSEPH JENNENS & CO.,ENGLAND,
1859,40-IN.CHAIN............................................... 90.00
SILVER,STERLING,WHISTLE,THREE SILVER ST.BERNARDS WITH KEGS
FORM HANDLE.................................................... 16.50
SILVER,STERLING,WINE,MONOGRAM,BY S.KIRK & SON,4 3/8 IN.HIGH,
SET OF 12...................................................... 180.00
SILVER,SWEDISH,CREAM BOAT,BY JONAS ELG,VASTERAS,1779........2,250.00
SILVER,SWEDISH,CREAMER,SCROLLS,FOLIAGE,PEHR WILHELM
HANNGREN,FALUN,1814............................................ 125.00
SILVER,SWISS,COFFEEPOT,CIRCA 1750.............................. 850.00
SILVER,TURKISH,MIRROR,EMBOSSED BACK,MILITARY TROPHY,FLORAL
WREATH,9 IN.................................................... 40.00


SINCLAIRE CUT GLASS WAS MADE BY H.P.SINCLAIRE &
COMPANY,NEW YORK,FROM 1905 TO 1929.
SINCLAIRE,BOWL,FINGER,ENGRAVED FLORAL,WREATH PATTERN,SIGNED,
PAIR........................................................... 30.00
SINCLAIRE,BOWL,FLARED,BLUE,7 1/2 IN........................... 12.50
SINCLAIRE,CARAFE,WATER,FANS,GEOMETRICS,STARS,TWENTY FOUR
STAR-BASE...................................................... 55.00
SINCLAIRE,PLATE,GREEN,SIGNED,8 1/2 IN......................... 22.50
SINCLAIRE,TUMBLER,EXPANDING RIM,THUMBPRINT TYPE DESIGN,
SIGNED......................................................... 14.00


SLAG GLASS IS STREAKED WITH SEVERAL COLORS. THERE WERE
MANY TYPES MADE FROM ABOUT 1880. CARAMEL OR CHOCOLATE
GLASS WAS MADE BY THE INDIANA TUMBLER AND GOBLET
COMPANY OF GREENTOWN,INDIANA,FROM 1900 TO 1903. PINK
SLAG WAS AN AMERICAN VICTORIAN PRODUCT OF UNKNOWN
ORIGIN. PURPLE AND BLUE SLAG WERE MADE IN AMERICAN AND
ENGLISH FACTORIES. RED SLAG IS A VERY LATE VICTORIAN
PRODUCT. OTHER COLORS ARE KNOWN,BUT ARE OF LESS
IMPORTANCE TO THE COLLECTOR.
SLAG,BLUE & MAROON MARBLE COLOR,TOOTHPICK,STRAIGHT PANELS... 18.50
SLAG,BLUE & WHITE,TOOTHPICK,URN,FOOTED........................ 15.00
SLAG,BLUE,DISH,BASKET-LIKE,RIBBED SIDES,SCALLOPED RIM,OVAL,

```
     4 1/2 X 3 IN.....................................   14.50
SLAG,BLUE,HEN,LACY-EDGED BASE,COVER,ATTERBURY...........  145.00
SLAG,BLUE,LAMP BASE,BLOWN,SIGNED,10 1/2 IN.HIGH.........   35.00
SLAG,BLUE,MUG,DWARF SCENES,GREENTOWN....................   28.00
SLAG,BLUE,VASE,ALLOVER PATTERN,FLARED TOP,5 IN. HIGH....   12.50
SLAG,CARAMEL,BOWL,CACTUS PATTERN,9 1/2 X 4 1/4 IN.......   55.00
SLAG,CARAMEL,BOWL,SHELL HANDLES,SHRIMP FINIAL,COVER,DIAMOND
     H MARK,5 IN........................................   12.50
SLAG,CARAMEL,CELERY,LEAF BRACKET,10 3/4 IN. LONG........   49.50
SLAG,CARAMEL,COMPOTE,CACTUS PATTERN,OPEN................   80.00
SLAG,CARAMEL,COMPOTE,CACTUS,5 1/4 IN. X 5 1/2 IN........   59.00
SLAG,CARAMEL,COMPOTE,CACTUS,7 1/2 IN. HIGH.........ILLUS..   95.00
SLAG,CARAMEL,COMPOTE,JELLY,CACTUS.......................   65.00
SLAG,CARAMEL,CREAMER,CACTUS,GREENTOWN...................   47.50
SLAG,CARAMEL,CREAMER,& SUGAR,PANELS,SCROLLS,FLORAL,COVER.   75.00
SLAG,CARAMEL,CREAMER,SHUTTLE PATTERN....................   50.00
SLAG,CARAMEL,CRUET,BLOWN,7 IN. HIGH.....................   15.00
SLAG,CARAMEL,CRUET,CACTUS...............................   65.00
SLAG,CARAMEL,CRUET,LEAF BRACKET,STOPPER.................   55.00
SLAG,CARAMEL,DISH,BUTTER,CACTUS.........................   75.00
SLAG,CARAMEL,DISH,CANDY,CACTUS PATTERN,ON STANDARD,5 1/4 X
     5 1/2 IN.HIGH......................................   76.00
SLAG,CARAMEL,DISH,ROBIN WITH BERRY,COVER,GREENTOWN......  300.00
SLAG,CARAMEL,ELEPHANT,POLISHED BASE,4 IN. HIGH,7 IN. LONG..   75.00
SLAG,CARAMEL,JAR,CRACKER,CACTUS PATTERN,COVER,GREENTOWN,
     8 3/4 IN.TALL......................................   65.00
SLAG,CARAMEL,JAR,CRACKER,CACTUS,COVER,GREENTOWN.........   95.00
SLAG,CARAMEL,LAMP BASE,OIL,CLEAR FONT,WILD ROSE,PEARL
     CHAINS,8 3/4 IN....................................   75.00
```

CACTUS CARAMEL SLAG COMPOTE

```
SLAG,CARAMEL,LAMP SHADE,TULIP SHAPE,BEADED BRASS FRAME,LEAD
     EDGE,PAIR..........................................   50.00
SLAG,CARAMEL,LAMP,TIFFANY-TYPE SHADE,TREE TRUNK-TYPE BASE,
     21 IN.............................................   89.50
SLAG,CARAMEL,LAMP,WILD ROSE,BOWKNOT,CLEAR FONT,GREENTOWN,
     8 IN.TALL..........................................  185.00
SLAG,CARAMEL,LEMONADE,CACTUS............................   28.50
SLAG,CARAMEL,MUG,BEADED RIB,HANDLED.....................   22.50
SLAG,CARAMEL,MUG,CACTUS.................................   45.00
SLAG,CARAMEL,MUG,HERRINGBONE............................   26.50
SLAG,CARAMEL,NAPPIE,CACTUS,TRICORNERED..................   40.00
SLAG,CARAMEL,NAPPIE,LEAF BRACKET,TRIANGULAR.............   29.00
SLAG,CARAMEL,NAPPIE,THREE CORNERS,HANDLE,4 1/2-IN.DIAMETER..   35.00
SLAG,CARAMEL,PITCHER,SHUTTLE PATTERN....................   65.00
SLAG,CARAMEL,PITCHER,WATER,SQUIRREL,GREENTOWN...........  195.00
SLAG,CARAMEL,SAUCE,CACTUS...............................   12.00
SLAG,CARAMEL,SHOT GLASS,FIERY OPAL,BOTTOMS UP...........   11.75
SLAG,CARAMEL,SUGAR,BASKET WEAVE BASE,KITTEN TOP.........   52.00
SLAG,CARAMEL,SUGAR,FERNS,CATTAILS,SWANS,OPEN,4 IN.-DIAMETER.   35.00
SLAG,CARAMEL,SUGAR,FLEUR-DE-LIS,2 HANDLES,LID,GREENTOWN.   47.50
SLAG,CARAMEL,SUGAR,OPEN.................................   35.00
SLAG,CARAMEL,SYRUP,BEAD & DRAPE.........................   77.50
SLAG,CARAMEL,SYRUP,CACTUS PATTERN,GREENTOWN.............   60.00
SLAG,CARAMEL,SYRUP,CACTUS,GREENTOWN.....................   49.00
SLAG,CARAMEL,SYRUP,CORD & DRAPERY.......................   50.00
```

```
SLAG,CARAMEL,TEAPOT,CACTUS.....................................    25.00
SLAG,CARAMEL,TOOTHPICK,CACTUS....................... 25.00 TO     55.00
SLAG,CARAMEL,TOOTHPICK,CACTUS,GREENTOWN.......................    32.50
SLAG,CARAMEL,TOOTHPICK,HOLLY...................................    42.00
SLAG,CARAMEL,TUMBLER,ADVERTISING,UNEEDA MILK BISCUIT.......       39.00
SLAG,CARAMEL,TUMBLER,CACTUS....................... 14.95 TO       35.00
SLAG,CARAMEL,TUMBLER,HEARTS....................................    25.00
SLAG,CARAMEL,TUMBLER,HOLLY.....................................    10.00
SLAG,CARAMEL,TUMBLER,OPALESCENT................................    12.50
SLAG,CARAMEL,TUMBLER,PALM LEAF.................................    19.50
SLAG,CARAMEL,TUMBLER,FLEUR-DE-LIS.............................     24.50
SLAG,CARAMEL,VASE,DEWEY,6 1/2 IN.HIGH.........................     45.00
SLAG,CREAM COLOR,SHADE,LIGHT,IRREGULAR EDGE,2-IN.FITTER,
   3 1/2 IN.HIGH..............................................    10.00
SLAG,GREEN,BOTTLE,COLOGNE,FLASK,GOLD CAP,RENAUD,PARIS,
   PATENT,1817................................................     6.00
SLAG,GREEN,BOWL,TEARDROP & TASSEL,GREENTOWN,8 1/2 IN.........     35.00
SLAG,GREEN,CAKE STANDARD,WAFFLE PATTERN,OPAQUE...............     72.50
SLAG,IVORY,VASE,SHELLS & SNAILS,CAMBRIDGE,OHIO,7 1/2 IN.....      18.50
SLAG,LAMP,CHOCOLATE,WILD ROSE,BOWKNOT,CLEAR FONT,GREENTOWN,
   9 1/2 IN..................................................    140.00
SLAG,ORANGE,JAR,JAM,APPLE SHAPE,BLOSSOMS,LEAF,STEM ON COVER.      25.00
SLAG,PINK,CUP,PUNCH,INVERTED FEATHER & FAN,HANDLE,
   FOOTED...............................................225.00 TO 350.00
SLAG,PINK,TUMBLER,INVERTED FEATHER & FAN............ 375.00 TO   450.00
SLAG,PURPLE,BOOT,WOMAN'S,6 IN.HIGH............................    65.00
SLAG,PURPLE,BOWL,ROSE,ALLOVER FLORAL,THREE-CORNERED,DOLPHIN
   FEET,1850.................................................     45.00
SLAG,PURPLE,BUTTER............................................    75.00
SLAG,PURPLE,CART,FOUR WHEELS,REG.MARK 1880,5 IN.LONG,
   3 1/2 IN.WIDE.............................................     40.00
SLAG,PURPLE,CART,FOUR WHEELS,REG.MARK 1880,5 IN.LONG,
   3 1/4 IN.HIGH.............................................     48.00
SLAG,PURPLE,CELERY............................................    45.00
SLAG,PURPLE,CELERY,8 1/4 IN.HIGH..............................    65.00
SLAG,PURPLE,COMPOTE,FLUTED TOP,THREADED BOWL,4 1/2 IN........     47.00
SLAG,PURPLE,COMPOTE,OPEN......................................   100.00
SLAG,PURPLE,COMPOTE,THREADED,TRANSLUCENT OPALESCENCE,
   4 1/4 IN.HIGH.............................................     70.00
SLAG,PURPLE,CREAMER,PEACOCK MARK,3 IN.........................    28.00
SLAG,PURPLE,CREAMER,SUGAR,FLOWER & PANEL PATTERN,
   CHALLINOR-TAYLOR..........................................     95.00
SLAG,PURPLE,DISH,COVER,FOOTED,5 1/2-IN.DIAMETER...............    62.50
SLAG,PURPLE,DISH,CROUCHING RABBIT COVER,6 IN.................     24.50
SLAG,PURPLE,DISH,DUCK COVER,WAVY BASE,6 IN....................    27.50
SLAG,PURPLE,DISH,HEN WITH CHICKS,COVER,MOTTLED COLORS........     25.00
SLAG,PURPLE,DISH,ROBIN,COVER,5 IN.............................    18.00
SLAG,PURPLE,MATCH HOLDER,ENGLISH REGISTRY MARK,1877..........     20.00
SLAG,PURPLE,MATCH HOLDER,FOOTED...............................    20.00
SLAG,PURPLE,MATCH HOLDER,FOUR PEG FEET,4 IN.HIGH.............     22.00
SLAG,PURPLE,MUG,BIRD & NEST...................................    22.00
SLAG,PURPLE,MUG,BIRD PATTERN....................... 20.00 TO      24.00
SLAG,PURPLE,MUG,BIRDS,NESTS,INTAGLIO CAT BOTTOM,HANDLE......      30.00
SLAG,PURPLE,MUG,BIRDS,TREE,3 1/4 IN.HIGH......................    25.00
SLAG,PURPLE,MUG,NEST,BIRD,FLOWERS,CAT UNDER BASE............      75.00
SLAG,PURPLE,MUG,THREE SINGING BIRDS,HANDLE...................      7.50
SLAG,PURPLE,PITCHER,BAMBOO,ENGLAND,3 IN.HIGH.................     18.50
SLAG,PURPLE,PLATE,CAKE,PEDESTAL,9-IN.DIAMETER,6 IN.HIGH.....      55.00
SLAG,PURPLE,PLATE,OPEN EDGE,10 IN.............................    73.50
SLAG,PURPLE,SPOONER,SCROLL WITH ACANTHUS.....................     30.00
SLAG,PURPLE,THIMBLE,INSCRIBED JUST A THIMBLE FULL,2 1/2 IN..      35.00
SLAG,PURPLE,TOOTHPICK,LOVING CUP STYLE,ENGLISH MARKING......      18.00
SLAG,PURPLE,VASE.......................................ILLUS..    25.00
SLAG,PURPLE,VASE,11 IN.TALL...................................    27.50
SLAG,RED,BOWL,CONSOLE,ON BLACK STAND.........................     35.00
```

PURPLE SLAG VASE

```
SLAG,RED,BOWL,PRINTED CITIZENS MUTUAL TRUST CO,1924,
   9 1/2-IN.DIAMETER.........................................    67.50
SLAG,RED,CANDLESTICK,NORTHWOOD,PAIR...........................   125.00
SLAG,RED,CONSOLE SET,BOWL 9-IN.DIAMETER,PAIR CANDLESTICKS
   9 IN.TALL............................................         135.00
SLAG,RED,DISH,CANDY,COVER,FOOTED.............................     12.50
SLAG,RED,PITCHER,WATER,BULBOUS,THORN HANDLE,7 1/2 IN.TALL...     45.00
SLAG,RED,VASE,BLACK AMETHYST BASE,FOOTED,6 3/4 IN.TALL......     37.50
SLAG,RED,VASE,SWIRL PATTERN,PEDESTAL,9 IN...................     48.00
SLAG,RED,WHITE,CIGARETTE HOLDER,OCTAGONAL,3 IN..............      8.00
SLAG,WHITE,BOWL,LOW,BASKET WEAVE,LATTICED RIM,GATEHEAD MARK,
   8 IN.....................................................     27.50
SLAG,WHITE,VASE,HORSE HEAD HANDLES...........................    10.00
SLAG,WHITE & GREEN,BOWL,EMBOSSED ROSES,THISTLE,SHAMROCK,
   5-IN.DIAMETER...........................................      22.50
```

SLIP IS A THIN MIXTURE OF CLAY AND WATER,ABOUT THE
CONSISTENCY OF SOUR CREAM,THAT IS APPLIED TO THE
POTTERY FOR DECORATION. IF THE POTTERY IS MADE WITH RED
CLAY,THE SLIP IS MIXED WITH YELLOW CLAY.

```
SLIPWARE,BOWL,GRAY,PENNSYLVANIA DUTCH,SHALLOW,
   7 1/4-IN.DIAMETER.......................................      15.00
SLIPWARE,PLATE,BROWN-RED,BLACK ON BOTTOM,9 1/2-IN.DIAMETER,
   2 IN.DEEP...............................................      35.00
SLIPWARE,PLATTER,BROWN,CREAM COLOR,ORNATE DECOR,OVAL........    125.00
SLIPWARE,POT,BEAN,RED,NEW ENGLAND...........................     27.50
SLIPWARE,POT,RED,BROWN GLAZE INSIDE,9 1/2 IN. X 9 1/2 IN....     15.00
```

SMITH BROTHERS GLASS WAS MADE AFTER 1878. THE OWNERS
HAD WORKED FOR THE MOUNT WASHINGTON GLASS COMPANY IN
NEW BEDFORD,MASSACHUSETTS,FOR SEVEN YEARS BEFORE GOING
INTO THEIR OWN SHOP. SOME OF THE DESIGNS WERE SIMILAR.

```
SMITH BROTHERS,BOWL,CREAM GROUND,WHITE SHASTA DAISIES,BEADED
   TOP.....................................................      75.00
SMITH BROTHERS,BOWL,MELON RIB,COVER,SIGNED...................    195.00
SMITH BROTHERS,BOWL,MELON SECTIONS,ROSE & BLUE
   CHRYSANTHEMUMS,5 1/2 IN.................................     125.00
SMITH BROTHERS,BOWL,MONUMENTAL,BLUE FEATHER SCROLLS,GILT,
   FLORAL,VINES............................................     275.00
SMITH BROTHERS,BOWL,PINK CARNATIONS,BEADED TOP,MELON RIB,
   MATTE,8 1/2 IN..........................................     135.00
SMITH BROTHERS,BOWL,ROSE,BEADED TOP,SHASTA DAISY DECOR......    100.00
SMITH BROTHERS,BOWL,ROSE,BEADED,PANSY DECOR..................     95.00
SMITH BROTHERS,BOWL,ROSE,CREAM GROUND,RIBBED,HAND-PAINTED
   VIOLETS.................................................     130.00
SMITH BROTHERS,BOWL,ROSE,FLORAL ON FRONT....................     85.00
SMITH BROTHERS,BOWL,ROSE,LAVENDER VIOLETS,CREAM GROUND,
   HAND-PAINTED............................................     130.00
SMITH BROTHERS,BOWL,ROSE,MELON RIB,PANSY DECOR,BEADING,
   RAMPANT LION MARK.......................................     150.00
SMITH BROTHERS,BOWL,ROSE,PUSSY WILLOW DECOR,CREAM GROUND,
   BEADED TOP..............................................      97.50
SMITH BROTHERS,CREAMER & SUGAR,WHITE,BLUE PANSIES,SILVER
   COLLAR..................................................     325.00
SMITH BROTHERS,CREAMER,MELON SECTION,AUTUMN COLOR OAK
   LEAVES,ACORNS,GILT......................................     125.00
SMITH BROTHERS,JAR,BEIGE,RIBBED,ALLOVER GOLD GLASS JEWELS,
   COVER,SIGNED............................................     275.00
SMITH BROTHERS,JAR,BISCUIT,BLUE SHADING,DAISIES,SILVER TOP,
   SIGNED..................................................     225.00
SMITH BROTHERS,JAR,COOKIE,DAISY DECOR,RESILVERED,SIGNED.....    225.00
SMITH BROTHERS,JAR,COOKIE,FLORAL,SIGNED.....................    185.00
SMITH BROTHERS,JAR,COOKIE,FLORAL,SIGNED,RAMPANT LION........    200.00
SMITH BROTHERS,JAR,COOKIE,MELON RIB,ACORN & LEAF DECOR,
   SIGNED..................................................     170.00
SMITH BROTHERS,JAR,COOKIE,MELON RIB,SATIN,WISTERIAS,GOLD,
   MARK....................................................     350.00
SMITH BROTHERS,JAR,CRACKER,BURMESE COLOR,GOLD FLORAL BAND,
   SILVER BAIL.............................................     275.00
SMITH BROTHERS,JAR,MELON RIB,SQUATTY,SILVER LID,BAIL,FACTORY
   MARK,5 IN...............................................     175.00
SMITH BROTHERS,JAR,PINK,YELLOW TO WHITE,FLORAL,MELON RIB,
   SILVER COVER............................................      65.00
SMITH BROTHERS,JAR,POWDER,MELON RIB.........................    175.00
SMITH BROTHERS,MUSTARD,RIBBED,BLUE DOTS,FLORAL,SILVER PLATE
   TOP.....................................................      55.00
SMITH BROTHERS,PLATE,SANTA MARIA............................     65.00
SMITH BROTHERS,PLATE,SANTA MARIA SHIP IN SEPIA COLOR,
   WORLD'S FAIR 1893.......................................     160.00
```

SMITH BROTHERS,PLATE,SANTA MARIA,7 IN.......................  95.00
SMITH BROTHERS,SALT & PEPPER,EGG SHAPE,BURMESE COLOR,ENAMEL
  FLORAL,1889.............................................  60.00
SMITH BROTHERS,SALT,MASTER,MELON RIB,GOLD BEADED TOP,PRUNUS
  BLOSSOMS................................................  65.00
SMITH BROTHERS,SALT,RIBBED,GOLD DECOR,PAIR..................  65.00
SMITH BROTHERS,SHAKER,SUGAR,RIBBED,OPAQUE WHITE,VIOLETS,
  SILVER TOP.............................................. 155.00
SMITH BROTHERS,SUGAR & CREAMER,SUGAR HANDLED & COVERED,
  ENAMELED,SIGNED......................................... 195.00
SMITH BROTHERS,SWAN,BLACK AMETHYST,SIGNED...................  35.00
SMITH BROTHERS,SWEETMEAT,CREAMY GROUND,PINK & BLUE VIOLETS,
  LEAVES,SIGNED........................................... 195.00
SMITH BROTHERS,TOOTHPICK,APPLE BLOSSOM DECOR................  90.00
SMITH BROTHERS,VASE,BIRD DECOR,GLOSSY,ENAMEL DECOR,NEW
  BEDFORD,MASS............................................ 115.00
SMITH BROTHERS,VASE,BLUE GROUND,GILT RINGS,HUMMINGBIRD,
  WOODLAND FLOWERS........................................  60.00
SMITH BROTHERS,VASE,BLUE,DOUBLE PROTRUDED RINGS &
  MEDALLIONS,8 IN.........................................  98.00
SMITH BROTHERS,VASE,BLUE,PROTRUDED RINGS & MEDALLIONS,8 IN..  98.00
SMITH BROTHERS,VASE,BURMESE,PINK TO YELLOW,RASPBERRIES,
  LEAVES,ACID CUT......................................... 115.00
SMITH BROTHERS,VASE,LIGHT TO DARK GREEN,TWO BIRDS,ARROWHEAD
  LEAVES................................................. 110.00
SMITH BROTHERS,VASE,OVOID,GREEN & GOLD GROUND,BIRDS,BRANCH
  BLOSSOMS................................................  35.00
SMITH BROTHERS,VASE,ROBIN'S-EGG BLUE,BIRD DECOR,JUTTED
  RINGS,8 IN.HIGH......................................... 120.00
SMITH BROTHERS,VASE,YELLOW-GREEN GROUND,RED SWAMP ROSE,BLUE
  LEAVES.................................................  60.00
  SNUFF BOTTLE,SEE BOTTLE,SNUFF

     SOAPSTONE IS A MINERAL THAT WAS USED FOR FOOTWARMERS
     OR GRIDDLES BECAUSE OF ITS HEAT-RETAINING PROPERTIES.
     CHINESE SOAPSTONE CARVINGS OF THE NINETEENTH AND
     TWENTIETH CENTURIES ARE FOUND IN MANY ANTIQUE SHOPS.
SOAPSTONE,ASHTRAY,RED MOTTLE...............................   3.50
SOAPSTONE,BED WARMER,6 IN. X 8 IN..........................   8.00
SOAPSTONE,BOOKEND,BEAVER,CARVED,DARK BROWN,PAIR............  15.00
SOAPSTONE,BOOKEND,CARVED FLOWERS & LEAVES,PAIR.............  65.00
SOAPSTONE,BOOKEND,CARVED POT WITH FLOWERS,5 IN.HIGH,
  4 IN.WIDE,PAIR.........................................  30.00
SOAPSTONE,BOOKEND,DARK BROWN FLORAL,BIRD,PAIR.............  25.00
SOAPSTONE,BOTTLE,SNUFF,RETICULATED,19TH CENTURY........... 725.00
SOAPSTONE,BOX,CARVED SCENE,3 IN. X 5 IN. X 2 IN...........  20.00
SOAPSTONE,CANDLEHOLDER,DOUBLE,CARVED LEAVES,3 1/2 IN.LONG,
  2 IN.HIGH..............................................   7.00
SOAPSTONE,CIGARETTE HOLDER,TWO CUP-SHAPED CONTAINERS,CARVED
  BASE...................................................  27.00
SOAPSTONE,DISH,PIN,FRUIT DESIGN,GRAY & BLACK,4 IN.DIAMETER..   5.00
SOAPSTONE,FIGURINE,CHINESE ELDER,CARVED,8 IN.HIGH..........  35.00
SOAPSTONE,FIGURINE,ELEPHANT,DOG AT THE BASE,CARVED,
  5 1/2 IN.HIGH..........................................  45.00
SOAPSTONE,FIGURINE,ELEPHANT,2 1/2 IN......................   6.50
SOAPSTONE,FIGURINE,ELEPHANT,3 IN..........................   7.50
SOAPSTONE,FIGURINE,KWAN YIN SEATED ON LOTUS THRONE,CARVED,
  GREEN,7 IN.............................................  38.00
SOAPSTONE,FIGURINE,LADY,DARK SOAPSTONE BASE,9 3/4 IN.HIGH...  75.00
SOAPSTONE,FIGURINE,MONKEYS,SEE,HEAR,SPEAK NO EVIL,CARVED,
  MARKED CHINA...........................................  17.00
SOAPSTONE,FIGURINE,OFFICIAL,ROBES,BEARD,HAT,WOODEN STAND,
  CHINA..................................................  15.00
SOAPSTONE,FIGURINE,WOMAN,WARRIOR,CARVED,1810,CHINA,
  5 1/2 IN.HIGH..........................................  97.50
SOAPSTONE,GROUP OF THREE FOO DOGS,CARVED,5 IN.TALL........  70.00
SOAPSTONE,HOLDER,CIGARETTE-MATCH,FLORAL,MONKEYS,VINES,CARVED  32.00
SOAPSTONE,HOLDER,CIGARETTE,CARVED,LEAVES,CORAL TYPE CARVING
  ON SIDE,BASE...........................................  25.00
SOAPSTONE,INCENSE BURNER,ALLOVER CARVINGS,MONKEYS,VINES,
  4 IN.DIAMETER..........................................  55.00
SOAPSTONE,MATCH HOLDER,NO EVIL MONKEYS ON OUTSIDE.........   6.50
SOAPSTONE,TOOTHPICK,FLORAL CARVING,MARKED CHINA,5 IN.WIDE,
  3 IN.HIGH..............................................  15.00
SOAPSTONE,TOOTHPICK,LEAF & NUT DECOR,TWO SECTIONS.........   8.50
SOAPSTONE,TOOTHPICK,THREE MONKEYS.........................   5.00
SOAPSTONE,TOOTHPICK,THREE MONKEYS,MOTTLED,2 1/2 IN.HIGH...   9.00
SOAPSTONE,VASE,BROWN MOTTLE,CARVED LEAVES,3 IN.HIGH.......   7.00
SOAPSTONE,VASE,CARVED FLORAL,LEAVES,NEUTRAL TO BROWN,DOUBLE,
  3 IN.TALL..............................................  18.00
SOAPSTONE,VASE,CARVED,FLOWER SPRAY.......................   6.50

SOAPSTONE,VASE,DOUBLE,CARVED PEONIES,BIRDS,AMBER TO GREEN
  COLOR,9 IN............................................ 65.00
SOAPSTONE,VASE,ETCHED,BROWN & BLACK,4 1/4 IN.............. 15.00
SOAPSTONE,VASE,FLOWERS & LEAVES CARVED ON FRONT,
  8 3/4 IN.HIGH......................................... 37.50
SOFT PASTE,BONBONNIERE,HEAD OF WILLIAM SHAKESPEARE......... 450.00
SOFT PASTE,BOWL,WHITE RESERVES,ORANGE,SIGNED ALI,GOUDA,
  HOLLAND,1856......................................... 32.00
SOFT PASTE,JUG,RIBBED BODY,INTERTWINED LEAF TERMINALS,
  HANDLES,6 X 4 IN...................................... 55.00
SOFT PASTE,MUG,BLACK TRANSFER SCENE,PINK LUSTER RIM,ENGLAND. 22.00
SOFT PASTE,MUG,PORTRAIT,VICTORIA,1837-1897................ 25.00
SOFT PASTE,PITCHER,DEER HUNTING SCENE,BLUE & PINK LUSTER,
  6 IN.HIGH............................................ 45.00
SOFT PASTE,PITCHER,FLORAL GARLANDS,SQUAT BODY,ORNATE HANDLE,
  10 3/4 IN............................................ 45.00
SOFT PASTE,PLATE,BIRD,POLYCHROME......................... 65.00
SOFT PASTE,PLATE,COTTAGE,CHILDREN,FISHING SCENE,BLUE,WHITE,
  6 3/4 IN............................................. 18.00
SOFT PASTE,PLATE,TODDY,BLUE WILLOW,ENGLAND,CIRCA 1800,
  5 1/2-IN.DIAMETER.................................... 10.00
SOFT PASTE,TEAPOT,SUGAR,CREAMER,TWO CUPS & SAUCERS,CHILD'S,
  1850,FRANCE.......................................... 75.00
SOFT PASTE,TUREEN,ENGLISH,18TH CENTURY................... 350.00
SOFT PASTE,VASE,COBALT,GREEN,RED,YELLOW UNDER CLEAR GLAZE,
  1864,FAIENCE......................................... 125.00
SOFT PASTE,VASE,FLOWER-ENCRUSTED,HANDLES,FOOT,PAIR 9 IN.,ONE
  10 1/2 IN............................................ 175.00
SOFT PASTE,VASE,YELLOW,MORGAN TYPE,9 IN.TALL.............. 195.00
SOUVENIR,1915 PAN PACIFIC EXPOSITION,BRONZE PENNY,
  1 3/4-IN.DIAMETER.................................... 7.50
SOUVENIR,ASHTRAY,PAN-AMERICAN EXPOSITION,BUFFALO,1901,WHITE
  METAL................................................ 6.50
SOUVENIR,BANNER,SAYS WELCOME LINDBERGH................... 3.50
SOUVENIR BASKET,CORONATION,KING GEORGE VI,1937,CLEAR,FLORAL,
  DEWDROPS............................................. 17.50
SOUVENIR,BEAKER,CORONATION,QUEEN VICTORIA,1837-1897,4 IN.
  TALL................................................. 25.50
SOUVENIR,BELL,WORLD'S FAIR 1893,GLASS,FROSTED SWIRL HANDLE,
  GLASS CLAPPER........................................ 35.00
SOUVENIR,BOWL,ROSE,1893 WORLD'S FAIR,NEW ENGLAND,PEACHBLOW.. 175.00
SOUVENIR,BUTTON,PRESIDENT WILSON,DAUGHTERS,WHITE HOUSE,
  9-IN.DIAMETER........................................ 6.00
SOUVENIR,CLOCK,SHELF,CENTURY OF PROGRESS EXP.,CHICAGO,1933,
  WIND-UP.............................................. 9.75
SOUVENIR,CREAMER & SUGAR,FOOTED,GOLD TRIM,LACY HANDLES,
  COBALT & WHITE....................................... 12.00
SOUVENIR,CREAMER,HEART BASE,MCKEESPORT,PA.,RUBY,CLEAR....... 8.00
SOUVENIR,CREAMER,HEART BASE,PHILADELPHIA,PA.,RUBY,CLEAR..... 8.00
SOUVENIR,CREAMER,LAURA DOCK,1903,GREEN,GOLD,COLORADO
  PATTERN,3 1/2 IN..................................... 16.50
SOUVENIR,CUP & SAUCER,BRIDGEPORT,VT.,PIERCED HANDLE,GOLD,
  FOOTED,GERMANY....................................... 8.50
SOUVENIR,CUP & SAUCER,IOWA COLLEGE FOR THE BLIND,VINTON,IOWA 4.00
SOUVENIR,CUP & SAUCER,SOUVENIR OF TILTON,NEW HAMPSHIRE...... 3.75
SOUVENIR,CUP,HEART BASE,AKRON,OHIO....................... 8.00
SOUVENIR,CUP,HOT SPRINGS,ARK.,RUBY & CLEAR............... 12.00
SOUVENIR,CUP,PAN AMERICAN EXPOSITION,1901,RED-FLASHED...... 7.50
SOUVENIR,CUP,SAUCER,PHILA,EXHIBITION,1876,PORTRAIT,MARTHA
  WASHINGTON........................................... 18.50
SOUVENIR,CUP,TRAVELING,PEWTER CASE,CENTENNIAL,T.H.SNYDER,
  PHILA.,1876.......................................... 20.00
SOUVENIR DISH,CORONATION QUEEN ELIZABETH II,1953,5 IN.LONG.. 3.95
SOUVENIR,DISH,IMPORTED FOR THE INDIAN STORE,OKLAHOMA CITY,
  OKLA.,PICTURE........................................ 6.50
SOUVENIR,DISH,MADE IN GERMANY ESPECIALLY FOR J.H.EBERS CANDY
  PARLOR............................................... 6.50
SOUVENIR DISH,SHELL SHAPE,SANKATY HEAD LIGHTHOUSE,NANTUCKET. 2.50
SOUVENIR,GOBLET,RUBY TOP,CLEAR BABY THUMBPRINT ON BASE,
  WATERLOO,IOWA........................................ 12.50
SOUVENIR HANDKERCHIEF,CENTENNIAL,MEMORIAL HALL ART GALLERY,
  PHILA.,1876.......................................... 15.00
SOUVENIR,HATCHET,WORLD'S FAIR,1893,CLEAR GLASS............ 17.50
SOUVENIR HATPIN,ST.LOUIS EXPOSITION,1904,PAIR............ 6.00
SOUVENIR,JAR,COOKIE,NEWCASTLE EXPOSITION,1929,BLUE,WHITE,
  CASTLES,PANELS....................................... 29.50
SOUVENIR,JUG,NEVILLE CHAMBERLAIN,LION HANDLES,PARAGON,
  5 1/4 IN.HIGH........................................ 80.00
SOUVENIR,MATCH SAFE,CONEY ISLAND........................ 5.00
SOUVENIR,MATCH SAFE,POCKET,ST.LOUIS WORLD'S FAIR,1904,
  STERLING SILVER...................................... 14.00

```
SOUVENIR,MATCH SAFE,ST.LOUIS EXPOSITION,1904..............     4.50
SOUVENIR,MUG,B.P.O.E.,ELK'S,BLUE..........................     9.50
SOUVENIR,MUG,BUTTON & ARCHES,RED..........................     6.50
SOUVENIR,MUG,CENTURY OF PROGRESS,1933,RED,BLUE,MARKED
   BAUSCHER................................................    10.00
SOUVENIR,MUG,CHILDS,INDIANAPOLIS,IND.,CHILDREN AT PARTY,
   3 CROWN,GERMANY.........................................     9.50
SOUVENIR,MUG,COLORADO,GREEN...............................    16.00
SOUVENIR,MUG,CORONATION KING EDWARD VIII,MAY 12,1937,
   PORCELAIN...............................................    10.00
SOUVENIR,MUG,CORONATION OF EDWARD VIII,PORCELAIN,
   4 1/2 IN.HIGH...........................................    10.00
SOUVENIR,MUG,PINK AROUND TOP & HANDLE,SCENE,MEMORIAL
   HAMIOTA,MANITOBA........................................     5.00
SOUVENIR,MUG,RICHMOND.VIRGINIA,MARKED GERMANY.............     8.50
SOUVENIR,MUG,SCENE OF NEW MACCABEE TEMPLE,PORT HURON,
   MICHIGAN................................................     5.00
SOUVENIR,MUG,WORLD'S FAIR,1893,RED BLOCK..................    12.50
SOUVENIR,PAPERWEIGHT,CITY HALL,KINGSTON,N.Y.,4 X 2 IN.....     2.95
SOUVENIR,PAPERWEIGHT,DEERING PARK,PORTLAND,MAINE,4 X
   2 1/2 IN................................................     2.95
SOUVENIR,PAPERWEIGHT,GOLDEN GATE INTERNATIONAL EXPOSITION,
   1940,3 IN.SQ............................................     5.00
SOUVENIR,PAPERWEIGHT,STATE BATH HOUSE,REVERE BEACH,MASS.,4 X
   2 1/2 IN................................................     2.95
SOUVENIR,PAPERWEIGHT,WASHINGTON STATUE,PUBLIC GARDENS,BOSTON    2.95
SOUVENIR,PAPERWEIGHT,WATERFRONT,BREWER,BANGOR,MAINE,STEAMER
   PENOBSCOT...............................................     3.95
SOUVENIR,PIN,SAN FRANCISCO EXPOSITION,1939,GOLDEN GATE
   BRIDGE.................................................     2.50
SOUVENIR,PITCHER,BLISS & NYE,NEW BEDFORD,MASS.,CENTENNIAL
   1787-1887..............................................    35.00
SOUVENIR,PLATE,ALASKA YUKON PACIFIC EXPO.,SEATTLE,1909,
   STAFFORDSHIRE..........................................    25.00
SOUVENIR,PLATE,ASBURY PARK,N.J.,SCENIC,BLUE..............    12.00
SOUVENIR,PLATE,BOSTON,FANEUIL HALL,WEDGWOOD,10 IN.DIAMETER..     8.00
SOUVENIR,PLATE,BREWSTER MEMORIAL HALL,WOLFSBORO,N.H.........     5.00
SOUVENIR,PLATE,CAPITAL ISLAND,MAINE,OLD SAILING SHIPS,
   8 1/2 IN.DIAMETER.......................................     2.95
SOUVENIR,PLATE,CAPITOL ISLAND,MAINE,SAILING SHIPS,PINK,
   WHITE,8 1/2 IN..........................................     4.75
SOUVENIR,PLATE,COURTHOUSE,MONTEVIDEO,MINNESOTA,
   7 1/4 IN.DIAMETER.......................................     2.95
SOUVENIR,PLATE,FANEUIL HALL,BOSTON,OPENWORK BORDER,7 IN.....     3.75
SOUVENIR,PLATE,HEAD OF NEWFOUNDLAND DOG,SOUVENIR OF
   SALAMANCA,N.Y..........................................     9.50
SOUVENIR,PLATE,HIGHLAND LIGHT,CAPE COD,MASS.,BLUE,WHITE,
   8 IN...................................................     4.95
SOUVENIR,PLATE,ISRAELI,MASADA,1968.......................     7.50
SOUVENIR,PLATE,ISRAELI,RACHEL'S TOMB,1969................     6.00
SOUVENIR,PLATE,ISRAELI,TOWER OF DAVID,1967...............    10.00
SOUVENIR,PLATE,ISRAELI,WAILING WALL,1967.................    10.00
SOUVENIR,PLATE,NEW YORK CITY,SCENIC,BLUE.................    12.00
SOUVENIR,PLATE,NEW YORK WORLDS FAIR,1939,AMERICAN POTTER....    12.50
SOUVENIR,PLATE,PLATTSBURGH,BLUE ON WHITE,ENGLAND MARK.......    10.00
SOUVENIR,PLATE,PROVIDENCE,R.I.,NEW R.R.STATION,ARCADE,CITY
   HALL,8 IN..............................................     4.95
SOUVENIR,PLATE,RHODES,PEARCE,MAHONEY FURNITURE CO.,TAMPA....     5.00
SOUVENIR,PLATE,ST.LOUIS WORLD'S FAIR,1904,PALACE,BUILDING,
   AUSTRIA................................................    10.00
SOUVENIR,PLATE,STEVENS POINT,WISCONSIN,GREEN & PURPLE
   GRAPES,GOLD............................................     4.50
SOUVENIR,PLATE,THE CAROLINA,PINEHURST,N.C.,HAND-PAINTED,
   8 1/2 IN...............................................     4.95
SOUVENIR,PLATE,TOWER,PARAGON PARK,NANTASKET BEACH,MASS.,
   7-IN.DIAMETER..........................................     3.75
SOUVENIR,PLATE,UTAH STATE,MORMON SCENES,9 IN..............     7.00
SOUVENIR,PLATE,W.ADAMS & CO...............................     8.50
SOUVENIR,PLATE,WASHINGTON,BLUE ON WHITE,ENGLAND...........    10.00
SOUVENIR,PLATE,WEST VIRGINIA CENTENNIAL,RED BIRD,BEAR,10 IN.     6.50
SOUVENIR,PLATE,WHEELOCK,INTERNATIONAL EXPOSITION,CALIF.,
   1915,SCENE.............................................    10.00
SOUVENIR,SHAKER,SALT,COLUMBIAN EXHIBITION,1893,WHITE SATIN,
   SIGNED LIBBEY..........................................    25.00
SOUVENIR,SHOE,COLUMBIAN EXPOSITION,1893,6 IN.LONG.........    35.00
SOUVENIR,SHOE,CURLED TOE,PINK LUSTER,BUFFALO,N.Y.,6 IN......    15.00
SOUVENIR,SHOE,FROSTED,BOW,GILLINDER & SONS,CENTENNIAL
   EXHIBITION,1876........................................    30.00
SOUVENIR,SHOE,WORLD'S FAIR,1893,CAMPHOR GLASS,LIBBEY GLASS
   CO.,TOLEDO.............................................    25.00
SOUVENIR,SHOT GLASS,MOERLEIN CAFE,211 W.FEDERAL ST.,
```

```
YOUNGSTOWN,OHIO.......................................      6.50
SOUVENIR,SHOT GLASS,R,E.JOHNSON,134 BALTO ST.,CUMBERLAND,
  MARYLAND...............................................     5.00
SOUVENIR,SLIPPER,EVANS HOTEL,HOT SPRINGS,S.D.,PORCELAIN,
  GERMANY................................................     9.50
SOUVENIR SPOON,ACTOR,RAMON NAVARRO......................      3.75
SOUVENIR SPOON,ACTOR,THOMAS MEIGHAN.....................      3.75
SOUVENIR SPOON,ACTRESS,GLORIA SWANSON...................      3.75
SOUVENIR SPOON,ACTRESS,MARION DAVIES....................      3.75
SOUVENIR SPOON,ACTRESS,NORMA TALMADGE...................      3.75
SOUVENIR SPOON,ACTRESS,POLA NEGRI.......................      3.75
SOUVENIR SPOON,ADVERTISING,TOWLE'S LOG CABIN SYRUP..........  2.00
SOUVENIR SPOON,GOLD-PLATED,ENAMELED, FROM AUSTRALIA.........  5.00
SOUVENIR SPOON,GOLD-PLATED,ENAMELED,FROM CZECHOSLOVAKIA.....  5.00
SOUVENIR SPOON,GOLD-PLATED,ENAMELED,FROM AUSTRIA...........   5.00
SOUVENIR SPOON,GOLD-PLATED,ENAMELED,FROM RUSSIA............   5.00
SOUVENIR SPOON,GOLD-PLATED,ENAMELED,FROM SWEDEN...........    5.00
SOUVENIR,SPOON,SILVER,BLOOMINGTON,ILLINOIS.................   8.00
SOUVENIR SPOON,SILVER PLATE,ACTRESS,POLA NEGRI.............   4.50
SOUVENIR SPOON,SILVER PLATE,HANDLE SHAPE OF FISH,
  TERCENTENARY 1939.....................................      2.75
SOUVENIR SPOON,SILVER PLATE,MARY PICKFORD,PORTRAIT,
  SIGNATURE,ONEIDA......................................      7.00
SOUVENIR SPOON,SILVER PLATE,OLD ORCHARD BEACH,MAINE.......    2.00
SOUVENIR SPOON,SILVER PLATE,PAN AMERICAN EXPOSITION,1901....  2.00
SOUVENIR SPOON,SILVER PLATE,PANAMA PACIFIC EXPOSITION,NEW
  JERSEY................................................      2.50
SOUVENIR SPOON,SILVER PLATE,TEASPOON,CHARLIE MCCARTHY.......  3.75
SOUVENIR SPOON,SILVER PLATE,TIP-TOP HOUSE,MT.WASHINGTON,N.H.  2.75
SOUVENIR SPOON,SILVER PLATE,WORLD'S FOOD FAIR,1896..........  2.00
SOUVENIR SPOON,SILVER PLATE,1893 COLUMBIAN EXPOSITION
  BUILDING..............................................      2.00
SOUVENIR SPOON,SILVER PLATE,1933 WORLD'S FAIR,CHICAGO,SCENE
  IN BOWL,6.............................................     12.00
SOUVENIR SPOON,SILVER PLATE,1939 WORLD'S FAIR,NEW YORK,SET
  OF 6..................................................     18.00
SOUVENIR SPOON,STERLING SILVER,ATLANTA,GEORGIA,BALE OF
  COTTON...............................................       3.95
SOUVENIR SPOON,STERLING SILVER,BEAUMONT,TEXAS,RICE-GROWING
  SCENE................................................       5.00
SOUVENIR SPOON,STERLING SILVER,BOSTON TEA PARTY,1773,INDIAN,
  BUNKER HILL..........................................       7.50
SOUVENIR SPOON,STERLING SILVER,BOSTON,PAUL REVERE,4 IN.....   9.00
SOUVENIR SPOON,STERLING SILVER,BRADFORD ACADEMY............   2.95
SOUVENIR SPOON,STERLING SILVER,BROWNS VALLEY,MINN.,DEMITASSE  5.00
SOUVENIR SPOON,STERLING SILVER,CALIFORNIA,MINER,REDWOOD,
  GOLDEN GATE..........................................       6.00
SOUVENIR SPOON,STERLING SILVER,CAPITAL ALBANY,CLAREMONT,
  ROBERT FULTON........................................       8.50
SOUVENIR SPOON,STERLING SILVER,CHARTER OAK,HARTFORD,
  CONNECTICUT,6 IN.....................................      14.50
SOUVENIR SPOON,STERLING SILVER,CHARTER OAK,TREE,ELK,WATER,
  DATES................................................       5.00
SOUVENIR SPOON,STERLING SILVER,CHICAGO LIBRARY,DEMITASSE....  4.75
SOUVENIR SPOON,STERLING SILVER,CLIFF HOUSE.................   5.50
SOUVENIR SPOON,STERLING SILVER,COLORADO STATE SEAL,WORD
  DENVER...............................................       6.00
SOUVENIR SPOON,STERLING SILVER,COLORADO,MINER,FULL FIGURE... 11.00
SOUVENIR SPOON,STERLING SILVER,COLORADO,WOMAN,STATE CAPITAL
  IN BOWL..............................................      10.00
SOUVENIR SPOON,STERLING SILVER,COLUMBIA WORLD'S FAIR
  EXPOSITION,1892......................................       8.50
SOUVENIR SPOON,STERLING SILVER,CONVENT OF LA RABIDA,
  COLUMBUS,SHIP,1898...................................       7.50
SOUVENIR SPOON,STERLING SILVER,COURTHOUSE,TAUNTON,MASS......  2.95
SOUVENIR SPOON,STERLING SILVER,CROSBY INN,BELFAST,MAINE.....  2.95
SOUVENIR SPOON,STERLING SILVER,DEMITASSE,MONTREAL,ENAMEL
  HANDLE...............................................       6.00
SOUVENIR SPOON,STERLING SILVER,DEMITASSE,SARATOGA..........   5.00
SOUVENIR SPOON,STERLING SILVER,DEMITASSE,WORLD'S FAIR,1892,
  NEW YORK.............................................       6.00
SOUVENIR SPOON,STERLING SILVER,DEMITASSE,INDIAN HEAD HANDLE,
  ALBANY,N.Y...........................................       8.00
SOUVENIR SPOON,STERLING SILVER,DEMITASSE,INDIAN WARRIOR,
  TWISTED HANDLE.......................................       7.00
SOUVENIR SPOON,STERLING SILVER,DEMITASSE,NORTH DAKOTA,
  GOLD-WASHED..........................................       7.50
SOUVENIR SPOON,STERLING SILVER,DETROIT/WINDSOR,HARBOR SCENE,
  INDIAN,CORN..........................................       5.00
SOUVENIR SPOON,STERLING SILVER,ENAMELED TOP,QUEBEC,CANADA... 2.95
SOUVENIR SPOON,STERLING SILVER,FRESNO,CALIFORNIA,FOUR
```

```
BUILDINGS,FRUIT.........................................   5.75
SOUVENIR SPOON,STERLING SILVER,G.A.R.,THE CAP.............   7.00
SOUVENIR SPOON,STERLING SILVER,GOLDEN GATE EXPOSITION,1939..   9.00
SOUVENIR SPOON,STERLING SILVER,GRAND UNION HOTEL,SARATOGA,
   N.Y.,4 IN.LONG........................................   3.50
SOUVENIR SPOON,STERLING SILVER,HAVRE,MONTANA.................   7.25
SOUVENIR SPOON,STERLING SILVER,HOT SPRINGS,CUTOUT ARK,JUG,
   SAW..................................................   9.00
SOUVENIR SPOON,STERLING SILVER,HOTEL DEL MONTE,4 IN.LONG....   3.50
SOUVENIR SPOON,STERLING SILVER,I.P.E.,1915,CUTOUT POLAR BEAR
   HANDLE................................................  15.00
SOUVENIR SPOON,STERLING SILVER,INDIANAPOLIS,INDIANA,BUFFALO,
   LOG CABIN.............................................   8.50
SOUVENIR SPOON,STERLING SILVER,IRELAND,SHAMROCKS,HARP,
   BLARNEY CASTLE........................................   5.50
SOUVENIR SPOON,STERLING SILVER,JUNEAU,MILWAUKEE,PIONEER
   HOLDING MUSKET........................................   5.00
SOUVENIR SPOON,STERLING SILVER,LOUISIANA PURCHASE
   EXPOSITION,1903.......................................   7.50
SOUVENIR SPOON,STERLING SILVER,MACCABEE TEMPLE,PORT HURON,
   MICHIGAN..............................................   3.95
SOUVENIR SPOON,STERLING SILVER,MANISTIQUE,MICHIGAN..........   3.95
SOUVENIR SPOON,STERLING SILVER,MARBLEHEAD,MASS.,COASTAL
   SCENE.................................................   5.00
SOUVENIR SPOON,STERLING SILVER,MIAMI,CUTOUT POINSETTIA
   HANDLE................................................   9.00
SOUVENIR SPOON,STERLING SILVER,MILES STANDISH,JOHN,PRISCILLA   6.50
SOUVENIR SPOON,STERLING SILVER,MILWAUKEE,SCENES,ENGRAVED
   8/11/1911.............................................   7.00
SOUVENIR SPOON,STERLING SILVER,MINNEAPOLIS..................   7.00
SOUVENIR SPOON,STERLING SILVER,MINNEHAHA FALLS..............   8.50
SOUVENIR SPOON,STERLING SILVER,MISSION INN,RIVERSIDE,CALIF.,
   ORANGES,BELL..........................................   6.50
SOUVENIR SPOON,STERLING SILVER,MOBILE,ALABAMA,DEMITASSE.....   4.50
SOUVENIR SPOON,STERLING SILVER,MORMON TEMPLE,SALT LAKE CITY,
   MASTER SALT...........................................   8.50
SOUVENIR SPOON,STERLING SILVER,MT.VERNON,VA.................   8.00
SOUVENIR SPOON,STERLING SILVER,NATIVITY SCENE IN BOWL,BELL,
   STAR,CROSS............................................  14.50
SOUVENIR SPOON,STERLING SILVER,NEW YORK,SKYLINE.............   8.50
SOUVENIR SPOON,STERLING SILVER,NEWPORT,TWISTED HANDLE,CLAM
   ON TIP................................................   6.00
SOUVENIR SPOON,STERLING SILVER,NIAGARA FALLS,INDIAN HEAD,
   6 IN..................................................  12.50
SOUVENIR SPOON,STERLING SILVER,OLD STATE HOUSE,BOSTON.......   2.95
SOUVENIR SPOON,STERLING SILVER,ORIENTAL,BIKE,SCIMITAR,
   WALTHAM MFG. CO.......................................   6.50
SOUVENIR SPOON,STERLING SILVER,ORLANDO,FLORIDA,CUTOUT PALM
   TREE..................................................   9.00
SOUVENIR SPOON,STERLING SILVER,PAN AMERICAN EXPOSITION,1901,
   INDIAN................................................   6.00
SOUVENIR SPOON,STERLING SILVER,PANAMA.......................   4.00
SOUVENIR SPOON,STERLING SILVER,PETOSKEY,MICH.,CUTOUT FULL
   LENGTH INDIAN.........................................   9.00
SOUVENIR SPOON,STERLING SILVER,PORTLAND,OREGON..............   5.50
SOUVENIR SPOON,STERLING SILVER,PORTRAIT WILLIAM SHAKESPEARE,
   STRATFORD.............................................   7.50
SOUVENIR SPOON,STERLING SILVER,PORTRAIT,JOHN HOOD,DAISIES,
   JAN.6,1929............................................   7.50
SOUVENIR SPOON,STERLING SILVER,RIVER FRONT,DETROIT,MICHIGAN.   3.95
SOUVENIR SPOON,STERLING SILVER,RIVERSIDE,CALIFORNIA,GRAPES..   6.75
SOUVENIR SPOON,STERLING SILVER,SACRAMENTO,CALIF.,SEPT.9,
   1907,INDIAN,CORN......................................   6.50
SOUVENIR SPOON,STERLING SILVER,SAN GABRIEL MISSION,LOS
   ANGELES,CAL.,BEAR.....................................   6.50
SOUVENIR SPOON,STERLING SILVER,SARATOGA SPRINGS,N.Y.........   2.95
SOUVENIR SPOON,STERLING SILVER,SEATTLE,WASHINGTON...........   7.50
SOUVENIR SPOON,STERLING SILVER,ST.AUGUSTINE,SUNNY SOUTH,
   NEGRO BOY.............................................   7.50
SOUVENIR SPOON,STERLING SILVER,ST.LOUIS,CROWN,FLEUR-DE-LIS..  10.00
SOUVENIR SPOON,STERLING SILVER,STATE NORMAL SCHOOL,CASTINE,
   MAINE.................................................   2.95
SOUVENIR SPOON,STERLING SILVER,SUTTER'S MILL,MINER,FULL
   FIGURE................................................  10.00
SOUVENIR SPOON,STERLING SILVER,TACOMA,WASHINGTON............   5.50
SOUVENIR SPOON,STERLING SILVER,TIP-TOP HOUSE,MT.WASHINGTON,
   N.H...................................................   5.00
SOUVENIR SPOON,STERLING SILVER,TURQUOISE & LAPIS LAZULI
   STONE,SCENE...........................................  28.50
SOUVENIR SPOON,STERLING SILVER,UTAH BANNER,SHIELD,MINER,
   PICK,SCENE............................................   9.00
```

SOUVENIR SPOON,STERLING SILVER,VICTORIA,B.C.,CHIEF KASKO,
TOTEM POLE.......................................................... 8.75
SOUVENIR SPOON,STERLING SILVER,WASHINGTON,D.C.,CAPITOL
BUILDING........................................................... 6.00
SOUVENIR SPOON,STERLING SILVER,WASHINGTON MANSION,MT.VERNON,
VA................................................................. 2.95
SOUVENIR SPOON,STERLING SILVER,WHITE LAKE,N.Y.................. 8.00
SOUVENIR SPOON,STERLING SILVER,WOONSOCKET,R.I.,4 IN.LONG.... 3.50
SOUVENIR SPOON,STERLING SILVER,WORLD'S FAIR,1904,ST.LOUIS... 6.50
SOUVENIR,SPOONER,SNAIL PATTERN,RED TOP,INSCRIBED MOTHER,
1893............................................................... 15.00
SOUVENIR,STICKPIN,ATLANTIC CITY,1907,ENAMELED TOP,STERLING
SILVER............................................................. 2.75
SOUVENIR,STICKPIN,ENAMEL TOP,MARKED ATLANTIC CITY,1907,
STERLING SILVER.................................................... 2.75
SOUVENIR,STICKPIN,GREEN OVAL CELLULOID,VICTOR DOG........... 9.00
SOUVENIR,STICKPIN,STERLING SILVER,ENAMELED TOP,ATLANTIC
CITY,1907.......................................................... 2.75
SOUVENIR,TOBY,NEW YORK WORLD'S FAIR,1939,GEORGE WASHINGTON,
BISQUE............................................................. 6.50
SOUVENIR,TOOTHPICK,STATE FAIR,1904,RED & CLEAR,BUTTON ARCHES 11.00
SOUVENIR,TOWEL,WORLD'S FAIR,1892,CHICAGO,RED BORDER,FRINGE.. 12.50
SOUVENIR,TRAY,CAFE MEDAGLIA D'ORO,NEW YORK WORLD'S FAIR,
1939,TIN........................................................... 9.50
SOUVENIR,TRAY,CHICAGO WORLD'S FAIR,SILVER ON COPPER......... 2.50
SOUVENIR,TRAY,PINE,COMMEMORATIVE,GEORGE VI CORONATION,
PORCELAIN.......................................................... 5.00
SOUVENIR,TUMBLER,BUTTON & ARCHES PATTERN,SAYS FATHER 1918,
RED,CLEAR.......................................................... 12.00
SOUVENIR,TUMBLER,SUNBURY,PENNSYLVANIA,RUBY & WHITE.......... 9.50
SOUVENIR,VASE,MANITOU,COLORADO,1905,FLASHED RED,7 IN........ 10.00
SOUVENIR VASE,BUD,PAN-AM EXPOSITION,BUFFALO,1901,
6 1/2 IN.HIGH...................................................... 3.95
SOUVENIR,WATCH CHARM,NIAGARA FALLS,SEE-THROUGH,ALABASTER.... 3.50
SOUVENIR,WOVEN SILK,ST.LOUIS EXPOSITION,1803-1904,JEFFERSON,
NAPOLEON........................................................... 20.00

SPANGLE GLASS IS MULTICOLORED GLASS MADE FROM ODDS AND
ENDS OF COLORED GLASS RODS. IT INCLUDES METALLIC
FLAKES OF MICA COVERED WITH GOLD,SILVER,NICKEL,OR
COPPER. SPANGLE GLASS IS USUALLY CASED GLASS WITH A
THIN LAYER OF CLEAR GLASS OVER THE MULTICOLORED LAYER.
SPANGLE GLASS,BASKET,DARK BLUE,PINK,MICA,MELON-RIBBED,FLUTED
RIM................................................................ 115.00
SPANGLE GLASS,BASKET,FLUTED,THORN HANDLE,6 1/2 IN.HIGH.... 48.00
SPANGLE GLASS,BASKET,WHITE,BLUE INTERIOR,SILVER FLECKS,THORN
HANDLE............................................................. 35.00
SPANGLE GLASS,JAR,COOKIE,SILVER PLATE TOP & HOLDER,
5 1/4 IN.HIGH...................................................... 45.00
SPANGLE GLASS,VASE,YELLOW GROUND,PEACH & GOLD FLECKS,FLORAL,
LEAVES,PAIR........................................................ 36.00
SPANISH LACE,BOTTLE,BARBER,CRANBERRY.......................... 20.00
SPANISH LACE,BOTTLE,BARBER,CRANBERRY,OPALESCENT.............. 55.00
SPANISH LACE,BOWL,BRIDE'S,BLUE,RUFFLED,SCALLOPED,SILVER
HOLDER,PEDESTAL.................................................... 65.00
SPANISH LACE,BOWL,BRIDE'S,PINK................................. 37.00
SPANISH LACE,BOWL,FINGER,BLUE,OPALESCENT SWIRLS.............. 18.50
SPANISH LACE,BOWL,ROSE,BLUE.................................... 42.75
SPANISH LACE,BOWL,ROSE,VASELINE GLASS......................... 35.00
SPANISH LACE,BOWL,ROSE,VASELINE,SERPENTINE RIM.............. 34.00
SPANISH LACE,CRUET,OPALESCENT,APPLIED HANDLE,TREFOIL LIP,
STOPPER............................................................ 39.50
SPANISH LACE,EPERGNE,CENTERPIECE,CRANBERRY,13 1/2 IN.HIGH,
9-IN.DIAMETER...................................................... 125.00
SPANISH LACE,LAMP,OIL,CRANBERRY,OPALESCENT,FENTON GLASS
WORKS.............................................................. 13.50
SPANISH LACE,SHAKER,SALT,VASELINE.............................. 18.00
SPANISH LACE,SHAKER,SUGAR,WHITE OPALESCENT,LID.............. 25.00
SPANISH LACE,TOOTHPICK......................................... 25.00
SPANISH LACE,TOOTHPICK,BULBOUS,VASELINE,1 1/4 IN. HIGH...... 18.50
SPANISH LACE,TOOTHPICK,WHITE,OPALESCENT....................... 25.00
SPANISH LACE,VASE,OPALESCENT,BLUE,CRIMPED TOP,6 IN.HIGH..... 35.00
SPANISH LACE,VASE,WHITE & CLEAR,BULBOUS BASE,RUFFLED TOP,
6 1/2 IN........................................................... 30.00

SPATTER GLASS IS A MULTICOLORED GLASS MADE FROM MANY
SMALL PIECES OF DIFFERENT COLORED GLASS.
SPATTER GLASS,BASKET,MELON RIB,RED,YELLOW,BLUE,GREEN,CASED,
BLOWN.............................................................. 50.00

```
SPATTER GLASS,BOWL,CLEAR-CASED,ENAMEL FLORAL,WHITE-LINED,
   RIGAREE FEET.................................................    58.00
SPATTER GLASS,BOWL,FINGER,PINK,YELLOW,WHITE LINING..........    25.00
SPATTER GLASS,CREAMER,CIRCA 1850,3 1/2 IN.HIGH..............    35.00
SPATTER GLASS,CREAMER,PANELED,6 IN.TALL....................    58.00
SPATTER GLASS,EWER,CRYSTAL GROUND,TORTOISE & OPALESCENT
   SPATTERS,GILT............................................    60.00
SPATTER GLASS,PITCHER,BLUE & WHITE,4 1/2 IN................     3.50
SPATTER GLASS,SLIPPER,RED,WHITE,GREEN,APPLIED RIGAREE.......    30.00
SPATTER GLASS,TOOTHPICK,PINK...............................    27.50
SPATTER GLASS,TOOTHPICK,RIBBED PATTERN,BOULTINGHOUSE........    22.50
SPATTER GLASS,TUMBLER,CREAM COLOR ON PALE AMBER,4 1/4 IN....    16.00
SPATTER GLASS,VASE,OCHER,RED,BRONZE COLOR,YELLOW FLAKES,FAN,
   6 1/2 IN................................................    18.00
SPATTER GLASS,VASE,YELLOW,WHITE,BROWN,COBALT TRIM,METAL
   GRILL MOUNT,PAIR........................................    45.00
```

```
       SPATTERWARE IS A CREAMWARE OR SOFT PASTE DINNERWARE
       DECORATED WITH SPATTER DESIGNS. THE EARLIEST PIECES
       WERE MADE DURING THE LATE EIGHTEENTH CENTURY,BUT MOST
       OF THE WARES FOUND TODAY WERE MADE FROM 1800 TO 1850.
       THE SPATTERWARE DISHES WERE MADE IN THE STAFFORDSHIRE
       DISTRICT OF ENGLAND FOR SALE IN THE AMERICAN MARKET.
SPATTERWARE,BOWL,BLUE,11 X 5 IN.............................    15.00
SPATTERWARE,BOWL,MIXING,BLUE,11 1/2 IN......................    29.00
SPATTERWARE,BOWL,ROSE,YELLOW,OXBLOOD,RED,PURPLE,WHITE,
   CRIMPED TOP,BLOWN.......................................    30.00
SPATTERWARE,CUP,CHILD'S,RAINBOW PATTERN,HANDLE.............    28.00
SPATTERWARE,CUP,SAUCER,HANDLELESS,WHITE,RED BANDS,FLORAL,
   PENNA.DUTCH.............................................    75.00
SPATTERWARE,JAR,YELLOW GROUND,BROWN DECOR,WHITE LINING,
   COVER,8 1/2 IN..........................................    35.00
SPATTERWARE,MUG,LEAF DECOR,GOLD,RED,GREEN,CLEAR CRYSTAL
   HANDLE,3 1/2 IN.........................................    65.00
SPATTERWARE,PITCHER,GREEN & CREAM,WHITE CAT FOR HANDLE,
   4 1/2 IN.TALL...........................................     8.50
SPATTERWARE,PLATE,BLUE & WHITE,EAGLE CENTER,8-IN. DIAMETER..   175.00
SPATTERWARE,PLATE,SCHOOLHOUSE.........................ILLUS..   220.00
```

SPATTERWARE SCHOOLHOUSE PLATE

```
SPATTERWARE,PLATE,WHITE,RED BANDS,TULIPS,GREEN FLORAL,
   PENNSYLVANIA DUTCH......................................    75.00
SPATTERWARE,VASE,WHITE CASING,CLEAR HANDLES,8 IN...........    50.00
   SPINNING WHEEL,SEE FURNITURE,SPINNING WHEEL
```

```
       SPODE POTTERY,PORCELAIN,AND BONE CHINA WERE MADE BY
       THE STOKE-ON-TRENT FACTORY OF ENGLAND FOUNDED BY
       JOSIAH SPODE ABOUT 1770. THE FIRM BECAME COPELAND AND
       GARRETT FROM 1833 TO 1847. THEN W.T.COPELAND OR W.T.
       COPELAND AND SONS UNTIL THE PRESENT TIME. THE WORD
       SPODE APPEARS ON MANY PIECES MADE BY THE COPELAND
       FACTORY. MOST ANTIQUE DEALERS INCLUDED ALL OF THE WARES
       UNDER THE MORE FAMILIAR NAME OF SPODE.
   SPODE,SEE ALSO,COPELAND SPODE
SPODE,BOUILLON,GREEN,FLORAL,SET OF 8.......................    40.00
SPODE,BOUILLON,GREEN,MULTICOLOR FLORAL,COPELAND NO.R8396K,
   SET OF 8................................................    40.00
SPODE,BOWL,WHITE,FLORAL,ENGLAND............................    25.00
SPODE,BREAKFAST SET,TURQUOISE,WHITE,FOUR EGG CUPS,FOUR
   PLATES,PLATTER..........................................    35.00
```

```
SPODE,COMPOTE,GOTHIC CASTLE PATTERN,12 1/4 IN. X 9 1/4 IN. X
   4 1/2 IN.............................................         88.00
SPODE,CUP & SAUCER,HANDLELESS,BLUE & RED BELL SHAPE FLOWERS,
   GOLD TRIM...........................................         38.00
SPODE,CUP & SAUCER,MAYFLOWER PATTERN......................          5.25
SPODE,CUP & SAUCER,SALESMAN'S SAMPLE SIZE,BILLINGSLEY ROSE
   SPRAY DECOR.........................................          7.50
SPODE,CUP,SAUCER,DESSERT PLATE,GREEN ORIENTAL PATTERN,
   WELLINGTON,6 EACH...................................         60.00
SPODE,DINNER SET,FRUIT GARDEN PATTERN,BLUE,WHITE,1784 MARK,
   65 PIECES...........................................        800.00
SPODE,DISH,FRUIT,BASKET OF FRUIT CENTER,FLORAL BORDER,1810,
   10 IN...............................................         65.00
SPODE,DISH,SHRIMP,BLUE,WHITE,CITADEL NEAR CORINTH,MARK,CIRCA
   1830................................................         39.00
SPODE,PITCHER,GREEN,CHINESE TABLE,FLORAL ARRANGEMENT,
   FELDSPAR,5 1/2 IN...................................         40.00
SPODE,PITCHER,WATER,COBALT GROUND,WHITE SPRAYS,BERRIES,
   SCENE,VINE HANDLE...................................         59.00
SPODE,PLATE,CASTLE PATTERN,SCENE IS THE GATE OF SEBASTIAN ON
   APPIAN WAY..........................................         22.00
SPODE,PLATE,D.A.R.,CONSTITUTION HALL,MEMORIAL CENTENNIAL
   HALL,PAIR...........................................         17.00
SPODE,PLATE,ITALIAN PATTERN,BLUE,10 IN....................         22.00
SPODE,PLATE,SCALLOPED FLORAL RIM,WICKER BASKET WEAVE,
   10 1/2 IN.,SET OF 4.................................         10.00
SPODE,PLATE,TOBACCO LEAF,8 IN.............................         14.00
SPODE,PLATE,TOGO PATTERN,BLUE,9 IN., SET OF 8.............         25.00
SPODE,PLATTER,BLUE WILLOW PATTERN,21 IN...................         48.00
SPODE,PLATTER,WHITE GROUND,BUTTERFLIES,FLOWERS,FOLIAGE,CIRCA
   1810,13 IN..........................................         55.00
SPODE,PLATTER,WILLOW PATTERN,THREE MEN ON BRIDGE,21 IN. X
   16 1/2 IN...........................................         48.00
SPODE,TOBY,WINSTON CHURCHILL,FULL FIGURE,8 1/2 IN.HIGH....         75.00
```

        SPONGEWARE IS VERY SIMILAR TO SPATTERWARE IN
        APPEARANCE. THE DESIGNS WERE APPLIED TO THE WARE BY
        DAUBING THE COLOR. MANY DEALERS DO NOT DIFFERENTIATE
        BETWEEN THE TWO WARES AND USE THE NAMES
        INTERCHANGEABLY.

```
SPONGEWARE,BOWL,BLUE,DEEP,8-IN.DIAMETER...................         29.50
SPONGEWARE,BOWL,BLUE & BROWN ON GREEN,GILT TRIM,SCALLOPED,
   FOOTED..............................................         15.00
SPONGEWARE,BOWL,RED & BLUE PATTERN,7 1/2-IN.DIAMETER......         25.00
SPONGEWARE,CUP & SAUCER,RED,BLUE,GREEN DECOR,MARKED ADAMS...       37.50
SPONGEWARE,CUSPIDOR,BLUE,BLUE BANDS......................         11.00
SPONGEWARE,CUSPIDOR,BUFF GROUND..........................         15.00
SPONGEWARE,DISH,SOAP,BLUE & WHITE,5 1/4 IN. X 3 1/2 IN....         18.00
SPONGEWARE,PITCHER,BATTER,BLUE,NEW ENGLAND...............         35.00
SPONGEWARE,PITCHER,BLUE,TANKARD,9 IN. X 9 IN. X 5 1/2 IN....       25.00
SPONGEWARE,PITCHER,BLUE,WHITE,THREE STRIPES AROUND MIDDLE,
   BULBOUS,8 IN........................................         24.00
SPONGEWARE,PLATE,BLUE,8 1/4-IN.DIAMETER..................         18.00
SPONGEWARE,PLATTER,BLUE,13 1/2 IN. X 10 IN...............         20.00
SPONGEWARE,POT,CHAMBER,BLUE,LID.........................         24.00
SPONGEWARE,SPITTOON,BLUE................................         15.00
ST.CLOUD,CUP & SAUCER,BLUE & WHITE,CIRCA 1740...........        175.00
```

        STAFFORDSHIRE IS A DISTRICT IN ENGLAND WHERE POTTERY
        AND PORCELAIN HAVE BEEN MADE SINCE THE 1600S.
        THOUSANDS OF TYPES OF POTTERY AND PORCELAIN HAVE BEEN
        MADE IN THE HUNDREDS OF FACTORIES THAT WORKED IN THE
        AREA. SOME OF THE MOST FAMOUS FACTORIES HAVE BEEN
        LISTED SEPARATELY. SEE ROYAL DOULTON,ROYAL WORCESTER,
        SPODE,WEDGWOOD,AND OTHERS.

```
STAFFORDSHIRE,SEE ALSO,FLOW BLUE
STAFFORDSHIRE,BASKET,GREEK KEY,HORSE & CHARIOT SCENE,CIRCA
   1810,PLATE..........................................        125.00
STAFFORDSHIRE,BONBONNIERE,LION HEAD,ENAMEL,2 IN......ILLUS..       275.00
STAFFORDSHIRE,BONBONNIERE,SHELL FORM,2 3/8 IN.LONG...ILLUS..       290.00
STAFFORDSHIRE,BOTTLE,PILGRIM,MULBERRY TRANSFER PRINT........        70.00
STAFFORDSHIRE,BOWL,SCENE,TEMPLE,DEER,TREES,SIGNED TAMS,
   ANDERSON & TAMS.....................................         55.00
STAFFORDSHIRE,BOX,BOY RIDING NEWFOUNDLAND DOG,COVER........         27.00
STAFFORDSHIRE,BOX,ENAMEL REPOUSSE,CAT,1 1/2 IN.......ILLUS..       260.00
STAFFORDSHIRE,BOX,GIRL IN CARRIAGE PLAYING WITH DOLL,COVER..        30.00
STAFFORDSHIRE,BOX,JEWEL,COVER,BABY CRAWLING TOWARD PLATE OF
   COOKIES.............................................         28.00
STAFFORDSHIRE,BOX,MATCH,WHITTE,STRIKER ON BOTTOM SIDE OF
```

STAFFORDSHIRE LION HEAD BONBONNIERE

STAFFORDSHIRE SHELL
FORM BONBONNIERE

STAFFORDSHIRE BOX,
ENAMEL REPOUSSE

```
  COVER........................................................    5.95
STAFFORDSHIRE,BOX,ROUGE,WATCH FORM,DIAL,HANDS,PAINTED SCENE
  ON BACK......................................................  425.00
STAFFORDSHIRE,BOX,SHOE SHAPE,ENAMEL,FLORAL SPRIGS,GOLD
  BUCKLE,LID,3 IN..............................................  125.00
STAFFORDSHIRE,BOX,TAPER,ENAMEL,FLORAL BOUQUETS,SPRIGS,SCREW
  TOP..........................................................  150.00
STAFFORDSHIRE,BOX,TRINKET,COVER IS FORMED BY STORK CARRYING
  BABY.........................................................   27.00
STAFFORDSHIRE,BOX,TRINKET,CUPID ON COVER......................   17.00
STAFFORDSHIRE,BOX,TRINKET,GIRL SITTING UP IN BED.............   12.50
STAFFORDSHIRE,BOX,TRINKET,MINIATURE,RECLINING SPANIEL WITH
  BUGLE........................................................   27.50
STAFFORDSHIRE,BOX,TRINKET,TOP HAS BABY WITH OARS,PADDLE YOUR
  OWN CANOE....................................................   22.50
STAFFORDSHIRE,CASE,NEEDLE,ENAMEL,BLUE-GREEN GROUND,BLUE &
  RED GARLANDS.................................................  130.00
STAFFORDSHIRE,CASTLE,5 1/2 IN.HIGH............................   45.00
STAFFORDSHIRE,CHAMBERSTICK,GOLD,GREEN,ORANGE,SEPARATE
  SNUFFER ATTACHED.............................................   15.00
STAFFORDSHIRE,CHARGER,WILD ROSE,BLUE,WHITE...................   35.00
STAFFORDSHIRE,CLOCK,TWO LOVERS,SCOTTISH COSTUMES,PAINTED
  CLOCK FACE...................................................   32.00
STAFFORDSHIRE,CREAMER & SUGAR,CHILD'S,STAG PATTERN,BLUE,
  WHITE........................................................   20.00
STAFFORDSHIRE,CREAMER,BLUE SWAN,ROYAL FENTON.................   10.00
STAFFORDSHIRE,CREAMER,BLUE,PARK SCENERY BY PHILLIPS,CIRCA
  1840.........................................................   14.00
STAFFORDSHIRE,CUP & SAUCER,HANDLELESS,HUNTING DOGS,FLORAL,
  MARKED CLEWS.................................................   45.00
STAFFORDSHIRE,CUP & SAUCER,PANAMA,LIGHT BLUE,CHALLINOR,
  HANDLELESS...................................................   10.00
STAFFORDSHIRE,CUP & SAUCER,PARADISE PATTERN,HANDLELESS......   17.50
STAFFORDSHIRE,CUP & SAUCER,SCENIC,MULBERRY,HANDLELESS.......   11.50
STAFFORDSHIRE,CUP & SAUCER,TRANSFER TITLED SYDENHAM BY
  J.CLEMENTSON.................................................   15.00
STAFFORDSHIRE,CUP PLATE,BLUE,CASTLE & BOAT SCENE,FLORAL
  BORDER,4 IN..................................................   10.00
STAFFORDSHIRE,CUP,POSSET,ONE HANDLE,MAJOLICA BAND,COVER,
  COPPER LUSTER................................................   85.00
STAFFORDSHIRE,DISH,CHEESE,BLUE & WHITE,SCENIC,BY J.KENT,
  FENTON,ENGLAND...............................................   37.50
STAFFORDSHIRE,DISH,HEN,WHITE BISQUE TOP,COLORED HEAD,BASKET
  WEAVE BASE...................................................  125.00
STAFFORDSHIRE,DISH,MEAT,BLUE & WHITE,CIRCA 1860,19 IN. X
  13 IN........................................................   39.00
STAFFORDSHIRE,DISH,PAIR,AMERICAN ARMS,CIRCA 1790,5 1/2-IN.
  DIAMETER.....................................................   50.00
STAFFORDSHIRE,DISH,SERVING,WILLOW PATTERN,COVER,MARKED YE
```

```
    OLDE WILLOW.............................................   15.00
STAFFORDSHIRE,DISH,SWAN,COVER,4 IN.LONG,3 1/4 IN.TALL.......   37.50
STAFFORDSHIRE,DISH,VEGETABLE,BLUE,FLORAL & FOLIATE BORDER,
    FLOWER FINIAL.........................................   42.00
STAFFORDSHIRE,DOG,PAIR...............................ILLUS..   65.00
STAFFORDSHIRE,DOG,PUG,PAIR.................................   85.00
STAFFORDSHIRE,ETUI,ENAMEL GROUND,PAINTED LANDSCAPES,GILT
    METAL BORDER..........................................  100.00
STAFFORDSHIRE,ETUI,ENAMEL,5 IN.LONG..................ILLUS..  350.00
STAFFORDSHIRE,FIGURE,CIRCA 1770,4 1/2 IN. HIGH,AGED WOMAN &
    PIPE..................................................  350.00
STAFFORDSHIRE,FIGURE,MAN AND LION....................ILLUS..   75.00
STAFFORDSHIRE,FIGURE,SPLATTER-GLAZED,CIRCA 1780,4 IN. HIGH,
    HUNTER................................................   60.00
STAFFORDSHIRE,FIGURINE,BOY,ALLEGORICAL OF AUTUMN,GIRL,
    SUMMER,PAIR...........................................   80.00
STAFFORDSHIRE,FIGURINE,CAT,GRAY,GREEN EYES,II IN.HIGH,PAIR..  150.00
STAFFORDSHIRE,FIGURINE,CERES,ALLEGORICAL,HANLEY,DAVID
    WILSON,5 1/2 IN.......................................   40.00
STAFFORDSHIRE,FIGURINE,CINDERELLA,MARKED,6 IN..............   24.50
STAFFORDSHIRE,FIGURINE,COCKEREL, TAIL PLUMAGE,BLUE,GREEN,
    YELLOW,8 1/2 IN.......................................  210.00
STAFFORDSHIRE,FIGURINE,COW,ORANGE,WHITE,GREEN,PAIR.........   89.00
STAFFORDSHIRE,FIGURINE,DOG,COPPER LUSTER,8 IN.HIGH,PAIR....   45.00
STAFFORDSHIRE,FIGURINE,DOG,SEATED,WHITE,CURLY,GILT CHAIN,
    12 IN.,PAIR...........................................   58.00
STAFFORDSHIRE,FIGURINE,DOG,WHITE,COPPER LUSTER,13 IN.HIGH,
    PAIR..................................................   65.00
STAFFORDSHIRE,FIGURINE,DOG,WHITE,14 IN.,PAIR...............   65.00
STAFFORDSHIRE,FIGURINE,DOGS,PINK LUSTER,7 1/2 IN.HIGH......   45.00
```

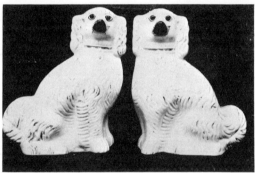

PAIR OF STAFFORDSHIRE DOGS

STAFFORDSHIRE
ENAMEL ETUI

STAFFORDSHIRE FIGURE, MAN AND LION

```
STAFFORDSHIRE,FIGURINE,DOGS,WHITE WITH GOLD LUSTER DECOR,
  8 1/2 IN.HIGH.........................................        48.00
STAFFORDSHIRE,FIGURINE,EUTERPE,ALLEGORICAL,HOLDS MUSICAL
  INSTRUMENT,1790.......................................        85.00
STAFFORDSHIRE,FIGURINE,FIREMAN,WHITE HELMET,ORANGE JACKET,
  4 1/2 IN.HIGH.........................................        15.00
STAFFORDSHIRE,FIGURINE,GRAY HOUND,RABBIT IN MOUTH,TREE,
  FLORAL,11 IN.TALL.....................................        23.50
STAFFORDSHIRE,FIGURINE,HORSE,BLUE PLAID SADDLE BLANKET,CIRCA
  1790,6 IN.............................................       250.00
STAFFORDSHIRE,FIGURINE,HORSE,STANDS,SADDLE BLANKET,BRIDLE,
  5 1/2 IN.HIGH.........................................        50.00
STAFFORDSHIRE,FIGURINE,HUNTER,DOG,GREEN,BROWN,ORANGE,
  12 1/2 IN.TALL........................................        40.00
STAFFORDSHIRE,FIGURINE,LOVERS IN A BOWER,14 1/2 IN.TALL....        28.00
STAFFORDSHIRE,FIGURINE,PRODIGAL'S RETURN,CIRCA 1860,17 IN...        35.00
STAFFORDSHIRE,FIGURINE,QUEEN VICTORIA IN HER CORONATION
  ROBES,17 IN.HIGH......................................        45.00
STAFFORDSHIRE,FIGURINE,RED RIDING HOOD,WOLF,TREE TRUNK,
  7 1/2 IN.,PAIR........................................        50.00
STAFFORDSHIRE,FIGURINE,ROBERT BURNS & HIGHLAND MARY,FLAT
  BACK,14 IN.TALL.......................................        22.50
STAFFORDSHIRE,FIGURINE,ROBIN HOOD,TITLE IN RAISED CAPITALS,
  15 1/4 IN.............................................        40.00
STAFFORDSHIRE,FIGURINE,WHITE COW,BOY,CALF,CIRCA 1800........       150.00
STAFFORDSHIRE,GIRAFFE,PAIR,CIRCA 1810......................       700.00
STAFFORDSHIRE,GRAVY BOAT,BLUE,MILLENIUM PATTERN............        45.00
STAFFORDSHIRE,GROUP,MOSES & VICAR,19TH CENTURY.............       175.00
STAFFORDSHIRE,HEN,10 IN. LONG.........................ILLUS..        85.00
STAFFORDSHIRE,HOLDER,MATCH,LITTLE GIRL WITH DOLL...........        18.00
```

STAFFORDSHIRE HEN

```
STAFFORDSHIRE,HOLDER,MATCH,PAIR BOOTS,STRIKER.............        12.50
STAFFORDSHIRE,HOLDER,WATCH,SCOTTISH DANCERS,12 IN.HIGH.....        25.00
STAFFORDSHIRE,HOUSE,COCKER SPANIEL AT DOOR,TREES,BIRDS IN
  NEST..................................................        34.00
STAFFORDSHIRE,ICE PAIL,RIBBED,CYLINDRICAL,LION MASK HANDLES,
  PAIR..................................................       425.00
STAFFORDSHIRE,INKWELL,BIRDS,COBALT WINGS,TULIP HOLDER,
  FLORAL,GOLD TRIM......................................        45.00
STAFFORDSHIRE,INKWELL,MASKS ON SIDE,CLAW FEET,FLORAL DECOR,
  COBALT BANDS..........................................       120.00
STAFFORDSHIRE,INKWELL,SANDER ATTACHED TO TRAY.............        22.50
STAFFORDSHIRE,INKWELL,TWO COBALT BIRDS,TULIP INK HOLDER,
  APPLIED FLORAL........................................        45.00
STAFFORDSHIRE,INKWELL,WHIPPET DOGS,COBALT BASE,7 1/4 IN.LONG        49.00
STAFFORDSHIRE,JAR,ROOSTER SHAPE,WHIELDON TYPE,COVER,
  9 IN.HIGH.............................................        50.00
STAFFORDSHIRE,JUG,BROWN,YELLOW DECOR,WILLOW,PAGODA,PORTO
  BELLO,5 1/2 IN........................................        75.00
STAFFORDSHIRE,JUG,PINK LUSTER DECOR,GREEN LEAVES,FLOWERS,
  6 IN..................................................        75.00
STAFFORDSHIRE,JUG,RUSTIC DESIGN MOLDED WITH HEAD OF BACCHUS,
  4 1/2 IN..............................................        40.00
STAFFORDSHIRE,JUG,TOBY,BLACKAMOOR,19TH CENTURY............       125.00
STAFFORDSHIRE,KEEP,HALF-ROUND PRISON,STEPS,LIONS,ROCKWORK,
  5 7/8 IN.HIGH.........................................        50.00
STAFFORDSHIRE,MANTEL GARNITURE,ENAMELED,THREE PIECES ILLUS..       175.00
STAFFORDSHIRE,MASTIFF,STANDING,BUFF,RED COLLAR,GOLD BELLS,
  6 1/2 IN..............................................        22.50
STAFFORDSHIRE,MATCH HOLDER,TWO BOOTS,BOOTJACK,SCRATCHER....        26.00
STAFFORDSHIRE,MATCH HOLDER,TWO BOOTS,OBLONG BASE,RELIEFS &
  COLORS,GILT...........................................        22.00
```

STAFFORDSHIRE MANTEL GARNITURE

```
STAFFORDSHIRE,MUG,MALE BACCHUS HEAD,CURLED BEARD,POINTED
   EARS,1800...........................................  150.00
STAFFORDSHIRE,MUG,SCENES,PEOPLE RIDING VELOCIPEDES,
   BLUE-GREEN,WHITE......................................   29.00
STAFFORDSHIRE,MUG,TAN,FIGURES IN RELIEF,CARRYING BOTTLES,
   SMOKING,FROGS.........................................   80.00
STAFFORDSHIRE,PASTILLE BURNER,FIGURAL,PARTIALLY-DRAPED
   FIGURES,ALTAR.........................................   90.00
STAFFORDSHIRE,PATCH BOX.................................   25.00
STAFFORDSHIRE,PENHOLDER,WHIPPET LYING DOWN,COBALT BASE,5 IN.   38.50
STAFFORDSHIRE,PITCHER,APPLE GREEN,12 IN. HIGH...........   60.00
STAFFORDSHIRE,PITCHER,BLUE,WHITE,TRANSFER SCENE,HUNT NEAR
   WINDSOR,1820..........................................   20.00
STAFFORDSHIRE,PITCHER,CLASSICAL GARDEN SCENE,BLUE,WIDE
   SPOUT,8 1/2 IN........................................   60.00
STAFFORDSHIRE,PITCHER,ENAMELED DECOR,INSCRIPTION,1812....   60.00
STAFFORDSHIRE,PITCHER,FISH,9 IN.HIGH....................   25.00
STAFFORDSHIRE,PITCHER,HUNTERS,HOUNDS,BALUSTER SHAPE,1790,
   6 1/2 IN..............................................   90.00
STAFFORDSHIRE,PITCHER,MILK,BLUE WILLOW,WOOD & SONS.......   30.00
STAFFORDSHIRE,PITCHER,MILK,SALT GLAZE,PEWTER TOP,SHEAF OF
   WHEAT.................................................   50.00
STAFFORDSHIRE,PITCHER,PEONIES,LARKSPUR,ROSES,MONOGRAM,
   5 1/2 IN.HIGH.........................................   90.00
STAFFORDSHIRE,PITCHER,PORTRAITS,PRINCE COBURG,DUKE OF YORK,
   1785..................................................   60.00
STAFFORDSHIRE,PITCHER,RED-BROWN & BUFF,HUNTING SCENES,MARK
   DOULTON,1890..........................................   35.00
STAFFORDSHIRE,PITCHER,SEPIA TRANSFER OF HOPE & FAITH,SILVER
   LUSTER DECOR..........................................  195.00
STAFFORDSHIRE,PITCHER,WHITE,FIGURES IN BAS-RELIEF,SALT
   GLAZE,MINTON..........................................   35.00
STAFFORDSHIRE,PITCHER,WILLOW PATTERN,MEN CROSSING BRIDGE,
   6 IN..................................................    9.00
STAFFORDSHIRE,PLATE,AMERICAN MARINE PATTERN,WHITE WITH BROWN
   TRANSFER..............................................   10.00
STAFFORDSHIRE,PLATE,AVON COTTAGE,BLUE,10 IN.,SET OF 6....   20.00
STAFFORDSHIRE,PLATE,BAKERS FALLS,HUDSON RIVER,BLACK & WHITE,
   8 3/4 IN..............................................   40.00
STAFFORDSHIRE,PLATE,BATTLE CREEK,MICHIGAN,10 IN.........    8.50
STAFFORDSHIRE,PLATE,BIRD,FLOWERS,BLUE BORDER,DAVENPORT,9 IN.    7.00
STAFFORDSHIRE,PLATE,BLACK BORDER,PURPLE CENTER,CALEDONIA,
   9 1/2 IN..............................................   28.50
STAFFORDSHIRE,PLATE,BLACK,BATTLE MONUMENT,BALTIMORE,9-IN.
   DIAMETER..............................................   48.00
STAFFORDSHIRE,PLATE,BLUE,BOSTON STATE HOUSE,BY ROGERS,
   7 1/2 IN..............................................   58.00
STAFFORDSHIRE,PLATE,BLUE,BOSTON STATE HOUSE,BY ROGERS,
   9 1/2 IN..............................................   65.00
STAFFORDSHIRE,PLATE,BLUE,DON QUIXOTE,HELMET,CLEWS,10 IN..   75.00
STAFFORDSHIRE,PLATE,BLUE,LANDING OF HENDRICK HUDSON,9 IN..   12.50
STAFFORDSHIRE,PLATE,BLUE,LANDING OF THE PILGRIM FATHERS,BY
   WOOD..................................................   45.00
```

```
STAFFORDSHIRE,PLATE,BLUE,SHEPHERD,FLOCK AMID RUINS,CIRCA
  1820.....................................................    28.00
STAFFORDSHIRE,PLATE,BLUE,WHITE,ELMS AT CAMBRIDGE,FRUIT &
  FLORAL BORDER...........................................    22.00
STAFFORDSHIRE,PLATE,BLUE,WHITE,FLOWERED BORDER,10 IN.......    20.00
STAFFORDSHIRE,PLATE,BLUE,WHITE,OLD SOUTH CHURCH,BOSTON,FRUIT
  BORDER..................................................    22.00
STAFFORDSHIRE,PLATE,BLUE,WHITE,WASHINGTON CROSSING DELAWARE,
  FLORAL..................................................    22.00
STAFFORDSHIRE,PLATE,BREAD,SCENE TRANSFER,BOAT,RIVER, GIVE US
  THIS DAY ...............................................    38.50
STAFFORDSHIRE,PLATE,BROWN,BAKERS FALLS,9-IN. DIAMETER......    37.00
STAFFORDSHIRE,PLATE,BROWN,GIRAFFE PATTERN,10 IN...........    25.00
STAFFORDSHIRE,PLATE,BROWN,PHILADELPHIA WATERWORKS,
  9-IN.DIAMETER...........................................    35.00
STAFFORDSHIRE,PLATE,BROWN,SANDY HILL,HUDSON RIVER,CLEWS,
  7 1/4 IN................................................    25.00
STAFFORDSHIRE,PLATE,BUDDHA PATTERN,PINK ON WHITE,BY WOOD,
  9 3/4 IN................................................     7.50
STAFFORDSHIRE,PLATE,BUNKER HILL MONUMENT,FLOWERS,FRUIT,
  10 IN...................................................    18.00
STAFFORDSHIRE,PLATE,CAT'S HEAD,ENGLAND,5 IN.SQUARE..........    15.00
STAFFORDSHIRE,PLATE,COMMERCE,GREEN,WHITE,6 1/2 IN.........     8.50
STAFFORDSHIRE,PLATE,COPPER LUSTER FLOWERS,7 IN.............     6.50
STAFFORDSHIRE,PLATE,CRYSTAL PALACE,BY T.GODWIN,CIRCA 1851,
  BORDER DECOR............................................    15.00
STAFFORDSHIRE,PLATE,CUP,BLUE,SCENE IN CENTER,FLOWERS & SCENE
  BORDER..................................................    12.50
STAFFORDSHIRE,PLATE,CUP,DARK BLUE FLORAL,WHITE GROUND,
  IMPRESSED ROGERS........................................    12.50
STAFFORDSHIRE,PLATE,DARK BLUE,MOULIN SUR LA MARNE,A
  CHARENTON BY WOODS......................................    55.00
STAFFORDSHIRE,PLATE,DARK BLUE,VUE DE CHATEAU ERMENONVILLE,BY
  WOOD,10 IN..............................................    55.00
STAFFORDSHIRE,PLATE,DICKENSWARE,MR.BUMBLE,4 IN.SQUARE......     8.00
STAFFORDSHIRE,PLATE,DON QUIXOTE & THE SHEPHERDESSES,CLEWS,
  10 IN...................................................    85.00
STAFFORDSHIRE,PLATE,DR.SYNTAX PAINTING A PORTRAIT,BLUE,
  10 1/4 IN...............................................   108.00
STAFFORDSHIRE,PLATE,ELM AT CAMBRIDGE,MASSACHUSETTS,FLORAL,
  FRUIT,10 IN.............................................    18.00
STAFFORDSHIRE,PLATE,FLOW BLUE, THE SPIRIT OF '76,  SCENES ON
  BORDER..................................................    10.00
STAFFORDSHIRE,PLATE,GREEN BORDER,PINK CENTER,CALEDONIA,
  10 1/2 IN...............................................    32.50
STAFFORDSHIRE,PLATE,HISTORIC BLUE,CANADIAN..........ILLUS..    85.00
STAFFORDSHIRE,PLATE,HOUSE,STEPHEN FOSTER,MY OLD KENTUCKY
  HOME,BLUE,WHITE.........................................    16.50
STAFFORDSHIRE,PLATE,ITALIAN VILLA,PURPLE,10 IN.............    11.00
STAFFORDSHIRE,PLATE,ITALY PATTERN,PINK,MARKED E.M.& CO.,
  7 1/2 IN................................................     7.50
STAFFORDSHIRE,PLATE,LIGHT BLUE,CALIFORNIA,TRANSFER,REG.1849,
  9 7/8 IN................................................     9.50
STAFFORDSHIRE,PLATE,LIGHT BLUE,CANOVA,9 1/2 IN.............     8.50
STAFFORDSHIRE,PLATE,LIGHT BLUE,PRIORY,TRANSFER,9 1/2 IN.....     7.50
```

CANADIAN STAFFORDSHIRE PLATE,
HISTORIC BLUE

STAFFORDSHIRE,PLATE,LIGHT BLUE,VENABLES MANN & CO.,BRITISH
 REG.2-17-1852.............................................. 15.00
STAFFORDSHIRE,PLATE,LONGFELLOW'S HOME,HISTORICAL PICTURES,
 COBALT..................................................... 22.50
STAFFORDSHIRE,PLATE,MADE FOR WRIGHT,TYNDALE & VAN RODEN,
 PHILA.,FLORAL.............................................. 9.50
STAFFORDSHIRE,PLATE,MASSACHUSETTS STATE HOUSE,FLORAL,FRUIT,
 10 IN...................................................... 18.00
STAFFORDSHIRE,PLATE,MAYFLOWER IN PLYMOUTH HARBOR,COBALT,
 SIGNED..................................................... 35.00
STAFFORDSHIRE,PLATE,MEDALLIONS,SCENES,YE OLDE HISTORICAL
 POTTERY,9 IN............................................... 18.50
STAFFORDSHIRE,PLATE,MILLENNIUM,PURPLE,9-IN.DIAMETER......... 22.00
STAFFORDSHIRE,PLATE,MOTHER GOOSE,SEPIA,WHITE,CAT & FIDDLE,
 7 IN....................................................... 10.00
STAFFORDSHIRE,PLATE,MULBERRY,KOREAN PATTERN,MARKED.......... 15.00
STAFFORDSHIRE,PLATE,NIAGARA FALLS,10 IN............. 8.50 TO 20.00
STAFFORDSHIRE,PLATE,OLD SOUTH CHURCH,10 IN................. 20.00
STAFFORDSHIRE,PLATE,PINK BORDER,GREEN CENTER,CALEDONIA,
 10 1/2 IN.................................................. 32.50
STAFFORDSHIRE,PLATE,PINK,THE BATTERY,NEW YORK,8-IN. DIAMETER 37.00
STAFFORDSHIRE,PLATE,PINK,VIEW NEAR CONWAY,9-IN.DIAMETER..... 32.00
STAFFORDSHIRE,PLATE,PORTRAIT,ROBERT BURNS,MRS.BURNS,
 9 5/8 IN.,PAIR............................................. 75.00
STAFFORDSHIRE,PLATE,SCENIC MARKED MANHATTAN,R.STEVENSON,
 ORCHID,1835............................................... 12.00
STAFFORDSHIRE,PLATE,SOUP,BEACH AT BRIGHTON,DARK BLUE,SHELL
 BORDER.................................................... 65.00
STAFFORDSHIRE,PLATE,SOUP,BLUE,DON QUIXOTE,SANCHO PANZA,
 CLEWS,9 IN................................................ 75.00
STAFFORDSHIRE,PLATE,SOUP,CANOVA,PINK,GREEN BORDER,T.MAYER
 1836...................................................... 20.00
STAFFORDSHIRE,PLATE,SOUVENIR OF ALBANY,FLOWERS,BUILDINGS,
 9 IN...................................................... 14.00
STAFFORDSHIRE,PLATE,THE ELMS AT CAMBRIDGE,10 IN............. 20.00
STAFFORDSHIRE,PLATE,THE SEA,BLUE,10 1/2-IN.DIAMETER........ 26.00
STAFFORDSHIRE,PLATE,TRANSFER BY R.HALL,CAROLINA PATTERN,
 PINK,7 3/4 IN............................................. 15.00
STAFFORDSHIRE,PLATE,TRANSFER,SCENES,FURTH,STEINHEIM,MARK,
 PAIR...................................................... 15.00
STAFFORDSHIRE,PLATE,VIEWS OF BETHLEHEM,PA.,BLUE............ 8.50
STAFFORDSHIRE,PLATE,WASHINGTON CROSSING THE DELAWARE,10 IN.. 20.00
STAFFORDSHIRE,PLATE,WEST POINT,10 IN....................... 8.50
STAFFORDSHIRE,PLATE,WHIRLPOOL RAPIDS,10 IN................. 20.00
STAFFORDSHIRE,PLATTER,BLUE WILLOW,MARKED,19 IN. X 15 IN..... 35.00
STAFFORDSHIRE,PLATTER,BLUE WILLOW,OPAQUE,15 IN. X 12 IN..... 15.00
STAFFORDSHIRE,PLATTER,BLUE,FRUIT,FLORAL,ARTIST STUBBS,
 16 1/4 IN.LONG............................................ 90.00
STAFFORDSHIRE,PLATTER,CASTLE SCENE MARKED KIRKSTALL ABBEY,
 YORKSHIRE................................................. 42.00
STAFFORDSHIRE,PLATTER,CASTLE,BRIDGE,BOATMEN,WILD ROSE
 BORDER,15 X 11 IN......................................... 26.00
STAFFORDSHIRE,PLATTER,CHESAPEAKE & SHANNON,BLUE,20 IN....... 375.00
STAFFORDSHIRE,PLATTER,DON'T GIVE UP THE SHIP,CHESAPEAKE &
 SHANNON,20 IN............................................. 360.00
STAFFORDSHIRE,PLATTER,DORNEY COURT,BUCKINGHAMSHIRE,BLUE,
 WHITE..................................................... 27.00
STAFFORDSHIRE,PLATTER,ESPLANADE & CASTLE GARDEN......ILLUS.. 500.00
STAFFORDSHIRE,PLATTER,FISH,9 IN............................ 27.50
STAFFORDSHIRE,PLATTER,FLORENTINE PATTERN,BLUE,T.J.& J.MAYER,
 CIRCA 1840................................................ 27.50
STAFFORDSHIRE,PLATTER,JENNY LIND,LANDSCAPE,CASTLE,HOLLY
 BORDER,11 IN.............................................. 13.00
STAFFORDSHIRE,PLATTER,LAMBTON HALL,DURHAM,CASTLE SCENE,DARK
 BLUE...................................................... 88.00
STAFFORDSHIRE,PLATTER,LANDING OF LAFAYETTE,DATE 1824,SIGNED
 CLEWS,10 IN............................................... 235.00
STAFFORDSHIRE,PLATTER,NAPOLEON WITH HIS TROOPS,BROWN,
 15 1/2 X 12 1/2 IN........................................ 35.00
STAFFORDSHIRE,PLATTER,ONTARIO,LAKE SCENERY,LIGHT BLUE,
 J.HEATH................................................... 15.00
STAFFORDSHIRE,PLATTER,SPARTAN,LIGHT BLUE,12 IN. X 18 IN..... 15.00
STAFFORDSHIRE,PLATTER,TRANSFER BY T.MEYER,OLYMPIC GAMES,THE
 SLING..................................................... 35.00
STAFFORDSHIRE,QUILL HOLDER,FORM OF TREE TRUNK,TWO WHITE
 POODLES................................................... 40.00
STAFFORDSHIRE,SERVICE,DESSERT,GREEN GLAZE,CIRCA 1840,
 15 PIECES................................................. 80.00
STAFFORDSHIRE,STATUETTE,DOG,BLACK JACKFIELD,14 IN. TALL,PAIR 65.00
STAFFORDSHIRE,STATUETTE,ZEBRA,PAIR,19TH CENTURY............ 750.00
STAFFORDSHIRE,TEA SERVICE,STRAWBERRY LUSTER,CIRCA 1825,

STAFFORDSHIRE PLATTER

| | |
|---|---|
| 24 PIECES.................................................... | 1,200.00 |
| STAFFORDSHIRE,TEAPOT,GREEN,PARKLIKE SCENES,LILY BORDER,1835. | 55.00 |
| STAFFORDSHIRE,TEAPOT,TRANSFER-PAINTED,CIRCA 1840............ | 40.00 |
| STAFFORDSHIRE,TOBY,BLACK,GREEN,BROWN,TOUCHES OF LUSTER, | |
| 9 3/4 IN................................................... | 150.00 |
| STAFFORDSHIRE,TOBY,GARDINER IMPRINTED ON BOTTOM,INITIALED A, | |
| 4 1/2 IN................................................... | 15.00 |
| STAFFORDSHIRE,TOBY,GRANNY,TOP OF BONNET IS REMOVABLE LID, | |
| 11 IN.HIGH................................................. | 140.00 |
| STAFFORDSHIRE,TOBY,JOLLY SIRE,LAUGHING,SHOWS DETAILED TEETH. | 45.00 |
| STAFFORDSHIRE,TOBY,MAN IN A TRI-CORNE,HOLDS PITCHER AND MUG. | 65.00 |
| STAFFORDSHIRE,TOBY,MAN,SEATED,HOLDS PITCHER & GLASS, | |
| 10 1/2 IN.................................................. | 200.00 |
| STAFFORDSHIRE,TOBY,MAN IN A TRICORNE,HOLDS PITCHER AND MUG.. | 65.00 |
| STAFFORDSHIRE,TOBY,MARSHAL FOCH,SIGNED CARROUTHERS GOULD.... | 135.00 |
| STAFFORDSHIRE,TOBY,PEPPER POT,MAN HOLDS MUG,WEARS | |
| THREE-CORNERED HAT......................................... | 22.00 |
| STAFFORDSHIRE,TOBY,RALPH WOOD TYPE,TRICORNE HAT,REMOVABLE | |
| LID,1815................................................... | 125.00 |
| STAFFORDSHIRE,TOBY,RALPH WOOD,10 IN.TALL................... | 75.00 |
| STAFFORDSHIRE,TOBY,TOP OF HAT IS REMOVABLE LID,9 IN.HIGH... | 85.00 |
| STAFFORDSHIRE,TUREEN,BROWN TRANSFER,COVER,ALCOCK,1884,8 X | |
| 10 X 6 IN.................................................. | 22.50 |
| STAFFORDSHIRE,TUREEN,SAUCE,COVER,CREAMWARE,WITH FIGURINE OF | |
| CHERUBS.................................................... | 70.00 |
| STAFFORDSHIRE,URN,NOTTINGHAM STONEWARE,DATED 1772,5 IN.HIGH, | |
| PAIR....................................................... | 200.00 |
| STAFFORDSHIRE,VASE,BOUGH,CIRCA 1810........................ | 200.00 |
| STAFFORDSHIRE,VASE,COW,HORSE,TROUGH,DOVES ON BRANCHES,TREE | |
| TRUNK TYPE................................................. | 35.00 |
| STAFFORDSHIRE,VASE,FLOWER-ENCRUSTED,LANDSCAPE,CURVED | |
| HANDLES,12 1/4 IN.......................................... | 70.00 |
| STAFFORDSHIRE,VASE,HORSE,COLT,TAN,GREEN TREE TRUNK TYPE, | |
| ORANGE LINING.............................................. | 30.00 |
| STAFFORDSHIRE,VASE,HORSES,COWS,TROUGH,BIRDS,BRANCH HANDLES, | |
| 11 IN.,PAIR................................................ | 65.00 |
| STAFFORDSHIRE,VASE,PAIR,BOUGH,CIRCA 1830................... | 240.00 |
| STAFFORDSHIRE,VASE,RED RIDING HOOD,WOLF,LOG TYPE........... | 49.50 |
| STAFFORDSHIRE,WASHBOWL & PITCHER,BLUE,SHAW,PERUVIAN HORSE | |
| HUNT,1850.................................................. | 130.00 |
| STAINED GLASS,WINDOW,SAINT SIMON,16TH CENTURY,ENGLAND, | |
| 66 IN.HIGH................................................. | 225.00 |

STAR HOLLY IS A MILK GLASS TYPE OF GLASS MADE BY THE
IMPERIAL GLASS COMPANY OF BELLAIRE,OHIO.
THE PIECES WERE MADE TO LOOK LIKE WEDGWOOD JASPERWARE.
WHITE HOLLY LEAVES APPEAR AGAINST COLORED BORDERS OF
BLUE,GREEN,OR RUST. IG IS MARKED ON THE BOTTOM OF EVERY
PIECE.

| | |
|---|---|
| STAR HOLLY,GOBLET,5 IN..................................... | 68.00 |
| STAR HOLLY,PLATE,GREEN BORDER,8 3/4 IN..................... | 25.00 |
| STAR HOLLY,SHERBET,BLUE...............................ILLUS.. | 90.00 |
| STEIN,3/10 LITER,BLUE BANDS AROUND BODY,PEWTER LID......... | 5.00 |
| STEIN,1/2 LITER,BUFF,GREEN,LIBERAL ARTS PALACE,ST.LOUIS | |

BLUE STAR HOLLY SHERBET

EXPOSITION,1904.......................................... 18.00
STEIN,1/2 LITER,FIGURE OF FAUST,LITHOPHANE BOTTOM,PORCELAIN,
GERMANY................................................. 125.00
STEIN,1/2 LITER,FLOWERS ON FRONT,BUM ANDENKEN,PORCELAIN,
PEWTER TOP.............................................. 20.00
STEIN,1/2 LITER,LITHOPANE,REGIMENT,DATED 1892.............. 75.00
STEIN,1/2 LITER,PICTURE ON FRONT,LITHOPANE IN BOTTOM,
PORCELAIN............................................... 42.50
STEIN,1/2 LITER,RELIEF,BLUE SALT GLAZE,M.G. IN PEWTER LID... 18.00
STEIN,1/2 LITER,ROSES,ANDENKEN,PORCELAIN IN PEWTER COVER.... 19.50
STEIN,1/2 LITER,SQUATTY,CASTLE SCENE,ILLERTISSEN-SCHLOSS,
PORCELAIN............................................... 22.00
STEIN,1/2 LITER,VERTICAL PANELS,HOTEL GIBSON ON INSET,CIRCA
1900.................................................... 18.00
STEIN,1/2 LITER,WEIHNACHTEN,1936,6 IN...................... 19.50
STEIN,1/2 LITER,YALE,PORCELAIN INSERT,CLASS SIGNATURES,
SCENICS,1901............................................ 65.00
STEIN,1 LITER,BLUE,WHITE BAND,DWARFS HOLD MEDALLION,VILLEROY
& BOCH.................................................. 39.00
STEIN,1 LITER,CREAM COLOR,MONKEY ON PEWTER RIM HOLDS FISH,
LETTERS H.B............................................. 75.00
STEIN,1 LITER,ETCHED DECOR,PORCELAIN LINING,ETCHED LIDS,PAIR 157.00
STEIN,1 LITER,ETCHED,PEWTER LID,GERMANY.................... 125.00
STEIN,1 LITER,HOLLOW BOTTOM RELIEF,THREE DRUNKS WALKING,
PEWTER TOP.............................................. 35.00
STEIN,1 LITER,MAN,WOMAN,DOG,HAND-PAINTED,PEWTER LID,
LITHOPHANE.............................................. 105.00
STEIN,1 LITER,MUSICIANS,BARMAID,ARTIST INITIALED B.K.,PEWTER
TOP,GERMANY............................................. 85.00
STEIN,1 LITER,PICTURE OF COUPLE IN BOTTOM,GRULS-AUD
LANDSHUT,PORCELAIN...................................... 34.00
STEIN,1 LITER,RELIEF IN GREEN,BROWN,BUFF,PEWTER TOP,
10 IN.HIGH.............................................. 30.00
STEIN,2 LITERS,RELIEF IN BLUE & BUFF,ORNATE PEWTER TOP,
15 IN.HIGH.............................................. 40.00
STEIN,3 LITERS,HEAVY RELIEF IN BUFF,BLUE,BROWN,PEWTER TOP,
17 IN.HIGH.............................................. 50.00
STEIN,BEIGE,GREEN,BROWN,HANDLE IN FORM OF BRANCH,PEWTER LID,
GERMANY................................................. 45.00
STEIN,BLUE ON GRAY,10 1/2 IN.............................. 16.00
STEIN,BREWERY,1/2 LITER,OLD HUBER BREWERY,CREST,GOLDENROD
DECOR,LID............................................... 32.00
STEIN,BURSLEM,HAND-PAINTED ROSES,GREEN BANDS,PEWTER LID,
7 IN.................................................... 25.00
STEIN,CAPO-DI-MONTE TYPE,14 IN. HIGH X 6 1/2 IN.-DIAMETER... 175.00
STEIN,CLEAR,HONEYCOMB PATTERN,PEWTER TOP,SAYS  DANZIG,
7 1/2 IN.HIGH........................................... 18.00
STEIN,CLEAR,THUMBPRINT,PEWTER LID,PORCELAIN CENTER,BUM
HOCHZEFSTAG............................................. 35.00
STEIN,CRYSTAL,ENGRAVED,DEER,FOREST,HORN OF PLENTY SHAPE,
PEWTER TRIM............................................. 135.00
STEIN,CUT GLASS CENTER,BISMARK IN MILITARY DRESS,PEWTER LID,
GERMANY................................................. 50.00
STEIN,ENAMEL BOY,GIRL,DANCING,PORCELAIN,LITHOPHANE BASE,
8 IN.TALL............................................... 48.00
STEIN,FAMILY CREST,PEWTER LID,DATE 1588,MARK
D.R.G.M.GESETZLICH,16 IN................................ 125.00
STEIN,FIGURES,SYMBOLS IN RELIEF,LATIN INSCRIPTIONS,BRASS &
COPPER.................................................. 100.00
STEIN,GEOMETRIC,THUMBPRINT,CUT CRYSTAL,PEWTER COVER,BOWLING
PIN..................................................... 35.00
STEIN,GESCHUT,NO.1102,1/2 LITER........................... 45.00
STEIN,GIRL PLAYING ZITHER,DOG,OUTDOOR SCENE,PEWTER TOP,
1/2 LITER,GERMANY....................................... 20.00

STEIN,GRAY GROUND,ALLOVER DECOR,SILVER TOP,925,ORNATE THUMB
 REST,GERMANY............................................. 35.00
STEIN,GREEN,CREAM GROUND,EMBOSSED NORSEMEN FIGURES,PEWTER
 LID,GERMANY............................................. 225.00
STEIN,HAND-PAINTED PEASANT SCENE,PEWTER LID,CIRCA 1917,
 GERMANY,9 1/2 IN........................................ 65.00
STEIN,HUNT SCENE,MEN,HORSES,DOGS,WILD BOARS,APPLIED ROPE
 HANDLE,BRASS........................................... 15.00
STEIN,HUNTERS ON HORSES,ROPE HANDLE,HINGED LID,REPOUSSE,
 BRASS.................................................. 12.00
STEIN,IMPERIAL GERMAN CREST,MIT GOTT FUR KAISER UND REICH,
 PEWTER TOP............................................. 62.00
STEIN,LITHOPHANE BASE,CANNON FINIAL,1899,REVERSE K & R MARK,
 9 IN.TALL.............................................. 37.50
STEIN,LITHOPHANE BASE,TRAIN FINIAL,1913,REVERSE K & R MARK,
 9 IN.TALL.............................................. 37.50
STEIN,LITHOPHANE SCENE,MILITARY SCENE ON SIDE,PEWTER LID,
 GERMANY,1902........................................... 75.00
STEIN,LITHOPHANE SCENE,MILITARY,REGIMENTAL,HAND-PAINTED,
 1902................................................... 68.50
STEIN,LITHOPHANE,NUDE,PEWTER TOP,GERMANY,10 IN.............. 55.00
STEIN,LITHOPHANE,NUN CHARACTER............................. 95.00
STEIN,LITHOPHANE,REGIMENTAL................................ 75.00
STEIN,LITHOPHANE,REGIMENTAL,SOLDIERS FAREWELL,PEWTER TOP,
 GERMANY,10 IN.......................................... 55.00
 STEIN,METTLACH,SEE METTLACH,STEIN
STEIN,MONKEY,SITTING,SMOKING PIPE,HOLDING STEIN,GREEN
 JACKET,BLUE HAT........................................ 36.50
STEIN,MUSTERSCHUTZ,CHARACTER,BISMARCK,MULTICOLORED......... 250.00
STEIN,MUSTERSCHUTZ,TURNIP.................................. 65.00
STEIN,MUSTERSCHUTZ,1/2 LITER,LAUGHING TURNIP.............. 80.00
STEIN,PEWTER TOP,BLACK ON CREAM,8 IN. HIGH................. 15.00
STEIN,PEWTER TOP,CLEAR GLASS,LOWENBRAU-MUENCHEN,5 1/2 IN.
 HIGH.................................................. 18.00
STEIN,PORTRAIT,MONK HOLDING DOG,PORCELAIN ANIMAL ON PEWTER
 COVER,FRANCE.......................................... 35.00
STEIN,PEWTER TOP,ONE LITER,DRINKING SCENES,BLACK ON CREAM,
 GERMANY............................................... 20.00
STEIN,RAISED FLORAL DESIGN,MEN IN COLONIAL DRESS,MURRAY CO.,
 SODA WATER............................................ 12.00
STEIN,REGIMENTAL,FIGURE HOLDING FLAG ON TOP,LITHOPHANE OF
 GIRL AT BOTTOM........................................ 30.00
STEIN,REGIMENTAL,LITHOPHANE BOTTOM,STANDING SOLDIER PEWTER
 TOP,1908.............................................. 60.00
STEIN,REGIMENTAL,LITHOPHANE,DATED 1900,PEWTER TOP......... 68.00
STEIN,REGIMENTAL,LITHOPHANE,MOTHER CRYING,PEWTER TOP,LION
 FINIAL,12 IN.......................................... 115.00
STEIN,SCENE,LADY,WOODSMEN,BLUE,GRAY,VERSES,PEWTER TOP,
 1/2 LITER,GERMANY..................................... 15.00
STEIN,SCENE,MAN & WOMAN AT TABLE,PEWTER TOP,THUMB LIFT,
 GERMANY,10 IN......................................... 32.00
STEIN,SCENE,MEN,WOMEN,TABLE,BLUE,BROWN,IMPRESSED GERMANY,
 10 IN.TALL............................................ 30.00
STEIN,SCENE,WOMAN PICKING GRAPES,4 IN.HIGH................ 9.00
STEIN,SCHULTZ & DOOLEY,UTICA CLUB BEER,PAIR............... 65.00
STEIN,SLEEPY EYE,8 IN..................................... 45.00
STEIN,STONEWARE,CREAM COLOR,PEWTER COVER,ONE LITER........ 15.00
STEIN,STONEWARE,1 LITER,HAUPTBAHNHOF MANCHEN,PEWTER LID,
 GERMANY............................................... 35.00
STEIN,THREE-DIMENSIONAL DECOR,1/2 LITER,GERMANY........... 125.00


  STEREO CARDS THAT WERE MADE FOR STEREOPTICAN VIEWERS
  BECAME POPULAR AFTER 1840. TWO ALMOST IDENTICAL
  PICTURES WERE MOUNTED ON A STIFF CARDBOARD BACKING SO
  THAT,WHEN VIEWED THROUGH A STEREOSCOPE, A THREE-
  DIMENSIONAL PICTURE COULD BE SEEN.
STEREO CARD,AMERICAN SCENERY,INDIAN,PACK TRAIN TO ALASKA,
 COLOR,11.............................................. 6.00
STEREO CARD,ARMY & NAVY,BLACK & WHITE,GROUP OF 7.......... 2.75
STEREO CARD,CALIFORNIA,COLORADO,CLIFF HOUSE,RIVERSIDE,
 DEVIL'S GATEWAY,13.................................... 2.75
STEREO CARD,CHILDREN,ANIMALS,21........................... 6.00
STEREO CARD,COMIC,CHILDREN WITH PETS & TOYS,WAR VIEWS,43... 3.00
STEREO CARD,COMIC,13...................................... 3.00
STEREO CARD,CUBA,1899,AFTER WAR,17........................ 7.00
STEREO CARD,FOREIGN SCENES,GROUP OF 8..................... 1.00
STEREO CARD,G.A.R.IN WASHINGTON,1892,FIVE VIEWS........... 3.00
STEREO CARD,INDIAN CHIEF,GROUP OF 6....................... 2.00
STEREO CARD,JAMAICA EARTHQUAKE,23......................... 12.00
STEREO CARD,MISSOULA,MONTANA,30........................... 5.00

```
STEREO CARD,NAVAL SHIPS,FIVE VIEWS.........................     3.00
STEREO CARD,NEW YORK SCENES,GROUP OF 9.....................     2.00
STEREO CARD,NUDIST SLAVE MARKET,FALL OF BABYLON,9..........     7.50
STEREO CARD,PRESIDENTIAL,GROUP OF 4........................     1.50
STEREO CARD,RAILROAD SCENES,BLACK & WHITE,GROUP OF 6.......     2.50
STEREO CARD,SAN FRANCISCO EARTHQUAKE,1906,GROUP OF 60......    35.00
STEREO CARD,SCENES ABROAD,COLOR,GROUP OF 16................     4.00
STEREO CARD,THEODORE ROOSEVELT'S INAUGURAL,COLOR,GROUP OF 7.    4.50
STEREO CARD,VICTORIAN VIEW..........................ILLUS..      .15
STEREO CARD,VIEWS OF U.S.,SOME OF NORTHFIELD,VERMONT,LOT OF
  36.......................................................     7.75
STEREO CARD,WORLD WAR I,50.................................    50.00
STEREO CARD,WORLD WAR I,74.................................    20.00
STEREO CARD,WORLD'S FAIR,ST.LOUIS,50 VIEWS IN COLOR........    15.00
STEREO CARD,30............................................    10.00
STEREO CARD,48 VIEWS......................................    10.00
```

```
        STEREOSCOPES OR STEREOPTICANS WERE USED FOR VIEWING THE
     STEREO CARDS. THE HAND VIEWER WAS INVENTED BY OLIVER
     WENDELL HOLMES,ALTHOUGH MORE COMPLICATED TABLE MODELS
     WERE USED BEFORE HIS WAS PLACED IN PRODUCTION IN 1859.
STEREOSCOPE.............................................ILLUS.   12.50
STEREOSCOPE AND 12 CARDS..................................    10.00
STEREOSCOPE,ENGRAVED ALUMINUM EYE SHIELD,UNDERWOOD,DATED
  1901,15 VIEWS..........................................     9.50
STEREOSCOPE,HAND TYPE VIEWER,SLIDING ADJUSTMENT..........     5.95
STEREOSCOPE,HAND TYPE,THREE PICTURES.....................     7.00
STEREOSCOPE,HAND TYPE,WALNUT.............................    10.50
STEREOSCOPE,HAND TYPE,WALNUT & EMBOSSED METAL,MARKED SUN
  SCULPTURE..............................................    10.50
STEREOSCOPE,HAND VIEWER,BRASS-MOUNTED FRONT & BACK,
  ADJUSTABLE LENS,1896...................................    20.00
STEREOSCOPE,KEYSTONE,80 CARDS,SOME WORLD WAR I TROOPS.....    15.00
STEREOSCOPE,LENSES,LIGHT BROWN WOOD,FRANCE................    12.50
STEREOSCOPE,MAGNIFYING GLASS,FOLDS LIKE A BOX,OAK........    38.50
```

STEREO CARD, VICTORIAN VIEW

STEREOSCOPE

```
STEREOSCOPE,NICKEL PLATE BRASS STAND,FOLDS,MAHOGANY,15 VIEWS        15.00
STEREOSCOPE,SLIDING ADJUSTER,MARKED PERFESCOPE,PATENT 1895,
  10 CARDS...............................................        12.00
STEREOSCOPE,SLIDING ADJUSTER,WOODEN,5 CARDS.................         7.50
STEREOSCOPE,SLIDING ADJUSTMENT,METAL,5 CARDS................         8.50
STEREOSCOPE,TABLE MODEL,WALNUT STAND,MARKED THE SATURNSCOPE,
  PATENT 1895...........................................        27.50
STEREOSCOPE,VIEWER AND 10 SCENIC VIEWS.....................        12.00
STEREOSCOPE,VIEWER,6 CARDS.................................        10.00
STEREOSCOPE,WITH 11 CARDS,CORONATION RUSSIAN CZAR..........        16.00
STEREOSCOPE,WITH 375 CARDS,OLD WEST,INDIANS,COMICS,ROGERS
  STATUARY..............................................        35.00
STEREOSCOPE,16 CARDS,SOME CIVIL WAR........................        10.00
STEREOSCOPE,89 CARDS.......................................        20.00
STEREOSCOPE,100 CARDS......................................        20.00
STEREOSCOPE,25 VIEW CARDS..................................        10.00
STEREOSCOPE,35 VIEW CARDS..................................        20.00
STEREOSCOPE,50 VIEW CARDS..................................        25.00
  STERLING SILVER SEE,SILVER,STERLING
```

```
    STEUBEN GLASS WAS MADE AT THE STEUBEN GLASS WORKS OF
    CORNING,NEW YORK. THE FACTORY,FOUNDED BY FREDERICK
    CARDER AND T.C.HAWKES,SR.,WAS PURCHASED BY THE CORNING
    GLASS COMPANY. THEY CONTINUED TO MAKE GLASS CALLED
    STEUBEN. MANY TYPES OF ART GLASS WERE MADE AT STEUBEN.
    THE FIRM IS STILL PRODUCING GLASS OF EXCEPTIONAL
    QUALITY.
STEUBEN,SEE ALSO,AURENE,CALCITE,VERRE DE SOIE
STEUBEN,BONBON,RIBBED DESIGN,GOLD AURENE ON CALCITE,
  6 1/4 IN.DIAMETER......................................        48.00
STEUBEN,BOTTLE,DRESSER,JADE GREEN,ALABASTER STOPPER,SIGNED,
  12 IN.,PAIR...........................................       650.00
STEUBEN,BOTTLE,PERFUME,STOPPER,ROSA,SIGNED WITH
  FLEUR-DE-LIS,8 IN.HIGH................................       145.00
STEUBEN,BOWL,BLUE AURENE,SIGNED,FOOTED....................       295.00
STEUBEN,BOWL,BLUE JADE,SILVER HOLDER,ORNATE,FOOTED,2 IN. X
  4 IN..................................................       125.00
STEUBEN,BOWL,BLUE,LABEL,SIGNED,AURENE,5 IN................       190.00
STEUBEN,BOWL,CALCITE,GOLD AURENE,FLARED,5 IN.TALL,
  11-IN.DIAMETER........................................       100.00
STEUBEN,BOWL,CALCITE,PEDESTAL BASE,12 IN.ACROSS,
  3 1/2 IN.HIGH.........................................       155.00
STEUBEN,BOWL,CALCITE,9 1/2 IN.............................       135.00
STEUBEN,BOWL,CENTER,IVORY COLOR,BLACK BASE,ONE PIECE,14 X
  4 IN.HIGH.............................................       165.00
STEUBEN,BOWL,CENTERPIECE,ACID CUT-BACK ROSALINE TO
  ALABASTER,12 IN.......................................       495.00
STEUBEN,BOWL,CENTERPIECE,CALCITE & GOLD AURENE,FLARING,
  12 1/4 IN.............................................       110.00
STEUBEN,BOWL,CENTERPIECE,YELLOW,ROLLED LIP,RIM FOOT,BRISTOL,
  11 1/2 IN.............................................        31.00
STEUBEN,BOWL,CONSOLE,GOLD AURENE ON CALCITE,7 IN..........        85.00
STEUBEN,BOWL,FINGER,UNDERPLATE,GREEN JADE,ALABASTER,ENGRAVED      85.00
STEUBEN,BOWL,GOLD AURENE,SIGNED & NUMBERED,10 1/4 IN.......       200.00
STEUBEN,BOWL,GOLD AURENE ON CALCITE,10-IN.DIAMETER........        87.50
STEUBEN,BOWL,GOLD AURENE ON CALCITE,DOME FOOT BASE,7 IN....        92.50
STEUBEN,BOWL,GROTESQUE,CLEAR,SIGNED S.G.D.,12 X 6 1/2 X
  6 IN.HIGH.............................................        95.00
STEUBEN,BOWL,JADE,8 IN.ROUND..............................        75.00
STEUBEN,BOWL,PANELED OPTIC AMETHYST,FOLDED RIM,
  12-IN.DIAMETER........................................       150.00
STEUBEN,BOWL,RIBBED,FOLD OVER EDGE,LABEL,TOPAZ,14 IN.ACROSS.      110.00
STEUBEN,BOWL,RIBBED,PINK/GOLD IRIDESCENT INSIDE & OUTSIDE,
  CALCITE,PLATE.........................................       125.00
STEUBEN,BOWL,SHALLOW,CALCITE,GOLD AURENE LINING,
  6-IN.DIAMETER.........................................        37.50
STEUBEN,BOWL,SWAN,GREEN,BLOCK LETTER MARK,5 1/2 IN. X 8 IN.
  X 6 IN................................................        95.00
STEUBEN,BOWL,SWIRLED,OPAL GREEN,CIRCULAR FOOT,SIGNED,
  5-IN.DIAMETER.........................................       135.00
STEUBEN,BOWL,THREADING,GOLD REEDING,BUBBLED GLASS,14 X 6 IN.       90.00
STEUBEN,BOWL,TOPAZ AMBER,RIBBED ROLLED EDGE...............        36.00
STEUBEN,BOWL,WHITE CALCITE,GILT LINING,2 1/4 IN.HIGH X
  5 1/2 IN.WIDE.........................................       140.00
STEUBEN,BOWL,YELLOW,FOLDED EDGE,ROLLED RIM,BRISTOL,
  FLEUR-DE-LIS MARK.....................................        72.00
STEUBEN,BOX,PUFF,OPAL,IVORY KNOB ON COVER,3 1/2-IN.DIAMETER.      115.00
STEUBEN,CANDLEHOLDER,BLACK GLASS,SIGNED WITH FLEUR-DE-LIS,
  PAIR..................................................       145.00
STEUBEN,CANDLEHOLDER,BLUE CUP,DOMED BASE,CLEAR TWISTED ROPE
```

| | |
|---|---|
| STEM,PAIR............................................ | 155.00 |
| STEUBEN,CANDLEHOLDER,GREEN SHADE,SWIRL PATTERN,HAND-BLOWN, SIGNED............................................ | 85.00 |
| STEUBEN,CANDLEHOLDER,SWIRL RIB,GREEN,CLEAR BERRY PRUNTS ON CUP,4 IN.TALL...................................... | 25.00 |
| STEUBEN,CANDLESTICK,BLUE AURENE,TWISTED STEM,8 IN.HIGH,PAIR. | 495.00 |
| STEUBEN,CANDLESTICK,BLUE IRIDESCENT,TWISTED STEM,SIGNED..... | 250.00 |
| STEUBEN,CANDLESTICK,CELESTE BLUE,SWIRL RIB BASE & SOCKET, 11 IN............................................ | 37.50 |
| STEUBEN,CANDLESTICK,CLEAR BASE,CERISE MORNING GLORY-SHAPED CUPS,PAIR.......................................... | 165.00 |
| STEUBEN,CANDLESTICK,CRYSTAL WITH AMETHYST,MAT-SU-NO-KE DECOR,17 IN......................................... | 48.00 |
| STEUBEN,CANDLESTICK,GREEN,PINK,GOLD AURENE ON CALCITE BOWL, 10 3/4 IN......................................... | 100.00 |
| STEUBEN,CANDLESTICK,GREEN,SWIRLED FOOT & HOLDER,SIGNED FDL, 10 IN.,PAIR....................................... | 80.00 |
| STEUBEN,CANDLESTICK,GREEN,TULIP-SHAPED,SWIRL TOP,CLEAR COLUMN,10 IN.,4...................................... | 200.00 |
| STEUBEN,CANDLESTICK,OPEN BALUSTER,CLEAR WAFER CONNECTIONS ON FOOT,RUBY............................................ | 70.00 |
| STEUBEN,CANDLESTICK,ROSE-COLOR,SIGNED.................... | 47.00 |
| STEUBEN,CANDLESTICK,SWIRLED STEM,SIGNED STEUBEN AURENE, 8 1/4 IN.,PAIR....................................... | 225.00 |
| STEUBEN,CENTERPIECE,GREEN JADE,ALABASTER BASE,SIGNED,14 X 4 IN.HIGH.......................................... | 225.00 |
| STEUBEN,CHAMPAGNE GLASS,HOLLOW STEM,SWIRLED,CRANBERRY....... | 75.00 |
| STEUBEN,CHAMPAGNE,GREEN JADE,ALABASTER,COPPER WHEEL-ENGRAVED 6 1/2 IN............................................ | 85.00 |
| STEUBEN,CHANDELIER,FIVE BELL-SHAPED AURENE SHADES,GOLD,BLUE, BRASS,36 IN......................................... | 450.00 |
| STEUBEN,CHANDELIER,FIVE SHADES,WHITE CALCITE OUT,GOLD AURENE IN,WIRED............................................ | 350.00 |
| STEUBEN,COCKTAIL GLASS,CRYSTAL,HOLDS 3 OUNCES,SET OF 9...... | 60.00 |
| STEUBEN,COCKTAIL SHAKER,BLACK REEDING ON BODY,BLACK FACETED STOPPER............................................ | 95.00 |
| STEUBEN,COLOGNE,GOLD AURENE,RED HIGHLIGHTS,SIGNED, 7 3/4 IN.HIGH........................................ | 165.00 |
| STEUBEN,COLOGNE,ROSALINE,ALABASTER STOPPER & BASE, 7 3/4 IN.HIGH........................................ | 225.00 |
| STEUBEN,COMPOTE,AMETHYST,OPTIC SWIRL PATTERN,CLEAR BALL STEM | 140.00 |
| STEUBEN,COMPOTE,BLUE,REEDED EDGE,TEARDROP STEM,7-IN.DIAMETER | 32.00 |
| STEUBEN,COMPOTE,CARDER,MICA AIR TWIST,AMETHYST,SIGNED, 7 IN.HIGH........................................... | 550.00 |
| STEUBEN,COMPOTE,COTTON TWIST STEM,SIGNED................. | 65.00 |
| STEUBEN,COMPOTE,GOLD AURENE & CALCITE,RIBBED,6 IN. X 3 IN.HIGH........................................... | 85.00 |
| STEUBEN,COMPOTE,GREEN ALABASTER,COVER.................... | 50.00 |
| STEUBEN,COMPOTE,GREEN JADE BOWL,TWISTED ALABASTER STEM,GREEN BASE,8 IN............................................ | 87.50 |
| STEUBEN,COMPOTE,ORIENTAL POPPY,PINK STRIPE TOP,GREEN STEM, FOOT,7 IN.HIGH........................................ | 250.00 |
| STEUBEN,COMPOTE,PEACOCK BLUE ON CALCITE,3 X 6 IN.WIDE...... | 275.00 |
| STEUBEN,COMPOTE,SWIRL PATTERN,SIGNED,AMBER,7 1/2 IN.HIGH.... | 99.00 |
| STEUBEN,COMPOTE,TOPAZ COLOR,COPPER WHEEL ENGRAVED,SIGNED, 8-IN.DIAMETER....................................... | 47.50 |
| STEUBEN,COMPOTE,YELLOW JADE,ALABASTER STEM & BASE, 6 1/2 IN.HIGH........................................ | 250.00 |
| STEUBEN,CORDIAL,TWISTED STEM,MONOGRAM,PAIR............... | 8.50 |
| STEUBEN,DISH,FRUIT,BLUE,SCALLOPED BORDER,FOOTED,SIGNED, 5-IN.DIAMETER....................................... | 65.00 |
| STEUBEN,EPERGNE,CLEAR,SILVER PLATE HOLDER................ | 38.00 |
| STEUBEN,EPERGNE,SIX TRIANGULAR-SHAPED VASES,VARIOUS HEIGHTS, CLEAR,16 IN.......................................... | 300.00 |
| STEUBEN,FIGURINE,PENGUIN,GREEN JADE,ALABASTER,SIGNED, 6 IN.TALL........................................... | 125.00 |
| STEUBEN,GLASS,CORDIAL,ETCHED MONOGRAM BBC,SIGNED, 3 1/8 IN.TALL,SET OF 8.............................. | 125.00 |
| STEUBEN,GOBLET,BLUE WAFER,ETCHED,STEM & FOOT,8 IN.TALL...... | 16.50 |
| STEUBEN,GOBLET,BLUE,BUBBLES IN SIDES,WIDE-THREADED TOP,8 IN. | 60.00 |
| STEUBEN,GOBLET,BUBBLY................................ | 22.50 |
| STEUBEN,GOBLET,CARDER,BUBBLES,REEDS,PRUNTS,WAFERS,PANELS, TOPAZ.............................................. | 75.00 |
| STEUBEN,GOBLET,CARDER,GOLD AURENE,SIGNED & NUMBERED, 6 1/4 IN.HIGH........................................ | 150.00 |
| STEUBEN,GOBLET,DOG CHASING RABBIT,ENGRAVED,SIGNED.......... | 35.00 |
| STEUBEN,GOBLET,GOLD AURENE,TWISTED STEM,SIGNED,4 1/4 X 6 1/4 IN.HIGH........................................ | 150.00 |
| STEUBEN,GOBLET,GOLFER,ENGRAVED,SIGNED................... | 35.00 |
| STEUBEN,GOBLET,GREEN JADE,ALABASTER,COPPER-WHEEL-ENGRAVED, 8 1/2 IN.TALL....................................... | 85.00 |

| | |
|---|---|
| STEUBEN, GOBLET, MARINA BLUE BOWL & BASE, CLEAR TWISTED STEM, SIGNED, 7 IN........ | 55.00 |
| STEUBEN, GOBLET, SAILING SHIP, ENGRAVED, SIGNED............... | 35.00 |
| STEUBEN, GOBLET, WATER, CRANBERRY, CLEAR STEM, 10 IN. HIGH....... | 95.00 |
| STEUBEN, GOBLET, WATER, ROSALINE, ALABASTER, PAIR.............. | 125.00 |
| STEUBEN, JAR, JADE TO ALABASTER, ACID CUT BACK, COVER........... | 550.00 |
| STEUBEN, JUG, BUBBLE GLASS, SIGNED STEUBEN, F. CARDER, 10 IN...... | 150.00 |
| STEUBEN, LAMP BASE, GREEN GROUND, ORIENTAL FLORAL, ACID CUT BACK, SIGNED....... | 235.00 |
| STEUBEN, LAMP, CONSOLE, BRONZE LATTICE BASE, GOLD AURENE SHADE, 15 IN., PAIR........ | 285.00 |
| STEUBEN, LAMP, DESK, BRONZE BASE, SILVER FLEUR-DE-LIS, WHITE CALCITE SHADES........ | 235.00 |
| STEUBEN, LAMP, DESK, TWO SHADES, WHITE CALCITE, FEATHER MOTIF, BRONZE BASE........ | 235.00 |
| STEUBEN, LAMP, PERFUME, AURENE, ART GLASS CHIMNEY, SIGNED....... | 195.00 |
| STEUBEN, LAMP, STUDENT, IVORENE SHADES, FEATHER MOTIF, BRONZE BASE, 1909........ | 180.00 |
| STEUBEN, LAMP, TABLE, AURENE, GOLD & BLUE IRIDESCENT, MATCHING SHADE, 14 IN........ | 375.00 |
| STEUBEN, LEMONADE, THREADED, CELESTE BLUE, FLEUR-DE-LIS MARK, 6 IN. HIGH........ | 25.00 |
| STEUBEN, PAPERWEIGHT, CUT, CLEAR, SIGNED........ | 70.00 |
| STEUBEN, PAPERWEIGHT, SILVER-FLECKED CUSHION IN BASE, MULTICOLORED FLOWER........ | 125.00 |
| STEUBEN, PAPERWEIGHT, SWIRL, SIGNED........ | 200.00 |
| STEUBEN, PARFAIT, ROSALINE, ALABASTER WAFER & BASE, 4 1/4 IN. HIGH........ | 67.50 |
| STEUBEN, PERFUME, GREEN JADE, GOLD, ALABASTER SNAKE ON NECK, SIGNED, 7 IN........ | 95.00 |
| STEUBEN, PERFUME, GREEN JADE, 10 IN........ | 75.00 |
| STEUBEN, PITCHER, CLEAR, CERISE THREADING, GREEN HANDLE........ | 65.00 |
| STEUBEN, PITCHER, IVORY, BLACK HANDLE, 9 1/4 IN. HIGH........ | 135.00 |
| STEUBEN, PITCHER, RIBBED, GREEN, CLEAR HANDLE........ | 65.00 |
| STEUBEN, PITCHER, WATER, ROSALINE, APPLIED ALABASTER HANDLE, 9 IN. HIGH........ | 150.00 |
| STEUBEN, PLAQUE, COMMEMORATION, THOMAS EDISON, MARKED........ | 750.00 |
| STEUBEN, PLATE, AURENE ON CALCITE, IRIDESCENT........ | 55.00 |
| STEUBEN, PLATE, AURENE-LINED CALCITE, PINK & BLUE HIGHLIGHTS, 8 1/2 IN........ | 60.00 |
| STEUBEN, PLATE, BLACK AMETHYST, STERLING SILVER HANDLES & TRIM, 7 IN........ | 17.50 |
| STEUBEN, PLATE, BLUE, BUBBLY, SELF-THREADING DECOR, 8 1/2 IN..... | 23.00 |
| STEUBEN, PLATE, BLUE, SIGNED, AURENE, 6 IN........ | 140.00 |
| STEUBEN, PLATE, GOLD CALCITE, 6 1/2-IN. DIAMETER........ | 125.00 |
| STEUBEN, PLATE, GREEN, 8 IN........ | 22.50 |
| STEUBEN, PLATE, RECESSED CENTER, YELLOW, BRISTOL, 8 1/2 IN....... | 12.00 |
| STEUBEN, PLATE, ROSALINE, 8 1/2 IN........ | 58.00 |
| STEUBEN, PLATE, YELLOW, BRISTOL, 8 1/2 IN........ | 12.00 |
| STEUBEN, SALT, AURENE, GOLD, FOOTED, SIGNED & NUMBERED........ | 105.00 |
| STEUBEN, SALT, CALCITE, GOLD INTERIOR, DOUBLE EDGE, 2 IN. X 1 1/4 IN........ | 95.00 |
| STEUBEN, SALT, CELESTE BLUE........ | 40.00 |
| STEUBEN, SALT, MASTER, AURENE, IRIDESCENT GOLD, FOOTED, SCALLOPED, SIGNED........ | 110.00 |
| STEUBEN, SHADE, BURNISHED, REWIRED, FIXTURE, SIGNED, GROUP OF 5... | 235.00 |
| STEUBEN, SHADE, CLEAR, GREEN FEATHER, GOLD BORDER, OPAL TOP, SIGNED, 4 5/8 IN........ | 37.50 |
| STEUBEN, SHADE, GAS LAMP, GOLD IRIDESCENT COLOR, SIGNED........ | 28.00 |
| STEUBEN, SHADE, GAS, GREEN, WHITE, SIGNED........ | 32.50 |
| STEUBEN, SHADE, GOLD AURENE, BLUE HIGHLIGHTS, SIGNED, 2 1/4 X 7-IN. DIAMETER........ | 60.00 |
| STEUBEN, SHADE, GOLD HEART & VINE DECOR, GOLD AURENE LINING, 5 1/2 IN., PAIR........ | 75.00 |
| STEUBEN, SHADE, GOLD IRIDESCENT, WIDE-RIBBED, SIGNED, 5 1/4 IN. TALL........ | 35.00 |
| STEUBEN, SHADE, GREEN DRAPE, GOLD INSIDE, IRIDESCENT, SIGNED, PAIR | 91.00 |
| STEUBEN, SHADE, IVORENE, ACID-CUT BACK, 2 1/4 IN. TOP OPENING, 5 IN. DEEP, 8........ | 300.00 |
| STEUBEN, SHADE, LIGHT, FLEUR-DE-LIS, RIBBED, SWIRLED, FLUTED, BRONZE-GOLD........ | 35.00 |
| STEUBEN, SHADE, WHITE, IVORY, FLEUR-DI-LIS, INTAGLIO CUT, 5 1/4 IN., SET OF 3........ | 110.00 |
| STEUBEN, SHADE, WIDE RIBS, MORNING GLORY COLORS, SCALLOPED, 2 1/4 X 5 IN........ | 30.00 |
| STEUBEN, SHERBET & PLATE, BLUISH GOLD, AURENE, SIGNED........ | 145.00 |
| STEUBEN, SHERBET, CALCITE, GOLD, IRIDESCENT, UNDERPLATE........ | 75.00 |
| STEUBEN, SHERBET, CARDER, BUBBLES, REEDS, PRUNTS, WAFERS, PANELS, TOPAZ........ | 65.00 |
| STEUBEN, SHERBET, GOLD AURENE ON CALCITE, PEDESTAL, UNDERPLATE.. | 135.00 |
| STEUBEN, SHERBET, GOLD-PURPLE, RIBBING, POLISHED PONTIL, SET OF | |

```
5.................................................................  60.00
STEUBEN,SHERBET,JADE & ALABASTER,SIGNED.......................  60.00
STEUBEN,SHERBET,ROSALENE,ALABASTER,FOOTED,UNDERPLATE.......... 125.00
STEUBEN,SHERBET,TOPAZ & CELESTE BLUE,SIGNED...................  25.00
STEUBEN,TAZZA,FLEUR-DE-LIS,ROSA INTAGLIO,8 3/4 IN.HIGH....... 145.00
STEUBEN,TAZZA,GOLD AURENE ON CALCITE,6 1/2 X 8 1/2 IN.WIDE.. 200.00
STEUBEN,TAZZA,SWIRLING MICA SQUARES ON BOWL,AMETHYST STEM,
  7 IN....................................................... 250.00
STEUBEN,TUMBLE-UP,CARDER,AMETHYST............................ 275.00
STEUBEN,TUMBLER,CLEAR,GREEN,MAT-SU-NO-KE DESIGN,GREEN HANDLE  65.00
STEUBEN,TUMBLER,GREEN-BLUE TO CLEAR,SILVER DEPOSIT RIM,
  BARREL SHAPE...............................................  35.00
STEUBEN,TUMBLER,ICED TEA,BLUE RIM,BLUE APPLIED HANDLE.......  65.00
STEUBEN,TUMBLER,ICED TEA,IVORY,BLACK HANDLE.................  85.00
STEUBEN,TUMBLER,ROSALINE,ALABASTER FOOT..................... 125.00
STEUBEN,URN,AURENE,GOLD IRIDESCENT,APPLIED BASE,EAR HANDLES,
  7 IN.HIGH.................................................. 295.00
STEUBEN,URN,CLEAR,HANDLES,6 3/4 IN.HIGH,PAIR................ 125.00
STEUBEN,VASE,AMETHYST,CLUTHRA,BUBBLES,SIGNED,8 IN........... 450.00
STEUBEN,VASE,AURENE,GOLD IRIDESCENT,RIBBED,FLARED TOP,
  SIGNED,6 IN.HIGH...........................................  85.00
STEUBEN,VASE,AURENE,PEACOCK BLUE,6 1/2 IN.TALL,5 1/4 IN.WIDE
  AT SHOULDER................................................ 395.00
STEUBEN,VASE,BLACK GLASS,SIGNED WITH FLEUR-DE-LIS,10 IN.HIGH 110.00
STEUBEN,VASE,BLACK RIM,GROUND PONTIL,THREE APPLIED BLACK
  FEET.......................................................  49.00
STEUBEN,VASE,BLUE,ACID-ETCHED GRAPEVINES,10 1/2 IN...ILLUS.. 475.00
STEUBEN,VASE,BLUE AURENE OVER YELLOW JADE,ARCHER,GAZELLE,
  ACID CUT,10 IN............................................. 795.00
STEUBEN,VASE,BLUE AURENE,SIGNED............................. 225.00
STEUBEN,VASE,BLUE AURENE,VERTICAL PANELS,FLARED RIM,SIGNED,
  8 IN.HIGH.................................................. 375.00
STEUBEN,VASE,BUBBLES,FLARE BASE,WIDE FLARE TOP,GREEN REEDING
  AT TOP.....................................................  35.00
STEUBEN,VASE,BUBBLY BLUE GLASS,PINK REEDING AROUND TOP,
  8 1/4 IN.HIGH.............................................. 125.00
STEUBEN,VASE,BUD,JADE,YELLOW,11 IN..........................  60.00
STEUBEN,VASE,CALCITE & VIBRANT,GOLD,AURENE,PEDESTAL BASE,
  PARFAIT.................................................... 120.00
STEUBEN,VASE,CAR,BLUE,GREEN,GOLD AURENE,CALCITE............. 175.00
STEUBEN,VASE,CELESTE BLUE,SLIGHTLY RIBBED,SIGNED,F.CARTER,
  12 IN.TALL................................................. 195.00
STEUBEN,VASE,CERISE,SILVERY WAVE DESIGN AROUND BODY,
  10 IN.HIGH.................................................  75.00
STEUBEN,VASE,CINTRA ACID-CUT BACK,SHADED WHITE MANSARD
  PATTERN,9 1/2 IN...........................................1,500.00
STEUBEN,VASE,CLEAR,APPLIED GREEN STRIPES,SILVER RIM,
  8 IN.TALL..................................................  85.00
STEUBEN,VASE,CLEAR,GREEN THREADING AROUND TOP,HANDLES,
  SIGNED,5 1/2 IN............................................  89.00
STEUBEN,VASE,CLEAR,HANDLE,SQUARE PEDESTAL,7 IN.TALL.........  40.00
STEUBEN,VASE,CLEAR,HONEYCOMB PATTERN,BLACK REEDING,
  9 1/4 IN.TALL..............................................  75.00
STEUBEN,VASE,CLEAR,RED THREADING,FLARED TOP,7-IN.DIAMETER...  48.00
STEUBEN,VASE,CLUTHRA,MARBLEIZED BROWN,SIGNED K,4 X
  4 1/4 IN.HIGH.............................................. 137.50
```

STEUBEN GRAPEVINE VASE

```
STEUBEN,VASE,DIAMOND-QUILTED,CLEAR,BLACK THREADS,FLARED,
  SCALLOPED,5 IN.........................................    48.00
STEUBEN,VASE,EMERALD GREEN REEDING,FLARE TOP,CRYSTAL,
  5 1/2 IN..............................................    22.00
STEUBEN,VASE,FAN,AMBER,BRISTOL,MARKED,8 IN.,PAIR..........   120.00
STEUBEN,VASE,FAN,GREEN,APPLIED GREEN LEAVES,SAUCER BASE,
  3 1/2 IN.TALL.........................................    35.00
STEUBEN,VASE,FAN,GREEN,DOUBLE-KNOB STEM,CLEAR BASE,SIGNED,
  6 1/2 IN..............................................    45.00
STEUBEN,VASE,FAN,GREEN,SIGNED WITH FLEUR-DE-LIS,PAPER LABEL.   67.00
STEUBEN,VASE,FAN,RIBBED,BLUE,8 1/2 IN.HIGH................    25.00
STEUBEN,VASE,FAN-SHAPED,BLUE,AMBER FOOT,8 3/8 IN.,PAIR....   160.00
STEUBEN,VASE,FAN-SHAPED,CARVED CHRYSANTHEMUMS,ALABASTER,
  8 IN.HIGH.............................................   450.00
STEUBEN,VASE,FLARE TOP,GOLD AURENE,BLUE BASE & RIM,SIGNED,
  7 IN..................................................   175.00
STEUBEN,VASE,FLUTED TOP,CUSTARD,8 IN. X 8 IN..............   135.00
STEUBEN,VASE,GOLD AURENE,BULBOUS,SIGNED FREDERICK CARDER,
  6 IN.HIGH.............................................   165.00
STEUBEN,VASE,GREEN,CRYSTAL,THREE PRONGS,RUSTIC,SIGNED.....    75.00
STEUBEN,VASE,IVORENE,FLARED,SIGNED,PAPER LABEL............   145.00
STEUBEN,VASE,IVORENE,FLARED TOP,RUFFLED,SIGNED,5 1/2 X
  4 1/2 IN.TALL.........................................   115.00
STEUBEN,VASE,IVORENE,SHEEN,SIGNED,5 1/4 IN................    87.50
STEUBEN,VASE,IVORENE,URN SHAPE...........................   195.00
STEUBEN,VASE,IVORENE,VERTICAL RIB,SIGNED,5 IN.HIGH........   185.00
STEUBEN,VASE,IVORY,FLARED TOP,5 1/2 IN....................    89.00
STEUBEN,VASE,IVORY,URN SHAPE,10 1/2 IN.TALL...............   225.00
STEUBEN,VASE,IVORY,URN SHAPE,8 IN.TALL....................   150.00
STEUBEN,VASE,JADE ON ALABASTER,CHINESE DECOR,10 IN.TALL...   400.00
STEUBEN,VASE,JADE,BLACK,OVAL FREE FORM,PEDESTAL,6 1/4 X
  8 1/4 IN..............................................   133.00
STEUBEN,VASE,OVAL FREE FORM TOP,BLACK JADE,PEDESTAL,
  6 1/4 IN.HIGH.........................................   133.00
STEUBEN,VASE,RED & BLUE STRIPES,9 3/4-IN.DIAMETER....ILLUS..  600.00
STEUBEN,VASE,ROSA,INTAGLIO CUT SAILBOAT,FULL SAIL,SIGNED,
  10 1/2 IN.HIGH........................................   115.00
STEUBEN,VASE,ROYAL PURPLE,DRAPE,6 IN.HIGH.................    45.00
STEUBEN,VASE,STICK,BLUE AURENE,SIGNED & NUMBERED..........   155.00
STEUBEN,VASE,STICK,GOLD COLOR,SIGNED STEUBEN AURENE 2556,
  10 IN.HIGH............................................   125.00
```

STEUBEN RED AND
BLUE STRIPED VASE

```
STEUBEN,VASE,STICK,IVORY,10 IN..........................    85.00
STEUBEN,VASE,SWIRL,JADE,SIGNED,2 1/2 IN.TOP OPENING,
  7 IN.HIGH............................................    95.00
STEUBEN,VASE,TREE TRUNK,THREE PRONGS,CLEAR GREEN,SIGNED..   145.00
STEUBEN,WINE,AURENE,KLAXON-LIKE TOP,VIBRANT GOLD,PEDESTAL,
  SIGNED..............................................    77.00
STEUBEN,WINE,BUBBLY,TOPAZ REEDING,7 IN.TALL.............    22.50
STEUBEN,WINE,FLEUR-DE-LIS,TULIP-SHAPED BOWL,RIBBED,GREEN,
  FOOTED,SET OF 4.....................................    60.00
```

```
     STEVENGRAPHS ARE WOVEN PICTURES MADE LIKE RIBBONS.
  THEY WERE MANUFACTURED BY THOMAS STEVENS OF COVENTRY,
  ENGLAND,AND BECAME POPULAR IN 1862.
STEVENGRAPH,BOOKMARK,2 IN.WIDE,9 IN.LONG................    35.00
STEVENGRAPH,BOOKMARK,CHRISTMAS MOTIF,VERSE,TASSEL,10 IN..,.   28.50
STEVENGRAPH,BOOKMARK,NEW YEAR MOTIF,VERSE,TASSEL,10 IN....   28.50
STEVENGRAPH,BOOKMARK,PORTRAIT,PRINCE ALBERT EDWARD &
  PRINCESS ALEXANDRIA.................................    35.00
STEVENGRAPH,COLUMBUS LEAVING SPAIN.....................    55.00
STEVENGRAPH,FARM WOMEN GLEANING WHEAT,7 IN. X 8 IN.....    45.00
STEVENGRAPH,FARMER,WIFE IN PRAYER,FRAME,7 IN. X 8 IN...    45.00
STEVENGRAPH,LANDING OF COLUMBUS,GILT LINER,WALNUT FRAME.    62.00
STEVENGRAPH,RACING SUBJECTS,THE START,THE FINISH,SILK,
  UNFRAMED,PAIR.......................................   115.00
```

STEVENGRAPH,SHAKESPEARE'S TERCENTENARY,APRIL 23,1864........ 35.00
STEVENGRAPH,SILK,DICK TURPIN'S LAST RIDE,FRAME,7 X 9 1/2 IN. 65.00
STEVENGRAPH,SPORTING SCENE,FRAME,FINAL SPURT,PAIR........... 100.00
STEVENGRAPH,THE ROYAL MAIL COACH.......................... 32.50
STEVENGRAPH,THE START,THE FINISH,SILK,MAT,PAIR............. 165.00


STEVENS AND WILLIAMS OF STOURBRIDGE,ENGLAND,MADE MANY
TYPES OF ART GLASS.
STEVENS & WILLIAMS,BASKET,CLEAR TO GREEN,RUFFLED,FLORAL,
CRYSTAL MOTIF............................................ 55.00
STEVENS & WILLIAMS,BOWL,CENTERPIECE,SWIRLS,CAMPHOR TO
CRANBERRY,HOLDER........................................ 65.00
STEVENS & WILLIAMS,BOWL,PINK,APPLIED ICICLE EDGING,WHITE
LINING,6 IN............................................. 125.00
STEVENS & WILLIAMS,BOWL,ROSE,CRANBERRY THREADING,YELLOW
INTERIOR,FOOTED......................................... 275.00
STEVENS & WILLIAMS,BOWL,ROSE,MOTHER-OF-PEARL,
DIAMOND-QUILTED,ROSE COLOR.............................. 178.50
STEVENS & WILLIAMS,BOWL,ROSE,OPALESCENT,STRIPED,APPLIED
CRANBERRY FLOWER........................................ 42.00
STEVENS & WILLIAMS,BOWL,ROSE,RED TO PINK,AMBER LEAVES,RING
HANDLES................................................. 450.00
STEVENS & WILLIAMS,BOWL,SWIRL-RIBBED,MOTHER-OF-PEARL,GREEN,
CRIMPED RIM............................................. 425.00
STEVENS & WILLIAMS,BOWL,WHITE ICY OVERSHOT GROUND,AMBER
LEAVES,6 IN............................................. 70.00
STEVENS & WILLIAMS,BOWL,YELLOW SEAWEED,MAT-SU-NO-KE DECOR,
BLUE LINING............................................. 225.00
STEVENS & WILLIAMS,DISH,JAM,RUBINA,PAIR SET IN FOOTED SILVER
HOLDER.................................................. 50.00
STEVENS & WILLIAMS,EWER,BLUE SATIN,ENAMELED RED BIRD,
CORALENE STEMS.......................................... 50.00
STEVENS & WILLIAMS,JACK-IN-THE-PULPIT VASE,VASELINE,
OPALESCENT,FLORAL....................................... 42.00
STEVENS & WILLIAMS,TAZZA,ROSALENE,BALUSTER STEM,8 IN.ACROSS. 295.00
STEVENS & WILLIAMS,TAZZA,ROSALENE,BALUSTER STEM,WIDE BASE,
8 IN.ACROSS............................................. 315.00
STEVENS & WILLIAMS,VASE,APRICOT COLOR & WHITE STRIPES,GOLD
COLOR FLORALS........................................... 90.00
STEVENS & WILLIAMS,VASE,CARDER,BLUE,PINK SWIRLED AIR TRAPS,
WHITE CASING............................................ 425.00
STEVENS & WILLIAMS,VASE,ENAMELED IRIS,ACID-CUT GREEN GROUND,
CAMEO,9 IN.............................................. 285.00
STEVENS & WILLIAMS,VASE,MELON RIB,CRANBERRY & YELLOW SWIRLS,
CRIMPED RIM............................................. 98.50
STEVENS & WILLIAMS,VASE,MELON RIB,CRANBERRY & YELLOW
STRIPES,8 IN............................................ 98.50
STEVENS & WILLIAMS,VASE,PANELED AMBER,CROCODILE ENCIRCLES
BODY.................................................... 75.00
STEVENS & WILLIAMS,VASE,PARFAIT,YELLOW JADE & ALABASTER,
F.CARDER,SIGNED......................................... 57.00
STEVENS & WILLIAMS,VASE,PEACH COLOR,ENAMELED FLORAL,
WHITE-LINED,BLOWN....................................... 45.00
STEVENS & WILLIAMS,VASE,PEACOCK,FLORAL,CLEAR,PEDESTAL BASE,
12 1/2 IN............................................... 185.00
STEVENS & WILLIAMS,VASE,PINK TO APRICOT TOP,WHITE LINING,
ENAMELED FLORAL......................................... 48.00
STEVENS & WILLIAMS,VASE,PINK TO DEEP ROSE,GOLD COLOR RIBS,
ENAMEL,SATIN............................................ 75.00
STEVENS & WILLIAMS,VASE,PINK TO ROSE COLOR,ENAMEL FLORAL,
CORALENE STEMS.......................................... 65.00
STEVENS & WILLIAMS,VASE,PINK TO WHITE,FROSTED HANDLE,IVES,
WHITE CASING............................................ 230.00
STEVENS & WILLIAMS,VASE,PUMPKIN RED & WHITE MOTTLING,WHITE
CASING,BEADED........................................... 58.00
STEVENS & WILLIAMS,VASE,REEDY TYPE DECOR,PEAR-SHAPED BASE,
OPAQUE,11 IN............................................ 30.00
STEVENS & WILLIAMS,VASE,TRUMPET,JADE,6 3/4 X 6 1/2 IN.TALL,
PAIR.................................................... 40.00
STEVENS & WILLIAMS,VASE,WHITE SATIN,ENAMEL FLORAL,RAINBOW
LINING,9 IN............................................. 125.00
STEVENS & WILLIAMS,VASE,ZIPPER PATTERN,MOTHER-OF-PEARL,PINK
LINING.................................................. 350.00
STONEWARE,BOTTLE,DOE,RAM,TREES,HILLS,STOPPER,SIGNED WITH
SEAL OF PERSIA.......................................... 125.00
STONEWARE,BOX,SALT,BUTTERFLY,BLUE......................... 20.00
STONEWARE,BOX,SALT,HANGING,BLUE,GRAY,PINE LID............. 12.00
STONEWARE,BUTTER BUCKET,TWO-TONE BLUE,DARK LETTERING,
SCROLLWORK,LID,BAIL..................................... 16.00
STONEWARE,CHARGER,CORAL PATTERN,13 3/4 IN.WIDE,

```
    17 1/4 IN.LONG....................................................    32.00
STONEWARE,CROCK,BLUE FLORAL,EARS,OTTMAN BROS.,FT.EDWARD,
    N.Y.,6 GALLONS................................................    20.00
STONEWARE,CROCK,BLUE SWAN,MARKED GARDINER STONEWARE,
    5 GALLONS.....................................................    25.00
STONEWARE,CROCK,GRAY,BLUE FLORAL DECOR,SIGNED LYONS,
    7 IN.HIGH.....................................................    15.00
STONEWARE,CROCK,GRAY,SAYS WEST & WALTER DEALERS IN DRYGOODS,
    CLOVERPORT....................................................    18.00
STONEWARE,GARDEN SEAT,BLUE & WHITE GLAZED,19 1/4 IN. HIGH...    400.00
STONEWARE,JAR,COVER,WIRE HANDLE,PATENT FEBRUARY 11,1896,
    2 QUARTS......................................................     3.50
STONEWARE,JAR,ROLLED RIM,BLUE PENNSYLVANIA DUTCH TULIP
    DECOR,2 GALLONS...............................................    26.50
STONEWARE,JUG,ADVERTISING,SALZMAN WHISKEY,1/2 GALLON.......     7.50
STONEWARE,JUG,BIRD,BLUE,HAXSTUN,OTTMAN & CO.,FT.EDWARD,N.Y.,
    1 1/2 GALLON..................................................    35.00
STONEWARE,JUG,BLUE EAGLE,BALLARD,BURLINGTON,2 GALLONS.......    27.00
STONEWARE,JUG,BLUE SCROLL DESIGN,2 GALLONS..................    20.00
STONEWARE,JUG,GRAY,COBALT FLORAL DECOR,INCISED WHITES,UTICA,
    2 GALLONS.....................................................    32.50
STONEWARE,JUG,1 GALLON.......................................     3.50
STONEWARE,JUG,ONION SHAPE,COBALT DECOR,STRAP HANDLE,SIGNED
    LYON,1 GALLON.................................................    23.50
STONEWARE,JUG,TRIPLE DESIGN,GEDDES OF NEW YORK,2 GALLONS....    22.50
STONEWARE,JUG,TRIPLE FLORALS,GEDDES,2 GALLONS...............    27.50
STONEWARE,JUG,WESTERN STONEWARE CO.,MONMOUTH,ILL.,ONE GALLON     4.00
STONEWARE,MEAT TENDERIZER,GRAY,PINE HANDLE,DATED 1877.......    23.00
STONEWARE,MOLD,PUDDING,CORN..................................    15.00
STONEWARE,MORTAR & PESTLE,WOODEN HANDLE,WHITE,
    5 1/2-IN.DIAMETER.............................................    18.00
STONEWARE,MUG,GRAY,BUST OF QUAKER,ENAMEL,HANDLE,BY KNESETTI
    HENISONS......................................................     6.50
STONEWARE,MUG,HANDLE,SALT GLAZE,3 3/4 IN.HIGH...............    17.50
STONEWARE,PITCHER,MILK,BLUE & GRAY,WOODLAND CASTLE SCENE....    15.00
STONEWARE,SALT BOX,HANGING,CREAM,FLOWER CENTER,WOODEN LID...     8.50
STONEWARE,STEIN,1 LITER,CREAM COLOR,FLAT PEWTER TOP.........    20.00
STONEWARE,TEAPOT,FORM OF A BUDDHA'S HAND CITRON,BROWN,
    YI-HSING,1800.................................................   115.00
    STORE,SEE ALSO,CASH REGISTER,COFFEE GRINDER,FIRE,MACHINE,
    SCALE,TIN BOX
STORE,ADDING MACHINE,AMERICAN,1912..........................    18.50
STORE,ANVIL,JEWELER'S,HANDMADE,BRASS,2 1/2 IN.HIGH,5 IN.LONG    12.50
STORE,BALANCE,LARGE,BRASS SCOOP.............................    24.00
STORE,BAR,SODA FOUNTAIN BACK,LEADED PILLARS,MIRROR,1880,
    7 FT.X 9 FT.HIGH.............................................3,500.00
STORE,BARREL,PICKLE,SPIGOT,HEINZ,10 IN,.....................    20.00
STORE,BARREL,VINEGAR,WOODEN PUMP,50 GAL.....................    12.00
STORE,BIN,CORNMEAL,HINGED TOP,PINE,37 IN.WIDE,30 IN.HIGH,
    22 IN.DEEP....................................................    75.00
STORE,BOX,BLACK,COLORED ENAMEL ON FRONT,14 1/2 IN.WIDE,
    12 IN.HIGH....................................................    18.00
STORE,BOX,CHEESE,COVER,HANDLE,WOODEN,15 POUNDS..............     4.50
STORE,BOX,CIGAR,E.BIERHAUS & SONS,STAMP READS SERIES OF
    1883,WOODEN...................................................     7.50
STORE,BOX,CIGAR,G.W.PIERCE,COVER,REVENUE STAMPS,LABEL,WOODEN     2.50
STORE,BOX,CRACKER,DUTCH TWIN,SQUARE,TIN,6 3/4 IN............     3.50
STORE,BOX,HERSHEY CHOCOLATE & COCOA,TIN,12 IN...............     6.00
STORE,BOX,HUNTLEY & PALMER BISCUIT BOOK,EIGHT BOOKS,HINGED
    LID...........................................................    65.00
STORE,BOX,LUNCH,UNION LEADER TOBACCO,TIN....................     4.50
STORE,BOX,PATTERSON'S CUT PLUG,WICKER TRUNK DESIGN,TIN......     5.00
STORE,BOX,READS MACROPOLIS BROWN PERFUMED CIGARETTE,BOMBAY,
    EST.1863......................................................     5.00
STORE,BOX,RED,EAGLE DESIGN,WAR EAGLE CIGARS,ROUND,TIN.......     5.00
STORE,BOX,UNION LEADER CUT PLUG,RED,EAGLES ON SIDES,WIRE
    HANDLE ON COVER...............................................     6.00
STORE,BREAD SLICER,WOODEN FRAME,EIGHT STEEL BLADES,
    14 IN.LONG....................................................    10.00
STORE,BREAD-SLICING MACHINE,DATED 1891......................    35.00
STORE,BROADSIDE,CRIMEAN LINIMENT,FOR MAN AND BEAST..........     2.00
STORE,BROADSIDE,PABST GENUINE BOCK BEER,GOATS' HEADS,
    CARDBOARD,EASEL...............................................    15.00
STORE,CABINET,DIAMOND DYE,TIN DOOR,CHILDREN JUMPING ROPE,
    LABEL,OAK.....................................................    70.00
STORE,CABINET,DYE,PUTNAM FADELESS,DYE ENVELOPES IN
    COMPARTMENTS,WHITE............................................    35.00
STORE,CABINET,PUTNAM DYE,HORSES,MEN,TIN.....................    26.50
STORE,CABINET,PUTNAM DYE,LITHOGRAPH ON SIDES,WOOD,TIN.......    35.00
STORE,CABINET,SPOOL,J.& P.COATS,REVOLVING BASE MODEL,SLIDING
    DOORS.........................................................    32.00
```

STORE,CABINET,WALL,FOUR SHELVES,RAISE-UP GLASS DOORS,6 X 27 X 27 IN...... 69.50
STORE,CAGE,POSTMAN,OAK...... 325.00
STORE,CALENDAR,HOOD'S SARSAPARILLA,1892,GIRLS LEARNING TO SEW,7 IN...... 3.00
STORE,CAN,ARBUCKLE TEA,PAINT...... 1.00
STORE,CAN,BAKING POWDER,ROYAL,LITHOGRAPH,1938...... 2.50
STORE,CAN,BAKING POWDER,STICKNEY & POOR,PAPER LABEL...... 2.00
STORE,CAN,BELFAST CUT PLUG,GREEN,TIN,POUND...... 2.00
STORE,CAN,CIGARETTE,HERBERT TAREYTON,WHITE,BLUE,PHOTO...... 3.00
STORE,CAN,COFFEE,CAPITOL BLEND,HINGED TOP,THREE POUNDS...... 6.00
STORE,CAN,CUT PLUG TOBACCO,LUNCH BOX...... 4.50
STORE,CAN,DILL'S BEST TOBACCO...... 3.50
STORE,CAN,DUTCH COCOA,1/4 POUND...... 3.00
STORE,CAN,GREEN LUCKY STRIKE PLUG TOBACCO,HINGED TOP,TIN.... 3.75
STORE,CAN,HERCULES BLACK POWDER...... 8.50
STORE,CAN,LUCKY STRIKE FLAT FIFTY...... 1.25
STORE,CAN,MCNESS BLACK PEPPER,ONE POUND...... 2.00
STORE,CAN,P.C.W.COUGH DROPS,2 IN. X 2 1/2 IN...... 5.00
STORE,CAN,PLANTERS PEANUT,5-POUND SIZE,9 IN.HIGH, 6-IN.DIAMETER...... 8.50
STORE,CAN,POWDER,DUPONT HF GUNPOWDER,WILMINGTON,DELAWARE, RED,TIN...... 7.00
STORE,CAN,TOBACCO,DILL'S BEST SMOKING,GIRL IN GREEN,OVAL ON BROWN,5 IN...... 6.00
STORE,CAN,TOBACCO,LUNCH BOX,GEORGE WASHINGTON...... 6.00
STORE,CANDY STAND,WALNETTO,RED,YELLOW...... 7.50
STORE,CARD,ADVERTISING,GLENWOOD RANGE,CHILD,EASEL TYPE...... 1.50
STORE,CARD,ADVERTISING,GOLD MEDAL FLOUR,DOORS OPEN...... 3.00
STORE,CARD,ADVERTISING,HISTORY OF AMERICAN FLAG,CHASE & SANBORN...... 3.00
STORE,CARD,ADVERTISING,HOOD'S PILLS TRANSPARENCY...... 4.50
STORE,CARD,ADVERTISING,PABST BREWING CO...... 1.50
STORE,CARD,ADVERTISING,WARNER'S CORALINE CORSETS...... 2.00
STORE,CARD,ADVERTISING,WHEAT BITTERS...... 1.25
STORE,CASH REGISTER,BRASS...... 50.00
STORE,CASH REGISTER,EMBOSSED,MICHIGAN...... 45.00
STORE,CASH REGISTER,NINE DRAWERS,1909,NATIONAL...... 300.00
STORE,CASH REGISTER,REGISTERS UP TO TEN DOLLARS,NATIONAL, 1900...... 125.00
STORE,CASH REGISTER,RINGS UP TO 9.99,HAND CRANK,WOODEN...... 40.00
STORE,CASHIER,AUTOMATIC,FOUR KEY ROWS,BRANDT JR., PAT.WATERTOWN,5/25/1909...... 55.00
STORE,CHEESE CUTTER...... 27.50
STORE,CHEWING GUM MACHINE,ONE CENT COIN-OPERATED,CLOCKWORKS, ZENO,1893...... 65.00
STORE,CIGAR CUTTER,BERDAN AND COMPANY...............ILLUS.. 18.00
STORE,CIGAR CUTTER,SCREWS INTO COUNTER...... 2.00
STORE,CIGAR CUTTER,TRAY,USED ON COUNTERS...... 55.00
STORE,CIGAR HOLDER,EAGLE BRAND SHOE POLISH,AMBER COLOR...... 4.50
STORE,CIGARETTE SLOT MACHINE,PENNY...... 85.00
STORE,COFFEE GRINDER,SEE COFFEE GRINDER
STORE,CONTAINER,ARTSTYLE CHOCOLATES,ONE POUND,TIN...... 2.00
STORE,CONTAINER,BLANKE'S HAPPY THOUGHT ROASTED COFFEE,GREEN,

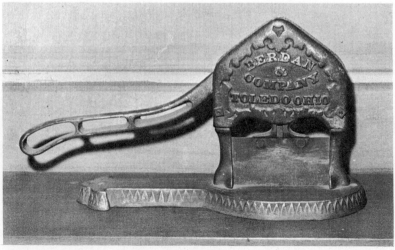

CIGAR CUTTER

BLACK,TIN.................................... 3.50
STORE,CONTAINER,CAMPFIRE MARSHMALLOWS,WHITE,BLUE,RED,LID,
TIN,6 IN.HIGH............................... 4.50
STORE,CONTAINER,CRISPO GRAHAM CRACKERS,BLUE,WHITE,SQUARE,
LID,TIN, .................................. 4.50
STORE,CONTAINER,CUTEX FIVE-MINUTE SET,TIN.................. 2.00
STORE,CONTAINER,FITCH'S IDEAL COLD CREAM,TIN............... 2.50
STORE,CONTAINER,HELEN HARRISON HOMEMADE CANDIES,ONE POUND,
TIN........................................ 2.00
STORE,CONTAINER,LIPTON'S TEA BAGS,HOLDS TWELVE BAGS,TIN..... 1.50
STORE,CONTAINER,MAVIS CHOCOLATES,ONE POUND,TIN............. 2.00
STORE,CONTAINER,MONARCH COCOA,TIN......................... 2.75
STORE,CONTAINER,STUFT CONFECTIONS,SQUARE,SCREW LID,TIN,
10 IN.HIGH................................. 2.50
STORE,CONTAINER,TO MEASURE PENNY CANDY,MILK GLASS.......... 1.00
STORE,CONTAINER,TOM MOORE CIGARS,CLARO,REVENUE STAMP....... 3.00
STORE,CONTAINER,VASSAR CHOCOLATES,ONE POUND,TIN........... 2.00
STORE,CONTAINER,WARSHIPS,U.S.S.IDAHO ON COVER,LOOSE WILES
BISCUIT CO................................ 6.50
STORE,CONTAINER,WHITMAN'S,CANDY,ONE POUND,TIN............. 2.00
STORE,CORK SIZER,DRUGGIST,FOOTED,IRON..................... 17.00
STORE,CROCK,LAMBRECHT'S BUTTER........................... 4.00
STORE,DISPENSER,MATCH BOOK,PENNY-OPERATED,RED PAINT,IRON,
10 IN.HIGH................................. 14.00
STORE,DISPENSER,PAPER,DRUGGIST,TWO TIERS,IRON & WOOD,
PAT.JULY 8,1894............................ 14.00
STORE,DISPENSER,ROOT BEER,BARREL SHAPE,SILVER PLATE TOP,
14 IN...................................... 75.00
STORE,DISPENSER,SMITH BROTHERS COUGH DROPS,TIN............ 15.00
STORE,DISPENSER,SODA FOUNTAIN,LABELED MISSION ORANGE,PINK
GLASS TOP.................................. 37.50
STORE,DISPENSER,WRAPPING PAPER,29 IN...................... 8.00
STORE,DISPLAY CABINET,PUTNAM DYE,RED,WHITE LETTERS,TIN,
245 DYE PACKAGES........................... 25.00
STORE,DISPLAY CASE,KNIFE,MARKED REMINGTON,WOODEN,GLASS PANEL 15.00
STORE,DISPLAY CASE,SUGAR PUFF MARSHMALLOW................. 5.50
STORE,DISPLAY JAR,GLASS,OWL DECOR,SAYS OPTIMO DOLLS FIVE
CENTS,5 IN................................. 67.75
STORE,DISPLAY,DYE,PUTNAM,TIN............................. 20.00
STORE,DRUGSTORE ADVERTISING FAN.......................... 1.25
STORE,EPICURE TOBACCO TIN................................ 8.00
STORE,FAN,CEILING,WOODEN BLADES,60 CYCLE,110 VOLTS,DAYTON
FAN CO.,59 IN.............................. 125.00
STORE,FAN,OVERHEAD,ICE CREAM PARLOR...................... 200.00
STORE,GUM MACHINE,SEE STORE,MACHINE,GUM.
STORE,HATCHET,FOR CUTTING TAFFY,MARKED KRANZ'S TAFFIES,
NICKLE-PLATED.............................. 2.95
STORE,HIGH BUTTON SHOE,USED FOR SIGN,IRON................. 22.50
STORE,HOLDER,ROLL,WRAPPING PAPER,COUNTER TYPE,15 IN........ 8.75
STORE,HOLDER,STRAW,METAL LID & INSERT.................... 15.00
STORE,HOLDER,STRING & BAG,CEILING,CHAINS,PAT.APRIL 29,1884,
IRON....................................... 45.00
STORE,HOOK,MEAT,CROWN TYPE,HAND-FORGED IRON,FIVE.......... 45.00
STORE,HOOK,MEAT,THREE PRONGS,IRON,9 IN.LONG............... 18.00
STORE,ICE TONGS.......................................... 2.00
STORE,IRON PLUG TOBACCO CUTTER........................... 6.00
STORE,JAR,NUT,TIN COVER,U.S.NUT CO.,LYNN,MASS.,RESTS ON
SIDE,8 IN.HIGH............................. 10.00
STORE,JUG,TOP LIFTS OFF,USED FOR PRETZELS,ADVERTISING,NEW
JERSEY,16 IN............................... 37.50
STORE,KEG,STAVED,BRASS-BOUND,SHUT-OFF SPOUT,6 IN. X 6 IN.... 50.00
STORE,KNIFE,BUTCHER,MARKED SHAPLEIGH HARDWARE............. 4.00
STORE,LADLE,PICKLE,GLASS,WOODEN HANDLE,DATED APRIL 21,1896.. 10.00
STORE,LAMP,HANGING,TIN,NO SHADE.......................... 12.50
STORE,LATHE,JEWELER,COLLETS,FOOT SPEED MOTOR,CRANK,DATED
1880,SWISS................................. 15.00
STORE,LICORICE TIN,GLASS WINDOW,YOUNG & SMYLIE............ 8.50
STORE,LITHOGRAPH,ADVERTISING DR.MC MUNN'S KINATE OF QUININE
& CINCHONINE............................... 18.00
STORE,MACHINE,CHECK WRITING,CIRCA 1920................... 15.00
STORE,MACHINE,GUM,COIN-OPERATED,BALL GUM VENDOR,IMP,KEY.... 45.00
STORE,MACHINE,GUM,COIN-OPERATED,NAIL MAZE,DRAWER,KEY, LITTLE
DREAM ..................................... 45.00
STORE,MACHINE,GUM,COIN-OPERATED,ZENO..................... 135.00
STORE,MACHINE,GUM,MECHANICAL,MADE BY PULVER.............. 165.00
STORE,MACHINE,GUM,MECHANICAL MAN,TURNS WHEN GUM IS
DISPENSED,PULVER........................... 55.00
STORE,MACHINE,GUM,RED,WOODEN,WHITE METAL ADVERTISING SIGN,
24 1/2 IN.HIGH............................. 50.00
STORE,MACHINE,GUM,WOODEN CABINET,ZENO.................... 87.00
STORE,MACHINE,POPCORN & PEANUT,ELECTRIC,CIRCA 1920.......... 800.00

```
STORE,MACHINE,VENDING,BOOK MATCH,OHIO.......................    25.00
STORE,MACHINE,VENDING,E Z BALL GUM,DATED 1908...............    27.00
STORE,MACHINE,VENDING,PEANUT,SAYS EMPIRE VENDOR.............    22.50
STORE,MACHINE,VENDING,SAYS MANSFIELD PEPSIN GUM MACHINE,
  DATED 1902................................................    65.00
STORE,MACHINE,VENDING,SMILIN' SAM....................ILLUS..   350.00
STORE,MEAT BLOCK,LEGS,MAPLE,REFINISHED,8 IN. X 1I IN. X
  30 IN.HIGH...............................................    125.00
STORE,MEAT CLEAVER,HAND-FORGED,PAIR........................     25.00
STORE,MILK BOTTLE CARRIER,EIGHT SECTIONS,WIRE..............      9.50
STORE,MILK CAN,10 GALLONS..................................      3.50
STORE,MILK CAN,10 GALLONS...........................ILLUS..     43.50
STORE,MIRROR,ADVERTISING,AMERICAN DRUGGISTS FIRE INSURANCE
  CO.......................................................      7.50
STORE,MIRROR,ADVERTISING,ANGELUS MARSHMALLOWS,CUPID,OVAL...      6.50
STORE,MIRROR,ADVERTISING,CALOX,THE OXYGEN TOOTH POWDER,OVAL.     4.50
STORE,MIRROR,ADVERTISING,DUFFY'S MALT WHISKEY,ROUND........      6.50
STORE,MIRROR,ADVERTISING,GARLAND STOVES AND RANGES,ROUND...      4.50
STORE,MIRROR,ADVERTISING,GOOD FOR TEN CENTS IN TRADE,GIRL
  WITH POSEY...............................................      6.50
STORE,MIRROR,ADVERTISING,OWL,A WISE OLD OWL LIVED IN AN OAK.    15.00
STORE,MIRROR,ADVERTISING,PLYMOUTH RUBBER COMPANY,ROUND.....      4.50
STORE,MIRROR,ADVERTISING,RAILROAD MEN'S CLOTHING...........      3.50
STORE,MIRROR,ADVERTISING,UNION STAMP BOOT AND SHOE COMPANY,
  OVAL.....................................................      4.50
STORE,MIRROR,ADVERTISING,UNION STAMPED SHOES...............      3.50
STORE,MOLD,CIGAR,FOR 20 CIGARS,WOODEN......................     12.50
STORE,MOLD,CIGAR,SPACE FOR 20 CIGARS,5 X 21 IN.............     10.00
STORE,MORTAR & PESTLE,BIRD'S-EYE MAPLE,3 1/2-IN.DIAMETER,
  4 1/2 IN.TALL............................................     20.00
STORE,MORTAR & PESTLE,BRASS,SALESMAN SAMPLE................      4.50
STORE,MORTAR & PESTLE,BRASS,2 1/2 IN.HIGH,2 3/4-IN.DIAMETER.    10.00
STORE,MORTAR & PESTLE,BRASS,3 IN.HIGH......................     19.50
```

VENDING MACHINE, SMILIN' SAM

MILKCAN

```
STORE,MORTAR & PESTLE,GLASS,2 IN.HIGH,2 1/4-IN.DIAMETER.....    5.50
STORE,MORTAR & PESTLE,HAND-CARVED,WOODEN...................   12.00
STORE,MORTAR & PESTLE,IRON,7 IN.DIAMETER,6 1/2 IN.HIGH.....   20.00
STORE,MORTAR & PESTLE,KNOB HANDLES,BRASS..................   25.00
STORE,MORTAR & PESTLE,MINIATURE,FOOTED,BRASS,2 1/4 IN. X
  2 3/4 IN.TALL........................................    9.50
STORE,MORTAR & PESTLE,NEW ENGLAND,BURL...................   45.00
STORE,MORTAR & PESTLE,PAINTED GREEN,IRON,7 1/2 IN.HIGH.....   22.00
STORE,MORTAR & PESTLE,PEDESTAL BASE,IRON,6 IN. X 6 IN......   20.00
STORE,MORTAR & PESTLE,ROSEWOOD..........................   24.50
STORE,MORTAR & PESTLE,TURNED MAPLE,8 IN.TALL..............   28.00
STORE,MORTAR & PESTLE,WEDGWOOD TYPE.....................   12.00
STORE,MORTAR & PESTLE,WOOD HANDLE,IMPRESSED TRADE MARK BRAND
  & ANCHOR.............................................    7.50
STORE,MORTAR & PESTLE,WOODEN...........................   20.00
STORE,MORTAR & PESTLE,WOODEN HANDLE ON PESTLE,WHITE,POTTERY.   15.00
STORE,MORTAR & PESTLE,WOODEN,HAND-CARVED.................   12.00
STORE,MUG,ADVERTISING,HIRES ROOT BEER....................   12.00
STORE,PAIL,PEANUT BUTTER,GREAT A & P TEA CO.,TIN,4 IN. X
  4 IN...............................................    6.50
STORE,PEANUT MACHINE,ROUND GLASS BALL IN CENTER,PAT.1932,
  18 IN.HIGH..........................................   22.00
STORE,PEANUT ROASTING MACHINE..........................  400.00
STORE,PEPSI-COLA SIGN,TIN,9-IN.DIAMETER..................    6.00
STORE,PIN ROLLER,APOTHECARY,WOODEN......................   28.50
STORE,PLAQUE,DEER RUN WHISKEY,DEER BY LAKE,TIN,
  12-IN.DIAMETER......................................   20.00
STORE,POSTER,DR.HALL CATARRH REMEDY,PICTURES PATENT
  MEDICINE,19 X 33 IN.................................    3.00
STORE,PRINT,ADVERTISING,J & P COATS THREAD,1880,FRAME......    3.00
STORE,PRINT,DIAMOND WINE CO.,LADIES SIPPING CHAMPAGNE,1896,
  27 X 19 IN..........................................   18.50
STORE,PUMP,BEER,COPPER.................................   20.00
STORE,RAZOR BLADE SHARPENER,1915.......................    6.00
STORE,REGISTER,REGISTERS UP TO $10,NATIONAL CASH REGISTER,
  1900..............................................  125.00
STORE,SAUSAGE STUFFER................................   24.50
STORE,SCALE,BALANCE,TIN SCOOP,WEIGHTS...................   22.50
STORE,SCOOP,ICE CREAM,WOODEN HANDLE,MECHANICAL..........    5.00
STORE,SHIELD,PLATE GLASS,DENNEHY'S OLD UNDERROOF RYE,CHAIN
  HANGER.............................................   85.00
STORE,SHOT GLASS,ADVERTISING,CALVERT....................    2.50
STORE,SHOT GLASS,ADVERTISING,OLD CROW...................    2.50
STORE,SIGN,ADVERTISING,GIRL ON SWING,CARDBOARD,26 1/2 IN. X
  17 IN.............................................   16.00
STORE,SIGN,ALKA SELTZER,THERMOMETER,ROUND...............   15.00
STORE,SIGN,ANHEUSER BUSCH,CARDBOARD,41 1/2 IN. X 28 1/2 IN..   15.00
STORE,SIGN,ATLANTIC PETROLEUM,PORCELAIN.................   15.00
STORE,SIGN,BARGAIN SHOW,ALL SEATS TEN CENTS,WOODEN,7 FEET X
  2 1/2 FEET.........................................   35.00
STORE,SIGN,BLACKHALL,CONNECTICUT POST OFFICE,PINE,1880,45 X
  21 IN.HIGH.........................................  250.00
STORE,SIGN,BOY CLUTCHING LEOPARD SKIN,MOTHER'S OATS,FRAME,
  22 X 32 IN.........................................   25.00
STORE,SIGN,BUDWEISER GIRL,COPYRIGHT 1907,18 IN. X 32 IN.....   20.00
STORE,SIGN,BUTTE CITY 5 CENT CIGAR,CANVAS,1910,12 IN. X
  36 IN.............................................    5.00
STORE,SIGN,CARLING'S ALE,KEYSTONE COPS,NINE PINTS OF THE
  LAW,TIN,19 IN......................................   12.50
STORE,SIGN,CHRISTIAN MOERLEIN BREWING,GYPSY,MAN,20 X 26 IN.,
  FRAME.............................................   35.00
STORE,SIGN,CIGARETTE POSTER,CIRCA 1900,FRAME,24 IN. X 31 IN.   35.00
STORE,SIGN,CIGARETTE,ALLEN & GINTER,ARMS OF NATIONS,14 X
  30 IN.............................................   30.00
STORE,SIGN,CITIZENS INSURANCE COMPANY OF NEW JERSEY,SILVER
  ON BLUE,FRAME......................................    9.00
STORE,SIGN,COLE'S PENETRATING LINIMENT,BLUE,WHITE,PORCELAIN,
  6 X 16 IN..........................................   13.00
STORE,SIGN,COLGATE'S RIBBON DENTAL CREAM,MAN,WOMAN,TIN,10 X
  14...............................................   12.50
STORE,SIGN,COLUMBIA BEVEL GEAR CHAINLESS,GIRL,BICYCLE,1900,
  7 X 5 IN...........................................    4.00
STORE,SIGN,COOK'S BEER,HAND HOLDING BOTTLE OF ALE,TIN,17 IN.
  X 14 IN............................................   15.00
STORE,SIGN,COOK'S BEER,TIN,SQUARE......................    4.75
STORE,SIGN,COUNTER,S & H QUALITY ICE CREAM,TIN,1923,9 1/2 X
  3 1/2 IN...........................................    5.00
STORE,SIGN,CREMO CIGAR,26 IN. X 13 IN...................    9.00
STORE,SIGN,DEVILISH FIVE CENT CIGAR,CHILDREN SMOKING,TIN,
  10 X 14 IN.........................................   12.50
STORE,SIGN,DOUBLE-FACED,COWHIDE BRAND OVERALLS & PANTS,
```

METAL,10 X 1I IN.......................................... 6.00
STORE,SIGN,DRINK GRAPE-OLA,BASKET OF GRAPES,BOTTLE,TIN,36 X
   12 IN..................................................... 5.00
STORE,SIGN,DRINK LIME CRUSH,OLIVE COLOR,EMBOSSSED,TIN,14 IN.
   X 19 IN................................................... 9.50
STORE,SIGN,DRINK ORANGE CRUSH,SHOWS BOTTLE,TIN,38 IN........ 12.00
STORE,SIGN,EL PRODUCTO CIGAR,31 1/2 IN. X 19 IN............. 12.50
STORE,SIGN,FRING CIGARS,YELLOW LETTERS ON BLACK SHIELD,TIN,
   3 1/2 X 9 IN.............................................. 2.50
STORE,SIGN,GASOLINE,MILK GLASS............................. 14.00
STORE,SIGN,GENERAL ARTHUR CIGAR,FRAME,21 X 19 IN........... 25.00
STORE,SIGN,HAMILTON WATCH,BLACK GROUND,GOLD LEAF,BEADED
   DECOR,FRAME............................................... 27.50
STORE,SIGN,HIGH GRADE SODA WATER,TREMONT BOTTLING CO.,TIN,
   7 X 10 IN................................................. 5.00
STORE,SIGN,JAMES LEWIS HAVANA FILLER FIVE CENT CIGAR,
   ALUMINUM,6 X 9 IN......................................... 3.50
STORE,SIGN,LADY,FARM MOWING MACHINERY,OSBORNE FARM
   MACHINERY,1905............................................ 45.00
STORE,SIGN,LET'S DRINK BLUE BIRD,YELLOW RED,EMBOSSED,TIN,
   36 IN..................................................... 9.50
STORE,SIGN,LET'S DRINK BLUE BIRD,YELLOW GROUND,1/ IN. X
   30 IN..................................................... 9.50
STORE,SIGN,LET'S DRINK BLUE BIRD,YELLOW GROUND,10 IN. X
   30 IN..................................................... 9.50
STORE,SIGN,MAN EATING AND HOLDING STEIN,BARTLE'S BEER,TIN,
   20 X 24 IN................................................ 25.00
STORE,SIGN,MAN ON BIKE,HOOPSKIRT LADY ON BIKE,TROLLEY,PIERCE
   BICYCLES.................................................. 50.00
STORE,SIGN,MARTINSBURG SODA WATER,DINING TABLE SCENE,CIRCA
   1885,20 IN................................................ 35.00
STORE,SIGN,MINSTREL POSTER,HARRY RIMYER'S MINSTREL DANDY,
   20 X 28 IN................................................ 275.00
STORE,SIGN,MISSION ORANGE,SHOWS HUGE BOTTLE,FIVE CENTS,TIN,
   45 IN.HIGH................................................ 12.00
STORE,SIGN,NEW ENGLAND PALE ALE,MT.PLEASANT BREWING CO.,TIN,
   14 X 7 IN................................................. 10.00
STORE,SIGN,NO MORE MALARIA,COLE'S PERUVIAN BARK & WILD
   CHERRY BITTERS............................................ 15.00
STORE,SIGN,OMAR CIGARETTE,TIN,8 X 14 IN.................... 3.50
STORE,SIGN,PRIMA BREWING CO.,METAL,34 IN. X 24 IN......... 12.00
STORE,SIGN,PURE OIL LUBRICATION CHART,DATED 1932,LISTS
   52 AUTOS,TIN.............................................. 12.50
STORE,SIGN,REUTERS LIFE SYRUP,RED,YELLOW,FRAME,TIN,15 1/2 X
   21 1/2 IN................................................. 35.00
STORE,SIGN,ROYAL TIRE COMPANY,PICTURE FRONT,CARDBOARD,
   6 1/2 X 14 1/2 IN......................................... 3.00
STORE,SIGN,SADDLEMAKER'S,MOLDED SHEET IRON HORSE........... 195.00
STORE,SIGN,SHOWS ORANGES,BOTTLE,EMBOSSED,TIN,27 IN.LONG.... 9.50
STORE,SIGN,SHUTTER TYPE,SPALDING BICYCLES,TIN LETTERING,OAK
   FRAME..................................................... 37.50
STORE,SIGN,STAND-UP DOLL,MARY JANE'PURE FOOD CANDY,ONE CENT,
   CARDBOARD................................................. 3.00
STORE,SIGN,STREETCAR SCENE,THERMOMETER,WOODEN,19 1/2 X
   4 1/2 IN.................................................. 20.00
STORE,SIGN,TIN,30 IN. X 20 IN.....................ILLUS.. 150.00
STORE,SIGN,UNSALTED CREAMERY BUTTER,WHITING MILK CO., VT.,
   BRASS,14 IN............................................... 5.00

TIN SIGN

```
STORE,SIGN,VICTOR BICYCLES,SCENE,BOY DELIVERING CYCLE,CIRCA
   1885,21 IN.......................................................    35.00
STORE,SIGN,VOLCANIC REPEATING FIREARMS,1864,DIRECTIONS FOR
   LOADING........................................................    10.00
STORE,SIGN,WE SELL COLUMBIAN PURE MANILA ROPE,AUBURN,N.Y.,
   12 X 18 IN.....................................................     8.50
STORE,SIGN,WELCH GRAPE,PICTURE OF BOTTLE,GRAPES,CIRCA 1920,
   18 X 40 IN.....................................................    12.50
STORE,SIGN,WILLARD STORAGE BATTERY,RED,WHITE,PORCELAIN,14 X
   30 IN..........................................................    18.00
STORE,SLICER,BALONEY,CLAMP-ON TYPE,ADJUSTABLE,EAGLE,1918....    15.00
STORE,SLOT MACHINE,CIGARETTE,REEL TYPE,PENNY.................    75.00
STORE,STAND,CLARK'S TEABERRY GUM............................     5.50
STORE,STAND,CLARK'S TEABERRY GUM,VASELINE...................    16.50
   STORE,STEREOSCOPE,SEE STEREOSCOPE
STORE,THERMOMETER,CHEW COPENHAGEN,4 IN. X 12 IN.............     3.00
STORE,THERMOMETER,CHEW MAIL POUCH TOBACCO,BLUE,YELLOW,3 X
   9 IN...........................................................     7.50
STORE,TIN,BLANKE'S COFFEE,2 LB..............................     3.50
STORE,TIN,CARNATION MALTED MILK,SCREW TOP,SQUARE,5-POUND....     7.50
STORE,TIN,FESTAL HALL COFFEE,3 LB...........................     3.50
STORE,TIN,GINGER,MING CRYSTALLIZED,LITHOGRAPH,SHIPS.........     3.00
STORE,TIN,GRANDMOTHER'S TEA,SOLE DISTRIBUTORES,GREAT A & P
   TEA CO.,GREEN..................................................     6.00
STORE,TIN,LUCKY STRIKE,FLAT FIFTIES,FOIL....................     3.00
STORE,TIN,LUCKY STRIKE,FLAT FIFTY...........................     5.00
STORE,TIN,MAYO TOBACCO,LUNCH BOX,BLUE.......................     7.00
STORE,TIN,MURAD TURKISH CIGARETTES,TURKISH TROOPER ON
   STALLION,CONTENTS..............................................    35.00
STORE,TIN,PATTERSON'S TUXEDO TOBACCO,GREEN BASE,GOLD
   LETTERS,1856-1906..............................................     8.50
STORE,TIN,TOBACCO,LORD SALISBURY TURKISH CIGARETTES.........     3.00
STORE,TIN,TOBACCO,RED & SILVER COLOR,OLD ENGLISH CURVE CUT
   PIPE TOBACCO...................................................     3.75
STORE,TIN,TOBACCO,TIGER CHEWING TOBACCO,HINGED LID,LUNCH BOX
   TYPE...........................................................     9.50
STORE,TOBACCO CABINET,COUNTER,PHONE BOOTH,RACKS,SHADES,
   100 FEET,1911..............................................3,500.00
STORE,TOBACCO CUTTER,MOUNTED ON WOODEN BOOTJACK-TYPE BASE,
   PAT.5-11-20....................................................    10.00
STORE,TOBACCO CUTTER,SAYS LORILLARD'S TOMAHAWK..............     8.50
STORE,TOBACCO CUTTER,WHEEL BLADE,DATED 1888,IRON,17 IN......    23.00
STORE,TOBACCO FELT,COLLEGES,FLAGS,RUGS,25...................     7.50
STORE,TOBACCO TIN,MAYO'S CUT PLUG TOBACCO,BAIL HANDLE,BLUE,
   GOLD...........................................................     5.50
STORE,TOBACCO TIN,UNION LEADER,RED,GOLD EAGLE,HINGED LID,4 X
   6 IN...........................................................     5.00
STORE,TOKEN,ADVERTISING,CASCARETS,BEST FOR THE BOWELS.......     2.50
STORE,TOKEN,ADVERTISING,GOOD FOR CAKE PALMOLIVE SOAP........     2.50
STORE,TONGS,ICE,IRON........................................     3.50
STORE,TRAY,ADVERTISING,CLARK'S TEABERRY GUM,CLEAR,7 X 5 X
   3 1/2 IN.......................................................     6.50
STORE,TRAY,ARCTIC ICE CREAM,ICEBERG SCENE,POLAR BEAR,METAL,
   10 IN.ROUND....................................................     9.00
STORE,TRAY,CHANGE,ADVERTISING GOEBEL BEER...................     5.00
STORE,TRAY,CHANGE,ADVERTISING,RED RAVEN SPLITS,GENTLEMAN,
   BOTTLE,RAVEN...................................................     6.00
STORE,WAFER IRON,DATED 1880.................................    27.50
STORE,WASHING MACHINE,HANDLE HAS TO BE ROCKED BACK & FORTH,
   PINE...........................................................    37.50
STORE,WHIP RACK,15 HOLES,IRON,21 X 2 IN.....................    18.50
STORE,WINE TESTER,DRUM-SHAPED BOWL,BONE RINGS,PIERCED HEART
   HANDLE,4 IN....................................................    12.00
STORE,WOODEN HOOK BOARD,11 HAND-FORGED HOOKS,FOR HANGING
   GAME & FOWL....................................................    30.00
STOVE,COAL & WOOD,MONTGOMERY WARD,10 IN.WIDE,37 IN.HIGH.....    50.00
STOVE,OIL,PORTABLE,IRON FONT,TIN TOP,ISINGLASS WINDOW,
   PAT.DEC. 28-83.................................................    12.00
STOVE,POTBELLY,BELLE NO.11,KEELEY STOVE CO.,PAT.1868,
   25 1/2 IN.HIGH.................................................    35.00
STOVE,POTBELLY,FED FROM THE TOP,THREE LEGS..................    95.00
STOVE,POTBELLY,IRON.........................................    40.00
   SULFIDE,MARBLE,SEE,MARBLE,SULFIDE
   SULFIDE,PAPERWEIGHT,SEE PAPERWEIGHT,SULFIDE
SULFIDE,PLAQUE,DUCHESSE DE BERRY,SIGNED MONTCENIS,FRAME,
   OVAL,2 3/4 IN..................................................    80.00
```

SUNBONNET BABIES WERE FIRST INTRODUCED IN 1902 IN THE
SUNBONNET BABIES PRIMER. THE STORIES WERE BY EULALIE
OSGOOD GROVER,ILLUSTRATED BY BERTHA CORBETT. THE

CHILDREN'S FACES WERE COMPLETELY HIDDEN BY THE
SUNBONNETS,AND HAD BEEN PICTURED IN BLACK AND WHITE
BEFORE THIS TIME. THE COLOR PICTURES IN THE BOOK WERE
IMMEDIATELY SUCCESSFUL. THE ROYAL BAYREUTH CHINA
COMPANY MADE A FULL LINE OF CHILDREN'S DISHES DECORATED
WITH THE SUNBONNET BABIES.

| | |
|---|---|
| SUNBONNET BABIES,BOWL, MENDING,  FOOTED,6 IN | 27.50 |
| SUNBONNET BABIES,BOWL,SUGAR,ROYAL BAYREUTH | 12.00 |
| SUNBONNET BABIES,BOX,PENCIL,PYROGRAPHY | 20.00 |
| SUNBONNET BABIES,CANDLEHOLDER,LAUNDRY,SAUCER TYPE,HANDLE, ROYAL BAYREUTH | 135.00 |
| SUNBONNET BABIES,COFFEEPOT,3 1/2 IN.PITCHER,11-IN.TRAY,TWO PLATES,TIN | 60.00 |
| SUNBONNET BABIES,CREAMER,CLEANING,ROYAL BAYREUTH | 75.00 |
| SUNBONNET BABIES,CREAMER,IRONING,PINCHED SPOUT,ROYAL BAYREUTH | 85.00 |
| SUNBONNET BABIES,CREAMER,ROYAL BAYREUTH | 12.00 |
| SUNBONNET BABIES,CREAMER,ROYAL BAYREUTH,BLUE MARK | 95.00 |
| SUNBONNET BABIES,CREAMER,WASHING,HANGING CLOTHES,ROYAL BAYREUTH,MARK | 125.00 |
| SUNBONNET BABIES,CUP & SAUCER,DEMITASSE,FISHING | 85.00 |
| SUNBONNET BABIES,CUP & SAUCER,WASHING,IRONING,HANGING CLOTHES | 23.00 |
| SUNBONNET BABIES,CUP,DEMITASSE,EATING,GERMANY | 15.00 |
| SUNBONNET BABIES,CUP,SAUCER,BOY FACING GIRL, I LOVE YOU, PORCELAIN | 37.50 |
| SUNBONNET BABIES,CUP,SAUCER,DEMITASSE,SPRINKLING CLOTHES, GERMANY | 38.00 |
| SUNBONNET BABIES,CUP,SAUCER,SEWING,MENDING,FOLDING,IRONING CLOTHES | 140.00 |
| SUNBONNET BABIES,DISH,SAUCE,AMBERETTE,ROYAL BAYREUTH | 12.00 |
| SUNBONNET BABIES,KISS & MAKE UP,SOUVENIR,7-IN.DIAMETER | 22.00 |
| SUNBONNET BABIES,MUG,MENDING,ROYAL BAYREUTH,BLUE MARK | 95.00 |
| SUNBONNET BABIES,PICTURE,BAKING,8 1/2 IN. X 6 1/2 IN | 5.00 |
| SUNBONNET BABIES,PICTURE,MENDING DAY,SERIES 601,FRAME, 8 1/2 X 6 1/2 IN | 19.50 |
| SUNBONNET BABIES,PICTURE,MENDING,FRAME,7 3/4 IN. X 5 3/4 IN. | 15.00 |
| SUNBONNET BABIES,PITCHER,MILK,IRONING,ROYAL BAYREUTH | 130.00 |
| SUNBONNET BABIES,PLATE,ADVERTISING,GIRL WITH DOLL,BOY WITH TOY | 58.00 |
| SUNBONNET BABIES,PLATE,CANDY FOR MY MANDY | 18.00 |
| SUNBONNET BABIES,PLATE,FISHING,ROYAL BAYREUTH,BLUE MARK, 6 IN | 55.00 |
| SUNBONNET BABIES,PLATE,HOT,FISHING | 105.00 |
| SUNBONNET BABIES,PLATE,HOT,FISHING,ROYAL BAYREUTH | 100.00 |
| SUNBONNET BABIES,PLATE,KISS AND MAKE UP,TRENLE CO.,VIRGINIA, 7 1/2 IN | 22.00 |
| SUNBONNET BABIES,PLATE,MOPPING,WINDOW CLEANING,ROYAL BAYREUTH,BLUE MARK | 45.00 |
| SUNBONNET BABIES,PLATE,TUESDAY,7 1/2 IN | 10.00 |
| SUNBONNET BABIES,POSTCARD | 1.00 |
| SUNBONNET BABIES,POSTCARD,DAYS OF WEEK,GROUP OF 7,FRAME | 10.00 |
| SUNBONNET BABIES,POSTCARD,MONDAY-WASHING,TUESDAY-IRONING, ETC.,7 | 35.00 |
| SUNBONNET BABIES,POSTCARD,NOVEMBER 1906,CARRYING TURKEY ON PLATTER | 5.00 |
| SUNBONNET BABIES,PRINT,B.L.CORBETT,1904,6 IN. X 8 IN | 5.00 |
| SUNBONNET BABIES,PRINT,FISHING,SWINGING,PRANG,1903,5 IN. X 10 IN.,PAIR | 10.00 |
| SUNBONNET BABIES,TEAPOT,CHILDS,MARKED GERMANY,5 IN.HIGH | 12.50 |
| SUNBONNET BABIES,TOOTHPICK,MILK GLASS,OPAQUE WHITE | 22.50 |
| SUNBONNET BABIES,TRAY,CHILD'S,WASHING,DARNING,IRONING, ALPHABET,NUMBERS | 15.00 |
| SUNBONNET BABIES,TRAY,FOLDING & IRONING CLOTHES,ROYAL BAYREUTH,10 IN | 185.00 |
| SUNBONNET BABIES,TRAY,TOOTHPICK,RING-A-ROSIE, HAND-PAINTED 14.00 TO | 15.00 |
| SUNBONNET BABIES,VASE,TEAL GLAZE,GREEN DRESS,WHITE BONNET, HOLDS BALLOON | 18.00 |

SUNDERLAND LUSTER IS A NAME GIVEN TO A CHARACTERISTIC
PINK LUSTER MADE BY LEEDS,NEWCASTLE,AND OTHER ENGLISH
FIRMS DURING THE NINETEENTH CENTURY. THE LUSTER GLAZE
IS METALLIC AND GLOSSY AND SOMETIMES APPEARS TO HAVE
BUBBLES AS A DECORATION.

| | |
|---|---|
| SUNDERLAND,CREAMER,RAISED COLORFUL FIGURES | 35.00 |
| SUNDERLAND,CUP & SAUCER,CIRCA 1880,LUSTER | 25.00 |
| SUNDERLAND,CUP & SAUCER,DECOR INSIDE CUP,PINK LUSTER LOOPINGS,1820 | 22.00 |
| SUNDERLAND,CUP & SAUCER,GREEN,PINK,FLORAL DESIGN,LUSTER | 22.00 |

SUNDERLAND,CUP & SAUCER,PINK,BLUE STRIPE,BOY & GIRL,
  TRANSFER,LUSTER............................................ 22.00
SUNDERLAND,CUP & SAUCER,PINK,SCENIC,PEOPLE,LUSTER........... 16.50
SUNDERLAND,JAR,BUTTON,PURPLE LUSTER,LACE PINCUSHION ON LID,
  1820...................................................... 65.00
SUNDERLAND,JUG,FARMER VERSE,BRIDGE,ODD FELLOW COAT OF ARMS,
  LUSTER,9 IN............................................... 100.00
SUNDERLAND,JUG,ODD FELLOW COAT OF ARMS,FARMER,BRIDGE,VERSE,
  9 IN.HIGH................................................ 100.00
SUNDERLAND,JUG,PINK LUSTER, WEST VIEW OF BRIDGE OVER RIVER
  WEAR,1796................................................ 350.00
SUNDERLAND,MUG,LUSTER,5 1/4 IN.HIGH........................ 150.00
SUNDERLAND,MUG,PINK,MARINER'S COMPASS DECOR,FROG INSIDE,
  LUSTER................................................... 150.00
SUNDERLAND,MUG,SHIP WITH SAILS,BRITISH FLAG,VERSE,4 IN.HIGH. 85.00
SUNDERLAND,PITCHER,LUSTER,9 IN.TALL........................ 650.00
SUNDERLAND,PITCHER,SHIP,SAILORS,VERSE,5 IN.HIGH............ 95.00
SUNDERLAND,PITCHER,SHIP SCENE,VERSE,VIEW OF IRON,BRIDGE,
  1836,LUSTER.............................................. 195.00
SUNDERLAND,PLAQUE,LUSTER,PREPARE TO MEET THY GOD........... 38.00
SUNDERLAND,PLAQUE,THOU GOD SEEST ME,LUSTER................. 19.00
SUNDERLAND,SHAVING MUG,PURPLE LUSTER,THE MARINERS,COMPASS,
  SAILOR POEM.............................................. 38.50
SUNDERLAND,SHAVING MUG,SCUTTLE,SHIP,MARINER COMPASS........ 35.00


    SWANSEA POTTERY WAS MADE AT THE CAMBRIAN POTTERY IN
  GLAMORGANSHIRE,WALES. IT WAS FOUNDED BY 1765 AND WORKED
  UNTIL 1870. THE EARLY WARES WERE OF A FINE-QUALITY SOFT
  PASTE. ALL TYPES OF STAFFORDSHIRE WARES WERE ALSO MADE.
SWANSEA,PLATTER,WILLOW PATTERN,14 1/2 IN. X 10 3/4 IN.,PAIR. 24.00
SWORD,SEE WEAPON,SWORD
SYRUP PITCHER,SEE PRESSED GLASS,PITCHER,SYRUP,PEWTER,ETC.


TAFFETA GLASS,SEE CARNIVAL GLASS
TAPESTRY,CARYATIDS,MUSICIANS,SATYRS,FRUIT CLUSTERS,RESTORED,
  100 X 58 IN.............................................. 850.00
TAPESTRY,COURT LOUIS XIV,FRANCE............................ 50.00
TAPESTRY,COURT SCENE,FRANCE 48 IN. X 70 IN................. 45.00
TAPESTRY,ENGLISH COURT PASTORAL SCENE,IRON RODS,36 X 18 IN.
  WIDE..................................................... 25.00
TAPESTRY,FIGURE OFFERS WINE TO STATUARY MONUMENT,AUBUSSON,
  47 X 101 IN.............................................. 75.00
TAPESTRY,JUNGLE SCENE,FLORAL BORDER,FRENCH,75 IN. X 112 IN.. 400.00
TAPESTRY,LANDSCAPE,CRANE,FISH,CASTLE,MOUNTAIN,FLORAL,FRANCE,
  80 X 90 IN............................................... 725.00
TAPESTRY,LARGE SHADE TREE,FLOWERING PLANTS,BLOSSOM BORDER,
  58 X 80 IN............................................... 50.00
TAPESTRY,NUDE NYMPH,VASE,FLOWERS,RIBBON BORDER,FRENCH,75 X
  25 IN.................................................... 100.00
TAPESTRY,ORIENTAL MARKET & STREET SCENE,4 3/4 X 2 FT........ 9.00
  TAPESTRY,PORCELAIN,SEE ROSE TAPESTRY
TAPESTRY,SHEPHERD,SHEPHERDESS,SHEEP,FRANCE,70 X 95 IN.......1,000.00
TAPESTRY,TROUBADOUR SERANADING LADIES,MADE IN BELGIUM,29 IN.
  X 39 IN.................................................. 10.00
TAPESTRY,TWO LADIES,MAN,HORSE,SERVANTS,DOGS,BUILDINGS,48 X
  39 IN.................................................... 60.00
TAPESTRY,VELVET,COLONIAL FIGURES,BLUE GROUND,WOVEN,38 IN. X
  57 IN.................................................... 125.00
TAPESTRY,VERDURE,WOODED GLADE,FLOWERING PLANTS,FLEMISH,156 X
  78 IN.................................................... 850.00
TAPESTRY,WINDMILL,MAN,WOMAN WORKING IN FIELD,50 IN. X 76 IN. 35.00
  TEA CADDY,SEE FURNITURE,TEA CADDY
  TEA LEAF,SEE LUSTER,COPPER TEA LEAF
TELEPHONE,BLACK,MAN,WOMAN PLAYING INSTRUMENTS,LOUIS XVI,
  1890,FRANCE.............................................. 90.00
TELEPHONE,BOX,PORCELAIN MOUTHPIECE......................... 9.50
TELEPHONE,CANDLESTICK TYPE............................ILLUS. 12.00
TELEPHONE,CASE,WALL,OAK................................... 10.00
TELEPHONE,CRANK TYPE,SHELF,OAK............................ 35.00
TELEPHONE,DESK,BRASS RECEIVER,1903........................ 25.00
TELEPHONE,DESK,CANDLE TYPE,BELL BOX....................... 48.00
TELEPHONE,DESK,DIAL,1928.................................. 23.00
TELEPHONE,DESK,1903...................................... 20.00
TELEPHONE,DOUBLE BOX,32 IN.TALL,11 IN.WIDE................ 50.00
TELEPHONE,FRENCH STYLE,BLACK ENAMEL METAL,GOLD STRIPES,
  CREST,FLAGS.............................................. 24.00
TELEPHONE,FRENCH TYPE,METAL PARTS ARE NICKLED BRASS,MADE IN
  CHICAGO.................................................. 35.00
TELEPHONE,PLATFORM AT BASE................................ 40.00
TELEPHONE,STICK TYPE,OAK BOX.............................. 25.00

CANDLESTICK TYPE TELEPHONE

| | |
|---|---|
| TELEPHONE,TWO BOXES,AMERICAN,WOODEN........................ | 80.00 |
| TELEPHONE,UPRIGHT.............................. 13.00 TO | 19.00 |
| TELEPHONE,WALL,CRANK,OAK BOX.............................. | 50.00 |
| TELEPHONE,WALL,HAND CRANK,WESTERN ELECTRIC................ | 200.00 |
| TELEPHONE,WALL,SETCHEL CARLSON........................... | 25.00 |
| TELEPHONE,WALL,KELLOGG,DATED 1901........................ | 50.00 |
| TELEPHONE,WALL,MAGNITO,OAK............................... | 25.00 |
| TELEPHONE,WALL,OAK,16 IN. X 30 IN........................ | 54.00 |
| TELEPHONE,WALL,SIDE CRANK,KELLOGG INCISED ON MOUTHPIECE,OAK. | 42.50 |
| TELEPHONE,WALL,TRANSMITTER & RECEIVER IN ONE PIECE,SHELF ON | |
| BOTTOM................................................ | 15.00 |
| TELEPHONE,WALL,TWO-BOX,REFINISHED,OAK.................... | 75.00 |
| TELEPHONE,WESTERN ELECTRIC,NOV.17,1891-NOV.1,1892,MARKED,NEW | |
| MOUTHPIECE............................................ | 25.00 |
| TELESCOPE,SEA CAPTAIN,MARKED HARRIS-LONDON,CIRCA 1860,BRASS, | |
| WOODEN CASE........................................... | 59.50 |
| TELESCOPE,THREE-DRAW,WOODEN TUBE,BRASS,16 IN.EXTENDED | |
| LENGTH,CASE........................................... | 60.00 |
| TEPLITZ,AMPHORA,POMEGRANATE CLUSTER,GREEN-BROWN GROUND, | |
| 10 IN.HIGH............................................ | 45.00 |
| TEPLITZ,BASKET,BEIGE,PINK & YELLOW ROSES,GREEN HANDLE....... | 18.00 |
| TEPLITZ,URN,CLASSIC FIGURES,LADY,CUPID,BLUE,TWO HANDLES, | |
| MARKED,3 IN.HIGH...................................... | 45.00 |
| TEPLITZ,VASE,AMPHORA,GREEN IRIDESCENT,BLUE SKY,TREES,BEES, | |
| FLORAL,9 IN........................................... | 48.00 |
| TEPLITZ,VASE,AMPHORA,IVORY COLOR,GREEN,RUST,THREE | |
| RETICULATED HANDLES................................... | 18.50 |
| TEPLITZ,VASE,AMPHORA,PORTRAIT ON FRONT,5 3/4 IN.TALL....... | 59.00 |
| TEPLITZ,VASE,BLUE & GREEN GROUND,RAISED DRAGONFLIES,SIGNED, | |
| 4 1/4 IN.TALL......................................... | 55.00 |
| TEPLITZ,VASE,PURPLE VIOLETS,GREEN LEAVES,IVORY GROUND, | |
| HANDLES,FOOTED........................................ | 15.00 |
| TEPLITZ,VASE,SHAPE OF ARTIST PALETTE WITH BRUSHES,HANDLES, | |
| MARKED,9 IN........................................... | 35.00 |

TIFFANY GLASS WAS MADE BY LOUIS COMFORT TIFFANY,THE
AMERICAN GLASS DESIGNER WHO WORKED FROM ABOUT 1876
TO 1933. HIS WORK INCLUDED IRIDESCENT GLASS,ART
NOUVEAU STYLES OF DESIGN,AND MANY ORIGINAL CONTEMPORARY
STYLES. HE WAS ALSO NOTED FOR HIS STAINED GLASS
WINDOWS,HIS UNUSUAL LAMPS,AND HIS BRONZE WORK.

| | |
|---|---|
| TIFFANY,ASHTRAY & MATCH HOLDER,GOLD DORE IN SPIDER WEB | |
| PATTERN,SIGNED........................................ | 25.00 |
| TIFFANY,BASE,GOLD IRIDESCENT,ENAMELED BRONZE BASE,SIGNED, | |
| 10 1/2 IN............................................. | 295.00 |
| TIFFANY,BASKET,FLOWERS ON HANDLE,STERLING SILVER, | |
| 5-IN.DIAMETER......................................... | 90.00 |
| TIFFANY,BASKET,STERLING SILVER,SIGNED,3 IN.HIGH HANDLE, | |
| 5-IN.DIAMETER......................................... | 65.00 |
| TIFFANY,BOOKEND,ZODIAC,BRASS,PAIR........................ | 30.00 |
| TIFFANY,BOTTLE,COLOGNE,CROWN FINIAL,SHAVING STICK,SILVER, | |
| 1893,SIGNED........................................... | 90.00 |
| TIFFANY,BOTTLE,CREAM TO YELLOW,SATIN,IRIDESCENT,GOLD DECOR, | |
| GOURD SHAPE........................................... | 225.00 |
| TIFFANY,BOTTLE,FLASK,HAND-CARVED & ENGRAVED FLORAL, | |
| THREE-DIMENSIONAL..................................... | 125.00 |
| TIFFANY,BOTTLE,PERFUME,BROWN & OCHER STRIPES,SILVER CAP, | |
| 3 3/4 IN.HIGH......................................... | 625.00 |

```
TIFFANY,BOTTLE,SCENT,FAVRILE GLASS,7 IN. HIGH..............    200.00
TIFFANY,BOWL,BERRY,GOLD IRIDESCENT,GREEN BORDER INSIDE,
   FOOTED,SIGNED..........................................    350.00
TIFFANY,BOWL,BLUE,IRIDESCENT,SIGNED,6-IN.DIAMETER.........    350.00
TIFFANY,BOWL,BLUE,WHITE,PASTEL,WHITE CALCITE UNDER,CUT
   LEAVES,SIGNED...........................................   200.00
TIFFANY,BOWL,BRONZE,GOLD FINISH,SIGNED,9-IN.DIAMETER......     28.00
TIFFANY,BOWL,CHRYSANTHEMUM PATTERN,STERLING SILVER,
   10-IN.DIAMETER.........................................    175.00
TIFFANY,BOWL,CLOVER PATTERN,STERLING SILVER,
   10 1/2-IN.DIAMETER.....................................    175.00
TIFFANY,BOWL,FAVRILE GLASS,15-IN. DIAM...................     250.00
TIFFANY,BOWL,FAVRILE GLASS,6-IN. DIAM.,INSCRIBED L.C.TIFFANY
   FAVRILE................................................    125.00
TIFFANY,BOWL,FINGER,FLORAL,TRANSLUCENT,IRIDESCENT,
   MILLEFIORI,PLATE.......................................    600.00
TIFFANY,BOWL,FINGER,GOLD................................     135.00
TIFFANY,BOWL,FINGER,GOLD IRIDESCENT,SCALLOPED PLATE,PAPER
   LABEL,SIGNED...........................................    195.00
TIFFANY,BOWL,FINGER,GOLD IRIDESCENT,UNDERPLATE,SIGNED.......  165.00
TIFFANY,BOWL,FINGER,UNDERPLATE,CLEAR OPALESCENT,GREEN FLORAL  695.00
TIFFANY,BOWL,FINGER,UNDERPLATE,STRETCHED EDGES,ORANGE-GOLD
   GROUND.................................................    300.00
TIFFANY,BOWL,FLORAL & FERN BORDER,FOOTED,CIRCA 1900,STERLING
   SILVER.................................................    175.00
TIFFANY,BOWL,FLORAL DECOR,BRONZE OVERLAY OVER POTTERY,
   L.C.T.,NO.150..........................................    285.00
TIFFANY,BOWL,FLOWER,FAVRILE GLASS,L.C.TIFFANY,
   11 1/2 IN.-DIAMETER....................................    325.00
TIFFANY,BOWL,GOLD COLOR,FLARING LIP,LABEL,12 IN.WIDE........  120.00
TIFFANY,BOWL,GOLD IRIDESCENT INSIDE & OUTSIDE,LOW BASE,
   L.C.T.FAVRILE..........................................    165.00
TIFFANY,BOWL,GOLD IRIDESCENT,BLUE HIGHLIGHTS,SWIRLED
   HANDLES,4 IN.HIGH......................................    375.00
TIFFANY,BOWL,GOLD IRIDESCENT,MELON RIB BASE,SCALLOPED TOP,
   7 X 3 IN.HIGH..........................................    150.00
TIFFANY,BOWL,GOLD IRIDESCENT,SIGNED L.C.T.,5-IN.DIAMETER....  150.00
TIFFANY,BOWL,GOLD IRIDESCENT,TURNED-IN RUFFLED EDGE,
   L.C.T.FAVRILE..........................................    150.00
TIFFANY,BOWL,GOLD IRIDESCENT,YELLOW,PINK,GREEN SWIRLS,
   PEDESTAL,12 IN.........................................    250.00
TIFFANY,BOWL,GOLD WITH PURPLE & GREEN IRIDESCENT,BISHOP HAT
   SHAPE..................................................    135.00
TIFFANY,BOWL,GOLD-BLUE IRIDESCENT,FLARES,SCALLOPED TOP
   RIDGES,SIGNED..........................................    145.00
TIFFANY,BOWL,GOLD-COLORED GLASS,HANDLES,WAFER PONTIL,SIGNED
   L.C.TIFFANY............................................    150.00
TIFFANY,BOWL,GOLD,BLUE HIGHLIGHTS,HANDLES,SIGNED,6 IN.WIDE,
   2 1/2 IN.HIGH..........................................    125.00
TIFFANY,BOWL,GREEN,LACY STRIPES,SIGNED,10 1/2-IN.DIAMETER,
   3 IN.HIGH..............................................    250.00
TIFFANY,BOWL,GREEN-GOLD GROUND,IRIDIZED,GREEN SWIRLS,SIGNED,
   1 1/2 IN...............................................    275.00
TIFFANY,BOWL,INTAGLIO,STRETCHED EDGE,GOLD COLOR,PEDESTAL,
   SIGNED,8 IN............................................    249.00
TIFFANY,BOWL,IRIDESCENT GOLD,8 1/2-IN.DIAMETER.............    75.00
TIFFANY,BOWL,IRIDESCENT BLUE,SIGNED,2 1/2 X 8 1/2 IN.WIDE...  375.00
TIFFANY,BOWL,LEAF,FERN,FOOTED,1900,STERLING SILVER,
   9 1/2-IN.DIAMETER......................................    175.00
TIFFANY,BOWL,NUT,GOLD,IRIDESCENT,ROLLED-OUT TOP,PEDESTAL
   BASE,2 1/2 IN..........................................     59.00
TIFFANY,BOWL,PASTEL YELLOW,OPALESCENT OPTIC PATTERN,TURNED
   EDGE,SIGNED............................................    235.00
TIFFANY,BOWL,PEACOCK BLUE,IRIDESCENT,RIBBED,FLARED TOP,
   FAVRILE................................................    250.00
TIFFANY,BOWL,PLATE,STRETCHED EDGE,IRIDESCENT,GOLD,RED
   HIGHLIGHTS,RUFFLED.....................................    147.00
TIFFANY,BOWL,PUNCH,PIERCED TOP,PEDESTAL...................    275.00
TIFFANY,BOWL,PUNCH,STERLING SILVER.......................    300.00
TIFFANY,BOWL,PURPLE SATIN GROUND,ENAMELED WHITE FLOWER,
   LEAVES,5 IN............................................     55.00
TIFFANY,BOWL,RED & BLUE HIGHLIGHTS,2 IN.HIGH,4 1/2 IN.WIDE..  125.00
TIFFANY,BOWL,REVERE,STERLING SILVER,7 IN..................     52.50
TIFFANY,BOWL,ROSE,TWISTED PRUNTS,GOLD,RAINBOW IRIDESCENT,
   1 1/4 IN.HIGH..........................................     75.00
TIFFANY,BOWL,SCALLOPED BORDER,EMBOSSED GRAPES,STERLING
   SILVER,9 IN............................................    150.00
TIFFANY,BOWL,SINGLE FLOWER CENTER,INTAGLIO CUT FLORAL IN
   BAND,AMBER.............................................    425.00
TIFFANY,BOWL,SWIRL,SCALLOPED,MONOGRAM,STERLING SILVER,
   9 1/4-IN.DIAMETER......................................     85.00
```

TIFFANY,BOWL,TEXTURED GROUND,FLORAL,UNGLAZED POTTERY,WHITE,
2 1/2 IN.............................................. 650.0
TIFFANY,BOWL,YELLOW,TWISTED PEDESTAL BASE,FAN SHAPE,
8 3/4 IN.TALL........................................ 275.00
TIFFANY,BOX,CIGARETTE,OVERLAY,BEADED,FOOTED,BRONZE,GREEN
SLAG LINING.......................................... 42.50
TIFFANY,BOX,HEXAGON,FAVRILE GLASS PANELS,FOOTED,BRONZE,
5 1/2 X 2 IN.HIGH.................................... 300.00
TIFFANY,BOX,LETTER,SIGNED TIFFANY STUDIO................. 175.00
TIFFANY,BOX,RING,FLOWERS,VINES IN RELIEF,BRASS FEET,HINGED
LID,MARKED........................................... 35.00
TIFFANY,BOX,STAMP,HINGED COVER,MARKED,3 3/4 IN.LONG,
2 IN.ACROSS.......................................... 30.00
TIFFANY,CAN,TALCUM POWDER,REVOLVING CAP,SCROLLS,FLORAL,
STERLING SILVER...................................... 45.00
TIFFANY,CANDELABRUM,BRONZE,11 3/4 IN. HIGH.............. 250.00
TIFFANY,CANDELABRUM,BRONZE,13 IN. HIGH................. 275.00
TIFFANY,CANDLE SHADE,STERLING SILVER,SIGNED............. 20.00
TIFFANY,CANDLEHOLDER,DOUBLE BOBECHE,DORE BRONZE,SIGNED,
8 IN.HIGH............................................ 160.00
TIFFANY,CANDLESTICK,BLUE,GOLD,TWISTED,10 IN............. 185.00
TIFFANY,CANDLESTICK,BRONZE,GREEN ENAMEL TRIM,2 IN.X
4 1/2 IN.SQUARE,PAIR................................. 85.00
TIFFANY,CANDLESTICK,FAVRILE GLASS...................... 175.00
TIFFANY,CANDLESTICK,GOLD IRIDESCENT,6 3/4 IN.HIGH,
4 1/2 IN.BASE........................................ 195.00
TIFFANY,CANDLESTICK,GREEN FEATHER FAVRILLE GLASS,SIGNED..... 175.00
TIFFANY,CANDLESTICK,PAIR,BRONZE,20 1/2 IN. HIGH........ 175.00
TIFFANY,CANDLESTICK,PATINA FINISH,BRONZE TOP,GOLD IRIDESCENT
PRISMS............................................... 300.00
TIFFANY,CANDLESTICK,PINK IRIDESCENT,OPALESCENT SOCKETS,
4 IN.HIGH,PAIR....................................... 485.00
TIFFANY,CANDLESTICK,SPIRAL TWIST,BLUE-GOLD,SIGNED,14 1/2 IN.
HIGH................................................. 250.00
TIFFANY,CANDLESTICK,ZODIAC PATTERN,SIGNED,BRONZE,
5 1/2 IN.HIGH,PAIR................................... 90.00
TIFFANY,CHAMPAGNE,PINK,OPALESCENT,OPTIC RIB BOWL,GREEN STEM,
SIGNED............................................... 335.00
TIFFANY,CHAMPAGNE,WHITE & VIOLET,SIGNED................. 300.00
TIFFANY,CHANDELIER,FAVRILE GLASS & BRONZE,TURTLE-BACK,19 IN.
HIGH................................................. 900.00
TIFFANY,CHARGER,SIGNED,BRONZE,12 IN.DIAMETER............ 52.00
TIFFANY,CLOCK,DESK,ENAMELED BRONZE,5 3/4 IN. HIGH....... 175.00
TIFFANY,CLOCK,DESK,IRIDESCENT GLASS AROUND BORDER OF FACE,
SIGNED............................................... 450.00
TIFFANY,CLOCK,MARBLE,BRONZE FIGURE ON TOP,PORCELAIN DIAL,
SIGNED............................................... 375.00
TIFFANY,CLOCK,MECHANICAL WATERFALL OF SPIRAL RODS,TWO
CANDELABRA,BRASS.................................1,995.00
TIFFANY,CLOCK,ROTATING SPIRAL GLASS RODS,TWO CANDELABRA,
BRASS,ONYX TRIM..................................1,995.00
TIFFANY,COFFEEPOT,CREAMER,SUGAR,SCALLOPED TRAY,ENGRAVED,
STERLING SILVER...................................... 500.00
TIFFANY,COMPOTE,BLUE,GOLD,GREEN,YELLOW,BROWN,LAVENDER
IRIDESCENT,L.C.T..................................... 245.00
TIFFANY,COMPOTE,DIAMOND-QUILTED,BRONZE DORE DECORATED
PEDESTAL,GREEN....................................... 400.00
TIFFANY,COMPOTE,FLARE EDGE,GOLD-ORANGE,SIGNED,4 1/2 IN...... 175.00
TIFFANY,COMPOTE,FLUTED,FULLY-SIGNED,4 1/2 IN.WIDE X
4 1/2 IN.HIGH........................................ 145.00
TIFFANY,COMPOTE,GOLD COLOR BRONZE,FOOTED,SIGNED,6 1/2 IN. X
4 IN.HIGH............................................ 45.00
TIFFANY,COMPOTE,GOLD COLOR,PURPLE HIGHLIGHTS,SIGNED &
NUMBERED............................................. 145.00
TIFFANY,COMPOTE,GOLD COLOR,STRETCHED EDGE,SIGNED.......... 195.00
TIFFANY,COMPOTE,GOLD-PURPLE IRIDESCENCE,SIGNED,NUMBERED,4 X
4 IN.HIGH............................................ 135.00
TIFFANY,COMPOTE,GREEN TO YELLOW,BLUE IRIDESCENT AT BASE,
PATTERN,6 IN......................................... 200.00
TIFFANY,COMPOTE,PASTEL GREEN TO YELLOW,BLUE IRIDESCENT AT
BASE,LOW............................................. 200.00
TIFFANY,COMPOTE,PASTEL GREEN,OPALESCENT LINING,SIGNED,
4 1/4 IN.TALL........................................ 385.00
TIFFANY,COMPOTE,PEACOCK BLUE,IRIDESCENT,ONION SKIN EDGE,
L.C.T.FAVRILE........................................ 375.00
TIFFANY,COMPOTE,TURQUOISE,IRIDESCENT,RICE PATTERN,
6 1/2-IN.DIAMETER.................................... 285.00
TIFFANY,CORDIAL,DIMPLED SIDES,SIGNED & NUMBERED.......... 90.00
TIFFANY,CORDIAL,GREEN-GOLD TO CLEAR,BLUE HIGHLIGHTS,SIGNED
L.C.T.FAVRILE........................................ 135.00
TIFFANY,CREAMER,FOOTED,18TH CENTURY,STERLING SILVER,

```
    4 3/8 IN.........................................    55.00
TIFFANY,CREAMER,MONOGRAM,GOLD-WASHED,STERLING SILVER.......    30.00
TIFFANY,CUP,MAYONNAISE,FLOWER-SHAPED UNDERPLATE,VIOLET,
    GREEN,BLUE,SIGNED.............................................   400.00
TIFFANY,CUP,NUT,CRENALATED RIM,SIGNED.........................    64.00
TIFFANY,CUP,NUT,CRENALATED TOP,SIGNED.........................    67.50
TIFFANY,CUP,NUT,SERPENTINE RIM,SIGNED.........................    74.00
TIFFANY,DESK CALENDAR,1933,BRASS & GLASS,FLIP PAGES,SIGNED..    75.00
TIFFANY,DESK SET,INKWELL,PEN TRAY,BRUSH HOLDER,AMBER GLASS..    85.00
TIFFANY,DESK SET,THREE PIECES,SIGNED & NUMBERED,BRONZE......   150.00
TIFFANY,DESK SET,ZODIAC MOTIF,INKWELL ATTACHED TO TRAY,
    BRONZE,8 PIECE.............................................   215.00
TIFFANY,DISH,BONBON,GOLD IRIDESCENT,SILVER & RED ACCENTS,
    RIBBED,SIGNED.............................................   110.00
TIFFANY,DISH,CANDY,ETCHED GLASS,STERLING SILVER COVER,KNOB
    FINIAL,MARK...............................................    18.50
TIFFANY,DISH,FAVRILE,VICTORY,INSCRIBED 1918,6 IN. DIAM......   125.00
TIFFANY,DISH,GOLD COLOR,FLORIFORM,STRETCHED EDGE,PEDESTAL,
    4 1/4 IN.TALL.............................................   225.00
TIFFANY,DISH,NUT,BLUE,L.C.T.FAVRILE,SIGNED...................   350.00
TIFFANY,DISH,NUT,DECOR,HANDLE,FOOTED,SIGNED,STERLING SILVER.    48.00
TIFFANY,DISH,NUT,GOLD WITH PURPLE-BLUE IRIDESCENCE,SIGNED
    L.C.T.FAVRILE.............................................   125.00
TIFFANY,EWER,ORMULU,BRONZE,SIGNED,1895,34 IN.HIGH...........1,850.00
TIFFANY,FLOWER FORM,GOLD,GREEN LEAVES,VINES,SIGNED,NUMBERED,
    8 1/2 IN..................................................   350.00
TIFFANY,FLOWER HOLDER CENTERPIECE,BRONZE GILT,INSERT,
    STERLING SILVER...........................................   500.00
TIFFANY,FORK,DINNER,KING WILLIAM PATTERN,STERLING SILVER,SET
    OF 12.....................................................    80.00
TIFFANY,FORK,ICE CREAM,STERLING SILVER,SET OF 6.............    35.00
TIFFANY,FORK,OYSTER,STERLING SILVER,PLAIN POINTED TIP
    HANDLE,MONOGRAM,12........................................    72.00
TIFFANY,GLASS,SHOT,PINCHED SIDES,GOLD,SIGNED................    72.00
TIFFANY,GOBLET,AMETHYST,WHITE FEATHERS,CLEAR STEM,SIGNED,
    8 1/2 IN..................................................   295.00
TIFFANY,GOBLET,GOLD,BLUE HIGHLIGHTS,SIGNED L.C.T.,T1924,
    5 1/2 IN.HIGH.............................................   150.00
TIFFANY,GOBLET,WATER,INTAGLIO LEAVES,GRAPES,GOLD IRIDESCENT,
    SET OF 10.................................................2,000.00
TIFFANY,GOBLET,WATER,VINTAGE PATTERN,ENGRAVED,RED & GOLD
    IRIDESCENT................................................   145.00
TIFFANY,GOBLET,WINE,SIGNED L.C.T.FAVRILE NO.5,5 1/2 IN.TALL.   125.00
TIFFANY,GOBLET,YELLOW,SCULPTURED,RIBBED STEM,BLUE RIM,
    FAVRILE,8 1/2 IN..........................................   160.00
TIFFANY,HOLDER,BLOTTER,GEOMETRIC DESIGN,DORE,SIGNED,BRONZE..    45.00
TIFFANY,HOLDER,LETTER,ZODIAC DESIGN,BRONZE..................    28.50
TIFFANY,HUMIDOR,BLUE IRIDESCENT,GOLD HIGHLIGHTS,CUT STAR
    FINIAL,FAVRILE............................................   595.00
TIFFANY,INKWELL,CALENDAR HOLDER,METAL......................    40.00
TIFFANY,INKWELL,DORE FINISH,MARBELIZED GLASS-LINED,SIGNED,
    SQUARE....................................................    40.00
TIFFANY,INKWELL,GREEN IRIDESCENT,RAISED ALLOVER PATTERN,
    HINGED LID................................................    95.00
TIFFANY,INKWELL,INDIAN MOTIF,DARK PATINA,BRONZE,5 IN. X
    3 1/2 IN.HIGH.............................................    45.00
TIFFANY,INKWELL,SPIDER WEB DESIGN,INITIALED H.T.S.,HINGED
    TOP.......................................................    45.00
TIFFANY,INKWELL,ZODIAC,BRONZE..............................    45.00
TIFFANY,INKWELL,ZODIAC,SIGNED..............................    75.00
TIFFANY,INKWELL,ZODIAC,SIGNED,BRONZE.......................    85.00
TIFFANY,KNIFE,DINNER,MONOGRAM,STERLING SILVER HANDLE,SET OF
    12........................................................   240.00
TIFFANY,LAMP,ACORN SHADE,GREEN,BRONZE BASE,SIGNED,24 IN.TALL   900.00
TIFFANY,LAMP,APPLE BLOSSOM,BRONZE BASE,BRONZE WEB SHADE,
    SIGNED....................................................5,500.00
TIFFANY,LAMP,BRIDGE,AURENE SHADE,GREEN,PLATINUM RIM,
    10-IN.DIAMETER............................................   375.00
TIFFANY,LAMP,BRIDGE,DAMASCENE SHADE,SIGNED,56 IN.HIGH.......   600.00
TIFFANY,LAMP,CANDLE,FOOTED SAUCER BASE,SCULPTED MUSLIN
    SHADE,BRONZE..............................................   275.00
TIFFANY,LAMP,CANDLE,GOLD COLOR SHADE & BASE,GREEN & WHITE
    CANDLE,SIGNED.............................................   350.00
TIFFANY,LAMP,CLEMATIS,GREEN,RED,YELLOW,LEADED,BRONZE BASE,
    33 IN.HIGH................................................4,250.00
TIFFANY,LAMP,DESK,FAVRILE & BRONZE,TURTLE-BACK,14 IN. HIGH..   575.00
TIFFANY,LAMP,DESK,FAVRILE GLASS & BRONZE,14 IN. HIGH........   325.00
TIFFANY,LAMP,DESK,OCTAGONAL SHAPE,FILIGREED SHADE,SIGNED....   290.00
TIFFANY,LAMP,DESK,ZODIAC,TURTLEBACK,SIGNED,15 IN.HIGH.......   675.00
TIFFANY,LAMP,FAVRILE GLASS & BRONZE,TURTLEBACK,24 IN.HIGH...   650.00
TIFFANY,LAMP,FLOOR,LILY,12-LIGHT,FAVRILE & BRONZE,55 IN.
```

HIGH..........................................................2,500.00
TIFFANY,LAMP,FOUR-COLUMN PEDESTAL,BRONZE,CLAW FEET,GREEN
   SHADE,16 IN............................................... 195.50
TIFFANY,LAMP,GREEN FAVRILE GLASS,17 1/2 IN. HIGH............ 350.00
TIFFANY,LAMP,MOTTLED BLUE & GREEN SHADE,16-IN.DIAMETER,BASE
   22 IN.HIGH................................................ 725.00
TIFFANY,LAMP,MURANO ART GLASS SHADE,GOLD,GREEN,WHITE CASING,
   BRONZE BASE............................................... 375.00
TIFFANY,LAMP,OPALESCENT GOLD,BRONZE BASE,SIGNED & NUMBERED,
   18 IN.HIGH................................................ 800.00
TIFFANY,LAMP,POPPY,FAVRILE & BRONZE,26 IN. HIGH......ILLUS..3,100.00
TIFFANY,LAMP,SNAIL SHADE,LEADED GLASS,BRONZE SWIVEL BASE.... 595.00
TIFFANY,LAMP,SNAIL SHADE,LEADED,GREEN,YELLOW,BRONZE BASE,
   13 1/4 IN................................................. 995.00
TIFFANY,LAMP,SNAIL,BRONZE & LEADED GLASS,GREEN & YELLOW,
   13 1/4 IN.HIGH...........................................1,150.00
TIFFANY,LAMP,STAINED GLASS & BRONZE,24 IN. HIGH............ 225.00
TIFFANY,LAMP,STUDENT,PINK & GREEN,SWIRLED MOIRE PATTERN,
   ADJUSTABLE,7 IN........................................... 335.00
TIFFANY,LAMP,TABLE,FAVRILE & BRONZE,PEONY...........ILLUS..4,100.00
TIFFANY,LAMP,TABLE,FAVRILE & BRONZE,WISTERIA........ILLUS..7,000.00
TIFFANY,LAMP,TABLE,FAVRILE GLASS & BRASS,8 1/2 IN. HIGH..... 400.00
TIFFANY,LAMP,TABLE,LEADED DOME SHADE,TULIP INLAYS,BRONZE
   STANDARD,LEAVES.......................................... 215.00
TIFFANY,LAMP,TABLE,ORANGE ACORN,GREEN GLASS,LEADED,SIGNED,
   16-IN.DIAMETER........................................... 575.00
TIFFANY,LAMP,TABLE,RED SHADE,ACORN BAND,LEAD,BRONZE BASE,
   22 1/2 IN.TALL........................................... 850.00
TIFFANY,LAMP,TRICOLORED,LEADED SHADE,SIGNED BASE & SHADE,
   10-IN.DIAMETER........................................... 350.00
TIFFANY,LAMP BASE,TABLE,HOLDS TWO GASLIGHT SHADES,SIGNED.... 250.00
TIFFANY,LAMPSHADE,GREEN GROUND,YELLOW ACORNS,SIGNED,16 IN... 495.00
TIFFANY,LETTER HOLDER,MOTHER-OF-PEARL INSERTS IN BRONZE,BALL
   FEET,SIGNED............................................... 55.00
TIFFANY,LIQUEUR,DIMPLED SIDES,SIGNED AND NUMBERED.......... 90.00
TIFFANY,LIQUEUR,GOLD DIMPLED,SIGNED L.C.T.................. 85.00
TIFFANY,LIQUEUR,GOLD IRIDESCENT,DIMPLED SIDES,SIGNED &
   NUMBERED.................................................. 91.00
TIFFANY,LIQUEUR,GOLD IRIDESCENT,SIGNED L.C.T............... 85.00
TIFFANY,MASTER SALT,WHITE,PINK INSIDE,SCALLOPED RIM,SIGNED,
   FAVRILE................................................... 375.00
TIFFANY,MATCH HOLDER,SAUCER TYPE,GLASS INSERT,SIGNED,
   NUMBERED,5 IN............................................. 50.00
TIFFANY,MEDALLION PORTRAIT OF THOMAS FENTON,BY O.L.WARNER,
   BRONZE,7 IN............................................... 750.00
TIFFANY,MUG,CHILD'S,MONOGRAM,STERLING SILVER.............. 19.00
TIFFANY,OWL,SIGNED TIFFANY STUDIOS:NO.892,BRONZE,3 IN.HIGH.. 215.00
TIFFANY,PANEL,PAIR,TAPESTRY-WOVEN PEACOCK FABRIC,5 FT. X
   33 IN..................................................... 450.00
TIFFANY,PANEL,PRINTED VELVET FABRIC,50 IN. LONG............ 60.00
TIFFANY,PAPERWEIGHT,FABRIQUE GLASS,SPIDER WEB DESIGN,SIGNED,
   NUMBERED.................................................. 40.00
TIFFANY,PAPERWEIGHT,MASTER SALT,INVERTED BISHOP'S HAT SHAPE,
   AMBER,SIGNED.............................................. 195.00
TIFFANY,PARFAIT,PASTEL YELLOW,UNSIGNED.................... 165.00
TIFFANY,PARFAIT,YELLOW FEATHERING WITH OPAL............... 175.00
TIFFANY,PEN,FOUNTAIN,INITIALS,SIGNED,14K GOLD............. 60.00
TIFFANY,PERFUME,BLUE & GOLD IRIDESCENT,STOPPER,L.C.TIFFANY
   FAVRILE................................................... 175.00
TIFFANY,PIPE RACK,FOUR PIPE,COPPER,TWO RAMS' HORNS,CRYSTAL
   BOWL,1915................................................. 85.00
TIFFANY,PITCHER,MILK,BLUE IRIDESCENT,PURPLE HIGHLIGHTS,
   SIGNED,4 IN.HIGH.......................................... 375.00
TIFFANY,PITCHER,WATER,SWIRL FLUTING,EMBOSSED LEAF MOTIF,
   11 3/4 IN.HIGH............................................ 650.00
TIFFANY,PLANTER,RAISED FLORAL DECOR,YELLOW GLAZE,POTTERY,
   15-IN.DIAMETER............................................ 180.00
TIFFANY,PLATE,BLUE,SIGNED,5 1/2 IN.ACROSS................. 175.00
TIFFANY,PLATE,PASTEL BLUE & YELLOW,SIGNED L.C.T.FAVRILE,
   6-IN.DIAMETER............................................. 50.00
TIFFANY,PLATE,PASTEL BLUE,SIGNED,11-IN.DIAMETER........... 187.00
TIFFANY,PLATE,PASTEL LIME,LABEL.......................... 175.00
TIFFANY,PLATE,PASTEL PINK,OPALESCENT OPTIC PATTERN,SIGNED,
   9 IN...................................................... 225.00
TIFFANY,PLATE,PASTEL YELLOW,GLAZED,SIGNED,10 3/4-IN.DIAMETER 175.00
TIFFANY,PLATE,SWIRL SCALLOP,DRESDEN-TYPE FLORAL,MARKED ROYAL
   TETTAU,6.................................................. 45.00
TIFFANY,RING TREE,STERLING SILVER........................ 15.00
TIFFANY,SALT,BLUE,OPEN,FOOTED,SIGNED & NUMBERED.......... 125.00
TIFFANY,SALT,FAVRILE,GOLD COLOR,GREEN STRIPES,GOLD INTERIOR,
   RUFFLED................................................... 60.00

TIFFANY LAMP, POPPY

TIFFANY LAMP, PEONY

TIFFANY LAMP, WISTERIA

TIFFANY,SALT,GOLD COLOR,PURPLE HIGHLIGHTS,CRIMPED,SIGNED &
  NUMBERED.............................................................. 68.00
TIFFANY,SALT,GOLD,CRIMPED,SIGNED...................................... 65.00
TIFFANY,SALT,GOLD IRIDESCENT,RUFFLED,SIGNED.................. 47.50
TIFFANY,SALT,GOLD IRIDESCENT,SIGNED.................................. 78.00
TIFFANY,SALT,GOLD WITH PURPLE HIGHLIGHTS,SIGNED............. 65.00
TIFFANY,SALT,GOLD,IRIDESCENT,FLUTED RIM,SIGNED.............. 60.00
TIFFANY,SALT,GOLD,PINK & LAVENDER HIGHLIGHTS,RUFFLED,
  L.C.T.FAVRILE......................................................... 58.00
TIFFANY,SALT,GOLD,RUFFLED,SIGNED L.C.T........................ 55.00
TIFFANY,SALT,MASTER,GOLD-PURPLE IRIDESCENT,CRIMPED,SIGNED,
  NUMBERED.............................................................. 65.00
TIFFANY,SALT,OPEN,FLARED RIM,FOOTED,SIGNED.................... 80.00
TIFFANY,SALT,OPEN,RUFFLED TOP,SIGNED.......................... 75.00
TIFFANY,SALT,PRUNTS ALL AROUND,SIGNED......................... 85.00
TIFFANY,SALT,RAINBOW HIGHLIGHTS,CRIMPED TOP,SIGNED........... 60.00
TIFFANY,SALT,RUFFLED,SIGNED,2 5/8 IN.......................... 57.00
TIFFANY,SALT,RUFFLED RIM,OPEN,SIGNED L.C.T.,1 IN.HIGH,
  3 3/4-IN.DIAMETER.................................................... 85.00
TIFFANY,SALT,RUFFLED TOP,RAINBOW HIGHLIGHTS,GOLD,SIGNED
  L.C.T................................................................ 60.00
TIFFANY,SALT,THORN PATTERN............................................ 75.00
TIFFANY,SALT,VIBRANT GOLD IRIDESCENT,RUFFLED,L.C.T.FAVRILE,
  2 1/2 IN............................................................. 57.00
TIFFANY,SAMOVAR,SILVER-SOLDERED,SIGNED,20 IN.HIGH........... 200.00
TIFFANY,SEAL,LETTER,WAX,INTAGLIO P IN BASE,BEETLES,FAVRILE,
  1 5/8 IN............................................................. 60.00
TIFFANY,SEAL,WAX,STAG BEETLE,GOLD..................................... 65.00
TIFFANY,SERVER,CAKE,TREE DESIGN,OPENWORK,REPOUSSED SHELLS ON
  HANDLE,1884.......................................................... 85.00
TIFFANY,SHADE,CREAM COLOR,GREEN FEATHER TRIM,GOLD LINING,4 X
  6 IN.WIDE........................................................... 130.00
TIFFANY,SHADE,ELECTRIC BULB,RIBBED,SIGNED L.C.T,FAVRILE,
  GOLD,5 IN.HIGH....................................................... 48.00
TIFFANY,SHADE,GAS,GREEN FEATHER DECOR,SIGNED................. 60.00
TIFFANY,SHADE,GAS,GREEN FEATHER,SIGNED....................... 50.00
TIFFANY,SHADE,GASLIGHT,GOLD IRIDESCENT,L.C.T.,
  2 1/8-IN.FITTER,5 IN.HIGH........................................... 50.00
TIFFANY,SHADE,GOLD & CREAM CAMEO CUT,SIGNED,12-IN.DIAMETER.. 250.00
TIFFANY,SHADE,HANGING,GREEN & AMBER TURTLEBACKS,CHAIN,
  OCTAGONAL,30 IN....................................................2,650.00
TIFFANY,SHADE,LAMP,PINK,BLUE,BEIGE,18 IN.WIDE,10 1/2 IN.HIGH  85.00
TIFFANY,SHADE,LIGHT,PAPERWEIGHT,SIGNED L.C.T. & NO.0116.....1,250.00
TIFFANY,SHAKER,COCKTAIL,CUT DIAMOND SQUARES,STERLING SILVER
  TOP,SIGNED.......................................................... 110.00
TIFFANY,SHAVING BRUSH & STICK,MONOGRAM,DATED 1890,STERLING
  SILVER,SIGNED........................................................ 75.00
TIFFANY,SHERBET,GOLD IRIDESCENT,PULLED PRUNTS,SIGNED,SET OF
  5................................................................... 500.00
TIFFANY,SHERBET,PEACOCK COLOR,ALL AROUND PUNTS,TRUMPET BASE,
  SIGNED.............................................................. 215.00
TIFFANY,SHIELD,HANGING DRAGONFLY,FAVRILE,10 IN. LONG........ 250.00
TIFFANY,SHOT GLASS,GOLD IRIDESCENT,GREEN DECOR,WEIGHTED,
  SIGNED.............................................................. 275.00
TIFFANY,SPOON,DEMITASSE,MONOGRAM,PAT.1885M,STERLING SILVER,
  4 1/2 IN.LONG........................................................ 12.50
TIFFANY,SPOON,MASTER SALT,LEAF AT END,GOLD WASH BOWL,
  STERLING SILVER...................................................... 10.00
TIFFANY,SPOON,SOUVENIR HUDSON-FULTON CELEBRATION,1909,
  STERLING SILVER...................................................... 15.00
TIFFANY,SPOON,STUFFING,CHRYSANTHEMUM PATTERN,STERLING
  SILVER,12 1/4 IN.................................................... 150.00
TIFFANY,STICKPIN,SCARAB,IRIDESCENT.................................... 35.00
TIFFANY,TABLESPOON,CLASSIC PATTERN,STERLING SILVER,1909..... 15.00
TIFFANY,TAZZA,FAVRILE GLASS,8-IN. DIAM.INSCRIBED
  L.C.T.FAVRILE....................................................... 150.00
TIFFANY,TAZZA,LAVENDER,SIGNED........................................ 575.00
TIFFANY,TAZZA,PASTEL,SIGNED LCT-FAVRILE,CIRCA 1919,5 1/2 X
  7 1/2 IN............................................................ 225.00
TIFFANY,TAZZA,SIGNED,6 1/2 IN. X 6 1/2 IN.................... 175.00
TIFFANY,TEA CADDY,ROUND,SLOPING SIDES,LOTUS LEAF,STERLING
  SILVER............................................................... 75.00
TIFFANY,TILE,FIREPLACE,DRAGON,MARKED PATENT APPLIED FOR,
  4 IN.SQUARE.......................................................... 15.00
TIFFANY,TILE,FIREPLACE,RAISED MEDALLION,MARKED PATENT
  APPLIED FOR,4 IN..................................................... 15.00
TIFFANY,TILE,12,FAVRILE GLASS,4 X 4 IN....................... 85.00
TIFFANY,TOOTHPICK,DIMPLED BODY,IRIDESCENT GOLD,SIGNED....... 85.00
TIFFANY,TOOTHPICK,FOUR DIMPLED SIDES,GOLD IRIDESCENT,SIGNED. 85.00

```
TIFFANY,TOOTHPICK,GOLD,DIMPLED,SIGNED & NUMBERED............   100.00
TIFFANY,TOOTHPICK,GOLD,RIBBED,FOOTED,SIGNED,2 3/4 IN.TALL,
   2 IN.WIDE...............................................   150.00
TIFFANY,TOOTHPICK,PULLED-OUT KNOBS,GOLD,BLUE HIGHLIGHTS,
   SIGNED,2 1/4 IN.........................................   165.00
TIFFANY,TOOTHPICK,RAISED FLORAL,SILVER......................    12.00
TIFFANY,TRAY,ALLOVER POCKMARKS,ORNATE BORDER,BRASS,
   14-IN.DIAMETER..........................................    59.00
TIFFANY,TRAY,HEART SHAPE,BLUE,WISHBONE HANDLES,IRIDESCENT,
   4 X 4 IN...............................................   345.00
TIFFANY,TRAY,PURPLE & GREEN IRIDESCENT,14-IN.DIAMETER.......   175.00
TIFFANY,TUMBLER,APPLIED LILY PADS PULLED DOWN INTO BASE,GOLD
   IRIDESCENT.............................................   135.00
TIFFANY,TUMBLER,GOLD IRIDESCENT,LOTUS DECOR,HORIZONTAL
   BANDS,SIGNED...........................................   125.00
TIFFANY,TUMBLER,GOLD,GREEN NETWORK NEAR BOTTOM,SIGNED
   625 L.C.T.TIFFANY......................................   185.00
TIFFANY,URN,BLUE,APPLIED CURLED & REEDED HANDLES,
   4 1/2 IN.HIGH..........................................   425.00
TIFFANY,URN,BLUE,ROLLED EDGE,APPLIED HANDLES,SIGNED,
   1064-959M,4 1/2 IN.....................................   525.00
TIFFANY,URN,WHITE,TWO HANDLES,SIGNED,1 1/2 IN.TALL..........   225.00
TIFFANY,VASE,AMBER IRIDESCENT,RED PEACOCK FEATHERS,SEPARATE
   BASE,19 IN...........................................1,500.00
TIFFANY,VASE,AZURE BLUE,GOLD & ENAMELED RAISED DECOR,10 IN..   150.00
TIFFANY,VASE,BLUE FAVRILE GLASS,11 IN. HIGH.................   400.00
TIFFANY,VASE,BLUE,BLACK VINES,GOLD SPARKLE,GREEN LEAVES,
   3 3/4 IN.HIGH..........................................   675.00
TIFFANY,VASE,BLUE,IRIDESCENT,RIBS,SCALLOPED,LABEL,SIGNED,
   13 1/2 IN.TALL.........................................   300.00
TIFFANY,VASE,BLUE,RIBBED,SIGNED & NUMBERED,9 IN.............   325.00
TIFFANY,VASE,BLUE,SWIRL DESIGN,BULBOUS TOP,NUMBERED PAPER
   LABEL,5 IN.............................................   250.00
TIFFANY,VASE,BOWL-SHAPED,GOLD,GREEN FEATHERY LEAVES,SIGNED,
   5 1/2 X 3 IN...........................................   180.00
TIFFANY,VASE,BRONZE COLOR POTTERY,SIGNED,8 1/2 IN..........    295.00
TIFFANY,VASE,BUBBLY WATER,FOAMY WATER LINE,LEAVES,FLORAL,
   AQUA,6 1/2 IN........................................2,500.00
TIFFANY,VASE,BUD,CALCITE,GREEN STRIATIONS,SIGNED L.C.TIFFANY
   FAVRILE................................................   125.00
TIFFANY,VASE,BUD,GOLD-BLUE IRIDESCENT,TEARDROP BODY,SLENDER
   NECK,7 IN..............................................   125.00
TIFFANY,VASE,BULBOUS,TAPERS TO NARROW NECK,LEAF,VINE DECOR,
   SIGNED,6 IN............................................   365.00
TIFFANY,VASE,CAGEWORK DECOR,SIGNED L.C.TIFFANY-FAVRILE,
   2 IN.HIGH..............................................   160.00
TIFFANY,VASE,CAMEO FAVRILE,MINIATURE,3 3/4 IN. HIGH..ILLUS..   750.00
TIFFANY,VASE,DARK GREEN,CASING,GOLD & BLUE FEATHERING,
   4 1/2 IN...............................................   275.00
TIFFANY,VASE,DEEP RED TO PURPLE,VINES,LEAVES,FREE FORM,
   10 IN.TALL.............................................   275.00
TIFFANY,VASE,EXTRUDED RIBS AND PUNTS,GOLD,BLUE,RED BAND,
   WAFER PONTIL...........................................   320.00
TIFFANY,VASE,FAVRILE & BRONZE,9 IN. HIGH,INSCRIBED
   L.C.TIFFANY FAVRILE....................................   375.00
TIFFANY,VASE,FAVRILE GLASS,BLUE,5 1/2 IN. HIGH.............   250.00
TIFFANY,VASE,FAVRILE GLASS,4 3/4 IN. HIGH,INSCRIBED 04633...   130.00
TIFFANY,VASE,FEATHER MOTIF,LAPPED RIM BASE,FLORIFORM,SIGNED,
   12 1/2 IN..............................................   565.00
TIFFANY,VASE,FIVE FLOWER FORM TOP RUFFLES,YELLOW,PEDESTAL,
   IRIDESCENT.............................................   145.00
TIFFANY,VASE,FLARED TOP,BLUE,SIGNED L.C.T.,14 3/4 IN........   350.00
TIFFANY,VASE,FLASHED-GREEN DECOR,FREE-FORM CHAIN ON BODY,
```

CAMEO TIFFANY VASE

```
SIGNED,8 IN.........................................   375.00
TIFFANY,VASE,FLORIFORM,BLUE,PETAL DECOR,SIGNED,12 IN.HIGH...   600.00
TIFFANY,VASE,FLORIFORM,ELONGATED TRIANGULAR BOWL,DOME FOOT,
  LEAVES............................................   825.00
TIFFANY,VASE,FLORIFORM,FAVRILE GLASS,11 1/2 IN. HIGH.......   350.00
TIFFANY,VASE,FLORIFORM,FAVRILE GLASS,12 1/2 IN. HIGH.......   375.00
TIFFANY,VASE,FLORIFORM,GREEN & WHITE LEAVES,RIBBED,
  12 1/2 IN.HIGH.....................................   450.00
TIFFANY,VASE,FLORIFORM,IRIDESCENT GLASS,13 IN. HIGH........   525.00
TIFFANY,VASE,GOBLET-LIKE,GREEN,OPAQUE STRIPES,DOME-SHAPED
  FOOT,SIGNED........................................   595.00
TIFFANY,VASE,GOLD COLOR,RIBBED,TULIP TOP,TAPERED,SIGNED,
  13 IN..............................................   285.00
TIFFANY,VASE,GOLD COLOR,RUFFLED TOP,PAPER LABEL,MARKED
  L.C.T.1558B,8 IN...................................   375.00
TIFFANY,VASE,GOLD IRIDESCENT,BLUE & LAVENDER HIGHLIGHTS,
  SIGNED,5 IN.WIDE...................................   145.00
TIFFANY,VASE,GOLD IRIDESCENT,BULBOUS,FLARED LIP,PULLED
  HANDLES,3 IN.HIGH..................................   130.00
TIFFANY,VASE,GOLD IRIDESCENT,EGG SHAPE,FITTED WOODEN BASE,
  SIGNED,7 IN........................................   125.00
TIFFANY,VASE,GOLD IRIDESCENT,FERN DESIGN,CUT BUTTERFLIES
  INSIDE,10 IN.......................................   625.00
TIFFANY,VASE,GOLD IRIDESCENT,FLOWER FORM,STRETCH TOP,
  RUFFLED,SIGNED.....................................   225.00
TIFFANY,VASE,GOLD IRIDESCENT,HANDLES,L.C.T.TIFFANY FAVRILE
  NO.3034...........................................   140.00
TIFFANY,VASE,GOLD IRIDESCENT,RIBBED,TAPERING NECK,FLARED
  LIP,5 IN.HIGH......................................   115.00
TIFFANY,VASE,GOLD IRIDESCENT,RIBBED BODY,BRONZE BASE,
  18 1/2 IN..........................................   175.00
TIFFANY,VASE,GOLD IRIDESCENT,SIGNED,NUMBERED 9424A,
  11 IN.HIGH.........................................   250.00
TIFFANY,VASE,GOLD IRIDESCENT,TAPERED STEM,FLARED TOP,SIGNED,
  12 IN..............................................   375.00
TIFFANY,VASE,GOLD IRIDESCENT,TRUMPET SHAPE,BRONZE HOLDER,
  8 1/4 IN.TALL......................................   250.00
TIFFANY,VASE,GOLD LEAF,TRUMPET SHAPE,SIGNED,15 IN.........   300.00
TIFFANY,VASE,GOLD LUSTER,GREEN LEAF DECOR,SIGNED,26 IN.HIGH.   350.00
TIFFANY,VASE,GOLD SWIRL DESIGN,IRIDESCENT,SIGNED L.C.T.,
  5 IN...............................................   150.00
TIFFANY,VASE,GOLD TO RED TO BLUE-GREEN,IRIDESCENT,RIBBED
  MIDDLE,8 IN.........................................   215.00
TIFFANY,VASE,GOLD,BLUE HIGHLIGHTS,URN SHAPE,HANDLE,SIGNED,
  3 IN...............................................    95.00
TIFFANY,VASE,GOLD,BLUE SHEEN,14 ROWS OF IRIDESCENT
  THREADING,SIGNED...................................   107.00
TIFFANY,VASE,GOLD,GREEN IVY LEAVES,VINES,BULBOUS,SIGNED
  FAVRILE,11 IN......................................   350.00
TIFFANY,VASE,GOLD,RIBBED,RUFFLED,MARKED L.C.T.,1558B,
  7 1/2 IN.HIGH......................................   375.00
TIFFANY,VASE,GOLDEN BRONZE COLOR,PLATINUM FEATHER DECOR,2 X
  2 IN.HIGH..........................................   495.00
TIFFANY,VASE,GREEN-GLAZED FINISH,PUSSY WILLOW DECOR,
  10 IN.HIGH.........................................   350.00
TIFFANY,VASE,IRIDESCENT BLUE,RIBBED,CURLED HANDLES,SIGNED,
  NUMBERED...........................................   400.00
TIFFANY,VASE,IRIDESCENT GREEN,STRETCHED EDGE,SIGNED,6 IN. X
  7 IN.HIGH..........................................   450.00
TIFFANY,VASE,JACK-IN-THE-PULPIT,FAVRILE,19 IN. HIGH.......   650.00
TIFFANY,VASE,LILY,GOLD IRIDESCENT,RIBBED,SCALLOPED RIM,
  SIGNED,8 1/2 IN....................................   145.00
TIFFANY,VASE,MILLEFIORI,GREEN-WHITE LINING,WAFER PONTIL,
  L.C.T.,3 1/4 IN....................................   375.00
TIFFANY,VASE,OPALESCENT STRIPES,TURQUOISE,WHITE,PETAL
  SCALLOPS,4 1/2 IN..................................   400.00
TIFFANY,VASE,PAPERWEIGHT,FAVRILE GLASS,11 1/2 IN. HIGH......2,500.00
TIFFANY,VASE,PEACOCK BLUE IRIDESCENT,7 1/2 IN.............   160.00
TIFFANY,VASE,PEACOCK EYE FEATHER,BRONZE PETAL BASE,SIGNED,
  11 7/8 IN.HIGH.....................................   250.00
TIFFANY,VASE,RED,FAVRILE,MINIATURE,1 1/4 IN. HIGH....ILLUS..   650.00
```

TIFFANY VASE, 1¼ INCHES HIGH

```
TIFFANY,VASE,RED,FAVRILE,MINIATURE,3 IN. HIGH........ILLUS..1,110.00
TIFFANY,VASE,RIB,SLENDER BASE TAPERING TO HEXAGON TOP,
  SIGNED,7 1/2 IN.............................................  150.00
TIFFANY,VASE,RIBBED PANELS,JUTTED ORNAMENTS,BURNISHED GOLD,
  4 1/2 IN...................................................  298.00
TIFFANY,VASE,RIBBED,SILVERY-GOLD IRIDESCENT,SIGNED L.C.T.,
  Y5660,6 IN.................................................  325.00
TIFFANY,VASE,SILVER-BLUE TO VIOLET BASE,BLACK SPIRAL DECOR,
  4 1/2 IN.HIGH..............................................  200.00
TIFFANY,VASE,SILVER,GOLD IRIDESCENT,WHITE LINING,PINK BAND,
  MOSQUE SHAPE...............................................  145.00
TIFFANY,VASE,STICK,FLOWER,AUTO,PEACOCK BLUE IRIDESCENT,
  FAVRILE,NO HOLDER..........................................   75.00
TIFFANY,VASE,STICK,GOLD IRIDESCENT,SIGNED,12 IN.............   48.50
TIFFANY,VASE,STRIPED GREEN LEAF DECOR,FLOWER FORM,TRIANGULAR
  BODY,9 IN..................................................  395.00
TIFFANY,VASE,TRANSLUCENT MATTE,GOLD & CREAMY OPAQUE,SWIRLS,
  2 1/2 IN...................................................  265.00
TIFFANY,VASE,TRUMPET SHAPE,AURENE,YELLOW,GREEN MARKING,
  BRONZE HOLDER..............................................  250.00
TIFFANY,VASE,TRUMPET,GOLD COLOR,SIGNED,18 IN................  295.00
TIFFANY,VASE,TRUMPET,GOLD,GREEN,ORANGE,FEATHER,BRONZE BASE,
  15 IN.,PAIR................................................  600.00
TIFFANY,VASE,TRUMPET,GOLD,YELLOW,ORANGE,BRONZE HOLDER,
  MARKED,8 1/2 IN............................................  250.00
TIFFANY,VASE,TRUMPET,GREEN VEINS,FEATHER DESIGN,GOLD,GREEN,
  BRONZE HOLDER..............................................  290.00
TIFFANY,VASE,TULIP,RIBBED,GOLD,BLUE HIGHLIGHTS,SIGNED &
  NUMBERED,15 IN.............................................  355.00
TIFFANY,VASE,URN SHAPE,ANTIQUE FINISH,6 1/2 X 6-IN.DIAMETER.   45.00
TIFFANY,VASE,WAVES OF COLORS & FORMS,IRIDESCENT,BULBOUS,
  5 5/8 IN.HIGH..............................................  175.00
TIFFANY,VASE,WHITE IRIDESCENT GROUND,GREEN FEATHER DESIGN,
  8 1/2 IN...................................................  250.00
TIFFANY,VASE,WHITE OPAQUE,GREEN FEATHER & LINE,GOLD
  INTERIOR,4 IN..............................................  300.00
TIFFANY,VASE,WHITE,PLATINUM & GREEN IRIDESCENT DECOR,1 1/2 X
  2 IN.HIGH..................................................  595.00
TIFFANY,VASE,YELLOW,LOOPINGS ON STEM,SIGNED
  V-452-LCT-FAVRILLE,8 3/4 IN................................  195.00
TIFFANY,VASE,ZIPPERED RIBS,GOLD COLOR,SIGNED,NUMBERED,LABEL,
  6 IN.......................................................  315.00
TIFFANY,WATCH,LADY'S,OPEN FACE,REPOUSSE SCENE ON BACK,FLORAL
```

TIFFANY VASE, 3 INCHES HIGH

```
  BORDER,1889................................................  195.00
TIFFANY,WATERCOLOR SUGGESTION FOR BRONZE MEMORIAL,SIGNED
  LOUIS C.TIFFANY............................................  225.00
TIFFANY,WINE,GOLD LUSTER,IRIDESCENT,SIGNED,5 1/2
  IN....................................................75.00 TO  85.00
TIFFANY,WINE,STEMMED,FOOTED,SIGNED..........................   96.00
TILE,DUTCH SCENE,SIGNED ROZENBURG,DEN HAAG,5 IN.SQUARE......   45.00
TILE,LANDSCAPE,BIRDS,TEAK & EBONY FRAME,BRONZE HANDLE,CHINA,
  1670,7.....................................................  225.00
TILE,SCENE,HAND-PAINTED,MAKER AM.ENCAUSTIC TILING CO.,6 IN..    7.50
TILE,TEA,FLORAL DECOR,PORCELAIN,MARKED GERMANY..............    3.50
TILE,TEA,PINK LUSTER BORDER,FLORAL CENTER,MARKED BONN.......   10.00
TIN,BASKET,PICNIC,PAINTED IN BASKET PATTERN,WOODEN HANDLES,
  LID........................................................    8.00
TIN,BATHTUB,BABY'S,OVAL,36 IN.LONG..........................   22.50
TIN,BOWL,EMBOSSED VIOLET DECOR,TWO HANDLES,SWEDEN...........   10.00
TIN,BOX,BISCUIT,HINGED LID,GLASS FRONT,PAT.JULY 18,1882,10 X
  10 X 11 IN.................................................   12.50
TIN,BOX,BISCUIT,SIR WINSTON CHURCHILL,PANELS WITH EVENTS,
  ENGLAND,9 IN...............................................    6.50
TIN,BOX,GLORIA SWANSON COVER................................    5.00
```

TIN,BOX,OPIA CIGAR,REVENUE STAMP,PICTURE OF WOMAN,SQUARE.... 4.00
TIN,BOX,SNUFF,DATED JAN.24,1860............................. 10.00
TIN,BOX,SNUFF,MURRAY SONS & CO.,BELFAST,LONDON,GLASGOW,ONE
    OUNCE.................................................. 4.00
TIN,BOX,SUGAR,HINGED LID,ORIGINAL LABEL,9 1/2 X 14 IN.TALL.. 12.00
TIN,BOX,TIGER CHEWING TOBACCO,TWO HANDLES,LUNCH BUCKET TYPE,
    HINGE COVER........................................... 6.50
TIN,BOX,TOBACCO,POCKET SIZE,TWIN OAKES MIXTURE.............. 3.50
TIN,BUCKET,LUNCH,UNION LEADER CUT PLUG TOBACCO.............. 8.50
TIN,BUGGY WARMER,CHARCOAL DRAWER,TAPESTRY-COVERED........... 8.00
TIN,CABINET,REVOLVING BASE,WEST ELECTRIC HAIR CURLER CO.,
    PHILA.,1921........................................... 28.00
TIN,CAN,KEROSENE,WITH SPOUT................................. 2.50
TIN,CAN,TOBACCO,PATTERSON SEAL CUT PLUG.................... 4.50
TIN,CANDLEHOLDER,PUSH-UP,RING HANDLE,SAUCER................ 7.50
TIN,CANNISTER,UNION LEADER SMOKING TOBACCO,RED............. 5.00
TIN,CHANDELIER,THREE CANDLE,SOCKET......................... 150.00
TIN,COFFEEPOT,BACK & SIDE HANDLES,3 QT..................... 13.00
TIN,COFFEEPOT,GOOSENECK.................................... 55.00
TIN,COFFEEPOT,ORNATE PEWTER HANDLE,FINIAL,SPOUT COVER,COPPER
    BOTTOM................................................ 25.00
TIN,COMB CASE,MATCH COMPARTMENT,COMB COMPARTMENT,MIRROR..... 7.00
TIN,COMB CASE,WALL,EAGLE & SHIELD DESIGN ON BACK PLATE...... 3.95
TIN,COMB CASE,WALL,TRAY FOR COMBS,MATCH CONTAINER,MIRROR.... 5.00
TIN,COMB CASE,WHISK BROOM COMPARTMENT,MIRROR,MATCHES........ 5.00
TIN,CONTAINER,COOKIE,GINGERBREAD HOUSE SHAPE,MOVABLE HANSEL,
    GRETEL,WITCH.......................................... 95.00
TIN,CUP,ADVERTISING INDIANAPOLIS SPEEDWAY,1914.............. 6.00
TIN,CUSPIDOR,RING HANDLE,5-IN.DIAMETER..................... 10.00
TIN,DISPENSER,MATCH BOOK,MECHANICAL,SAYS DIAMOND MATCH BOOK,
    2 FOR 1 CENT.......................................... 15.00
TIN,DUTCH OVEN,FIREPLACE,ROTATING SPIT..................... 50.00
TIN,EASTER EGG,COLORED TRANSFERS OF PETER RABBIT FAMILY,
    TWO-PIECE,5 IN........................................ 13.50
TIN,EGG BOILER,C.1860..............................ILLUS.. 15.00

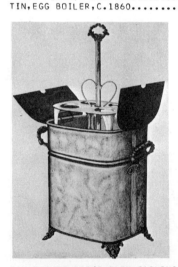

TIN EGG BOILER

TIN,FIGURE,EAGLE,FROM SAILING VESSEL,28 IN.HIGH,
    59 IN.WINGSPAN........................................ 350.00
TIN,FIGURINE,HORSE,20 IN.LONG,20 IN.HIGH,AMERICAN.......... 150.00
TIN,FOOT WARMER,PIERCED,HEART-DESIGNED WOODEN FRAME,TURNED
    CORNER POSTS.......................................... 18.00
TIN,FOOT WARMER,PIERCED,WOOD FRAME,TURNED POSTS............ 16.00
TIN,FOOT WARMER,SQUARE BOX,PERFORATED,CHARCOAL BURNER,USED
    IN BUGGY.............................................. 18.00
TIN,FOOT WARMER,WOODEN POSTS,CHARCOAL PAN,PIERCED HEART
    DECOR................................................. 32.50
TIN,GRATER,NUTMEG.......................................... 4.00
TIN,HOLDER,MATCH,THREE CONTAINERS,5 3/4 IN.ROUND........... 5.00
TIN,HORN,BICYCLE,CRANK-OPERATED,PAT.1905,SEISS MFG.CO.,
    TOLEDO,TIN,BLACK...................................... 5.00
TIN,LADLE,14 IN.LONG....................................... 2.00
TIN,LANTERN,CANDLE,PIERCED,PAUL REVERE TYPE,GEOMETRIC DESIGN 85.00
TIN,LANTERN,SKATERS........................................ 8.50
TIN,LUCKY STRIKE PLUG,GREEN,8 OUNCES....................... 7.50
TIN,MATCH HOLDER,COMPARTMENTS FOR MIRROR,COMBS,MATCHES...... 7.00
TIN,MATCH HOLDER,GREEN,COVER,SAYS MATCHES.................. 4.00

```
TIN,MATCH HOLDER,MIRROR,WHISK BROOM COMPARTMENT.............    5.00
TIN,MATCH HOLDER,TWO COMPARTMENTS,MIRROR,5 IN.HIGH..........    5.00
TIN,MATCH SAFE,WALL,COVER,SAYS MATCHES.....................    4.00
TIN,MEASURE,ONE QUART......................................    3.50
TIN,MOLD,CANDLE,2 TUBES,CRIMPED TOP,APPLIED HANDLE,
   10 IN.LONG..............................................   32.00
TIN,MOLD,CANDLE,2 TUBES,NO-BASE TYPE.......................   30.00
TIN,MOLD,CANDLE,4 TUBES,HANDLE.............................   20.00
TIN,MOLD,CANDLE,6 TUBES....................................   22.50
TIN,MOLD,CANDLE,6 TUBES,FOOTED.............................   75.00
TIN,MOLD,CANDLE,6 TUBES,STRAP HANDLE.......................   25.00
TIN,MOLD,CANDLE,8 TUBES...........................16.50 TO   30.00
TIN,MOLD,CANDLE,8 TUBES,HANGING............................   25.00
TIN,MOLD,CANDLE,12 TUBES...................................   35.00
TIN,MOLD,CANDLE,12 TUBES,FOUR IN LINE......................   42.50
TIN,MOLD,CANDLE,24 TUBES,6 IN LINE.........................   67.50
TIN,MOLD,CANDLE,32 TUBES,2 HANDLES.........................   65.00
TIN,MOLD,CANDLE,91 TUBES,WOODEN FRAME,22 1/2 IN.HIGH,
   25 1/2 IN.LONG..........................................  265.00
TIN,MOLD,CANDLE,BENCH,6 TUBES..............................  145.00
TIN,MOLD,CANDLE,HANGING,8 TUBES............................   25.00
TIN,MOLD,CANDLE,SIDE HANDLE,FLUTED LIP,SINGLE,18 IN.LONG....   25.00
TIN,MOLD,CANDY,DEVIL,8 IN. X 3 1/2 IN......................   10.00
TIN,MOLD,CANDY,KNIFE,8 IN. X 3 1/2 IN......................   10.00
TIN,MOLD,CANDY,SANTA CLAUS,8 IN. X 3 1/2 IN................   10.00
TIN,MOLD,COPPER BOTTOM,SHEAF OF WHEAT......................   14.00
TIN,MOLD,HEART.......................................ILLUS..   15.00
```

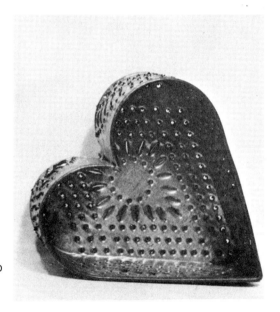

HEART MOLD

```
TIN,MOLD,MAN IN THE MOON,OVAL,4 X 3 IN.....................    7.50
TIN,MOLD,PUDDING,MELON SHAPE,BALL,FRICTION LID,2
   QUARTS..........................................12.00 TO   12.50
TIN,MOLD,PUDDING,MELON SHAPE,FLUTED,COVER,HANDLED,
   8 1/4 IN.LONG...........................................   10.00
TIN,MOLD,PUMPKIN,4 X 3 1/2 IN..............................    6.50
TIN,MOLD,ROOSTER,8 IN. HIGH..........................ILLUS..   22.50
TIN,MOLD,STAR,9 X 2 1/2 IN.................................    4.75
TIN,MUG,RAILROAD,MARKED WRECK CAR..........................   14.00
TIN,PAIL,BERRY,COVER.......................................    4.00
TIN,PAN,ANGEL FOOD,SWANSDOWN,DATED 1923....................    3.50
TIN,PAN,MILK,MADE IN FIVE SECTIONS,15 IN...................    7.50
TIN,PITCHER,VINEGAR,HANDMADE,CURVED SPOUT,GREECE,
   9 1/2 IN.TALL...........................................   12.00
TIN,PLATE,ADVERTISING,FALSTAFF,9 1/2 IN....................   10.00
TIN,PLATE,ARBOUR,BARRETT WARE,ENGLAND,10 IN................    8.50
TIN,PLATE,COTTAGE,BARRETT WARE,ENGLAND,10 IN...............    8.50
TIN,PLATE,GRECIAN SCENE,GREEN BORDER,MARKED H.D.BEACH CO.,
   COSHOCTON,OHIO..........................................    8.00
TIN,PLATE,GRECIAN SCENE,RED BORDER,MARKED VIENNA ART PLATES.   8.00
```

ROOSTER TIN MOLD

TIN,PLATE,LOVE LETTER,BARRETT WARE,ENGLAND,10 IN.............     8.50
TIN,PLATE,PORTRAIT,LADY,PROFILE,RED & GOLD SKULLCAP,GOLD
    SHOULDER DROP.........................................    18.00
TIN,PLATE,PORTRAIT,MINIATURE HAND-PAINTED SCENE ON BACK,
    1907.................................................    24.00
TIN,PLATE,PRIMROSE & VIOLETS,BARRETT WARE,ENGLAND...........     3.50
TIN,PLATE,ROSES,BARRETT WARE,ENGLAND.......................     3.50
TIN,PLATE,THE LOVE LETTER,BARRETT WARE,ENGLAND.............      8.50
TIN,RED PASTIME PLUG TOBACCO...............................    28.00
TIN,SCONCE,CANDLE,WALL,TOOLED FLOWER BORDER,ROLLED EDGES,
    15 IN.HIGH...........................................    60.00
TIN,SCONCE,FLUTED TOP,WITH TALLOW CANDLE,PAIR..............   125.00
TIN,STAND,CHRISTMAS TREE,CONE SHAPE,PAINT,GOLD STENCIL,
    PATENT NOV.5,1915....................................     6.50
TIN,STRAINER,SCREEN,DAIRY SIZE.............................     7.50
TIN,SYRUP,HINGED COVER.....................................     3.95
TIN,TALLOW DIPPER FOR CANDLEMAKING,24 IN...................    18.00
TIN,TRAY,ADVERTISING,EAST SIDE BEER.......................     10.00
TIN,TRAY,BALLARD'S OBELISK,LOUISVILLE,EGYPTIAN SCENE,4 IN...     4.50
TIN,TRAY,CANDLE,CANDLESNUFFER SCISSORS.....................    25.00
TIN,TRAY,DOG,SIGNED,12 IN. X 17 IN.........................     7.00
TIN,TRAY,HAND-PAINTED FLORAL,OVAL,SIGNED,17 X 14 IN........    10.00
TIN,TRAY,HEPTOL SPLITS THE ONLY PERFECT LAXATIVE,COWBOY,
    HORSE,1904...........................................     8.00
TIN,TRAY,LADY IN PUFFED BLUE FROCK,16 1/2 X 14 IN..........    16.00
TIN,TRAY,WOMAN IN WHITE MANTILLA,16 1/2 X 14 IN............    13.00
TIN,WALL SAFE,BLADE CONTAINER,RAZOR CONTAINER, GEM, ,
    2 1/4 IN.HIGH........................................     2.00


        TOBY JUGS HAVE BEEN MADE SINCE THE SEVENTEENTH CENTURY.
TOBY,CREAMER,BLUE & WHITE DELFT TYPE PORCELAIN,FULL FIGURE..    20.00
TOBY,DUTCH MAN,WOMAN,SIGNED,HOLLAND,DELFT,CIRCA 1869,PAIR...   150.00
TOBY,JUG,GEORGE WASHINGTON'S HEAD,MARKED PAT.1892,9 IN......    65.00
TOBY,JUG,OLD GENTLEMAN,GAUDY-COLORED,SEATED,HOLDS JUG,1850,
    STAFFORDSHIRE........................................    80.00
TOBY,JUG,ONE HAPPY FACE,ONE SAD FACE,MARKED SARREGUEMINES,
    8 1/2 IN.............................................    65.00
TOBY,MAN,SITTING,HOLDS JUG & PIPE,10 IN....................   150.00
TOBY,MUG,ADMIRAL PERRY,PORCELAIN,GESCHUTZT,5 IN.HIGH........    32.00
TOBY,MUG,MADE IN OCCUPIED JAPAN,5 IN.HIGH..................     6.00
TOBY,PITCHER,FULL FIGURE,GERMANY,7 IN......................    35.00
TOBY,PITCHER,SCOT IN COLORFUL COSTUME,PORCELAIN,6 IN.TALL...    21.00
TOBY,SCROOGE,WEARING NIGHTCAP,BESWICK,ENGLAND,7 IN.HIGH.....    18.00
TOLE,BANK,BUILDING FORM,SPIRED ROOF,GRAY-BLUE PAINT,STILL,
    4 1/2 IN.TALL........................................     9.00
TOLE,BOX,ADVERTISING,PANELS,DEPICTS LORD NELSON'S BATTLES,
    7 1/2 IN.............................................    25.00
TOLE,BOX,BLACK.....................................ILLUS..     35.00
TOLE,BOX,DOCUMENT,BLACK,GOLD LINES.........................     7.00
TOLE,BOX,FLOWERS,LEAVES,HINGED & DOMED LID,4 IN. X 3 IN.....    11.00
TOLE,BOX,MATCH,DOMED LID,PIERCED,8 IN......................    12.50
TOLE,BOX,ROUNDED TOP,OVAL BRASS ON TOP,PENNSYLVANIA DUTCH,
    4 1/2 X 9 IN.........................................    35.00
TOLE,BOX,STENCIL  BREAD,  HINGED LID,HANDLES...............    12.00
TOLE,BOX,TEA,FLOWERS,BUTTERFLIES,SQUARE,HINGED LID,ENGLAND..     5.00
TOLE,CADDY,TEA,LITHOGRAPHED PORTRAITS,MUSICAL INSTRUMENTS,
    10 1/2 X 8 IN........................................    22.00

BLACK TOLE BOX

```
TOLE,CANDLESTICK,SAUCER BASE,RING HANDLE,BLACK,PAIR........        6.00
TOLE,CHAMBER STICK,DEEP SAUCER,RED,FLUTED CUP,IRONSTONE
  INSERT,6 IN.........................................            20.00
TOLE,LAMP,BRACKET,REFLECTOR,CHIMNEY.........................      16.00
TOLE,LANTERN,HAND,PANELS,IRON CHANDELIER,SPANISH,23 IN.,
  CHESTNUT ROASTER.......................................         40.00
TOLE,LANTERN,PROCESSIONAL,GILT FRAME,LEAFAGE,CROSS,ON STAFF,
  98 IN.,PAIR...........................................          75.00
TOLE,MOLD,CANDLE,12 TUBE,FLAT STRAP HANDLE,11 IN.TALL.......       35.00
TOLE,PIPE,BUBBLE,HANDMADE.................................         3.00
TOLE,PITCHER,WOODLIKE DECOR,CROOKNECK SPOUT,YELLOW BANDING,
  COVER,11 IN..........................................           28.00
TOLE,PLATE,FOLDED EDGE,RING DECOR ON EDGE,AMERICAN,CIRCA
  1830,9 IN............................................            9.00
TOLE,PLATE,PAINTING,STILL LIFE,PINK & RED ROSES IN VASE,
  10 IN................................................            7.00
TOLE,SUGAR,DECOR,COVER,CIRCA 1860.........................        95.00
TOLE,SYRUP,DECOR,CIRCA 1860...............................        75.00
TOLE,TEAPOT,CHILD'S,WASH BOILER,TEAKETTLE,COVERED POT.......       20.00
TOLE,TRAY,BLUE GROUND,GILT LEAVES,FLORAL,STAND,BAMBOO LEGS,
  18 IN.HIGH...........................................          230.00
TOLE,TRAY,BREAD,DECOR,CIRCA 1860..........................        55.00
TOLE,TRAY,CRUMB,BLACK,WHITE LILIES OF THE VALLEY,BRUSH......        7.00
TOLE,TRAY,FREE-HAND DECOR,YELLOW,ORANGE,IRIDESCENT BRONZE,
  13 3/4 IN.LONG.......................................           22.00
TOLE,TRAY,MOUNTAIN LANDSCAPE,YELLOW GROUND,EVERTED RIM,
  HANDGRIPS,28 IN......................................           50.00
TOLE,TRAY,OPEN HANDLES,STENCIL MAN,WOMAN,COLONIAL-TYPE
  DRESS,TIN,26 IN......................................           65.00
TOLE,TRAY,RED,PINK,WHITE ROSES,B.F.EARLES,MORLEY,MISSOURI...        7.50
TOLE,TRAY,ROSES,MORNING GLORIES,HAND-PAINTED,OPEN HANDLES,
  20 X 28 IN...........................................           39.50
TOLE,TRAY,SWEETMEAT,MOTHER-OF-PEARL DECOR,HANDLES...........       15.00
  TOOL,SEE ALSO,KITCHEN,STORE,WOODEN,IRON,TIN
TOOL,ADZE,CARPENTER'S,CURVED HANDLE,28 1/2 IN...............       12.00
TOOL,ANVIL,JEWELER'S,BRONZE,3 1/2 IN......................         4.00
TOOL,AUGER,PATENT QUICK CHANGE CROSS HANDLE,MARKED P.S.&
  W.CO.,1884...........................................            6.50
TOOL,BIT,TAPER SHANK CENTER,GIMLETS,COUNTERSINKS,
  SCREWDRIVERS,LOT OF 18...............................            4.00
TOOL,BRACE,CARPENTER'S,EMBOSSED WITH EAGLE,MARKED SUPERIOR,
  BRASS................................................           14.00
TOOL,DRILL,ALFALFA.......................................         35.00
TOOL,FOR LOADING AND MEASURING POWDER IN SHOTGUN............        4.50
TOOL,GAUGE,DOUBLE MARKING,WOODEN,PATENT 1873,BRASSBOUND.....        4.50
TOOL,KNIFE,DRAW,HAND-FORGED,21 IN.........................         4.00
TOOL,MALLET,KEYSTONE SHAPE WOODEN HEAD....................         3.50
TOOL,MOLDING PLANE,WOODEN.................................         2.50
TOOL,PLANE...........................................ILLUS.        8.00
TOOL,PLANE,COOPER........................................         25.00
TOOL,PLANE,PLOW,CARVED-OUT SAW HANDLE,FENCE ON WOODEN
  SCREWS,BEECHWOOD......................................          16.50
TOOL,PLANE,PLOW,HANDLE,ADJUSTED WOOD NUTS ON THREADED ROD,
  WOODEN...............................................           10.00
TOOL,SAW WREST,HAND-FORGED, 10 IN. LONG...................         4.00
TOOL,SAW WREST,HAND-FORGED,DOUBLE END,8 IN................         4.50
TOOL,SAW WREST,HAND-FORGED,RING ON END,9 1/2 IN.LONG.......        4.50
TOOL,SAW WREST,HAND-FORGED,7 1/2 IN.LONG..................         3.50
TOOL,SHEARS,WOOL,HAND,DISSTON............................          2.50
TOOL,SHIP AUGER BIT,1/2 IN.-7/8 IN., 28 IN. LONG,SET OF 4...        6.00
TOOL,SLICK CHISEL,CARPENTER'S,ROUND END HICKORY HANDLE,MAKER
  DOUGLAS CO...........................................           12.50
TOOL,SPOKE SHAVE,COOPER..................................          8.00
TOOL,SPOKE SHAVE,WOODEN,WITH BRASS THROAT.................         3.50
```

PLANE

TOOTHPICK HOLDERS ARE SOMETIMES CALLED TOOTHPICKS BY
COLLECTORS. THE VARIOUSLY SHAPED CONTAINERS MADE TO
HOLD THE SMALL WOODEN TOOTHPICKS ARE MADE OF GLASS,
CHINA, OR METAL. MOST OF THE TOOTHPICKS ARE VICTORIAN.
TOOTHPICK, SEE ALSO, OTHER CATEGORIES SUCH AS BISQUE, SLAG,
ETC.

| | |
|---|---:|
| TOOTHPICK, 1000-EYE, CLEAR | 10.00 |
| TOOTHPICK, AIREDALE DOG, CUPS ATTACHED | 9.00 |
| TOOTHPICK, ALLIGATOR, GREEN | 12.50 |
| TOOTHPICK, ALLOVER HOBNAIL | 3.50 |
| TOOTHPICK, ANTHRACITE, POLISHED RIM AT TOP & BASE, CARVED MIDDLE, 2 IN. HIGH | 6.00 |
| TOOTHPICK, BABY CHICK & EGG, NESTING ON MAPLE LEAF | 10.50 |
| TOOTHPICK, BABY'S BOOTIE, FROSTED | 13.50 |
| TOOTHPICK, BALL BASE, FAN TOP, COBALT BLUE | 10.50 |
| TOOTHPICK, BARREL, CHARLIE CHAPLIN AT SIDE, CLEAR | 20.00 |
| TOOTHPICK, BARREL, HANDLE, STIPPLED, CLEAR | 6.50 |
| TOOTHPICK, BASE TAPERS TO RED TOP, ALLOVER CUT IN THUMBPRINT, MEDALLIONS | 9.50 |
| TOOTHPICK, BASKET, ANVIL SHAPE, TWO HANDLES, CLEAR, PURPLE | 10.00 |
| TOOTHPICK, BLOCK PATTERN, CLEAR | 6.00 |
| TOOTHPICK, BLUE PAINTED DAISIES, FLAMELIKE EMBOSSED BASE, CLEAR | 5.00 |
| TOOTHPICK, BLUE, INTAGLIO, FOOTED | 4.00 |
| TOOTHPICK, BOOT, STAR ON HEEL, GREEN | 7.60 |
| TOOTHPICK, BOTTOM IS CUT IN FACETS, BULBOUS, SCALLOPED | 12.50 |
| TOOTHPICK, BOY & DOG ON PEDESTAL, PINK, BLUE, BISQUE | 9.50 |
| TOOTHPICK, BOY AGAINST BASKET, CHICKS ON BASE, MARKED GERMANY, PARIAN | 20.00 |
| TOOTHPICK, BUCKET SHAPE, BAIL, GRACE & HOWARD, 1924, FLARED, RUBY GLASS | 8.50 |
| TOOTHPICK, BULLDOG & TOP HAT ON FOOTED BASE, AMBER | 28.00 |
| TOOTHPICK, CAMPHOR GLASS | 5.00 |
| TOOTHPICK, CANNONBALL, ATLAS | 7.00 |
| TOOTHPICK, CANOE, LIGHT BLUE | 6.50 |
| TOOTHPICK, CARNIVAL GLASS, BLUE, FOUR KITTENS | 55.00 |
| TOOTHPICK, CARNIVAL GLASS, BLUE, ICE, HOLLY PATTERN | 5.00 |
| TOOTHPICK, CARNIVAL GLASS, BLUE TO PINK, PASTEL, HAT SHAPE, BRIM TOP | 33.00 |
| TOOTHPICK, CARNIVAL GLASS, FIVE FLUTES, RAT, CAT, MARIGOLD | 48.50 |
| TOOTHPICK, CARNIVAL GLASS, FLUTE, GREEN | 55.00 |
| TOOTHPICK, CARNIVAL GLASS, MARIGOLD, FLUTE PATTERN.... 25.00 TO | 50.00 |
| TOOTHPICK, CARNIVAL GLASS, MARIGOLD, KITTENS | 65.00 |
| TOOTHPICK, CARNIVAL GLASS, MARIGOLD, PANELED | 40.00 |
| TOOTHPICK, CARNIVAL GLASS, ORANGE, PANELED | 40.00 |
| TOOTHPICK, CARNIVAL GLASS, PURPLE, FLUTE................ 65.00 TO | 95.00 |
| TOOTHPICK, CARNIVAL GLASS, PURPLE, TWIG | 79.00 |

TOOTHPICK,CAT STANDING IN FRONT OF A SACK,WHITE PORCELAIN,
  2 3/4 IN.TALL................................................. 7.50
TOOTHPICK,CHICK,EGG,GILLINDER & SONS CENTENNIAL EXHIBITION,
  CAMPHOR GLASS.............................................. 20.00
TOOTHPICK,CHICKEN ON WISHBONE,SAYS JUST PICKED OUT,BARBOUR
  SILVER CO.................................................. 15.00
TOOTHPICK,CLEAR GLASS,IN METAL STAND........................... 10.50
TOOTHPICK,COBALT BLUE WITH SILVER OVERLAY DESIGN.............. 3.00
TOOTHPICK,COBALT,SILVER TRIM.................................. 5.00
TOOTHPICK,COLORADO,GREEN,FOOTED,DATED 1909.................... 15.00
TOOTHPICK,COLORADO,SOUVENIR................................... 12.50
TOOTHPICK,CONE SHAPE,ROUND PEDESTAL,EMBOSSED DESIGN ON TOP &
  BASE,PAIR.................................................. 7.50
TOOTHPICK,CORSET,SAPPHIRE BLUE................................ 85.00
TOOTHPICK,CROSSBAR,OPAL,BLUE,BEATTY................ 28.00 TO 45.00
TOOTHPICK,CUT GLASS,EGG-SHAPED,STANDARD,4 1/4 IN.HIGH......... 55.00
TOOTHPICK,DAISY & BUTTON WITH ORNAMENT,PRESSED GLASS.......... 12.00
TOOTHPICK,DAISY & BUTTON,FUCHSIA,FOOTED...................... 115.00
TOOTHPICK,DE LAVAL SEPARATOR,2 SECTIONS,TIN.................. 5.50
TOOTHPICK,DOG WITH HAT,CANARY COLOR.......................... 32.00
TOOTHPICK,DOUBLE FACE,MONK,BRONZE............................ 19.00
TOOTHPICK,EMERALD GREEN,SILVER OVERLAY,...................... 3.50
TOOTHPICK,ENAMELED FLORAL,WHITE GROUND,SATIN GLASS,
  MT.WASHINGTON.............................................. 45.00
TOOTHPICK,ETCHED SARATOGA,1896,RUBY,FLASHED.................. 10.00
TOOTHPICK,FIGURAL,FACE,EMBOSSINGS,TWO HANDLES FORM EARS..... 10.00
TOOTHPICK,FLASHED RUBY,CLEAR BUTTON ARCH BASE............... 12.50
TOOTHPICK,FLORAL BAND,PEDESTAL BASE,PORCELAIN............... 3.00
TOOTHPICK,FRANCISWARE....................................... 40.00
TOOTHPICK,FROG HOLDING TULIP BLOSSOM,CLEAR.................. 12.50
TOOTHPICK,FROSTED MEDALLION................................. 5.00
TOOTHPICK,GOOSEBERRY DECOR,GOLD TRIM,HAND-PAINTED,SIGNED,
  HANDLES.................................................... 18.00
TOOTHPICK,GREEN PATTERN,THREE SMALL HANDLES................. 35.00
TOOTHPICK,GREEN,BULBOUS,SCALLOPED TOP....................... 10.00
TOOTHPICK,GREEN,GOLD,COLORADO............................... 15.00
TOOTHPICK,GREEN,RED,GOLD,SPRIG,CUSTARD GLASS,MARKED
  NORTHWOOD.................................................. 80.00
TOOTHPICK,HAND HOLDING A BUD VASE,FLASHED RED,IRIDESCENT,
  4 IN...................................................... 13.00
TOOTHPICK,HAT-SHAPED,DEEP PINK CASED IN OPAL,POLISHED PONTIL 40.00
TOOTHPICK,HAT,BLUE THREADS.................................. 15.00
TOOTHPICK,HAT,HORSE & RIDER SCENE,SAYS ROAD RIDING,PORCELAIN
  DE PARIS.................................................. 8.00
TOOTHPICK,HAT,YELLOW,WAFFLE................................. 15.00
TOOTHPICK,HERON IN RUSHES,CLEAR............................. 15.00
TOOTHPICK,HOBNAIL,OPAL,FOOTED............................... 12.00
TOOTHPICK,HOBNAIL,YELLOW.................................... 11.00
TOOTHPICK,HORIZONTAL,SIGNED KRISTOL PATENT FEBRUARY 5,1907.. 10.00
TOOTHPICK,HORSE & CART,CLEAR................................ 4.50
TOOTHPICK,HORSE AND BARREL CART,CLEAR....................... 15.00
TOOTHPICK,JEWEL WITH DEWDROP................................ 8.00
TOOTHPICK,JUST OUT,CHICK & EGG.............................. 16.00
TOOTHPICK,KETTLE,WITCH'S,CANE PATTERN,CLEAR,WIRE BAIL....... 10.00
TOOTHPICK,KITTEN STANDING ON HIND LEGS,SIGNED JAMES W.TUFTS,
  BOSTON.................................................... 18.50
TOOTHPICK,LACY MEDALLION,GREEN,GOLD......................... 17.50
TOOTHPICK,LAPIDARY CUT,CUT GLASS............................ 12.00
TOOTHPICK,LOBSTER IN FRONT,SOUVENIR BROCKTON FAIR,WHITE
  PORCELAIN................................................. 6.00
TOOTHPICK,MADE LIKE DICE,PLAYING CARD FIGURES,MILK GLASS.... 29.00
TOOTHPICK,MELON RIB,FLORAL DECOR,BEADED TOP................. 45.00
TOOTHPICK,MILK RUFFLED EDGE,VASELINE GLASS.................. 15.00
TOOTHPICK,MONKEY AND STUMP,CLEAR............................ 16.50
TOOTHPICK,MONKEY WITH LANTERN,SILVER PLATE.................. 15.00
TOOTHPICK,MOON & STAR,CLEAR................................. 5.00
TOOTHPICK,MOSS ROSE ON APPLIED AQUA GROUND,OPALWARE......... 22.00
TOOTHPICK,MT.WASHINGTON,ROUND,BLUE,AUTUMN-COLORED LEAVES.... 35.00
TOOTHPICK,OLD ORCHARD,RED & CLEAR........................... 7.00
TOOTHPICK,OPALESCENT RIM,VASELINE GLASS..................... 13.50
TOOTHPICK,OPALESCENT,BLUE................................... 18.50
TOOTHPICK,OVAL,3 GOLD FEET,WHEAT DESIGN IN GOLD............. 3.00
TOOTHPICK,PAINTED MARSH SCENE,CRANE,CATTAILS,MILK GLASS..... 12.50
TOOTHPICK,PANELED,FLEUR-DE-LIS,SCALLOPED TOP,PURPLE......... 20.00
TOOTHPICK,PANELS,CLEAR,STAR BOTTOM,FOOTED................... 6.00
TOOTHPICK,PICKET PATTERN,CLEAR,3 IN......................... 6.50
TOOTHPICK,PINEAPPLE & FAN................................... 6.00
TOOTHPICK,PINK & GOLD FLOWERS,THREE GOLD HANDLES,MARKED
  VIENNA,AUSTRIA............................................ 10.00
TOOTHPICK,PINK & WHITE,GOLD OPENWORK,PORCELAIN.............. 6.50

TOOTHPICK,PINK CASE GLASS,QUILTED............................. 15.00
TOOTHPICK,PINK PIG SITS BESIDE GREEN STRAWLIKE BASKET,
  PORCELAIN...................................................  8.00
TOOTHPICK,PONY & TWO-WHEELED CART,CLEAR......................  7.50
TOOTHPICK,PORCELAIN,HAND-PAINTED.............................  5.50
TOOTHPICK,PORTLAND AND HOBNAIL PATTERN,PRESSED GLASS.........  6.75
TOOTHPICK,RED BLOCK......................................... 26.00
TOOTHPICK,RED DEVIL STANDS IN BACK OF GREEN HAT,PORCELAIN...  8.50
TOOTHPICK,RED,GRAY,POTTERY,SIGNED H. HANNELL................  4.50
TOOTHPICK,RIBBED OPAL....................................... 18.50
TOOTHPICK,RIBBED,BLUE OPAL.................................. 15.00
TOOTHPICK,ROADSTER,BLUE.................................... 17.00
TOOTHPICK,ROW OF FLOWERS AROUND TOP,THREE GOLD-COLORED FEET,
  GREEN......................................................  6.00
TOOTHPICK,RUBY & CLEAR,PATTERN............................. 15.00
TOOTHPICK,RUBY TOP,CLEAR PATTERN BASE,HAGGETT BROS.,
  WISCASSET,ME...............................................  7.50
TOOTHPICK,SADDLE ON BARREL,BLUE............................ 32.00
TOOTHPICK,SADDLE,SAPPHIRE BLUE............................. 45.00
TOOTHPICK,SCATTER BALL CANNON,PRESSED GLASS................ 11.25
TOOTHPICK,SCROLL,CANE BAND,GOLD............................  9.50
TOOTHPICK,SEWING THIMBLE ON LEAF,RESILVERED................ 16.00
TOOTHPICK,SHELL & SEAWEED,GREEN,OPAQUE..................... 37.00
TOOTHPICK,SHELL & WREATH,SCALLOPED RIM,CLEAR BOTTOM,WHITE
  TOP,2 1/2 IN............................................... 18.00
TOOTHPICK,SOUVENIR,OMAHA EXPOSITION,1898,RED & CLEAR GLASS.. 16.50
TOOTHPICK,SOUVENIR,RED & CLEAR,1910........................  8.50
TOOTHPICK,STANDING BEAR EATING HONEY,TWO HONEY POTS......... 12.50
TOOTHPICK,STANDING CHERUB BESIDE BASKET,BRONZE COLOR,WHITE
  METAL......................................................  7.50
TOOTHPICK,STRAIGHT PANELS,CLEAR............................ 28.50
TOOTHPICK,SUNFLOWERS,GOLD,CLEAR............................  9.50
TOOTHPICK,SWIRL & DOT......................................  4.00
TOOTHPICK,THIN-RIBBED,ENAMELED DAISIES,PINK,GREEN,YELLOW,
  SATIN GLASS................................................ 55.00
TOOTHPICK,THREE BROWN MONKEYS ATTACHED TO HOLDER............  6.00
TOOTHPICK,THREE DOLPHINS,CLEAR GLASS....................... 18.50
TOOTHPICK,THUMBPRINT RUBY BAND AT SCALLOPED TOP,CLEAR...... 10.00
TOOTHPICK,TOP HAT,BLUE CANE PATTERN........................ 15.00
TOOTHPICK,TWO MEDALLIONS,FIGURES,FLORAL BETWEEN,BLUE,GOLD,
  PORCELAIN.................................................. 10.00
TOOTHPICK,U.S.BATTLESHIP MAINE,DESTROYED 1898,PEWTER........ 10.25
TOOTHPICK,UMBRELLA LEAF PATTERN,CRANBERRY.................. 37.50
TOOTHPICK,URN SHAPE,CLEAR..................................  3.50
TOOTHPICK,VIOLETS,HAND-PAINTED,PORCELAIN...................  6.50
TOOTHPICK,WHITE CAMEO CUT & CLEAR GLASS,COVER.............. 25.00
TOOTHPICK,WHITE DOG,BLACK & WHITE CAT ON SIDE,PORCELAIN.....  9.50
TOOTHPICK,WHITE FLOWERS,HAND-PAINTED,PANELS,GOLD & FLUTED
  TOP........................................................  3.50
TOOTHPICK,WHITE GROUND,PINK ROSES,MARKED GERMANY,PORCELAIN..  8.00
TOOTHPICK,WHITE,BLUE MORNING-GLORY,PANEL,GOLD RIM,FOOTED,
  PORCELAIN..................................................  6.00
TOOTHPICK,WHITE,EMBOSSED PANSY DESIGN,GOLD OUTLINE,PORCELAIN  8.00
TOOTHPICK,WHITE,FLARED BASE,STAFFORDSHIRE,2 3/4 IN.TALL.....  5.00
TOOTHPICK,WHITE,PINK LINING,GOLD-MOLDED SCALLOPED EDGE,
  PORCELAIN..................................................  3.25
TOOTHPICK,WOODSMAN WITH AXE AT TREE STUMP,METAL............ 12.00
TORTOISE,BOTTLE,SNUFF,CORAL STOPPER....................... 375.00
TORTOISE,CASKET,ORMOLU-MOUNTED,19TH CENTURY............... 375.00
TORTOISE,COMB,FLORAL BORDER,SEVEN ROWS OF COLORED STONES,
  SPANISH.................................................... 18.00
TORTOISE,COMB,SPANISH,FOR DOLL.............................  3.50
TORTOISE,COMB,TWO ROWS OF TURQUOISE STONES,PAIR............ 35.00
TORTOISE,DRESSER SET,BUTTONHOOK,COMB,BRUSH,MIRROR,12 PIECES. 50.00
TORTOISE,HAIRPIN...........................................  4.00


        TORTOISESHELL GLASS WAS MADE DURING THE 1880S AND AFTER
        BY THE SANDWICH GLASS WORKS OF MASSACHUSETTS AND SOME
        FIRMS IN GERMANY. TORTOISESHELL HAS BEEN REPRODUCED.
TORTOISESHELL GLASS,BOWL,ROSE,4 3/4 IN.TALL................ 75.00
TORTOISESHELL GLASS,COMPOTE,AMBER FEET................ILLUS.. 65.00
TORTOISESHELL GLASS,MELON RIB,ELONGATED BODY,FOOTED,FLINT,
  SANDWICH GLASS............................................. 195.00
TORTOISESHELL GLASS,TUMBLER................................ 48.00
TORTOISESHELL GLASS,TUMBLER,MUTTON FAT..................... 58.00
TOTEM POLE,CEDAR,CARVED,OUTSTRETCHED THUNDERBIRD,6 FT.,PAIR. 750.00
TOTEM POLE,THUNDERBIRD,WHITE,ORANGE,BLACK,5 1/2 X 6 FEET
  HIGH,PAIR.................................................. 795.00
TOURNAY,SAUCEBOAT & STAND,18TH CENTURY,4 PIECES,

TORTOISE SHELL GLASS COMPOTE,
AMBER FEET

```
9 3/4 IN.LONG.............................................    30.00
TOY,SEE ALSO,DOLL,TIN,WOODEN,CARD,MARBLES,MACHINES
TOY,ACROBAT,WIND,TIN......................................     4.50
TOY,AIRPLANE,DARNIER,MARKED HUBLEY,RED WING,ENGINES,NO.DO-X,
  IRON....................................................    28.00
TOY,AIRPLANE,LINDBERGH TYPE,SILVER PAINT,TOOTSIE TOY,
  3 1/2 IN................................................     4.50
TOY,AIRPLANE,MICKEY MOUSE IN COCKPIT,WHEELS,HARD RUBBER,
  5 IN.LONG...............................................    15.00
TOY,AIRPLANE,SPIRIT OF ST.LOUIS,STRAUSS...................     7.50
TOY,ALABAMA COON JIGGER,DANCES WHEN WOUND,MECHANICAL......    48.00
TOY,ALPHABET & NUMBER BOARD,FOXY TOYS,11 1/2-IN.DIAMETER..    25.00
TOY,ALPHABET GAME,SLIDING,LITHOGRAPH,PAT.1916.............     8.50
TOY,ALPINE STATION,TRACK,TWO TOUR BUSES,WIND,OHIO ART CO.,
  TIN....................................................    10.00
TOY,AMBULANCE,SOLDIERS,MOTOR UNIT,CANNON,DOCTOR,WORLD WAR I,
  23 PIECES...............................................    32.50
TOY,AMOS & ANDY,FRESH AIR TAXI,MECHANICAL.................    49.50
TOY,ANIMALS MADE AT BENSON'S ANIMAL FARM,N.H.,PLATFORM,
  WHEELS,WOODEN,6.........................................    50.00
TOY,ARMY TANK,WORLD WAR I,KEY WIND,POP-UP SOLDIER,TURRET
  GUN,MARX,TIN............................................    29.50
TOY,AUTOMOBILE,SIGNED ARCADE,IRON,4 IN....................    28.00
TOY,BAND,LIL ABNER,WIND,TIN...............................    23.00
TOY,BASKET,COVER,HANDLE,OVAL,PETER RABBIT ON PARADE,TIN...     5.00
TOY,BATHTUB,FOR DOLL HOUSE,PORCELAIN,GERMANY,4 1/2 IN.LONG..   8.50
TOY,BATHTUB,DOLL'S,WOODEN.................................     2.00
TOY,BEAR BEATING DRUM,MONKEY ON BACK,2 1/4 X 2 1/4 IN.....    20.00
TOY,BED,CHEST,VANITY,CRADLE,CHAIRS,CLOTH-COVERED CARDBOARD,
  DOLL'S.................................................    14.00
TOY,BED,DOLL'S,FOUR POSTER,MATTRESS,PILLOWS,COVERLET,
  MAHOGANY,29 1/2 IN......................................    38.50
TOY,BED,DOLL'S,STRAW & FEATHER MATTRESSES,PILLOW,SPREAD,
  BOLSTER,WALNUT..........................................    45.00
TOY,BED,DOLL'S,PAINTED TO LOOK LIKE IRON BED,GILT KNOBS,
  FOLDS,WOODEN............................................     7.00
TOY,BED,DOLL'S,ROPE STYLE,STENCIL,IRON,13 IN..............    20.00
TOY,BED,FOUR-POSTER,WOODEN PEGS,CANNONBALL,RED,
  10 1/2 IN.LONG,10 IN.HIGH...............................    35.00
TOY,BELL RINGER,FOUR BELLS ON HEART WHEELS,IRON...........     8.00
TOY,BICYCLE,HAND BRAKE,BRASS LABEL,POPE MFG. CO.,PAT.1877...  525.00
TOY,BIRD,PECKING,PAT.1927,WIND,TIN........................    16.50
TOY,BIRD,PECKING,WINDUP,TIN,5 1/2 IN......................     4.00
TOY,BIRD,WIND,HOPS,TIN,1927,5 1/4 IN......................    12.00
TOY,BLOCKS,SHAPED AND DECORATED TO LOOK LIKE BUILDINGS,
  PENNA.DUTCH,23..........................................    12.50
TOY,BLOCKS,WOODEN,COVERED IN COLORED LITHOGRAPH PAPER,CIRCA
  1910,12................................................    12.00
TOY,BOAT,OUTBOARD,LINDSTROM,WIND,TIN......................    22.50
TOY,BOMBO THE MONK,WIND,HANGS FROM TREE,SOMMERSAULTS,ART
  MFG.CO.................................................    14.00
TOY,BOY ON TRICYCLE,WINDUP,MARKED KIDDY CYCLIST...........    29.00
TOY,BOY RIDING TRICYCLE,WIND,TIN..........................    14.00
TOY,BUBBLE PIPE,MADE IN ST.JOHNSBURY,VERMONT,1871,TIN.....     7.00
TOY,BUGGY,DOLL'S,MOVABLE TOP,TIN & IRON,4 1/2 X 2 3/4 IN,..   15.00
TOY,BUGGY,DOLL'S,REED,1917................................     8.50
```

TOY,BUGGY,DOLL'S,REED,BRAKES,WINDOWS,ADJUSTABLE BACK,CIRCA
   1900................................................................. 25.00
TOY,BUGGY,DOLL'S,SWIVEL UMBRELLA,OPENWORK SILVER,DATED
   AUG.13,1895,5 IN................................................... 39.50
TOY,BUGGY,DOLL'S,WICKER.............................................. 20.00
TOY,BUGGY,DOLL'S,WOODEN WHEELS,FRINGED SUNSHADE,STENCIL,
   WOODEN,1820....................................................... 89.50
TOY,BUNNY,PAPIER-MACHE,PULLING TWO-WHEELED WOODEN CART,
   12 IN............................................................. 15.00
TOY,BUREAU,DOLL'S,THREE DRAWERS,PINE................................. 35.00
TOY,BUREAU,DOLL'S,TWO DRAWERS,PORCELAIN PULLS,VICTORIAN.............. 60.00
TOY,BUTTERFLY ON STICK,FLAPS ITS WINGS,TIN.......................... 15.00
TOY,CANNISTER SET,CHILD'S,TAN,GOLD,TEA,COFFEE,SUGAR,FLOUR,
   CAKE,BREAD........................................................ 10.00
TOY,CAR,FIVE-WINDOW COUPE,SPARE TIRE,METAL WHEELS,IRON,
   3 1/2 IN.......................................................... 10.00
TOY,CAR,GAS,CAST ALUMINUM............................................ 50.00
TOY,CAR,HUBLEY RACER NO.7,DRIVER,IRON,5 1/2 IN....................... 22.00
TOY,CAR,MODEL A FORD,TOOTSIE,1939.................................... 4.00
TOY,CAR,OPEN,WIND,TWO SEATS,WYANDOTTE TOY,TIN,12 IN.................. 5.50
TOY,CAR,POLICE PATROL COUPE,WIND,SIREN,GREEN,MARX,1936,TIN,
   15 IN............................................................. 25.00
TOY,CAR,TOURING,DATED APRIL '09,TIN................................. 50.00
TOY,CARPET SWEEPER,FOR DOLL HOUSE,BRITANNIA,6 IN.LONG............... 6.00
TOY,CARPET,ORIENTAL,FOR DOLL HOUSE,8................................ 25.00
TOY,CARRIAGE,DOLL,IRON,3 IN.LONG.................................... 4.95
TOY,CARRIAGE,OPEN,MAN & WOMAN SEATED,TWO HORSES,MARKED
   STANLEY TOYS,IRON................................................. 42.50
TOY,CART,DUMP,TWO-WHEELED,DONKEY,DRIVER,MECHANICAL,MARX,
   8 1/4 IN.......................................................... 15.00
TOY,CART,RED,HORSES,WOODEN,MOVABLE TIN LEGS,GRAY BEAUTY
   PACERS,GIBBS...................................................... 65.00
TOY,CASTOR SET,CHILD'S.............................................. 35.00
TOY,CAT ON WHEELS,GRAY,TIN,3 1/2 IN................................. 3.00
TOY,CAT,PUSHES BALL,MECHANICAL,5 1/2 IN............................. 15.00
TOY,CHAIR,DOLL,GERMANY,8 IN.HIGH.................................... 2.00
TOY,CHAIR,DOLL'S,SLAT-BACK,RUSH SEAT,BLACK,FLORAL DECOR,
   16 IN.,PAIR....................................................... 35.00
TOY,CHAIR,DOLL'S,CAPTAIN'S,PLANK SEAT,RED PAINT,8 IN.TALL........... 12.00
TOY,CHARLIE MC CARTHY,WIND,OPENS MOUTH,WALKS,TIN,8 IN.TALL.. 16.00
TOY,CHEST OF DRAWERS,DOLL'S,SIX DRAWERS,PINE,PAINTED WHITE,
   VICTORIAN......................................................... 18.50
TOY,CHEST,DOLL'S,FOUR DRAWERS,WOODEN................................ 8.00
TOY,CHICKEN,LAYS EGGS,BALDWIN CO.,TIN,5 1/4 IN.LONG X
   4 3/4 IN.TALL..................................................... 15.00
TOY,CHICKEN,WHEELBARROW,PUSH TOY,J.CHEIN,TIN,7 IN............ 3.50
TOY,CIRCUS BANDWAGON,HORSES,RIDERS,MUSICIANS,DRIVER,OVERLAND 125.00
TOY,CIRCUS CAGE,BEAR,DRIVER,OVERLAND,PAIR........................... 110.00
TOY,CLOCK,CUCKOO,FOR DOLL HOUSE,STANDING,METAL.............. 9.00
TOY,CLOCK,MANTEL,TICKING MECHANISM,HANDS MOVE,BRASS,TIN,2 X
   2 1/2 IN.......................................................... 12.50
TOY,CLOSET,TWO DOORS,TOP DRAWER,INSIDE SHELF,WOODEN,
   12 7/8 IN.HIGH.................................................... 25.00
TOY,CLOTHES WRINGER,RED,GREEN PAINT,RUBBER,BRITANNIA,2 X
   2 IN.............................................................. 5.50
TOY,CLOWN & BUCKING DONKEY,CART,LEHMAN,WIND,TIN.............. 38.50
TOY,CLOWN ON BAR,PRESS LEVER FOR ACTION,TOE-JOE,OHIO........ 15.00
TOY,CLOWN,DONKEY CART,TIN,LEHMAN,RUNS............................... 16.00
TOY,COACH,HORSES,LEAD,3 FEET LONG................................... 600.00
TOY,COACH,RAILROAD,OPEN VESTIBULE,RED,IRON WHEELS,6 1/2 IN.. 15.00
TOY,COAL HOD,IRON................................................... 2.75
TOY,COAL HOD,SCUTTLE,IRON........................................... 2.75
TOY,COFFEE GRINDER,CHILD'S,IRON & WOOD.............................. 14.50
TOY,COFFEE GRINDER,CHILD'S,PAPER LABEL SAYS DAISEY,HANDLE,
   IRON,2 IN.HIGH.................................................... 10.00
TOY,COVERED WAGON,IRON WHEELS,METAL FRAMES,CLOTH TOP,
   11 IN.LONG........................................................ 27.50
TOY,COWBOY ON HORSE,WIND,CELLULOID.................................. 9.50
TOY,CRADLE,DOLL'S,BENTWOOD,15 X 28 X 18 IN.DEEP............... 25.00
TOY,CRADLE,DOLL'S,HOOD,WICKER,18 IN.LONG............................ 25.00
TOY,CRADLE,DOLL'S,RED PAINT,PINE,8 IN. X 16 IN..................... 20.00
TOY,CRADLE,HOODED,TIN,6 1/2 IN.LONG X 4 5/8 IN.WIDE X
   6 IN.TALL......................................................... 22.00
TOY,CRADLE,PAINTED GOLD & WHITE,FILIGREE,BRITANNIA,SIGNED
   W.G.,2 IN.LONG.................................................... 9.50
TOY,CURLING IRON,CHILD'S............................................ 2.50
TOY,DESK,BLACKBOARD,ROLL PAPER TOP,PORTABLE,1913............. 12.50
TOY,DISH,BUTTER,CHILD'S,COVER,COBALT BASE,CLEAR PRESSED
   GLASS COVER....................................................... 7.00
TOY,DOG,CELLULOID,CIRCLES TIN KENNEL,WIND,JAPAN............... 22.50

TOY,DOG,LEAD,ENGLAND,2 IN.HIGH,LOT OF 6...................... 4.50
TOY,DOG,SCOTTIE,KEY WIND,BLACK,PLAID COAT,WEE SCOTTIE BY
    MAR,TIN.............................................. 8.50
TOY,DOG,SOMERSAULT,S.G.,WIND,TIN............................ 18.50
TOY,DOG,TERRIER,SCOTTY,COCKER,WHITE METAL,1 1/2 IN. TO
    3 1/2 IN.LONG,8..................................... 12.00
    TOY DOLL,SEE DOLL
TOY,DOLL BED,BAMBOO,MATTRESS,PILLOW,FOR 20-IN.DOLL.......... 25.00
TOY,DOLL HOUSE BATHROOM,FIXTURES,ARCADE,IRON,11 X 10 1/2 X
    10 IN.HIGH.......................................... 175.00
TOY,DOLL HOUSE DINING ROOM,FURNITURE,ARCADE,IRON,15 X 20 X
    10 IN.HIGH.......................................... 175.00
TOY,DOLL WARDROBE,BAMBOO,MIRRORED DOOR,DRAWER BELOW,
    13 IN.HIGH.......................................... 30.00
TOY,DOLL,MICKEY MOUSE,RUBBER............................... 2.50
TOY,DOLL'S DRESSING TABLE,BAMBOO,MARBLE TOP,MIRROR,SHELF,
    15 IN.HIGH.......................................... 30.00
TOY,DONALD DUCK,PLAYING XYLOPHONE,PULL,WOODEN.............. 14.50
TOY,DONKEY,WIND,TAIL & EARS WIGGLE,HEAD NODS,5 IN.LONG..... 10.00
TOY,DRESS FORM,DOLL'S...................................... 25.00
TOY,DRESSER,ATTACHED MIRROR,TWO DRAWERS,MARBLE TOP,HONEY
    MAPLE,3 1/4 IN...................................... 25.00
TOY,DRESSER,DOLL'S,THREE DRAWERS,PINE,4 1/2 X 7 X
    5 3/4 IN.TALL....................................... 8.50
TOY,DRIVER,BUTTERFIELD STAGE LINE,TIN,4 HORSES............. 25.00
TOY,DRUM MAJOR,WIND,TIN,10 IN.HIGH........................ 35.00
TOY,DUCK,MECHANICAL,YELLOW,BLUE,RED,CHEIN,4 IN.TALL........ 15.00
TOY,DUCK,WIND-UP,J.CHEIN,TIN.............................. 6.50
TOY,EGG WITH TWO RABBITS,CART,WIND,TIN.................... 27.50
TOY,ENGINE,TENDER,RAILROAD,RED,FRICTION,1900,17 IN. X
    5 IN.HIGH........................................... 25.00
TOY,ERECTOR SET,1923...................................... 5.00
TOY,FARM ANIMALS,LEAD,ENGLAND,2 IN.HIGH,LOT OF 6.......... 4.50
TOY,FELIX THE CAT,JOINTED WOOD,FELIX TRADEMARK,7 IN.TALL.... 4.50
TOY,FELIX THE CAT,MEOW NOISEMAKER,BLACK,WHITE,ORANGE,PAPER,
    7 IN.TALL........................................... 3.50
TOY,FELIX THE CAT,RUBBER FACE,WOODEN JOINTS................ 35.00
TOY,FIGURE,CHARLIE CHAPLIN,LEAD,2 3/4 IN.HIGH............. 1.25
TOY,FIGURES,CIVIL WAR CANNON,INDIANS,REGIMENT SOLDIERS,LEAD,
    20.................................................. 10.00
TOY,FILLING STATION,BRIGHTLIGHT,MARX,BATTERY,CIRCA 1925..... 15.00
TOY,FIRE ENGINE,FOUR MEN,LADDER,DRIVER,WIND,RED,TIN,
    6 IN.LONG........................................... 10.00
TOY,FIRE ENGINE,IRON,4 3/4 IN............................. 15.00
TOY,FIRE ENGINE,PUFFER,HORSE,DRIVER,SILVER COLOR,
    6 1/2 IN.LONG....................................... 15.00
TOY,FIRE ENGINE,THREE HORSES,IRON......................... 50.00
TOY,FIRE HOSE WAGON,DRIVER,TWO HORSES,IRON,REPAINTED....... 49.00
TOY,FIRE PUMPER,HORSE,FOUR WHEELS,IRON,8 IN............... 20.00
TOY,FIRE TRUCK,DRIVER,TWO LADDERS,RED,IRON,4 IN........... 10.00
TOY,FIRE TRUCK,LADDER,APPARATUS MOVES UP & DOWN,
    INTERNATIONAL,IRON.................................. 48.00
TOY,FIREPLACE,GAS LOG,IRON,4 IN. X 6 1/2 IN.HIGH.......... 20.00
TOY,FIREPLACE,WHITE,GOLD,SERPENTINE MANTLE,FILIGREE,
    BRITANNIA,4 IN.WIDE................................. 15.00
TOY,FLIP THE JUMPING DOG,MARX,WIND,TIN.................... 16.50
TOY,FOOD CHOPPER,CHILD'S,MARKED PONY,IRON,4 7/8 IN......... 5.00
TOY,FOUR HORSE BEER WAGON WITH DRIVER CARVED OF WOOD &
    LEATHER............................................. 65.00
TOY,FURNITURE,DOLL,COUCH,ROCKER,CHAIR,WICKER.............. 45.00
TOY,FURNITURE,DOLL,LYRE BASE TABLE,TWO CHAIRS,IRON........ 25.00
TOY,G I JOE,K-9 PUPS,HELMET MOVES,WIND,UNIQUE ART MFG.,TIN,
    8 3/4 IN............................................ 18.50
TOY,GAMING SET,AUSTRIAN CARVED AND TINTED WOOD.......ILLUS.. 600.00
TOY,GOOSE,LAYS EGGS,MARX,WIND,TIN......................... 15.00
TOY,GRAIN SHOVEL,IRON,4 3/4 IN.LONG....................... 2.75
TOY,GRIDDLE,IRON,2 3/4-IN.DIAMETER........................ 2.75
TOY,GUITAR,MICKEY MOUSE,SAYS GETAR JR.,TURN HANDLE & MUSIC
    PLAYS,14 IN......................................... 25.00
TOY,GUN,CAP,EMBOSSED GEM ON BARREL,3 IN................... 5.00
TOY,GUN,CAP,EMBOSSED PUCK PAT.MAR.22,1987-JUNE 17,1997,
    3 3/4 IN............................................ 8.50
TOY,HAPPY HOOLIGAN,CHEIN,WIND,TIN......................... 32.50
TOY,HEN,LITHOGRAPHED,CACKLES,LAYS EGGS (MARBLES).......... 15.00
TOY,HIGHCHAIR,DOLLS,SPOOL-TYPE,LOWERS TO PLAY TABLE,
    17 IN.HIGH.......................................... 37.50
TOY,HOBBYHORSE,PINE,19TH CENTURY,AMERICAN,47 IN.LONG....... 100.00
TOY,HOBBYHORSE,RED ROCKERS,WICKER SEAT,CUSHION,GOLD
    STENCILING,1890..................................... 75.00
TOY,HORSE & CART,WIRE SPRING,WIND,TIN..................... 33.50

AUSTRIAN WOOD GAMING SET

```
TOY,HORSE,FOOT PEDALS,JOINTED LEGS,ON ROLLERS,PRESSED METAL,
   30 IN.HIGH..................................................  79.50
TOY,HORSE,IRON,TIN CART,ORIGINAL PAINT,7 IN..................  15.00
TOY,HORSE,JOINTED LEGS AND HEAD,ON ROLLERS,CAST ALUMINUM,
   26 IN.HIGH..................................................  79.50
TOY,HOUSE,VICTORIAN,TWO CHIMNEYS,AWNINGS,DORMERS,BAY
   WINDOWS,TIN.................................................  15.00
TOY,HUTCH,DOLL'S,MIRROR BACK,OAK,26 IN. X 15 IN..............  20.00
TOY,ICE CREAM FREEZER.........................................  45.00
TOY,ICE SKATE,CHILD'S,WOODEN PLATFORM,STRAP,PAIR.............   4.50
TOY,ICE SKATE,TURNED-UP FRONT,PAIR............................  18.50
TOY,ICE SKATE,WOODEN,STEEL RUNNER & SPIKE,PAIR...............  15.00
TOY,IRON,CHILD'S,FLAT,OPENWORK TRIVET,FOOTED.................  18.00
TOY,IRON,CHILD'S..............................................   5.00
TOY,IRONING BOARD,CHILD'S,WOODEN..............................   3.00
TOY,JENNY THE BALKING MULE,FARMER & CART,STRAUSS,WIND,TIN...  32.00
TOY,JOLLY JOE,MARX,TIN,MECHANICAL,6 IN.LONG..................  10.00
TOY,KAISER,KAISERINA,FOOTMEN,CARRIAGE,SIX HORSES.............  75.00
TOY,KETTLE,BAIL HANDLE,THREE FEET,IRON,2 1/4-IN.DIAMETER....   2.75
TOY,KETTLE,BAIL,FOOTED,IRON,2 3/8-IN.DIAMETER................   2.75
TOY,KIDDIE CAR,MARKED KILGORE,IRON............................   4.75
TOY,KNIFE,POCKET,HOPALONG CASSIDY,3 IN.......................   9.00
TOY,LANTERN,CHILD'S,BAIL, JEWEL,  TIN........................   5.00
TOY,LAUNDRY BASKET,TWO HANDLES,FOR DOLL HOUSE,5 IN.LONG,
   3 IN.WIDE..................................................   2.25
TOY,LOCOMOTIVE,COAL CAR,IRON,6 1/2 IN........................  27.50
TOY LOCOMOTIVE,MICKEY MOUSE...................................  50.00
TOY,LOCOMOTIVE,STEAM,WHISTLE,BRASS...........................  40.00
TOY,MAN DOLL,TALL HAT,WIND,WALKS,DRINKS,8 IN.TALL...........  60.00
TOY,MAN PLAYS XYLOPHONE,5 STONE RECORDS,TIN,WOLVERINE,
   PAT.PENDING 204............................................  78.00
TOY,MARIONETTE,HOWDY DOODY,...................................   8.00
TOY,MEAT GRINDER,CHILD'S,IRON.................................   6.75
TOY,MEAT GRINDER,CHILD'S,METAL,4 IN..........................   5.00
TOY,MEAT GRINDER,CHILD'S,THREE EXTRA CUTTING BLADES,IRON,
   7 IN.......................................................  13.50
TOY,MERRY-GO-ROUND,THREE FIGURES,UMBRELLA,WINDUP,TIN........  15.00
TOY,MERRY-GO-ROUND ROOSTER WITH STAND,RESTORED.............. 500.00
TOY,MERRY-GO-ROUND,WOLVERINE NO.31,WIND,TIN..................  19.50
TOY,MICKEY MOUSE,DANCES WHEN BASE IS PRESSED,PLAYS DRUMS....  15.00
TOY,MICKEY MOUSE,WINDUP.......................................   6.50
TOY,MINNIE MOUSE,ROCKING & KNITTING IN CHAIR,TIN............  15.00
TOY,MONKEY,CLIMBS CORD,DRESSED IN RED & GREEN,PAT.1903,TIN..  12.50
TOY,MOTHER GOOSE & CAT,WIND,TIN..............................  30.00
TOY,MOTORCYCLE,DRIVER,BLUE,IRON,CHAMPION,7 IN................  20.00
TOY,MOTORCYCLE,DRIVER,IRON WHEELS & TIRES,CHAMPION,IRON,
   4 3/4 IN...................................................  20.00
TOY,MOTORCYCLE,DRIVER,IRON,RUBBER TIRES,7 IN.................  20.00
TOY,MOTORCYCLE,DRIVER,SIDECAR,WHITE TIRES,IRON,4 3/4 IN.....  15.00
TOY,MOTORCYCLE,POLICEMAN,BLUE,RED SIDECAR,RUBBER TIRES,
   CHAMPION,IRON..............................................  26.00
TOY,MOTORCYCLE,POLICEMAN,HARLEY-DAVIDSON,BLUE,WHITE RUBBER
   TIRES,IRON.................................................  19.00
TOY,MOTORCYCLE,POLICEMAN,IRON,IRON TIRES,4 IN................  20.00
TOY,MOTORCYCLE,POLICEMAN,RED PAINT,SAYS COP,IRON,4 IN.......  12.50
TOY,MOTORCYCLE,POLICEMAN,WIND,TIN,MARX TOY,8 IN.LONG........  12.00
TOY,MOTORCYCLE,RED,THREE WHEELS,IRON,RUBBER TIRES,INDIAN
   CRASH CAR..................................................  20.00
TOY,MOTORCYCLE,WHITE RUBBER TIRES,GAS TANK,SAYS CHAMPION,
   4 3/4 X 3 IN...............................................  15.00
TOY,MOUSE ON WHEELS,TIN.......................................   2.00
TOY,MOVIE PROJECTOR,MICKEY MOUSE,KEYSTONE....................  48.00
TOY,MOVIE THEATER,TIN BUILDING,PAPER CARTOON MOVIE,MARX.....  14.50
```

```
TOY,MULE,MOVABLE LIMBS,WOODEN,SCHOENHUT.....................    12.00
TOY,ORGAN,CHILD'S,16 KEYS,ELECTRIC..........................     5.00
TOY,OVER AND UNDER,WIND,TIN.................................    19.50
TOY,PAN,FRY,FOOTED,IRON,2 1/2-IN.DIAMETER...................     2.75
TOY,PENGUIN,FRICTION WIND,WINGS FLAP WHEN MOVING,TIN........     7.00
TOY,PHONE,CHILD'S,UPRIGHT,METAL & WOOD,7 IN.................     3.00
TOY,PIANO,CHILD'S,SCHOENHUT,19 3/4 IN.LONG,10 IN.DEEP,
   19 IN.TALL...............................................    39.50
TOY,PINBALL GAME,HAND-PAINTED,DATED 1902,12 X 28 IN.........    22.00
TOY,PISTOL,BUCK ROGERS U235 ATOMIC,HOLSTER..................   100.00
TOY,PISTOL,CAP,AUTOMATIC SHOOTER,MARKED K,OVERALL 7 IN......    10.00
TOY,PISTOL,CAP,BIG BILL,MARKED K,U.S.A.,6 IN.LONG...........    14.00
TOY,PISTOL,CAP,BIRD-HEAD GRIP,SHEATHED TRIGGER,BULLDOZER,
   1874,5 1/4 IN............................................    16.00
TOY,PISTOL,CAP,COLT,PAT.1890,IRON,3 1/2 IN..................   120.00
TOY,PISTOL,CAP,EAGLE,PAT.1890,5 IN..........................    20.00
TOY,PISTOL,CAP,IRON,LEATHER HOLSTER,BELT,PICTURE OF BUFFALO
   BILL,11 IN...............................................    15.00
TOY,PISTOL,CAP,K SIX-SHOOTER AUTOMATIC,IRON,7 1/4 IN........    10.00
TOY,PISTOL,CAP,KILGORE......................................    10.00
TOY,PISTOL,CAP,LONGBOY,IRON.................................     7.50
TOY,PISTOL,CAP,MARK D,IRON,6 1/2 IN.........................     5.00
TOY,PISTOL,CAP,MARK DAISY,IRON,4 1/2 IN.LONG................     7.00
TOY,PISTOL,CAP,MARK DICK,AUTOMATIC,IRON,NICKEL FINISH,4 IN..     6.00
TOY,PISTOL,CAP,MARK ECHO,U.S.A.,5 IN........................     6.00
TOY,PISTOL,CAP,MARK FLINTLOCK MIDGET,HUBLEY,WHITE METAL,
   6 IN.....................................................     8.00
TOY,PISTOL,CAP,MARK HUB,MADE IN U.S.A.,ZINC,6 1/2 IN........     6.00
TOY,PISTOL,CAP,MARK JAX S.W.,PAT.1923,IRON,4 1/4 IN.,PAIR...    20.00
TOY,PISTOL,CAP,MARK OH BOY..................................    10.00
TOY,PISTOL,CAP,MARK PET,IRON,5 IN...........................     6.00
TOY,PISTOL,CAP,MARK PUP,WHITE METAL,6 IN....................     6.00
TOY,PISTOL,CAP,MARK TEDDY,IRON,6 IN.........................    10.00
TOY,PISTOL,CAP,OPENING FOR CAPS,SMOKE-ESCAPE SLOT,U.S.A.,
   5 IN.....................................................     6.00
TOY,PISTOL,CAP,PAT.1890,IRON,3 IN...........................    18.00
TOY,PISTOL,CAP,PATENT 1890,COLT,PAIR........................     8.00
TOY,PISTOL,CAP,SCOUT,PAT.1890,7 1/4 IN......................    10.00
TOY,PISTOL,CAP,SMOKE SLOT,SAYS ECHO,MADE IN U.S.A.,5 IN.....     6.00
TOY,PISTOL,CAP,SPUR TRIGGER,IRON,MARKED PLUCK,HOLSTER,BELT,
   3 3/4 IN.................................................    25.00
TOY,PISTOL,MARKED U.S.A.LIQUID PISTOL,PAT.1896,IRON,
   5 1/2 IN.LONG............................................    15.00
TOY,PITCHER,WASHBOWL,POTTY,BEIGE,RASPBERRY,GREEN,DOLL HOUSE
   SIZE.....................................................    22.50
TOY,PITCHER,WASHBOWL,WHITE,BLUE STRIPES,DOLL HOUSE SIZE.....    20.00
TOY,POLICEMAN ON BICYCLE,RIDES STRING,JOINTED LEGS & ARMS,
   TIN......................................................    22.00
TOY,POLICEMAN,MOVING ARMS,PAINTED,IRON...............ILLUS..    21.00
```

IRON TOY POLICEMAN, MOVING ARMS, PAINTED

| | |
|---|---|
| TOY,PORTRAIT,FOR DOLL HOUSE,TINTYPE,CHILDREN,1 X 3/4 IN..... | .50 |
| TOY,POT,SIDE HANDLE,THREE FEET,IRON,2 1/2-IN.DIAMETER....... | 2.75 |
| TOY,PROJECTOR,MOVIE,CRANK FOR FILM,ELECTRIC BULB,KEYSTONE, ONE FILM..................................................... | 30.00 |
| TOY,PROJECTOR,MOVIE,10 ROLLS OF 100-FOOT FILM FROM EARLY THIRTIES.................................................. | 110.00 |
| TOY,PULL,FELT-COVERED HORSE PULLING BREWERY WAGON,WOODEN.... | 35.00 |
| TOY,PUNCH & JUDY THEATER,FOLDS,WOODEN,SEVEN PUPPETS......... | 100.00 |
| TOY,PUPPET,BY-LO,CELLULOID HANDS,CRY BOX,PINK BUNTING,SIGNED G.PUTNAN............................................ | 95.00 |
| TOY,PUSHCART,PEDDLER'S,HANDLE,IRON WHEELS,TIN,7 IN.HIGH..... | 4.95 |
| TOY,RABBIT ON MOTORCYCLE,SIDECAR,TIN....................... | 5.75 |
| TOY,RACER,IRON............................................ | 7.00 |
| TOY,RADIATOR,GOLD PAINT,FOR DOLL HOUSE,BRITANNIA,2 1/2 X 2 1/2 IN................................................ | 8.00 |
| TOY,RAILROAD COACH,RED,OPEN VESTIBULE,FOUR WHEELS,IRON, 6 1/2 IN............................................... | 15.00 |
| TOY,RAILROAD ENGINE AND TENDER,RED,FRICTION,1900,17 X 5 IN.. | 25.00 |
| TOY,RAILROAD HANDCAR,TWO MEN,WINDUP,TIN.................... | 18.50 |
| TOY,RATTLE,BABY'S,ALPHABET,WHISTLE HANDLE,TIN.............. | 8.00 |
| TOY,RATTLE,WHISTLE,SAYS FOR A GOOD CHILD,A.B.C. ON SIDES.... | 18.00 |
| TOY,REINDEER,CLOTH-COVERED,METAL ANTLERS,GLASS EYES,SADDLE, BRIDLE,11 IN............................................ | 22.50 |
| TOY,RIDE 'EM COWBOY,MARX,WIND,TIN......................... | 37.50 |
| TOY,ROCKER,DOLL'S,OAK,7 IN................................ | 6.50 |
| TOY,ROCKER,DOLL'S,WICKER,BLUE............................. | 2.50 |
| TOY,ROCKET,BUCK ROGERS,MECHANICAL,DATED 1927,MARX,12 IN.LONG | 32.50 |
| TOY,ROCKING HORSE,RIDER,WIND,PAINT,WOODEN,6 1/2 IN.HIGH..... | 25.00 |
| TOY,ROLLING PIN,CHILD'S,CORRUGATED,ONE PIECE,1 1/2 IN. X 12 IN.LONG.............................................. | 8.50 |
| TOY,ROOSTER PULLING CART,WIND,S.G.,TIN.................... | 32.50 |
| TOY,RUBBER STAMP SET,EXCELSIOR NO.3....................... | 20.00 |
| TOY,SADIRON,BLACK WOODEN HANDLE,REMOVABLE TOP,SIGNED DOVER U.S.A.,IRON............................................. | 8.50 |
| TOY,SADIRON,CHILD'S,DATED 1900............................ | 14.00 |
| TOY,SADIRON,CHILD'S,POINTED ENDS,WOODEN HANDLE,MARKED ASBESTOS,1900.......................................... | 7.00 |
| TOY,SADIRON,CHILD'S,REMOVABLE HANDLE...................... | 7.50 |
| TOY,SADIRON,MARKED DALE CO.,IRON,3 1/2 IN.LONG............. | 3.95 |
| TOY,SALT DIP,VINEGAR CRUET,PEPPER SHAKER,TRAY,CHILD'S, PRESSED GLASS.......................................... | 32.50 |
| TOY,SANTA CLAUS & SLEIGH,TWO REINDEER,PAINTED,IRON, 16 IN.LONG............................................. | 75.00 |
| TOY,SCALE,MINIATURE,TIN SCOOP,5 IN........................ | 9.50 |
| TOY,SCUTTLE,COAL HOD,IRON................................. | 2.95 |
| TOY,SEDAN,GREEN,ARCADE MFG.,FREEPORT,ILL.,IRON,2 1/2 IN. X 5 IN.LONG.............................................. | 7.50 |
| TOY,SET OF DISHES,CHILD'S,BLUE WILLOW,BY BUFFALO CHINA,1915, 29 PIECE............................................... | 75.00 |
| TOY,SEWING MACHINE,BLACK ENAMEL,RED & GOLD DECOR,SIDE HANDLE,6 1/2 IN........................................ | 12.50 |
| TOY,SEWING MACHINE,CHILD'S,HAND TURN,SINGER,IRON........... | 18.00 |
| TOY,SEWING MACHINE,CHILD'S,PEERLESS,DATED 1897,IRON........ | 18.00 |
| TOY,SEWING MACHINE,CHILD'S,CASIGE,MADE IN GERMANY.......... | 7.00 |
| TOY,SEWING MACHINE,CHILD'S,STAND ON OVAL BASE,HANDWHEEL ON SIDE,SINGER............................................ | 12.50 |
| TOY,SEWING MACHINE,CHILD'S,TIN............................ | 10.00 |
| TOY,SEWING MACHINE,HAND TURN,GERMANY,6 IN. HIGH X 6 1/2 IN.LONG........................................... | 18.50 |
| TOY,SHOVEL,CHILD'S,RED,WOODEN............................. | 9.50 |
| TOY,SKATE,ACORN TIP,WOODEN,PAIR........................... | 15.00 |
| TOY,SKATE,IRON RUNNERS,WOODEN,PAIR........................ | 8.50 |
| TOY,SKATE,WOOD,BRASS HARDWARE,STEEL BLADES,PAIR............ | 16.00 |
| TOY,SKATE,WOODEN,STEEL RUNNER,PAIR........................ | 16.00 |
| TOY,SLATE,SCHOOL,CHILD'S.................................. | 10.00 |
| TOY,SLEDGEHAMMER,IRON,4 IN.LONG........................... | 2.00 |
| TOY,SLEIGH PULLED BY TWO HORSES,IRON,15 IN.LONG........... | 85.00 |
| TOY,SOFA,DOLL,RED VELVET,2 1/2 X 7 IN..................... | 10.00 |
| TOY,STAKE WAGON,BLACK & WHITE HORSES,RED WAGON,GREEN WHEELS, DRIVER,IRON............................................ | 35.00 |
| TOY,STEAM ENGINE,ALCOHOL-FIRED............................ | 25.00 |
| TOY,STEAM ENGINE,VERTICAL ALCOHOL BURNER,PAT.MAY,1885,WEEDEN | 65.00 |
| TOY,STEAMROLLER,DRIVER,WIND,6 IN.LONG..................... | 15.00 |
| TOY,STOVE,A-1 BRAND,4 1/4 IN. X 6 1/4 IN.................. | 25.00 |
| TOY,STOVE,BARREL,CHIMNEY,TOP OPENS,LID,FOUR CURVED LEGS, IRON,7 IN.TALL......................................... | 6.50 |
| TOY,STOVE,COAL,HOT WATER TANK,FOUR COVERS,SHELF,MARKED CRESCENT,IRON.......................................... | 18.50 |
| TOY,STOVE,COKE,PAN,BOILER,COAL BUCKET,IRON,6 IN.WIDE, 7 IN.HIGH,9 IN.LONG..................................... | 50.00 |

```
TOY,STOVE,EMPIRE METAL WARE CORP.,TWO RIVERS,WISC.,ELECTRIC.      25.00
TOY,STOVE,FOUR BURNERS,OPEN GRATE AT FRONT,POT,IRON,3 X
   2 1/2 IN.TALL.................................................      11.50
TOY,STOVE,GAS,KENT,IRON...........................................      24.00
TOY,STOVE,GAS,ROYAL,IRON..........................................       8.00
TOY,STOVE,GAS,ROYAL,IRON,4 1/2 IN.HIGH............................      10.00
TOY,STOVE,IMITATION GAS,JACK & JILL DESIGN ON BACK,TIN,10 X
   4 IN........................................................       2.50
TOY,STOVE,LIDS,RESERVOIR,GRATE,IRON...............................      30.00
TOY,STOVE,LIFTER,POT,SKILLET,SCUTTLE,SHOVEL,QUEEN,IRON,
   3 5/8 X 6 IN................................................      22.50
TOY,STOVE,LITTLE PET,10 1/2 IN.TALL...............................      40.00
TOY,STOVE,NICKEL-PLATED,COAL GRATE,FOUR BURNERS,LIDS,MARKED
   HOME,IRON...................................................      25.00
TOY,STOVE,ORPHAN ANNIE............................................       7.00
TOY,STOVE,QUICKMEAL IRON & NICKEL RANGE,SALESMAN'S SAMPLE...      275.00
TOY,STOVE,WOOD-HEATING............................................      10.00
TOY,STREETCAR,CHEIN,TIN,8 1/4 IN.LONG.............................      22.00
TOY,SURREY,FRINGE ON TOP,TWO HORSES,COACHMAN,LADY PASSENGER,
   IRON.......................................................      45.00
TOY,TABLE,CARD,TOP INLAID WITH FANS,SIDES INLAID WITH
   SQUARES,7 3/8 IN...........................................      12.50
TOY,TABLE,DOLL'S,DROP LEAF,TURNED LEGS,OVAL,OPENS,
   12 1/2 IN.TALL.............................................      22.50
TOY,TABLE,DROP LEAF,FOUR TURNED LEGS,CAN BE REMOVED & STORED
   UNDER TOP..................................................      22.50
TOY,TABLE,DROP LEAF,SIX LEGS,SALESMAN'S SAMPLE,WOODEN,20 IN.
   X 14 IN....................................................      45.00
TOY,TABLE,MARBLE TOP,TAPERED LEGS,WOODEN,FOR DOLL HOUSE,
   2 1/4 IN.HIGH..............................................      18.00
TOY,TABLE,SETTEE,TWO CHAIRS,REED,FOR DOLL.........................      25.00
TOY,TABLE,TWO ARMCHAIRS,SETTEE,DOLL'S,WICKER......................      45.00
TOY,TABLE,TWO CHAIRS,LOVE SEAT,TABLE,DOLL'S,WICKER,5 IN.HIGH      18.00
TOY,TANK,PLANET PATROL,MARX,WIND,TIN..............................      30.00
TOY,TANK,SOLDIERS,JOINTED,GUTMAN,PAT.1918,TIN.....................      30.00
TOY,TANK,TURNOVER,NO.3,MARX,WIND,TIN..............................      30.00
TOY,TANK,WIND,TIN,10 IN.LONG X 5 1/4 IN.TALL......................      20.00
TOY,TEA SET,CHILD'S,BLUE WILLOW,12 PIECES.........................      10.00
TOY,TEA SET,CHILD'S,LUSTER,FLORAL,JAPAN,26 PIECES,
   SILVERWARE,GERMANY.........................................      23.00
TOY,TEA SET,CHILD'S,WHITE,GOLD TRIM,MARKED AURORA,16 PIECES.      28.00
TOY,TEAPOT,CHILD'S,WHITE,TWO KITTENS,PLAYING,5 1/2 IN.......       8.50
TOY,TEAPOT,CREAMER,SUGAR,6 CUPS,SAUCERS,GIRL,EGGS IN APRON,
   STAFFORDSHIRE..............................................      50.00
TOY,TELEPHONE,DESK,WOODEN.........................................       2.00
TOY,TELESCOPE,CHILD'S,FOLDING.....................................       5.98
TOY,TIDY TIM,WINDUP,DSC TRADEMARK,TIN.............................      18.00
TOY,TOP,ADVERTISING,CRACKER JACK..................................       5.00
TOY,TRACTOR,DRIVER,IRON,RUBBER TIRES,MCCORMICK DEERING,
   7 1/2 IN...................................................      25.00
TOY,TRACTOR,GRAY,RED WHEELS,WIND,TIN..............................       7.50
TOY,TRAIN,AMERICAN FLYER,WIND,LOCOMOTIVE,TENDER,TRACK.......      75.00
TOY,TRAIN,BLACK ENGINE,RED CAR,IRON,9 IN..........................      25.00
TOY,TRAIN,BLACK,IRON,10 1/2 IN....................................      17.50
TOY,TRAIN,CIRCUS,AMERICAN FLYER...................................     150.00
TOY,TRAIN,COAL CAR,IRON,11 1/2 IN.LONG............................      35.00
TOY,TRAIN,KEYSTONE,25 IN.LONG.....................................      18.00
TOY,TRAIN,LIONEL O GAUGE,1930.....................................      20.00
TOY,TRAIN,LIONEL STANDARD GAUGE,1920..............................      35.00
TOY,TRAIN,STATION,TUNNEL,MECHANICAL,TIN,MARKED GERMANY......      10.00
TOY,TRAIN,WIND,CARS,MICKEY MOUSE..................................       5.00
TOY,TRAIN,WIND,TIN................................................      16.00
TOY,TRICYCLE,1882.................................................     100.00
TOY,TRIVET,CHILD'S,MATCHING HANDLED SADIRON,IRON............      12.00
TOY,TRIVET,IRON,3 IN.LONG.........................................       3.95
TOY,TRUCK,COCA-COLA,RUNNING BOARDS,YELLOW BODY,SIGNS,RACKS,
   11 IN......................................................      52.50
TOY,TRUCK,DUMP,INTERNATIONAL HARVESTER CO.,ARCADE,IRON,
   11 IN.LONG.................................................      50.00
TOY,TRUCK,HOOK & LADDER,BUDDY L,LABELS,29 IN.LONG...........      85.00
TOY,TRUCK,LADDER,FOLDING LADDER,DRIVER,WINDUP,TIN...........      50.00
TOY,TRUCK,RUBBER,RED,1940.........................................       3.00
TOY,TRUCK,STAKE,RED,BLACK,MARKED WYANDOTTE TOYS,10 IN.......      12.00
TOY,TRUCK VAN,RUBBER TIRES,PAINT,BUDDY L,STEEL,8 1/2 X
   23 IN.LONG.................................................      36.00
TOY,TRUNK,DOLL,DOME TOP,TRAY,RESTORED,9 X 16 IN.............      17.50
TOY,TRUNK,WARDROBE,DOLLS,METAL BOUND,EXELSIOR,STAMFORD,
   CONN.,12 X 23 IN...........................................      10.00
TOY,TUREEN,PLATTERS,VEGETABLE BOWL,COMPOTE,WHITE,BLUE DECOR,
   PORCELAIN..................................................      25.00
```

```
TOY,TURTLE,BLACK,RED BABY TURTLE ON BACK,MECHANICAL,
   4 1/2 IN.......................................................  15.00
TOY,TYPEWRITER,CHILD'S,PAINT,TIN...............................   9.00
TOY,WAFFLE IRON,CHILD'S,DATED FEB.,1910,BROWN WOODEN HANDLE,
   IRON..........................................................  15.00
TOY,WHEELBARROW,IRON,6 1/2 IN.LONG,2 1/2 IN.HIGH...............   6.75
TOY,WHISTLE,ALLIGATOR,CARVED IVORY,HAS LOOP...................   7.00
TOY,WICKER SET,DOLLS,SOFA,ARMCHAIR,ROUND TABLE................  21.50
TOY,YELLOW CAB & DRIVER,IRON,7 1/2 IN.LONG....................  50.00
TOY,ZEPPELIN,WIND,SAYS LOS A,TIN,9 1/2 IN.....................  27.00
```

        TRIVETS ARE NOW USED TO HOLD HOT DISHES. MOST OF THE
        LATE NINETEENTH- AND EARLY TWENTIETH-CENTURY TRIVETS
        WERE MADE TO HOLD HOT IRONS. IRON OR BRASS
        REPRODUCTIONS ARE BEING MADE OF MANY OF THE OLD STYLES.

```
TRIVET,CHRISTMAS TREE,COLOR,IRON..............................   5.50
TRIVET,DIAMOND T,IRON.........................................   7.50
TRIVET,E.P. IN CENTER,ENTERPRISE,PHILADELPHIA AROUND EDGE,
   IRON,6 IN.....................................................   8.00
TRIVET,EAGLE & HORSESHOE,ANCIENT ORDER OF FORESTERS,IRON....  13.50
TRIVET,FORESTAL URN IN CENTER,THREE LEGS,IRON.................   5.50
TRIVET,GEOMETRIC,IRON.........................................   6.50
TRIVET,GRAPES,LEAVES,SILVER INLAY,6 IN........................  15.00
TRIVET,HEART CENTER,HEART AT HANDLE END,FOOTED,PENNSYLVANIA
   DUTCH,IRON....................................................  18.00
TRIVET,HEART HANDLE,CENTER DESIGN,ROUND,IRON,10 IN.LONG.....  15.00
TRIVET,HORSESHOE SHAPE,GOOD LUCK,EAGLE,IRON..................  12.50
TRIVET,IRON,WOODEN HANDLE...........................ILLUS..   5.00
```

IRON TRIVET, WOODEN HANDLE

```
TRIVET,LACY FILIGREE,CHILD,DOG,HOUSE,RING & FAN BORDER,
   HANDLE,BRONZE.................................................  19.50
TRIVET,LACY,SIX PAW FEET,IRON.................................  10.50
TRIVET,LYRE TOP,18TH CENTURY,AMERICAN,BRASS..................  45.00
TRIVET,MAN-O'-WAR,IRON........................................  16.00
TRIVET,ONE POINTED END,MARKED 674V,3820,VULCAN,IRON,7 IN....   8.00
TRIVET,OPENWORK,BURNISHED,BRASS,10-IN.DIAMETER..............   9.00
TRIVET,PINK ROSES,GOLD RUFFLED EDGE,PORCELAIN,GERMANY,7 IN..  12.00
TRIVET,ROUND,THREE CLAW FEET,STAR CENTER,BRASS,MARKED CHINA.   8.50
TRIVET,SADIRON CHAIN..........................................   7.00
TRIVET,STAR CENTER,HANDLE,FOOTED,IRON.........................  15.00
TRIVET,SWAN,FOOTED,IRON.......................................   6.50
TRIVET,TRIANGLE,THREE 3-INCH LEGS,IRON........................   7.50
TRUNK,CHINESE DECORATED LEATHER,19TH CENTURY,25 IN. LONG.... 290.00
TRUNK,CHINESE,DECORATED LEATHER,STAND,19TH CENTURY.......... 300.00
TYPEWRITER,BLICKENSDERFER,1892,CASE..........................  39.00
TYPEWRITER,CORONA,DATED 1917..................................  18.50
TYPEWRITER,CORONA,PORTABLE,PATENT 1904........................  15.00
TYPEWRITER,CORONA,1915........................................  20.00
TYPEWRITER,GUNDKA,BALL TYPE...................................  20.00
TYPEWRITER,HAMMOND NO.12......................................  25.00
TYPEWRITER,IDEAL,GERMANY......................................  25.00
TYPEWRITER,JOST NO.10.........................................  50.00
TYPEWRITER,LAMBERT............................................  10.00
```

```
TYPEWRITER,OLIVER.................................. 25.00 TO    30.00
TYPEWRITER,PORTABLE,SIDE LEVER RAISES TYPE,REMINGTON........    22.00
TYPEWRITER,REMINGTON STANDARD,KEYS STRIKE ROLLER FROM
  BOTTOM,PATENT..............................................    25.00

VAL ST.LAMBERT,BOTTLE,COLOGNE,CAMEO,CRANBERRY SCROLL,FROSTED
  GROUND....................................................    50.00
VAL ST.LAMBERT,BOWL,ROSE,CLEAR,SIGNED.......................    23.00
VAL ST.LAMBERT,BOX,BLUE GROUND,GOLD CAMEO FIGURES,SIGNED,
  5 IN.ROUND................................................    45.00
VAL ST.LAMBERT,BOX,CAMEO,CRANBERRY COLOR FLORAL,ETCHED
  GROUND,LID,3 IN...........................................    95.00
VAL ST.LAMBERT,BOX,CAMEO,CRANBERRY FLOWERS,FLEUR-DE-LIS,
  FROSTED GROUND............................................    45.00
VAL ST.LAMBERT,BOX,CLEAR,FROSTED TO ORANGE,ACID-CUT IRIS,
  LEAVES,COVER..............................................    55.00
VAL ST.LAMBERT,BOX,JEWEL,CAMEO,FLORAL,ACID-CUT,OVAL,MATCHING
  RING TREE.................................................    95.00
VAL ST.LAMBERT,JAR,BISCUIT,CAMEO,ENAMEL LAVENDER FLORAL,
  SILVER COVER..............................................   145.00
VAL ST.LAMBERT,JAR,GARLANDS & ROSES,COVER...................    35.00
VAL ST.LAMBERT,PLATE,COMMEMORATIVE,REMBRANDT,300TH
  ANNIVERSARY,1669-1969.....................................    50.00
VAL ST.LAMBERT,PLATE,GAME BIRD,FROSTED,MARKED,8 IN..........    22.50
VAL ST.LAMBERT,PLATE,MOTHER'S DAY,1968,PAIR.................   100.00
VAL ST.LAMBERT,PLATE,PILGRIM................................   400.00
VAL ST.LAMBERT,PLATE,REMBRANDT,RUBENS,1968,PAIR.... 85.00 TO    95.00
VAL ST.LAMBERT,RING TREE,RED FLOWERS,CLEAR..................    11.50
VAL ST.LAMBERT,VASE,CAMEO GLASS,DEER,SCENIC,RED,SIGNED,
  9 IN.HIGH.................................................   235.00
VAL ST.LAMBERT,VASE,CRANBERRY CUT TO CLEAR,SCRIPT SIGNATURE,
  6 1/2 IN..................................................    54.00
VAL ST.LAMBERT,WINE,TULIP SHAPE TOP,PINK-RED,CLEAR STEM.....    37.50
VALLERYSTAHL,DISH,BLUE,DOG ON BLANKET ON COVER,FLORAL ON
  BASE,SIGNED...............................................    40.00
VALLERYSTAHL,DISH,RETRIEVER DOG COVER,SIGNED................    95.00
VALLERYSTAHL,GOBLET,BLUE,SCALLOPED,FOOTED,SIGNED,MATCHING
  PLATE....................................................    50.00
VALLERYSTAHL,HEN ON NEST,MARKED,MILK GLASS..................    18.50
VALLERYSTAHL,HEN,8 IN.......................................    50.00
VALLERYSTAHL,SALT DIP,COVER,COVERED HEN,SIX EGG CUPS,CHICK
  BASES,TRAY................................................   350.00
```

VAN BRIGGLE POTTERY WAS MADE BY ARTUS VAN BRIGGLE IN
COLORADO SPRINGS,COLORADO,AFTER 1901. MR. VAN BRIGGLE
HAD BEEN A DECORATOR AT THE ROCKWOOD POTTERY OF
CINCINNATI,OHIO,AND HE DIED IN 1904. HIS WARES WERE
ORIGINAL AND HAD MODELED RELIEF DECORATIONS WITH A
SOFT DULL GLAZE.

```
VAN BRIGGLE,BOWL,BLUE,BEE DESIGN,SHALLOW,8 1/2 IN...........    10.50
VAN BRIGGLE,BOWL,DRAGONFLY,TURQUOISE,THREE FROG FLOWER
  HOLDER...................................................    35.00
VAN BRIGGLE,BOWL,FIVE PETALS,BLUE...........................     7.00
VAN BRIGGLE,BOWL,FLOWER,TULIPS IN RELIEF,MAROON GROUND,
  MATCHING FROG............................................    13.00
VAN BRIGGLE,BOWL,ROSE,GREEN TO BLUE,LEAF DECOR,4 IN.HIGH....    12.00
VAN BRIGGLE,BOWL,SWIRLS,LEAF PATTERN AT TOP,MAUVE,SIGNED,
  7 IN.....................................................    24.50
VAN BRIGGLE,BOWL-VASE,FLOWER HOLDER,BLUE,DRAGONFLIES,FROGS..    49.50
VAN BRIGGLE,CANDLEHOLDER,MAROON,HOLDS TWO CANDLES,PAIR......    12.00
VAN BRIGGLE,CREAMER & SUGAR,MAROON,COVER....................    18.00
VAN BRIGGLE,CREAMER,BLUE....................................     8.50
VAN BRIGGLE,PITCHER,MAROON,4 1/4 IN.TALL....................    10.00
VAN BRIGGLE,PITCHER,WHITE...................................     4.00
VAN BRIGGLE,PLANTER,WHITE,CRESCENT SHAPE,7 1/2 IN.TALL,
  8 IN.ACROSS..............................................     7.50
VAN BRIGGLE,SEASHELL,TURQUOISE TO BLUE,OPEN,12 IN.LONG,
  4 1/2 IN.HIGH............................................    19.50
VAN BRIGGLE,VASE,BLENDED TURQUOISE,MARKED,7 IN.HIGH.........    10.00
VAN BRIGGLE,VASE,BLUE TO GREEN,EMBOSSED ARCH DESIGN,SIGNED,
  7 1/2 IN.................................................    16.50
VAN BRIGGLE,VASE,BLUE,CORSET SHAPE,DATED 1906...............    15.00
VAN BRIGGLE,VASE,BROWN,GREEN,THREE MOLDED INDIANS HEADS,
  11 IN.HIGH...............................................    65.00
VAN BRIGGLE,VASE,DEEP TOAST SHADE,GREEN BUTTERFLY ON SIDES,
  BOWL SHAPE...............................................    11.00
VAN BRIGGLE,VASE,EMBOSSED TULIPS,BLUE-GREEN,2 1/2 IN........    14.50
VAN BRIGGLE,VASE,GREEN,MATTE FINISH,5 IN.TALL,3-IN.DIAMETER.     4.50
VAN BRIGGLE,VASE,GREEN TO BLUE,LEAF DECOR,4 1/2 IN.HIGH.....    12.00
```

VAN BRIGGLE,VASE,LEAVES AT BASE,LONG-STEMMED FLOWER TO TOP,
4 1/2 IN.................................................... 12.00
VAN BRIGGLE,VASE,LIGHT TO DARK MAROON,LEAF PATTERN AROUND
TOP,4 1/2 IN................................................ 4.95
VAN BRIGGLE,VASE,LORELEI,BLUE-GREEN,MARK,10 1/2 IN.TALL..... 18.00
VAN BRIGGLE,VASE,MAROON..................................... 12.00
VAN BRIGGLE,VASE,MAROON,BLUE,RAISED INDIAN FACES,
11....................................... 45.00 TO 75.00
VAN BRIGGLE,VASE,PLUM COLOR,TWO HANDLES,SIGNED,4 IN.HIGH.... 15.00
VAN BRIGGLE,VASE,RED,FLORAL DESIGN,DATED 1918,MARKED,3 1/2 X
3 1/2 IN................................................... 22.00
VAN BRIGGLE,VASE,RED,LEAF PATTERN AROUND TOP,MARKED,
4 1/2 IN.HIGH.............................................. 4.95
VAN BRIGGLE,VASE,ROSE BOWL SHAPE,DARK RED,SIGNED,DATED...... 6.50
VAN BRIGGLE,VASE,SHADED BLUE,EMBOSSED FLORAL,COLORADO
SPRINGS MARK............................................... 10.50
VAN BRIGGLE,VASE,SWIRL,MAROON TO PURPLE TOP,SIGNED,
7 1/4 IN.TALL.............................................. 12.00
VAN BRIGGLE,VASE,WHITE SATIN FINISH,CRESCENT SHAPE,SIGNED... 7.50

VASA MURRHINA IS THE NAME OF A GLASSWARE MADE BY THE
VASA MURRHINA ART GLASS COMPANY OF SANDWICH,
MASSACHUSETTS,ABOUT 1884. THE GLASSWARE WAS TRANSPARENT
AND WAS IMBEDDED WITH SMALL PIECES OF COLORED GLASS AND
METALLIC FLAKES. SOME OF THE PIECES WERE CASED. THE
SAME TYPE OF GLASS WAS MADE IN ENGLAND. COLLECTORS
OFTEN CONFUSE VASA MURRHINA GLASS WITH AVENTURINE,
SPATTER,OR SPANGLE GLASS. THERE IS MUCH CONFUSION ABOUT
WHAT ACTUALLY WAS MADE BY THE VASA MURRHINA FACTORY.

VASA MURRHINA,BASKET,BLUE & WHITE SWIRLS,SILVER MICA,STEVENS
& WILLIAMS................................................. 45.00
VASA MURRHINA,BASKET,LAVENDER,8-IN.DIAMETER................ 175.00
VASA MURRHINA,BASKET,WHITE CENTER,RED RUFFLES,MICA
FLECKINGS,6 IN.LONG........................................ 65.00
VASA MURRHINA,BASKET,WHITE,CASED,YELLOW OVERLAY,GOLD FLECKS,
RUFFLED.................................................... 30.00
VASA MURRHINA,BOWL,PINK,RED,BLUE FLECKS,SILVER MICA,CRYSTAL
FRILL,10 IN................................................ 85.00
VASA MURRHINA,BOWL,ROBIN'S-EGG BLUE,BLUE MICA,APPLIED
CRYSTAL PETALS............................................. 30.00
VASA MURRHINA,BOWL,ROSE,APRICOT,GOLD FLAKES,WHITE CASING,
DAISY RIGAREE.............................................. 50.00
VASA MURRHINA,BOWL,ROSE,CRANBERRY,WHITE & SILVER FLECKS,
4 IN.HIGH................................................. 65.00
VASA MURRHINA,BOWL,ROSE,YELLOW TO WHITE,4 1/2 IN. X
4 1/4 IN.................................................. 57.50
VASA MURRHINA,BOWL,SPATTERS OF BLUE,BROWN,GREEN,WHITE,SILVER
MICA....................................................... 30.00
VASA MURRHINA,BRIDE'S BASKET,TAN,GOLD FLECKS,WHITE CASING,
RUFFLED.................................................... 95.00
VASA MURRHINA,COMPOTE,BLUE FLUTES,ORANGE TO BLUE,SANDWICH,
PAIRPOINT CO............................................... 100.00
VASA MURRHINA,CREAMER,RAINBOW,CASED,4 IN................... 55.00
VASA MURRHINA,PAPERWEIGHT,APPLE............................ 35.00
VASA MURRHINA,PITCHER,AMBER GROUND,SPLASHES,GOLD SPECKS,
CLEAR HANDLE............................................... 85.00
VASA MURRHINA,TRAY,BROWN-RED,6 IN.......................... 28.00
VASA MURRHINA,TUMBLER,PINK,WHITE,SILVER FLECKS............. 35.00
VASA MURRHINA,VASE,BLACK,WHITE SPATTER,RED AVENTURINE,BLUE,
8 1/2 IN.................................................. 58.00
VASA MURRHINA,VASE,COBALT,GOLD,SCALLOPED,CRIMPED,9 X
3 1/2 IN.HIGH............................................. 50.00
VASA MURRHINA,VASE,DEEP PINK OUTSIDE,LIGHT PINK INSIDE,
FLECKS,PAIR............................................... 185.00
VASA MURRHINA,VASE,DOUBLE GOURD SHAPE,CASED,PINK,GOLD
FLECKS,14 IN.............................................. 85.00
VASA MURRHINA,VASE,MULTICOLOR,RUFFLED,9 IN.HIGH........... 43.00
VASA MURRHINA,VASE,MULTICOLORED,SILVER MICA,WHITE CASING,
9 1/4 IN.................................................. 42.50
VASA MURRHINA,VASE,OXBLOOD,RED,BLUE,SILVER MICA,CRYSTAL
RIBBON EDGE............................................... 30.00
VASA MURRHINA,VASE,RUFFLED TOP,9 IN.HIGH.................. 45.00
VASART,BOWL,PINK & WHITE CLUTHRA-TYPE GLASS,SIGNED,4 3/4 X
1 1/2 IN.HIGH............................................. 38.00
VASART,TUMBLER,YELLOW..................................... 10.00
VASART,VASE,BLUE-TURQUOISE,SIGNED,8 IN.HIGH............... 45.00
VASART,VASE,CRANBERRY TO DEEP BLUE,BLOWN,BULBOUS,
7 3/4 IN.HIGH............................................. 95.00

VASELINE GLASS IS A GREENISH YELLOW GLASSWARE
RESEMBLING PETROLEUM JELLY. SOME VASELINE GLASS IS
STILL BEING MADE IN OLD AND NEW STYLES. PRESSED GLASS
OF THE 1870S WAS OFTEN MADE OF VASELINE-COLORED GLASS.
THE OLD GLASS WAS MADE WITH URANIUM,BUT THE
REPRODUCTIONS ARE BEING COLORED IN A DIFFERENT WAY.
SEE PRESSED GLASS FOR MORE INFORMATION ABOUT PATTERNS
THAT WERE ALSO MADE OF VASELINE-COLORED GLASS.

VASELINE GLASS,BASKET,FLOWER,OPALESCENT BLUE TOP,ROPELIKE
HANDLE.............................................. 22.50
VASELINE GLASS,BOWL,BERRY,HOBNAIL,OPALESCENT,8 IN.,FIVE
SAUCES............................................. 87.50
VASELINE GLASS,BOWL,BUTTON & DAISY,CROSSBAR,FOOTED,
8 1/4-IN.DIAMETER.................................. 35.00
VASELINE GLASS,BOWL,DIAMOND QUILTED,FOOTED,8 1/4 IN......... 18.75
VASELINE GLASS,BOWL,FINGER,THREADED LUTZ................... 30.00
VASELINE GLASS,BOWL,ROSE,EMBOSSED IRIS,RUFFLED TOP,
OPALESCENT........................................ 30.00
VASELINE GLASS,BOWL,ROSE,EMBOSSED POPPIES................. 18.00
VASELINE GLASS,BOWL,ROSE,FOOTED........................... 35.00
VASELINE GLASS,BOWL,ROSE,OPALINE SWIRL,GREEN RIM,FLUTED TOP,
3 1/2 IN.......................................... 35.00
VASELINE GLASS,BOWL,SUGAR,DAISY,BUTTON,CROSSBAR............ 22.50
VASELINE GLASS,BOWL,SUGAR,OPALESCENT HOBNAIL,TWO HANDLES,
OPEN.............................................. 19.50
VASELINE GLASS,BOWL,THREE PANELS,ON STANDARD,10-IN.DIAMETER. 24.00
VASELINE GLASS,BUTTER,DAISY & BUTTON,INVERTED THUMBPRINT
DECOR ON COVER.................................... 60.00
VASELINE GLASS,CAKE STAND,DAISY & BUTTON,7 3/4 X
11 1/8-IN.DIAMETER................................ 77.50
VASELINE GLASS,CAKE STAND,MEDALLION,10 1/2 IN............. 29.50
VASELINE GLASS,CAKE STAND,PANELED BLOCK.................... 24.50
VASELINE GLASS,CANDLESTICK,FACET CUT,FLOWER SPRAYS,STEMS,
8 5/8 IN.,PAIR.................................... 85.00
VASELINE GLASS,CASTOR,PICKLE,DIAMOND-POINT PATTERN,SILVER
COVER,HOLDER...................................... 68.00
VASELINE GLASS,CASTOR,PICKLE,CRISSCROSS PATTERN,SILVER
HOLDER,TONGS...................................... `67.50
VASELINE GLASS,CASTOR,PICKLE,DIAMOND POINT,SILVER HOLDER,
COVER,TONGS....................................... 70.00
VASELINE GLASS,CELERY,1000-EYE,6 IN....................... 25.00
VASELINE GLASS,CELERY,DAISY & BUTTON,CROSS BAR............ 22.50
VASELINE GLASS,CELERY,PRESSED DIAMOND,7 IN.TALL........... 17.50
VASELINE GLASS,CELERY,TWO PANELS,7 1/4 IN.HIGH............ 32.50
VASELINE GLASS,COMPOTE,1000-EYE,KNOB STEM,THREE MOLD,OPEN,
7 1/2 IN.......................................... 25.00
VASELINE GLASS,COMPOTE,1000-EYE,THREE KNOBS,8 3/4 IN....... 30.00
VASELINE GLASS,COMPOTE,CUT SATIN FLORAL SPRAYS,2 3/4 X
11 IN.WIDE........................................ 18.00
VASELINE GLASS,COMPOTE,DOLPHIN STEM,OPALESCENT RIM,6 IN. X
5 1/2 IN.HIGH..................................... 27.50
VASELINE GLASS,COMPOTE,FLOWER SPRAYS,LOW FOOT,11-IN.DIAMETER 55.00
VASELINE GLASS,COMPOTE,PETTICOAT,DOLPHIN,OPALESCENT RIM,
PITTSBURGH........................................ 110.00
VASELINE GLASS,COMPOTE,PINK IRIDESCENT INSIDE TOP,STRETCHED
EDGE.............................................. 35.00
VASELINE GLASS,COMPOTE,QUILTED DIAMOND,OPEN,8-IN.DIAMETER,
5 3/4 IN.HIGH..................................... 13.00
VASELINE GLASS,COMPOTE,ROSE SPRIG,OPEN,OVAL,5 1/4 IN.HIGH... 32.50
VASELINE GLASS,COMPOTE,SWAG WITH BRACKETS,OPALESCENT RIM,
5 IN.HIGH......................................... 18.00
VASELINE GLASS,COMPOTE,THREADED,FLUTED OPALESCENT EDGE,
4 1/2 IN.TALL..................................... 22.00
VASELINE GLASS,COMPOTE,WILLOW OAK,COVER,10 IN. HIGH,
6 1/4 IN.-DIAMETER................................ 25.00
VASELINE GLASS,CREAMER,ALASKA,LION LEG.................... 50.00
VASELINE GLASS,CREAMER,COVERED SUGAR,SPOONER,THREE PANELS... 65.00
VASELINE GLASS,CREAMER,DAISY & BUTTON,THREE-CORNERED....... 22.00
VASELINE GLASS,CREAMER,LION'S LEG,OPALESCENT.............. 28.00
VASELINE GLASS,CREAMER,MAPLE LEAF,FOOTED.................. 25.00
VASELINE GLASS,CREAMER,SUGAR,BUTTER,SPOONER,ADONIS,COVERS... 100.00
VASELINE GLASS,CREAMER & SUGAR,OPAL TRIM.................. 12.50
VASELINE GLASS,CRUET,HOBNAIL............................. 18.00
VASELINE GLASS,CUP,SAUCER,IMPRESSED PANSIES,LIBBEY GLASS
CO.,TOLEDO,OHIO................................... 27.50
VASELINE GLASS,DECANTER,ENAMEL BIRD DECOR,CLEAR BLOWN
STOPPER........................................... 25.00
VASELINE GLASS,DESSERT,CLEAR TO OPALESCENT,RUFFLED........ 10.00
VASELINE GLASS,DISH,BANANA SHAPE,HINGED HANDLES,CLEAR,8 X

6 IN.HIGH.............................................. 10.00
VASELINE GLASS,DISH,BANANA,HOBNAIL,OPALESCENT,HANDLES,
5 1/2 X 6 1/2 IN..................................... 15.50
VASELINE GLASS,DISH,BOAT-SHAPED,TURNED-UP ENDS,PIERCED FOR
HANGING,8 IN........................................ 22.50
VASELINE GLASS,DISH,CANDY,ROUND BASE,SHORT STEM,GREEN,
7-IN.DIAMETER....................................... 10.00
VASELINE GLASS,DISH,CANDY,SPANISH LACE,OPALESCENT EDGE,
RUFFLED,6 1/2 IN.................................... 11.00
VASELINE GLASS,DISH,CELERY,DAISY & BUTTON,CROSSBAR.......... 27.50
VASELINE GLASS,DISH,PICKLE,LOVE'S REQUEST IS PICKLES,
ACTRESS,5 X 9 IN.................................... 21.00
VASELINE GLASS,DISH,RELISH,WHISK BROOM,CIRCA 1886,PAT.APP.
ON HANDLE........................................... 25.00
VASELINE GLASS,DISH,SAUCE,1000-EYE,FOOTED.............. 10.00
VASELINE GLASS,DISH,SAUCE,SHELL & WREATH............... 8.00
VASELINE GLASS,DISH,TWO COMPARTMENTS,OVAL,7 IN......... 7.00
VASELINE GLASS,EPERGNE,CREAM OPALESCENT CRESCENTS,LILY,
16 IN.HIGH.......................................... 88.00
VASELINE GLASS,GOBLET,BASKET WEAVE..................... 15.00
VASELINE GLASS,GOBLET,ROSE IN SNOW,FOOTED,CIRCA 1931... 18.00
VASELINE GLASS,INKWELL,DIAMOND SHAPE,HINGED TOP,BRASS HINGE
& RIM............................................... 25.00
VASELINE GLASS,JAR,BISCUIT,IRIS,LEAVES,HINGED BRASS COVER,
7 1/2 IN.TALL....................................... 45.00
VASELINE GLASS,JAR,BISCUIT,THREADED,BLOWN,SILVER COVER &
HANDLE,6 IN......................................... 50.00
VASELINE GLASS,JAR,BISCUIT,THREADED,SILVER COVER,BAIL,
6 IN.HIGH........................................... 50.00
VASELINE GLASS,JAR,CRACKER,DAISY & BUTTON,CROSSBAR,COVER.... 42.50
VASELINE GLASS,MUG,CHILD'S,RABBIT PATTERN.............. 16.00
VASELINE GLASS,PAPERWEIGHT,BUDDHA,SIGNED GILLINDER..... 55.00
VASELINE GLASS,PAPERWEIGHT,PAIRPOINT,LARGE CORE OF TINY
BUBBLES,3 IN........................................ 22.50
VASELINE GLASS,PERFUME,RIBBED,PANELED,PETAL STOPPER,
SANDWICH,4 IN.TALL.................................. 55.00
VASELINE GLASS,PITCHER,APPLIED AMBER HANDLE............ 18.00
VASELINE GLASS,PITCHER,DAISY & BUTTON,CROSSBAR,QUART SIZE... 25.00
VASELINE GLASS,PITCHER,DAISY & BUTTON,CROSSBARS,6 IN....... 20.00
VASELINE GLASS,PITCHER,DAISY & BUTTON WITH CROSSBAR,
6 3/4 IN.HIGH....................................... 22.00
VASELINE GLASS,PITCHER,INVERTED THUMBPRINT,POLISHED PONTIL,
REEDED HANDLE....................................... 37.50
VASELINE GLASS,PITCHER,MILK,DAISY,BUTTON,CROSSBAR.. 22.50 TO 35.00
VASELINE GLASS,PITCHER,OVERLAY........................ 135.00
VASELINE GLASS,PITCHER,WATER,BASKET WEAVE,TRAY,SIX GOBLETS.. 147.50
VASELINE GLASS,PITCHER,WATER,DAISY & BUTTON,ELONGATED
BULBOUS BODY........................................ 55.00
VASELINE GLASS,PLATE,CAKE,WILD FLOWER,10 IN.SQUARE. 17.50 TO 25.00
VASELINE GLASS,PLATTER,DAISY & BUTTON,OPEN HANDLES,OVAL,13 X
9 IN................................................ 29.50
VASELINE GLASS,POT,GYPSY,DAISY & BUTTON PATTERN,WIRE BAIL... 10.00
VASELINE GLASS,PUMP & TROUGH,OPALESCENT............... 85.00
VASELINE GLASS,RELISH,ROSE SPRIG,BOAT SHAPE,SCALLOPED EDGE.. 18.00
VASELINE GLASS,SALT,DAISY & BUTTON,BANDMASTER CAP.......... 22.50
VASELINE GLASS,SALT,DAISY & BUTTON,TRIANGULAR......... 7.50
VASELINE GLASS,SALT,INDIVIDUAL,DIAMOND................ 4.50
VASELINE GLASS,SAUCE,DAISY & BUTTON,OCTAGON........... 10.00
VASELINE GLASS,SAUCE,DAISY & BUTTON,5 IN.............. 7.50
VASELINE GLASS,SAUCE,DIAMOND-QUILTED,FLAT,4 IN........ 7.50
VASELINE GLASS,SAUCE,MAPLE LEAF,FOOTED................ 5.00
VASELINE GLASS,SAUCE,RETICULATED CORD,FLAT,4 3/8 IN... 6.00
VASELINE GLASS,SAUCE,SUNKEN BUTTONS,FLAT,4 IN......... 5.00
VASELINE GLASS,SAUCE,TREE OF LIFE..................... 15.00
VASELINE GLASS,SAUCE,WILD FLOWER,FLAT,4 IN............ 6.00
VASELINE GLASS,SHADE,GAS,HOBNAIL,4-IN.OPENING......... 20.00
VASELINE GLASS,SHAKER,SALT,1000-EYE................... 12.00
VASELINE GLASS,SHOE,DAISY & BUTTON,5 IN............... 22.50
VASELINE GLASS,SLIPPER,DAISY & BUTTON,NAILHEAD DECOR,6 IN... 12.00
VASELINE GLASS,SLIPPER,ON SKATES,DAISY & BUTTON....... 22.50
VASELINE GLASS,SPOON TRAY,ROLLED UP SIDES,OPEN EDGES,
SUNBURST............................................ 19.00
VASELINE GLASS,SPOONER,ALASKA,LION LEG................ 45.00
VASELINE GLASS,SPOONER,DAISY & BUTTON,CROSSBAR,FOOTED...... 22.50
VASELINE GLASS,SPOONER,INVERTED THUMBPRINT............ 18.00
VASELINE GLASS,SPOONER,OAKEN BUCKET................... 13.75
VASELINE GLASS,SPOONER,THREE PANELS................... 17.50
VASELINE GLASS,SPOONER,WREATH & SHELL,OPALESCENT,FOOTED.... 16.50
VASELINE GLASS,STAND,TEABERRY GUM.............. 4.95 TO 15.00
VASELINE GLASS,SUGAR & CREAMER,INVERTED THUMBPRINT,COLLARED

BASE,COVER............................................... 28.00
VASELINE GLASS,SUGAR,LION'S LEG,ALASKA,SQUARE.............. 37.50
VASELINE GLASS,TOOTHPICK,DAISY,BUTTON,CAT ON CUSHION....... 28.50
VASELINE GLASS,TOOTHPICK,DAISY,BUTTON,WITH V............... 12.00
VASELINE GLASS,TOOTHPICK,FAN.............................. 16.00
VASELINE GLASS,TOOTHPICK,FLOWER BORDER,FOOTED............. 10.00
VASELINE GLASS,TOOTHPICK,HAT,DAISY & BUTTON............... 16.50
VASELINE GLASS,TOOTHPICK,HAT,RIBBED....................... 8.50
VASELINE GLASS,TOOTHPICK,OAKEN BUCKET,BAIL................ 17.50
VASELINE GLASS,TRAY,BASKET WEAVE,RURAL SCENE IN CENTER..... 32.50
VASELINE GLASS,TRAY,BASKET WEAVE,RURAL SCENE,BOY,DOG,HOUSE,
   TREES,BRIDGE............................................ 32.00
VASELINE GLASS,TRAY,BREAD,MAPLE LEAF,OVAL,SCALLOPED,9 1/2 X
   13 1/2 IN............................................... 22.50
VASELINE GLASS,TRAY,DAISY & BUTTON,CROSSBAR,11 IN. X 18 IN.. 25.00
VASELINE GLASS,TRAY,DOUGHNUT,IMPERIAL JEWELS,CENTER POST,
   PAINTED DECOR........................................... 16.00
VASELINE GLASS,TUMBLER,HOBNAIL............................ 22.00
VASELINE GLASS,TUMBLER,MEMPHIS,DARK GREEN,GOLD BAND,
   NORTHWOOD............................................... 8.50
VASELINE GLASS,TUMBLER,SEQUOIA............................ 10.00
VASELINE GLASS,TUMBLER,TOY,DAISY,BUTTON,FOOTED,HOBBS,
   BROCUNIER,1880.......................................... 22.50
VASELINE GLASS,TUMBLER,WREATH AND SHELL,OPALESCENT........ 15.00
VASELINE GLASS,VASE,AUTO,METAL HANGER,PAIR................ 35.00
VASELINE GLASS,VASE,BULBOUS IN CENTER,9 IN................ 12.00
VASELINE GLASS,VASE,CELERY,DAISY & BUTTON,CROSSBAR........ 27.50
VASELINE GLASS,VASE,ENAMELED ORANGE,TAN,RED ROSES,SIGNED
   LEA,13 IN.,PAIR......................................... 98.00
VASELINE GLASS,VASE,OPALESCENT TOP,SQUATTY,HAND-BLOWN...... 12.00
VASELINE GLASS,WINE,GREEN,CLEAR STEM & FOOT,PAIR.......... 12.00
VASELINE GLASS,WINE,PANELED JEWELS....................... 22.50
VASELINE GLASS,WINE,VINTAGE PATTERN,RIBBED STEM,BOHEMIA,
   6 IN.HIGH.............................................. 18.00

VENETIAN GLASS HAS BEEN MADE NEAR VENICE,ITALY,FROM
THE THIRTEENTH TO THE TWENTIETH CENTURY. THIN,COLORED
GLASS WITH APPLIED DECORATIONS IS FAVORED,ALTHOUGH
MANY OTHER TYPES HAVE BEEN MADE.

VENETIAN GLASS,BASKET,FLANGE BASE,APPLIED CLEAR HANDLE,
   MURANO,ITALY............................................ 22.50
VENETIAN GLASS,BOWL,BLUE,WHITE STRIPES,RUFFLED EDGE PULLED
   TO 3 POINTS............................................ 17.50
VENETIAN GLASS,BOWL,FINGER,RUFFLED,SAUCER,PINK,GREEN,AMBER,
   BLUE,SET OF 8........................................... 195.00
VENETIAN GLASS,BOWL,PAPERWEIGHT,RED,WHITE RODS ON RIM,RED TO
   GREEN,8 IN............................................. 900.00
VENETIAN GLASS,BOX,POWDER,GOLD & WHITE SNOWFLAKE-LIKE
   DAISIES,COVER........................................... 8.50
VENETIAN GLASS,DISH,CANDY,ENAMELED,ROSES,LEAVES,GOLD,
   6-IN.DIAMETER........................................... 23.50
VENETIAN GLASS,DISH,NUT,GREEN,GOLD,RUFFLED,AMBER SQUIRREL
   HANDLES,6.............................................. 49.50
VENETIAN GLASS,EPERGNE,GREEN & BLUE OPALESCENT,FLOWERS,
   BLOWN,21 IN............................................ 65.00
VENETIAN GLASS,FINGER BOWL SET,STRIPED GLASS,COBALT & ORANGE
   PANELS................................................. 95.00
VENETIAN GLASS,GOBLET,RUBY STEM,CLEAR GOLD-DUSTED HOLLOW
   KNOB IN CENTER.......................................... 20.00
VENETIAN GLASS,PARFAIT,YELLOW,PEACH-ROSE FLORAL,ENAMEL,GOLD,
   SET OF 6............................................... 165.00
VENETIAN GLASS,PITCHER,WATER,ENAMELED,LILIES,GOLD,SIX
   GLASSES................................................ 55.00
VENETIAN GLASS,PLATE,PINK THREADING,BERRY PRUNTS,GOLD DUST,
   7 IN.................................................. 35.00
VENETIAN GLASS,SWAN,GREEN & GOLD......................... 8.00
VENETIAN GLASS,VASE,CLEAR,GREEN SWIRL DESIGN,RUFFLED TOP.... 10.00
VENETIAN GLASS,VASE,GREEN TO OPALESCENT,GREEN RIGAREE AROUND
   STEM,12 IN............................................. 37.50
VENETIAN GLASS,VASE,GREEN,THREADS,BULBOUS,10 IN.HIGH....... 18.00
VENETIAN GLASS,VASE,PORTRAIT,PORCELAIN MEDALLION,GREEN
   GROUND,GOLD............................................ 135.00
VENETIAN GLASS,VASE,PUMPKIN,GREEN,GOLD DECOR,SET WITH OPALS
   & GARNETS............................................. 50.00

VERLYS GLASS WAS MADE IN FRANCE AFTER 1931. VERLYS WAS
ALSO MADE IN THE UNITED STATES. THE GLASS IS EITHER
BLOWN OR MOLDED. THE AMERICAN GLASS IS SIGNED WITH A

DIAMOND-POINT-SCRATCHED NAME BUT THE FRENCH PIECES ARE
MARKED WITH A MOLDED SIGNATURE.

VERLYS,BOWL,ACORNS,BLUE,SIGNED,6 1/4 X 1 3/4 IN.............. 18.00
VERLYS,BOWL,BLUE FLYING GULLS MAKE FOOTREST,MOLDED FISH,
  SATIN GROUND.................................................. 90.00
VERLYS,BOWL,BLUE,THISTLE PATTERN,FOOTED BASE,
  CAMPHOR-FROSTED,SIGNED....................................... 35.00
VERLYS,BOWL,CAMPHOR SATIN,ORCHIDS IN HIGH RELIEF,SHALLOW,
  14 IN......................................................... 65.00
VERLYS,BOWL,CENTER,YELLOW,LEAF DECOR,SIGNED,
  8 1/2-IN.DIAMETER............................................ 59.00
VERLYS,BOWL,CENTERPIECE,FLYING BIRDS,FISH,SATIN,FROSTED,
  SIGNED,14 IN................................................ 125.00
VERLYS,BOWL,FROSTED CUPID WITH HEARTS IN BOTTOM,6 IN. X
  2 IN.TALL.................................................... 27.50
VERLYS,BOWL,FROSTED,PALM TREES,MARK,4 1/2-IN.DIAMETER....... 15.00
VERLYS,BOWL,LARGE POPPIES,LEAVES,SIGNED,13 1/2-IN.DIAMETER.. 47.50
VERLYS,BOWL,PINECONE,STEMS,NEEDLES,AMBER,FOOTED,SIGNED,
  6 1/8 IN..................................................... 18.00
VERLYS,BOWL,POPPY,13 1/2 IN................................. 65.00
VERLYS,BOWL,ROSES,SIGNED,5 IN.............................. 25.00
VERLYS,BOWL,TASSELS,SIGNED,11-IN.DIAMETER.................. 27.50
VERLYS,BOWL,THREE BIRDS IN FLIGHT,TWO FISH,
  13 1/2-IN.DIAMETER.......................................... 47.50
VERLYS,BOX,AMBER COLOR,FROSTED FLOWER DECOR,COVER,BEVELING,
  SIGNED...................................................... 37.50
VERLYS,BOX,POWDER,BUTTERFLIES,SIGNED,7-IN.DIAMETER......... 75.00
VERLYS,DISH,EMBOSSED WATER LILIES,LILY PADS,SIGNED,
  11 3/4 IN.DIAMETER.......................................... 70.00
VERLYS,DISH,THREE SPREAD-WINGED DUCKS IN FLIGHT,TWO FISH IN
  WATER....................................................... 60.00
VERLYS,RELISH,PINEAPPLE,ROUND,THREE-FOOTED,SIGNED........... 22.00
VERLYS,TRAY,CAR,NUDE WOMAN,SIGNED.......................... 38.00
VERLYS,VASE,FROSTED LOVEBIRDS,FOOTED,4 1/2 IN.HIGH......... 40.00
VERLYS,VASE,LADIES GATHERING WHEAT,EMBOSSED,FROSTY CRYSTAL,
  10 IN.HIGH.................................................. 65.00
VERLYS,VASE,LOVEBIRDS,SIGNED,6 1/2 X 4 1/2 IN.HIGH......... 45.00
VERLYS,VASE,OPALESCENT,DANCING FIGURES,CAMPHOR,SIGNED,
  8 IN.TALL................................................... 95.00

VERRE DE SOIE GLASS WAS FIRST MADE BY FREDERICK CARDER
AT THE STEUBEN GLASS WORKS FROM ABOUT 1905 TO 1930. IT
IS AN IRIDESCENT GLASS OF SOFT WHITE OR VERY,VERY PALE
GREEN. THE NAME MEANS GLASS OF SILK AND IT DOES
RESEMBLE SILK. OTHER FACTORIES HAVE MADE VERRE DE
SOIE,AND SOME OF THE ENGLISH EXAMPLES WERE MADE OF
DIFFERENT COLORS. VERRE DE SOIE IS AN ART GLASS AND IS
NOT RELATED TO THE IRIDESCENT PRESSED WHITE CARNIVAL
GLASS MISTAKENLY CALLED BY ITS NAME.
VERRE DE SOIE,SEE ALSO STEUBEN
VERRE DE SOIE,BONBON,ROUND BASE,PULLED SQUARE TOP,SWIRLS,
  IRIDESCENT.................................................. 40.00
VERRE DE SOIE,BOTTLE,COLOGNE,ORIGINAL STOPPER,STEUBEN....... 65.00
VERRE DE SOIE,BOWL,ATOMIC CLOUD........................... 75.00
VERRE DE SOIE,BOWL,ENGRAVED,FLARED BASE,SIGNED HAWKES...... 75.00
VERRE DE SOIE,BOWL,FLORAL CUTTING,BLUE & PURPLE HIGHLIGHTS,
  8 X 3 1/2 IN................................................ 60.00
VERRE DE SOIE,BOWL,ROSE,WHITE & GOLD FEATHERING,PULLED
  RUFFLES..................................................... 42.50
VERRE DE SOIE,BOWL,SLANTING SIDES,POLISHED PONTIL,STEUBEN,
  6-IN.DIAMETER............................................... 25.00
VERRE DE SOIE,BOX,PUFF,GREEN KNOB......................... 45.00
VERRE DE SOIE,COLOGNE,MELON RIB BASE & STOPPER,STEUBEN,
  6 1/2 IN.................................................... 90.00
VERRE DE SOIE,COMPOTE,INTAGLIO CUT FLORAL,LEAVES,SIGNED
  HAWKES,5 X 7 IN............................................. 49.50
VERRE DE SOIE,PERFUME,GREEN JADE STOPPER.................. 145.00
VERRE DE SOIE,SALT,IRIDESCENT,PEDESTAL,STEUBEN............. 50.00
VERRE DE SOIE,SHADE,GAS,IRIDESCENT,GREEN,IVORENE RIM,
  STEUBEN,5 IN.HIGH.......................................... 65.00
VERRE DE SOIE,SHADE,SCALLOPED BOTTOM,SIGNED STEUBEN,SET OF
  6........................................................... 175.00
VERRE DE SOIE,SHERBET,UNDERPLATE,SET OF 6................. 250.00
VERRE DE SOIE,URN,SWIRL-RIBBED DESIGN,STEUBEN,SIGNED,
  7 IN.HIGH................................................... 98.00
VERRE DE SOIE,VASE,BULBOUS BASE,SHORT NECK,CUT............. 82.50
VERRE DE SOIE,VASE,BULBOUS,SHORT NECK,FLARED TOP,STEUBEN,
  HAWKES,7 IN................................................. 82.50
VERRE DE SOIE,VASE,ENAMEL DECOR,PAIR FIGHTING COCKS,SIGNED

```
DR.W.MEITZER.......................................................  65.00
VERRE DE SOIE,VASE,FLARE TOP,FOOTED,10 IN.TALL.................  35.00
VERRE DE SOIE,VASE,GREEN,SILVER OVERLAY,SIGNED ALVIN,
   3 1/2 IN....................................................... 137.00
VERRE DE SOIE,VASE,IRIDESCENT,STEUBEN..........................  95.00
VERRE DE SOIE,VASE,IRIDESCENT,8 IN.HIGH........................ 115.00
VERRE DE SOIE,VASE,OPENWORK RIM,GREEN LINING,SIGNED STEUBEN. 165.00
VERRE DE SOIE,VASE,YELLOW,SWIRL-RIBBED BODY,TRUMPET-SHAPED,
   STEUBEN,4 IN...................................................  75.00
```

```
        VILLEROY AND BOCH POTTERY OF METTLACH,GERMANY,WAS
     FOUNDED IN 1841. THE FIRM MADE MANY TYPES OF POTTERY
     INCLUDING THE FAMOUS METTLACH STEINS.
   VILLEROY & BOCH,SEE ALSO,STEIN
VILLEROY & BOCH,BOWL,BLUE,WHITE LINING,WHITE DECOR,MARKED
   DRESDEN,SAXONY................................................  14.00
VILLEROY & BOCH,BOWL,WHITE,BLUE DECOR,MARKED,DRESDEN,
   9 1/2-IN.DIAMETER.............................................  15.00
VILLEROY & BOCH,CANDLEHOLDER,SAUCER TYPE,SIDE FINGER HANDLE,
   GREEN,MARK....................................................  10.00
VILLEROY & BOCH,CUP & SAUCER,SWIRLED CREAMY BEIGE GROUND,
   FLORAL,MARK...................................................  15.00
VILLEROY & BOCH,MUG,B.P.O.E.....................................  10.00
VILLEROY & BOCH,MUG,WHITE GROUND,BLUE & WHITE FLAG,DATED
   1884,1/2 LITER................................................  35.00
VILLEROY & BOCH,PITCHER,GRAVY,ATTACHED TRAY,ONION,BLUE......  22.50
VILLEROY & BOCH,PLAQUE,SCENE,STEAMBOAT,SAILBOAT,MOUNTAINS,
   12 1/2 IN.....................................................  43.00
VILLEROY & BOCH,PLAQUE,TAVERN SCENE,PIERCED FOR HANGING,
   12 1/2 IN.....................................................  43.00
VILLEROY & BOCH,PLAQUE,WALL,DOE,FAWN,STREAM,GEESE,
   12 1/2-IN.DIAMETER............................................  40.00
VILLEROY & BOCH,PLATE,CASTLE,DOCK,BOATS,BLUE ON WHITE,11 IN.  43.00
VILLEROY & BOCH,PLATE,DUTCH SCENE,WALLERFANGEN,PIERCED,
   10 IN.........................................................  30.00
VILLEROY & BOCH,PLATE,FRUIT,THREE PURPLE PLUMS ON RIM,GREEN
   BAND..........................................................  14.50
VILLEROY & BOCH,PLATE,LORELEI,12 IN.............................  75.00
VILLEROY & BOCH,PLATE,SAILBOAT & WINDMILL SCENE,
   10 1/2-IN.DIAMETER............................................  17.50
VILLEROY & BOCH,PLATE,SCENIC,HEIDELBERG CASTLE,PIERCED TO
   HANG,12 IN....................................................  12.50
VILLEROY & BOCH,PLATE,WHITE,GOLD FLOWER IN CENTER,GOLD TRIM,
   8 IN..........................................................   4.50
VILLEROY & BOCH,PLATE,WHITE,GOLD TRIM,METTLACH,7 IN.........   3.50
VILLEROY & BOCH,PLATTER,BLUE LEAVES,YELLOW ROSES,11 IN. X
   8 IN..........................................................  10.00
VILLEROY & BOCH,POT,PLANT,WHITE FAIENCE,GREEN BANDS,IRIS
   SPRAYS,BASE...................................................  30.00
VILLEROY & BOCH,RAMEKIN,SAUCER,DRESDEN PATTERN,BLUE & WHITE
   DECOR.........................................................   7.00
VILLEROY & BOCH,SUGAR,PASTORAL SCENES,MULBERRY TRANSFER,
   COVER.........................................................  15.00
VILLEROY & BOCH,TEAPOT,CHILD'S,ONION PATTERN,PITCHER,SIX
   CUPS,SAUCERS..................................................  52.00
VILLEROY & BOCH,TUMBLER,1/4 LITER,PEASANT GIRL,FLORAL,BORDER
   DESIGN........................................................  22.50
VILLEROY & BOCH,VASE,BLUE & WHITE,CASTLE MARK,5 3/4 IN.TALL.  17.00
VILLEROY & BOCH,VASE,GRAY GROUND,WHITE CAMEO FIGURES OF
   GIRL,MAN,10 IN................................................  60.00
VINCENNES,VASE,PAIR,TURQUOISE BLUE & GOLD,DATED 1753........2,300.00
WALLPAPER,VENUS,PSYCHE,CUPID,HAND PRINT,LINEN,JOSEPH DUFOUR,
   FOUR PANELS................................................... 300.00
```

```
        WARWICK CHINA WAS MADE IN WHEELING,WEST VIRGINIA,IN A
     POTTERY FACTORY FOUNDED IN 1887.
WARWICK,JAR,CRACKER,IVORY SATIN FINISH,FLORAL,GOLD,MARK,
   8 IN.TALL.....................................................  42.50
WARWICK,PITCHER,MONK............................................  25.00
WARWICK,PITCHER,MONK,4 MUGS.....................................  95.00
WARWICK,TUREEN,SOUP,BROWN DECOR,PINK & BLUE FLOWERS.........  45.00
WARWICK,VASE,BROWN TONES,FACE OF WOMAN,10 IN.TALL...........  25.00
WARWICK,VASE,BROWN TONES,FLORAL,12 IN.TALL......................  25.00
WARWICK,VASE,PORTRAIT,GIRL,BROWN & TAN,MARKED A 17 IN RED,
   10 1/2 IN.....................................................  30.00
WASHING MACHINE,COPPER BOILER,1900 CATARACT.................. 500.00
WASHING MACHINE,HAPPY HOME STEAM,HAND TURN,MADE TO SIT ON
   STOVE.........................................................  14.00
```

WATCH,ALBERT BURGER,MINUTE REPEATER,SILVER SNAKESKIN CASE,
OPEN FACE.......................................................... 450.00
WATCH,BABE RUTH................................................... 21.00
WATCH,CASED,DUTCH-TYPE COCK,WITH SILVER REPOUSSE VERGE,1780,
TWO PIECES........................................................ 100.00
WATCH,CHAIN,WITH SLIDE,GOLD-FILLED,52 IN.......................... 32.00
WATCH,CHAIN,WITH SWIVEL,GOLD-FILLED,52 IN......................... 12.00
WATCH,CORN GRAIN GUILLOCHE CASE,HUNTING CASE,18K GOLD,TWO
PIECES............................................................ 125.00
WATCH,CYLINDER MOVEMENT,KEYWIND,GOLD KEY,GOLD..................... 165.00
WATCH,DICK TRACY.................................................. 35.00
WATCH,ELGIN,KEYWIND,HUNTING CASE,GOLD-FILLED,1882................. 125.00
WATCH,ENAMEL,ROSES,SPLIT PEARLS,KEY WIND,GOLD........ILLUS.. 100.00

GOLD WATCH, ENAMEL, ROSES, SPLIT PEARL

WATCH,ENAMEL,SIZE 18 LIGNE,GIRL,PINK DRESS,SLEEPING BOY,
TREES,FRANCE...................................................... 495.00
WATCH,ENGINE-TURNED,SCROLL BORDER,LEAFAGE,FLORAL,1870,SWISS,
14K GOLD.......................................................... 50.00
WATCH,ENGLISH,OPEN FACE,KEY WIND,CYLINDER ESCAPEMENT,
M.J.TOBIAS,1800................................................... 22.50
WATCH,ENGLISH,SILVER HUNTING CASE,KEYWIND,MAKER BANKS,1812.. 45.00
WATCH,ENGLISH,STEM-WIND,DECORATED FACE,FOUR INSET DIALS,
GUN-METAL CASE.................................................... 55.00
WATCH,ENGRAVED HUNTING,25 YEAR CASE,MINUTE HAND IN RED...... 65.00
WATCH,FIVE-MINUTE REPEATER,SILVEROID CASE,8 DAY,BAILEY,
BANKS,BIDDLE CO................................................... 400.00
WATCH,FOB,KEY WIND,ENAMEL DIAL,BLANC FRERE ET FILS...ILLUS.. 375.00

WATCH, FOB, ENAMEL DIAL, BLANC FRERE ET FILS

WATCH,GOLD FILLED CASE,ELGIN...................................... 65.00
WATCH,HAMILTON,SIZE 12,BRUSHED SILVER FACE,ARABIC NUMERALS,
MODEL 917......................................................... 28.00
WATCH,HAMPDEN,HUNTING CASE,GOLD-FILLED............................ 65.00
WATCH,HENRY SANDOZ,MINUTE REPEATER,CHRONOGRAPH,ENAMEL DIAL,
SWISS............................................................. 800.00
WATCH,HOWARD,SIZE 14,OPEN FACE,GOLD-FILLED CASE,MARKED NO.1,
226,800........................................................... 50.00
WATCH,HUNTING CASE,CHAIN,ENGRAVED,15 JEWELS,ELGIN,14 KT..... 160.00
WATCH,HUNTING CASE,ENGRAVED FLORAL,ORNATE SHIELD,WALTHAM,
GOLD-FILLED....................................................... 32.00
WATCH,HUNTING CASE,ENGRAVED,COIN SILVER TRIMMED INSIDE WITH
GOLD.............................................................. 75.00
WATCH,HUNTING CASE,GOLD INLAY,MARE,FOAL,HUNTER,DOG,SILVER,
NIELLO,SWISS...................................................... 60.00
WATCH,HUNTING CASE,GOLD-FILLED,11-JEWEL MOVEMENT,SIZE 12,
J.A.FIELD......................................................... 25.00
WATCH,HUNTING CASE,JEWELED MOVEMENT WITH BUTTON SET,SWISS,
COIN SILVER....................................................... 22.00
WATCH,HUNTING CASE,KEYWIND,DATED 1874,TO C.J.PETERSON,ELGIN,
COIN SILVER....................................................... 36.00
WATCH,HUNTING CASE,KEYWIND,J.BARTH ET FILS,GENEVE....ILLUS.. 150.00
WATCH,HUNTING CASE,MINUTE REPEATER,GILT,CHAUX DE FONDS,
ULLMAN & CO....................................................... 500.00
WATCH,HUNTING CASE,PENDANT,RED ENAMEL GUILLOCHE GROUND,ROSE
DIAMOND,GOLD...................................................... 150.00
WATCH,HUNTING CASE,ROSE DIAMONDS,W.REDARD & SONS,GENEVE,
1880,GOLD......................................................... 200.00
WATCH,HUNTING CASE,STIPPLE-ENGRAVED,BLANK SHIELD,15 JEWELS,

HUNTING CASE WATCH, J. BARTH ET FILS, GENEVE

```
ELGIN,GOLD.................................................  75.00
WATCH,HUNTING CASE,STIPPLE,FLORAL,15 JEWELS,WALTHAM,
  SILVEROID................................................  25.00
WATCH,HUNTING,MAN'S,ELGIN,ENGRAVED BIRDS,25 YEAR CASE.......  30.00
WATCH,INRO,BRASS MOVEMENT,WOODEN CASE,JAPAN,3 IN.HIGH....... 350.00
WATCH,J.DOBLER,QUARTER HOUR REPEATER,CALENDAR,OPEN FACE,KEY,
  1830.................................................... 590.00
WATCH,KEY WIND,SILVER,CIRCA 1867...........................  37.50
WATCH,LADY'S,ALLOVER ENGRAVING,SCENE IN ARCHED FRAME,1880,
  WALTHAM.................................................  70.00
WATCH,LADY'S,BELT,GOLD,CRYSTAL,SILVER PADLOCK FORM,PEARLS,
  TWO PIECES.............................................. 225.00
WATCH,LADY'S,CHATELAINE,FRANCE,GOLD,5 1/2 IN.LONG....ILLUS.. 375.00
```

LADY'S GOLD CHATELAINE WATCH, FRANCE

```
WATCH,LADY'S,CLOSED CASE,COVERS ENGRAVED WITH DAFFODILS,
  GOLD,WALTHAM ...........................................  50.00
WATCH,LADY'S,ELGIN,SIZE O,GOLD-FILLED HUNTING CASE,FLORAL
  BORDER,BEADING.........................................  40.00
WATCH,LADY'S,ELGIN,SIZE 6,GOLD HUNTING CASE,ENGRAVED FLORAL,
  SCENE,14K..............................................  65.00
WATCH,LADY'S,ENGRAVED BIRD,DUEBER CASE,GOLD,ELGIN.......... 135.00
WATCH,LADY'S,ENGRAVED BUTTERFLIES,FLOWERS,FAN,GOLD BEADING,
  1888,ELGIN............................................. 285.00
WATCH,LADY'S,HAND-PAINTED ENAMEL DIAL,48-IN.CHAIN,STERLING
  SILVER.................................................  48.00
WATCH,LADY'S,HUNTING CASE,BIRDS,NEST,HILLS,LAKE,BOAT,
  WALTHAM,14K GOLD....................................... 188.00
WATCH,LADY'S,HUNTING CASE,DRUM SHAPE,JEWELED MOVEMENT,ELGIN,
  14K GOLD............................................... 125.00
WATCH,LADY'S,HUNTING CASE,ENGRAVED FLORAL,KEYWIND,SWISS,GOLD  55.00
WATCH,LADY'S,HUNTING CASE,ENGRAVED GEOMETRIC,BLANK SHIELD,
  U.S.WATCH CO...........................................  30.00
WATCH,LADY'S,HUNTING CASE,FLORAL,GEOMETRIC DESIGN,SCENE,
  1887,14K GOLD..........................................  75.00
WATCH,LADY'S,HUNTING CASE,HAMPDEN,MOLLY STARK..............  47.50
WATCH,LADY'S,HUNTING CASE,STEM WIND,ENAMEL,DIAMONDS,GOLD,
  HOWELL & JAMES......................................... 650.00
WATCH,LADY'S,KEYWIND,SILVER ENGRAVED CASE.................  21.00
```

WATCH,LADY'S,LAPEL,DECORATED HUNTER CASE,GOLD............... 25.00
WATCH,LADY'S,LAPEL,STERLING SILVER CASE,CARVED ROSES,FLEUR
DE LIS PIN............................................. 40.00
WATCH,LADY'S,LAPEL,TWO BIRDS,THREE MINE-CUT DIAMONDS,LADY
RACINE,GOLD............................................ 25.00
WATCH,LADY'S,LONGINES,SIZE 6,GOLD HUNTING CASE,FLORAL
WREATH,SCENE........................................... 60.00
WATCH,LADY'S,OPEN FACE,VERGE,ENAMEL MINIATURE ON BACK,
VAUCHEZ A PARIS........................................ 125.00
WATCH,LADY'S,PAIR CASE,JACQUES COULIN & AMY BRY,GENEVA,GOLD. 400.00
WATCH,LADY'S,PENDANT,ENAMEL SCENE,SCROLLWORK,TWO PIECES,
FRANCE,14K GOLD........................................ 125.00
WATCH,LADY'S,PENDANT,OPEN FACE,SAYS BRUNET A GENEVE,THREE
PIECES,18K............................................. 275.00
WATCH,LADY'S,PENDANT,SIZE 9 LIGNE,OPEN FACE,DIAMOND-SET
CROWN,GOLD,SWISS....................................... 150.00
WATCH,LADY'S,PENDANT,SPLIT PEARLS IN BORDER,CAMEO SET IN
BACK,SWISS,GOLD........................................ 150.00
WATCH,LADY'S,PIN,FLORAL & LEAF ENGRAVING,MARKED U.S.ASSAY
14K GOLD............................................... 75.00
WATCH,LADY'S,SILVER CLOSED CASE,SCENE & ETCHED FLOWERS ON
SILVER PIN............................................. 21.50
WATCH,LADY'S,SILVER HUNTING CASE,BUTTERFLY,WREATH OF LEAVES,
N.Y.STANDARD........................................... 25.00
WATCH,LADY'S,SIZE 0,CRACKLE BANDS ON EDGES,U.S.BETSY ROSS
MOVEMENT............................................... 40.00
WATCH,LADY'S,SIZE 0,GOLD-FILLED HUNTING CASE,MONOGRAM,
WALTHAM................................................ 35.00
WATCH,LADY'S,SIZE 0,HUNTING CASE,HAMPDEN DIADEM MOVEMENT,
GOLD-FILLED............................................ 35.00
WATCH,LADY'S,SIZE 0,HUNTING CASE,ORNATE DIAL,FLORAL,SCENE,
POTOMAC................................................ 32.00
WATCH,LADY'S,SIZE 0,20 YEAR GOLD-FILLED HUNTING CASE,SCROLL,
FLORAL,SCENE........................................... 47.00
WATCH,LADY'S,SIZE 6,HUNTING CASE,DRUM SHAPE,FLORAL,SCENE,
GOLD,WALTHAM........................................... 65.00
WATCH,LADY'S,SIZE 6,HUNTING CASE,ENGRAVED FLORAL,SCENE,1880,
14K GOLD............................................... 65.00
WATCH,LADY'S,SIZE 6,HUNTING CASE,LEAF,SCROLL,SCENE,
GOLD-FILLED,ELGIN...................................... 35.00
WATCH,LADY'S,SIZE 6,HUNTING CASE,STAG,LEAVES,TWO SMALL
RUBIES,DIAMOND......................................... 55.00
WATCH,LADY'S,SIZE 8,GOLD DRUM-SHAPED CASE,FLORAL,SWAN,
AGASSIZ MOVEMENT....................................... 65.00
WATCH,LADY'S,STERLING HUNTING CASE,ELGIN................... 22.00
WATCH,LADY'S,STIPPLE-ENGRAVED,FLOWERS,SCROLLS,GOLD HUNTING
CASE,VALLIER........................................... 70.00
WATCH,LADY'S,WALTHAM,GOLD-FILLED HUNTING CASE,ENGRAVED
FLORAL,FOLIATE......................................... 40.00
WATCH,LADY'S,WALTHAM,SIZE 0,GOLD HUNTING CASE,STIPPLE
GROUND,14K............................................. 57.00
WATCH,LADY'S,WALTHAM,SIZE 6,GOLD-FILLED CASE,ENGRAVED
SCROLL,HEART........................................... 37.50
WATCH,LADY'S,WRIST,ADJUSTABLE BRACELET,ULYSSE NARDIN
CHRONOMETER,14K........................................ 130.00
WATCH,LAPEL,LADY'S,OPEN FACE,20 YEAR CASE,ENGRAVED BAND,
ELGIN.................................................. 28.00
WATCH,LONE RANGER......................................... 45.00
WATCH,MAN'S,CHAIN DRIVE,FLORAL,VINES,GOLD HANDS,KEY WIND,
COIN SILVER............................................ 125.00
WATCH,MAN'S,DECORATED HUNTER CASE,14K GOLD,WALTHAM......... 30.00
WATCH,MAN'S,ELGIN,GOLD HUNTING CASE,ENGRAVED AMERICAN EAGLE. 65.00
WATCH,MAN'S,ELGIN,HUNTING CASE,GOLD-FILLED................. 30.00
WATCH,MAN'S,ELGIN,NATIONAL,GOLD-FILLED CASE................ 25.00
WATCH,MAN'S,FUSEE,KEYWIND,OPEN FACE,BULL'S-EYE CRYSTAL,J.&
J.JOHNSON.............................................. 30.00
WATCH,MAN'S,GOLD-FILLED,ETCHED CLOSED CASE,HOWARD.......... 59.50
WATCH,MAN'S,HUNTING CASE,EMBOSSED,STERLING SILVER,ELGIN.... 27.50
WATCH,MAN'S,HUNTING CASE,PORCELAIN FACE,20 YEAR GOLD CASE,
ELGIN.................................................. 27.50
WATCH,MAN'S,HUNTING CASE,STEMWIND,14K GOLD,E.HOWARD & CO.,
BOSTON................................................. 95.00
WATCH,MAN'S,NEW YORK STANDARD,HUNTING CASE................. 25.00
WATCH,MAN'S,OPEN FACE,ENGRAVED HORSE HEAD ON BACK,GOLD,
ROCKFORD............................................... 65.00
WATCH,MAN'S,ORNATE ENGRAVING,MARKED DUEBER STERLING 925,
WALTHAM................................................ 25.00
WATCH,MAN'S,POCKET,HUNTING CASE,ENGRAVED DOG'S HEAD,KEY
WIND,1851.............................................. 185.00
WATCH,MAN'S,POCKET,VEST CHAIN,SOLID GOLD SLIDE,ROMAN FOB,

| | |
|---|---|
| ELGIN | 25.00 |
| WATCH,MAN'S,POCKET,WALTHAM,DIAL INLAY | 25.00 |
| WATCH,MAN'S,POCKET,WALTHAM,GOLD-FILLED | 25.00 |
| WATCH,MAN'S,ROCKFORD,17 JEWEL,CHAIN,25 YEAR CASE | 35.00 |
| WATCH,MAN'S,SILVER CASE OPENS FROM BACK,INSIDE CASE LIFTS OUT,ELGIN | 35.00 |
| WATCH,MAN'S,SILVER HUNTING CASE,APERTURE IN COVER REVEALS DIAL,ROSKELL | 35.00 |
| WATCH,MAN'S,SIZE 12,FLORAL,SCROLL,BLANK ROCOCO SHIELD,SCENE, ELGIN | 25.00 |
| WATCH,MAN'S,SIZE 16,COIN SILVER HUNTING CASE,PROFUSE FLORAL, LEAF,ELGIN | 22.50 |
| WATCH,MAN'S,SIZE 16,PAIR CASE,PORCELAIN DIAL,17 JEWEL,GOLD, HAMILTON | 25.00 |
| WATCH,MAN'S,SIZE 18,SILVER-CASED,KEYWIND,WALTHAM | 25.00 |
| WATCH,MAN'S,SIZE 18,SILVEROID HUNTING CASE,STIPPLE ENGRAVING,WALTHAM | 30.00 |
| WATCH,MAN'S,SIZE 18,STEMWIND,PHOTO TRANSFER OF WOMAN INSIDE COVER,MARION | 35.00 |
| WATCH,MAN'S,STEM WIND,KEYSTONE WATCH CASE SILVEROID,WALTHAM. | 14.75 |
| WATCH,MAN'S,WALTHAM,15 JEWEL,20 YEAR CASE | 30.00 |
| WATCH,MAN'S,WALTHAM,17 JEWEL,25 YEAR CASE | 35.00 |
| WATCH,MICKEY MOUSE,CHARACTER ON DIAL WITH HANDS TELLING TIME | 25.00 |
| WATCH,MICKEY MOUSE,INGERSOL | 65.00 |
| WATCH,MICKEY MOUSE,INGERSOL,MICKEY & MINNIE METAL BAND | 75.00 |
| WATCH,MICKEY MOUSE,SILVER COLOR DIAL,RED NUMBERS,ARMS FORM HANDS | 37.50 |
| WATCH,MICKEY MOUSE,WRIST,INGERSOL,NEVER WORN | 145.00 |
| WATCH,MICKEY MOUSE,WRIST,SILVER MICKEY MOUSES ON BAND | 100.00 |
| WATCH,N.Y.STANDARD,SIZE 12,GOLD-FILLED HUNTING CASE,MONOGRAM | 22.50 |
| WATCH,NO.18,HUNTING CASE,20 YEAR CASE,HAMPDEN,14K GOLD PLATE | 18.00 |
| WATCH,OPEN CASE,BULL'S-EYE CRYSTAL,KEY WIND,15 JEWELS,SWISS, SILVER | 20.00 |
| WATCH,OPEN FACE,ARABIC NUMERALS,LEVER-SET,17 JEWEL,HAMILTON, GOLD-FILLED | 20.00 |
| WATCH,OPEN FACE,COIN SILVER CASE,SIZE 18,WALTHAM,NO.3,061, 913,1880 | 20.00 |
| WATCH,OPEN FACE,CUTOUT DECOR,ENGRAVED SCENE,KEY WIND,SILVER. | 30.00 |
| WATCH,OPEN FACE,CYLINDER MOVEMENT,CUTOUT BRIDGES,ENGRAVED MOOSE,SILVER | 40.00 |
| WATCH,OPEN FACE,CYLINDER,ENAMEL BACK & BEZEL,MOULINIER, GENEVA,GOLD | 100.00 |
| WATCH,OPEN FACE,ENAMEL,FLORAL,PEARL BEZEL,BOVET FLEURIER, GILT METAL | 500.00 |
| WATCH,OPEN FACE,ENGRAVED BRIDGES,SWEEP SECOND HAND,KEY WIND, SILVER | 50.00 |
| WATCH,OPEN FACE,ENGRAVED GOLD FACE,BULL'S-EYE CRYSTAL, ENGLAND,1820,18K | 72.00 |
| WATCH,OPEN FACE,ENGRAVED RURAL SCENE,15 JEWELS,WALTHAM, SILVEROID | 22.00 |
| WATCH,OPEN FACE,FULL-JEWELED,KEY WIND,HAMPDEN,COIN SILVER... | 22.50 |
| WATCH,OPEN FACE,FULL-JEWELED LEVER MOVEMENT,SWISS,COIN SILVER | 18.00 |
| WATCH,OPEN FACE,LEVER,SPLIT PEARLS,ENAMEL,SCENE,TIGER HUNT, SWISS,GILT | 500.00 |
| WATCH,OPEN FACE,QUARTER REPEATER,SCENE GALANTE,FRANCE,18K GOLD | 525.00 |
| WATCH,OPEN FACE,VERGE,C.CABRIER,LONDON,NO.626,CIRCA 1770, SILVER | 150.00 |
| WATCH,OPEN FACE,VERGE,MINIATURE OF GIRL,ENAMEL DIAL,GILT METAL | 175.00 |
| WATCH,OPEN FACE,VERGE,PAINTED MINIATURE ON DIAL,CUROISIER FRERES,SILVER | 125.00 |
| WATCH,OPEN FACE,WINDS BY STEM OR KEY,ILLINOIS,SILVEROID..... | 25.00 |
| WATCH,PAIR-CASED,DATE CALENDAR,SILVER REPOUSSE,MAY,LONDON, CIRCA 1740 | 225.00 |
| WATCH,PAIR-CASED,GILT METAL,TORTOISESHELL,GEORGE PRIOR, LONDON,1780 | 200.00 |
| WATCH,PAIR-CASED,MASONIC EMBLEMS,SILVER,MORRIS TOBIAS, WAPPING,LONDON | 70.00 |
| WATCH,PAIR-CASED,TILT,F.DE VIGNE,LONDON,NO.1321,CIRCA 1780.. | 600.00 |
| WATCH,PAIR-CASED,VERGE,REPOUSSE,DUTCH MINUTE MARKING, CABRIER,LONDON,GOLD, | 500.00 |
| WATCH,PAIR-CASED,VERGE,TORTOISESHELL OUTER CASE,ENAMEL SCENE,SILVER | 100.00 |
| WATCH,PENDANT,GOLD HUNTING CASE,POCKET,PAIR-CASED,SILVER,TWO PIECES | 70.00 |
| WATCH,PENDANT,HUNTING CASE,ENAMELED FLORAL ON BACK,THREE PIECES,14K GOLD | 125.00 |
| WATCH,PENDANT,LADY'S,OPEN FACE,WHITE ENAMEL DIAL,ENAMELED | |

```
  BACK,GOLD.............................................  125.00
WATCH,PENDANT,OPEN FACE,ENGINE-TURNED BACK,VAUCHER A PARIS,
  1780,GOLD.............................................  300.00
WATCH,PENDANT,OPEN FACE,VERGE,ENAMEL,FLORAL,JEAN BTE.LE
  NOIR,GOLD.............................................  200.00
WATCH,PENDANT,PLATINUM-SET ROSE DIAMONDS,FRANCE......ILLUS..  425.00
```

PLATINUM WATCH, PENDANT

```
WATCH,PENDANT,PURPLE ENAMEL,PANSY,ROSE DIAMOND,RED
  CARTOUCHE,18K GOLD...................................  100.00
WATCH,PENDANT,SCALLOPED BORDERS,ENGRAVED DECOR,FRANCE,18K
  GOLD.................................................   80.00
WATCH,PLUTO,BLACK DIAL,GREEN NUMBERS,WRIST...............   15.00
WATCH,POCKET,ALARM,CIRCA 1670,P.D.LAGISSE,GENEVA,SILVER,
  DAMAGED CASE.........................................  200.00
WATCH,POCKET,BLUE GROUND,ENAMEL,FLORAL,PEARL BORDER,GOLD,
  BOVET FLEURIER.......................................  850.00
WATCH,POCKET,COIN SILVER CASE,13 JEWELS,KEY WIND,M.J.TOBIAS
  CO.,ELGIN............................................   28.00
WATCH,POCKET,COMBINATION HUNTING CASE & OPEN FACE,THOMAS
  HOWARD,18K GOLD......................................  350.00
WATCH,POCKET,DUPLEX,NEW ENGLAND,FOUR JEWEL ESCAPEMENT,1866..  500.00
WATCH,POCKET,ELGIN,GOLD CASE,ENGRAVED,1883...............   37.50
WATCH,POCKET,ENGINE-TURNED,DELAUNOY,ELEVE DE BREGUET,PARIS,
  18K GOLD.............................................  175.00
WATCH,POCKET,HUNTING CASE,ENAMEL DIAL,CHASED & ENGRAVED
  BACK,SCENE,ELGIN.....................................  125.00
WATCH,POCKET,HUNTING CASE,INSCRIBED AUDEMARS FRERES,BRASSUS,
  GENEVE,GOLD..........................................  100.00
WATCH,POCKET,HUNTING CASE,LEAF DESIGN,WALTHAM,18K GOLD......  250.00
WATCH,POCKET,HUNTING CASE,LEVER ESCAPEMENT,R & G BERSLEY,
  LIVERPOOL,GOLD.......................................  100.00
WATCH,POCKET,HUNTING CASE,QUARTER REPEATER,CALENDAR,SWISS,
  18K GOLD.............................................  450.00
WATCH,POCKET,HUNTING CASE,SILVER,CENTER SECOND,STOP,SWISS,
  TWO PIECES...........................................   50.00
WATCH,POCKET,HUNTING CASE,TURKISH NUMERALS,ENGRAVED,HOURIET,
  SWISS,GOLD...........................................  150.00
WATCH,POCKET,MAN'S,17 JEWEL,GOLD-FILLED CASE,ILLINOIS WATCH
  CO...................................................   19.95
WATCH,POCKET,OPEN FACE,BLUE & WHITE ENAMEL DECOR,PEARL
  BORDER,18K GOLD......................................  225.00
WATCH,POCKET,OPEN FACE,BLUE ENAMEL,PEARLS,VERGE,ROSE
  DIAMOND,FRANCE,GOLD..................................  450.00
WATCH,POCKET,OPEN FACE,BREGUET,GOLD,WRIST WATCH,OLLENDORF,
  FRENCH GOLD..........................................  350.00
WATCH,POCKET,OPEN FACE,DATE,DAY,MONTH,MOON PHASES,GUNMETAL,
  SWISS................................................   70.00
WATCH,POCKET,OPEN FACE,ENGINE-TURNED,GILT DIAL,WREATH
  ORNAMENT,18K GOLD....................................  100.00
WATCH,POCKET,OPEN FACE,ENGRAVED SCENE,HYDE & SON,WATCH
  CASES,FOUR PIECES....................................  100.00
WATCH,POCKET,OPEN FACE,GILT DIAL,DAY,DATE,HUNTING CASE,14K
  GOLD.................................................  250.00
WATCH,POCKET,OPEN FACE,GILT DIAL,M.I.TOBIAS,LIVERPOOL,18K
  GOLD.................................................   60.00
WATCH,POCKET,OPEN FACE,GREEN ENAMEL GROUND,THISTLE,GOLD,HAAS
  NEVEUX...............................................  175.00
WATCH,POCKET,OPEN FACE,HAMILTON,24-HOUR DIAL,HOWARD,GOLD,TWO
  PIECES...............................................  100.00
WATCH,POCKET,OPEN FACE,KEY WIND,COIN SILVER,G.M.WHEELER,
  ELGIN,ILL............................................   20.00
WATCH,POCKET,OPEN FACE,LEVER ESCAPEMENT,ENAMEL DIAL,ROBERT
  ROSCOE,GOLD..........................................   60.00
WATCH,POCKET,OPEN FACE,MINUTE REPEATER,HOLDER,GOLD,TIFFANY,
  NO.18994.............................................  450.00
WATCH,POCKET,OPEN FACE,QUARTER REPEATER,KEY WIND,
  ENGINE-TURNED BACK,GOLD..............................  175.00
WATCH,POCKET,OPEN FACE,QUARTER REPEATER,BREGUET A PARIS,
  1800,18K GOLD........................................  175.00
WATCH,POCKET,OPEN FACE,VERGE,ENAMEL DIAL,STEEL HANDS,FRANCE,
  18K GOLD.............................................   75.00
```

WATCH,POCKET,OPEN FACE,VERGE,POLISHED CASE,ENAMEL DIAL,1800,
  18K GOLD...............................................    75.00
WATCH,POCKET,PAIR-CASED,ROSE DIAMOND END STONE,S.TOULMIN,
  LONDON,GOLD...........................................   300.00
WATCH,POCKET,QUARTER REPEATER,MUSICAL,OPEN FACE,GOLD,FRANCE,
  1830..................................................   950.00
WATCH,POCKET,TOWER,CATERPILLAR FOB......................     7.50
WATCH,POCKET,TWO CASES,VERGE,ENAMEL DIAL,THO.EUSTACE,EXETER,
  NO.0619...............................................    50.00
WATCH,PORCELAIN DIAL,TO THEIR MAJESTIES,SIZE 30,OPEN FACE,
  SILVER................................................    45.00
WATCH,QUARTER REPEATER,HUNTING CASE,KEY WIND,GOLD,FREUNDLER
  A GENEVE..............................................   375.00
WATCH,RAILROAD,ENGRAVED TRAIN,TRACK,GOLD,WALTHAM........    40.00
WATCH,RAILROAD,WALTHAM,ENGRAVED TRAIN,SMOKE,TRACK,GOLD..    50.00
WATCH,RING,OVAL,VISIBLE BALANCE,ENAMEL DIAL,FRANCE,1820,GOLD   450.00
WATCH,SCROLLED CASE,KEY WIND,STERLING SILVER,ENGLAND,CHAIN..    40.00
WATCH,SILVER CASE,VERGE,DUTCH-TYPE MOVEMENT,ENGLISH
  HALLMARKS,CIRCA 1760..................................    50.00
WATCH,SILVEROID CASE,ENGRAVED STEAM LOCOMOTIVE,OPEN FACE,
  SIZE 18,WALTHAM.......................................    25.00
WATCH,SILVEROID CASE,OPEN FACE,ENGRAVED STAG,SIZE 18,WALTHAM    17.50
WATCH,SILVEROID,STEM WIND,AMERICAN WALTHAM WATCH CO,KEYSTONE
  WATCH CASE............................................    14.75
WATCH,SNOW WHITE.......................................     7.50
WATCH,SOLID GOLD CASE,ELGIN............................   165.00
WATCH SYNCHRONIZER,EARLY TIMING DEVICE,WOODEN CASE,
  INSTRUCTIONS,BENNET...................................    35.00
WATCH,VERGE,ENAMEL,1800,PENDANT,ENGRAVED,CIRCA 1850,TWO
  PIECES................................................   200.00
WATCH,VERGE,MULTICOLOR GOLD,JOHAN EUSEPIUS LODERER,AUGUSTA,
  1770..................................................   500.00
WATCH,VERGE,REPOUSSE OUTER CASE,DUTCH MARKINGS,IN SANDERS,
  LONDON,GOLD...........................................   400.00
WATCH,WALTHAM,SIZE 0,OPEN FACE,SWIVEL PENDANT,ENAMEL DIAL,
  14K GOLD..............................................    65.00
WATCH,WALTHAM,SIZE 12,GOLD-FILLED HUNTING CASE,MONOGRAM,
  15 JEWELS.............................................    25.00
WATCH,WALTHAM,SIZE 14,HUNTING CASE,OVERLAY DESIGN ON BOTH
  COVERS,1880...........................................   175.00
WATCH,WALTHAM,SIZE 16,ENGRAVED FLORAL,SAILBOAT,14K.........    85.00
WATCH,WALTHAM,SIZE 16,GOLD-FILLED HUNTING CASE,ENGRAVED
  FLORAL,15 JEWELS......................................    32.00
WATCH,WALTHAM,SIZE 18,KEY WIND,COIN SILVER HUNTING CASE,
  WM.BARTLETT...........................................    40.00


    WATCH FOBS WERE WORN ON WATCH CHAINS. THEY WERE POPULAR
    DURING VICTORIAN TIMES.
WATCH FOB,ADVERTISING POWER SHOVELS,LEATHER STRAP...........     6.50
WATCH FOB,ADVERTISING,BOTTLE OPENER,SHAPE OF TOURING CAR,
  PAT.NOV. 1911........................................     4.00
WATCH FOB,ADVERTISING,WEST VIRGINIA TRACTOR,NO STRAP.......     3.00
WATCH FOB,AUTO,MAXWELL VELIE..........................     2.50
WATCH FOB,JACKHAMMER...................................     2.50
WATCH FOB,METAL,SAYS WILHELM 1797-1897.................    10.00
WATCH FOB,PRESENTATION,TORTOISESHELL,CLASSIC HEAD ON FRONT,
  1890..................................................    20.00
WATCH FOB,ROCHESTER DISTILLING CO.,PICTURES FACTORY,NO STRAP     7.00
WATCH FOB,SALOVET WORM DESTROYER.......................     5.00
WATCH FOB,STRAP,MAN USING JACKHAMMER,INGERSOL RAND..........     8.75
WATCH FOB,THREE SILVERED INDIAN HEAD CENTS LINKED TOGETHER..     5.00
WATCH FOB,TOBACCO CUTTER,GOLD-FILLED....................     6.50
WATCH FOB,WORLD WAR I,U.S.SEAL,BRASS...................     2.50


    WATERFORD TYPE GLASS RESEMBLES THE FAMOUS GLASS MADE IN
    THE WATERFORD GLASS WORKS IN IRELAND. IT IS A CLEAR
    GLASS THAT WAS OFTEN CUT FOR DECORATION. MODERN GLASS
    IS STILL BEING MADE IN WATERFORD,IRELAND.
WATERFORD TYPE,BOWL,ALLOVER STRAWBERRY DIAMOND,NOTCHED RIM,
  RAYED BASE............................................    43.00
WATERFORD TYPE,BOWL,CUT GLASS,14 1/2 IN. X 8 IN.HIGH........   150.00
WATERFORD TYPE,BOWL,ROSE,6 IN.HIGH,6-IN.DIAMETER.......    95.00
WATERFORD TYPE,DECANTER,BAND OF DIAMOND POINT,CUT PANELS,
  THREE RIGAREES........................................    38.50
WATERFORD TYPE,RING TREE,RIB DESIGN,CRYSTAL............    14.00
WATERFORD TYPE,SHERBET,CUT PANELS,SCALLOPED EDGE,KNOB IN
  STEM,3 1/2 IN.........................................     6.00
WATERFORD TYPE,WINE,DIAMOND CUT........................    **12.00**

WATERFORD TYPE,WINE,DOUBLE KNOB TEARDROP STEM............... 7.50

 

WAVECREST GLASS IS A WHITE GLASSWARE MANUFACTURED BY
THE PAIRPOINT MANUFACTURING COMPANY OF NEW BEDFORD,
MASSACHUSETTS,AND SOME FRENCH FACTORIES. IT WAS THEN
DECORATED BY THE C.F. MONROE COMPANY OF MERIDEN,
CONNECTICUT. THE GLASS WAS PAINTED PASTEL COLORS AND
DECORATED WITH FLOWERS. THE NAME WAVECREST WAS USED
AFTER 1898.

WAVECREST,BASKET,SWIRL DESIGN,BLUE FLORAL,GREEN,SILVER PLATE
  HANDLE................................................... 79.50
WAVECREST,BOWL,DECOR,BRASS COLLAR & HANDLES,4 IN.WIDE....... 35.00
WAVECREST,BOWL,DECORATED,BRASS COLLAR,SIGNED............... 22.00
WAVECREST,BOWL,ENAMELED BLUE FLORAL,EMBOSSED WHITE & PINK
  GROUND,GOLD............................................. 37.50
WAVECREST,BOWL,ORMOLU COLLAR,TWO HANDLES,MT.WASHINGTON...... 34.50
WAVECREST,BOWL,RABBITS,BRASS COLLAR,OPEN,SIGNED NAKARA,
  4-IN.DIAMETER........................................... 65.00
WAVECREST,BOWL,SUGAR,IVORY GROUND,SWIRL PATTERN,FLORAL,LEAF,
  SILVER.................................................. 85.00
WAVECREST,BOWL,SWIRL PATTERN,PINK FLORAL,GREEN LEAVES,
  5-1/2 IN.DIAMETER....................................... 62.50
WAVECREST,BOWL,TRINKET,SWIRL RIBS,RAISED DECOR,GOLD METAL
  COLLAR.................................................. 26.00
WAVECREST,BOX,APPLE BLOSSOMS DECOR,HINGED,SIGNED,3 1/2 IN... 48.00
WAVECREST,BOX,BLUE & WHITE GROUND,RED,PINK,GRAY DECOR,OPEN,
  BRASS RIM............................................... 68.00
WAVECREST,BOX,BLUE FORGET-ME-NOTS,HINGED,LINING,3 IN........ 65.00
WAVECREST,BOX,COLLAR & CUFF,WRITTEN IN GILT,BILLOWED PUFFS,
  FLORAL,SQUARE........................................... 275.00
WAVECREST,BOX,CREAM GROUND,RAISED SWIRLS,ENAMELED
  FORGET-ME-NOTS,LINING................................... 60.00
WAVECREST,BOX,CUPID DECOR,LINING,SIGNED,8 IN............... 150.00
WAVECREST,BOX,EMBOSSED,MULTICOLOR FLORAL DECOR,OVAL,HINGED,
  LINING.................................................. 110.00
WAVECREST,BOX,ENAMELED FLORAL & RIBBON DECOR,HINGED,
  5 3/4 IN.ACROSS......................................... 67.50
WAVECREST,BOX,FLORAL DECOR,OPEN,ROUND,SIGNED............... 12.00
WAVECREST,BOX,FLORAL SPRAYS,ENAMEL ACCENTS,HINGED,
  5 1/2-IN.DIAMETER....................................... 95.00
WAVECREST,BOX,FLORAL,BIRDS,ROUND,OPEN,SIGNED............... 19.00
WAVECREST,BOX,GOLD SCROLLS,VIOLETS,BLUE FLOWERS,SILVER
  EMBOSSED RIM............................................ 125.00
WAVECREST,BOX,GREEN GROUND,FLORAL,HAND-PAINTED,
  4 1/2-IN.DIAMETER....................................... 75.00
WAVECREST,BOX,GREEN,PINK FLORAL,SILVER COLLAR,OVAL,OPEN,
  5 1/4 X 4 IN............................................ 65.00
WAVECREST,BOX,HELMSCHMIED SWIRL PATTERN,YELLOW,IVORY COLOR,
  FLORAL.................................................. 52.00
WAVECREST,BOX,JEWEL,ANGEL IN FIELD OF WHEAT SHOCKS,SIGNED... 165.00
WAVECREST,BOX,JEWEL,ANGEL,FIELD OF WHEAT,OVAL,HINGED LID.... 175.00
WAVECREST,BOX,JEWEL,BRASS & SCROLLWORK,OVAL,OPEN,5 IN....... 45.00
WAVECREST,BOX,JEWEL,ENAMELED FORGET-ME-NOTS,HINGED COVER,
  SATIN LINING............................................ 115.00
WAVECREST,BOX,JEWEL,HELMSCHMIED SWIRL PATTERN,FLORAL DECOR,
  2 3/4 X 4 IN............................................ 50.00
WAVECREST,BOX,JEWEL,ORMOLU CONNECTIONS,BLUE FLOWER SPRAYS,
  HINGED,ENAMEL........................................... 98.00
WAVECREST,BOX,JEWEL,ORMOLU CONNECTIONS & HINGE,ANGEL OVER
  WHEAT FIELD............................................. 185.00
WAVECREST,BOX,JEWEL,OVAL,SCENIC,HINGED,SIGNED,2 3/4 X
  5 IN.LONG............................................... 175.00
WAVECREST,BOX,JEWEL,PAINTED & ENAMELED DECOR,METAL BAND,
  SIGNED,7 IN............................................. 160.00
WAVECREST,BOX,JEWEL,PINK GROUND,HAND-PAINTED FLOWERS........ 55.00
WAVECREST,BOX,JEWEL,QUILTED,WHITE GROUND,BLUE & WHITE FLORAL
  ON COVER................................................ 75.00
WAVECREST,BOX,JEWEL,S SCROLLS,PLUMES,FORGET-ME-NOTS,HINGED
  LID,SIGNED.............................................. 158.00
WAVECREST,BOX,JEWEL,SWIRL DESIGN,ENAMELED VIOLETS,HINGED,4 X
  3 IN.TALL............................................... 45.00
WAVECREST,BOX,JEWEL,SWIRLED BASE & COVER,ENAMELED
  FORGET-ME-NOTS.......................................... 47.50
WAVECREST,BOX,JEWEL,SWIRLED SHAPE,HAND-PAINTED FLORAL ON
  LID,LINING.............................................. 30.00
WAVECREST,BOX,OPEN,HAND-PAINTED BIRDS,FLORAL,RED BANNER
  SIGNATURE............................................... 25.00
WAVECREST,BOX,PIN,HAND-PAINTED DECOR,BRASS COLLAR,OPEN...... 25.00
WAVECREST,BOX,PINK & WHITE GROUND,MULTICOLORED FLORAL,

LINING,SIGNED.......................................... 90.00
WAVECREST,BOX,PINK & WHITE SHELL,HINGED,FOOTED,SIGNED,
4-IN.DIAMETER......................................... 125.00
WAVECREST,BOX,PINK ENAMELED FLOWERS,SIGNED IN RED,7 IN...... 155.00
WAVECREST,BOX,POWDER,PALE BLUE,PINK FLORAL,ATTACHED SWIVEL
MIRROR,6 IN........................................... 125.00
WAVECREST,BOX,RING,OPEN,EMBOSSED FLORAL,FILIGREE BRASS
HANDLES,LINING........................................ 65.00
WAVECREST,BOX,SHELL PATTERN,COVER,PINK APPLE BLOSSOMS,GREEN
LEAVES,MOORE.......................................... 146.00
WAVECREST,BOX,SWIRL RIBS,RAISED DECOR,HINGED COVER,GOLD
METAL COLLARS......................................... 65.00
WAVECREST,BOX,SWIRL,FLORAL ON TOP,C.V.HELMSCHMIED,PATENTED.. 50.00
WAVECREST,BOX,WHITE & BLUE FORGET-ME-NOTS,4 1/2 IN......... 60.00
WAVECREST,BOX,WHITE GROUND,FLORAL,HAND-PAINTED,HINGED LID,
6-IN.DIAMETER......................................... 110.00
WAVECREST,BOX,WHITE GROUND,SWIRLS,ENAMELED FLORAL,BRASS RIM,
OPEN.................................................. 85.00
WAVECREST,BOX,WILD-FLOWER DECOR,WHITE & PINK GROUND,OPEN,
BRASS COLLAR.......................................... 40.00
WAVECREST,BOX,YELLOW & BROWN FLOWERS,3 IN.HIGH,
3 1/2 IN.DIAMETER..................................... 85.00
WAVECREST,CASE,JEWEL,BLUE TO WHITE,SCROLLS,PINK FLORAL,GOLD
BANDS................................................. 75.00
WAVECREST,CREAMER,HAND-PAINTED FLOWERS,RESILVERED RIM &
HANDLE................................................ 55.00
WAVECREST,DISH,DRESSER,BLUE ENAMEL FLORAL,PINK SCROLLS,BRASS
COLLAR,OPEN........................................... 36.00
WAVECREST,DISH,JEWEL,FLORAL,WIDE GOLD RIM & HANDLES,
5-IN.DIAMETER......................................... 88.00
WAVECREST,DISH,PIN,BEIGE,HAND-PAINTED FLOWERS.............. 30.00
WAVECREST,DISH,PIN,BLUE FORGET-ME-NOTS,PUFFY CORNERS,BRASS
COLLAR,OPEN........................................... 18.00
WAVECREST,DISH,PIN,HAND-PAINTED FLOWERS,HANDLES,OVAL,SIGNED. 40.00
WAVECREST,DISH,RING,WHITE GROUND,HAND-PAINTED WILD ROSE,
BRASS HANDLES......................................... 75.00
WAVECREST,EWER,WHITE,HAND-PAINTED CUPID,GOLD,17 1/2 IN.TALL. 65.00
WAVECREST,FERNERY,PUFF PATTERN,FERNS,FLOWERS,PINK,BLUE
BROWN,7 IN.ACROSS..................................... 75.00
WAVECREST,HOLDER,GLOVE,CREAM GROUND,DAISY BOUQUET,BRASS
COLORS,FRAME.......................................... 225.00
WAVECREST,HOLDER,STATIONERY,YELLOW GROUND,SCROLLED,PINK
ROSES,6 1/2 IN........................................ 95.00
WAVECREST,HOLDER,STATIONERY,YELLOW,SCROLLS,ROSES,6 1/4 X
4 1/4 IN.............................................. 115.00
WAVECREST,JAR,BISCUIT,ENAMELED PINK & YELLOW ROSES,SILVER
COVER & BAIL.......................................... 75.00
WAVECREST,JAR,CANDY,SHADED BUFF GROUND,ENAMELED GOLD
POPPIES,COVER......................................... 49.50
WAVECREST,JAR,COOKIE,BISQUE PANELS,FLORAL & LEAF DECOR,
C.F.MONROE............................................ 110.00
WAVECREST,JAR,COOKIE,BLUE FIELD,RED CHRYSANTHEMUM IN WHITE
CARTOUCHE............................................. 145.00
WAVECREST,JAR,COOKIE,PINK FLORAL,CERISE,YELLOW LEAVES &
STEMS,SILVER LID...................................... 43.00
WAVECREST,JAR,COOKIE,PINK,RAISED SCROLL,FLORAL PANELS,SILVER
LID,HANDLE............................................ 55.00
WAVECREST,JAR,COOKIE,PUFF PATTERN,MORNING GLORY DECOR,SQUARE
SHAPE................................................. 85.00
WAVECREST,JAR,COOKIE,WHITE GROUND,PINK WILD ROSES,SIGNED,
6 IN.HIGH............................................. 95.00
WAVECREST,JAR,COOKIE,YELLOW GROUND,WHITE PANELS,EMBOSSED
SCROLLS,FLORAL........................................ 95.00
WAVECREST,JAR,CRACKER,EMBOSSED BLUE DESIGN,HAND-PAINTED
FLOWERS............................................... 55.00
WAVECREST,JAR,CRACKER,EMBOSSED SCROLL PATTERN,FLORAL DESIGN. 55.00
WAVECREST,JAR,CRACKER,FLORAL,HAND-PAINTED,BEIGE BORDER,
SILVER COVER.......................................... 85.00
WAVECREST,JAR,CRACKER,FLOWERS,SCROLLS,SILVER-PLATED RIM,
HANDLE,COVER.......................................... 42.50
WAVECREST,JAR,CRACKER,FUCHSIA FLOWERS,SCROLLS,SILVER PLATE
LID,VAN BERGH......................................... 85.00
WAVECREST,JAR,CRACKER,PEACH COLOR,FLORAL PANELS,RAISED
SCROLLS,UNSIGNED...................................... 65.00
WAVECREST,JAR,CRACKER,YELLOW GROUND,FLORAL SCROLLS,
HAND-PAINTED FLORAL................................... 85.00
WAVECREST,JAR,CRACKER,YELLOW,PANSY DECOR,BARREL SHAPE,SILVER
LID,BAIL.............................................. 59.00
WAVECREST,JAR,JEWEL,OPEN TOP,COLLAR,SIGNED C.F.M.CO.,3 X
1 1/2 IN.HIGH......................................... 32.00

WAVECREST,JAR,PIN,PINK CLOVER DECOR,AQUA SCROLLING,EMBOSSED
  BRASS COVER.......................................................... 45.00
WAVECREST,JAR,POWDER,HINGED,SIGNED.................................... 125.00
WAVECREST,SALT & PEPPER,SCROLLS,PINK FLORAL,BLUE GROUND,PAIR 59.00
WAVECREST,SALT & PEPPER,WHITE & BLUE GROUND,PINK FLORAL,
  GREEN LEAVES......................................................... 45.00
WAVECREST,SALT SHAKER,SWIRLED,FLORAL DECOR............................ 15.00
WAVECREST,SUGAR & CREAMER,FLORAL,HAND-PAINTED,SILVER BEADED
  TRIM................................................................. 135.00
WAVECREST,TRINKET,BLUE,ENAMEL,SWIRL DESIGN,BRASS COLLAR,OPEN 32.00
WAVECREST,TRINKET,SWIRL RIBS,RAISED DECOR,RAISED INNER RIM,
  OPEN................................................................. 22.00
WAVECREST,VASE,APPLE BLOSSOMS,SCROLLS,SIGNED,7 1/2 IN........ 85.00
WAVECREST,VASE,WHITE & BLUE GROUND,YELLOW COSMOS,METAL
  COLLAR,FEET.......................................................... 350.00
WAVECREST,VASE,YELLOW GROUND,MEDALLIONS,PINK MUMS,WHITE,BLUE
  ENAMEL............................................................... 235.00
WEAPON,ARMOR,ONE AND ONE-HALF SETS,ONE SWORD,SAMURI.......... 950.00
WEAPON,AXE,BOARDING,TOMAHAWK-LIKE HEAD,SIDE STRAPS,BRITISH
  MARKINGS............................................................. 125.00
WEAPON,AXE,TONG WAR,BAMBOO HANDLE.................................... 25.00
WEAPON,BAYONET,BOWIE,FOR KRAG RIFLE,IRON SHEATH,BLUE FINISH,
  1898................................................................. 145.00
WEAPON,BAYONET,BOWIE,FOR KRAG RIFLE,NICKEL FINISH SHEATH &
  BELT LOOP............................................................ 135.00
WEAPON,BAYONET,BRASS,WOOD HILT,NO.11757,D ARMES D ST.ETIEMS,
  AVRIL 1876........................................................... 27.50
WEAPON,BAYONET,BRASS HANDLE,SCABBARD FOR MODEL 1855 RIFLE... 45.00
WEAPON,BAYONET,BRASS HILT,FOR BRUNSWICK RIFLE,MARKED V R,
  BRITISH.............................................................. 39.50
WEAPON,BAYONET,BRASS TRIM,SABER TYPE,CIRCA 1878,PAIR........ 33.50
WEAPON,BAYONET,PLUG,BRASS CROSS GUARD,WINGED CHERUB DESIGN,
  CIRCA 1680........................................................... 145.00
WEAPON,BAYONET,SPADE,SCABBARD FOR MODEL 1873 SPRINGFIELD.... 40.00
WEAPON,BLUNDERBUSS,ENGLISH,CIRCA 1650,DOG LOCK,16-INCH
  BARREL,FLINTLOCK..................................................... 950.00
WEAPON,BLUNDERBUSS,ROUND BARREL,MARKED NH,CIRCA 1700,
  ENGLAND,BRASS........................................................ 650.00
WEAPON,BOMB LANCE & DARTING HARPOON,EBEN PIERCE............. 900.00
WEAPON,BROADSWORD,BASKET HILT,1720,ARMORER'S MARK,SCOTTISH
  HIGHLAND............................................................. 295.00
WEAPON,BROADSWORD,BRASS HILT,SHARKSKIN-COVERED GRIPS,CIRCA
  1770,SCOTLAND........................................................ 225.00
WEAPON,BROADSWORD,GERMAN,TWO-HANDED,IRON CROSS GUARD,16TH
  CENTURY,6 FT......................................................... 235.00
WEAPON,BROADSWORD,SCOTTISH HIGHLAND,BASKET HILT,IRON GUARD,
  1740................................................................. 325.00
WEAPON,BROADSWORD,SCOTTISH HIGHLAND,FULL BASKET HILT,1740,
  SHOWS AGE............................................................ 215.00
WEAPON,BROADSWORD,SCOTTISH HIGHLAND,IRON FULL BASKET HILT,
  1796,SHOWS AGE....................................................... 125.00
WEAPON,BROADSWORD,SCOTTISH HIGHLAND,IRON HILT,ORNATE
  PIERCINGS,1720....................................................... 350.00
WEAPON,BROADSWORD,SCOTTISH,BASKET HILT,IRON GUARD,HEART
  MOTIF,1790........................................................... 195.00
WEAPON,CANNON BALL,CIVIL WAR,51 POUNDS............................... 25.00
WEAPON,CANNON,BRITISH NAVAL,SWIVEL,CIRCA 1800,110 POUNDS.... 255.00
WEAPON,CARBINE,BREECH-LOADING,FRENCH MILITARY,MARKED CARONE
  B'TE-PARIS........................................................... 135.00
WEAPON,CARBINE,CIVIL WAR,BALL REPEAT,MAGAZINE CUTOFF ON LEFT
  FRAME,MARK..........................................................1,450.00
WEAPON,CARBINE,CIVIL WAR,BURNSIDE,PERCUSSION,UNFIRED,
  UNISSUED............................................................. 275.00
WEAPON,CARBINE,CIVIL WAR,CAVALRY,PERCUSSION,MARKED U.S.,
  GIBBS................................................................ 325.00
WEAPON,CARBINE,CIVIL WAR,JOSLYN,BRASS MOUNTINGS,LACKS FRONT
  SIGHT................................................................ 175.00
WEAPON,CARBINE,CIVIL WAR,MAYNARD,PERCUSSION,UNISSUED,
  UNFIRED,.50 CALIBER.................................................. 185.00
WEAPON,CARBINE,CIVIL WAR,WARNER,.50RF,LACKS UPPER LEAF ON
  REAR SIGHT........................................................... 325.00
WEAPON,CARBINE,COCHRAN-WHITNEY,LACKS BUTT PLATE,STOCK SHOWS
  WEAR................................................................. 175.00
WEAPON,CARBINE,EXPERIMENTAL,AMERICAN,MAKER WHITNEY FULLER,
  PATENT 1865.......................................................... 325.00
WEAPON,CARBINE,NAVY,PERRY,BREECH-LOADING,PERCUSSION,
  .54 CALIBER.......................................................... 575.00
WEAPON,CARBINE,TRANSITIONAL MODEL,BURNSIDE,CIVIL WAR,SERIAL
  NO.6933.............................................................. 275.00
WEAPON,CONTAINER,POWDER CHARGE,NAVAL,MARKED 12 PDR-LIGHT,

LEATHER........................................................ 44.50
WEAPON,CUTLASS,BRITISH NAVAL,IRON GRIPS,LEATHER SHEATH,BRASS
TIP,STUD....................................................... 59.50
WEAPON,CUTLASS,BRITISH NAVAL,IRON GRIPS,RIBBED PATTERN,1830,
29 IN.......................................................... 39.50
WEAPON,CUTLASS,FRENCH NAVAL,BRASS HILT,LIBERTY CAP & ANCHOR
DESIGN,1790.................................................... 225.00
WEAPON,CUTLASS,NAVAL,REVOLUTIONARY PERIOD,IRON HILT,
AMERICAN,28 IN.BLADE........................................... 225.00
WEAPON,CUTLASS,NAVAL,WAR OF 1812 PERIOD,IRON HILT,GRIPS,
GUARD,RIBBED................................................... 69.50
WEAPON,DAGGER,CARVED,IVORY,15 IN............................... 45.00
WEAPON,DAGGER,ITALIAN,IVORY HANDLE,BRASS CROSS GUARD,FLORAL
MOTIF,1750..................................................... 275.00
WEAPON,DAGGER,IVORY HANDLE,WALRUS HEAD SHAPE POMMEL,IVORY
SHEATH......................................................... 64.50
WEAPON,DIRK,BRITISH NAVAL,BRASS HILT,CROWN & GR PATTERN,
SHEATH,1810.................................................... 79.50
WEAPON,DIRK,BRITISH NAVAL,LION-HEAD POMMEL,ENGRAVED DECOR ON
GRIPS,1790..................................................... 79.50
WEAPON,DIRK,GERMAN NAVAL OFFICER,BONE GRIPS,ANCHOR CENTER,
SHEATH,1914.................................................... 74.50
WEAPON,DIRK,IVORY HANDLE,IRON CROSS GUARD,SAYS J.BATES-SELF
DEFENCE,1850................................................... 97.50
WEAPON,DIRK,NAVAL,BIRD HEAD POMMEL,FLAGS,CANNON,IVORY GRIPS,
1810........................................................... 67.50
WEAPON,DIRK,NAVAL,CARVED IVORY GRIPS,PILLOW-POMMEL MOTIF,
1790,SHEATH.................................................... 84.50
WEAPON,DIRK,NAVAL,FLORAL MOTIF ETCHED ON BLADE,MAKER
GILLOTT-LONDON................................................. 74.50
WEAPON,DIRK,NAVAL,GERMAN SILVER,IVORY HANDLE,SHEATH,1850,
7-IN.BLADE..................................................... 57.50
WEAPON,DIRK,NAVAL OFFICER,IVORY HANDLE,OVAL BRASS GUARD,
FLORAL,1800.................................................... 87.50
WEAPON,DIRK,NAVAL OFFICER'S,BRASS & GILT,BIRD HEAD,LION
HEAD,IVORY GRIPS............................................... 94.50
WEAPON,DIRK,SCOTTISH HIGHLAND,EBONY HANDLE,CAIRNGORM STONE,
SHEATH,1840.................................................... 235.00
WEAPON,DIRK,SCOTTISH HIGHLAND,SHEATH,KNIFE,FORK,SILVER
MOUNTS,1810.................................................... 250.00
WEAPON,DIRK,SHEATH,BRITISH NAVAL OFFICER,IVORY GRIPS,BRASS
POMMEL,1810.................................................... 94.50
WEAPON,DIRK,SHEATH,SILVER-MOUNTED,HORN HANDLE,LEAF-SHAPED
CROSS GUARD.................................................... 97.50
WEAPON,DIRK SET,SCOTTISH HIGHLAND,CARVED EBONY HANDLE,
CAIRNGORM STONE................................................ 97.50
WEAPON,ENGLISH OFFICER'S,1770, JOHNSTON-LATE BLAND,MAKER TO
HIS MAJESTY ................................................... 84.50
WEAPON,FLASK,POWDER,SHELL DESIGN,MARKED IMPROVED PATENT,
COPPER & BRASS................................................. 22.00
WEAPON,FOWLING PIECE,MINIATURE,ITALIAN,CIRCA 1740,33 IN.
OVERALL........................................................ 325.00
WEAPON,GUN,BB,RED RYDER........................................ 12.00
WEAPON,GUN,BB,WOODEN ROD PUMP,WALNUT HANDLE.................... 15.00
WEAPON,GUN,BREACH-LOADING,PERCUSSION CARBINE,CAL.52,
MASS.ARMS CO................................................... 165.00
WEAPON,GUN,BROWN BESS,MARKED HIRST NO.33,38-IN.BARREL,CIRCA
1760,BRITISH................................................... 550.00
WEAPON,GUN,ELEPHANT,FUSE-IGNITED,INDIA,FLARED MUZZLE,WEIGHT
25 POUNDS...................................................... 185.00
WEAPON,GUN,MUZZLE-LOADING,FLINTLOCK,BRASS BUTT PLATE &
TRIGGER GUARD.................................................. 135.00
WEAPON,GUN,PERCUSSION,BREECH-LOADING,CIVIL WAR,GALLAGER,
PATCH BOX...................................................... 150.00
WEAPON,GUN,POACHER,PIN FIRE,ESCLOPETTE,FOLDING STOCK,MAKER
CARONE,FRANCE.................................................. 425.00
WEAPON,GUN,POCKET COLT,6-SHOT,1849............................. 400.00
WEAPON,GUN,RAMPART,BROWN BESS,BRITISH,1785,WEIGHS 35 POUNDS,
6 FEET LONG.................................................... 850.00
WEAPON,GUN,WALL,MUZZLE-LOADING,INDIA,29-IN.ROUND IRON
BARREL,40 POUNDS............................................... 225.00
WEAPON,GUNS,SWORDS,AXES,SPEARS,DAGGERS,SHIELDS,80-PIECE
COLLECTION..................................................4,500.00
WEAPON,KEG,POWDER,LABEL,KENTUCKY RIFLE GUN POWDER,HAZARD
POWDER CO.,WOOD................................................ 15.00
WEAPON,KNIFE-BAYONET,FOR MUSKET,SAYS WINCHESTER REPEATING
ARMS CO........................................................ 17.50
WEAPON,KNIFE,BOWIE,GRIP HAS INDIAN ON HORSE,BRASS HILT,
LEATHER SHEATH................................................. 94.50
WEAPON,KNIFE,BOWIE,STAG GRIPS,SAYS R.BUNTING & SONS,

SHEFFIELD, 1850.......................................... 32.50
WEAPON,KNIFE,CLASP,FOLDING BLADE,TORTOISESHELL HANDLE,1850,
   20 IN.................................................. 69.50
WEAPON,KNIFE,HUNTING,HANDLE IS DEER'S FOOT,CASE,MARKED
   GERMANY............................................... 7.50
WEAPON,KNIFE,NEPAL GHOORKA KUKRI,12-IN.BLADE,BRASS-FITTED
   HORN POMMEL........................................... 16.95
WEAPON,KNIFE,SEMINOLE INDIAN,LEATHER SCABBARD SHEATH....... 22.00
WEAPON,KNIFE,TRENCH,BRASS HILT,IRON SHEATH,SAYS U.S. 1918,AU
   LION.................................................. 59.50
WEAPON,KNIFE,TRENCH,MODEL 1917............................ 30.00
WEAPON,KUKRI,FLORAL MOTIF,FIGURAL DESIGN,WARRIORS,INCURVED
   15-IN.BLADE........................................... 39.50
WEAPON,LANCET,SPRING-LOADED BLADE,STEEL SIDE TRIGGER,18TH
   CENTURY,CASE.......................................... 15.00
WEAPON,MACE,BULL HEAD SHAPE,PIERCED NOSTRILS,EARS,INDIA,
   IRON,25 IN............................................ 29.50
WEAPON,MEASURE,GUNPOWDER,CUP SWIVELS,NOTCHED GAUGE ON SIDE,
   BRASS................................................. 9.00
WEAPON,MUSKET,AMERICAN COLONIAL,CLUB BUTT,CIRCA 1765,FRENCH
   STYLE................................................. 650.00
WEAPON,MUSKET,AMERICAN COMMITTEE OF SAFETY,REVOLUTIONARY
   WAR,.60 CALIBER....................................... 950.00
WEAPON,MUSKET,AMERICAN INDIAN FUR TRADE,MARKED BARNETT,1831. 185.00
WEAPON,MUSKET,AMERICAN REVOLUTIONARY COMMITTEE OF SAFETY,
   MAKER'S MARK.......................................... 950.00
WEAPON,MUSKET,BRASS BAND BARREL FASTENINGS,SAYS
   PALMETTO-COLUMBIA,1852................................ 550.00
WEAPON,MUSKET,BRITISH,MADE FOR COLONIAL TRADE,EAST INDIA
   CO.,1801.............................................. 125.00
WEAPON,MUSKET,BROWN BESS,AMERICAN REVOLUTIONARY,SAYS
   W.GOODWIN,CARPENTER................................... 550.00
WEAPON,MUSKET,BROWN BESS,AMERICAN REVOLUTION,MARKED GR-TOWER
   WITH CROWN............................................ 650.00
WEAPON,MUSKET,BROWN BESS,AMERICAN REVOLUTION,MARKED TOWER,
   FLINTLOCK............................................. 850.00
WEAPON,MUSKET,BROWN BESS,FLINTLOCK,DATED 1805,BEARS
   BATTALION MARKINGS.................................... 395.00
WEAPON,MUSKET,BROWN BESS,FLINTLOCK,DATED 1779,LACKS SLING
   SWIVEL................................................ 425.00
WEAPON,MUSKET,BROWN BESS,FLINTLOCK,MARKED TOWER,DATED 1813,
   WALNUT STOCK.......................................... 175.00
WEAPON,MUSKET,BROWN BESS,39-INCH BARREL,MARKED GR-TOWER..... 375.00
WEAPON,MUSKET,CIVIL WAR,.58 CALIBER,PERCUSSION,MARK
   U.S.-WATERTOWN-1863................................... 97.50
WEAPON,MUSKET,CIVIL WAR,.58 CALIBER,PERCUSSION,MARKED
   TOWER-1861............................................ 110.00
WEAPON,MUSKET,CIVIL WAR,COLT SPECIAL,UNISSUED,UNFIRED,MARK
   COLT-1863............................................. 295.00
WEAPON,MUSKET,CIVIL WAR,EXPERIMENTAL,MARKED PARKER
   SNOW-MERIDEN 1864..................................... 350.00
WEAPON,MUSKET,CIVIL WAR,MARKED SPRINGFIELD-1864,LACKS
   SWIVELS,REAR SIGHT.................................... 125.00
WEAPON,MUSKET,CIVIL WAR,MILLER CONVERSION TO BREECH LOAD,
   PARKER,1864........................................... 54.50
WEAPON,MUSKET,CIVIL WAR,PERCUSSION,MARKED SPRINGFIELD 1864,
   .58 CALIBER........................................... 325.00
WEAPON,MUSKET,CIVIL WAR,TAKES TWO LOADS,PERCUSSION,LINDSAY,
   SHOWS WEAR............................................ 165.00
WEAPON,MUSKET,COLONIAL AMERICA,CLUB BUTT,RELIEF-CARVED,
   WALNUT,RESTORED.....................................1,450.00
WEAPON,MUSKET,CONTRACT,U.S.1808,SAYS BROOKE,SIDE LUG,
   PERCUSSION............................................ 155.00
WEAPON,MUSKET,FLINTLOCK,U.S.M1812,MARK HARPER'S FERRY 1817,
   NEEDS SWIVELS......................................... 275.00
WEAPON,MUSKET,FRENCH,CIRCA 1728,ST.ETIENNE MANUFACTURER MARK 795.00
WEAPON,MUSKET,HARPER FERRY,BAYONET,DATED 1824.............. 130.00
WEAPON,MUSKET,HUDSON BAY INDIAN FUR TRADE,MARKED HOLLIS &
   SONS.................................................. 250.00
WEAPON,MUSKET,INDIAN FUR TRADE,FLORAL ENGRAVING,WALNUT
   STOCK,CIRCA 1765...................................... 195.00
WEAPON,MUSKET,INDIAN FUR TRADE,35-IN.OCTAGON BARREL,MARK
   BARNETT-1835.......................................... 110.00
WEAPON,MUSKET,MILITIA,NEW ENGLAND MAKER,CIRCA 1780,BRASS
   MOUNTINGS............................................. 155.00
WEAPON,MUSKET,NORTHWEST AMERICAN INDIAN FUR TRADE,SIDE LUG,
   PERCUSSION............................................ 225.00
WEAPON,MUSKET,PRESENTATION,ENGRAVED,INLAID,U.S.SPRINGFIELD
   M1816,1829............................................ 650.00
WEAPON,MUSKET,REVOLUTIONARY WAR,BROWN BESS,MAKER WILSON,

DATED 1779................................................ 350.00
WEAPON,MUSKET,REVOLUTIONARY,AMERICAN,GERMANIC-HESSIAN-STYLE
 LOCK PLATE............................................... 795.00
WEAPON,MUSKET,U.S. M1816,ARSENAL CONE,PERCUSSION,MARKED
 WHITNEY-1834............................................. 74.50
WEAPON,MUSKET,U.S.,PERCUSSION,CADET,M1858,MAYNARD TAPE
 PRIMER,BAYONET........................................... 475.00
WEAPON,MUSKET,U.S.CADET,M1841,RIFLED BORE,MARKED
 SPRINGFIELD,1852,U.S..................................... 325.00
WEAPON,MUSKET,U.S.M1812,TYPE II,FLINTLOCK,STUD SPRING
 FASTENERS................................................ 450.00
WEAPON,MUSKET,U.S.M1816,FLINTLOCK,MARKED SPRINGFIELD-1820,
 RESTORED................................................. 145.00
WEAPON,MUSKET,U.S.NAVY M1816,IRON BUTT PLATE,MARKED
 U.S.WATERS-1832.......................................... 225.00
WEAPON,MUSKET,U.S.NORWICH,1862................................ 90.00
WEAPON,MUSKET,WINCHESTER,MORTISED DUST COVER,SERIAL NO.2705,
 M1873................................................... 750.00
WEAPON,PISTOL,AMERICAN REVOLUTION,CHARLEVILLE FLINTLOCK,
 NEEDS HAMMER............................................. 125.00
WEAPON,PISTOL,ENGLISH CAVALRY,FLINTLOCK,MARKED G.R.TOWER.... 150.00
WEAPON,PISTOL,FLINTLOCK,SILVER INLAY ON WOOD,18TH CENTURY... 95.00
WEAPON,PISTOL,MARKED SMOKER NO.2.............................. 25.00
WEAPON,PISTOL,PERCUSSION,ENGLAND.............................. 80.00
WEAPON,PISTOL,POCKET,OCTAGON BARREL,31 COLT,1849,WELLS FARGO 450.00
WEAPON,PISTOL,REFORMA 312-1,2 MM,CASE,REAMER,BRUSH,MEXICAN,
 2 1/2 IN................................................. 35.00
WEAPON,POWDER FLASK,AMERICAN CAP & FLASK CO.,RIBBED DECOR,
 CORD,TASSELS............................................. 25.00
WEAPON,POWDER FLASK,BRASS..................................... 20.00
WEAPON,POWDER FLASK,BRASS MEASURE TOP,EMBOSSED DEAD GAME,
 SCENE.................................................... 35.00
WEAPON,POWDER FLASK,BRASS MEASURE TOP,PEWTER................. 17.50
WEAPON,POWDER FLASK,BRASS TOP,GAME SCENE,9 IN................ 20.00
WEAPON,POWDER FLASK,BUGLE DECOR,MARKED PUBLIC PROPERTY,1812. 80.00
WEAPON,POWDER FLASK,EMBOSSED HOUNDS,HUNTER,BIRDS,COPPER..... 28.50
WEAPON,POWDER FLASK,HUNTING SCENES,MARKED SHEFFIELD,BRASS,
 8 IN.LONG................................................ 75.00
WEAPON,POWDER FLASK,PEACE,CLASPED HANDS,EAGLE,U.S.EMBLEM,NO
 SPRING,BRASS............................................. 60.00
WEAPON,POWDER FLASK,PHEASANT,SHELL,COPPER,AMERICA,7 IN...... 16.50
WEAPON,POWDER FLASK,SHELL DESIGN,BRASS....................... 25.00
WEAPON,POWDER HORN,BRASS..................................... 16.00
WEAPON,POWDER HORN,BULBOUS WOOD END,ENGRAVED JAMES CROCKER,
 12 IN.LONG............................................... 25.00
WEAPON,POWDER HORN,CARVED INITIALS & CO.H,1847,1817 ON WOOD
 BASE.................................................... 35.00
WEAPON,POWDER HORN,CARVED LARGE BIRD,NAME WILLIAM MOSS,
 16 IN.LONG............................................... 26.50
WEAPON,POWDER HORN,CARVED NECK,INITIALS & 1831 DATE ON
 WOODEN BOTTOM............................................ 16.00
WEAPON,POWDER HORN,CARVED,VESSELS,BRITISH FLAG,CHURCH,BIRDS,
 BRASS PIN................................................ 95.00
WEAPON,POWDER HORN,CIRCA 1760,MARKED JOHN FROST,KITTERY,ME.,
 10 IN.LONG............................................... 300.00
WEAPON,POWDER HORN,COW HORN................................... 8.00
WEAPON,POWDER HORN,INITIALS AND 1837 DATE,LEATHER STRAP,
 13 IN.................................................... 14.50
WEAPON,POWDER HORN,MARKED EXTRA QUALITY SYKES PAT.,COPPER,
 8 IN.LONG................................................ 30.00
WEAPON,POWDER HORN,PELLET HOLDER,CONTENTS.................... 12.00
WEAPON,POWDER HORN,PEWTER.................................... 10.00
WEAPON,POWDER HORN,RELIEF CARVED TOWN,FORTS,WARRIOR,HORSE,
 CREST,FLAGS............................................. 100.00
WEAPON,POWDER HORN,REVOLUTIONARY WAR,8 IN.................... 9.50
WEAPON,POWDER HORN,SHELL,ACANTHUS LEAF,BRASS,7 3/4 IN....... 22.00
WEAPON,POWDER HORN,STARS,WHALE,CARVING SAYS MAINE,JABEZ
 WALKER,21 IN............................................. 75.00
WEAPON,POWDER HORN,WITH POWDER & THONG,12 IN................. 13.00
WEAPON,RAPIER,SWEPT HILT,BRAIDED WIRE GRIPS,16TH CENTURY,
 ITALIAN,43 IN............................................ 425.00
WEAPON,RAPIER,SWEPT HILT,IRON GUARD,WIRE-WRAPPED GRIPS,
 ITALY,35-IN.BLADE........................................ 225.00
WEAPON,RIFLE,BENCH,PERCUSSION,DELANEY,READING,PENNA.,WALNUT
 HALF STOCK............................................... 425.00
WEAPON,RIFLE,BOAR HUNTING,AMERICAN,MARKED ZETTLER,CIRCA
 1860.................................................... 475.00
WEAPON,RIFLE,BRASS BUTT PLATE,TRIGGER GUARD,HEX BARREL,
 KENTUCKY................................................. 165.00
WEAPON,RIFLE,BUFFALO,SHARPS,PERCUSSION,.44 CALIBER,OCTAGONAL

BARREL.......................................................... 295.00
WEAPON,RIFLE,BURNSIDE,SOLID UNHINGED BREECH BLOCK,NO FORE
END,PERCUSSION................................................. 265.00
WEAPON,RIFLE,CIVIL WAR,ARTILLERY MODEL,BRITISH ENFIELD,POTTS
& HUNT......................................................... 110.00
WEAPON,RIFLE,CURLY MAPLE STOCK,ETCHED PATCH BOX,42 CALIBER,
KENTUCKY....................................................... 350.00
WEAPON,RIFLE,FLINTLOCK,19TH CENTURY,ENGLAND.................... 85.00
WEAPON,RIFLE,FLINTLOCK,ENGLAND................................. 85.00
WEAPON,RIFLE,FLINTLOCK,WALNUT STOCK,MUZZLE CAP,PATCH BOX,
S.SIEGFRIED.................................................... 165.00
WEAPON,RIFLE,GERMAN MAUSER,MODEL 98,WORLD WAR II,MARKED
S/42-1936...................................................... 32.50
WEAPON,RIFLE,KENTUCKY FULL STOCK,MARKED DERINGER,CURLY MAPLE
STOCK.......................................................... 375.00
WEAPON,RIFLE,KENTUCKY,FLINTLOCK,SAYS TRUITT BROS. & CO.,
MAPLE STOCK.................................................... 795.00
WEAPON,RIFLE,KENTUCKY,RELIEF-CARVED,MARKED E.LANNING,CURLY
MAPLE STOCK.................................................... 425.00
WEAPON,RIFLE,LEFT-HAND LOCK,CHEEKREST ON RIGHT SIDE,CIRCA
1840,KENTUCKY.................................................. 375.00
WEAPON,RIFLE,MATCH,KENTUCKY,PERCUSSION,.52 CALIBER........... 165.00
WEAPON,RIFLE,MAYNARD TAPE PRIMER UNIT,MARKED JENKS
U.S.N.1847 REMINGTON........................................... 350.00
WEAPON,RIFLE,PLAINS,PERCUSSION,MARKED J.V.HOFFMAN-ATTICA,
INDIANA........................................................ 275.00
WEAPON,RIFLE,REMINGTON,M1863,BLUE FINISH,UNFIRED,PATCH BOX.. 450.00
WEAPON,RIFLE,REMINGTON,ZOUAVE,CIVIL WAR,UNISSUED,PERCUSSION,
BLUE BARREL.................................................... 475.00
WEAPON,RIFLE,REPEATER,FULL STOCK,BROWN METAL,SPENCER........ 120.00
WEAPON,RIFLE,SAVAGE MODEL 99,.22 CALIBER,22-IN.-ROUND BARREL 59.50
WEAPON,RIFLE,SIDE HAMMER,MUZZLE-LOADING,PERCUSSION,REAR PEEP 115.00
WEAPON,RIFLE,SPORTING,MARKED C.OAK & SON,JACKSONVILLE,
FLORIDA,REMINGTON.............................................. 950.00
WEAPON,RIFLE,SPORTING,STRIPED DAMASCUS FINISH,NEEDS ONE
RAMROD,ENGLAND................................................. 135.00
WEAPON,RIFLE,TARGET,BENCH REST,PERCUSSION,MARK NELSON
DELANEY-PENNA.................................................. 450.00
WEAPON,RIFLE,U.S.M1819,MARKED HALL-H.FERRY-U.S.-1834,UNFIRED 325.00
WEAPON,RIFLE,WALL GUN,LONG RANGE,CIRCA 1760,GERMAN,
.82 CALIBER,67 IN.............................................. 850.00
WEAPON,RIFLE,WINCHESTER,.32 SPECIAL,26-IN.ROUND BARREL,1894. 145.00
WEAPON,RIFLE,WINCHESTER,1895,SERIAL NO.97,FLAT FRAME,BLUE
METAL OUTSIDE.................................................. 395.00
WEAPON,RIFLE,WINCHESTER,32/20,24-IN.-ROUND BARREL,1892,FULL
MAGAZINE....................................................... 195.00
WEAPON,SABER,CAVALRY,ORNATE LEATHER & BRASS HANDLE,AMES MFG.
CO............................................................. 59.00
WEAPON,SABER,CAVALRY,ORNATE LEATHER,BRASS HANDLE,METAL
SCABBARD,AMES CO............................................... 65.00
WEAPON,SABER,DRAGOON,FRENCH,NAPOLEONIC,THREE-BRANCH GUARD,
BRASS HILT..................................................... 97.50
WEAPON,SABER,DRAGOON,IRON HILT,CARVED WOODEN GRIPS,CIRCA
1775,BRITISH................................................... 110.00
WEAPON,SABER,SCABBARD,GERMAN NAVAL OFFICER,BRASS HILT,LION
HEAD POMMEL.................................................... 84.50
WEAPON,SABER,SCABBARD,ORNATE MOTIF,31-IN.CURVED BLADE,
NAPOLEONIC,FRANCE.............................................. 425.00
WEAPON,SABER,U.S.CAVALRY,IRON HILT,SAYS U.S.-1906,SHEATH.... 34.50
WEAPON,SABER,U.S.CAVALRY,MARKED U.S.-1913,SHEATH,MAKER
GEORGE PATTON.................................................. 47.50
WEAPON,SCIMITAR,MASON,SIMULATED RUBY,HORN CRESCENT,PHARAOH
HEAD,ISLAM..................................................... 15.00
WEAPON,SHOT BAG,LEATHER,WOODEN STOPPER....................... 9.00
WEAPON,SHOT POUCH,BELT-TYPE,LEATHER,22 IN.LONG............... 7.50
WEAPON,SHOT POUCH,EMBOSSED DEAD GAME SCENE,MEASURE. 16.00 TO 18.00
WEAPON,SHOT POUCH,LEATHER,BRASS TOP.......................... 6.75
WEAPON,SHOTGUN,ENGLISH,DOUBLE BARREL,PERCUSSION,MARKED
PERKINS........................................................ 135.00
WEAPON,SHOTGUN,FACTORY-ENGRAVED MARLIN,MODEL 24,PUMP,FLYING
BIRDS,GEESE.................................................... 165.00
WEAPON,SHOTGUN,FACTORY-ENGRAVED MARLIN,MODEL 24,26-IN.
BARREL,12 GAUGE................................................ 140.00
WEAPON,SHOTGUN,5-SHOT,COLT-HARTFORD MARKINGS,SERIAL NO.2,
DATED 1856.................................................1,950.00
WEAPON,SHOTGUN,FOWLING PIECE,HALF STOCK,ENGLISH,PERCUSSION,
CIRCA 1850..................................................... 225.00
WEAPON,SHOTGUN,FRANCOTTE,HAMMERLESS,MARKED VON LENGERKE &
DETMOLD........................................................ 350.00
WEAPON,SHOTGUN,PERCUSSION,DOUBLE BARREL,SINGLE TRIGGER,

GERMANY,MARK.................................................... 195.00
WEAPON,SHOTGUN,SLOPING BREECH,PERCUSSION,MARKED S.G.SHARPS,
.56 CALIBER..................................................... 225.00
WEAPON,SHOTGUN,TUBE LOCK,DOUBLE BARREL,12 GAUGE,MARK
R.LANCASTER,LONDON.............................................. 425.00
WEAPON,SKEIN DHU,SCOTTISH HIGHLAND,STOCKING DAGGER,BASKET
WEAVE,BOAR...................................................... 39.50
WEAPON,SWORD,ANCIENT ORDER OF HIBERNIANS,1890,SCABBARD......... 18.00
WEAPON,SWORD,BRASS HILT,LION HEAD POMMEL,IVORY GRIPS,CIRCA
1803,ENGLAND................................................... 59.50
WEAPON,SWORD,BRASS HILT,LION HEAD POMMEL,29-IN.BLADE,
GOLD-ETCHED DECOR.............................................. 79.50
WEAPON,SWORD,BRITISH INFANTRY OFFICER,M1803,CIPHER GR,CROWN,
IVORY GRIPS.................................................... 59.50
WEAPON,SWORD,BRITISH INFANTRY OFFICER,URN-SHAPED POMMEL,
BRASS HILT,1785................................................ 110.00
WEAPON,SWORD,BRITISH OFFICER,ALLIGATOR-LIKE POMMEL,FLAG,
SHIELD DECOR................................................... 84.50
WEAPON,SWORD,BRITISH OFFICER,DIVIDED GUARD,IVORY GRIPS,SHOWS
AGE,1750....................................................... 125.00
WEAPON,SWORD,BRITISH OFFICER,DRESS,RELIEF CARVING,BUDDHAS,
IVORY HILT..................................................... 295.00
WEAPON,SWORD,BRITISH OFFICER,PRESENTATION,FLORAL,SCROLL,
1862,SCABBARD.................................................. 155.00
WEAPON,SWORD,BRITISH OFFICER'S,IRON HILT,CIRCA 1750,
26-IN.CURVED BLADE............................................. 175.00
WEAPON,SWORD,CIVIL WAR,DATED 1860,BRASS SCABBARD,EAGLE,BELT,
BRASS BUCKLE................................................... 85.00
WEAPON,SWORD,CIVIL WAR,DATED 1862.............................. 135.00
WEAPON,SWORD,CIVIL WAR,SHEATH.................................. 48.00
WEAPON,SWORD,DRESS,INDIA ROYAL CAVALRY......................... 12.00
WEAPON,SWORD,ENGLISH COURT,IRON HILT,FLORAL,MAKER SPINHOSA,
CIRCA 1740..................................................... 225.00
WEAPON,SWORD,ENGLISH FOOT OFFICER,IRON HILT,EBONY GRIPS,
1750,26 IN..................................................... 97.50
WEAPON,SWORD,ENGLISH FOOT OFFICER,IRON HILT,CUT SPIRAL ON
POMMEL,1760.................................................... 175.00
WEAPON,SWORD,ENGLISH MOUNTED OFFICER,KNUBLEY-SWORD & GUN
MANUFACTORY,1790............................................... 165.00
WEAPON,SWORD,ENGLISH OFFICER,INFANTRY,IRON GUARD,HALF BASKET
SHAPE,1850..................................................... 34.50
WEAPON,SWORD,ENGLISH OFFICER,IRON HILT,SHARKSIN GRIPS,WIRE
WRAPS,1750..................................................... 145.00
WEAPON,SWORD,ENGLISH VICTORIAN MILITARY........................ 35.00
WEAPON,SWORD,EXECUTIONER,TWO-HANDED,BRASS CROSS GUARD,1731,
GERMANY........................................................ 550.00
WEAPON,SWORD,EXECUTIONER,TWO-HANDED,JAPANESE STYLE TSUBA,
51 IN.LONG..................................................... 295.00
WEAPON,SWORD,FOOT ARTILLERY,CIVIL WAR,BRASS HILT,MARKED
MOLLER N.YORK.................................................. 97.50
WEAPON,SWORD,FOOT OFFICER'S,BRASS HILT,LEATHER GRIPS,1740,
GERMANY........................................................ 175.00
WEAPON,SWORD,FRATERNAL,HORSTMANN,ETCHED,IVORY HANDLE,ORNATE. 85.00
WEAPON,SWORD,FRENCH FOOT OFFICER,BRASS HILT,HELMET POMMEL,
SCABBARD,1840.................................................. 34.50
WEAPON,SWORD,FRENCH OFFICER'S,GILTED BRASS HILT,WING & LEAF
MOTIF,1820..................................................... 69.50
WEAPON,SWORD,FRENCH OFFICER'S,SILVER HILT,SCROLLS,FLORAL,
CIRCA 1820..................................................... 135.00
WEAPON,SWORD,GILDED BRASS HILT,SCROLLED POMMEL,PRUSSIAN
OFFICER,1871................................................... 29.50
WEAPON,SWORD,HANDLE CARVED FROM A WHALE'S TOOTH,METAL BLADE,
COPPER GUARD................................................... 900.00
WEAPON,SWORD,IRON HILT,HAND-ENGRAVED SERRATIONS,CIRCA 1650,
FRANCE......................................................... 79.50
WEAPON,SWORD,JAPANESE NAVY OFFICER............................. 35.00
WEAPON,SWORD,JAPANESE POLICE OFFICER........................... 25.00
WEAPON,SWORD,JAPANESE,FLOWER DESIGN,BRONZE HILT,METAL
SCABBARD....................................................... 22.00
WEAPON,SWORD,LION-HEAD POMMEL,ENGLISH FOOT OFFICE,1760,
23-IN.BLADE.................................................... 250.00
WEAPON,SWORD,NAVAL OFFICER'S,CIVIL WAR,LEATHER-COVERED
SCABBARD,HORSTMAN.............................................. 75.00
WEAPON,SWORD,OFFICER,MAMELUKE HILT,SAYS UNITED STATES
MARINES,SCABBARD............................................... 44.50
WEAPON,SWORD,OFFICER,PRESENTATION,FLORAL MOTIF,ENGRAVED
INSCRIPTION,1862............................................... 175.00
WEAPON,SWORD,ONE-PIECE BRASS GRIPS,SPIRAL FLUTED MOTIF,CIRCA
1700,29 IN..................................................... 150.00
WEAPON,SWORD,OPENWORK MEDALLION-LIKE MOTIF OF EAGLE,PRUSSIA,

| | |
|---|---:|
| 1870.................................................... | 37.50 |
| WEAPON,SWORD,PIERCED,NAMBAM TYPE......................... | 45.00 |
| WEAPON,SWORD,PRESENTATION,WORLD WAR I,GERMAN,REVERSE P | |
| GUARD,IRON SHEATH....................................... | 32.50 |
| WEAPON,SWORD,ROOSTER HEAD POMMEL,LIONESS QUILLON,SHEATH, | |
| 1800,FRANCE............................................. | 175.00 |
| WEAPON,SWORD,SAMURAI,IVORY HANDLE,SCABBARD,TSUBA,CARVED, | |
| 39 IN.LONG............................................. | 450.00 |
| WEAPON,SWORD,SAMURAI,COPPER,BRASS ON TSUBA,METAL SCABBARD... | 85.00 |
| WEAPON,SWORD,SAPPER/PIONEER,ROOSTER HEAD POMMEL,BRASS HILT, | |
| FRANCE,1800............................................ | 175.00 |
| WEAPON,SWORD,SCABBARD,FRENCH OFFICER,DATED 1916,FLORAL | |
| MOTIF,EBONY GRIPS...................................... | 32.50 |
| WEAPON,SWORD,SCABBARD,IMPERIAL GERMAN OFFICER,PRUSSIAN | |
| EAGLE,CROWN............................................ | 175.00 |
| WEAPON,SWORD,SCABBARD,PRUSSIAN GRENADIER OFFICER,EAGLE, | |
| CROWN,1830,22 IN....................................... | 125.00 |
| WEAPON,SWORD,SCOTTISH HIGHLAND,IRON HILT,SAYS VENER OMORIR | |
| PORMIRE 1650........................................... | 395.00 |
| WEAPON,SWORD,SIKH,HAND-FORGED,CIRCA 1868,ROYAL TROOPS OF THE | |
| MAHARAJAH.............................................. | 19.50 |
| WEAPON,SWORD,SIKH,ROYAL TROOP OF THE MAHARAJAH,SCABBARD, | |
| 1866................................................... | 19.50 |
| WEAPON,SWORD,SPANISH OFFICER,SILVER HILT,CARVED GRIPS,1820, | |
| 33 IN.................................................. | 115.00 |
| WEAPON,SWORD,SPANISH,CUP HILT,SHELL-LIKE GUARDS,MARKED,1795, | |
| 32-IN.BLADE............................................ | 84.50 |
| WEAPON,SWORD,TACHI,JAPANESE,RAYSKIN GRIPS,SILK COVERING, | |
| MENUKI SYMBOLS......................................... | 79.50 |
| WEAPON,SWORD,TALWAR,INDIA,COPPER HILT,RELIEF MOTIF, | |
| ELEPHANTS,TIGERS....................................... | 64.50 |
| WEAPON,SWORD,U.S.ARTILLERY OFFICER,EAGLE HEAD MOTIF,CIRCA | |
| 1800................................................... | 79.50 |
| WEAPON,SWORD,U.S.INFANTRY OFFICER,BRASS HILT,EAGLE ON | |
| LANCET,1820............................................ | 125.00 |
| WEAPON,SWORD,U.S.INFANTRY OFFICER,BRASS HILT,INDIAN HEAD | |
| POMMEL,1820............................................ | 74.50 |
| WEAPON,SWORD,U.S.INFANTRY OFFICER,MARKED U.S.1861, | |
| AMES-CHICOPEE,SHEATH................................... | 79.50 |
| WEAPON,SWORD,U.S.MILITIA OFFICER,GILT BRASS HILT,CIRCA 1820, | |
| 32-IN.BLADE............................................ | 64.50 |
| WEAPON,SWORD,U.S.MILITIA STAFF OFFICER,BRASS HILT,BONE | |
| GRIPS,1850............................................. | 195.00 |
| WEAPON,SWORD,U.S.NAVY,CURVED BLADE,1864.................. | 60.00 |
| WEAPON,SWORD,U.S.OFFICER,AMERICAN EAGLE,THREE-LEAF CLOVER, | |
| SCABBARD............................................... | 275.00 |
| WEAPON,SWORD,WAKIZASHI,JAPANESE,RAYSKIN GRIPS,CIRCA 1673, | |
| IRON TSUBA............................................. | 49.50 |
| WEAPON,SWORD,WALSCHEID SCHLINGER,U.S.A.,33-IN.BLADE,STEEL | |
| SCABBARD............................................... | 38.00 |
| WEAPON,SWORD CANE,LONG BLADE,COMPLETE DISGUISE............ | 13.00 |
| WEAPON,TACHI,SWORD & SHEATH,JAPANESE,RAYSKIN GRIPS,BRAIDED | |
| SILK COVER............................................. | 79.50 |
| WEATHERVANE,ANTLERED RUNNING DEER,FULL BODY,COPPER........ | 250.00 |
| WEATHERVANE,COCKRELL,THREE-DIMENSIONAL,ARCHED TAIL,SPURS, | |
| COPPER................................................. | 165.00 |
| WEATHERVANE,EAGLE ON ARROW,LETTERS,ROD,PAINTED GOLD, | |
| 8-IN.WINGSPREAD,IRON................................... | 125.00 |
| WEATHERVANE,EAGLE,LETTERS N.S.E.W.,PAINTED GOLD,23 IN.HIGH.. | 125.00 |
| WEATHERVANE,EAGLE,SPREAD WINGS,ON ORB,ROD STANDARD,COPPER, | |
| 64 IN.HIGH............................................. | 400.00 |
| WEATHERVANE,GILDED COPPER,ROD STANDARD,64 IN.HIGH....ILLUS.. | 850.00 |
| WEATHERVANE,HORSE,COPPER,BRONZE,HANDMADE,32 IN.LONG, | |
| 26 IN.TALL............................................. | 400.00 |
| WEATHERVANE,HORSE,COPPER,15 1/2 IN.LONG.................. | 50.00 |
| WEATHERVANE,HORSE,RACING,JOCKEY,WIND INDICATORS,COPPER, | |
| 62 IN.HIGH............................................. | 525.00 |
| WEATHERVANE,HORSE,RIDER,AUTOMATED,FAN MECHANISM,WOODEN, | |
| 61 IN.HIGH............................................. | 700.00 |
| WEATHERVANE,HORSE,TROTTING,ON ORB,ROD STANDARD,COPPER, | |
| 65 IN.HIGH............................................. | 200.00 |
| WEATHERVANE,HORSE,TROTTING,ROD STANDARD,ZINC,62 | |
| 1/2.....................................150.00 TO | 200.00 |
| WEATHERVANE,OWLS,SHEET IRON............................. | 45.00 |
| WEATHERVANE,POINTER DOG,LETTERS,ARROW,COPPER,20 1/2 IN. X | |
| 19 IN.WIDE............................................. | 45.00 |
| WEATHERVANE,ROOSTER ON CONE,ARROW SAYS JAMES,TIN,BLUE MILK | |
| GLASS BALL............................................. | 58.00 |
| WEATHERVANE,ROOSTER,ON ORB,DIRECTIONAL SIGNALS,COPPER, | |
| 55 IN.HIGH............................................. | 400.00 |

GILDED COPPER WEATHERVANE

```
WEATHERVANE,SILHOUETTE DIRECTIONAL ARROW,LEAF SCROLLS,TIN,
   61 IN.HIGH............................................    275.00


      WEBB GLASS WAS MADE BY THOMAS WEBB & SONS OF
      STOURBRIDGE,ENGLAND. MANY TYPES OF ART AND CAMEO GLASS
      WERE MADE BY THEM DURING THE VICTORIAN ERA.
WEBB,BOTTLE,PERFUME,LAY-DOWN,CRANBERRY,WHITE DECOR,CAMEO,
   SILVER LID...........................................    145.00
WEBB,BOTTLE,TOPAZ COLOR,ENGRAVED BIRDS,EIGHT STEMMED WINES,
   SIGNED...............................................    150.00
WEBB,BOWL,COIN SPOT DESIGN,PINK TO RED,WHITE INSIDE,
   MOTHER-OF-PEARL......................................    125.00
WEBB,BOWL,MELON-RIBBED,FISHSCALE,CREAM-COLOR GROUND,SEA
   PLANTS,FISH..........................................    145.00
WEBB,BOWL,ROSE,ARABESQUE PATTERN,OPALESCENT CRACKLE,CRIMPED
   TOP..................................................     45.00
WEBB,BOWL,ROSE,DECORATED,SIGNED.........................    465.00
WEBB,BOWL,ROSE,MOTHER-OF-PEARL,PINK,RUFFLED TOP.........    110.00
WEBB,BOWL,ROSE,POLYCHROME ACORNS & LEAVES,CRIMPED RIM,
   2 1/2 IN.HIGH........................................    325.00
WEBB,BOWL,ROSE,PROPELLOR,OVOID,ENAMELED PINK APPLE BLOSSOMS,
   MEDALLIONS...........................................     55.00
WEBB,BRIDE'S BASKET,APPLIED FLORAL,GOLD,SATIN GLASS,ATTACHED
   STAND................................................    165.00
WEBB,CENTERPIECE,SATIN,WHITE-CASED,ROSE-COLOR LINING,SILVER
   PEDESTAL.............................................     75.00
WEBB,COMPOTE,FLORAL,LEAVES,COPPER WHELL-ENGRAVED,SIGNED,
   5 IN.,PAIR...........................................     65.00
WEBB,CREAMER & SUGAR,INTAGLIO,CERISE,W IN OPAL PONTIL,3 IN..1,500.00
WEBB,DECANTER,WINE,SQUARE,CUT GLASS.....................     35.00
WEBB,FLASK,PERFUME,CAMEO,DUCK HEAD,WHITE OVER CITRON,SILVER
   TOP..................................................    395.00
WEBB,FLASK,PERFUME,DUCK HEAD,WHITE CAMEO OVER CITRON GROUND,
   GORHAM TOP...........................................    395.00
WEBB,INKWELL,CUT GLASS,BUBBLES THROUGHOUT,SIGNED........     45.00
WEBB,JAR,BISCUIT,INTAGLIO CUT FLORAL,LEAVES,STEMS,CRANBERRY,
   SILVER COVER.........................................     85.00
WEBB,LAMP,FAIRY,ALLOVER INTAGLIO CUT FLORAL,CRANBERRY,SATIN,
   CLARKE BASE..........................................     85.00
WEBB,LAMP,FAIRY,BLUE MOTHER-OF-PEARL RIBBON SATIN SHADE,TIER
   DECOR BASE...........................................    185.00
WEBB,LAMP,FAIRY,BLUE-CASED SATIN SHADE,HAND-PAINTED FURLS,
   CLARKE BASE..........................................    145.00
WEBB,LAMP,FAIRY,WHITE SATIN,QUATREFOIL SHADE,ENAMELED PINK
   FLORAL...............................................    225.00
WEBB,MUFFINEER,SILVER PLATE TOP,SIGNED..................     33.00
WEBB,PERFUME,BLUE,ENAMEL DECOR,BUTTERFLY,AMBER STOPPER..     20.00
WEBB,PERFUME,CAMEO,RED,WHITE,VIOLETS,WHITE PICKET BAND,
   CARVED,3 3/4 IN......................................    350.00
WEBB,PERFUME,CAMEO,YELLOW,CARVED PINK & WHITE FLORAL,SILVER
   TOP,5 IN.............................................    650.00
WEBB,PERFUME,PINK TO APRICOT COLOR,FLORAL,BEADING,SATIN,
   BRASS COVER..........................................    135.00
WEBB,PITCHER,MOTHER-OF-PEARL,SILVERY CREAM,HERRINGBONE,
```

```
SQUARE,5 IN.TALL.....................................................1,650.00
WEBB,PITCHER,RED,CASED,WHITE LINING,GOLD COLOR FLORAL,BIRDS,
    BUTTERFLY........................................................ 250.00
WEBB,PITCHER,WATER,WHITE SATIN,DECOR................................. 195.00
WEBB,SALT DIP,RED OVER WHITE,APPLIED CLEAR BERRIES,SIGNED... 110.00
WEBB,VASE,APPLIED FLOWERS & FRUIT,DEEP ROSE,PAIR,MATCHING
    CORNUCOPIA....................................................... 500.00
WEBB,VASE,BLUE,CARVED CLEMATIS BLOSSOMS,LEAFY SPRAYS,RINGS,
    CAMEO,4 IN....................................................... 350.00
WEBB,VASE,BRONZE COLOR,GROUND PONTIL,10 IN.HIGH.............. 115.00
WEBB,VASE,CAMEO RELIEF DESIGN OF TULIPS & LEAVES ON ETCHED
    GROUND,10 IN..................................................... 225.00
WEBB,VASE,CAMEO-CUT GLASS,2-COLOR DECORATION,10 1/4 IN. HIGH 500.00
WEBB,VASE,CAMEO,FOUR-LAYER,WILD ROSE,BUDS,LEAVES,WHITE,PINK,
    YELLOW,4 IN...................................................... 385.00
WEBB,VASE,CAMEO,RELIEF DESIGN,PINK TULIPS,ETCHED CRYSTAL,
    6 1/2 IN......................................................... 225.00
WEBB,VASE,CRANBERRY,4 IN.HIGH,PAIR.................................... 75.00
WEBB,VASE,CREAM GROUND,FLORAL,BUTTERFLY,DRAGONFLY,GOLD,
    BROWN,7 3/4 IN................................................... 78.00
WEBB,VASE,CUT VELVET,RIBBED TRIANGLE PATTERN,WHITE CASING,
    BLUE,5 IN.TALL................................................... 110.00
WEBB,VASE,DIAMOND-QUILTED,MOTHER-OF-PEARL,BLUE,PEDESTAL
    BASE,6 1/2 IN.................................................... 90.00
WEBB,VASE,GOLD MOTHER-OF-PEARL,RAINDROP PATTERN,STICK NECK,
    BLOWN,7 IN....................................................... 65.00
WEBB,VASE,HONEY-AMBER BRONZE IRIDESCENT CASING,RUBBED TO
    WHITE ON TOP..................................................... 145.00
WEBB,VASE,IVORY CAMEO,STICK,SIGNED,10 IN.HIGH.................1,750.00
WEBB,VASE,IVORY GROUND,GOLD FLORAL,BUTTERFLY,SIGNED
    PROPELLER MARK................................................... 85.00
WEBB,VASE,LAVENDER HIGHLIGHTS,BRONZE,4 IN.HIGH.............. 45.00
WEBB,VASE,MOTHER-OF-PEARL,DIAMOND-QUILTED,PINK AT BASE,WHITE
    SATIN GLASS...................................................... 115.00
WEBB,VASE,PINK & GOLD STRIPES,FLORAL,GOLD BUG,BORDER AT TOP,
    6 1/2 IN......................................................... 90.00
WEBB,VASE,PINK & WHITE STRIPES,GOLD-ENAMELED FLORAL,WHITE
    LINING,SATIN..................................................... 95.00
WEBB,VASE,PINK TO RASPBERRY,CREAM LINING,BASKET WEAVE,SATIN,
    7 IN.TALL........................................................ 325.00
WEBB,VASE,PINK,WHITE,CHARTREUSE,CAMEO........................ 798.00
WEBB,VASE,PURPLE,GOLD DECORATION,6 1/2 IN............ILLUS.. 875.00
```

WEBB VASE

```
WEBB,VASE,PURPLE PLUMS,HAND-PAINTED,GOLD LEAVES,BEIGE
    GROUND,7 1/2 IN.................................................. 135.00
WEBB,VASE,ROSE COLOR GROUND,ENAMEL BIRDS & FLOWERS,SIGNED,
    11 IN........................................................... 100.00
WEBB,VASE,ROSE TO PINK,GOLD FLORAL,SATIN,6 IN.HIGH......... 250.00
WEBB,VASE,VASELINE GLASS,ENAMEL PINK & VIOLET FLORAL,
    BUTTERFLIES,10 IN............................................... 70.00
WEBB,VASE,WHITE THREADINGS,MELON RIB,VASELINE SATIN,3 X
    4 IN.TALL....................................................... 105.00
WEBB,VASE,WHITE,GOLD DECOR,TWO HANDLES,SIGNED,10 IN.TALL.... 175.00
WEBB,VASE,YELLOW,WHITE CASING,MULTICOLOR ENAMEL DOTS,LEAVES,
    FLORAL,8 IN..................................................... 125.00
WEBB BURMESE,BOWL,ROSE,ENAMEL FLORAL,CRIMPED TURNED-IN TOP,
    2 1/4 IN.TALL................................................... 275.00
WEBB BURMESE,BOWL,ROSE,FLORAL & LEAVES,LABEL,2 1/2 IN.HIGH.. 415.00
```

```
WEBB BURMESE,BOWL,ROSE,FLORAL DECOR,CRIMPED TOP,2 1/2 X
  2 1/2 IN.HIGH..................................................  225.00
WEBB BURMESE,BOWL,ROSE,SIGNED......................................  395.00
WEBB BURMESE,BOWL,ROSE,SIGNED QUEEN'S BURMESE,THOS.WEBB &
  SONS..........................................................  590.00
WEBB BURMESE,BOWL,ROSE,VERY LITTLE YELLOW,ALMOST ALL PINK,
  2 1/2 IN.HIGH.................................................  185.00
WEBB BURMESE,BOWL,ROSE,3 IN.TALL..................................  295.00
WEBB BURMESE,EPERGNE,UNDER GLASS DOME,SEVEN PARTS,PATENT
  QUEEN'S BURMESE.............................................3,750.00
WEBB BURMESE,FAIRY LITE,ENAMEL,CLARKE MARK ON BASE & HOLDER,
  THREE PARTS...................................................  225.00
WEBB BURMESE,JAR,SWEETMEAT,DECOR,SIGNED WEBBS QUEENS BURMESE   450.00
WEBB BURMESE,JAR,SWEETMEAT,DECORATED,SIGNED WEBBS QUEENS
  BURMESE.......................................................  450.00
WEBB BURMESE,LAMP,FAIRY........................135.00 TO   138.00
WEBB BURMESE,LAMP,FAIRY,3 PART.....................ILLUS..  700.00
```

WEBB BURMESE FAIRY LAMP

```
WEBB BURMESE,LAMP,FAIRY,RUFFLED DISH 7 1/2-IN.DIAMETER,
  5 1/2 IN.TALL.................................................  650.00
WEBB BURMESE,LAMP,FAIRY,SIGNED QUEENS.............................  750.00
WEBB BURMESE,PITCHER,ENAMEL DECOR,GILT,SIGNED IN PONTIL,
  6 IN.TALL.....................................................  650.00
WEBB BURMESE,SWEETMEAT,DECOR,COVER,5 1/2-IN.DIAMETER........  425.00
WEBB BURMESE,TOOTHPICK,ENAMEL FLORAL,SQUARE NECK,
  2 5/8 IN.TALL.................................................  275.00
WEBB BURMESE,TUMBLER,JUICE,IVY VINE SPRIGS,SHADED GREEN
  LEAVES,3 IN.HIGH..............................................  285.00
WEBB BURMESE,VASE,ACID FINISH,4 IN.TALL...........................  195.00
WEBB BURMESE,VASE,APPLE SHAPE BODY,FLOWER FORM,SIGNED,
  3 1/2 IN......................................................  470.00
WEBB BURMESE,VASE,BULBOUS BOTTOM,CRIMPED-IN EDGE TOP,
  3 IN.TALL,PAIR................................................  365.00
WEBB BURMESE,VASE,DECOR,3 1/4 IN.TALL.............................  350.00
WEBB BURMESE,VASE,FIVE-POINTED STAR TOP,SIGNED,2 1/2 X
  3 1/4 IN.HIGH.................................................  325.00
WEBB BURMESE,VASE,LEMON COLOR,SALMON-PINK ROLLED RIM,
  PEDESTAL BASE.................................................  325.00
WEBB,BURMESE,VASE,PIECRUST SIX-POINTED-STAR TOP,QUEEN'S
  WARE,3 1/2 IN.................................................  275.00
WEBB BURMESE,VASE,PINK RIBS,FLARING COLLAR,ACID FINISH,
  4 1/2 IN......................................................  375.00
WEBB BURMESE,VASE,ROSE TO LEMON COLOR,STAR TOP,QUEENS,
  SIGNED,3 1/2 IN...............................................  330.00
WEBB BURMESE,VASE,SWIRL PATTERN,BLOWN-MOLDED,ACID FINISH,
  PINK TO YELLOW................................................  115.50
WEBB CAMEO,BOTTLE,PERFUME,VASELINE GROUND,WHITE FLORAL,SCREW
  TOP...........................................................  185.00
WEBB PEACHBLOW,VASE,DEEP ROSE TO PINK,SCALLOPED,CREAM
  LINING,ACID FINISH............................................  425.00
```

WEBB PEACHBLOW,VASE,STICK,DEEP ROSE TO PINK,COIN GOLD PRUNUS
    BLOSSOMS...................................................  285.00
WEBB PEACHBLOW,VASE,STICK,GOLD DECOR........................  135.00
WEBB PEACHBLOW,VASE,STICK,GOLD DECOR,7 1/2 IN...............  250.00


        WEDGWOOD POTTERY HAS BEEN MADE AT THE FAMOUS WEDGWOOD
    FACTORY IN ENGLAND SINCE 1759. A LARGE VARIETY OF WARES
    HAS BEEN MADE,INCLUDING THE WELL-KNOWN JASPERWARE,
    BASALT,CREAMWARE,AND EVEN A LIMITED AMOUNT OF
    PORCELAIN.
WEDGWOOD,SEE BASALT,JASPER
WEDGWOOD,BASKET,QUEEN'S WARE,CRESS,IMPRESSED WEDGWOOD AND
    BRB,TRAY...................................................   57.50
WEDGWOOD,BOWL,EGYPTIAN BLACK BASALT,TURNED-IN RIM,WINDOW
    MARK ON BASE...............................................  135.00
WEDGWOOD,BOWL,FAIRY LUSTER,DRAGONS,PAINTED GOLD,
    8 1/2-IN.DIAMETER..........................................  300.00
WEDGWOOD,BOWL,FAIRYLAND,MOTHER-OF-PEARL,ORANGE LINING,
    BUTTERFLIES,MARK...........................................  285.00
WEDGWOOD,BOWL,MOTTLED BLUE,GOLD DRAGONS,INTERIOR DECOR,
    DRAGONS,8 IN...............................................  325.00
WEDGWOOD,BOWL,SOUP,FERN PATTERN,SET OF 6,ENGLAND,5 SAUCERS..   35.00
WEDGWOOD,BOX,BLUE,WHITE CLASSICAL FIGURES,DIANA,CHARIOT,LID,
    JASPERWARE.................................................   60.00
WEDGWOOD,BOX,BLUE,WHITE STAG HEADS HOLDING GARLANDS OF
    ROSES,SILVER LID...........................................   42.00
WEDGWOOD,BOX,GREEN & WHITE,COVER,JASPERWARE,ENGLAND.........   20.00
WEDGWOOD,BOX,GREEN,WHITE,FIGURES IN RELIEF,FINIAL,MARKED,
    3 1/2 IN.HIGH..............................................   27.50
WEDGWOOD,BOX,MATCH,BLUE,CLASSIC FIGURES,ENGLAND.............   23.50
WEDGWOOD,BOX,PATCH,BLUE,WHITE GRECIAN FIGURES,COVER,
    1 1/2-IN.DIAMETER..........................................   20.00
WEDGWOOD,BOX,PIN,GREEN JASPERWARE,WHITE CLASSICAL FIGURES,
    LID,4 IN...................................................   35.00
WEDGWOOD,BOX,POWDER,KIDNEY SHAPE,COVER,BLUE,MARKED WEDGWOOD,
    ENGLAND....................................................   16.00
WEDGWOOD,BOX,STAMP,BLACK,WHITE RELIEF,DATED 1904,JASPERWARE.   18.50
WEDGWOOD,BROOCH,BLUE,WHITE,OCTAGONAL MEDALLION,STERLING
    SILVER MOUNT...............................................   38.00
WEDGWOOD,BROOCH,LIGHT BLUE,CLASSIC FIGURE,MARKED,STERLING
    SILVER MOUNT...............................................   30.00
WEDGWOOD,CANDELABRUM,ORMOLU,BASALT PEDESTAL,CUT GLASS STEM,
    DROPS,PAIR..............................................3,250.00
WEDGWOOD,CANDLESTICK,CLASSIC FIGURES,DARK BLUE,JASPERWARE,
    7 IN.,PAIR.................................................  140.00
WEDGWOOD,CANDLESTICK,ENAMELED FLORAL DECOR,MARKED,7 IN.TALL,
    PAIR.......................................................  185.00
WEDGWOOD,CANDLESTICK,MARKED MADE IN ENGLAND,WEDGWOOD,
    8 IN.HIGH,PAIR.............................................   50.00
WEDGWOOD,CANDLESTICK,WILLOW,ETRURIA,ENGLAND,4 IN.,PAIR......   22.50
WEDGWOOD,COFFEEPOT,ORANGE & GOLD AUTUMN FLORAL,SHEFFIELD
    TOP,10 IN..................................................   35.00
WEDGWOOD,COMPOTE,BULLFINCH,STEM,9 1/4-IN.DIAMETER,
    5 1/2 IN.TALL..............................................   32.00
WEDGWOOD,COMPOTE,FAIRY,LUSTER,PEDESTAL,SIGNED,4 1/4 X
    3 1/4 IN.HIGH..............................................  250.00
WEDGWOOD,COMPOTE,LATTICEWORK EDGES,DRAPED,ROSES,MEDALLIONS,
    FOOTED,1850................................................  125.00
WEDGWOOD,CREAMER & SUGAR,BLACK JASPERWARE,WHITE FIGURES,
    MARKED,ENGLAND.............................................   45.00
WEDGWOOD,CREAMER & SUGAR,WILLOW PATTERN,MARKED ETRURIA......    8.00
WEDGWOOD,CREAMER,BLACK BASALT,HELMET SHAPE,PEDESTAL BASE,
    MARK,5 IN.HIGH.............................................   55.00
WEDGWOOD,CREAMER,BLUE GROUND,WHITE CLASSICAL FIGURES,SQUATTY
    SHAPE......................................................   28.00
WEDGWOOD,CREAMER,BLUE,CLASSIC FIGURES IN RELIEF,ENGLAND,
    2 IN.HIGH..................................................   19.00
WEDGWOOD,CREAMER,CLASSIC DESIGN,BLACK BASALT................   45.00
WEDGWOOD,CREAMER,JASPERWARE,YEAR MARK DVR,ENGLAND..........   45.00
WEDGWOOD,CREAMER,LIGHT BLUE,WHITE CLASSICAL FIGURES,MARKED,
    ENGLAND....................................................   40.00
WEDGWOOD,CUP & SAUCER,MUSTACHE,WHITE WITH BLUE BAND.........   14.00
WEDGWOOD,DISH,BONE,COBALT BORDER,GOLD,IMPERIAL PORCELAIN....    4.50
WEDGWOOD,DISH,CHEESE,BLUE JASPERWARE,CLASSIC FIGURES,
    11 IN.HIGH.................................................  125.00
WEDGWOOD,DISH,CHEESE,FIGURES ANGEL CHORUS,LEAF,SCROLL,
    JASPERWARE,BLUE............................................  135.00
WEDGWOOD,DISH,CHEESE,LIGHT BLUE,EMBOSSED WINGED CHILDREN,
    GRECIAN COLUMNS............................................  100.00

```
WEDGWOOD,DISH,SOUP,WHITE,FLORAL,DOUBLE-HANDLED,MATCHING
   SAUCER.............................................................   10.00
WEDGWOOD,DISH,TURQUOISE GROUND,WHITE & ROSE FLORAL,REG.MARK
   FOR 1883..........................................................   41.50
WEDGWOOD,FIGURINE,LORD MAYOR,HAND-PAINTED,8 1/2 IN.HIGH.....   25.00
WEDGWOOD,FISH SET,SHELL & SEAWEED PATTERN,MAJOLICA,PLATTER,
   5 PLATES..........................................................  285.00
WEDGWOOD,INKWELL,TWO ON SMALL PLATTER......................  175.00
WEDGWOOD,JAR,BISCUIT,BLUE,WHITE CLASSICAL FIGURES,ANIMALS,
   TREES.............................................................   65.00
WEDGWOOD,JAR,BISCUIT,GREEN,WHITE CLASSICAL FIGURES,ANIMALS,
   TREES.............................................................   75.00
WEDGWOOD,JAR,COOKIE,DEEP BLUE,STRAIGHT SIDES,MARK,FOOTED,
   5 3/4 IN.HIGH.....................................................   75.00
WEDGWOOD,JAR,COOKIE,GREEN,WHITE CLASSIC FIGURES,SILVER LID &
   HANDLE............................................................   75.00
WEDGWOOD,JAR,COOKIE,RESILVERED TOP RIM,BAIL,COVER,BASE,
   MARKED............................................................   75.00
WEDGWOOD,JAR,CRACKER,BLUE,CLASSIC FIGURES,MADE IN ENGLAND...   48.00
WEDGWOOD,JAR,CRACKER,BLUE,WHITE CLASSICAL FIGURES,SILVER
   FEET,COVER........................................................   52.00
WEDGWOOD,JAR,CRACKER,GREEN,SIGNED,ENGLAND,5 1/2 X
   5 1/2-IN.DIAMETER.................................................  100.00
WEDGWOOD,JAR,MUSTARD,HIGH RELIEF DECOR,WHITE ON BLUE,SILVER
   COVER.............................................................   60.00
WEDGWOOD,JARDINIERE,BLUE JASPERWARE,ENGLAND,6 IN. X
   5 1/2 IN..........................................................   55.00
WEDGWOOD,JARDINIERE,CLASSIC FIGURES,LIONS' HEADS,GRAPE
   GARLANDS,MARK.....................................................   60.00
WEDGWOOD,JARDINIERE,GREEN JASPERWARE,ENGLAND,7 1/4 IN. X
   8 IN..............................................................   60.00
WEDGWOOD,JARDINIERE,LIGHT GREEN,CIRCA 1860,JASPERWARE,6 X
   5 1/2 IN.HIGH.....................................................   90.00
WEDGWOOD,JARDINIERE,RAISED WHITE FIGURES FROM FLAXMAN
   DESIGNS,JASPERWARE................................................   13.00
WEDGWOOD,JUG,DARK BLUE JASPERWARE,CIRCA 1820,8 IN.........   35.00
WEDGWOOD,MATCHBOX,BLUE,LADY TEACHING CHILD TO SEW,4 X
   1 3/4 IN..........................................................   29.50
WEDGWOOD,MEDALLION,CLASSIC SCENE,WHITE ON BLUE,
   3 1/2-IN.DIAMETER.................................................   60.00
WEDGWOOD,MORTAR & PESTLE,1856..............................   25.00
WEDGWOOD,MUG,BLUE & WHITE JASPERWARE,STERLING SILVER RIM,
   MARK..............................................................   58.50
WEDGWOOD,MUG,BLUE,WHITE,GRAPES & LEAVES,2 3/8 IN.TALL.......   45.00
WEDGWOOD,MUG,CLASSIC FIGURES,GREEN,5 1/2 IN................   49.00
WEDGWOOD,MUG,GRAPES & LEAVES,BLUE,WHITE,2 3/8 IN.TALL.......   45.00
WEDGWOOD,MUG,PORTRAIT,PRINCESS MARGARET,ROYAL VISIT TO
   CANADA,U.S.,1939..................................................    6.00
WEDGWOOD,MUG,SILVER LUSTER ON SCENE,DOG HANDLE.............   12.00
WEDGWOOD,PITCHER & BOWL SET,WHITE,GREEN BORDER,1879,PITCHER
   8 IN.TALL.........................................................   69.00
WEDGWOOD,PITCHER,BLACK GROUND,WHITE LADIES,CHILDREN,CHERUBS,
   7 1/2 IN..........................................................   84.50
WEDGWOOD,PITCHER,BLACK,7 3/4 IN.HIGH,4 1/2 IN.BASE..........  125.00
WEDGWOOD,PITCHER,BLUE TRANSFER UNDER GLAZE,CIRCA 1850,
   SIGNED,7 IN.......................................................   55.00
WEDGWOOD,PITCHER,BLUE,CLASSICAL DESIGN,GRAPE BORDER,MARKED &
   NUMBERED..........................................................   30.00
WEDGWOOD,PITCHER,BLUE,WHITE CATTAILS,7 1/2 IN.HIGH.........   45.00
WEDGWOOD,PITCHER,BLUE,WHITE CLASSIC FIGURES,JASPERWARE,
   6 1/2 IN.TALL.....................................................   42.50
WEDGWOOD,PITCHER,BOWL,TWO POTS,SOAP & CLOTH DISH,WHITE,BLUE
   DRAGONS,MARK......................................................  150.00
WEDGWOOD,PITCHER,COMMEMORATION,INDEPENDENCE HALL,EXPOSITION
   BLDG.,MARKED......................................................   65.00
WEDGWOOD,PITCHER,COMMEMORATION,MAYFLOWER,PILGRIM MEMORIAL,
   BLUE,WHITE........................................................   20.00
WEDGWOOD,PITCHER,CREAMY,PURPLE,GOLD,LUSTER,5 3/4 IN.HIGH,
   5-IN.DIAMETER.....................................................  325.00
WEDGWOOD,PITCHER,DARK BLUE,EMBOSSED GRAPE,CLASSIC FIGURES,
   JASPERWARE........................................................   50.00
WEDGWOOD,PITCHER,DARK BLUE,TANKARD,4 IN.TALL...............   30.00
WEDGWOOD,PITCHER,DORIC,BLACK & GOLD,10 IN.HIGH.............  150.00
WEDGWOOD,PITCHER,GOLD GARGOYLE FACE,DORIC TRIM,PEWTER TOP,
   9 IN..............................................................  150.00
WEDGWOOD,PITCHER,GRECIAN FIGURES,GRAPE BORDER,DARK BLUE,
   3 3/4 IN.HIGH.....................................................   28.00
WEDGWOOD,PITCHER,GREEN,METAL TOP..........................  125.00
WEDGWOOD,PITCHER,GREEN,WHITE RELIEF,SPOUT.................   95.00
WEDGWOOD,PITCHER,ORCHID,CLASSIC FIGURES,DANCING,HOLDING
```

```
HANDS,ONE QUART......................................... 125.00
WEDGWOOD,PITCHER,RELIEF DESIGN IS THISTLES,CLOVER,FLORAL,
  BLACK,5 1/4 IN......................................... 40.00
WEDGWOOD,PITCHER,TANKARD,TWISTED HANDLE,BLACK BASALT,
  ENGLAND,MARK.......................................... 37.50
WEDGWOOD,PLAQUE,BENTLEY BLACK BASALT,CIRCA 1768-80......... 200.00
WEDGWOOD,PLAQUE,FEMALE,CUPID,BLACK BASALT,FRAME,6 1/2 X
  4 3/4 IN.............................................. 300.00
WEDGWOOD,PLAQUE,SARAH,JOSIAH WEDGWOOD,18TH CENTURY,SIGNED
  FLAXMAN,PAIR.......................................... 400.00
WEDGWOOD,PLAQUE,UNDERGLAZE PAINTING,BIRDS,DATED 1912,
  12 1/2-IN.DIAMETER.................................... 78.00
WEDGWOOD,PLATE,BLACK KNIGHT,FRIAR TUCK,FOREST DECOR,ETRURIA,
  ENGLAND............................................... 16.50
WEDGWOOD,PLATE,BLUE WILLOW,ENGLAND,9 IN.................. 7.50
WEDGWOOD,PLATE,BLUE,ETRURIA,ENGLAND,8 IN.,SET OF 6....... 40.00
WEDGWOOD,PLATE,BLUE,PARSON'S HOME,NORTHAMPTON............ 7.50
WEDGWOOD,PLATE,BOSTON 1768 HARBOR SCENE,BLUE,FLORAL BORDER,
  9 IN.................................................. 16.00
WEDGWOOD,PLATE,CAKE,LANDSCAPE,BLUE DECOR,ETRURIA,ENGLAND,
  7 IN.,SET OF 4........................................ 25.00
WEDGWOOD,PLATE,CATTLE SCENE CENTER,THREE SCENES IN BLUE
  BORDER,10 IN.......................................... 12.00
WEDGWOOD,PLATE,CENTER UNION PARK CONGRESSIONAL CHURCH,
  CHICAGO,1860.......................................... 13.50
WEDGWOOD,PLATE,CHILDREN,HOME SCENE,VERSES,BROWN,WHITE,
  OPAQUE,10 IN.......................................... 18.00
WEDGWOOD,PLATE,CHOP,MULBERRY ON WHITE,FERRARA PATTERN,
  12 1/2 IN............................................. 15.00
WEDGWOOD,PLATE,COMMEMORATION,HOOSAC TUNNEL,BLUE,WHITE,FLORAL
  BORDER................................................ 10.50
WEDGWOOD,PLATE,COMMEMORATION,MONTICELLO,BLUE,FLORAL BORDER.. 18.50
WEDGWOOD,PLATE,COMMEMORATIVE,COLUMBIAN EXPOSITION,1892,PINK
  ON WHITE.............................................. 9.00
WEDGWOOD,PLATE,COMMEMORATIVE,COLUMBIAN EXPOSITION,1892,
  BLACK,WHITE........................................... 9.00
WEDGWOOD,PLATE,CORNFLOWER,6 1/2 IN....................... 1.25
WEDGWOOD,PLATE,CREAM COLOR,SCENES OF SMITH COLLEGE....... 3.50
WEDGWOOD,PLATE,DARK BLUE,FAIRBANKS HOUSE 1656,DEDHAM,MASS.,
  MADE 1904............................................. 18.00
WEDGWOOD,PLATE,GREEN MAJOLICA,MAPLE LEAVES & STEMS PATTERN,
  8 1/2 IN.............................................. 18.00
WEDGWOOD,PLATE,GREEN,BASKET TYPE CENTER,GRAPE BORDER,9 IN... 15.00
WEDGWOOD,PLATE,GREEN,RAISED GERANIUM LEAF PATTERN,
  8-IN.DIAMETER......................................... 15.00
WEDGWOOD,PLATE,HISTORICAL,BLUE,KING'S CHAPEL,BOSTON,1897.... 15.00
WEDGWOOD,PLATE,IVANHOE SCENE,BLUE,WHITE,OPAQUE PORCELAIN,
  10 IN................................................. 18.00
WEDGWOOD,PLATE,IVANHOE,BLACK KNIGHT,FRIAR TUCK,10 1/2 IN.... 20.00
WEDGWOOD,PLATE,IVANHOE,BLUE, BLACK KNIGHT EXCHANGES BUFFETS,
  10 IN................................................. 22.50
WEDGWOOD,PLATE,IVANHOE,WAMBO & GURGH,10 1/2 IN........... 20.00
WEDGWOOD,PLATE,IVORY COLOR,SCENES OF SMITH COLLEGE,EMBOSSED,
  9 1/2 IN.............................................. 2.50
WEDGWOOD,PLATE,LIGHT BLUE,SCENES OF HARVARD UNIVERSITY,1927,
  SET OF 12............................................. 85.00
WEDGWOOD,PLATE,MEMORIAL CONTINENTAL HALL,WASHINGTON,D.C.,
  BLUE,FLORAL........................................... 12.00
WEDGWOOD,PLATE,MOTTOS FROM CHAUCER,ETRURIA,ENGLAND,10 IN.... 15.00
WEDGWOOD,PLATE,NAPOLEON CREST,CIRCA 1800,QUEEN'S WARE,9 IN.. 60.00
WEDGWOOD,PLATE,OLD BOSTON THEATRE,1794.................. 8.00
WEDGWOOD,PLATE,PORTRAITS,IVANHOE,REBECCA REPELLING THE
  TEMPLAR,SIGNED........................................ 28.00
WEDGWOOD,PLATE,PRISCILLA & JOHN ALDEN,DATED 1901,BLUE,WHITE,
  9 1/4 IN.............................................. 12.00
--WEDGWOOD,PLATE,RAISED GRAPE LEAVES & STEMS,OPAQUE PORCELAIN,
  8 IN.................................................. 15.00
WEDGWOOD,PLATE,SALAD,CREAMY GROUND,ROOSTER & HEN SCENE,GREEN
  BORDER................................................ 8.00
WEDGWOOD,PLATE,SCENE,OLD FARM MANOR,TREES,COWS,10 1/4 IN.... 9.00
WEDGWOOD,PLATE,SHELL & SEAWEED DECOR,CREAMWARE,CIRCA 1770,
  9 IN.................................................. 45.00
WEDGWOOD,PLATE,SKI SCENES OF BANFF,SUNSHINE VALLEY,
  MT.NORQUAY,PAIR....................................... 17.50
WEDGWOOD,PLATE,TOWN OF MILTON,250TH ANNIVERSARY,1662-1912,
  TOWN CREST............................................ 14.00
WEDGWOOD,PLATE,WELLESLEY COLLEGE,1952,SCENE,10 1/2 IN....... 6.00
WEDGWOOD,PLATE,WESLEYAN UNIVERSITY,10 IN................. 8.50
WEDGWOOD,PLATTER,BLUE ON WHITE,CYPRUS PATTERN,ETRURIA,
  ENGLAND,18 IN......................................... 22.00
WEDGWOOD,PLATTER,BLUE,WHITE,SCENE,COWS,WATER,CROWN MARK,17 X
```

```
     13 1/2 IN.............................................    65.00
WEDGWOOD,POT,FLOWER,DARK BLUE,WHITE FIGURES,ENGLAND,7 1/4 X
     6 1/2 IN.............................................    65.00
WEDGWOOD,SAUCER,LANDSCAPE,BLUE DECOR,ETRURIA,ENGLAND,SET OF
     5...................................................    20.00
WEDGWOOD,SUGAR,BLACK BASALT,OPEN,MARK,3 IN.HIGH..........    55.00
WEDGWOOD,SUGAR,EASTERN FLOWERS PATTERN,COVER.............     6.50
WEDGWOOD,SYRUP,DARK BLUE,JASPERWARE,PEWTER TOP,6 1/4 IN.HIGH  60.00
WEDGWOOD,TANKARD,BLUE,CLASSIC FIGURES,SILVER RIM,WREATH
     AROUND HANDLE.......................................    65.00
WEDGWOOD,TEA CADDY,CAULIFLOWER,C.1780.............ILLUS..   120.00
```

WEDGWOOD CAULIFLOWER TEA CADDY, C. 1780

```
WEDGWOOD,TEA SERVICE,CREAMWARE,MINIATURE,CIRCA 1790,9 PIECES   350.00
WEDGWOOD,TEA SERVICE,OLIVE GREEN & BLUE JASPERWARE,NINE
     PIECES.............................................    325.00
WEDGWOOD,TEA SET,DARK BLUE,WHITE CLASSIC FIGURES,JASPERWARE,
     THREE PIECES.......................................    125.00
WEDGWOOD,TEA SET,1939,CENTENNIAL,SHIP,EAGLE,FLOWERS,TEAPOT,
     SUGAR,CREAMER......................................     87.50
WEDGWOOD,TEAPOT,BASKET WEAVE,SHEAF OF WHEAT FINIAL,CANE WARE    95.00
WEDGWOOD,TEAPOT,BLUE JASPERWARE,WHITE FIGURES,MARKED,ENGLAND    50.00
WEDGWOOD,TEAPOT,BLUE,CLASSICAL DECOR,WREATHS AROUND SPOUT,
     LID................................................     65.00
WEDGWOOD,TEAPOT,BLUE,WHITE GRECIAN DECOR,SIGNED,ENGLAND.....    70.00
WEDGWOOD,TEAPOT,CREAMER,SUGAR,BLUE JASPERWARE,WHITE
     CLASSICAL FIGURES..................................    125.00
WEDGWOOD,TEAPOT,DARK BLUE,ENGLAND.......................     35.00
WEDGWOOD,TEAPOT,LAUREL PATTERN,IRONSTONE................     37.50
WEDGWOOD,TEAPOT,ONE-CUP,GREEN,JASPERWARE,7 IN...........     48.50
WEDGWOOD,TEAPOT,SEPIA,OLD PARK THEATRE ON BOSTON POST ROAD,
     1851,10 IN.........................................     60.00
WEDGWOOD,TEAPOT,WIDOW FINIAL,BASALT,ETRURIA,ENGLAND,8 1/2 X
     5 IN...............................................     96.00
WEDGWOOD,TILE,BLUE GROUND,BOY,GIRL,CHRISTMAS TREE,WIRE FRAME   45.00
WEDGWOOD,TILE,ETRURIA BLUE & WHITE TRANSFER,CHILDREN IN
     MARCH WIND,4 IN....................................     30.00
WEDGWOOD,TILE,FLORAL,WALNUT FRAME,BRASS FEET,6 IN. X 6 IN...    12.00
WEDGWOOD,TOOTHPICK,DARK BLUE,MARKED WEDGWOOD,ENGLAND........    22.00
WEDGWOOD,TRAY,BLUE,VIEW OF FERRARA,TRIANGULAR SHAPE,ETRURIA,
     ENGLAND............................................     15.00
WEDGWOOD,TRAY,BLUE,WHITE FIGURES & MEDALLION,BERRIES,10 X
     7 1/2 IN...........................................     62.00
WEDGWOOD,TRAY,PIN,DARK BLUE,GRECIAN FIGURES,4 X 2 IN........    17.50
WEDGWOOD,TUREEN,BLUE,WHITE,HANDLES,COVER,FLORAL FINIAL,
     PLATTER,CLASSICAL..................................     75.00
WEDGWOOD,TUREEN,CREAM,BROWN,CIRCA 1770,14 1/2 IN.LONG,
     9 1/2 IN.HIGH......................................    350.00
WEDGWOOD,VASE,BASALT,SIGNED BY ARTIST,KEITH MURRAY,
     8 1/4 IN.HIGH......................................    125.00
WEDGWOOD,VASE,BLUE GROUND,WHITE FIGURES OF CHILDREN,
     5 IN.TALL..........................................     32.00
WEDGWOOD,VASE,BLUE,WHITE CLASSICAL DANCING FIGURES,
     5 1/4 IN.TALL......................................     34.00
WEDGWOOD,VASE,BLUE,WHITE,MEDALLION BASE,NUDE FIGURES,
     JASPERWARE,PORTLAND................................    320.00
WEDGWOOD,VASE,BUST FIGURE OF GIRL WITH LARGE HAT,TWO
     HANDLES,5 IN.HIGH..................................     22.50
WEDGWOOD,VASE,COBALT GROUND,GOLD ENAMEL CHINOISERIE,
     PORCELAIN..........................................     45.00
WEDGWOOD,VASE,COIN GOLD POPPIES,CREAMY GROUND,QUEEN'S WARE,
     9 IN.TALL..........................................    125.00
WEDGWOOD,VASE,LAVENDER,GREEN,WHITE......................    525.00
WEDGWOOD,VASE,ORANGE OUTSIDE,MOTHER-OF-PEARL INSIDE,MARKED
     PORTLAND...........................................    220.00
WEDGWOOD,VASE,PORTLAND,BLUE & WHITE JASPERWARE,10 IN.HIGH...   500.00
WEDGWOOD,VASE,PORTLAND,COIN GOLD POPPIES,QUEEN'S WARE
     POTTERY,9 IN.......................................    125.00
WEDGWOOD,VASE,PORTLAND,DRAGON,FAIRYLAND LUSTER,MARKED,
     ENGLAND,10 IN.HIGH.................................    350.00
```

```
WEDGWOOD,VASE,RAM HEAD DECOR,THREE COLOR,TWO HANDLES,
   8 IN.HIGH.............................................. 235.00
WEDGWOOD,VASE,THREE COLORS,COVER,9 IN.HIGH,PAIR............. 900.00
WEDGWOOD,VASE,2-HANDLED,PAINTED BY E.LESSOR,3 PIECES........ 550.00
WEDGWOOD,WASHBOWL,PITCHER,BLUE FLORAL.......................  50.00
```

WELLER POTTERY WAS MADE IN FULTONHAM,OHIO,FROM 1873 TO
1900. THE MOST FAMOUS POTTERY MADE AT THE FACTORY WAS
ART POTTERY THAT RESEMBLED ROOKWOOD,AND A TYPE OF GOLD
METALLIC LUSTER POTTERY.

```
WELLER,BASKET,GREEN,BASKET WEAVE,PINK ROSES,ROPE HANDLES....   6.50
WELLER,BOTTLE,WATER,IVORY & RED,GOURD SHAPE,SIGNED..........   6.00
WELLER,BOWL,AURELIAN,YELLOW FLORAL,KIDNEY SHAPE,FOUR-FOOTED,
   10 X 10 IN.............................................  75.00
WELLER,BOWL,COPPERTONE,FROG ON EDGE,OVAL,6 IN.HIGH,
   10 IN.WIDE............................................   35.00
WELLER,BOWL,DEEP BLUE,PINK FLOWERS,GREEN LEAVES,4 X 6 IN....   12.00
WELLER,BOWL,DRAPERY,BLUE,3 1/4 IN.HIGH,5 1/2-IN.DIAMETER....   15.00
WELLER,BOWL,FREE-FORM SWAN PERCHED ON SIDE,CHARCOAL GRAY,
   5 IN.WINGSPAN.........................................   50.00
WELLER,BOWL,GREEN,DRAGONFLIES IN RELIEF,SIGNED,3 1/2 IN.WIDE  18.00
WELLER,BOWL,ROSE,AURELIAN,GOLD & GREEN FLORAL ON FRONT,
   SCALLOPED,FOOTED......................................   57.50
WELLER,BOWL,WATER LILY SHAPE,FROG,GREEN....................   18.00
WELLER,BOWL,WOODCRAFT,IMPRESSED SQUIRRELS ALL AROUND,
   5-IN.DIAMETER.........................................   25.00
WELLER,BOWL,WOODCRAFT,LATTICEWORK,ROUND,SHALLOW,
   8-IN.DIAMETER.........................................   25.00
WELLER,BOWL,WOODCRAFT,OPENWORK LATTICE,FLORAL,4 IN.SQUARE...   20.00
WELLER,CANDLESTICK,BROWN GROUND,FLORAL DECOR ON FRONT,
   5 1/2 IN.HIGH.........................................   38.50
WELLER,CANDLESTICK,EOCEAN,DARK GRAY TO BLACK,CHERRIES,
   FOLIAGE,10 IN.HIGH....................................   42.00
WELLER,CANDLESTICK,LILY PAD,HALF VASE MARK,3 IN.TALL,PAIR...   15.00
WELLER,CANDLESTICK,LOUWELSA,BALUSTER SHAPE,HAND-PAINTED
   NARCISSUS.............................................   50.00
WELLER,CANDLESTICK,LOUWELSA,YELLOW-ORANGE FLORAL,GREEN
   LEAVES,7 IN.HIGH......................................   35.00
WELLER,CANDLESTICK,ROMA LINE,11 IN.HIGH...................    10.00
WELLER,CANDLESTICK,WOODCRAFT TREE TRUNK,BRANCHES WITH
   FLOWERS,PAIR..........................................   30.00
WELLER,CENTERPIECE,PEACH COLOR,WHITE FLORAL,MARKED,7 IN. X
   5 IN.HIGH.............................................   10.00
WELLER,CREAMER & SUGAR,ZONA,MARKED........................    14.00
WELLER,CUP,CUSTARD,BROWN,BLOCK LETTERS ON BASE,SET OF 3.....  10.00
WELLER,DECANTER,ROZANNE,BERRIES & LEAVES,HANDLED,
   ARTIST-SIGNED.........................................   42.00
WELLER,EWER,AURELIA,ORANGE,RED FLORAL,GREEN LILY PADS,SIGNED
   M.MITCHELL............................................   78.00
WELLER,EWER,LOUWELSA,DAFFODIL,6 IN........................    45.00
WELLER,EWER,ROZANNE,FLOWERS & LEAVES,7 3/4 IN..............   45.00
WELLER,FIGURINE,FROG,HOLDS FLOWER,PODLIKE BASE,GREEN DECOR
   OVER RUST.............................................   18.50
WELLER,FLOWER HOLDER,TOADSTOOL,BEE ON TOP..................   18.00
WELLER,FLOWERPOT HOLDER,FOREST PATTERN,GREEN,BROWN,5 X 5 IN.  22.50
WELLER,FLOWERPOT,CREAM,FLORAL,BLOCK LETTER.................    12.00
WELLER,HOLDER,FLOWER,CENTERPIECE,ISADORA DUNCAN,DANCE POSE,
   SCARF,8 IN............................................    6.50
WELLER,JARDINIERE,BABYLONIAN DECORATION IN RELIEF,UNGLAZED,
   8 1/2 IN.HIGH.........................................   28.50
WELLER,JARDINIERE,BUFF BUTTERFLIES,DAISIES,BROWN GROUND,12 X
   10 IN.TALL............................................   38.50
WELLER,JARDINIERE,DARK CHESTNUT COLOR,POPPY-LIKE FLORAL
   SPRAY,SIGNED..........................................   22.00
WELLER,JARDINIERE,DICKENSWARE,GLOSSY DARK GREEN,FLORAL DECOR  55.00
WELLER,JARDINIERE,EOCEAN,TURQUOISE GROUND,PURPLE IRIS,
   LEAVES,7 1/2 IN.......................................   65.00
WELLER,JARDINIERE,ETNA,SHADED GRAY GROUND,PURPLE IRIS,10 X
   8 IN.HIGH.............................................   57.00
WELLER,JARDINIERE,LARGE FLORAL,SHINY GLAZE FINISH,9 IN. X
   8 IN.HIGH.............................................   25.00
WELLER,JARDINIERE,LOUWELSA,BROWN,FLORAL,ARTIST-SIGNED
   MITCHELL,9 IN.HIGH....................................   60.00
WELLER,JARDINIERE,LOUWELSA,ORANGE IRIS DECOR,FLUTED RIM,10 X
   9 IN.HIGH.............................................   42.00
WELLER,JARDINIERE,LOUWELSA,UNDERGLAZE FLOWERS,ARTIST INITIAL
   L.B...................................................   80.00
WELLER,JARDINIERE,ORANGE FLORAL,IMPRESSED BLOCK MARK,
   6 1/2 IN.HIGH.........................................   36.00
```

```
WELLER,JARDINIERE,RAISED DESIGN,OVERLAPPING MAPLE LEAVES,
   STONEWARE..........................................................    35.00
WELLER,JARDINIERE,RIBBED DESIGN,GEOMETRIC BORDER,YELLOW,
   BROWN,OLIVE........................................................    24.00
WELLER,JARDINIERE,TAN,BROWN,GREEN GRAPE PATTERN.............    45.00
WELLER,JUG,LOUWELSA,DARK BROWN GROUND,YELLOW SNOWDROPS,
   3 3/4 IN.HIGH......................................................    11.50
WELLER,JUG,LOUWELSA,ORANGE POPPY DECOR,5 1/2 IN.HIGH........    46.00
WELLER,JUG,LOUWELSA,POPPY & WHEAT DECOR,6 IN.HIGH..........    37.00
WELLER,JUG,LOUWELSA,RAISED UNDERGLAZE DECOR,SIGNED,6 IN.....    65.00
WELLER,JUG,TOBY,UMBRELLA FORMS HANDLE,7 IN.HIGH.............    18.00
WELLER,LAMP BASE,BROWN,UNSIGNED,11 1/2 IN...................    15.00
WELLER,LAMP BASE,METALLIC LUSTER,ROSE,BLUE,GREEN,BRONZE,RED,
   5 1/2 IN...........................................................    45.00
WELLER,MATCH HOLDER,ROZANNE,BROWN GROUND,YELLOW MATCHES,4 X
   2 IN.HIGH..........................................................    30.00
WELLER,MUG,DICKENSWARE,INDIAN,ARTIST INITIALS,SGRAFFITO.....   185.00
WELLER,MUG,ETNA,GRAY-BLUE,PURPLE GRAPES,6 IN.HIGH...........    35.00
WELLER,MUG,ETNA,GREEN-GRAY TO CREAM,PURPLE GRAPES,PAIR......    55.00
WELLER,MUG,ETNA,LIGHT TO DARK GRAY,PURPLE GRAPES...........    35.00
WELLER,MUG,ETNA,PURPLE GRAPES,GREEN LEAVES,BROWN VINES,GRAY
   GROUND.............................................................    32.50
WELLER,MUG,FLORETTA,OLIVE GREEN TO CREAM,PURPLE GRAPES,5 IN.    37.50
WELLER,MUG,INDIAN POTTERY DECOR,BROWN,TAN,RUST COLOR........    25.00
WELLER,MUG,ROZANNE,PINECONE DECOR,4 IN.HIGH................    32.00
WELLER,MUG,TANKARD,LOUWELSA,ORANGE FLORAL,5 1/2 IN.HIGH.....    26.00
WELLER,PEDESTAL,HOLDS JARDINIERE,VASE,OR FIGURINE,GNARLED
   TREE,23 IN.........................................................    28.50
WELLER,PITCHER,BLUE TO YELLOW,FLORAL,TREE TRUNK HANDLE,6 IN.    12.00
WELLER,PITCHER,OLIVE COLOR TO PALE GRAY,BLUE FLORAL,
   7 IN.HIGH..........................................................    65.00
WELLER,PITCHER,TANKARD,DUTCH SCENE,6 MUGS...................    50.00
WELLER,PITCHER,YELLOW WARE,BROWN BANDS,4 IN.................    12.00
WELLER,PLANTER,BLUE DRAPERY LINE,14 1/2 IN.LONG,
   4 1/2 IN.HIGH......................................................    35.00
WELLER,PLANTER,BLUE,PINK SHELL,CORNERS & FEET ARE GREEN
   FISH,SIGNED........................................................    14.00
WELLER,PLANTER,BOXWOOD TREES,BIRDS,MESH GROUND,PINK RIBBONS,
   SIGNED.............................................................    13.50
WELLER,PLANTER,GARDEN WALL & LATTICE WITH ROSEBUSHES,
   5 1/2 IN.HIGH......................................................     8.75
WELLER,PLANTER,LILY SHAPE,HELD BY FROG,GREEN,YELLOW,
   3 1/2 IN.LONG......................................................    30.00
WELLER,PLANTER,STANDING DACHSHUND ON FRONT,BROWN,
   7 1/2 IN.LONG......................................................    20.00
WELLER,PLANTER,WOODCRAFT,HANGING,6-IN.DIAMETER.............    17.00
WELLER,PLAQUE,LINCOLN,MARKED,4 1/2 IN.......................    15.00
WELLER,PLAQUE,MCKINLEY,MARKED,4 1/2 IN......................    15.00
WELLER,PLATE,MAP OF U.S.,WORLD'S FAIR,ST.LOUIS,1904,
   ZANESVILLE,OHIO....................................................    50.00
WELLER,SUGAR,NEGRO CHILDREN HANDLES,WATERMELON FINIAL ON
   COVER,SIGNED.......................................................    42.00
WELLER,SYRUP,RED-BROWN,WHITE LINING,MARK,DEEP UNDERTRAY.....    26.00
WELLER,TANKARD,WOMAN IN SHEER GOWN,FLOWERS,PINK,GREEN,MATTE,
   11 1/2 IN..........................................................    60.00
WELLER,UMBRELLA STANDARD,RED,GREEN & GOLD TULIPS,SIGNED,
   20 IN.HIGH.........................................................    32.00
WELLER,VASE,AETNA,SHADED GRAY GLOSS,LAVENDER FLOWERS,7 IN...    30.00
WELLER,VASE,ALLOVER PERSIMMON-ORANGE GLAZE,CLASSIC FORM,
   7 1/4 IN...........................................................    13.50
WELLER,VASE,AURELIAN,BROWN GROUND,YELLOW FLORAL SPRAYS,
   ARTIST J.IMLAY.....................................................    38.00
WELLER,VASE,BALDIN,CREAM COLOR,PASTEL FLOWERS,7 IN.HIGH.....    30.00
WELLER,VASE,BASKET WITH ROSES,TWO HANDLES,4 IN.HIGH,
   6 IN.DIAMETER......................................................    10.50
WELLER,VASE,BEIGE,BLUE & BROWN FLOWERS,SIGNED BY ARTIST.....     8.50
WELLER,VASE,BLONDE LADY IN SEE-THROUGH GOWN,MATTE GLAZE,
   SIGNED,10 IN.......................................................    60.00
WELLER,VASE,BLUE DRAPERY....................................    17.00
WELLER,VASE,BLUE DRAPERY,PINK ROSE GARLAND CASCADES,
   3 1/2 IN. X 7 IN...................................................    14.50
WELLER,VASE,BLUE DRAPERY,7 IN...............................     5.00
WELLER,VASE,BLUE MATTE GROUND,YELLOW & BLUE PANSIES,LEAVES,
   PILLSBURY..........................................................    52.50
WELLER,VASE,BLUE,DOUBLE CORNUCOPIA,INITIAL A,CAMEO LINE,
   6 IN...............................................................    15.00
WELLER,VASE,BLUE,HAND-PAINTED FLORAL,GREEN,LAVENDER,YELLOW,
   9 3/4 IN.HIGH......................................................    35.00
WELLER,VASE,BLUE,PINK DOGWOOD,BLOCK LETTERS INCISED,
   8 1/2 IN...........................................................    10.00
```

```
WELLER,VASE,BLUE,SIGNED,7 IN.HIGH,4 1/4-IN.DIAMETER AT TOP..      7.50
WELLER,VASE,BROWN,YELLOW & PINK ROSES,BULBOUS,NARROW NECK,
   11 IN.TALL.................................................     28.50
WELLER,VASE,BUD,ROSE ON RED CLAY,MARKED,8 IN.,PAIR..........     12.00
WELLER,VASE,BULBOUS,NARROW FLARED NECK,ORANGE FLOWER,GREEN
   LEAVES,SIGNED..............................................     14.50
WELLER,VASE,CONICAL,SPLOTCHY PURPLE-PINK LUSTER,MARKED,
   4 1/2 IN..................................................     22.00
WELLER,VASE,CREAM,FLORAL,11 1/2 IN......................     25.00
WELLER,VASE,CREAMY WHITE,LAVENDER FLORAL,GREEN TWIG HANDLES,
   10 IN....................................................     10.50
WELLER,VASE,DAFFODIL SPRAYS,SIGNED LQUWELSA WELLER,
   10 1/4 IN................................................     35.00
WELLER,VASE,DELSA,GREEN GROUND,PINK FLORAL DECOR,12 IN.TALL.     17.50
WELLER,VASE,DICKENSWARE,GLADIATOR DECORATION,SIGNED,7 IN....     75.00
WELLER,VASE,DICKENSWARE,INDIAN HEAD PORTRAIT,SGRAFFITTO
   DECOR,SIGNED..............................................    175.00
WELLER,VASE,DICKENSWARE,PASTEL BLUE,BROWN,DUTCH GIRL,SIGNED
   J.H.......................................................     95.00
WELLER,VASE,DOME SHAPE,BLUE-GREEN,10 IN....................     29.00
WELLER,VASE,DOUBLE BUD,GREEN GROUND,ACORN,OAK LEAVES,SIGNED,
   7 IN.TALL.................................................     15.00
WELLER,VASE,DOUBLE,BLUE-GREEN,OAK LEAF,ACORN,SIGNED M.......     16.00
WELLER,VASE,EMBOSSED FRUIT ON TREE LIMB,MARKED,9 IN.........     12.50
WELLER,VASE,EOCEAN,BLUE-GRAY,PINK THISTLE,ARTIST-SIGNED,
   10 IN....................................................     75.00
WELLER,VASE,ETNA,GRAPE DECORATION,14 1/2 IN................     30.00
WELLER,VASE,ETNA,GRAY & WHITE GROUND,PINK WILD ROSES,
   4 1/2 IN. X 9 IN.........................................     35.00
WELLER,VASE,ETNA,GRAY GROUND,LAVENDER FLORAL,SIGNED,
   6 IN.TALL.................................................     35.00
WELLER,VASE,ETNA,RED THISTLES ON LIGHT TO DARK GRAY GROUND,
   11 IN....................................................     45.00
WELLER,VASE,ETNA WELLER,HIGH GLAZE,ROSE DECOR,MARKED,
   14 IN.TALL................................................     75.00
WELLER,VASE,FINGER,FRUIT TREE IN RELIEF,BLOCK LETTER-SIGNED,
   7 1/2 IN..................................................     27.00
WELLER,VASE,FLORETTA,BROWN GLAZE,BERRY DECOR,TWO HANDLES,
   5 3/4 IN.TALL.............................................     45.00
WELLER,VASE,FLORETTA,BROWN GLAZE,TWO BUNCHES OF GREEN
   GRAPES,6 IN...............................................     15.00
WELLER,VASE,FLORETTA,BROWN TO ORANGE,FLORAL & LEAF DECOR,URN
   SHAPE,7 IN................................................     35.00
WELLER,VASE,FLORETTO,BULBOUS,EMBOSSED BERRIES,MARKED,
   5 IN.HIGH.................................................     36.50
WELLER,VASE,FOREST LINE,SIGNED............................     15.00
WELLER,VASE,FOREST SCENE,8 IN.HIGH........................     15.00
WELLER,VASE,FOX HUNTING SCENE,WEDGWOOD TYPE,5 1/2 IN.HIGH...     38.00
WELLER,VASE,GRAY-GREEN,GRAPE DECOR,8 IN...................     29.00
WELLER,VASE,GRAY,PURPLE MORNING-GLORY DECOR,HIGH GLAZE,
   5 IN.TALL.................................................     40.00
WELLER,VASE,GRAY,YELLOW & RED FLORAL PAINTED UNDER GLAZE,
   9 IN.HIGH.................................................     40.00
WELLER,VASE,GREEN GROUND,EMBOSSED FLOWERS,HANDLES,SIGNED....     12.50
WELLER,VASE,HANGING,GREEN-RIBBED,FLOWER ON BASE,CATTAILS ON
   BODY,DOUBLE...............................................     18.00
WELLER,VASE,HUDSON,DEEP BLUE FLORAL,9 IN.HIGH..............     28.00
WELLER,VASE,HUDSON,GRAY,WATER LILY DECOR,BULBOUS,8 IN.HIGH..     35.00
WELLER,VASE,LADY HOLDS WREATHS,BLUE GROUND,FLORAL DECOR,
   7 1/2 IN..................................................     23.00
WELLER,VASE,LASA,GREEN PALM TREES,GOLD & LAVENDER SKY,FISH,
   7 IN.....................................................     65.00
WELLER,VASE,LASA,SIGNED,6 1/2 IN..........................     75.00
WELLER,VASE,LOUWELSA,BERRIES DECOR,HIGH GLOSS,16 IN........     55.00
WELLER,VASE,LOUWELSA,BLUE GROUND,WHITE FLORAL,SIGNED,BIRD
   MARK,9 IN.HIGH............................................     89.00
WELLER,VASE,LOUWELSA,BROWN,11 1/2 IN......................     25.00
WELLER,VASE,LOUWELSA,BROWN GLAZE,ORANGE POPPY,HEART SHAPE,
   SIGNED....................................................     25.00
WELLER,VASE,LOUWELSA,BROWN GROUND,LEAVES,FRUIT,7 IN.HIGH....     35.00
WELLER,VASE,LOUWELSA,BROWN GROUND,YELLOW FLORAL,HIGH GLAZE,
   12 IN....................................................     45.00
WELLER,VASE,LOUWELSA,BULBOUS BODY,LONG NECK,ROSEBUD,LEAVES,
   5 3/4 IN.HIGH.............................................     32.50
WELLER,VASE,LOUWELSA,CLOVER DECOR,FOOTED,4 1/2 IN.HIGH......     28.00
WELLER,VASE,LOUWELSA,FLORAL & LEAF DECOR,6 IN.HIGH,NECK
   3 1/2 IN..................................................     35.00
WELLER,VASE,LOUWELSEA,GREEN TO APRICOT,RUSSET POPPIES,SEED
   HEADS,15 IN...............................................     65.00
WELLER,VASE,LOUWELSA,ORANGE ROSES,ARTIST SIGNED,MARKED,
```

```
     7 1/2 IN.TALL.....................................................    40.00
WELLER,VASE,LOUWELSA,ORANGE WILD ROSE DECOR,CLASSIC SHAPE,
     6 1/2 IN.HIGH....................................................    48.00
WELLER,VASE,LOUWELSA,ORANGE WILD ROSE,CLASSIC SHAPE,
     ARTIST-SIGNED,4 IN...............................................    38.00
WELLER,VASE,LOUWELSA,OVOID SHAPE,CLOVER LEAVES,BLOSSOMS,
     10 1/2 IN.HIGH...................................................    52.00
WELLER,VASE,LOUWELSA,OVOID,BROWN GLAZE,ORANGE FLOWERS,YELLOW
     CENTERS ........................................................    29.00
WELLER,VASE,LOUWELSA,PILLOW,BROWN,GREEN,HOLLY,5 1/4 IN.HIGH.    30.00
WELLER,VASE,LOUWELSA,UNDERGLAZE PANSY DECOR,PILLOW-FOOTED,
     5 X 4 IN........................................................    40.00
WELLER,VASE,LOUWELSA,YELLOW FLORAL,TRIANGULAR RUFFLED MOUTH,
     SQUAT,3 IN......................................................    45.00
WELLER,VASE,LOUWELSA,YELLOW FLOWERS,GREEN STEMS & LEAVES,
     BROWN GLAZE.....................................................    42.50
WELLER,VASE,MORNING-GLORY SHAPE,BLUE GROUND,YELLOW & GREEN
     FLORAL..........................................................     7.50
WELLER,VASE,OPEN HANDLES,BLUE,NASTURTIUMS,LEAVES,SIGNED
     MCLAUGHLIN......................................................    24.00
WELLER,VASE,PANSY,ETNA,6 IN..........................................    38.00
WELLER,VASE,PASTEL COLORS,FLORAL DECOR,HANDLES,7 1/2 IN.....    14.00
WELLER,VASE,PINK WISTERIA,GRAY,WHITE,MATTE,MARK,10 IN.HIGH..    47.50
WELLER,VASE,PINK-BANDED BASE,YELLOW TOP & HANDLES,FLORAL,
     6 1/2 IN.HIGH...................................................    12.00
WELLER,VASE,POINSETTIAS,BULBOUS,4 1/2 X 6 1/2 IN.HIGH.......    10.50
WELLER,VASE,PORTRAIT,GIRL,GRAY,TWO HANDLES,6 IN.HIGH........    35.00
WELLER,VASE,PURPLE & GOLD IRIDESCENT,BLACK PAPER LABEL,
     5 1/2 IN........................................................    25.00
WELLER,VASE,RED GLAZE TOWARD TOP,FLORAL,SIGNED J.L.,
     9 IN.HIGH.......................................................    75.00
WELLER,VASE,ROZANNE,BERRIES,GREEN LEAVES,EWER,MARKED
     R.P.CO.,7 1/4 IN................................................    32.50
WELLER,VASE,ROZANNE,CLOVER DECOR,LARGER THROUGH CENTER,
     7 1/2 IN.TALL...................................................    30.00
WELLER,VASE,ROZANNE,MATTE,GLAZED ORANGE IRIS,GREEN STEMS,
     9 IN.HIGH.......................................................    65.00
WELLER,VASE,ROZANNE,SHADED BROWN,LEAVES,STEMS,BUDS,HANDLES,
     7 1/2 IN........................................................    35.00
WELLER,VASE,SABRINIAN,BLUE-PINK GLAZE,PEACOCK EYE,FEATHER
     HANDLES,1915....................................................    45.00
WELLER,VASE,SICARD,BURGUNDY,GREEN,SIGNED,4 IN...............    85.00
WELLER,VASE,SICARD,GREEN & GOLD FLORAL,LEAVES,PURPLE GROUND,
     MARK......................................................9,135.00
WELLER,VASE,SICARD,GREEN,PURPLE,IRIDESCENT,GOURD SHAPE,
     4 1/2 IN........................................................   115.00
WELLER,VASE,SICARD,IRIDESCENT SWIRLS IN PURPLE,BLUE-GREEN,
     SIGNED,6 IN.....................................................    75.00
WELLER,VASE,SICARD,PURPLE,GREEN,BLUE,SILVER IRIDESCENT,
     FLORAL,LEAF.....................................................   115.00
WELLER,VASE,STICK,ROZANNE,BRONZE COLOR,YELLOW & GREEN
     FLORAL,SIGNED...................................................    28.50
WELLER,VASE,STIPPLED GROUND,FLORAL,6 IN.HIGH................    18.00
WELLER,VASE,STRAWBERRY JUG SHAPE,GREEN,BROWN,8 1/2 X 7 IN..    45.00
WELLER,VASE,TREE TRUNK,BROWN,GREEN,FLOWER DECOR,SIGNED IN
     BLOCK...........................................................    17.50
WELLER,VASE,TREE TRUNK,10 1/2 IN.TALL,4 1/4-IN.BASE........    16.50
WELLER,VASE,URN TYPE,LEAVES & BERRIES,2 HANDLES,7 IN........    17.50
WELLER,VASE,WALL,BRANCH WITH APPLE BLOSSOMS,INCISED BLOCK
     LETTERS,9 IN....................................................    18.00
WELLER,VASE,WALL,GREEN GROUND,PINK FLORAL,CONE SHAPE,6 X
     5 IN............................................................    12.75
WELLER,VASE,WOODCROFT,TWO SMALL HANDLES,5 1/2 IN.TALL.......    15.00
WELLER,VASE,YELLOW,IVORY,ROMAN KEY DESIGN AT BASE & TOP,
     12 IN...........................................................    18.50
WELLER,WALL POCKET,WOODCRAFT,FREE-FORM SQUIRREL ON BOTTOM...    45.00
WHEILDON,CREAMER,CAULIFLOWER PATTERN,LID ATTACHED BY METAL
     CHAIN,1760......................................................   450.00
WHEILDON,PLATE,BROWN TORTOISESHELL MOTTLING,18TH CENTURY,
     7-IN.DIAMETER...................................................    35.00
WHIELDON,PLATE,MOTTLED BROWN,OCTAGONAL,CIRCA 1760...........   100.00
WHIELDON,PLATE,TORTOISESHELL,STAFFORDSHIRE,CIRCA 1770,9 IN..   115.00
WILLOW,SEE BLUE WILLOW
WOOD CARVING,ALMS BOX,FIGURES,MALTESE CROSS,1840,MAHOGANY...    89.50
WOOD CARVING,ALMS BOX,MAHOGANY,FIGURES,SILVER MALTESE CROSS,
     1840............................................................    89.50
WOOD CARVING,ANGEL,GILT TUNIC,WINGS,SPANISH,48 IN.HIGH,PAIR.   200.00
WOOD CARVING,BUDDHA,LACQUER,GILT,18TH CENTURY,8 IN. X 9 IN..    84.50
WOOD CARVING,BUST,GEORGE WASHINGTON,19 IN. HIGH............   425.00
WOOD CARVING,CHERUB HEAD,GILT SCROLLWORK,BAVARIAN,
```

```
    10 1/4 IN.HIGH,PAIR.................................     70.00
WOOD CARVING,CHERUB HEAD,RELIEF,OUTSPREAD WINGS,BAVARIAN,
    16 IN.LONG........................................     20.00
WOOD CARVING,CHERUB,SEATED,GILT WINGS,ITALY,27 IN.LONG,PAIR.   230.00
WOOD CARVING,CHINESE WOMAN,SITTING,TEAKWOOD,6 1/2 IN.HIGH...    25.00
WOOD CARVING,DUCK,BUTTERMILK PAINT FINISH,STAMPED CHINA.....     5.00
WOOD CARVING,DUCKS,MALE,FEMALE,PINTAIL,ON PLATFORM,7 1/2 IN.    19.00
WOOD CARVING,EAGLE,GILDED,18TH CENTURY......................   225.00
WOOD CARVING,EAGLE,GILDED,19TH CENTURY......................   200.00
WOOD CARVING,EAGLE,SHIELD,REPAINTED.................ILLUS..   800.00
```

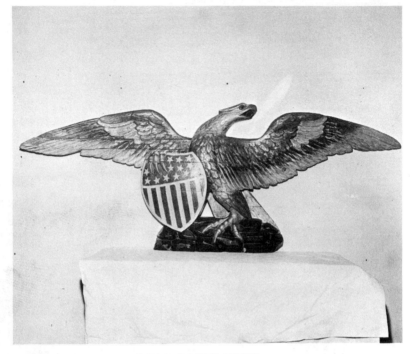

EAGLE SHIELD WOOD CARVING

```
WOOD CARVING,ELEPHANT,BLACK FINISH,7 IN.HIGH,7 1/2 IN.LONG..    18.50
WOOD CARVING,ELEPHANT,TAN FINISH,4 1/2 IN.TALL,4 1/2 IN.LONG    12.50
WOOD CARVING,FIGURE OF FRUIT PEDDLER,CHINA,CIRCA 1840,
    17 IN.TALL......................................   120.00
WOOD CARVING,FIGURINE,ST.MARTHA,GILT ROBE,WIMPLE,SPAIN,1700,
    12 1/2 IN.......................................   110.00
WOOD CARVING,FIGURINE,THE VIRGIN,ROBES,CLOAK,FLEMISH,PINE,
    21 1/2 IN.HIGH..................................    90.00
WOOD CARVING,HEAD OF CHRIST,GLASS EYES,SPANISH,16 IN.HIGH...    60.00
WOOD CARVING,HOUSE,TREES,CLIFF,WOODEN STAND,11 1/4 IN.TALL.    80.00
WOOD CARVING,NEGRO EATING WATERMELON,SEATED ON POLKA-DOT
    PINCUSHION......................................     5.50
WOOD CARVING,PLAQUE,DOG,FOLIAGE,HOUSE,HAND-CARVED,CHESTNUT,
    OVAL,PAIR.......................................    95.00
WOOD CARVING,TOTEM POLE,THUNDERBIRD WINGS,COWICHAN BAND,
    6 FT.HIGH,PAIR..................................   795.00
WOOD CARVING,TURKEY,WILD,SIGNED W.J.M.......................    14.00
WOOD CARVING,WARLORD MOUNTED ON HORSEBACK,WIRE INLAID IN
    WOOD,18 IN.HIGH.................................   750.00
    WOODEN,SEE ALSO,KITCHEN,STORE,TOOL
WOODEN,AUTOMATON,NEGRO FIGURE,TURN KNOB,PLAYS DRUM..........    50.00
WOODEN,AUTOMATON,NEGRO FIGURE,TURN KNOB,DANCES..............    50.00
WOODEN,AUTOMATON,NEGRO FIGURE,TURN KNOB,STRUMS GUITAR.......    50.00
WOODEN,BARBER'S SHAVING SOAP BOX BY COLGATE,1900,9 X 13 X
    5 IN............................................     6.50
WOODEN,BARREL,METAL STRAPS,SPIGGOT,19 IN....................    10.00
WOODEN,BASKET,BUSHEL,HANDMADE,HICKORY.......................    15.00
WOODEN,BEAM,HAND-CARVED,OAK,FROM CABIN OF SAILING SHIP,CIRCA
    1760,PAIR.......................................   475.00
WOODEN,BELLOWS,PINE.........................................    12.00
WOODEN,BIBLE BOX,CARVED FRONT,17TH CENTURY,OAK,23 X 14 3/4 X
    9 1/2 IN........................................    95.00
```

| | |
|---|---|
| WOODEN,BIBLE BOX,CARVED HARP,LEAVES,CROSS,BOOK-SHAPED,DRAWER | 25.00 |
| WOODEN,BIT BRACE,CIRCA 1700.............................. | 85.00 |
| WOODEN,BOOTJACK,ADULT,16 IN............................... | 10.00 |
| WOODEN,BOOTJACK,CHILD'S,8 IN............................... | 10.00 |
| WOODEN,BOOTJACK,HANDLE,36 IN............................... | 15.00 |
| WOODEN,BOOTJACK,HANDLES AT TOP,WALNUT,31 1/2 IN............ | 15.00 |
| WOODEN,BOOTJACK,LYRE STYLE,SPRING AT TOP,19 1/2 IN......... | 15.00 |
| WOODEN,BOOTJACK,PAT.1869,35 IN.LONG....................... | 27.50 |
| WOODEN,BOWL,BIRD'S-EYE MAPLE,15-IN.DIAMETER,4 1/2 IN.DEEP... | 40.00 |
| WOODEN,BOWL,BUTTER,OVAL,MAPLE,17 IN....................... | 15.00 |
| WOODEN,BOWL,SMALL,RUSSIA.................................. | 2.25 |
| WOODEN,BOX,BIRD'S-EYE MAPLE,COVER,4 X 2 3/4 IN.HIGH,PAIR.... | 16.00 |
| WOODEN,BOX,BRIDE'S,PENNSYLVANIA DUTCH,PINE,VILLAGE SCENE, 6 1/2 X 11 IN............................................ | 55.00 |
| WOODEN,BOX,CANDLE,DOVETAILED,CHERRYWOOD,SLANT LID,DARK PATINA,18TH CENTURY 11500&'M &'NA&)GO1&H&2HGO1MA&+ZN)&-G&O | 115.00 |
| WOODEN,BOX,CANDLE,RED PAINT,DOVETAILED,12 1/2 IN.WIDE...... | 27.50 |
| WOODEN,BOX,CARVED INDIAN CHIEF HEAD ON LID,ROUND,4 IN...... | 5.00 |
| WOODEN,BOX,CIGAR,THREE COMPARTMENTS,CLOTH-LINED TOP,BRASS HANDLES,OAK.............................................. | 17.00 |
| WOODEN,BOX,COAL,CARVED LIFT UP DOOR ON FRONT,SHOVEL FITS IN BACK POCKET.............................................. | 85.00 |
| WOODEN,BOX,KNIFE,FLORAL MEDALLION,SHERATON,MAHOGANY,CONTAINS CUTLERY................................................. | 210.00 |
| WOODEN,BOX,KNIFE,SERPENTINE FRONT,INLAY,MAHOGANY,PAIR....... | 300.00 |
| WOODEN,BOX,KNIFE,SHERATON,MAHOGANY,14 1/2 IN.,PAIR......... | 185.00 |
| WOODEN,BOX,LETTER,LADY'S,BURLED WALNUT,BRASS STRAPS, PORCELAIN MEDALLIONS.................................... | 145.00 |
| WOODEN,BOX,SPILL,SCALLOPED SHIELD,BACK HOLE FOR HANGING,3 X 3 X 11 IN................................................ | 65.00 |
| WOODEN,BOX,STATIONERY,ORMOLU TRIM,HAND-PAINTED PORCELAIN PLAQUE,FRANCE.......................................... | 110.00 |
| WOODEN,BOX,TRINKET,BURNED ALLOVER DECOR,WOMAN'S HEAD ON LID, BRASS HINGES............................................ | 4.25 |
| WOODEN,BOX,WRITING,SLANT TOP,BRASS TRIM,DRAWER,MAHOGANY..... | 85.00 |
| WOODEN,BUCKET,SAP,CEDAR................................... | 3.00 |
| WOODEN,BUCKET,SAP,LACED HOOPS,HOLE FOR HANGING,PAINTED RED.. | 12.00 |
| WOODEN,BUTTER PAT,PARTRIDGE............................... | 45.00 |
| WOODEN,CADDY,APPLE SHAPE,TINTED RED,BROWN,LOCK,FRUITWOOD, 4 IN.HIGH............................................... | 275.00 |
| WOODEN,CADDY,GOURD SHAPE,MOTTLE GREEN STAIN,HANDLE, FRUITWOOD,5 1/2 IN...................................... | 400.00 |
| WOODEN,CADDY,MOTTLED BROWN STAIN,FLUTED BODY,FAN-SHAPED THUMBPIECE,HINGE...................................... | 575.00 |
| WOODEN,CADDY,PEAR SHAPE,CURVED STEEL LOCK,OVAL ESUTCHEON, FRUITWOOD............................................. | 250.00 |
| WOODEN,CADDY,PEAR SHAPE,HONEY COLOR,LOCK,FRUITWOOD,6 IN.HIGH | 275.00 |
| WOODEN,CADDY,PEAR SHAPE,STEEL LOCK,FRUITWOOD,6 1/4 IN.HIGH.. | 275.00 |
| WOODEN,CADDY,PEAR SHAPE,STEEL LOCK,OVAL ESCUTCHEON,HINGE, FRUITWOOD,5 IN......................................... | 225.00 |
| WOODEN,CADDY,PINEAPPLE SHAPE,LACQUER BASE,ESCUTCHEON & FINIAL MISSING........................................ | 250.00 |
| WOODEN,CADDY,PUMPKIN SHAPE,STAINED BROWN,GREEN,CURVED HANDLE,6 1/8 IN........................................ | 325.00 |
| WOODEN,CADDY,TEA,COVERED WELLS INSIDE,CUT GLASS BOWL,COVER, MAHOGANY.............................................. | 50.00 |
| WOODEN,CADDY,TEA,HINGED COVER,CUT GLASS MIXING BOWL,BRASS TRIM,MAHOGANY......................................... | 90.00 |
| WOODEN,CADDY,TEA,LIFT TOP,SHELL MOTIF INLAY,BOXWOOD STRINGING,MAHOGANY...................................... | 40.00 |
| WOODEN,CADDY,TEA,MIXING BOWL,LEAF PATERAE INLAY,SHERATON, SATINWOOD............................................. | 70.00 |
| WOODEN,CANDLESTICK,TURNED,GREEN,9 1/2 IN.HIGH,PAIR......... | 3.50 |
| WOODEN,CANE,CARVED,ROPE DESIGN,IVORY-TIPPED,SOLID EBONY..... | 12.00 |
| WOODEN,CANTEEN,DRUM SHAPE,PEWTER SPOUT,IRONBOUND,DATED 1812, 8 IN.................................................. | 55.00 |
| WOODEN,CHEST,SEAMAN,DATED 1774,PINE....................... | 60.00 |
| WOODEN,CIGAR STORE INDIAN,BRAVE,PAINTED,6 FT.HIGH.......... | 375.00 |
| WOODEN,CIGAR STORE INDIAN,CHIEF,HAND-CARVED,UNPAINTED,1895, 4 FEET TALL............................................ | 395.00 |
| WOODEN,CIGAR STORE INDIAN,PAINTED WOOD............ILLUS..2,700.00 | |
| WOODEN,CIGAR STORE INDIAN,PRINCESS,HOLDS CIGARS & TOBACCO BOX,LIFE-SIZE......................................... | 550.00 |
| WOODEN,CIGAR STORE INDIAN,SQUAW,HALF-LENGTH FIGURE, 44 IN.HIGH............................................. | 600.00 |
| WOODEN,COFFEE JUG,MASK SPOUT,WHITE PORCELAIN INTERIOR,METAL TRIM,8 1/2 IN.......................................... | 72.50 |
| WOODEN,COMB,CURRY,ANIMAL HAIR,HAND-FORGED METAL TEETH,CARVED HANDLE,1750........................................... | 10.00 |
| WOODEN,DESK,LAP,BRASS CORNERS,SUPPORTS,NAMEPLATE,WALNUT..... | 15.00 |

CIGAR STORE INDIAN

WOODEN,DESK,LAP,BRASS TRIM,WALNUT,12 IN. X 9 IN. X 4 IN.....    12.00
WOODEN,DESK,LAP,MOTHER-OF-PEARL INLAY,INKWELL,ROSEWOOD......    59.00
WOODEN,DESK,LAP,ONE INKWELL,8 IN. X 11 IN. X 3 1/2 IN.HIGH..    12.00
WOODEN,DESK,LAP,SLANTED TOP,GLASS INKWELLS,WALNUT...........     9.75
WOODEN,DESK,LAP,TWO DRAWERS,FOLDING BRASS HANDLES,CIRCA
  1890,WALNUT..............................................    50.00
WOODEN,DIPPER,BURL,9 1/2-IN.BOWL,3 IN.HIGH,5-IN.DIAMETER,
  OVAL.....................................................    30.00
WOODEN,DOORFRAME,CARVED,FLOWERS,FOLIAGE,URNS,PINE,114 X
  70 IN.,PAIR..............................................   425.00
WOODEN,DRUM,BUDDHIST TEMPLE,MOKUGYO,TWIN DRAGON HEAD DESIGN,
  CIRCA 1880...............................................    47.50
WOODEN,FIGURE,BLACKAMOOR,VENETIAN,70 IN.,PAIR........ILLUS..1,400.00
WOODEN,FOO DOG,RED LACQUER FINISH,CARVED,CHINESE,9 IN.TALL..    75.00
WOODEN,HIGHCHAIR,CANE SEAT,WICKER FOOT REST,LEGS,WOODEN
  BEADS....................................................    85.00
    WOODEN,HORSE,SEE CAROUSEL HORSE
WOODEN,INKSTAND,DRAWER IN BASE,THREE INK BOTTLES,MAHOGANY,
  CANDLE BOX...............................................    90.00
WOODEN,JEWEL CASE,MIRROR RAISES WHEN OPENED,6 DRAWERS,TEAK,
  INLAID,BRASS.............................................   650.00

VENETIAN WOODEN BLACKAMOORS

WOODEN,KNIFE BOX,SHEFFIELD PLATE HANDLES,ESCUTCHEONS,
  MAHOGANY,PAIR.............................................. 180.00
WOODEN,KNIFE BOX,SHELL MEDALLIONS,ROSEWOOD & SATINWOOD
  BANDS,MAHOGANY............................................. 260.00
WOODEN,KNIFE TRAY,MAHOGANY...........................ILLUS.. 18.00
WOODEN,MASK,JAPANESE,BOY,SERIOUS EXPRESSION,LACQUER,FLESH
  TONE...................................................... 100.00
WOODEN,MASK,JAPANESE,CHILD,CARVED,SNUB NOSE,SMILING MOUTH... 30.00
WOODEN,MASK,JAPANESE,GIRL,PIERCED EYES,NOSTRILS,MOUTH,
  BLACK-STAINED TEETH....................................... 30.00
WOODEN,MASK,JAPANESE,GIRL,PIERCED EYES,NOSTRILS,WHITE TEETH,
  LACQUER................................................... 100.00
WOODEN,MASK,JAPANESE,HYOTTOKO,HAIR PROTRUDING FROM NOSTRILS,
  PAINTED,GILT.............................................. 35.00
WOODEN,MASK,JAPANESE,YAKKO,RED LACQUER FACE,PAINTED GOLD
  EYES,MUSTACHE............................................. 40.00
WOODEN,MASK,JAPANESE,YAKKO,WHITE FACE,PIERCED EYES,MUSTACHE,
  PAINTED................................................... 40.00
WOODEN,MOLD,BUTTER,FIVE PETAL FLOWER,FIVE SCATTER LEAVES,
  4 7/8 IN.WIDE............................................. 18.00

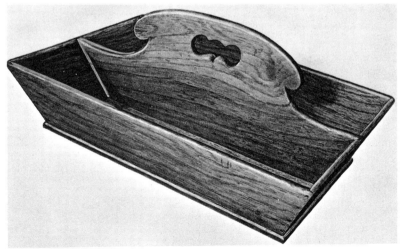

MAHOGANY KNIFE TRAY

| | |
|---|---|
| WOODEN,MOLD,CIGAR,TWO-PIECES,20 MOLD,22 IN.LONG............. | 18.50 |
| WOODEN,MOLD,MAPLE SUGAR,HAND-HEWN,ONE PIECE,FOUR<br>   COMPARTMENTS,11 IN.LONG........................................ | 25.00 |
| WOODEN,MORTAR & PESTLE,DESIGNS,DATED 1822.................... | 45.00 |
| WOODEN,MORTAR & PESTLE,HAND-CARVED.......................... | 12.00 |
| WOODEN,NIDDY-NODDY,MORTISE & TENON,WOODEN PINS,WIND SKEINS<br>   OF YARN BY HAND............................................. | 10.00 |
| WOODEN,PHONE,WALL,CRANK TYPE,SHELF,BELL,OAK................. | 60.00 |
| WOODEN,POTATO MASHER,CURLY MAPLE,14 IN...................... | 5.00 |
| WOODEN,RACK,COMB,TOWEL BAR,MIRROR,OAK,REFINISHED............ | 22.00 |
| WOODEN,SCOOP,HANDMADE,11 1/4 IN X 4 1/2 IN. X 1 1/2 IN.HIGH. | 15.00 |
| WOODEN,SHIP WHEEL,42-IN.DIAMETER........................... | 345.00 |
| WOODEN,SHIP WHEEL,EIGHT SPOKES,BRONZE HUB & INLAY,OAK,36 IN. | 250.00 |
| WOODEN,SIGN,FRACE'S HOTEL,43 1/2 IN. X 55 1/2 IN.....ILLUS.. | 275.00 |

WOODEN SIGN

| | |
|---|---|
| WOODEN,SPOON,HAND-CARVED,7 IN.LONG.......................... | 3.25 |
| WOODEN,SPOON,SHALLOW BOWL,HAND-HEWN,BROAD HANDLE,CHERRYWOOD,<br>   9 1/2 IN................................................... | 6.00 |
| WOODEN,STOOL,MILKING,ROUND,THREE LEGS,HANDLE................ | 8.00 |
| WOODEN,TEA CADDY,MOTHER-OF-PEARL INLAY,CIRCA 1860,ENGLAND,<br>   9 1/8 IN.LONG.............................................. | 64.00 |
| WOODEN,TEA CADDY,RESTS ON GILT WINGED DRAGONS,TEAK,PEWTER<br>   INSERT,CHINA............................................... | 225.00 |
|    WOODEN,TELEPHONE,SEE TELEPHONE | |
| WOODEN,TOWEL RACK,HAND-CARVED NUDES,OAK,PAIR................ | 27.50 |
| WOODEN,TRAY,BUTLER,HAND GRIPS,STAND,SQUARE LEGS,MAHOGANY,<br>   22 IN.HIGH................................................. | 190.00 |
| WOODEN,TRAY,BUTLER,SHAPED HINGE SIDES,GRIPS,STAND,SQUARE<br>   LEGS,MAHOGANY.............................................. | 300.00 |
| WOODEN,TRAY,KNIFE,DOVETAILED CORNERS,MIDDLE DIVIDER,HEART<br>   HANDLE,WALNUT.............................................. | 15.00 |
| WOODEN,TRAY,KNIFE & FORK,DOVETAIL,HANDLE,ASH,2 IN. X 8 IN. X<br>   12 IN..................................................... | 15.00 |
| WOODEN,TRAY,SERVING,BLACK,HAND-PAINTED FLOWERS,14 X 18 IN... | 5.00 |
| WOODEN,TROUGH,BREAD,BOAT SHAPE,TWO DIVISIONS,CASTERS,<br>   MAHOGANY.................................................... | 80.00 |
| WOODEN,VASE,BLACK,DRAGON,CARVED STAND,LACQUER,FOOCHOW,CHINA. | 12.50 |
| WOODEN,WALKING STICK,ORNATE,CARVED,TEAK..................... | 15.00 |
| WOODEN,WASHBOARD,BUCKET,WRINGER,DRYER,ECLIPSE............... | 15.00 |
| WOODEN,WHEEL,SHIP.......................................... | 175.00 |
| WOODEN,WHEEL,SHIP,BRONZE HUB,EIGHT SPOKES,36-IN.DIAMETER.... | 250.00 |
| WOODEN,WINE PAIL,BRASS BANDS,HANDLES,METAL LINER,1800,<br>   MAHOGANY,7 1/4 IN.......................................... | 130.00 |
| WOODEN,WRITING BOX,UPRIGHT SLANT TOP,PULLS DOWN FOR WRITING<br>   BOARD,10 IN................................................ | 15.00 |
| WOODEN,YARN HOLDER,SIX TREE BRANCHES,OPENS LIKE UMBRELLA, | |

```
CLAMPS,MAPLE.......................................     13.00
WOODEN,YARN WINDER,DATED 1864,RESTORED.....................     65.00
   WORCESTER,SEE ALSO,ROYAL WORCESTER
WORCESTER,BOWL,BLUE & WHITE TRANSFER PRINTED,DR.WALL PERIOD.    100.00
WORCESTER,BOWL,ORIENTAL DECOR,BARR FLIGHT & BARR,
   6 3/4-IN.DIAMETER.........................................    100.00
WORCESTER,BOWL,QUEEN CHARLOTTE,DR.WALL PERIOD,6-IN.DIAMETER.    250.00
WORCESTER,CANDLESTICK,PAIR,9 IN. HIGH......................    120.00
WORCESTER,COFFEEPOT,BLUE SCALE DECORATION,DR.WALL....ILLUS..    700.00
WORCESTER,CUP & SAUCER,APPLE GREEN BORDERS,DR.WALL PERIOD...    500.00
WORCESTER,CUP,QUAIL DECORATION,DR.WALL PERIOD..............     80.00
WORCESTER,DISH,CANDY,PINK-BEIGE,SQUARE BASKET,TWO HANDLES,
   1 1/4 IN.HIGH............................................     25.00
WORCESTER,DISH,DUKE OF CLARENCE,1789-92....................1,150.00
WORCESTER,DISH,LEAF FORM,TWIG HANDLE,FLORAL DECOR,DR.WALL
   PERIOD..................................................    275.00
```

WORCESTER COFFEEPOT

```
WORCESTER,HAND,WHITE,GOLD BRACELET,SIMULATED JEWELS,MARK,
   1865...................................................     62.50
WORCESTER,PLATE,CHAMBERLAIN'S,ARMORIAL,CIRCA 1800...........    550.00
WORCESTER,PLATE,MAUVE,GOLD,ARMORIAL,BARR FLIGHT & BARR,
   9 1/4 IN.,PAIR..........................................    190.00
WORCESTER,TEA BOWL & SAUCER,GREEN & GOLD,DR.WALL PERIOD.....    175.00
WORCESTER,TEA SERVICE,PINK,GOLD,FLIGHT,BARR & BARR,1830,
   30 PIECES...............................................    450.00
WORCESTER,TEAPOT,ORIENTAL DECOR,DR.WALL PERIOD,5 3/4 IN.HIGH    300.00
WORLD'S FAIR,ASHTRAY,1892,CHICAGO,PEWTER,2 IN.SQUARE........      5.00
WORLD'S FAIR,BANK,1939,CASH REGISTER,UNDERWOOD TYPEWRITER,
   2 1/2 IN................................................      8.00
WORLD'S FAIR,BOTTLE,1939,ANCHOR ON BOTTOM..................      9.00
WORLD'S FAIR,BOTTLE,1939,MILK GLASS........................     15.95
WORLD'S FAIR,BOTTLE,1939,MILK GLASS,PAIR...................     10.00
WORLD'S FAIR,BOTTLE,1939,NEW YORK,OPAQUE WHITE GLASS,
   9 IN.HIGH...............................................      4.95
WORLD'S FAIR,BOTTLE,1939,PORTION OF ORIGINAL VINEGAR LABEL..      8.50
WORLD'S FAIR,BUS,1934,GREYHOUND,SIGHT-SEEING...............     16.00
WORLD'S FAIR,CREAMER,1893,RED BLOCK,MARY O'CONNOR,3 1/4 IN..     18.00
WORLD'S FAIR,HOT PLATE,1939................................      3.00
WORLD'S FAIR,MATCH HOLDER,1939,CHINA.......................      3.00
WORLD'S FAIR,MUG,MINIATURE,1893,RUBY & CLEAR...............      3.50
WORLD'S FAIR,NAPKIN RING,1903,CHICAGO......................      5.00
WORLD'S FAIR,PASTRY SERVER,1939,NEW YORK,SILVER PLATE.......      3.75
WORLD'S FAIR,PITCHER,1939,POTTERY..........................     10.00
WORLD'S FAIR,PLATE,1904,ST.LOUIS,CLEAR,LATTICE,FLORAL
   BORDER,GOLD SCENE.......................................     12.50
WORLD'S FAIR,RING,LADY'S,1938-39,STERLING SILVER...........      7.00
WORLD'S FAIR,SPOON,1893,ART PALACE.........................      2.00
WORLD'S FAIR,SPOON,1939....................................      4.00
```

WORLD'S FAIR,STEIN,1893,CHICAGO,STONEWARE,BLUE ENAMEL,
  4 3/4 IN.HIGH......................................................... 12.00
WORLD'S FAIR,TRAY,1939,METAL,5 IN.......................................... 5.00
WORLD'S FAIR,TRAY,1939,NEW YORK,8 IN. X 17 IN.............................. 7.50
WORLD'S FAIR,TEA CADDY,1934,CHICAGO,SHAPE OF TEAKETTLE ON
  SAUCER,INITIAL....................................................... 15.00
WORLD'S FAIR,TEASPOON,1933,CENTURY OF PROGRESS,LEBOLT....... 13.50
WORLD'S FAIR,TOOTHPICK,1893,RED TOP........................................ 11.50
WORLD'S FAIR,TOOTHPICK,1904,RUBY-FLASHED.................................. 10.00
WORLD'S FAIR,TUMBLER,1893,RED TOP,BUTTON ARCHES............. 18.00
WORLD'S FAIR,UMBRELLA,1933,CHICAGO,PAPER & STICK............ 3.00
WORLD'S FAIR,VASE,1939,CRANBERRY & CLEAR,GOLD.............. 5.00


YELLOW WARE,BOWL,DOUGH,POURING LIP,NEW ENGLAND,
  13-IN.DIAMETER....................................................... 45.00
YELLOW WARE,BOWL,8 1/2-IN.DIAMETER,4 IN.HIGH................ 8.00
YSART,PAPERWEIGHT,COILED BLUE & WHITE SNAKE,GREEN GROUND.... 425.00


    ZSOLNAY POTTERY WAS MADE IN HUNGARY AFTER 1855.
ZSOLNAY,BOWL,BASKET-TYPE,PINK,MEDALLION ON FRONT AND BACK,
  SIGNED............................................................... 72.00
ZSOLNAY,BOWL,GOLD-GREEN IRIDESCENT,BOAT IN FULL SAIL,TREE ON
  LAND,10 IN........................................................... 85.00
ZSOLNAY,BOWL,GREEN,BLUE,GOLD,TULIPS,ROUND BASE,SQUARE TOP,
  5 IN.HIGH............................................................ 90.00
ZSOLNAY,BOX,IVORY COLOR,BLUE,GILT,FIGURES IN RELIEF,DOME
  TOP,SIGNED........................................................... 20.00
ZSOLNAY,DISH,ANGEL ASTRIDE DRAGON,BRONZE,MULTICOLORED FLORAL
  INSIDE............................................................... 65.00
ZSOLNAY,DISH,CANDY,BLUE,YELLOW,CARAMEL,GOLD,ELONGATED,SIGNED 30.00
ZSOLNAY,DISH,SOAP,CREAM GROUND,GREEN & BROWN LEAVES,ROSES,
  COVER................................................................ 10.00
ZSOLNAY,FIGURINE,FROG,WEARS CROWN,GOLD,BLUE IRIDESCENCE,
  3 IN................................................................. 95.00
ZSOLNAY,PITCHER,CHICKEN-SHAPED,ENAMELED,SIGNED,8 IN.HIGH.... 68.00
ZSOLNAY,SWEETMEAT,RETICULATED,ENAMELED,PEDESTAL,COVER,
  SIGNED,4 1/2 IN...................................................... 48.00
ZSOLNAY,TEAPOT,CREAMER,SUGAR,THREE CUPS,SAUCERS,CAKE PLATES,
  FLORAL............................................................... 185.00
ZSOLNAY,VASE,BLUE & PLATINUM COLOR IRIDESCENT,5 IN.......... 45.00
ZSOLNAY,VASE,COMPLETELY RETICULATED,SIGNED,7 1/4 IN......... 48.00
ZSOLNAY,VASE,EWER,FLORAL,LEAVES,BLUE,GRAY,OVERLAY DECOR,
  13 IN................................................................ 145.00
ZSOLNAY,VASE,TAN,IVORY,GOLD COLORS,TURQUOISE FLORAL,HANDLES,
  RETICULATED.......................................................... 55.00

# NOTES

# Notes

# NOTES

# NOTES

NOTES

# NOTES

NOTES

# NOTES